ORLD AGRICULT

House Document No. 27

77th Congress, 1st Session

1941

YEARBOOK OF AGRICULTURE

+

CLIMATE
YEARBOOK OF

1941

UNITED STATES
DEPARTMENT OF AGRICULTURE
WASHINGTON, D. C.
UNITED STATES GOVERNMENT PRINTING OFFICE

and MAN

AGRICULTURE

FOR SALE BY THE
SUPERINTENDENT OF DOCUMENTS
WASHINGTON, D. C.
PRICE $1.75

Yearbooks

IN THIS SERIES

1936: Better Plants and Animals. Vol. 1

1937: Better Plants and Animals. Vol. 2

1938: Soils and Men

1939: Food and Life

1940: Farmers in a Changing World

1941: Climate and Man

YEARBOOK COMMITTEE

1941

F. W. Reichelderfer, Weather Bureau, *Chairman*

Louis H. Bean, Bureau of Agricultural Economics

Joseph B. Kincer, Weather Bureau

Larry F. Page, Bureau of Agricultural Economics

C. G. Rossby, Weather Bureau

Charles F. Sarle, Bureau of Agricultural Economics

C. Warren Thornthwaite, Soil Conservation Service

Edgar W. Woolard, Weather Bureau

Gove Hambidge, Office of Information, *Editor*

Marion J. Drown, Office of Information, *Assistant Editor*

At the time of the appointment of the 1941 Yearbook Committee and throughout most of the committee's active work in shaping the book, the Weather Bureau was part of the Department of Agriculture. Subsequently it was transferred to the Department of Commerce.

The committee lost one of its ablest members in Larry F. Page, who died June 10, 1940. Mr. Page's exceptional knowledge in the field of long-range weather forecasting gave him a dynamic part in the Department's work in this field.

Special acknowledgment should be made of the assistance given by the Work Projects Administration in preparing material for Part 5 of this volume. Under the direction of J. P. Kohler, of the Weather Bureau, a small staff of WPA workers combed the vast number of records necessary to compile many of the tables in that part of the book and prepared most of the numerous maps. Without this assistance, the data given could not have been so complete.

FOREWORD

NEXT TO CROP PRICES, nothing is more important to the farmer's business than the weather, and in fact the weather often has a strong influence on prices. So every farmer takes a keen interest in the weather, and in many cases he is a weather prophet of no mean ability, at least for his own local area. One of the first things he is likely to do when he gets up in the morning is to scan the sky, note the direction of the wind, and plan his day's work according to what he thinks the weather is going to be. This remains true even though the radio and the newspaper now give him Government forecasts for his general area.

Weather science is one of the large family of sciences closely tied up with agricultural operations, from the smallest to the largest. The intelligent farmer today hardly makes a move in which some science or other is not involved, even if he does not consciously realize it. Most intelligent farmers, however, realize that they do constantly use the findings of science in their work.

The present Yearbook of Agriculture carries on the work of the preceding volumes, each of which has covered some major aspect of science fundamental to the use of our agricultural resources. This volume takes up weather and climate. Although the Weather Bureau was transferred from the Department of Agriculture to the Department of Commerce in a Governmental reorganization that took place after this book was under way, work on it was continued because no series of volumes on science in agriculture could be complete without including weather. For example, the very important long-range forecasting work on which the Weather Bureau is now engaged grew originally out of the needs of agriculture.

Naturally, a large part of the present volume is devoted to detailed discussion of the relation of climate and weather to crops. There is also a good deal of material on the newer developments that now promise to remake the whole science of meteorology—developments in which American scientists have played a leading part and which are of great significance to agriculture. The second half of the book contains tables and maps filled with a wealth of detail on climate in all parts of the United States. This material may seem dry and uninteresting to urban people, but it has a direct bearing on farm operations in every agricultural community.

As in other volumes in this series, the shortcomings of knowledge in the science concerned are emphasized rather than glossed over. The first step in increasing knowledge is to have a healthy awareness of what we do not know.

CLAUDE R. WICKARD, *Secretary.*

June 15, 1941.

ORGANIZATION

of the United States Department of Agriculture

CLAUDE R. WICKARD, *Secretary of Agriculture*

PAUL H. APPLEBY, *Under Secretary*
GROVER B. HILL, *Assistant Secretary*

DIRECTOR OF INFORMATION, Morse Salisbury.
DIRECTOR OF EXTENSION WORK, M. L. Wilson.
DIRECTOR OF FINANCE, W. A. Jump.
DIRECTOR OF PERSONNEL, Roy F. Hendrickson.
DIRECTOR OF RESEARCH, James T. Jardine.
DIRECTOR OF MARKETING, Milo R. Perkins.
SOLICITOR, Mastin G. White.
LAND USE COORDINATOR, M. S. Eisenhower.
OFFICE OF PLANT AND OPERATIONS, Arthur B. Thatcher, *Chief.*
OFFICE OF C. C. C. ACTIVITIES, Fred W. Morrell, *Chief.*
OFFICE OF EXPERIMENT STATIONS, James T. Jardine, *Chief.*
OFFICE OF FOREIGN AGRICULTURAL RELATIONS,
Leslie A. Wheeler, *Director.*
AGRICULTURAL ADJUSTMENT ADMINISTRATION,
R. M. Evans, *Administrator.*
BUREAU OF AGRICULTURAL CHEMISTRY AND ENGINEERING,
Henry G. Knight, *Chief.*
BUREAU OF AGRICULTURAL ECONOMICS, H. R. Tolley, *Chief.*
AGRICULTURAL MARKETING SERVICE, C. W. Kitchen, *Chief.*
BUREAU OF ANIMAL INDUSTRY, John R. Mohler, *Chief.*
COMMODITY CREDIT CORPORATION, J. B. Hutson, *President.*
COMMODITY EXCHANGE ADMINISTRATION, Joseph M. Mehl, *Chief.*
BUREAU OF DAIRY INDUSTRY, O. E. Reed, *Chief.*
BUREAU OF ENTOMOLOGY AND PLANT QUARANTINE, Percy N. Annand, *Chief.*
FARM CREDIT ADMINISTRATION, A. G. Black, *Governor.*
FARM SECURITY ADMINISTRATION, C. B. Baldwin, *Administrator.*
FEDERAL CROP INSURANCE CORPORATION, Leroy K. Smith, *Manager.*
FOREST SERVICE, Earle H. Clapp, *Acting Chief.*
BUREAU OF HOME ECONOMICS, Louise Stanley, *Chief.*
LIBRARY, Ralph R. Shaw, *Librarian.*
BUREAU OF PLANT INDUSTRY, E. C. Auchter, *Chief.*
RURAL ELECTRIFICATION ADMINISTRATION, Harry Slattery, *Administrator.*
SOIL CONSERVATION SERVICE, H. H. Bennett, *Chief.*
SURPLUS MARKETING ADMINISTRATION, Milo R. Perkins, *Administrator.*

CONTENTS

Part 3.—Climate and the Farmer

Part 4.—The Scientific Approach to Weather and Climate

Part 5.—*Climatic Data, With Special Reference to Agriculture in the United States*

Climates of the States—Continued.

Climates of the Territories and the West Indian Islands:

Climate and Man—A Summary

By Gove Hambidge [1]

THIS YEARBOOK is the sixth in a series designed as a set of reference volumes for modern farmers dealing with all the important aspects of present-day agriculture in the United States. As in the other volumes, all the articles are summed up briefly in this introduction. Any reader who wishes to do so can get a view of the whole subject by reading the summary. For more details, he can then turn to particular articles in which he may be especially interested. As a further guide in helping the reader to pick out what interests him, each article has a short introductory statement below the title telling what it is about.

[1] Gove Hambidge is Principal Research Writer, Office of Information.

EVERY HOUSEHOLDER is familiar with the difficulties he encounters in heating his home. Heated air in the rooms rises toward the ceiling, cold air enters through cracks and descends, and the floor is swept by chilly drafts. Moisture collects on cool windowpanes in the form of "steam," and on winter nights they are coated over with frost crystals. There is a constant movement of air currents, and it obeys strictly physical laws, but the movement cannot be seen because air is totally invisible. The movement of the currents would become visible, however, if a smoke-producing device were placed at some spot in the house. The smoke would be seen to swirl in one place, drift lazily in another, blow along rapidly somewhere else, and circulate all over the house, from cellar to garret, in curious patterns.

Multiply all this millions of times, add a few hundred complications, and you have what happens to the atmosphere surrounding the earth. Just as a furnace is a heat source in a house and the outdoors is a cold source, so the equatorial region is a heat source for the earth's atmosphere, and each polar region is a cold source. Instead of little currents of air moving a few feet, there are immense masses moving hundreds, thousands of miles, rising, sinking, whirling in majestic spirals, battling bitterly with one another where warm and cold masses meet, forming huge horizontal waves, drifting along as gentle breezes in one place, creating hurricanes and tornadoes somewhere else. Instead of a little steam or frost forming on a windowpane from condensation of moisture, the condensed moisture in the atmosphere forms clouds and is dumped on the earth as rain, snow, hail.

The general circulation of the atmosphere over the earth is the cause of all the climate and all the weather we have. And just as the circulation within a house obeys strictly physical laws, so does the far larger circulation over the earth. There is no mystery about it—or rather, the mystery is that we do not yet know exactly how it operates. If we knew in full detail exactly how the laws of physics apply to the circulation of the atmosphere, if we could measure exactly what forces are involved here, there, and elsewhere all over the earth, then we could predict the weather with much greater accuracy and much farther in advance than we do now.

Scientists have realized this for a long time, but only in recent years—since the first World War, in fact—have they begun to get a picture of the circulation of the atmosphere that is really comprehensive and detailed. At the time of the World War, the Norwegians and Swedes, cut off from outside reports, which are so vital in weather forecasting, began trying to do a more intensive job within their own limited territory. Since they could no longer cover a wide area on land and sea, they went in for intensive studies of wind flow and local cloud forms and from these deduced what happens in the upper atmosphere. A brilliant and resourceful group of weather scientists were engaged in this work, and as the saying goes, they found out plenty. Present-day weather science is based solidly on the idea that changes in weather are caused by the conflict of great, sweeping masses of warm and cold air along a "polar front." This idea stems directly from the work of the Norwegian group, who first glimpsed the magnificent drama of the forces involved.

The discoveries of the Norwegian school were a great stimulus to progress in weather science in other countries. It is not too much to say that the modern theories about air masses and the polar front, together with a number of related theories, have given weather science a powerful drive not unlike that given to genetics by the discoveries of Mendel and to the science of nutrition by the discovery of vitamins. Science moves forward in spurts, and each spurt seems to be started by a great theoretical advance which serves as a key to unlock a whole series of doors formerly closed. Weather scientists have unquestionably had such a stimulus. They are baffled by a score of difficult new problems, but they are beginning to see their way through. They are no longer stagnating and marking time. The best of them are working extremely hard trying to round out the new knowledge, and they feel that they are making real progress.

The United States played no small part in building up the new knowledge that is on its way to transforming weather science. In the Massachusetts Institute of Technology, the California Institute of Technology, and various services connected with aviation, weather scientists vigorously took hold of the new ideas. In particular, they emphasized actual observations and measurements in the upper air rather than sheer reasoning about what happens up there; and as a result of these observations and measurements they were able to work out practical techniques for forecasting based on the new knowledge, and also to make valuable additions to the fundamental theory.

The Department of Agriculture has had a hand in advancing this work. Because a better understanding of the general circulation of the atmosphere and the laws behind it is so vital to modern weather science, and especially to long-range forecasting, which is of particular interest to agriculture, the Department set up a cooperative research project with the Massachusetts Institute of Technology in 1937 to study this subject. Out of this project was developed the most comprehensive picture yet available of the hows and whys of atmospheric circulation over the earth and its relation to climate and weather. This picture is summed up in Rossby's article in this book. The article is semitechnical—too technical for most general readers—but it deals with pioneering work of great importance to agriculture.

Weather science, then, has left the ground and gone up into the air where all our weather comes from. The final outcome of this momentous change cannot, of course, be foretold. Right now weathermen are busy making their measurements in the upper air, collecting data, going through intricate calculations, creating new techniques. Perhaps a whole new generation of weathermen will have to be trained to think in terms of the new knowledge before it can be used to the full. Meanwhile, forecasting has gone over to the new techniques as far as is possible with limited equipment, observation points, and personnel. The work is beset with difficulties. For one thing, few laymen have any idea of the complicated mental juggling that is the everyday job of the modern forecaster; he seems to the outsider to be trying to keep a dozen billiard balls, knives, and forks in the air all at once without dropping or forgetting one. There is a large job ahead merely to reduce this complication to more manageable proportions by developing short cuts—formulas that include a number of factors in a single, inclusive, usable equation like those used in engineering.

One very significant result of the new knowledge of the upper air is the experiment now being carried on in limited long-range forecasting (forecasts for a period of 5 days). This too was initiated by the Department of Agriculture in cooperation with the Massachusetts Institute of Technology. At the beginning of the project a study was made of all the serious efforts at long-range forecasting based on physical data that have been started in various parts of the world in comparatively recent times. Only a few were found to suggest methods of genuine value or to give more accurate forecasts than would result from chance alone. It is impossible as yet to predict the possibilities of long-range forecasting beyond some such limited range as that now being tried. Weathermen are cautious about being too optimistic, but on the other hand they are certainly not pessimistic. For the farmer, perhaps no one thing would be more valuable than ability to know a year, a season, even a month in advance what the weather conditions will be.

The distinction between climate and weather is more or less artificial, since the climate of a place is merely a build-up of all the weather from day to day and the weather is merely a day-by-day break-down of the climate. It seems to be a useful distinction, however, and there will probably continue to be meteorologists concentrating on the daily weather and climatologists concentrating on the longer time range. Climate is of special interest to agriculture primarily because it divides the earth into zones, regions, and smaller areas each of which is suitable for certain crops and not suitable for others.

Climatology, the branch of weather science concerned with climate, feels the stirring of new needs in addition to the ideas that have had such a profound influence on weather science in general. Modern soil conservation work furnishes an example. The conservationists are much concerned with overcoming the hazards of erosion, soil exhaustion, floods. In many cases this involves getting the right kind of plant cover on the land, permanently, temporarily, or in rotation with certain crops. The climate of an area fundamentally determines the kinds of plants that can be used there. This statement is too broad to be useful, however; it means nothing in a particular case until you determine just what elements in the climate affect the plant and just what the effects are.

Here the conservationist runs into difficulties. Certain kinds of data about climate have been carefully collected for decades—figures on rainfall, for instance; but when the conservationist or the crop specialist tries to connect these figures with the behavior of plants, he finds that they do not work. A plant will thrive in one region with a certain amount of rainfall and fail miserably in another with the same amount. Rainfall does not tell the story. Further investigation shows why. It is not the amount of rainfall that counts but the amount of water the plants can get, and this depends on a great many things besides the amount of rainfall. It depends on the nature of the soil, the amount of wind, the sunshine and cloudiness, the humidity of the air, the temperature—above all, the rate of evaporation and transpiration, which are affected by these other factors. But there are no figures on evaporation and transpiration from the soil and growing plants, and until recently there has not even been any practicable way of making the measurements necessary to get the data.

There is the same lack of necessary facts elsewhere. Climate, including weather, affects the yield and quality of crops, the spread and intensity of attacks by diseases and insects, and undoubtedly the well-being and performance of animals. But how does it affect these things? Some of the ways are known, but others, perhaps even more significant, can only be guessed at, and still others are probably totally unsuspected. Our inability to forecast just what will happen to a given crop as a result of certain climatic and weather conditions is evidence of our lack of knowledge. Could we not do a better job of forecasting if we had the right kinds of facts to begin with? No amount of weather data was of much use in forecasting the prospects for wheat during the coming season in the Great Plains. Then someone hit on the simple method of measuring the depth of moisture in the soil at planting time, and it did the trick. There were plenty of facts before that—but not the right facts.

It should be the job of the climatologists to discover what facts are needed to throw light on a wide range of agricultural and other problems related to climate, and they are eager to push ahead with it.

The importance of this whole business of climate and weather to agriculture hardly needs to be emphasized. Weather science is important to everyone, but agriculture and navigation on the sea have traditionally been the two fields in which it was most vital; hence the long tie-up between the Department of Agriculture and the Weather Bureau in the United States. Today it happens that aviation is more critically in need of certain kinds of weather information than any other industry; moreover, it operates in those same upper levels of the air where the most significant work in weather science is now being done. Largely for this reason, the Weather Bureau is now officially connected with the Department of Commerce, the department most closely concerned with aviation. But advances in weather science are no less important to agriculture than they were before.

Few occupations of man, in fact, involve such varied knowledge and skill as farming. It looks simple to drop some seed into the ground, let it grow up under the blessed influence of sun and rain, and then harvest the crops. But at least as far back as the days of the Romans, men realized that the business was not so simple after all. A Roman named Columella wrote a large treatise on agriculture in which he summed up the best knowledge of his time—and it was by no means simple even then. In the 2,000 years since then, it has not become any simpler.

Today a comparative handful of able or successful farmers are required to feed all the rest of the population, and this vast undertaking would be impossible without the aid of science. Indeed, it can hardly be said any longer that science aids agriculture; rather, agriculture under modern conditions is itself a science, and one with many complicated and indispensable divisions. Whether he knows it consciously or not, the modern farmer constantly uses the results of research in genetics, soil science, the science of nutrition, medicine (including physiology, bacteriology, and parasitology), entomology, plant pathology (the medical science of the plant world), engineering, weather science, and many others. They all have an intensely prac-

298737°—41——2

tical bearing on his everyday work with soils, crops, and herds. Moreover, the farmer cannot stop with these so-called natural sciences. He must also know how to gear his operations into a market affected in a hundred ways by the complications of modern industry, commerce, and government. He is forced to form and act on judgments about social institutions and economic and political events in his own country and in other countries, because these things, too, have a direct practical bearing on his affairs.

In our modern society each group does a particular kind of work for all the other groups. Each must do a very efficient job in its own field or "gum up the whole works." Each group must also learn to understand and cooperate fully with all the other groups. From one standpoint, this staggering job can be considered the penalty of a high degree of specialization. But looked at in another way, it is a great opportunity to build a superb civilization.

SUMMARY OF THE YEARBOOK

The book is divided into five parts.

Part 1, Climate as a World Influence, gives some of the evidence concerning long-time changes in climate during the history of the earth; tells how climate divides the world into regions that have different kinds of natural vegetation and soils and different types of agriculture; and describes the operation of the Nation-wide weather service in gathering information about weather and climate and putting it to many vital uses, particularly the making of forecasts.

Part 2, Climate and Agricultural Settlement, tells about the part climate has played in the lives of those who peopled the United States and its territories, shaping their agriculture and their ways of doing things in each major climatic region. Fortunately, as Carl O. Sauer has shown, the original settlers came from regions in Europe with climatic conditions not too unlike those they found in the eastern and midwestern parts of the United States, so that they could adapt their native customs, which in turn had been strongly influenced by the climates they knew back home, to the new land. This section of the book ends with two contributions on climate and health—one of the continuing problems of people who live in any climatic region.

Part 3, Climate and the Farmer—the longest section in the first half of the book—deals in considerable detail with the effects of climate and weather on each of the major and many of the minor crops produced by farmers in the United States, and in addition takes up problems of livestock production, soils, forestry, plant diseases, insects, and animal parasites in relation to climate. It is very evident from these articles that climate is not something the farmer accepts passively. He constantly works to take advantage of favorable elements and counteract unfavorable ones, and much of our modern agricultural science has a direct bearing on this effort.

Part 4, The Scientific Approach to Climate and Weather, takes up the problem of floods and flood forecasting and discusses land use practices in relation to flood control, tells how our daily weather forecasts are made, and finally gives a résumé of the present state of our knowledge of the physical forces back of the whole range of weather phenomena.

Part 5, Climatic Data, prepared under the direction of J. B. Kincer, includes a wealth of facts about climate and weather in the United States, with special relation to agriculture. The material is so arranged that farmers practically anywhere in the country should be able to find the pertinent facts about their own locality or one nearby. The section has several main divisions. (1) First there is some selected material on climate in other parts of the world. (2) Next there is a set of maps covering weather and climate throughout the United States. These give data on temperature at different times of the year, precipitation and droughts, snowfall, thunderstorms, hail, relative humidity, fog, sunshine, cloudiness, dates of killing frost, length of growing season, depth of frost penetration. (3) Next, data are given for the individual States. The material for each State includes tables on precipitation, temperature, and frost for at least one station in every county where official observations are made; additional frost tables designed to show conditions in more detail for certain selected stations; a set of seven maps giving temperature, precipitation, and frost data in graphic form; and brief supplementary notes on the climate of the State. (4) Finally there are tables giving for Alaska, Hawaii, and Puerto Rico the same information given for the States.

PART 1. CLIMATE AS A WORLD INFLUENCE

Climatic Change Through the Ages

The history of the earth can be traced back some billion and a half years by geologists. Suppose we imagine this vast period as a single year of time—imagine that a billion and a half years ago it was January 1, the present moment is the stroke of midnight on December 31, and the entire history has been telescoped into the 365 days between.

During practically the whole of that year, according to geologic evidence, the climate of the earth was much more genial and uniform than it is today. It was as though the earth were experiencing a long succession of balmy summer days. Toward the end of April (millions of years ago, of course), there was a brief, severe cold snap lasting a matter of hours on our condensed time scale—actually, an ice age. In the latter part of August there was another cold snap; still another around the middle of November; a somewhat less severe one about the middle of December; and finally another severe one beginning along toward this evening, December 31.

In our condensed time scale, man appeared on earth about 6 hours ago, around suppertime on December 31, and he began to keep historical records of his activities about 1 minute and 12 seconds before midnight. Thus he came here in an ice age, and he has never known any other kind of climate. But the fact is that all of the ice ages put together have lasted only about 3 days out of the year on our time scale.

Human beings, then, have seen only the more violent moods of the earth. They were not here during the immense stretches of time when it was comparatively quiet and peaceful.

The long periods of climatic geniality—never known by man—are called "normal" times by the geologist; the brief intervals of comparative violence are called revolutions. Two outstanding features, Russell points out, characterize the revolutions. (1) There is unrest in the crust of the earth—earthquakes, volcanoes, an upthrusting of high mountains, extensive deserts, retreat of the oceans. We are now in a period of as violent crustal unrest as the earth has ever seen. For example, 325 volcanoes are now active. (2) There are ice caps—frozen seas—in the polar regions, and sometimes the ice extends, in the form of glaciers, far down over the normally warmer parts of the earth. Out of these icy regions sweep cold winds; stormy battles occur where cold and warm air masses meet; there are violent changes from day to day and season to season, and the contrast is strong between hot equatorial latitudes and those toward the Poles. In "normal" times, on the other hand, the earth's crust is quiet, its surface is more level, oceans are more extensive and warmer, and there are open, unfrozen seas around the Poles. Over the earth, the climate is more like that in maritime regions today—not so hot around the Equator, much less cold toward the Poles, much less variable from day to day and season to season.

The key to the climatic difference between normal and revolutionary times, Russell holds, is the existence of the polar ice cap. During all times, normal or revolutionary, climate obeys the same physical laws, set by the nature of the earth as a rotating ball with an inclined axis, moving around the sun and surrounded by an atmosphere. But the difference between polar ice and no polar ice is very great over the whole earth. Yet the balance between the two conditions is delicate. "A rise of 2° F. in the temperature of the earth now would be sufficient to clear polar seas of all ice." We would then be living in a "normal" climate.

What starts the formation of polar ice in the first place? Russell does not say specifically, but he thinks it is probably an indirect result of the crustal unrest of revolutionary periods. What causes the crustal unrest? The true explanation is yet to be discovered.

Our interest in the normal times that existed long before we came on earth is theoretical. We have a strong practical interest in glacial ages, however, because we live in one. Such ages are marked by periods of advance and retreat of the ice. We are now living in a period of ice retreat. It may be the beginning of the end of the present ice age, though the evidence rather indicates that the retreat is temporary. Temporary retreats during past glacial epochs have brought the earth much nearer to a normal climate than it is now. Considerable evidence exists to show that in our ice age there have been five major stages of advance of the ice and five major retreats. During the maximum advance, the ice extended as far south as New York City and the Ohio and Missouri Rivers in the eastern half of the United States.

There are various kinds of evidence available for tracing climatic history since the last great ice advance. For the early part of the period there is chiefly the evidence of rocks and the fossil remains of ancient life. Further along in the period, it is possible to count varves—annual layers of clay and silt deposited in lakes. Each varve has a summer zone and a winter zone, and much is revealed by the thickness of the layer and the character of the material. An incomplete varve chronology in North America goes back about 28,000 years. Tree rings also give evidence of climatic peculiarities in individual years. The succession of plant types in peat bogs indicates that there have been several climatic waves during the past 30,000 to 35,000 years. Bones of animals tell a similar story. Tools and weapons left by early man testify to migrations that depended on the extent of glaciers. Finally, about 7,000 years ago, records of various kinds began to be kept, and from these it is possible to reconstruct the state of the earth, dimly at first, but with increasing clarity.

From all these types of evidence, Russell pieces together the story of climatic change in the Northern Hemisphere from about 35,000 years ago until the middle of the nineteenth century, when mountain glaciers began retreating after an advance that had begun toward the end of the eighteenth century. The record is spotty and scattered, and on any large scale the more recent changes indicated are comparatively slight; yet they have been significant in shaping history through their influence on the activities of man.

Modern meteorology, made possible by the use of instruments, began only about the middle of the nineteenth century. Instrumental records are still comparatively meager, but climatic change can be studied from now on with an accuracy and a detail not before possible.

Russell finds no adequate evidence of recurring climatic cycles; there is no proof that short-time climatic changes, at least, are anything more than matters of chance. Of the many theories that have been advanced to account for long-time changes, especially the occurrence of glacial epochs, he discusses several briefly—changes in the angle of the ecliptic (the inclination of the earth's axis), precession of the equinoxes (a cycle occurring every 26,000 years), variations in the sun's radiant energy as indicated by sunspots, changes in the atmosphere that might affect the amount of radiant energy reaching the earth, changes in the amount of carbon dioxide in the atmosphere, volcanic dust. In most cases, he concludes, the cause suggested is not adequate to produce the effect, or there are other serious objections to the theory.

The size of continents and oceans and the elevation of mountains, on the other hand, have a profound influence on climate, as we know from present-day evidence; and these are the very things that are most profoundly affected by crustal revolutions. Russell concludes that these revolutions somehow produce the glacial epochs—brief periods when all life on earth is tested to the utmost and has to adapt itself to new conditions or perish.

Essentially, the central problem of Russell's article is the effect of the earth upon climate—especially the influence of an enormous cold source, a supergigantic cake of ice, which has formed occasionally in the course of a billion and a half years at each of the Poles, lasted for a while, and vanished.

Climate and the World Pattern

Blumenstock and Thornthwaite, on the other hand, are concerned with the effects of climate on the earth. They describe a great climatic pattern made by moisture and dryness, heat and cold. This in turn has created a pattern of natural vegetation, and both together have been the principal forces—though not the only ones—in creating the general pattern of soils.

The forces that make the world's climate what it is are discussed briefly by the authors, and at greater length elsewhere in this book. They result in eight major climatic divisions. Five of these are in regions where the prevailing temperatures are hot, warm, or cool, so that moisture, not temperature, is the chief factor affecting plant growth. These five divisions, then, are classified on the basis of moisture as (A) superhumid—very moist, (B) humid—moist, (C) subhumid—inclined to be dry, (D) semiarid—quite dry, (E) arid—very dry. The three additional divisions occur where the prevailing temperature is cold enough so that it, rather than moisture, is the chief factor affecting plant growth. These divisions are (D′) the cold regions called taiga after the dominant vegetation, (E′) the very cold regions called tundra, also after the dominant vegetation, and (F′) the regions of perpetual frost.

It should be noted that total rainfall is not the sole factor in determining the moisture divisions. Thornthwaite makes them on the basis of what is called effective precipitation—the amount of moisture that remains in the soil long enough to be available for plant growth. In general, effective precipitation is the difference between the amount of water that falls as rain or snow and the amount that runs off from the surface or is evaporated too quickly to be of use to plants. Since the rate of evaporation depends primarily on temperature, the climatic divisions really represent a combination of rainfall and temperature, worked out according to simple mathematical formulas.

It is the distribution of these climatic provinces over the earth that makes the climatic pattern.

Superhumid (A) climates are in equatorial regions (Central America, for example), and also in high middle latitudes on west coasts—as in coastal Oregon, Washington, and British Columbia. At the other moisture extreme, the arid (E) climates occur on the west coasts of continents in low middle latitudes—as in southern California—and extend as great lobes or tongues into continental interiors, as in Arizona, Nevada, Utah.

Between these extremes lie the other three moisture divisions. Next to the superhumid are the humid (B) climates, occupying extensive areas in the Tropics and also in the middle latitudes, as in the eastern and northwestern United States. Next to them are the subhumid (C) climates, as in our Central States. The semiarid (D) climates form broad belts around the arid deserts, as in the western United States.

The cold taiga (D′) and the very cold tundra (E′) climates cover large areas northward in our hemisphere—as in Canada. Around the Pole is the climate of perpetual frost (F′). The last three climates also occupy limited areas on high mountains.

Although the examples mentioned are all in North America, these climates are found in the same relative positions on other continents. The boundaries between divisions shift somewhat from year to year, and the shifts are often extremely important for agriculture.

The pattern of natural vegetation depends on the fact that each climatic region has a characteristic, dominant group of plants, built up by thousands of years of adaptation to a particular set of moisture and temperature conditions.

The superhumid climates nourish the dense growth called rain forest. In the humid climates, with somewhat less moisture, forests occupy the land. Tall prairie grasses are dominant in the subhumid regions where there is too little moisture for forests. In the still drier semiarid regions, short grasses grow, making plains or steppes. In the arid regions there are desert grasses and shrubs adapted to very little moisture. Taiga is the name applied to the coniferous forests (mostly spruce and fir) that cover cold regions. Where it is still colder, only mosses and lichens and some stunted trees (tundra) can grow. In the climate of perpetual snow and ice, there is no vegetation.

Climate and vegetation play the largest part in making the broad soil pattern of the earth, though locally other factors may be more important. For example, the kind and amount of organic matter available for soil building depends on the prevailing vegetation. Its rate of decay, and also the rate of chemical change in the soil, depends on temperature and moisture. Whether chemicals are leached out of the upper soil layers and where and how they accumulate lower down, depend on moisture. The character of a given soil depends on a combination of these effects.

There are two very broad soil divisions—in moist climates, the Pedalfers, characterized by the leaching of minerals out of the upper layers and by a moderate amount of generally acid humus from the prevailing forest cover; in dry climates, the Pedocals, characterized by less leaching, an accumulation of lime below the surface, a greater abundance of humus from the grass cover (except in arid regions), and a less acid or even a neutral or alkaline reaction.

These two major divisions in turn can be subdivided into groups characteristic of each climatic region. In the superhumid and humid climates, the Pedalfers include: (1) Lateritic soils in the Tropics, where heat favors rapid decomposition of organic matter (laterization), making the soil rather low in productivity. (2) Red and Yellow Podzolic soils in the wetter and hotter parts of the humid regions—as in our Southeast. These soils are also laterized, but they are less acid and more fertile than the first group. (3) Gray-Brown Podzolic soils in the parts of the humid regions with less heat—as in much of our Northeast. These are rather acid soils formed under deciduous and mixed forests. (4) Podzol soils in still colder humid regions—as in our extreme Northeast. Formed under coniferous forests, these soils are very acid. (5) Prairie soils, formed under tall grass in the eastern, more humid part of the Corn Belt—almost as fertile as the Chernozems, into which they merge toward the west.

The Pedocals, characteristic of the drier climates include: (1) Chernozems in the subhumid regions—as in the western part of our Corn Belt. Formed under tall grass, these soils have a deep-buried layer of accumulated lime, very slight acidity, high organic-matter content, and high fertility. (2) Chestnut and Brown soils in the semiarid regions—as in our High Plains. These soils, formed under short grass and with less moisture, are neutral or slightly alkaline in reaction, and the lime layer is not far below the surface. (3) Sierozems and Desert soils in the arid regions—as in the Great Basin and the Southwest. There is little organic matter in these soils, and the small amount of rainfall leaves the lime layer at or near the surface.

The taiga has very acid Podzol soils formed under coniferous forest. Under the mosses and lichens of the tundra are waterlogged soils underlain at greater or less depth by ground that never thaws. No differentiated soils have been able to develop in the regions of perpetual frost.

The three broad patterns of climate, vegetation, and soil can now be given side by side:

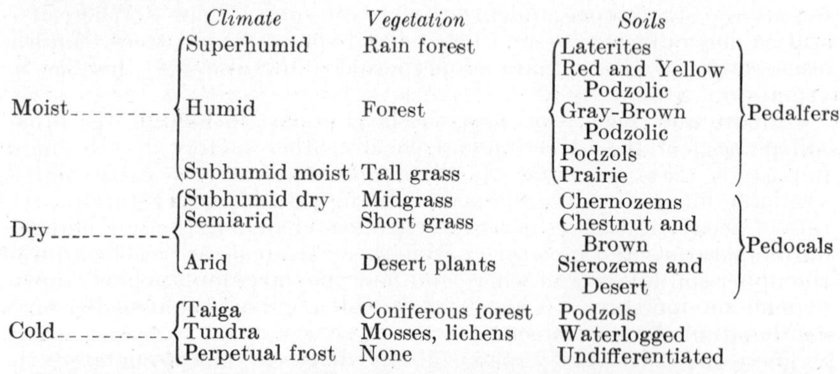

	Climate	*Vegetation*	*Soils*	
Moist	Superhumid	Rain forest	Laterites	Pedalfers
	Humid	Forest	Red and Yellow Podzolic	
			Gray-Brown Podzolic	
			Podzols	
	Subhumid moist	Tall grass	Prairie	
Dry	Subhumid dry	Midgrass	Chernozems	Pedocals
	Semiarid	Short grass	Chestnut and Brown	
	Arid	Desert plants	Sierozems and Desert	
Cold	Taiga	Coniferous forest	Podzols	
	Tundra	Mosses, lichens	Waterlogged	
	Perpetual frost	None	Undifferentiated	

Soil erosion is also markedly related to climate. Under natural conditions, there is a balance between the forces of destruction and those of maintenance. For example, maximum erosion occurs in regions of high rainfall, but there is also the maximum amount of vegetation to prevent it. In drier regions there is less protective vegetation but also less erosion. The gently rolling country characteristic of warm, humid climates is itself a product of the wearing-down of erosion. In cold regions and in arid regions where there is little erosion, hills are sharp and slopes abrupt.

Removing vegetation and cultivating the land upsets the natural balance and tends to speed up erosion without at the same time speeding up soil-forming processes. There are then characteristic hazards in each climatic region. In superhumid regions, the high rainfall favors gullying, sheet washing, trenching, siltation. In the humid regions, there is gullying and sheet washing where rainfall is highest—that is, toward the Equator. Farther away from the Equator, this kind of erosion is less likely to occur because of the longer period during which the ground is frozen and covered by snow; but snow and deforestation increase the hazard of floods, and heaving produced by frost favors mass movement of soil down slopes. In subhumid regions there is not much risk of gullying and sheet washing because the soil, rich in organic matter, can absorb a great deal of water; but drought becomes a hazard, depleting vegetation, altering soil structure, and making the soil susceptible to erosion by rain. In semiarid regions, cropping exposes the soil to erosion by wind, and overgrazing exposes it to gullying and sheet-wash by running water.

In addition to the three great natural patterns discussed, there is a fourth imposed on the earth by man—the pattern of agriculture. This too is strongly subject to climatic influences, including the erosion hazards already mentioned. Man can and does vary the agricultural pattern considerably within climatic limits, however, according to his culture, habits, and needs. As a single example, consider Chernozem soils in subhumid regions. In India they are used for raising cotton; in Africa, for grazing cattle; in the United States, for commercial wheat farming and cotton production.

In our modern industrial civilization, land that was or might have been used for subsistence farming is divided into highly specialized areas each devoted to one or a few crops produced on a commercial scale. In general, each area is especially suited by climate and soil to produce what it does. Sometimes, however, climate is not adequately considered, and the result is often failure of crops, of land, of human beings. This is notably true where cultivation is pushed out into areas that are climatically risky for crop production—as in parts of our semiarid West. It is possible to prevent this kind of failure by taking the climate fully into account.

The How and Why of Weather Knowledge

Like the postal service, the weather service is a governmental function for the benefit of everyone and an indispensable one in our complex modern civilization. Production and communication today are divided into an immense number of specialized compartments. In each compartment comparatively few workers perform vital services for all the rest of the population; a few citrus growers, for instance, supply 130 million people with oranges and grapefruit. The separate compartments are closely dependent on one another—those citrus growers, for example, on transportation interests, on buyers in big cities, on manufacturers of spray materials. Any upset or interruption at one point throws a mass of related activities out of gear.

One of the greatest upsetters and interrupters of human plans and activities is climate, including weather; it must constantly be taken into account in the calculations of agriculture and industry if smooth operation is to be achieved. Hence the pressure in modern times for a more and more elaborate, refined, and accurate weather service. Much depends on it.

Superficially, the weather service has not changed much for many years; we get the same daily weather reports and maps we have been accustomed to. But under the surface, as Reichelderfer shows, it has been going through something of a revolution not evident to the public. This revolution is in the science of meteorology itself.

During the World War, Norway was cut off from outside weather reports, and this crippled forecasting in that small country. To make up for the loss, the able and vigorous Norwegian School of meteorologists began to do a more intensive job within their own borders. Studying especially what occurs along the boundary between warm, moist air currents from the south and cold, dry currents from the north, they found that an actual air battle on a gigantic scale goes on along this front. Their discoveries proved to be the key to some of the most important aspects of weather. With further study, these discoveries were elaborated into the present-day "polar front" theory and "air mass analysis"—methods for analyzing vast masses of air and their movements and changes.

Hitherto meteorologists have worked largely from observations of conditions at or near the ground. Now they study the upper air as well—primarily, in fact—and the more they find out about it, the better they understand the mysteries of weather.

Meteorologists in the United States have been responsible for some very significant extensions and applications of the new methods. In particular, they have taken these methods out of the realm of theory into that of everyday practice, using first-hand measurements of upper-air conditions instead of merely making deductions about them. Potent tool in this work is a new invention, the radiosonde—an uncanny little device that goes 10 miles up attached to a balloon, sends back radio signals telling what the pressure, temperature, and humidity are up there, and then floats back to earth by way of a small parachute. The first practical system of radiosonde observations—30 stations altogether—was established by the Weather Bureau as recently as 1938. Kites and balloons are also used for upper-air soundings.

This whole development has given present-day meteorology a new direction and a new stimulus. It is only at its beginning and it has other aspects not touched on here. There is little doubt that out of it will come important changes in weather forecasting. Eventually, a close radiosonde network over lands and oceans might practically replace surface observations for use in preparing the daily weather map, giving a vastly improved picture of the atmospheric conditions that spell weather.

One of the significant results of the new development so far is the 5-day forecast, now issued by the Weather Bureau every Tuesday and Friday on an experimental basis. The possibilities for long-range forecasting—which would be of immense value to agriculture—begin to look a little better now than they ever have before.

Fundamentally, weather forecasting depends on what is called synoptic meteorology. (The word "synoptic" simply means a bird's-eye view.) This is the way a daily forecast is made: Promptly at 7:30 a. m., eastern standard time, observers at the weather stations that pepper the United States send their reports on local conditions to the central district offices. As the messages pour in, beginning about 8 o'clock, they are immediately decoded, and the data are entered on charts showing such conditions as surface weather, atmospheric pressure trends, winds aloft, and pressure, temperature, and moisture at various levels aloft. Within three-quarters of an hour—by 8:45—most of the mapping and charting is done. The forecaster meanwhile has begun his job of studying upper-air charts and surface weather, identifying air masses, sketching fronts and pressure lines, working out atmospheric formations, and estimating rates of movement, characteristics, and interactions of air masses. Out of this mass of complicated material and welter of calculations, he works out his picture of what the weather in his district will be. He has to work fast, too; his forecast is usually sent out by 10:15.

The information used by the district forecasters comes from 315 first-order weather stations, equipped for complicated and detailed observations. Climatological bulletins, on the other hand, are prepared from the observations of some 5,000 voluntary cooperators who serve without pay and furnish accurate but simpler data. The dense network of cooperators makes it possible to keep records of local conditions that are invaluable in the study of climate in relation to crops, land utilization, erosion, aeronautics, and other fields. Such a network is necessary because one of the most significant facts about climate and weather is that there are great differences within relatively small areas.

In addition to the daily forecast sent out by radio and telephone and through the press, there are the daily weather map and daily reports and bulletins. Weekly, monthly, and annual summaries are published. Much special work is done in connection with such services as frost warnings in fruit and vegetable regions, crop-weather advices in the cotton, corn, and wheat belts, specialized reports for aviation, storm warnings along the coasts, flood forecasts. In an infinite number of ways this information is used not only by agriculture, industry, business, and the professions, but by every citizen in such commonplace daily decisions as whether to wear his rubbers, put antifreeze in the automobile radiator, or lay in a ton of coal.

Three factors are of prime importance in this work. (1) Observations must be accurate, adequate, and uniform. (2) Interpretation and forecasting must be done by thoroughly trained technicians. Adequate weather forecasting is a complicated and difficult job, not only because it is so highly technical but because so many different factors must be kept in the mind and weighed at one time. (3) There must be a system of constant follow-up observations so that forecasts can be modified as later information is received. In weather work continuous vigilance is peculiarly the price of success because changes can occur so rapidly.

Few people understand the disciplines and technicalities involved in this work. Many, for example, continue to have faith in almanac forecasting, which attempts to foretell the future by using the climatic records of past years. If the weather service were better understood by the public, better use could be made of it.

Scientific weather forecasting has certain limitations. The public demands, for instance, that a forecast be expressed as nearly as possible in one word—clear, fair, cloudy, rain—whereas a much longer account is necessary to give an adequate description of what the weather will be during a period of 24 or 36 hours. There are also some difficult situations that need to be clarified through more research; but with the exception of these, everyday forecasting has been greatly improved as a result of the developments of recent years, and there is rarely a miss on such important items as storm warnings. The ccasional forecast that is wrong, however, is the one that is likely to stick in the mind, rather than the immensely greater number that are successful day by day.

PART 2. CLIMATE AND AGRICULTURAL SETTLEMENT

The Settlement of the Humid East

"This was indeed a lustier land to which the settlers had come," says Sauer, "a land of hotter summers and colder winters, of brighter and hotter sun and more tempestuous rain, a land suited to and provided with a greater variety of vegetation than the homelands of

Europe." In other words, even the climate in our eastern regions was more continental in character than that in the British Isles and northern Europe; but it was at any rate a humid climate, and this quality made it sufficiently like the climate at home to be congenial.

As Sauer points out, neither in New England nor in the South did the early explorers and settlers come here primarily to farm. They expected to make money in almost any other way except agriculture, and they were driven to farming reluctantly to keep from starving. Even so, they might have starved if they had not quickly adopted Indian agricultural methods and crops. European agriculture was based on grain and livestock; it involved cleared and plowed fields, seeded in rows or by broadcasting, and was entirely unsuited to a densely forested land. The Indians had worked out the best way to farm such a land with a minimum of labor and practically no equipment except a digging stick or mattock. They killed the trees by girdling, burned them over, and planted their crops—mostly corn, beans, squash—in hills among the stumps.

In the southern Colonies, two money crops of tropical origin soon came to be dominant. Virginians discovered that their climate was well adapted to the growing of tobacco—and they made the discovery just as the English were acquiring the tobacco habit. Eventually, tobacco culture spread all the way across the upper South. The second great discovery was that the southern climate was adapted to cotton—first, sea-island cotton, introduced around Charleston from the Barbados, along with sugarcane, indigo, and rice; next, upland cotton, a Mexican plant introduced probably from southern Europe. Cotton growing under the plantation system gradually spread westward across the deep South.

New England, meanwhile, grew corn, beans, and pumpkins alongside grains from Europe. A major shortcoming was the poor quality of native eastern pasture grasses. When European grasses and clover were introduced and became established, livestock production was greatly stimulated. New England would have had difficulty, however, in supporting itself on agriculture alone.

But "the basic pattern of the American farm," says Sauer, "is derived chiefly from the middle Colonies," which saw the greatest influx of settlers who were true tillers of the soil. Here there were neither southern plantations, nor close-knit New England townships, but scattered single-family farmsteads. Swedes and Finns contributed the log cabin; the Dutch, better breeds of livestock, European grasses and clovers, an interest in dairying. The Irish and Scots contributed intrepid backwoodsmen—and potatoes; the Germans, improvements in grain growing and stock breeding, the basic American barn, the rifle, the Conestoga wagon, the stove instead of the fireplace.

In the middle Colonies, "the Old World pattern of general farming, with emphasis on the feeding of livestock, was transferred . . . to the New World with one major modification"—Indian corn, which greatly increased livestock production. Spreading westward, this general-crop and livestock farming readily became the corn-hog economy of the Prairie States and the dairy-potato-small-grain agriculture of the Great Lakes region.

Climate and Settlement of the Subhumid Lands

"By 1850 . . . the first period of American colonization, that of the forest, was at an end, and the second, that of the grasslands, was beginning," writes Trewartha. What manner of land lay beyond the humid eastern forests?

The prairies lie between the Canadian border on the north and the Gulf of Mexico on the south. On the east they are bounded by a line representing 1 dry year in 20, on the west by a line representing 10 dry years in 20. Climatically the region is one of strong contrasts, as is the interior of every great continental land mass. Winters are nearly 50° F. warmer in southern Texas than in North Dakota, but the great thrusts of polar air that spill suddenly out of the Arctic may sweep all the way down into the Gulf States. The growing season lasts only 3 to 4 months in northern North Dakota, 8 to 9 months in Texas; but midsummer days in the north may be almost as hot as in the south. Over the region in general, rainfall does not greatly exceed evaporation, so that drought is the chief hazard. Fortunately, the rain is almost everywhere concentrated in the warm season, especially in early summer, the time when grain needs it most. Originally the prairies were covered with grass that grew 3 to 10 feet high and was studded with wildflowers. Trees were rare except among the "oak openings" on the eastern boundary and along the river valleys; where the subsoil was moist enough to support forests, they perhaps could not survive because of prairie fires and grazing buffalo. The soil in the drier western area is the deep black Chernozem, one of the richest on earth, while farther east are the only slightly less fertile Prairie soils.

Many pioneers from the East were afraid of this too bright, too level land where there were so few friendly trees, and shade and water both were scarce. They eased into it by first settling the river valleys and oak openings, which seemed familiar. What was needed was the development of new techniques for farming and living. Houses made out of sod instead of logs; cow chips and knots of twisted grass for fuel; wells sometimes 200 feet deep, dug with pick and shovel; windmills to harness the strong winds for pumping; barbed-wire fencing, better than the almost nonexistent split rails; steel plows that would scour clean and bright in the prairie soil and not stick like the old iron and wooden plows; oxen, plenty of oxen, to pull the plows through the thick, tough virgin sod; reapers and mowers and threshers replacing slow hand labor; and perhaps more than anything else, railroads to haul the products of the new lands to distant markets.

One by one, these things and these techniques were provided. Once conquered, the prairies yielded enormously. No need here to grub out trees laboriously and endlessly; a man could have the land producing within a year. No need to think of conserving this soil—it looked inexhaustibly fertile. Eastward, great industrial cities were growing up that needed to be fed cheaply. The prairies, with cheap land and large-scale methods of production, could do the job. Quickly they swung into the production of wheat, corn, cattle, hogs on a vast scale; and to the south, cotton. Droughts, searing winds, insect plagues, blizzards took their toll, but they were incidents. The prairies were such an agricultural treasure house as has seldom existed in the world, and they lived up to their destiny.

Climate and Settlement in the Great Plains

An old song says that "woman is fickle." So also, Thornthwaite makes clear, are the Great Plains. In one mood they seem like a comfortable, loving housewife. Next they lash out with a sharp tongue and a long blacksnake whip. To live with these moods, a man must be wise and cautious.

The moods of the Great Plains have a climatic basis. Rainfall in the humid East is caused mostly in this way: Warm air, laden with moisture from the ocean, travels northward; it meets a wall of cold, dry polar air; it is forced upward and chilled; the moisture condenses and comes down as rain. Normally, this moisture-laden air from the south curves eastward and so never reaches the Great Plains. Most of the warm air that does reach the Plains comes from Mexico; it is so dry to begin with that it has little or no water to spill when it is forced up by cold polar air from the north. But sometimes the moist ocean air goes westward and gets to the Plains. A third of the year's rainfall may then be dumped on the land in a single day.

The climate, then, is one of extremes. In 1905, for example, hardly any part of the Great Plains had a semiarid climate. Parts were as moist as Ohio; other parts had the climate of Iowa and western Illinois. Five years later, in 1910, most of the southern and parts of the northern Plains were experiencing a climate as dry as that of a desert. Hail, frost, hot winds are particularly severe in this region; seasonal contrasts in temperature are great. Different types of air masses sweep over the Plains in succession and make it a meteorological battleground.

Originally the region was like a vast close-cropped meadow, covered with short grasses that could stand prolonged drought. Pioneers accustomed to trees thought it a desert and hurried across. After the Civil War there was an immense expansion of ranching, preceded by the great cattle drives from Texas. Meanwhile settlers learned to farm the treeless prairies to the east, and some began experimenting on the Plains. A period of comparatively high moisture made the prospects seem good. More settlers moved in. A severe drought came along in the nineties, ruined many, drove them out. Then special dry-farming methods were developed to conserve moisture, and the problem seemed to be solved. The treatment given the soil, however, made it blow away.

Cattle ranching expanded next as a result of the World War. After the war, the development of mechanical methods for wheat farming, high prices for wheat, and a series of comparatively rainy years made the Plains look like a bonanza region again. By 1930 most of the land had been plowed. Then during the whole of the next decade there were droughts, coming on top of the depression. Once more great numbers of people were ruined and forced to emigrate.

There is not much sense, Thornthwaite argues, in this feverish alternation of false hopes and ruin. The character of the climate in the Great Plains is now clear enough. Over a period of years, wheat farming can pay, at current prices, only in a few locations where supplementary water is available. The general pattern imposed by the climate is a grazing economy, with additional forage and feed crops produced in rainy years and where flood irrigation is possible. This involves restoration of the range, larger and fewer farms, considerable cooperative planning, and restraints on further inrushes of settlers. So a man can live with the Great Plains and take its moods in his stride.

Climate and Settlement of the Arid Region

"I will lift up mine eyes unto the hills, from whence cometh my help," is a literally true saying for the dweller in the arid region of the United States. The region is barricaded on the west by the long Sierra Nevada-Cascade Range. Moist winds from the Pacific are forced up these mountains and spill their load of water invariably on the western slopes. The same thing occurs at each successive range eastward. Thus, though the region as a whole is parched, it is also spotted with moist areas. Too high, too cold, too rough in topography to be used for agriculture, these humid islands are wonderful sources of life-giving water for the valleys below, especially since much of the moisture is held in winter as snow and released later on when it is needed for crops. The combination of mountain, valley, and flat desert makes for abrupt changes in both precipitation and temperature. Salt Lake City, for example, has about 16 inches of rainfall a year, whereas 40 miles west, over the desert, there is only 6 inches, and 20 miles east, in the Wasatch Range, there is 43 inches.

People settled at the mouths of canyons, where water poured out, and at the base of mountains, just as in the Sahara they settled in scattered oases. Later on, engineering developments made it possible to bring water farther away from the mountains, but the pattern of settlement is still determined by the availability of water.

Ranching and dry farming are both practiced in the arid region, but irrigation dominates its agriculture. Modern irrigation agriculture was begun by the Mormons in 1847. Today about half the farms in 11 Western States are irrigated, and the value of irrigated land is well over half the value of all farm land. In Utah each acre of irrigated land is entirely dependent for its productiveness on the water from 7 acres of forest and range up in the mountains.

Irrigation agriculture seems ideal because moisture is fully controlled. But it involves very difficult problems. It cannot be successful without disciplined cooperation among the water users. Water conservation must be practiced high up in the mountains, and this involves regulation of other uses of the watershed to avoid erosion, floods, and siltation. Much land can be ruined by heavy concentration of salts carried in the irrigation water unless management practices are sound. Settlement must be carefully planned; it is easy to bring in more people than a given irrigated area will support or to put more land under cultivation than the available water justifies.

"Future expansion of irrigation," says Bailey, "depends primarily upon engineering developments." Available water and good soil seldom occur side by side; only engineering can bring them together. But the best engineering is no guaranty of success. That depends on a common understanding and acceptance of the peculiar necessities that arise when water has to be carefully collected, saved, and rationed out to make production possible.

Settlement and Cultivation in the Summer-Dry Climates

Not far inland from the Pacific coast a long stretch of mountains reaches from Canada almost to Mexico. East of these mountains lies the arid region already described. West of them is a strip of country that receives much more rainfall. But the peculiarity of this precipitation is that it comes mostly in winter. In summer the cyclonic storms caused by air battles along the polar front stay far to the north, and this strip of country has little or no precipitation. Thus it is characterized by drought in summer, moisture in winter—the reverse, in general, of what occurs in other agricultural regions of the United States. It is also characterized by mild winter temperatures because air coming from the Pacific is always comparatively warm, and cold air coming from the east is warmed by compression in dropping from the high mountains to the valley floors. In summer, sunshine is intense and temperatures are likely to be high, except where they are moderated by the ocean or by high elevations.

Native plants in the region are adapted to the peculiar climate. Trees in the moister areas and shrubs (chaparral) in the drier areas have deep enough roots to draw on ground water and so withstand summer drought. Grasses make their growth in late winter and early spring and ripen in early summer before drought becomes severe. Many of the common cultivated crops, however, are not suited to these conditions. For them, irrigation must be provided.

The first settlements were in the south, and they were made by Spanish missionaries from Mexico. Accustomed to a dry climate, the Spaniards were equipped to succeed. They had extensive herds; they produced grain by dry-farming methods; they raised fruits and vegetables with the aid of small-scale irrigation from the streams. Mission agriculture was suitable for the support of a small population. In the north, where there was more moisture, settlement followed the typical eastern pattern—trapper, trader, and finally pioneer farmer.

The gold rush brought a huge influx of fortune hunters who could not be adequately fed by the native agriculture. After 1860 there were four periods of agricultural development—1860–70, wheat; 1870–80, wool; 1880–90, fruit; 1890–1900, dairying. One type of agriculture did not displace another; they grew side by side, and each was due to the search for a new way to sell land to settlers.

Today agriculture in the summer-dry regions is based on the natural advantage of mild winters and a long growing season. Citrus fruits, the less hardy deciduous fruits, fresh vegetables in winter—these are grown for distant markets. The rainless summers are admirably adapted to the drying of prunes, raisins, peaches, apricots. Irrigation does not have quite the same function it has in truly arid regions; it is supplementary to the winter precipitation and is often provided by pumping directly out of the ground on individual farms. Winter run-off has gone mostly unused to the sea. The next step, says Leighly, is large-scale storage of winter precipitation, as in the Central

Valley water project, now being developed. The intensity of agriculture in the region as a whole depends almost entirely on how extensive are the means for overcoming summer drought.

The Colonization of Northern Lands

Stefansson, one-time Arctic explorer, has long been an enthusiast about northern lands. Here he gives his views about why they have not been more heavily colonized and what their resources and possibilities are. Most of the discussion concerns Alaska.

There are several fundamental reasons why the north has not been more thickly settled, and they go far back in history. Some of them, Stefansson thinks, are based mostly on misconceptions.

(1) The ancient Greeks divided the earth into five zones, of which only the two Temperate Zones were inhabitable. In the Arctic, they said, no life could exist. Not until 1937 was the existence of a lifeless region at the Pole finally disproved. In one way or another the old Greek doctrine, bolstered by a fear of the north natural to southerly peoples, has influenced our viewpoints for centuries.

(2) Southerly peoples, thinking only in terms of their own ways of doing things, cannot imagine how it is possible to live comfortably in the north. But it is in the main a question of doing things in different ways. Our winter clothes, made for looks, would not keep us warm in the Arctic; the Eskimo keeps warm with clothes designed for efficiency. Houses must be different from ours; for instance, the Eskimo's door is in the floor. Ice, an inconvenience to travel in the south, is a superb highway in the north, with proper equipment.

(3) The north can produce certain food products economically—reindeer meat, for example; wheat in certain regions. But farmers farther south already have a hard enough time getting along and naturally oppose further competition. Since they have a voice in governments, their opposition is a factor in holding back northern development.

(4) Some say the northern regions are too far away for colonization. With modern methods of transportation, this is not true. Scandinavia and Finland have about 16 million people. They are as far north as Alaska with its 73,000 inhabitants (of whom 39,000 are whites), and they are not so rich in some important resources. The pioneering, subsistence-farming psychology necessary for the settlement of Alaska is lacking today.

Average annual temperatures are not the only important factors in agricultural production, Stefansson argues. The long period of daylight in summer in the north makes up for the shortness of the growing season in the case of several crops. Wheat can be grown successfully where the summer temperatures are high enough, as they are in various northern regions. Where wheat cannot be grown, other crops often can be. The caribou (reindeer) is a very economical source of meat and hides; the musk ox, of meat, hides, and wool.

In spite of his enthusiasm for the north, Stefansson foresees no very rapid growth in the colonization of Alaska in the next decade. There might be such a rapid growth, he thinks, if the development of Alaskan resources were handed over to one or more huge privately owned corporations, somewhat like the old Hudson's Bay Co.; or to big coopera-

298737°—41——3 +

tives like those in Iceland or Palestine; or to the Government, which would imply some form of socialism. He believes that such things as fostering the development of the reindeer industry will result in a moderate increase in population with a cheap source of food, which in turn will make possible the further development of other resources, notably gold.

Climate and Settlement in Puerto Rico and the Hawaiian Islands

It has long been argued that white people cannot live normally in the Tropics. For the milder tropical climates, at least, this is disproved by experience in Puerto Rico and Hawaii. Not climate but economic conditions seem to be the determining factor.

More than two-thirds of the population of Puerto Rico was white in 1935, as compared with less than half in 1802. Of the serious diseases apparently brought in with slaves from Africa, yellow fever and smallpox have been conquered since the American occupation in 1898; hookworm and malaria are still prevalent. But improved health conditions increased the rate of population growth. In 1935 it was 501 to the square mile—more than the present agriculture of the island can support.

The chief product today is sugar, from large plantations made by consolidating small farms. This has crowded people into cities and factory centers or onto the poorer, rougher land. Employment is seasonal. Labor is cheap. Earnings are meager, and they go for imported rice, beans, codfish, supplemented by some home production of vegetables and fruits. Around the coffee plantations in the higher areas there is less crowding, but at present coffee production faces serious difficulties. Tobacco production alone is carried on on small farms.

Every student of Puerto Rican conditions realizes the seriousness of its economic problems. Large-scale migration to the United States or to other islands might solve them—if it were possible. Some have suggested that division of the sugar estates into small subsistence farms would be a solution, but studies also show that wages on sugar plantations will buy 3½ times as much food as can be raised on the same land. What is needed most, Thorp suggests, is the introduction of more industries, either privately owned or cooperative, with water power developed to make up as far as possible for the lack of coal.

The Hawaiian Islands, on the other hand, are relatively prosperous and could support a larger population than they have. Health conditions are better than in many parts of the United States; there is little unemployment; wages are sufficient for a good standard of living. Sugarcane produces the highest average yields in the world, through the use of scientific methods; the pineapple industry is prosperous; high-quality beef is produced on large ranches on some of the islands.

Climate does not account for the difference in the condition of the people in these two regions. Puerto Rico has a relatively small amount of normally arable land, which makes it easier to reach the point of extreme population pressure. Both regions have about the same minimum rainfall in certain areas, but there is a much greater maximum in the wet portions of the Hawaiian Islands—almost 500 inches a year, as compared with 150 in Puerto Rico.

Climate and Future Settlement

Broek takes up the question of pioneering in new lands. After 400 years of migration by the European peoples, there are still large areas which they have avoided or only thinly settled. This is mainly because people go to new lands in order to have better opportunities than they had at home, and the good lands, offering better opportunities, have all been taken. The remaining sparsely settled regions are those in which climate is a serious draw-back—the hot wet regions, the hot dry regions, the cold regions. At least it is not considered today that these regions are uninhabitable; the problem is to find techniques for overcoming the climatic draw-backs; but this usually involves high costs. There is an increased interest in colonization at present because of the search for places where European refugees can settle. Broek discusses each of the three types of regions in turn.

Draw-backs to white settlement in the hot wet regions of tropical rain forest include monotonous weather, deficient diets, overpowering vegetative growth, leached soils, diseases carried by insects. There is now a more optimistic view about the white man's ability to stay healthy in these regions, however; it seems quite possible with a good diet, proper sanitation and other precautions, enough regular exercise, and perhaps suitable air conditioning. But all these things imply a high standard of living. This is not difficult for colonial officials, business managers, and others in well-paid positions, but it becomes a real problem in the case of a complete white settlement where the majority of the people have to earn a living by manual work. The serious problem, then, is economic. Among the elements of this problem are the health menace from natives with a low standard of living; economic competition from the same quarter; high costs of cultivation and comparatively low yields. Colonization in these regions, Broek concludes, must have expert leadership and be preceded by adequate experimentation. In the cooler uplands of the Tropics and in the lowlands on the edges of the Tropics chances are better than in the true rain-forest regions.

The hot dry regions (the deserts) are healthy enough. Soils are often rich in minerals. The great draw-back to agricultural production is lack of water. Extensive irrigation costs a great deal, and it is profitable only with crops of high value. In the semiarid areas on the edges of deserts the problem is mainly the uncertainty and irregularity of rainfall, as discussed by Thornthwaite in the article on the Great Plains.

The cold polar climate seems to be the most formidable of the three, judging by sparseness of settlement. The shortness of the growing season, the rather poor character of the soils, and the inaccessibility of the north are draw-backs. Far north of the Arctic Circle, in the tundra (the region of mosses and lichens), extreme measures, such as the production of vegetables in hothouses, must be resorted to to support any large population; hence there will not be much settlement in this region unless there are powerful reasons for it. In the taiga (the region of coniferous forests farther south) conditions are more favorable for agriculture. Potatoes and other vegetables, flax, forage crops, and early-maturing grains can be raised. The northward push of agriculture here will be determined largely by the demand for foodstuffs in mining and lumbering areas. One advantage for the farmer is that he can work in mines or mills during the winter. Careful planning is required, however, to avoid temporary exploitation of resources, leaving stranded communities.

Comfort and Disease in Relation to Climate

Hirsh deals with some of the broad general relations of climate to comfort and disease.

Through extremes of heat and cold, from −40° F. in the Dakotas in winter to 130° in a southwestern desert in summer, the body maintains a constant temperature of about 98°, largely through its own heat-regulating mechanism. Contrary to common opinion, it does not depend much on such external aids as clothing. In cold weather it speeds up the rate of heat production; skin and fatty tissues serve as insulation against heat loss; surface blood vessels contract to save heat; we may even produce extra heat by shivering. In hot weather the surface blood vessels dilate so that heat can be carried more quickly from the inside to the outside, where it can be lost by convection and radiation; the evaporation of sweat also has a cooling effect.

Comfort, however, does not depend on temperature alone but on other factors as well. High humidity in particular helps to prevent heat loss from the body and makes high temperatures much less bearable. Fanning and dehumidifying the air both help the body to lose heat. But beyond certain limits reduction in the moisture content of warm air becomes harmful; in a dry parched atmosphere the mucous membranes of nose and throat tend to become dry, and susceptibility to respiratory troubles increases.

The practical objective in clothing and housing should be to help the body maintain the balance between heat production and heat loss with a minimum of effort. House heating in winter and cooling in summer should not be overdone, however, because too great a contrast with outdoor conditions makes it difficult to become readjusted to them. In heating a house it is especially important to provide for the thorough mixing of cold and warm air; too often, in an ordinary room, the head is in a warm stagnant atmosphere, and the feet are in a cold drafty one.

Acclimatization, or adjustment to a different climate from that one has been used to, often presents serious problems. The southerner coming north, writes Hirsh, may find that his body is suddenly called on to produce more heat than it has been accustomed to producing; the northerner going south may find himself uncomfortable because his heat production and activity are at too high levels for a warm climate. Serious consequences may follow sudden changes unless precautions are taken while the body is making new adjustments—a process that may take considerable time.

Few diseases are caused directly by climate; among them are heat exhaustion, heatstroke, snow blindness, frostbite, mountain sickness. But climate favors the organisms that cause some diseases, such as malaria and hookworm, and it also affects the individual's resistance to disease.

Hirsh gives several examples of climatic influences in relation to disease, including the seasonal rise and fall of the common cold, pneumonia, and infantile paralysis, and the occurrence of the three major troubles caused by heat—heat cramps, heat exhaustion, and heatstroke. Of the three, heatstroke is the most sudden and dangerous; it may cause death within a short time and requires immediate and constant attention by a physician. Excessive loss of salts from the body by sweating is a major factor in causing heat exhaustion and heat cramps. Taking extra salt is a preventive.

In general, Hirsh notes, climate is less to blame for diseases in many regions than such factors as poor nutrition, overcrowding, and lack of adequate sanitation and medical care.

Health in Tropical Climates

Stone has been particularly concerned with what happens to people, physiologically, in the Tropics, but his discussion is of much wider interest for the light it throws on our reactions to excessive heat whether we live in the Tropics or not. It might almost have been called Men in Hot Weather.

It would be useful to have an absolute scale of comfort in relation to temperature and humidity, but every attempt to make such a scale runs up against two basic difficulties. There is a marked difference in what different individuals call comfortable; and what is comfortable to an individual at one time may not be at another. People agree only on certain extremes. For instance, everyone will say it is very hot when the temperature is 95° F. and the humidity 70 percent, and everyone will agree that it is cool when the temperature is below 60° or 65°.

So far as health is concerned, the monotony of the tropical climate is more harmful than the heat and humidity. Where climatic variations are slight from day to day and season to season, the body loses its ability to adapt itself to changes and thus becomes more sensitive to whatever changes do occur. Hence the danger, for example, of "chills" in the Tropics; bodily resistance to cold has been lost. Moreover, if there is enough variation in the climate, it is possible to withstand extreme conditions for a while, even though they might be dangerous if long-continued. Hot days are bearable if the nights are cool enough for sleep, but a long stretch of hot days and nights can be very exhausting. Some of the summer heat waves in the United States are much worse than any weather that ever occurs in parts of the subtropics, but the heat waves have not been a serious drawback to settlement because they are temporary.

The simplest way to maintain physical tone and make up for the lack of variation in a tropical climate is to take regular, vigorous exercise—in spite of contrary opinion in the past. The worst substitute for climatic stimulation—but one commonly resorted to—is overindulgence in alcohol.

What does "comfort" mean physiologically? It means that heat losses are balancing heat production in the body without sensible strain. When the air becomes very cold, this balance still occurs—down to a certain temperature—through more severe internal adjustments. These adjustments to cold can be made to operate very promptly by training, but they can also be impaired by disuse.

Adjustments to high temperatures are also made by the body, though they are not made so well by the very young, the aged, the sick, and those with weak hearts; these are the individuals most likely to succumb to heat. The process of acclimatization to heat, says Stone, consists largely in learning to sweat more volume with less salt in it, and this must be accompanied by taking more water and more salt. Other adjustments are involved, too, though some of the ones suggested are questioned by some authorities. The basal metabolism may decrease somewhat; the number of sweat glands may increase; some of the internal glands may alter their level of secretion.

Exposure to sunlight is one of the problems of life in the Tropics. It is well to acquire a tan if possible because this increases the resistance of the skin to ultraviolet radiation, but extreme exposure is dangerous. Shade and white clothing help to reduce the heat from the sun. Why then are not Negroes, with dark skins, more sensitive to heat than the whites? Because they have more sweat glands, start to sweat sooner, and sweat more copiously. Moreover, they have a tough skin that withstands infection better than that of the whites.

Not much can be said with certainty about the effects of a tropical climate on the body because only very inadequate records have been kept so far. There seems to be a lowering of blood pressure; the volume of blood presumably increases, but it is more diluted; sweating takes a toll of plasma, fluid, and salts which must be made up; there is a decrease in gastric secretions, accompanied by constipation and impaired appetite and digestion; there is also reduced energy for work, but this may often be only a sign of malnutrition or some other trouble. Those who have high energy production because of an overactive thyroid are likely to become neurasthenic in the Tropics. There is less oxygen per cubic foot in hot than in cold air, and this may reduce the effectiveness of all bodily functions unless the body becomes adjusted to it.

All in all, says Stone, the most important conclusions seem to be that the constant sweating and the increase of blood flow to the capillaries induced by warmth have a harmful effect on blood chemistry and the tone of the internal organs, lowering resistance to infection. With more knowledge, it may be quite possible to overcome these difficulties by suitable hygienic measures. Selection of individuals especially adapted to live in the Tropics, much as Army and Navy fliers are selected, is another promising possibility.

PART 3. CLIMATE AND THE FARMER

Climate and Soil

Kellogg does not confine his discussion strictly to the tie-up between soil and climate but endeavors to answer these five broad questions: (1) How is a soil formed? (2) What is the relationship between climatic factors and soil? (3) What are the principal soil types and their characteristics? (4) What factors are involved in soil fertility and productivity, soil exhaustion and renewal, and erosion? (5) What considerations guide the farmer in his use of the soils on an individual farm?

(1) As an example of soil formation he takes a soil in a humid, temperate climate like that of West Virginia or Maryland. Begin with an exposed granite rock. Sun, rain, changes in temperature, ice in the cracks, all cause it to crumble. Some of the minerals are changed and dissolved by water. At some time plants appear and take hold—at first, maybe only mosses and lichens; eventually, trees. They die and their organic material is added to the crumbled rock substance, together with the minerals they have pulled up and built into their bodies. Bacteria and other micro-organisms bring about the break-down and decay of the organic material; some "fix" nitrogen from the air and add it to the soil.

This particular soil, formed under a humid-climate forest, would be acid, partly because no great amount of basic (alkaline) substances are pulled up by tree roots to be added to the surface. Trees also make comparatively little humus. Rain in this humid climate would wash some minerals down entirely below the soil. Some of the clay, in fine particles, would also be washed down and deposited in a layer below the surface. Eventually there would be a number of layers of different kinds, one above another. Together, they would make a profile with distinctive characteristics, determined by the climatic and other conditions under which this soil was formed. The two top layers (horizons) would be the true soil. The normal erosion is constantly removing some of this as soil-forming processes extend into the rocks beneath. Under them would be loose material; under that, solid rock. Changes would constantly be going on in the soil, but in time gains and losses would be in a state of balance.

Other soils, formed under different conditions, would be quite different from this one. Strong differences in climate make strong differences in vegetation and the soils formed under the vegetation.

(2) In discussing climate and soil, Kellogg emphasizes the refinements and complexities rather than the broader and simpler relationships. There are many variations to be taken into account. Vegetation, for example, modifies climate locally; wind, sunlight, rain, snow are different under a dense forest, under grass, under sparse desert vegetation. Within the soil itself, the climate is again modified. Steep slopes and gentle slopes, slopes facing the sun and those facing away from it, even small mounds and shallow pits, all have different effects on the climate at the surface and under the soil. Changes in air pressure at the surface are recorded instantly in the soil, even deep down, because of the pore spaces into which the air enters.

Soil temperatures are different on south slopes and on north slopes, and a vegetative cover makes a difference also. The temperature of the soil is especially influenced by the amount of water and the amount of organic matter it contains; the less water and the less organic matter, the more quickly the soil responds to changes in air temperature. The temperature of the rain itself also has an influence. Evaporation, of course, has a cooling effect and greatly modifies the heat coming from the sun.

The internal structure of the soil is a very important factor in determining how much rainfall it will absorb; an impervious soil on a steep slope will take in little water and be arid even in a moist climate. A soil is seldom uniformly moistened by rain; thus there are differences in internal climate not only between different soils in the same region but between the different horizons of the same soil.

In view of all these complexities and major and minor variations, Kellogg implies, it is impossible to make sweeping statements. All the factors in a given situation at a given time must be known and taken into account.

(3) Leaching or lack of leaching, directly due to the amount of rainfall, makes a vast difference in soil types. In humid regions, the more soluble constituents are washed out; in subhumid regions only the most soluble minerals, leaving the less soluble ones, such as lime, to accumulate below the surface. In semiarid regions there is still less leaching.

There are three main kinds of soils—those chiefly influenced by climate and vegetation, called zonal soils; those in which local factors have overbalanced climate and vegetation, called intrazonal soils; and those characterized by extreme youth or other conditions that have prevented normal soil formation, called azonal soils.

Of the zonal soils, Kellogg describes the four most sharply different groups—Podzols, Laterites, Chernozems, and Desert soils. These have already been briefly characterized in this summary in connection with Thornthwaite's article, Climate and the World Pattern. All the other groups of zonal soils, Kellogg points out, are more or less transitional between these four.

Intrazonal soils include those that are poorly drained—in the humid regions, Bog, Half-Bog, and meadow soils (Wiesenboden); in the arid regions, saline and alkali soils, in which salts have accumulated. Also included are Planosols, which have a hard claypan or siltpan under the surface owing to lack of natural erosion, and Rendzinas—black soils developed from soft calcareous marl or chalk. Azonal soils include the barren, rocky soils on steep slopes and the frequently rich Alluvial soils of actively growing deltas and flood plains.

(4) Soil fertility is measured by the amount, balance, and availability of the chemical compounds that influence plant growth. Soil productivity is quite different and much more complex. The productivity of a soil depends not only on its chemical nutrients but also on its physical condition, its slope, the amount and distribution of rainfall, seasonal temperatures, the frequency and severity of droughts and frost. Lack of fertility can often be corrected by management practices if it pays to do so, and many soils of comparatively low fertility have been made very productive by management.

In considering soil exhaustion, Kellogg again emphasizes the complexity of the problem. Maintaining the soil is not simply a matter of replacing nutrients or of any other single treatment, because no one factor acts by itself. The climate, the slope, the amount of nutrients, the rate at which they become available for plants, the depth of plant roots, the ability of the plant to use certain nutrients—all these things act together. Cultivation does not necessarily reduce the productivity of the soil or even lead to erosion; whether it does or not depends on particular management practices in relation to these other factors. Nor are deficiencies of nutrients in the soil necessarily due to wholesale removal of chemicals by crops. Rather, there are specific deficiencies related to particular soil types and management practices. The structure of the soil—its permeability to water and to roots—is as important as the nutrient supply. "In order to maintain good structure," says Kellogg, "most soils must be devoted periodically to grass or close-growing legumes."

(5) Kellogg concludes that there is no "best use" for any combination of soil and climate in the abstract. The range of possible uses is less with some soils than with others, but many soils can be used in a dozen or more different ways, and which one is chosen depends on prices of farm products, available credit, transportation, and various other factors—including what the farmer can do best and wants to do most. Each farm unit is an individual problem. To illustrate, Kellogg describes five different farms—two in the Southeast with different soils, three in Michigan with the same soils—and shows how various factors would combine to determine what would be produced in each case.

Effects of Climatic Factors on Growing Plants

Climate and weather are as decisive in the development of a plant as home surroundings are in the life of a growing child. Hildreth, Magness, and Mitchell show how and why in considerable detail.

Temperature, moisture, and light are the big three that have the most power over plant life. They always work together to produce a given effect, but we can understand them better if we consider them separately.

Hopkins worked out a "bioclimatic law" that covers mainly a response to temperature: For each degree of latitude north or south of the Equator, and also for each 400-foot increase in altitude, the date of flowering of plants of the same species is retarded 4 calendar days; for each 5 degrees of longitude from east to west on land areas it is advanced 4 calendar days.

Temperature influences every chemical and physical process in plants and determines the great production belts for various crops. Though plant life as a whole is enormously adaptable (there are algae that thrive in hot springs at 200° F., and arctic plants that survive −90°), most plants will grow only within a much narrower range. For each species and variety there is a minimum below which growth is not possible, an optimum at which growth is most rapid, a maximum beyond which growth stops; and these temperatures may vary with different stages of development (seedlings, for example, may grow well at comparatively low temperatures). The optimum temperature is not always the best for commercial production, since it may produce too rapid growth, but some temperature near the optimum is usually essential.

Plants escape cold injury in various ways. Some complete their life cycle before cold weather arrives; others die down to the roots; others have developed the power to resist cold during a dormant or semidormant period, though no one has yet discovered what this resistance really consists of. Nevertheless, damage from cold is a universal hazard throughout the United States, even in subtropical fruit-growing areas, because for economic reasons production is always being extended beyond the safe seasonal and geographic limits. One of the objects of plant breeding is to make this extension possible by creating hardier strains.

The authors describe several types of cold injury. Many plants make a surprising recovery because not all their parts are equally affected by cold. Nor is cold always harmful. All of our deciduous fruit trees, for example, go into a rest period during which no growth occurs, and under natural conditions only a cold spell will break this rest and enable the plant to start growing again. This is the reason for the cold storage of bulbs and the chilling of rhubarb roots as commercial practices. Again, winter wheat requires a cold period in the germination and early seedling stages, or it will not head later on. An artificial cold treatment ("vernalization") of the partly germinated seed will accomplish the desired result.

Several types of heat injury are also described by the authors. They point out that heat treatment of floral parts is now used to increase the number of chromosomes in the cells—a method under investigation for producing new types of plants.

Moisture relationships divide plants into three broad groups. The camels of the plant world are the xerophytes; they have remarkable adaptations to drought. At the other extreme are the hydrophytes—the ducks of the plant world (rice is practically a hydrophyte). In between are the mesophytes, the average citizens of the plant world. They include practically all agricultural crop plants and they can usually adapt themselves somewhat to extremes if they have to.

Actively growing plant parts (not woody parts) usually contain 75 to 90 percent of water. In addition, relatively large amounts of water are constantly passing through the plant and being evaporated (transpired) by the leaves. Root systems to supply this steady flow of water are far more extensive than most people realize; grass roots often go down 16 feet. Good soil structure is perhaps more important than anything else from a moisture standpoint; a soil with a right structure will often hold enough available water to mature a crop even if there is no rain throughout the entire growth period. Plants as well as soils differ in moisture efficiency; in one study, a variety of alfalfa used 963 pounds of water to build a pound of dry matter and another variety only 651 pounds; one variety of millet required 444 pounds and another only 261. This of course is a fundamental factor in the adaptation of agricultural plants to various regions; it means, too, that not only water-conserving farm practices but plant breeding can be used to overcome limitations in the water supply.

Light, the third great climatic factor, has effects as fundamental as those of temperature and moisture. The less light, the more a plant grows in length; hence growth speeds up at night and slows down in the daytime; hence, too, seedlings grow relatively fast under the soil. For the process of food manufacture within the plant, on the other hand, light is essential. With many plants, day length rather than temperature sets the time of maturity; they will flower and produce seed only when the days are of the right length—some requiring long, some short days. Varieties of the same plant (soybeans, for example) may differ in these requirements, and this too is sometimes important in crop distribution and plant breeding. The intensity of the light has different effects on different plants. Some reach maximum production with high light intensity—as in irrigated areas in arid regions. Others—sunflower, buckwheat, tobacco—produce more when slightly shaded.

Influence of Climate and Weather on Growth of Corn

Corn is more widely distributed over the world than any other cereal, which means that it has exceptionally wide adaptability. Each climate has its characteristic varieties, ranging from those less than 2 feet tall, with 8 or 9 leaves, maturing in 60 to 70 days, to those over 20 feet tall, with 42 to 44 leaves, maturing in 10 to 11 months. For this achievement, which has no equal in plant-breeding history, Jenkins gives credit to the American Indians, who originally developed types suited to the places where they lived, from Canada to Peru. The white man has been carrying on this work of breeding for adaptability to climate.

The outstanding fact emphasized by Jenkins is the difference in the adaptability of different strains of corn to climatic factors. Though most corn cannot germinate satisfactorily below 50° F. and is very susceptible to seedling diseases below 55°, inbred and open-pollinated strains show enough differences to warrant efforts to breed strains suitable for planting in cold soil. The same thing holds true for resistance to excessive heat, especially when combined with drought. Some inbreds and hybrids are very much less damaged than others, and there is definite evidence that heat tolerance is inherited. Similarly, some strains produce viable pollen and have receptive silks at temperatures too high for others.

For best growth and production corn requires a plentiful supply of moisture well-distributed throughout the growing season. The rate of evaporation has a great influence on the water demands of the plant, and in some seasons evaporation is very much higher than in others. In moisture needs too there is a difference in strains. The Pueblo Indians in the Southwest have an ancient type of corn that can be planted a foot deep to be near moisture in ground dry on top. Other varieties could not push up to the surface from this depth, but this variety can produce fair crops in semiarid New Mexico and Arizona. Modern plant breeders have developed varieties that are somewhat drought-resistant, and special farm practices also are useful in overcoming the handicap of deficient moisture.

Again, strains differ in their ability to recover from freezing injury during the seedling stage; a corn grown by Indians in the mountains of Mexico is said to withstand severe freezing when it is 2 feet tall. Some strains can withstand a fall temperature of 32° F. for several hours without great injury.

Length of day has a marked effect on the time of flowering and of ripening. Northern varieties grown near the Equator, where the summer days are short, ripen more quickly; southern varieties moved to the north ripen later. In general, a variety ripens 1 day earlier or later for each 10 miles north or south of a given starting point, if altitude remains the same. This means that southern varieties of corn can be used in the north to produce a greater amount of silage because they have a longer period of vegetative growth.

Many of the new corn hybrids are exceptionally resistant to lodging—often caused by high winds—and this is of great importance in machine harvesting.

Jenkins discusses a number of other relations of climate to corn growing and gives figures showing the distribution of corn production throughout the world.

Climate and Small Grains

There are ways of partly overcoming the hazards of climate and weather in the case of small grains. Plant explorers search the earth for varieties that will stand up against drought and cold, mature quickly, and resist the diseases prevalent in certain climates; and these introductions are used by breeders to develop still better varieties. Special cultural practices are also used—for example, early preparation of the ground, planting at just the right time, seeding in stubble or furrows.

Salmon first tells how climate affects the distribution of small grains; then how climate and weather affect growth, yields, and quality.

Precipitation, length of growing season, and winter temperatures are the main factors limiting the regions of production. Most of these regions have not less than 15 and not more than 45 (preferably not more than 30) inches of rainfall a year, though with special practices and suitable distribution of the rainfall, wheat is grown where there is only 10 inches. Diseases, leached soils, excessive growth and lodging, and other difficulties prevent production (except in the case of rice) in regions of high rainfall. In general, a frost-free growing season of at least 100 days is necessary for the small grains, though here again the limits are sometimes extended, in spite of the extra hazards, to 90 days or less. Where there is a short season, only spring-sown grains can be grown. Winter temperatures as well as the length of the growing season limit the production of winter (fall-sown) grains; rye is the most cold-resistant and can be grown farthest north. Toward the Poles the extra length of summer days becomes a factor in grain growing, overcoming some of the handicap of a short season by enabling the crop to mature earlier.

In discussing the effects of weather on growth, Salmon considers first the fall, then the winter, then the spring and summer.

Fall weather is of some importance to grains seeded the following spring because it affects the amount of available moisture and plant foods, especially nitrates; but it has more extensive effects on winter grains. With them the amount of moisture determines whether the seed will germinate promptly, or not at all, or not until spring. If it does not germinate until spring, the crop may not mature, or it may mature late and be subject to damage by rust, heat, and drought. The amount of fall growth is also important. In the East, it is desirable to have large plants to resist soil heaving; in the semiarid areas, too much fall growth may deplete moisture and nitrates or result in lodging. The hardening of plants to resist winter temperatures is extremely important; warm, rainy weather in the fall may be disastrous from this standpoint. Just what "hardening" really is is not known, but it seems to be related to the accumulation of sugars in the plant, induced by cold weather.

Winter weather is important chiefly for its relation to winter killing, which is caused by the freezing of the crowns or roots, heaving of the soil, "smothering" of the plant under ice or snow, and drought within the plant tissues. Salmon thinks it is debatable whether this internal, or physiological, drought really causes winter killing; external drought, however, can kill plants in winter as well as at any other time of the year. Heaving, caused by alternate freezing and thawing, is most important in the East. It is doubtful whether plants really "smother" under snow and ice, though this may occur if they are covered by water when the snow or ice melts. Actual freezing of crowns or roots seems to depend largely on the quantity of ice formed within the cells. Hardened plants can withstand some freezing without injury, but hardiness decreases in late winter.

The most important factors in spring and summer weather are late frosts, high temperatures, and moisture supply. Spring-planted grains usually escape freezes without much damage, but winter grain is sometimes extensively damaged, and this has forced the use of late-maturing varieties in the southern Great Plains. There are marked differences in cold resistance between different varieties of the same kind of grain—a fact that makes it possible to reduce losses considerably by using the hardier varieties. High temperatures are especially harmful at the heading stage or between heading and ripening, probably because they are accompanied by excessive transpiration, which rapidly reduces the available moisture.

Weather is undoubtedly the most important factor in grain yields, but the relationships are extremely complicated, Salmon points out, and it is not yet possible to forecast a crop accurately from a study of weather data—desirable as that would be for farmers and the grain industry. It is possible, however, to make very general advance estimates of yields of winter wheat in the Great Plains by determining the depth of moisture in the soil at seeding time in the fall and correlating this with the subsequent rainfall during the winter. Similar methods have recently been worked out for spring wheat.

Salmon discusses at some length the relation of climate and weather to the quality of grain, and especially the protein content of wheat. There have been several theories about the latter. He comes to the conclusion that protein content is high in dry climates and in dry years because (1) there is more nitrogen in the soil under these conditions, partly because of reduced leaching; (2) vegetative growth is reduced, so that less nitrogen is used for this purpose and more is left to make protein in the seeds; (3) yields may be reduced, so that a given amount of nitrogen is concentrated in a smaller total quantity of seeds.

Salmon concludes his article with an account of the production of each of the small grains throughout the world, going into considerable detail regarding the principal producing areas in the United States and Canada.

Climate and Sorghum

Martin gives much useful information about sorghum in a brief space. Among his facts are these:

Until recently grain sorghums could be grown only where there was a frost-free season of at least 160 days, a mean July temperature of at least 75° F., and an average precipitation of at least 17 inches. New varieties developed by plant breeders can be grown with a season as short as 130 days, a mean July temperature of 70°, an average precipitation of 15 inches.

Sorghums can produce a crop under hot, dry conditions because they have a corky skin covered with wax, which reduces transpiration and drying; they are actually perennials under frost-free conditions and can remain dormant during a short drought, sending up new tillers when moisture again becomes available; and they have a large number of fibrous roots.

Sorghums should not be planted until after all danger of spring frosts is over. Damage from fall frosts can be minimized by the right choice of varieties and planting dates. The earliest sorgo varieties (not grain sorghums) will ripen in 80 days.

Heading is hastened by short days and delayed by long ones. Most tropical varieties will not head in the United States for this reason, but some developed in this country will mature grain with days as long as 16 hours. Early-maturing varieties grown under the long-day conditions in the North may produce larger plants than they do in the South.

At least 11 to 12 inches of rain on sandy soils and 13 to 14 on loam soils is required to produce any grain worth harvesting; each inch of rain above these lower limits may mean an additional 2 to 2½ bushels per acre. Failures can be reduced by thin planting, wide spacing of rows, and the use of drought-escaping varieties.

An inch of water saved by cultural practices is as good as an extra inch of rainfall. Yields of milo in the southwestern Great Plains have been increased 50 to 90 percent by summer fallowing, which conserves soil moisture.

Climate and Cotton

Cotton is being planted and picked somewhere in the world every day in the year. So useful is the fiber that many efforts have been made to extend production beyond the naturally favorable climatic regions, and in modern times some of these efforts have been successful through the breeding of rapid-fruiting, early-maturing varieties. It is now generally agreed, Doyle writes, that the climatic requirements for successful commercial production are a mean annual temperature of not less than 60° F. or, under certain otherwise favorable conditions, of not less than 50°; a frost-free season of 180–200 days; annual rainfall of not less than 20 and not more than 75 inches, with suitable seasonal distribution; open, sunny weather at least half the time throughout the year.

Weather conditions have an enormous influence on yield and quality. Cotton thrives best when there is a mild spring with light, frequent showers; a moderately moist summer, warm both day and night; sunny weather during the period of bloom; a dry, cool, prolonged autumn. On the other hand, there is a long list of unfavorable conditions. Cold wet weather in spring may rot the seed, retard seedling growth, favor cutworms and seedling diseases. Rains that cause the soil to pack or crust at planting time may ruin the stand, and too little moisture may prevent germination. Cold winds, sandstorms, and duststorms early in the season may kill seedlings. Cold nights and hot days while the plants are young favor the cotton louse. Heavy rains and low temperatures in May and June favor diseases and insects. A wet summer induces too much vegetative growth and favors the boll weevil. Severe summer drought often stunts the plants and causes too early maturity. Rainy weather at picking time retards maturity, interrupts picking, damages the exposed fiber. Hailstorms during the growing or harvesting season may do much damage.

Doyle points out that the peculiar fruiting habit of the cotton plant makes it sensitive to weather conditions over an exceptionally long period. Flowers appear progressively every 2½ days on the fruiting branches that develop up the main stalk, and every 6 or 7 days outward along the fruiting branches. Throughout the entire period of progressive fruit formation, weather influences the quantity of fruit formed, the amount of shedding, the size of bolls, and the quality of the fiber. Among the causes of shedding are insects and diseases, high temperatures that result in excessive loss of moisture through transpiration and evaporation, heavy and continous rain, abrupt changes in weather, imperfect pollination due to rain, and root injury. The principal cause is probably lack of sufficient soil moisture.

Boll weevils increase rapidly as the season advances, and practically all the buds developed later than July are apt to be destroyed. This major handicap of cotton production has been met by breeding rapid-fruiting, early-maturing varieties and working out cultural practices that favor earliness.

Federal and State cooperative studies carried out in great detail have proved that both inherited characteristics and weather govern the yield and fiber qualities of cotton. It has not been possible, however, to work out an accurate method of local crop forecasting based on local weather conditions. Doyle believes this is partly because the right kind of weather data are not available—there is little or no information, for example, on such extremely important factors as soil moisture and transpiration—and partly because the long fruiting period of the cotton plant makes drastic changes in yields possible up to the last minute. For the Cotton Belt as a whole, however, seasonal reports and crop forecasts have been remarkably accurate.

Cotton is bought on the basis of grade standards, and Doyle points out that exposure to the weather through careless harvesting and storing is responsible for enormous losses to growers, much of it preventable. Cotton that is dull, grayed, or blue as a result of delayed picking and exposure in the field sells for about $15 less per 500-pound bale than high-grade white (⅞-inch staple). Seed too is greatly damaged by careless harvesting and storing. A 500-pound bale of cotton left uncovered flat on the ground had only 130 pounds undamaged at the end of 8 months as compared with 499 pounds undamaged in a bale stored in a warehouse.

At the end of his article Doyle discusses the areas of production of all the commercial types of cotton throughout the world, yields in the principal regions, and the soils and climate of the Cotton Belt of the United States.

Climate and Tobacco

Tropical in origin, tobacco is now grown under a wide range of climatic and soil conditions as far north as central Sweden, as far south as southern Australia. The moisture requirements of the plant are high because of its great leaf area and the desirability of rapid growth. Heavy yields, on the other hand, are not desired because they mean lower quality. Among the most serious weather hazards are hail and high winds, which can seriously damage the large leaves. The ravages of the wildfire disease also usually depend on weather, as it attacks the leaves of certain tobacco types when they are water-soaked by wind-driven rain. If plants resistant to water soaking can be bred, they should also be resistant to wildfire.

Garner discusses some of the more important growth requirements of tobacco but emphasizes the relation of climate and weather to quality. Certain specific qualities divide tobacco into different types suitable for different uses, and each type in turn has its own special quality requirements. The size, shape, color, veining, elasticity, combustibility, minute structure, and chemical composition of the leaf determine these qualities, and each of these factors is affected by the environment of the plant.

For example: Too low temperatures may prevent the full ripeness necessary for the best quality. High temperatures reduce the water content of the plant and favor strong aroma and thickening of the leaf. Optimum moisture conditions, partial shade, and absence of wind favor the production of a large, broad, thin, fine-veined, open-textured, elastic, light-colored, bright leaf with low nicotine content, weak aroma, and little resinous matter—the type required for cigar wrappers. Less favorable moisture conditions mean a smaller, narrower, denser, heavier, thicker-veined, less elastic, darker colored, duller, slower burning leaf with more nicotine, stronger aroma, and more resin—qualities desired in different degrees in cigar-filler, cigarette, pipe-smoking, chewing, and snuff tobaccos.

Seasonal variations in weather will naturally affect the quality of leaf, just as regional differences in climate affect both type and quality. Research in recent years has shown how to modify moisture conditions to some extent by fertilizer practices and the use of the right kind of organic matter in the soil. The methods of topping and suckering also have some effect on moisture relations.

In general, what the tobacco grower wants is rapid, uninterrupted growth throughout the season, somewhat limited rainfall during the early stages, light and infrequent rains during the ripening period, not too much humidity during curing (if this is done without artificial heat), and a period of damp weather after curing.

By way of illustrating his points, Garner describes a few of the most famous tobaccos in the world and the conditions under which they are produced.

Climate and Vegetable Crops

Boswell and Jones think Mark Twain was wrong when he said that nobody does anything about the weather though everyone talks about it. From a vegetable grower's standpoint a good deal has been done about the weather. The native range of many vegetable plants was very narrow and they had very exacting climatic requirements, yet they are now grown over much of the earth in climates quite different from those in their old homes. There are many ways of accomplishing this. Seed is produced in the most favorable regions, often far removed from the places where the plants are grown for food. Short-season plants are grown to follow the march of the seasons, northward in the spring, southward in the fall. Young plants are started in the South, shipped to the North for transplanting to the field weeks later. Greenhouses, hotbeds, coldframes, plant covers are employed to lengthen the growing season. Irrigation is used to overcome drought and make deserts productive. New varieties of plants are bred to overcome some climatic handicaps. Fresh products are hauled long distances because of modern developments in refrigeration and transportation. Finally, the vegetable grower can generally take more chances with the weather than producers of some other crops—tree fruits, for instance.

All this means that it is at least possible to get around the weather if not to change it. Nevertheless, climate (including weather) is still the most important single factor in vegetable production.

One of the major requirements in the production of fresh vegetables is to avoid regions subject to sudden and extreme weather changes. They may be ruinous to very early and very late crops—and the market gardener tries to get as close to the edge of the season as possible because that is the time when there is the least competition in his own region. Thus the great market and truck-gardening areas in the United States are near large bodies of water, which reduce climatic extremes, or in protected valleys. Boswell and Jones list these areas as (1) a belt along the Atlantic and Gulf coasts from Massachusetts to Texas, (2) a broad area along the Great Lakes from New York into Minnesota, (3) certain intermountain valleys in Colorado, Utah, and Idaho, (4) the Rio Grande Valley in Texas, (5) the Pacific coast and intermountain valleys of Arizona and California. The last three areas grow vegetables mostly under irrigation.

Climatic extremes of spring and fall do not matter so much in the case of vegetables for canning and freezing because it is not necessary to concentrate on early or late production. Thus they can be grown outside the great market-garden areas—in the Corn Belt, for instance.

There is much commercial production in the South in the spring and fall, but Boswell and Jones point out that midsummer production there is a serious problem. High temperatures speed up maturity, shorten the harvest period, and hasten deterioration after harvesting. Some important crops are directly damaged by excessive heat and sunlight. Certain insects and plant diseases flourish and take a heavy toll. There is great need in the South for new varieties, and perhaps for special cultural practices, that will overcome these handicaps, not only for commercial production for shipment but also for the sake of improving the local supply of summer vegetables. The

298737°—41——4

breeding problem is being tackled by the United States Vegetable Breeding Laboratory at Charleston, S. C., in cooperation with the experiment stations in the Southeastern States. Another area that needs special varieties is the high plateau region of the Rocky Mountains, where the main difficulty is the shortness of the growing season. That problem is being tackled by the United States Cheyenne Horticultural Field Station. Various State stations are dealing with the same problem for other areas in the country.

Boswell and Jones divide the vegetable crops into four main groups according to certain climatic requirements:

(1) Cool-climate crops, growing best at mean temperatures of 60°–65° F., and not tolerant of mean summer temperatures above 70°–75°. These include (a) very hardy crops not usually injured by freezing—cabbage, brussels sprouts, turnips, rutabagas, kohlrabi, collards, horseradish, spinach, beets, parsnips; (b) crops usually damaged by freezing—cauliflower, lettuce, carrots, celery, peas, potatoes.

(2) Crops adapted to a wide range of temperature but not tolerant of freezing. These include (a) crops adapted to monthly mean temperatures of 55°–75° F.—onions, garlic, leeks, shallots (all these can stand frost under certain conditions); (b) crops adapted to monthly mean temperatures of 65°–80°, killed by frost or prolonged exposure near freezing—melons, cucumbers, squash, pumpkins, tomatoes, peppers (hardier varieties), sweet corn.

(3) Warm-season crops that will not thrive below a monthly mean temperature of 70° F.—watermelons, sweetpotatoes, eggplant, peppers (tender varieties), okra.

(4) Perennial crops—asparagus, globe artichoke, rhubarb.

The authors take up each of these crops in turn. They discuss the weather conditions under which it thrives or is damaged, its special peculiarities and problems, the results or the possibilities of breeding work to overcome major difficulties, and the principal areas of production. This part of the article contains so many detailed facts for most of the crops that no attempt will be made to summarize it here.

Climatic Adaptation of Fruit and Nut Crops

Climatic adaptation divides fruits and nuts into three main groups. (1) The tropical group. Bananas, an example of this group, will not grow well where the temperature ever goes below 50° F. Strictly tropical fruits are grown very little in the United States. (2) The subtropical fruits—usually evergreen plants that can stand temperatures slightly below freezing but do not do well in tropical climates. (3) The hardy group—deciduous plants that require cold weather to break a dormant period and are therefore not adapted to tropical climates.

Traub writes about the subtropical and Magness about the hardy group. In this brief summary of the article only a few examples of the many important effects of climate and weather on these crops can be given.

Of the citrus fruits, the Satsuma orange, which can stand 18° F., can be grown farthest north. The lime is injured at 28°. Other citrus fruits are in between these limits. Apparently, says Traub, temperatures in February and March control flowering and influence the time of ripening. Grove heating, banking up soil above the bud union, and the selection of hardy varieties (Marsh grapefruit, for instance) are used as methods of combating cold. High temperatures result in a green or yellowish-green rind color, cooler temperatures in a deep yellow or orange color. Normal production requires 35 inches of water a year from rainfall or irrigation. High relative humidity apparently has a favorable effect on smoothness and thinness of skin, juiciness, richness; low humidity, with high temperatures, causes dropping of immature fruits. Both insects and diseases are related to climate; certain pests develop in humid areas, certain others in dry areas.

For commercial production, dates have rather strict temperature and moisture requirements. Old trees can stand occasional temperatures as low as 12° F. High temperatures (110° or more) during the growing season are apparently beneficial, but Deglet Noor fruit ripening in late August and September is inferior to that ripening in October and November, when the weather is cooler. Dates require irrigation, a minimum of rainfall, and low humidity during the maturing season; high humidity favors diseases and spoilage of fruit. During hours of full sunlight, leaf growth ceases; it is now thought that light of certain wave lengths makes some growth substance in the plant inactive.

Dormant mature fig trees can stand a temperature of 15° F., but cold injury is not uncommon. Figs for drying need long sunny days, low humidity, maximum temperatures of about 100° F.; but temperatures much higher than this are harmful. Rains while blossoms are being fertilized or fruit is drying can cause serious damage. It is reported that climatic differences affect the shape, skin color, pulp color, and sweetness of figs.

The buds of hardy fruits do not open in the spring if the trees are not exposed to sufficient cold, Magness points out, and this is the chief reason why apples cannot be grown within 150 miles of the Gulf. Peaches can be grown farther south, and pears of Asiatic types still farther. To the north, on the other hand, the growing of these fruits is limited by their ability to withstand cold. Roots, which fortunately are protected by soil and often by snow, are the most tender part of the tree in the dormant season. Next most tender is the bark around the collar, or crown; next, the buds. Injury is always greatest when warm weather immediately precedes cold. Apples, sour cherries, and American plums can usually stand winter temperatures down to −30° F., and pears, sweet cherries, and Japanese and European plums down to −20°, but peaches and apricots are likely to be severely injured at −15°, and fruit buds of peaches at −10°. Since buds are most tender after opening, the likelihood of cold injury in spring depends on the time when they open. Apples require the equivalent of about 30 days at 70° before blossoms will open, peaches 15–20 days, apricots a still shorter time; thus apricots are the most likely and apples the least likely to be injured by cold in the spring.

All the hardy tree fruits require ample moisture, but some American-type plums are rather highly drought-resistant. All can stand a wide range of summer temperatures, though sour cherries like rather cool conditions, apples medium temperatures, and peaches and certain pear varieties rather high temperatures.

Diseases depend a great deal on weather. Apple scab thrives in areas where and in parts of the season when temperatures are under 70° F. and rainfall is ample. Bitter rot is a high-temperature disease. Fire blight of pears is worst where spring temperatures are high and rainfall abundant. Brown rot and scab of peaches are favored by abundant spring or summer rains. In general, fungus and bacterial diseases of fruits are least troublesome in the dry irrigated regions.

Grapes of the vinifera (Old World) varieties need only a short rest period and are grown in the warm regions where there is little rainfall to favor fungus diseases. In the humid regions, American or American-vinifera hybrids are grown; they are less subject to disease and some are as cold-hardy as apples. The Southeast grows the so-called muscadines, which require a long, warm season and are very resistant to fungus diseases.

Strawberries are adapted to a wide range of climates, but they are very subject to winter killing and must be well protected in cold regions. Most varieties form their fruit buds during the short days of September and October, but in the South they get a second bud-forming period on the new, early spring growth, and this greatly lengthens the fruiting period. Disease resistance is important in choosing varieties for the humid East. Strawberries are subject to drought injury because of their shallow roots. Raspberries are best adapted to regions with cool summers; disease limits production in the South, as it does also in the case of currants and gooseberries. Blackberry production, on the other hand, is limited in the North by winter cold. High-bush blueberries (except the rabbiteye group) cannot be grown in the South because of lack of winter cold.

The most important of the hardy and semihardy nut crops are walnuts, pecans, chestnuts, almonds, and filberts. Most of the pecans in the United States require a long, hot growing season, free of frost for more than 200 days; and they need ample moisture. The Persian (English) walnut varies in its cold requirement and cold resistance according to variety; it is not grown in humid regions because of its susceptibility to disease. The almond has about the same climatic requirements as the apricot. The filbert does best with a relatively dry growing season and moderate summer temperatures. Oriental chestnuts, now being widely tested in the United States, have about the same climatic range as the black walnut but can be grown farther south.

Climatic Relations of Sugarcane and Sugar Beet

Brandes and Coons clearly bring out a very important point about climate and agricultural production.

The climate of a given region is seldom entirely favorable to all the crops we may need or wish to grow within that region. High temperatures may interfere with satisfactory crop production, or low temperatures, usually taking the form of shortening the cropping season, may reduce yields or quality. Similarly, moisture variations may be beyond the adjustment limits of the crop, the common experience being a short crop because drought stopped plant growth. It might be advantageous, especially in the matter of seed production, to have a somewhat different length of day. Further, the climatic conditions very decidedly affect the severity of plant diseases, and if these are favored, they may be limiting factors in production.

It would be nice, of course, if we could tailor the climate like a suit of clothes to make it fit the crop more exactly. We cannot, and anyway it might then be a worse fit for other crops. What we can do is to change the plant so that it is indifferent to the adverse conditions or actually thrives under them. Nature imposes her limits, and to adapt a plant to a drastically changed environment requires that some distant cousin which can thrive under such conditions be available for the plant breeder to use in hybridization.

How can this be done? By studying all the close relatives of the plant (those in the same species) and the more distant relatives (those in the same genus), and finding out how they respond to climatic conditions all over the world. Here and there one will be found that responds much better to some condition of our own region than the plant we are using. By suitable breeding work a number of desirable qualities can then be combined to make a new plant that will meet the handicaps we need to overcome. All this involves thorough, systematic studies and the complicated methods used in modern genetics. It is no easy trial-and-error business, but it can give revolutionary results, as modern agricultural science has proved again and again.

This is the fundamental story back of Brandes' discussion of climate in relation to sugarcane production. He takes the reader on an imaginary tour of the regions where sugarcane is produced throughout the world and shows that though there are similarities in climates, the differences are even more striking. Then he shows how all our sugarcane in the Western Hemisphere came originally from one small spot, the Melanesian Islands, in the Pacific Ocean northeast of Australia. These islands are in the Tropics, and the cane grown there was closely adapted to particular tropical conditions that are duplicated only in very limited areas in our part of the world, and certainly not in Temperate Zone areas such as Louisiana. But although this cane never did very well in our producing regions, nothing was done to improve it. Meanwhile, there are many different kinds of sugarcane in other parts of the world—northern India, for example, has wild and garden varieties that are very well adapted to temperate regions—but nobody used them elsewhere, even for breeding purposes.

This situation has been completely changed within the past few years. To prevent the total collapse of the sugar industry in Louisiana, a breeding project was started that not only saved the industry but gave it new varieties of cane that are far better producers than those used in the past. Out of this work came the thoroughgoing study of climate in relation to sugarcane, the collection and testing of varieties from all over the world, and systematic breeding. For the first time, cane-producing regions in the Temperate Zone are on the way to really efficient production based on varieties suited to temperate climates.

The sugar beet is grown in regions north of those suitable for sugarcane. Coons discusses its climatic requirements—temperature, moisture, day length—in some detail, and then shows what is being done to meet specific problems posed by climate.

In recent years sugar beets have been introduced into the Imperial Valley of California. This means completely reversing the normal growth season, planting in the fall instead of the spring. Now the sugar beet is a biennial, producing seed the second year after it has passed through its first cold season. But if it is grown in winter instead of summer, there may be enough cold, even in the Imperial Valley, to make half of the plants or more produce seed (bolt) in the first year—and this interferes with sugar production. To make efficient production possible, then, it has been necessary to obtain strains or varieties that will resist bolting under these conditions. Selection for this characteristic, however, created another problem; the resistant plants would not produce seed when handled by the usual methods in certain established seed-producing areas with mild winter climates. This necessitated finding new areas adapted to growing these nonbolting types. The Pacific Northwest, with its long, cool winters, proved to be well adapted, and the problem was met by introducing sugar-beet-seed growing as a new enterprise for this area. Fitting the sugar-beet variety to the environment suited to its requirements for seed production has necessitated close study of bolting in relation to temperature, day length, and genetic constitution.

Sugar-beet production was driven out of favorable western areas by curly top, a virus disease carried by the beet leafhopper, which lives on certain range plants. Climate controls the range plants, hence the size and extent of the leafhopper population, hence the prevalence of curly top. The breeding of curly-top-resistant beet varieties has made it possible to grow the crop again in districts once abandoned. More recently, beets have been bred that are resistant to leaf spot, a fungus disease that becomes epidemic in some areas under conditions of high temperature and rainy weather.

Climate and Forage Crops

A vast carpet of grasses and legumes covers more than half the land in the United States. Where there is no carpet there are tilled acres, forests, deserts, and cities; though even in cities green grass is cherished in yards and parks. The pattern of this immense carpet is more complicated and varied than that of an Oriental rug, for it is woven by climate, and different plants must be used for the weft in different places, cold and hot, wet and dry.

For thousands of years, only nature had anything to do with the making of the carpet. Within the past 300 years in our country, man has taken a hand. He tore up nature's work, wore the carpet out in many places, patched it up with plants brought in from other countries, and at present is engaged in a sincere effort to weave a good stout fabric again. In this effort, science plays a large part. There are thousands of plants to choose from, but each different environment sets conditions that only a few of them can meet. The job of science is to find or develop the right ones for each place and purpose.

Alfalfa was born in a region of cold winters, hot dry summers, and limited rainfall—southwestern Asia. Naturally it rather prefers these climatic conditions when it is moved elsewhere. In a humid climate like that of the eastern part of the United States, it is not so long lived as in the drier Midwest and West. Moisture is also associated with certain troublesome diseases—bacterial wilt and black stem, for example. Nevertheless, the plant has a high water requirement, and under dry conditions the roots have been known to exhaust all the moisture 40 feet down in the soil. Hence in a very dry climate, irrigation is needed for abundant production. Winter killing is often associated with lack of moisture, which reduced the vigor of the plants during the previous growing season.

From the standpoint of adaptability to temperature extremes, alfalfa seems to be a combination of Eskimo and Fiji Islander, surviving winter temperatures down to −84° F. and summer temperatures up to 120°. Three types, or groups, are now used in the United States—nonhardy in the far South, midhardy farther north, hardy up to the Canadian border.

All of our useful true clovers and sweetclovers are foreign plants, brought here by design or accident, but some are now quite different from what they were in their original homes. Red clover, for example, was exposed to a variable climate when it first came to this country; only the adapted plants survived. When it moved west, only the heat-resistant and more drought-resistant plants survived. It was attacked by leafhoppers, and only the hairy types, avoided by hoppers, survived. Diseases also got in their work along the line. Nowadays the plant breeder is taking a hand in shaping improved varieties.

Clovers need a plentiful and uniform supply of moisture, cool temperatures preferably, and ample light. Shading often cuts down the stand, and in fact clovers did not originally thrive over a very wide area until man began destroying other vegetation. The sweetclovers, some of which are annuals and some biennials, originated in drier regions than the true clovers and are grown in the Corn Belt, the Great Plains States, and the Southwest, as well as in the intermountain region; biennial sweetclovers will stand drought once they are established. Of the true clovers, the red, white, alsike, and strawberry species are perennials, adapted to the Northeast, the Pacific Northwest, and the Intermountain States wherever enough moisture is available; they may behave as annuals under severe conditions. Crimson, low hop, least hop, Persian, cluster, subterranean, and lappa species are true winter annuals, adapted to the Southeast and Pacific Northwest. In addition to its direct effects on the distribution of clovers, climate has indirect effects through its influence on diseases, the activity of pollinating insects, and the acidity of the soil.

There are 1,100 species of grass in this country. Of these, some 100 are important—about 50, mostly foreign-born, in the humid regions, and another 50, mostly native-born, in the dry regions. Temperature and moisture both govern distribution.

In the humid regions, certain species thrive in the colder North (bluegrass, orchard grass, redtop, timothy), certain others in the warmer South (Bermuda, carpet, Dallis grasses); certain ones in the wetter areas (carpet grass, St. Augustine grass in the South—reed canary grass, redtop in the North), and certain others in the drier areas (Bermuda grass, Bahia grass in the South—Canada bluegrass, bromegrass in the North).

In the dry western regions, on the other hand, some species spread over a wide range of temperatures. Moisture, however, makes a considerable difference; some of the bluestems and western wheatgrass, for example, thrive in the moister areas of the semiarid region, whereas grama and buffalo grasses can do well in the more droughty areas. Moisture also affects winter survival; much winter killing in the northern Great Plains is due not to cold but to drying out of the plant tissues.

Breeding work with the grasses is now actively going on. Among the objectives related to climate are resistance to drought, diseases, insects, extreme temperatures, and repeated defoliation. Good seasonal growth habits, productivity, and ability to thrive in plant mixtures are also sought.

A number of miscellaneous legumes are vitally important in our agriculture, particularly in the South where northern clovers will not grow on poor soil. Lespedeza, which requires high rainfall, humidity, and temperature, and tolerates acid soils, now covers 20 million acres between the Great Lakes and the Gulf, and the Atlantic coast and the Ozarks. Common lespedeza is grown in the southern part of this region, Korean in the central and northern parts. Crotalaria, another poor-soil plant, needs higher temperatures and thrives on sandy and sandy loam soils in the Southeast. Velvetbeans and cowpeas are cover-crop plants vital to the agriculture of the lower South. Field peas, vetches, and bur-clovers are grown in winter in the South (as winter annuals) and some varieties are used as summer cover crops in the North.

In the case of soybeans, different varieties are closely adapted to different climates, often within narrow ranges. This has made the extensive use of soybeans possible in the United States. Some varieties will mature in 75 days; others require 200. The total heat accumulation and the total amount of available moisture during the growing season are important factors. The soybean is also sensitive to day length, and this strongly affects the adaptability of varieties to the north or south.

Climate and Grazing

A billion or more acres of this country's land, Chapline and Cooperrider note, is grazed at least part of every year. In general, where moisture and soils are such that a comparatively large amount of forage is produced per acre, cultivated pastures have been developed. Where there is less moisture, grazing land is left as uncultivated range. Thus at the outset climate determines how the land will be handled.

The object in pasture management is to keep a maximum of young nutritious growth coming along for the animals. In the northeastern part of the United States, grazing capacity is high, but there can be no grazing in winter; animals must be winter-fed. Kentucky and Canada bluegrasses, timothy, and clovers are among the principal plants used for pasturage. In the Southeast, improved pastures can be used throughout most of the year. Bermuda grass, carpet grass, Dallis grass, and lespedeza produce during the warm season and are grown in permanent pastures, which are sometimes supplemented by temporary pastures of Napier grass and pearl millet. Winter pasturage consists mostly of grains and ryegrasses. In the West, pasture conditions along the Pacific coast are somewhat similar to those in the East. In dry-farming regions, pasture production is uncertain, depending on rainfall, but some of the unevenness can be ironed out by the use of drought-resistant species such as crested wheatgrass. In small, scattered areas in the semiarid region there are highly productive irrigated pastures, used to supplement the range.

Over the vast range area of the West, climate determines the kind and amount of forage produced, and it must be closely studied and obeyed to insure success and prevent disaster in livestock operations. The principal forage plants consist of drought-resistant bunchgrasses and semi-turf-forming grasses which do not form a complete ground cover even under the most favorable climatic conditions. On especially arid areas the stand often covers less than 10 percent of the soil surface, and the number of acres required to feed an animal increases correspondingly. Studies show that present grazing capacities are considerably below what they would be if ranges in general were in good condition. They also show that in order to absorb a large proportion of the rainfall the ground must have a good cover of perennial grasses or much of the water will be lost in run-off. Annual weeds and grasses are less effective in preventing run-off and erosion than is a perennial plant cover.

Drought may occur on the range in any year or in a series of years together. During the past 25 years precipitation has been lower in most of the West than during the previous 30 to 35. Downward trends over even longer periods have been noted in places. Range plants adapt themselves to drought by producing smaller tufts and fewer and shorter stems and leaves, and even by dropping leaves. Then they recover when heavier rainfall returns, but studies show that they do not recover as well or as rapidly under heavy as under conservative grazing. When they are overgrazed, a severe drought (as in 1934 and 1936) will also kill off a considerably larger percentage of the plants than it will under moderate grazing.

Temperature is an important factor in forage production chiefly in the spring. Some plants produce well in cool weather and afford a limited amount of early grazing, but the important palatable plants usually develop in warmer weather, and thus care must be exercised to avoid injury to these plants from too early grazing. In the Southwest, where winter temperatures are mild, grazing is yearlong, livestock being moved from winter to summer ranges with the season.

No climatic factor acts alone. Relative humidity, temperature, and wind movement, for example, influence evaporation, and evaporation influences the amount of moisture available for plants. It takes 21 inches of rainfall in Texas to produce the same amount of growth that would be produced with 14 inches in Montana. Hot, drying winds can make a drought much worse.

The problem on the range is to lick the weather hazards by good management. First, there are the submarginal areas. Where the rainfall is less than 5 inches a year, there can be only occasional, limited grazing. Where it is between 5 and 10 inches, it usually takes

200 or more acres to feed a cow for a year, and costs of fencing, water, and handling are so high that only large outfits can effectively use the range and meet the drought risk. In many areas with up to 15 inches, however, there is range land that is submarginal only because it has been ruined by plowing. This land can be restored to usefulness, though often only at considerable cost.

On range land that is not submarginal, it has been proved again and again that the best insurance against weather is conservative grazing. This means (1) stocking the range 15 to 25 percent below its capacity in average years, which will insure enough forage in all but severe drought years and will also favor quick recovery after drought; (2) building up reserves of feed for years of severe drought; (3) keeping a flexible herd in areas with less than 10 inches of rainfall—that is, part breeding herd, part steers, the steers to be sold off in years of short feed; (4) restocking the range cautiously after a drought.

Chapline and Cooperrider conclude their article with a fairly detailed discussion of the principal types of herbage on the range, particularly in relation to climate.

Climate and the Nation's Forests

A dense forest, says Zon, is like an enormous umbrella with holes in it covering the earth. Naturally the climate—moisture, temperature, light—under the umbrella is modified. More than that—the climate near but not under the vast umbrella is somewhat modified too. In other words, even though man can do nothing to affect the climate in general, he can influence it to some extent locally by adding or taking away forests. And different kinds of forests have different effects.

What are some of these effects? The mean maximum monthly temperature in a forest in a temperate region is about 4° F. lower during the summer than the temperature outside; in winter, it is about 2° lower. Light is reduced 50 to 90 percent within the forest, the amount of reduction depending on the kinds of trees. Forest soil is warmer by 2° in winter and 5° to 9° cooler in summer than that outside, and freezing, if any, is much less deep than outside. Humidity is greater by 3 to 12 percent within the forest. A considerable amount of precipitation is intercepted by the trees and evaporates before it can reach the ground. Dew and fog form readily over fields adjoining forests, and early spring frosts and summer hail are effectively prevented. Evaporation from the soil under the forest is greatly reduced. Wind velocities are immensely reduced within the forest. The water-storing capacity of the soil is greatly increased. The significance of this underground storage is indicated by the fact that a rise of 6 inches in the water table of the Tennessee Valley would mean an additional storage, in the ground itself, of four times as much water as the Norris Reservoir holds.

Shelterbelts well illustrate the influence of trees on the area nearby. A shelterbelt at right angles to the prevailing winds affords good protection on the leeward side for a horizontal distance 20 times the height of the trees, and some protection more than twice as far as that. There is also considerable protection on the windward side. This means that evaporation is reduced, temperatures are lowered, relative humidity is increased, snow is more effectively retained to supply moisture, soil blowing is reduced or stopped, fuel consumption in farmhouses is reduced by as much as 30 percent, animals are protected from exposure.

Much of the present forest land in the United States is cut-over or burnt-over land and second-growth timber; there is only a tenth as much old-growth timber as there was in the days of the original forests. It would be hard to prove what effects this reduction has had on local climates, but a 7,000-acre area completely stripped of forest by smelter fumes in eastern Tennessee gives some indication. Careful comparisons were made between this area and nearby forested land. Average temperatures were 3° to 4° F. higher on the denuded area; average wind velocity was 7 to 10 times greater in winter, 34 to 40 times in summer; evaporation was twice as great in winter, 7 times as great in summer. Elsewhere in the United States, soil destruction following destruction of forests has been amply proved. Measurements made in various places also prove the great value of forest cover in preventing run-off and reducing flood hazards.

If forests affect climate to some extent, to a far greater extent climate affects forests. An understanding of the interrelationships between climate and forests is the basis of modern forest practice.

For instance, the drying out of inflammable material depends on relationships between weather and the density of the forest cover. Dense cover retards drying and greatly reduces fire risks; partial cutting has a similar effect; clear cutting vastly increases the fire hazard. Fire-danger meters have been devised that measure the risk for any combination of weather and inflammability of fuels.

Burning over after cutting down a forest changes the climatic environment so drastically that the succeeding growth consists of entirely different kinds of trees. The forest then has to go through several stages before conditions are right for the return of the original type of growth. If it is desirable, any one of these stages can be made permanent by suitable management practices, and further change in the forest type can be prevented. The chief factor in this control is adjustment of light, moisture, and temperature through control of the thickness of the stand. Reforestation by planting also involves a knowledge of these factors in relation to different kinds of trees. Some trees will flourish under conditions that injure or kill others.

This kind of knowledge, the basis of forest management, is gained largely from the study of the relations between climate and natural forests. Forests cannot be managed as artificially as crops. The forester must find out what nature does and learn how to work closely with her requirements.

All the great forest belts of the world are adjacent to oceans. There are two of these belts in the United States, along the Atlantic and the Pacific. In between, farthest from the oceans, and therefore farthest from the primary sources of moisture, the land grows grass, not trees. In the western belt, three successive mountain ranges interfere with the passage of the sea-born moisture eastward. The west side of each range is moist, and forests grow there but not on the drier eastern side. These western forests consist largely of coniferous trees because the soils are comparatively young and thin. In the eastern part of the United States, on the other hand, there are no great mountain barriers to stop moisture-laden air, and the forest is continuous. It consists mostly of deciduous trees (hardwoods) because the soils are older, deeper, and more fertile.

These are gross differences. There are many finer variations that depend on local climate. Nowhere else in the Temperate Zone is there so rich a variety of forest types and species as in the United States. In the East, at least five strikingly different types correspond to differences in climate: The mangrove thickets, the southern pineries, the oak forest, the northern hardwood forest (beech, birch, maple), the spruce-fir forest. In the West there are two main types: The western red cedar-Douglas fir-redwood combination, and the ponderosa pine forests.

Even these subdivisions are too broad to give a real picture of the variations in forest growth produced by climate. Every difference in elevation and exposure affects heat and moisture and therefore vegetation. Many different combinations of climatic factors are possible, and each has characteristic effects. Zon discusses some of them. They are the things the modern forester is studying.

Climate and Plant Diseases

Ever since agriculture began, it has been scourged by plant diseases and insects, and many times they have caused widespread famines. Modern research has revealed much about the relationships between the diseases of plants and the weather. Sometimes weather conditions favor the disease organism itself, sometimes an insect carrier, and sometimes they make the host plant more receptive to the disease. Humphrey gives several examples, with special attention to cereal rusts.

He tells how rust spores are swept from Canada all the way to Texas by northern winds blowing in the fall and early winter. In the South the infective organisms winter over and cause local epidemics, and the spores from these in turn sweep northward in spring and summer, sometimes spreading from region to region like wildfire.

Four favorable conditions must be present at the same time to cause an epidemic: (1) Favorable temperatures, (2) abundant rain or dew, (3) a large number of spores, (4) a susceptible host—grain or grass. The first two of these conditions cannot be controlled, but the last two can be. If rust-resistant plants are developed, the host will not be susceptible and the quantity of infective material will also be cut down.

Thatcher rust-resistant wheat, developed by plant breeders, now covers 17½ million acres in the United States and Canada. Such an acreage in 1935, 1937, and 1938 would have prevented the disastrous epidemics in the hard red spring wheat area in those years. A new resistant wheat will soon be distributed in the South to help in eliminating overwintering infections there. New rust-resistant varieties of oats and barley are being introduced. Farmers can look forward to extensive conquests of plant diseases by such means, though the work is bound to be long and difficult.

Insects and the Weather

Hyslop gives many remarkably interesting examples of the effects of weather on insects. At each stage of its development (egg, larva, pupa, adult, for example) each insect has a definite temperature and moisture tolerance. There is a low point below which it cannot live, an optimum favoring the greatest development in the least time, and a high point beyond which it cannot live. Near the low point and the high point many insects live in a state of suspended animation.

The longer optimum weather conditions last, the greater the number of generations the insect can produce in a single season; codling moths, for instance, produce three broods (though not always) in the Ozarks, two in the Shenandoah Valley of Virginia, one in the Northeast. The following are other examples of effects of weather: A temperature of −20° F. in November destroys all exposed gypsy moth eggs. Cool, delayed springs favor the seed-corn maggot and many species of cutworm. Hot, dry weather favors egg laying by the codling moth. The boll weevil is killed by temperatures near zero, harmed by hot, dry summers, favored by wet summers. Mild winters bring pickleworms and the harlequin bug northward from the south Atlantic and Gulf regions and favor the spread of the corn-ear worm north of its normal habitat. Drought when young grasshoppers are hatching means a serious oubreak of this pest. Heavy rains at hatching time mean fewer chinch bugs; under certain weather conditions, too, fungus diseases kill off the bugs. The hessian fly is practically eliminated when a late, dry fall retards the germination of wheat seed; late planting accomplishes the same result. Weather is also a major factor in the effectiveness of parasites—insects that prey on the harmful insects.

Climate and Livestock Production

Since climate has a marked effect on the amount and the nutritive value of feedstuffs produced within a region, there is no question about its indirect effect on livestock production. Does it also have a more direct influence? Rhoad gives examples to show that it does.

High-quality dairy cows of European breeds produce best at relatively cool temperatures. A study under controlled conditions showed that milk production gradually declined from 29 pounds a day to 17 as the temperature rose from 40° to 95° F. In tropical Singapore, a group of Holsteins kept in an air-conditioned barn at 70° averaged 24 pounds of milk a day; a similar group in a barn exposed to outdoor temperatures averaged only 9 pounds. Registry of Merit Jersey cows were compared in Maine and Georgia; in summer they produced more butterfat in Maine, where it was cool, but in winter, more in Georgia, where they were kept outdoors, than in Maine, where they were kept in warm barns. In tropical Brazil, purebred imported European dairy cattle produced little more than half of their apparent capacity.

Studies indicate that pullets produce larger eggs at cool than at warm temperatures, and that the rate of gain of hogs in Texas is reduced during the high temperatures of summer. In the case of sheep, rainfall is important. In South Africa, the best wool-growing areas have less than 20 inches of rainfall, but fat lambs cannot be produced where there is less than 30 inches. In general, the distribution of British breeds is largely influenced by rainfall and temperature.

Reproduction also is affected by temperature. Various reports show that high temperatures markedly reduce breeding efficiency, especially in male animals. Some studies even indicate that continued high temperatures result in sterility of males. The influence of temperature probably accounts for the seasonal breeding habits of some classes of livestock, especially sheep.

There are distinct differences between species and breeds in adaptability to various factors in climate. The Jersey cow has more heat tolerance than some other breeds, and this is probably why it is so extensively used in the South. Studies in Louisiana showed that purebred and half-bred Brahmans were much less affected physically by high temperatures than quarter-breds and purebred Aberdeen Angus. Breeding, then, offers a practical solution for some climatic problems in livestock production. Cross-breeding tropical and European breeds of cattle (both dairy and beef) is giving promising results in Jamaica, Brazil, the Philippines, South Africa, Australia, and the Gulf coast region of the United States. The first truly American beef breed is the Santa Gertrudis, the shorthorn × Brahman cross produced in Texas. In the Philippines a new breed of hogs, the Berkjala, a cross between the Berkshire and the native Jalajala, is being developed to meet tropical conditions.

Rhoad implies that much more of this kind of work will be done in the future as more is discovered about the adaptability of animals to climate.

Climate in Relation to Worm Parasites of Livestock

Adults and sometimes larvae of worm parasites live inside the bodies of warm-blooded animals, but all except those taken from the blood and tissues by biting insects are exposed directly to the outside environment for part of their lives. During this time, favorable or unfavorable climatic conditions have a marked influence. Lucker gives a considerable number of examples, but he points out that much of the available information on this subject is based on laboratory experiments on the effects of temperature, moisture, etc., on the free-living stages of the parasites. The influence of climate on the distribution of the parasite is then deduced from these experimental data. There is a dearth of field studies designed to bring out just how observed climate and weather actually affect the distribution and intensity of the parasitic diseases of livestock. More is known about this, however, in the case of parasites affecting man.

Only a few of Lucker's examples can be given here.

The eggs of roundworms and flukes that go through certain stages of development on pastures must have moisture. They differ in their resistance to drying out, and this affects the distribution and prevalence of these parasites in different regions and different seasons. The large intestinal roundworm of man can stand much drier conditions in the egg stage than can the whipworm; there is some evidence that the same thing applies to the corresponding types infesting hogs. Studies of the prevalence of the common stomach worm which causes parasitic gastritis in sheep have shown that relatively high moisture, regionally or seasonally, favors infestation. On the other hand, an unusually dry season, under certain conditions, can also bring an outbreak of certain parasites, and exceptionally heavy rains may cleanse pastures of eggs and larvae.

Temperature controls the speed of development of eggs and larvae when moisture is adequate, as has been shown with the swine whipworm and the common liver fluke. Many laboratory experiments and some field observations brought out marked differences in the ability of various parasites to survive low temperatures in the egg and larval stages. These free-living stages of the nodular worm and the stomach worm of sheep, for example, are not resistant to winter conditions in eastern Canada. Eggs and larvae of the swine kidney worm lack resistance to cold, but eggs of two of the swine stomach worms are quite resistant to freezing.

High temperatures also kill parasite eggs and larvae, but in the field it is hard to distinguish the effects of high temperatures from those of drying out and of sunlight. It has been proved experimentally that sunlight alone can kill eggs and larvae, irrespective of temperature and moisture.

Some parasites must pass part of their lives in the body of an intermediate host—fish, snails, insects, for instance; and, of course, climate affects the distribution of these hosts. Wet weather that brought a great increase in the numbers of a certain snail and favored its spread has been known to result in an outbreak of liver fluke disease in sheep. This disease is caused by a parasite that spends part of its life in the snail's body.

Some measures for preventing or controlling parasitic diseases have been worked out on the basis of such findings—for example, raising pigs on clean, dry, well-drained, sunlit soil to avoid infestations of the kidney worm and the nodular worm. As Lucker indicates, however, there is need for much more precise information about the influence of local, general, and seasonal climatic differences on the distribution and prevalence of animal parasites.

PART 4. THE SCIENTIFIC APPROACH TO WEATHER AND CLIMATE

Flood Hazards and Flood Control

The Hydrologic Cycle

The earth has a fixed supply of water, which is used over and over again, appearing in three forms as part of a great hydrologic cycle—(1) water in oceans, lakes, streams, and underground storage places, (2) water in the soil, (3) water in the atmosphere. A balance is maintained among these three forms; losses from one mean gains for another. The land gains water from the atmosphere by precipitation; the sea gains it by precipitation from the atmosphere and by run-off from the land; the atmosphere gains it by evaporation from the sea and the land. The amount of water received by the land from precipitation equals the amount that runs off the land plus the amount that evaporates from it.

Thus the land loses water, Holzman points out, in two ways: (1) As liquid, by run-off, both above ground and underground. This water, which swells streams, lakes, and seas, is useless to plants. (2) As vapor, by evaporation and transpiration. Much of this water has stayed in the soil long enough to be used by plants; they then give it up to the atmosphere by transpiration. Some, however, is lost to the atmosphere by direct evaporation from the soil.

Probably only about 30 percent of all the water received by the land from precipitation runs off. The other 70 percent stays in the soil awhile and is then evaporated and transpired. Nevertheless, this 70 percent evaporated and transpired from the land is not the principal source of rain and snow. In fact, it is a very minor source. Almost all our rain and snow is water that has been evaporated from the sea and has then been carried by great air movements over the land. Warm air laden with moisture from tropical seas moves northward, chills, and drops its moisture over the land. Cold, dry air from the north, on the other hand, steals a certain amount of moisture from the land it passes over.

Nothing man can do will ever appreciably change the amount of precipitation on the land; the forces that produce it are too vast. But man can to some extent control the amount of water that runs off the land, thereby increasing the amount available for his use and reducing the amount that causes disastrous floods.

Run-off

Since run-off equals the total amount of precipitation minus the amount of water absorbed by the land, Musgrave writes, it is important to know how absorption is increased or decreased.

The structure of the soil counts a great deal. A loose soil with large pore openings absorbs more water—often many times more—than a dense soil with small openings. Intensive cultivation and loss of humus favor the latter condition. Dry soil generally absorbs more water than wet soil, but the amount of moisture in the soil is not always an indication of how much more it will absorb. Good drainage and a permeable subsoil favor increased absorption.

More water enters a warm than a cold soil, and a frozen wet soil absorbs little or none unless frost has fluffed it up and made it porous. Soil frozen deeply absorbs less water than soil frozen lightly; deep snow and a cover of vegetation both tend to decrease the depth of frost penetration. Even though run-off may be high on frozen ground with a good vegetative cover, erosion is less than on the same ground left bare. In general, there is more run-off in northern than in southern climates, largely because of the various influences of a prolonged cold period each year.

The characteristics of each storm are also important in determining the amount and rate of run-off. Most storms that produce floods are of long duration or high intensity or both. Even these storms are less damaging, however, when the three protective factors—favorable soil structure, warm temperatures, and a good vegetative cover—are present to bring about maximum absorption. Though on a large watershed some of the water absorbed by the soil will eventually reach the streams by seepage underground, it is at least usually delayed enough to reduce flood crests.

Evaporation and Transpiration

Rainfall can be measured rather easily, but the information tells nothing about the amount of water that runs off the land or the amount evaporated from the soil and transpired by plants. Run-off too can be measured, though only with considerable difficulty and expense. It has never hitherto been possible to measure evaporation from a land surface (including transpiration by plants, which is also loss of water as vapor) with any accuracy. A simple method of doing this would be enormously useful. It would tell what the farmer wants to know—how much water is available for plants under different conditions of temperature, humidity, soil, and vegetation. And by telling how rapidly the soil is drying out, it would help in predicting how much water would be absorbed during a given rainfall and how much would run off.

Such a method has recently been worked out, and it is described here by Thornthwaite and Holzman. The layer of air near the ground is in a state of turbulent mixing. Thus its moisture is evenly distributed throughout the layer so long as no moisture is being added at the bottom by evaporation or withdrawn by condensation (as in dewfall). If moisture is being added, there will be more in the air at ground level than there is, say, 25 feet up. The reverse will be true if moisture is being withdrawn at the bottom. As soon as addition or withdrawal ceases, the air will again have a uniform moisture content above and below. To discover whether moisture is being added or withdrawn, then, it is only necessary to measure the moisture content of the air near the ground at two levels, one above, one below. The rate of evaporation or condensation can be measured by determining the wind velocity at the two levels, since this gives the intensity of the turbulence, or the rate of mixing.

This method has been used only for a short time at a few places, but already some interesting results have been obtained.

In the central and eastern United States floods are produced mainly by general storms. They must ordinarily fill up the soil with the water it has already lost before run-off will occur. The greatest loss of water from the soil comes through transpiration by plants. In this region, then, it is important to know what type of plant cover gives the greatest transpiration. In dry regions, on the other hand, it is important to know what type of plant cover gives the least transpiration so that water can be saved. This is the kind of problem that can be attacked by the new method of determining just how much moisture is evaporated from the land under different conditions.

Storms and Floods

Two general types of storms, described by Holzman and Showalter, are responsible for floods.

One causes flash floods—quick flooding of streams in a comparatively small watershed, say one or two thousand square miles in extent. Such a storm lasts only a short time and is usually accompanied by thunder and lightning. It occurs when a warm air mass heavily laden with moisture from southern seas is suddenly and violently forced upward. As it expands and cools at high levels, its vapor

298737°—41——5 +

condenses, like water on the outside of a cold jug during a hot day, and falls as heavy rain, causing excessive run-off. Storms and floods of this type are hard to predict in advance.

The other type of storm lasts much longer, is much more widespread, and produces general floods over large watersheds. It occurs along the polar front—the southern edge of the great mass of cold air pushing down from the north. Warm, moist air from the south meets this front, is pushed up over the cold air, and drops its moisture as rain. As the two types of air masses meet and struggle, great waves, moving from west to east, are formed along the front, producing alternating periods of warm and cold, rainy and clear weather. Under certain conditions, however—chiefly when there is a strong push of cold air southward at high levels—the large eastward-moving waves are halted and broken up into much shorter waves, and during this time storms are likely to be especially violent. A series of such halts, each producing intense rainfall, may occur one after another with successive pushes of cold air at high levels. When this happens, streams over a large area receive a fresh flood of water before they can get rid of the previous one, and there is a build-up, perhaps increased by melting snow, in the main rivers, which may also be dammed with ice. Floods of this type, fortunately, can usually be predicted pretty well in advance. More knowledge of what causes the halting or stagnation of part of the normal polar-front movement should make still better prediction possible.

Snow Melt

In the far West, the Lake States, and the Northeast, where snow reaches great depths, snow melt alone may release enough water in the spring to cause floods. In the Middle Western States and the central Ohio and Mississippi Valleys, on the other hand, it is merely one factor contributing to floods, and then only if there is a deep accumulation of snow which melts rapidly during the occurrence of heavy rains.

Rapid melting, especially on frozen ground, is the chief risk. Warm, moist winds, rather than rain, cause the most rapid melting, Forsling points out. On a large watershed where snow is a flood hazard, then, the aim should be to prevent it from melting at the same time over the entire area. If there are different rates of melting in different parts of the area, the water will be released over a considerable period and not be poured into the streams all at once.

This can be achieved by varying the ground cover according to local conditions. For example, hardwood and open coniferous forests favor a heavy accumulation of snow, little or no soil freezing, a moderate rate of melting; dense coniferous forests favor little snow accumulation, moderate soil freezing, slow melting; cleared areas favor intermediate snow accumulation, maximum soil freezing, rapid melting. Thus the depth of snow, the amount of soil freezing, and the rate of melting can all be varied by using different types of cover.

Land Use in Flood Control

It is evident from the discussion so far that land use is necessarily an important factor in controlling floods, and Congress has passed laws that take this into account. They provide for cooperative Federal, State, and local action on whole drainage basins. The War Department has the responsibility for major engineering works downstream—that is, along the big rivers and their main tributaries. Farther up, among the scores, hundreds, and thousands of smaller streams that feed the big ones, it is the job of the Department of Agriculture, in cooperation with other agencies, to devise and put into effect measures that will help in controlling floods at their source by retarding run-off and decreasing the flow of silt that chokes up stream channels and reservoirs.

Among the measures that have been proved effective in reducing run-off and erosion are such practices as crop rotation, strip cropping, terracing, contour cultivation, contour ridging, contour furrowing, rotation grazing, reforestation. Which ones to use is an individual problem in each area and each locality, and extensive studies are under way to determine the facts. Climate, topography, and soils are not the only things to be considered. Expense is also a factor. Will the most effective flood-control program in a given area pay for itself in public benefits, or should something less effective but cheaper be considered? The amount of cooperation that can be expected from farmers and others is also important in determining what steps are most practical. Finally, any given program should aim to improve and stabilize the local agriculture as far as possible, in addition to reducing flood hazards.

Ringland and Guthe make it clear that our knowledge of how to reduce flood hazards by upstream land use practices is still far from complete. Much can be done, but research continues in order to develop more facts and determine what methods really are most effective for different conditions.

Flood Forecasting

Perfect flood prevention would consist in (1) having the maximum amount of rainfall and snow melt soak into the land, and (2) catching all the excess in natural and artificial reservoirs. Since prevention is far from perfect, it is vital to have adequate warning in advance to reduce the damage and loss of life when floods do occur—and they occur somewhere in the United States almost every month in the year. The Weather Bureau is the warning agency. It is well aware, Bernard writes, of the shortcomings of the flood-forecasting service, which are due to lack of sufficient facilities for promptly gathering and analyzing data as well as to lack of fundamental knowledge on certain points; but it also makes vigorous efforts to reduce these draw-backs and make the service more nearly perfect.

Bernard describes two types of flood forecasting.

On the lower reaches of the larger rivers it is usually only necessary to know the stage, or height, of the river at a given place and a given time upstream in order to know what it will be a certain number of hours (or days) later—long enough for effective preparation—at a given place downstream.

Farther up the main rivers, and on tributary streams, the problem is much more complicated. Rates of flow are not uniform because slopes are steeper; many streams, short distances apart, are pouring into one; changes are swift because of the short distances. It is necessary to base forecasts on such fundamentals as weather predictions, especially of amounts of rainfall; the condition of the ground, especially its capacity to absorb water; run-off from melting snow. Not only the seasonal conditions but, during the danger season, the day-to-day and finally the hour-by-hour changes must be studied and reported to central stations by a network of observers working under carefully prepared instructions.

To show vividly how the system operates, Bernard describes the procedure during a flood on the Shenandoah River in late January and early February 1939. At the beginning of the storm, only 10 percent of the water was running off the ground. At the end, 75 percent was running off. Bernard shows just what information the forecaster had at each step and how his forecasts compared with the actual flood conditions later on. In this case it was possible to predict the crest of the flood 40 hours in advance.

How the Daily Forecast Is Made

The brief daily weather forecast we get in the newspaper and over the radio is familiar to everyone, and everyone uses it in one way or another. It is put in words as commonplace as those a doctor uses when he tells us we have such-and-such a disease and the outlook for recovery is such-and-such. Back of the doctor's diagnosis and prognosis, however, there is a complicated process of observation, testing, and reasoning based on painfully acquired knowledge. So with the daily weather forecast. It will never be possible, Mitchell believes, to predict weather with 100-percent accuracy for more than a few hours in advance even for an area as small as a single State; the changes that result from conditions great distances away are too involved in their nature and origin. Nevertheless, by spreading the network of observations, by rapid communication, and by developing a more scientific approach to meteorology, modern forecasting has made notable strides toward the goal that it will perhaps never quite reach.

Because of the importance of upper-air observations in present-day forecasting, Wexler gives a brief summary of the history of these observations since the time when Alexander Wilson, of Glasgow, began sending thermometers up on kites in 1749. Subsequent developments included the use of mountaintop stations, free balloons, box kites, pilot balloons, and finally, in very recent years, the radiosonde.

Mitchell then outlines the network of observation points from which data flow in daily to a district forecasting center. From this information, plotted on charts by specially trained men, the forecaster sees the areas of low and high barometric pressure at sea level; the principal "fronts" between different kinds of air masses; the temperature, dew point, cloudiness, and precipitation, and the 3-hour and the 12-hour pressure changes, at each reporting station. He also sees the vertical structure of the atmosphere for several miles up. This upper-air information includes the direction and velocity of the wind and the temperature and humidity conditions at various levels, and again the distribution of pressure, including the position of pressure centers and troughs of low pressure.

All of these data come in in code messages, which are translated while the charts are being made. Translating and charting takes up most of the time—at least 1½ hours. The forecaster does not get a really complete picture until the last moment; but after the charting is completed, the actual making of the forecast takes only 15 or 20 minutes. Meanwhile, however, the forecaster has been studying, digesting, and comparing data, checking and rechecking the charts and diagrams against each other, and deciding which conclusion to use in cases where two or more are in conflict.

To illustrate the procedure in some detail, Mitchell takes a specific case—the weather forecast made on the morning of March 29, 1939, for the Eastern District, which covers 16 States and the District of Columbia. It is an "easy" case, without major complications, but to the general reader it will seem quite complicated enough.

Mitchell reproduces several of the charts used by the forecaster on that date—the sea level weather chart, the upper-air chart for the 10,000-foot level, the flow pattern for a selected upper-air surface, and two vertical cross sections through a low-pressure disturbance over the Middle West. He discusses what is happening at various places along the cold front, where cold air pushes against warm air; the location of the warm fronts, where the reverse occurs; the nature of the wave disturbances in various places; why there is clear, cloudy, and rainy weather at certain points; and the significance of various kinds of pressure changes. He analyzes the upper-air charts in some detail and shows what is happening to "islands" of dry air and "tongues" and currents of moist air aloft. Finally he extends or "extrapolates" into the future the past movements of the high- and low-pressure centers and of a low-pressure cold-front trough and indicates where they will be located by the end of another 24 hours.

From the knowledge thus gained as to the arrangement of surface air masses in relation to fronts, troughs, wedges, and centers, the forecaster predicted the wind directions and approximate velocities, the changes in temperature, and the precipitation that would occur during the forecast period in the 16 States in his district.

The reader realizes that much is omitted—all of the highly technical calculations, in fact. To include these would make the account unreadable except by the expert. As it is, the procedure is obviously not one for the amateur, though the latter can become rather expert in a certain limited kind of local forecasting.

The Scientific Basis of Modern Meteorology

Early in this introduction to the Yearbook it was pointed out that weather science has gone through revolutionary developments within the past few years, and one or another aspect of the newer knowledge of the science has been discussed in various articles. Rossby's article is a survey of the present state of the science as a whole. He gives the physical basis of modern meteorology insofar as it is now understood, apologizing for the fact that his account is much oversimplified.

This summary attempts, not very successfully, to simplify it still further. Readers who, like this editor, find even a semitechnical discussion of the physics of meteorology rather hard going can get a good deal of information from the unusual set of charts and diagrams accompanying Rossby's article. The editor would like to point out that to visualize even the more elementary aspects of atmospheric circulation over the earth is not easy, since you have to imagine that you are a mile or two up in the air, on your stomach with your head toward the North Pole, a clock nearby lying on its back so you can readily tell which is clockwise and which counterclockwise rotation—also a mirror so you can see how everything would be reversed if you were in the Southern instead of the Northern Hemisphere; and you have to remember constantly that a south wind is a northward-moving wind, an east wind a westward-moving wind, and vice versa.

The atmosphere is a turbulent fluid subjected to strong heat influences from the earth and the sun and to strong mechanical influences because it moves over a rough, rotating surface. Theoretically, what happens under such conditions can be fully explained by the physical laws of mechanics and heat. There are large gaps, however, in our knowledge of how to apply these laws under some of the conditions involved, and also in our observations of the conditions themselves. Long-range weather forecasting will be relatively crude and lacking in accuracy until the gaps of both types are more nearly filled.

Rossby shows (1) the atmospheric conditions that would result purely from the heating of the earth by the sun, disregarding the uneven distribution of heat, the earth's rotation, and the uneven distribution of land and water. Then he shows (2) how uneven heating—torrid Equator and cold extremities—would modify this first set of conditions; then (3) how the earth's rotation would modify both sets; and finally (4) how the existence of great land masses in the Northern Hemisphere would modify all three sets.

(1) Of the radiant energy reaching the earth's outer atmosphere from the sun, about 40 percent is stopped by clouds, air molecules, and dust; 60 percent reaches the earth's surface, where it is absorbed, turned into heat, and radiated back to space. Here part of it is absorbed by water vapor in the lower atmosphere, which in turn sends some of it upward, some of it back to earth. Thus the ground receives heat from two sources—the sun and the blanket of atmosphere—and its mean temperature is always higher than that of the air, which is losing heat in two directions, upward and downward. The atmosphere is warmest at the bottom. It loses heat rapidly in the lower layers, more slowly with increasing height. At great heights, in the stratosphere, the temperature is nearly constant up to perhaps 15 miles above sea level.

When gases and liquids are heated, they expand and lose weight. When they are cooled, they become heavier and settle. This accounts for the familiar process of convection—the same process that keeps the water circulating in a hot-water heating system. If only radiation were involved and the earth were uniformly heated all over, the circulation of the atmosphere would be confined to up-and-down currents. There would be no organized, horizontal north-and-south circulation (this is called meridional circulation by meteorologists).

(2) North-and-south, or meridional, circulation is brought about because the Equator faces the sun directly whereas the Poles face it at a slant; thus the same amount of heat has to spread over a larger area at the Poles, and they are colder than the Equator. Since the heated air at the Equator moves up toward space and the cold air at the Poles tends to sink and hug the earth, there is less air and therefore less pressure in the upper atmosphere at the Poles. Gases tend to move from an area of greater to an area of less pressure. The upper air, then, moves toward the Poles. As it piles up there, it puts the lower air at the Poles under more pressure while at the Equator the lower air is losing pressure. Thus the air near the earth's surface flows from the Poles (area of higher pressure) toward the Equator (area of lower pressure).

(3) Warm air, then, drifts northward in the upper atmosphere; cold air drifts southward in the lower atmosphere. But this simple, rather slow circulation is greatly complicated by the fact that the earth spins from west to east, dragging the atmosphere along with it.

A ring of air extending around the earth and starting out at the Equator with the same west-to-east speed as the earth (that is, stationary with relation to the earth) and moving northward will be traveling in a constantly smaller circle as it approaches the Pole and will therefore pick up speed in relation to the speed of the earth rotating under it. In other words, at any place north of its starting point, it will be traveling faster than the earth but in the same direction, west to east; so it will appear as a circumpolar west wind to an observer on the earth. The upper air does drift northward; hence west winds develop in the upper atmosphere.

On the other hand, a circumpolar ring of air starting southward from the polar regions at the same speed as the earth will be traveling in a constantly larger circle as it approaches the Equator and will therefore lose speed in relation to the speed of the earth at any place south of its starting point. Since it is going slower than the earth, it will appear to be moving backward; in other words, it will be an east wind. The lower air does drift southward from the Pole; hence east winds develop in the lower atmosphere.

This arrangement—east winds below, west winds aloft—does not hold over the entire Northern Hemisphere, however. Other things occur to complicate it.

The west winds in the upper atmosphere are moving faster than the earth. Thus they tend to be thrown away from the earth's axis, outward, by their own excess of centrifugal force. This means that they tend to be flung southward toward the Equator—the latitude that is farthest away, vertically, from the axis. On the other hand, the east winds at the surface are moving slower than the earth; hence they tend to be flung downward, toward the axis—that is, northward, since northern latitudes are nearest the axis—by their own deficiency of centrifugal force.

As a ring of air is flung southward, it piles up or banks on the south side. It keeps piling up until there is enough pressure on this side to stop any further movement in that direction. West winds (the ones that tend to be flung southward) thus build up high pressure toward the south and have lower pressure toward the north. East winds (the ones that tend to be flung northward) do the opposite;

they build up high pressure toward the north and have lower pressure toward the south.

For an observer facing downwind, then, there is always high pressure on the right, low pressure on the left; that is, the pressure drops from right to left. When air goes around an area of low pressure it goes to the left (counterclockwise), creating what is called a cyclone. When it goes around an area of high pressure, it goes to the right (clockwise), creating what is called an anticyclone.

Now what happens as a result of these various forces?

Heated air in the lower latitudes, near the Equator, rises upward, drifts northward, and appears as west winds at high levels. As it moves northward it loses heat fairly rapidly and sinks. By the time it reaches 30° north latitude some of it has sunk to the ground level, where it spreads out fanwise, part of it going south, part north.

The part that goes south builds up high pressure on the south side, bends around clockwise, and becomes an east wind. The part that goes north similarly becomes a west wind.

Thus, in general, there are east winds at the ground from 30° N. toward the Equator, but west winds at the ground from 30° N. toward the Pole.

Meanwhile, near the North Pole, the southward-drifting air at the surface appears as an east wind. Eventually, at about 60° N., it meets the warmer northward-drifting west winds that had started at about 30°. The latter are forced upward over the cold air from the Pole and tend to move back toward the Equator.

Thus instead of uniform east winds at the surface throughout the Northern Hemisphere, there are actually three different belts, or cells, as the meteorologist calls them—east winds from the Equator to 30° N., west winds from 30° to 60° N., and east winds again from 60° to the Pole.

In the upper air, there are west winds from the Equator to 30° N., and again from 60° N. to the Pole. Between 30° and 60° N. the upper air moving back toward the Equator should appear as east winds, but it is forced to move in the opposite direction by friction from and mixing with the west winds to the north and south of it. At high levels, then, the wind is uniformly west over the entire hemisphere.

Not only the east-and-west but the north-and-south movement of air breaks up into three cells, it will be noted. From the Pole to 60° N., the surface air drifts southward, the upper air northward. From 60° to 30° N., the surface air drifts northward, the upper air slightly southward. From 30° N. to the Equator, the surface air drifts southward, the upper air northward. Circulation in the middle cell (30° to 60° N.), then, is in general opposite to that in the two extreme cells, and it acts as a brake on both of them.

In the northernmost cell, where there are east winds at the surface, the sea level pressure drops toward the south (the left), reaching its lowest point at 60° N. Sea level pressure in the middle cell, with west winds, drops toward the north (the left), also reaching its lowest level at 60° N. At this latitude, then, there is a belt (trough) of low pressure.

In the middle cell, pressure rises southward until it reaches its highest point at 30° N. This also coincides with the highest pressure in the southernmost (east wind) cell, where there is a pressure build-up northward, a drop southward. Thus around latitude 30° N. there is a belt (ridge) of high pressure. Below 30° N. the pressure falls steadily toward the Equator.

In the upper air, on the other hand, with west winds prevailing everywhere, the pressure rises southward from the Pole all the way to the Equator.

From the standpoint of weather, the most interesting and critical zone is around latitude 60° N., the boundary between the northernmost cell and the middle cell. This is a belt of low pressure where the cold air from the Pole, with prevailing east winds, meets the warmer air moving northward in the middle cell, with prevailing west winds. Here the cold, dry polar air and the warm, moist subtropical air are in constant battle. Wedgelike tongues of cold air push under the warm air, forcing it to higher levels, where the moisture condenses, forming clouds and falling as rain or snow. Strong temperature contrasts and a rapid succession of wet and dry spells characterize this polar front.

Along the polar front there are great horizontal waves and eddies formed in a very complicated way and due fundamentally to the rotation of the earth on its axis.

This rotation gives the ground under our feet, and any object on the ground—such as a column of air—a counterclockwise (cyclonic) rotation in the Northern Hemisphere and a clockwise (anticyclonic) rotation in the Southern Hemisphere; and the speed of this rotation decreases toward the Equator. A column of air near the North Pole with a cyclonic rotation equal to that of the earth itself is of course at rest in relation to the earth's surface. But if, keeping its original speed of rotation, it moves southward, it will be rotating faster and faster in relation to the surface of the earth the nearer it gets to the Equator. A narrow current from the north, consisting of a number of such columns, will twist or bend to the left over the surface, traveling first eastward (as a west wind), then northward (as a south wind). As it moves back northward, it will lose some of its relatively greater rotation speed because the earth itself rotates faster northward, and eventually it will reach a point where it will be rotating more slowly than the earth's surface. In relation to the ground, it will then have a right-to-left or anticyclonic rotation, and it will bend to the right, traveling first eastward (as a west wind), then southward (as a north wind). At some point to the south it will again have a stronger cyclonic rotation than the earth's surface, and the whole process will be repeated.

There is a pronounced difference in behavior between narrow currents, which move rapidly from one latitude to another, and broad circumpolar rings of air, which slowly, almost imperceptibly, change their latitude. The current of air moves in a series of waves, oscillating back and forth across a latitude circle. If a west wind is deflected northward at some point, it will form just such great waves.

On the other hand, for similar reasons connected with relative rotation speeds, east winds tend to form large spiral eddies, instead of waves—cyclonic eddies if the wind is originally deflected northward, anticyclonic eddies if it is deflected southward.

The stronger the wind in either of these cases, the longer the wave or the larger the eddy.

Thus when the west winds in the middle cell are disturbed, they set up a wavelike pattern along the polar front, and the disturbed east winds in the northern cell set up circular eddies. The cold eddies from the north push southward in the troughs of the waves; warm air from the south pushes northward in the crests. As a result of these opposing forces, the polar front as a whole constantly shifts. It breaks up into separate parts, individual polar fronts, extending from southwest to northeast. Along these fronts minor waves, the typical cyclone waves, form, also normally moving northeastward.

The dominating major wave length depends on the speed of west winds. The stronger they are, the longer the waves and the fewer the troughs in which cold air pushes southward. These west winds set the pattern of individual polar fronts along which polar air can push southward. The interaction of cold and warm air masses in each major front in turn is responsible for the storms that control day-by-day weather changes during the cold half of the year, when the polar front sometimes extends all the way to or even beyond the southern boundary of the United States.

It is therefore extremely important to develop some index of the intensity of the west winds in the middle latitudes. From week to week there are very great fluctuations in this intensity as measured by the difference in mean pressure between latitude 35° N. (near the subtropical high-pressure ridge—southern boundary of the middle cell) and latitude 55° N. (near the low-pressure trough—northern boundary of the middle cell). Until these fluctuations are understood, Rossby points out, there can be no adequate long-range weather forecasting.

From a mechanical standpoint, the middle-cell west winds are not, as it were, self-generated; they are largely the resultant of atmospheric circulation between heat sources in the southern or equatorial cell and cold sources in the northern or polar cell. Thus a satisfactory understanding of variations in circulation intensity depends on getting fairly complete daily temperature and humidity data from the upper atmosphere not only in the middle cell but throughout the Northern Hemisphere.

(4) In the Southern Hemisphere the polar-front pattern works out with considerable regularity. In the Northern Hemisphere, however, the existence of large continents greatly disturbs the regularity of the pattern. The snow cover over immense areas of land in winter reflects back most of the sparse heat from the sun and makes these areas manufacturing plants for cold air. In effect, over a large continent the polar front is pushed far to the south, and it tends to be parallel to the boundaries of the continent. Rossby describes in some detail the circulation of the atmosphere and the polar-front zones that result from the massing of continents in the Northern Hemisphere, as well as the profound effects of strong and weak circulation, with their accompanying pressure changes, on weather in the United States. He is particularly interested in working out, as far as possible, two idealized pressure patterns—one for maximum and one for minimum circulation intensity—as an aid in classifying and understanding weather types.

Finally, on the basis of the previous ground work, he discusses three other points in addition to the four already given: (5) What happens along a polar-front wave; (6) summer circulation patterns, which are quite different from those in winter; and (7) long-range (5-day) forecasting.

(5) Along each of the several disconnected polar fronts running from southwest to northeast there will be minor waves (the typical cyclone waves responsible for our daily weather) traveling from southwest to northeast. In the advanced crest of such a wave the warm air pushes up over and replaces the cold air. This portion of the front is called the warm front of the wave. In the rear, or trough, of the wave the wedge of cold air pushes southward under and replaces the warm air. This part of the front is called the cold front. The advancing cold air in the trough of the wave moves faster than the advancing warm air in the crest; and, constantly bending around counterclockwise with a spiral motion, the trough eventually overtakes the crest and wipes it out, or occludes it. This merely means that all of the warm air has been forced upward and the cold air has spread out over a larger area next to the ground. Meanwhile some of the shallow layer of cold air brought southeastward is eventually warmed and in turn is ready to be forced upward.

At the cold front, the forced ascent of warm air is violent and intermittent, resulting in squally winds and cumulus-type clouds. At the warm front, the air ascends more steadily and condensation aloft produces steady rain. Once the fronts have occluded, with the warm air above and the cold air below, the arrangement is more stable, and there is a tendency for it to hold for some time as a large-scale cyclonic spiral.

(6) In summer the same general principles hold, but they work out in a different and less clear-cut pattern. The polar front moves back northward—farther back over the continents than over the oceans. In summer the continents manufacture warm rather than cold air, and there is much less contrast between temperatures in the north and those in the south than in winter. In fact, the temperature contrast between ocean and land is now greater than that between northern and southern land areas; consequently the oceans become the cold-air factories and dominate the general circulation. But the cold air generated over the oceans spreads very slowly and thus tends to form large anticyclonic cells. Because the large-scale changes are slow, local factors have more time to act, and they are more important in determining summer than winter weather.

Rossby gives a fairly detailed account of the summer air circulation over North America. Since circulation patterns are not clearly established next to the ground, it is necessary to study them in the upper air. Temperature, humidity, and wind data are used in special ways and combined on what is called an isentropic chart. A succession of these charts shows that over North America in summer the circulation of the free (upper) air is dominated by anticyclonic (clockwise) vortices or spirals. Great tongues of moist and of dry air are brought in over the continent. The clockwise eddies change so slowly that one pattern will be repeated day after day on a set of charts over a considerable period of time. Since the available humidity over a given area can be worked out from the data used, it is possible to predict whether rain will result if a given set of conditions occur, or whether the weather will be dry because there is not enough available humidity to produce rain.

(7) It has already been pointed out that it will not be possible to do very specific long-range weather forecasting until there is a better understanding of the changes in circulation intensity that are associated with (and probably cause) changes in the circulation pattern. The relative slowness of large-scale changes, however (there is an average time interval of about 6 weeks between one peak of circulation intensity and the next), means that the general trend at any given time will persist long enough to make some prediction possible—for, say, a week in advance. It is possible, for instance, to predict fairly well for a week ahead the position and development of the principal centers of action and the principal polar-front zones, and hence of the prevailing storm tracks.

In the present 5-day forecasting project the forecaster (a) studies the behavior of the circulation index and the large centers of action, determines their trends, and on this basis constructs a chart giving a 5-day forecast of the mean pressure at sea level. The main problem here is to decide whether the circulation intensity is going to increase or decrease, and as yet there are little more than persistence tendencies on which to base prediction. (b) Constructs a similar pressure chart for the upper atmosphere at the 3-kilometer level (about 2 miles up). From these two charts the forecaster gets the locations and movements of the principal frontal zones and also works out what the mean temperatures will be between sea level and 3 kilometers. With this knowledge he can work out the moisture content of the air and determine the probability of precipitation. (c) During the warm half of the year, constructs a chart of probable flow patterns for the next 5 days—the isentropic chart already mentioned.

All of these charts are checked against one another and modified until they show a consistent picture of the probable departures from normal temperature and rainfall for the coming period.

Even this limited and not very specific long-range forecasting can be of great value in agriculture, flood control, water supply, and other services. Rossby considers it a crude first step that is certain to be developed further.

In concluding his article, he gives a brief historical résumé of the development of the main ideas he presents.

Following this article Rossby gives a number of cloud photographs, accompanied by a brief text, to illustrate certain weather changes along a polar front as these changes are observed from the ground. Cloud observations, he points out, have always been extremely useful in amateur forecasting.

PART ONE

Climate as a World Influence

Climatic Change Through the Ages

By Richard Joel Russell [1]

IT WILL be news to many people that man, during his geologically brief existence on earth, has never known a "normal" climate. We are now at the tail end of an ice age and living in a period of crustal and climatic violence as great as any the earth has known. This is why we have to think so much about the weather. Such periods of revolution have occurred briefly several times in the history of the earth. Between them have been the far longer periods of crustal peace and a genial climatic uniformity—the "normal" times of the geologist. Here is the story.

---

[1] Richard Joel Russell, Professor of Physical Geography, Louisiana State University, is a Collaborator, Soil Conservation Service.

To THE AVERAGE MAN, "as old as the hills" has long been a synonym for antiquity. Climate, on the other hand, is commonly regarded as changeable and unstable, and it is widely suspected of possessing cyclic tendencies. Both of these beliefs are reversed by scientific research. Hills are only incidental features of the landscape, incapable of defense against long-continued ravages of erosion. The history of the earth is conclusive, however, in demonstrating climatic uniformity. Climate varies, but the actual amplitude of change between the coldest and the warmest geological periods is surprisingly small.

During most of geologic time the climate at any particular place on the surface of the earth has been milder than that experienced today. The contrasts between summer and winter have been less pronounced. Fewer storms have occurred. The precipitation has been somewhat lighter, and less of it fell as snow or hail. During these genial times there was less contrast between the climates of differing latitudes than is experienced today and less also between oceanic coasts and continental interiors. Such were the conditions during several periods which are thought to have been many tens of millions of years in length and which constitute almost all of the geologic time scale. These periods are recognized by geologists as "normal" times from the climatic standpoint. They have been separated by shorter intervals of geologic and climatic upset, or "glacial" periods. Man is experiencing one of the latter now and has been throughout the geologically short interval that includes the whole of his struggle for domination of the earth.

The object of this article is to place climatology in its geological perspective and to examine various evidences of climatic change. Starting with information contained in rocks, the article outlines the history of climates for the enormous period of time that ended with the introduction of instrumental observation.

CLIMATIC CHANGES OVER LONG PERIODS OF TIME

HISTORIC VS. GEOLOGIC CHANGES—A COMPARISON OF TIME SCALES

Geologists are historians whose archives are the earth's surface and whose manuscripts are rocks. By custom the historian of mankind limits himself to written documents and leaves to the archeologist the whole "prehistoric" period, an interval many times longer than that of written history and also one far more significant in terms of racial development. By a similar custom the geologist relinquishes to the astronomer, physicist, or other interested scientist the major questions concerning the actual origin of the earth and its evolution down to the time represented by the oldest rocks on its surface. The geologist's story begins there.

The essential techniques of geology are simple. Age sequence is determined chiefly through the line of reasoning that overlying rocks are younger than those which support them. Layers of rock overlie one another like so many blankets in a pile. Each layer has been formed by processes that can be observed at present. Some are sheets of lava that have come out of volcanoes. Others are layers of alluvium deposited by flooded streams, layers of sand accumulated on old beaches, or beds of ancient seas or lakes. In any case the uppermost layer is the youngest, just as the topmost blanket was the last to be placed on the pile.

There are complications, of course. Not all layers have the same horizontal extent. In some parts of the earth the rocks have been broken, folded, or subjected to other changes which blur the record. Running water, expansion of ice during freezing, chemical decay, and many other agencies of weathering and erosion have removed vast quantities of rock, so that the geologist often finds his manuscript in a very crumpled and fragmentary condition. Patient research has by no means resulted in a completely deciphered record, but it has advanced knowledge to a point where the main outlines of geologic history have been firmly established.

Preserved in some rocks are the fossil remains of such living things as were occupying the earth while the rocks were formed. The study of fossils is a special branch of geology—paleontology. This science is subdivided into paleozoology and paleobotany, for rocks contain both animal and plant remains. The age sequence established by stratigraphic geological methods—the study of layers of rock—indicates progressive changes in both plant and animal life during earth history.

The oldest rocks show absolutely no trace of life. This condition existed for about half of geologic time. The oldest known fossils are the remains of animals that lived in water. It was only later that amphibians, insects, scorpions, worms, and various other animals managed to inhabit the surface of the land. Still later came the reptiles, birds, and mammals. A similar history is exhibited by fossil plants. The earliest were blue-green algae, water dwellers. Land plants appeared much later, and the first types were structurally simple. The development of seeds came very late in earth history, as did the first grazing mammals.

If geologic history is thought of in terms of a set of books, individual volumes are called eras, chapters are periods, sections of chapters are epochs, and paragraphs are stages. These terms refer to time. Various other names are given to the rocks formed during such intervals, but these need not concern us here, except that the rocks formed during a stage are called a formation. Each formation consists of a great number of individual layers, called beds, sheets, lentils, strata, laminae, etc. Formations are designated by geographical names referring to the place where they were first described. Larger subdivisions have been given geographical names in some cases and descriptive names in others. Jurassic, for example, refers to the Jura Plateau of Switzerland, whereas Cretaceous refers to the chalk content typical of certain rocks in England, Texas, and elsewhere.

Though various methods are used for tabulating geologic time, and customs differ in different countries, the simplified scale shown in figure 1 is typical of modern practice.

298737°—41——6

ERA	PERIOD	EPOCH	ROUGH PROPORTION OF GEOLOGICAL TIME (PERCENT)	NOTES	WORLD-WIDE REVOLUTIONS
ARCHEAN (ARCHEOZOIC)			32+	GEOLOGICAL EVENTS INDEFINITE	
ALGONKIAN (PROTEROZOIC)			32-	A FEW TRACES OF LIFE	
PALEOZOIC	CAMBRIAN		7-	ABUNDANT LIFE IN THE SEAS	
	ORDOVICIAN		4	OLDEST KNOWN FISHES	
	SILURIAN		2-	OLDEST LAND PLANTS AND ANIMALS	
	DEVONIAN		3-	AMPHIBIANS AND FORESTS ON LAND	
	MISSISSIPPIAN (CARBONIFEROUS)		2-	AMPHIBIANS DOMINANT ON LAND	
	PENNSYLVANIAN (CARBONIFEROUS)		3	EARLY REPTILES ON LAND	
	PERMIAN		3-	EXTINCTION OF MUCH PALEOZOIC LIFE	
MESOZOIC	TRIASSIC		2-	PRIMITIVE MAMMALS ON LAND	
	JURASSIC		2-	REPTILES DOMINANT, FIRST BIRDS	
	LOWER CRETACEOUS (COMANCHEAN)		1+	SPREAD OF MODERN INSECTS AND PLANTS	
	UPPER CRETACEOUS		3-	EXTINCTION OF LARGE REPTILES	
CENOZOIC	TERTIARY	PALEOCENE	2+	RAPID SPREAD OF MAMMALS	
		EOCENE		MODERN MAMMALS, GRASSES, AND FRUITS	
		OLIGOCENE		RISE OF ANTHROPOIDS	
		MIOCENE	2-	"GOLDEN AGE" OF MAMMALS	
		(PLIOCENE?)			
	QUATERNARY	PLEISTOCENE		MAN APPEARS, EXTINCTION OF MANY MAMMALS	
		RECENT		DOMINANCE OF MAN	

FIGURE 1.—A geological time scale. The beginning of the Archean era at the top of the scale is believed by many geologists to have been a billion and a half years ago. The percentage column represents middle-of-the-road opinion concerning the duration of epochs, periods, and eras. In the last column, the duration of geological revolutions is indicated roughly by the height of the black sections, and their intensity by the width of the sections.

If the entire period from the beginning of the Archean until today were considered to be equivalent to 1 year, the various divisions would be spaced on the calendar like this:

Archean	January 1–April 27.
Algonkian	April 28–August 22.
Paleozoic:	
Cambrian	August 23–September 17.
Ordovician	September 18–October 2.
Silurian	October 3–October 9.
Devonian	October 10–October 20.
Mississippian	October 21–October 27.
Pennsylvanian	October 28–November 7.
Permian	November 8–November 18.
Mesozoic:	
Triassic	November 19–November 25.
Jurassic	November 26–December 2.
Lower Cretaceous	December 3–December 6.
Upper Cretaceous	December 7–December 17.
Cenozoic:	
Tertiary	December 18–December 31, 6 p. m.
Quaternary	December 31, 6–12 p. m.

[Historic time begins about 1 minute, 12 seconds before midnight December 31]

It is believed that some billion and a half years are represented by this time scale, evidence being furnished chiefly through the effects of disintegration of radioactive minerals in rocks. Just how much "cosmic time" elapsed prior to the formation of the oldest rock is unknown to geologists.

From the climatic standpoint it is interesting to know that the oldest rocks, the Coutchiching series of Rainy Lake, in western Ontario, include conglomerates (old gravels) which were deposited by running water under physical conditions not greatly different from those of today. The geologic time scale does not extend back to a time when the earth was molten, or even to a time when the crust had any significantly higher temperature than at present.

The details of geologic history grow dimmer with age and thus resemble the history of man. The historian knows as little about the details of stone or bronze age history as does the geologist about the details of the Archean and Algonkian eras. Ancient history is known from a small but very significant group of documents, something like the geologist's knowledge of the early Paleozoic. Vastly more detail is available for the study of medieval history, as for the Mesozoic, and an overwhelming amount of fact requires that the student of modern history, or of the Cenozoic, become a specialist in some small portion of the field.

Reconstruction of Geologic Climates

That "the present is the key to the past" is one of the fundamental working hypotheses of the geologist. Departures from this rule must be applied with caution; yet the evidence shows that many must be made. Many geologists believe that continents have occupied rather fixed positions throughout geologic time, but there are some who adduce evidence to show that continental drifting has shifted their relative positions. All geologists agree that vast areas have been upheaved into mountains or plateaus only to have been worn down again. Geologists also agree that seas have expanded at various times so that no part of any continent has escaped flooding at one time or another during geologic history. Thus, at best, the details of the present are only roughly those of the past.

Both physical and biological evidence leads to the conclusion that the present is in many ways a poor guide for the reconstruction of climates of earlier geologic periods. Yet it is from evidence of today's earth that we must obtain the climatological knowledge to back such a conclusion. We must reconstruct the climates of the past on the basis of such correlations as now exist between soils, plant and animal life, erosional conditions, and their climatic settings. A sound paleoclimatology, the science of ancient climates, can be established only by persons well grounded in such fields as meteorology, climatology, ecology, and geography of the present who also possess a substantial background of geologic information.

On the biological side we must accept the general hypothesis that today's restrictions in the distribution of plants and animals are guides to climates of the past. It is reasonable to believe, for example, that cold-blooded reptiles, today sharply restricted in geographic range by their physical inability to stand long periods of freezing or prolonged exposure to intense heat, must have been similarly handicapped in the past. If the skeletal remains of reptiles are found in the rocks of such places as the Antarctic Continent, where reptilian life is now impossible, one naturally concludes that temperatures there were more genial while the animals were living. But one must always use caution in drawing such conclusions. The mammoth bones of Alaska and Siberia might be interpreted as suggesting tropical conditions there at some time, but we know that these animals, unlike their naked close relatives of Africa and India, the elephants, were covered with a thick coat of wool and thus were able to penetrate into a truly cold climate.

Plant distribution is particularly useful as a guide to existing climatic boundaries and assists greatly in reconstructing climates of the past (*17*).[2] It is very unlikely that these simple organisms had means of adjusting themselves to rapid climatic change. It is true that individual types, such as the tough-skinned succulent cactus of the desert, the flaring-based bald cypress of the Gulf-coast swamps, and the dwarfed, small-leaved chaparral of the southern California hills, are remarkably adapted to their environments. Such adaptations must have been made slowly. In the face of rapid climatic change most plants must either migrate or perish. Temperature and moisture conditions limit many species sharply, and it is reasonable to believe that this has always been the case. The presence in comparatively young silts in Europe of fossils of certain mosses now living only in subpolar regions and of such northern species as white spruce, larch, and white cedar in some of the younger deposits of southern Louisiana is valid evidence that colder climates were experienced in those places not long ago.

From the strictly inorganic standpoint the paleoclimatologist must recognize such facts as the restriction to beach or desert environments of peculiar rocks, called ventifacts, which have been polished by

[2] Italic numbers in parentheses refer to Literature Cited, p. 95.

sandblast. If found widespread in the rocks of a certain formation, ventifacts constitute good evidence of aridity in the past. Glaciers scratch and polish rocks in a characteristic manner and also have the unique distinction of transporting material of any size. Their deposits—moraines—ordinarily consist of jumbled masses of rock particles which may range in size from fine clay to large boulders, a fact which makes ancient moraines easily recognizable. By analogy with the drying enclosed lake basins of Utah, Nevada, and parts of South America, Africa, and Asia, the geologist recognizes salt deposits in beds of earlier ages as indicative of arid climates. Heavily oxidized soil remnants from warm, humid regions, certain types of peat from cold-temperate or subpolar regions, coral reefs from warm, clear seas, and many other lines of evidence are regarded as reliable guides to the climates of the past.

The evidence of the geologist or paleontologist must always be weighed against the background of meteorological probability. A rotating earth with its axis inclined about 23.5° toward the plane of the ecliptic, heated most effectively in its equatorial region, with an atmosphere such as ours, has the major features of its atmospheric circulation pretty well stamped out for it. The equivalent of our easterly trade winds, comparatively stagnant polar caps, and zones of cyclonic disturbance are bound to be set up as the result of differences in temperature, or more accurately temperature gradients (a temperature gradient is the rate of change in temperature between one point and another), and rotation. Climates must be cooler toward the Poles. The interiors of continents will naturally exhibit greater seasonal ranges in temperature than coastal locations. Since the amount of atmosphere appears to have been quite constant during geologic time, higher pressures in one region must have been balanced by lower pressures elsewhere, since the sum total of all pressures is a constant—the weight of the atmosphere. If continents were larger during some periods of earth history than during others and their central parts during those times therefore suffered greater seasonal temperature contrasts, barometric gradients (a barometric gradient is the rate of change in atmospheric pressure between one point and another) must have steepened appreciably, so that average wind velocity also increased and storminess became a more general condition. Considerations such as these are as necessary in paleoclimatology as are observations concerning plant and animal life.

The Changing Surface of the Earth in Relation to the Climatic Pattern

The ancient Greeks developed a simple climatology based on geographic areas, a portion of which we inherit and commonly use in dividing the earth into Tropical, Temperate, and Frigid Zones. Modern areal climatology adds many refinements to this old latitudinal system. Temperature belts are now bounded by isotherms—lines of equal temperature. Many precipitation characteristics are recognized, such as total amount, rate of fall, kind (rain, snow, hail), season of fall, etc. Other climatic elements, such as fog, overcast skies, and various types of storms, assist the modern climatologist to recognize climatic types. Köppen, Herbertson, Thornthwaite, and others have made maps showing the areal distribution of climates differentiated upon such criteria.

All systems of modern areal climatology arrive at very similar conclusions. Warmer climates lie toward the Equator; raininess is concentrated along the Equator, windward coasts, and mountain flanks; continental interiors are dry in higher latitudes, etc. Such broad generalizations naturally result in a similarity between the general pattern of one map and that of another. There is a general symmetry with respect to the Equator, less symmetry between opposite sides of a continent. The land masses of the Old World have climates closely resembling those of the New. Discrepancies are caused by topography and extent of land. They result in contrasts in shape and extent rather than in relative position.

The great arid belt of the northern lands of the Old World extends from the west coast of Africa to the Desert of Gobi, in Mongolia. The equivalent dry region in North America extends from the coast of Lower California to the lowlands of Montana. The west coast north of each of these dry belts is characterized by a climate of wet winters and dry summers. The widespread development of this "Mediterranean climate" in the Old World in comparison with its restriction to only a part of California in North America results from the differing trends of mountain systems, parallel to the coast in the New World and at right angles to it in the Old.

It is not the purpose here to develop the distribution of modern climates but only to emphasize the idea of a climatic pattern, well exemplified in the distribution of types as classified by Thornthwaite or other modern climatologists. This pattern varies from continent to continent in accordance with such facts of physical geography as the size and extent of land masses; the number, trends, and heights of mountain ranges and plateaus; and trends of coast lines. There is not land enough in appropriate latitudes in the Southern Hemisphere for the development of extensive areas of cool-temperate climate of the northwestern European type; but if there were, it would be found along west coasts on the poleward side of places receiving their maximum precipitation in winter.

It is reasonable to suppose that ancient climates followed substantially today's patterns. The geologic record confirms this belief, but it also indicates many wide departures from today's proportional distribution of types. The present is a good key to the past with regard to the establishment of climatic patterns, but it gives a distorted notion as to the relative extent of each climatic type during the greater part of geologic time.

The late Cenozoic era, including the Recent epoch, is in many respects geologically abnormal. There are more and higher mountains now than have existed during most of the earth's history. Continents are larger. There are more volcanoes and earthquakes. We are living in the midst of what geologists call a revolution, a time of acute crustal unrest.

Revolutions are by no means new in earth history. There have been at least four great revolutions during geologic time and several other fairly important times of crustal unrest. These periods are indicated in figure 1, on page 70. The duration has in each case been short in comparison with the long periods of quiet between revolutions. Most of geologic time has been marked by stability of the crust. Seas have been more extensive than they are today. The continents, smaller in size, have had few mountains or extensive plateaus. Streams have carried less sediment. Only at a few places in the geologic column are records found of intense folding of the crust, faulting, volcanic activity over extensive areas, and other signs of igneous activity. During such times there were extensive deserts, glaciation, and rapidly flowing streams capable of laying down coarse deposits of gravel and sand.

Generally speaking, the geologist has attempted to mark the ends of eras by the appearance of major revolutions and the ends of periods by minor, yet significant, signs of crustal unrest.

Geologic Climates

There are two broad types of climatic pattern indicated by the geologic record, the normal and the glacial.

The characteristic of glacial climates is the existence of frozen seas during the summer in polar regions. Such is the case today. The absence of polar ice is the characterist c of normal times from the geologic standpoint. The difference between glacial and normal climates is sharply defined, and transitions from one to the other occupied inconsequential intervals of time. It is probable that less than 1 percent of geologic time—about 3 days out of the year on our previous scale—has experienced glacial climatic patterns.

Normal geologic periods were times of quiet between revolutions during which normal climates prevailed. Rocks deposited at such times indicate a minimum of relief—unevenness in height—and few signs of crustal unrest. The paleontologic record is one of widespread ranges in both plant and animal distribution. The early Cenozoic was such a time. Plants closely allied to some of our warm-climate types were flourishing in places such as Greenland, Spitzbergen, and other lands in high latitudes where their growth is impossible today. Even more strikingly uniform were the temperatures in all latitudes during most of the Paleozoic and Mesozoic eras.

For a planet to have an experience characterized by alternations between normal and glacial climatic patterns its surface must be covered by extensive oceans and the temperature of its polar regions must remain not far from the freezing temperature of water. Only the earth among the planets falls within the slight range in these essential requirements. The sharp contrast between glacial and normal climates is a reflection of the sharp discontinuity between liquid water and solid ice. Water is penetrated for a considerable distance by solar radiation and thus slowly becomes warmer. Ocean currents and convection spread temperature effects widely. The marine influences in climate are well known, the most significant effect being the tendency toward uniformity of temperature. Ice is fixed in position and in many ways resembles land surface from the climatic standpoint. The effect of an open arctic ocean is that of adding area to marine climatic influences, but a polar ice cap has a different climatic effect similar to an addition of continental area, which makes for comparatively rapid and violent changes in temperature. The balance is so delicate in terrestrial climatic patterns that a swing from one condition to the other—a polar ice cap or no polar ice cap—means the change from normal to glacial climates for the whole of the earth's surface.

Brooks (*4*) has shown that a surprisingly small variation in temperature causes a change from open to ice-capped polar seas. As long as winter temperatures remain above 28° F., the approximate freezing point of ocean water, the polar seas remain open. At slightly lower temperatures, the ice frozen during the winter melts again in the following summer, and the seas remain effectively open. But if the winter temperature falls about 5° F. lower than the freezing point of ocean water, an ice cap will form. Its growth will be slow at first, but summer melting will not quite offset the effect of winter freezing. After its radius has reached about 600 miles, the growth of the ice cap becomes rapid because the ice itself has a cooling effect on surrounding areas and the rate of summer melting is thus reduced. Growth continues until the ice extends so far from the polar areas that its margins encounter temperatures sufficiently high to stop further extension. Glacial climates have their optimum development at such times. Rising temperatures cause retreat of the ice and the modification of climatic patterns. The cooling effect of the ice cap is so great that retreat is slow until the ice has diminished in area to its critical point—a radius of about 600 miles—after which the ice disappears very rapidly. For a complete explanation of the theory behind these conclusions the reader is again referred to Brooks (*4*), Climate Through the Ages.

Polar ice now lowers the temperatures in Canada and the United States many degrees. It profoundly affects ocean temperatures, especially at great depths. There is a sort of vicious circle in ice-cap and temperature relationships. Brooks (*4*) calculates that lowering of polar temperatures 5° F. under the freezing point ultimately results in a drop of 50° F. in polar winter temperatures. The initial drop causes the growth of the polar ice cap; the cooling effect of the ice itself is responsible for the remainder of the drop. A rise of 2° F. in the temperature of the earth now would be sufficient to clear polar seas of all ice. We are thus in a world where the balance is extremely delicate between normal and glacial climates.

During most of geologic time mountains were low, seas widespread, and normal climates prevalent. Extremely low winter temperatures were unknown, even in the central parts of continents in high latitudes. Distinctions between tropical and polar regions were less evident than at present, the cooling toward higher latitudes being gradual over both oceans and continents. Climatic zones of animal and plant life existed, but the contrasts between zones were not great. Polar air covered the highest latitudes, but its outrushes toward the Equator were less sharp than those today, and the temperatures carried by its winds were by no means so low because the polar air mass was much more restricted in extent and developed over regions neither ice-covered nor near any polar ice cap. All temperature boundaries were shifted poleward, so that subpolar lands experienced conditions about like those of today's Temperate Zones and middle latitudes were subtropical. At the same time, the Tropics themselves were probably only slightly warmer than at present.

Gentle meridional (north-and-south) temperature gradients during normal geologic times were accompanied by less intensified pressure belts. The physical contrast between air masses to the north and those to the south produced a belt of cyclonic disturbance and lower pressures at about 60° of latitude. This zone of storminess was located some distance poleward from its present position, and the intensities in cyclonic disturbance were far less than are now experienced. Middle latitudes had rather monotonous weather, with few invasions of sharp fronts between air masses causing abrupt weather changes. Farther toward the Equator conditions varied little from those today. Poleward temperature gradients and rotation set up systems of high pressures just outside the Tropics, trade winds, and a doldrum belt of calms, but all these had somewhat less intensity than the same phenomena have now.

Precipitation was less during normal times. Fewer and lower mountains meant the absence of much precipitation caused by the ascent of air upslope. Less sharply defined fronts between air masses meant less precipitation of cyclonic origin. Higher temperatures and extended ocean surfaces undoubtedly resulted in atmospheric humidity in excess of that of today, but the absence or toning down of immediate causes of precipitation left lands drier on an average than they are today.

The question of desert climates during normal times is still unsettled. It seems probable that rather mild deserts existed in continental interiors and that intense aridity was restricted to times of revolution. Smaller continents, subdued relief, and a humid atmosphere were not favorable factors for the development of deserts as they exist today.

In reconstructing the areal climatology of normal geologic periods today's climatic pattern may be used as a guide, but it must be modified to harmonize with the physical geography concerned.

The land areas on somewhat more than half of the earth had a climate much like that of tropical lowlands today. Had higher plants existed, the landscape would have been broad savanna grassland rather than tropical rain forest, because of prevailingly low relief. Zones toward the Poles were feebly expressed in landscapes until some such latitude as 60° was reached, where the climate resembled that of the savannas of northern Texas today. Still farther poleward the zones became more pronounced, but even around the open waters of the Arctic Ocean winters were not particularly cold. Rainfall diminished gradually from Equator to Pole and somewhat more sharply toward continental interiors in high latitudes.

Occasional storms reached the Tropics, but the main belt of storminess was centered well toward the Poles, and all latitudes experienced less frequent and less severe weather changes than today. Snow occurred only in higher latitudes, and bodies of glacial ice were extremely rare.

The oceans of normal times were much warmer than those of today. In the absence of polar ice, from which cold water, heavy because of its temperature, now creeps to abysmal depths and accumulates, it is probable that bottom temperatures were considerably higher.

The distribution of both plant and animal fossils bears out these generalizations. Many authors have concluded that temperature zones of plants and animals became effective only as recently as

Pliocene times, but this is an exaggeration (*3*). Zonation has always existed in a mild form during normal times and has always become more pronounced at times of revolution and glacial climatic patterns.

Today's climatic pattern may be regarded as typical of times of revolution. Its distinctive features are glaciation, sharp division into zones according to latitude, and the development of deserts.

It is possible that geologists exaggerate the extent of desert climate in past periods. Many cautions must be observed in interpreting the evidence. Extensive deposits of salts occur in various parts of the geologic column and may be considered as rather good indicators of aridity. The meaning of coarse fragments—detrital materials—is less certain. It is true today that enclosed arid basins accumulate sand, gravel, and coarse detritus in great quantities, but it must be pointed out that erosional conditions were quite different prior to the establishment of today's vegetational types, in the late Mesozoic. Rocks unprotected by modern vegetation and soil, even in humid climates, would have eroded in much the same way as they do in desert basins today. Many geologists attach great importance to red beds—red sands and shales—as indicators of aridity, but this idea rests upon very uncertain interpretations. The oxidized iron content of such deposits suggests a surface condition more closely allied to tropical savanna than to desert in today's landscapes. The amphibia, reptiles, and plants contained in lignite in the red beds of west Texas suggest life in at least a fairly well watered country.

There is a theory popular among geologists that aridity caused many eventful adaptations in life, but little proof supports it. The first land dwellers appear in the middle of the Paleozoic and include scorpions, amphibia, and several other animal types. Many geologists believe that such animals were forced out of pools in arid regions. It is more reasonable to suppose that the change took place in an environment of seasonal flooding and drying, such as now exists along the sides of many streams in humid climates (*24*). The first land plants appeared at about the same time. They may have been scattered about by the animals or may have emerged as the result of seasonal recession of water levels and stranding. To suppose that the animals appeared because plants had paved the way implies that such creatures as the fringed ganoid [3] had information concerning the availability of food on adjacent land, which is not reasonable. As a matter of fact, all of the earliest animals on land were carnivorous and returned to water for feeding and egg laying. The close dependence upon nearby waters was something that animals gave up slowly. It is quite certain that the earliest land animal lived during Silurian times, but it seems likely that the first definitely land plant occurred in the following period, the Devonian (*26*).

The Ice Ages

According to the old idea that the earth's crust gradually formed on a molten mass, it was reasonable to suppose that the Pleistocene ice age was evidence of a refrigeration the progress of which would bring fatal temperatures to all life in the not too distant future.

[3] The fringed ganoid was a primitive fish, closely related to the garfish of the southern United States, which developed its fins into four legs and is believed to be ancestral to all amphibia, reptiles, and mammals.

Polar ice caps appeared to be evil omens of conditions destined to become more and more widespread, eventually taking over the whole of the earth. The discovery of evidences of glaciation in rocks much older than the Quaternary, even in some formed well toward the start of geologic time, might well have come as agreeable, even joyful, news to a public deeply concerned over such possibilities as the freezing out of the human race. Even more comforting might have been the discovery that at least four major glaciations have occurred, at intervals of about 250 million years, plus several minor glaciations, each cold spell being comparatively short and representing only a slight interruption in the long-continued geniality of normal climatic conditions.

There is a distinct relationship between crustal unrest and glaciation. Associated with rocks containing evidences of continental ice are records of folding, faulting, and volcanic activity, all of which are rarities during normal times. Normal times have had little to do with shaping the destinies of physical or biologic history. Both plant and animal life suffered abrupt and extensive change during each revolution.

The greatest break in the continuity of biologic and physical history occurred at the close of the Paleozoic and is called the Hercynian revolution by geologists. A great range of mountains was formed in western Europe whose roots may now be observed in Wales and in a broad belt extending across northern France, Germany, and Bohemia and far into central Asia. A slightly later phase of unrest in North America, called the Appalachian revolution, affected all parts of the continent.

Somewhat less intense was a mid-Paleozoic revolution, the Caledonian, which resulted in a mountain range extending northwestward from Europe to Greenland. Its North American phase, the Acadian revolution, formed mountains in New England and westward.

The end of the Mesozoic witnessed the Cordilleran revolution—the Andean of South America—which resulted in mountains along nearly all borders of the Pacific Ocean.

The world today is witnessing a revolution probably as intensive as any of those of the past. The highest ranges on earth are its topographic results. In Europe it is called the Alpine revolution, but the greater significance of the Himalaya Ranges has caused many geologists to adopt the name Himalayan revolution. Continental relief is probably as great now as at the time of any earlier revolution, and continental areas are probably at maximum extent.

Volcanic activity has always accompanied revolutions. During the Caledonian revolution much igneous rock found its way to the surface in the northeastern part of the United States and eastern Canada. The mountain from which Montreal takes its name was one of a chain of volcanoes which extended across southern Quebec. Other volcanoes were active in Arkansas, Oklahoma, and elsewhere. The Hercynian revolution has been considered the greatest of all volcanic periods (*2*). The Cordilleran revolution brought volcanic activity to many parts of the earth. The most widespread of all existing lava masses, the Dekkan traps of lower India, which originally covered an area of 500,000 square miles, date from that time. In places they have a thickness of 6,000 feet. Today, during the

Himalayan revolution, there are at least 325 active volcanoes on earth and many others which were active not long ago.

The relationships between revolutions and glacial climatic patterns are among the more obvious lessons of the earth's history. Though the earliest records are dim, it is certain that the first glaciation occurred millions of years before the appearance of life on earth. The revolution which closed the Archean era was accompanied by glaciation in southern Australia and in the vicinity of the Great Lakes of North America. A somewhat more recent, late-Algonkian, glaciation is recorded in the rocks of Greenland, Norway, Scotland, central and south Africa, India, China, and Australia.

The greatest of all glaciations occurred toward the end of the Paleozoic, during the Hercynian revolution. The records are very clear. Most amazing is the fact that widespread glacial deposits occur in tropical India. Boulders up to 15 feet in diameter are embedded in a matrix of poorly assorted rocks, angular and scratched from having been ground during glacial transportation. At places they rest on a polished rock floor as fresh and unaltered as if it were of Quaternary age. Similar evidences of glaciation occur in Cape Colony, Transvaal, Southwest Africa, Tongoland, Madagascar, Tasmania, all parts of Australia including Queensland, Brazil, Argentina, Uruguay, Bolivia, England, France, Germany, the Ural Mountains, Afghanistan, Alaska, and in Massachusetts near Boston.

The appearance of so many evidences of late Paleozoic glaciation in tropical regions and in the Southern Hemisphere has aroused lively controversy regarding the climatic conditions of the time. An elaborate thesis of continental drift has been advanced by Köppen and Wegener (*18*), who visualize the glaciation as having actually taken place in high latitudes of a southern continent which later split into several fragments and drifted toward the Equator, carrying the glacial deposits with them. This theory is attractive and has many followers, but it has been challenged sharply on the basis of conflicting geologic evidence and the failure of its authors to suggest a mechanism capable of causing the drift (*4*). It was advanced in a somewhat legalistic manner, with great emphasis on such points as seemed to fit the theory and a bland indifference to evidence against it. It is probable that Joly (*16*) has suggested a better mechanism for continental drift, but most geologists, especially in the United States, regard the theory as being far from demonstrated.

Brooks (*4*) finds it unnecessary to adopt the idea of continental drift to explain late Paleozoic glaciation in tropical regions. He has reconstructed a paleogeography in which continental outlines and relief features would permit such glaciation without violating accepted principles of climatology. The whole question, however, is by no means settled and promises to be an active rallying point for geologic controversy for many years.

The ice age best known to us occurred during the Quaternary and has been accompanied by the glacial climatic patterns we are now experiencing. Various waves of ice advance were interrupted by interglacial stages of retreat, some of which may have been warmer and more prolonged than the one in which we are now living. During maximum advance the ice covered some 7 million square miles in the Northern Hemisphere and 5 million in the Southern. Enough water had been evaporated out of the oceans and locked up as ice on continents to lower general sea levels about 300 feet (*1*). That we have not fully emerged from an ice age is evident from the fact that complete melting of the Greenland and Antarctic ice caps would result in raising sea level another 100 to 160 feet.

Between the great ice-age revolutions which closed the Archean, Algonkian, Paleozoic, and Quaternary eras there have been some lesser times of crustal unrest, volcanic activity, and glaciation. The most pronounced of these occurred during the mid-Paleozoic (Caledonian-Acadian revolution) and at the end of the Mesozoic (Cordilleran revolution). Still other evidences of glaciation are known from the geologic record, but they were not widespread and are unimportant in any general survey of paleoclimatology.

CLIMATIC CHANGES SINCE THE LAST GLACIATION

The Recent and Pleistocene epochs, which together constitute the Quaternary period, are abnormal from the standpoint of paleoclimatology, being a time of revolution and glaciation. The entire history of the genus *Homo*, of which living man is today's representative, has been confined to this period. No true man has known from personal experience the normal geologic climatic pattern. He has always been extremely conscious of weather changes, for he has always had to cope with conditions resulting from alternate swings of the delicate balance, first toward advance and later toward retreat of ice.

The Pleistocene ice age was a compound affair during which there were four or five main stages of ice advance separated by important stages of retreat and numerous lesser swings. Each time of ice advance is called a glacial stage, and each time of retreat is called an interglacial stage. It is an open question whether we are now experiencing an interglacial stage or the actual ending of the whole ice age. The weight of evidence suggests the former, but there is no actual proof. It is certain that some of the interglacial stages of the past have come closer to normal geological climates than that of today, and it is also certain that some of them had greater duration than the Recent epoch. Even during the Recent there has not been a constant retreat in ice fronts. Some have made minor advances within historic time.

During maximum ice advance practically all of North America was covered north of a line extending from near New York City westward along the Ohio and Missouri Rivers, swinging northward nearly to the Canadian border in Montana and Idaho, and reaching the Pacific near Puget Sound. Isolated ice caps covered parts of the Rockies, the Sierra Nevada, and other high ranges.

The contrasts between landscapes formerly covered with ice and those which escaped are striking. The great majority of all natural lakes and ponds occur in regions that had glaciers in the past (deglaciated regions). Irregular hills of gravel, boulders, and poorly sorted debris cover large parts of the lowlands. Ice overdeepened valleys in mountains, polished rock surfaces, scoured lake basins, and caused many of our most spectacular waterfalls. The recognition of the existence of the Pleistocene ice age, the approximate extent of land covered with ice, and the fact of its recency are all based upon observations such as any intelligent layman can make and fully understand.

The reconstruction of climates during times of maximum ice advance is more difficult and requires an intimate knowledge of several fields of science. The detailed story of climatic changes during the several advances and retreats of glaciers is so complex that it still baffles experts. It is not known whether the advance of ice was simultaneous in both hemispheres, or even whether the same number of advances occurred at similar times in the western and eastern parts of the United States, though it seems probable that such was the case.

Many of the major details of Pleistocene history appear more clearly in the records of regions not at any time covered by ice than in those of the deglaciated regions themselves. The climatic upset accompanying maximum ice advance was sufficient to be felt in all parts of the world. Even the Tropics, which throughout geologic time have shared only to a minor degree in climatic changes, furnish valuable clues concerning Pleistocene conditions.

From the Tropics, in fact, came one of the most significant facts concerning glacial history.

Among the East and West Indies and in the tropical Pacific, the Indian, and the tropical Atlantic Oceans are curious islands called atolls, consisting of corals and other marine organisms and having the shape of rings broken at one or more points along the leeward coast. Many atolls occur in places where surrounding oceans are deep, showing that they are perched upon islands of quite another origin, because corals live only in shallow water and could not have established themselves on the ocean floor. Similar reefs form rings around existing islands. It is generally believed that atolls were originally fringing reefs and that either the subsidence of islands or a rise in sea level accounts for their present condition. Against the first of these suggestions is the fact of widespread distribution. It seems improbable that islands in all parts of tropical oceans would sink together. More probably the seas have risen. From this consideration came the recognition of the fact that each major glacial advance caused a lowering of general sea levels and each major glacial retreat caused a subsequent rise (*1, 6*).

From the desert came additional information concerning Pleistocene glacial history.

In the great arid region between the Wasatch Range of Utah and the Sierra Nevada of California are many enclosed basins between a complex of impressive mountain ranges. Lakes exist in some of these basins today—among them Great Salt Lake, Winnemucca, Pyramid, Walker, Tahoe, and others. Most of these lakes are low today, and many of them are dry-floored, being known as playas; conspicuous examples are Carson Sink, Black Rock Desert Playa, and the Surprise Valley lakes. Similar lakes exist in the dry regions of all other parts of the world. They have been called "Nature's rain gages," because heavier precipitation deepens their waters and diminished precipitation lowers them or even dries them up completely.

Beaches, perched deltas, wave-cut cliffs, and other evidences of high shore lines have long been known above the lakes of the arid

West (*13*, *25*). Buried layers of salt attest even more arid conditions than occur today. The piecing together of such lines of evidence reveals a complex history of alternation between arid and pluvial (rainy) stages that have been identified as alternations between ice advance and retreat.

The lakes of enclosed basins could not rise or fall without affecting all streams entering them. Deltas and flood plains, formed while waters were high, became perched terraces when waters were low. Thus times of building of valley floors by deposition at high levels were times of glacial advance, and glacial retreat witnessed the intrenchment of such surfaces as water levels dropped.

Terraces are also formed along streams entering the seas, but the interpretation of them is quite the reverse of that of terraces in the enclosed basins of the arid West. Sea levels were lowered not as the result of diminished precipitation but because water evaporated from oceans was being imprisoned as ice caps on continents. The pluvial period of the arid regions was the low-level period for the seas. On the other hand, the arid times of low waters in enclosed lakes witnessed a return of glacial-melt water and rising seas. Terraces along streams entering the sea thus represent interglacial stages, and those of streams leading to enclosed lakes in arid climates represent glacial stages.

The number of major terraces or terrace levels along streams entering the sea is universally four. The existing flood plains and deltas—the Quaternary alluvium of the geologist—constitute a fifth level. This record indicates the probability of five major stages of glacial advance, each a time of valley cutting as the sea level sank, followed by five major stages of retreat, each a time of valley filling as the sea level rose. This terrace record occurs around the Mediterranean Sea, along the Atlantic seaboard of Europe and Africa (*9*), around the Black Sea (*19*), along the Gulf coast of the United States (*12*), and elsewhere. The tilting of land surfaces during the Quaternary has resulted in the preservation of individual terraces, so that they are quite easily recognized.

Different terrace tilts along the Gulf coast indicate longer intervals between the first three than the last two glacial stages. Similar evidence comes from the study of fossils, soils developed on glacial deposits, and the chemical decomposition of weathered rock.

While today's climates are glacial rather than normal from the geologic standpoint, it must be recognized that the Recent epoch of the geologist is a time of waning glaciation, rising seas, and return toward normal climatic patterns. The general trend has been fairly uniform for several thousand years, but interruptions have occurred, and short reversals in trend can be demonstrated.

Evidence of Change During Post-Glacial Times

Types of Climatic Evidence

From the standpoint of types of evidence there are four kinds of climatology:

(1) Geologic climatology, or true paleoclimatology, is based on evidence from rocks. The period of time to which this kind of climatology is applied extends from the oldest pre-Cambrian to a

somewhat uncertain date in the Quaternary, a date which is being pushed farther back as geologists succeed in deciphering the record. The discussion so far has been concerned almost wholly with geologic climatology. Its main conclusion is that normal climates have characterized most of earth history, being interrupted now and then by glacial conditions.

(2) Geochronologic climatology covers a period from near the start of the Recent epoch to the appearance of historic records. It begins earliest in certain favored localities and ends soonest where man first established the habit of documentation. It differs from geologic climatology in that its events can be identified as to year, precisely in some cases, roughly in most. It is confined chiefly to a time which has witnessed amelioration of maximum glacial conditions and is very interesting from the standpoint of fluctuations, or possible cyclic changes.

(3) Documental climatology is based upon written records. Its methods, in general, may first be applied in Asia Minor, Egypt, and Mediterranean lands several centuries before the advent of the Christian Era. In remote parts of the earth it is even now only gradually being replaced. The chief value of documental climatology lies in its indications of possible cyclic changes.

(4) Instrumental climatology, the precise, modern science based upon actual measured observations, dates only from the middle of the nineteenth century. The thermometer and barometer were invented two centuries earlier, but systematic observations were not taken. The earliest rainfall record, in the modern sense, started at Padua, northern Italy, in 1725. Sunspots have been recorded since 1749. At the beginning of the nineteenth century there were only 5 places in the United States and 12 in Europe where worth-while observations were being taken. The Challenger Expedition, 1872–76, brought back the first significant observations taken at sea. Even today the climatologist finds data too meager for satisfactory conclusions in nearly all parts of the world.

Varves

The longest and most satisfactory geochronology is based upon annual layers of clay and silt deposited in quiet waters subject to freezing during winter and thawing in summer. In a frozen lake the only material being deposited on the bottom is very fine clay held in suspension by the water. Surface ice prevents new material from entering. The layer formed under such conditions is thin and is composed of materials so fine that several months may have been required for individual particles to settle a few feet. Thaw brings in fresh water and new sediment. If inflowing waters are rapid this sediment may be quite coarse. The lake bottom then receives a thick layer, ordinarily of much coarser material than that deposited in winter. Each annual deposit of this kind is called a varve. It has a thick summer zone and a thin winter zone. By counting varves one is able to extend investigations back year by year. This idea originated in the mind of Gerard De Geer in 1878 (*8*), was first published by him in 1882, was demonstrated before the Geological Society of Stockholm in 1884, and was applied on a large scale as the result of extensive studies starting in 1904. Since then many workers have used it; notable among them have been Sauramo, Sayles, and Antevs.

Varves are studied by methods similar to the stratigraphic correlation of the geologist. No one place has a complete record, so conclusions have to be based on evidence extended from one locality to the next. Since few individual varves extend more than a few miles, their time identification depends upon techniques other than following individual layers from place to place.

One of the simplest methods used in correlation of varves depends upon the fact that they are variable in thickness. No two successive years are likely to leave exactly the same amount of deposit on a lake floor. Patient measurement of the thickness of each varve in a sequence can be plotted on a scale that exaggerates thickness. A similar record from another sequence might match the first record, or it might disagree in some or all respects. Suppose, for example, that several varves in one place could be expressed by such thicknesses as 3, 8, 5, 8, 15, 4, in sequence, and that from some other place the record contains the sequence 5, 8, 15, 4, 7, 7, 11; it is reasonable to suppose that there is an actual overlapping of records in the years 5, 8, 15, 4. The second record extends information slightly in a direction opposite to the first 2 years of the first record. This is essentially the method by which varves have been patiently measured across Scandinavia, parts of the United States, and in various other parts of the earth.

Of course, the example given above is highly simplified. Actual records from a single place often contain hundreds or thousands of varves, and the overlapping between nearby exposures often includes half or more of each record. Then, too, the best modern techniques do not depend entirely on varve thickness. Some investigators prefer to use such things as the ratio between the thicknesses of summer and winter zones. The significant thing is that each varve represents a single year and that a geochronology has been based upon varve evidence.

Varve geochronology has been tied into our own chronology as the result of a very fortunate event. Lake Ragunda, in Sweden, was totally drained in the year 1796, and thus the date of its uppermost varve is definitely known. Below are 1,100 beautifully preserved varves. This record was correlated with those of nearby localities, and eventually a geochronology was developed that covered nearly all of Scandinavia. The matching of this record with that of varves in the United States is not as yet thoroughly established.

As the formation of varves requires annual freezing and thawing they cannot exist under glaciers. They start to form only after ice has retreated. The oldest varves in Scandinavia are thus found in the extreme south, and the appearance of younger varves northward makes it possible to follow the retreat of the ice front on practically a year-to-year basis. About 13,700 years are represented in the Scandinavian records (7). Similar studies elsewhere will drive the varve geochronology back through many additional centuries.

Tree Rings

A second type of geochronology is based on the amount of wood added as tree rings each year. Records of this kind extend back only

298737°—41——7 +

about 3,000 years in living trees, but careful research may add another thousand or so.

Tree-ring studies were first undertaken in the plateaus of Arizona by A. E. Douglass (*10*), who demonstrated a close relationship between annual rainfall and the widths of rings in yellow pine trees. Ellsworth Huntington (*15*) extended investigations to the big tree of California (*Sequoia gigantea*), a specially desirable species for study because of its phenomenal longevity. Antevs and others have refined techniques in more recent studies. By a method very similar to that used for varve correlation, Douglass and others have studied wood preserved in the pueblos of the Southwest and have thus extended their chronology beyond the lives of any trees whose stumps remain standing (*11*). On the whole, however, the climatic generalizations based on North American tree rings have not been driven back as far as documental evidence in the eastern Mediterranean. The identification of individual years marked by climatic peculiarities in many cases appears to be more precisely determined through tree rings than by means of documental evidence.

Other Evidences of Climatic Change

Less certainly dated than the years represented by varves or tree rings are conclusions as to climate depending on other types of geochronological evidence.

The succession of plant types in peat shows that "there have been several climatic waves since the last glacial period, each of relatively long duration" (*5*). A period of some 30,000 to 35,000 years is included in this generalization. In the British Isles climatic changes based on peat studies carry back to about 11,000 B. C. and have been correlated with stages in the cultural development of man (*26*).

Quaternary animal remains yield a similar story. The bones of arctic land mammals far south of the limits of present-day distribution are regarded as evidence of colder conditions than those now existing. The presence of the bones of certain steppe and desert animals in western Europe indicates drier conditions in the past. Many marine animals of lower orders are extremely sensitive to temperature change and their migrations along coasts yield interesting source material for the historian of the Quaternary period.

Man's history is practically coincident with the Quaternary. He left little trace of his presence in the early part of this period, but his records become relatively rich as time advances. At one time he was restricted to caves in the Alps above the highest evidences of ice in valleys, suggesting his presence during a time of intense glaciation. Artifacts (tools and weapons) incorporated in moraines of England and elsewhere yield a story of migrations conditioned by various advances and retreats in the ice front (*28*).

Many of the most significant predocumental records of man from the standpoint of climatic change are concerned with variations in the depths of lakes on the shores of which he built dwellings. About 2,400 B. C. the lakes of central Europe stood well below today's levels, and an early Neolithic people built homes in the marshes around them. A period of increased precipitation caused a "high-water catastrophy," when floods destroyed many of the dwellings. By the end of the bronze age, about 1,000 B. C., the lakes reached a second low stage, permitting an advance of dwellings and agriculture into lands now too moist for such purposes. European climates were warm enough at that time to permit the growing of crops high in the mountains, in places now glaciated. A new period of flooding, starting about 850 B. C., drove the people to drier and warmer localities. Similar histories have been traced for dwellers around lakes in northern Africa and the enclosed lakes of western and central Asia (*4*).

The blending of geochronologic and documental evidence of climatic change occupies a long transitional period. The foreshadowing of the documental stage appeared first in western Asia about 7,000 years ago. In such places as Tasmania, much of North and South America, and much of northern Asia the documental stage had not been reached at the time of their discovery by western Europeans.

An excellent example of transition between geochronologic and documental methods of climatic research is cited by Brooks (*4*), with reference to the alternate settlement and abandonment of Anau, in northern Persia. Evidence first appears in the form of artifacts, later as historical documents. Estimates of time during the early part of the record are based on the thickness of sedimentary deposits between various cultural horizons, but later they become matters of actual chronology. As Anau is on the arid margin today and agriculture is just barely successful, each abandonment is regarded as the result of increased aridity and each reoccupation as the sign of increased precipitation. This conclusion is strengthened by geologic interpretations of the deposits, archeologic interpretation of culture habits, and the negative evidence of the absence of indications of conquest, diseases, or other nonclimatic causes of migration. Stated briefly, the record shows an occupation of Anau about 9,000 B. C., again in 6,000 B. C., again in 5,200 B. C.; a short abandonment about 3,000 B. C.; complete abandonment in 2,200 B. C. not only of Anau but of a large adjacent territory as well; and a final reoccupation about 750 B. C.

Documental climatology ordinarily deals with manuscripts written for purposes other than climatic description. Research in this field often means going through hundreds or thousands of pages to glean a single pertinent observation. Interpretations are often risky. About 438 B. C., for example, Herodotus happened to mention the shape of the Caspian Sea in such a way as to imply a length about six times its width. Huntington (*14*) has investigated the configuration of the land and finds that this would be the case if the water level were 150 feet higher than it is now. This suggests that precipitation was then much greater.

Many workers have used statistical methods in documental climatology. Manuscripts have been scanned for mere mention of drought, floods, rainless years, and so on, and climatic curves have been constructed on the basis of the frequency of such observations per century. Some documents are quite to the point. Records of water level in the Nile are almost continuous between A. D. 641 and 1480. Flood stages alone have been recorded for most years between 1480 and 1830. Records of grape yields, success and failure of wheat and other cereals, migrations of man to less arid regions, etc., all help in reconstructing climatic history.

What the Records Show

Geochronological climatology demonstrates a gradual amelioration, or lessening, of extreme glacial conditions during the Recent epoch and sheds much light on the major oscillations which have at times opposed and at other times accelerated the general trend. Its conclusions are dated only in relative terms toward the beginning, but become fixed as to year as the record progresses.

The climatic pattern of the last major glacial advance is the real starting point from which amelioration proceeded; hence a brief summary of those conditions is now in order. The discussion will be confined to the Northern Hemisphere, where records are most completely known. It must always be borne in mind that the Southern Hemisphere approaches being a reverse or mirror image of the Northern, with important modifications resulting from more widespread development of oceans south of the Equator.

Along the borders of the ice cap there was a strip of tundra, just as now, but in Europe it extended as far south as northern Spain. The evidence is that of arctic plants in peat and the remains of such animals as the arctic fox, reindeer, musk ox, and arctic lemming (a small rodent). A similar belt in North America has been demonstrated by the finding of such animals as the musk ox in Indiana, Illinois, West Virginia, Missouri, and Iowa and reindeer in New Jersey, Connecticut, and Vermont.

Between tundra and true forest climates in Europe was a zone of cold steppe similar in many ways to the treeless plains of southern Siberia today. Here lived the dry-climate jerboa (a jumping rodent), red suslik (a ground squirrel), steppe marmot (related to the woodchuck), and saiga antelope. This zone appears to have been narrower in North America, where forests approached ice margins more closely as they do today in parts of Alaska and particularly in New Zealand, where luxuriant tree ferns and other plants of tropical aspect almost reach the ice itself. The contrast between European and American steppe climates is readily explained by the difference in trends of mountain systems.

True deserts were more limited in extent than now, partly as the result of greater precipitation but chiefly because lower temperatures reduced the evaporation rates. They were somewhat farther south where topography permitted.

Forest climates in Europe were split into two groups, one confined to narrow strips along the Atlantic seaboard and the other in the highlands toward the southeast. Glaciation so upset pre-Quarternary conditions that most of the Tertiary flora vanished, and Europe today is poor in plant species. The ice crowded plants against mountain ranges they could not cross. In North America the open belt of land south of the ice permitted southward migration of plants, and they again moved northward as the ice retreated. Many plants have remained behind as disjuncts or relics of ice-age distribution.

Tropical climates were somewhat cooler during glacial maxima. The glaciers on Mount Kenya, 8 miles south of the Equator, are now confined to elevations in excess of 15,000 feet. During the Pleistocene they extended down to 10,000 feet. A similar record exists in Mexico.

The glaciers on Popocatepetl came down about 4,725 feet below present levels and those on Ixtaccihuatl, 3,860 feet.

Recession of glaciers shifted climatic belts toward existing positions (*1*, *23*). As land formerly covered with ice was exposed, tundra vegetation was established upon it, steppes expanded in continental interiors, deserts grew in size and shifted northward. Forests followed in the path of migrating tundras both northward and upward into mountains as temperatures ameliorated.

It is thought that the last general recession of continental glaciers began about 30,000 to 40,000 years ago. Varves in North America account for some 28,000 years, but the record is incomplete and has not been tied into the European geochronology. From a climatic standpoint it is convenient to consider this epoch of retreat, the Recent of the geologist, in four parts, differentiated chiefly on the basis of evidence: (1) From about 30,000 to 40,000 years ago to about 12,000 B. C., a time of glacial recession, with halts and minor advances indicated by varves and types of evidence that are essentially geologic; (2) from 12,000 to 120 B. C., a time when the record is fairly clear with respect to minor climatic oscillations, the evidence being essentially archeologic or paleontologic and the dating depending chiefly on varves; (3) from 120 B. C. to the middle of the nineteenth century, with documental evidence of climatic swings; and (4) since the middle of the nineteenth century, the instrumental period, with precise data. The major events during ice retreat do not coincide with these periods.

In northwestern Europe the Arctic period, characterized by extreme glacial climates, gradually passed into the Subarctic period in about 12,000 B. C. A Baltic ice lake, which did not communicate with the Atlantic Ocean, was then established along the southern and eastern fringe of the melting ice. Accelerated melting occurred in about 8,000 B. C., and the ice retreated far enough northward to permit the entrance of saline Atlantic waters into the Baltic, and a cold-water Yoldia fauna (a group of shelled animals, the most common of which was *Yoldia arctica*, which today lives only in waters at least as cold as 32° F.) was established. The lands of central Europe then experienced a northern (Boreal) climatic period, the diminishing intensity of which permitted northward migration of forests. After some complications in Baltic history, which are chiefly of geologic interest and need not concern us here, in about the year 5,000 B. C. the Baltic became warm enough to support types of life that demand temperatures warmer than those of today. Geologists speak of this time as the Littorina period, naming it after one of the dominant species of snails living in the Baltic at that time. Men living in western Europe were making kitchen middens, or refuse heaps, which are now being excavated for the purpose of examining their culture, a stage called Epipaleolithic. From the climatic standpoint, warm and moist conditions lasted from about 5,000 to 3,000 B. C., and the time is called the Atlantic period. Temperatures were high enough so that all small mountain glaciers of the Alps and the present United States disappeared completely (*21*).

The Atlantic period was followed, about 2,000 B. C., by the dry and warm Subboreal period, which lasted well over a thousand years. Men were leaving curious piles of rock—dolmens—in western Europe and practicing mass burials of their dead. Others, the "lake dwellers," were building houses in marshy places which later became lakes. The cultural stage was Neolithic in western Europe. Some lines of evidence lead us to believe that the actual minimum in precipitation occurred in about 2,200–2,000 B. C., but there was also very dry weather centering about 1,000 B. C. In all probability there were two times of extreme dryness separated by a short period of intense rainfall, for it has been established that the lake villages in Switzerland were destroyed by flood in 1,275 B. C.

Subboreal times were followed by increasing rainfall and cooler weather in western Europe, during a period known as Subatlantic, which reached typical development between 850 and 300 B. C. Bronze and iron ages were blended into historic times. The Hallstat and La Tène cultures of central Europe characterize most of the period. From peat bogs of Subatlantic times come not only a rich record of human events but also a detailed botanical record of sequential climatic changes.

The climatic history just sketched is quite definite for western and central Europe. Was it universal? Instrumental records from recent decades plainly tell us that many extreme departures from normal conditions at one place have little or no expression elsewhere. On the other hand, certain sympathetic swings seem to be related even though appearing in observations as widely spaced as different continents or hemispheres. Unfortunately we know less about the geochronologic period in other continents than Europe. The record from western Asia is in rather close agreement as far as it is known. Anau was occupied during the wet period of about 5,000 B. C. Drought occurred there in about 2,000 B. C., during the European Subboreal period. Western Asia was again wet during the moist Subatlantic period of Europe. About 400 B. C. a precipitation maximum is indicated in North America, Africa, western Asia, and Europe. All of these places record very dry conditions about A. D. 700. There is thus considerable evidence in favor of world-wide climatic swings. On the other hand, the records indicate some notable exceptions, particularly between European and Chinese precipitation (*4*).

The documental period of European climatic history indicates many swings in climatic conditions. During the first century after Christ precipitation conditions over Europe and southwestern Asia appear to have closely resembled those of today. This fact has been widely used as an argument against climatic change. The evidence is strong, however, that considerable variability has occurred during the interval. Advocates of climatic stability who use first-century *vs.* twentieth-century comparisons have no stronger case than would a person who might visit Duluth each January and advocate a theory that average annual temperatures there are below freezing.

From about A. D. 180 to 350 Europe experienced a wet period. The fifth century was dry in Europe and western Asia and apparently also in North America. Many of the lakes in the western United States appear to have dried out completely. Europe was both warm and dry in the seventh century. Glaciers retreated to such an extent that a heavy traffic used Alpine passes now closed by ice. Tree rings in the western United States indicate minimum precipitation at this time. Nile floods were low until about A. D. 1000.

The beginning of the ninth century brought heavier precipitation to Europe. The levels of lakes rose, and people living around their borders were pushed upslope. Documental evidence from southwestern Asia and American tree rings give similar testimony. Warm, dry conditions returned during the tenth and eleventh centuries. This was a time of great exploratory activity among northwestern Europeans. The Arctic ice cap may have disappeared entirely. In any event the logs of Greenland voyagers show routes of travel where they would now be impossible because of ice floes. Greenland was settled in 984 and abandoned about 1410 (*22*). During the eleventh and twelfth centuries it was in rather close touch with Iceland and Europe, even to the point of having its own bishop. The decline of the colony was due to unsatisfactory conditions both in Greenland and in northwestern Europe. The first half of the thirteenth century was a period of great storminess, as shown by documents describing conditions on the North Sea. The early fourteenth century was unusually cold and snowy in Iceland and Denmark. America, too, experienced cold and wet weather during this general period. The Aztecs settled Mexico in 1325, when lakes stood at levels higher than today's levels. Drought and lower levels followed, but in 1550 lakes again reached high stages.

The early seventeenth century in Europe was particularly wet. Alpine glaciers extended far down valleys, and northern Italy suffered from disastrous floods. Glaciers retreated between 1640 and 1770 and then advanced until the middle of the nineteenth century. Since then they have retreated back to sixteenth-century positions (*21*). This appears to be a world-wide condition and suggests that the last century has had higher summer temperatures than the eighteenth century just preceding.

Rate of Change of Climate

Long-Time Trends, Short-Time Fluctuations

One normally considers that a flea and an elephant differ greatly in size. In relation to the sun, however, the difference is inconsequential. To a geologist a long-time trend in climatic change might occupy a million years or so. To a climatologist, especially one who is dealing with the instrumental period, a long-time trend might be a matter of half a century to several centuries. Short-time fluctuations would involve only a small number of years.

The time during which instrumental observations have been made in sufficient quantity and under well enough standardized conditions to permit comparative studies has been so short that climatologists have been severely handicapped in their attempts to find systematic changes in weather conditions. Precise studies can do little more than call attention to short-time fluctuations. Our surest long-time trends are established so far on documental evidence.

A list of more than 50 "climatic cycles," varying in length from a few days to nearly 2 centuries, has been compiled by Mascart (*20*). Each man who has proposed one or more of these cycles has become convinced that he has found a particular rhythm in which climatic conditions have changed from a minimum, through a maximum, and back to the minimum observational value. It may be possible that there is true significance in some of these cycles, but it is also apparent that the climatic experience resulting from various combinations of cycles is indeed complex.

Though firm advocates of climatic cycles will sharply disagree, such facts as we possess today neither definitely demonstrate nor disprove the existence of any real cycle. Such climatic variability as has been observed may be explained as resulting wholly from random fluctuations.

Climatic Variations From Year to Year

While the changes in climate over such long ranges of time as geologic epochs or periods are primarily of practical interest only to students of earth history, and such variations as occur during decades are of practical utility only in such fields as long-range economic or cultural planning, the ordinary citizen, especially if he is concerned with agriculture, finds his interests chiefly centered about the question of variation from one year to the next. The problems of long-range forecasting are discussed elsewhere in this volume. Here it need be stated only that new concepts are arising continually in the minds of climatologists and that their testing in the light of increasingly valuable instrumental observation is gradually building a secure footing for the complete understanding of the causes and nature of climatic variations from year to year.

SOME THEORIES OF CLIMATIC CHANGE

Climate and Changes in the Earth's Surface

The close relationship shown in the geologic record between times of revolution and glacial climatic patterns leaves slight room for doubt that crustal unrest is responsible for the major breaks in the continuity of normal geologic climates.

At times of revolution continents are most extensive, and their topography is most complex and has greatest relief. These factors make for increased temperature ranges between opposite seasons, increased pressure ranges both between seasons and from place to place, higher wind velocities, and numerous other changes in weather conditions, all of which in turn make for climatic complexity.

The fact that glacial deposits are almost wholly restricted to the formations originating at times of revolution strongly favors the idea of a cause-and-effect relationship. Most salt layers, the greatest deposits of coarse sediment, and the most extensive deposits of nonmarine sediment also come from these times of crustal unrest. Volcanic activity is most pronounced at such times (*27*).

In sharp contrast to the glacial climatic patterns of revolutions is the moderate, uniform, subdued-zonal, "normal" climatic pattern of the long intervals of geologic quiet. These were times of reduced continental area, low relief, diminished volcanic activity, and crustal rest.

No widely accepted theory explains the underlying cause of more or less periodic geologic revolutions. Their occurrence is widely accepted as geologic fact. Their climatic relationships appear to be well established. Their causes may be regarded as matters for the future to decide.[4]

---

[4] Possibly the most attractive theory today relates them to contrasts between the escape of heat generated by radioactive substances under conductive versus convective conditions. The earth's radius might lengthen slowly—that is, the earth might expand in size—during long intervals in which the crust and subcrust gained radioactive heat more rapidly than conduction dissipated it. Eventually a time would come when an important zone would liquefy, causing rapid expansion and geologic revolution. A relatively rapid heat loss by convection through the liquefied portion would permit crustal and subcrustal cooling, the shortening of earth radii (contraction of the earth), a return to solidity, and original conductive conditions (*16*).

Possible Astronomic Effects on Climate

Several theories of climatic change based on causes not related to the earth's crust or atmosphere are, or have been, held in widespread popular esteem. The more significant will be sketched here.

The annual revolution of the earth around the sun takes place in a plane called the ecliptic. The axis of the earth is inclined toward this plane at an angle of about 23°27′3″. This inclination of the earth's axis is the principal cause of seasons. It is responsible for the differing lengths of night and day experienced in various latitudes, causes seasonal shifting of wind belts, and in other ways materially affects climatic distribution. If the axis were exactly at right angles to the ecliptic, days and nights would always have the same length in all latitudes. This would keep winter days from being shorter and reduce cold in higher latitudes.

It is thoroughly established that the angle between the axis and the ecliptic is not constant. It will reach a minimum of about 22°30′ some 9,600 years from now. Arguments that climatic changes result from this cause are sound enough in quality but are not impressive from the quantitative standpoint. The variation is altogether too small to account for contrasts indicated by the geologic record. The cycle recurs too often to explain the small number of glacial climatic experiences since the beginning of the Paleozoic era. It may contribute to certain cycles "long range" in terms of nongeologic climatology.

Another astronomic fact is that the axis of the earth does not always point approximately toward the North Star. This means that existing conditions whereby the earth's nearest approach to the sun (the perihelion) occurs only a few days after the shortest day of the northern winter (winter solstice) will gradually change to an opposite extreme in which the earth will be closest to the sun in northern midsummer. This cycle occurs each 26,000 years and is called the precession of the equinoxes. Northern Hemisphere seasonal contrasts should be somewhat intensified as the perihelion approaches the summer solstice. This effect also may contribute to "long-range" cycles in nongeologic climatology.

There are catastrophic possibilities in astronomic speculation. Many believe that the earth originated from the passage of some great star so close to the sun that long filaments of solar material were drawn out as tides. These filaments broke into several fragments which solidified and became planets, with rotations and revolutions resulting from the original speed of the passing star. Lesser gravitational disturbances originating outside the planetary system could conceivably jolt the earth now and then so as to upset the direction of its axis or the relative positions of continents and bring about catastrophic climatic changes. However, the geologic record contains no evidence that this has ever happened.

The sun is a variable star. This means that the amount of radiant energy it emits changes from time to time. Some of the shorter periods of change have been considered to be cyclic, but instrumental observations extend back for only a few decades. Changes in solar radiation have been related to the numbers, positions, and polarity of sunspots. The relation between sunspots and terrestrial magnetism is very close, but no conclusive evidence indicates any simple climatic relationships. Our knowledge on this subject is increasing from year to year. The possibilities of long-range forecasting on the basis of sunspot cycles are being investigated seriously by students in various parts of the earth.

Whether variations in the sun's radiant energy could cause such contrasts as exist between glacial and normal geologic climates is unknown. Against the idea is the close correlation between glacial conditions and crustal revolutions. If the sun is the underlying cause, some mechanism whereby revolutions and increased volcanic activity result from varying amounts of radiant energy must be found.

Climate and Changes in the Atmosphere

One of the most popular explanations of glacial climates relates them to changes in the earth's atmosphere. The ability of the sun's radiant energy to travel from the outer limits of the atmosphere to the earth's surface may change with changes in the atmosphere itself; on a clear day the coefficient is higher than on a day with a heavy cloud layer. Such variations might produce results similar to those caused by variations in the emission of radiant energy by the sun itself. It is unfortunate that much fallacious argument has been advanced along these lines and that many of the ideas advocated fail to consider all consequences of the conditions postulated.

If the atmosphere had a perpetual cloud layer, a great deal of solar radiation would be reflected back to space, and consequently the amount of energy available to the earth's surface in the form of heat would be diminished. A cloud blanket, however, would also cut off a good deal of terrestrial radiation, tending to conserve such heat as might exist beneath it. Temperature ranges between day and night, one season and another, and higher and lower latitudes would be reduced. Arguments as to whether the loss in the sun's heat reaching the surface (insolation) exceeds the energy value of heat trapped by a cloud layer are of interest only if it can be demonstrated that such a layer is a possibility. The ascent of air to form cloud in one place must be matched by descent elsewhere. Rotation and equatorial heating are bound to produce an atmospheric circulation in which definite belts of descending air occur. The cloud blanket would be broken at all places where air descends, and it would also be punctured as the result of topographic irregularity such as exists on earth today. An extensive, though not world-wide, cloud blanket could best form over an earth of small continents having subdued relief. Tendencies in this direction are most readily realized during normal geologic periods and might have contributed to the minor zonal differences characteristic of normal climatic patterns. They may be regarded as impossible of realization over the earth today or at any other time of geologic revolution. As far as the contrast between normal and glacial climatic patterns is concerned, we may regard crustal stability as the true cause of contrasts, cloud layering as a possible conditioning factor.

Much has been written about varying amounts of carbon dioxide in the atmosphere as a possible cause of glacial periods. The theory received a fatal blow when it was realized that carbon dioxide is very selective as to the wave lengths of radiant energy it will absorb, filtering out only such waves as even very minute quantities of water vapor dispose of anyway. No probable increase in atmospheric carbon dioxide could materially affect either the amount of insolation reaching the surface or the amount of terrestrial radiation lost to space.

Large amounts of volanic dust in the atmosphere have also been considered as a possible cause of glacial climates. Lowered temperatures have followed great dust-producing volcanic explosions during the period of instrumental observation. Volcanoes have been particularly active during times of glacial climate. It seems most reasonable, however, to relate both the volcanic activity and the climate to crustal unrest and to regard the former more in the light of a modifying influence than as the underlying cause of the latter.

Variations in the Earth's Heat

There is a slow radiation into the atmosphere of heat that slowly escapes from the earth's interior. It has been suggested that variations in the rate of escape could produce changes in climates. The rate of escape, however, is too slow to have an appreciable effect upon such things as daily or seasonal temperature ranges today. These are controlled by solar rather than by terrestrial energy.

A possibility exists that cyclic variations in the rates of escape of the earth's heat have occurred during the course of geologic time (*16*). If such is the case, they have followed the general history of normal versus revolutionary conditions. The idea is highly speculative, and at most such changes have acted only as conditions modifying climatic patterns determined by crustal behavior.

CLIMATE AND MAN

The world pattern of climates today depends primarily upon definite facts of atmospheric behavior related to surface conditions such as the relative proportion of oceanic cover, shapes and sizes of continents, their positions with reference to the Poles and Equator, and the distribution of plains, plateaus, and mountains upon land surfaces. The world pattern during any part of the geologic past was, in general, related to exactly the same phenomena. Many of the facts of atmospheric behavior have remained practically constant throughout geologic time. The amount of atmosphere has not changed appreciably nor has its average temperature, viscosity, composition, or other significant physical property. The speed and direction of the earth's rotation, the rate of escape of heat from the earth's interior, the amount of solar radiation received by the earth, and similar fundamental climatic factors have either remained constant or varied by only inconsequential amounts. The most variable factors affecting climate have been those relating to continental sizes and elevations. It is thus reasonable to regard these as the most probable causes of such climatic change as is indicated by geological evidence. This conclusion finds strong support in numerous divergent, but not wholly unrelated, fields of geological investigation.

For reasons that are today unknown, the earth has experienced several relatively brief periods of crustal unrest, each of which has been accompanied by evidences of glaciation in various parts of the earth's surface and by intense aridity in other parts. Between these revolutionary periods have been vastly longer intervals of quiet and climatic monotony. Such is the general outline of climatic history of geological proportions.

Man appeared on the scene during a revolutionary period and has experienced glacial climates. In the geologically recent portion of his experience, during which he has progressed through a cultural development which has culminated in such scientific advances as the introduction of modern instrumental observation, he has witnessed a slow, and possibly permanent, amelioration of extreme glacial climates, but he has at no time experienced the normal climate indicated by most of the geologic record.

Man has observed that climatic conditions fluctuate rather widely from time to time at a given place, and in seeking to understand such natural phenomena he has been tempted to explain such fluctuations on the basis of recurring cycles. As yet, however, no definite proof has been advanced to contradict the opinion that all such relatively short-term climatic changes are nothing more than matters of chance. The world pattern of climates today is the product of climatic variations, not the expression of recurring mean, or normal, conditions. The extent of desert climate will not be the same next year as this. The humid margin of the desert is the product of an ever-changing distribution of extreme aridity. The time may come when such changes will be well enough understood to be of definite forecast and economic value, but it is likely that such information will be the fruit of long-continued and patient research.

Interest in changes of geologic proportions will remain intellectual. There is satisfaction in learning the secrets of earth history, even though our investigations are based almost entirely upon evidence that accumulated long before the appearance of man on the earthly scene and all forecasts relate to a time when he may no longer be present to verify or contradict them.

LITERATURE CITED

(1) Antevs, Ernst.
1928. THE LAST GLACIATION, WITH SPECIAL REFERENCE TO THE ICE RETREAT IN NORTHEASTERN NORTH AMERICA. Amer. Geog. Soc., Res. Ser. 17, 292 pp., illus.

(2) Arldt, Theodor.
1919–22. HANDBUCH DER PALEOGEOGRAPHIE. 2 v., illus. Leipzig.

(3) Berry, Edward Wilber.
1923. tree ancestors; a glimpse into the past. 270 pp., illus. Baltimore.
(4) Brooks, C. E. P.
1926. climate through the ages; a study of the climatic factors and their variations. 439 pp., illus. London.
(5) Dachnowski, Alfred P.
1922. the correlation of time units and climatic changes in peat deposits of the united states and europe. Natl. Acad. Sci. Proc. 8: 225–231.
(6) Daly, Reginald A.
1929. swinging sealevel of the ice age. Geol. Soc. Amer. Bul. 40: 721–734.
(7) ———
1934. the changing world of the ice age. 271 pp., illus. New Haven and London.
(8) DeGeer, Gerard.
1910. a geochronology of the last 12,000 years. 11th Internatl. Geol. Cong. (Stockholm), Compt. Rend. 1: 241–258, illus.
(9) Depéret, Charles.
1918. essai de coordination chronologique des temps quaternaires. [Paris] Acad. des Sci. Compt. Rend. 166: 480–486, 636–641, 884–889.
(10) Douglass, A. E.
1914. a method of estimating rainfall by the growth of trees. Carnegie Inst. Wash. Pub. 192, pp. 101–121, illus.
(11) ———
1921. dating our prehistoric ruins. how growth rings in timbers aid in establishing the relative ages of the ruined pueblos of the southwest. Amer. Museum Nat. Hist., Nat. Hist. 21: 27–30, illus.
(12) Fisk, H. N.
1938. geology of grant and la salle parishes. La. Dept. Conserv. Geol. Bul. 10, 246 pp., illus.
(13) Gilbert, Grove Karl.
1890. lake bonneville. 438 pp., illus. U. S. Geol. Survey Monog. 1.
(14) Huntington, Ellsworth.
1907. the pulse of asia, a journey in central asia illustrating the geographic basis of history. 415 pp., illus. Boston and New York.
(15) ———
1925. tree growth and climatic interpretations. Carnegie Inst. Wash. Pub. 352, pp. 155–204, illus.
(16) Joly, John.
1925. the surface-history of the earth. 192 pp., illus. Oxford.
(17) Knowlton, Frank Hall.
1927. plants of the past; a popular account of fossil plants. 275 pp., illus. Princeton.
(18) Köppen, W., and Wegener, A.
1924. die klimate der geologischen vorzeit. 255 pp., illus. Berlin.
(19) Lungerhausen, L.
1938. fauna of the dniester terraces. (In Russian, with brief summary in English.) Ukraine Acad. Sci., Jour. Geol. 5: 119–236, illus.
(20) Mascart, Jean.
[1925.] notes sur la variabilité des climats. Docs. Lyonnais, Études de Climatologie, pt. 1, 382 pp. Lyon.
(21) Matthes, François E.
1939. report of committee on glaciers. Amer. Geophys. Union Trans. 20 (4): 518–523.
(22) Nansen, Fridtjof.
1911. in northern mists; arctic exploration in early times. 2 v., illus. London.
(23) Penck, Albrecht.
1914. the shifting of the climatic belts. Scot. Geog. Mag. 30: 281–293, illus.

(24) RAYMOND, PERCY E.
1939. PREHISTORIC LIFE. 324 pp., illus. Cambridge, Mass.
(25) RUSSELL, ISRAEL COOK.
1885. GEOLOGICAL HISTORY OF LAKE LAHONTAN, A QUATERNARY LAKE OF NORTHWESTERN NEVADA. 288 pp., illus. U. S. Geol. Survey Monog. 11.
(26) SEWARD, A. C.
1931. PLANT LIFE THROUGH THE AGES; A GEOLOGICAL AND BOTANICAL RETROSPECT. 601 pp., illus. Cambridge, England.
(27) SNIDER, LUTHER C.
1932. EARTH HISTORY. 683 pp., illus. New York.
(28) WRIGHT, W. B.
1914. THE QUATERNARY ICE AGE. 464 pp., illus. London.

Climate and the World Pattern

BY DAVID I. BLUMENSTOCK AND C. WARREN THORNTHWAITE [1]

THREE GREAT patterns dominate the earth and are of tremendous importance to man—the pattern of climate, the pattern of vegetation, and the pattern of soils. When the three patterns are laid one upon another, their boundaries coincide to a remarkable degree because climate is the fundamental dynamic force shaping the other two. The relationships between these three patterns have been the object of considerable scientific study, and some of the results are here broadly outlined. A fourth pattern laid upon the three is that of human culture, or civilization. Though modern man has some freedom to vary this pattern because of his control of other forces, he too cannot go beyond certain limits set fundamentally by climate.

[1] David I. Blumenstock is Assistant Climatologist and C. Warren Thornthwaite is Chief, Climatic and Physiographic Division, Office of Research, Soil Conservation Service.

THE MOST obvious difference in appearance between one region and another is found in surface configuration, with such contrasts as those between flat, open plains and rugged mountains or low marshland and high, rocky plateaus. Vegetation also varies; forests, for example, contrast sharply with open grassland or desert. Forest areas in turn can be distinguished from one another by the kind of trees that compose the stands. The coniferous forests of the Pacific coast are quite different in appearance and aspect from the deciduous forests of Ohio or Indiana. Grassland areas too present important contrasts, as between the tall-grass prairies of Iowa and the short-grass plains of eastern Colorado or the bunchgrass regions of Utah and Nevada. Again, underneath the mantle of vegetation there are great variations in soil characteristics between one area and another.

All of these factors—surface configuration, vegetation, soils—vary from place to place. Yet there are extensive areas where each is relatively homogeneous, and it thus becomes possible to identify and map regions with uniform characteristics of surface, vegetation, and soil. The regions thus identified form a general pattern or arrangement that can be best interpreted in climatic terms. The influence of climate on the growth of plants is a predominant factor affecting their distribution; and the relationship between soil formation on the one hand and vegetation and climate on the other is so close that the pattern displayed by a soils map likewise reflects climatic conditions. Surface configuration, being due in part to great internal diastrophic forces (forces responsible for the formation of the earth's surface) is less influenced by climate than is either vegetation or soil, but the influence is great enough for the minor surface features to reflect the climate of the area in which they occur.

THE CLIMATIC PATTERN

The pattern formed by the distribution of climatic types over the surface of the earth is a reflection of the nature of the general circulation of the atmosphere. The tilting of the earth on its axis to form an angle of 66½° with the plane in which it revolves about the sun (plane of the ecliptic) causes the rays of the sun to fall more directly on tropical than on polar regions. As a result, lower latitudes are warmed more than higher ones. Air, heated at the Equator, expands upward and flows poleward aloft. Thus the total weight of air over the Poles increases, and this causes high pressure at the ground in very high latitudes; whereas the outflow of air aloft around the Equator causes the air at the ground to have less weight. The difference in surface pressures thus set up creates a return flow of air along the ground, from the Poles equatorward, since fluids tend to move from areas of higher pressure to areas of lower pressure.

The earth, however, is rotating on its axis from west to east. Hence the return flow does not follow a simple, direct line from the Poles to the Equator. Rather, winds are deflected because of the rotation, being thrown off to the right in the Northern Hemisphere and to the left in the Southern. In addition, friction produced by the earth's surface causes modifications in the simple flow pattern. The result is a series of belts with prevailing east winds in the polar regions and near the Equator, but with west winds in the middle latitudes. The

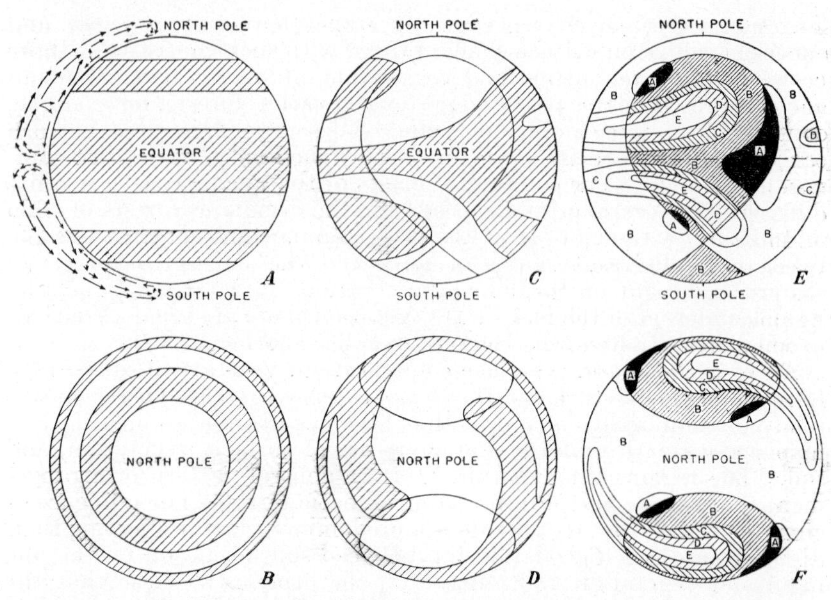

FIGURE 1.—*A, B,* The general circulation of the atmosphere and the rainfall belts as they would appear on a uniform earth—that is, one without irregular masses of continents and oceans. *A* is the view looking down on the Equator; *B*, that looking down on the North Pole. Arrows show how the atmospheric circulation is split into three cells in each hemisphere. Shaded portions are areas of maximum rainfall; unshaded portions are dry areas. *C, D,* Generalized rainfall pattern. This shows how the rainfall pattern in *A* and *B* is modified by continents and oceans. Shaded portions are areas of heavy rainfall; unshaded areas are dry. The loop formed by the black line in C (looking down on the Equator) is a generalized continental area; it roughly represents North and South America in the Western Hemisphere, and Europe, Asia, and Africa in the Eastern Hemisphere. In *D* (looking down on the North Pole) the continents are represented by an egg-shaped loop in each hemisphere. *E, F,* The distribution of the principal climatic types on the generalized continental area. *E,* looking down on the Equator, shows the generalized continent outlined as a loop in *C. F,* looking down on the North Pole, shows the two egg-shaped continental masses outlined in *D.* The letters and shadings in these two diagrams represent the climatic divisions of the earth according to Thornthwaite's classification, described in the text.

simple drift of air equatorward in the lower levels and poleward aloft is broken down into a series of subdivisions or cells with air ascending in the equatorial region and in high middle latitudes and descending in the subtropics and in polar regions. This cellular pattern of atmospheric circulation is shown by the arrows in figure 1, *A* (*25*).[2] Because of the difficulty of representing clearly all features of the climatic pattern of the earth on a flat map or diagram, the pattern is presented from two angles in figure 1—first as it would look from over the Equator, and second, as it would look from over the North Pole.

Precipitation occurs from air which is cooled by being forced aloft where two currents converge. Thus, were it not for the uneven distribution of land and sea there would be rainy belts corresponding to the belts of ascending air in low latitudes and in high middle latitudes as shown by the shaded areas in figure 1, *A* and *B*. But land heats and cools more rapidly than do the oceans, which act as great

[2] Italic numbers in parentheses refer to Literature Cited, p. 126.

heat reservoirs, and the distribution of the continents therefore has a marked effect on the circulation pattern. There are certain preferred positions or routes, like main highways, along which cold air moves down from the Poles to meet the warmer air moving up from low latitudes. The modified pattern which results is shown in the two hemisphere diagrams in figure 1, *C* and *D*. The area within the loop in figure 1, *C*, represents a much-generalized continental land mass, either North and South America or Eurasia and Africa, surrounded by water. The triangular area to the south represents Antarctica. The polar view, figure 1, *D*, shows the portions of the two continents which lie north of the Equator. As brought out in the polar view, the relatively dry area (unshaded) forms an S in the Northern Hemisphere, the center of the S being at the Pole. In the Southern Hemisphere, where large continental masses in high middle latitudes are entirely lacking, the pattern is less pronounced. Insufficient data make any definite conclusion impossible, but it is reasonable to believe that there too the dry tongues produce an analogous pattern, but with three tails comprised in a reverse S.

Annual precipitation varies enormously over the earth, the minimum being less than 1 inch and the maximum in excess of 900 inches. As a result, types of vegetation have developed which vary greatly in their moisture requirements. At one extreme, the water available for vegetation is vastly more than sufficient for the most extravagant users of water; and at the other, there is insufficient to permit the development of the most abstemious of water-using plants. On the basis of varying moisture requirements, five principal types of vegetation have developed over the earth's surface. Because of their dependence on precipitation for moisture, these vegetation types correspond to climatic regions as follows:

Vegetation type	*Climatic region*
Rain forest	A—superhumid
Forest	B—humid
Grassland	C—subhumid
Steppe	D—semiarid
Desert	E—arid

Since some of the water that falls on the land evaporates directly and some runs back to the sea, only a part of the precipitation is available for plants. This remainder, which the plants may use, is called effective precipitation. As temperature decreases from the Equator to the Poles, losses due to evaporation and run-off diminish and consequently the effectiveness of a given amount of rainfall increases. Thus, the diagrammatic representation of the distribution of rainfall in figure 1, *C* and *D*, fails to give an adequate picture of the pattern of climates. Even though the annual rainfall in the polar regions is small, the evaporation is smaller still, and the resultant climate is humid.

At present, no meteorological instrument for measuring effective precipitation exists. Total precipitation falling on any part of the earth can be measured, but the proportion not lost as evaporation or run-off and available for plants cannot be measured directly. Vegetation itself serves as the most satisfactory existing measure of effective precipitation; thus, the five principal climatic types are mapped by means of natural vegetation. The distribution of soil types and, to a

298737°—41——8

lesser degree, patterns of drainage and land surface and of land use, verify the fivefold climatic division suggested by the distribution of vegetation (*25*).

In figure 1, *E* and *F*, the generalized distribution of the five climatic types is shown, the land areas being shaded from solid black to white to conform to the range from superhumid (A) to arid (E). The relations between *C* and *E* and between *D* and *F* of figure 1 can readily be seen.

A number of climatic elements in addition to precipitation are important in determining the distribution of vegetation, soils, surface features, and land utilization. They include temperature, evaporation, sunshine, cloudiness, and fog. Those of greatest significance are precipitation, evaporation, and temperature.

Lack of adequate evaporation measurements has made it necessary to combine precipitation and evaporation through developing indices of effective precipitation based on the general principle that an increase in temperature tends to cause an increase in evaporation.[3] These indices have been devised to show not the actual total precipitation, but that portion of the total which remains in the soil available for plant use. In some areas nearly all of the precipitation enters the soil and is accessible to growing plants, while in others only a very small percentage reaches the subsoil before being evaporated. Indices of effective precipitation, therefore, are more satisfactory than total-rainfall figures in any study of plant, soil, or agronomic relationships.[4]

When figures showing mean annual precipitation effectiveness are plotted on a map, it can be seen that there is a close relationship between them and the type of natural vegetation and soil to be found from area to area. By locating the transition zones between vegetation and soil regions, critical values for precipitation effectiveness that have practical meaning in terms of plant growth and soil develop-

---

[3] Evaporation measurements have been made from pans, but pan evaporation is not equal to true evaporation from a land surface, since pans, unlike the ground, are kept supplied with water and evaporation from a free water surface is not equivalent to evaporation from the soil or transpiring leaf surfaces. The statement that evaporation increases with temperature although not strictly true holds in a general way.

[4] De Martonne (*14*), Meyer (*15*), Lang (*12*), Köppen (*11*), and others have devised indices of precipitation effectiveness. The one used here was developed by Thornthwaite (*23*, *24*) and is defined as follows:

Thornthwaite's index of precipitation effectiveness, which is used in defining the moisture provinces, rests on the basic assumption that evaporation and transpiration tend to increase with increase in temperature and hence that the effectiveness of any given amount of precipitation decreases with temperature increase. Meyer developed an index of precipitation effectiveness which employed this principle in its simplest form. His index was simply P/T, where P is mean annual precipitation in millimeters and T is mean annual temperature in degrees centigrade. De Martonne modified Meyer's formula, making it $\left(\frac{P}{T+10}\right)$ in which P and T retain the same values assigned by Meyer. Thornthwaite's index, based on careful analysis of climatic records and vegetation distributions, led to the formulation of a monthly index $\left(\frac{P}{T-10}\right)^{10/9}$ where P=precipitation in inches and T=temperature in degrees Fahrenheit. Not only does this represent a refinement of the form of the index, but whereas Meyer and De Martonne used mean annual values, Thornthwaite calculates an index for each month and then sums them to obtain the annual index. By so doing allowance is made for variations in temperature and precipitation from month to month so that greater weight is given precipitation occurring in cold months, when evaporation and transpiration are low, than during hot months, when they are relatively high.

Through introducing a constant term into the precipitation effectiveness (*PE*) index as given above, Thornthwaite has obtained whole numbers for *PE* values separating the principal moisture regions. He found that the superhumid climates had values above 128, the humid between 64 and 128, the subhumid between 32 and 64, the semiarid between 16 and 32, and the arid below 16. There is no ready explanation as to why these successive values happen to form a geometric series.

The temperature-efficiency index which is used in defining the temperature divisions rests on the principle that only temperatures above freezing are beneficial to plant growth. Accordingly 32° F. is subtracted from each mean monthly temperature (where these temperatures are expressed in degrees Fahrenheit), and the 12 differences are then summed. This sum is divided by 4 for the purpose of making the magnitude of the index comparable to that of the *PE* index. By analogy with the moisture regions, the following temperature-efficiency regions are then recognized: Macrothermal, above 128; mesothermal, from 64 to 128; microthermal, between 32 and 64; taiga, from 16 to 32; tundra, 0 to 16; and perpetual snow and ice, below 0 (that is, all mean monthly temperatures below freezing).

ment have been determined. On this basis the principal moisture provinces already listed as climatic regions are defined—superhumid, humid, subhumid, semiarid, and arid.

In areas where summers are short and temperatures are generally low throughout the year—that is, near the North or South Poles and on high mountains—temperature efficiency rather than precipitation effectiveness becomes critical in influencing plant distribution and soil genesis. Three major temperature provinces have been recognized and delimited in terms of temperature efficiency—the taiga (coniferous forests), the tundra (mosses, lichens, and stunted trees), and the climate of perpetual frost. It will be noted that the first two of these have been named after vegetation types. There are three additional temperature divisions—macrothermal (hot—literally, great heat), mesothermal (moderate—literally, middle heat), and microthermal (cool—literally, little heat). These do not constitute major provinces because temperature is not a limiting value, but they are of importance in interpreting the distribution of soil and vegetation. The five moisture provinces and three major temperature provinces distinguished above constitute the eight principal climatic divisions of the world.

Superhumid (A) climates appear in equatorial regions, particularly on east coasts, and in high middle latitudes on west coasts. Arid (E) climates appear on the west coasts of continents in low middle latitudes and extend as lobes into continental interiors. Humid (B), subhumid (C), and semiarid (D) climates make up broad bands which lie between the superhumid and arid climates.

The three climates characterized by low temperature efficiency, taiga (D′), tundra (E′), and the climate of perpetual frost (F′), form concentric bands around the Poles and appear on higher mountain slopes.

Irregularities in the shape of the continents and in the distribution of mountains and lowlands result in some departure from the generalized pattern. However, as can be seen from the map of world climates (fig. 2), the general arrangement as delineated on the generalized continent is preserved. Superhumid climates appear in the equatorial region and include the East Indies and part of the Philippines, the Malay Peninsula and the coastal parts of Burma and Indo-China, the west coast of India, the Guinea coast and the Niger Delta in Africa, Central America, and the northwest coast of South America. Superhumid climates are found also on continental west coasts in high middle latitudes, as in western Europe, western North America, and southwestern Chile in South America.

Arid climates are found on the west coasts of continents in low middle latitudes and inland to continental interiors. The largest arid regions occur in Eurasia and Africa, and include the Sahara, the Arabian deserts, the deserts of Iran and Turkestan, the Thar Desert of India, and the Gobi Desert of Mongolia. The arid regions of North America, restricted largely to northern Mexico, southern California, Arizona, Nevada, and Utah, are much less extensive than the Old World deserts, but they occupy identical positions in the climatic pattern. Arid regions in the Southern Hemisphere include the Atacama and Patagonian Deserts in South America, the Kalahari Desert of South Africa, and the Great Australian Desert.

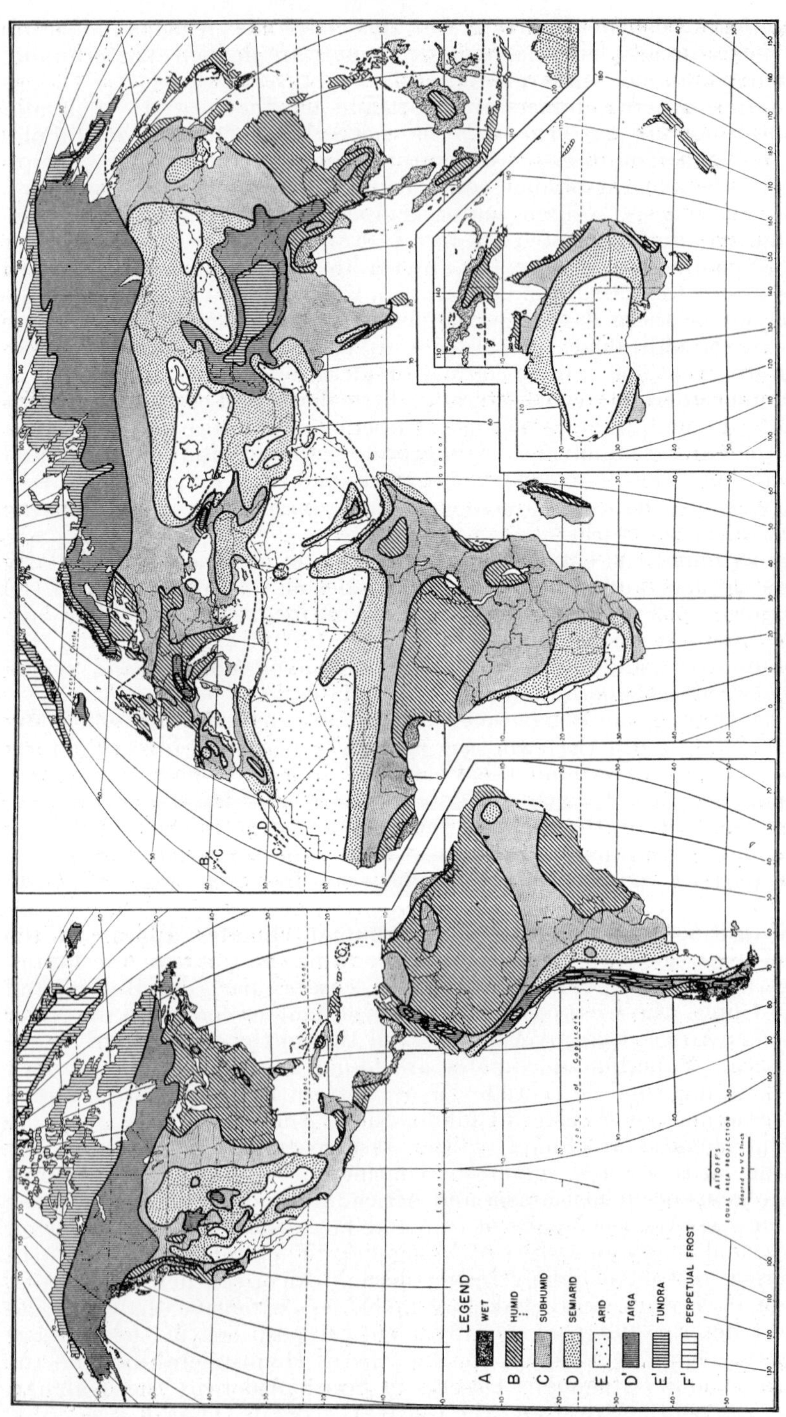

FIGURE 2.—Distribution of the principal climates of the earth.

Semiarid climates occupy broad belts around the deserts and are most extensive in Eurasia and North Africa. Other large areas are found in western North America, Australia, and South Africa. The semiarid part of South America is relatively small.

The humid climates occupy extensive areas in the Tropics and middle latitudes, being found in the equatorial regions of South America and Africa and in eastern and northwestern United States, central and western Europe, China and eastern Australia, and southeastern South America.

The subhumid climates occur between the humid and semiarid climates. They are found chiefly in central United States and Canada, northeastern Argentina and interior South America, south and central Africa, eastern Australia, north China and peninsular India, and in a belt from central Germany eastward into Siberia.

Extensive areas of taiga and tundra climates are found in Canada and Siberia. The climate of perpetual frost appears in the interior of Greenland and other polar islands and occupies the whole continent of Antarctica.

The world map shown in figure 2 represents the mean (average) position of the climatic regions. Actually, the boundaries shift from year to year, the regions themselves expanding or contracting, and these shifts are of critical importance in agriculture. However, it is the mean position of the climatic regions which is most strongly related to the distribution of natural vegetation and soils and the development of minor land forms, and these ramifications of the climatic pattern will now be considered.

CLIMATE AND VEGETATION

Since very early times it has been recognized that there is a close relationship between vegetation and climate, and many terms have come to be used to describe both climate and vegetation. The word "desert" calls to mind a region which is excessively dry and is characterized by sparse vegetation peculiarly adapted to arid conditions. "Steppe" is a term at once descriptive of a semiarid climate and of short-grass vegetation. "Tundra" applies to those cold subarctic lands, frozen much of the year, where only mosses, lichens, and occasional stunted trees grow. Many other terms apply interchangeably to climate and vegetation.

The close identification of climate and vegetation is the consequence of thousands of centuries of plant differentiation and adaptation. Since plants first appeared upon the earth, they have been subjected to the influence of climate. Through the elimination of nonadapted species and through the frequent origin of new forms (mutants), many different types of plants have become adapted to widely different climatic conditions. Plants capable of withstanding prolonged drought have developed—for example, cacti, with their extensive root systems for drawing moisture from a wide area and thick spiny leaves, which decrease transpiration; junipers, which can withstand drier climatic conditions than can most conifers; and short grasses, such as grama and buffalo grasses, whose low growing habit makes them drought-resistant as compared with the taller, more luxuriant prairie grasses (*21, p. 98*).

Because of this adaptation, each major climatic region has a dominant vegetation group made up of several plant species, each of which is adjusted to the climate of that region. These groups constitute major vegetative units called plant formations. The plant formation is a product of the climate and is controlled by it. It is not to be thought that only the plants making up the formation are to be found in one climatic region. Other species exist. But the members of the formation are dominant and are referred to as the climax vegetation for the region, since they represent the highest plant development—the climax—that will be attained under the existing climatic conditions. Locally the climax may not exist at all because of edaphic (soil) conditions or because fire has destroyed the dominant vegetation and it has not had sufficient time to become reestablished. Under such conditions it may appear as though the climax has been reached, but the "only true climax is the climatic climax: edaphic, biotic, fire, and all other so-called climaxes are capable of partial or complete explanation on the basis of the climatic climax" (*17, p. 240*).

Rain-forest and forest vegetation represent the climax in superhumid and humid climates; tall grass is the climax in subhumid regions; short grasses (steppe) are found in semiarid regions; and desert grasses and shrubs occur in desert areas. As already noted, in the taiga are found coniferous forests, mainly of spruce and fir—dense stands along the equatorward border of the province and scattered stunted trees along the poleward margin. Tundra is characterized by the presence of moss, lichens, and sedges. In the climate of perpetual snow and ice, vegetation is absent since the temperature remains below freezing throughout the year, except, perhaps, for occasional days during the summer. Here occur the barren arctic and antarctic lands, occupying, as in Greenland and Antarctica, the plateau areas in very high latitudes.

A comparison between the world-climate map (fig. 2) and the world-vegetation map (fig. 3) reveals the correspondence between climate and vegetation patterns. In the hot, superhumid Tropics and adjacent portions of the humid tropical lands, rain-forest vegetation occurs. Rain-forest conditions, characterized by tall trees with interlocking crowns and a dense understory of shrub, bush, and smaller trees, occur extensively throughout the Amazon Basin, the Congo Basin, along the African Gold Coast, and throughout the East Indies. Rain-forest areas are typically characterized by high precipitation and temperatures throughout the year. In the moderate and cool superhumid regions, on the west coasts of continents in middle latitudes, the forest growth, though dense, is somewhat different from true rain forest. Tall coniferous stands with heavy crowns replace the mixed forests of the hot, superhumid regions, and the understory does not contain so many smaller trees and vines but rather displays dense fern and moss growths.

With a decrease in effective precipitation but with high temperatures, the rain forest passes into lighter tropical forests such as occur in northeastern Australia and in parts of central America and southeastern Africa. Where precipitation totals remain high but the rainfall assumes a markedly seasonal aspect with a dry season of appreciable length, the rain forest grades into savanna. Near the rain-forest areas this is of the parkland-savanna type. As the rainfall becomes

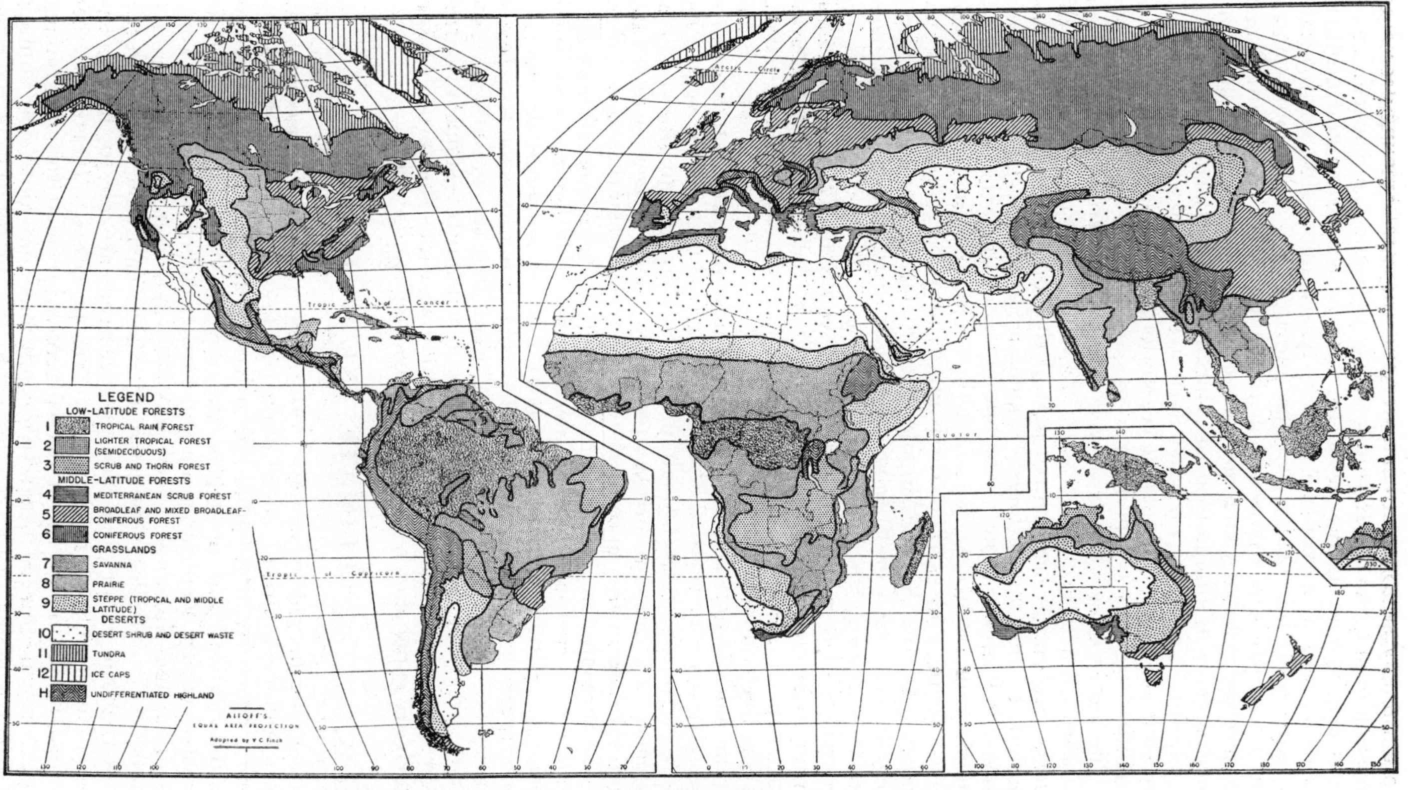

FIGURE 3.—World distribution of the principal vegetative formations.

more strongly seasonal in character and the total amount decreases, the subhumid areas of the true savanna grassland are reached. Such areas are extensively developed in southeastern Brazil and northern Australia and in a wide belt across Africa about 10° north of the Equator from the Atlantic to the Indian Ocean. In south-central Africa and southern India and in the plateau area of eastern Brazil, scrub forest is found which does not seem to represent the true climax since it occurs in subhumid areas typically characterized by herbaceous vegetation. These scrub and thorn areas are so widespread, however, that on any world map of vegetation they deserve recognition as a distinct vegetative type.

The progressive change in vegetative types from warm to cool climates is well exemplified by the banding of vegetation in the United States. In the eastern part of the country are the deciduous, coniferous, and mixed forests which occupy the regions of humid climate. Westward, in the subhumid zone, are the prairie grasslands. Still farther westward, in the semiarid plains, are found the short steppe grasses, and these grade into the desert shrubs and grasses. In the Rocky Mountain area and throughout the Sierra Nevada and the Coast Ranges increased precipitation effectiveness largely resulting from increased elevations is associated with the occurrence of forest vegetation, mainly coniferous. Along the California coast and in the Interior Valley are found Pacific bunchgrass and chaparral, which are characteristic of subhumid climatic regions having dry summers and wet winters.

The world-vegetation map illustrates how this same banding is exemplified over the earth. From humid to arid regions, the vegetation changes from forest, through prairie and steppe, to desert. This sequence is displayed, for example, inland from Chosen (Korea) and from the coastal area of southeastern Australia or southeastern Africa.

The three principal high-latitude climatic types—taiga, tundra, and climate of perpetual frost—are best developed in Eurasia and North America. Although the actual moisture in the ground is abundant in these areas it remains largely unavailable to plants since it is frozen throughout much of the year. As a result only the warmest of these three climatic provinces, the taiga, is capable of supporting tree growth, and it is largely limited to conifers such as the spruce and fir, which are capable of withstanding physiological drought.

CLIMATE AND SOILS

The part played by climate in soil genesis and the consequent climatic influence on soil distribution was first brought out by Dokuchaiev, Sibertsev, and Glinka (*3*) in Russia, and by Hilgard (*5*) in the United States. The principles they developed in the latter part of the last century were taken up and further elaborated by later workers, including Ramann in Germany (*19*) and Marbut in the United States (*13*). Studies conducted by these men and others clearly show that the major differences between soils are due to the effect of climate operating through soil-forming processes. It is true that locally the nature of the underlying rock, peculiarities in drainage conditions, or unusual vegetative conditions may outweigh climatic factors in influencing soil character, but the distribution of the great soil groups can be best interpreted in climatic terms. This is partly due to the direct influence of climate on soil formation and partly to the fact that soils are strongly influenced by vegetation, which in turn is related to climate.

The recognition of the importance of climate in soil genesis led soil scientists to investigate the relationship between climatic conditions and the distribution of soils of various kinds. In 1893 Hilgard (*5*), realizing that the amount of precipitation as compared with the amount of evaporation was of critical significance, emphasized the existence of a climatic boundary along which the effect of precipitation was balanced by the effect of evaporation. This boundary, which lies between the moist and dry subhumid climates (not differentiated on the generalized climatic map in fig. 2), divides the humid soils from the arid soils. The humid soils (Pedalfers), formed under climates in which the precipitation exceeds the evaporation, are leached soils—that is, the predominantly downward movement of water has removed material from the top zone into lower zones. Arid soils (Pedocals), on the other hand, are characterized by carbonate accumulation at or within a few feet of the surface resulting from the comparatively small downward percolation and the upward movement of water which evaporates from the soil and deposits basic salts

The effective precipitation (that is, precipitation minus evaporation) has an effect not only on the amount of leaching but also on the acidity, the nitrogen content, and the amount of fine clay minerals or colloids present in the soil (*9, 10*). Increased effective precipitation is associated with increased acidity and nitrogen content, concentration of clay minerals, and decreased carbonate accumulation.

Temperature as well as precipitation is an important factor in soil distribution. A great variety of alteration products can be formed only under high temperatures. Thus with an increase in temperature there is an increase in chemical weathering. In addition, the rate of accumulation of organic matter in the soil tends to increase with increase in temperature (*20*). This relationship is frequently masked by the more important influence which vegetation has on organic-matter content. Grasses yield more humus than does a forest cover, and maximum organic-matter content is therefore found in warm subhumid areas.

Vegetation is also of great significance in its effect on the mineral content of the soil. In northern coniferous forests, leaf fall constitutes the principal source of humus, and this kind of leaf litter, being low in mineral constituents, leads to the formation of a highly acid, peaty surface layer. In a deciduous forest the leaf fall is higher in mineral matter, and mineral compounds are added from plants covering the forest floor, so that a more nearly neutral humus is formed. The highest mineral accretions to the soil from plants are realized under grassland conditions where plants are high in mineral content and where their disintegration both below and above the surface insures the dissemination of this mineral matter throughout the upper portion of the soil mass.

In studying soils and relating soil conditions to such fields as agriculture it is convenient to use a classification of some sort. Most classifications rest primarily on distinctions made on the basis of the physical and chemical properties of the soil as they occur in the different horizons. The differentiation of soil horizons through leaching or through carbonate accumulation causes the soils to possess distinctive profile characteristics which are of marked practical significance. The soils of the world have been classified on such a basis, and 10 principal world groups can be distinguished.[5]

Conditions of excessive precipitation resulting in leaching have produced the humid soils or Pedalfers, the chief types of which are lateritic soils, Red and Yellow Podzolic soils, Gray-Brown Podzolic, Podzols, and the Prairie soils, which include degraded Chernozems. The arid soils, or Pedocals, which are predominantly influenced by evaporation, include the Chernozem, Chestnut, and Brown soils, and the Sierozem and Desert soils. Tundra soils are classed separately as a waterlogged type, the ground under tundra climatic conditions remaining saturated throughout most of the year. In the climate of perpetual snow and ice there is little or no soil differentiation beneath the snow-ice cover; hence these soils also fall outside the general division of Pedalfer and Pedocal groups. The distribution of the great soil groups over the earth is given in figure 4. The close correspondence with the distribution of climate and natural vegetation may be seen by comparing this map with figures 1 and 2.

The process of podzolization, which assumes an important role in the genesis of all of the humid soils, varies directly with the precipitation effectiveness. The essential features of podzolization are the accumulation of an acid, peaty top (A_{00} and A_0) horizon, the leaching of materials from the horizon just below the surface (A_1 and A_2), and the concentration through leaching of iron and aluminum compounds in the lower (B) horizon, sometimes accompanied by the deposition in this lower horizon of organic material as well (*2, p. 972*). In the taiga climate and in the colder parts of the humid and wet regions the precipitation effectiveness is high and the comparatively low temperatures prohibit extreme alteration of leached material, so that in these regions the podzol profile is particularly well developed. True Podzols of this type are found throughout most of southern Canada, in New England and the Lake States, and in central Russia and southern Siberia, usually associated with coniferous forests. They are for the most part absent in the Southern Hemisphere except at high elevations, since land masses in that hemisphere do not extend sufficiently far south to produce the requisite climatic conditions.

A soil group closely affiliated with the true Podzols, the Gray-Brown Podzolic soils, occupies the humid and superhumid climatic regions where temperatures are higher than in the Podzol zone. The Gray-Brown Podzolic soils are not so acid as the Podzols and seldom display a marked zone of concentration of organic matter. Like the Podzols, they are formed under forest conditions, but under deciduous and mixed forest stands. They are found in areas contiguous to the Podzol belts, principally in the northeastern part of the United States, throughout much of central Europe, and in northeastern China.

The Red and Yellow Podzolic subtropical soils and the lateritic soils fall naturally into the same general class since they have both

[5] Only the zonal soil groups are treated here. In addition there are intrazonal soils, which are strongly influenced by factors other than climate and vegetation. Such, for example, are Rendzina soils, developed on limestone and markedly influenced by it. There are also azonal soils, which do not display profile differentiation. Of these, the alluvial soils are the most important to agriculture.

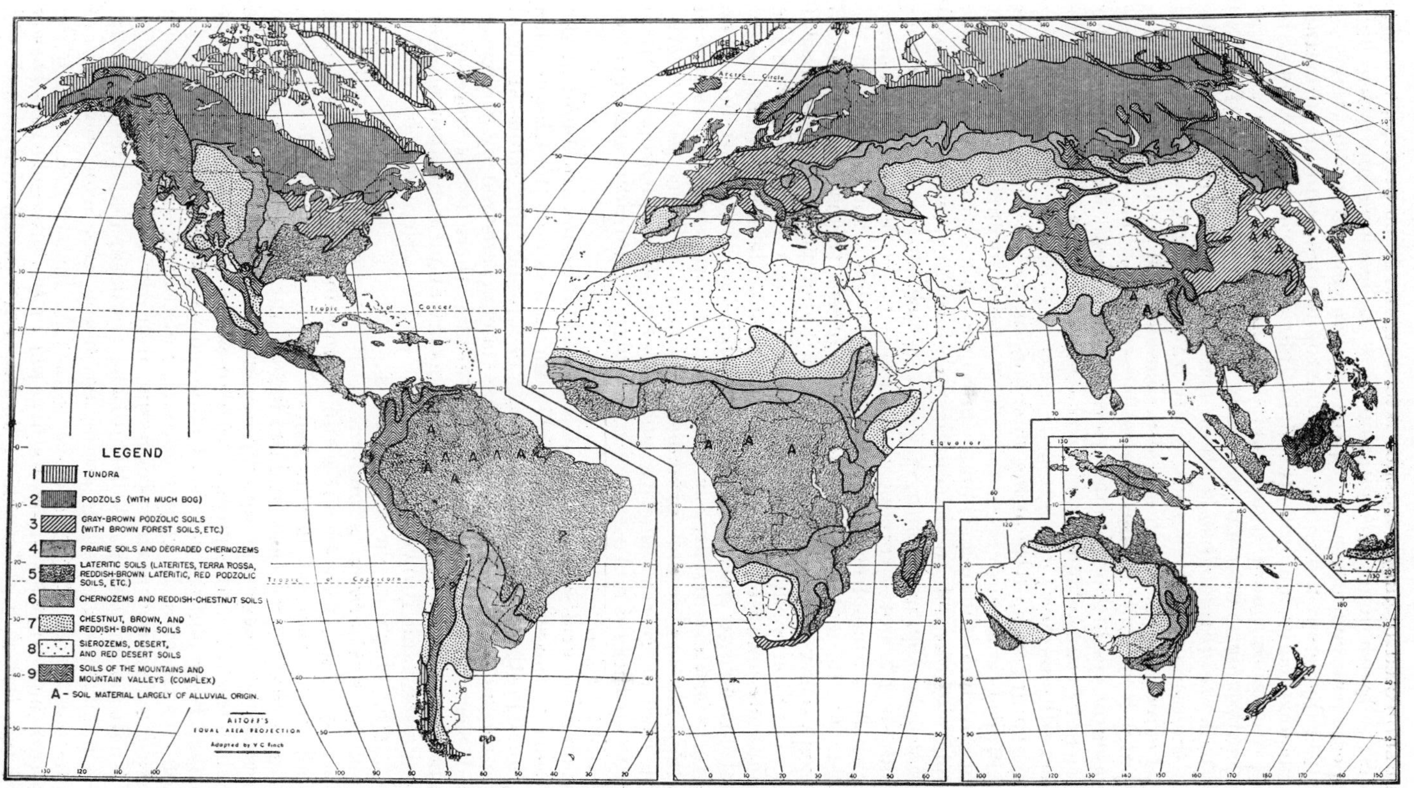

FIGURE 4.—World distribution of the principal zonal soil groups.

been subjected to the process of laterization. This process, which is associated with high precipitation causing leaching and with high temperatures conducive to extreme chemical alteration, tends to result in the removal of silica from the top horizons and the formation of silicious clays underneath. The high temperatures favor the rapid decomposition of organic matter, which makes these soil groups poor in organic matter and generally low in productivity. The Red and Yellow subtropical soils are in general less acid and more fertile than the tropical lateritic soils, podzolization being greater in the Red and Yellow groups, which are also characterized by less strong laterization. Red and Yellow Podzolic soils are the middle-latitude representatives of the general lateritic group, from which they differ somewhat because they were formed under more moderate temperature conditions.

On the dry side of the other members of the Pedalfer group occur the Prairie soils and degraded Chernozems, occupying the moist portion of the subhumid climatic province. Fluctuations of climatic boundaries from year to year result in occasional invasions of semiarid and even arid climates into this zone, which on the average is subhumid; so it is not surprising that these soils, though not truly arid, frequently contain free lime (calcium carbonate), particularly in the lowest (C) horizon. In addition, the clays themselves in the B horizon usually are high in calcium even though no free lime is present (*2*). The Prairie and degraded Chernozem soils are classed with the humid soils because, although they contain calcium, they are sufficiently leached to show that some podzolization has occurred. They are very fertile and only slightly acid. Prairie soils and degraded Chernozems are found principally in the western part of the Corn Belt of North America and in east-central Europe, central Africa, northeastern Australia, and Uruguay and adjacent parts of Argentina.

Among the arid soils or Pedocals the Chernozems are found in the dry part of the subhumid zone. On the dry side of the Chernozems lie the Chestnut and Brown soils, occupying the semiarid area, while the most arid zone—the desert—is characterized by Sierozems and Desert soils. With increase in aridity there is an increase in alkalinity, so that while the Chernozems are about neutral in reaction the Chestnut and Brown soils are basic and the Sierozems even more so. Lime, which in the Chernozems occurs in the free state only deep in the soil horizon, is found in the B horizon in the Chestnut and Brown soils and may occur within a few inches of the surface or actually at the surface in the case of the Sierozem and Desert soils. The progressive decrease in leaching as the effective precipitation decreases is responsible for these contrasts, since the greater the leaching the lower the mean depth to which the lime is carried by downward-percolating waters. Combined with this change in precipitation effectiveness the change in nature of the vegetation results in a decrease in organic matter progressing from the Chernozems through the Chestnut and Brown soils into the Sierozem and Desert group. The Chernozems themselves are highly productive, being very high in organic matter and neutral in reaction. Productivity is lower in the Chestnut and Brown soils and still lower in the Sierozem and Desert soils, but this is a reflection of decrease in rainfall and not of soil

FIGURE 5.—Schematic representation of:

A, The distribution of climatic types;

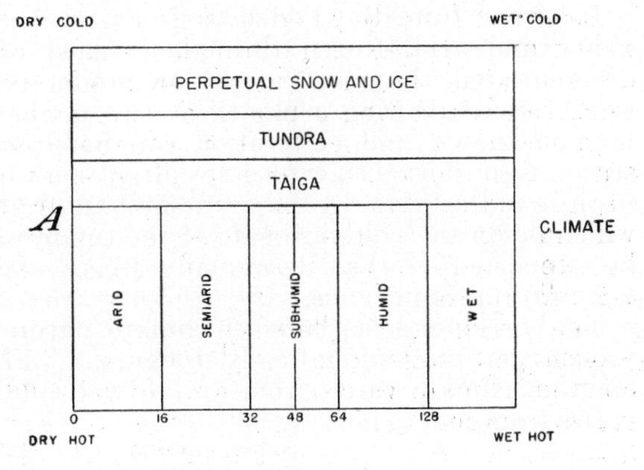

B, The distribution of vegetative formations, on a climatic base;

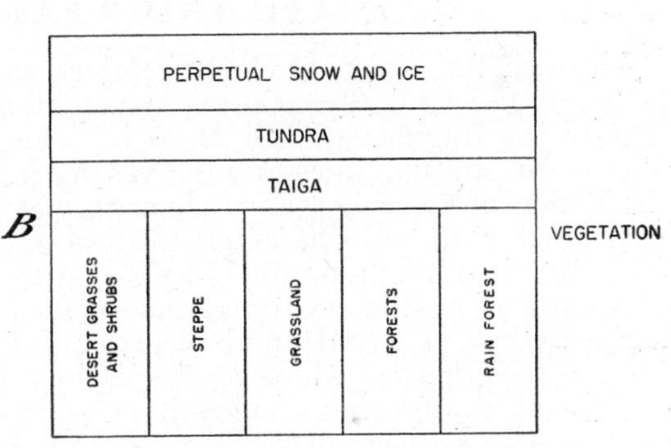

C, The distribution of the major zonal soil groups on a climatic base.

PERPETUAL SNOW AND ICE
TUNDRA SOILS
PODZOLS
C
SOILS
SIEROZEMS AND DESERT SOILS
CHESTNUT AND BROWN SOILS
CHERNOZEMS
PRAIRIE SOILS– DEGRADED CHERNOZEMS
PODZOLS
GRAY-BROWN PODZOLIC SOILS
RED AND YELLOW PODZOLIC SOILS
LATERITIC SOILS
32
48
64
128

fertility. Desert soils, when properly irrigated and drained, frequently prove to be highly productive.

The typical distribution of the arid soils in bands is well exemplified in North America, where the Chernozems of the eastern Wheat Belt grade into the Chestnut and Brown soils of the High Plains, which in turn give way to the Sierozems and Desert soils of the Great Basin and the arid Southwest. The same banding is displayed in concentric form around most of the great desert areas of the world—the Sahara, the Kalahari Desert in southwest Africa, the Thar in northwest India, the Great Australian Desert, and the Mongolian Desert of interior China.

Poleward from the Podzol soils lie the waterlogged Tundra soils. Peaty and acid, frozen throughout most of the year, largely undifferentiated, these soils are of low productivity and minor economic significance. During a month or two in the summer the upper soil horizon thaws, and cultivation can be practiced, but the growing season is so short that extensive cultivation is not carried on anywhere in the tundra belt. In the arctic and antarctic lands of snow and ice which lie on the poleward side of the tundra, no vegetation at all can be supported so that perpetually frozen soils are entirely without agricultural significance.

The correspondence between climate, natural vegetation, and soils is brought out diagrammatically in figure 5. From left to right in each diagram climate varies from dry to wet, and from top to bottom it varies from cold to hot.

CLIMATE AND WEATHERING

Through the action of climatic forces, notably precipitation, temperature, and wind, the rocks and rock materials at or below the earth's surface are fragmented and altered. This weathering is intimately related to erosion, since it prepares materials for removal through the action of running water, glaciers, and wind. It is also closely associated with soil characteristics, since soil in its first stages of formation is simply a product of weathering.

It has been customary to recognize three principal types of weathering—physical, chemical, and biological. These types are interrelated. Physical weathering, which results in the fragmentation of rock without chemical alteration, makes it possible for chemical processes to operate with greater effectiveness, since more total rock surface is exposed because of the smaller pieces. Chemical changes alter the regolith—the mantle of loose material overlying the solid rock beneath—and this in turn affects the amount of surface exposed to the action of physical forces. Biological weathering, such as the disrupting of rock through root penetration and the pitting of rock through the action of lichens, tends to influence both the chemical and physical phases of the total weathering complex. In addition it is impossible to understand chemical alterations without considering the action of such micro-organisms as nitrogen-fixing bacteria (nitrobacters), fungi, and algae.

Physical weathering includes the splitting of rock in thin layers (exfoliation) through heating and cooling; disruption of rock surfaces and regolith through frost action; abrasion through sand blast and by particles carried in running water; breaking of rock due to ice formation in crevices and interstices; and rock plucking at the head, sides, and base of glaciers. Chemical weathering, which involves hydration, solution, oxidation, reduction,[6] and carbonization, occurs significantly only in the presence of water and increases with an increase in temperature. The same is true of microbiologic activity. Hence in dry areas and in very cold ones physical weathering is far more important than either chemical or biological weathering; whereas in moist, hot regions conditions are most favorable for chemical and biologic alteration, and physical weathering is of less significance.

[6] Frequently reduction is not considered as being an important part of chemical weathering, but as Polynov (*18*) points out, it may attain considerable importance even where unassociated with the activity of such micro-organisms as *Bacterium coli*.

The greater the effective precipitation and the higher the temperature efficiency, the greater the amount and degree of chemical weathering, while with a constant decrease in either or both of these factors physical weathering assumes greater and greater importance. The forms of weathering, then, like the vegetation and soil characteristics, are primarily associated with temperature and precipitation.

CLIMATE, NATURAL EROSION, AND MINOR LAND FORMS

The variation in the natural landscape from one climatic region to another is a reflection of gross differences in the effectiveness of various forces that strip or denude the surface. Streams, waves, ground water, sheet wash, frost, winds, and glaciers are the agents which participate in the leveling of the land surface. In opposition to these one must place the forces that thrust up rock and other formations (tectonic forces), volcanic activity (vulcanism), and the action of winds and glaciers. These are the agents responsible for the formation of positive relief features.

The agents of denudation act in a variety of ways in molding the natural landscape. It is necessary only to consider briefly those forces the importance of which depends on climate. Thus wave action may be eliminated from consideration, although in a certain sense it is true that the character of coastal climates does have an effect on the intensity and effectiveness of waves in promoting erosion.

Virtually all erosion occurs through the action of running water, through mass movement, as a result of wind, or in association with glacial movement. These four categories include the work of all the agents mentioned above. Running water includes stream action, sheet wash, and ground-water flow. Mass movement is the general term applied to soil flow (solifluction), soil creep, rock creep, mudflow, soil slump, rockslide, and subsidence over mines, caverns, etc. Scouring, dune building, wind sculpturing, and general soil mixing are the chief results of wind action. Glaciers are responsible for the formation of deposits such as moraines, rock plucking as in the formation of circular hollows on mountainsides (called cirques or corries), scouring, and the transport of debris and soil.

Figure 6 brings out how the effectiveness of running water, mass movement, wind, and glaciers varies with differences in temperature and precipitation effectiveness. These diagrams are meant only to present the general relationship and should not be interpreted in a strictly quantitative manner. The diagram in figure 6, *A*, shows the variation in the effectiveness of these four types of denudation with a variation in temperature, where the effective precipitation remains constant and relatively high—equal, approximately, to that of the southeastern part of the United States. Running water becomes less and less important as the temperature decreases, since with a decrease in temperature the period of freezing temperatures increases in length. Mass movement remains an important mechanism throughout the entire thermal range except, perhaps, for the very lowest portion of the scale. At the warm end of the scale, soil slumping is the principal mass-movement type; at the cold end of the range, solifluction becomes significant; and for intermediate values, soil creep as related to frost and ice action becomes highly significant (*22*). It will be

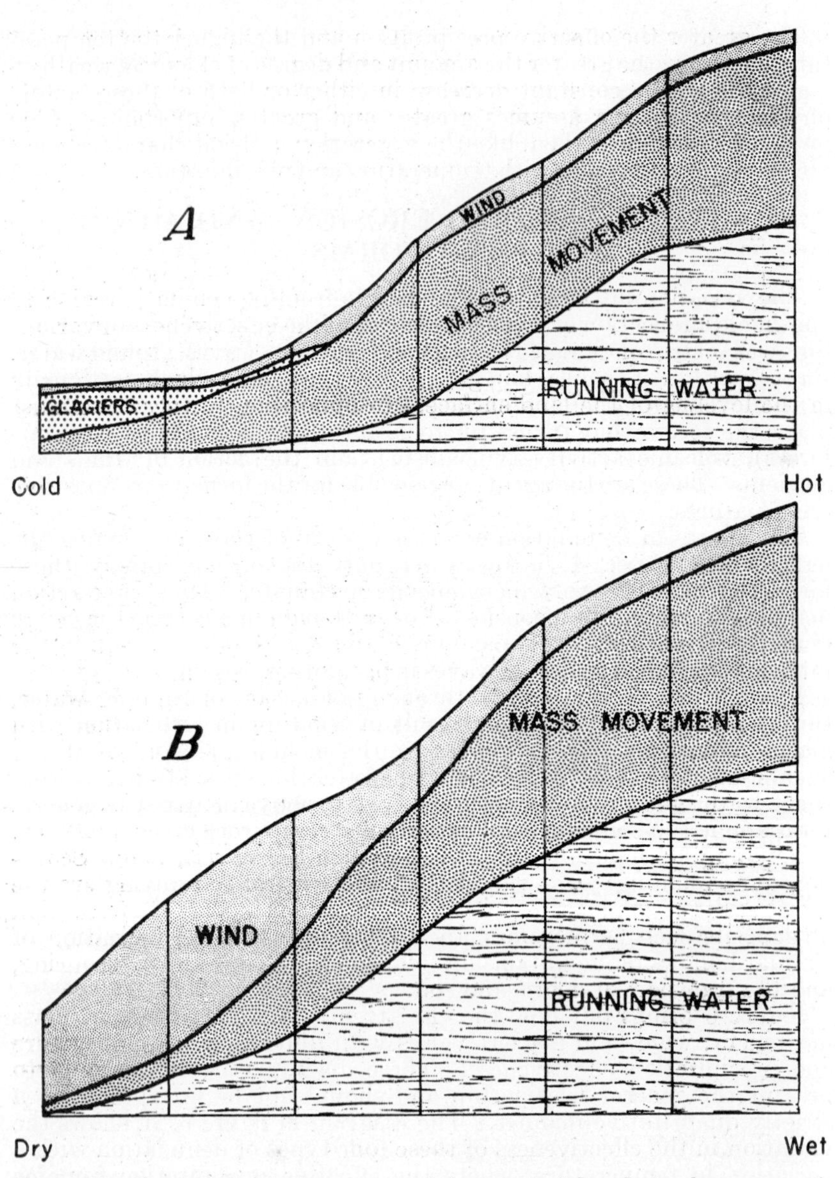

FIGURE 6.—The variation in importance of the principal denudational processes: *A*, Variations in thermal efficiency; *B*, Variations in precipitation effectiveness.

noted that wind has relatively little influence where effective precipitation is high. Principally this is because under hot and warm conditions with no deficiency in effective precipitation, the ground surface is, in a natural state, well protected by vegetation, whereas, with very low temperatures, frozen ground and snow cover both aid in protecting the land surface against wind erosion. Glacial action becomes significant only at temperature values below freezing—although some glaciers are encountered higher up on the temperature scale. One may obtain a general idea of the varying rates of denudation for different temperatures by considering the varying height of the diagram shown in figure 6, *A*. There can be no doubt that there is a decrease in the total amount of denudation in a given period of time from areas of high to those of low thermal efficiency. Quantitative data, however, are not available; hence the diagram is highly schematic.

Just as there are differences in the rate of erosion and in the importance of various types of denudation with a variation in temperature, so are there such differences with variations in precipitation effectiveness, if temperature is constant. Figure 6, *B*, indicates the general nature of this variation when the temperature conditions are constant and lie near the center of the mesothermal range. It is evident that erosion through running water will decrease as precipitation becomes less. Similarly, mass movement will become less and less effective, for water in either the liquid or the solid state is an important element in the mass-movement mechanism, and in arid regions mass movement is restricted to rockslides. The effectiveness of wind, however, varies inversely with precipitation effectiveness, as indicated in the diagram. As the effective precipitation decreases, so in general does the density of the natural vegetation, and the exposure of the soil makes it possible for wind to work with maximum efficiency. That glaciers do not enter this second diagram is explained by the fact that mesothermal conditions are represented.

As figure 6, *B*, shows, the variation in total denudation as effective precipitation changes does not parallel the variation resulting from temperature differences (fig. 6, *A*). More erosion will occur in dry climates, with very low precipitation effectiveness, than in cold climates, with very low thermal values; and the same is true where the values are very high (in moist climates and hot climates). It

FIGURE 7.—Desert landscape, Mojave Desert, Calif. Note the rocky desert floor, the sharp angular slopes, and the steep alluvial fans.

298737°—41——9 +

would be erroneous, however, to conclude from this that precipitation efficiency is more significant than temperature in influencing denudation processes.

Low values of either temperature or effective precipitation result in low rates of denudation. This accounts for the general similarity in local relief between polar and arid regions, as noted by A. Penck (*16*) and others. The fact that erosional forces are not particularly active means that in these areas there are sharp breaks in relief, for tectonic displacements of the earth's crust are not readily leveled but are long perpetuated as surface expressions. Cliff walls are common in desert and polar regions alike (figs. 7 and 8); small plateaus—erosional remnants—are likewise typical of both polar and arid regions; the hammada (plateau of stones) of the desert finds a rough counterpart in the Blockmeere (rock streams) of the cold climates; the broad valleys without external drainage (bolsons) and the alluvial fans of arid basins resemble in form the stone fields and rock-debris slopes of the tundra (*6*).

But although in broad outline these two climatic regions are alike with respect to land forms, there are numerous important minor differences. Wind, which is far more significant in desert than in polar regions, is responsible in arid lands for the formation of dunes, the scouring of dry basins (playas), the carving of solid rock through sand blast, and the development of "desert pavement." In polar climates the wind can seldom attack the surface with any degree of effectiveness, because the ground is usually frozen or protected with snow and the wind is not provided with sand particles which can be used as blasting tools. On the other hand, solifluction and glacial action, which are so characteristic of tundra and climates of perpetual frost, are absent in arid regions; so that such minor land forms

FIGURE 8.—Subarctic landscape, Yukon Territory, Canada. The rock-strewn surface, angular profiles, and steeply sloping debris fans bear a strong outward resemblance to desert forms as shown in figure 7.

FIGURE 9.—Humid landscape, western Maryland. Note the gently rounded slopes, as contrasted with the angular slopes of desert and subarctic landscapes, figures 7 and 8.

as cirques and moraines, while occurring in cold climates, are not to be found in arid regions unless, indeed, they date back to earlier, colder times.

Whereas the desert and polar regions are characterized by a landscape with angular breaks, steep slopes, and flat plains and plateaus, the warm humid regions of the earth where denudation is proceeding at a maximum rate are typically regions of gently rolling slopes well covered with vegetation (fig. 9). A fine network of streams and the gradual movement of soil particles downhill soon obliterate surface breaks caused by faults or sharp folds. The vegetation protects the land against the scouring action of the winds, and the temperatures are too high for the formation of glaciers. Thus regions of warm and hot climates display a natural landscape markedly different from that of arid or polar regions.

CLIMATE AND ACCELERATED EROSION

Under natural conditions there is a tendency for a balance to be maintained between the soil-forming and the soil-eroding forces. Where rainfall is most abundant, surface waters are most extensive and stream networks are the finest. But under these conditions vegetation is also most abundant, and the protection it affords against erosion through the action of running water acts as a check against excessive gullying and sheet wash. Toward the drier regions there is a decrease in the degree of protection afforded by the vegetation, but there is a corresponding decrease in the amount and intensities of rainfall so that an approximate balance is still maintained. Even in sparsely vegetated desert areas soils are formed and maintained under natural conditions, particularly in basins and depressions and along the flood plains of rivers which rise in adjacent wet or humid regions and flow through the desert lands.

Nor do winds or glaciers normally cause great soil wastage. In all but desert regions vegetation serves to protect the soil against erosion through blowing. Glaciers, which are active only in high latitudes and at high elevations, affect only a relatively small portion of the land surface of the world at present and are operative only in scouring and moving soils which, because they are frozen, would be largely untillable in any case.

The natural balance between soil erosion and soil formation is upset, however, when cultural modifications are introduced. Erosion takes place at an accelerated rate, and since the rate of soil formation is not similarly accelerated, excessive soil wastage occurs. The clearing of land for agriculture both removes natural checks to erosion and impedes the processes of soil regeneration. Rain waters coursing down a hillside are enabled to operate more effectively on fallow ground or on land which is only partially protected by crops. Wind, which under natural conditions would be ineffectual in causing the widespread blowing of soils, is provided with bare surfaces upon which to work. And the lack of natural vegetation deprives the soil of an abundant source of organic matter as it is usually only partially replaced through the planting of crops.[7]

The form which accelerated erosion assumes and the extent to which it occurs are closely related to the climatic conditions and to the nature of the soil. Adjustments in cropping practices made to minimize erosion losses must be based on an understanding of the climatic and soil conditions which determine the erosion hazard. Since there is a correspondence between the broad climatic regions and the principal soil provinces, these erosion hazards can be defined as they apply to each climatic region. In each such region the clearing of land for cultivation results in the creation of different erosion hazards, both as to the types of accelerated erosion which are apt to occur and as to their intensity (*1*).

In the superhumid climates both the intensity and the amount of rainfall are high.[8] Gullying, sheet wash, trenching, and siltation therefore constitute the principal erosion hazards. The lateritic soils of the wet climatic regions are characterized by deep clays which are highly resistant to erosion. But the topsoil, comparatively low in organic matter, is not resistant and can be easily sluiced away.

In the humid climates the intensity and amount of rainfall are highest in the equatorward regions, decreasing poleward. Gullying and sheet wash are therefore more serious in the warm humid regions, such as the southeastern United States, than in the cool parts of the humid areas, such as New England. In the cooler humid climates the prevalence of snow during the winter leads to the existence of a flood hazard, which is accentuated by deforestation. In addition, frost action in these areas, which, particularly on unprotected sod, results in soil heaving, promotes the mass movement of materials downslope. The Red and Yellow Podzolic soils of the warm humid climates have a deep clay B horizon which does not readily erode; but once this clay horizon has been removed, the rate of downward gully cutting may increase enormously, and extensive areas may be laid waste within a

[7] An exception to this statement may be pointed out. Where forests are cleared and close-growing grasses are planted, the supply of organic matter for soil replenishment is increased, and after a considerable period of time this increase is reflected in an increase in the organic matter in the soil.

[8] The highest 24-hour rainfall intensities in the world probably occur in the subtropical areas which, because of their seasonal distribution of precipitation, are classed as being humid. Thus at Crohamhurst, Australia, 35.7 inches of rain has fallen in 24 hours, while at Baguio, P. I., 46.0 inches in 24 hours has been recorded (8). However, intensities in the superhumid climates are generally higher than in the humid ones, with the exception of those superhumid climates occurring in high middle latitudes on the west coasts of continents. In these west-coast areas intensities are low to moderate.

few years (7). The Podzols and Gray-Brown Podzolic soils are not so resistant as the Red and Yellow soils, but since they occur in areas where rainfall intensities are lower and since in the winter they are protected from erosion through freezing, not so much gullying and sheet washing is apt to occur.

The soils of subhumid regions, formed under tall-grass conditions, are generally high in organic matter, particularly in the warm subhumid areas. As a result the surface horizon is capable of absorbing considerable amounts of water so that gullying and sheet wash are decreased. Drought constitutes a hazard. Not only does it result in the depletion of vegetal cover, but it alters the physical structure of the surface soil, making it peculiarly susceptible to erosion by running water. If, as is frequently the case, a drought is broken by an intense downpour, gullying and sheet wash can set in in spite of the high organic-matter content of the A horizon.

The wind-erosion hazard becomes critical in semiarid regions. Most of the semiarid lands of the world are relatively flat so that high wind velocities can develop without being impeded by the presence of topographic barriers. In spite of the relatively low rainfall intensities in semiarid regions, serious gullying and sheet washing occur where the resistance of the land to erosion has been lowered through overgrazing.[9] The bottom lands, usually the most productive areas of these regions, are particularly susceptible.

Accelerated erosion in desert regions is similar to that which occurs under natural conditions, and except where irrigation has made it possible to utilize desert lands, its economic significance is not great. The effect of irrigation is to provide the soil with a more effective erosion-control cover than it possessed before; hence the establishment of irrigated tracts aids soil preservation. Some portions of the desert may be used for grazing, but the quality of the forage is such that many acres of land must be provided for each animal. Under such conditions the normal rate of erosion is not greatly accelerated. The most serious soil erosion in desert lands occurs in the small areas where drainage conditions have provided a source of water that permits the growth of nondesert plants. In such instances overgrazing is as great a hazard as in semiarid regions.

The taiga and tundra lands are more free from accelerated erosion than any of the warmer regions of the world. This is partly because these lands have not been extensively cleared, and where clearing has occurred the growing season is so short that the lands are under a crop cover throughout the frost-free period. When freezing does set in, it serves to preserve the soil against erosion by wind or water, although frost heaving and ice action may cause local soil disruption.

CLIMATE AND LAND UTILIZATION

The distribution of climates and their associated soil and vegetative types provides the basis upon which all agricultural land utilization rests. Where the occurrence of minerals makes mining possible or where nearness to sea lanes, rivers, and centers of production and consumption make it possible for urban areas to become established,

[9] THORNTHWAITE, C. WARREN, SHARPE, C. F. STEWART, and DOSCH, EARL F. CLIMATE AND ACCELERATED EROSION IN THE SOUTHWEST WITH SPECIAL REFERENCE TO THE POLACCA WASH DRAINAGE BASIN, ARIZONA. (In manuscript.)

man can engage in highly specialized forms of land utilization with less concern for climate and its attendant natural conditions. But in agricultural use of the land, whether for crop production or grazing, certain natural limitations are imposed which for the most part cannot be surmounted.[10]

But while variation in the climatic complex from place to place sets limits beyond which certain crops cannot be grown or certain types of agriculture practiced, it does not follow that land utilization and climate correspond as do soils and climate. On the subhumid Chernozem lands of India the Hindu peasant raises cotton. On similar lands in Africa the Buganda natives raise cattle. In northeastern Australia the natives left the subhumid Chernozem lands untilled and virtually unused prior to the arrival of Europeans. In our country these same lands provide the most productive areas for commercial wheat farming and cotton production that the continent possesses. It may seem, then, that there is no one use to which land can or should be put. The economy of the culture determines what constitutes optimum use, and even optimum use varies with fluctuations in economic conditions.

In our own economy, which like that of western Europe is the product of the industrial revolution, pressure on the agricultural lands is equaled only in the most densely populated oriental countries. The creation of a large industrial and commercial population has laid upon the farmer the task of feeding and clothing millions of persons engaged in other than agricultural pursuits. Whereas the subsistence farmer of the Amazon Basin or in India has only to provide for the feeding and clothing of his immediate family group, the American or European farmer must produce huge surpluses over and above the relatively small quantities he himself consumes. The subsistence farmer produces only a very minor portion of his crops for trade or exchange, but the farmer of our occidental society must produce cash crops in abundance in order to obtain the other foods and industrial goods he needs.

All of this has led to a specialization in farming which has tended toward the establishment of one-crop systems. Except for truck farming and dairying there is little real diversity in crop production in the occidental economy. The Corn Belt farmer may produce a variety of crops, but the emphasis is on hogs and corn. The farmer in the Southeast depends largely on cotton. Wheat is the cash crop on the western prairies and eastern plains. Citrus fruits are the specialty in the Los Angeles Basin.

The development of transportation in North America, Europe, Australia, and throughout much of South America and Asia has drawn most of the land areas of the world into the realm of influence of the western economy. Since in most parts of the world comparatively efficient transportation is afforded for the dispersal of agricultural products and since those cash crops have been raised which would yield the greatest monetary return, there has been a tendency to raise crops on the lands most suitable for them from the standpoint of climate, soils, and topographic conditions. This tendency has been fulfilled only in part because of such economic factors as variation in

[10] Irrigation of desert areas forms the principal exception to this statement. Yet even in the case of irrigation natural conditions must be such as to favor this cultural modification.

price, availability of labor, and distance to market. Nevertheless the tendency has been sufficiently marked so that in areas strongly influenced by the western economy a crop pattern roughly corresponding to the general climatic pattern has become established. The tendency has been furthered by mechanization, particularly in the newly settled areas of the world, even though farmers, like all people, are slow to abandon their traditional techniques.

The general conformity between types of land utilization and climate in the occidental economy is brought out by comparing the distribution of these types in Europe and in the United States and Canada. On both continents, Mediterranean agriculture, consisting of the production of mixed vegetable and orchard crops (the latter principally citrus fruits and olives), is found in the summer-dry subhumid climates (*4*). Corn, wheat, and livestock are the chief products of the humid and subhumid lands in which occur the Gray-Brown Podzolic soils and the Prairie soils and degraded Chernozems. Throughout extensive areas of Europe, and in a narrow belt in North America extending eastward from southern Michigan into Canada and western New York, small grains and livestock are raised. These occupy a position north of the corn-wheat-livestock agricultural complex. Still farther north, in the cool humid climates, hay production, dairying, and livestock raising constitute a distinct agricultural association.

In the warm humid and subhumid southeastern part of the United States cotton is the principal cash crop. The climatic belt it occupies has no counterpart in Europe—a fact that partially explains the lack of such a quasi-plantation economy on the European continent. In the semiarid and dry subhumid lands commercial grain farming predominates, grading into commercial grazing in the more arid regions. Climate, soils, and topography favor the establishment of commercial grain operations in the broad rich lands of the Ukraine and the fertile lands of the Spring and Winter Wheat Belts of North America. The low precipitation results in low yields and necessitates the use of large-scale methods since costs of production must be kept at a minimum.

Truck farming and commercial fruit growing in the eastern and southeastern United States is only partly determined by climate; the principal factor is the location of centers of consumption. The particular crops raised, however—for example, citrus fruits in Florida—are directly related to the climate. Throughout the taiga zone uncultivated forest lands are the rule because of the shortness of the growing season.

Correspondence between land use and climate such as that in Europe and North America does not exist throughout the world. An entirely different classification of major agricultural regions is necessary outside the occidental economy (*26*). Vast areas of desert and semiarid land are devoted to nomadic herding which would be used for commercial livestock ranching in Europe or America. Tropical wet and humid lands devoted to shifting cultivation under primitive societies give way to plantations of rubber, sugarcane, coffee, and other crops when under European or American control. In many areas in several climatic regions subsistence agriculture is practiced, with rice or some similar crop as the staple and with or without livestock.

The general farming types already identified for Europe and North America are carried over into other parts of the world which have been settled by Europeans—Australia and South Africa, for instance.

Adjustments in Land Utilization

Because a land-utilization pattern tends to match the climatic pattern, this does not mean that it will or should remain fixed. Industrialization, with its commercialization of agriculture, is a recent development, and adjustments are constantly being made. The agricultural pattern will probably never be fixed over very long periods of time.

But in this constant process of adjustment there are more crop failures and land failures than there need be. Too often the method of trial and error is followed, and too little attention is paid to the year-to-year conditions under which a given crop must grow. A series of years of "good" climatic conditions results in overexpansion of agricultural lands, and crops are pushed outward into areas which are climatically submarginal. Then when "average" or "poor" years occur, crop and land failures result. So far as climatologists can determine, the year-to-year fluctuations in climate are almost entirely fortuitous. Good years may occasionally be bunched together, or a series of bad years may occur, but there is nothing systematic about the variations.

While the complexity of interacting meteorological phenomena has thus far made it impossible to evolve an accurate long-range forecasting method, this does not preclude the development of some such method in the future. With an increase in climatic data, the extension of upper-air observations, and the growth of meteorological knowledge will come a clearer understanding of how long-range forecasts can best be carried out; and long-range forecasts sufficiently accurate to be useful in year-to-year land use planning may eventually be made.

The present inability to make long-range forecasts does not mean that climatic knowledge cannot be usefully employed in effecting adjustments in land utilization. Highly pertinent information is available if the problem is viewed simply as a statistical one. The principle involved is the same as that applied in vital statistics. The population expert, knowing the incidence of mortality in different age groups, can accurately predict the number of deaths annually in each group. The utility of this knowledge is not negated merely because he cannot predict the time of death of a particular person. In an analogous manner, the climatologist can state how many serious droughts, flood-producing rains, or periods of abnormally high temperature are likely to occur in an area during a 20-year period. And—following the analogy—the utility of this knowledge is not impaired merely because he is unable to predict what particular years or seasons will produce these conditions.

Through applying climatic-risk data organized on such an actuarial basis the expected incidence of crop failure, depletion of the range, occurrence of floods, etc., can be readily ascertained, given the local economic, soil, and topographic conditions. In marginal areas where climatic fluctuations are particularly critical, this knowledge is especially applicable in determining what crops should be raised, what agronomic techniques and calendars will prove most effective, whether supplemental irrigation is required, and, in general, what type of farm economy is best suited to the particular area. By proceeding in this way adjustments in land utilization can be made on a basis other than the expensive, and often disruptive, method of trial and error.

CLIMATE AND LANDSCAPE

Landscapes are the integrated combinations of natural and cultural features that characterize the surface of the earth. Land forms, surface waters, vegetation, animal life, soils, and rocks are foremost among the natural elements of the landscape; crops, domesticated animals, buildings, roads, railroads, and canals are a few of the many cultural elements. In the interactions between climate, vegetation, soils, erosion, and the molding of land forms, climate plays a dominant role; it is therefore readily understandable that the natural landscape—solely the product of natural forces in the sense that the influence of man has not been felt—is closely bound to climate. To a somewhat lesser degree is the cultural landscape related to climate. The elements of the cultural landscape, such as buildings, roads, and distribution of crops, are strongly influenced by cultural heritage; yet they remain the outward manifestations of an economy and social organization which is in delicate balance with the natural environment. So while a wide variety of cultural landscapes may exist under any one set of natural conditions, each displays certain characteristics that are in harmony with the natural landscape and hence with the climatic complex.

Where the natural landscape has remained unaltered, the expression of the climate in the landscape is readily discernible. The dense forests, deep Red and Brown clay soils, fine stream network, and gently rounded slopes of the superhumid Tropics all reflect the high temperatures and high, well-distributed precipitation which characterize these climatic regions. So too is the sharp angular landscape of the desert with its alkaline soils and sparse growth of drought-resisting plants an expression of climatic conditions. Similarly, in all of the climatic regions, the individual elements of the natural landscape—land forms, vegetation, soils, weathering and erosion characteristics—each of which is strongly influenced by climate, combine and interact to form the total landscape.

In the cultural landscape the climate is a passive rather than an active agent, setting limits beyond which certain human activities cannot reasonably be pursued. As has been seen, the climate influences the crops grown and the techniques used to cultivate them. Climate also influences human activities indirectly through the medium of the natural landscape. Thus shifting cultivation, for example, is limited to the humid and superhumid climates where acid soils and dense tree growth make this type of agriculture the only practicable one for primitive peoples. Though climates fluctuate in distribution from year to year, their mean positions change very slowly; hence the average conditions and normal fluctuations are operative over long periods of time. The result is that the cultural as well as the natural landscapes tend more and more to reflect climatic conditions, though the cultural landscape forms themselves may vary within one climatic region because of the different cultural backgrounds of the peoples inhabiting it.

The world landscape pattern, then, whether or not the landscapes are altered by man, constitutes the integration of the world patterns formed by vegetation, soils, land forms, and land utilization. And the study of climate, which helps to make possible an understanding of all these patterns and the landscape pattern as well, is a mode of approach which, though not sufficient in itself, is indispensable in determining how man can most intelligently utilize the resources and environment with which nature has provided him.

LITERATURE CITED

(1) Bennett, Hugh Hammond.
1939. soil conservation. 993 pp., illus. New York and London.

(2) Byers, H. G., Kellogg, Charles E., Anderson, M. S., and Thorp, James.
1938. formation of soil. U. S. Dept. Agr. Yearbook 1938: 948–978, illus.

(3) Glinka, K. D.
1935. the great soil groups of the world and their development. Transl. from the German by C. F. Marbut. 150 pp. Ann Arbor, Mich. [Processed.]

(4) Hartshorne, Richard, and Dicken, Samuel N.
1935. a classification of the agricultural regions of europe and north america on a uniform statistical basis. Assoc. Amer. Geog. Ann. 25: 99–120, illus.

(5) Hilgard, E. W.
1892. a report on the relations of soil to climate. U. S. Weather Bur. Bul. 3, 59 pp.

(6) Högbom, Ivar.
1923. ancient inland dunes of northern and middle europe. Geog. Ann. 5: [113]–[243], illus.

(7) Ireland, H. A., Sharpe, C. F. S., and Eargle, D. H.
1939. principles of gully erosion in the piedmont of south carolina. U. S. Dept. Agr. Tech. Bul. 633, 143 pp., illus.

(8) Jarvis, C. S.
1931. rainfall characteristics and their relation to soils and run-off. Amer. Soc. Civil Engin. Trans. 95: [379]–458, illus. [Discussion, pp. 424–458.]

(9) Jenny, Hans.
1935. the clay content of the soil as related to climatic factors, particularly temperature. Soil Sci. 40: 111–128, illus.

(10) ——— and Leonard, Chester D.
1934. functional relationships between soil properties and rainfall. Soil Sci. 38: 363–381, illus.

(11) Köppen, W.
1936. das geographische system der klimate. *In* Handbuch der Klimatologie, Bd. 1, Teil C, 44 pp., illus.

(12) Lang, Richard.
1920. verwitterung und bodenbildung als einführung in die bodenkunde. 188 pp., illus. Stuttgart.

(13) Marbut, C. F.
1935. soils of the united states. *In* Atlas of American Agriculture, Part 3, U. S. Dept. Agr., Adv. Sheets 8, 98 pp., illus.

(14) Martonne, Em. de.
1926. aréisme et indice d'aridité. [Paris] Acad. des Sci. Compt. Rend. 182: 1395–1398.

(15) Meyer, Alfred.
1926. über einige zusammenhänge zwischen klima und boden in europa. Chem. der Erde 2: [209]–347, illus.
(16) Penck, Albrecht.
1905. climatic features in the land surface. Amer. Jour. Sci., ser. 4, 19: 165–174.
(17) Phillips, John.
1935. succession, development, the climax, and the complex organism: an analysis of concepts. part ii. development and the climax. Jour. Ecol. 23: [210]–246.
(18) Polynov, B. B.
1937. the cycle of weathering. Transl. from the Russian by Alexander Muir. 220 pp., illus. London.
(19) Ramann, E.
1928. the evolution and classification of soils. Transl. by C. L. Whittles. 127 pp., illus. Cambridge, England.
(20) Robinson, Gilbert Wooding.
1936. soils, their origin, constitution, and classification; an introduction to pedology. Ed. 2, rev. and enl., 442 pp., illus. London and New York.
(21) Shantz, H. L.
1923. the natural vegetation of the great plains region. Assoc. Amer. Geog. Ann. 13: 81–107, illus.
(22) Sharpe, C. F. Stewart.
1938. landslides and related phenomena; a study of mass movements of soil and rock. 137 pp., illus. New York.
(23) Thornthwaite, C. Warren.
1931. the climates of north america according to a new classification. Geog. Rev. 21: 633–655, illus.
(24) ———
1933. the climates of the earth. Geog. Rev. 23: 433–440, illus.
(25) ———
1941. atlas of climatic types in the united states, 1900–1939. U. S. Dept. Agr. Misc. Pub. 421.
(26) Whittlesey, Derwent.
1936. major agricultural regions of the earth. Assoc. Amer. Geog. Ann. 26: 199–240, illus.

The How and Why of Weather Knowledge

By F. W. Reichelderfer [1]

CLIMATE AND WEATHER are basic natural resources, but they must be understood if they are to be turned to good advantage. No one has better reason to know this than the farmer. As civilization has become more complex, our dependence on intimate and accurate knowledge of climate and weather has increased. Today this knowledge is so indispensable that every civilized country has an elaborate weather service. In the United States this service functions 24 hours a day and endeavors to bring up-to-date information to every individual in the land who needs it. For 50 years the service was part of the Department of Agriculture, and it is still closely associated with agricultural activities. What does it do? How does it work? How can we make the best use of its activities? The Director of the service explains.

[1] F. W. Reichelderfer is Director, United States Weather Bureau.

WEATHER AND CLIMATE are as vital to human life as the soil itself. They are among our most valuable natural resources. If the weather is too dry or too wet, crops fail, and the farmer suffers—but not the farmer alone. Permanent changes in climate could bring ruin to our entire business structure and make our continent practically uninhabitable. Fortunately the supply of weather, unlike the reserves of some natural resources, appears to be inexhaustible. Although there are fluctuations in rainfall, temperature, and other atmospheric elements from day to day, month to month, and year to year, "permanent" changes in climate within the records of civilized man have been small. But even the yearly fluctuations have such profound influence on man's livelihood and pursuit of happiness that no matter what his occupation—farmer, aviator, engineer, industrialist, laborer, merchant, clerk—he daily takes keen interest in the weather. It is usually the first thing he thinks of when he lays his plans for the day's work and decides what clothes to wear. In this country 2 million businessmen every morning turn at once to the weather report when they pick up the daily paper. More than a million people listen for the weather forecast by radio once or more each day, and a hundred thousand, desiring more than is given in the press or over the radio, telephone or visit Weather Bureau offices daily to obtain further information.

The Nation-wide meteorological service of the Weather Bureau provides reports and advices of value to almost every kind of business and profession and probably ranks close to the postal service in universal interest and application.[2]

In a recent survey of the utilization of weather service in the United States, it was found that the protection to property afforded by the weather reports and forecasts of the Weather Bureau, and the increased profits through reduction in loss or increase in production from use of weather information, account for savings and profits totaling more than 3 billion dollars annually. Large as this sum is, it does not represent the fullest practicable utilization of the weather service available to agriculture, commerce, and industry.

In view of the fundamental influence of weather and climate on man's food, clothing, and shelter, and therefore on his health and happiness, it is not surprising to find that from the earliest times he has taken notice of seasonal variations and that long ago he looked for signs or omens that would foretell the weather, particularly the approach of storms. In an attempt to court supernatural aid in warding off unfavorable weather he made supplication to meteorological deities. Some of the weather signs picked up by man through the ages contain an element of truth; others were mere superstitions. A surprisingly large number of these superstitious notions about the weather still persist. These are slowly giving way to a more scientific viewpoint and a better understanding of how a modern weather service functions, its possibilities, and its limitations.

[2] An act of Congress dated October 1, 1890, created the Weather Bureau and made it responsible for the general weather service of the Nation. Subsequent legislation and Executive decisions extended the Bureau's responsibilities in the science of weather and climate until its service now applies to civil aeronautics and other modern fields as well as to general agricultural, commercial, industrial, and transportation interests. The Fourth Plan of Government Reorganization, 1940, transferred the Weather Bureau from the Department of Agriculture to the Department of Commerce, effective June 30, 1940. This transfer has not modified the Weather Bureau's service to any of the general interests of the country, including agriculture. H. Doc. 692, 76th Cong., 3d sess., states that the transfer "will permit better coordination of Government activities relating to aviation and to commerce generally, without in any way lessening the bureau's contribution to agriculture."

THE DEVELOPMENT OF MODERN WEATHER SCIENCE

Although man's observations of the weather began with the dawn of consciousness, meteorology,[3] or weather science, is still a comparatively young member of the family of modern sciences. Accurate observations, truly representative of open-air conditions—that is, unmodified by purely local or accidental influences—are not easy to obtain. Prior to the invention of meteorological instruments, it was impossible to measure accurately atmospheric pressure, temperature, humidity, wind velocity, and other elements. The barometer and thermometer were developed during the seventeenth century. Thereafter weather records became more accurate, but daily weather service as it is now known could not be established until the telegraph was invented and a widespread system of daily synoptic reporting was organized.

Synoptic Weather Reports

A synoptic weather report is a concise synopsis, or summary, usually in a simple code for brevity, describing the weather conditions in a locality at a certain time. (The word "synoptic" comes from two Greek words meaning "general view.") It is important to understand the role of the synoptic report in modern meteorology. The study of daily synoptic reports as represented on the weather map is the basis of our understanding of weather changes.

A single isolated weather observation tells little of the general state of the atmosphere or of the changes that are about to take place in it. Experienced outdoor observers like farmers and mariners may recognize the approach of a storm from a single observation of clouds or the appearance of the sky, but such an observation does not enable them to describe the weather in detail or for a large area each day. As may be seen from the article on The Scientific Basis of Modern Meteorology, page 599, the moisture that falls as rain is usually transported by air from some distant ocean. Vast bodies of air, technically known as air masses, come together from widely separated regions and by their contrasting characteristics produce changes in weather. Clouds and rain usually occur along the boundaries of air masses and are the result of their overlapping. An air mass is frequently composed of millions of cubic miles of air more or less homogeneous in character, and it may pass over many lands and seas before encountering an air mass of opposite characteristics, interaction with which causes clouds and rain. In order to have a comprehensive understanding of weather and climate, it is necessary to view a major portion of the atmosphere as a whole, such as a polar hemisphere or the quadrant or octant encompassing the region under consideration.

The state of the atmosphere at any instant may be likened to a great jigsaw puzzle in which one local weather observation is a single piece that reveals little or nothing of the whole picture. The synoptic

[3] The word "meteorology" comes from the ancient Greek term for the atmosphere. General meteorology includes the subjects weather and climate. It does not include the study of meteors and other heavenly bodies, which properly belongs to astronomy. In the popular mind meteorology is often confused with astronomy and sometimes with metrology, which deals with weights and measures. Meteorology has little to do with the heavenly bodies except for the sun as a source of radiant energy.

weather reports from well-distributed observing points make up the numerous pieces of the weather puzzle. Many simultaneous observations are necessary to reveal the pattern. Pieced together in the form of the daily weather map, they give the complete view of the weather as seen by observers on the ground. This branch of weather science is called synoptic meteorology. It is the foundation of the modern weather service.

The Daily Weather Map

The daily weather map of the United States, made possible by synchronized observations throughout the country collected quickly by telegraph, was first published by the United States Government in 1871.[4] This was a great step toward modern meteorology. However, the surface map represents the weather conditions over a portion of the globe as viewed from the ground, and except for cloudiness it gives little direct information of conditions in the air high above. Since some of the most important processes of weather formation take place in the upper air, the surface weather map obviously cannot give a complete understanding of weather. Meteorological instruments installed at the surface of the earth ordinarily measure the conditions only within 50 or 100 feet of the ground. The surface air represents scarcely one one-thousandth by volume of the atmosphere which enters into the formation of weather changes. The upper air, meaning all of the air above 100 feet or so, holds most of the secrets as to why the day is clear, cloudy, or showery. Only a guess as to upper-air conditions can be made from the evidence on the surface weather map.

The Polar-Front Theory and Air-Mass Analysis

During the World War interruption of ocean weather reports led Norwegian scientists to intensive studies of air currents in the effort to develop improved methods of weather forecasting. The studies focused attention on the fact, already mentioned, that most weather changes are related to the boundaries between air currents having different conditions of temperature and humidity. The more or less continuous conflict between warm, moist currents, usually from the south or west, and cold dry currents, from the north or east (in the Northern Hemisphere), so resembled the tide of battle along the western European battle front that the Norwegian school applied the name "front" to the boundary between different air currents—or air masses, as they are now called. This concept led to a great step in meteorology—the evolution of the polar-front theory and the air-mass method of weather analysis, which systematized and simplified the picture of the atmospheric formations most frequently the cause of weather changes. Air-mass analysis of the surface weather map gives a logical explanation of the observed weather through a kind of extension or extrapolation of surface observations known as indirect aerology. It guesses at the upper-air structure to account for the weather experienced on the ground.

[4] Synoptic reports were collected by telegraph in 1849 but were not published in the form of a weather map.

Balloon Observations and the Radiosonde

Direct air-mass analysis, substituting factual data on the state of the upper air for the deduction and conjecture involved in indirect aerology, was impossible until means were invented for observing and measuring the weather elements far above the ground. Upper-air soundings, as these observations are called, were obtained by sending up a manned balloon as early as 1784, but the instruments carried were not accurate, and the ascents were never sufficiently frequent to be used in a daily weather service. Still earlier, about 1749, crude temperature soundings of the upper air had been made by attaching a thermometer to a kite. Benjamin Franklin was one of the experimenters in this field. Beginning about 1900 unmanned balloons carrying a meteorograph, which automatically records air conditions during its ascent, were used for occasional soundings. These were later supplemented by the box kite and subsequently by the airplane, and for several years such daily observations were made at a number of stations in connection with the regular forecast service. Neither the kite-observation network nor the airplane network, however, was developed to give the frequent and numerous synchronized soundings necessary for adequate sampling of air pressure, temperature, and humidity at altitudes where important weather processes take place.

In 1938 a system of radiosonde observations was inaugurated. A radiosonde (fig. 1, *L*, and fig. 2, *C*) consists of a combination measuring instrument, or meteorograph, and an extremely lightweight radio that transmits signals translatable in terms of air pressure, temperature, and humidity, the assembly being released with a small gas-filled free balloon which carries it up to 50,000 feet or more. A radio receiver on the ground records the signals. Wind direction and velocity in the upper air can also be obtained by observations of the balloon with a theodolite during its ascent. In practice, wind aloft is more economically observed by the use of a much smaller balloon, called a pilot balloon. Upper-wind observations by means of the latter are usually made four times daily; by radiosondes only once or twice daily. The radiosonde and pilot-balloon network gives for the first time sufficiently numerous direct measurements to enable the meteorologist to analyze changes in air-mass structure from day to day and thus to piece together an accurate picture of the physical causes of weather and the course of its development.

Daily air-mass analysis based on the direct measurements by radiosondes throughout the country opens a new phase in modern meteorology. The upper-air data from the radiosonde records do not, however, displace the ground observations and the surface weather map. They may do so eventually when the radiosonde observing network is widespread over the continents and oceans, but for the next few years they will serve to complement the partial picture shown by the surface weather map and provide knowledge to replace conjecture in ascertaining the physical processes of the upper air which account for weather.

In bringing about this important step in weather science, aeronautics had a prominent role. Aeronautical inventions and research, the balloon, the airplane, and the lightweight aircraft radio led the way to the radiosonde. The urgent needs of civil and military aviation for specialized weather reports and forecasts supplied the driving force and enlisted the necessary support for meteorological research and development.

HOW A NATIONAL WEATHER SERVICE FUNCTIONS

Brief reference has been made to the fact that the modern weather service depends upon synoptic meteorology. It is obvious, therefore, that the first requisite is a widespread system of observations and reports collected daily by telegraph, telephone, or radio. In general, the greater the area covered by the reporting system, the more comprehensive and satisfactory the meteorological service. The atmosphere is boundless and never motionless. Storms develop, travel, and dissipate without regard to national boundaries and with relatively little influence from coast lines or other topographical features except high mountain ranges. In normal times international agreements provide for a rather complete exchange of weather observations twice daily or oftener. Thus the Weather Bureau is able to draw weather maps for almost the entire Northern Hemisphere each morning and evening. Thorough international cooperation in exchange of weather reports is indispensable to optimum weather service.

Requirements for Observations

Cooperation is necessary also to provide uniformity in time and form of observations so that the reports assembled on the weather map will be synchronized and comparable. An international weather code, which provides for observations to be taken in accordance with recognized procedure and expressed in standard units, is used. This is quite necessary. The meteorological observations all over the earth must be coordinated and integrated if a complete understanding of atmospheric circulation and weather processes is to be reached. For example, observations of atmospheric pressure at different places or at the same place at different times are not comparable unless they are reduced to a common standard of temperature, altitude, and gravity.

The requirements of synoptic meteorology for uniformity go even further than the immediate observations. Great care is necessary in selecting the exposures for meteorological instruments, as well as in obtaining the readings and reducing them to comparable standards. The importance of this point is illustrated by temperature variations on a calm, clear night. The air is often several degrees warmer a few feet above the ground than right next to the ground. Fifty or a hundred feet above the ground, or on the crest of a slope a few hundred feet distant, it may be 15° F. or more warmer. Under such conditions two neighboring points within the same air mass may appear to belong to two different air masses unless the temperature observations are taken under standard conditions. Variations such as these, large enough to be significant in air-mass analysis and in identification of weather conditions, are common with other meteorological elements also, particularly humidity, wind, and shower-type precipitation. The possibility of such characteristic weather vagaries or variations, often within a comparatively short distance, must be kept in mind when

298737°—41——10

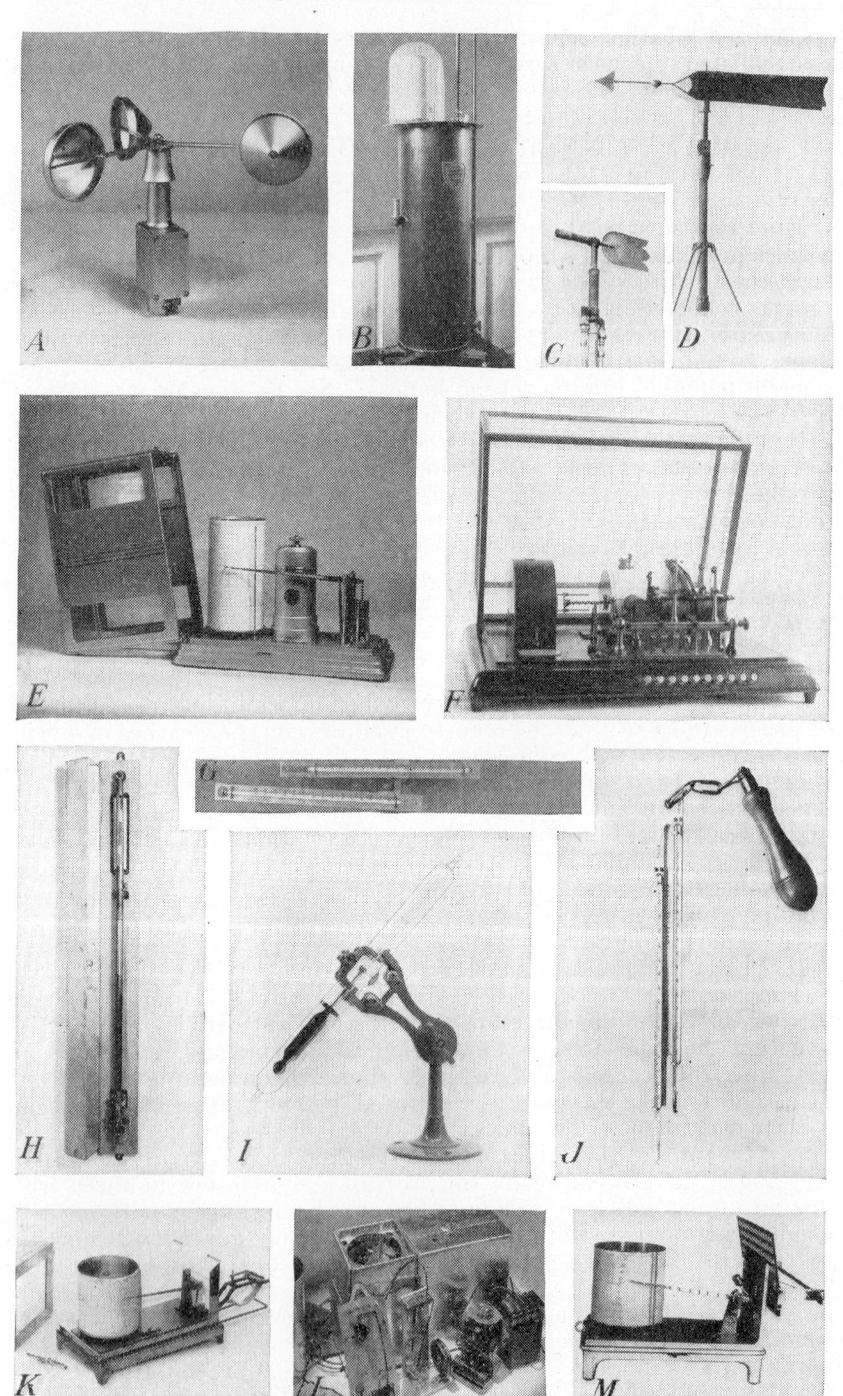

FIGURE 1. (*Legend on opposite page.*)

interpreting weather reports and forecasts. They are frequently a source of confusion and dispute.

Significant local variations in atmospheric conditions are found not only near the ground but also in the upper air. Time as well as space is a factor. It is evident that a thorough sampling of upper-air conditions by radiosonde and pilot balloon is necessary to reveal these variations. If observations are so far apart geographically or chronologically that a significant atmospheric condition is not detected, the meteorologist makes his analysis and forecast from incomplete information. The omitted condition may cause a serious error in his picture of the weather.

Meteorological Instruments

Observations that are both accurate and adequate are therefore essential to a good meteorological service. Weather Bureau observers throughout the country are equipped with instruments to measure the weather elements as accurately as possible and are trained to use them with precision. Even a common instrument like the thermometer may read wrong by several degrees, no matter how accurately it has been calibrated, unless it is properly shaded and ventilated and carefully read. Illustrations of the instruments used by Weather Bureau observers are shown in figures 1 and 2, and descriptions of these instruments and their uses are given in the legends.

Not every Weather Bureau observer has all of the instruments pictured in figures 1 and 2. Cooperative observers—discussed in detail later—have only thermometers and a rain gage. Airport offices where more detailed measurements are required have more equipment. Each station is equipped to accomplish the special purposes for which it was established.

Figure 1.—Instruments used by weather observers. *A*, A three-cup anemometer which, installed on a tower or mast, measures the wind velocity at the earth's surface; it gives a continuous record through an electric circuit to an element of the recorder, *F*. *B*, a wind-gustiness recorder, useful in aviation, is operated through the wind-tube, *C*. The large vane, *D*, is joined electrically to the recorder, F, to show continuously the wind direction near the ground. Instruments for measuring atmospheric pressure: *E*, A barograph, which records the pressure by means of a partially evacuated metal bellows arrangement, and *H*, a mercurial barometer, which gives the most precise determinations of static air pressure. *I*, A black bulb in a vacuum tube operates through a column of mercury and an electrical circuit to record sunshine on another element of the recorder, *F*. Temperature instruments: *G*, Maximum- and minimum-indicating thermometers in the horizontal position in which they are installed to give the highest and lowest temperatures each day at the observation point; *J*, a sling psychrometer consisting of wet-and-dry-bulb thermometers which are whirled by the observer to obtain the depression of the wet bulb, from which is computed the humidity or amount of moisture in the air, as well as the dew point, or, if the temperature is below freezing, the frost point; and *K*, the thermograph, which continuously records the air temperature, the record sheet being turned by a clock inside the drum at the rate of one rotation a week. *M*, A hygrograph, the humidity-recording instrument operated on the principle that a strand of hair lengthens or shortens when the humidity increases or decreases. *L*, The radiosonde measures upper-air pressure, temperature, and humidity. In this view the instrument is disassembled, with the container, or case, shown at the rear, the measuring units near the center front, and the radio tube and battery at the right front. The entire assembly weighs only about 2 pounds. It is carried up by the balloon shown in figure 2, *C*. All the instruments pictured here with the exception of that shown in *L* are used in measuring air conditions near the ground, that is, in surface observations.

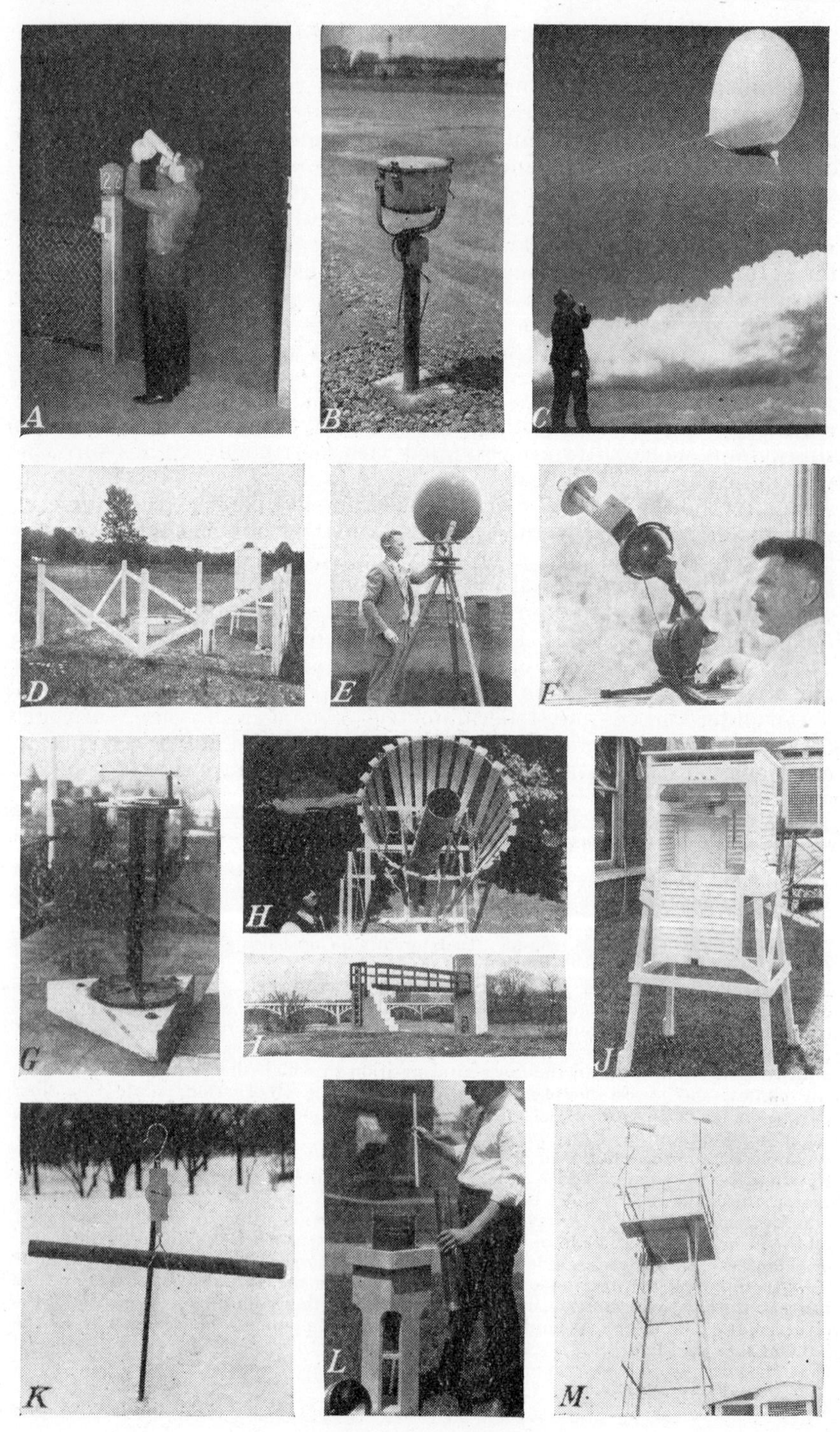

Figure 2. (*Legend on opposite page.*)

Observations and Reports

At present there are about 30 radiosonde observation points in the United States and about 140 pilot-balloon stations. Since clouds and fog obscure a pilot balloon, the soundings are often interrupted by cloud layers. Radiosonde observations, however, may be made regardless of cloud cover or fog. These two types of upper-air observations are the basis for upper-air charts and direct air-mass analysis. They furnish information used continuously in civil and military aviation. In the preparation of surface weather maps, on the other hand, it is necessary to have a larger number of observation points than for upper-air charts. The system of daily synoptic reports is built upon the network of the Weather Bureau's airport and city offices, which have been established to serve local agricultural, aviation, and business interests everywhere. These stations are known as primary or first-order weather stations; they now number approximately 315. They not only report their synoptic observations but also keep watch for significant changes in the weather and distribute weather bulletins and forecasts to farmers, business interests, and the general public. In addition they assist in the computation and compilation of climatological information.

Some Weather Bureau offices telegraph their synoptic reports once daily, others four times daily, and still others send them hourly or, under rapidly changing conditions, more frequently, depending upon the significance of the local weather conditions. These reports by telegraph giving the synchronous observations at 1:30 a. m., 7:30 a. m., 1:30 p. m., and 7:30 p. m., eastern standard time, for the four daily weather maps, are dovetailed with the observing networks for the hurricane-warning service, the cold-wave, frost-warning, and farm crop-weather services, the flood-warning and forest-fire-warning

---

Figure 2.—Other instruments designed to give accuracy in meteorological observations. *A* and *B* are an alidade and its searchlight projector for measuring the altitude of clouds for aviation uses. *C* shows the release of a radiosonde. The parachute, which lowers the instrument gently after the rubber balloon bursts at an altitude of 50,000 or 75,000 feet, is carried just underneath. The radiosonde instrument, shown in figure 1, *L*, is attached to the end of the light rope and is held in the hands of the attendant until the release of the balloon. The instrument and parachute usually land many miles from the starting point. A notice printed on the container instructs the finder to return it to the Government. A small fee is paid for its return. *D*, A standard exposure for meteorological instruments; in the center is shown an evaporation apparatus to measure the rate at which moisture is taken up by the air—a matter of much importance in studies of crop growth and other subjects in argonomy, hydrology, and meteorology. At the right are two rain gages, which measure the rate and amount of precipitation received at the ground, and a louvered thermometer shelter which provides proper shade and ventilation for the maximum and minimum thermometers and other temperature and humidity instruments. A close-up view of the interior of a thermometer shelter is given in *J*. *E* shows a theodolite and pilot balloon by means of which the different wind currents in the upper air are computed. *F*, A solar-radiation observation. *G*, A nephoscope, or cloud mirror, which gives an indication of wind direction and velocity at cloud level through observations of cloud drift. *H*, A shielded snow gage to measure depth of snow. The shield prevents errors in snow catch which would result from wind eddies around an unshielded gage. *I*, A river-stage station which gives the height of the river, used in the Bureau's daily river-navigation service and in flood warnings in times of high water. *K*, A second form of snow gage, in which a cylindrical sample of snow is taken in the open and weighed by the spring scale shown. *L*, A standard nonrecording gage to measure depth of rainfall. *M*, A typical exposure tower at a Weather Bureau office, with its installation of wind vanes, anemometer, and thermometer shelter.

services, and the general climatological service of the Weather Bureau.

Coordination and integration are first essentials to successful weather service. Observations taken at irregular times or by nonstandard instruments and methods would not be adaptable for use with the regular Nation-wide observations and would be of little value in the general weather service. One reason why the meteorological service in every country is organized as a government activity is to provide for uniform and coordinated observations. The International Meteorological Committee, an official organization of the directors of the government meteorological services of every nation, promotes uniformity and coordination in these observations and reports throughout the world.

The Forecast

The synoptic reports from all over the country are collected at certain meteorological centers. There they are plotted on charts and analytical forms preparatory to study by expert forecasters. After the working chart is drawn and the analysis completed, the meteorologist makes his weather forecasts for the locality and for the regions in his district. The reader may be interested in a glimpse of the forecast room of a district center while the maps and forecasts are being prepared. The activities in connection with a typical 7:30 a. m. map will serve to illustrate the procedure.

The Bureau's synoptic observers throughout the United States start observations early enough to send their reports by telegraph promptly at 7:30. A few minutes later the first reports are received in the forecast room at the district center. A translator decodes the messages, reading them aloud to various assistants who plot the data on working charts as the decoding proceeds. The number of charts depends on the functions of the center and the technique of the individual forecaster. There is always the surface weather map and usually a pressure-trend chart, as well as upper-air charts showing (1) winds aloft, and (2) significant surfaces of pressure, temperature, and moisture (sometimes also entropy, an expression for energy under certain conditions) at various altitudes. Some centers also draw profiles of temperature and winds aloft and separate temperature-trend and cloud charts.

By 8 a. m. the messages are arriving in large volume and by 8:45 a. m. most of the 300–400 weather reports have been plotted on the map. The forecaster in the meantime has been studying the upper-air charts, which have been completed somewhat earlier, and he now turns to analysis of the surface weather map. He identifies the air masses, sketches the fronts and isobars (lines through localities having the same pressure) and studies the atmospheric formations that produce the weather pictured on the map. He compares the upper-air charts with the surface analysis and estimates the rates of movement of air masses and the factors which may change not only their movements but their characteristics and their interactions with one another. He thus arrives at his conclusions which he crystallizes either in the form of a prognostic (prediction) chart or as a mental image, on the basis of which he describes the weather he expects. His forecasts are immediately distributed by telegraph, telephone, radio, mail, and press. Time is the essence of effective weather service, and forecasts are usually completed and dispatched by 10:15 a. m., within 3 hours after the synoptic observations are begun.

The weather map serves not only for the preparation of forecasts. It is the basis for summaries and bulletins of weather in various parts of the country. These play a vital part in the daily plans of farmers and those in industries allied to farming—shippers, manufacturers, brokers—and persons in many other business and commercial activities. Any delay in the daily distribution of the reports, bulletins, and forecasts disrupts important business plans and occasions loud protests from the press and other interests.

A general description of the technique of weather forecasting is given in the article on page 579. Although the process is not simple, neither is it mysterious. In its present stage it has many of the characteristics of an art as well as of a science. Expertness is the result of a combination of training, experience, and native ability. However, as progress is made in three-dimensional analysis of the weather and as the knowledge of its physical processes increases through factual observations of the upper air, the science will become more systematic and exact. Gradually a methodology of forecasting is being built up which diminishes the importance of personal factors. Treatises on the principles of weather forecasting are contained in recently published works.[5]

The Observation Networks

One of the essentials of effective weather service is adequate sampling—with emphasis on the word adequate—of significant air masses by means of representative observations. For some purposes, only sparse observations are required; for others a very dense network is necessary. The general weather map of the United States requires 300 to 400 observation points. Additional stations are needed in some regions to amplify this network for special services, such as hurricane warnings along the Gulf and south Atlantic coasts during the summer and autumn, frost warnings in horticultural belts during the winter, and crop-weather advices in the Cotton, Corn, and Wheat Belts during the growing season.

Voluntary Cooperative Observers

The most intensive network of weather-observing stations in the United States is composed of the Weather Bureau's voluntary cooperative observers, who serve without pay. Their observations, referred to in a later article (p. 689), supplement the synoptic network of the weather map. The records of the 5,000 unpaid cooperators in this dense network reveal the local variations in weather and are the foundation of present knowledge of the climate of the United States. The differences in rainfall, temperature, and certain other elements from point to point within a radius of a few miles sometimes make it necessary to have a very intensive network of cooperative observers, in some cases one for each 100 to 200 square miles, if significant local

[5] Petterssen, Sverre. Weather analysis and forecasting; a textbook on synoptic meteorology. 505 pp., illus. New York. 1940.
Byers, H. R. Synoptic and aeronautical meteorology. 279 pp., illus. New York. 1937.
See also the article by C. G. Rossby in this Yearbook, p. 599.

variations are to be determined. The present rainfall-observing network is shown in figure 3.

The different observing networks to which reference has been made are organized each for its special use, but they are so dovetailed that they supplement one another. No one of them, operating independently, could accomplish its intended purpose without the duplication of some of the reports and functions now provided through the mutually supplementary reports. The observers who voluntarily give their services in reporting climatological observations furnish a noteworthy contribution to the public welfare. The types of observation points or field stations are shown in figure 4 and are described in the accompanying legend.

Field Organization

The district forecast centers also serve as administrative offices for the districts into which the networks and special weather services are organized. For some purposes large districts are suitable; for others, such as the climatological and crop-weather services, smaller districts are necessary. The latter are organized by States. Figure 5 shows the general-forecast districts, figure 6, the crop-weather districts. Still other district boundaries have been found necessary to fill the special requirements in the airways-weather and the river and flood-warning services.

What appears to be a complex system of superimposed districts is in reality a rather simple organization of regional offices, some functioning for all phases of Weather Bureau service wherever relatively large areas make satisfactory administrative units, others limited to a single phase where small districts are necessary. All of these centers are regular field-service offices, their administrative work being additional to their functions of observing, reporting, forecasting, and distributing. The organization is suited to an activity with various phases as interwoven as are those of a meteorological service.

THE USES OF METEOROLOGICAL SERVICE

Climatological information has innumerable uses and applies directly or indirectly to almost every human activity. It is used by hydrologic engineers everywhere for such purposes as designing flood-control works and water-conservation and irrigation projects, as well as in planning ordinary drainage systems. It is used by manufacturers and heating engineers in designing their plants and conducting their operations; by agriculturists in studying crop relations, land utilization, and prevention of soil erosion; by aeronautical engineers in laying out airports and making air-line routes and schedules; and by economists and sociologists in studying mass migrations. The radiosonde's report of conditions at 10,000 or 20,000 feet altitude is as essential to the farmer, whose stock or crops may be damaged by a storm or cold wave unless forewarning enables him to protect them, as it is to the aviator whose airplane may be grounded by icing conditions in the clouds.

The purpose of the Weather Bureau as defined in its organic act is to provide meteorological information which contributes to the success

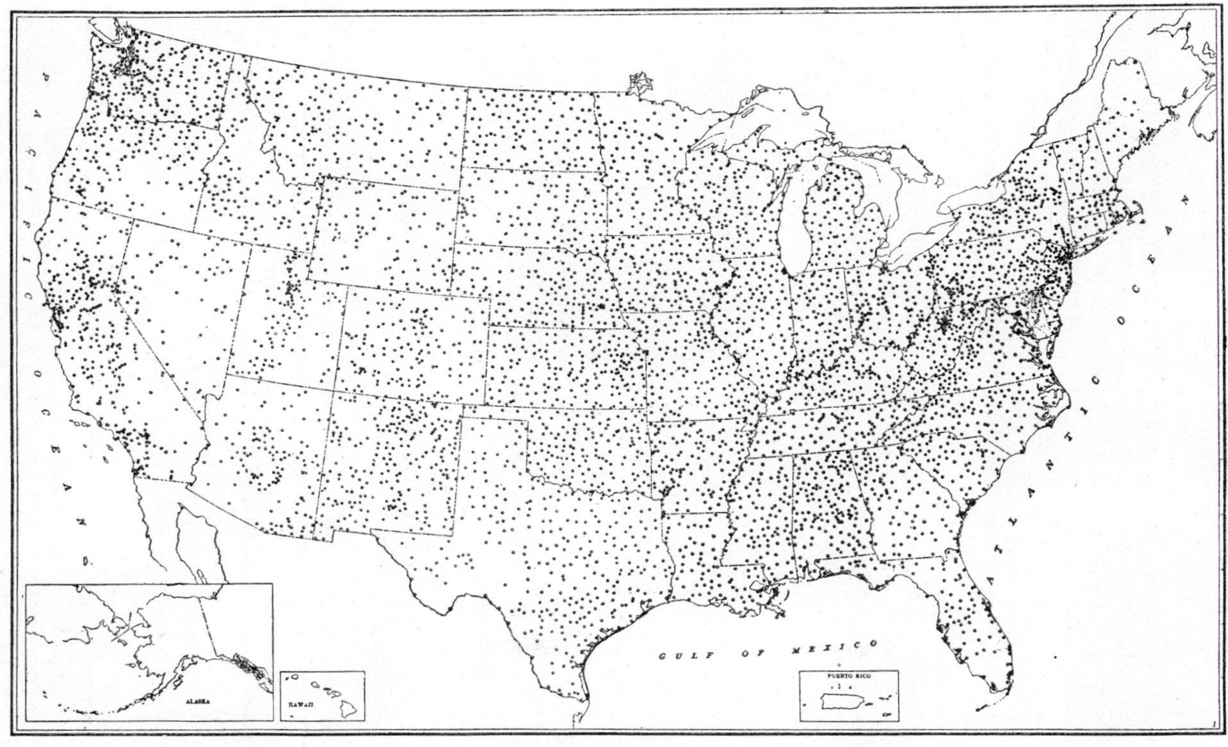

FIGURE 3.—Location of precipitation observers in the United States, 1940.

FIGURE 4. (*Legend on opposite page.*)

of agriculture and other business and commercial activities of the Nation. The Bureau's field offices distribute timely reports, bulletins, and forecasts daily by radio, telephone, and press. The weekly, monthly, and annual summaries are published as soon as they can be compiled.[6]

Figure 7 illustrates a few of the diverse uses of information on weather and climate.

Some of the less well-known uses of the weather service are of interest also. For instance, in some methods of spraying fruit trees and vegetables to protect them from pests it is important to know not only that there will be no rain to wash away the chemical soon after spraying but also that a certain temperature will not be exceeded, because at high temperatures a chemical reaction sometimes takes place that injures the plant.

In many processing methods for preparing cereals, flour, baked goods, and confectionery for market, advance knowledge of temperature and humidity is important. The processing is regulated to fit the changing conditions. Forecasts of temperature extremes—either cold waves or excessively warm spells—enable shippers of perishables to protect their shipments. In some cases shipments are rerouted to avoid damage.

Power companies in large cities plan to meet the peak loads in heating and lighting on the basis of forecasts of temperature and unusual cloudiness. Without advance knowledge of these conditions, uneconomical operation and perhaps power failure would result. Hydroelectric companies regulate their use of water power in the light of forecasts of rainfall, even going to the expense of starting steam auxiliary plants when a long period of dry weather is in prospect.

In winter when a great mass of cold air is about to engulf the country, the forecast leads to precautionary activities in almost every field. Water pipes and valuable shrubs are wrapped for protection. Automobile radiators are filled with antifreeze solutions, and wholesalers of antifreeze products rush their advance shipments to areas that will be affected. Retailers increase their advertisements of fur coats and other winter articles. Fuel dealers increase their supplies of coal and oil and ration their sales to customers if there is likely to be a shortage. Farmers drive their stock to shelter. In some parts of the country the first forecast of cold weather in the fall is the signal for preparation of the winter's meat supply and the completion of fall harvesting. Other precautionary measures affecting almost every walk of life in one way or another follow the publication of forecasts of hurricanes and floods.

[6] Additional information about these bulletins, forecasts, and other forms of meteorological service can be obtained from local Weather Bureau offices or from the main office in Washington. In cities where there is a local office of the Bureau its facilities are available to furnish further information on weather and climate insofar as the scope of the science and the capacity of the staff permit.

FIGURE 4.—Types of observation points or field stations. *A*, Thermometer shelter and rain gage of a rural cooperative observer. *B*, A river-gage station. *C*, A mobile unit for field work with forest-fire-fighting parties. A weather forecaster accompanies this unit, and through his local observations and weather maps furnishes forecasts of wind shifts and thunderstorms, foreknowledge of which often enables the fire fighters totdispatch men to threatened points in time to prevent serious spreading of fires. *D*, A city office of the Weather Bureau. *F*, An airport office. Mountain observations of importance in airway operations and in upper-air analysis are illustrated in *E* and *G*. *H*, Releasing a radiosonde at an upper-air sounding station . *I*, A ship at sea which reports its weather observations by radio four times daily while en route.

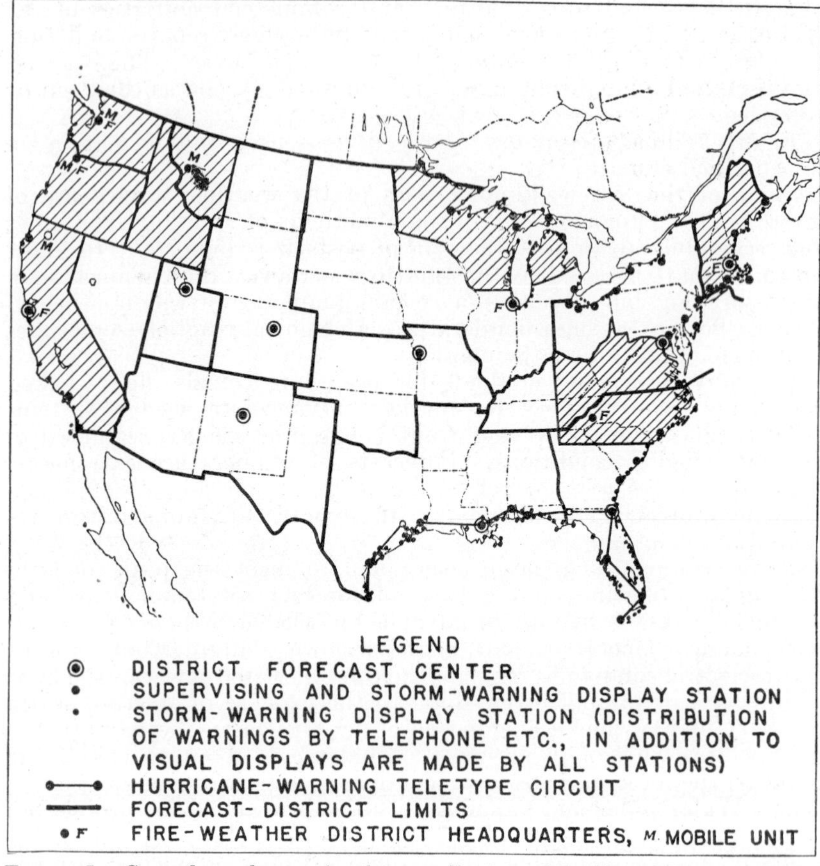

FIGURE 5.—General weather-service forecast districts of the United States. Shaded areas are fire-weather districts.

A specialized type of meteorological service which is very important at the present time is the furnishing of information on weather and climate in connection with national defense. Individualized weather services for military and naval operations are usually provided by specialists on the staffs of the organizations concerned. The general synoptic weather reports of the Bureau are the basis for such special services, supplemented by additional observations in the theater of operations. Individualized forecasts are prepared from the combined data.

The value of climatological statistics, as distinguished from the current reports and forecasts, is sometimes overlooked. The influence of climate in first encouraging settlement and later causing mass migration from the same area is shown in figure 8. Although there is at present no reliable method of predicting the occurrence of such periods of drought as occurred in the Plains States in 1930–39, the Weather Bureau, in the light of its information on average rainfall, advised in 1919 against overcultivation. Wet years such as those from 1920 to 1929 lead to unsound exploitation unless the public is guided

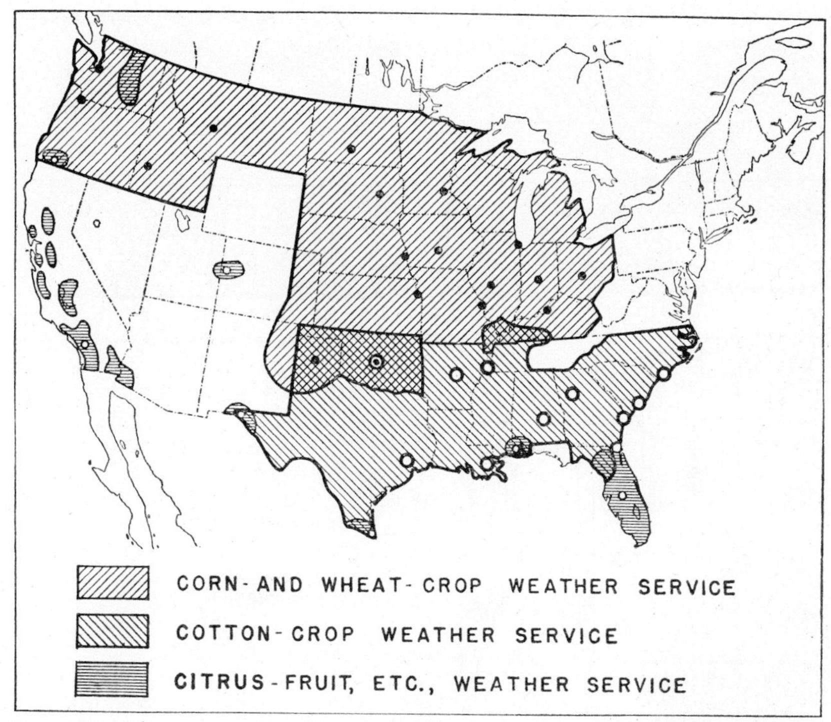

FIGURE 6.—States covered by the special agricultural weather service for the important crop regions.

by knowledge of climatology. Applications such as this are of profound importance to the entire social and economic order of the affected areas. The value of accurate methods for predicting long-time rainfall and temperature fluctuations would be enormous. This subject is discussed elsewhere in this volume.

SOME FALLACIES AND PROBABILITIES

An old proverb says that tubers should be planted during the dark of the moon because they grow under the ground where there is no light. Superstitions like this no longer guide the farmer in his potato planting, but many equally ridiculous weather proverbs handed down from the dark ages of meteorology still enjoy popular belief. It is not easy to distinguish the weather myth that is accepted merely because it is often repeated from the respectable proverb based on sound observations. The myth, usually lacking in definiteness, is now and then corroborated by pure coincidence. These cases keep it current.

Neither is it always easy to distinguish mere guesswork like that sometimes found in weather calendars and almanacs from authentic forecasts based on sound synoptic meteorology. Their wording does not distinguish them; both must be phrased in the same popular terms. Like the myth, the guess is occasionally confirmed by chance, and its spuriousness is then revealed only by knowledge of its origin.

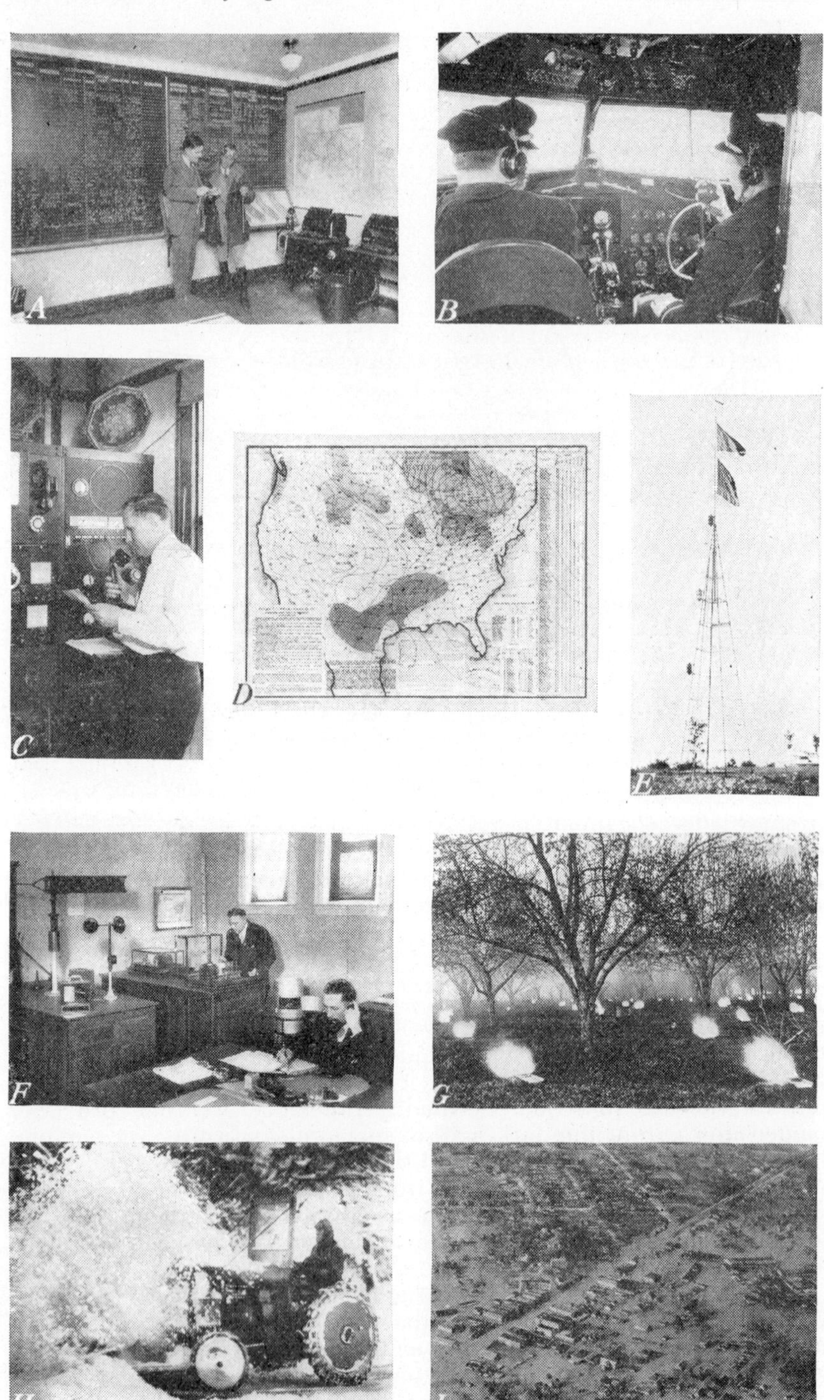

FIGURE 7. (*Legend on opposite page.*)

The source of a forecast is an index to its trustworthiness. Obviously anyone may keep account of forecasts from day to day and check their accuracy by comparison with the weather he observes. But few persons except those in occupations which use forecasts for daily business activities take the time and trouble to compare them with observations over a period sufficiently long for a careful, impartial appraisal.

These facts are important because they have a direct bearing upon the usefulness of meteorological service to the general public. The value of any advisory service, whether it be medical advice, business counsel, or weather information, depends not only upon its reliability but also upon the user's confidence in it. Agriculture, business, and industry in general have learned to utilize weather bulletins and forecasts with confidence. Many individuals, however, remain suspicious of the science and skeptical of its possibilities because they are confused by the diversity of weather prognostications and know little about the principles of meteorology. A better understanding of the character of weather service, particularly forecasts, and of some common fallacies about weather forecasting would lead to more intelligent interpretation and increased benefit to the public from the service now available.

The fact that daily weather analysis and forecasts must be based upon synoptic meteorology is recognized in the official meteorological services of all civilized countries. Weather forecasts based upon the phases of the moon or the direct influences of planets or other astronomical bodies have been tested again and again and found to be as lacking in justification as those based on the weather of a particular day, such as ground-hog day or St. Swithin's day.[7] Although tendencies toward certain periodicities or cycles have been discovered by investigators, none of these have so far proved to be sufficiently constant and

[7] For interesting treatises on these subjects see: HUMPHREYS, W. J. WEATHER PROVERBS AND PARADOXES. Ed. 2, 126 pp., illus. Baltimore. 1934.
BROOKS, C. F., BROOKS, E. M., AND NELSON, JOHN. WHY THE WEATHER? Rev. and enl. ed., 295 pp., illus. New York. 1935.

FIGURE 7.—Important everyday uses of information on weather and climate. *A*, A pilot receives up-to-the-minute airways reports just before he leaves the ground in an air-transport plane loaded with passengers and mail. *B*, Other pilots listening in flight to weather forecasts which tell them about terminal landing conditions. *C*, An announcer broadcasting a weather bulletin to the general public. *D*, A daily weather map as published by the Weather Bureau. About 10,000 copies of weather maps are printed each day by offices of the Bureau in large cities and are posted in prominent places for the use of the public and mailed to private subscribers. *E*, A storm-warning tower on the coast. The Weather Bureau cooperates in the operation of about 375 of these towers at coastal points, including the shores of the Great Lakes. They are used to warn small craft as well as larger vessels of the approach of storms and enable ships to remain in port or seek sheltered waters. *F*, Answering one of the numerous telephone inquiries received each day at Weather Bureau offices. A recent innovation in weather service by telephone has been introduced in several large cities. At the telephone exchange an automatic device (magnetic-tape principle) repeats the forecast continuously, permitting a large number of callers to hear it simultaneously without the delay of calling the office by regular connection when the line is busy. This makes the Bureau's latest 36-hour forecast available to telephone callers at any time of the day or night. *G*, Orchard heaters to protect against frost, started as the result of a frost warning. *H*, The daily forecasts are particularly valuable in assisting city street departments and utilities to prepare in advance for removal of heavy snow. *I*, Flood warnings aid in evacuating areas in advance of floods. Predictions of flood crests in the principal river basins are remarkably accurate. It is often possible to predict the crest stage several days ahead with an accuracy of within a few inches.

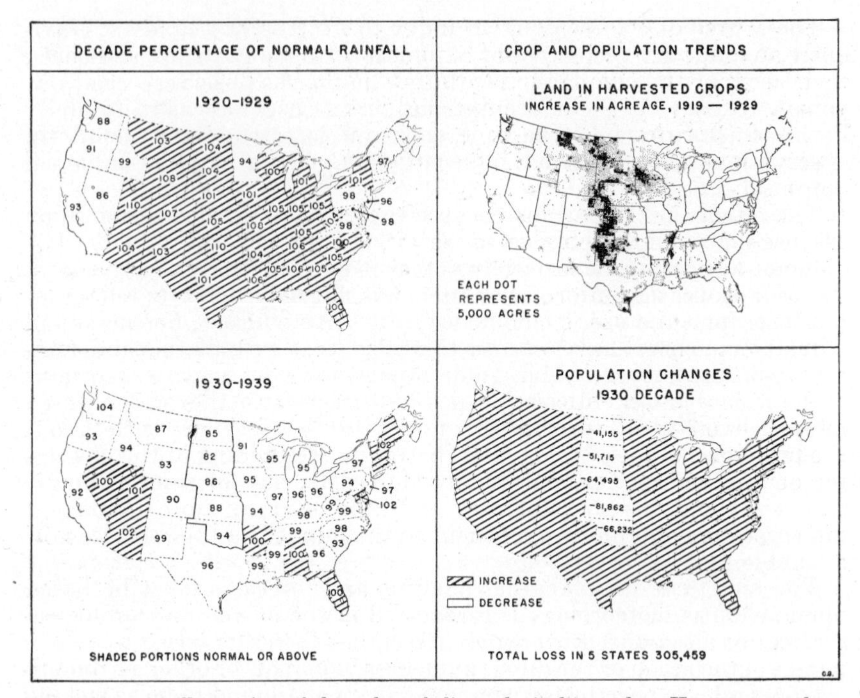

FIGURE 8.—An illustration of the value of climatological records. How greater-than-normal rainfall encouraged settlement in the Great Plains in the 1920's and subnormal rainfall in the 1930's drove many of the new settlers out.

definite to furnish a basis for specific daily weather forecasts. Most of the day-to-day forecasts for a year or more, like those printed in calendars and almanacs, are without scientific foundation and fail to stand the test of impartial comparison with the actual weather. Many such predictions are no better than a random guess. Yet a surprising number of persons still think that almanac forecasts are reliable.

A sound weather forecast must tell specifically what, when, and where. It must also rest upon knowledge that affords a basis for detecting unusual conditions such as severe storms. These stipulations are not so obvious as they may at first appear to be. It is a statistical fact, for example, that in most parts of the country a relatively high degree of accuracy may be attained if the forecast "fair" is used for every day in the year. Normally, more than 60 percent of the days are fair. Yet the guess "fair" is not a true forecast, even though it turns out to be correct; it is based wholly on "playing the averages," a method that would fail completely to warn of storms, cold waves, or other unusual conditions and departures from normal. A guess based on averages is of little practical value in planning for a particular day and usually fails to foretell severe weather conditions of which farmers and businessmen need to be warned in advance.

Perhaps the most frequent source of misinterpretation in forecasts a week or more in advance arises from failure to take into account this element of time. Studies show that in many months the forecasts "rain" and "no rain" can both be rated more than 80-percent accurate for the same 30 days if the forecaster is allowed a tolerance of 1 day before and 1 day after each date for which the prediction is made.

Some are deceived by the general expression "stormy weather," which is sometimes applied to a period of several days in predictions printed months in advance. Such predictions are usually indefinite as to when and where the storm will occur and what kind of storm it will be; they are equivalent to saying "The sun will rise." One or more storms of some kind occur somewhere every day.

It is quite possible to use a generalized statement of average conditions for a week or a month based on climatological records as an indication of the probabilities. The expectancy for extreme conditions or departures from normal may be expressed in terms of frequency, as shown by long climatological records. A summary of this kind can be applied to its analogous period a month or a year or more in the future, and such generalizations are often very useful. They are sometimes offered as forecasts. Since, however, climatological averages do not show the departures from normal for a specific time, they are not forecasts in the accepted sense and cannot be relied upon to foretell unusual conditions for that time. To take an extreme case as an illustration: Climatological records show that the average temperature in the United States is higher in July than in January. With that knowledge one may safely predict that July will be warmer than January. But this is not truly a forecast because it does not tell whether a particular July will be much warmer or cooler than the average July.

Another cause of misuse or misunderstanding of meteorological facts, including climatological records and current bulletins as well as forecasts, is the failure to recognize the variable character of weather and climate. The science of meteorology is reasonably exact in its measurements of the state of the weather at any particular time and place, but unless the user of factual observations remembers that changes in weather occur frequently and often rapidly from time to time and from place to place, he may misinterpret the observations. An exact measurement is made of the rate and amount of rainfall at a particular place for a certain period. A few hundred feet away or a few minutes later the rate and amount may be very different. Variations of 50 percent or more are common in showers. Similar variations are found in wind direction and velocity, in temperature, and in cloudiness.

These variations complicate climatology, and they greatly increase the difficulties of forecasting. This is not due entirely to the fact that the variations are hard to anticipate. Indeed, with modern synoptic reports and analyses, a meteorologist is often able to forecast the weather in great detail. But practical necessity makes him describe it concisely. The press and the radio want brevity in weather bulletins and forecasts, and if the presentation is too lengthy, the public declines to read or hear all of it, or becomes so confused in the details that misunderstanding follows. People want the weather characterized in a few words, or preferably one word—clear, rain, snow. On a typical day this is almost like asking the astronomer to describe the stars in one word.

298737°—41——11 +

An accurate description of the weather in one place for a single day often requires several hundred words. It should be remembered that when the forecaster says "rain" he is typifying the day's weather and rarely expects it to rain the entire day. When he says "clear" he usually means the weather will be clear most of the day and without rain at any time, though during many days characterized by this term a few clouds are visible at one time or another. If he were to forecast "partly cloudy" in order to describe the occasional cloudiness, the description would not apply during the hours when the sky is completely clear. Only when it is uniformly clear or uniformly cloudy or rainy does a single term describe conditions for the entire day, and such uniformity in weather is rare. Again, the public places various interpretations upon common words like "clear." To most people a summer day is clear if the sun is bright enough to cast a faint shadow, even though the sky is covered by thin cirrus clouds. To the photographer who wants bright sunlight for aerial mapping or the farmer who desires the sunshine to ripen his crops, such a day is not clear but cloudy.

In the present state of meteorology an explicit forecast in the accepted sense of the term is not usually justifiable from the scientific viewpoint for longer than 48 hours beyond the time of issue. Occasionally atmospheric conditions are sufficiently stable or stagnant to permit the forecaster to foretell the weather with accuracy 3 or 4 days in advance. Official meteorological services sometimes publish a general statement or outlook for a somewhat longer period based upon an extension of the hemisphere weather map or other synoptic procedure. These outlooks are necessarily in more general terms than the regular daily forecast. Predictions for periods longer than a week are still in the experimental stage except for pure statements of climatological probabilities, which strictly speaking are not forecasts. Samples of those with claims to scientific consideration have been carefully checked by independent observers and have so far been found lacking in practical value when used as specific forecasts for definite dates.[8] But though a climatological outlook is not a forecast, it has value as an index to future weather, and climatic studies are of real use for general planning in agriculture and commerce.

The conditions just discussed have such influence upon the interpretation of meteorological information, particularly forecasts, and therefore upon their value to the public, that some further brief comment on the principal sources of misinterpretation seems desirable.

Although the state of the atmosphere, which we call weather, may be observed at any time and place with accuracy, its large and sometimes rapid variations must be kept in mind in interpreting these observations, whether in the form of current reports or as climatological statistics. Weather phenomena are not static as are, for example, the conditions studied in geology, which, once ascertained, remain unchanged for long periods. Nor have weather changes been reduced to mathematical expressions as have the motions of the planets and the stars, so that they can be computed accurately long in advance. Atmospheric changes are of an extremely complex nature, and in our present state of knowledge their causes are not completely understood.

[8] UNITED STATES BUREAU OF AGRICULTURAL ECONOMICS. REPORTS ON CRITICAL STUDIES OF METHODS OF LONG-RANGE WEATHER FORECASTING. U. S. Monthly Weather Rev. Sup. 39, 130 pp., illus. 1940.

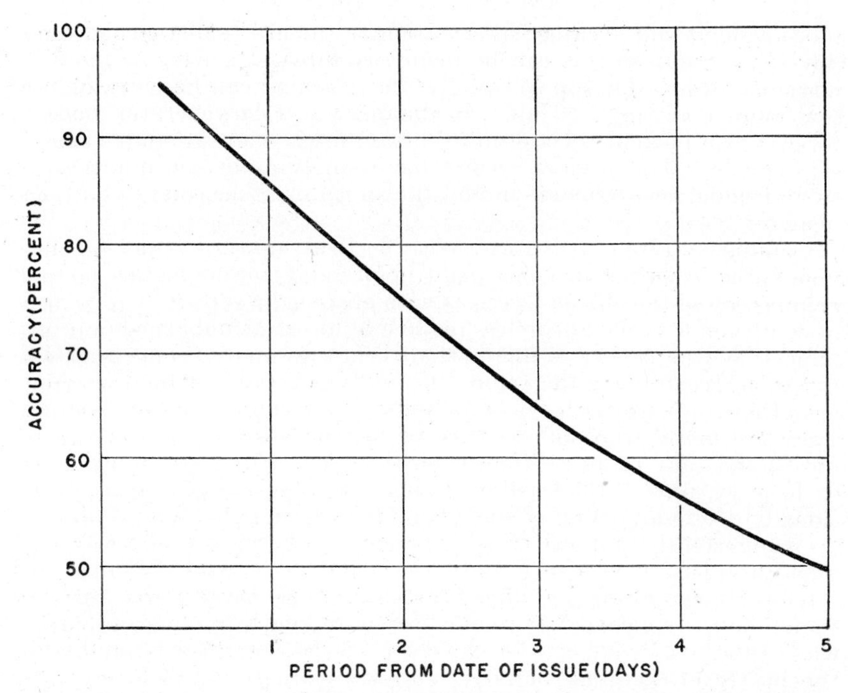

Figure 9.—Approximate practical limits of forecast accuracy at the present time. Average percentage value of forecasts of the state of the weather of the single-term type up to 5 days after date of issue.

The rapid changes in intensity, speed, and direction of movement of air masses, and the large variations consequently found along the boundaries or transition zones of these masses impose practical limitations making it difficult to give explicit descriptions of weather—particularly forecasts—in statistical or other concise forms. The accuracy that may at present be expected over a period of time in forecasts of the single-term type, like "clear," "rain," etc., is indicated by figure 9.

Besides these technical limitations, there is frequent misunderstanding of meteorological information. Accuracy in meteorology compares favorably with accuracy in many other sciences and professions—engineering, medicine, economics. The cases of unforeseen changes in air masses that lead to erroneous forecasts are obvious to everyone after they occur. But since weather service is a daily activity and errors in forecasts occur three to five times a month in most parts of the country, the errors are remembered and seem more frequent than they really are.

There are seldom significant errors in the forecasting of severe storms and other very dangerous conditions; storm and cold-wave warnings are very trustworthy. Preliminary warnings are often given 3 or 4 days in advance, and specific forecasts are issued as the storm or cold wave develops and comes closer. All modern forecasts should be viewed as having two general stages—(1) preliminary advices based on first indications and (2) subsequent revisions giving more explicit and accurate information as the atmospheric conditions develop. Some storms can be definitely forecast 2 days or more in advance; others develop so rapidly that warning can be given only a few hours in advance. Unlike an almanac guess, however, the modern forecast can be kept revised up to the minute as more complete analysis is made. The advices become increasingly exact and informative as additional reports come in and the storm or other condition draws near.

Comments received by the Weather Bureau show that popular views of weather forecasts are made up of many factors besides factual comparison of the official forecasts with observed weather. One source of confusion is hasty or careless reading of forecasts published in newspapers; another source is the inattentiveness of many people in listening to forecasts over the radio. Conditions predicted for tomorrow are often confused with those for today. During every severe storm there are many who suffer injury or loss because of their failure to notice and take proper action when they read about storm warnings or hear warnings broadcast by radio. Moreover, newspapers occasionally delete a portion of the official forecast for the sake of brevity or inadvertently publish an old forecast, and radio broadcasts frequently inject advertising and other comments which distort the intended meaning of the official forecast. Surprisingly, too, there is sometimes a subconscious tendency to reproach the meteorologist when the weather is not what we wish, just as we instinctively blame the bearer of any bad news. Indications are that this reaction is much more general among the public than might be expected. Broader education in meteorology and increased interest and understanding are dispelling the irrational views and superstitions that have been handed down from the dark ages of the science and are leading to rational use of climatological data, current observations, and weather forecasts, thus greatly extending the usefulness and value of the service.

The science of meteorology and the technique of the daily weather service have advanced greatly during the last two decades. A broader public interest and the spread of education in the science are removing the limitations which have prevented the most effective use of weather service. Recently developed observations of the upper air add to the knowledge of the atmosphere and promise eventually to give a much better understanding of the basic causes of weather and climate and their changes. With this knowledge a more basic interpretation of climatic influences and more systematic and reliable methods for determining future weather conditions may be expected. The economic benefits will be enormous if methods can be developed for making reliable forecasts of weather for a week, a month, or a season in advance, and although progress is uncertain, meteorologists are justified in seeking techniques which now appear remote. Modern studies in three-dimensional meteorology—that is, in the upper air as well as on the ground—are growing in importance to various branches of agriculture—for example, in the interpretation of climatic factors through studies carried on by the Soil Conservation Service, in the fire-prevention work of the Forest Service, in the periodical crop estimates of the Agricultural Marketing Service, and in the long-range forecast research conducted with Bankhead-Jones research funds.

Research is the means of progress. Meteorological research has only recently arrived at the threshold of its laboratory, the atmosphere as a whole. Its studies are certain to open the way to a more comprehensive science, with results that will be of benefit to all.

PARTIAL LIST OF REGULAR WEATHER BUREAU SERVICES TO THE PUBLIC

Approximate time of issue (eastern standard time)	*Service*
10 a. m.	Thirty-six-hour weather forecast issued daily through radio, telephone, and press. This forecast is revised in the light of subsequent weather maps about 5 p. m., 11 p. m., and 5 a. m. the following day if necessary during periods of rapid change.
10:30 a. m.	Amplified local 36-hour forecasts issued through radio and press by about 75 field offices of the Weather Bureau.
11 a. m.	Daily weather map published by about 30 Weather Bureau offices throughout the country on week days. Daily weather bulletin containing tabulation of weather observations from other cities. Published on cards and in the daily press by local Weather Bureau offices.
Every 6 hours	Airways weather forecasts available at airport offices.
When occurring	Special warnings of storms, cold waves, etc. Published by radio, press, etc., whenever severe weather conditions are expected.
Noon on Tuesdays and Thursdays.	General weather forecast or outlook for the ensuing 5 days. Published in newspapers throughout the country.
Wednesday	Weekly Weather and Crop Bulletin. Published by Weather Bureau, Washington, D. C.
	Weekly Cotton Region Bulletin. Published by Weather Bureau at New Orleans during the growing season.
	Weekly Corn and Wheat Region Bulletin. Published by Weather Bureau at Chicago during the growing season.
	Less complete weekly bulletins issued by a number of other district centers.
Periodically	Monthly Weather Review.
	Annual Meteorological Yearbook of the United States.
	Bulletin W (3 volumes) giving tables and summaries of climatological data for the United States. Published every 10 years, last 1930.
	A number of other publications, a complete list of which is available through the Superintendent of Documents, Government Printing Office, Washington, D. C.

PART TWO

Climate and Agricultural Settlement

The Settlement of the Humid East

By Carl O. Sauer [1]

BY MIGRATIONS and settlement man has spread over the earth and settled it. To each new land he brings the ways of production familiar to him in his old home—ways fundamentally influenced by climate. In the new land some of these ways may suit the climate, some may not. The struggle of adaptation, modification, and discovery then begins. Here is the first of a group of articles dealing with this struggle in the United States and its territories. The settlement of this country represented the greatest mass migration of all time, and the climates, from Alaska to Puerto Rico and Hawaii to New England, cover almost the entire range found on the earth.

[1] Carl O. Sauer is Chairman of the Department of Geography, University of California.

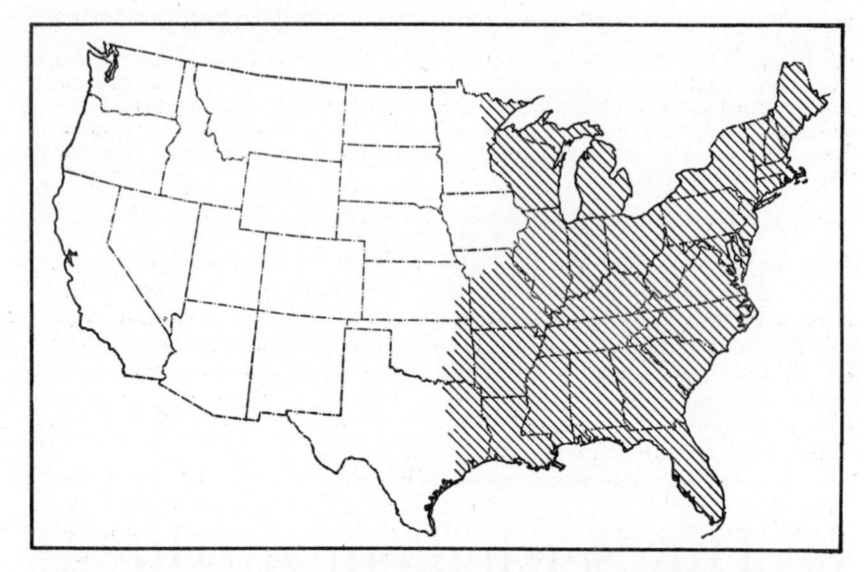

Whereas ocean air flows freely during all seasons over the European shores of the Atlantic, the Atlantic seaboard of the United States is only occasionally and in part influenced by its position on the ocean. Since the weather usually moves from west to east, the usual storm tracks pass from western Canada or the Rockies eastward by way of the Great Lakes and New England. Much of the air that gets to our Atlantic coast has passed over a wide stretch of land beforehand. Such continental air may have been greatly chilled in winter or similarly heated in summer before it reaches the seaboard. Thus our eastern seaboard areas are largely subject to extremes of heating and chilling like those in the interior of the continent, although they have intervening periods of weather that is tempered by air from the ocean. Our Atlantic States have hotter summers and colder winters than the countries of western Europe. Other continental qualities of the climate are a rather abrupt change from winter to summer and the fairly marked development of summer thunderstorms, with rains more intense but of shorter duration than in coastal Europe.

The European colonists became well aware of these differences while recognizing the generally familiar nature of the weather. One of the earliest observations was by Capt. John Smith, who likened the summers of Virginia to those of Spain but its winters to those of England, and who said also, "The like thunder and lightening to purefie the air, I have seldome either seene or heard in Europe."

Peter Kalm, visiting this country from Sweden, wrote under date of September 23, 1748:

It is true that in Pennsylvania, and even more so in the lands farther to the north, the winters are often as severe as in Sweden, and therefore much colder than in England and the southern countries of Europe. I found, for instance, that in Pennsylvania, which lies by 20 degrees farther south than some provinces of my fatherland, the thermometer of Celsius fell 24 degrees below freezing. And yet I was assured that the winters which I spent there were not of the coldest, but quite ordinary. It is also true, however, that if the winters are at times hard, they do not last usually a great while. One can say properly that in

Pennsylvania ordinarily they do not endure more than 2 months, and sometimes not that long. It is unusual if winter holds for as much as 3 months. Further, the summer heat is very strong and constant. In Pennsylvania, most of April, all of May, and the following months until October are as warm as June and July in Sweden. Cherries are often ripe in Philadelphia on the 25th of May; and, not infrequently, wheat is harvested in Pennsylvania by the middle of June. All of September and half, if not all of October, constitute the pleasantest season in Pennsylvania.

EUROPEAN AND AMERICAN VEGETATION

In most cases, the colonists were at no loss to identify the native plants and animals which they found on the western side of the Atlantic. It would be impossible, indeed, to cross an ocean anywhere else and find as little that is unfamiliar in nature on the opposite side. In all the lands of earliest colonization, from Massachusetts Bay south to Virginia, flora and fauna were closely related to those in the European homeland and indicated to the settlers that they were still under familiar skies and seasons.

Except for some stretches of sand, the east coast was a land abounding in hardwoods. Above all, there were oaks of divers kinds. Ash, elm, beech, birch, maple, poplar, willow, linden, and holly were other familiar trees, even though the American species differed somewhat from those of Europe.

Hardwoods conspicuously different from those of north Europe were the chestnut and walnut; the English had enough experience of the Mediterranean to guess right as to the names of both of these, but they also found hickories and pecans, for which Indian names were adopted, and the noble tulip tree, which they misnamed "yellow poplar." In the north, the colonists found white and red pine mingled with the hardwoods; on the sandy coast, pitch pine; southward from Virginia, forests of yellow pine. Such stands were a new experience to the immigrants, for pines are few in western Europe. Still more novel were the coniferous trees met with in the swamps from Chesapeake Bay south. For want of a better name, the colonists called these trees cypresses, though they are not closely akin to the Old World cypresses. The eastern juniper was similarly mislabeled "red cedar." It was obvious that America possessed a wealth of fine trees far beyond that of the European homelands.

The wild berries were remarkably similar on both sides of the Atlantic and served as an important food supply to the more northerly English colonists. The wild grapes of the New World attracted much attention from the settlers, for in most of northwestern Europe, grapes, either wild or cultivated, did not grow. English, Swedish, and German settlers commented upon the abundance and merits of the American grapes.

This was indeed a lustier land to which the settlers had come, a land of hotter summers and colder winters, of brighter and hotter sun and more tempestuous rain, a land suited to and provided with a greater variety of vegetation than the homelands of Europe. In one important respect only was it strikingly inferior to northwest Europe—the quality of the grasses. There was grass aplenty, both in wet, low meadows and parklike openings or glades in the upland woods, but mostly it furnished rather poor feed. Some, like the broomsedge or broomstraw (eastern *Andropogons*), became coarse and harsh as it grew. Almost none of the native grasses withstood trampling and grazing. The annual grasses died off if heavily pastured, because they did not get a chance to seed; the perennials had delicate crowns that ill stood the abuse of heavy grazing. In clovers and other herbaceous legumes, a similar inferiority may be noted for the eastern American flora as compared with the European.

INDIAN ECONOMY OF THE EASTERN WOODLANDS

All the native tribes encountered by the early colonists had basically similar ways of making a living. They are usually all classed by anthropologists as Eastern Woodland Indians. Their houses were made of logs or poles set upright; or in some cases strips of heavy bark, as of the chestnut, were tied to a framework of poles. They made dugout canoes by hollowing the trunk of a tulip tree or some other light, strong wood, or used bark canoes, as in the north. The household vessels were largely of wood and bark. The hard maples were carefully tapped for the spring sap, which was boiled down to sugar. From woods borders, berries and edible roots were gathered in quantity. Walnuts, hickory nuts, chestnuts, and the sweeter acorns provided winter foods of importance. Woodland browse and glade and marsh grasses supported game in an amount and variety that greatly impressed the newly come Europeans, who rarely had been given the chance to hunt at home. Many of the Indian uses of forest resources were copied or adapted by the settlers. The products of the woodlands were important to them for many years, as these products had been to the Indians.

From the woodland Indians, the colonists learned ways of farming that greatly helped, if indeed they did not make possible, the successful establishment of settlements in the new country. First of all the whites learned a valuable short cut to land clearing, the deadening of trees by girdling. In Europe, where they were accustomed to open fields of plow land, when additional land was cleared the trees were carefully cut down and the stumps dug out for firewood. In the New World, the clear field, the plow, and the seeds of Old World agriculture all gave way largely to the Indian methods of forest girdling and planting in hills and the use of Indian crops.

The basic Old World crops were field crops, such as small grains, planted in plowed ground, either broadcast or seeded in rows. The Indians used digging stick and hoe for farming, had no regular, rectangular fields, such as plowing requires, and disregarded stumps and dead trees. The planting was usually done in "hills," often by setting several kinds of seed, such as corn, beans, and squash, in each heaped-up mound of earth. By such procedure, the cultivator secured a much greater food supply than would have been possible under European modes of farming, without the labor of getting the soil ready for the plow and without requiring draft animals or equipment other than hoe or mattock.

Not only in the early colonial days of the Atlantic seaboard but for two and a half centuries thereafter the pioneer settler used Indian tillage and Indian crops. He continued to do so until he had advanced westward to the far interior margin of the lands of humid climate. The best known solution of how to farm in a hardwood country, with a minimum of tools and without the necessity of costly clearing, had been worked out by the aboriginal agriculturists of the New World.

The barking or girdling of trees let the full sunlight onto the forest floor in a few months' time and thus made it ready for planting. The ground commonly was burned over before being planted, to free it of dead branches, dry leaves, and the light herbaceous vegetation that was present. The forest topsoil was dark with leafmold, rich in potash, and congenial to the heavily feeding Indian corn. In a few years wind and weather completed the task of bringing down the dead timber. The deadened hardwood trunks and roots decayed rapidly in the moist, warm summers.

With one or two exceptions the plants cultivated by the Indians had originated far to the south of the United States under tropical or subtropical conditions. The list of native crops includes several kinds of corn, such as dent, flint, and sweet corn, various kidney or navy beans, squashes or pumpkins, the common sunflower, and the Jerusalem-artichoke. Somewhat doubtfully the last two are credited to the eastern United States as the original place of domestication. Excepting the Jerusalem-artichoke, these are all annual plants which, in contrast to most of the crops of northern Europe, require warm weather for starting. A large part of our humid East is as warm in summer as a tropical region. Summer in the middle Mississippi Valley is as warm by day or night as summer in the Tropics, perhaps warmer. Hence, carrying the warmth-loving domesticated American annuals northward from Mexico and Central America to the eastern woodland areas involved no very serious problems for the aboriginal cultivators. It may be assumed, however, that it took many generations for agriculture to spread from Mexico to Chesapeake Bay. As it spread, a gradual selection of plants that would mature in a shorter and shorter growing season took place. These in turn became the parents of our modern commercial corn, beans, and pumpkins.

COLONIAL BEGINNINGS NOT AGRICULTURAL

When the English first began their activities in the New World, they had little concern about places suitable for agricultural settlement. Farming was forced upon the colonists; it was not the object of their coming. The early Englishmen who came to America came to seek a northern way to the Orient, to bar the way of Spanish or French expansion, to seek wealth in furs and in codfish, herring, and mackerel, to find precious metals like those of Mexico and Peru, or at least to secure profitable cargoes of medicines, spices, dyewoods, or naval stores. Stockholders in trading ventures put up the funds on which attempt after attempt at settlement was made and failed—in Newfoundland, in Maine, in North Carolina, and in the Tropics—largely because settlements were started for all reasons but the suitability of climate and soil for farming. The fact that any group of overseas colonists needed above all else to sustain themselves by the products of their agriculture was understood very slowly.

PLANTATION CROPS FROM TROPICAL LANDS

Even the Colony of Virginia, first overseas English settlement that endured, was extremely reluctant to engage in agriculture. In its floundering beginnings, it depended on imported supplies and food traded or taken from the Indians. Four miserable years after the founding of Virginia, the new government of Sir Thomas Dale applied a rigorous regime of enforced agricultural labor, which pulled the Colony through. The Englishmen gave some attention to the growing of Indian crops, and European livestock was turned out to range through the woods. Swine in particular did well on the mast of the hardwoods and increased rapidly. Smith reported as late as 1618 that only 30 or 40 acres of European grain had been sown—in soil prepared with a single plow.

Meanwhile, apparently in 1612, the cultivation of tobacco was begun. This was not the harsh native tobacco (*Nicotiana rustica*) used by the Indians of the eastern woodlands, but the cultivated tobacco (*N. tabacum*) of the American Tropics. During the sixteenth century Spaniards and Portuguese had introduced this Indian ceremonial plant to European trade and its seeds to European gardens. The use of tobacco spread rapidly into France and England. In both countries it was planted to some extent before the founding of Virginia. It is not definitely known how this tropical tobacco came to Virginia. The first plantings probably were of seed that had been brought from England. Fortunately for the success of the Virginia Colony, the experimental introduction of tobacco was made just at the time when the English were acquiring the tobacco habit, before any English colony had been established in the Tropics, and under an economic policy that emphasized production of goods by Englishmen.

It cannot be claimed that Virginia had any peculiar climatic advantage in the growing of tobacco. But Virginia had an advantage in being the only English colony at the time and in the indifferent quality of the leaf tobacco produced in England; and the long and equable summers of Virginia, amply supplied with moisture, free of hot dry winds and sudden sharp drops in temperature, proved sufficiently congenial to the growth of this delicate plant of tropical origin. This was the climatic discovery the Virginians made for New World agriculture.

In later years the major expansion of tobacco was westward in the same latitude as Virginia, continuing to the western edge of the woodland country. A secondary spread took place southwestward, through the Piedmont. After Virginia, Kentucky became the next great tobacco State. Soon Tennessee and the lands north of the Ohio were involved in tobacco planting, and by the middle of the nineteenth century, St. Louis was the greatest tobacco market, with tobacco fields stretching west across Missouri to the Plains.

The next introduction of tropical crops came principally by way of Charleston, S. C. Shortly after Virginia became a tobacco-planting colony, English settlements were established in the smaller West Indian islands, most significantly in Barbados. The rapid growth of settlement and plantations soon crowded this and other islands, and an overflow of population was directed to South Carolina after 1670. Sugarcane, indigo, Barbados, or sea-island, cotton (*Gossypium barba-*

dense), and rice were introduced as plantation crops in the lowlands around Charleston. Similar introductions took place around New Orleans in the eighteenth century by the French, largely influenced from Haiti. Florida entered only slightly into this plantation development, not because of unsuitable climate but because of lack of rich lowlands with deep soil. From the sea-island coast of South Carolina to the Delta of the Mississippi, tropical climatic conditions prevail during most of the year. The principal difference in practice here as compared with that in the West Indies was that whereas such tropical crops as sugarcane and sea-island cotton were treated as perennials in the islands, winter frosts required annual planting in South Carolina and Louisiana.

Last and greatest of the plant introductions in the southern plantations was that of upland cotton (*Gossypium hirsutum*). The manner of its appearance in the South is obscure. A domesticated plant of Mexico, it was, like many New World plants, taken to the Mediterranean by Spaniards in the sixteenth century, and soon it was cultivated to some extent along the entire length of the Mediterranean shores. Its introduction to the English Colonies was perhaps by way of southern Europe. In the eighteenth century upland cotton was rather commonly planted on a small scale in the southern Colonies, chiefly for domestic use. Commercial planting was made possible by the invention of the cotton gin, and the first area of upland, or short-staple, cotton plantations was in South Carolina and Georgia, inland from the old sea-island cotton section.

The climatic background of upland cotton is quite different from that of the sea-island species. The latter needs a large and frequent supply of moisture and a very long, warm growing season, reflecting its fully tropical origin. The upland, or Mexican, cotton was bred in a land with much less moisture and a shorter growing season. The spread of upland cotton was principally westward from South Carolina. Historically, tobacco dominated the upper South and cotton the deep South. This segregation of the Cotton Belt from a tobacco and general-farming belt to the north was not wholly a matter of length of growing season. Two quite different farming systems were in process of spreading westward. Cotton planting pioneered the westward movement through the warmer section of the humid eastern hardwood country. The black prairies of Alabama and Mississippi proved the suitability of the crop to prairie-land cultivation. When settlement reached them, the rich prairies of central Texas were rapidly and most successfully added to the Cotton Belt.

It is somewhat doubtful whether the history of our cotton culture proves the superior climatic adaptability of our South, in particular of the Southeast, for cotton. Perhaps it records only the establishment of a crop in an area with a reasonably suitable climate, the long dominance of the South in world markets resting largely upon its prior development of cotton growing and marketing.

AGRICULTURE IN THE NORTHERN COLONIES

New England was not settled because of agricultural attractions, nor did agriculture become the chief interest of the colonists. Fish and furs, oaken ship timbers, spars and masts of white pine, and iron made from ore raked from the floors of cool bogs were early products, characteristic of the natural resources of New England. Farming was in many cases a part-time occupation. It appears that New England has scarcely grown enough food for its needs at any time. Lack of sufficient areas of good soil and a climate marked by a brief growing season and little summer heat placed it at a disadvantage with the Colonies farther south.

In the planted fields local kinds of short-season Indian maize, beans, and pumpkins were grown side by side with small grains from England, and it appears that the Indian crops gave the more satisfactory returns.

In the second half of the seventeenth century, English grasses began to make a noticeable improvement in pastures and meadows. The manner of their spread is obscure, but it appears that, sown here and there, they naturalized themselves rapidly and soon displaced the poor native grasses. The cool New England climate was fully congenial to the introduced European grasses and to white clover, in contrast to that in the southern Colonies. In the eighteenth century, one of these European grasses, long established in New England, became perhaps the first important sown hay crop of America, first under the name of "Herd's grass" and then as "Timothy grass." With the improvement of hay and pasture, more attention was given to livestock, especially for meat production. Rhode Island and the Connecticut Valley were especially known in later colonial times for their beef, mutton, and draft horses. These are the chief earlier expressions of the climatic suitability of New England for grass rather than grain and other tilled crops.[2]

DOMINANT QUALITIES OF AMERICAN FARMING DERIVED FROM THE MIDDLE COLONIES

The basic pattern of the American farm is derived chiefly from the middle Colonies, and thus from a continental European as well as from an English background. It was to the middle Colonies that the greatest number of people came who were by birth and training tillers of the soil. Their coming was delayed sufficiently so that they brought with them some of the new agriculture that changed western Europe so greatly in the eighteenth century.

Unlike New England, the middle Colonies were not generally settled as closely knit township communities but as single farmsteads. Unlike the owners of plantations on the southern seaboard, the land operators to the north were themselves the tillers of the soil, occupants of single-family farms.

The contributions of Europeans to the Colonies from the Hudson to the upper Chesapeake were varied. The Swedes and Finns are credited in particular with the introduction of the log cabin, which became the standard house of the frontier until the sod house of the western prairies took its place. The Dutch contributed better

[2] From Jared Eliot's First Essay on Field Husbandry in New England (1747): "English Grass will not subsist without a Winter. In the Southern Colonies the less Winter the less Grass. In Virginia, North and South Carolina, they have no English Grass at all. Where there is no English Grass, it is difficult to make Cattle truly fat; so that Winter brings its good as well as its evil Things." In his Second Essay (1748) he added: "Red Clover is of a quick Growth and will supply our Wants for the present; a few Months brings it forward to an high Head: There are few People yet know the Value of this beneficial Grass." (In Essays Upon Field Husbandry in New England and Other Papers, 1748–1762, Columbia Univ. Studies, 1934.)

breeds of livestock and interest in dairying, and played a role in the introduction of European grasses and clovers. The Scotch-Irish, under which term Irish and Scots are also included, provided a large proportion of the intrepid backwoodsmen who first ventured into the wilderness. It is also probable that they established the culture of the potato.[3]

The German settlers as a group were most preoccupied with becoming permanently established as farmers wherever they settled. They were less mobile than the Scotch-Irish and so are often considered as forming a second wave of settlement behind the latter, who constituted an advance guard in the movement inland. The Germans were general farmers, accustomed to animal husbandry. They practiced manuring and, largely, crop rotation. Notable improvements in grain growing and stock breeding are credited to them. Architecturally they were the creators of the basic American barn, combining barn, stable, granary, and wagon shed under one commodious roof in the so-called Swiss, Mennonite, or bank barn. In contrast to the English colonists, they stabled animals in bad weather and were accustomed to stall feeding. Other items of importance to American farm settlement credited to the colonists from the Rhine are the introduction of the rifle, the Conestoga wagon, and the stove to replace the English fireplace.[4]

From all northwestern Europe, farmers poured into the Colonies during the eighteenth century, settling from the Mohawk Valley to Pennsylvania and in the back country of Maryland. Here lay the largest bodies of rich land, with a familiar climate, convenient to the seaboard. All the accustomed crops and livestock of Europe thrived here. The Old World pattern of general farming, with emphasis on the feeding of livestock, was transferred here to the New World with one major modification—Indian corn was fitted quickly into the agricultural economy and greatly increased the livestock capacity of the farms. Maize was found to be a stock feed superior to anything known then or now in northern Europe. Corn, oats, wheat, rye, clover, and European grains formed a crop combination that provided the means of keeping more livestock and of obtaining sustained high yields. In late colonial and post-colonial times, these general-crop and stock farmers spread this basic American way of farming westward and southwestward. Indeed, when these farmers, reinforced by New Englanders and new arrivals from the north of Europe in the second quarter of the nineteenth century, encountered the prairies in the Old Northwest Territory between the Ohio River and the Great Lakes, they quickly found the technical means of occupying them. The prairies are still a part of the humid East, scarcely differentiated climatically from the woodlands by which they are surrounded on the north, east, and south. The same crops succeed in both areas. The summers of Iowa are as hot as those of Pennsylvania and as much characterized by rains from thunderstorms, and so Indian corn found admirably suited conditions across the whole breadth of the prairie country. Fall, winter, and spring

[3] Earlier introductions of potatoes occurred, but their cultivation did not become common until the eighteenth century. Then they appear in localities with colonists from Ireland, such as New York, and in the back country of New England where Scotch-Irish settlements were made.

[4] A brief account and a good bibliography will be found in: SHRYOCK, RICHARD H. PENNSYLVANIA GERMANS IN AMERICAN HISTORY. Pa. Mag. Hist. and Biog. 63: 261–281. 1939.

weather in the prairie States are equally congenial to the small grains, grasses, and clovers from northern Europe. Hence the middle-colony pattern of farming easily became the famous corn-clover-oats rotation of the prairie States, with hogs as the primary market product.

In the development of the forested Great Lakes States, corn was largely eliminated by reason of the reduced summer warmth. Here the pattern of agriculture became almost identical with that of the climatically very similar Baltic countries. Dairy products, potatoes and other root crops, and some small grains constitute an agricultural complex suited to short, cool summers. New Englanders and Scandinavians were dominant groups that found a continuation of accustomed climatic conditions in the new country.[5]

[5] General references: CARRIER, LYMAN. THE BEGINNINGS OF AGRICULTURE IN AMERICA. 323 pp., illus. New York. 1923. BIDWELL, PERCY WELLS, and FALCONER, JOHN I. HISTORY OF AGRICULTURE IN THE NORTHERN UNITED STATES, 1620-1860. Carnegie Inst. Wash. Pub. 358, 512 pp., illus. 1925.

Climate and Settlement of the Subhumid Lands

By Glenn T. Trewartha [1]

"THIS IS A REGION of most unusual natural potentialities," says the author. "No other region of the earth of equal size is so well endowed physically—in surface configuration, soil, and climate—for agricultural use. Drought is the one serious natural handicap. . . . Never before had white settlers entered into such a 'promised land,' and never can they again, for no such frontiers remain. The occupying of the American prairies was an event of epochal significance for the Nation and for the world."

[1] Glenn T. Trewartha is Professor of Geography, University of Wisconsin. This article was prepared while the writer was on leave of absence subsidized by a grant from the Special Research Fund of the University. The writer wishes to acknowledge the assistance of Clarence Vinji, graduate student at the University of Wisconsin, in the collection of material.

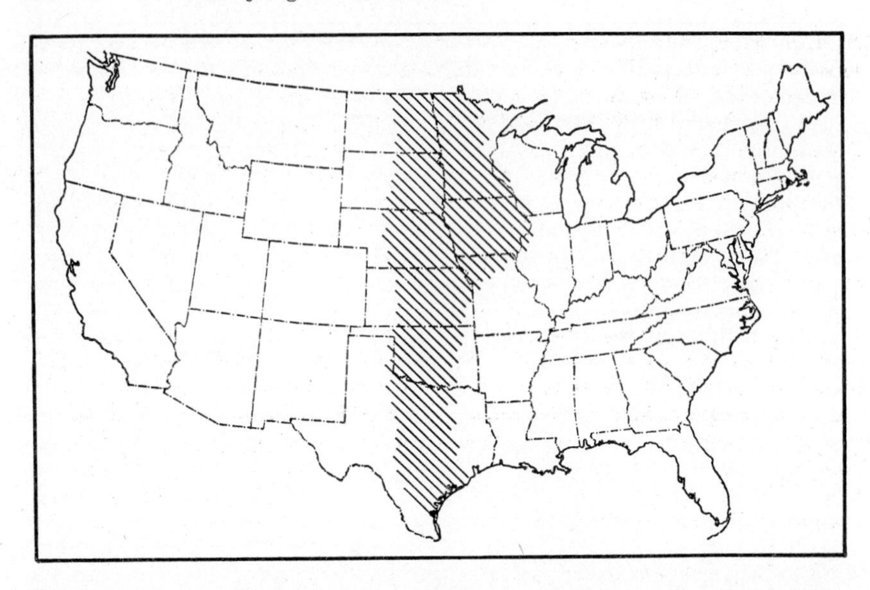

The interior subhumid lands of the United States are intermediate in climate as well as in position between the humid East and the dry West. Within this extensive belt of territory stretching from beyond the Canadian border to the Gulf of Mexico, annual precipitation exceeds potential evaporation but usually not by a very great margin. Generally, therefore, the climate of the subhumid lands errs on the side of having too little precipitation and too many droughts rather than too much rainfall. The dryness increases from east to west. In a general way the interior subhumid lands are coincident with the prairies, the region of tall grasses—only in central Illinois do extensive prairies extend eastward well beyond the subhumid region.

CLIMATE AND ASSOCIATED ELEMENTS OF EARTH EQUIPMENT

Temperature [2]

Lying as it does in the heart of a great land mass, the region has a climate strikingly continental in character, with winters relatively cold and summers relatively warm for the latitude. Since the subhumid lands extend through such a spread of latitude, from near the subarctic margins well into the subtropics, there are bound to be marked differences in temperature from north to south. Midwinter months in North Dakota and northwestern Minnesota have an average temperature of about 5° F.; in Nebraska and Kansas the comparable figures are 25° and 30°, while in southern Texas the January mean is 50° to 55°. Thus it becomes evident that winters are nearly 50° warmer in the extreme southern prairies than in the northern. The temperature gradient is remarkably steep, averaging about 2.5° F.

[2] Maps showing the distribution of annual rainfall and of the seasoned temperatures in the prairie States are given in Part 5 of this book.

for each latitude degree of approximately 70 miles. Rapid and irregular rises and falls in temperature are much more characteristic of winter than of summer.

On typical midwinter days in northern North Dakota the night temperatures drop to about −10° F., while the highest daytime temperatures are below 20°. Throughout most midwinter days temperatures remain well below freezing. In southern Texas on the other hand the thermometer remains above freezing on the majority of January nights, and midday temperatures rise to over 60°. During a normal winter in North Dakota the thermometer sinks to −35° or −40°, and lows of −50° to −60° have been recorded. Toward the southern limit of the prairies in southern Texas the usual winter has one or more cold spells when temperatures may reach 20° or below, and on occasions they have sunk nearly if not quite to zero. Such occasional low temperatures for subtropical latitudes of 30° and less in a region where the average January temperatures are relatively high are characteristic of the American South. The great thrusts of polar air that spill out of the arctic plains of Canada in winter spread rapidly southward over a relatively level surface with few orographic barriers so that this polar air is still cold when it arrives in the normally mild Gulf States.

Winter weather is variable in character as a result of the procession of cyclones and anticyclones that cross the region with their associated tropical and polar air masses. Certain winter-weather types such as the blizzard and the cold wave are especially well known on the prairies. In Texas the cold wave is called a "norther," and this blast of arctic air may bring a sudden drop in temperature of 50° F. or more in 2 or 3 hours. Even more to be feared is the blizzard with its driving winds, bitter cold, and fine, dry snow. Fortunately these blinding snow squalls are not frequent, for they are dangerous alike to men and to beasts exposed to their fury. Shut in by a shroud of snow one loses all sense of direction, and people have perished within calling distance of their homes.

In summer the temperatures of the prairie lands show less contrast from north to south. July averages 65° F. or less in the north, about 75° in Kansas and Nebraska, and 80° to 85° in Texas. The rate of change in temperature between north and south in the warm season, therefore, is only about one-third of that in winter. Midsummer days have maximum temperatures of 80° and more in North Dakota, while in Texas they characteristically exceed 90°. Over the prairies in general temperatures have been known to exceed 110°.

These great contrasts in temperature between the northern and southern parts of the subhumid lands create equally great contrasts in their potentialities for human use and lead to marked differences in agricultural specialization. Thus the growing season is only 3 to 4 months in northern North Dakota, while it is 8 to 9 months in Texas.

Precipitation

Although the region under discussion is all classed as subhumid, there are considerable regional contrasts in the total average amount of precipitation received each year. The western boundary separating the subhumid from the dry lands receives close to 18 inches of precipitation in the north and about 25 inches in Texas. Higher temperatures and consequent increased evaporation in the south cause the rainfall there to be relatively less effective for plant growth. Rainfall on the eastern or humid boundary of the subhumid lands varies from less than 30 inches in northeastern Minnesota to 45 inches in Texas. Probably 30 inches is not far from the median for the whole area.

Throughout much of the larger part of the region precipitation is concentrated in the warm season of the year when it is most effective for the growing crops. This concentration in summer is especially significant for agriculture in the northern sections where the growing season is relatively short, and in the western sections where the total amount of rainfall is less. In both of these sections a high degree of coincidence between rainfall and the growing season is essential.

The concentration of the year's rainfall in the summer season is associated with the prevalence over the region of warm tropical air masses in summer, in contrast to cold polar air masses in winter. The former not only have a higher capacity for moisture because of their higher temperatures, but they have their origin over the Gulf of Mexico. To be sure, a considerable part of the moisture is precipitated before the Gulf air reaches the prairies, which accounts for their being less humid than regions farther east.

Not only does most of the precipitation fall during the warm season, but it is concentrated in the early part of summer, June usually, or occasionally even May, being the rainiest month. In cereal-growing regions this early-growing-season precipitation is very significant, for it assures the grain crops of adequate water during the stalk-forming period, when it is most needed. A somewhat drier July and August aid in ripening the grain and hardening the kernels. The fact that the maximum rainfall precedes the time of greatest heat is associated with the steeper lapse rate in early summer. A relatively meager snow cover allows for a rapid advance of spring; the ground and the lower air warm rapidly, and the upper air more slowly. As a consequence the temperature contrasts between upper and lower air are at a maximum in early summer, with resulting instability and strong convection currents.

Much of the summer precipitation falls in the form of sharp convectional showers, often accompanied by thunder and lightning. In the southern and central prairies a large number of the warm-season showers are of this type—a result of excessive surface heating of unstable Gulf air. These are the so-called local or heat thunderstorms associated with towering cumulo-nimbus clouds on sultry summer afternoons. Farther north this type of storm becomes less common, and more of the rain is caused by the forcing up of warm Gulf air over a wedge of cooler polar air. Where this upthrust is strong, severe cold-front or wind-shift thunderstorms with occasional hail are likely to result.

Summer rains of the convectional type are likely to be relatively vigorous but not of long duration. On sloping plowed fields such rains are powerful removers of topsoil. On the other hand they permit a maximum of sunshine for the amount of rain that falls, a combination that is ideal for a crop such as corn. Winter precipitation is almost exclusively frontal or cyclonic in origin and is associated with gray overcast skies. Snow falls throughout the entire subhumid region although southern Texas receives less than 1 inch a year. The average number of days with snow cover decreases with considerable regularity from 120 along the Canadian border to less than 1 in southern Texas. Most of the Winter Wheat Belt has a protective snow cover during only 30 days or less. But no matter what the season or the type of precipitation, the source of moisture for the subhumid lands is largely tropical air brought in from the Gulf of Mexico.

Although rainfall is much less fickle than in the semiarid Great Plains farther west, years of deficient rainfall are by no means uncommon in the subhumid lands. Dependability becomes increasingly greater from west to east on the prairies. Over the western prairies in particular occasional hot dry summers may cause disastrous reductions in crop yields. Russell has shown that the subhumid prairie lands are fairly well bounded on the west by the line between 10 and more than 10 dry or semiarid years in 20, and on the east by the line between 0 and 1 dry year in 20. In other words, in the subhumid lands from 1 to 10 years out of 20 are likely to be so deficient in rainfall as to be designated as dry or semiarid (*6, pls. 31 and 32*).[3]

Native Vegetation

The original native vegetation of much the larger part of the subhumid lands was a cover of tall prairie grasses which at maturity attained heights of 3 to 10 feet. A great variety of gay flowering plants such as phloxes, spiderworts, shootingstars, and violets grew among the tall grasses so that in the spring the prairies had the appearance of a great flower garden. Except along watercourses trees were largely absent. On the east the prairies were bounded by forests while on the west they were terminated by the short-grass steppes or plains. Both boundaries are transitional or gradual rather than abrupt. Decreasing and uncertain precipitation determines the prairie-steppe boundary, which fairly well coincides with the line (isarithm) of 10 dry years in 20 (*6, pl. 32*). Here the zone of moist soil extends to a depth of less than 2 feet below the surface, and the subsoil is permanently dry.

The prairie-forest boundary is not entirely understood. It coincides reasonably well with the isarithm of 1 dry year in 20 (*6, pl. 32*) and with Thornthwaite's precipitation-effectiveness isarithm of 64 (*8, fig. 2, p. 642*). This seems to suggest a climatic explanation (*9, pp. 10–13*). Many ecologists, however, differentiate between the western or true prairie, where there is a permanently dry subsoil, and the eastern prairies which, they suggest, are an induced grassland growing in a climate satisfactory for trees (*7, p. 16; 10, p. 843*). Prairie fires and possibly buffalo are often mentioned as the nonclimatic factors which tended to prevent the establishment of forest in the eastern prairie lands, where rainfall is sufficient to maintain a moist subsoil (*3, pp. 79–81; 7, p. 16; 10, p. 843*). The boundary between the western and eastern prairies extends through western Minnesota, eastern Nebraska, and eastern Kansas.

[3] Italic numbers in parentheses refer to Literature Cited, p. 176.

Soils

Two of the earth's most fertile zonal soils are characteristic of the American subhumid prairie lands. Toward the drier margins, and therefore roughly coinciding with the area known as the true prairie, is the Chernozem (*10, pp. 843, 1075*). Dark brown to black in color, high in organic matter and mineral plant foods, excellent in structure, Chernozem outranks all other zonal soils. Because rainfall is relatively meager, water does not penetrate deeply, and a zone of lime accumulation occurs at a depth of several feet. Farther east where the greater rainfall penetrates deeper to form a moist subsoil and the zone of lime accumulation is lacking, Chernozems give way to Prairie soils (*10, pp. 843, 1052*). Subjected to somewhat more leaching than Chernozems and not quite their equal in fertility, the Prairie soils are nevertheless excellent soils. Moreover, they exist in a somewhat better climatic environment and consequently are somewhat easier to use.

It becomes obvious from the foregoing analysis of the climate and associated physical elements of the American subhumid lands that this is a region of most unusual natural potentialities. No other region of the earth of equal size is so well endowed physically—in surface configuration, soil, and climate—for agricultural use. Drought is the one serious natural handicap. The natural prairies provided superb grazing, but the total physical environment was of too high a grade for settlers to permit the original native vegetation to remain, and during the three decades from 1850 to 1880 most of it went under the plow. Today native prairie is almost a museum specimen. Never before in modern world history had white settlers entered into such a "promised land," and never can they again, for no such frontiers remain. The occupying of the American prairies was an event of epochal significance for the Nation and for the world.

SETTLEMENT OF THE PRAIRIES

By 1840 to 1850 the westward movement of settlers had emerged from the timber and reached the eastern edge of the prairies. For over 200 years pioneers had been developing frontier homes in the eastern forests. The ax and the log cabin were symbols of this conquest. But now as they faced the open grasslands they hesitated, for this strange environment posed new and difficult problems of settlement. Whether to attempt to occupy the prairie in front of them or to move on to the humid timbered country of the Pacific Northwest where they would feel more at home was a difficult decision to make. Many chose the long and difficult overland trip to the Oregon country rather than attempt to develop homes on the adjacent Illinois and Iowa prairies. "They were bound for the land where the simple plow, the scythe, the ox, and the horse could be used according to the tradition that had been worked out in two centuries of pioneering in a wooded country" (*11, p. 149*). They sought the familiar and shunned adaptation to the grasslands.

It is no doubt true that many settlers coming from the East were skeptical about any soil that did not grow trees (*1, 4*). For decades they had come to recognize the quality of land from the kind and abundance of timber it produced (*1, p. 158*). Where there were no trees the fertility of the soil was, temporarily at least, under suspicion. In Kentucky large tracts without trees had been termed "barrens" (*4, p. 92*). Moreover the American settlers had developed a feeling of companionship with timber; it gave them a sense of protection. They had developed technological skills for clearing the forest and establishing farms in its midst. It is only natural that they should at first shrink from the openness and strangeness of the exposed prairie.

Fortunately they were introduced to the grasslands in something less than their most formidable form—the oak openings (*1, p. 267*). These they did not seem to avoid, for timber not only surrounded these local prairies, but excellent trees dotted the openings, giving them somewhat the appearance of an orchard. Moreover, in such locations the sod was much less tough than on the genuine prairies farther west. Up to about 1850 settlement had been chiefly in the oak openings near the junction of prairie and timber, while the open prairie remained largely unoccupied. The earliest advance into the real grasslands was by way of the river valleys so that the settlement pattern distinctly followed the rivers (*2, pp. 126, 255–256*). Here were water and timber and some protection against the elements. Gradually settlement spread laterally from the valleys to the wide grass-covered areas between the rivers, but this stage presented a number of serious problems to the pioneer farmer, requiring important adjustments in farming techniques and the development of new types of equipment.

The lack of timber, a resource which had been prodigal in the humid East and on which the American pioneer had come to depend, was a most serious handicap. From timber he had built his house, barns, and other outbuildings. Fuel and fencing materials were obtained from the same source. Out of wood many of his tools, or parts of them, were constructed, and his household furnishings as well. The forest likewise sheltered numerous animals which were an important source of food.

Water as well as timber was a resource which the pioneer had somewhat taken for granted in the humid East. But on the prairie uplands, away from the rivers, it was not easy to obtain. Ground water was not uncommonly 100 to 200 feet below the surface, and timber and rock for shoring the walls of such deep wells were often lacking.

The roads on the prairies were nearly impassable because of mud in the spring, and surfacing materials were scarce in many places. Rivers were fewer and less navigable than in the East, and the problem of getting produce to market was discouraging. The prairie sod was so tough that several yoke of oxen were required on the breaking plow, and many pioneer farmers lacked sufficient capital to purchase the required draft animals. Moreover, the wooden moldboard plow and even the cast-iron plow used in the forest soils of the East would not scour properly in the prairie soil. A new type of plow was required.

Somewhat compensating for these handicaps was the soon-discovered advantage of an unusually fertile soil and the quickness with which that soil could be made to produce. The grubbing of trees and removal of undergrowth to open a farm of 100 acres in the forest had required years of arduous labor. Here was country that could be brought into production within a year.

By 1850 the American frontier lay close to the eastern margins of the subhumid or prairie lands (*5, p. 430*). The first period of American colonization, that of the forest, was at an end, and the second, that of the grasslands, was beginning. Webb has described the boundary between the civilization of the grasslands and that of the eastern timberlands as an "institutional fault," using fault in the geological sense of a sharp break or dislocation (*11, p. 8*). At this fault the ways of living changed; many of the institutions carried across it were either broken and remade or else greatly altered. Methods of tilling the soil, agricultural machinery, weapons, methods of transportation, and even laws were greatly modified. In the quarter century following 1850 a combination of events occurred that was critically favorable for the advance of settlement into the grasslands. There were practically no railroads on the prairies in 1850; by 1860 9 or 10 had reached the Mississippi north of St. Louis and at least half a dozen had crossed the river into Iowa and northern Missouri; by 1870 the western prairies had been crossed in Nebraska and Kansas. The meat and wheat from the cheap western lands were thus carried to the eastern markets. Contemporaneously there was taking place in the East, as a result of increasing industrialization and urbanization, a rapid increase in population and therefore of potential markets for the food products of the West. Invention, or at least widespread use, of such farm equipment and machinery as barbed wire, the drilling machine, the windmill, reaper, steel plow, mower, and thresher during this period overcame many of the natural handicaps to settlement on the prairies.

As settlement crept farther and farther west toward the Great Plains there was increasing dependence upon sod as a building material. The crudest form of house was an excavation in the side of a hill, with a front wall of cut turf or logs and a roof made of poles covered with grass and dirt sloping back to the hill. The sod house was not so quickly made but it was more satisfactory. To obtain the sod slabs for building, furrows were turned on about half an acre where the sod was strongest and then a spade was used to cut it into blocks about 3 feet long (*2, pp. 110–113*). Houses of these materials, although dark and hard to keep clean, were cool in summer and warm in winter and they could not be destroyed by prairie fire. Their average life was 6 or 7 years.

With his home built, the prairie settler had to plan immediately for obtaining fuel and water. Just as the first settlers built along the streams because of the availability of wood and water, so the upland pioneers also went to the valleys for wood. There they cut fuel from the railway grants and from the lands of eastern speculators, often hauling firewood of the poorest quality as far as 20 to 40 miles to their homes. Stove ovens were kept full of green cottonwood, drying it out to make it fit to burn. Later settlers even grubbed the stumps. Buffalo and cow chips also were collected for fuel. Settlers welcomed having a cowboy bed his trail herd on their land, for this meant several hundred pounds of cow chips. The most universal fuel on the prairies probably was dry grass twisted into knots called "cats" (*2, pp. 255–260*). Homes were piled full of "cats" in winter and a large pile of hay was kept near the house to provide fuel during an occasional severe storm. Even special hay-burning stoves were invented and put on the market. After the corn crop was established, new fuel in the form of corncobs and stalks was available.

The first settlers on the uplands hauled not only fuel but likewise water, stored in barrels, from the river valleys. Such hauling took a great deal of their time. Cisterns were dug, rain barrels were employed, and hollows were even excavated in which surface run-off would collect to form ponds. Sooner or later, however, a deep well had to be dug. Some were over 200 feet in depth, and all of the excavating was done with pick and shovel. Drilled wells were expensive, costing approximately $1 a foot, but after the windmill was invented and came into general use in the late sixties and early seventies the water problem of the prairie farmer was solved (*2, p. 261*). On the level grasslands of the interior United States where friction is small, wind velocities are higher on the average than in most of the country. To such a region the windmill is ideally suited. Webb is responsible for the statement, "Barbed wire and windmills made the settlement of the West possible" (*11, p. 280*).

The high cost of fencing in the grasslands was one of the important factors retarding their settlement. In 1871 it was estimated that the cost of fence on the prairie was 100 to 400 percent higher than in the East and maintenance was 90 to 200 or more percent higher (*11, p. 286*). Some writers go so far as to say that the invention of barbed wire in the early 1870's, even more than the railroads, made close settlement of the western prairies possible (*11, p. 317*). It was invented by a prairie farmer in the early seventies and was particularly adapted to the grasslands. Cheap and easy to set up, a barbed-wire fence was an excellent barrier against animals, collected no snowdrifts, and was not demolished by high winds.

Prairie farming was predatory in character, no thought being given to conserving the soil. To the easterner this looked like poor farming, but at least it was the most profitable type on the rich black soil of the prairies. To his steel plow the pioneer farmer hitched his two to six yoke of oxen, some of them probably borrowed from a neighbor, and broke the tough virgin sod. This was hard work, but chiefly for the draft animals, for the human labor required was negligible when compared with that necessary to clear a woodland farm. On the prairie the requirement was in the form of animal power and efficient machines. After 2 or 3 years the sod was so decomposed that the prairie soil was easily worked. Even in the freshly turned sod a settler might obtain an immediate crop of sod corn and potatoes, while crops of wheat, barley, and oats were possible the second year. With such extraordinarily fertile soils and the use of all kinds of improved labor-saving machinery easily operated on the level land the prairie farmer produced cheaply and sold to the rapidly expanding eastern markets. Cattle and sheep were adjuncts of general farming to the prairie settler, who found that the range provided excellent feed. His animals were often allowed to graze all year round with only the protection offered by a straw stack or a board fence. Wheat early became the great commercial crop of the northern prairies, while corn was used for feeding cattle and hogs. The reaper, threshing machine, and mower had all been invented and adapted before 1860, so that extensive cereal farming was made relatively easy. By approximately 1900 the present specialized agricultural regions of the prairies (spring wheat, winter wheat, corn, and cotton) had become definitely established.

Prairie farming, however, was not entirely a bonanza. Nature was not always smiling. In summer, drought and hot winds too often withered the flourishing crops, and insect pests likewise took a heavy toll. In late summer and autumn the disastrous prairie fires swept the grasslands, destroying crops, fences, and sometimes farmsteads as well. In winter the dreaded blizzards caused large losses among the animals. But in spite of these handicaps the American prairies hold their own as the heart of agricultural America and one of the world's superior farming regions.

LITERATURE CITED

(1) BIDWELL, PERCY WELLS, and FALCONER, JOHN I.
1925. HISTORY OF AGRICULTURE IN THE NORTHERN UNITED STATES, 1620–1860. Carnegie Inst. Wash. Pub. 358, 512 pp., illus.

(2) DICK, EVERETT.
1937. THE SOD-HOUSE FRONTIER, 1854–1890; A SOCIAL HISTORY OF THE NORTHERN PLAINS FROM THE CREATION OF KANSAS AND NEBRASKA TO THE ADMISSION OF THE DAKOTAS. 550 pp., illus. New York and London.

(3) GLEASON, HENRY ALLEN.
1922. THE VEGETATIONAL HISTORY OF THE MIDDLE WEST. Assoc. Amer. Geog. Ann. 12: 39–85.

(4) HALL, JAMES.
1838. NOTES ON THE WESTERN STATES; CONTAINING DESCRIPTIVE SKETCHES OF THEIR SOIL, CLIMATE, RESOURCES, AND SCENERY. 304 pp.

(5) PAXSON, FREDERIC L.
1924. HISTORY OF THE AMERICAN FRONTIER, 1763–1893. 598 pp., illus. Boston and New York.

(6) RUSSELL, RICHARD JOEL.
1932. DRY CLIMATES OF THE UNITED STATES. II. FREQUENCY OF DRY AND DESERT YEARS, 1901–20. Calif. Univ. Pubs., Geog. 5 (5): 245–274, illus.

(7) SHANTZ, H. L.
1924. NATURAL VEGETATION. *In* Atlas of American Agriculture, Part I, The Physical Basis of Agriculture, Sect. E, U. S. Dept. Agr. Adv. Sheets 6, 29 pp., illus.

(8) THORNTHWAITE, C. WARREN.
1931. THE CLIMATES OF NORTH AMERICA ACCORDING TO A NEW CLASSIFICATION. Geog. Rev. 21: 633–655, illus.

(9) TRANSEAU, EDGAR NELSON.
1935. THE PRAIRIE PENINSULA. Ecology 16: 423–437.

(10) UNITED STATES DEPARTMENT OF AGRICULTURE.
1938. SOILS AND MEN. U. S. Dept. Agr. Yearbook 1938, 1232 pp., illus.

(11) WEBB, WALTER PRESCOTT.
1931. THE GREAT PLAINS. 525 pp., illus. Boston.

Climate and Settlement in the Great Plains

By C. Warren Thornthwaite [1]

IN A DESERT, you know what to expect of the climate and plan accordingly. The same is true of the humid regions. Men have been badly fooled by the semiarid regions because they are sometimes humid, sometimes desert, and sometimes a cross between the two. Yet it is possible to make allowances for this too, once the climate is understood. The author argues that the semiarid regions are now understood well enough to do a good job with them and avoid the failures and tragedies of the past.

[1] C. Warren Thornthwaite is Chief, Climatic and Physiographic Division, Office of Research, Soil Conservation Service.

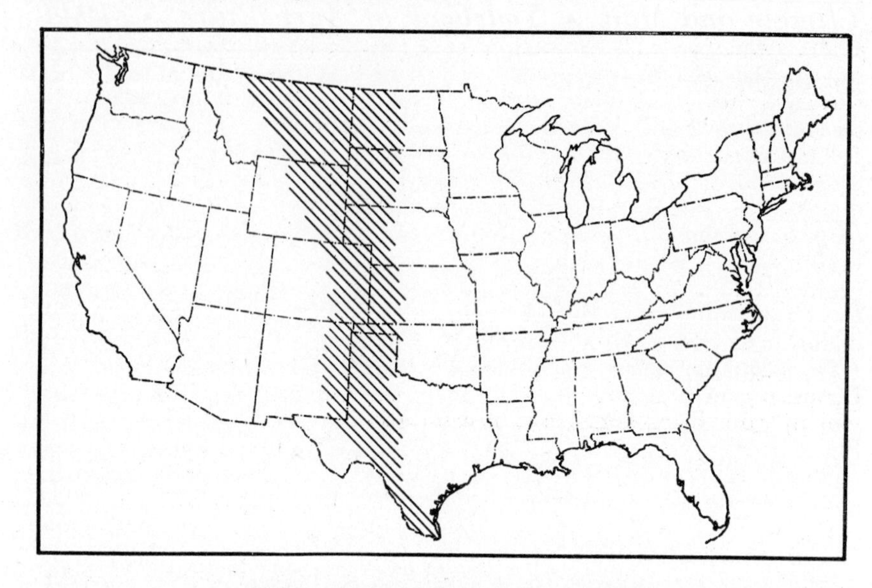

THE CLIMATIC SETTING

THE GREAT PLAINS, extending in a continuous belt 300 to 400 miles wide from Mexico into Canada, comprise the largest uninterrupted area with semiarid climate in North America. For the most part they are high plains ranging from 3,000 feet above sea level along their eastern margin to more than 4,000 feet where they give way to the steep eastern slopes of the Rocky Mountains. Rainfall is scanty, averaging less than 20 inches annually except in the warmer southern portion, and only slightly more than 10 inches in the north. The variability of the rainfall is great; almost everywhere the driest year brings less than 10 inches and the rainiest more than three times as much.

In the eastern part of North America nearly all rainfall is caused by the interaction of great masses of air originating over the vast arctic tundra of northern Canada and over the Gulf of Mexico and the Atlantic between Bermuda and the Bahamas.[2] In the northern region the air becomes cold, dry, and heavy and is called polar continental; in the southern, it becomes warm, very moist, and light and is called tropical maritime. At irregular intervals the polar continental air masses advance southward and eastward, spreading across the area east of the Rockies, where they generally encounter along their route maritime air advancing northward from the Gulf or the Atlantic. Being lighter and more moist, the maritime air is forced to ascend, is cooled, and yields a portion of its water vapor as precipitation.

The path followed by the tropical maritime air characteristically curves across the Gulf, up the Mississippi Valley, and thence eastward to the Atlantic, thus tending to avoid the Great Plains altogether. The tropical air masses which flow northward across the

[2] A more detailed discussion of air masses and their interaction is presented in The Scientific Basis of Modern Meteorology, p. 599.

Plains come generally from the dry plateau of Mexico and are warm but contain little water vapor. When this air comes in contact with the cold, heavy air from the north it, too, is forced up, but little precipitation results from the consequent cooling.

The moist air from the Gulf, however, does not always avoid the Great Plains. Most of the precipitation there, as farther east, is due to the incursions of tropical maritime air. The farther the tropical air has traveled from its source of moisture, the drier it becomes and the less will be the precipitation that results from its cooling. Thus there is a gradual decrease in average annual precipitation from approximately 25 inches in south Texas to less than 12 inches in northern Montana.

Occasionally masses of especially moist tropical air enter the Plains region and collide with dry polar air with such force that violent rainstorms and heavy precipitation occur. Anywhere in the Plains, such an event may bring as much as a third of the average annual supply of precipitation in a single day, or a fifth in a single hour. These invasions and interactions are rare, and sometimes periods as long as 120 days may occur during which no rain falls.

Thus, throughout the Great Plains region, great variability of rainfall from season to season is produced as a result of differences in the moisture content of the northward-moving warm air masses, the routes followed, and the force of the impact between the warm and cold air masses.

CLIMATIC HAZARDS TO AGRICULTURE

The excessively high and low temperatures which are characteristic of the Plains are also associated with the interactions of tropical and polar air masses. The displacement of warm tropical air by an advancing mass of cold polar air may bring about a drop in surface temperature of as much as 60° F. in a few hours.

Maximum summer temperatures in excess of 110° F. have been experienced nearly everywhere in the Plains, and records of 117° have been reported from both Texas and Montana. Below-zero temperatures have occurred throughout the region, but the minimum becomes lower with increase in latitude and reaches a record of −63° at Poplar, in northern Montana. In 1893 at Glendive, Mont., the absolute minimum was −47° for February, and the absolute maximum was 117° for July, a range of 164° (*3*, *5*).[3]

The hazards of hail, frost, and hot winds are all particularly severe in the Plains and are also due to the alternate inundation of the region by various types of air masses and to their interactions. A vigorous upward displacement of warm air along the advancing front of a cold polar air mass is responsible for most of the hailstorms, which are common during the summer. In spring and autumn an advance of polar air may cause killing frost, accompanied by great damage to crops. Equally serious is the hazard presented by the hot, dry winds of summer that are at times experienced in all parts of the Plains.

Throughout the Great Plains the drought hazard is greatest in winter and least in late spring and early summer. Seasonal and

[3] Italic numbers in parentheses refer to Literature Cited, p. 187.

annual drought frequencies for three representative stations are shown in figure 1. From the graphs it is possible to determine the number of consecutive days without rain [4] experienced in various periods of years. Drought periods of 35 or more consecutive days may be expected annually and periods of between 60 and 70 days once in 10 years. Less frequently a drought period may reach 90 days in the northern Great Plains and 120 days in the southern Plains. The drought hazards in autumn and winter are approximately equal in the central and northern Plains, but in the southern Plains the winter hazard greatly exceeds that of any other season. Throughout the Plains prolonged periods of drought are least likely to occur in summer.

THE EXTENT OF CLIMATIC VARIATIONS

The Great Plains, so situated as to be inundated successively by moist and dry, cold and hot air masses, suffer meteorological excesses and in consequence experience large fluctuations in climate. Although the climate is classed as semiarid, there are years when other climatic types prevail—in fact, every type from humid to arid may occur. A similar range is experienced in parts of the subhumid region to the east, and in some desert areas farther west the range may be nearly as great. There is, however, a great difference in the frequency of occurrence of the various climatic types, as is indicated in table 1.

TABLE 1.—*Climatic variability at Jamestown, N. Dak., Fort Stanton, N. Mex., and Independence and Indio, Calif.*

Station	Length of record	Climatic type [1]	Climatic distribution					
			Superhumid	Humid	Moist subhumid	Dry subhumid	Semiarid	Arid
	Years		*Years*	*Years*	*Years*	*Years*	*Years*	*Years*
Jamestown, N. Dak.	35	Dry subhumid	0	1	15	13	5	1
Fort Stanton, N. Mex.	37	Semiarid	0	1	1	5	25	5
Independence, Calif.	37	Arid	0	0	1	1	1	34
Indio, Calif.	36	do	0	0	0	0	0	36

[1] Based on effective precipitation as determined in Thornthwaite's classification of climates (7).

The fluctuation of the climate within wide limits, as at Jamestown and Fort Stanton, creates one of the most serious of the climatic risks to agriculture. In some years the amount and seasonal distribution of rainfall is entirely adequate for successful agriculture; in others, the rainfall is so reduced that crop production is impossible. No corresponding risk exists in a continuously arid climate, as at Indio, because in no year does the weather encourage an attempt at agriculture. In the Great Plains the rainfall surpasses that of semiarid climates with sufficient frequency to encourage agricultural extension, but not to make successful agriculture possible over a period of years.

The normal pattern of climatic distribution in the Great Plains and adjacent areas and the patterns in 3 extreme years, 1905, 1910, and 1934, are shown in figure 2.[5]

[4] In the computation of these curves less than 0.10 inch of precipitation in 48 hours was not considered sufficient to be counted.

[5] These maps have been selected from the Atlas of Climatic Types in the United States, 1900–1939 (9).

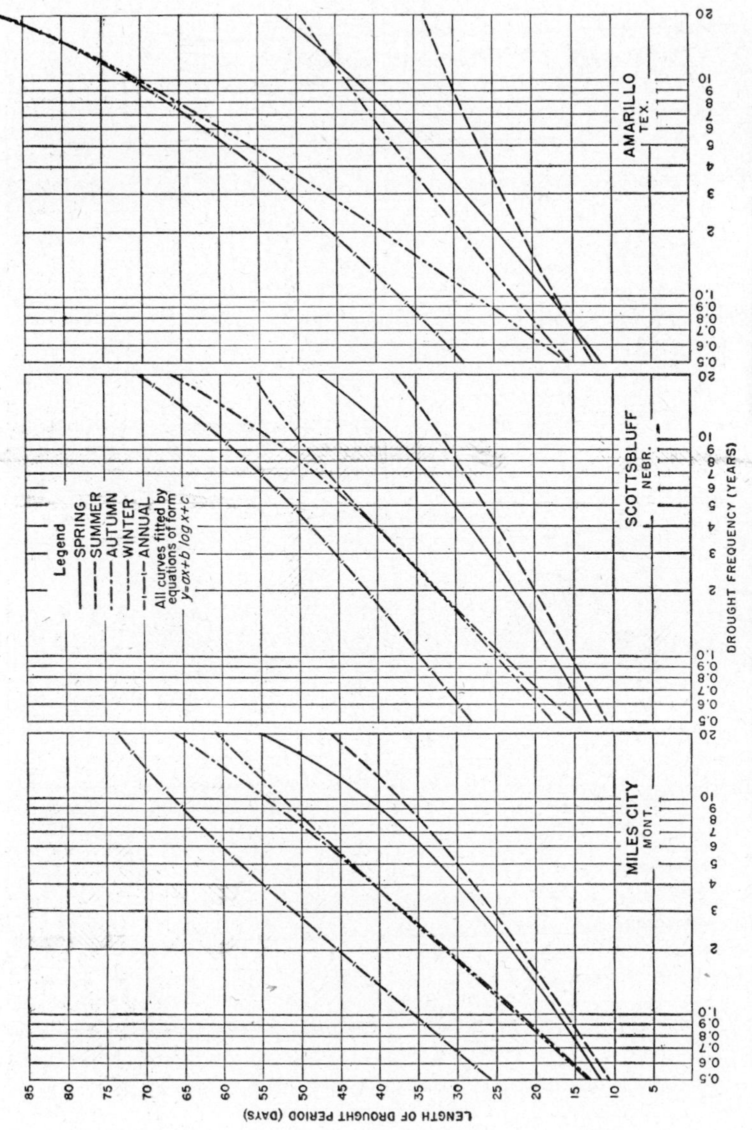

FIGURE 1.—Seasonal and annual drought frequency for three representative Great Plains stations.

298737°—41——13 +

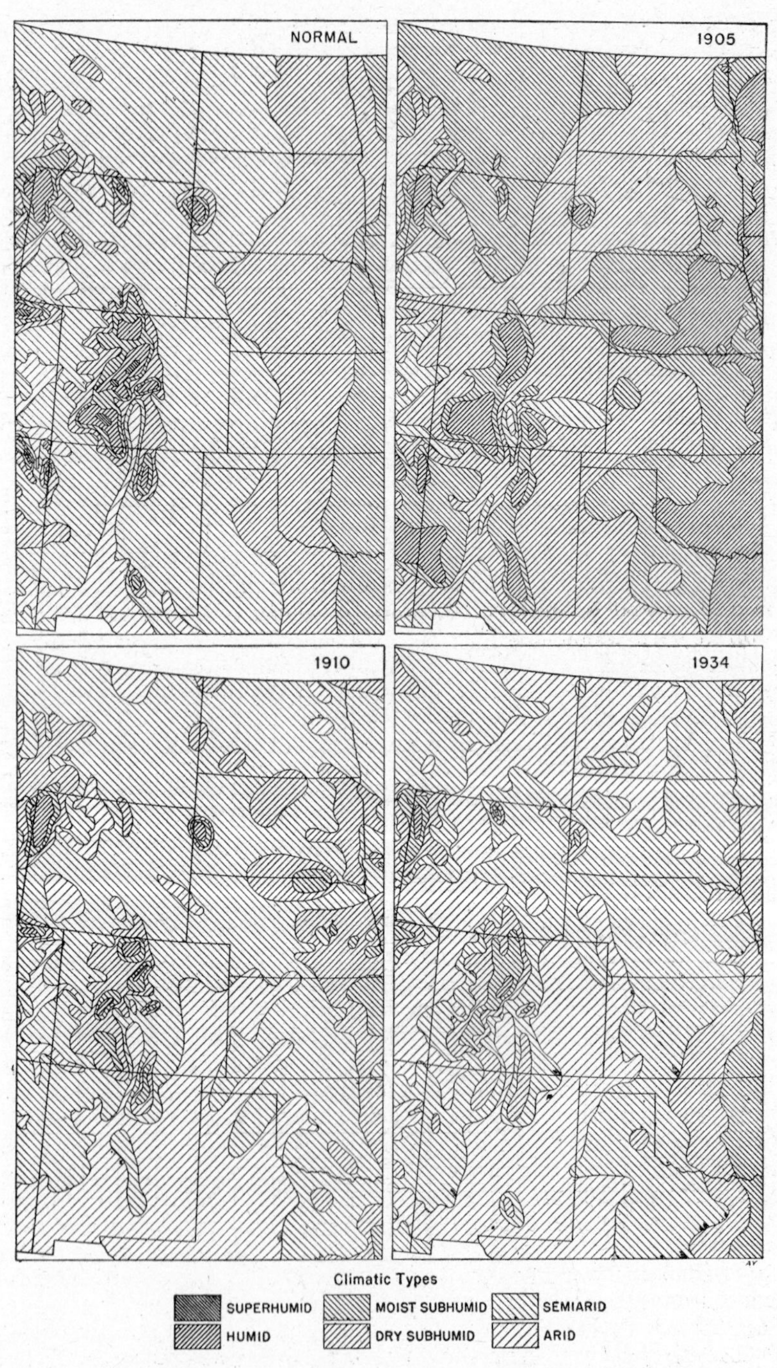

FIGURE 2.—Normal pattern of climatic distribution in the Great Plains as compared with the patterns in 3 extreme years, 1905, 1910, and 1934.

The year 1905 was one of the rainiest in the history of the Great Plains, and semiarid climate disappeared from the region altogether, except in a small island in southeastern Colorado. Moist-subhumid climate, normal to Iowa and western Illinois, occupied most of Montana and extended in two great lobes westward across Nebraska and Oklahoma. Humid climate, characteristic of Ohio, pushed into the Plains in two places. The years 1910 and 1934 were 2 of the driest on record. In 1910 desert climate covered most of the southern Plains; there were a few islands of desert climate in the northern Plains, and semiarid climate was displaced by arid eastward as far as Wisconsin. In 1934 nearly half of the area of the Great Plains experienced desert climate.

THE BEGINNINGS OF SETTLEMENT

The natural vegetation of the Plains resembles that of a closely pastured meadow. It consists of species of drought-enduring short grasses such as grama and buffalo grass, which can enter a drought rest stage when necessary and produce seed in a remarkably short time after moisture becomes available. Prior to settlement the almost universal cover of short grass and the character of the soil combined to reduce run-off to a minimum even after the heaviest rains and served to protect the smooth, gently sloping surface from erosion (*6*). Except immediately after heavy rains, surface water was almost completely absent in the broad upland areas between the through-flowing streams, which themselves often became completely dry. Consequently, to the first wave of migrants, the Great Plains and the desert zone to the west appeared as uninhabitable areas which had to be traversed in order to reach the Oregon country and California.

At the end of the Civil War, the Great Plains were chiefly wasteland occupied by roving herds of buffalo and scattered bands of nomadic Indians. The few existing settlements were trading posts and forts that had developed along the various trails to the West. By 1870 two railroads had been extended across the Great Plains, from Omaha across Nebraska to the Pacific, and from Kansas City across Kansas to Denver. Originally intended to tap the trade of the far West, they encouraged the activities of buffalo hunters, who during the following decades exported enormous quantities of hides, horns, and bone and virtually exterminated the buffalo (*8, pp. 207–217*).

The Civil War had produced a shortage of cattle in the North but had left Texas fairly overflowing with them. Before 1885 nearly 6 million head were driven from Texas north over the trails to the railroads leading to the northern and eastern markets. Real and anticipated profits from cattle raising led to a phenomenal extension of ranching throughout the Great Plains. The ranges were soon overstocked, and the devastating drop in prices which followed so impoverished the ranchers that they were unable to combat the subsequent droughts, blizzards, and plagues of grasshoppers.

The day of the cattlemen in the Great Plains, however, was brief. Even before the Civil War the eastern farmers had discovered that absence of trees did not indicate lack of soil fertility and had made tentative advances into the prairies of Iowa, Missouri, and eastern

Kansas. Gradually a new culture evolved in which dependence upon trees and a surface-water supply was reduced greatly by the use of sod houses, hedge fences, barbed wire, drilled wells, windmills, and the steel plow. Encouraged by the Homestead Act, passed while the Civil War was still in progress, and by subsequent legislation, agricultural settlement slowly advanced across the prairies and into the Plains of western Kansas and Nebraska along the lines of the two transecting railroads.

By 1890 a vanguard of settlers had pushed beyond Kansas and Nebraska into eastern Colorado. The majority had come from the humid Northeastern States, and previous experience had in no way prepared them for the climatic hazards they now encountered. The initial settlement occurred during one of the rainier periods, and the settlers were predisposed to believe that the climate was becoming permanently more humid. In fact many thought that it was the spread of cultivation that brought about an increase in rainfall. Aughey (*1, pp. 44–45*), in writing about Nebraska in 1880, said:

> It is the great increase in absorptive power of the soil, wrought by cultivation, that has caused, and continues to cause an increasing rainfall in the state. * * * After the soil is broken, a rain as it falls is absorbed by the soil like a huge sponge. The soil gives this absorbed moisture slowly back to the atmosphere by evaporation. Thus year by year as cultivation of the soil is extended, more of the rain that falls is absorbed and retained to be given off by evaporation, or to produce springs. This, of course, must give increasing moisture and rainfall.

This delusion was destroyed by the drought of the nineties. Not only was further immigration stopped, but there was instead a considerable emigration of earlier settlers. In some of the western Kansas counties, two-thirds of the farm population was forced to leave because of the drought. Many entire towns were completely abandoned.

EFFORTS TO EXTEND THE AGRICULTURAL AREA

One almost immediate reaction to the drought was a phenomenal increase in dry farming throughout the Plains. To a large extent this can be attributed to the efforts of one man, H. W. Campbell (*2*), of Lincoln, Nebr., who had invented a subsoil packer in 1885. Dry farming was further publicized by railroads, whose profits depended upon population, and in 1894 a dry-farming experiment station was established at Cheyenne Wells, Colo. Before the end of the nineteenth century dry farming was hailed as the solution to all agricultural problems of the Great Plains, and settlers again began to pour into the region.

All dry-farming practices focused upon the single aim of conserving the scant moisture supply by reducing or eliminating run-off and evaporation and by increasing to a maximum the absorption and retention of moisture by the soil. It was thought that this could be accomplished by summer fallowing and by maintaining a dust mulch through cultivation after every summer rain. The mechanical treatment considered necessary for moisture conservation resulted in rapid deterioration of the soil structure and destruction of humus and in consequence introduced wind erosion as a menace to permanent settlement (*3*). Before the beginning of the World War the enthusiasm for dry farming had waned, and it was recognized that climatic risks still existed in the Great Plains.

The skyrocketing of agricultural prices during the war tended to expand cattle production rather than crop production in the Great Plains; but, with the crash of the cattle market during the depression of 1920–22, many ranchers were financially ruined. In the years following the war rapid progress was made in agricultural mechanization. Various machines designed for use on the level land, including a manageable tractor, a disk plow, a disk drill, and a small combine harvester, made it possible to plant and harvest wheat in the Plains at a cost less than half that involved on the smaller, rougher farms in the East.

The economic distress of the rancher, the development of power machinery for planting and harvesting wheat, the maintenance of high prices for wheat, and a series of rainier-than-average years resulted in renewed land speculation. At a time when land values the country over were falling toward pre-war levels, land in the Great Plains, purchased from the ranchmen at $2 to $4 an acre, was resold for $30 to $40 to investors and speculators from as far east as Iowa and Illinois, who were ignorant of the physical deficiencies of the area. Despite the speculative nature of much land purchase and the fact that a great deal of the crop production was by "suitcase farmers," who did not live on the farms and frequently stayed in the region only long enough to harvest one crop and sow the next, the population throughout most of the Great Plains continued to increase until after 1930.

Since wheat farming could be reduced to a part-time occupation, the increase in population did not parallel the increase in the amount of land brought under cultivation. By 1930 virtually all of the land had been plowed, and the native short-grass sod was nearing extinction in many of the Great Plains counties. Farm prices of wheat, the dominant crop, hovered around $1 a bushel during the entire decade of the 1920's. Year after year, the climatic conditions favored agriculture; first one part of the Plains and then another enjoyed a climate normal to the subhumid prairies to the east.

ECONOMIC ASPECTS OF DROUGHTS

In 1931 a disastrous drought was experienced in the northern and central Great Plains, with desert climate prevailing in most of eastern Montana and in parts of eastern Colorado and western Kansas. Thereafter, in every year until the end of the decade, some part of the Plains was affected by serious drought; and in 1934 and 1936 the region from end to end was scourged with drought.

The depression, coming simultaneously with the onset of the drought, carried prices of agricultural products down to the lowest levels on record. The Great Plains farmers, burdened with expensive power machinery and land that had been overcapitalized, were bankrupted almost immediately, and Federal relief in many forms poured into the region. Despite the fact that the administration of relief tended to discourage movement of population, there was a tremendous emigration from the Plains region between 1930 and 1940.

In many respects the period from 1920 to 1940 resembled the earlier period between 1880 and 1900. In both a series of rainy years was followed by a disastrous drought. Both wet periods occurred when there was great pressure for more farm land and encouraged rapid immigration that led to extension of the cultivated area and to overgrazing. Each drought period set in motion an emigration that grew into a rout. In both cases the series of rainy years had been mistaken for normal climate, with disastrous results.

Relief measures were instituted in the 1890's as well as in the 1930's and experts were assigned the task of working out programs for rehabilitation and for the permanent occupancy of the Great Plains. In certain major aspects there is a striking resemblance between the report of the Great Plains Committee of 1936 (*10*) and that on The High Plains and Their Utilization, by Willard D. Johnson, in the annual reports of the United States Geological Survey for 1899–1901 (*4*). Both contain vivid accounts of the overextension of agriculture during preceding years, emigration and the abandonment of farms, the shift of land ownership from individuals to loan companies, and reversion of land to the county or Federal Government. In 1899, as in 1936, counties were burdened with bonded indebtedness incurred for public improvements during the boom years. The plight of the farmers who remained was desperate. Although the farmer who managed to remain on his land through the drought of the 1890's was forced to depend almost exclusively upon stock for his livelihood, Johnson (*4, Rpt. 21, p. 690*) commented that—

> * * * as a rule his hope and his ambition are, after the temporary unfavorable conditions—as he regards them—shall have passed, to return to growing wheat for export.

These two disastrous droughts have demonstrated that permanent agricultural settlement based on the production of grain for export is not possible. Despite the fact that the mechanization of agriculture has, in recent years, greatly reduced the cost of production, wheat yields over a period including both favorable and unfavorable years are not sufficient, at current wheat prices, to justify the initial expense and the maintenance of expensive equipment except in favored locations where supplementary water is available.

THE FUTURE

In a semiarid climate like that of the Great Plains, wide climatic fluctuations are to be expected. Although it is not yet possible to forecast a specific drought year, it is possible to determine drought frequency and the probability of its occurrence. A stable economy can be achieved only if agriculture is adapted to the entire range of climatic conditions. This would necessitate returning to a grazing economy, in which pasturing of cattle on the natural and restored range is supplemented by the production of forage and feed crops in areas where flood irrigation is possible, and elsewhere in the rainy years on soils that are resistant to deterioration by wind and water. Such a change in land use requires an increase in the size of farms to a point where cultivation and grazing can both be controlled. Permanent agriculture, if not perpetually subsidized, also requires further diminution of population and a reduction in services, such as schools and improved roads. Through planned cooperation and the elimination of duplicate expenditures, such a reduction would be possible without materially lowering the standard of living.

It must be recognized that in the future there will be a recurrence of rainy years that will attract settlers and invite extension of wheat production and land speculation. Past experience has shown conclusively the need for setting up restraints before the onset of a series of years favorable to commercial grain production in order that the population of the future may be less vulnerable to the terrors of inevitable future droughts.

LITERATURE CITED

(1) AUGHEY, SAMUEL.
1880. SKETCHES OF THE PHYSICAL GEOGRAPHY AND GEOLOGY OF NEBRASKA. 326 pp. Omaha.

(2) CAMPBELL, HARDY W.
1914. CAMPBELL'S SOIL CULTURE PRIMER. Rev. and ed. by Richard A. Haste, 108 pp., illus. Lincoln, Nebr.

(3) CHILCOTT, E. C.
1912. SOME MISCONCEPTIONS CONCERNING DRY FARMING. U. S. Dept. Agr. Yearbook 1911: 247–256.

(4) JOHNSON, WILLARD D.
1901–2. THE HIGH PLAINS AND THEIR UTILIZATION. U. S. Geol. Survey Ann. Rpt. (1899–1900) 21 (4): 601–741 illus.; (1900–1901) 22 (4): 631–669, illus.

(5) KINCER, JOSEPH B.
1923. THE CLIMATE OF THE GREAT PLAINS AS A FACTOR IN THEIR UTILIZATION. Assoc. Amer. Geog. Ann. 13: 67–80, illus.

(6) SHANTZ, H. L.
1923. THE NATURAL VEGETATION OF THE GREAT PLAINS REGION. Assoc. Amer. Geog. Ann. 13: 81–107, illus.

(7) THORNTHWAITE, C. WARREN.
1931. THE CLIMATES OF NORTH AMERICA ACCORDING TO A NEW CLASSIFICATION. Geog. Rev. 21: 633–655, illus.

(8) ———
1936. THE GREAT PLAINS. *In* Goodrich, Carter, Allin, Bushrod W., Thornthwaite, C. Warren, and others, Migration and Economic Opportunity, the Report of the Study of Population Redistribution, pp. 202–250, illus. Philadelphia and London.

(9) ———
1941. ATLAS OF CLIMATIC TYPES IN THE UNITED STATES, 1900–1939. U. S. Dept. Agr. Misc. Pub. 421.

(10) UNITED STATES GREAT PLAINS COMMITTEE.
1936. THE FUTURE OF THE GREAT PLAINS. 194 pp., illus. Washington.

Climate and Settlement of the Arid Region

By Reed W. Bailey [1]

GAMBLING ON the climate may be possible in semiarid regions, but the dweller in an arid region has to play safe or perish. He learns to know where the water is, to husband it, to use just the right amount when it is needed, to protect his watersheds; and by this skill, knowledge, and discipline, he makes rich gardens in the desert. Theoretically; but theory and the practice do not always dovetail, and no type of agriculture has stricter requirements than irrigation farming.

[1] Reed W. Bailey is Director of the Intermountain Forest and Range Experiment Station, Forest Service.

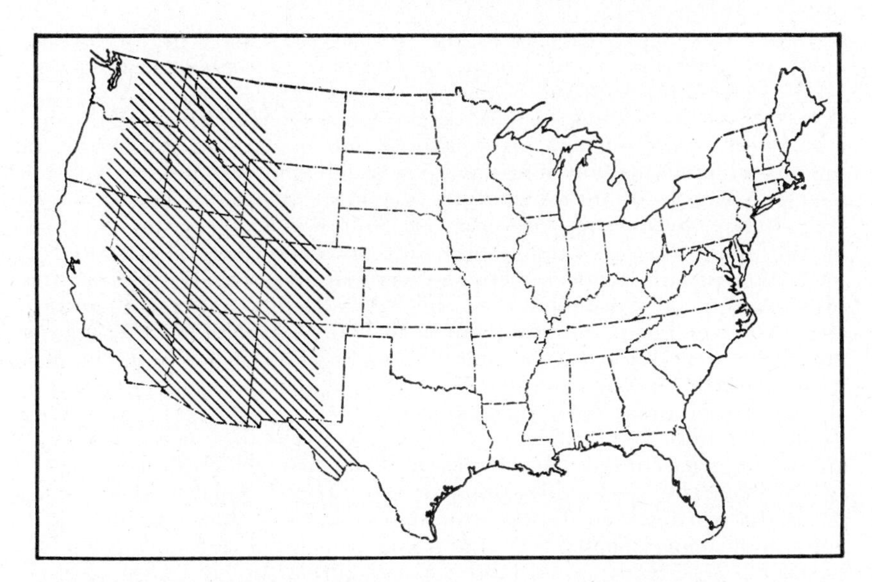

Nowhere in the United States has climate influenced the patterns of settlement and culture more definitively than in the arid region of the West. Together with topography and soils, it has determined rather rigidly the location of most settlement, whether in individual farms, rural communities, or larger population centers. It has even largely conditioned settlement incident to mining. Within relatively narrow limits, it has restricted the number of people that the region as a whole can support, and as a result many rural communities already are experiencing population pressures of fairly severe intensity. It has been primarily responsible for the development of irrigation, a distinctive and highly specialized type of agriculture. Finally, it has given rise to certain basic problems inherent in an environment where man has had to utilize meager resources to the fullest possible extent and resort to specialized techniques and disciplines in order to make agricultural development possible and settlement a success.

GENERAL CLIMATIC CHARACTERISTICS

The arid region comprises a broad belt of mountain, valley, and desert land some 600 miles wide and nearly 1,100 miles long lying between the western margins of the Great Plains and the crests of the Sierra Nevada-Cascade barrier, which extends along a north-south axis from Canada to the Mexican border. Within its boundaries are found the driest areas of the North American continent; in fact, general aridity is the predominant characteristic of the regional climate as a whole. There is, however, a great diversity of local climates ranging between the extremes of humid cold and torrid dry. These wide local variations are due primarily to topography but also depend to some extent on general air circulation, the relative position in the continental land mass, and latitude.

On the basis of general climatic characteristics the region can be divided into two major zones: (1) A southern zone, comprising most of New Mexico, Arizona, and the southeastern part of California, and (2) a northern zone, including, roughly, the area between the Utah-Arizona line and the Canadian border.

In the southern zone the summer winds sweep over the region from a southerly direction and are relatively moist, causing the period of maximum precipitation to coincide with the hottest months of the year. Nearly half of the annual precipitation occurs during July, August, and September, preceded and followed by very dry periods. In the mountains and higher plateaus, however, there is a period of winter maximum in addition to the wet summer period. The winter precipitation falls principally in the form of snow. For the section as a whole the mean annual precipitation ranges from a low of 3 inches in the vicinity of Yuma to a high of more than 30 inches in the mountains of northern Arizona and New Mexico. Temperatures in general are high, with great daily fluctuations.

The northern section lies in the zone of prevailing westerly winds and receives its climatic characteristics from the cyclonic storms which sweep from the west. Maximum precipitation comes in the winter and early spring months, the summer months of July, August, and September being usually very dry. August is often rainless in valleys, as in the Boise Valley in Idaho. Mean annual precipitation for the section as a whole ranges from a low of about 4 inches in the desert valleys west of Salt Lake to highs of over 60 inches in the mountains of central Idaho and central Washington. For a contrast of precipitation patterns for the northern and southern zones see figure 1. The temperatures exhibit extremes characteristic of the continental climatic type.

Growing seasons are variable but generally shorter in the arid valleys of the northern zone than in those of the southern zone. Yakima, Wash., has 183 frost-free days; Boise, Idaho, 169; Logan, Utah, 155; whereas Albuquerque, N. Mex., has 196, Phoenix, Ariz., 295, and Yuma, Ariz., 355.

INFLUENCE OF TOPOGRAPHY ON CLIMATE AND SETTLEMENT

The factor that significantly alters the general climate of the region is topography. Within any latitudinal zone, topography largely determines the precipitation pattern in space, just as general air circulation determines it in time. The Sierra Nevada-Cascade mountain crests rising to a maximum elevation of about 14,000 feet act as a barrier to eastward-moving storms and are responsible for much of the relatively heavy precipitation on the west slopes and the aridity of the Great Basin and the Columbia River Plateaus. Similarly each successive mountain range eastward acts in turn to increase precipitation on the western slopes and to make for greater aridity on the slopes and valleys to the east. It is not uncommon to find some valleys receiving only 4 to 5 inches of precipitation, while mountain slopes less than 40 miles away receive in excess of 40 inches. The influence of topography on precipitation is illustrated in figure 2, which gives mean annual precipitation values for certain points along a topographic profile from San Francisco to Denver.

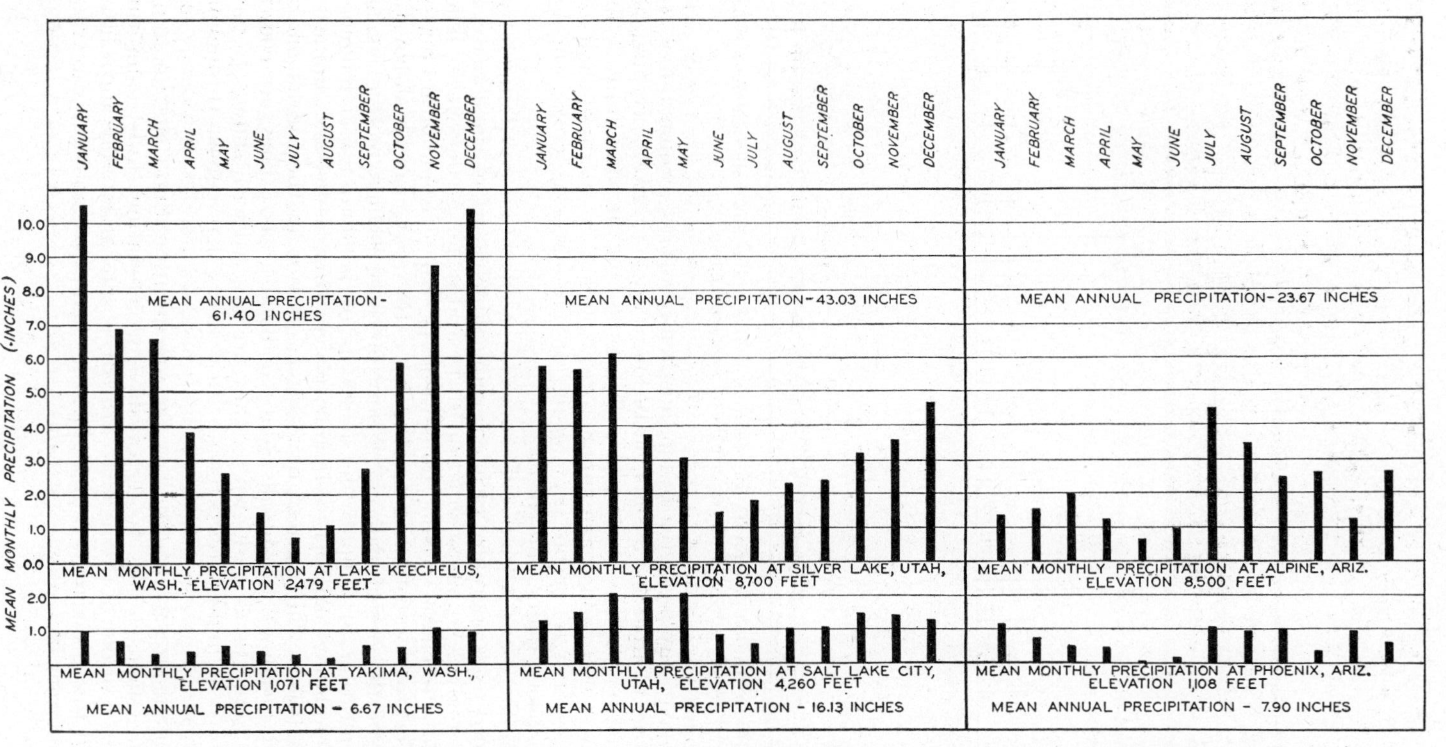

FIGURE 1.—Valley and mountain precipitation by months at Yakima, Wash., Salt Lake City, Utah, and Phoenix, Ariz.

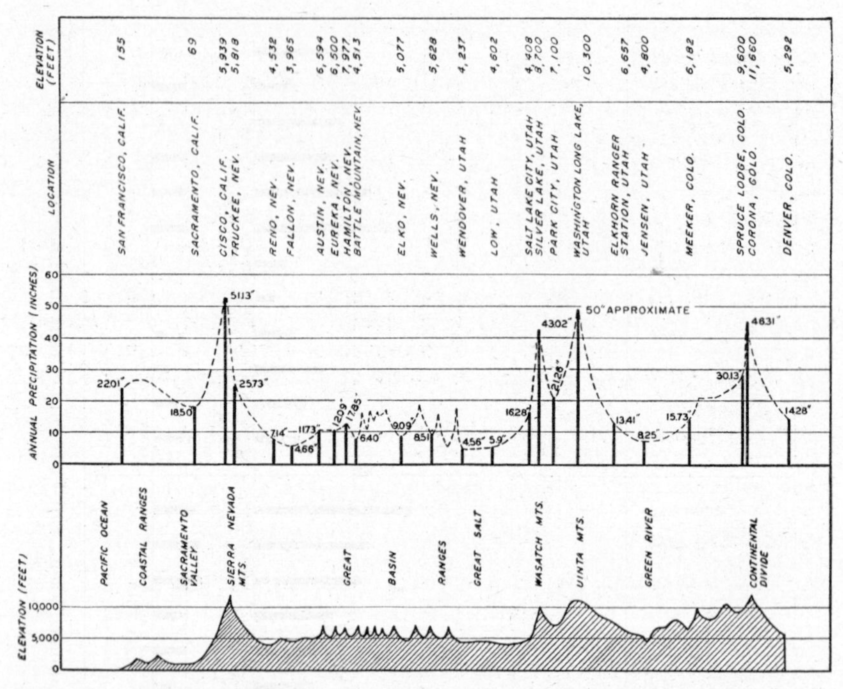

FIGURE 2.—Annual precipitation in relation to mountains and valleys along a course between San Francisco and Denver.

Topography also greatly modifies temperatures. Some valleys are not free of frost for a sufficiently long period to grow anything but the hardiest grains and forage, while others in the same latitude but at lower elevations have summer growing seasons warm enough and long enough to permit the raising of late-maturing crops, such as sugar beets, fruits, and corn.

The large and abrupt differences in precipitation and temperature induced by topography form the important feature of the climate, at least so far as human occupation of the arid region is concerned. They give rise to characteristic "humid islands" wherever mountain masses project to a substantial height above the gray, sagebrush-covered floor of the desert valleys. Many of these islands receive enough precipitation to support dense stands of ponderosa and lodgepole pine, quaking aspen, Engelmann spruce, Douglas-fir, and alpine fir, as well as a wide variety of lesser vegetation in the forests and in alpine meadows, brushfields, and woodland areas. They are cool in the summer and in the winter they are covered with snow. In fact, some of the higher areas contain snow fields that persist throughout the year.

The disproportionately heavier precipitation that falls upon the humid islands is largely responsible for generating the streams that flow into or out of the region. Moreover, snow in late fall and winter, stored for spring and summer melting, makes possible and maintains the summer flow of most streams.

The importance of this interrelationship between cool, humid mountain islands and warm, arid valleys cannot be too strongly emphasized. The islands in themselves, for the most part, are not habitable, because of steep slopes, low temperatures, rocky soils, short growing season, deep snow mantle, inaccessibility, and similar factors, but they are the gathering grounds for creeks and rivers that flow to the valleys. Indeed, one of the more striking and important features of the mountain-valley relationship is the nearness of the points between which large differences in climate may, and usually do, exist. Salt Lake City, for example, is located in the semiarid zone at the base of the Wasatch Mountains at an elevation of 4,408 feet and receives 16.13 inches of moisture annually. Forty miles west of the city the desert receives less than 6 inches of rainfall a year; 20 miles east of the city, Silver Lake, at an elevation of 8,700 feet in the Wasatch Range, has a mean annual precipitation of 43 inches. Similar relationships exist throughout both northern and southern climatic sections; these are further emphasized in figure 1, in which the three locations for which mean precipitation is given represent essentially the extremes and the midpoint of the latitudinal range of the arid region.

THE PATTERN OF SETTLEMENT AND AGRICULTURE

With a knowledge of the climatic characteristics and the mountain-valley relationship of this region it is readily understandable why the early settlers established their homes, farms, and industries for the most part near the mouths of canyons and at the bases of mountains. These locations were selected in part because of the availability of fertile soils and favorable temperatures, but primarily because the adjacent mountains provided sources of timber for their homes, forage for their flocks, and above all, the water that was necessary for sustaining life throughout the dry summer months on the valley floors. Later, engineering developments were introduced in the form of storage reservoirs and elaborate canal systems, and these made it possible to extend settlement farther out into the valleys and away from the natural streams.

The dependence of settlement both on mountain streams originating in the humid islands and on favorable valley temperatures and soils has not only restricted the number of people that the country can support, but has rather rigidly determined the location of farms and other population centers. Today, after nearly a century of settlement, practically all of the population of the region is still concentrated where the mountain waters meet the soils of the desert valleys. A map of the arid region showing population density would strikingly illustrate how available water and soil control and determine the pattern of settlement. A concentration of population would plainly mark the course of the Snake River in Idaho and the base of the Wasatch Mountains in Utah. The effect of availability of water on population concentrations is further illustrated by the condition in Utah. Today the density of the population for that State as a whole is 6.2 persons per square mile while along the Wasatch Front from Santaquin to the north end of Cache County, in an area 2 to 10 miles wide by 160 miles long and totaling only 1,000 square miles, or 1.2 percent of the land area, the density is 338 per square mile.

The relationship between humid islands and dry valleys is responsible for the development of an irrigation agriculture wherein crops are not dependent on precipitation that falls on the cultivated lands but on that which accumulates on the more remote range and forest lands.

Historically, modern irrigation culture began crudely in July 1847, when Brigham Young and his group of Mormon pioneers started diverting water from City Creek near the site on which Salt Lake City developed. The Mormon occupancy of the arid land is characteristic of much of the settlement that has occurred throughout the whole region, and nowhere is the relationship of the environmental factors of climate and topography to settlement more clearly pictured than in the Utah valleys. Compact villages have been established on almost every stream along the west front of the Wasatch Mountains and high plateaus. They are situated at the mouths of canyons, and around them are spread green irrigated fields which give way to the gray sagebrush landscape at the end of the ditch. From an airplane they appear as small varicolored oases in a great expanse of "desert" landscape.

The inhabitants of the irrigated valleys, living in the faith of continuing stream flow, have gradually acquired a consciousness of the dependence of the irrigation enterprise upon the mountain watersheds. In Utah it is estimated that at least 80 percent of the usable stream flow is derived from mountain lands above 7,000 feet in altitude, or generally at elevations 2,500 to 6,000 feet above the valley floor. The implication is clear when one considers that every acre of the 1⅓ million of irrigated land in Utah is dependent upon approximately 7 acres of range and forest watershed land.

Similar mountain-valley relationships prevail on the Snake River in southern Idaho, where agricultural developments such as those in the Boise Valley and Twin Falls sections have been made on valley plains receiving only 7 to 12 inches of precipitation annually. For their water supply these developments depend entirely upon the Boise and Snake Rivers, which originate on mountain lands comprising only 30 percent of the drainage area but receiving up to 60 inches of precipitation annually. Relationships of like character are found throughout the entire arid region.

Settlement of the arid region was also made possible by ranching and dry farming, a form of agriculture which adapted itself to the topography, native vegetation, and climate, in contrast to the irrigation enterprise, in which the environment was modified. Such development, however, has not always been independent of irrigation, for even the livestock industry has greatly expanded as a result of forage production by the artificial application of water to croplands.

Although irrigation agriculture is not the sole source of livelihood in the arid regions, it colors all other activities and determines in a large measure how far these others may develop. Table 1 gives the acreage and value of irrigated lands in comparison with the total of all agricultural lands for the 11 Western States, some of which have areas in other climatic zones.

TABLE 1.—*Acreage and value of irrigated lands in the 11 Western States* [1]

State	Total crop-land	Irrigated land	All farms	Irrigated farms	Value of all farm lands	Value of irrigated land
	Acres	*Acres*	*Number*	*Number*	*Dollars*	*Dollars*
Arizona	649,000	576,000	14,173	8,523	160,854,000	131,239,000
California	8,390,000	4,747,000	135,676	85,784	2,976,155,000	2,145,451,000
Colorado	8,449,000	3,394,000	59,956	31,288	510,955,000	309,266,000
Idaho	4,073,000	2,181,000	41,674	27,953	340,256,000	233,067,000
Montana	11,399,000	1,595,000	47,495	11,925	442,941,000	156,067,000
Nevada	494,000	487,000	3,442	3,031	53,665,000	50,145,000
New Mexico	1,799,000	527,000	31,404	14,347	180,721,000	73,630,000
Oregon	4,173,000	899,000	55,153	11,387	501,947,000	130,246,000
Utah	1,495,000	1,324,000	27,159	23,847	174,341,000	157,832,000
Washington	6,275,000	499,000	70,904	15,949	608,373,000	154,327,000
Wyoming	2,293,000	1,236,000	16,011	7,308	174,464,000	99,704,000
Total	49,489,000	17,465,000	503,047	241,342	6,124,672,000	3,640,974,000

[1] Data from 1930 Census of Irrigation of Agricultural Lands.

CLIMATE AND THE PROBLEMS OF IRRIGATION AGRICULTURE

Irrigation agriculture has many advantages, but it also has many hazards which constantly threaten its permanency.

Theoretically, irrigation affords an ideal form of husbandry wherein man attains a high degree of control over his crops through regulation of water, averts the consequences of drought, and takes advantage of the long, warm growing seasons and fertile soils of the semidesert valleys to produce high yields in a variety of crops. Actually, however, the realization of all these benefits is difficult, for the whole process is beset with many important problems.

Experience with floods and erosion in the arid West, together with knowledge, gained through research, of the factors affecting run-off and soil stability on mountain watersheds, shows the dangers that threaten irrigation and the necessity of establishing and maintaining a sound watershed-management program based on knowledge of the factors determining the quantity and quality of water delivered to the irrigated lands.

Upon invading the arid West, settlers found that the normally low summer flow of the streams did not furnish enough water for their needs. Accordingly dams and elaborate diversion works were constructed in order to conserve winter and spring run-off and to convey water to the thirsty soils. In addition, people took to the hills to dig mine shafts, to cut timber, to graze flocks, and to build spiraling roads to scenic and recreational areas. In doing these things, man not only altered the age-old characteristics of stream flow, but he also tampered with the equally long established physical and biological features of the watershed lands from which the water is derived. The use of watershed lands for these purposes is essential, but it must be tempered by the requirements of soil and water conservation.

The watersheds where the streams originate can be so impaired by improper use that the character of the natural stream regimen is changed, resulting in increased frequency and destructiveness of floods and siltation. Moreover, through improper irrigation and land-management practices, the application of these mountain waters can damage and has damaged the soils by the leaching of plant foods, increased erosion of the topsoil, concentration of salts beyond the toxic tolerance of the plants, accumulation of stagnant water in soil horizons, and the sealing of pore spaces essential to plant growth in the soil. Locally these destructive processes already presage the downfall of irrigation agriculture if they are allowed to spread unchecked.

Perhaps the most serious problem in irrigation is that of alkali. Soils in an arid region generally contain large quantities of alkali salts, formed in the process of weathering. The rainfall is insufficient to wash them away or leach them out. Application of irrigation water quickly concentrates the more soluble salts at or near the surface of the soil. Alkalinity is also associated with waterlogging, when too much water is added to the soil and the water table is raised into the root zone of field crops, not only "drowning" the plants but increasing the salt concentration above the tolerance of the species grown.

In certain instances concentration of salts in streams flowing through arid territory may reach such a high point as to make the water unsuitable for use in ordinary methods of irrigation. Moreover, salt concentrations in reservoirs may become so great that the disposal of the resultant brine is a major problem.

Overexpansion and inadequate planning for settlement and land use have created other serious problems. On some projects more land has been brought under cultivation than the available stream flow would justify; on others it has not always been possible to divert the water to the areas having the best soils.

Future expansion of irrigation depends primarily upon engineering developments. There are still many areas of fertile land, and also there is much undeveloped water, but these two elements seldom occur side by side. The problem of engineering is to bring together the undeveloped water and the fertile soils through transmountain diversion, the extension and enlargement of canal systems, the construction of additional reservoirs, and in other ways. But an enduring irrigation culture cannot be built by engineering alone. On the contrary, the permanence of the enterprise, and indeed the permanence of all agriculture in the arid region, rests upon a full understanding and an adequate solution of the basic problems of land use and water conservation.

Settlement and Cultivation in the Summer-Dry Climates

By John Leighly [1]

A STRIP of country all along our western coast has a climate that in some ways reverses what occurs in other agricultural regions. It includes California, western Oregon, western Washington. Here is a clear-cut account of why the climate in this region is different and why it has favored the development of a distinctive type of agriculture.

[1] John Leighly is Associate Professor of Geography, University of California.

298737°—41——14

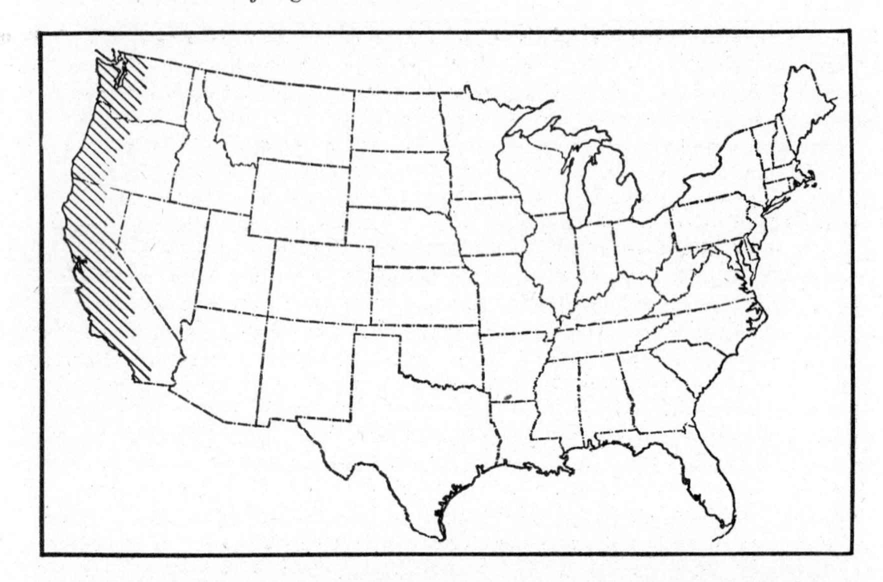

A LINE DRAWN from the northeastern corner of the State of Washington, through the intersection of the eastern boundary of Nevada with the Colorado River and prolonged to the Mexican boundary, passes, along most of its length, through the driest parts of the United States. Eastward from this line the increasing annual total of precipitation falls mainly in summer, while westward from it, toward the rainier areas nearer the Pacific Ocean, more precipitation falls in winter. Westward as far as the barrier formed by the Cascade and Sierra Nevada Mountains, which stretch from the Canadian border to the Mojave Desert, the winter precipitation is too scanty to raise the country out of the general class of arid lands; but from these mountain ranges to the coast, except in interior valleys, it is sufficient to support a natural cover of grass, brush, and forest much more abundant than is found in true steppe and desert. In coastal mountains, where the annual precipitation is from 40 to 100 inches and more, the heaviest forests of the United States grew, and in many places still grow. The boundary between the arid lands and the area of summer-dry climates follows approximately the barrier formed by the Sierra and the Cascades.

The average annual precipitation along the Pacific coast increases from 9.7 inches at San Diego to 83.5 inches at Tatoosh Island at the entrance of the Strait of Juan de Fuca. Inland from the coast there is a comparable increase northward, if stations at comparable elevations and exposure are compared. The principal increase is in the amount of precipitation that falls in winter. The months of December, January, and February, though comprising only one-fourth of the year, provide 40 to 60 percent of the annual total. The difference between south and north is less marked in summer, when June, July, and August bring only 1 to 10 percent of the total annual precipitation. The dry season becomes shorter and the amount of rain that falls in the summer months becomes greater from south to north, but in the lowlands, where agriculture is important, the dry summer produces a shortage of water in the soil all the way from the Mexican to the Canadian border. Summer drought is the most conspicuous feature of the climates of both mountain and valley in the Pacific Coast States.

Except for occasional local summer thunderstorms in the mountains, the rains are brought by cyclonic storms that move in from the Pacific. In summer the tracks followed by these storms lie far to the north. In winter the storms are both more numerous and more intense than in summer, and they follow paths lying far enough south to give rain (frequently snow in the mountains) to the Pacific States. The summer-dry area of our Pacific coast is the southern, drier edge of the rainy belt of northwestern North America, which includes the coasts of British Columbia and Alaska, throughout which there is a winter maximum and a summer minimum of precipitation.

A further prominent characteristic of the Pacific coastal climates is the mildness of the winters at low elevations as compared with those in the same latitudes in the interior of the continent and on the Atlantic coast. In popular opinion outside the Pacific States, the mild winters are perhaps more familiar than the dry summers. They are the product of two influences—the presence of the Pacific Ocean to the west and the mountain barrier, generally with high plateau country behind it, to the east. Air coming from the sea in winter is everywhere warmer than air that has been refrigerated by passage over snow-covered land. The high and continuous wall of mountains acts as a mechanical check to air that has been cooled over the snow-covered interior of the continent. This continental air does at times spill over the mountains and through the few breaks in them, but it must descend anywhere from 2,000 to 5,000 or 6,000 feet in order to reach the low elevations where most of the population lives. In descending to lower levels, where higher pressures prevail than on the plateaus, the air is compressed and thereby warmed mechanically. The coldest air experienced in winter in the lowlands of the Pacific States is sometimes low enough to injure the less hardy cultivated plants, but it would be considered mild in the same latitudes in the Mississippi Valley.

In the dry summer only elevation and proximity to the sea moderate the high temperatures attained by ground surface and air under the daily flood of sunshine. The sea, cool for its latitude, maintains low temperatures along the coast, where "high fog" contributes further toward keeping temperatures low by screening off the sun's rays. This effect rapidly becomes weaker inland; the valleys of the Coast Ranges are notably warmer than the immediate coast. Still farther inland, midday temperatures of over 100° F. are observed day after day in summer. These high temperatures rapidly exhaust the water retained in the soil from the winter rains and make the drought of the rainless summer more severe.

PLANTS IN THE SUMMER-DRY CLIMATES

When the Pacific coast of the present United States was first explored by Europeans the country was covered by a mosaic of forest, grassland, and scrub (chaparral) distributed mainly in accordance with the dryness of the surface in summer. This dryness is not merely the effect of varying amounts of winter rain but depends also in part on varying exposure to the sun's rays in summer. North- and northeast-facing slopes are less dry than those facing south and southwest and, under natural conditions, are occupied by plants requiring more moisture. The gradation from forest through chaparral to desert is easily interpreted as the consequence of decreasing winter precipitation and rising summer temperature from north to south and from highland to lowland; but the climatic relations of the grasslands occurring at irregular intervals from the middle California coast northward are still a problem. Woody plants with deep and extensive root systems may draw in summer on the ground water accumulated during the winter. Grasses and the herbaceous plants associated with them make their vegetative growth in late winter and spring, when there is still a supply of soil water, and ripen their seeds early in the dry summer.

The relation of the native plants to the seasonal conjunction of deficient soil water and high temperature underlay early agriculture and underlies agriculture today where the land is not irrigated. Unirrigated crops must either be able to subsist through the summer on ground water collected by deep, perennial root systems, as do the native trees, or, if annuals, must ripen their seeds in summer after making their vegetative growth in spring before the soil water within reach of their roots is exhausted. Many of the crops that have a firm place in modern agriculture do not conform to these requirements. Besides common garden vegetables, the reader will immediately think of such important crops as corn and potatoes. These cannot be grown in the summer-dry climates without irrigation, except in favored spots where, as on low valley floors close to permanent streams, ground water is within reach of their shallow roots.

AGRICULTURAL BEGINNINGS

The sparse European settlements in the Pacific Coast States found by the American pioneers in the late forties of the past century are shown in figure 1. This map emphasizes the two nuclear areas of settlement that existed before the great influx of immigrants from the eastern part of the United States—California (more properly Upper California at that time) and the Oregon country. The beginnings of agriculture had been made in both areas before the great immigration.

Agriculture was introduced into California along with other elements of Spanish-colonial ways of life late in the eighteenth century. In the early days of Spanish colonization the missions were the centers and examples of agricultural practice. The Spanish missionaries were undoubtedly the best equipped among the early European immigrants into California to introduce agriculture there. Much of Mexico, whence the colonists came, is dry; horticulture, production of grain under dry-farming methods, and the herding of livestock, all well-established in Mexico, were easily transplanted to Upper California. The Spaniards had brought from Spain, also a country with dry summers, tree crops and grains that could flourish in this part of North America. Mission agriculture included extensive herding of livestock on the ample tracts assigned to the missions,

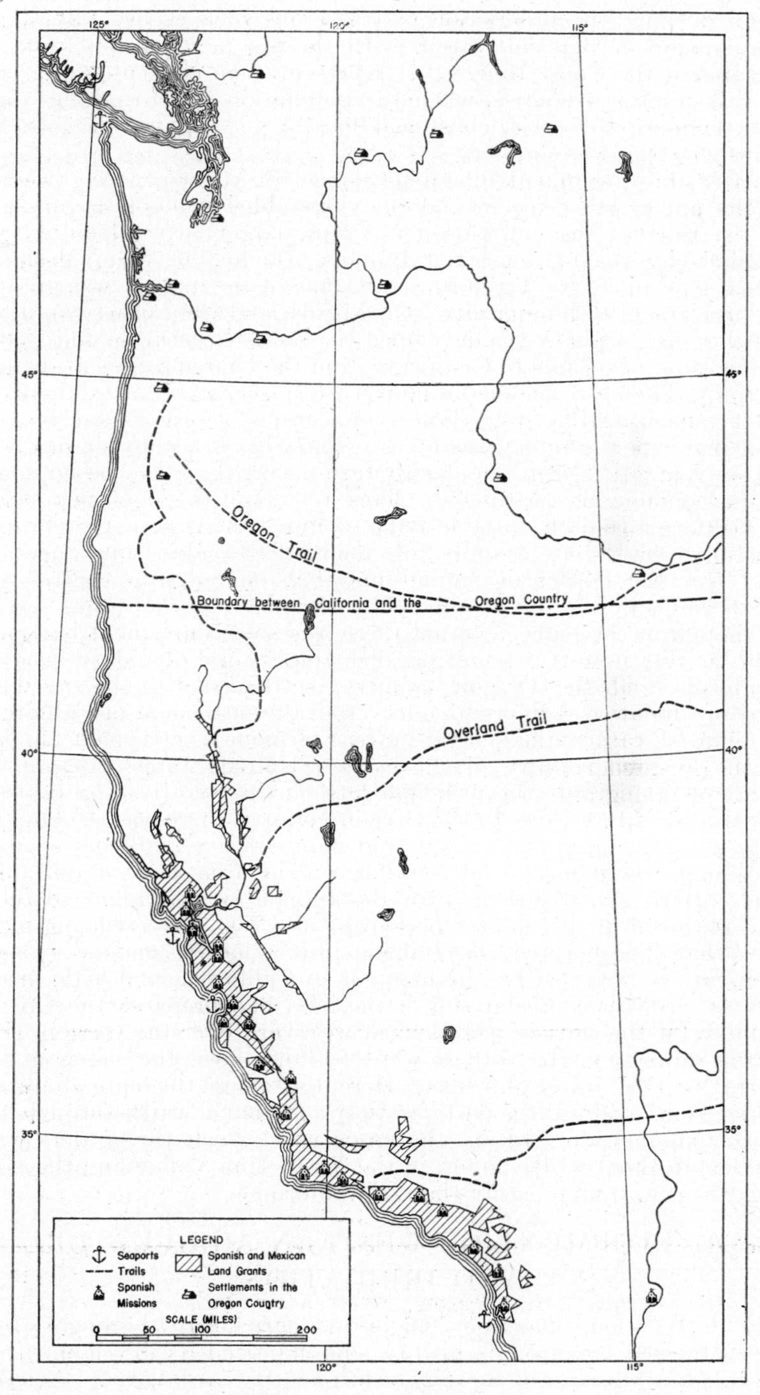

FIGURE 1.—Nuclei of settlement in the far West before the California gold rush.

grain farming, the production of tree crops such as figs, olives, and grapes, and garden cultivation with the aid of irrigation from the streams of the Coast Range. It represented an efficient use of land and of climatic resources when the population had to produce only a little more than was consumed locally and export markets and transportation were limited.

After the attainment of independence by Mexico in the twenties of the nineteenth century and the disestablishment of the missions in the thirties, the cultivation of crops, largely carried out at the missions by the half-enslaved Indians attached to them, declined. Much land in coastal California and some in the interior was granted in large tracts to immigrants from Mexico and from other countries. On these large tracts was developed the social structure found by the immigrants who came to California from the United States in the late forties. The chief use of the land was for grazing immense herds of cattle, sheep, and horses. Trade connections by sea existed, but the principal export product was hides. Early life in California has been highly romanticized in popular literature, but there can be no doubt of its economic backwardness. Thus in spite of the small population of California and the productivity of much of its soil, there was a woefully inadequate supply of foodstuffs—aside from "jerked" beef—for the hordes of immigrants that poured into central and northern California during the gold rush.

Though in the pioneer period there was some movement back and forth across the forty-second parallel, the historic boundary between California and the Oregon country, settlement of the northern territory followed a different course from the settlement of California. It followed, rather, the general pattern of pioneer settlement familiar in the forested country of the eastern United States. Before the influx of immigrants the principal settlements were trading posts of the Hudson's Bay Co. In the Oregon country there was the familiar sequence of trapper and Indian trader, missionary and frontiersman, and finally the pioneer settler staking out his frontier farm on public land. Here, too, relations with the Indians were similiar to those that obtained in the pioneer period in the East. No civilizing influence that incorporated the Indians into a local economic system, such as was exercised by the missions in California, and little in the way of large-scale preemption of the land had prepared the Oregon country for the settlers who flocked westward over the Oregon Trail at the same time that others were "rolling down the slopes of the Sierra Nevada" into California. Here, too, where the more abundant winter rains maintain a better supply of ground water through the shorter summer-dry season, the crops with which the settlers were familiar in their earlier homes in the Mississippi Valley and the East could be grown more easily than in California.

DEVELOPMENT OF WESTERN AGRICULTURE AND IRRIGATION

E. J. Wickson, who knew California agriculture thoroughly and had witnessed much of its history, characterized its development in the last four decades of the nineteenth century as follows:[2] 1860–70,

[2] WICKSON, E. J. RURAL CALIFORNIA. 399 pp., illus. New York. 1923. See pp. 100–101.

decade of wheat; 1870–80, decade of wool; 1880–90, decade of fruit; 1890–1900, decade of dairy awakening. A parallel development was followed in the western parts of the two Northern Pacific States. The agricultural practices mentioned gave character to the decades to which Wickson assigned them by great expansion rather than by wholesale replacement of practices dominant in earlier years. All of the branches mentioned, as well as the forms of agriculture current in the Spanish and Mexican periods, made permanent contributions to the varied agricultural life of the Pacific States.

Successive shifts in emphasis on different agricultural products were the reflection of a prevailing speculative interest in the use of land. Production of one crop after another, each promising large returns, was expanded until prices were depressed and the use and sale of land for that crop ceased to be profitable. Then the attention of speculative producers and vendors of land turned to a new product. The speculative sale of land to newcomers from the Middle West and East has been a means of dividing large land holdings into tracts of one-family size.

Intensification of the use of the land, the consequence of continued heavy immigration, has involved particularly an increase in the area devoted to fruits and vegetables grown for eastern and foreign markets and has been associated with steadily increased use of water for irrigation. From north to south irrigation increases in importance as the total annual precipitation decreases. But only in dry interior valleys and in southern California does it dominate agriculture to the extent of being absolutely necessary for crop production. Throughout the greater part of this climatic region irrigation is a supplementary source of water for crops and so is a feature of intensification of agriculture rather than a necessary basis for it. The place of irrigation in the summer-dry climates differs in this respect from its place in the true dry climates.

Aside from its climatic effects, the topography of the Pacific States has had a further effect on agriculture by determining the distribution of lands smooth enough for tillage and especially for irrigation. Population and cultivation of the soil are almost wholly confined to valleys. In this valley agriculture, the neighboring mountains play an important part. Everywhere they receive more precipitation than the valley floors. Run-off from them goes into the valleys as surface streams or as ground water and so becomes available in part to supplement the scantier rainfall of the valleys. Development of agriculture has been closely linked with increasingly more efficient use of run-off from the mountains. In the Spanish and Mexican periods California agriculture used strictly local water supplies, but these local supplies have been inadequate where large aggregations of population have been built up. Constantly larger amounts of water have been required for direct use by cities and for irrigation.

Thus far, water-supply systems as large as those built by cities have not been built for irrigation. On thousands of farms, water is pumped directly out of the ground for the irrigation of its surface. Natural summer run-off through streams supplied by melting snow in the Sierra Nevada and Cascade Mountains has provided a further supply. Winter run-off has mostly gone unused to the sea. The next step in the better utilization of the winter precipitation involves the large-scale storage for use during the summer of this water that has heretofore run off unused in winter and spring. Already work has begun on the largest of the projects for such storage and distribution of water, the Central Valley water project in California. Comparable in function though not in magnitude is the coordinated water plan for the Willamette Valley in Oregon. These systems of dams and canals will represent a long step toward what must be the ultimate goal—namely, as complete use as is practicable of winter precipitation for crop production during the dry summer.

THE SUMMER-DRY CLIMATES IN THE ECONOMY OF THE UNITED STATES

The prime value in our national economy of the lands of summer drought on the Pacific coast is as a source of plant products that require mild winters and long growing seasons. Citrus fruits, the less hardy deciduous fruits, fresh vegetables in winter—these are their most important contributions at present. Rainless summers make possible the inexpensive drying of fruits, which puts into the market prunes, raisins, dried peaches, and apricots. In its present relation to American economy in general, the primary technical problem of agriculture in the Pacific Coast States is to make increasingly more effective use of the mild winters and the long growing season in the face of the great obstacle presented by the rainless summers. To overcome that obstacle supplementary irrigation is necessary. Hence the key position of water in Pacific coast agriculture. The volume of water flowing through ditches to supply thirsty crops in summer has been the measure of the intensity of agriculture in this region, from the meager trickle that watered a mission garden over a century ago through the period of local irrigation districts of the past generation, and it will continue to be the measure when the Kings and Sacramento Rivers and the tributaries of the Willamette are subjugated tomorrow.

The Colonization of Northern Lands

By Vilhjalmur Stefansson [1]

THIS IS MORE than a matter-of-fact discussion of the possibilities of settlement in Alaska and other northern lands. The author is an enthusiast about his subject and shows it; he even gets some of the flavor and feel of life in the north into the discussion. The primary question that concerns him is: Why is it that Scandinavia and Finland have 16 million inhabitants while our own northern Territory of Alaska has only 72,500?

[1] Vilhjalmur Stefansson began his scientific career as an anthropologist, but his work developed along geographical lines and the history of geographic discovery. Among his published books are Anthropological Papers; The Friendly Arctic; The Northward Course of Empire; Adventures in Error; Iceland: The First American Republic; and The Arctic Manual.

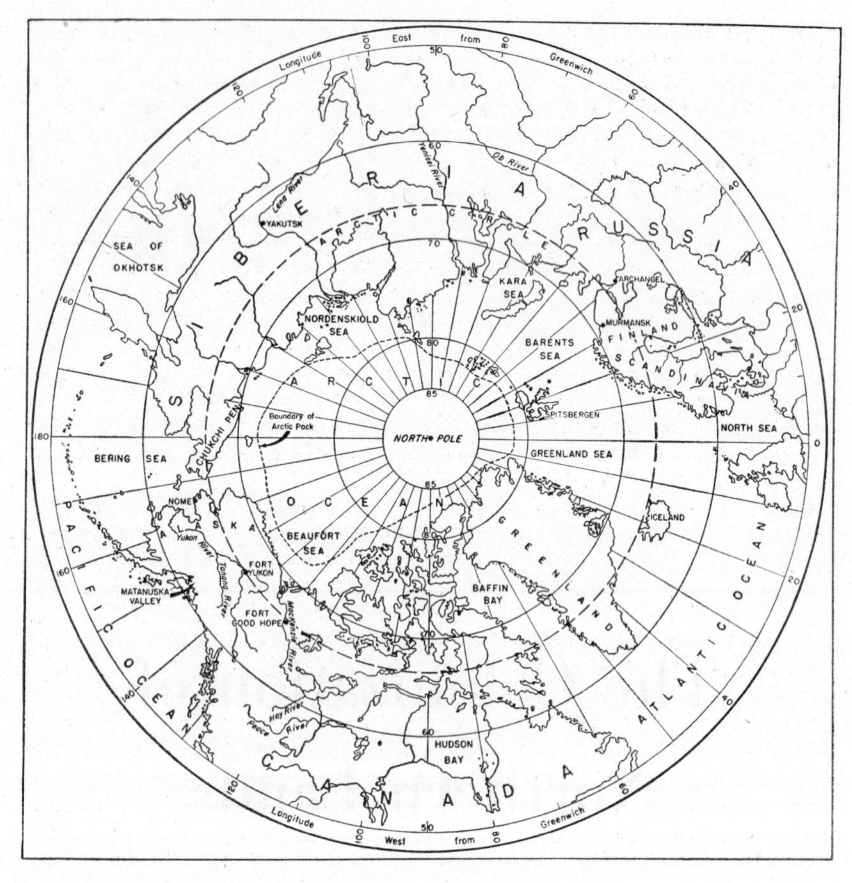

Lands north of the Arctic Circle have as yet been "colonized," in the usual meaning of the word, only in Europe; elsewhere, uncolonized lands spread a long way south of the technical Arctic boundary.

The answer to sparseness of settlement and lack of modern development in northern lands comes, I think, less from the physical sciences than from the humanities. A study of geography, geology, climatology, and the rest is needed; but the answer is more pertinent and more readily grasped when the inquiry begins with history, sociology, and economics.

REASONS FOR SPARSE NORTHERN SETTLEMENT

The Answer From History

It is doubtful whether there has been any biological adaptation of man to his northward movement from the Tropics or subtropics; at any rate, it seems clear that the Eskimos, most northerly people in the New World, get their faces frozen as easily, shiver as often, and make all similar responses to chill as readily as whites, Negroes, or South Sea Islanders.

Man's ability to spread northward is, then, either wholly or chiefly cultural and depends mainly on clothes, housing, and the use of fire. Secondarily it depends on the solution of numerous other problems of environmental change resulting from a northward movement.

The lands of the south are the lands of our past, understood because they are known to us through history, literature, and tradition. By contrast, the lands of the north are the lands of the future, unknown as the future is unknown. Their problems, insofar as they differ from those of the ancestral south, are new; the solutions remain to be discovered. We fear the unknown north—and with good reason, for conditions which knowledge and skill might turn to our advantage prove hostile and even deadly when we lack the mental and physical equipment needed to meet them.

That fear and misunderstanding of the north are basic to our thinking could be shown by a hundred examples. For instance, a New Yorker would undoubtedly assume that an unusually cold winter is hard luck for both the east coast of Florida and the west coast of Greenland. Let him visit Florida, and everyone there will support him. Indeed, no proof is needed; for the experience of a thousand generations has taught that frosts in the subtropics are destructive. But in west Greenland he would receive no confirmation of his view. Eskimos and veteran whites alike would tell him that a colder winter, or at least a winter that has more ice than usual in the sea, gives better harvests of the crops on which the Greenlanders rely—the beasts that come with the ice and go with the ice, that are primarily dependent on frozen water, as the Eskimos are secondarily dependent on it.

The fear of the north which pervades Mediterranean culture is not based merely on such common-sense reasons as I have given. That Europeans did not attempt to cross the Tropics during the 1,500 years preceding Henry the Navigator (1394–1460) was due to their firm belief that neither man nor plant could endure the terrific heat of a middle zone of the earth, which was too near the sun or too directly below it. This was based on the Greek doctrine that the earth was divided into five zones, only two of which—the Temperate Zones—were habitable. Since Henry's time colonization of the Tropics has been retarded by a survival of the old belief in a modified form—that although the Tropics were livable they were so hot as to be very uncomfortable for Europeans, as well as demoralizing to them, mentally and physically. Similarly, a "knowledge" that the Arctic was lifeless because of distance from the sun or because the sun's rays there were too slanting, at first prevented exploration and development. More recently, with the Arctic, as with the Tropics, development has been hindered by residual beliefs derived from the original Greek doctrine.

A northern limit beyond which animals and plants do not go was believed in so recently that even polar explorers said in print less than 20 years ago that the accounts in my book, The Friendly Arctic,[2] of how a party of us lived by hunting on the moving pack ice of the open sea several hundred miles north of Alaska, were fiction. Roald

[2] STEFANSSON, VILHJALMUR. THE FRIENDLY ARCTIC; THE STORY OF FIVE YEARS IN POLAR REGIONS. 784 pp., illus. New York and London. 1921.

Amundsen, for instance, said in his autobiography, published at Oslo in 1927,[3] among other things of similar trend:

> A more unreasonable distortion of conditions in the North has never been set forth than that a skilful marksman "can live off the land." Stefansson has never done it, although he says he has. Furthermore, I am willing to stake my reputation as a Polar explorer, and will wager everything I own, that if Stefansson were to attempt it he would be dead within eight days, counted from the start, provided that this test takes place on the Polar ice, which is constantly adrift over the open sea.

The Mediterranean doctrine about a region too far north for any life was not finally destroyed until, in May and June of 1937, a group of four explorers from the Union of Soviet Socialist Republics, led by Ivan Papanin, reported from the immediate vicinity of the North Pole more than half a dozen species of birds, a mother polar bear with cubs so young that they must have been born on the drifting sea ice in the vicinity, shrimps moving sluggishly in the leads, seals eating the shrimps, and a gradient of animal and plant life from surface to bottom of the ocean that resembled the life gradient of well-known parts of the north Atlantic.

The Answer From Sociology

The sociological, or perhaps better the ethnological, handicap has been similar to the historical. Consider but one sample element—our cultural attitude toward water.

It is fundamental in southern thinking that water is useful and desirable as a liquid, but that it is undesirable, hostile, and even deadly when a solid. In the north, the attitude is the reverse. There water is considered to be most friendly and useful when it is cold and hard. In the south, people think of water in its relation to travel as something in which you swim, or on which you move by oar, sail, or steam power. With southerners it is a miracle to walk on water. To northerners the most commonplace use of water is to walk on it; thereafter they think of it as a highway, or highway material, for sledges, tractors, skis, snowshoes, skates, and airplanes.

Few landscapes are so naturally adapted for the use of caterpillar tractors as those of the far north where, through half the year or more, every river is a winding boulevard and every lake as flat and hard as a tennis court. In nonmountainous regions, lakes cover 50 to 60 percent of the landscape on an average, the remainder being largely swamp that is impassable to tractors or wheeled vehicles in summer but becomes hard as concrete in winter. By laying out routes of travel that cross isthmuses between lakes where they are low and not wide, it is possible, with such small labor as to be scarcely credible to southerners, to open up practically the whole Arctic and subarctic throughout the winter to tractor movement.

Two other sample handicaps from this division of the cultural field may be mentioned—southern clothes and southern-type house doors.

The anthropologists are in general agreement that clothes had a large part of their origin in motives of decoration. A New Yorker dressed for returning home from his office in January wears an outfit

[3] Amundsen, Roald. On Stefansson. *In* Explorers Club Tales, pp. 1–8, illus. New York, 1936. [Transl. from Mit Liv Som Polarforsker, 1927.]

weighing perhaps 15 pounds that would not keep him reasonably warm for 15 minutes if he sat still at −15° F. An Eskimo of northern Alaska wears in January a 10-pound suit in which he would be less chilled after 50 minutes at −50°. The Eskimo designs his clothing for warmth, mobility, and comfort; fundamentally we design ours to look at.

The second sample cultural handicap is the typical European door, perhaps 7 feet high and 3 feet wide, which is located in the wall of a house. Those are good doors for the Tropics. At −50° F. you have to dodge in and out of such a door. When it is opened, volumes of chilled air roll in along the floor to make the room noticeably colder; volumes of heated air rush out through the upper half of the door, without making the outdoors noticeably warmer.

The sensible door for cold weather is of the Eskimo type. It may be of the same dimensions, 3 feet by 7, but it is a horizontal door in the floor. Such a door is typically kept open both day and night, for (apart from a slight "diffusion of gases") gravity prevents the warm air which fills the house from sinking down, while the cold air from below the door cannot press up into the house because it is already full of warm air. Ventilation is assured by a stovepipelike ventilator in the roof, through which the warm air rushes out under terrific pressure from an atmosphere that has been weighted by the outdoor chill, while cold air rises gradually through the comparatively large door and spreads along the floor without any draft or any other effect that discommodes the occupants.

By making a few score, or perhaps a few hundred, adjustments like those suggested for transportation, clothing, and houses, a system of comfortable living in regions of the longest and coldest winters may be devised—a comfort upon which is based the nearly universal verdict of those who have lived in the north that they prefer the winter season to the summer.

The Answer From Economics

On my first journey north through Canada down the Mackenzie River system in 1906 I learned that for decades before my time the Hay River Valley had been recognized as nearly ideal for cereals and for the type of mixed farming associated with States like Wisconsin. There were few if any summer frosts that would interfere with wheat—not so many, for instance, as in that part of North Dakota where I was brought up, the Red River Valley. The soil was rich; there was a variety of prairie, meadowland, and timber. There were fewer blizzards than in North Dakota, and they were less violent. There was a more dependable rainfall.

But the Hay River district remains uncolonized to this day, although tapping it would bring into production one of the potentially richest food regions of even that great food-producing country, the Dominion of Canada. The wheat growers of the prairie Provinces do not feel themselves any too prosperous on what they are now able to get for their crops and consider that if additional millions of bushels of the world's best wheat were to start pouring in from a new district there would be a further depression of prices. This accounts also for opposition by wheat farmers to railway extension into the Hay

Valley, which would not be technically difficult. The Hay district is also a potential source of dairy products, wool, and honey, which accounts for the opposition of still more groups of voting Canadians. So there is a tacit agreement in Canada that under the present economic set-up it is not feasible to colonize the Hay.

Another example comes from Alaska. Some years ago a company with offices in Seattle and Nome got several railways to agree to serve reindeer meat in their dining cars. The venture was so successful that rumors of the new food and how much people were liking it spread rapidly through the cattle and sheep region, and it was not long until protests began to come in from farmers in the United States. At least two States boycotted the meat—Kansas and Nebraska. There was the equivalent of an ultimatum: "If you want to handle our business you will have to eat our meat." Reindeer meat was withdrawn from the dining cars. When it is realized that perhaps the easiest money crop to produce in Alaska, after gold and fish, is reindeer beef, one more of the ways in which the present economic and political set-up tends to hold back the colonization of Alaska is evident. I am not saying here whether this ought to be so; I am merely pointing out that it is so.

The Answer From Geography

To say that the development of the far north is being retarded by mileage distance from commercial centers is really begging the question. A 1941 voyage from Seattle to Nome is shorter in time, safer, and easier than a 1641 voyage from London to Boston. If our civilization were still in the expanding phase of the seventeenth and eighteenth centuries, distances would mean less now than they did then.

If you are willing to be an old-fashioned pioneer—a Lincoln of Illinois, a Nordic of a Swedish inland valley, or a Mongol of central Finland—you can make their type of living in the Alaska of today. But there are few places where it is more difficult than in Alaska to be a successful "economic man." The Finns and the Swedes colonized their northern lands when they were subsistence hunters, subsistence fishers, and subsistence farmers—when they were in a Lincoln or pre-Lincoln stage of economic and social development.

There are said to be 12 million people now in the whole of Scandinavia, which, speaking alphabetically, is Denmark, Iceland, Norway, and Sweden. The total is 16 million including Finland, and Finland must be included in order to make a reasonable comparison with Alaska on an area basis.

Scandinavia-Finland, then, is a northern land developed through an earlier culture. Alaska is a northern land which is at least open for development under our present culture—if a district can be called open that is fenced off by so many economic, sociological, and psychological barbed-wire fences.

Scandinavia (including Iceland) and Finland cover about 500,000 square miles; Alaska about 586,000. The climate of northern Alaska is similar to that of northern Finland; southern Alaska resembles southerly Scandinavia. The central Alaskan climate has more violent extremes than are found even in central Finland, but that is perhaps in Alaska's favor, at least economically speaking. For when winter temperatures once go below −50° F. it makes little difference to man's comfort or freedom of movement whether the low limit is −58°, as in Finland, or −71°, as in the Yukon Basin of Alaska. A fall of 10° in midwinter is of negligible importance; a rise of 10° in midsummer is of profound importance. The central Yukon Valley of Alaska suffers more from heat and danger of sunstroke is greater there than anywhere in Finland (though in neither country is there much danger if proper care is taken). But with certain economic plants—wheat, for instance—a rise of 10°, or even 5°, can be of vast consequence. There is, accordingly, no reason to doubt that on the average wheat culture will be more successful on and just south of the Arctic Circle in Alaska, where there is this additional summer heat, than it is in the same latitudes in Finland.

There are a few known resources in which Scandinavia-Finland excels Alaska. The most important is probably iron. It is likely, too, that for cattle and sheep grazing there is a higher percentage of suitable country in Scandinavia. But for reindeer Alaska has more land—and reindeer grazing is really more valuable than sheep or cattle grazing, in that reindeer meat, because of its quality, commands as high prices as any meat where it is known (as in Scandinavia) and is much cheaper than any other meat to produce in a climate of long winters, since the animals require no barns to shelter them and no hay to feed them. Reindeer are as native to Arctic prairies as cattle are to the prairies of the Argentine.

Both Alaska and Scandinavia-Finland have great wealth in their surrounding waters. In herring, cod, halibut, and some other commercially valuable fishes, Alaska may fall behind; but it is so far ahead in salmon that there is little doubt the total Alaskan fisheries are potentially more valuable than the Scandinavian. So much for ocean fishing. In river fisheries, Alaska far excels Scandinavia.

A comparison of forest resources is difficult, for so much depends on what a given tree is used for in a given decade. Disregarding species and thinking only of cordage or board feet, Alaskan forest resources are about as great as those of Norway and Sweden combined.

In several important resources, Alaska is so far ahead of Scandinavia that there can be scarcely any comparison. Alaska is known to be rich in coal; Scandinavia has little. Alaska has in various parts of the Territory promising oil districts; Scandinavia has not even one of known consequence. Alaska is famous for its gold, a mineral negligible in Scandinavia-Finland.

There is little doubt, then, that if Alaska had been settled as long ago as Scandinavia by people of European culture it would now be supporting a larger population than Scandinavia and supporting it more easily. Instead of having fewer than 75,000 people, as now, the Territory could easily have more than 10 million.

Alaska has been used as an example to show that, in general, the north is colonizable. But some of the ways in which Alaska and Scandinavia differ from the Canadian and Siberian Arctic and subarctic regions are not necessarily to the disadvantage of the latter from the standpoint of colonization. The ratio of forest to prairie is much higher in Alaska and Scandinavia, generally speaking, than in continental northern Canada and Siberia. But is it from the colonization point of view a handicap that hundreds of thousands of square miles should be grassland instead of spruce forest? The forest can be looked upon commercially as eventual pulpwood. But a time when we need more meat is as likely to come as a time when we need more newsprint. The prairie still carries, according to a recent Canadian estimate, 3 million head of caribou north of the tree line. The caribou has long been domesticated under the name of reindeer; the musk ox is now being domesticated. These two beasts annually convert millions of tons of edible northerly vegetation into millions of pounds of that musk ox beef which Admiral Peary has said is better than any domestic beef, and into that favorite food of Scandinavians, reindeer beef.

Besides meat, the northern animals supply leather. The skins of the reindeer make the best clothes known for cold weather, and the wool of the musk ox, by the findings of the textile department of the University of Leeds, has the softness of cashmere, the warmth of merino, good wearing qualities, and will not shrink.

One may jump to the conclusion that the more intense winter cold of northern Canada and Siberia would make these regions noticeably less desirable for human residence than are corresponding latitudes of Alaska or Scandinavia. But Canadian travelers and residents at Good Hope on the Mackenzie River complain no more of −78° F. than the Americans of the Yukon River do of −68° at Fort Yukon; and the Russians are no more troubled by their −88° in Yakutsk province than the Canadians are by their −78° in the Northwest Territories.

But it is otherwise with the summer heat. A warmth of 80° F. in the shade at Matanuska may give only a poor grade of wheat, or wheat that has not ripened, while a warmth of 90° on the Tanana, a few hundred miles farther north, would give a high-grade, well-ripened product.

It has been assumed by many that ground frost, more extensive in Siberia and Canada than in Alaska and Scandinavia, is a draw-back. Experience shows, however, that while in some ways this is true, in others ground frost is advantageous. To begin with, a frozen layer some inches or feet below the surface will prevent rain and thaw water from sinking beyond the reach of plant roots, as it may do where the ground is not frozen. Then ground frost provides a reserve of moisture, for if a summer is unusually dry, the surface thaw will penetrate 1 or a few inches deeper than usual, whereupon the very thawing of the muck produces water that plants can use. How this works out in practice may be studied, among other sources, in the series of reports by C. C. Georgeson on his experiments in Alaska, made on behalf of the United States Department of Agriculture.

THE NORTHERN GROWING SEASON

It must be kept in mind that the northern season of relative discomfort is the summer, when there are stifling temperatures and the mosquitoes come out in numbers unknown to tropical or Temperate Zone experience. Generally, the worst mosquito season is from May to early July. Before the mosquitoes noticeably decrease, however, sand flies begin to increase and are troublesome during July and

August. But experience shows that biting insects, the greatest handicap of the Arctic and subarctic, can be dealt with by protective clothing. There are also special northern ways of dealing with the heat. One can sleep during the hottest part of the day, say from 10 a. m. to 6 p. m. True, nights are not nearly so much cooler than days where the sun does not set as they are in the Tropics and the Temperate Zone; but even so, they are cooler. You can find cool sleeping quarters in a basement, where the permanently frozen ground lowers temperature, if not elsewhere in the house. Then there is the blessing that the northern summer is short. Autumn is as delightful, where Temperate Zone and Arctic meet, as it is in New England; and after that comes the long, clean, clear winter, the time of year all northerners prefer, the time of free movement and varied activity.

The shortness of summer pleases the northerner because of his dislike for heat and biting insects; it makes the southerner uneasy because he fears too short a growing season for vegetation. For southerners may not realize that wheat and many other plants do not grow by days of the calendar but by hours of sun. There are in midsummer 24 hours of sun a day on that bend of the Yukon where it crosses the Arctic Circle; there are not much more than 12 on the Amazon. So wheat in the Amazon highland works only one 12-hour shift each calendar day; wheat in the Yukon lowland works two shifts of that length. From this it may be assumed that wheat can grow as much in 1 Yukon day as in 2 Amazon days. Some say it ripens on the Yukon in two-thirds of the Amazon time; others make it three-quarters.[4]

In June 1938 the first crop of cucumbers in the Chukchi Peninsula of northeastern Siberia was produced out of doors. From the time the cucumbers were planted to the time they were full-grown was 42 days. In Moscow the time would have been about 60 days. During this season 12,000 cucumbers were grown.

Another common failure to grasp northern principles is to suppose that in the north, summer frosts destructive to wheat necessarily increase. The contrary is true. At Lacombe, near the southern boundary of Canada, during 15 years the average frost-free period was only 69 days; but at Beaverlodge, 200 miles farther north, it was 80 days, and at Fort Vermilion, 230 miles farther north than Beaverlodge, it was 88 days. This increasing length of the frost-free period has, of course, nothing to do with Japan Current, Chinook wind, or any other fanciful explanation; it is due to the simple and constantly observed fact that in the wheat country which runs north through the center of the continent, much of it originally prairie, a July frost results from a gradual accumulation of chill during a long absence of the sun, the actual deadly nip usually coming just before or just after

[4] A copy of this paragraph, or a paraphrase of it, was sent to half a dozen authorities for their comment. One thought it completely wrong—believed that wheat would grow as much during a warm dark night as during a warm sunshiny day and that the calendar time between planting and ripening would be about the same in the Red River Valley of Arkansas and in the Tanana Valley of Alaska if the average temperatures for the 24 hours were the same. However, this statement apparently was based on theory, not on statistics of observed growth. Another specialist was in general agreement with the paragraph and gave as his own rough estimate that from Oklahoma north to Peace River the calendar growing season of wheat would shorten about 1 day for each 200 miles, on which basis Tanana wheat should ripen in 12 days' less time than Oklahoma wheat. Several correspondents thought that the speedy growth reported from the Arctic Circle was probably due only in part to the factors mentioned in my paragraph. I agree, but let the paragraph stand, since this is a popular statement and I feel I have been guilty of extreme simplification rather than oversimplification—that I am giving the nontechnical reader an approximately correct point of view.

298737°—41——15 +

sunrise. Northward from Lacombe to Fort Vermilion the summer nights get shorter rapidly, which accounts for the northward increase in length of the frost-free period; north of Vermilion the darkness does not last long enough in midsummer to produce a sufficiently low temperature for a destructive frost.

From the wheat-raising point of view, it is a handicap to some northern lands that they are too much affected by warm ocean currents. Iceland, for instance, where on the south coast January temperatures are like those of Philadelphia or Milan, cannot raise wheat successfully—it seldom ripens properly, for the summers, though long, are not sufficiently hot. The same may be true for considerable parts of the southward-facing coast of Alaska. However, if communities like Matanuska are not very well adapted for wheat, they are well adapted for hay, for garden vegetables, and perhaps for cereals other than wheat. In Alaska the chief wheat production will no doubt be so far north that the Alaska Range will protect it from the sea influence. The bulk of it is likely to be in the Yukon Basin.

POSSIBILITIES OF ALASKAN DEVELOPMENT

On the possibility that Alaska may develop into a greater Scandinavia in population, just because it is on the whole greater than Scandinavia in resources, further light is shed by a study of Alaska census figures. The United States, of which Alaska is a part, had what are now considered to have been good times between 1910 and 1920; but during that decade the white population of Alaska decreased from 36,400 to 27,883. During another period of what are now thought of as good times, from 1920 almost to 1930, Alaska's population gained by 757 persons, probably a few more than can be accounted for by excess of births over deaths. Times have been hard since 1930, but there has been an increase to 40,000 whites in 1940, usually said to be due in the main to the rise in the price of gold.

It has been recognized by Canadians for some time that their only notable recent development beyond the frontier has been related to the precious minerals, gold, platinum, and radium. Even in spite of the present set-up and its current disapproval of subsistence living, Alaska may possibly be able to do a little better. For in addition to mining, the fisheries may be expanded considerably, and the exploitation of forest resources may be developed with some rapidity.

Reindeer will perhaps be the significant test for Alaska under the new policy of the Department of the Interior. With the quarter of a million head (estimated by the Department of the Interior as now in Alaska) to go on, a reindeer industry could be developed so rapidly that in a few decades the permanent safe grazing limit of the various large and small Alaska prairies would be reached. With this industry established, not only would there be a small resident population throughout the Territory depending on it, but also a cheap and excellent source of food would be available, which would make it easier to show profit on an exporting and importing basis from a development of some of the other resources. One of the first industries to benefit from success with reindeer would be gold mining—properties now unworkable would begin to pay through a more abundant labor supply from the pastoral population and a cheaper food supply from their herds. Gold is, of course, from the point of view of the Alaska chambers of commerce, an ideal product, for you cannot eat it and therefore have to sell it; butter, eggs, and meat are not nearly so good from the point of view of commerce, for they may be eaten instead of sold.

When I wrote The Northward Course of Empire, published in 1922,[5] I was capable of seeing only the resources of the north—a climate liked by those who know it, a country rich in many of the raw materials of our culture. In 1922 my eyes were still holden by the pioneer concepts of the time before 1890 and by an outlook derived from a boyhood in that Territory which is now North and South Dakota. Since then I have grown sufficiently realistic to understand that the qualities which would have brought a flood of immigrants in 1890 may draw only a baker's dozen in 1940.

It seems to me, then, that what The Northward Course of Empire says is so practically true that it could have been made true in practice—at any time before 1890. Now its conclusions regarding rapid development and large resident populations in the near future have to be judged against the following economic and social backgrounds, among others:

(1) Under conditions as they are at present in northern Canada and Alaska, there can be no rapid development. A guess would be that, except for a possible war stimulus, Alaska's white population of 40,000 would not reach 100,000 in the next 10 years.

(2) But once upon a time there was a system of more or less capitalistic exploitation under great corporations that might still prove successful. Examples are the seventeenth-century companies, typically British or Dutch, of which the Hudson's Bay Co. is perhaps the best example. If such a corporation had the rights and privileges it had before 1869, it could perhaps justify to its stockholders a large-scale Canadian Arctic and subarctic program promoting rapid development, involving many activities, and including a swift increase in population. If we in the United States wanted to, we could authorize one or more such huge corporations for the development of Alaska.

(3) Judging from such near miracles as have been accomplished by cooperatives during the last 10 years, say in Palestine and Iceland (also in several other countries, among them parts of mainland Scandinavia), it would seem that an Alaskan population growth, which I have estimated at a top of 100,000 whites in 10 years with the present system, might be increased to at least a million in 10 years through such encouragement of cooperatives in Alaska as they receive in Iceland.

(4) Then there is, of course, outright socialism—government ownership and development. During the last 10 years, Soviet Arctic shipping has increased many thousand percent. The population of several Arctic and subarctic towns has increased several hundred and even several thousand percent. The Archangel population figures are 76,774 for 1926 and 281,091 for 1939, an increase of 266.1 percent. The corresponding figures for Murmansk are 8,777 and 117,054, which is 1,233.6 percent in 13 years. Such is the growth

[5] STEFANSSON, VILHJALMUR. THE NORTHWARD COURSE OF EMPIRE. 274 pp., illus. New York. 1922.

of places that were already cities. Where villages have grown to cities, the percentages are frequently colossal; as, for instance, Igarka, which had less than 500 inhabitants 10 years ago and now has more than 15,000. Under socialism, then, it might reasonably be expected that many now living would see the time when Alaska would support as many people as the Finno-Scandinavian region and support them in a comparable degree of well-being. That, however, is a most academic consideration; for the United States shows fewer signs of going socialist than almost any country. With the possible exception of Wall Street, Alaska is the least socialistically minded place in America.

Climate and Settlement in Puerto Rico and the Hawaiian Islands

By James Thorp [1]

HERE ARE two regions, both situated in the milder outer Tropics, with rather similar climates and some of the same natural advantages. In one, much of the population faces serious economic difficulties like those found in parts of the continental United States. In the other, the general level of living is considerably higher. What makes the difference? Not climate, the author argues, but the balance between population and available resources.

[1] James Thorp is Soil Scientist, Division of Soil Survey, Bureau of Plant Industry.

It is a common belief that white people cannot lead normal lives in the Tropics but must make frequent and prolonged visits to temperate regions in order to maintain their health and ability to reproduce.[2] While this may be true of certain limited areas in the Tropics, it is interesting to consider the facts concerning white settlement in relation to climate in the milder tropical areas of Puerto Rico and the Hawaiian Islands. Experience in these areas seems to warrant the conclusion that climate alone in the milder Tropics offers no great obstacle to settlement by white people. Poverty and disease, which accompany overpopulation and bad economic and social conditions, are the chief causes of distress and misery, as they are in more temperate regions.

SETTLEMENT IN PUERTO RICO

The first colonization of Puerto Rico by the Spaniards was in 1508, following its discovery by Columbus in 1493. It is estimated (*6*) that there were 80,000 to 100,000 Carib Indians on the island at that time. Although these people at first were friendly to the strangers, friendship was soon replaced by hate when the greedy settlers began forcing them to work the gold deposits. In the following years there was a bloody struggle between the whites and Caribs which ended in the killing or driving out of practically all of the latter by 1582. Even as early as 1515 it was estimated that scarcely more than 4,000 Caribs remained.

Negro slaves were first introduced about 1510, and their number in proportion to whites gradually increased. According to Price (*6*), who collected data from many sources—

> In 1815 the "Schedule of Grace" opened the island to world commerce, and immigrants, including practical farmers from Louisiana, came in. In 1845 the island contained 216,183 whites, 175,791 free colored persons and 51,265 slaves. By the time of the Treaty of Paris, 1898, there were 570,187 whites, 239,808 persons of mixed color, and 75,824 negroes.

The census of 1930 showed a population of 1,543,913, and that of 1935–36 indicates that there were about 1,750,000, or 501 to the square mile, on the island at that time. Of this number it is estimated that somewhat less than one-third are colored. This is in contrast to a total of 52 percent colored in 1802 (Price) and indicates that the whites are competing sucessfully with the blacks for settlement of the island. The decrease in the proportion of colored people appears to be partly due to the fact that there is relatively little race prejudice among the mass of the people and consequently the whites are absorbing the blacks through miscegenation. Furthermore, the importation of Negro slaves was of course discontinued long ago, and there has been a considerable influx of white people since.

When the island was discovered in 1493 the Indians were raising corn, sweetpotatoes, manioc, or cassava, and other vegetables and fruits (*3*). Their only meat was fowl and fish, although it is possible that they may occasionally have eaten the flesh of the manatee (sea cow).

[2] The gist of this old controversy has been outlined by Hanson (*5*). (Italic numbers in parentheses refer to Literature Cited, p. 226.)

Sugarcane was first introduced into Puerto Rico from Haiti in 1515, and the first sugar mill was built in 1548. Crude sugar was being exported to Spain before the landing of the Pilgrims in New England. From that time on, commercial sugar has been produced continuously, but the total amount has been great only in the last two or three generations.

At present the greater part of the rich alluvial flood plains and river terraces and of the gently sloping uplands is devoted to sugarcane. Much of this land has gradually been combined to form large holdings for efficiency in management of land and manufacture of sugar. Small farms have been purchased by the large companies, and the dispossessed landowners have been obliged to settle in small villages around the sugar mills, where they obtain seasonal employment, or to move to the rough hilly lands which formerly were covered by forests. At present, the people of Puerto Rico are concentrated in urban centers, in sugar-factory communities, and on the lands that are too rough and broken to be suitable for cane production. The result is that the rural people of the lowlands and middle highlands live on the least productive soils, and many of them eke out their existence by walking daily to the cane fields and sugar factories during the seasons of rush work. They are able to raise enough vegetables and fruits to supply part of their subsistence but must obtain sufficient cash to pay for imported rice, beans, and codfish. In the higher country where there are many coffee plantations, the rural people are less concentrated than in areas adjacent to cane fields, although even here most of them live in small communities around the hacienda headquarters.

Apparently tobacco is indigenous to the island, but according to Dorsey (7) its cultivation was forbidden by papal bulls and royal decrees until 1614. By 1836 production of tobacco had increased sufficiently for nearly 5,000,000 pounds to be exported in 1 year, and since that time there have been great fluctuations in the amount raised and exported. Tobacco is produced both in the rolling plateau country of the region near Cayey and Aibonito and in the lowlands along the northern coast. Since most of the tobacco is produced on small farms, the population is more evenly distributed than in areas where sugarcane is the main crop.

Coffee has been produced in Puerto Rico since the eighteenth century. The amount produced has fluctuated greatly. Coffee trees and the shade trees necessary for the production of high-quality coffee have been destroyed or severely damaged during each of several very severe hurricanes. With these losses and the present low price of coffee it is difficult for the growers to make a living, even though the Puerto Rican type of coffee commands a premium in the European market.

Coffee growers are nearly all southern-European whites; the black and mulatto people have penetrated little into the highlands where coffee is raised. The Negroes and mulattoes are largely concentrated along the seacoast near the sugar factories and in the large cities.

It appears that health conditions were fairly good in the early days of the settlement of Puerto Rico, but the Negro slaves introduced in 1510 brought with them the diseases common to the black race in Africa. Hookworm, malaria, yellow fever, and smallpox have taken a terrific toll of life in Puerto Rico. When the island was taken over from Spain by the United States in 1898, campaigns were started to eradicate some of the more dangerous diseases, and yellow fever and smallpox have practically disappeared from the island. Malaria and hookworm continue to cause a great amount of sickness and loss of life. Before the occupation of the island by the United States, the population was increasing rapidly, and with the eradication of the more deadly plagues and the amelioration of the less deadly diseases, the rate of increase has been further augmented.

At the present time, the island has a larger population than can be well supported by its own agriculture. It appears that it is headed toward serious difficulties unless industries that will employ more people and increase their income can be introduced. Mass migration to other less densely populated islands of the West Indies or to the United States is a possible solution. There has already been a considerable migration to the United States, but the population increase has more than offset this loss. Recently enacted insular laws permit education in methods of birth control, but since this solution of the problem is not in harmony with the religious beliefs of many of the people, its effectiveness remains to be proved.

Nearly every humanitarian who visits Puerto Rico realizes the desperate condition of a large proportion of the people and proposes some sort of remedy. One of the most common is that the lands now devoted to sugarcane should be divided into small farms and that the people should be encouraged to raise subsistence crops instead of sugarcane. It seems extremely doubtful whether such a method of distribution of wealth would improve conditions, since sugarcane produces a greater value per acre than any other crop that might be grown, and the wages earned are sufficient to buy a considerably greater amount of food than could be produced on the land.[3]

It seems as if the introduction of more industries, either privately owned or cooperative, to absorb the available cheap labor of the island would furnish a better solution if satisfactory working conditions for the laborers and a fair degree of security for the owners could be provided. A limiting factor in such a program is the lack of coal and timber. Water power could be developed, however, to furnish considerable energy for industrial plants.

Whatever may be the solution, the present inhabitants of Puerto Rico are undeniably in a serious economic plight, which is becoming worse as the already overcrowded island becomes more densely populated.

In Puerto Rico it has been demonstrated beyond question that southern-European whites can settle successfully in the milder tropical areas and can compete with the black race, although it is necessary to control the many diseases that thrive in tropical regions, particularly where a large part of the people are poverty-stricken.

[3] It has been estimated (*8, pp. 41–43*) that wages earned on sugar plantations will buy three and one-half times as much other food as could be raised on the same land. The estimate is based on the average yields of common food crops in Puerto Rico. Probably more food could be produced by using superior strains of plants and by following scientific methods of culture, but even then it is doubtful whether food crops would equal sugar in value to the laborer.

GEOGRAPHIC SETTING AND CLIMATE OF PUERTO RICO

Geographically, Puerto Rico, the least of the four Greater Antilles, lies in about the same latitude as the Sahara Desert and is slightly farther south than the island of Hawaii. It is nearly rectangular in shape, a little more than 100 miles long from east to west, and more than 35 miles wide. The total area is 3,435 square miles, including Vieques, Culebra, Mona, and other small dependent islands (*7*).

The northern coastal plain is an area of limestone hills and solution valleys (formed by water dissolving part of the limestone) crossed by several streams with their level alluvial plains and terraces. Much of the central part of the island is a deeply dissected plateau with general elevations ranging from 1,500 to 2,500 feet. A few mountain peaks extend above this level to about 3,000 feet. The "backbone" of the island is an east-west chain of mountains the top of which varies in distance from about 8 to about 15 miles north of the southern coast. The higher peaks exceed 3,000 feet, and the highest, Cerro de Punta, is 4,398 feet high. The high Luquillo Range, on the eastern end of the island, is separated from the backbone by the broad Caguas Valley. The southern escarpment of the highest mountain ranges is precipitous. The southern coastal plain is narrower than that of the northern coast and consists of a series of coalescing level alluvial fans and terraces adjacent to the sea, separated from a series of narrow inner plains by a range of low hills composed of limestone, shale, and volcanic tuff.

According to reports of early explorers (*1*) Puerto Rico was originally forested from the tops of the mountains to the seashore, but there is plenty of evidence that the "forests" of the semiarid and arid southern coast consisted chiefly of scattered trees, desert shrubs, and cactus. The forests of the humid and wet areas, however, were originally luxuriant.

The rugged interior of the island, with its lush tropical vegetation, and the milder landscapes of the coastal areas offer an unusual variety of scenic splendor to the traveler; but the small proportion of normally arable land increases the problem of population pressure.

Records of rainfall in Puerto Rico, available from about 50 stations, cover periods ranging from 7 to 30 years [4] and indicate a maximum average annual precipitation of 136 inches and a minimum of 27 inches. The character of the vegetation and information from local residents indicate that the rainfall may average less than 20 inches in small areas in the southwestern part of the island and exceed 150 inches on a few of the higher mountain peaks.

The mean winter temperature of the northern and eastern coastal towns is about 75° F. and the mean summer temperature about 80°. Mean temperatures are probably 2° or 3° higher on the drier southern coast in both seasons. The temperature seldom exceeds 90°, even on the southern coast, and rarely falls below 50° except on the highest mountain peaks. Temperatures average about 5° lower in the mountainous interior than on the coast.

Because of the high mean temperatures, the effectiveness of the

[4] Data assembled from Weather Bureau records and other sources by R. C. Roberts and others (*7*).

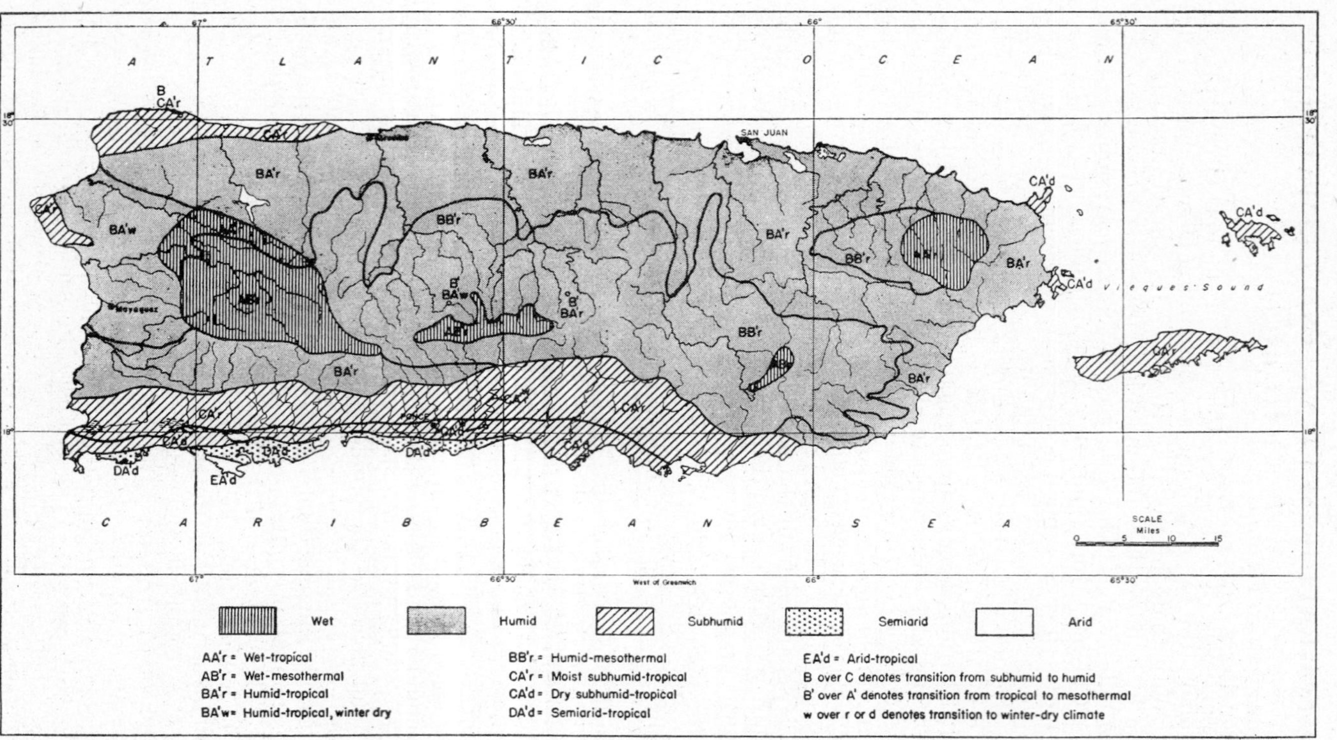

FIGURE 1.—Climatic map of Puerto Rico, according to the Thornthwaite system of classification (prepared by the writer under the guidance of C. W. Thornthwaite).

rainfall is considerably less than it would be in cooler climates, and it is further reduced below that of many cooler regions because of the almost constant air movement.

The northeasterly trade winds blow almost continuously winter and summer during the daytime; they are less persistent at night when cool air currents drift down to the coast from the mountainous interior. The strongest winds blow on the eastern end and the northwestern corner of the island.

The climatic types of Puerto Rico, according to Thornthwaite's system of classification (*9*), are shown in figure 1. Thornthwaite's system is designed to recognize the well-known principle that more rain is needed in warm countries to support a given type of vegetation than in cool countries.

The primary cause of rain in Puerto Rico seems to be that the moisture-laden winds of the Atlantic are forced upward by the hills and mountains, which causes the moisture to precipitate. The maximum amount of rain falls on the high mountain peaks, and as soon as the winds begin to descend on the southern side of the main mountain range, there is a rapid decrease in rainfall. From wet mountaintops south of the center of the island the descent is rapid to the semiarid and arid southern coastal plain, where in places the rainfall probably is less than 20 inches and precipitation effectiveness is very low. This rapid decrease in rainfall is partly due to the fact that the air loses most of its moisture in the cool mountains and therefore picks up rather than drops moisture as it descends to the warmer lowlands.

The island lies in the belt of West Indian hurricanes (Spanish "huracán" or "juracán," supposedly a corruption of the Carib name (*3*))—great whirling storms which are essentially the same as the typhoons of the Philippine area. Periodically these storms are violent enough to destroy most forests, crops, and buildings in their path. Violent storms of this type visit some part of the island about every 7 to 10 years, and hurricanes of less intensity come more frequently. They bring great quantities of rain as well as high winds.

Nearly everywhere in Puerto Rico rainfall is markedly lower in winter than in summer and autumn. Seasonal differences in rainfall are least marked along the northern and eastern coasts and most marked in the humid west-central and western parts of the island, where summer rainfall is several times that of winter. At Mayaguez the average rainfall is 1.89 inches in January and 11.26 in August. At Guajataca Reservoir 4 inches of rain falls in January and 11.42 in September.

SETTLEMENT IN THE HAWAIIAN ISLANDS

The history of the settlement of the Hawaiian Islands has been quite different from that of Puerto Rico. At the time of his first visit to the islands in 1778, Capt. James Cook found settlements of Polynesians making their living by farming and fishing. A few whites established themselves soon after Cook's visit, but permanent occupation by white settlement really began in earnest about the time of the arrival of the first Christian missionaries in 1820 (*4*). Since that time people of many countries have gone to the islands to settle, and at present only a relatively small proportion of the population consists of pure-blooded Polynesians. They have mixed with the white and the yellow races. A large proportion of the present population consists of Japanese, Chinese, Filipinos, and people of mixed racial origin.

Health conditions on the islands are better than in many parts of the United States proper, and not only is there little unemployment but wages are sufficient to sustain a high standard of living. A lack of strong racial prejudice in the islands results in the rather free mixing of various racial groups, and in general it appears that the resulting crosses are of desirable types.

The introduction of sugarcane into the Hawaiian Islands has resulted in the development of a prosperous sugar industry which has been able, through the use of scientific methods in cultivation and development of good varieties of cane, to produce some of the highest average yields in the world. The pineapple industry also is prosperous and employs a large number of people. Cattle are raised on a large scale on some of the islands and high-quality beef is produced. Ranching conditions in these areas are much like those of the western part of the United States except that the climate is less rigorous and good pasture grasses can be produced the year round. Dairying is important, especially near Honolulu.

The Hawaiian Islands are an excellent demonstration of the fact that white people can live comfortably in the milder tropics generation after generation without deterioration from the effects of climate, provided sanitary conditions reduce dangers from tropical diseases. It may be of some importance in this connection that relatively few Negroes have been introduced into the islands and that the diseases considered to be characteristic of that race are not prevalent.

In contrast with Puerto Rico, the Hawaiian Islands can support more than the present population.

GEOGRAPHIC SETTING AND CLIMATE OF THE HAWAIIAN ISLANDS

The following description is quoted from the 1938 Yearbook of Agriculture (*10*):

> The Hawaiian Archipelago is a chain of islands nearly 1,600 miles long near the center of the North Pacific Ocean. The larger islands form a group about 375 miles long at the east end of the chain and entirely within the Tropics. [The areas of the principal, inhabited islands are: Hawaii, 4,030 square miles; Maui, 728; Oahu, 604; Kauai, 555; Molokai, 260; Lanai, 141; Niihau, 72; and Kahoolawe, 45 square miles.[5]] The total area of the remaining small islands is only about 6 square miles.
>
> The islands are great volcanic mountains rising from ocean depths of 15,000 to 18,000 feet to a maximum elevation (Mauna Kea) of 13,825 feet above sea level. The islands at the west end of the group are apparently older than those farther east, where there is still extensive active volcanism. These western islands have more deeply and thoroughly weathered mantles of soil material and are more maturely dissected—titantic erosion has produced canyons 3,000 feet deep on the island of Kauai. The island of Hawaii, comprising two-thirds of the area of the archipelago, consists of five volcanic mountains, some of them active, connected by saddles formed by coalescing or overlapping lava flows. There is little dissection and there are no streams except in heavy rains.
>
> The isolation of the islands and their great diversity of soil, relief, drainage,

[5] The area figures given are those of the General Land Office revised to 1940.

and climate has led to the development of a unique flora and one that is extremely diversified. Many of the native species are found nowhere else. There are more than 1,000 native flowering plants, including 300 kinds of trees, about 150 species of ferns, among them tree ferns 25 to 30 feet high, and hundreds of species of mosses, fungi, and algae.

The character of the rainfall of the Hawaiian Islands is much like that of Puerto Rico, but the range in precipitation is very much greater.

The northeast trade winds, blowing in from cool ocean currents, modify the temperatures and carry a heavy load of moisture, much of which is dropped on the islands. Rough relief and great range in elevation produce great differences in temperature and rainfall within short distances. Temperatures are generally lower than in similar latitudes and altitudes elsewhere. There is a decrease of about 1° F. for each rise in elevation of 300 feet. At Honolulu, 50 feet above sea level, the mean annual temperature is 74.4°; at Humuula on Hawaii, at an elevation of 6,685 feet, it is 52°. Freezing temperatures, frost, and snow very rarely occur below 4,000 feet but are common in winter above 6,000 feet.

Rainfall varies extremely from place to place—the range being from less than 20 inches to almost 500 inches annually. It is heaviest on windward slopes from 300 to 5,000 feet above the sea. The lowlands receive less moisture, and the lower leeward slopes and plains are arid or semiarid. The higher mountains have relatively low rainfall on the upper reaches, the moisture-laden winds having lost most of their rain below 6,000 feet. There are no extreme wet and dry seasons as in much of the Tropics, but there is usually more rainfall in summer than in winter. The distribution of rainfall on Oahu is shown on the sketch map (fig. [2]), which illustrates the effect of topography and elevation on rainfall in the trade-wind belt, though the high mountain masses on Hawaii and Maui have some modifying effect.[6]

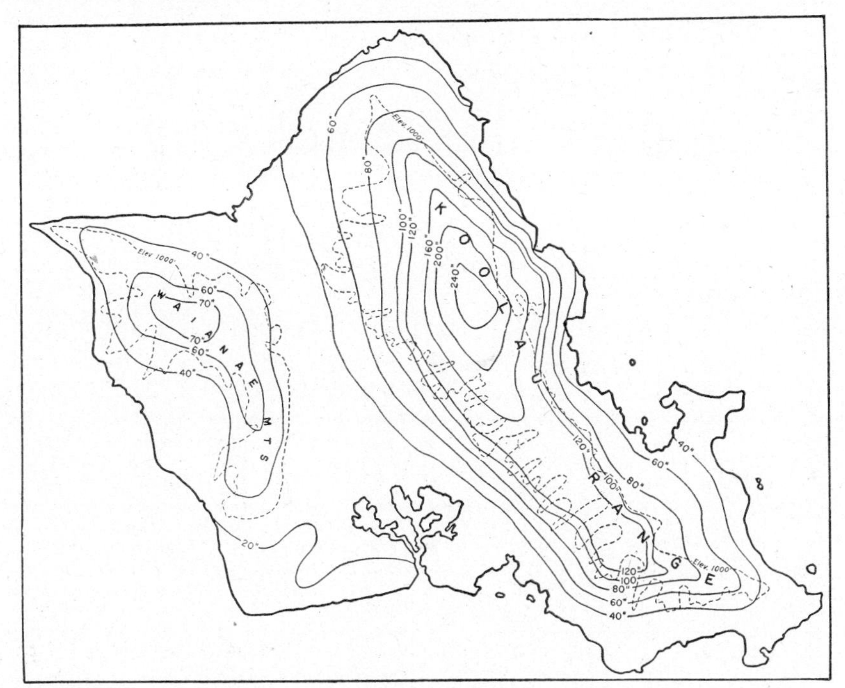

FIGURE 2.—Map of Oahu, showing the effect of topography and elevation on distribution of rainfall.

[6] Climatological data from records of the Weather Bureau, Hawaii section.

LITERATURE CITED

(1) Britton, N. L.
1930. THE PLANTING OF A STAHLIA ON ARBOR DAY IN PORTO RICO. N. Y. Bot. Gard. Jour. 31: 45–47.

(2) Dorsey, Clarence W., Mesmer, Louis, and Caine, Thomas A.
1903. SOIL SURVEY FROM ARECIBO TO PONCE, PORTO RICO. U. S. Dept. Agr., Bur. Soils Field Oper. 1902, Rpt. 4: 793–839, illus.

(3) Enamorado Cuesta, J.
[1929.] PORTO RICO, PAST AND PRESENT, THE ISLAND AFTER THIRTY YEARS OF AMERICAN RULE . . . 170 pp. [New York.]

(4) Frear, Walter Francis.
1937. HAWAII. Encyc. Brit. 11: 264–273, illus.

(5) Hanson, Earl P.
1940. GEOGRAPHY GOES FLUID. Harper's Mag. 1077: [245]–253.

(6) Price, A. Grenfell.
1939. WHITE SETTLERS IN THE TROPICS. Amer. Geog. Soc. Spec. Pub. 23, 311 pp., illus.

(7) Roberts, R. C., and others.
1941. SOIL SURVEY OF PUERTO RICO. U. S. Dept. Agr. [In press.]

(8) Smith, Dudley, and Requa, William M.
1939. PUERTO RICO SUGAR FACTS. 125 pp., illus. (Assoc. Sugar Producers of Puerto Rico.)

(9) Thornthwaite, C. W.
1931. THE CLIMATES OF NORTH AMERICA ACCORDING TO A NEW CLASSIFICATION. Geog. Rev. 21: 633–655, illus.

(10) United States Bureau of Chemistry and Soils, Soil Survey Division.
1938. SOILS OF THE HAWAIIAN ISLANDS. U. S. Dept. Agr. Yearbook 1938: 1151–1161, illus.

Climate and Future Settlement

By Jan O. M. Broek [1]

AFTER COLUMBUS discovered America, there were several centuries of intense pioneering and emigration all over the world. This long period has come to an end. Yet there are still large areas on the earth where there is plenty of room for more people. Where are these regions? What are they like? Why are they so thinly populated? What are the chances of successfully colonizing them in the future?

[1] Jan O. M. Broek is Associate Professor of Geography, University of California.

ANY ATTEMPT to prophesy is hazardous, and to evaluate climate as a factor in future settlement is particularly difficult. Not only is our knowledge of climate incomplete, but the function of climate varies with the cultural level of the occupying group. Man is not a passive creature who merely submits to the forces of his milieu. By setting his own standards, by rebelling against restrictions of the environment, he has gradually overcome obstacles and harnessed resources. There is no reason to believe that he has reached the end of his conquest.

This is not to say, however, that all climates are equally favorable. A study of the present distribution of population clearly reveals that certain zones offer stubborn resistance to dense settlement (fig. 1). In general, these regions belong to the following three climatic extremes: (1) Areas with low rainfall—the deserts; (2) areas with low temperatures—the polar regions; (3) areas with a combination of year-round high precipitation and high temperatures—the equatorial rain-forest regions. On the margins of these are the transition zones to the so-called temperate climates—respectively, the semiarid steppes, the subpolar forests, and the seasonally dry outer Tropics (fig. 2).

No doubt one could speculate in various ways on eventual changing relations between settlement and climate in the already well-populated regions; but this article will focus attention on regions with unsolved climatic problems in other parts of the world than the United States. The discussion will also be limited to the possibilities of settlement by peoples of European stock (*1*, *2*, *4*).[2]

SETTLEMENT IN TROPICAL LANDS

Of the three climatic extremes, the equatorial lowlands with their excessive moisture and heat appear to be least repellent to human settlement. They may not have a high density of population, but neither do they show the empty spaces typical of the deserts and the polar lands. To high forms of cultural achievement, however, this environment seems unfavorable. There is no record of any advanced indigenous civilization in the Amazon and Congo Basins or in the equatorial parts of the Malay Archipelago.

Why this is so remains a matter of speculation. Perhaps the uniformity of climate is not conducive to foresighted action, as are climates with seasonal contrasts. More important, it may be that the overpowering vegetative growth and the leached soils offer tremendous resistance to human effort. Also the prevalence of diseases, which are carried from person to person by a multitude of insects, the monotonous and deficient diets, and perhaps the direct influence of the climate on human physiology should be considered. But one should take care to avoid purely environmental explanations. In many instances European exploitation, alcohol, disease, and the slave trade have caused the population to diminish and the native economic and social structure to deteriorate. Whatever the reasons, the fact remains that the equatorial lands are sparsely populated and are thus potential regions for immigration.

The majority of whites who at present live in the Tropics, either temporarily or permanently, belong to the social-economic upper

[2] Italic numbers in parentheses refer to Literature Cited, p. 236.

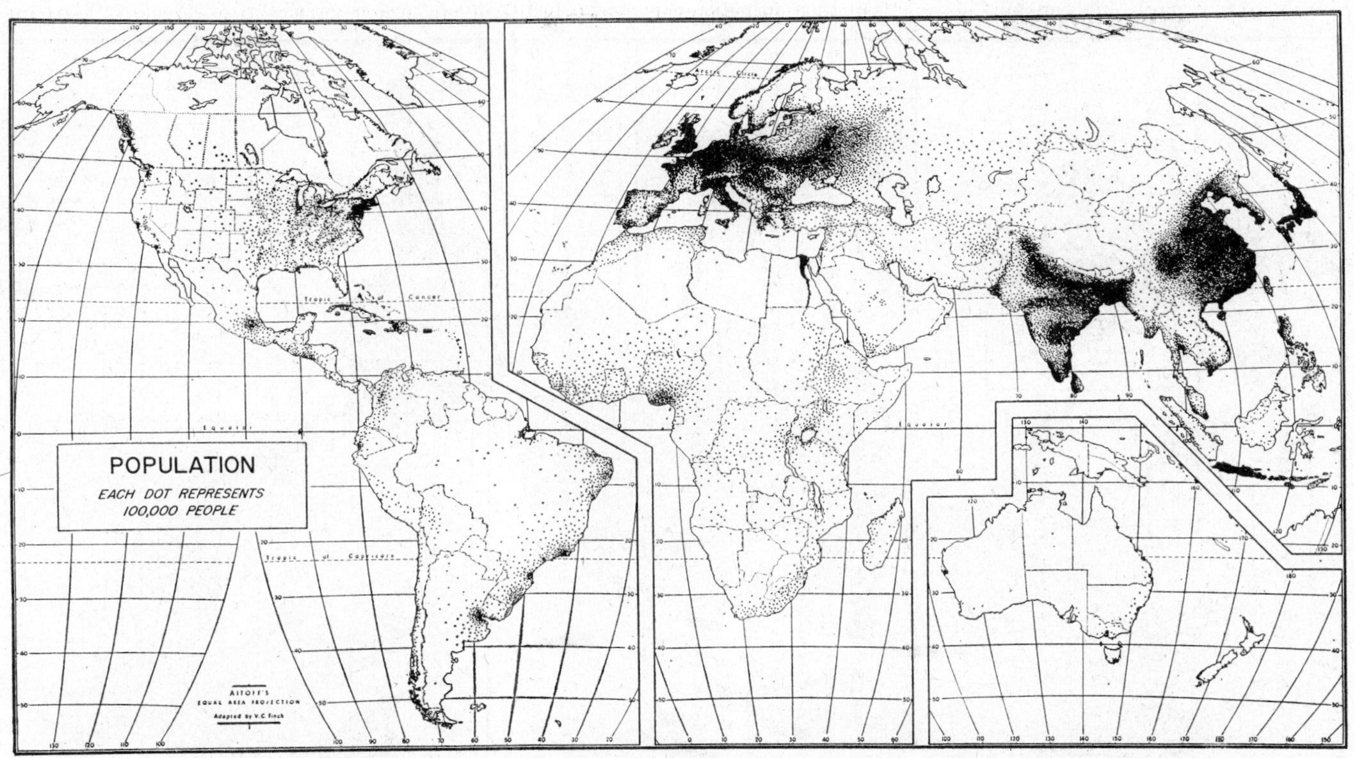

FIGURE 1.—World population, showing concentration of settlement in regions of more favorable climates.

298737°—41——16

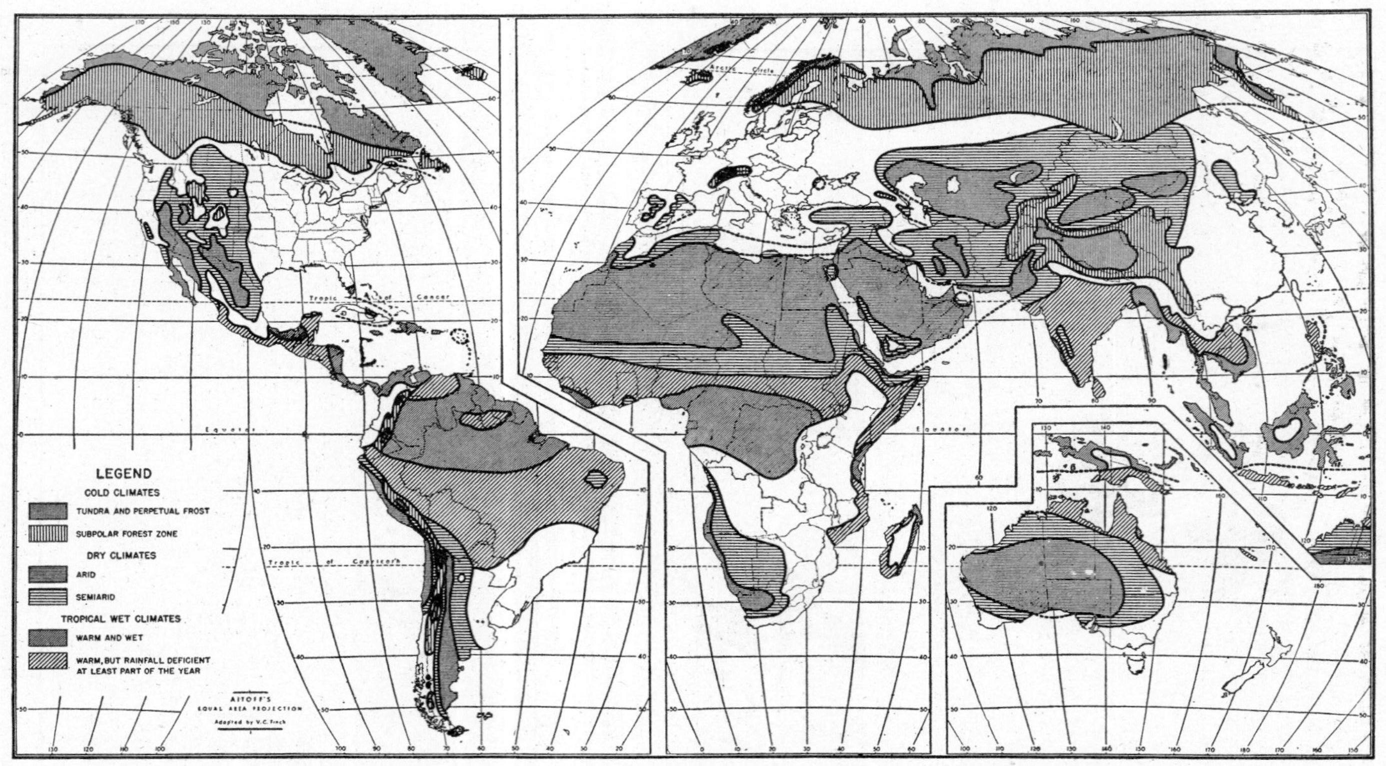

FIGURE 2.—Climates of the earth, showing the extent of regions dominated by cold, dry, and wet climates unfavorable to settlement.

strata, relying upon other races for physical labor. Immigration of whites in large numbers, however, implies the establishment of complete communities in which they would perform all functions. There are very few such colonies in the equatorial lowlands. The suitability of these territories for white settlement is still a hotly debated question.[3]

There are two main aspects to the problem: (1) Can the whites maintain physical and mental health in the Tropics? and (2) can they be economically successful there? The answer to the first question was long held to be in the negative, as far as the tropical lowlands are concerned. But in recent decades there has been a definite swing to a more optimistic view, and for good reasons. Causes and cures have been found for such "tropical" diseases as malaria, dysentery, yellow fever, African sleeping sickness, hookworm, and others. Formerly physical labor in the Tropics was regarded as dangerous; modern evidence strongly indicates that it is instead an effective means of keeping fit, bodily as well as mentally. Moreover, air conditioning may in time become as significant in fighting heat as the traditional means of fighting cold are in temperate climates.

It cannot be denied, however, that the health problem requires constant vigilance, certain expenditures for sanitation, a balanced diet, and other precautionary measures. In other words, there must be a relatively high standard of living. This leads directly to the economic question. As a matter of fact, health and income are more closely intertwined in the Tropics than anywhere else. Although a discussion of economic problems is outside the scope of this article, a few points must be mentioned because of their fateful relation to the climatic struggle.

The leached soils of the tropical rain forest on the whole give low yields. This may be counterbalanced by obtaining two harvests a year, but that is not everywhere possible. Furthermore, there is reason to believe that cultivation requires more labor per acre of cropland than in the Temperate Zone, chiefly because of the need for frequent weeding (*3, pp. 125–130*). If these observations are correct, it means that the productivity of labor in the Tropics is low. This might be one explanation of why the white man usually has found small-scale farming unprofitable.

Even if this were not true, most tropical countries present problems associated with the presence of an indigenous population. Not only is the native because of his carelessness a constant source of infection, but, more important economically, he works for a far smaller reward than can the white man because he has much more restricted material and cultural wants. This competition naturally has a tendency to pull down the white farmer's income. Theoretically, this may be overcome in various ways—for instance, by producing high-value crops which the native does not raise or by using machinery for large-scale farming. But there is always the chance that the native will imitate him and plant the same crops; and as far as farming with machinery is concerned, there are various obstacles to success, especially the cultivation requirements of most tropical crops and, again, the presence of a cheap labor supply.

In view of these difficulties most experts agree that, although white settlement in equatorial lowlands is physically possible, the economic

[3] For informative and up-to-date discussions of this problem see (*3*) and (*5*).

handicaps in comparison with those of other regions are such that at present intensive colonization seems inadvisable. Where colonies are contemplated, they should be preceded by experimental farms and established only under expert leadership.

Chances for settlement are considerably better in the cooler uplands of the Tropics. This is proved by a number of communities scattered through the Cordilleras of Central and South America as well as the African highlands. On the East African plateaus and the Rhodesian and Angolian uplands, at altitudes between 3,000 and 6,000 feet, white colonists raise cotton, coffee, sisal, maize, wheat, and livestock. Health conditions appear to be satisfactory. These colonies could be expanded if transportation were improved. It should be noted, though, that the Negro population, rapidly increasing in recent years, restricts the area available. Also, in most of these African settlements the white owner relies upon cheap native farm labor for much of the work; in other words, the farm economy resembles more the plantation or hacienda type than the small-scale family-farm community.

The highlands of central Brazil may be climatically well suited to white occupation; moreover, the natives are comparatively few. But various institutional and social factors and lack of transportation facilities are formidable barriers to the development of this territory.

The lowlands of the outer Tropics have a comparatively cool season, which makes them better suited for the white man than are the equatorial lowlands. The climatic limitations lie in the distribution of the precipitation. Many parts of the outer Tropics have a protracted dry season and a highly variable rainfall. This is notably true of northeastern Brazil and northern Australia. In small areas irrigation may be possible. For the remainder, the great problem is to find commercial crops adapted to the short (and very warm) rainy season.

A good example of the effect of rainfall is the part of Australia located in the outer Tropics. Here the population is extremely sparse except on the east coast of Queensland, where there is sufficient rainfall for a variety of crops and sugarcane is the main commodity. The whites themselves do the heavy field work and seem none the worse for it. But two points should be noted: (1) Queensland is a white man's country since the colored labor formerly employed was forced to leave; (2) the Commonwealth subsidizes the cane growers by a high tariff on imported sugar. Even under these favorable conditions only the humid eastern part has been occupied. To the west and north lie almost empty semiarid wastes. The "white Australia" policy is understandable, but it places a heavy responsibility upon the leaders of the Commonwealth. There is an urgent need for effective occupation of North Australia by acclimatized whites.

SETTLEMENT IN THE DRY LANDS

In comparison with the tropical regions, the desert offers no particular obstacles to acclimatization. As a matter of fact, the dry air and the absence of disease-carrying insects are, in most cases, favorable to health. Generally speaking, desert soils are rich in mineral nutrients; the fundamental condition needed for their development is the procurement of water. Modern techniques have greatly increased the means of conquering the desert, but they require a very large capital investment, profitable only if high-value crops are produced. The extensive irrigation works on the Indus, Nile, and Niger Rivers are well known. Obviously these areas are outlets for native rather than white farmers. Given favorable economic conditions, there is no doubt that the irrigated desert area could be enlarged. Outside the United States there are some possibilities in the west-coast deserts of South America and—probably of wider scope—in Mesopotamia, the lower Volga region, and Turkestan.

The rainfall in the semiarid fringes, although meager on the average, may in some years be considerable. These variations make the steppe a far more hazardous land with which to deal than is the desert. As far as climate is concerned, successful occupation depends upon how well the farming methods are adapted to these special conditions. These problems have been discussed in a preceding article on the Great Plains. It may be noted that substantially the same struggle characterizes settlement in the steppes of Argentina, South Africa, southern Australia, Manchuria, Mongolia, and southern Siberia. These semiarid regions, formerly the habitat of the roaming hunter or herdsman, have for the greater part been settled during the last century. This has been made possible through modern means of transportation and cultivation. In some of these areas the frontier is still moving forward, but in general it can be said that already the best steppe lands are occupied. The main task now is to consolidate the conquest in terms of a better adjustment to the peculiar environment. It is even quite likely that the forward surge into the dry realms has gone further than is wise under present conditions. Wherever further advance is possible it will require heavy capital investment. Clearly it is not production per acre that counts here, but production per man. Settlement, therefore, will always be sparse.

SETTLEMENT IN THE POLAR LANDS

The low-temperature climate appears to be the most formidable of the three extremes, if one may judge by the very scanty population. Even in the broad belt of the subpolar forest, or taiga, settlement has scarcely made a dent. Yet for the man from the middle latitudes acclimatization is fairly easy here; it seems that the contrast of light and dark seasons is harder to bear than is the intense cold of the long winters. The chief obstacle is the short season for growing crops. There are two other environmental factors, however, that restrict opportunities. One is the generally poor soils and the glacial morphology of the landscape; the other is the inaccessibility of most of this zone, since the continents of the Northern Hemisphere have their greatest width in these high latitudes and the Arctic Ocean has (or had until recently) no value as a communication route. But even in northern Scandinavia, adjacent to the open sea, the age-long struggle of European civilization against the subpolar forest has resulted in only a sparse population.

The areas of perpetual frost around the North and South Poles are obviously out of the question for permanent settlement, even though the establishment of metereological stations, airplane bases, and mining camps may be expected as the ice caps gain in significance for the inhabited world. The tundra—the treeless, moss-covered polar steppe—has too short a summer to allow normal agriculture. The mean temperature of the warmest month is below 50° F., and only the top layer of the soil thaws during the warm season. For the settlement of people other than native nomads a new way of living must be found.

In this respect the recent policy of the Union of Soviet Socialist Republics is of great interest (*8*). The main goal is to create a safe navigation route through the arctic waters, practically a private corridor of some 6,000 miles, linking the western and eastern extremities of the country. In the last few years a score of ships have each season (July until October) made the through passage. The development of this route requires that various navigation facilities and ports of call be created along the arctic coast; this in turn will make possible the exploitation of the mineral resources as well as the export of timber from the southward forest zone. Because these extreme northern settlements are so remote, it is of crucial significance for the tenability of the whole position that the food problem be solved. The Central Administration of the Northern Sea Route, which has jurisdiction over the whole Russian Arctic (in Siberia as far south as the 62d parallel) is therefore charged with the development of its agriculture. The extreme north, as an official statement declares, must supply the industrial and trading population with vegetables and milk, organize forage bases for livestock, and establish hothouse production of antiscurvy greens.

Reindeer raising and hothouse culture are the only possibilities for the coastal fringe; it is claimed, however, that farther south, though still well north of the Arctic Circle, various berries and vegetables such as radishes, carrots, cabbages, and onions are grown successfully in the open. In view of the peculiar character of the Soviet regime and the baffling contradictions in the statistics, it is hard to say what the actual state of affairs is. Yet as an experiment in subduing the Arctic it deserves full attention.

Whatever the future possibilities of the tundra may be, it is unlikely that it will ever support a large number of people at a relatively high level of living. In this respect the taiga offers a somewhat better outlook. Climatic conditions there are not adverse to the production of well-selected crops. The limiting factors are principally the low temperature of air and soil in the spring and fall, but the shortness of the summer is partly counterbalanced by the great number of hours of daylight. Potatoes, flax, and various vegetables do well; even early-maturing grains and forage crops can be raised. The growing period of grains can be materially shortened by so-called vernalization, which consists in starting the germination process artificially, after which the plants are kept for a time in cold storage. If this procedure is economically feasible it will be an important means of pushing agriculture farther poleward.

The northward move of the farmer is determined not so much by the agricultural possibilities in themselves as by the demand for foodstuffs in areas of forest and mineral exploitation. Often he can supplement his income in winter by working in the mine, the forest, or the lumber mill. Agricultural expansion, therefore, depends upon the expansion of the latter industries and especially upon their degree of stability. When the policy is one of "cut out and get out," it leaves stranded farm communities in its wake and demoralizes the pioneer fringe. Only by carefully planning and coordinating the various activities can a thriving settlement be established.

In the Eurasian taiga the boundary of agriculture lies, on an average, farther north than in its American counterpart, owing to earlier settlement and greater population pressure. In the somewhat protected river valleys of central and eastern Siberia—as for instance in the Lena River Basin—farming is carried on as far as 65° N. In western Canada the 58th parallel is about the limit. The Northwest Territories of Canada beyond the 60th parallel comprise about 1,300,000 square miles but contain not more than 1,000 whites plus some 10,000 natives. Southern Alaska, while having no worse climate than Finland, has as yet only a very small farming population. Far-flung explorations, mostly by airplane, have been going on in the last decades, but no great undertaking like the opening of the Northeast Passage on the other side of the Arctic has as yet provided the inspirational stimulus for a determined assault on the Far North.[4]

IN CONCLUSION

It is clear from the foregoing review that there are large areas still potentially available for human settlement. But it must be kept in mind that migration is essentially not a flow from densely populated areas to sparsely populated ones, but from areas of lesser to those of better opportunities. For some 400 years the European peoples have swarmed out into nearly empty lands, which were at the same time—broadly speaking—good lands. The situation is different now; land that has not yet been taken is mainly of a marginal nature, often because of its climate.

Controlling a new environment requires learning the laws of its behavior and devising ways to use them to the greatest advantage. No doubt science and technology will find further means of overcoming the present obstacles; even so, the borderlands with unfavorable climates can be won only with considerable effort and at high cost. This imposes a heavy burden on the modern pioneer, diminishing his chances of gaining a better living than he had in his home country.

This is not to say that the frontiers have become stagnant. At present there is an intensive search for lands suitable for European refugees. This need may well give new impetus to colonization of hitherto neglected territories. Nevertheless, it seems beyond doubt that the advance will take place more slowly than before. But just because expansion will be slower, it may be more substantial and may lead to a more secure grip on the climatic problem areas.

[4] For a vivid and optimistic account of the potential value of the polar lands, see (*6*) and (*7*); see also The Colonization of Northern Lands, p. 205 of this Yearbook.

LITERATURE CITED

(1) Bowman, Isaiah.
1931. THE PIONEER FRINGE. Amer. Geog. Soc. Spec. Pub. 13, 361 pp., illus.

(2) ——— ed.
1937. LIMITS OF LAND SETTLEMENT; A REPORT ON PRESENT-DAY POSSIBILITIES. 380 pp., illus. New York. (Council on Foreign Relations.) [Bibliography, pp. 339–372.]

(3) International Congress of Geographers.
1938. GÉOGRAPHIE COLONIALE. Cong. Internatl. de Geog., Amsterdam, Compt. Rend., Tome 2, sect. 3c, 364 pp. [Many contributions in English.]

(4) Joerg, W. L. G., ed.
1932. PIONEER SETTLEMENT; COOPERATIVE STUDIES BY TWENTY-SIX AUTHORS. Amer. Geog. Soc. Spec. Pub. 14, 473 pp., illus.

(5) Price, A. Grenfell.
1939. WHITE SETTLERS IN THE TROPICS. Amer. Geog. Soc. Spec. Pub. 23, 311 pp., illus.

(6) Stefansson, Vilhjalmur.
1921. THE FRIENDLY ARCTIC; THE STORY OF FIVE YEARS IN POLAR REGIONS. 784 pp., illus. New York and London.

(7) ———
1922. THE NORTHWARD COURSE OF EMPIRE. 274 pp., illus. New York.

(8) Taracouzio, Timothy Andrew.
1938. SOVIETS IN THE ARCTIC; AN HISTORICAL, ECONOMIC AND POLITICAL STUDY OF THE SOVIET ADVANCE INTO THE ARCTIC. 563 pp., illus. New York. [Bibliography.]

Comfort and Disease in Relation to Climate

By Joseph Hirsh [1]

THE PEOPLE in every region are interested in how to be comfortable and healthy under a given set of climatic conditions; perhaps this is the main reason why the weather is a universal topic of conversation. Here is a broad general discussion of the way the body adjusts itself to changes in temperature; why we are uncomfortable under certain extreme conditions of temperature and humidity, and what we can do to be more comfortable; and what diseases are influenced in one way or another by climate.

[1] Joseph Hirsh is Specialist in Health Education, Vocational Training for Defense Workers, United States Office of Education; when this article was prepared he was Assistant Health Education Specialist, United States Public Health Service.

CLIMATE AND COMFORT

THERE is probably no one on earth who has not been affected in one way or another, mentally, emotionally, and physically, by climate and by changes in the weather. Some of the more obvious effects are expressed from day to day in our attitude toward other people, in restlessness or complacency, in the amount of work we accomplish or feel too sluggish to accomplish.

In a report on human reactions to changes in weather (*9*),[2] Winslow, of the Yale School of Public Health, found that a group under study thought the weather in fall and winter more refreshing and pleasant than at any other time of the year. A rising barometer, sunshine, and moderately low humidity were generally regarded as important in these subjective evaluations. A long period of the same kind of weather—of bright days or cloudy days, humid days or rainy days—frequently becomes depressing or irritating. Mills (*6*), Ward (*8*), and others have pointed out that this is especially common in the Tropics and in the subtropics of the United States. The characteristic high temperature and high humidity of the Tropics and subtropics, with only slight variation from day to day, have some well-established psychological and physiological effects. (These are discussed in the article by Robert G. Stone, p. 246.)

In the temperate sections of the United States, where people are subjected to wide day-to-day and seasonal changes in the weather, they become adjusted psychologically and physiologically with greater ease. Unless cold is too severe or prolonged, it serves as a stimulant to body and mind, just as a cool shower in hot weather refreshes. There is not the unbroken monotony of just one kind of weather or just one season.

TEMPERATURE REGULATION IN THE BODY

In the United States, people experience a wide range in weather conditions. In winter in the Dakotas, the temperature may drop to as low as 40° below zero F. and even lower. In summer in the hot, low-lying desert regions of Utah and Arizona, it may be as high as 130°. How does man adjust himself to such extremes? The human body maintains a fairly constant internal temperature averaging 98.6°. This is accomplished by the balance the body maintains between heat production and heat loss.

The main source of body heat is the food we eat, approximately 80 percent of which is used for growth, tissue repair, and heat production. The other 20 percent furnishes the energy necessary for daily activities. Every time we walk or turn or run, muscles as well as internal organs are involved in producing heat. Seventy percent of the heat produced by muscular exercise is waste and must be lost to the environment. To retain this heat would have the same effect experienced in a hot stuffy room. Vitality would be lowered, and we would be overcome with a general weakness of the kind experienced in fever.

The body automatically maintains a nearly constant temperature by the regulation of internal heat production—that is, the metabolic

[2] Italic numbers in parentheses refer to Literature Cited, p. 245.

rate—and the control of heat retention and heat loss through respiration, blood circulation, and secretion by sweat glands. The skin and the fatty tissue immediately underlying it form a natural garment for the rest of the body. During cold days this garment serves as a protection against the weather. On such days, the blood vessels near the surface contract and lie deeper in the skin, conserving the body's heat, and the skin is left pale and pinched. When we are physically active or the day is warm, the surface blood vessels dilate, the skin takes on a rosy hue, and we may become flushed. The blood carries heat to the surface, where it can be lost to the air outside. Heat is also lost in the evaporation of sweat and in exhaling.

Children adapt themselves more readily than adults to changes in weather and to wide ranges in climate. The exceptions to this rule are premature and very small infants. They require incubators and air-conditioned rooms which have fixed temperature and humidity levels necessary to maintain constant body temperature (*3*). Most people after middle age, especially those with poor circulation, adapt themselves poorly to changes in weather and require warm and not overstimulating climatic conditions.

The body possesses thermostatic equipment which makes it possible for man to adapt himself to varying conditions of weather and climate. Important as this physical equipment is, adaptation depends also upon some intangible neuropsychological factor. Most of us readily adapt ourselves to summer and winter conditions of comfort, so that many individuals who feel uncomfortably cool in a summer temperature of 68° F., in winter consider such a temperature uncomfortably warm.

Other Factors Responsible for Comfort

Our sensations of comfort, however, depend not only upon temperature but upon a number of other factors as well. Air motion, humidity, smoke and dust, and overcrowding are some of these.

Temperature alone indicates only the degree of warmth or coldness; by itself it is not a complete index of comfort. On a day with little moisture in the air, for example, a temperature of 78° may be comfortable, but the same degree of comfort can be experienced on a damp day with the temperature as low as 73° F.

In moving air, loss of body heat is accelerated so that comfort can be attained at relatively high temperatures. According to Hill, "Under ordinary . . . conditions most of the body heat is lost by radiation and convection, the loss by evaporation in comparison being insignificant" (*4*). When people are crowded together indoors in an atmosphere devoid of air motion, or on hot, muggy, windless days out of doors, loss of heat by these three mechanisms is limited. The air surrounding the body becomes warmed by the body temperature and saturated with moisture. The body becomes hot, flushed, and uncomfortable. If body heat cannot be dissipated, heat exhaustion, a condition characterized by dizziness, a sense of oppression, lassitude, weakness, and occasionally by fainting spells, may follow. Moist air permits little evaporation of moisture from the body and, when coupled with high temperature, aggravates these symptoms.

Heat exhaustion and heatstroke can be forestalled in crowded rooms by proper ventilation and especially by dehumidifying or circulating the air. Circulating the air brings "fresh" and comparatively dry air in contact with the body surface, and a sense of comfort is preserved. Out of doors, cool, shaded, breezy places should be sought, though if the temperature is lowered too much, continued evaporation of residual sweat will give the skin a sensation of chilliness. Removal of clothes is another obvious way of getting relief. In the Tropics, natives customarily wrap themselves in wet sheets and cloths as a protection against heatstroke, a practice that is followed generally in the treatment of this condition.

Important as high humidity is as an inhibiting factor in heat loss and in its relation to our sense of comfort, it plays an even greater role in its relation to health. While no upper limit to the amount of moisture in the air is generally accepted as the standard for good health, it is commonly agreed that warm, very dry air is less pleasant and, more important, less healthful than air of a moderate humidity, since dry air irritates and dries the mucous membranes of the nose and throat and increases susceptibility to colds and other respiratory disorders. Cool air with a relative humidity of 30 percent or more enhances both the flow of blood through the membranes lining the breathing passages and the circulation of fluids, which acts as a cleansing mechanism.

In normal health, people are sensitive to such weather factors as changes of temperature and humidity and possibly to changes in barometric pressure due to the passage of storms. Heat generally relaxes the tissues of the body and brings blood and lymph into them so that pain is relieved. Cold, on the contrary, contracts the skin tissues, and causes a tingling of the skin. Moist air lessens the insulating power of the skin and the clothes, and in a draft or a wind the evaporation of moisture on the skin often leads to chills. On a cold damp day we may experience these effects acutely. We literally shake with cold, and our lips may turn blue. Shivering, an involuntary reflex to cold, increases body heat by muscular contractions.

Indoor Climate

The major problem in controlling indoor atmospheres is to maintain the balance between heat production and heat loss in the body.

In cold weather the body automatically offsets excessive heat loss by more rapid heat production and constriction of the blood vessels in the skin; in warm weather it banks its internal fires and dilates skin blood vessels (*10*). If we were to remain in a constant relatively comfortable temperature all the time, the problem of maintaining the balance would be relatively simple. But in the Temperate Zone people spend a considerable part of their time outdoors where they have no control over atmospheric conditions. In conditioning homes in these latitudes, therefore, indoor temperatures should approximate outdoor conditions as much as possible without detracting from our sense of comfort. In passing from one to the other we can thus adjust with greater ease. Houses should not be kept too hot in winter or too cool in summer.

In very hot climates, homes should be built to afford free ventilation, with large shaded windows and wide verandas so as to catch the wind, and with thick walls and double roofs with an air space between so as to dissipate heat. In temperate climates, frame houses should have double walls, if possible containing moisture-resistant materials. Dryness can be secured by liming and papering walls. Floors should be elevated above the ground.

Radiant heat, a warm floor, and an agreeable movement of air are essential in warming and ventilating rooms. Open fires, steam and hot-water pipes, and stoves give radiant heat. Unless there is adequate ventilation, however, heat, moisture, and dust may become oppressive and irritating to the nose and throat. When cold air enters through windows and doors or inside air is chilled through contact with cold glass panes, it will flow down next to the floor unless there are vigorous currents of air in the room to mix the cold with the warm air. In the winter most rooms have temperature differences of 5° to 30° F. between the floor and the ceiling (*1*). When feet and ankles are chilled by a draft blowing over the cold floor and the head is immersed in warm stagnant air, we feel chilled and stuffy; the nose becomes congested, the mucous membranes swollen and full of fluid; we may experience discomfort and become susceptible to colds. Radiators, hot-water pipes, and stoves, therefore, should be placed near or under windows so as to warm and mix the incoming air. Satisfactory outlets are necessary for air circulation, but they must be so constructed as to prevent drafts.

Though much has been written about temperature levels that are comfortable and conducive to good health, there is a dearth of accurate information on proper atmospheric conditions as they relate to different age groups, sex, states of health, working conditions, seasons of the year, and climatic conditions. These and many other problems must be solved before air conditioning becomes universal.

Adjustment to Climate

The ideal climate for the mental and physical health and comfort of most people is one that is marked by frequent but moderate changes in weather, variations in temperature from day to night, and gradual seasonal changes. Such a "middle" climate has been found bodily invigorating and stimulating.

A climate that is neither invariably hot nor continuously cold, that is neither monotonously rainy or foggy nor arid and cloudless—in other words, the climate common to the central region of North America—is most conducive to exercising the body's power of adaptation and reaction and keeping people fit and comfortable.

Relative humidity of between 30 and 70 percent [3] is considered most satisfactory from the point of view of good health and comfort.

Low body-heat production means less energy and less protection against disease. This relates directly to the problems that many people from the South experience when they travel north. They cannot stand abrupt changes in weather and require protection against the cold and other inclement conditions. When the southerner journeys north, while his imagination too may come into play, it is something much more basic that makes him chill in the northern cold spells. He really does not produce as much heat or increase it in

[3] At 100 percent the air is completely saturated with water vapor, and precipitation, or rain, takes place.

response to cold as quickly as do northerners who are already adjusted to the climate.

The problem of adaptation applies equally to the northerner when he goes south. In northern cold, people develop a higher rate of combustion. Their energy levels and capacity for activity are proportionate on the average (in a general way only) to the heat they produce. When they go south, therefore, they experience great difficulty in finding comfort at what southerners would call a pleasant temperature, because their heat production and energy levels continue high for many weeks and often for months after arrival. Adaptation to the southern climate comes after a period of time; it is immediately after their change from one climate to another that northerners are particularly sensitive to heat and susceptible to heat exhaustion and heatstroke (or sunstroke).

The adjustment that takes place in people who move from one climate to another is based in principle on the adjustment made when a man travels from sea level to mountain regions. Before he becomes acclimatized to the rarefied atmosphere his blood and internal organs must adjust to the changes in pressure and other conditions.

The northerner traveling in the Tropics or subtropics should live a temperate life, avoid an excessive amount of fat in his diet, and wear light, loose, white clothing. The return to northern latitudes should be made if possible in the late spring or summer, when adjustment to the climate will be greatly facilitated. People moving from the South to the North must guard especially against cold until they are fully adjusted to the weather, which may take anywhere from a week to as much as several years. They should be protected against inclement conditions by adequate clothing, and their diets should be fortified with fat and energy-producing foods.

Though climate and weather play an important role in the way we feel and act, such factors as food, clothing, housing, customs, and emotional, physical, economic, and social well-being are often more important in conditioning human beings and influencing their behavior.

CLIMATE AND DISEASE

Diseases caused directly by climate are few in number. Among the more familiar ones are heat exhaustion, heatstroke, snow blindness, frostbite, and mountain sickness. But climate may strengthen or weaken the individual's resistance to many diseases by influencing the metabolic rate, the level of activity, and the mental and physical states. Thus, an individual with tuberculosis may be benefited by the invigorating air of mountain regions provided he also has adequate rest, proper treatment, and freedom from worry. Rest, medical care, and good social adjustment are often more important than a change of air or the most favorable climatic conditions in the world. On the other hand, exposure to chilling rain, for example, may so lower an individual's resistance that he may easily fall victim to pneumonia or other respiratory infections.

Climate has an indirect influence also in favoring or inhibiting the growth and virulence of some of the microscopic organisms that cause disease. This is especially true of malaria and hookworm; the causal organisms require special conditions of temperature and moisture in order to live. In malaria, moreover, not only the plasmodium that causes the disease but also the mosquito that carries it require certain climatic conditions to thrive. Malaria mosquitoes breed in swamps produced by high rainfall and lack of drainage in southern regions.

Thus while climate may influence the onset, prevalence, and severity of disease, it is only one of many factors. Such factors as nutrition, degree of crowding, income, and medical care are more important in many regions than climate. It is common knowledge, for example, that those with high incomes, and consequently with better conditions of living and access to more medical care, have fewer illnesses and lower death rates from all causes than poorer people,[4] regardless of climate and weather.

Some Relationships Between Diseases and Climatic Factors

The effects of some climatic factors on disease will be briefly touched on here.

Many (if not most) diseases, such as the common cold, pneumonia, infantile paralysis, and others, exhibit a seasonal pattern. During some months of the year the number of cases is relatively small, while in other months the number is large. The greatest number of cases of the common cold, for example, occur during the winter months of January, February, and March, and the least during July and August. Conversely, cases of infantile paralysis reach a maximum during late summer and are generally absent during the winter.

Altitude is not precisely a variable of climate. However, a number of climatic factors are associated with it—increased sunlight and wind and lower temperature, humidity, and air pressure. Certain well-recognized physiological effects are related to altitude, both in mountainous regions and in airplane flights. For example, high altitude increases the number of red blood cells, accelerates respiration, and increases the metabolic rate. In connection with other factors previously noted, moderately high altitudes are conducive to good health generally, and in suspected and active cases of tuberculosis specifically, unless otherwise indicated in individual cases. On the other hand, a rapid change to a high altitude is exceedingly bad for people with some diseases of the heart and blood vessels.

Data for New York City (*5*) show that the death rate from all diseases is high (in all seasons) when there is a few days' rise or fall from the mean (weekly) temperature. While general mortality rates seem to be related to such departures in temperature, sickness and death rates due to specific diseases are often statistically unrelated to them or related only in an obscure secondary way.

Although pneumonia is more common in cities than in rural districts, it is found in both. It occurs more frequently in the Temperate Zone than in the Tropics. This is well expressed by Cecil (*2*): "A cold, damp changeable climate predisposes to the disease. When it occurs in a warm climate . . . it is doubtless referable to changes of temperature. Pneumonia is a disease of the late winter and early spring. In New York City, January, February, and March are the

[4] United States Public Health Service, National Institute of Health. illness and medical care in relation to economic status. U. S. Pub. Health Serv., Natl. Health Survey 1935–36, Sickness and Med. Care Ser., Bul. 2, 8 pp. 1938. [Mimeographed.]

months during which the disease occurs most frequently—July, August, and September show the lowest incidence."

In studies of pain in arthritis, rheumatism, and gout, many physicians have found that a significant number of patients suffer most during certain changes of weather. Increased pain is experienced during storms, either rain or snow, and even on cloudy days. Patients occasionally complain on a clear sunny day, usually when it precedes a storm.

Extreme dryness (5 to 25 percent relative humidity), whether atmospheric or in the home during the wintertime, affects the delicate membranes of the nose, throat, and upper respiratory tract and makes people susceptible to such infections as the common cold. High winds that scatter dust also favor infections of the upper respiratory tract.

Sunshine has a beneficial effect in preventing and treating rickets and is of definite value in the treatment of wounds and certain skin disorders.

Excessive heat produces not only heat exhaustion, already discussed, but heatstroke, which comes on rapidly and often with drastic consequences. There are certain well-recognized symptoms—for example, headache, dizziness, nausea, high temperature, deep breathing, and loss of consciousness. Death may follow quickly. Heat stroke demands the immediate and constant attention of a physician. Before the doctor comes, "ice-water baths, cold sprays, ice-packs, and ice-water enemata may be used until the temperature is reduced to about 102° F.; cold sponges may then be employed" (*2*).

In industry, and occasionally on the farm, the most common disturbance resulting from exposure to high temperatures is heat cramps. This condition is characterized by severe pain in the muscles, especially in the abdomen, nausea, vomiting, and usually high temperature. People exposed to high temperatures can prevent the condition by taking some salt in their drinking water, drinking plenty of milk, or eating salted food. When overcome by heat cramps, they should take warm baths, rest in bed, and drink fluids to which sodium chloride (table salt) has been added.

While there seems to be some relationship between climate and the incidence of tuberculosis, social and economic factors play a more important role. Certain climates are exceedingly beneficial in prevention and treatment, provided other conditions are satisfactory. In general the best climate for tuberculosis cure depends to a considerable extent on the stage and type of the disease.

No evidence exists that climate is in any way a direct causative agent in "heart trouble" and arteriosclerosis (hardening of the arteries). It is, however, definitely related to the progress of these diseases, and they are more common in stormy regions because they begin at a younger age there, owing to the stress of adapting the body to strong, frequent weather changes. People suffering from these conditions do much better in the moist warmth of Florida, the Gulf States, and southern California, which does not demand the level of activity and the rapid circulation necessary in northern cold.

More than 60 years ago, the old idea that "night air" and "bad air" caused disease fell before the microscopes of Pasteur and other bacteriologists. Later, fresh air was recognized as a positive factor in health when it was found that air and sunlight were important in the prevention and treatment of tuberculosis. Like many new ideas and innovations in medicine, fresh-air fads mushroomed all over the country. People became "air conscious." Salt air, pine air, and high altitudes all became popular. Distressed and even acutely ill persons would demand, and doctors would prescribe, what is commonly spoken of as "a change of climate." But people, especially those living in large cities, began to learn that a change of climate, like choice food, is often expensive. F. C. Smith, of the United States Public Health Service, who originally made this comparison, goes on to say that "excellence of climate is no more essential to a cure than excellence of some other things, and there is no climate so good that it will always make up for the increased work, worry, or poorer housing, or scantier fare" (7).

LITERATURE CITED

(1) American Public Health Association, Committee on the Hygiene of Housing.
1939. BASIC PRINCIPLES OF HEALTHFUL HOUSING. Ed. 2, 32 pp. [New York.]

(2) Cecil, Russell L., ed.
1939. A TEXTBOOK OF MEDICINE BY AMERICAN AUTHORS. Ed. 4, rev. and reset, 1614 pp., illus. Philadelphia and London.

(3) Drinker, Cecil K.
1936. THE EFFECTS OF HEAT AND HUMIDITY UPON THE HUMAN BODY. Jour. Indus. Hyg. and Toxicol. 18: 471–485, illus.

(4) Hill, Leonard.
1933. VENTILATION, SUNSHINE, AND CLOTHING. Lancet 225: 933–936.

(5) Huntington, Ellsworth.
1930. WEATHER AND HEALTH, A STUDY OF DAILY MORTALITY IN NEW YORK CITY . . . Natl. Res. Council Bul. 75, 161 pp., illus.

(6) Mills, Clarence Alonzo.
1934. LIVING WITH THE WEATHER. 206 pp. Cincinnati.

(7) Smith, F. C.
1938. CLIMATE AND TUBERCULOSIS. U. S. Pub. Health Serv. Rpts., Sup. 136, 6 pp.

(8) Ward, Robert De Courcy.
1918. CLIMATE, CONSIDERED ESPECIALLY IN RELATION TO MAN. Ed. 2, 380 pp., illus. New York and London.

(9) Winslow, C.-E. A., and Herrington, L. P.
1935. SUBJECTIVE REACTIONS OF HUMAN BEINGS TO CERTAIN OUTDOOR ATMOSPHERIC CONDITIONS. Heating, Piping and Air Conditioning 7: 551–556, illus.

(10) Yaglou, C. P.
1937. PHYSICAL AND PHYSIOLOGIC PRINCIPLES OF AIR CONDITIONING. Amer. Med. Assoc. Jour. 108: 1708–1713, illus.

298737°—41——17 +

Health in Tropical Climates

By Robert G. Stone [1]

ALTHOUGH this article deals primarily with the problem of keeping healthy in the Tropics, it contains much interesting material for those who have to face hot weather anywhere. The author has assembled the available information on what happens to the human body exposed to prolonged high temperatures, and he discusses it with vigorous contributions from his own viewpoint and experience.

[1] Robert G. Stone is Librarian and Research Fellow, Blue Hill Meteorological Observatory of Harvard University; Editor of the Bulletin of the American Meteorological Society; Editor of the Section of Bioclimatology and Biometeorology of Biological Abstracts; and Research Associate in Meteorology, New York University.

Practically all draw-backs and difficulties of civilization in tropical countries have been more or less blamed on the climate. Insofar as a tropical climate favors many diseases of men and plants that are difficult to control, tends to induce lassitude or debility in man, and plays an important role in the distribution and character of soils, crops, vegetation, and wildlife, this notion is true. But it is equally true that man, with his instinct and intelligence, his science and social organization, has great ability to avoid, take advantage of, or partly overcome these influences of nature, not without certain costs and sacrifices, but in the long run and as a rule effectively and profitably.

Hence to deny, as we do nowadays, that the climate is a rigidly determining force upon man is not to say that it does not have a profound indirect influence pervading nearly all aspects of life in some form and measure. Indeed, some relationship with the climate can usually be found for almost anything. Important direct effects of climate uncomplicated by other factors hardly exist, but there are many circumstances in which weather or climate is one of the most important factors to be considered. For example, sunstroke and frostbite are certainly directly caused by the weather, though, at the same temperature, clothing, age, health, and length of exposure will determine whether or not the injury is suffered. Pneumonia is caused by a germ, but the season of the year and sudden changes of weather indirectly influence the likelihood and time of getting the disease. The climate does not force one to eat certain foods, but it may have much to do with the choice of foods available and with the amounts of vitamins they contain. That is an example of a relatively indirect influence.

In spite of much contradictory opinion there is some fairly definite evidence of a scientific and historical character on the subject of the effect of tropical climates on human beings. This article deals principally with the relatively direct effects and only incidentally with those that are relatively indirect.

HOW "HOT" IS THE CLIMATE?

Scarcely a prospective tourist to the low latitudes or a person who intends to reside in the Tropics fails to wonder or worry about what the climate will be like and whether he can "take it." He has probably heard that San Juan in February is perfectly delightful, that Panama is rather too warm most of the year, that Calcutta is awful at any time, and that some desert hole is "simply hell."

Generally a comparison of the ordinary monthly average dry-bulb temperatures gives a good indication of the broader contrasts. Mean annual temperatures are more apt to be misleading and should not be given serious weight from a practical standpoint. There are many places for which not only the mean monthly but even the daily dry-bulb temperatures are misleading as to the sensible "comfort" or "heat" experienced there. For everyone knows that an increase of wind or a decrease of humidity makes a high temperature more tolerable if not comfortable. In view of this, it is customary to counsel a consideration of the relative humidity and wind as well as of the temperature. The intensity of the sunshine should also be considered if it is possible to find records of it. It is exceptional to find observations of this element taken in the Tropics, whereas temperature, humidity, and wind data are often at hand. Records of the amount of cloudiness or of the duration of sunshine will serve to give some idea of the frequency with which intense sunlight occurs.

Comfort and Discomfort at High Temperatures

In estimating the feeling of warmth or discomfort of a place in terms of the instrumental weather observations usually available, it would be desirable to have some standard criteria to mark off the degrees of warmth or comfort. Unfortunately this is not a simple problem. Various formulas are available for computing a single index of comfort from weather observations, and some of them do indicate fairly well the relative stress which different climates put upon the average body's heat- and temperature-regulating mechanism. Not one of them, however, has escaped criticism from many persons who find that their own sensations do not accord with the scale. This dilemma focuses attention on several important factors determining bodily sensations of warmth or comfort which are not taken into account by any mere measurements of the temperature, humidity, wind, and sunshine.

One of these factors is the remarkable ability of the body to adapt itself, after a certain length of exposure, to a new level of climatic conditions by shifting its "comfort zone," and another is the existence of great differences between different individuals in their responses, voluntary and involuntary, to given atmospheric conditions or changes. These differences are due to many causes; some are inherited, others acquired; some are due to disease, some to training and habits of living, to diet, to clothing habits, to sex and age, to race, and to other factors. The comfort zone of a group of people, then, is only an average of differing individual comfort zones. The air-conditioning engineers have found it impracticable or impossible to design installations that will make more than 50 to 65 percent of an average group of workers, shoppers, or movie-goers comfortable at any given season. Both the average as well as each individual's comfort zone shifts markedly with the season, the latitude, the climate, and living habits. Hereditary racial differences are less important, it seems.

These facts render futile attempts to make any but rather crude and largely statistical predictions of the relative or absolute comfortableness of a climate. Very extreme conditions can be faithfully indicated, but in such cases no complex method is needed. When the temperature and humidity together exceed certain levels, even in the shade, all men will rate the condition as "very hot," and heatstroke is likely if the exposure continues many hours. This level, as shown by various experiments, is at about a wet-bulb temperature of 85° F., which corresponds to dry-bulb and relative-humidity combinations of 85° and 100 percent, or 95° and 70 percent, or 110° and 30 percent, respectively. Likewise any conditions below 60° or 65° F., dry-bulb, are rated "cool" or "cold" by everyone. Between these extremes a wide variety of comfortable and uncomfortable conditions are found according to individual circumstances (fig. 1).

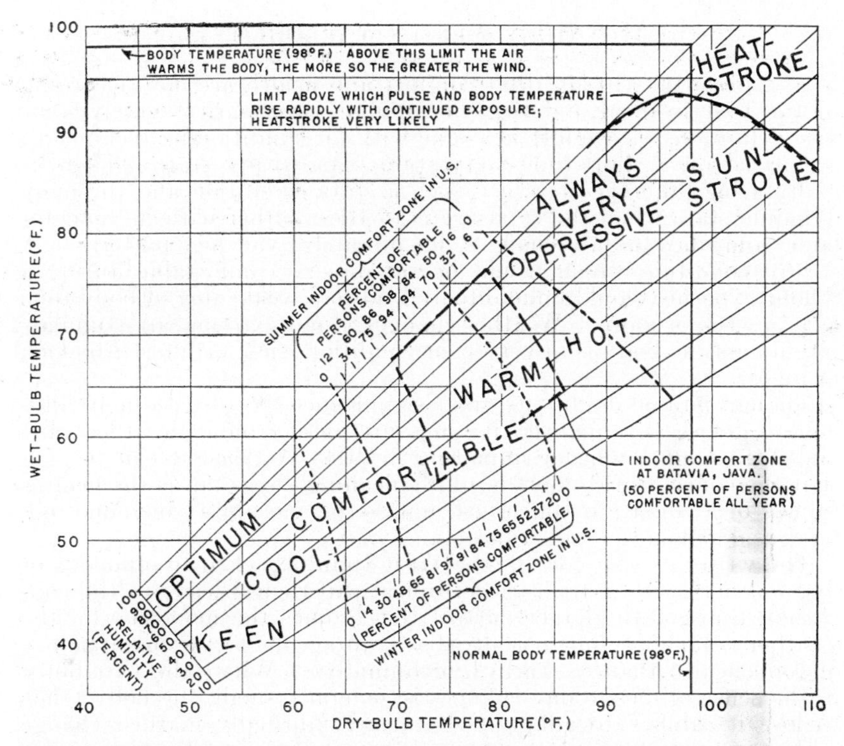

FIGURE 1.—Comfort and subjective sensations at various temperatures and humidities for normally clothed and resting persons according to indoor-chamber experiments and ordinary experience outdoors. The indoor comfort zones shown are based on controlled-chamber studies with almost still air and no sunshine; the effect of wind would be to shift the zone some degrees to the lower left of the chart, that is, toward lower wet- and dry-bulb temperature, while the effect of sunshine would be to shift the zone to the upper right (toward higher wet- and dry-bulb temperature). The terms in capital letters describing various subjective sensations, "COOL," "COMFORTABLE," "WARM," etc., give the outdoor feelings of most people when the general outdoor temperatures are in the regions where the terms are located on the diagram, assuming average conditions of wind and sunshine, customary clothing, and moderate activity, and that the individuals are used to those temperatures. There is considerable overlapping of the zones of neighboring sensations on the chart, owing to differences in sun and wind and in acclimatization and clothing of the individual. A comparison of the Java and United States winter indoor comfort zones indicates the magnitude of the shift in the comfort zone from the cooler climates to the Tropics or vice versa. Comparing the indoor with the outdoor sensations of warmth or coolness, one notes that with some sunshine, proper clothing, and physical exercise it is likely to be comfortable at lower temperatures outdoors than indoors at rest. On the too-warm side, however, exercise, sunshine, and clothing make one more uncomfortable at lower temperatures outdoors than indoors at rest. In the lower left of the diagram is an "optimum for civilization" zone, which extends to still lower temperatures (35° F.) than shown. This is roughly the climate which Ellsworth Huntington has suggested as most conducive to human physical and intellectual activity, for he found some evidence that people are healthier, produce more goods, and have more advanced culture in regions of the earth where mean temperatures in this approximate range prevail, along with sufficient yearly range and day-to-day variability to be stimulating. It is not a "comfort zone," however, as one can readily see. All of the data for this figure are so crude and subject to so many limitations of interpretation that one should not attempt to read it in much detail; it rather serves to illustrate the general principles and very approximate order of magnitude of the contrasts.

Monotony Versus Variability

It is important to add that comfort and health are not, according to the best medical and hygienic opinion, necessarily synonymous. The definitions of comfort in vogue with air-conditioning technicians are based on a short-time adaptation to a steady state. There is really a big difference between such a static condition and the more dynamic state when the exposure is to the weather with its hour-to-hour and day-to-day changes in infinitely varying patterns. A steady condition which would be rated very comfortable during a 3-hour exposure would undoubtedly lead to a weakening of body tone after a week or more. Weather changes, if not extreme, are stimulating, unless the body is in very poor condition, sick, or unused to such changes.

Though no one doubts its great significance, it is exceedingly difficult to devise any quantitative measure of the role of weather variability in maintaining or impairing health. At least it can be said that the concept of comfort is quite meaningless so far as the healthfulness of a climate is concerned, unless the variability or monotony be considered at the same time.

The writer's experience in the West Indies, backed by opinions of many others with more varied tropical experience, leads to the conclusion that for the larger part of the Tropics the monotony of the weather is far more intrinsically disadvantageous to the maintenance of good health than its warmth or humidity. Where the variability in the sense of day-to-day changes is generally small, the body tends to lose its ability to adapt itself to any unusually marked change without some pathological or atonal consequences. This fact underlies the danger of "chills" in many tropical regions, which is strongly emphasized in all handbooks on tropical medicine and hygiene.

The effect of monotony, then, is to increase the sensitivity to changes, so that a small change which would pass unnoticed in a more variable climate may contribute to some definite malaise in the monotonous environment. This is a phenomenon almost universally observed with tropical residents of all races, though this also varies greatly with individuals, and a few unusually robust persons can always be found to deny it. In tropical locations where sudden cool spells, such as northers, enduring cool rains, squalls, sea breezes, and other disturbances occur occasionally in the midst of generally monotonous weather, this sensitivity becomes a real factor in public health. Colds of a mild sort are very common in the Tropics, and people often attribute them to weather changes. When a cold norther strikes the highlands of Central America, many natives contract fatal pneumonia. Better diet, clothing, and housing, and the habit of exercising vigorously would remove the danger of these weather effects; but even such apparently simple therapy is largely hindered by economic and social conditions.

A wide daily range of temperature or of wind velocity may produce a similar problem, though these conditions are sometimes the healthiest. We have yet to learn just what kind of changes are harmful. A careful study of the frequencies of small weather variations in the Tropics would be of more value than many of the averages usually available for climatic statistics.

Need and Possibilities of Hygienic Precautions

Some hygienic precautions to offset the effects of monotony are possible. If one lives in a tropical lowland near an accessible highland, frequent or regular visits to the higher and therefore usually cooler locality, even if only overnight or for week ends, will serve as a general tonic stimulus as well as a temporary relief from heat. Such trips are actually taken at every opportunity by those who are able to do so. In addition, and especially where no other alternative source of stimulating change can be found, the habit of regular vigorous exercise, even under very warm conditions, is one of the best substitutes for weather variability in keeping up body tone. This may seem a radical suggestion in view of the fact that we have been told for years that a white man, at least, could not endure hard labor in the Tropics. That myth, however, is now well exploded. In fact, in extremely tropical locations it is the exceptional white man who stands up well for any long period of time unless he exercises sufficiently. Various military campaigns and experiences on plantations and public works leave no doubt that continual hard labor is very beneficial. However, neither whites nor Negroes should be expected to work as hard or for such long hours under very warm conditions as under cooler ones, and thus labor can never be so efficient in the Tropics as in cooler and more variable climes. Proper clothing and moderation are desirable for health as well as comfort.

There are many colonies of white farmers, such as the Germans in Brazil, who have thrived for years, even for several generations, under somewhat unfavorable climatic conditions. Many other tropical white settlements have failed or degenerated, but the climate cannot be held more than indirectly responsible. Without adequate knowledge and observance of present-day hygienic principles, without favorable economic and political conditions, without strong, well-selected stock willing to overcome difficulties at some sacrifice, no colonization effort could be expected to succeed in the Tropics. The greatest success has of course been achieved in the subtropical climates, which are cooler.

But the equatorial zone is not yet generally regarded as suitable for white settlers except as overlords of workers of the darker races, largely because of the prohibitive cost of the necessary hygiene on an extensive scale. The Panama Canal Zone colony is commonly regarded as proof that good sanitation and public health can be achieved locally in such climates. It is safe to say that any tropical environment can be made tolerably habitable for civilized whites in small groups under strict control. The health of a dense, widespread native population in an equatorial climate has never yet been raised to the standards of the United States or western Europe. Such populations remain vast reservoirs of disease which render the health of any white man among them very precarious, for he cannot fully or effectively observe the best precautions in such an environment. Clearly this is a case where economic and social conditions are of more direct consequence than the climate, which by itself might be more successfully faced.

The subtropical and highland tropical regions offer innumerable examples of unbroken generations of cultural existence; at least in many of them it is hard to prove any real degeneration, though refreshing contacts from the outside have no doubt done much to maintain them. Trade-wind climates, particularly in windward seacoast exposures, are quite comfortable for 1 to 6 months of the year; this rudimentary winter provides some much-needed stimulation, though in many cases it is insufficient to maintain a healthy tone.

For every tropical white who boasts of his continued good health, his fine children, etc., one can find a repatriate many years sick or broken for life. Much repatriation for reasons of health is in a sense unnecessary; so also are many premature deaths. Overindulgence in alcohol is a well-known affliction which directly or indirectly may explain a large fraction of the casualty list. It is worth noting that the attention to the bar in warm countries springs fundamentally from a need for stimulation which the climate fails to give. A daily set of tennis or some other vigorous exercise in place of the extra highballs would be the best solution. However, unsatisfactory social environment is often the immediate cause for seeking alcohol.

Range of Temperature and Humidity

This emphasis upon the question of monotony versus variability is not intended to give the impression that heat, humidity, and sunshine are of only minor significance in themselves. Insofar as any or all of these elements may exhibit average values which approach limits of tolerance by the body, monotony will aggravate their effect, and variability will lessen it. It may be safely assumed that the most extreme degrees of these elements that can be borne for short spells without apparent harm will be pathological or lethal under sufficiently long exposures. That is a matter of common observation, experimentally substantiated for temperature and the ultraviolet part of sunlight, at least. This observation emphasizes again that the significance of any definite temperature, humidity, sunshine, or wind value cannot be realistically estimated apart from its duration —that is, apart from its montony or variability.

The extreme maximum temperatures in the Americas are recorded from the dry or desert regions, where they occur with low relative humidities and where the night temperatures are often rather low. If water and food can be supplied, it is quite feasible to live in such a region without serious heat effects once a certain degree of acclimatization is attained. The dustiness, extreme dryness, and static electrical discharges seem to cause much irriation to membranes and skin, as well as nervousness. The excessive sunshine, often but not always rich in ultraviolet rays, is a strain on those who must be outdoors by day. The large dosage of ultraviolet in these regions is a cause of the high incidence of skin cancer observed there. The monotony in tropical desert weather is not as serious as elsewhere, owing to the great change between day and night, which, if anything, may be too stimulating for some constitutions.

In the more moist parts of the continental Tropics rather high maximum temperatures may occur in the dry season, resulting in oppressive and exhausting weather owing to the accompanying moderate humidity and insufficiently cool nights. Inability to sleep well because of hot nights can be very exhausting when it persists for a season, and often explains why some climates with generally hot days are well tolerated and others are not. The trade-wind islands and coasts, however, rarely suffer daytime temperatures of over 95° F.; in winter the steady wind and more moderate humidity make even sunny days there quite comfortable, but in the summer and autumn warm, muggy weather is the rule. Even so, the combinations of high temperature and humidity experienced yearly in the familiar summer heat waves of the United States are much more oppressive than the worst combinations that ever occur at many places on windward shores in the subtropics. But in the subtropics the weather of one summer day will not differ from that of the next day by an average of more than a degree or two in temperature, though the humidity, sunshine, and wind will show relatively more variation. A native Puerto Rican will invariably prefer to spend the summer on the island to going to the United States, but most Americans living in Puerto Rico find it more stimulating to spend the summer in the States in spite of its heat waves; this is partly due to the pull of family and racial ties but also reflects a difference in acclimatization.

Some important contrasts to note between the interior continental and the trade-wind island or coastal parts of the American Tropics lie in the annual and daily ranges of the weather elements. The generalization can be made that the highland and maritime windward locations of the trade-wind zone have rather mild but monotonous conditions during much of the year, whereas the lowland continental locations (except those in the monotonous rainy equatorial belt) are given to extreme conditions during at least part of the year. In specific cases it is often practically impossible to decide which of these types of climate is the more healthful; for example, is the continental location with a very uncomfortable season of limited duration healthier than a maritime place which is milder the year round but more monotonous? The latter kind of environment has over the centuries certainly attracted more numerous and successful settlers, but possibly only because it has had the advantage of greater accessibility. Perhaps after a decade of serious research in tropical physiology we may be able to answer such questions better.

PHYSIOLOGY OF COLD AND HEAT RESPONSES

One is comfortable when the loss of heat from the body closely balances the production of heat within the body (that is, its metabolism) without sensibly straining the heat-regulating mechanism. When the environment begins to cool below comfortable levels, first the outer capillaries close, and their blood shifts to the interior, which has the effect of reducing the heat loss to the air by conduction and convection, and the heat loss by radiation also decreases because the skin temperature lowers. Then if the environment becomes still colder, certain endocrine gland secretions are released which increase the internal heat production to balance the extra heat loss. Involuntary shivering also produces extra heat in the muscles. In these ways the constant body or blood temperature of 98° F. is maintained unimpaired, unless the cooling becomes too extreme. This reaction to the stimulus of cold can be trained by cold baths or by frequent exposures to cold weather to operate very promptly and adequately, so that "one doesn't mind the cold," so to speak. If no coolness is experienced for a long time, however, the mechanism of reaction becomes so slow and inadequate from disuse that when the next strong chill does come it may lead to shock, illness, and even death. Continuous exposure to warmth thus renders exposure to chill more serious.

When the normal state of comfort and metabolism is restored, if the environment becomes sufficiently warmer, the capillaries rapidly dilate to let more blood reach the skin, from which conduction, convection, and radiation can pass heat more rapidly to the surroundings. With further increase in warmth to temperatures between 80° and 90° F. the sweat glands suddenly begin to secrete; the evaporation of the sweat takes up latent heat and greatly augments the cooling power of the air, unless the air is already saturated. At about this point, however, the increasing warmth also begins to increase the metabolism (heat production); the added cooling from evaporation of sweat thus merely serves to maintain the balance between heat production and heat loss. But the balance is finally destroyed if the air closely approaches or surpasses the body temperature of 98° F. Discomfort, however, is usually complained of as soon as sweating begins, although the discomfort would of course be much greater if one could not sweat—and some people do not sweat as soon or as much as others.

With air temperatures higher than body temperature, the pulse rate, rate of breathing, and body temperature all tend to rise, for the heat loss is not keeping up with heat production. In some individuals, principally the very young, the aged, the sick, and those with weak hearts, such a condition rapidly leads to one of the various types of heat sickness, stroke, exhaustion, heart failure, or acute symptoms of any other disease they may have. A great many of the recorded "heat deaths" occur among these predisposed victims. There are, of course, limits to what even the healthiest and most acclimated man can stand. Heatstrokes and deaths, however, are far more common in the midlatitudes than in the Tropics, probably owing to lack of acclimatization and to improper clothing in places where heat waves are only occasional.

ACCLIMATIZATION TO HEAT

A healthy man well acclimated to working under such conditions may for hours run a body temperature of 103° or even 104° F. while exercising in the heat without marked ill effects. The process of acclimatization to heat consists in "learning" to sweat more freely but with a smaller total amount of salt in the sweat; this must be accompanied by a greater water intake and an adequate amount of salt in the diet or water. Failure to eat enough salt while sweating heavily and continually depletes the salts in the blood, altering its colloidal balance and impoverishing other organs of the body. Insufficient salt is the main cause of heat cramps as well as other less acute effects of heat.

The shift of the comfort zone to higher limits of temperature and humidity is also a mark of acclimatization, but it is not certain just what this signifies beyond a reduction of the thresholds of nervous sensitivity to heat; possibly it decreases metabolism and delays nervous exhaustion.

There is evidence that acclimatization to heat probably involves still other mechanisms, some of which are questioned by many authorities. For example, the basal metabolism—the production of heat for internal needs, without muscular movement—is said to decrease somewhat; there seems to be an unconscious tendency to choose a diet of less protein and more carbohydrate; the number of sweat glands may increase, at least after years of exposure; breathing may become slower and deeper; the adrenal, thyroid, and suprarenal glands may alter their levels of secretion, causing lower metabolism and blood pressure. These are difficult physiological problems that await more careful investigation.

SUNLIGHT

The ultraviolet component of the sunshine can cause a skin burn which makes one ill; yet in limited dosage these rays are valuable for the vitamin D they form in the skin. Many tropical climates are very sunny and rich in ultraviolet. One must therefore be careful of sunburn until a tan is acquired, and even then sun sickness is readily possible. Many tropical residents deliberately dodge much sun exposure, thus acquiring the familiar tropical pallor. A tan is desirable, however, if it can be acquired, as it prevents much of the ultraviolet from penetrating too deep into the skin. A good tan is regarded as a sign of good constitutional powers in the case of tuberculosis patients. Though heliotherapy, or sun treatment, is widely used for tuberculosis, the sunny Tropics have a very high incidence of that disease. This apparent anomaly is explained by the fact that tuberculosis flourishes most where crowding, malnutrition, and lack of hygiene is worst.

The sun's rays also add much ordinary heat to the body when they strike the skin or clothes. In the Tropics, where the body is usually having difficulty in losing its own heat to the environment, the sunshine aggravates the discomfort. Indeed, for San Juan, P. R., it has been computed that the full sunlight of midday generally decreases the cooling power of the environment by about one-fourth to one-half. Under such conditions the difference between the shade and the sunshine is often the difference between comfort and discomfort. Type of clothing may make a similar difference. A black surface absorbs nearly all the incident solar rays, while a white surface reflects a large part of them. Light-colored clothes are therefore preferable.

Speaking of black, one wonders why the Negro would not feel the sun more than a white man. The Negro's skin does absorb more solar heat, to be sure, but it has more sweat glands; hence the Negro sweats very copiously and because of his blackness starts to sweat sooner, for skin temperature controls the sweat reaction. Wearing clothes, however, puts the Negro and white more on a par. The Negro skin is tough and withstands infection better than the white skin, which becomes soggy with continual sweating, making skin ailments hard to cure. The origin and significance of the pigmentation of the races is a mystery. It is observed, however, that the darker races are considerably better suited to the Tropics; even Italians, Portuguese, and Spaniards have an advantage over blonds from higher latitudes. One must be cautious about such reasoning, however, for the Maya-Aztec-Inca group of Indians of Central and South America do not thrive in the hot, moist lowlands much better than the whites.

Frequent exposure to high intensities of both the heat and ultraviolet rays of the sun may induce cataract of the eye.

TROPICAL PHYSIOLOGY

The notion that there is an organized science of tropical physiology is really a fiction, for very little scientific work has yet been done directly in that field; nearly all the numerous observations quoted in medical and other books, purporting to show that physiological norms in the Tropics differ from those of cooler lands, have been severely criticized or contradicted. Doctors have generally averaged their readings from routine medical tests without sufficient regard to whether the patients were sick or well, young or old, male or female, obese or slim, acclimatized or not, of pure or mixed blood, sane or feeble-minded, well or poorly nourished, of low or high economic and social position; and they have lumped together readings from different seasons, climates, and times of the day. Such a mélange of routine medical observations could hardly be expected to provide bases for sound or useful physiological conclusions. Many of the individual observations of tropical physicians are doubtless quite valid, but they are not very suitable for scientific generalization.

Nevertheless, a few remarks can be made on some very general or typical effects of a tropical climate. A slight lowering of blood pressure seems to be very common and probably results from the suffusion of the capillaries under warm conditions. The volume of blood presumably increases to compensate for the supply withdrawn from the interior of the body to fill the dilated capillaries; otherwise the viscera would become impaired. This is accompanied by a decrease in hemoglobin from the dilution and by the entrance of new red corpuscles from the spleen into the circulation. Such a diluted blood is an adaptation that makes greater sweat volume possible. The decrease in blood viscosity has given rise to the saying that "one's blood is thinner in the Tropics." Profuse and prolonged sweating takes a toll of plasma, fluid, and salts from the blood which of course must be made up by the system if serious symptoms (even death) are not to result. Ordinarily, an adequate diet, with salt and plenty of water, permits the system to stand the effects of sweating. Nevertheless, temporary deficiencies of sodium, chlorine, potassium, and calcium from the blood and serum may frequently occur, with accompanying fatigue or exhaustion. Frequent or steady reduction of the blood volume and of salts supplied to the viscera leads to impaired appetite and digestion, through a decrease in gastric secretions, and to an atonic condition of the intestines, with constipation. High temperatures and a rich carbohydrate diet seem to pave the way for infection in the intestines, perhaps by altering the bacterial flora or the permeability of the membranes. Intestinal and gastric complaints are very common in the Tropics.

The depression of basal metabolism generally reported from lower latitudes is often cited as an adaptation to the climate. Some authorities doubt that it is a real phenomenon, owing to questions about the method of determining the metabolism. If it is real, then it is not clear how it serves as an adaptation. Without considering the accompanying changes in diet, height, weight, and body temperature no conclusions about the basal metabolism can be safely drawn, and few reliable records of this sort are available. The development of a "tropical build," the tall rangy or slender type, is also claimed as an adaptation. For the same weight a slender person has more surface area per unit weight than a stocky one, and he can thus lose heat more easily. But it is hard to prove that the climate rather than some other factors results in such a build.

The "working" metabolism (the heat production when one is active rather than resting and fasting) certainly averages less in warmer than in cold climates, a tendency which is probably associated with some reduction in weight. This is an adaptation in many cases, resulting from eating less heating foods and from less physical activity; but it may also often be a sign of malnutrition, poor tone, gastric troubles, or other disease. Heavy or fat persons do not necessarily have difficulty in acclimatization, however. Muscular activity produces a large amount of body heat, only 30 to 40 percent of which is actually used by the muscles; the rest must be stored or given off to the environment as surplus, unless the environment is so cold that it is needed to maintain body temperature. The disinclination to work or to engage in any physical activity when it is warm is probably largely due to the anticipated discomfort of this heat surplus from muscular activity. Any tendency to chronic overactivity of the thyroid keeps the metabolism high and in the Tropics is apt to drive the victim to neurasthenia. Those with subnormal thyroid are sent to the Tropics for safety against cold, which they cannot stand.

Women and children have been reported to withstand the Tropics less well than men. The women often neglect to exercise sufficiently and fail to find suitable social conditions. This failure contributes toward neurasthenia. Also their tendency to obesity may make warmth more trying. Childbirth is said to be more difficult and risky. Yet there is no conclusive proof that these troubles are inherent or inevitable; probably better hygiene and medical service can largely eliminate them. Mothers face some difficulty in feeding babies properly in a hot climate and in obtaining good milk. Whether children mature as well in the Tropics as in cooler climates is still a question of heated debate in colonial medical circles, but the social conditions seem of greater moment than the climate.

The amount of oxygen is less in a cubic foot of hot air than in a cubic foot of cold air, which means that in some degree the tropical resident has less available oxygen. Oxygen is of course a vital requirement; its restriction even in small amounts over a long time may either diminish the effectiveness of all bodily functions or force the body to learn to use the available oxygen more efficiently. There is some indication that both effects probably do occur, but their full significance for tropical acclimatization, if any, remains to be explored.

The most interesting conclusion from this meager knowledge of tropical physiology seems to be that the most effective mechanisms of physical heat regulation under warm conditions—sweating and capillary suffusion—have a tendency to produce rather deleterious effects on the blood chemistry and on the tone of the internal organs, with the result of lowering resistance to infection. Thus the human body's defenses against heat do not seem by nature to be well designed for more than short exposures. It would be very premature, however, to conclude at this time that there is no hope for man to discover a practical tropical hygiene which will insure him against progressive deterioration of tone due to the climate. We have hardly begun to learn the adaptive possibilities of the human organism. Careful studies carried over several generations will be required.

PRESELECTION

There is good reason to expect that in a few years a system of preselection of men who will acclimatize well to the Tropics can be worked out. This sort of thing is now very effectively done in selecting pilots for the Army and Navy Air Corps. Over a decade ago Borchardt [2] attempted to select those who would sweat well by placing them in a heated chamber for some hours. The ideal type of man for the Tropics, however, must do more than sweat; he should have nervous and emotional stability, no trace of hyperthyroidism, no abnormally high metabolism; he must tolerate regular doses of quinine and other prophylactic drugs; obesity, fondness for alcohol, and some other tendencies do not augur well. But research is needed on the role of various constitutional factors, such as the flexibility and efficiency of the coordination between metabolism, circulation, muscles, and nervous system, before any satisfactory procedure of selection can be applied.[3] When it can be, it will save great sums of money and many broken lives. Studies on the physiology of exercise being pursued at the fatigue laboratory of Harvard University are very promising to this end.

AIR CONDITIONING

There are possibilities that air conditioning can make certain uncomfortable climates not only more bearable but more healthful, but the cost is so high that its general use will be greatly limited by economic conditions. The enervating effects of certain equatorial climates where hot nights are frequent could probably be diminished materially by air-conditioned sleeping rooms. In general, however, marked cooling of interiors is dangerous in the Tropics owing to the chill and shock experienced when the hot moist body suddenly passes into a cool dry place. Consequently considerable dehumidification of the air with only a small degree of cooling is recommended to obtain comfort indoors.

---

[2] See Selected References, p. 259, for citation.

[3] Mason in a report of a recent study (see Selected References, p. 260.) doubts that the basal metabolism will give any indication of tropical acclimatability, but the present writer considers the scope of her inquiry too narrow and sees no reason for pessimism yet.

SELECTED REFERENCES [4]

BLACKHAM, ROBERT J.
1937. INFANT FEEDING IN WARM CLIMATES. Jour. State Med. 45: 462–473.

BORCHARDT, W.
1931. DIE BEDEUTUNG DER GEFÄSSREAKTIONEN DES PERIPHEREN UND DES SPLANCHNICUSGEBIETES FÜR DEN TROPENBEWOHNER. Arch. f. Schiffs u. Tropen Hyg. 35: [69]–73, illus.

CASTELLANI, ALDO.
1938. HYGIENIC MEASURES AND HOSPITAL ORGANISATION OF THE ITALIAN EXPEDITIONARY FORCES DURING THE ETHIOPIAN WAR, 1935–36. Roy. Soc. Arts Jour. 86: 675–689.

CHAMBERLAIN, WESTON P.
1929. TWENTY-FIVE YEARS OF AMERICAN MEDICAL ACTIVITY ON THE ISTHMUS OF PANAMA, 1904–1929. A TRIUMPH OF PREVENTIVE MEDICINE. 74 pp., illus. Mount Hope, C. Z.; also pub. in New England Jour. Med. 203: 669–680, illus. 1930.

CROWDEN, G. P.
1934. INSULATION AGAINST HEAT AND COLD FOR HUMAN COMFORT. THE USES OF BRIGHT METALLIC SURFACES. Lancet [London] 226: 37–40, illus.

CULPIN, MILLAIS.
1933. AN EXAMINATION OF TROPICAL NEURASTHENIA. (Abstract) Roy. Soc. Med. Proc. 26: [911]–922. [Discussion, pp. 917–922.]

DAVENPORT, C. B., STEGGERDA, MORRIS, and others.
1939. RACE CROSSINGS IN JAMAICA. Carnegie Inst. Pub. 395, 516 pp., illus.

DILL, DAVID BRUCE.
1938. LIFE, HEAT, AND ALTITUDE; PHYSIOLOGICAL EFFECTS OF HOT CLIMATES AND GREAT HEIGHTS. 211 pp., illus. Cambridge, Mass.

GIEMSA, G., AND NAUCK, E. G.
1937. RASSE UND GESUNDHEITSERHALTUNG SOWIE SIEDERLUNGSFRAGEN IN DEN WARMEN LÄNDERN. Arch. f. Schiffs u. Tropen Hyg. 41: 9–21.

HOFFMAN, FREDERICK LUDWIG.
1924. PROBLEMS OF MORTALITY AND ACCLIMATIZATION IN THE CENTRAL AMERICAN TROPICS. Internatl. Cong. Health Prob. in Trop. Amer. 1924: 657–708.

HOLDRIDGE, DESMOND.
1940. TOLEDO; A TROPICAL REFUGEE SETTLEMENT IN BRITISH HONDURAS. Geog. Rev. 30: 376–393, illus.

INTERNATIONAL GEOGRAPHICAL CONGRESS.
1939. SYMPOSIUM ON THE POSSIBILITIES AND EXPERIENCE OF WHITE SETTLEMENTS IN THE TROPICS. (Many papers by leading authorities.) Internatl. Cong. Geog., Amsterdam, 1938, v. 2, sect. 3, part c.

JAMES, E. PRESTON.
1925. THE CLIMATE OF TRINIDAD, B. W. I. U. S. Monthly Weather Rev. 53: 71–75, illus.

KEENAGH, PETER.
1937. MOSQUITO COAST; AN ACCOUNT OF A JOURNEY THROUGH THE JUNGLES OF HONDURAS. 286 pp., illus. London.

KENRICK, G. W., and DEL TORO, GEORGE, JR.
1940. STUDIES IN SOLAR RADIATION AND THEIR RELATIONSHIP TO BIOPHYSICS AND THE GENERAL PROBLEM OF CLIMATE AND HEALTH. Puerto Rico Jour. Pub. Health and Trop. Med. 15: 387–419, illus.

KUNO, YAS.
1934. THE PHYSIOLOGY OF HUMAN PERSPIRATION. 268 pp., illus. London.

LAURENS, HENRY
1936. SUNLIGHT AND HEALTH. Sci. Monthly 42: 312–324, illus.

LEE, DOUGLAS H. K.
1936. PHYSIOLOGY AND THE TROPICS. Malayan Med. Jour. 11: 105–108.

——— and COURTICE, R.
1940. ASSESSMENT OF TROPICAL CLIMATES IN RELATION TO HUMAN HABITATION. Roy. Soc. Trop. Med. and Hyg. Trans. 33: 601–614, illus.

[4] The references in this list have been selected out of perhaps a thousand papers in many languages. Bibliographies of wider scope are contained in many of the works cited.

MANSON, PATRICK.
1935. MANSON'S TROPICAL DISEASES; A MANUAL OF THE DISEASES OF WARM CLIMATES. Ed. 10, rev. and enl. by Philip H. Manson-Bahr, 1003 pp., illus. London, Toronto, [etc.].

MARTINI, E.
1936. WEGE DER SEUCHEN; LEBENSGEMEINSCHAFT, KULTUR, BODEN UND KLIMA ALS GRUNDLAGEN VON EPIDEMIEN, UNTER BERÜCKSICHTIGUNG DER TROPENKRANKHEITEN DARGESTELLT. 109 pp. Stuttgart.

MASON, E. D.
1940. EFFECT OF CHANGE OF RESIDENCE FROM TEMPERATE TO TROPICAL CLIMATE ON BASAL METABOLISM, WEIGHT, PULSE RATE, BLOOD PRESSURE, AND MOUTH TEMPERATURE OF 21 ENGLISH AND AMERICAN WOMEN. Amer. Jour. Trop. Med. 20: 669–686.

MILLS, CLARENCE A.
1939. MEDICAL CLIMATOLOGY; CLIMATIC AND WEATHER INFLUENCES IN HEALTH AND DISEASE. 296 pp., illus. Springfield, Ill., and Baltimore, Md.

MOM, C. P.
1940. AIR CONDITIONING IN THE TROPICS. Heating, Piping and Air Conditioning 12: 633–636, illus.

NELIGAN, A. R., CASTELLANI, ALDO, and others.
1931. DISCUSSION ON THE ADAPTATION OF EUROPEAN WOMEN AND CHILDREN TO TROPICAL CLIMATES. Roy. Soc. Med. Proc. 24: 1315–1333. [Reply by M. W. Toms, in Brit Med. Jour. 1: 1091–1092. 1931. See also Ronnefeldt, F.]

PRICE, A. GRENFELL.
1939. WHITE SETTLERS IN THE TROPICS. Amer. Geog. Soc. Spec. Pub. 23, 311 pp., illus.

RAGATZ, LOWELL JOSEPH.
[1928.] THE FALL OF THE PLANTER CLASS IN THE BRITISH CARIBBEAN, 1763–1833; A STUDY IN SOCIAL AND ECONOMIC HISTORY. 520 pp., illus. New York and London.

RONNEFELDT, F.
1930. MATERIAL ZUR FRAGE DER AKKLIMATISATION VON FRAUEN UND KINDERN IM TROPISCHEN WESTAFRIKA. Arch. f. Schiffs u. Tropen Hyg. 34: 319–323.

SAWYER, WILBUR A.
1938. THE IMPORTANCE OF ENVIRONMENT IN THE STUDY OF TROPICAL DISEASES. Amer. Jour. Trop. Med. 18: 9–18.

SHATTUCK, GEORGE CHEEVER, and HILFERTY, MARGARET M.
1936. DISTRIBUTION OF ACUTE HEAT EFFECTS IN VARIOUS PARTS OF THE WORLD. New England Jour. Med. 214: 458–468.

STARKEY, OTIS P.
1939. THE ECONOMIC GEOGRAPHY OF BARBADOS: A STUDY OF THE RELATIONSHIPS BETWEEN ENVIRONMENTAL VARIATIONS AND ECONOMIC DEVELOPMENT. 228 pp., illus. New York.

STONE, R. G.
1939. SOME RESULTS OF MODERN PHYSIOLOGICAL RESEARCH IN RELATION TO ACCLIMATIZATION IN THE TROPICS; COMFORT ZONES AND ACCLIMATIZATION; A NOTE ON THE COOLING POWER. *In* Price, A. Grenfell, White Settlers in the Tropics, Amer. Geog. Soc. Spec. Pub. 23, App. I–III, pp. 275–299. (Contains an extensive bibliography.)

STRONG, RICHARD P.
1935. THE IMPORTANCE OF ECOLOGY IN RELATION TO DISEASE. Science 82: [307]–317.

SWITZER, J. ELMER.
1925. WEATHER TYPES IN THE CLIMATES OF MEXICO, THE CANAL ZONE, AND CUBA. U. S. Monthly Weather Rev. 53: 434–437, illus.

VAN WULFFTEN PATHE, P. M.
1933. PSYCHIATRY AND NEUROLOGY IN THE TROPICS. Malayan Med. Jour. 8: 133–145.

VASSALLO, S. M.
1934. TROPICAL NEURASTHENIA: ITS POSSIBLE RELATIONSHIP TO HYPERTHYROIDISM. Roy. Soc. Trop. Med. and Hyg. Trans. 27: 625–627.

VISHER, STEPHEN S.
1930. RAINFALL AND WIND CONDITIONS RETARDING TROPICAL DEVELOPMENT. Econ. Geog. 6: [152]–165, illus.

WAIBEL, LEO.
1939. WHITE SETTLEMENT IN COSTA RICA. Geog. Rev. 29: [529]–560, illus.
WERNER, H.
1936. SOLL DER WEISSE TROPENBEWOHNER KÖRPERLICHE ARBEIT VERRICHTEN? Deut. Med. Wchnschr. 62: 27–29.
YAGLOU, C. P.
1937. PHYSICAL AND PHYSIOLOGIC PRINCIPLES OF AIR CONDITIONING. Amer. Med. Assoc. Jour. 108: 1708–1713, illus.

298737°—41——18

PART THREE

Climate and the Farmer

Climate and Soil

By Charles E. Kellogg [1]

FIVE BROAD QUESTIONS are discussed in this article: (1) How is a soil formed? (2) What is the relationship between climatic factors and soil? (3) What are the principal soil types and their characteristics? (4) What factors are involved in soil fertility and productivity, soil exhaustion and renewal, and erosion? (5) What considerations guide the farmer in his use of the soils on an individual farm? Throughout the author emphasizes the complexity of the soil and the problems relating to it.

[1] Charles E. Kellogg is Principal Soil Scientist and Chief of the Division of Soil Survey, Bureau of Plant Industry.

HOW A SOIL IS FORMED

IMAGINE a great mass of granite or some similar rock thrust above the ocean or otherwise exposed in a part of the earth having a humid, temperate climate like that of West Virginia or Maryland. Soon after exposure to the sun and rain the bare surface of the rock begins to crumble. Changes in temperature from night to day and from season to season cause strains and stresses in the rock. Water freezes in the cracks and expands, thus helping to break the rock to pieces. Water changes some of the minerals and dissolves out some of the more soluble materials, moving them to other places, into deep channels or surface lakes and streams. As the water rushes over the surface of the rock mass, some of the small fragments may be moved and redeposited at the base of slopes, in lakes and ponds, along streams, or in deltas.

This whole process, physical and chemical, is called weathering. Weathering is a destructive process, and by it loose deposits of fine rock material are produced, either directly above the weathering rock or at some distance from it. At some time during weathering, plants and other forms of life appear in the rock material and soil formation begins. The soil results from the meeting and fusion of the physical processes and the biological processes; it is the great bridge between the inanimate and the living. Some of the same reactions involved in weathering continue to operate, but they are modified, and new ones are added by the growing plants, animals, and micro-organisms.

Trees send their roots deep into the fine rock material and, with the other plants growing with them, serve as partial protection from erosion, allowing loose rock material to accumulate over the solid rock on gentle slopes. The roots of plants absorb nutrients like phosphorus, calcium, and potassium from the whole mass. These pass into the bodies of the plants and into the leaves, where, under the influence of sunlight, organic compounds are manufactured from the carbon dioxide of the air and from the water and other materials taken up through the roots.

As the trees grow they shed their leaves, and finally they themselves die and return to the soil. With this return of organic matter, the nutrients extracted from the whole soil are returned to its surface. Nutrients pass in a continuous cycle from the soil to the plant and back again to the soil.

Bacteria and other micro-organisms that feed on organic matter are important in this cycle. They cause the decomposition of the organic matter and the release of its minerals and nitrogen compounds in forms that may be used by other living plants or leached into the deeper strata. Certain bacteria are able to take the relatively inert nitrogen from the air and build it into their bodies. Some kinds of these bacteria live on the roots of particular plants—the legumes, such as alfalfa and clover. As the bacteria die, the nitrogen is released in forms available to plants.

Where the soil is acid, fungi take an important part in decomposing the organic matter, and under the native forests of temperate regions not enough bases (alkaline substances) are brought to the surface by plants to keep the soil from becoming acid. The products of decomposition by fungi are relatively more soluble than those of decomposition by bacteria. Not nearly so much humus (partially decomposed and relatively stable organic matter) accumulates as under grass vegetation, and few legumes are found in these forests.

When it rains, water enters the soil and moves down by vapor movements, by capillary movements, and freely under the force of gravity in the open pore spaces and cracks (fig. 1). During periods without rain, moisture moves upward by vapor and capillary movements from the lower horizons, or layers. Under the forest in humid regions some of the soluble materials may be washed down below the soil. Part of the fine clay particles in the acid surface layers become dispersed or suspended in the soil water and move down during periods of moistening, to be redeposited in a lower layer. Thus the layers, or horizons, developed within the soil have very different contents of fine clay and consequently different physical properties.

As the result of all these actions, chemical, physical, and biological, in time a distinct soil profile—a sequence of soil layers, or horizons—is developed. This profile reflects the total effect of all the factors in the environment and in the history of the soil; it is the complex result of the meeting and blending of the physical and biological forces of the earth. For the particular case under consideration the profile would be about as follows:

A_{00} horizon (2–3 inches).[2] A thin layer of recently fallen leaves and twigs. As this material becomes moist it is attacked by small animals and micro-organisms and passes into the next horizon.

A_0 horizon (0–2 inches). A mat of partially decomposed leaves and twigs. Much of this material has lost its identity and is being rapidly decomposed.

A_1 horizon (0–3 inches). Very dark gray or very dark brown soil consisting of a mixture of organic and inorganic materials with the soil particles grouped into granular or crumblike aggregates. This is a layer of intense activity of organisms, including bacteria, fungi, and small animals such as earthworms. Since the organic matter is decomposing just above it and in it, the minerals being released from this material keep the soil nearly neutral or only slightly acid, while the soil beneath is more acid.

A_2 horizon (3–10 inches). Brownish-gray soil with the particles arranged in thin, faintly developed plates, easily crushed into a crumblike mass. This horizon is the lightest in color of any, the lowest in clay content, and the most acid. Part of the fine clay has been removed by the percolating soil water into the lower horizon.

A_3 horizon (10–12 inches). Transitional to the next above.

B_1 horizon (12–15 inches). Transitional to the next below.

B_2 horizon (15–30 inches). Brown soil with the particles arranged in nut-sized, angular, blocky aggregates about ¼ inch to 1½ inches in diameter. On the faces of the little blocks can be seen the recent deposition of the fine particles from above as a sort of gluelike coating. This horizon has the highest content of clay of any, and the soil is quite hard when dry and plastic and sticky when wet. The soil is acid and leached of soluble materials but has received clay from the A_2 horizon above.

B_3 horizon (30–36 inches). Transitional.

C horizon (below 36 inches). Weathered rock.

The horizons (A plus B) above the weathered rock, or parent material, taken together, make up the solum, or true soil. Sometimes soil formation follows weathering so closely that there is little if any loose material between the soil and the underlying rock, but in this example, after a long time, the solid rock may lie at a depth of several feet beneath the surface.

[2] The depth of soil horizons is reckoned from the top of the A_1 horizon in inches. Thus the A_{00} horizon is 1 inch thick and lies between 2 and 3 inches above A_1, while A_2 is 7 inches thick and lies between 3 and 10 inches beneath A_1.

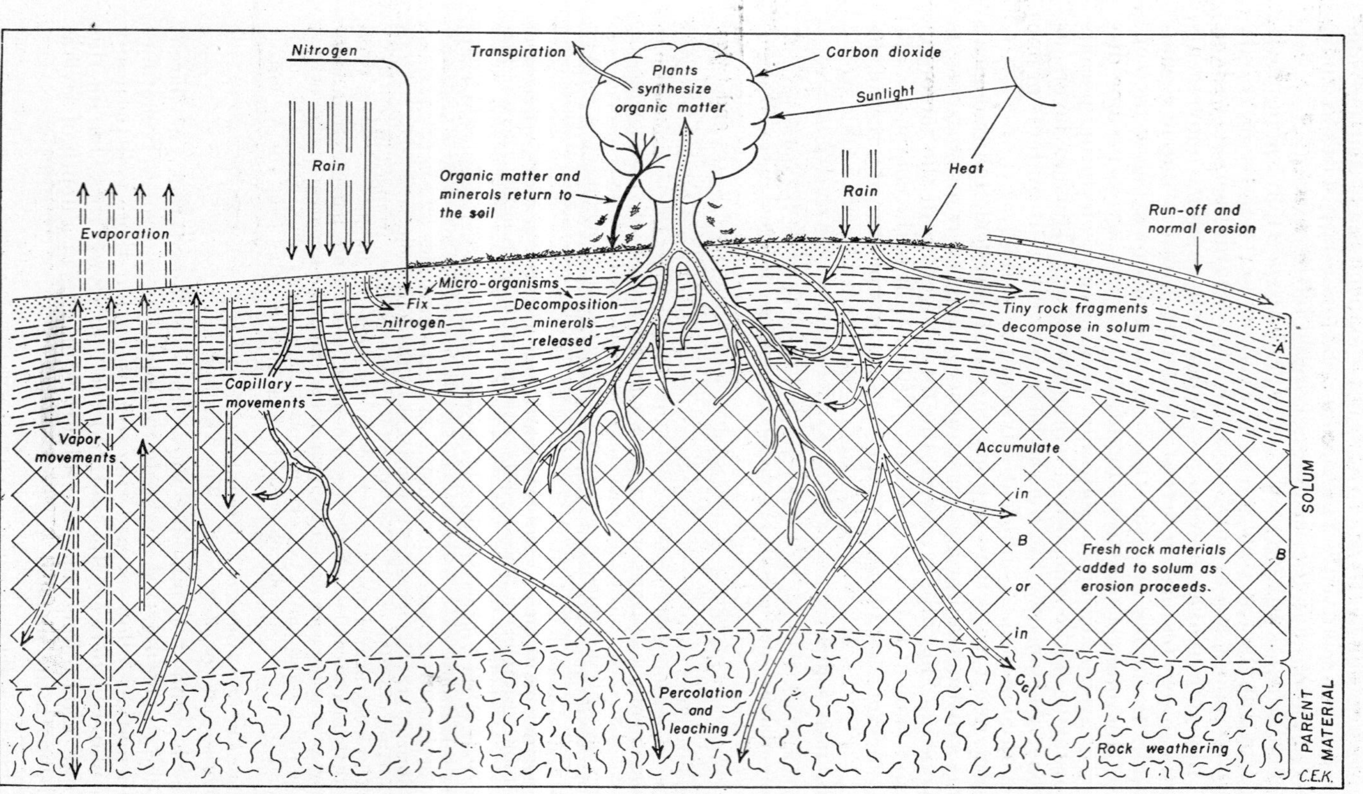

FIGURE 1.—The principal dynamic processes in a soil, much simplified. The plant is hypothetical. In humid forested regions the B horizon is a zone of accumulation of clay, while under subhumid to arid grasslands calcium carbonate accumulates in the C_c horizon.

As such a soil develops, some material is constantly lost through normal erosion—only a tiny bit in a single year, but in 500 years a great deal. With continuous erosion and weathering the whole soil slowly sinks; new minerals constantly come into the lower horizons, and old materials leave the surface. Finally a sort of balance is approached; the losses from erosion and leaching balance the gains from new minerals and the activities of plants and micro-organisms. Such a soil is said to be mature. If there are any changes in the environment—in the climate, vegetation, slope, or kind of parent rock in lower strata—the forces of soil formation will be modified and will work toward the evolution of a different soil. But until there are such changes, the soil remains the same. Some of the processes involved, greatly simplified, are shown in figure 1.

This brief description of the formation of a soil has dealt with a Gray-Brown Podzolic soil, which is only moderately fertile but is responsive to good management. Other combinations of factors result in other kinds of soils, many entirely different in every important respect.

THE SOIL DEFINED

Soil may be defined as the natural medium for the growth of plants. It is an essential part of a place or area on the earth, not something detached or separated from the other physical features. A useful description of a soil includes not only the internal characteristics of structure, texture, color, content of organic matter, consistence, and thickness of each horizon of the solum, but also the geological substratum, slope, native vegetation, and climate. In the system of soil classification used by scientists attention is given to all the characteristics, external and internal. Certainly man uses the soil in its total environment.

Every type of soil is characterized in four ways: (1) Functionally, according to its productivity for plants; (2) morphologically, by the chemical, physical, and biological characteristics of the several layers or horizons that, taken together, make up its profile; (3) geographically, according to the climate, vegetation, relief, and other features of the landscape where it is found; and (4) socially, according to the patterns of human occupancy it can provide. Thus, from a social point of view, a productive soil must furnish compounds that contain the necessary nutritive elements, in proper form and balance, for the normal growth and composition of the plants that man requires for his own growth, health, and reproduction. Production of plants must be possible under such systems of land management that a satisfactory labor income will be returned to the farmer over the years, assuming suitable economic and social conditions. The fact that many farmers are not accomplishing these objectives with the soil they cultivate—either their produce is unsatisfactory in quality or the production does not return a satisfactory income on a secure basis—is an added incentive to study the different types of soil and attempt to understand them.

The soil, climate, plants, and animals of any place are closely interrelated. With each broad climatic type are associated certain plants and soils. Native tall grasses and dark-colored soils are associated with a subhumid temperature climate, acid light-colored soils and coniferous forests with a cool moist climate, strongly leached red soils and tropical rain forests with hot humid climates, and unleached light-colored soils with desert shrubs in hot dry climates. The distribution of soil groups, plant associations, and climatic zones are thus roughly parallel. But frequently at the fringes of climatic belts the divisions are not sharp; local variations in rocks, slopes, and geological age may give rise to important local variations in soils and plants within any climatic type, such as those found in swamps, alluvial valleys, sand hills, and salty lake basins.

THE CLIMATIC FACTOR IN SOIL FORMATION

There is a close relationship between soil and climate, partly direct but more largely indirect. An absolute relationship cannot be expected, since climate is only one of five main factors responsible for soil formation. These are (1) climate, (2) living matter, (3) parent rocks, (4) relief, and (5) age. The first two influence the characteristics of soils over broad areas, while the others give rise to local differences—the differences one sees between neighboring fields and farms. Since there are also direct relationships between some of these factors, as between climate and living matter and between relief and the character of the rocks, it is not always possible to know precisely the influence of the individual factors. The indirect effect of climate—as it acts through the vegetation, for example—is probably greater than its direct influence on the soil. But any natural soil is the product of all these forces acting together. In some soils the characteristics inherited from the parent rocks may be very noticeable, while in other places the long-time influence of climate and vegetation may have erased these differences, and very similar soils existing side by side may have developed from quite different rocks. Besides these natural factors there is the influence of man's use of the soil, which may have changed it, either for better or for worse.

Climate within the soil is unlike that above the soil. The usual climatic data are obtained from recording instruments placed on the surface of the ground or at some distance above it. As the climate enters the soil, to speak loosely, it is modified according to soil conditions. First of all, the climate is modified locally by the vegetation. Inside a dense forest, wind velocity is lower than outside, rain strikes the surface of the soil with less force, and the humidity of the air just over the ground is higher during rainless days than that of air over barren soil. The degree of modification depends upon the height and density of the vegetation and the kind of plants. Grasses afford a great deal of protection but only in a thin layer of air just above the surface. Even the widely spaced shrubs of the desert are not without their modifying influence upon wind, sunlight, and falling rain or snow.

Local variations in slope modify the climatic conditions. On steep slopes more of the rain runs off than on gentle slopes, leaving less to penetrate the soil and less for growing plants. On slopes facing the sun during the warmer parts of the day the surface becomes warmer and drier. Near the boundary between climatic types in the Northern Hemisphere, trees grow on the north slopes and grasses on the south slopes, or grasses on the one and desert shrubs on the other, or shrubs on the north slopes and no vegetation on the south slopes. Even small local differences in relief, as in a landscape of small mounds or shallow pits, will modify the climatic conditions at the surface and within the soil; the mounds may be dry and the small pits moist.

There is an exchange of air between the atmosphere above the soil and the pore space within it. Changes in air pressure at the surface are recorded instantly in the lower horizons, unless these are frozen or completely saturated with water. The great changes in pore space available for air caused by water entering the soil during rains and its removal during fair weather are even more important. Thus air is being pushed into the soil and drawn out in a sort of breathing process. Unlike the air above the soil, that within all soils is essentially saturated with moisture except under extremely dry conditions—drier even than the very minimum of moisture for plant growth. The roots of plants, the animals, and the micro-organisms within the soil remove oxygen from the soil air and give to it carbon dioxide. Other gases, such as marsh gas, ammonia, and hydrogen sulfide, sometimes escape into the soil air from decomposing organic matter.

The temperature conditions are greatly modified by the soil. One of the principal sources of heat coming to the soil is direct radiation from the sun. This is greater in summer, when the rays strike the soil directly, than in winter, when they are slanting. In the United States the sun warms the south slopes more than the north-facing slopes. When the soil is covered with vegetation many of the rays are intercepted by the plants and do not reach the surface of the soil itself. Bare soil in the Tropics that receives the rays of the sun directly day after day may become so hot as to kill most forms of life in the surface horizon. Temperature variations from season to season depend upon cloudiness, air temperature, and the relative position of the sun with reference to the soil surface. Generally the average temperature of the surface soil is higher than that of the air above during both summer and winter. The daily fluctuations of the soil temperature are much less than those of the air temperature above and lag behind them, especially in the lower horizons. That is, the maximum temperature of the soil is reached later in the afternoon than the maximum temperature of the air, and the minimum temperature of the soil is reached later at night than the minimum temperature of the air. The daily variations are largely in the surface horizons and rapidly fade out with depth, so that below 6 to 20 inches the soil temperature does not reflect daily changes at the surface. Even though the soil may be frozen for 3 to 4 feet in depth, only the very surface layer ordinarily reaches temperatures significantly below the freezing point of water. There is also a lag in soil temperature following seasonal variations in the average air temperatures. The maximum temperature of the lower horizons is reached a long time after the average air temperature has passed the seasonal maximum. The amount of these variations also decreases rapidly with depth, and at a depth of 3 to 10 feet most soils are nearly constant in temperature.

Although some minor differences in the amount of heat absorbed by soils are due directly to the color and conductivity of the soil material, by far the most important differences result from variations in moisture content and organic matter. In order to change the temperature of soil so much heat is required to change the temperature of the water in it that other differences in specific heat are relatively insignificant. Thus porous, well-drained soils, such as sandy soils or those with well-developed pore spaces through which water may pass rapidly, warm up earliest in the spring—that is, they follow more closely the changes in the average air temperature. Soils with poorly developed structure, such as massive clays and clay loams, are frequently so moist that they warm very slowly in springtime.

Since organic material is a poor conductor of heat, the surface layers of peats and mucks may become very hot or cold in comparison with the layers underneath. It is not at all uncommon to find frozen soil a few inches beneath the surface in peat soils of the northern Lake States during July. Also, when cold snaps come during the growing season, heat is not transferred to the surface as rapidly as in mineral soils, so that in the temperate regions tender plants are much more susceptible to frost injury on muck and peat soils than on mineral soils, other conditions being similar.

The temperature of the rain falling on pervious soils also has a pronounced influence on soil temperature. Warm rains delay the cooling of the soil in the autumn and hasten its warming in the spring. In certain situations important soil movement or serious erosion may follow the falling of warm rains on frozen soil. If the lower horizons remain frozen and impermeable to water during such rains the surface horizons may become so saturated as to cause the soil to flow down the slope. In the far north this action is very important, especially among Tundra soils with ever-frozen subsoils. As soil freezes at the surface, lenses of ice are formed as water is drawn upward by capillary action. In very fine sandy or silty soils with a water table near enough to the surface for water to be drawn to the place of ice formation, this action may be sufficient to cause serious heaving of pavements or of plants, especially during alternate freezing and thawing weather. On slopes this freezing and thawing may cause soil to move down the slope and fall into small streams or rivulets that carry it away.

The direct effect of the sun's heat on the surface of the soil is greatly reduced by the cooling effect of the evaporation of water from the soil. Although the cooling influence of evaporation, as well as the high specific heat of water, delays the warming of soils in the spring, it protects the organisms in the soil and tender plants on the surface from death or injury due to very high temperatures during hot days in summer.

The amount of water that enters the soil depends only in part on the climate. If the soil is pervious to water, the total annual rainfall may soak into the ground, as in very sandy soils or those wtih large pore spaces like many soils of the Tropics. Thus on extremely porous soils very little water runs off, and on extremely impervious soils very little water enters, regardless of the slope. Most soils fall between these two extremes, and the penetration of water depends on both the internal structure and the slope. Thus in a region having, say, 30 inches of annual rainfall, only a small part may enter some of the relatively impervious soils on steep slopes, which may be essentially arid from the point of view of soil climate. Adjacent soils on gentler slopes, besides drinking in the water that falls on them directly, may absorb some of the water that has run off the steeper slopes and as a result may have a humid or even wet soil climate. Thus soils developed from identical rock material and lying side by side may have profiles that are quite different, especially in the thickness and depth of the several horizons. This is because the more humid soil climate on gentler slopes results in more luxuriant vegetation and greater intensity of the soil-forming processes than occur on the steeper slopes, where the soil climate is less humid.

The amount and distribution of the water in the soil influences every phase of soil formation as well as the relationships between the soil and growing plants. If soils containing considerable clay are alternately dry and very moist, the swelling and shrinking of the clay leads to the development of particular structural forms. Many of the soils of the semiarid regions, for example, are characterized by prismatic structure. In this type of structure the soil particles are arranged in vertical prisms, usually roughly six-sided. When the soil is very wet these prisms can scarcely be seen, but when it is dry they stand out prominently. Their size and the width of the structural cracks, or cavities, between them depend upon the amount and nature of the clay and the other factors of the environment.

The wetting of the soil during rains is rarely uniform. A shower moistens the surface first, then the water moves downward until some time after the rain has ceased. The surface may begin to dry out before the water has ceased moving down into the lower horizons. Only by rains of long duration can the soil be said to be uniformly moistened. In most parts of the country in only a small percentage of the showers does it rain long enough to moisten the soil sufficiently to start percolation into the rocks beneath. Especially in the drier

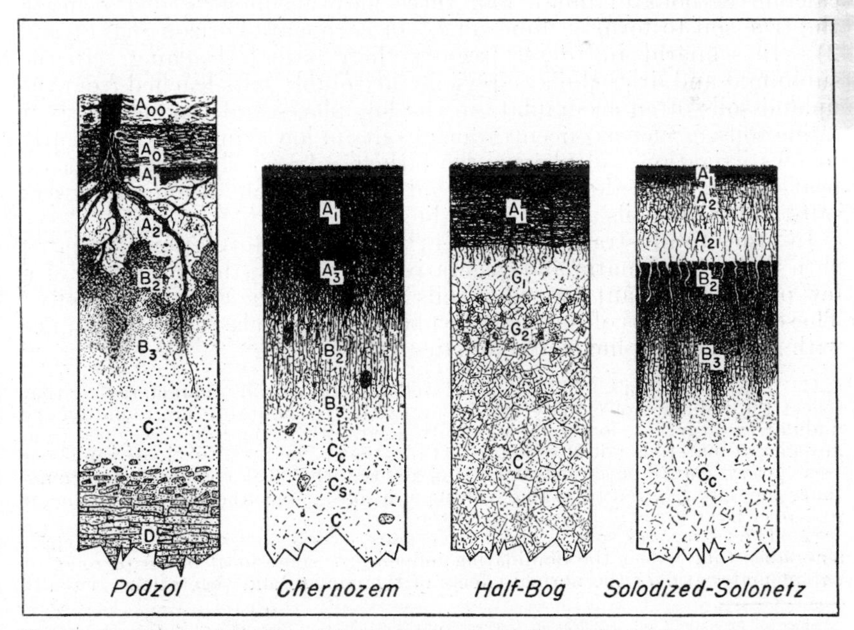

FIGURE 2.—Four soil profiles. The locations of the Podzol and Chernozem soils are shown on the map, figure 3. The Half-Bog soils are found in small areas associated with the podzolic soils of the humid region. The solodized-Solonetz soils are found in the semiarid regions in small areas that were once salty.

regions the horizons at some depth beneath the surface—the B horizons (figs. 1 and 2)—are ordinarily more moist for more of the time than the surface horizons above or the parent material beneath. Thus what is called soil climate varies among different horizons of the same soil as well as among different soils in the same climatic region.

Perhaps enough has been said to emphasize the intimate relationship between soil conditions and climatic conditions. It is convenient to think of the soil as the meeting place of the strictly physical processes and the biological processes. It is also the meeting place of the underlying rocks and the atmosphere.

FORMATION OF THE PRINCIPAL TYPES OF SOILS [3]

Climate and vegetation as they impinge upon the parent rock may be regarded as the active forces in soil formation. They are conditioned by slope and act over a period of time. The chief components of climate—rainfall, temperature, and humidity—influence the amounts of various chemical elements and compounds in the soil. In humid regions where there is a large excess of rainfall over evaporation, leaching takes place, and the more soluble constituents are lost from the soil. In subhumid climates, as in the eastern Dakotas, there may be sufficient leaching to remove from well-drained soils the more soluble compounds, such as sodium chloride (common salt) but not enough to remove completely the less soluble salts such as calcium carbonate (lime), and these may accumulate just beneath the true soil to form a "lime zone," or carbonate horizon (figs. 1 and 2). In semiarid and desert regions there is little leaching. In the subhumid and drier climatic regions the soluble salts leached from the upland soils often accumulate in the low places and produce salty or saline soils. Such a concentration of salts in low-lying soils frequently follows irrigation and plagues the farmer. In poorly drained places, peat or Bog soils develop in humid regions, while accumulations of salts and saline soils are found in the arid regions.

In order to illustrate the different types of soil formation associated with different climatic and vegetative conditions, the formation of a few of the important groups of soils (fig. 3) will be explained briefly.[4] These great groups of soils may be placed in three classes in accordance with their geographic characteristics:

(1) The zonal soils. These have well-developed soil characteristics that reflect the influence of climate and living matter. These soils are found on the undulating or gently sloping uplands with good drainage and are developed from any parent materials not of extreme texture (that is, neither very loose sands nor very heavy clays) or of extremely unbalanced chemical composition. Sometimes they are referred to as the "continental soils," since they are the dominant soils over large areas in many parts of the world.

(2) The intrazonal soils. These have more or less well developed soil characteristics that reflect the dominating influence of some local factor of relief or parent material over the normal effects of the climate and vegetation. Usually

---

[3] Since soil formation, soil classification, soil geography, soil depletion, and similar topics are dealt with in considerable detail in the Yearbook of Agriculture for 1938, Soils and Men, only a general treatment will be given here—just enough to bring out some of the more important relationships between these processes and climate. The reader interested in more detail regarding the soils of the United States and their formation and use should consult the 1938 volume.

[4] The distribution of the great soil groups in the United States is shown in figure 3. For descriptions of all of them the reader is referred to Soils and Men.

such soils are found intermingled in small areas with those of two or more zonal groups, although such a condition as poor drainage may prevail over a wide area.

(3) The azonal soils. These are without well-developed soil characteristics, owing to their extreme youth or to conditions of parent material or slope that prevent normal soil formation. Such soils are found on steep rocky slopes, on fresh alluvial deposits, and on formations of loose, nearly pure sand.

Zonal Soils

Of the zonal groups, the Podzol, Chernozem, Laterite, and Desert soils illustrate the main types of soil formation, and other zonal groups are more or less intermediate in their characteristics.

The Podzol soils are developed in a cool, moist climate under coniferous or mixed coniferous and hardwood forests, as in the northern Lake States, northern New England, and some of the high mountains. They are also found in northern Europe and Asia. In the evergreen forest the ground is well-shaded, and the trees are shallow-rooted. The needles are highly resinous and decompose slowly. There is a minimum of small flowering plants. The forest trees, especially the pines and spruces, feed relatively lightly on bases and return less of these to the surface to counteract the leaching influence of the rainfall than do the grasses; under the forest the soil becomes acid, and decomposition of the organic matter is accomplished more by fungi and less by bacteria than in grassland areas. The relatively soluble products of this decomposition are leached down in the soil and rapidly reduced to water and carbon dioxide. There is only a little humus as compared with the abundant amount in the soils of the grasslands. The surface layers become gray and are strongly leached of both organic matter and plant nutrients, while in the subsoil some of the clay and other relatively insoluble materials accumulate (fig. 2).

This process is called podzolization, and with modifications it is important in the development of all zonal soils of the humid regions. Under the hardwood forests farther south, bases are returned to the soil more rapidly by the vegetation—both the trees and the associated plants—and more humus is formed. In the soil region a little south of the Podzols are the Gray-Brown Podzolic soils like the example described at the beginning of this article.

The Laterite soils are less well understood, and there are many varieties. They are developed in humid or wet hot climates, under the tropical rain forest. Here weathering and all chemical and biological processes are intense. The nutrients circulate very rapidly from soil to plant and back to the soil again. Two principal processes may be involved. One is laterization, perhaps more strictly a process of weathering than of soil formation. The bases and silica are leached out of the original rock material, leaving it very rich in aluminum and iron. The material is usually red in color and very pervious to water. Under conditions of restricted drainage, streaked and mottled material develops which hardens upon exposure to the air. In India and elsewhere bricks and building stones, even statues, have been made of it. The name "laterite" was originally given to this material, but it is now applied more generally to a broad group of red tropical soils, and the soils with crusts or hardened material are called Ground-Water Laterites. After this process of intense weathering has gone on until the soil becomes acid and low in bases, podzolization, with the formation of leached layers underlain by horizons of accumulated clay, may go forward. In between the regions occupied by Laterite and Podzol soils are other soils, such as the Red Podzolic soils of the southern United States, influenced by both processes.

The Chernozem soils are developed in temperate subhumid regions under tall-grass vegetation. The grasses are heavy feeders on bases and return them to the surface fast enough to prevent the soil from becoming acid under the comparatively low rainfall. Large amounts of humus accumulate, and the soils are nearly black in color for 1 to 3 feet in depth. Since there is little movement of insoluble material, except as surface soil material falls into cracks, there is little difference in clay content between the different layers of the soil profile, whereas in podzolized soils the surface layers have less clay than the subsoils. In the Chernozem the soil particles are grouped into granular or crumblike aggregates and provide an excellent structure for crop plants. There is sufficient leaching to remove the most soluble salts but not enough to remove the calcium and magnesium carbonates completely. These accumulate in the lower part of the true soil, or just beneath it, in what is called a lime zone or carbonate horizon. Beneath this horizon there is frequently a layer of accumulation of the slightly more soluble calcium sulfate or

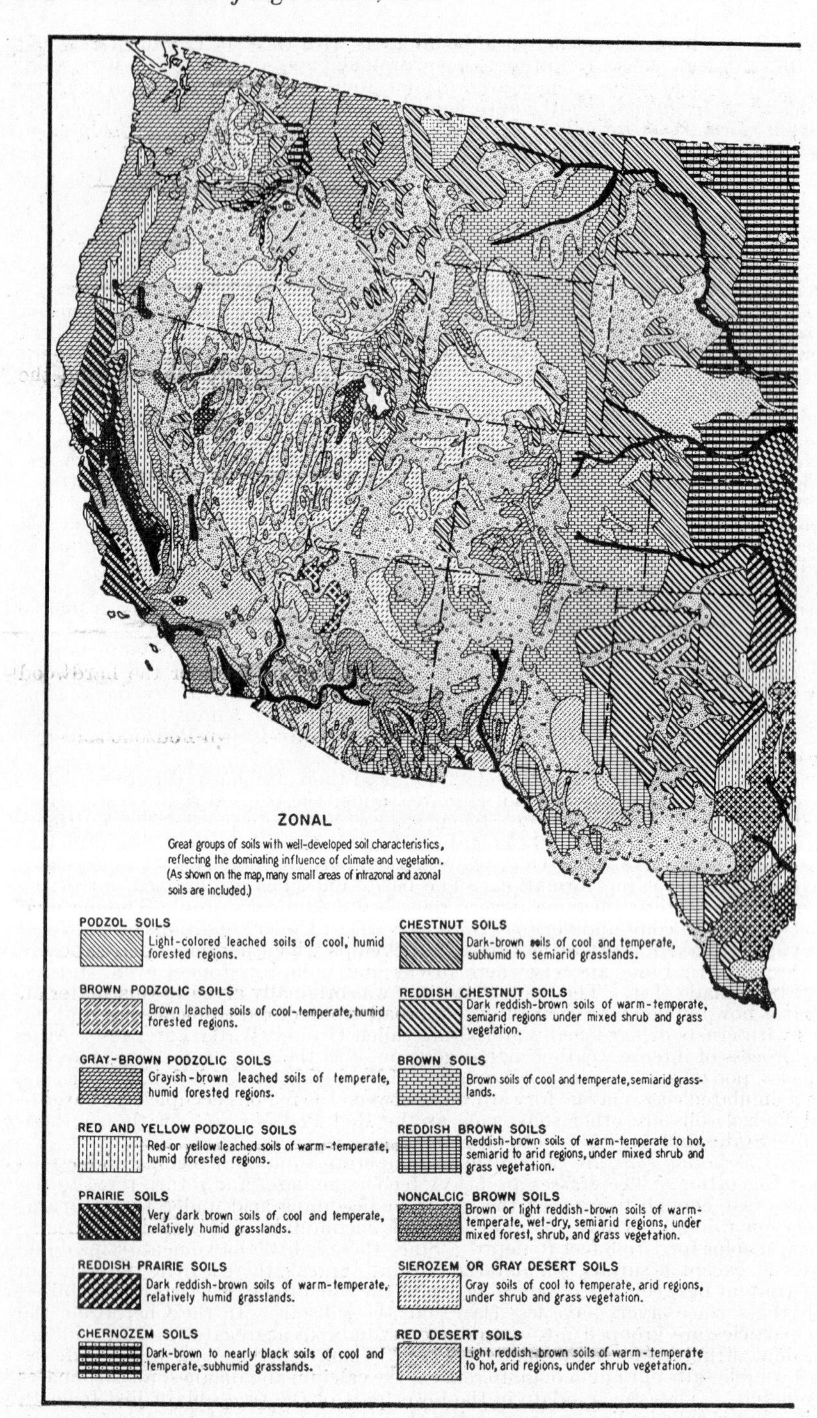
ZONAL
Great groups of soils with well-developed soil characteristics, reflecting the dominating influence of climate and vegetation. (As shown on the map, many small areas of intrazonal and azonal soils are included.)
PODZOL SOILS
Light-colored leached soils of cool, humid forested regions.
BROWN PODZOLIC SOILS
Brown leached soils of cool-temperate, humid forested regions.
GRAY-BROWN PODZOLIC SOILS
Grayish-brown leached soils of temperate, humid forested regions.
RED AND YELLOW PODZOLIC SOILS
Red or yellow leached soils of warm-temperate, humid forested regions.
PRAIRIE SOILS
Very dark brown soils of cool and temperate, relatively humid grasslands.
REDDISH PRAIRIE SOILS
Dark reddish-brown soils of warm-temperate, relatively humid grasslands.
CHERNOZEM SOILS
Dark-brown to nearly black soils of cool and temperate, subhumid grasslands.
CHESTNUT SOILS
Dark-brown soils of cool and temperate, subhumid to semiarid grasslands.
REDDISH CHESTNUT SOILS
Dark reddish-brown soils of warm-temperate, semiarid regions under mixed shrub and grass vegetation.
BROWN SOILS
Brown soils of cool and temperate, semiarid grasslands.
REDDISH BROWN SOILS
Reddish-brown soils of warm-temperate to hot, semiarid to arid regions, under mixed shrub and grass vegetation.
NONCALCIC BROWN SOILS
Brown or light reddish-brown soils of warm-temperate, wet-dry, semiarid regions, under mixed forest, shrub, and grass vegetation.
SIEROZEM OR GRAY DESERT SOILS
Gray soils of cool to temperate, arid regions, under shrub and grass vegetation.
RED DESERT SOILS
Light reddish-brown soils of warm-temperate to hot, arid regions, under shrub vegetation.

FIGURE 3.—General pattern of great

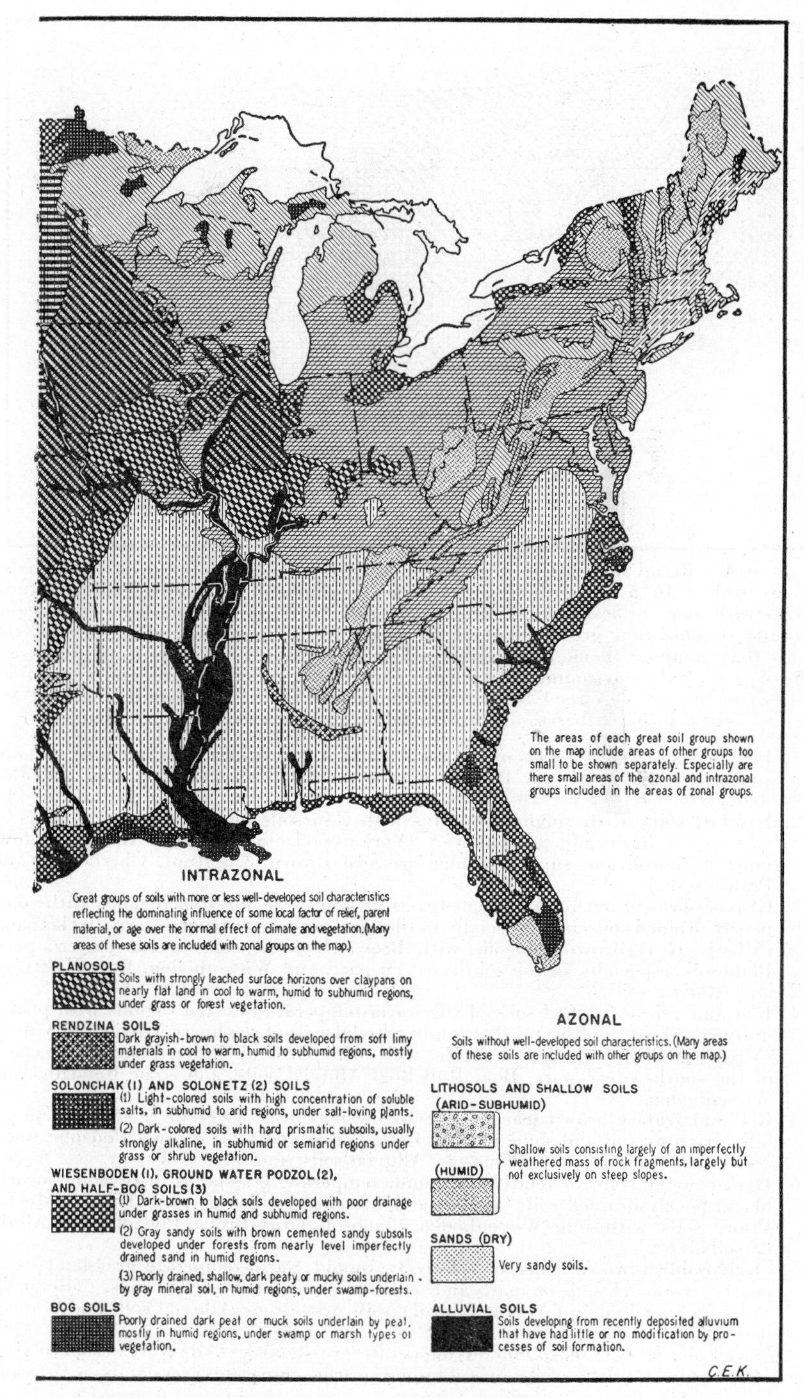
The areas of each great soil group shown on the map include areas of other groups too small to be shown separately. Especially are there small areas of the azonal and intrazonal groups included in the areas of zonal groups.
INTRAZONAL
Great groups of soils with more or less well-developed soil characteristics reflecting the dominating influence of some local factor of relief, parent material, or age over the normal effect of climate and vegetation. (Many areas of these soils are included with zonal groups on the map.)
PLANOSOLS
Soils with strongly leached surface horizons over claypans on nearly flat land in cool to warm, humid to subhumid regions, under grass or forest vegetation.
RENDZINA SOILS
Dark grayish-brown to black soils developed from soft limy materials in cool to warm, humid to subhumid regions, mostly under grass vegetation.
SOLONCHAK (1) AND SOLONETZ (2) SOILS
(1) Light-colored soils with high concentration of soluble salts, in subhumid to arid regions, under salt-loving plants.
(2) Dark-colored soils with hard prismatic subsoils, usually strongly alkaline, in subhumid or semiarid regions under grass or shrub vegetation.
WIESENBODEN (1), GROUND WATER PODZOL (2), AND HALF-BOG SOILS (3)
(1) Dark-brown to black soils developed with poor drainage under grasses in humid and subhumid regions.
(2) Gray sandy soils with brown cemented sandy subsoils developed under forests from nearly level imperfectly drained sand in humid regions.
(3) Poorly drained, shallow, dark peaty or mucky soils underlain by gray mineral soil, in humid regions, under swamp-forests.
BOG SOILS
Poorly drained dark peat or muck soils underlain by peat, mostly in humid regions, under swamp or marsh types of vegetation.
AZONAL
Soils without well-developed soil characteristics. (Many areas of these soils are included with other groups on the map.)
LITHOSOLS AND SHALLOW SOILS
(ARID-SUBHUMID)
(HUMID)
Shallow soils consisting largely of an imperfectly weathered mass of rock fragments, largely but not exclusively on steep slopes.
SANDS (DRY)
Very sandy soils.
ALLUVIAL SOILS
Soils developing from recently deposited alluvium that have had little or no modification by processes of soil formation.
C.E.K.

soil groups of the United States.

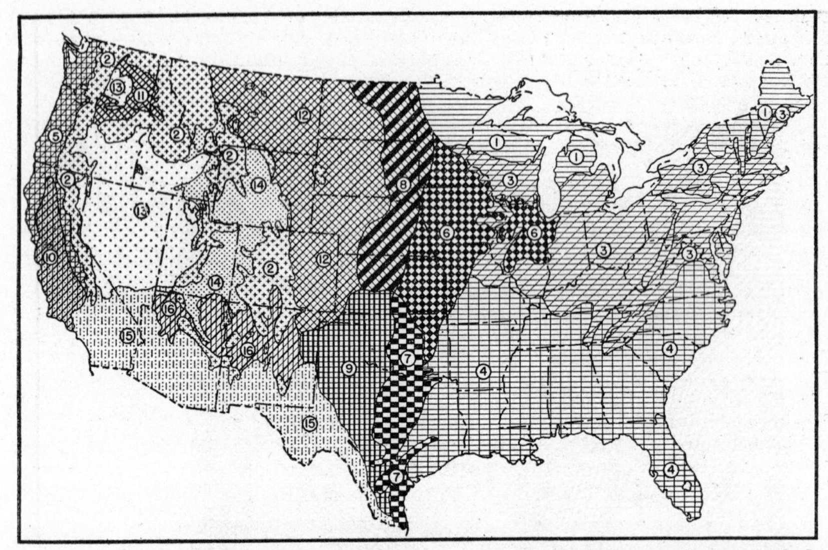

FIGURE 4.—Broad associations of great soil groups. Each of the associations includes many soils. In a sense these regions may be thought of as broad rural cultural areas with more or less distinct, broadly defined types of farming and rural community organization growing out of the character, proportion, and pattern of the soils that compose them, considering soil in its broadest sense as a synthetic expression of all the environmental factors—parent rock, relief, climate, and vegetation. These regions are described briefly, and the names of the broad units included are given in parentheses. (For detailed descriptions see Soils and Men.)

1. Light-colored leached soils of the northern forested regions with included swamps and stony soils. (Mostly Podzols with associated Lithosols, Bog, and Half-Bog soils.)
2. Leached soils of the high mountains with thin soils on the slopes and areas of various soils in the adjacent valleys. (Various podzolic soils, some Alpine Meadow, much Lithosol, and small irregular areas of Brown, Chestnut, Chernozem, and Prairie soils.)
3. Grayish-brown and brown leached soils of temperate forested regions, with some poorly drained soils and, especially in the southwestern portion, soils with claypans. (Mostly Gray-Brown Podzolic with Brown Podzolic soils in the eastern part, Planosols, especially in the southwestern part, and Wiesenboden, Bog, Half-Bog, and Alluvial soils.)
4. Red and yellow leached soils of the warm-temperate forested regions with poorly drained soils of the Coastal Plains and alluvial soils of the lower Mississippi Valley. (Mostly Red and Yellow Podzolic soils with Ground-Water Podzol, especially in the southeastern part, Bog, Half-Bog, Alluvial soils, and some Rendzina and Wiesenboden.)
5. Red and grayish-brown leached soils of the northwest forested region with much hilly or stony soil and some alluvial soils. (Red and Gray-Brown Podzolic soils, and Lithosols, with some Planosols, Alluvial soils, and other soils.)
6. Dark-colored soils of relatively humid, temperate grasslands with some nearly black, poorly drained soils and some light-colored soils on steep slopes. (Mostly Prairie soils, with some Wiesenboden, Planosols, Gray-Brown Podzolic, and Alluvial soils.)
7. Dark reddish-brown soils of relatively humid warm-temperate grasslands with nearly level black soils on marls and spots of light-colored leached soils. (Reddish-Prairie, Rendzina, and Yellow Podzolic soils, with some Alluvial soils and Wiesenboden.)
8. Dark-colored soils of subhumid temperate grasslands. (Mostly Chernozems.)
9. Dark reddish-brown soils of subhumid warm-temperate grasslands with some hilly soils. (Mostly Reddish-Chestnut soils with some Lithosol.) *(Legend continued at bottom of opposite page.)*

gypsum. All of the zonal soils of the semiarid and arid regions have such a layer of carbonate accumulation. One of the most significant differences between the Chernozem soils of eastern North Dakota, South Dakota, and Nebraska and the Prairie soils of Iowa and Illinois is that the Prairie soils have no horizon of accumulated carbonates.

The Desert soils are developed in arid regions under a scanty vegetation. They are light-colored and are unleached except in the uppermost part. Because of the scanty vegetation and extremely variable precipitation, run-off and erosion are great. In humid regions, where there is a protective cover of vegetation, hills are rounded and slopes are curved, whereas the desert landscape is characterized by sharp angles and an abundance of erosion features. Large areas are swept by the wind, and the finer particles are removed until a layer of protecting pebbles and stones, called the desert pavement, has accumulated on the surface. When the soil is barren of vegetation, a surface crust relatively impermeable to water commonly forms. Only the water from long gentle rains sinks into such soil. Elsewhere in the desert are large areas of shifting or partially stabilized sand dunes. There is, therefore, a great variation in the physical characteristics of Desert soils. Those developed on smooth alluvial fans and along broad stream valleys are frequently suitable for farming under irrigation if water can be supplied and if natural drainage conditions are favorable or proper drainage is supplied artificially.

The other great soil groups shown in figures 3 and 4 are more or less transitional, with regard to their formation, between these four principal groups—Chernozem, Podzol, Laterite, and Desert soils.

Intrazonal Soils

The soils of the intrazonal groups reflect the influence of some local factor of relief or parent material as well as that of climate and vegetation. In the humid regions the Bog soils occur in very poorly drained areas in which the remains of plants decompose so slowly that thick deposits of them accumulate. With less poor drainage the Half-Bog soils develop under a forest vegetation, and the Wiesenboden (meadow soils) under a grass vegetation. In the arid regions salts accumulate in the poorly drained places, giving rise to saline soils (Solonchak) and alkali soils (Solonetz).

In the humid and subhumid regions, areas of soils of medium to heavy texture have developed on such smooth relief that there is little or no erosion under natural conditions. In such instances the acid leached material accumulates in the surface horizon, and a hardpan or claypan develops beneath it. In normal soils, on the other hand, as the surface soil is gradually removed by erosion the profile gradually sinks into the parent material, and in this way new, fresh minerals are incorporated into the soil from beneath. The soils developed on smooth relief and having a claypan or siltpan are called Planosols. Although during their previous history erosion was too little for the formation of a productive soil, any accelerated erosion after clearing is very serious, because it exposes at the surface the claypan, from which a suitable surface soil for cultivated plants cannot be developed by tillage operations.

---

10. **Dark-colored to light-brown soils of the California valley and coastal mountains. (Chernozem, Prairie, Chestnut, Reddish-Chestnut, Desert, and Alluvial soils, Lithosols, Planosols, etc.)**
11. **Dark-colored to light-brown soils of the Northwest (Palouse) region. (Chernozem, Prairie, Chestnut, and Brown soils, with some Lithosol.)**
12. **Brown to dark-brown soils of the semiarid grasslands with some hilly soils, sandy soils, and badlands. (Mostly Chestnut and Brown soils, with some Lithosol, Dry Sands, and other soils.)**
13. **Grayish soils of the arid West (and Northwest) with soils of arid and semiarid mountains and mountain slopes. (Mostly Sierozem or Gray Desert soils, with much Lithosol and some Brown, Chestnut, and Alluvial soils.)**
14. **Grayish soils of the arid and semiarid intermountain plateaus and valleys. (Mostly Sierozem or Gray Desert soils and Brown soils, with some Lithosol and other soils.)**
15. **Reddish soils of the semiarid to arid Southwest. (Red Desert, Reddish-Brown, and Noncalcic Brown soils, with much Lithosol.)**
16. **Brown to reddish-brown soils of semiarid southwestern high mountain plateaus and valleys. (Mostly Brown and Chestnut soils, with much Lithosol and some Desert and other soils.)**

In some places soil is developed from soft limestone or rocks very rich incalcium carbonate. Under such conditions the soil cannot become acid, and grasses form the dominant vegetation even in humid regions. In the United States such black soils, called Rendzina soils, developed from soft calcareous marl or chalk, are found in Alabama and Texas.

Azonal Soils

Azonal soils have no well-developed soil charactertistics, largely because of the extreme youth of the parent material. They may be found in any climatic region. Of greatest extent are the Lithosols, very shallow soils consisting largely of an imperfectly weathered mass of fine or coarse rock fragments. These are found especially on steep slopes where little or no true parent material for soil has accumulated, and their characteristics are essentially those of the nearly barren rock. Of great importance agriculturally are the Alluvial soils, those developing from very recently deposited alluvium that has been modified little or not at all by processes of soil formation. Such soils are confined to recent or actively growing deltas or flood plains along streams. As soon as these soils acquire well-developed soil characteristics they are grouped with the appropriate great soil group. Thus a great many different soils, entirely unlike, may be developed from similar alluvium, depending upon the other factors of soil formation, especially the vegetation and climate. Soils developed from well-drained deposits of nearly pure sand are also included with the azonal group as Dry Sands because of the similarity of their character wherever they are found.

These several groups of soils in continental United States have been grouped further into broad associations in accordance with their characteristics and their relationships to one another (fig. 4).

SOIL FERTILITY AND PRODUCTIVITY

When man undertakes to use the soils built up through the long years of formation, he introduces changes, sometimes drastic ones, into the natural environment. Soils react differently to these changes. Furthermore, production from soil, in an economic or social sense at least, requires husbandry or management. The management practices may be very simple, such as building drift fences for range cattle; or they may be very complex and include tillage, green manuring, fertilization, drainage, and irrigation. If a soil is said to be highly productive for some crop, say corn, it is implied that a high yield of corn can be obtained in relation to the labor required or to the cost of production. Some soils may give relatively high yields of corn if the land is simply cleared of the native vegetation, plowed, and seeded. Others that do not give good yields under this treatment may be responsive to a management practice that includes the use of fertilizers and rotations with legumes. Thus soil productivity may be most clearly conceived as being a response to management. Yields alone are inadequate guides to soil productivity—the management under which the yields are obtainable must be known as well. Furthermore, the term "soil" in this sense must include the whole physical environment—all the characteristics of the soil itself, including depth, acidity, content of nutrients, slope, texture, degree of erosion if any, and so on, plus the climate. Not only the average rainfall and temperature during the various seasons must be considered, but also the frequency and severity of droughts and off-season frosts.

Soil fertility is included in the concept of soil productivity but refers only to the content, balance, and availability of chemical compounds in the soil that influence plant growth. As with productivity, however, reference must be made to some particular plant or group of plants. Soils fertile for strawberries—that is, well supplied with the proper nutrients and with no toxic substances—may not be fertile for alfalfa. Furthermore, soils may be fertile for crops but unproductive because of poor internal physical conditions that prevent normal root growth, slopes too steep for the use of machinery, or too many seasons with unfavorable climatic conditions. Thus fertile soils are not always productive, and productive soils are not always fertile naturally. Some of the most productive soils in this country, in an economic and social sense, are the loams and sandy loams of the eastern parts of the country developed originally under a forest cover in a humid climate. These soils are not naturally fertile for most crop plants. They have been thoroughly leached and have a low content of plant nutrients, but because of their good structure and the dependable climate they respond well to careful management. With proper fertilization, liming, drainage, and carefully planned crop rotations, they produce bountifully: they are productive. In the same region other soils on steep slopes underlain by limestone or weathered granite, for example, may be more fertile naturally because, through a greater degree of natural erosion, they are kept supplied with relatively fresh minerals, but they are less productive for crops.

Factors in Plant Growth

For normal plant growth several factors must be reasonably well adjusted to the needs of the plant. It is not always possible to determine the influence of any single factor, since the plant grows in response to all of them combined. Nature must make a great many right combinations to get even a mediocre corn plant. All of the factors are directly or indirectly influenced by climate, and the soil conditions may modify or be modified by seasonal climatic conditions. These factors influencing the growth of plants may be grouped under (1) temperature, (2) water supply, (3) air supply, (4) nutrient supply, (5) depth and stability of substratum, and (6) injurious influences such as diseases, insects, and toxic substances.

The temperature is determined by climatic conditions and soil temperature. How local soil conditions modify the temperature within the soil has already been discussed. Local variations in relief and in drainage may have the effect of raising or reducing the temperature in the neighborhood of the plant. Similar soils sometimes have slight differences in "frostiness" that are important to tender plants.

The water available to plants depends upon the precipitation (except as supplemented by irrigation) and the water-retaining capacity of the soil. The ideal soil for crop plants, from the point of view of water supply, is one that takes in the water that falls, allows the excess to drain away, and holds enough for plants between periods of moistening. Certain heavy clay soils hold water so tenaciously that plants are unable to get much of it, and very sandy soils allow too much to drain away. In the humid regions the very sandy soils are the most droughty; but under arid conditions these soils may be the least droughty, since they allow the water that falls to penetrate and they readily give water back to the plants. In very dry or very wet years the sandy soils have the advantage, while in "normal" years the soils of medium texture—loams, silt loams, and clay loams—have the advantage.

The supply of air to plant roots depends upon the structure of the soil and especially its drainage—factors only indirectly related to climate.

The nutrient supply is determined directly by the soil conditions, but these in turn are partly a result of leaching and of other processes related to climate. The nutrient supply depends also upon the plants that have been growing in the soil.

The rate of evaporation and the infiltration of water are influenced by plant cover, slope, and internal soil conditions. Thus there is a very intimate relationship between vegetation and climate, vegetation and soil, and climate and soil. The growth of plants is vitally affected by the nature of the environment, and at the same time the plants themselves do much to condition or modify this environment.

Soil Exhaustion and Renewal

People once thought that the fertility of a soil could be expressed according to a simple balance sheet. If the amounts of the several elements removed by various crops were known and the content of those elements in the soil was determined through chemical analysis, they believed a simple calculation would indicate the duration of soil fertility under any system of management. Unfortunately such a simple concept is not even approximately true, for many reasons. (1) The soil is not a static thing like a storage bin. Each year some elements are being lost through leaching and erosion, and new minerals are being added, either to the top of the soil by the action of wind or water, or to the bottom as the rock beneath becomes soil. (2) Within the soil itself minerals slowly come into solution at entirely different rates. Soils with the same total amounts of potassium or phosphorus, let us say, vary greatly as to the amounts of these nutrients available to different plants. (3) When fertilizers are added to different soils the degree to which they are held by the soil varies greatly. In some instances they are held so loosely they may be leached easily; in other instances large proportions are "fixed" so tightly as to be unavailable to plants. (4) Some plants are shallow-rooted; others are deep-rooted; some are strong feeders—that is, they can get nutrient elements from relatively insoluble minerals; others are weak feeders; some (the legumes) harbor nitrogen-fixing bacteria; others do not. (5) The influence of any one factor in plant growth, such as climate, amount of any particular nutrient available, depth of soil, or slope, depends upon the other factors. Thus in plant growth we are not dealing with a simple group of factors, each of which has a definite influence under all conditions, but with a complex combination, and the significance of any one or of variations in any one depends upon the others.

Each soil must be understood as a complex, changing thing, in some respects like a living thing, subject to the combined forces of the environment. In time, the soil approaches an equilibrium in which the forces of depletion (leaching, erosion, and removal of materials by plants and animals) balance the forces of renewal (addition of new minerals to the top or bottom of the soil layer, release of materials by plants and animals, and the decomposition of minerals within the soil). If any factor of the environment—the vegetation, climate, slope, or parent rock—varies or changes, the soil will take on a different character and will veer toward a new point of equilibrium.

Many such changes occur in nature, usually very slowly. Climates may change gradually. With climatic changes, or for other reasons, vegetation may change. There are instances in which a dark-colored soil with a layer of lime in the lower portion, developed under a tall-grass vegetation (Chernozem) has been changed to a light-colored, acid soil (Podzol) after coniferous trees have encroached on it. The most important recent changes have been caused by man. When man removes the native vegetation and replaces it with plants of his own choosing, an enormous change is sometimes made. This change may improve the soil and make it more productive for the future, or it may reduce its productivity, depending upon the crops grown, the management practices, and the soil conditions. Although such changes may not be fundamentally different from those taking place in the natural environment, they are brought about much more quickly and may even be drastic and sudden, like the change from natural tall grasses to cultivated corn or from pine trees to clover meadows. Certainly many of the soils of western Europe are more productive now than when they were first cleared. So are many in the eastern part of the United States and elsewhere in this country. Others have been allowed to become acid, deficient in nutrients, and eroded.

Losses[5] from the natural soil after it has reached essential equilibrium with its environment in the natural landscape are thus balanced with gains or additions. Although man's changes may be drastic and may greatly change the productivity of the soil for a time, the fundamental characteristics of the soil are ordinarily changed only very slowly, except in instances of extremely accelerated erosion. There are other instances where continued flooding, as in rice culture, the long-continued use of chemicals and drainage, irrigation, silting, and similar practices may lead to certain fundamental changes.

Cultivation may reduce losses from leaching, especially where a less vigorous plant growth is substituted for the native vegetation with a resulting increase in run-off. The most important loss from cultivated soils through leaching is that of nitrogen. To grow most farm crops successfully the soil must contain abundant supplies of soluble nitrogen compounds—larger supplies than are required by most native plants. In humid regions where there is plenty of rainfall, soils very permeable to water, such as the sandy soils, may suffer large losses of soluble nitrogen compounds, especially on barren ground, where there is no growing vegetation to take up the nitrogen. This is one of the reasons for growing cover crops. Such crops use part of the water, thus reducing the total amount passing through the soil, and also take up the nitrogen, which is released again to the soil by decomposition when the plants are plowed under. In applying nitrogen fertilizers to soils subject to much leaching, slowly available forms must be used along with soluble materials if one application is to serve the crop throughout the growing season; otherwise two or three smaller appli-

[5] The nature and extent of soil losses are described more fully in the 1938 Yearbook of Agriculture, Soils and Men, especially on pages 84 to 96, to which the reader is referred.

cations of the soluble materials will have to be used during the season. If a large application of soluble nitrogen fertilizer were used in the spring on a sandy soil in the southeastern part of the United States, say, much of the nitrogen might be leached out of the soil and lost to the plants before the latter part of the growing season.

Under natural conditions the materials taken up by vegetation are returned to the surface, but when crops are harvested these materials are removed. In many instances such withdrawals from the soil may be insignificant as compared with the total supply, especially if erosion is constantly uncovering fresh minerals. Thus, in many soils the content of calcium, magnesium, zinc, or any other nutritive element may be so large, or the natural processes of renewal so effective, that compensating additions are unnecessary to maintain the yield and quality of crops. Yet with many other soils this is not true. Frequently the demand made upon particular nutrient elements by planted crops is so much greater than that of the native vegetation that after a few crops have been harvested additions in the form of fertilizer or manure must be made. Many of the sandy soils developed under a forest vegetation in humid regions, for example, are deficient in most of the nutrient elements. On the other hand, some of the silt loam soils developed under luxuriant grass vegetation in subhumid regions may contain abundant supplies of all or at least most of the nutrient elements.

The matter of nutrient deficiencies is specific for each type of soil and management practice. It is a matter not of "replacing" what the plants remove but of supplying those particular nutrients in which the soil is deficient for the growth of some crop or sequence of crops in order to have good yields, or good quality, or both. The long-continued growth of harvested crops on any soil will ultimately deplete the soil of nutritive elements, provided there is no erosion or deposition, but it will do this very unequally for the different elements. As more is being learned about soils, fertilizers are being more and more adapted to particular soils in accordance with their specific deficiencies and the system of management. If a soil needs only one or two elements, it is not necessary to put on a complex, more expensive fertilizer containing several others in addition. Increasing deficiencies of many of the secondary nutritive elements like manganese, zinc, copper, boron, and iron are being found, especially in some of the soils that have been long cultivated. The matter of nutrient deficiencies may be expected to receive enormously greater attention from the point of view of human and animal health and nutrition as well as that of yield of crops in the years to come.

In addition to the chemical influences, growing crops have physical influences on the soil. For good crop growth it is necessary for the soil to be pervious to water and permeable to roots. Such a soil has a granular or crumblike structure, that is, it is made up of soft, irregular granules or aggregates of soil particles. Granular structure is best developed under grass vegetation; the Prairie or Chernozem soils are examples. Excessive plowing and cultivating, especially when the soil is very wet or very dry, tend to destroy the granular structure and cause the soil to run together, or puddle, when wet and to bake into hard crusts or large clods when dry. On many soils the continuous growing of corn or other cultivated crops injures the structure and causes a decline in production before any serious nutrient deficiencies have developed. Erosion sometimes removes a mellow surface soil and exposes a massive subsoil, thus greatly injuring soil structure. Without doubt accelerated erosion does more harm to the physical qualities of the soil than to its fertility, although both may be impaired. In order to maintain good structure most soils must be devoted periodically to grass or close-growing legumes. The good influence of alfalfa and the clovers grown in rotation, in humid regions especially, may be due as much to their good effect on structure as to their ability to maintain the nitrogen supply.

Erosion

Under natural conditions some erosion is constantly taking place from the upland soils, and some deposition is taking place on the lowland soils. Some soils are not subject to either influence, especially those on nearly level uplands, and in humid regions unproductive soils develop in such situations because of the slowness or lack of these normal processes for renewal. The removal of the native vegetation and the use of the soil for cultivated crops may accelerate the erosion process if the land is sloping, if the soil is not easily permeable to water, and if the soil material is easily suspended in water. Thus the amount of erosion that may be expected depends upon the erodibility of the soil under particular management practices, including the kind of crops grown, the lay-out of the fields, the methods of tillage, and so on. If a type of soil management is adopted that permits a great increase in the speed and amount of run-off, growing plants may suffer from a shortage of water, and erosion may be greatly accelerated. With proper control of run-off, losses of either water or soil are reduced or avoided.

Soil and rock erosion are always going on under natural conditions. Through this natural process, drainage systems are developed. In a geologically young country like the Lake States there are large areas of swamps and imperfectly drained lands even though the whole area lies well above sea level. As time goes on the streams may be expected to deepen and lengthen and gradually drain the lakes and swamps. When, through major geological processes, a great area becomes elevated as a plain, this normal cutting of a drainage system begins. In desert regions without the buffering influence of vegetation these processes go on very actively. In areas where rainfall is sufficient to promote a continuous cover of perennial vegetation the erosion process is much slower. Erosion proceeds in the natural landscape at the same rate as or slower than soil formation. In addition there is movement by slips and slides, in which the whole soil moves more or less as a mass. Some of these movements are very slow—"creeps," they are sometimes called. In regions of high temperatures and rainfall the tropical vegetation grows so luxuriantly and rapidly that sheet or gully erosion, that is, ordinary soil washing, is very slow indeed.

The amount of natural erosion in the different regions varies greatly, depending upon the seasonal amount and intensity of the rainfall, the angle, length, and shape of the slopes, the permeability of the soil, and the character of the vegetation. Sharp, sudden showers cause more erosion than slow, gentle rains. This is, perhaps, a principal reason for the very small amount of accelerated erosion in central and western Europe, where gentle rains are the rule. Sudden rains, like many of the winter and early spring rains in the United States, are especially destructive if they come at times when an erosive soil is nearly barren of vegetation. The greater the angle or the length of slopes, the greater is the amount and speed of the run-off. With the same length and degree of slope, there is more rapid run-off and more erosion on concave than on convex slopes.

Thus the erodibility of any particular soil is not easy to estimate. Rains may come with violence, and the slope may be steep, but if the soil is sufficiently permeable the water goes into the ground and does not run over the surface. Many of the strongly lateritic soils in the Tropics are of this type. Any factor that injures the vegetation, such as fire, severe drought, severe grazing, or clearing may greatly increase erosion, provided, of course, that the other factors are also favorable to such an increase. Some soils are so erosive that, even on a very gentle slope, if they are exposed to sudden rains great damage may be done swiftly. The several horizons of the same soil sometimes vary in erodibility. In the southern Piedmont region, for example, some soils have highly erodible surface (A) horizons, less erodible B horizons, and very highly erodible substrata (C horizons). Once gullies have cut through the solum in such soils, the problem of control is increased enormously.

In the United States erosion has increased on many soils as a result of placing lands under cultivation and intensive grazing. This has happened on soils subject to erosion where the system of management has allowed too much run-off. Erosion has become most noticeable on the sloping soils of the Central and especially the Southern States. There has been serious erosion and soil blowing in many parts of the West because of overgrazing and attempts to cultivate land by farming methods developed in more humid regions.[6]

Since the degree and effect of erosion depend upon both the type of soil and the management practices, they are not correlated directly with either one alone. Careless husbandry may lead to erosion on one soil and not on another; and some moderately erosive soils have eroded badly under poor husbandry—that is, under management practices not suited to the particular soil type—whereas under good husbandry the same soils may not have suffered accelerated erosion at all and may even be much more productive than under natural conditions.

It must be remembered that erosion, low yields, and rural poverty are all symptoms, not primary causes, of maladjustments between the people and the soil—maladjustments that lead to improper use or management of the soil. Of course, after a decline in soil productivity has begun, a proper adjustment may be even more difficult to effect. Thus soil depletion, once begun, may appear to be a cause of the difficulties of which it is really the result.

Whether or not a soil is productive depends on both soil and management. The use to which any soil can be put depends upon the economic and social conditions within which that use must be made. That is, if prices were high enough, most soils could be used for crops; if prices are very low, few soils can be used. Frequently people have been persuaded to attempt to farm land that cannot yield a satisfactory labor income under existing prices and costs of production on a secure basis. For example, farms have been established on strongly

[6] A more extended discussion of erosion, with maps, may be found in the Yearbook for 1938, Soils and Men.

sloping soils, extremely stony soils, dry sandy soils, the dry soils of the semiarid regions, and elsewhere where yields in proportion to the labor and other costs are too low to give returns sufficient for the support of a family. Exploitive methods of farming that lead to even lower yields may have been followed in an attempt to make a go of things, with the result of making a bad situation worse.

THE FARM AS A UNIT

The individual farm is the place where the several agricultural practices come together into one pattern. Success depends frequently upon ability to fit the several pieces together and to keep them in proper relationship to one another as economic and social conditions change and as agricultural science progresses. Although research may be conducted on single items, such as soil fertility, crop diseases, marketing arrangements, cattle feeding, and machinery design, in practice things are done together. One cannot do some perfectly and neglect the others. Failure to treat seed for disease may nullify other good practices. What are sometimes regarded as single problems such as soil erosion, rural health, tenancy, low farm prices, climatic hazards, and animal diseases, are not soluble individually. Many of them are rather effects than causes of farmers' difficulties. The study and analysis of the farm problem is handicapped by a modern tendency toward oversimplification—the attempt to find some one cause, for which there is some equally simple cure. Many years ago scientists hoped to find a fundamental cause; and though science has long since abandoned the search, many people, even leaders of the people, still advocate some single remedy for their ills. But there is no single road to ruin or success.

Each farm has its own peculiar physical make-up; almost no two farms are alike so far as soil and climate are concerned. Many are enormously complex. Part of the land may be hilly, some nearly level; part may be stony and some not; part sandy and some heavy. The effects of climate—droughts, sharp rains, hot winds—are different on these different soil types. Crops suffer from drought on some soil types much more than on others on the same farm. Soil type also determines the effect of sudden hard rains on erosion.

The farmer is trying to make a living and to develop a home—the kind of home he wants. Now there is a great deal of difference among people as to what they want, as to how hard they are willing to work for the extra comforts, as to what things give them most satisfaction. No one can set up a standard for all the rest—at least not in a democracy. Farmers are unlike in personal traits and have unequal amounts of worldly goods. What may be practical for one who has a little capital may be quite impractical for one without any.

Changes in transportation systems, in the development of electric power, in prices, in credit facilities, in machinery, in crop varieties, in all phases of our cultural and economic life, influence individual farmers quite differently. A new all-weather road may enable one farmer to produce whole milk but not help another. The price fluctuations of wheat and corn may not have much influence on the vegetable growers in eastern Virginia.

There is no such thing as a "best" use for any combination of soil and climate in the abstract. Of course, the range in possibilities for some soils is greater than for others; each has a certain elastic limit beyond which it cannot be improved. But for many soils there are 10 or even 20 "best" uses, depending upon the other factors in the combination—soil, climate, and farmer.

One can say that most farmers want secure production—income now and for the years ahead. This requires careful planning involving the relationship of all the many factors in the combination that is the farm unit to achieve maximum production with a system of farming that will maintain soil productivity for the future. Conservation is the byproduct of a properly adjusted farming system and not the direct purpose of the farmer. There are no one or two practices that will give the desired results. For example, terraces are useful on many soils to control run-off, provided that any deficiencies in lime, phosphorus, or other nutrients are supplied and proper rotations including legumes are planned. But terraces without the other accompanying practices may cause more injury that good by concentrating the water and starting gullies in places where they become broken. Similarly there is no advantage in using high-quality seed unless the land is well tilled, the soil fertilized where necessary, and run-off controlled.

Because the problem of the adjustment of people to the soil is complex and because several management practices must be fitted to a variety of physical conditions, each farm unit offers a unique problem and must be studied in detail. Certain facts may be true for many practices and for the same soil on many farms. But the combination of conditions is individual for each farm.

This fitting of a pattern of social and economic conditions to a pattern of soil conditions is illustrated by the hypothetical farms shown in figures 5 and 6. Although much simplified, these farm lay-outs may illustrate the point.

In the farms of figure 5 a slight difference in soil changes the use of all of the other soils in the farm unit. Thus, the "best use" of the same soils on adjoining farms is quite different. In figure 6, the soils on the three farms are the same, but the market facilities and the desires and abilities of the farmer as a manager are different. Consequently, the soils are used differently in order to achieve the ends of production on a secure basis. Although some one or two plants may grow best on a certain soil, most soils can be used reasonably well for several crops. Considering the economic advantages of diversification and the physical advantages of crop rotations, it may be better to grow several crops on a soil than only one or two. Some soils are much more elastic than others, and a few, as in the illustrations, have no elasticity under existing conditions.

It is clear, therefore, that generalizations about good practices for all soils or all farms, even in the same climatic region, are impractical. Each practice must be harmonized with the others on the farm. And for the farmer to make this adjustment on his own farm, the broader, community pattern of roads, tax policies, and so on must be in accord with the physical condition of the community. When these adjustments are made as conditions change, the fundamental basis for a secure, healthy rural people has been achieved. When they fail, from internal or external causes, discord, poverty, and soil depletion follow.

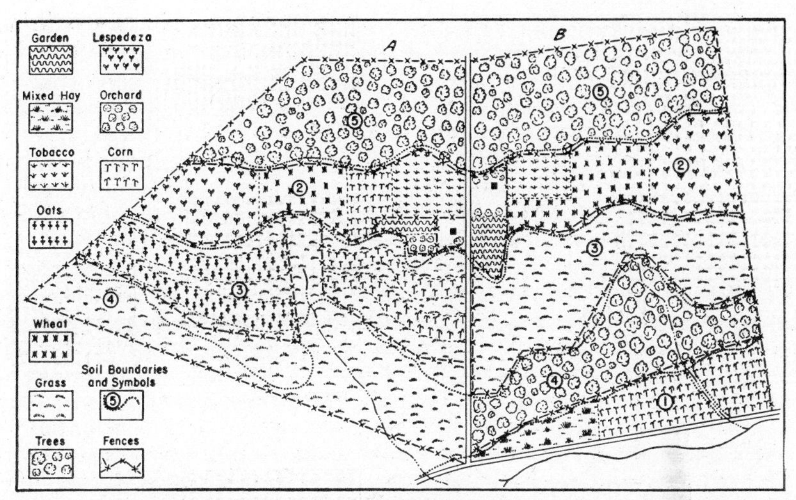

FIGURE 5.—These two adjoining hypothetical farms in the ridge-valley region of the Southeast, of about 140 acres each, consisting chiefly of relatively poors oils, illustrate the influence of a small area of one particular soil type on the use of others in the farm unit. The growing season is a little too short for cotton. Since the rainfallis high and is characterized by sudden showers, run-off and erosion are serious on sloping lands not well covered with vegetation. The soils on the two farms may bedescribed briefly as follows:

1. Huntington silt loam. Highly fertile soil of nearly level stream bottoms. Although occasionally subject to overflow for short periods, it is easy to till, and there is little hazard from erosion. Crops suffer little from drought on this soil. If this soil is devoted to mixed hay containing legumes every third or fourth year and if a little phosphate is used, excellent crops of corn may be obtained.
2. Clarksville cherty silt loam. Soil with good physical condition for crops, but relatively low in fertility, cherty and slightly stony, and found on undulating or gently sloping surfaces. It is comparatively easy to till, but care must be taken that legume hay crops are grown frequently, that the soil does not remain bare during the winter, and that tillage operations are conducted on the contour. In a few places strip cropping may be necessary for best results. Applications of both lime and phosphate, together with some potash, will be necessary for good yields. If legumes are grown and manure is properly conserved and applied, little nitrogen fertilizer will be required.
3. Fullerton silt loam, rolling phase. Moderately fertile soil with good physical condition for crops, but slightly stony and on steep slopes. With applications of lime and phosphate, good pastures with legumes can be grown easily. Crops can be grown with less fertilizer and lime than on soil No. 2, but great care to avoid excessive run-off and erosion must be taken through strip cropping and the maintenance of grassed areas in the drainageways.
4. Fullerton cherty loam, hilly phase. Soil with fair physical condition, quite stony, strongly sloping, and relatively low in fertility. Forest trees grow well on this soil, and grasses for pasture can be grown through the use of lime, heavy applications of phosphate fertilizer, and careful management to prevent overgrazing and the formation of little rills that could easily grow into gullies.
5. Clarksville stony loam, steep phase. Soil so stony and steeply sloping that only forest trees can be grown.

A system of farming that will support a family and conserve the soil must include livestock and some cash crop. This is much more easily arranged on farm B than on farm A because of the small area of soil on B highly productive for corn. Sufficient corn can be grown on farm B on soil No. 1 so that soil No. 2 can be used for tobacco, small grains, and legumes, soil No. 3 for pasture, and soil No. 4 for forestry. Since there is no soil highly productive for corn on farm A, soil No. 3 must be used partly for corn or other feed crops and soil No. 4 for pasture, with rather difficult management practices required in both instances. Soil No. 5 cannot be used for crops or pasture under any known system of management that would be practical.

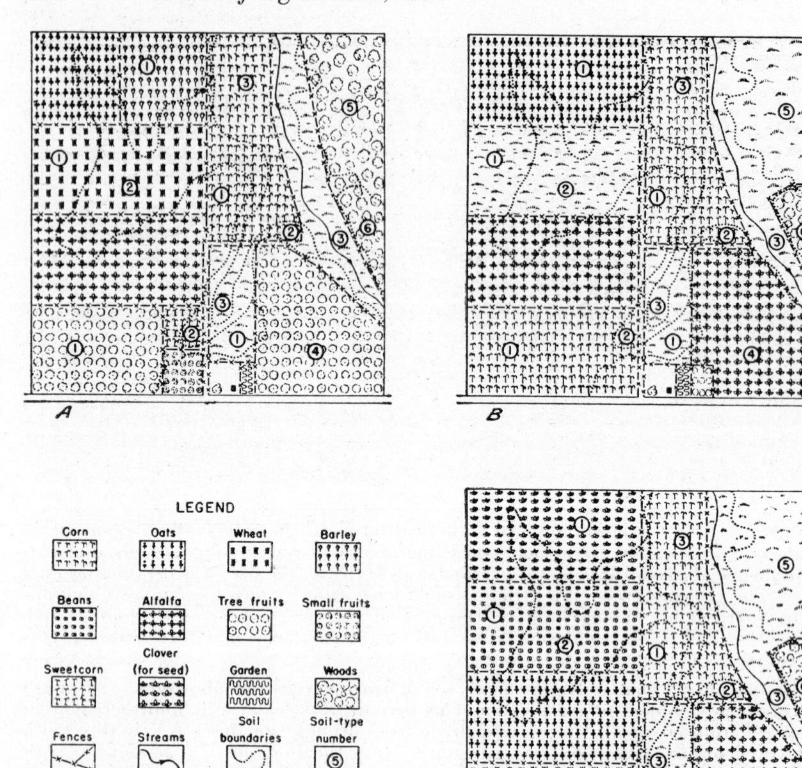

FIGURE 6.—These three hypothetical farms in southern Michigan of about 160 acres each have the same pattern of relatively good soils; yet different management systems to achieve both production and conservation may be easily developed in accordance with market facilities and the desires and capabilities of the farmers. Because of the soil and climatic conditions, erosion is not a serious hazard, but rotations must be sufficiently flexible to allow for shifts in abnormally wet or dry seasons. The soils may be described as follows:

1. Miami loam. Fertile soil, easy to till, well-drained, and undulating or very gently sloping. For best results lime must be applied and occasional applications of phosphates made. Unless manure is used and legumes grown, potash and nitrogen will be necessary also. Crops are not much affected by excessive or deficient rainfall.
2. Conover loam. Fertile soil, easy to till, imperfectly drained, and nearly level. Occasional applications of phosphate are necessary, and sometimes a little lime is needed. The soil must be tile-drained for best results, and during abnormally wet seasons crops may suffer somewhat.
3. Brookston silt loam. Highly fertile soil, poorly drained, nearly level, and comparatively easy to till unless the season is unusually wet. This soil must be tile-drained for the production of field crops, although pastures can be grown fairly well without such drainage. Phosphates are required for best results. During abnormally wet seasons crops may suffer somewhat and machinery be hard to handle.
4. Bellefontaine sandy loam. Moderately fertile soil, well-drained, easy to till, and gently rolling. During dry seasons crops may suffer somewhat. Lime and phosphate are needed but not much potash and nitrogen if manure is used and legumes are grown. (*Legend continued on following page.*)

5. Bellefontaine sandy loam, slope phase. Moderately fertile soil, excessively drained, difficult to till (because of the slope), and strongly sloping. With the use of lime and phosphate, pastures may be grown on this soil, although the grasses may suffer somewhat from lack of moisture during the summer, especially if the season is dry. Care must be taken to prevent excessive run-off and erosion. Unless pasture is very necessary in the farm unit, the soil may be devoted to forest trees, which will grow well.
6. Rodman gravelly loam. Relatively infertile soil, excessively drained, very difficult to till, and on steep slopes. Sweetclover can be grown, but with difficulty, and ordinarily the best use is for forest trees. Some areas of this soil are excellent sources of gravel for use in making concrete.

All three farms have rather long flexible rotations that allow for sudden shifts if seasons are bad and permit the growing of corn, oats, and beans mostly on soils 1, 2, and 3, and alfalfa and fruit on soils 1 and 4, although any of the field crops or emergency crops can be grown on any of the soils except 5 and 6. It might be said that the use of soil 6 was the least flexible, then that of 5, 3, 4, 2, and 1, in order, although soil 4 is superior to any except 1 for fruit trees. All three are "general farms," but farm A is specializing in fruit, farm B in dairying, and farm C in cash grain.

Effects of Climatic Factors On Growing Plants

By A. C. Hildreth, J. R. Magness, and John W. Mitchell [1]

THE AUTHORS of this article have brought together a wealth of facts regarding the effects of cold and heat, moisture and dryness, and differing amounts of light on growing plants. These are the fundamentals that govern the successful growing of crops in various regions, the breeding of plants to overcome climatic limitations, and some important farm practices designed to fit in with climatic requirements.

[1] A. C. Hildreth, Principal Physiologist, Cheyenne Horticultural Field Station, Bureau of Plant Industry, prepared the section on Temperature and Plant Growth; J. R. Magness, Principal Pomologist, Bureau of Plant Industry, the section on Water Supply and Plants; and J. W. Mitchell, Associate Physiologist, Bureau of Plant Industry, the section on Light and Plant Growth.

CLIMATE largely determines the type of vegetation that grows naturally in any part of the world and the kinds of agricultural production that are possible. The three most important factors in climate from the standpoint of plant response are temperature, water supply, and light. Temperature is the main factor that determines where native species or crop plants can be grown in great belts north and south of the Equator. Precipitation or water supply is the most important factor in determining the distribution of plants and crops within these great belts of somewhat similar temperature conditions. Light varies greatly in intensity in different areas, and the length of daily illumination varies in different regions and at different seasons of the year. Both light intensity and the length of the daily illumination period profoundly affect plant behavior.

Other elements of climate are less important from the standpoint of crop production. Wind increases the water requirement of plants. Hailstorms, tornadoes, or hurricanes may destroy crops locally. Near salt water, the salt spray may be destructive to many forms of vegetation.

All of these elements of climate are interrelated in their effect on the plant organism. Temperature and light affect the water requirement. The available moisture supply greatly influences the effects of high temperatures and light intensities. Although these elements of climate are discussed separately, the reader should keep in mind that the plant is a complicated organism, affected by all factors in its environment, nutritional as well as climatic, and that these effects are usually interrelated in plant response.

Numerous attempts have been made to evaluate geographical location and elevation in terms of plant response. These really are evaluations of location and elevation as they affect the elements of climate, since it is the climatic environment rather than geography that determines the rate of plant development. Hopkins (see Selected References, p. 306), in a recent study of these relationships—sometimes referred to as bioclimatics—has suggested the following values for latitude, longitude, and elevation in determining the time at which plants of the same species will flower:

1. For each degree of latitude north or south of the Equator, flowering is retarded 4 calendar days.
2. For each 5 degrees of longitude, from east to west on land areas, flowering is advanced 4 calendar days.
3. For each 400-foot increase in altitude, flowering is retarded 4 calendar days.

These values are quite similar to other and earlier estimates, and seem to apply very well to many of our crop plants.

TEMPERATURE AND PLANT GROWTH

In one way or another, temperature influences every chemical and physical process connected with plants—solubility of minerals, absorption of water, gases, and mineral nutrients, diffusion, synthesis—as well as vital processes such as growth and reproduction. Since these processes are necessary for plants to become established and survive, temperature limits to a considerable extent the distribution of plants on the earth and largely determines the flora of the different regions. Moreover, temperatures delimit the areas of successful

298737°—41——20

production of most agricultural crops. Such well-defined areas as the Cotton Belt, the Corn Belt, the winter and spring wheat areas, and the Michigan fruit belt are determined essentially by temperatures. This limiting influence on crop distribution results primarily from (1) too short a period of favorable temperature for crop maturity; (2) unfavorably high or unfavorably low growing-season temperatures for proper development of the crop; (3) occurrence of temperatures, either high or low, that cause injury or death to growing plants; (4) winter temperature conditions that injure or kill dormant plants; and (5) temperature conditions particularly favorable to the development of injurious diseases or insect pests.

In its evolution the plant kingdom has become adapted to a wide range of temperatures. There are few places on earth too hot or too cold to sustain some form of plant life. Certain blue-green algae thrive in hot springs where the water is constantly near the boiling point. Plants of arctic regions survive where winter temperatures reach −90° F. Many plants can adapt themselves to great extremes of temperature by entering resting stages. Dormant trees that withstand −65° F. in winter are killed when they are in summer growing condition by temperatures a few degrees below freezing. Dried seeds and spores withstand temperatures of liquid air and liquid oxygen. Spore stages of certain fungi can survive temperatures up to 130° C. (266° F.).

The temperature range within which growth takes place is much more limited than that within which plants in inactive stages can survive. Mention has already been made of the hot-springs algae that grow at temperatures of about 93° C. (199.4° F.). At the other extreme are fungi that develop in cold storage at about −6° C. (21.2° F.) and certain marine algae that complete their life cycle in sea water below 0° C. (32° F.). These, however, are exceptional cases, interesting because they show the enormous adaptability of plant protoplasm. By far the greater number of both higher and lower plants are capable of carrying on growth only within a comparatively narrow range, from about 0° C. (32° F.) to about 50° C. (122° F.).

For each species and variety there is a temperature below which growth is not possible—the minimum growth temperature. There is likewise a maximum temperature above which growth ceases. Between these limits there is an optimum temperature at which growth proceeds with greatest rapidity. These three points are called the cardinal growth temperatures. At the minimum point growth proceeds very slowly. From somewhat above the minimum to the optimum, the rate of growth follows van't Hoff's law; that is to say, for every 10° C. (18° F.) rise in temperature the rate of growth approximately doubles. Above the optimum, the growth rate falls off rapidly until the maximum is reached, beyond which growth stops. Thus the optimum and maximum points are closer together than are the optimum and minimum.

These cardinal growth temperatures vary considerably among the different kinds of plants. With typical cool-season crops, such as oats, rye, wheat, and barley, these points are all comparatively low—minimum 0°–5° C. (32°–41° F.), optimum 25°–31° C. (77°–87.8° F.), and maximum 31°–37° C. (87.8°–98.6° F.). For hot-season crops, such as melons and sorghums, the temperatures are much higher—mimimum 15°–18° C. (59°–64.4° F.), optimum 31°–37° C. (87.8°–98.6° F.), and maximum 44°–50° C. (111.2°–122° F.). However, there are other crops such as hemp that embrace the whole range of growth temperatures, having the minimum of the cool-season crops and the maximum of the hot-season crops. The cardinal temperatures for growth may vary considerably with the stages of plant development, such as germination, seedling stage, and maturity. Thus seedlings often have lower temperature requirements than plants in later stages.

It should be emphasized that the optimum temperature that produces the highest growth rate is not necessarily the most favorable for the general welfare of the plant and is often undesirable from an agricultural standpoint. Too-rapid growth may delay or entirely prevent fruiting; it may produce plants that are structurally weak, susceptible to disease or insect attacks, and subject to damage by wind, hail, or other climatic influences. It is evident, however, that wide departures from the optimum will so reduce the growth in most cases as to make production unprofitable.

A number of investigators have attempted to determine the total "heat units" required to mature a crop. Using as a base the minimum temperature at which growth occurs, they have computed the total "degree-hours" or "degree-days" required, a degree-hour being 1 degree of temperature above the base for the duration of an hour. Livingston (see Selected References, p. 306) has published the temperature summations for different parts of the United States and has suggested their value in studies of plant distribution and adaptation.

The temperature summations found for the same variety of plant frequently have varied greatly under different growing conditions. Generally, in cooler sections the summation is lower than in hotter sections, probably owing mainly to the fact that excessively high temperatures may reduce rather than increase the rate of growth or development. Also the greater light duration during the summer in more northern latitudes may partly compensate for less heat. Thus, while plants may be classed as requiring much, moderate, or little total heat, a definite number of degree-hours or degree-days does not result in similar development under widely varying conditions.

Unlike warm-blooded animals, plants have no mechanism for controlling temperature independent of environment or for maintaining a uniform temperature throughout the organism. In general, plants and plant parts have approximately the same temperature as their surroundings.

Effects of Low Temperatures

Wherever freezing temperatures occur, plants are in danger of frost injury. There are, however, many habits and modifications by which they are able to survive in regions having temperatures at or below the freezing point. Tender annuals escape freezing by completing their life cycle, from seed to seed, during the period between frosts. Herbaceous perennials die back to the ground but maintain life in underground organs—roots, bulbs, tubers, or rhizomes—which produce new tops when temperatures are favorable. Beneath the soil these organs are either entirely protected from freezing or subjected to much less cold than are aerial parts. Coverings of snow or leaves also afford protection from low temperatures, and many low-growing half-hardy plants are able to survive in cold regions because of such covering during periods of extreme cold. Natural protection is frequently supplemented in farming by such practices as mulching.

Cold-hardy plants have the ability to develop cold resistance within their tissues. The degree of resistance varies with different species and varieties. Some herbaceous types, such as cabbage, withstand ice formation in their leaves but are killed by winter temperatures in the colder parts of the country. Hardy woody plants —trees, shrubs, and vines—that endure cold winters without protection develop the greatest degree of cold resistance among higher plants. The exact nature of this remarkable physiological adaptation to cold is still unknown. Within limits, it is possible to secure increased resistance in many species by breeding.

Many correlations have been noted between cold resistance and certain plant characteristics, such as structure and the chemical and physical properties of the cells. None of these factors, however, seems to be common to all cold-hardy plants and none can therefore be regarded as the causal mechanism of cold resistance. The exact nature of cold resistance, as well as the mechanism of injury from freezing, must await a better knowledge of the structure and the physiology of plant protoplasm.

Bark, bud scales, and hairy coatings, often regarded by enthusiastic amateur naturalists as a means of keeping the plant warm, actually have little value in protecting it from cold. At best such coverings only slightly retard the rate of temperature fall, and the plant soon comes to equilibrium with the temperature surrounding it.

In their efforts to extend production into colder regions, farmers and gardeners have persistently carried plants beyond the temperature range to which they are naturally adapted. Consequently, cold injury is common in cultivated plants. Since frost occurs in practically every part of the continental United States, low-temperature injury is an agricultural problem of the entire country, and none of our agricultural areas are entirely free from this hazard.

The nature of freezing damage to crops varies in different regions and with the different kinds of crop plants. In winter-garden sections frosts may kill outright fields of tender crops, such as beans, melons, and tomatoes. Subtropical-fruit districts may experience winter frosts that freeze and ruin green or ripening fruit on the trees. With more severe freezing, the leaves and even the trees are killed.

Over much of the United States late-spring frosts constitute a major hazard of plant production. They may damage or kill young plants of corn, flax, potatoes, cotton, tender garden vegetables, and even seedlings of such comparatively hardy crops as wheat and alfalfa. Plants such as tomatoes, which are normally transplanted into the fields, are usually started in the South or under glass to escape the frost hazard. Deciduous fruits and nuts suffer damage to opening buds, flowers, or young fruit, often to the extent of completely destroying the crop. Flowers, shoots, and leaves of ornamental trees, shrubs, and perennials may be killed or damaged so that their esthetic value is largely lost for the season. Forest trees suffer damage from late spring frosts through destruction of the seed crop, killing back or injury of new growth, and development of frost rings in the wood, which later yields lumber of inferior quality.

Plants overwintering in cold regions are subject to various types and degrees of cold injury. Since not all parts, organs, or tissues are equally cold-resistant, one part may be killed or badly injured while another is undamaged. For this reason, plants apparently hopelessly injured by cold often make a surprising recovery. On the other hand, the effects of winter injury are not always immediately evident. Injured trees or branches may suddenly wither and die after opening their buds, or they may flourish until summer and even flower and fruit before dying. Injury to roots or interference with the conducting system by excretions or outgrowths from cold-injured tissue in the wood may be the cause of such surprising behavior.

Winter injury to herbaceous plants may consist in complete killing, as frequently happens with winter wheat, grasses, alfalfa, clover, strawberries, and many ornamental perennials. Less severe cold may kill buds or injure crowns or roots, as is common with alfalfa and strawberries.

Woody plants may have terminals killed back, and with lower temperatures killing may extend to the snow cover or to the ground. Injury to certain tissues or internal structures of woody stems is common and is generally recognizable by discoloration of the affected part. "Black heart" is an extreme case of such injury prevalent in cold regions, in which pith and often one or more annual rings of wood will be dark-colored. The cambium—the region between the wood and bark where new wood and bark cells are formed—is usually one of the most cold-resistant parts of a dormant stem and often remains uninjured, later laying down new rings of sound wood outside the discolored layers.

Roots are sometimes killed or injured even though the top is unharmed. Hardy fruit or nut varieties budded or grafted on tender rootstocks are likely to suffer from root killing. Winter killing of flower buds is common in many parts of this country, particularly on such crops as peach, cherry, and almond. It also occurs on apple, pear, and many ornamental plants. Local killing of the bark occurs on trees at crotches, at the base of the trunk, and in patches variously located on branches and trunk. Frost cracks and splitting and loosening of bark are mechanical injuries to trees resulting from freezing.

Sunscald is a cold injury occurring on the south and west sides of tree trunks and branches. In cold weather, sunlight falling directly on the bark may warm it several degrees above shaded parts. At sunset the temperature drops suddenly, and killing of the bark results either from the rapid fall in temperature or from freezing of tissues temporarily started into growth by the heating effect of the sun. Such practices as shading or wrapping the trunk or whitewashing to reduce absorption of heat from the winter sun reduce the sunscald type of injury.

Indirect effects of low temperatures on overwintering plants are heaving of soil, resulting in breakage or exposure of roots; the smothering effect of ice sheets; and breaking of trees and shrubs by snow and sleet.

Deleterious effects may result when plants are subjected to low temperatures above freezing. Growth is slowed down, elongation is reduced, and plants become dwarfed and more compact in habit. Definite injuries result from chilling many typically warm-climate plants. Exposure of a day or two at temperatures from slightly above 0° C. (32° F.) to 10° C. (50° F.) may result in yellowing of foliage, dead areas in the leaves, the dropping of leaves, and even the death of the plant.

Not all low-temperature effects are harmful. Many plants, including all of our deciduous fruit trees, have a "rest period," during which no growth takes place, even when all external conditions are favorable for growth. Shoots of woody plants, seeds, bulbs, tubers, and crown buds may exhibit this phenomenon. Some rather drastic treatments, by cold, chemical vapors, or heat, are necessary to break this rest. Cold is the natural means of accomplishing this result. Seed stratification, cold storage of bulbs, and chilling of rhubarb roots and flowering stems of lilac and other woody plants before forcing are commercially applied to break the rest period.

Certain plants seem to require a period of low temperature during germination and early seedling stages in order that later stages of development may be normal. Winter wheat sown in spring does not head; but if the seed is partly germinated and held from 1 to 2 months at temperatures around freezing and then spring-sown, a crop will be produced. This method of shortening the vegetative period and hastening seed production is called vernalization. Many cool-climate plants respond favorably to this treatment.

Effects of High Temperatures

The effects of high temperatures on plants are difficult to separate from the usually accompanying factors of high light intensity and rapid transpiration. Above the optimum growth temperature the rate of growth drops rapidly, and plants become dwarfed. Temperate Zone plants under tropical conditions tend to make only vegetative growth and to fruit sparingly or not at all. Fruits grown where summer temperatures are excessive for the variety ripen their crop prematurely, and the fruit is poor in flavor, color, and keeping quality. High temperatures cause in certain varieties and strains pollen abnormalities that result in sterility and failure to produce seed or fruit. Heat treatment of floral parts is used as a means of inducing polyploidy (multiplication of the number of chromosomes) in plants. Tissue injuries resulting from high temperatures may kill local areas on leaves, as in tipburn of lettuce and potatoes; scald fruits—such as strawberries and gooseberries; discolor and cause malformation of flowers, as in early blooming chrysanthemums and dahlias; and produce heat cankers on tender plants such as flax, and on the bark of fruit trees. General effects of excessive heat are defoliation, premature dropping of fruits, and, in extreme cases, death of the plant.

WATER SUPPLY AND PLANT DEVELOPMENT

Water supply, from rainfall or irrigation, ranks with temperature as the great determiner of where plant species grow naturally or can be grown agriculturally. Within the great belts of similar temperature conditions, it is more important than any other factor in determining the distribution of plant species and agricultural crops.

Plants may be divided into three great groups on the basis of the moisture condition to which they are adapted: (1) Hydrophytes—water plants or water-loving plants; (2) mesophytes—plants adapted to medium moisture conditions; and (3) xerophytes—plants able to survive under conditions of extreme moisture shortage.

Hydrophytes may grow entirely under water, or, more frequently, with part of the plant structure above water or floating on water. Plants in this group are usually large-celled and have thin cell walls and thin epidermal covering. They often have a relatively poorly developed root system that can survive in the absence of oxygen. They have relatively little protection against water loss. Among important agricultural crops, rice most nearly approaches the typical hydrophyte. Such crops can be grown only where water, from either rainfall or irrigation, is extremely abundant.

The mesophytes, requiring a medium amount of water, include the greater proportion of our agricultural crops. Such plants need moderate soil moisture and also good aeration around their roots, as the root system must have oxygen for development. They have moderately large root systems in proportion to the tops. Their structures are composed of medium-sized cells with surface covering well developed to prevent excessive water loss. Stomata, or pores, in the leaves usually close under conditions of incipient leaf wilting. Thus the plants are moderately well protected against water loss.

The third class, xerophytes, includes plants highly resistant to drought conditions. Usually their structure is such that water loss is reduced to a minimum—leaves are small, all epidermal coverings are thick and heavily covered with waxy material (cutinized), stomata are small and are frequently set in pits instead of on the surface of the leaves, and cells are small and thick-walled. Much of the true xerophytic vegetation has large root systems. Such plants usually grow slowly when moisture is available but are highly resistant to water loss and can survive long periods of drying. Since they are generally slow growing, they are not of great importance agriculturally. However, the native xerophytic vegetation of arid sections provides some feed for livestock and is important in reducing soil erosion.

In arid regions, in addition to xerophytic plants, there is usually an additional flora of quickly maturing plants that grow from seed and produce flowers and fruits during short seasons when rainfall occurs. The seeds then remain in the ground until moisture and temperature conditions are again favorable for growth. Such plants are mesophytic in type and develop only when moisture is ample.

A plant properly classed as a mesophyte tends to assume some of the characteristics of xerophytes when grown with a shortage of moisture and some of those of hydrophytes under conditions of abundant moisture. Thus the individual plant grown with abundant moisture will generally have larger leaves, larger cells, thinner cell walls, and less highly developed surface coverings than plants of the same variety or species grown under conditions of deficient water.

The Role of Water in Plants

Most growing plants contain much more water than all other materials combined. C. R. Barnes has suggested that it is as proper to term the plant a water structure as to call a house composed mainly of brick a brick building. Certain it is that all essential processes of plant growth and development occur in water. The mineral elements from the soil that are usable by the plant must be dissolved in the soil solution before they can be taken into the root. They are carried to all parts of the growing plant and are built into essential plant materials while in a dissolved state. The carbon dioxide from the air may enter the leaf as a gas but is dissolved in water in the leaf before it is combined with a part of the water to form simple sugars—the base material from which the plant body is mainly built. Actively growing plant parts are generally 75 to 90 percent water. Structural parts of plants, such as woody stems no longer actively growing, may have much less water than growing tissues.

The actual amount of water in the plant at any one time, however, is only an infinitesimal part of what passes through it during its development. The processes of photosynthesis, by which carbon dioxide and water are combined—in the presence of chlorophyll and with energy derived from light—to form sugars, require that carbon dioxide from the air enter the plant. This occurs mainly in the leaves. The leaf surface is not solid but contains great numbers of stomata, or pores, through which the carbon dioxide enters. The same structure that permits the one gas to enter the leaf, however, permits another gas—water vapor—to be lost from it. Since carbon dioxide is present in the air only in trace quantities (3 to 4 parts in 10,000 parts of air) and water vapor is near saturation in the air spaces within the leaf (at 80° F. saturated air would contain about 186 parts of water vapor in 10,000 parts of air), the total amount of water vapor lost is many times the carbon dioxide intake. Actually, because of wind and other factors, the loss of water in proportion to carbon dioxide intake may be even greater than the relative concentrations of the two gases. Also, not all of the carbon dioxide that enters the leaf is synthesized into carbohydrates.

While the air spaces inside the leaf are normally at or near saturation in plants not in a wilted condition, the moisture in the air surrounding the leaf may vary from full saturation to as low as 10-percent saturation. The drier and hotter the air surrounding the plant in general the more rapid the water loss in proportion to carbon dioxide intake. Thus in the drier, hotter areas the total water required to grow a plant to a given size will be greater than in areas where the air contains greater average quantities of moisture. Also water loss is more rapid when there is much wind than on a still day with the same temperature and humidity.

Water enters the plant primarily through the root system, which in most plants, at least those growing in a medium to dry environment, is usually more extensive than is generally realized. Weaver and Clements, in Plant Ecology (see Selected References, p. 307), state that corn in open soil will root almost as deeply as the height of the stalk; that the roots of a single lima bean or cabbage plant may ramify through 200 cubic feet of soil; and that many grasses and legumes have roots 16 feet deep in the soil. In open soils planted to such crops it may be impossible to find even a cubic inch of soil in the upper 2 or 3 feet that is not penetrated by roots.

The amount of moisture that the soil will hold against the downward force of gravity is termed the "field capacity" and varies in general with the fineness of the particles making up the soil. The moisture is held in the soil as films of water around the soil particles, and the total amount held is roughly proportional to the total amount of these surfaces. As the young roots penetrate the soil they are in contact with these moisture films, and the water enters them largely as a result of the physical process called osmosis.[2]

Not all the water in the soil, however, can be absorbed by the plant. If the films of water surrounding each soil particle become thin, the rate of capillary flow becomes less until the root is no longer able to absorb water. If this condition is reached in much of the root zone the plant wilts, because water is lost more rapidly from the top than it is supplied by the roots. The point at which the roots are no longer able to absorb appreciable moisture from the soil is termed the "wilting percentage," the moisture below that point being unavailable for plant use. The available moisture capacity of the soil is the amount of water available for plant use that it will store, or the amount between field capacity and wilting percentage. In general, the moisture content at the wilting percentage is a little less than half that of field capacity, though this varies in different soils.

The amount of available water that the soil will hold varies greatly with the soil texture and structure. Thus coarse, sandy soils may not hold more than half an inch of available water per foot of depth. Moderate-textured loam soils will usually hold 1½ to 2 inches of available water per foot of depth, while some clay soils will hold as much as 3 inches. Thus the light, coarse-textured soils that hold little available water are known as droughty and are of value agriculturally only under conditions of very frequent and regular rainfall or where abundant irrigation water is available. On the other hand, soils of high available water-holding capacity frequently will store enough water to mature satisfactory crops even though no rainfall occurs during the period of crop growth.

It is possible to determine the relative water efficiency of different plant species by determining the number of grams or pounds of water that the plant uses for each gram or pound of dry matter it builds. The ranges for a number of agricultural plants, as grown under arid conditions at Akron, Colo., are given in table 1, summarized from the work of Briggs and Shantz (p. 306). The water used per pound of dry matter produced would have been less with these same plants under more humid atmospheric conditions. The table indicates that the most efficient crops from the standpoint of water utilization used 250 to 300 pounds of water per pound of dry matter formed, while less efficient crops used as much as 1,000 pounds of water for each pound of dry matter produced.

Generally it may be said that the most critical period for water shortage in any plant species is the period during which it is making its most rapid growth, or when cell division is occurring most rapidly.

---

[2] When water containing dissolved substances is separated by a membrane from water without such substances or with a smaller concentration of them, the water will pass through from the side having less dissolved substances to the side having more dissolved substances. The membrane must be one that is permeable to water but not to the dissolved substances. The roots absorb water from around the soil particles with which they are in contact. This water is in turn replaced by capillary flow from other adjoining or nearby soil particles. Soil water does not move through great distances by capillary action to the roots, as was once supposed. But, wherever the root concentration is high, the movement through short distances is sufficient to dry the whole mass of soil occupied by the roots quite uniformly.

In crops grown for their seed, the most critical period is likely to be at the time of fertilization of the flowers, since lack of water at that time is likely to result in failure to form seed. In plants grown primarily for their leaves and stems, such as the forage crops, water shortage is likely to reduce production more during the earlier stages of development than during the later stages before harvest. With tree fruits such as cherries and peaches, which grow rapidly just prior to maturity, water shortage during that period of rapid increase in size is the most serious from the standpoint of reducing production.

TABLE 1.—*Water usage of plants, Akron, Colo., 1911–13*

Plant	Varieties tested	Water used per gram of dry matter		Plant	Varieties tested	Water used per gram of dry matter	
		Range in varieties tested	Mean			Range in varieties tested	Mean
Grain crops:	*Number*	*Grams*	*Grams*	Legumes–Continued	*Number*	*Grams*	*Grams*
Proso	3	268–341	293	Beans	2	682–773	728
Millet	5	261–444	310	Soybeans	2	672–815	744
Sorghum	14	285–467	322	Sweetclover	1		770
Corn	11	315–413	368	Peas, Canada field	2	775–800	788
Teosinte	2	376–390	383	Vetch	4	690–935	794
Wheat	7	473–559	513	Clover	2	789–805	797
Barley	4	502–556	534	Alfalfa	4	651–963	831
Buckwheat	1		578	Other crops:			
Oats	4	559–622	597	Beets, sugar	1		397
Rye	1		685	Potatoes	2	554–717	636
Rice	1		710	Crucifers	[1] 3	539–743	640
Flax	1		905	Cotton	1		646
Legumes:				Cucurbits	[1] 5	600–834	791
Cowpeas	1		571				
Chickpeas	1		663				

[1] Kinds rather than varieties.

In perennial plants, which form their flower buds during the season preceding that in which the buds flower and fruit, moderate water shortage tends to result in increased fruit-bud formation. Thus seasons of moderate water shortage usually are followed by abundant bloom the following spring in many fruit and forest trees.

Many of the basic farm practices, particularly in regions of limited rainfall, are based on conservation of the supplies of water available. The practice of summer fallowing is primarily to secure 2 years' rainfall for the production of one crop. Such practices as contouring and mulching are based in part on securing penetration into the soil of all water that falls. Clean tillage of cultivated crops during the growing season removes the competition of weeds for the available water. Irrigation, whether it be sprinkling a lawn or projects embracing millions of acres, is supplying water to plants that could not develop properly without it.

Finally, much has been accomplished and more is possible in breeding varieties of agricultural plants that will thrive and produce crops under conditions of limited water supply.

LIGHT AND PLANT GROWTH

The effect of light on the growth and development of green plants is manifest throughout nearly their entire life cycle. When the embryonic plant is resting in the seed under relatively dry conditions, it can be exposed to daylight or stored in darkness without appreciably affecting the subsequent germination of the seed or the growth of the plant. However, if placed under suitable conditions of humidity and temperature so that germination begins, the seeds of some plants such as Bermuda grass, bluegrass, and lettuce become light-sensitive even before the seed coat is broken, and germination can then be controlled to some extent by exposure to light.

After emergence from the seed, the plant in most instances becomes extremely photosensitive—sensitive to light—with respect to growth in length. The presence of light decreases and the absence of light increases the rate at which the stem elongates. Thus the seed, buried in the soil and germinating in darkness, sends out a stem that pushes upward very rapidly until it reaches the surface. The rate of elongation is then checked by sunlight and increases during the night. This rhythmic growth rate by day and night is manifested by many plants. If the light intensity is high, the stems are short and sturdy, but if dark, cloudy weather prevails the stems are often long and thin. Thus light affects the germination of the seeds of some plants and the rate of elongation and the sturdiness of the stems of many kinds of plants. The sensitivity to light and darkness with respect to stem length is maintained in most succulent plants through the growing season.

Light also becomes an important factor in connection with the manufacture of food soon after the young plant extends above the soil level. Sufficient food is stored in such seeds as beans and corn to last the seedlings grown in darkness approximately 2 weeks, after which they can no longer survive in darkness because of an inadequate supply of food. The leaves of plants grown in darkness do not become fully expanded, the stems grow thin and elongated, and the plants do not mature seed. On the other hand, seedlings supplied with light soon after germination and well before the food supply in the seed is exhausted soon become capable of manufacturing carbohydrates, protein, and other plant foods. Under favorable conditions of illumination and temperature, seedlings often turn green very rapidly when first exposed to light, sometimes within 1 to 3 hours. With the production of the green pigment, chlorophyll, the process of carbohydrate synthesis begins, and the plant becomes independent of the food stored in the seed.

Light also affects the development of plants through the effect of the length of the daily periods of illumination on the production of flowers, fruits, and seeds. Some kinds of plants grow vegetatively during the long days of summer and flower only in the short days of fall. Others grow vegetatively when exposed to short periods of daily illumination and flower only under a long photoperiod (period of light). Still others are not sensitive at all to the relative lengths of day and night. A plant that more readily produces flowers when grown with a relatively short daily period of illumination is generally classified as a short-day plant and one that flowers more readily under relatively long daily periods of illumination as a long-day plant. A few typical short-day and long-day plants are listed in table 2, together with others not sensitive to day length.

Sensitivity to the relative length of daily illumination often varies among several varieties of the same kind of plant. Certain varieties

TABLE 2.—*Typical short-day and long-day plants and plants not sensitive to day length*

Short-day plants	Long-day plants	Plants not sensitive to day length
Maryland Mammoth tobacco (*Nicotiana* sp.).	Hibiscus (*Hibiscus* sp.).	Asparagus (*Asparagus plumosus*).
Biloxi soybean (*Soja max*).	Goldenrod (*Solidago cutleri*).	Cyclamen (*Cyclamen persicum*).
Ragweed (*Artemisia* sp.).	Timothy (*Phleum pratense*).	Tomato (*Lycopersicon esculentum*).
Aster (*Aster linarifolius*).	Radish (*Raphanus sativus*).	Narcissus (*Narcissus poeticus*).
Bean (*Phaseolus multiflorus*).	Ryegrass (*Lolium perenne*).	Primrose (*Primula obconica*).
Cosmos (*Cosmos sulphureus*).	Chrysanthemum (*Chrysanthemum maximum*).	Foxglove (*Digitalis purpurea*).
Chrysanthemum (*Chrysanthemum morifolium*).	Cineraria (*Cineraria multiflora*).	

of chrysanthemum will flower only in the relatively short photoperiod of late summer. The same is true of varieties of radishes and soybeans. The time required for some plants to mature seed is dependent to some extent upon the relative lengths of day and night. As an example, Biloxi soybeans planted in the spring and grown during the relatively long days of summer at Washington, D. C., failed to mature seed. Comparable plants grown at the same time but given only 8 hours of daily illumination matured seeds within 2½ months.

Thus, by artifically controlling the length of the daily period of illumination, it has been possible to bring plants into flowering at a desired time and to induce them to mature seed. In breeding experiments the effect of the relative length of daily periods of light and darkness on flower initiation in plants has been of importance. By controlling the length of the daily period of illumination it has been possible to induce flowering and make crosses between plants with which this would not have been possible under natural conditions. It is also possible to induce some commercially important flowering plants to bloom at the desired time by artifically controlling the length of day under greenhouse conditions.

Although the mechanism through which plants respond to the relative length of day and night is not thoroughly understood, many interesting observations have been made by studying plants under artificially controlled conditions. Thus, if the stems of Biloxi soybeans are exposed to 8 hours of light daily and the leaves are kept in the dark, the plants do not initiate flowers, whereas if the leaves are exposed, the plants produce flowers. From this experiment it is evident that the leaves of Biloxi soybeans are sensitive to the relative lengths of day and night and that the stem is not sensitive. From similar experiments it has been shown that relatively young expanded leaves are most sensitive to day length. From numerous experiments of this nature the important effect of the length of the daily period of illumination upon plant reproduction has been demonstrated.

Thus light affects the development of crop plants mainly through affecting: (1) Their structural development, (2) their food production, and (3) the time required for certain species or varieties to produce seed.

Most plants are sensitive not only to the presence of light but to its quality and intensity. Under artificially controlled conditions light quality has been found to affect the height of some plants, those grown in red light often attaining a greater height than others grown in blue light or in daylight. In general, however, it has been found that plants produce more solid matter per unit of light intensity under the complete solar spectrum than under any portion of it. Variations in the quality of daylight are not so great as to produce a significant effect on plant growth.

Light intensity, however, varies greatly under natural conditions, and since most plants show marked response to these changes, the intensity of the light is relatively important in its effect on growth. As an example, bean plants can be made to attain a height of 10 to 12 inches within 4 days after they emerge from the soil by growing the plants in relatively dim light, while comparable plants grown in sunlight will attain a height of only 3–4 inches.

Light intensity also has an important effect on the amount of solid matter synthesized by plants. In general, this is limited by cloudy weather and increases noticeably when clear weather prevails. Excessively high light intensities, however, are sometimes deterimental to the growth of certain plants. Experiments have shown that sunflower, buckwheat, dahlia, and tobacco grown during June and July produced greater dry weight of tissues when slightly shaded. Many species, however, produce the maximum dry matter under high light intensity, if available water is ample. Thus crop production of many species reaches its maximum under irrigation in arid regions of high light intensity.

The response of plants to day length does not depend on the intensity of light. The flowering of a plant such as the Biloxi soybean can be delayed for a prolonged period by supplementing daylight with the dim light from a 20-watt incandescent lamp. An intensity no greater than 1/20000 of full sunlight has delayed flower initiation in this plant over prolonged periods. Thus light intensity under natural conditions affects principally the type of growth and amount of food synthesized by the plant but is relatively unimportant with respect to photoperiodic responses.

Although light affects the growth, synthesis of food materials, and seed production of many kinds of plants, it is, to be sure, only one of several environmental factors that interact to cause the responses observed under field conditions. Thus, a plant growing under natural conditions is often subjected to a period of high light intensity, high temperature, and low soil moisture at the same time, or during dark, cloudy weather it may experience a period of low light intensity, high humidity, and relatively low temperature. The plant responds not to these and other environmental factors separately but rather to all factors blended to make up a composite environment.

The farmer can do nothing to modify light conditions for most crops. High-priced crops, such as certain types of tobacco and such drug plants as ginseng and goldenseal, are grown under partial shade. Greenhouse operators may supply additional light for some crops during the winter and partially shade their houses in summer. In general, however, light intensity and duration are beyond the control of the plant grower.

SELECTED REFERENCES

Temperature and Plant Growth

Chandler, W. H.
1913. the killing of plant tissue by low temperature. Mo. Agr. Expt. Sta. Res. Bul. 8, pp. 143–309, illus.

Gardner, Victor Ray, Bradford, Frederick Charles, and Hooker, Henry Daggett, Jr.
1922. temperature relations of fruit plants. *In their* The Fundamentals of Fruit Production, pp. 234–387, illus. New York and London.

Hartley, Carl.
1918. stem lesions caused by excessive heat. Jour. Agr. Res. 14: 595–604, illus.

Heald, Frederick Deforest.
1926. diseases due to high temperatures. diseases due to low temperatures. *In his* Manual of Plant Diseases, pp. 135–176, illus. New York and London.

Hopkins, Andrew Delmar.
1938. bioclimatics—a science of life and climate relations. U. S. Dept. Agr. Misc. Pub. 280, 188 pp., illus.

Livingston, Burton Edward.
1916. physiological temperature indices for the study of plant growth in relation to climatic conditions. Physiol. Res. v. 1, No. 8, pp. 399–420, illus.

Lutman, B. F.
1919. tip burn of the potato and other plants. Vt. Agr. Expt. Sta. Bul. 214, 28 pp., illus.

McKinney, H. H., and Sando, W. J.
1933. earliness and seasonal growth habit in wheat as influenced by temperature and photoperiodism. Jour. Hered. 24: 169–179, illus.

Mix, A. J.
1916. sun-scald of fruit trees: a type of winter injury. N. Y. (Cornell) Agr. Expt. Sta. Bul. 382, pp. 235–284, illus.

Sellschop, Jacq. P. F., and Salmon, S. C.
1928. the influence of chilling, above the freezing point, on certain crop plants. Jour. Agr. Res. 37: 315–338, illus.

Weaver, John E., and Clements, Frederic E.
1929. temperature. *In their* Plant Ecology, pp. 275–297. New York.

Water and Plant Growth

Briggs, Lyman J., and Shantz, H. L.
1914. relative water requirement of plants. Jour. Agr. Res. 3: 1–64, illus.

Knight, R. C.
1922. further observations on the transpiration, stomata, leaf water content, and wilting of plants. Ann. Bot. 36: 361–383, illus.

Kramer, Paul J.
1937. the relation between rate of transpiration and rate of absorption of water in plants. Amer. Jour. Bot. 24: 10–15, illus.

Magness, J. R.
1935. status of orchard soil moisture research. Amer. Soc. Hort. Sci. Proc. (1934) 32: 651–661. [Presidential address.]

Maximov, N. A.
1929. the plant in relation to water; a study of the physiological basis of drought resistance. 451 pp., illus. London.

Shantz, H. L.
1927. drought resistance and soil moisture. Ecology 8: 145–157.

Veihmeyer, F. J., and Hendrickson, A. H.
1934. some plant and soil-moisture relations. Amer. Soil Survey Assoc. Bul. 15: 76–80, illus.

WEAVER, JOHN E.
1926. ROOT DEVELOPMENT OF FIELD CROPS. 291 pp., illus. New York.
——— and CLEMENTS, FREDERIC E.
1929. PLANT ECOLOGY. 520 pp., illus. New York, London [etc.].

LIGHT AND PLANT GROWTH

ARTHUR, JOHN M., and STEWART, W. D.
1931. PLANT GROWTH UNDER SHADING CLOTH. (Abstract) Amer. Jour. Bot. 18: 897.
BLACKMAN, F. FROST, and MATTHAEI, GABRIELLE L. C.
1905. EXPERIMENTAL RESEARCHES IN VEGETABLE ASSIMILATION AND RESPIRATION. IV.—A QUANTITATIVE STUDY OF CARBON-DIOXIDE ASSIMILATION AND LEAF-TEMPERATURE IN NATURAL ILLUMINATION. Roy. Soc. London, Proc., Ser. B, 76: 402–460, illus.
BORTHWICK, H. A., and PARKER, M. W.
1938. PHOTOPERIODIC PERCEPTION IN BILOXI SOYBEANS. Bot. Gaz. 100: 374–386.
DUGGAR, BENJAMIN M., ed.
1936. BIOLOGICAL EFFECTS OF RADIATION; MECHANISM AND MEASUREMENT OF RADIATION, APPLICATIONS IN BIOLOGY, PHOTOCHEMICAL REACTIONS, EFFECTS OF RADIANT ENERGY ON ORGANISMS AND ORGANIC PRODUCTS . . . 2 v., illus. New York and London.
FLINT, LEWIS H.
1934. LIGHT IN RELATION TO DORMANCY AND GERMINATION IN LETTUCE SEED. Science 80: 38–40.
GARDNER, WRIGHT A.
1921. EFFECT OF LIGHT ON GERMINATION OF LIGHT-SENSITIVE SEEDS. Bot. Gaz. 71: 249–288.
GARNER, W. W., and ALLARD, H. A.
1920. EFFECT OF THE RELATIVE LENGTH OF DAY AND NIGHT AND OTHER FACTORS OF THE ENVIRONMENT ON GROWTH AND REPRODUCTION IN PLANTS. Jour. Agr. Res. 18: 553–606, illus.
MASON, SILAS C.
1925. THE INHIBITIVE EFFECT OF DIRECT SUNLIGHT ON THE GROWTH OF THE DATE PALM. Jour. Agr. Res. 31: 455–468, illus.
MILLER, EDWIN C.
1938. PLANT PHYSIOLOGY. Ed. 2, 1201 pp., illus. New York and London.
PALLADIN, VLADIMIR I.
[1918.] PLANT PHYSIOLOGY. English transl. by Burton E. Livingston, 320 pp., illus. Philadelphia.
POPP, HENRY W[ILLIAM].
1926. EFFECT OF LIGHT INTENSITY ON GROWTH OF SOY BEANS AND ITS RELATION TO THE AUTO-CATALYST THEORY OF GROWTH. Bot. Gaz. 82: 306–319, illus.
———
1926. A PHYSIOLOGICAL STUDY OF THE EFFECT OF LIGHT OF VARIOUS RANGES OF WAVE LENGTH ON THE GROWTH OF PLANTS. Amer. Jour. Bot. 13: 706–736, illus.
SCHANZ, F.
1919. WIRKUNGEN DES LICHTS VERSCHIEDENER WELLENLÄNGE AUF DIE PFLANZEN. Ber. Bot. Ges. 37: 430–442.
SHIRLEY, HARDY L.
1928. THE INFLUENCE OF LIGHT INTENSITY AND QUALITY UPON THE GROWTH OF PLANTS. (Abstract) Amer. Jour. Bot. 15: 621–622.
SPOEHR, H. A.
1926. PHOTOSYNTHESIS. 393 pp., illus. New York. [Amer. Chem. Soc. Monog. Ser.]

Influence of Climate and Weather On Growth of Corn

By Merle T. Jenkins [1]

THE GREATEST plant-breeding job in the world was done by the American Indians. Out of a wild plant not even known today, they developed types of corn adapted to so wide a range of climates that this plant is now more extensively distributed over the earth than any other cereal crop. Modern breeders are carrying on this work and making important discoveries of their own. Here is the story of what climate means in corn growing.

[1] Merle T. Jenkins is Principal Agronomist, Division of Cereal Crops and Diseases, Bureau of Plant Industry.

Corn is grown today on more than 200 million acres in all the suitable and several unsuitable agricultural regions of the world. The annual crop exceeds 4 billion bushels and is produced from latitude 58° N. in Canada and the Union of Soviet Socialist Republics to latitude 40° S. in the Southern Hemisphere. Corn is grown below sea level in the Caspian Plain and above 12,000 feet in the Peruvian Andes. It is in fact cultivated in more widely diverse climates than any other cereal crop. No other cereal is distributed over so large an area, and only one other—wheat—occupies a larger acreage.

The wide distribution of corn throughout the agricultural regions of the world is even more remarkable when it is realized that the maize plant is of American origin and that its world-wide distribution has occurred in the 450 years since the plant was discovered by Columbus. This rapid and extensive distribution has been possible because of the previous existence in America of widely divergent types developed by the American Indian as he gradually spread the culture of this important plant over much of the Western Hemisphere.

Corn is unique among the cereals in the enormous differences that exist among strains developed to meet the needs of diverse conditions of temperature, moisture, length of growing season, and other environmental factors. Some strains grow less than 2 feet tall, require 60 to 70 days to mature, and have only 8 or 9 leaves, whereas others require 10 to 11 months to mature, grow more than 20 feet tall, and have 42 to 44 leaves (*16*).[2] Plant height and number of leaves are correlated with the length of the growing period.

Each climate has its characteristic varieties. Those in the Northern States are 5 to 8 feet tall, have 12 to 16 leaves, mature in 90 to 120 days, and may develop several tillers. In the Corn Belt the varieties are 8 to 10 feet tall, have 18 to 21 leaves, mature in 130 to 150 days, and usually have few if any tillers. Varieties in the South Atlantic and Gulf States may grow to a height of 10 to 12 feet on fertile soils, have 23 to 25 leaves, and require 170 to 190 days to reach maturity. Most of the varieties in this section are prolific—that is, they produce two or more ears to a plant. They also tiller profusely when available soil fertility and moisture permit.

All of these widely divergent climatic types of corn have been developed by selection over a very long period. Unlike most of our other cereals, corn is totally unable to survive in the wild. It has been dependent for its existence upon the care and attention of man for so long that its ancestral form even is unknown. Unquestionably the early American Indian was responsible for the development of this efficient plant from its primitive or ancestral form to a high state of perfection. He must likewise have bred the climatic types that permitted the extension of corn from its place of origin in Central America or Peru (*18*) into the other agricultural sections of the Western Hemisphere. These include Canada, with its short growing season, the semiarid regions of the Southwest, the subtropical regions adjoining the Gulf of Mexico, and the extremely high elevations of the Andes. This plant-breeding accomplishment of the American Indian is unrivaled in history. While the accomplishments of the white man seem dwarfed by comparison, the work of developing strains better suited to withstand the rigors of climate is still actively pursued.

[2] Italic numbers in parentheses refer to Literature Cited, p. 320.

298737°—41——21 +

CLIMATIC REQUIREMENTS

Temperature

Corn is a warm-weather plant that requires high temperatures both day and night during the growing season. Finch and Baker (*7*) state that practically no corn is grown where the mean summer temperature is less than 66° F., or where the average night temperature during the 3 summer months falls below 55°. The production of corn along the northern border of the United States and at the higher elevations in the West is consequently unimportant in spite of constant efforts to develop strains better suited to these regions. The region of greatest production in the United States has a mean summer temperature of 70° to 80°, a mean night temperature exceeding 58°, and a frostless season of over 140 days. The results of a study (*13*) of the average temperatures and yields during the 16-year period 1914–29 for the 24 States from New York westward and southward which produce large crops of corn without irrigation, show that the States with the largest average yields had average summer temperatures for the months of June, July, and August of 68° to 72° F.

While strains of corn differ somewhat in their temperature requirements for germination and seedling development, few are able to germinate satisfactorily below 50° F. Warm weather after planting hastens germination and early growth. At 55° and below, the germinating seedlings of most strains are inclined to be very susceptible to seedling diseases. Appreciable differences exist among both inbred and open-pollinated strains in this respect, however, and efforts have been made to select strains suited to planting in cold soil. The strains to be compared have been planted in the field very early in the spring, or their germination has been determined at low temperatures in an ice box. Cold Resistant Golden Glow, a selected strain of Golden Glow developed by the Wisconsin Agricultural Experiment Station, was produced in this manner.

The hard seeds of the flint varieties are able to withstand more adverse conditions of soil temperature and moisture after planting than the dents. They also mature more rapidly, and the grain is less injured by unfavorable weather in the fall. During the past hundred years much has been accomplished in this country in extending the dent varieties west and north into territory where flint varieties formerly were grown. Even yet, however, the principal varieties grown along the northern and western margins of the corn-producing areas are flints.

Corn flowers and ripens much sooner when grown at 80° than at 70° F., and temperatures as low as 60° greatly retard flowering and maturing. In these respects temperature produces effects upon the corn plant similar to those resulting from variation in the length of day.

Although corn grows best in warm weather, extremely high temperatures, especially when accompanied by deficient moisture, may be injurious. Plants are most susceptible to injury by high temperatures at the tasseling stage, when a combination of high temperature and low humidity, resulting in extreme desiccation, may kill the leaves and tassels and prevent pollination.

Inbred lines of corn and hybrids among them exhibit great differences in injury from heat and drought. Some strains survive with little apparent damage while others are severely damaged. Figure 1 shows the differences in leaf injury suffered by two inbred lines at the Kansas Agricultual Experiment Station in 1940.

Hunter, Laude, and Brunson (*12*) and Heyne and Laude (*9*) reported that it was possible to distinguish between strains with respect to drought tolerance by testing seedling corn plants under controlled conditions. They obtained essentially the same order of relative resistance among strains with seedlings subjected to artificial heat as was noted for mature plants subjected to drought and heat in the field. Heyne and Brunson (*8*) studied the inheritance of tolerance to heat and drought in inbred lines of corn and crosses among them. Their data definitely indicate that heat tolerance is inherited. The evidence presented by all these workers suggests that a high-temperature test of seedling plants would be a valuable aid in the breeding of strains resistant to heat and drought.

Field observations on inbred lines and hybrids have shown that some strains are able to produce viable pollen at temperatures at which the pollen of other strains is not viable. Likewise, the silks of some inbred lines remain viable and receptive for a longer period in extremes of heat and drought than do those of other strains. Both these kinds of differences are important in breeding improved strains for the areas where heat and drought are severe.

Mattice (*19*) studied the correlations between corn yields and numerous climatic factors in eight Corn Belt States. In Minnesota high yields were associated with warm weather during the summer. South of Minnesota high yields accompanied warm weather in September and usually in April, May, or early June. In Missouri high tem-

FIGURE 1.—Every third row in this 1940 cornfield was planted with a susceptible inbred line. Injury from heat and drought has made it easy to identify these rows in comparison with the rows of a resistant line. (Courtesy of the Kansas Agricultural Experiment Station).

peratures in July and August resulted in low yields. In South Dakota and Kansas large yields were associated with high relative humidity.

Precipitation

The annual precipitation in the regions of the world where corn is cultivated varies from only 10 inches in the semiarid plains of Russia to more than 200 inches in tropical Hindustan (*16*). In the United States the western limit of production coincides approximately with the line of mean summer (June, July, and August) precipitation of 8 inches, extending somewhat beyond this line in Nebraska and Colorado, while in Texas, where the evaporation and the loss through torrential rains are greater, this line is scarcely reached. The annual precipitation in the Corn Belt is 25 to 50 inches, 7 inches of which fall in July and August (*7*).

For optimum growth and grain production, corn requires a plentiful supply of moisture, well distributed throughout the growing season. Moisture requirements reach a maximum during silking and tasseling. The seasonal moisture requirements are associated with seasonal evaporation, which in turn is influenced by temperature, humidity, and wind movement. The areas in the United States which have well-distributed rains during June, July, and August, averaging 3 to 6 inches a month, have the largest average yields.

Early experiments by King (*15*) in Wisconsin indicated a requirement of 2.64 and 2.14 acre-inches of water per ton of dry matter for dent corn and flint corn, respectively, under the conditions there. Kiesselbach (*14*) found that at Lincoln, Nebr., the transpiration ratio—that is, the number of pounds of water used by the plant in the production of 1 pound of dry matter—varied from 261 to 445 in different seasons. This is equivalent to 2.30 to 3.93 acre-inches of water per ton of dry matter. Fully half of the total water was transpired during a period of about 5 weeks—usually the hottest and driest part of the season—after the plants developed their maximum leaf area. The water requirements in the different seasons were closely associated with the amount of evaporation.

The limiting effects of deficient moisture on corn production have been met to a certain extent by the development of strains that have lower water requirements or are drought-resistant and by agronomic practices that conserve the moisture supply and make it more available to the plant. The lister method of planting and the use of wide spacing, both between rows and between plants within rows, are common in areas with low rainfall. Conversely, the practice of planting on top of beds, with intervening water furrows to drain off the excess water, is common in areas of excessive rainfall.

Briggs and Shantz (*1*, *2*) determined the water requirements of several varieties of corn and of the hybrids among some of them. Esperanza, a hairy Mexican variety, had the lowest water requirements of any tested. Collins (*5*) describes this variety as having an extremely shallow root system. It was developed on the tablelands of Mexico, where the rainfall is very light. The rain that falls during the growing season comes in the form of light, misty showers in amounts insufficient to penetrate the soil deeply. Kiesselbach (*14*) has shown that in Nebraska strains of corn with relatively few narrow leaves and a low total leaf area are best suited to areas deficient in moisture.

Collins (*4*) has described an interesting drought-resisting adaptation of the corn varieties grown by the Hopi, Zuñi, and Navajo Indians in the semiarid sections of New Mexico and Arizona. These southwestern Indians have preserved from pre-Columbian times a type of corn able to produce fair crops in regions where the better known varieties of the East fail for lack of sufficient water. They commonly plant their crop in large hills which may contain 10 to 20 plants and be spaced as much as 20 feet apart in each direction (fig. 2). The soil is sandy in the localities selected by them for corn growing and the surface layers are dry in the spring, so that deep planting is necessary in order to place the seed in contact with moist soil. When planted at a depth of a foot or more, the varieties grown by these Pueblo Indians are able to force the growing shoot of the seedling to the surface of the soil. At such depths the seedlings of less specialized varieties die before reaching the surface.

The effects of short periods of severe summer drought are sometimes avoided by the early or late planting of specially developed strains. For example, the Mexican June variety is used widely for late planting in Texas, Oklahoma, New Mexico, and neighboring areas. It produces more satisfactory yields under these conditions than other strains. This variety is grown also in the irrigated valleys of Arizona, where it produces pollen satisfactorily even at the high desert temperatures.

The "Williamson plan" of corn culture (*20*) was introduced into South Carolina about 1906 and still is used to a limited extent there and in neighboring States in areas with sandy soils and deficient summer rainfall. The essential features of the plan consist of a severe early stunting of the plants to reduce their vegetative development and better enable them to withstand the dry weather which

FIGURE 2.—Field of Zuñi corn near Zuñi, N. Mex. Ten to twenty plants are in each of the widely spaced hills.

comes later in the season. The stunting is followed at the proper time by liberal applications of fertilizer to promote grain production.

Sunshine

Corn requires abundant sunshine for maximum yields and fails to grow normally in the shade or during extended periods of cloudy weather. Burtt-Davy (*3*) states, "It is noticeable in South Africa that in cloudy seasons, like that of 1909–10, when there was nearly twice as much cloud as usual during the months of January and February, the maize crop is light." Most of the important corn-growing areas in the United States probably have adequate sunshine, although Mattice (*19*) found acre yields in several of the Corn Belt States associated with the percentage of possible sunshine during certain periods. It is questionable, however, whether this indicates a direct effect of sunshine or an indirect effect due to higher temperatures.

OTHER CLIMATIC INFLUENCES

Cold, Frost, and Hail

The corn plant is injured by freezing temperatures occurring at any time during the growing season, but early fall frosts are most serious. Strains differ in their ability to recover from freezing injury during the seedling stage. At elevations of 9,000 feet the Tarahumare Indians of the Sierra Madre Mountains of Mexico grow corn which is said to withstand severe freezes even when the plants have reached a height of 2 feet. Most strains, however, are unable to recover from freezes occurring when they are 6 inches tall or taller.

Strains of corn also differ in the injury they suffer in the fall from low temperatures appreciably above freezing. Holbert and Burlison (*10*) report that some strains are killed by a temperature of 45° F., whereas others are able to withstand 32° for several hours before being seriously injured. Frosts early in the fall before the grain is mature not only reduce yield but damage quality. In occasional seasons extremely early frosts have resulted in large amounts of "soft" corn, which it is extremely difficult to save from complete loss.

Damage to corn from hail occurs somewhere every year, although the annual losses in percentage of the national crop are not large. In local areas, however, loss is occasionally complete. As judged by the amount of hail insurance sold, hail losses are largest in the midwestern States of Kansas, North Dakota, Iowa, South Dakota, Nebraska, Minnesota, and Oklahoma (*6*).

The most frequent hail injury consists of shredding of the leaves, causing loss of part of the leaf tissue. In severe cases the entire leaf blade is stripped from the midrib. When the hailstones are large, the stalks and ears may be bruised and broken or even beaten into the ground.

Reductions in yield due to loss of leaf tissue are roughly proportional to the amount of tissue lost. The reduction in yield of grain from hail injury is relatively slight when the plants are young, increases gradually to a peak at the period just preceding tasseling, and decreases again as maturity is approached.

Length of Day

Through many generations of selection the strains of corn grown in different latitudes from the Equator to the northern and southern limits of corn growing have become adapted to the length of day in the locality in which they are grown. Although the response of the corn plant to changes in day length is not so pronounced as that of some other plants, the times of flowering and of ripening are modified readily by changing the length of the daylight period.

The period from emergence to flowering is reduced by short days and increased by long days. The flowering of early-maturing northern varieties adapted to long summer days is hastened when they are grown nearer the Equator, where the summer days are shorter. Conversely, the growing season of southern varieties is lengthened and a larger and more luxuriant vegetative growth is produced when they are moved north, away from the Equator, to areas where the summer days are longer.

When tropical varieties of corn are grown in the Corn Belt they do not flower until fall, when the days are short. Plants of a tropical variety grown at Arlington, Va., subjected to an 8½-hour day for 34 days beginning the last week in June, began flowering during the second week in August, whereas those grown with the natural day length did not flower until late in September.

The later ripening and more luxuriant vegetative growth resulting when varieties are grown where the summer days are longer than those to which they are accustomed are two reasons for the use of southern varieties of corn for silage in many northern latitudes. Hunt (*11*) states that, "In general it may be said that as we go north or south of a given latitude a variety becomes one day later or earlier for each 10 miles of travel, the altitude remaining the same."

Wind

Wind probably has little direct influence on the distribution of corn, although it often has had an important effect on lodging and on the methods of harvesting the crop. Corn binders and pickers do not function satisfactorily when the plants are badly lodged. Many of the new corn hybrids are much more resistant to lodging than the older open-pollinated varieties, and machine harvesting has increased greatly in the sections with large acreages of hybrid corn.

Along the Gulf coast corn suffers severe lodging as a result of occasional tropical hurricanes. As a protection against wind damage it is common practice in the southern Mississippi Delta to "bend" the stalks at about the midpoint so that the upper portion of the stalk and the ears hang downward (fig. 3). The bending is done when the stalks are nearly ripe but still have sufficient moisture so that they do not break. The practice of bending, or doubling, is common in Central America and other tropical sections where the plants grow extremely tall and heavy winds may cause serious lodging. In some sections where wind is not a factor the practice is followed as insurance against rain and bird damage.

FIGURE 3.—A hill of corn plants in Mexico, with the stalks doubled as a protection against damage by wind, rain, and birds.

EFFECT OF CLIMATE ON INSECTS AND DISEASES

In the Tropics the insects and diseases which attack corn are much more numerous than in the more temperate climates. In these regions tropical flints are grown extensively because of their resistance to these pests, particularly those that attack the ears in the fall. Because of their horny texture the seeds of flint varieties suffer much less injury from the weevils common in these regions. In the United States the varieties commonly grown in the "Sugar Bowl" of Louisiana and in Florida are Creole Yellow Flint and Cuban Yellow Flint, both of which are of tropical origin. The distribution of flour corn, on the other hand, is governed by the demand of natives for a soft grain adapted to primitive methods of grinding rather than by climatic requirements.

EFFECT OF CLIMATE ON CHEMICAL COMPOSITION

Climate influences the chemical composition of corn, although the influence is less marked than in some other cereals. Under favorable

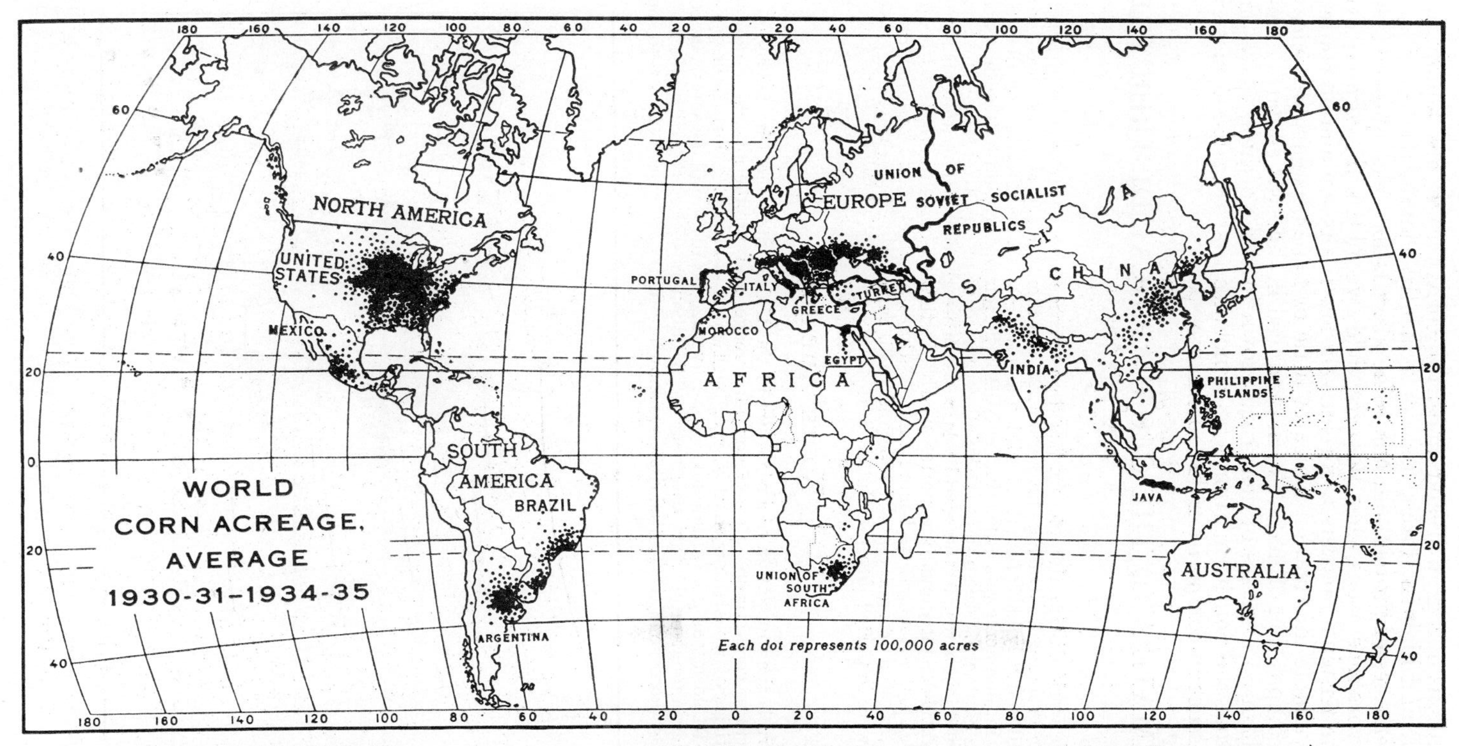

FIGURE 4.—World distribution of corn acreage, average 1930–31, 1934–35. (Bureau of Agricultural Economics map.)

conditions for growth and maturity corn kernels are plump, well filled, and high in starch, and consequently contain relatively lower percentages of protein, oil, and minerals. It has been observed that in favorable seasons when the acre yields were high, the corn received at the terminal markets was relatively low in protein and oil content.

Available information indicates little or no consistent difference in the composition of mature corn produced in different climates. As a result of 35 analyses of dent corn grown in the Northern States and 49 from the Southern, Hunt (*11*) concludes that there is no material difference in composition due to climate.

CLIMATE AND THE GEOGRAPHICAL DISTRIBUTION OF CORN

The world distribution of corn based on average acreages from 1930 to 1934 is shown in figure 4. During this period 221.4 million acres of corn (*21*) was grown annually, nearly half of it, 103.5 million acres, in the United States. Of the total, 184.3 million acres was grown in the Northern Hemisphere and 37.1 million acres in the Southern. In spite of the small corn acreage in the latter, Argentina, with 10.9 million acres, is the world's largest corn-exporting country. During the period 1930–34 it annually exported nearly six times as much corn as its nearest competitor (Rumania) and more than 40 times as much as the United States. Following the drought years of 1934 and 1936, appreciable quantities of Argentine corn were imported into the United States.

North America

Corn is the foundation of agriculture in the United States and by far the most important cereal crop. It exceeds in acreage and production the combined quantities of wheat, oats, barley, rye, buckwheat, and rice. During the period 1930–34 corn was grown annually on an average of 103.5 million acres, and the average annual production was nearly 2.3 billion bushels. The distribution of the corn acreage in the United States is shown in figure 5. Corn is grown to some

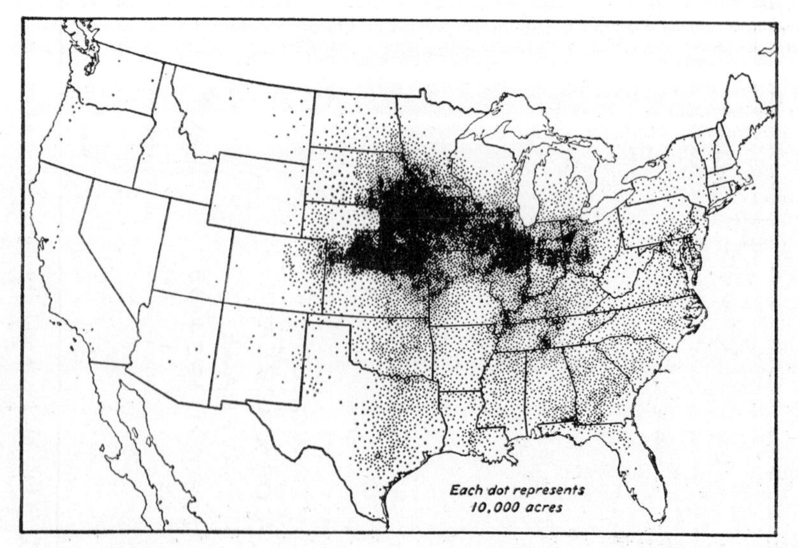

Figure 5.—Distribution of corn acreage in the United States. (Prepared by the Bureau of Agricultural Economics from 1929 census figures.)

extent in every State in the Union. During the past century corn production has moved westward (*17*) and now centers in the Corn Belt, the region of fertile prairie soils extending from Ohio westward and northward.

Mexico annually grows nearly 8 million acres of corn, the acreage about equaling that of all other crops combined (*7*). Most of the corn is grown in small patches of a few acres by very primitive methods, and the yields are the lowest of any important corn-growing country. The principal centers of production are in the southern section of the country, mostly on the high plateau and in Yucatan.

In Canada, corn is confined largely to Kent and Essex Counties in the Province of Ontario. Corn production in this area was practically wiped out by the European corn borer about 10 years ago, but the acreage is increasing gradually at the present time.

South America

The Argentine Republic, with an average of 10.9 million acres in 1930–34, and Brazil, with 9.5 million acres, are the principal corn-producing countries of South America.

Argentina ranks second to the United States among corn-producing countries of the world. Although corn is grown to some extent throughout the Republic, except in southern Patagonia, the principal corn-producing region is the central area of the grain belt. This region embraces practically the entire Provinces of Buenos Aires, Santa Fé, Cordoba, Entre Ríos, and the eastern part of the Territory of La Pampa. The annual rainfall ranges from more than 40 inches in Entre Ríos on the eastern edge to 18 inches in the west. Acre yields decline markedly from the central portion where rainfall is ample to the drier marginal area. The temperature differences between the northern and southern limits also are large. The corn crop usually suffers from excessively high temperatures in the north and in general lacks sufficient hot weather in the extreme south.[3]

Brazil normally grows nearly as many acres of corn as Argentina, but since the country is much larger the percentage of cropland planted to corn is lower.

Europe, Asia, Africa, and Australasia

The most important corn-growing regions of Europe are the Danube Basin, the U. S. S. R., Italy, and Spain. Although these regions lie in a latitude about 5° farther north than the Corn Belt of the United States, they have, with the exception of Italy, very similar conditions of temperature and rainfall. In the Danube Basin, Rumania, Yugoslavia, Hungary, and Bulgaria rank in corn production in the order named.

In Italy most of the corn is grown under irrigation. The chief producing region is the Po River plain, though one-fifth of the total land under corn is classed as mountainous. The corn acreage of Spain is concentrated in the northwest section of the country.

The principal corn-producing countries of Asia are China, India, Manchuria, and the Philippine Islands. The rather large corn acreage of India is concentrated mainly on the alluvial lands of the Ganges Valley and the irrigated lands of the Punjab district. Although corn has become a staple article of food in India, especially among the hill peoples, its relative importance is small, and it occupies less than 3 percent of the cropped land.

In the Philippine Islands corn is second to rice as a grain crop and leads rice as a staple food in a limited area.

The principal corn-producing sections of Africa are the Union of South Africa and Egypt. In the Union of South Africa most of the corn is produced in the eastern Provinces where the average rainfall for the three summer months is approximately 12 inches. In the Transvaal the better corn-producing sections are at elevations above 2,000 feet. In the warm coastal region of Natal the acre yields are larger, but relatively less corn is grown.

Corn in Egypt is grown entirely under irrigation. The crop is planted in July and harvested in October and November. It is irrigated about every 10 days.

In Australasia, Java and Madura have 5 million acres in corn.

[3] Nyhus, Paul O. argentine corn. U. S. Bur. Agr. Econ., Foreign Agr. 1: 393–418, illus. 1937. [Processed.]

LITERATURE CITED

(1) Briggs, Lyman J., and Shantz, H. L.
1914. relative water requirements of plants. Jour. Agr. Res. 3: 1–63, illus.

(2) ——— and Shantz, H. L.
1915. influence of hybridization and cross-pollination on the water requirement of plants. Jour. Agr. Res. 4: 391–401, illus.

(3) Burtt-Davy, Joseph.
1914. maize; its history, cultivation, handling, and uses, with special reference to south africa . . . 831 pp., illus. London and New York.

(4) Collins, G. N.
1914. a drought-resisting adaptation in seedlings of hopi maize. Jour. Agr. Res. 1: 293–302, illus.

(5) ———
1918. tropical varieties of maize . . . Jour. Hered. 9: 147–154, illus.

(6) Eldridge, John C.
1935. the effect of injury in imitation of hail damage on the development of the corn plant. Iowa Agr. Expt. Sta. Res. Bul. 185, 61 pp., illus.

(7) Finch, V. C., and Baker, O. E.
1917. geography of the world's agriculture. U. S. Dept. Agr. Unnumb. Pub., 149 pp., illus.

(8) Heyne, E. G., and Brunson, Arthur M.
1940. genetic studies of heat and drought tolerance in maize. Amer. Soc. Agron. Jour. 32: 803–814, illus.

(9) ——— and Laude, H. H.
1940. resistance of corn seedlings to high temperatures in laboratory tests. Amer. Soc. Agron. Jour. 32: 116–126, illus.

(10) Holbert, James R., and Burlison, W. L.
1930. some questions and answers on cold injury to corn. Ill. Farmers' Inst. Unnumb. Pub., 14 pp., illus.

(11) Hunt, Thomas F.
1904. the cereals in america. 421 pp., illus. New York and London.

(12) Hunter, James W., Laude, H. H., and Brunson, Arthur M.
1936. a method for studying resistance to drought injury in inbred lines of maize. Amer. Soc. Agron. Jour. 28: 694–698, illus.

(13) Huntington, Ellsworth, Williams, Frank E., and van Valkenburg, Samuel.
1933. economic and social geography. 630 pp., illus. New York and London.

(14) Kiesselbach, T. A.
1916. transpiration as a factor in crop production. Nebr. Agr. Expt. Sta. Res. Bul. 6, 214 pp., illus.

(15) King, F. H.
1894. the number of inches of water required for a ton of dry matter in wisconsin. Wis. Agr. Expt. Sta. Ann. Rpt. 11: 240–248.

(16) Kuleshov, N. N.
1933. world's diversity of phenotypes of maize. Amer. Soc. Agron. Jour. 25: 688–700, illus.

(17) Leighty, C. E., Warburton, C. W., Stine, O. C., and Baker, O. E.
1922. the corn crop. U. S. Dept. Agr. Yearbook 1921: 161–227, illus.

(18) Mangelsdorf, P. C., and Reeves, R. G.
1939. the origin of indian corn and its relatives. Tex. Agr. Expt. Sta. Bul. 574, 315 pp., illus.

(19) Mattice, W. A.
1931. weather and corn yields. U. S. Monthly Weather Rev. 59: 105–112, illus.

(20) Newman, C. L.
1906. the "williamson plan" of corn culture. S. C. Agr. Expt. Sta. Bul. 124, 20 pp.

(21) United States Department of Agriculture.
1939. agricultural statistics, 1939. U. S. Dept. Agr. 597 pp.

Climate and Small Grains

By S. C. Salmon [1]

THERE ARE definite climatic factors that determine where each of the small grains can be grown economically, less economically, or not at all. Within the areas favorable to production, weather conditions during fall, winter, spring, and summer have a marked influence on growth, yields, and the quality of the harvested crop. All of these relationships are interesting, most of them are important to producers, and some are by no means simple. They are discussed in considerable detail in this article.

[1] S. C. Salmon is Principal Agronomist, in Charge of Wheat Investigations, Division of Cereal Crops and Diseases, Bureau of Plant Industry.

SINCE SMALL GRAINS are usually grown on an extensive rather than an intensive scale, protection from unfavorable climate or weather such as is sometimes possible for truck, garden, and orchard crops is impractical. Much has been accomplished, however—and more can be accomplished—by growing the varieties least likely to be damaged and by modifying cultural practices so that losses are avoided or reduced to a minimum.

The Old World—especially the Union of Soviet Socialist Republics and northern Africa—has been extensively explored for varieties that are resistant to drought and to diseases of various kinds, are winter hardy, or mature early and thus escape some of the damage that would otherwise occur. Many of the varieties now grown in the United States were introduced for the express purpose of avoiding or reducing losses from these hazards, and many others have such a variety as a parent. Losses from drought and hot winds have been materially reduced in this way. Likewise, rust-resistant varieties have greatly reduced losses in areas where climate and weather have especially favored these diseases, and varieties with stiff straw have been effective in reducing lodging in wet seasons. Methods of reducing losses, made possible by a more complete knowledge of climatic and weather hazards, include early preparation of the ground to assure as far as possible a supply of moisture and nutrients for the subsequent crop, and timely planting and seeding in small-grain or corn stubble or in furrows to reduce winter killing.

CLIMATE AND THE DISTRIBUTION OF SMALL GRAINS

Small grains, except rice, are generally grown where the annual precipitation is between 15 and 45 inches and are grown most extensively where it does not exceed 30. Neither the minimum nor the maximum limit is sharply defined, since the possibility of growing a crop depends on many other climatic factors and on economic conditions as well. Many difficulties can be overcome if the value of the crop is sufficient to pay the extra cost of production. Wheat is grown in Australia (*52*) [2] and in the Big Bend area of Washington State, in both of which places the annual precipitation is only 10 inches or less (*21, 25, 43*), as well as in Argentina (*26*), South Africa (*49*), and the northern Great Plains of the United States, where rainfall is as low as 15 inches. In the southern Great Plains, where evaporation is high, the minimum limit is about 17 inches. Barley is grown without irrigation in Egypt where the annual rainfall is about 8 inches. Production year after year with these small amounts of moisture is possible only where the distribution of rainfall during the year and other climatic conditions are favorable and where the moisture falling in two or more years is stored for one crop.

The scarcity of small grains other than rice in areas of high rainfall is due in the main to indirect effects such as the prevalence of diseases, including rust, scab, mildew, and leaf spots of various kinds; to the leaching of plant food from the soil; to excessive growth and lodging; and to difficulties in preparing the ground, in seeding, and in harvesting and caring for the crop. In India wheat is grown where the annual

[2] Italic numbers in parentheses refer to Literature Cited, p. 339.

rainfall is 60 inches or more, but most of the rain falls during the season of the year when the crop is not growing. Fortunately, rice, with its high moisture requirement, is not attacked by rust and is resistant to many of the diseases that seriously injure other small grains.

The distribution of crops in relation to temperature is determined mainly by the length of the growing season, the minimum winter temperature, and the mean and mean maximum temperatures immediately preceding harvest.

In most areas where crops are seriously limited by a short growing season, spring-sown cereals only are grown. They are generally seeded as early in the spring as possible, usually several weeks before the last killing frost. The young plants usually emerge before the last frost but because of their greater tolerance of cold, as compared with such crops as corn or sorghums, they are not often seriously injured. Heavy frost in the late summer or early fall, however, before the crop has matured, kills the plants and results in the production of immature grain. With feed crops this may not be serious, but wheat that is severely frozen before it is mature is likely to be unsuitable for milling. A light frost may cause the bran to wrinkle; the result is a low-grade product, though there may be little damage to the intrinsic quality of the grain (*39, 48, 59*).

Winter wheat and winter rye may come into head before the danger of late spring frosts has passed. Even a light frost (28° to 30° F.) may kill the pollen and partly or completely prevent fertilization of the flowers. Damage of this kind is not uncommon in the United States and is said to be especially destructive in Argentina.[3]

Since the length of the frost-free period is a matter of record in most countries, it is a convenient measure of the likelihood of frost injury and a useful index of the possibility of growing small grains in mountain valleys or near the northern limits of crop production. It should be noted that the frost-free period is shorter than the growing season available for most small grains. Extensive production of small grains in general is limited to areas with a frost-free period of 100 days or more (*60*). Where this period is less than 90 days, production is precarious (*14*) and is possible only by prompt seeding and use of the earliest maturing varieties. Spring barley is grown farther north and at higher elevations than other small grains, followed closely by oats and wheat (*24, 25, 62*). In general, rice and flax require a somewhat longer frost-free period than other small grains.

The temperature preceding harvest is also important. If temperatures are too low grains ripen slowly, and if the growing season is short they are likely to be caught by early frost. High temperatures before harvest also may be injurious, especially if accompanied by drying winds.

It is generally considered that the northern limits of fall-seeded grains in the Northern Hemisphere are largely determined by winter temperatures; yet there are many apparent exceptions. Young plants of rye, wheat, oats, and barley do not die as long as the crown remains alive (*36, 56*). The crown is usually located an inch or more below the surface of the ground and is protected more or less by the soil,

[3] SHOLLENBERGER, J. H. THE GRAINS OF ARGENTINA (PARTICULARLY WHEAT AND CORN). U. S. Bur. Agr. Chem. and Engin., ACE-20, 8 pp. 1940. [Mimeographed.]

by snow, and by stubble, cornstalks, or other crop residues. The soil is almost always warmer than the air during the winter and much warmer following severe and sudden drops in temperature, because the air responds much more rapidly to such changes (*15*). The degree to which the plants have been hardened before the onset of winter is also fundamentally important. In addition, winter grains are sometimes killed by heaving, by "smothering" (see p. 327), and possibly by physiological drought, all of which conditions are only indirectly related to winter temperatures.

Winter rye is far more resistant to low temperatures and is grown farther north than any other winter cereal. Next in order are winter wheat, winter barley, and winter oats. There are no true winter varieties of flax, rice, or buckwheat, although flax is sometimes seeded in the fall in mild climates and under favorable conditions will survive moderate degrees of cold. Neither rice nor buckwheat is able to survive temperatures appreciably below freezing.

Winter temperatures, together with length of day, appear to be important in relation to the southern limit of winter grains and also to the choice of varieties. All winter grains have a certain degree of "winterness," which can be satisfied only if they are subjected to low temperatures, or short days, or both (*39*, *42*), for a period of several weeks. In tropical and subtropical regions the relatively long winter days and short period of low temperature or the absence of one may fail to satisfy these requirements, and true winter varieties may head only late in the spring or not at all. The behavior is analogous to that of true winter grains when they are sown in the spring in temperate regions. For this reason varieties of the cereals grown in or near the Tropics are true spring types.

The fact that a light snow cover protects the plants during the winter is so well known as to require no extended comment. Many investigators have called attention to this and have cited evidence to show that soil temperatures during winter are generally much higher under snow than where there is no snow (*11*, *15*).

The relation of snow cover to the distribution of winter grain, however, is not so simple as it might seem. One would expect to find winter wheat surviving colder winters in the eastern part of the United States than in the Great Plains, because of the heavier snowfall and the longer period the snow lies on the ground (*29*), but this is not the case. One reason is the lesser resistance to cold of the varieties generally grown in the East, but probably more important is the fact that winter killing is frequently due to heaving and other causes to which winter temperatures are only indirectly related.

In general, the available sunshine is more than adequate for the growth of small grains wherever they are produced. Jones (*27*), however, mentions lack of sunshine as a limiting factor in the growth of barley and other small grains at high elevations in South America. Cloudy weather in certain years has been shown by Tippett (*53*) to affect yields of grain in England, and Suneson and Peltier (*51*) have shown that variations in degree of cloudiness and solar radiation from one year to another is related to the hardening of winter wheat. Kossowitsch (*30*) found that shading induced the formation of higher crowns in small grains and that this in turn is accompanied by more winter killing.

It is well known that the greater length of the summer day toward the Poles is an important factor in crop production. In Alaska (*17*), for example, grain matures at Rampart (65°30′ N.) earlier than at Matanuska (5° farther south) because of the influence of a longer period of daylight during the growing season. The importance of a long day in growing crops at northern latitudes has been emphasized by Albright (*3*), Jasny (*24*), and Zinserling (*62*).

The world distribution of small-grain production as related to climate is discussed at the end of this article.

SEASONAL INFLUENCES ON GROWTH

The growth of the plants and the final yield and quality of the grain depend very materially on the weather conditions during the year. The effect of weather on growth and yield can most conveniently be considered in relation to the time of year or the stage of development of the plant.

Fall Weather

Fall weather affects the growth and development of spring-seeded small grains mainly through the quantity of water stored in the soil and the quantity of plant foods, especially nitrates, made available for subsequent growth.

For fall-seeded small grains, autumn weather determines also whether the seeds germinate, the amount of growth that takes place before winter, and whether the plants become sufficiently hardened to enable them to survive low winter temperatures. Each of these factors may have a profound influence on the growth of the crop the following spring. If moisture in the surface soil is deficient, the seed may not germinate at all, or it may germinate the following spring. If it does not germinate until spring and temperatures remain high after emergence, the plants will not head because the "winterness" requirements are not satisfied. In any event the crop will mature late and consequently is more likely than usual to be injured by rust, heat, and drought later in the year.

The amount of growth made during the fall is also of some importance, though the value of a good fall growth is frequently overestimated or even wrongly estimated. In the Eastern States, where heaving is apt to occur, a vigorous growth such as may be secured by good preparation of the ground, the use of fertilizers (*32*), and timely seeding (*23*) reduces the degree to which plants are pulled out by heaving and tends to increase yields. In semiarid areas excessive fall growth may deplete stored moisture and nitrates, or when moisture and nitrates are more abundant, it may result in lodging, in either case giving a smaller yield than would be obtained with less vegetative development of the plants. It is therefore not always safe to conclude that large plants in the fall insure a good crop or that small plants forecast a poor crop.

It is well known that the survival of winter grains during cold weather depends very largely on whether they have become hardened before winter sets in (*12*, *50*). Unhardened winter-wheat plants may be severely injured by exposures for any extended period to temperatures of 15° to 20° F., whereas the same varieties when fully hardened

298737°—41——22

will survive temperatures considerably below zero without serious injury.

The practical effect of subjecting unhardened or incompletely hardened grain to low temperatures is illustrated by the loss of more than 60 percent of the acreage of winter wheat in Ohio, Indiana, and Illinois in December 1927 as a result of a severe freeze following a period of warm, rainy weather during which the plants made considerable growth and had no opportunity to become hardened. Similarly, more than half the acreage of winter wheat in Oregon and Washington was killed by unusual cold preceded by warm weather in late November 1924 (*16*, *21*), and it was necessary to reseed to spring wheat in the spring of 1925. Winter grains are not infrequently injured by sudden cold following spells of warm weather during the winter.

Just what takes place when winter grains are hardened is far from clear. It appears to be generally accepted that the important changes include (1) a slight though not always consistent decrease in moisture content, (2) a marked decrease in the amount of water (sap) that can be extracted from the living tissue by pressure, (3) an increase in the sugar content, and (4) a decrease in free water, that is, the water in the tissue from which ice will be formed at any given temperature. An increase in permeability and a lowered viscosity of the protoplasm accompanying hardening in certain plants has recently been reported (*47*).

It is not entirely clear, either, just what effect weather during the fall may be expected to have on these various changes. Permeability is increased by low temperature, drought, and other conditions that check the growth of the plants (*47*). It has been known for many years that low temperature causes starch in the plants to change to sugar, and weather conditions, principally sunshine and temperatures favoring photosynthesis, would be expected to increase the total quantity of starch and sugar in the plants. The evidence supporting a relation between hardening and the accumulation of sugars both as a result of increasing the total quantity of carbohydrates and by transformation from starch is especially convincing.

Winter Weather

In areas with mild climates, fall-seeded grains continue to grow during the winter. Of more general importance, however, is the relation of weather to winter survival or winter killing. Four general causes of winter killing have been recognized, and naturally the weather conditions that determine each are quite different. They are (1) the freezing of the plant tissue (crowns or roots of small grains), (2) heaving, (3) "smothering," and (4) physiological drought. Drought as such has often been suggested as an important cause of the death of grain plants in dry climates. There can be no doubt that fall-seeded small grains die as a result of winter drought, and since the cause of death appears to be the same as during droughts at other times of the year, such losses probably should not be attributed to winter killing.

Many theories have been proposed to account for the death of plants exposed to low temperature. The oldest and the one that appears to be most generally accepted is that the protoplasm is injured by the formation of ice within the cells or in the intercellular spaces (*22*, *47*). It is not merely the fact that ice forms that is fatal, for it is well known that hardened leaves of winter wheat, winter rye, and other plants may be frozen stiff without injury. Rather it appears to be the quantity of ice as well as certain conditions of the plant cell that determines the degree of injury. Continued lowering of the temperature results in an increase in the quantity of ice formed, until the lethal point is reached. Under field conditions the rate of fall of the air temperature and the duration of the period of low temperature are important because of the very material lag, already referred to, in the temperature of the soil surrounding the crowns and roots of the plants.

As shown by several investigators (*33*, *36*, *47*), or as may be inferred from their work, plants decrease in hardiness during the latter part of the winter season. It would be expected therefore that cold weather of equal severity would do more damage in late than in early winter.

Heaving occurs as a result of alternate freezing and thawing of soil containing an excess of moisture. Ice crystals forming beneath the soil surface lift the soil and the plants along with it (*6*). When ice melts, the soil falls back into place, but the plants do not. Repeated freezing day after day soon raises the crowns above the soil surface and breaks the roots (*61*) or at least exposes them and the crowns to freezing temperatures and the desiccating effects of dry winds. Plants that have made a good growth in the fall either because of their variety or because of favorable conditions for development have stronger roots (*33*) and are less likely to be injured. Heaving occurs principally in the Eastern States, where it has usually been regarded as the most frequent cause of winter killing. Recent studies indicate, however, that freezing of the plants is more important than has generally been realized (*5*).

Smothering, under an ice sheet in the United States and under deep snow in northern Europe, is often referred to as a cause of winter killing of winter grains (*24*). In Europe, infection with snow mold (*Fusarium nivale*) is common, especially when the plants have grown rapidly in the fall (*46*). That death is due to lack of oxygen, as the term "smothering" implies, is an assumption rather than a proved fact. Experimental evidence (*55*) indicates that there is no lack of oxygen under a deep snow cover and that death is due rather to carbohydrate exhaustion and the breaking down of the protein substances, which, it is suggested, favors the development of snow mold. Often when ice or snow melts, the subsoil is frozen, and in the absence of surface drainage the plants may be covered with water for some time. Injury may then be due to an excess of water rather than to ice or snow as such.

The evidence that physiological drought causes winter killing of small grains is circumstantial rather than direct. The assumption of a causal relation appears to have arisen from the common observation that varieties best able to survive the cold winters of continental climates have narrow leaves, make little growth in the fall, and are drought-resistant as compared with many less winter-hardy varieties. Whether physiological drought is a factor of importance in the winter killing of small grains cannot be stated with present information.

Spring and Summer Weather

The principal spring-weather factors that merit consideration are late spring freezes, high temperatures, and moisture supplies.

Early spring freezes usually are not very destructive to spring-seeded small grains, since, with the exception of buckwheat and rice, they are not easily killed and usually recover very quickly. Losses do occur, however; and, as noted by several observers (*19, 57*), the damage may be greater than is commonly supposed even though the plants are not killed. Occasionally spring freezes may be sufficiently late to catch winter rye and very early varieties of winter wheat in the boot stage. If the freeze is severe, damage may be extensive. The prospect of such damage has without doubt caused the growing of later maturing varieties of winter wheat in the southern Great Plains than would otherwise be the case.

Small grains differ widely in susceptibility to injury from the freezing of the young plants. In general, rye is the most hardy, followed in order by wheat, oats, barley, flax, and buckwheat. Winter wheat and winter rye in the unhardened condition are more resistant than corresponding spring varieties. There are marked differences among crop varieties (*2, 19, 41, 57*), in many cases greater than the average or commonly observed difference among the crops themselves. The growing of the more resistant varieties has undoubtedly reduced losses considerably.

The period from shooting to shortly after heading is often referred to as a criticial stage of development, especially with reference to the need for adequate supplies of water. It is in reality a critical stage of development with respect to any weather factor because the plants have little opportunity to recover and make a crop if they are injured and because at this period they are very susceptible to certain types of injury. Pollen may be killed either by low temperatures or by high temperatures that do not destroy other portions of the plants (*54*).

It is common knowledge that high temperatures, especially if accompanied by wind (that is, hot winds), when the plant is at the heading stage or between heading and ripening, may seriously interfere with its growth and development, resulting in shrunken grain of low test weight and low yield. Since the air temperatures are usually considerably below what is believed to be lethal, it seems probable that much of the injury is due to transpiration in excess of the ability of the roots to absorb moisture from the soil (*1, 31*). The ill effects of moisture deficiency during the shooting, heading, and filling period are easily understood in the light of the large transpiring surface, the rapid growth usually being made under the influence of the favorable temperatures that commonly prevail, and the inability of the plant to recover from severe injury at this time of the year. It should be noted also that it is often during these stages of development that leaf and stem rust and other diseases first make their presence known. Conditions favorable for their spread and development can in a short time change a good crop prospect into a dismal failure. Under such conditions, the best of weather preceding this period may mean very little so far as the final yield of the crop is concerned.

EFFECTS OF WEATHER ON YIELD OF SMALL GRAINS

Experienced observers usually have no difficulty in determining whether conditions generally have been favorable or unfavorable for the growth of a crop. It is quite another matter to translate these conditions into prospective bushels per acre. Yet that is what each observer would like to do, be he a farmer, a processor of grain, a grain merchant, or a crop forecaster. Crop forecasts in general are based on the observed condition of the growing crop in comparison with that in past years. Since the variations from year to year are mostly due to weather, the question naturally arises, "Why cannot yield predictions be made directly from the weather records?" Such a procedure if successful might have several advantages—for example, earlier predictions and greater accuracy.

Apparently the earliest attempt to estimate a crop from the weather was in 1874, when the Governor of the Barbados Islands showed that the size of the sugar crop was related to the rainfall of the preceding season (*7*). Many attempts to correlate weather and yield have been made since that date.

Since about 1907 most such attempts have made use of formal statistical methods in which deviations from the average of the weather factors being studied are compared with the deviations in yield from the average yield. Thus, if over a period of years it is found that fall precipitation below the average is usually followed by below-average yields, and vice versa, this fact may be useful in estimating yields in future years. Studies of this kind have been very valuable in providing information regarding crop-weather relations, but the method has not been extensively used in actually making yield predictions prior to harvest. The relations are very complex (*4*, *20*) and much more must be known before reliable estimates of yields may reasonably be expected by this method.

The moisture content of the soil at seeding time, which is largely determined by rainfall in summer and early autumn, has recently been used as a guide in determining the acreage of winter wheat to be seeded in the western Great Plains States and in making very general estimates of the yield that may reasonably be expected (*18*). With dry soil or soil wet to a depth of a few inches only, poor yields or failures usually occur. If dry weather continues after seeding and throughout the winter, the probability of failure is so great that abandonment of the crop and use of the land for some other purpose is usually advisable. If, on the contrary, the soil is wet to a depth of 3 feet at seeding time, only unusually adverse conditions subsequent to seeding may be expected to result in low yields or failure. More recently the study of the relation between yield and moisture in the soil at seeding time has been extended to spring wheat in the Great Plains with gratifying results (*9*).

CLIMATE AND THE QUALITY OF SMALL GRAINS

It is well known that climate has important effects on the quality of small grains. The term "quality," however, has quite different meanings depending on the use to be made of the grain. Good quality always suggests freedom from damaged grains such as may result from sprouting or molding in the field or heating in the bin after threshing, etc. To the miller making flour for bread, good quality also means high test weight and high protein content; to the miller making cake or pastry flour, high test weight and low or moderate protein content; to the maltster, high test weight, uniformly plump grain, high starch content, and viability; and to the flaxseed processor, high oil content and satisfactory drying qualities of the oil (as indicated by iodine number). The farmer who needs feed for his domestic animals wants grain that is high in digestible nutrients and has a high test weight.

Plump, well-filled grain of high test weight may usually be expected whenever weather conditions after heading are favorable for the continued development of the crop. That is, an ample but not excessive supply of moisture; temperatures favorable for growth; sunshine; and especially the absence of conditions that induce lodging, burning, or firing of the crop, damage from diseases, etc. Such conditions in general are well known and require no further discussion.

Probably there is no relation between climate and crops that has attracted more interest from investigators or has proved more confusing than that between climate and the protein content of grain. The interest arises from the great importance of protein in determining the suitability of grains for various purposes, and the confusion because of the great multiplicity of factors that determine protein content, of which climate is only one.

It is generally admitted that the protein content of all small grains tends to be high in hot, dry climates and low in moist, cool climates. The Great Plains of the United States and Canada, the plains of Russia, and the Danubian countries, characterized in general by deficient moisture and generally high temperatures preceding harvest, are noted for grain that is hard and of high protein content. Great Britain, Germany, and the eastern section of the United States, on the other hand, with ample rainfall and moderate summer temperatures, produce grain that is generally soft, high in starch, and low in protein. Most early investigators attributed to climate the principal or only role in determining protein content.

There was evidence to show that most of the nitrogen (a necessary constituent of protein) used by the plant was absorbed before it came into head, whereas photosynthesis and the elaboration of carbohydrates continued until the grain was practically ripe. Lawes and Gilbert, at Rothamsted, noted in 1884 that long periods of growth after heading tended to produce plump, well-filled grain with a high starch but a low protein content. A long growth period after heading, often referred to as the fruiting period, is known to be characteristic of grain grown in cool, moist climates, and a short fruiting period of those grown in hot, dry climates. The length of the fruiting period, therefore, came to be regarded as the determining factor. It seemed logical that if nitrogen absorption ceased at the time of heading or soon thereafter and photosynthesis continued until the grain was ripe or nearly so, any factor that reduced the length of the fruiting period would reduce the amount of starch without affecting the total amount of protein and hence would increase the percentage of the latter. It was known that a shorter fruiting period also was often associated with low yields, but the possible relation of this to percentage of protein in the grain seems not to have been noted. Also it was known that nitrogenous fertilizers sometimes increased the protein content of the grain, but this effect was dismissed as being "so small as to have no practical value" and apparently also because the effect of fertilizers on yield and the complementary relations of yield and protein content (*34*) were overlooked.

Recent investigations (*44*, *58*) and a reevaluation of earlier research in the light of new knowledge show quite clearly that both absorption and translocation of nitrogen may continue as long as photosynthesis and translocation of carbohydrates continue, provided there is an ample supply of available nitrogen in the soil. The fact that summer fallow in dry areas generally not only increases the yield but also the protein content of grain is significant in this connection (*8*, *37*).

The pertinent facts as now known appear to be about as follows: In dry, hot regions, the nitrogen content of the soil and the rate of nitrification are in general higher, sometimes considerably higher, than in humid areas, and there is less leaching; hence the supply of available nitrogen in the soil at seeding time is greater. When moisture is limited, the plants make less vegetative growth and use less of the available nitrogen in producing leaves, stems, chaff, etc. (*44*); consequently more nitrogen is left for the production of grain. When yields are lowered by drought, as is often the case, the nitrogen is distributed among fewer bushels. The respiration rate during the fruiting period may be greater where temperatures are high, and since this affects carbohydrates only, the net result is an increase in the protein content. All of these relations, it may be noted, tend to favor a higher protein content for hot, dry areas than for cool, moist ones.

The effect of weather can be explained in a similar manner. Temperature and moisture conditions favorable for nitrification without leaching, a moderate vegetative growth in the fall and spring, and a yield limited by moisture rather than by available nitrates would be expected to leave a surplus of nitrogen for high-protein grain. This agrees with the well-known fact that high-protein grain is produced in dry years and low-protein grain in wet years.

A marked deficiency of moisture during the latter part of the growth period would be expected to lead to a higher protein content of grain, not so much because of any direct effect on nitrogen supplies as because of reduced photosynthesis and a lower yield. Frost (*38*, *40*, *48*) and stem rust, which abruptly terminate the fruiting period, have little or no effect on the percentage of protein in the grain, because absorption and translocation of nitrogen and photosynthesis and translocation of carbohydrates are stopped at approximately the same time.

Climate is also believed to be important in relation to the oil content and drying qualities of the oil of flaxseed. The drying quality of linseed oil appears to depend largely on the full development of the flaxseed. Where the crop is forced to premature ripening by drought and high temperatures, the seed is likely to be shrunken, and the quality of the oil is often impaired. In general, therefore, the best quality of flaxseed is produced in the cooler northern climates and where rainfall is adequate. Seed of high quality is produced under irrigation in California, where flax is grown as a winter crop, and in the northern Intermountain States—Montana, Idaho, and Utah—where flax is grown to a limited extent. It is certain that temperatures of 95° to 100° F. or higher are injurious to flax in the filling stage, that is, between blossoming and ripening. For this reason, flax of lower quality is generally produced in the Central States and in hot seasons in more northern areas. In California and Texas the crop matures in late April, before high temperatures occur.

WHERE SMALL GRAINS ARE GROWN

The average annual world production of small grains, exclusive of that of China, is, in millions of short tons: Wheat, 137; oats, 72; rye, 51; barley, 48; rice, 65; and flaxseed, 4. China is known to be an important producer of rice, wheat, and barley (*10*), but records of acreage and production are mostly lacking; recent estimates (*10*) [4] suggest a rice crop roughly two-thirds of that of the remainder of the world, a wheat crop about equal to that of the United States, and barley equal to or exceeding that of the United States and Canada combined. Buckwheat is of minor importance, occupying in Europe only about 2 percent and in the United States less than one-half of 1 percent as many acres as are devoted to other small grains.

The principal small-grain-producing regions are North America, Europe, China, India, Argentina, and Australia. Northern Africa grows considerable barley and wheat. Small grains are also grown in South Africa, on the west coast of South America, and in Mexico. The production in the latter regions, though important locally, is of little consequence in world volume. The acreage of wheat in various countries of the world is indicated in figure 1.

Production in Other Countries

Europe is the most important more or less continuous small-grain-producing area in the world. More than 95 percent of the rye, 60 percent of the oats, about one-half the wheat and barley, about 23 percent of the flaxseed, and nearly 1 percent of the rice of the world (excluding China) are produced there. Climatic conditions generally are favorable. Precipitation is deficient in portions of Spain and in the southern and eastern European parts of the Union of Soviet Socialist Republics but is reasonably ample and well-distributed elsewhere. Summers generally are cool, and evaporation is moderate or low. Except in the eastern, central, and northern European parts of the Soviet Union, the winters are relatively mild. To a considerable degree, therefore, and throughout much of the continent, soil and economic considerations rather than climate determine the crops that are grown. Some of the most productive varieties now grown in the United States had their origin in some part of Europe.

A large percentage of the small-grain crops of Argentina, principally wheat and flax, enters international trade. About half the world's crop of flaxseed is produced in that country. The small grains are grown mostly in a broad belt about 600 miles long beginning near the northern border and extending southward through the eastern half of the country.[5] The annual rainfall of the region varies from a minimum of about 15 inches in the west and southwest to about 40 inches in the northeast (*26*). Winters are open and mild, the mean temperatures corresponding roughly with those of the Cotton Belt of the United States.

India, including Burma, produces more than 50 percent of the world's rice crop, exclusive of that of China, about half as much wheat and barley as the United States, and slightly more flaxseed than the United States. The rice is grown principally on the lower flood plain of the Ganges River in northeast India and along the coasts of the Indian Peninsula. The temperature is high, and rainfall in many places is so plentiful that irrigation is not necessary. Wheat, barley, and flax are grown in the interior, where the rainfall is less and the temperature, especially during the winter and early spring, when the crop is grown, is lower. These grains are seeded in the fall after the monsoon rains and are harvested in the spring before the onset of hot weather.

---

[4] Rossiter, Fred J. agriculture in china. U. S. Dept. Agr., Off. Foreign Agr. Relations, Foreign Agr. 3: [429]-498, illus. 1939. [Processed.]

[5] Nyhus, Paul O. argentine wheat. U. S. Bur. Agr. Econ., Foreign Agr. 2: 323-348, illus. 1938. [Processed.]

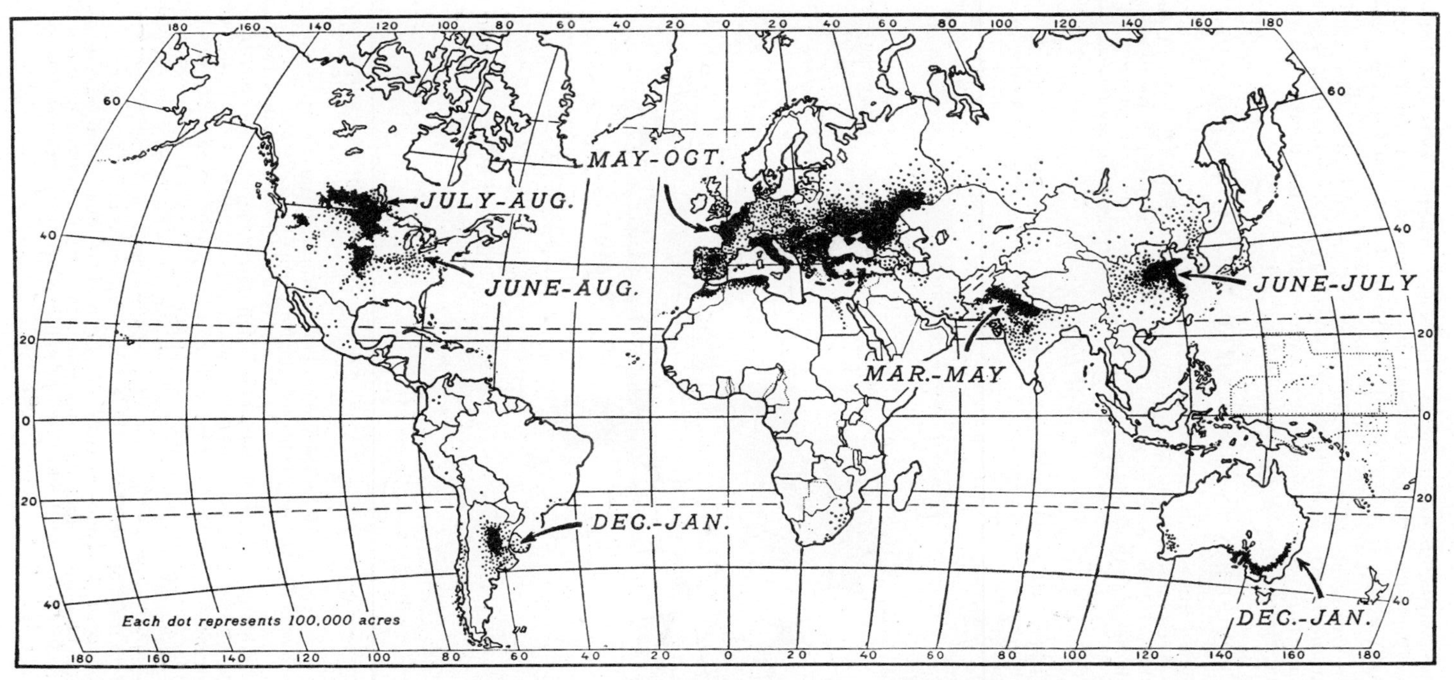

FIGURE 1.—World acreage and important harvest periods of wheat (average 1930–31, 1934–35). Wheat is grown in nearly every important political division of the world and is being harvested somewhere in every season of the year.

The principal small-grain crop of Australia is wheat. Oats and barley are grown, but they are relatively unimportant. Practically all the small grains of Australia are grown in a narrow belt paralleling the sea coast on the south and bordering the interior desert. The annual rainfall ranges from about 10 to 25 inches, occurring mostly during the winter. The winters are so mild that spring varieties may be seeded in the fall without danger of winter injury. Federation, which is one of the principal varieties grown in the Pacific Northwest of the United States, was introduced from Australia.

Production in the United States and Canada

The United States and Canada combined grow about one-sixth of the world tonnage of small grains. Of this, wheat accounts for about 47.5 percent, oats 38 percent, barley 12.5 percent, and flaxseed and rice about 1 percent each, rice production being limited to the United States.

Wheat

Four rather distinct wheat-producing areas may be recognized (fig. 2). These are (1) the eastern winter-wheat, (2) the hard winter-wheat, (3) the hard red

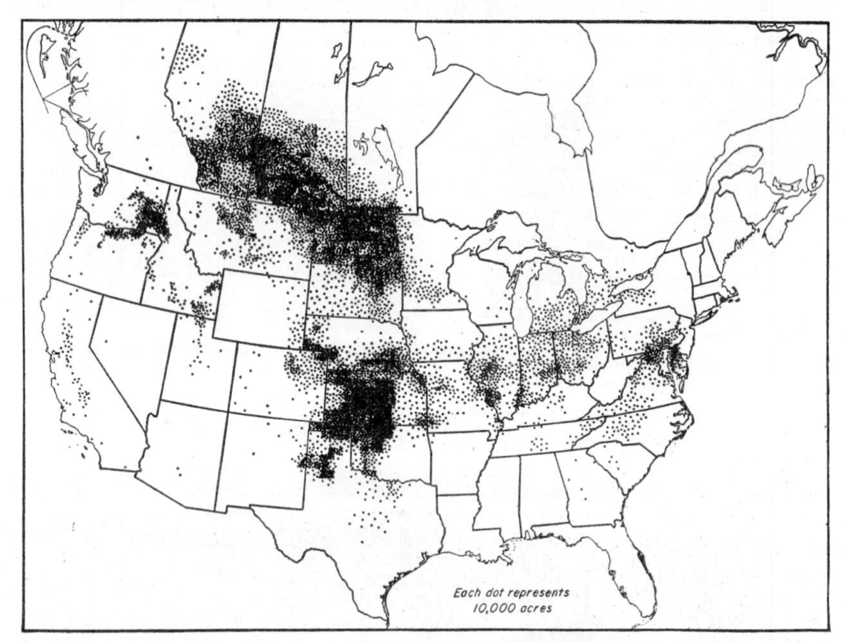

Figure 2.—Wheat acreages and regions of the United States and Canada.

spring, and (4) the western region. The eastern winter-wheat region grows principally soft red winter varieties but also a small amount of soft white and hard red winter varieties.

The eastern region is characterized by usually ample and seldom excessive rainfall, and by moderately cool but not severe winters, except in the northern part, where the ground is usually covered with snow during the coldest part of the year. The boundary between the eastern region and the hard red winter-wheat region on the west is indistinct, but is generally considered to be roughly the isohyet (line of equal rainfall) of 30 or 35 inches of annual rainfall. Because of the relatively high rainfall, most of the wheat of this region has soft grain of low protein content which produces a flour most satisfactory for pastries, such as cakes, cookies, pies, etc. When because of growing conditions the protein content of the wheat is high or when it is blended with high-protein wheats from other regions, most of it makes very satisfactory bread flour.

The hard red winter-wheat region centers in Kansas, Nebraska, central Oklahoma, and the Panhandles of Oklahoma and Texas. The annual precipitation varies from about 17 to 20 inches in eastern New Mexico and western Texas and 15 inches in eastern Colorado, Wyoming, and Montana to 30 or 35 inches in eastern Kansas and Oklahoma. Winters are moderately cold, especially along the northern border of the region, and generally dry with little or at best uncertain snow cover. The grain is hard, generally high in protein content, and highly rated for bread-making purposes. New varieties recently produced by breeding promise wheat of even better bread-making quality than those now grown.

In the hard red spring-wheat region the winters in general are too severe for winter wheat. The area includes the two Dakotas, the western border of Minnesota—especially the Red River Valley—northeastern and north central Montana, and an area in Canada approximately as far north as Winnipeg on the east and the Peace River district northwest of Edmonton on the west. The northern limits are determined largely by the length of the growing season and the mean summer temperatures. The annual rainfall varies from a minimum of about 15 inches in the west to about 25 inches along the eastern border of South Dakota and in western Minnesota. Diseases, especially stem rust and scab, and competition with crops such as barley, corn, and flax, are the chief factors determining the eastern limits.

Hard red spring wheat is noted for its high protein content and excellent bread-making characteristics and is used extensively for blends with weaker wheats throughout the world.

In the hard red spring-wheat region there is also grown annually about 35 to 40 million bushels of durum wheat, concentrated mostly in northeastern North Dakota and extending slightly into South Dakota and in recent years into Canada. Because of its greater resistance to stem rust, durum wheat has until recently had a yield advantage as compared with the prevalent varieties of hard red spring, but this has largely disappeared with the introduction of rust-resistant varieties of spring wheat, notably the variety Thatcher.

The principal wheat-growing area of the western part of the United States is in the Big Bend and Palouse districts of Washington and the adjoining portions of Oregon and northern Idaho. There are also scattered areas in southern Idaho, northern and central Utah, and California. Numerous varieties are grown, representing all market classes of wheat except durum.

The multiplicity of types and varieties suggests the great variety of climatic conditions under which wheat is grown in this area. The region as a whole is characterized by a limited precipitation occurring mostly in the fall, winter, and spring, necessitating or favoring an alternate fallow and cropping system. In general the winters are mild to moderately cold; only at high elevations and occasionally elsewhere is it so cold that winter wheat cannot be grown. The relative acreage of winter and spring varieties is determined more by fall moisture at seeding time than by winter cold and varies with the season as fall conditions are favorable or otherwise. An exception is California, where, because of mild winters, true spring varieties are grown from fall seeding. Spring and summer may be very hot, as in some of the interior valleys, where only early-maturing varieties are satisfactory. In other areas, especially at the higher elevations, moderately cool summer weather may prevail. In much of the area yields are relatively high and protein content low.

Small Grains Other Than Wheat

Of the small grains in the United States and Canada oats rank second in importance to wheat. The principal region of production circles south of the Great Lakes in a broad, irregular band extending from eastern Canada in the east to the Peace River district in west-central Alberta, Canada, on the west and north (fig. 3). The greatest concentration coincides very closely with the center of the Corn Belt, a reflection of the need for oats to complete most rotations in which corn is an important crop. In this area oats compete successfully with spring wheat and barley, since the latter are subject to scab and other diseases to which oats are more resistant. An important hazard in the production of oats in the southern and more moist areas is crown rust. Recently distributed varieties that are highly resistant to this disease promise a Nation-wide reduction in losses.

Barley perhaps is limited less by climate and more by competitive relations with other crops than any other of the small grains. Malting barley brings the

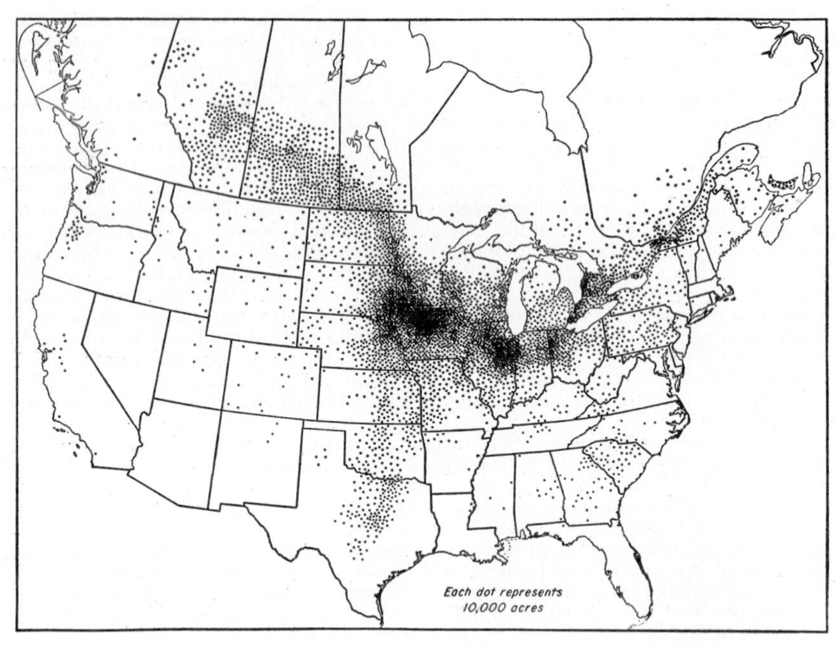

FIGURE 3.—The acreage of oats in the United States and Canada.

best price, but in general it is produced only in areas of moderately high rainfall. Elsewhere barley is grown mostly for feed and must compete with other crops on a feed basis.

The principal barley-producing area centers in Minnesota and the two Dakotas, with a northern extension into Manitoba and Saskatchewan, Canada (fig. 4), and an eastern extension across southern and central Wisconsin to northern Illinois. Higher yields as compared with those of oats and spring wheat and in much of the area the need for a feed crop to replace corn, which cannot be grown there satisfactorily, account for this rather extensive production. A second area of considerable importance is in northwestern Kansas, southwestern Nebraska, and northeastern Colorado. Here barley is often grown where winter wheat has not survived the winter. Barley also fits in well with corn in this area. Barley is likewise grown in scattered localities throughout the intermountain area and the Pacific Northwest, where it is used mainly for feed. In all these areas the crop is grown from spring sowing.

Winter barley is grown sparingly throughout the South, with some tendency toward increased production there in recent years. As with other winter crops, the northern limits are determined by winter temperature and the western limits largely by winter temperature and moisture for germination in the fall.

Barley is also grown from fall seeding in the central valleys of California, the varieties, however, being of spring type, as is the case with wheat in the same area.

Rice is grown in the United States only in sections where the growing season is relatively long, the summer temperatures relatively high, and supplies of water for irrigation abundant. Comparatively level land with good surface drainage and a tight soil or subsoil that will hold water is also essential. There are three principal producing areas: (1) the broad level prairies of southwestern Louisiana and southeastern Texas, (2) the Grand Prairie section of eastern Arkansas, and (3) the Sacramento and San Joaquin Valleys of California (*28*) (fig. 5).

In the Arkansas, Louisiana, and Texas areas the land is prepared and the rice seeded in much the same way as for other small grains. After the rice emerges the ground is flooded for 60 to 90 days or more during the growing season. In California the common practice is to submerge the land and then broadcast the rice on the surface of the water. Airplanes are commonly used for this purpose.

Flax has been grown at one time or another in most of the States from the

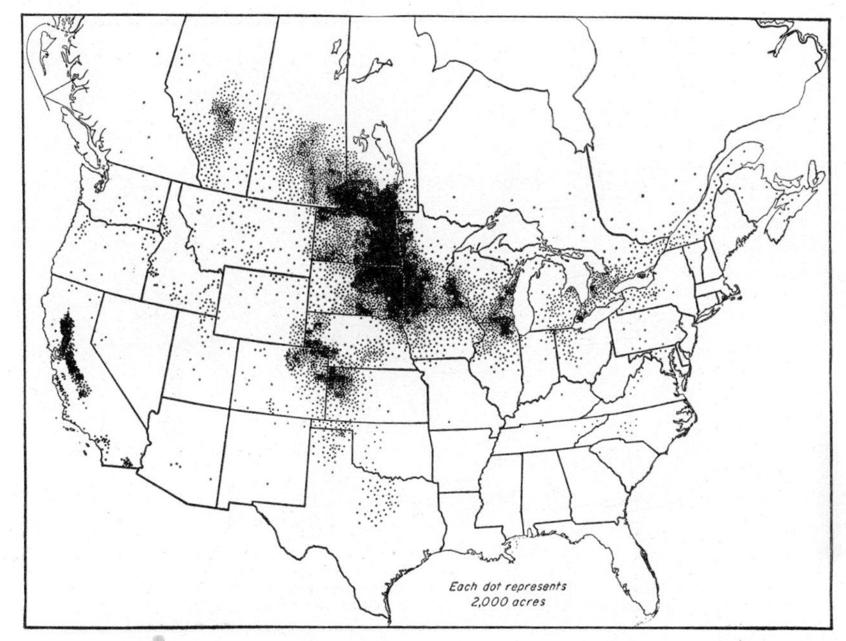

FIGURE 4.—The acreage of barley in the United States and Canada.

Atlantic coast west to its present principal area of production. So far as climatic requirements are concerned, the crop can be grown with more or less success anywhere within this range.

Rye is relatively unimportant in the United States and Canada. On most of the good soils yields of rye are less than those of other small grains. Before the World War, much of the rye of the United States was grown on the sandy soils of Wisconsin and Michigan with smaller areas on depleted soils of New York and Pennsylvania. There has since been a marked shift in acreage to the Spring Wheat Belt. Rye is also used as a winter cover and green-manure crop in the South, especially on sandy soils. The present principal area of production centers in North Dakota and Minnesota, extending far north into Canada, with scattered areas south of the Great Lakes to Pennsylvania and Maryland and southwest to Nebraska and Kansas (fig. 5). Rye is more resistant to low winter temperatures than any other cereal. The ability of the crop to grow more rapidly at low temperatures increases its efficiency in using moisture and may be important in dry areas. The lower temperature optimum of winter rye also makes it useful for winter pasture in the South, and its early maturity allows it to escape much of the injury from drought suffered by other crops.

The present principal seed-flax-producing area coincides very closely with that of spring wheat, extending, however, slightly farther east (fig. 6). A second area of considerable importance is in southeastern Kansas. Flax wilt and weeds have been the principal factors in crowding flax out of older cultivated areas. Wilt-resistant varieties are now available and the crop probably could be produced wherever it was formerly grown, although economic conditions, rather than climatic factors, have operated against this.

In recent years flax has become an important crop in California, and much interest in it has developed also in Arizona and in south Texas, where it is grown as a cool-season or winter crop. Flax has been grown for fiber and seed in western Oregon and Washington for 40 years or more and to a limited extent as a seed crop in Idaho. Seed flax was first grown commercially in California in 1934 as an outgrowth of experiments begun in 1927 by the California Agricultural Experiment Station and the United States Department of Agriculture at El Centro. About 1,700,000 bushels were grown on 108,000 acres in 1939. A somewhat

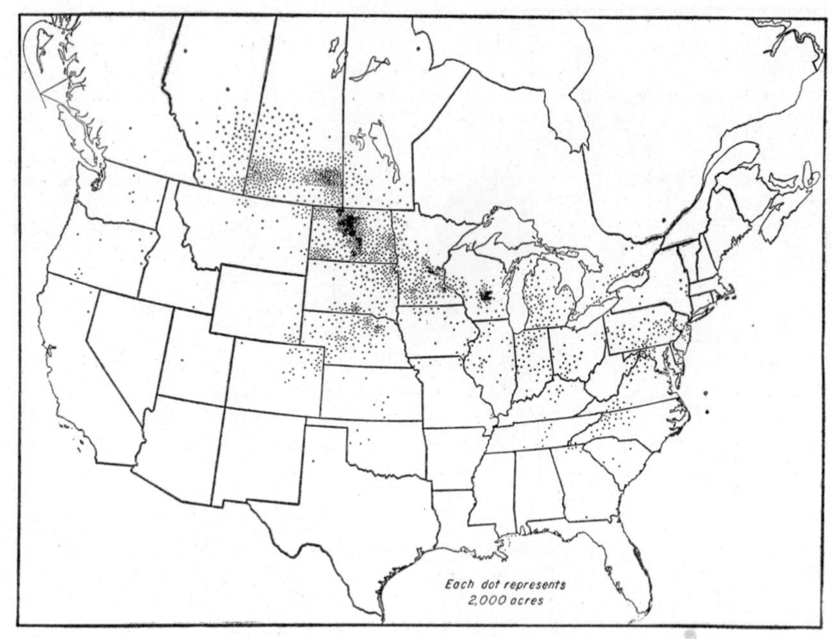

FIGURE 5.—The acreage of rye in the United States and Canada.

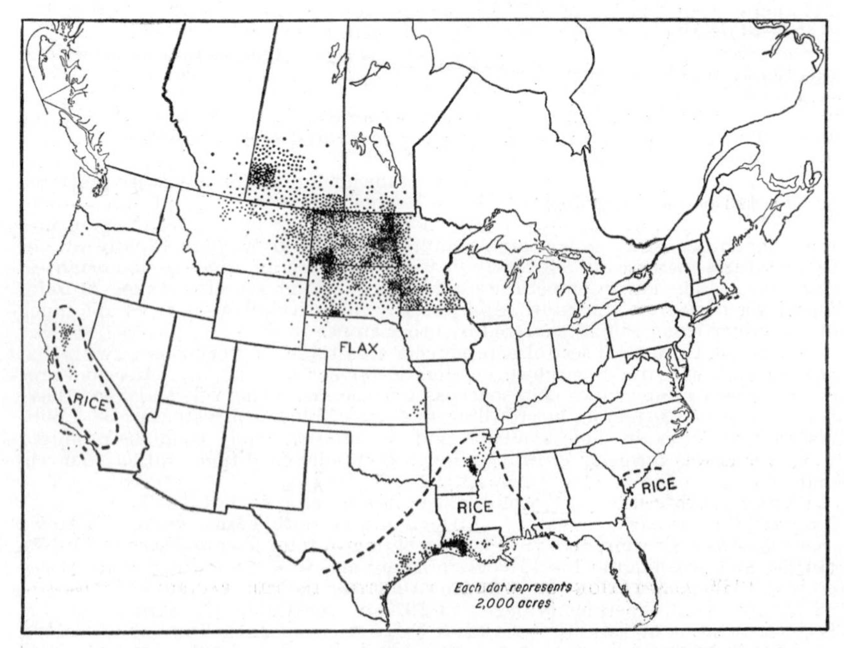

FIGURE 6.—The acreage of flax grown for seed and that of rice in the United States and Canada.

similar development along the Gulf coast in south Texas resulted in a crop of about 200,000 bushels on about 18,000 acres in 1939.

Both in California and Texas flax is sown in the fall. Flax is not a true winter annual, however, and will not survive as low temperatures as rye, wheat, barley, and oats. January temperatures as low as 15° to 20° F. and even lower have been reported in some cases to have caused little or no permanent damage to flax seeded the preceding fall (*13*). Hard freezes at later stages of development—for example, the blossom or green-boll stage—are more serious. The plant not only is more susceptible to injury at this stage but also has little time to recover and mature before the onset of hot summer weather. Frosts in late February and March, when the plants are in blossom or near the blossoming stage, are among the most serious hazards to flax growing in the San Joaquin and Sacramento Valleys.

LITERATURE CITED

(1) Aamodt, O. S., and Johnston, W. H.
1936. studies on drought resistance in spring wheat. Canad. Jour. Res. Sect. C, Bot. Sci. 14: 122–152, illus.

(2) ——— and Platt, A. W.
1934. resistance of wild oats and some common cereal varieties to freezing temperatures. Sci. Agr. 14: 645–650, illus.

(3) Albright, W. D.
1933. crop growth in high latitudes. Geog. Rev. 23: 608–620, illus.

(4) Alsberg, Carl L., and Griffing, E. P.
1928. forecasting wheat yields from the weather. Stanford Univ., Food Res. Inst. Wheat Studies 5: 1–44.

(5) Bayles, B. B., and Taylor, J. W.
1939. wheat improvement in the eastern united states. Cereal Chem. 16: 208–223, illus.

(6) Bouyoucos, George J., and McCool, M. M.
1928. the correct explanation for the heaving of soils, plants, and pavements. Amer. Soc. Agron. Jour. 20: 480–491, illus.

(7) Brooks, Charles F.
1922. forecasting the crops from the weather. Geog. Rev. 12: 305–307.

(8) Burke, Edmund.
1922. the influence of nitrate nitrogen upon the protein content and yield of wheat. Jour. Agr. Res. 31: 1189–1199, illus.

(9) Cole, John S., and Mathews, O. R.
1940. relation of the depth to which the soil is wet at seeding time to the yield of spring wheat on the great plains. U. S. Dept. Agr. Cir. 563, 20 pp., illus.

(10) Cressey, George B.
1934. agricultural regions of asia. part vi. china. Econ. Geog. 10: [109]–142, illus.

(11) Croxton, W. C., and Nicholson, Page.
1937. the extent to which the snow blanket influences the temperature beneath it. Minn. Acad. Sci. Proc. 5: 46–49, illus.

(12) Dexter, S. T.
1933. effect of several environmental factors on the hardening of plants. Plant Physiol. 8: 123–129, illus.

(13) Dillman, A. C., and Goar, L. Gordon.
1937. flaxseed production in the far western states. U. S. Dept. Agr. Farmers' Bul. 1793, 22 pp., illus.

(14) Finch, V. C., and Baker, O. E.
1917. geography of the world's agriculture. 149 pp., illus. Washington, D. C. (U. S. Dept. Agr.)

(15) Fitton, Edith M., and Brooks, Charles F.
1931. soil temperatures in the united states. U. S. Monthly Weather Rev. 59: 6–16, illus.

(16) Gaines, E. F., and Schafer, E. G.
1932. adaptation of wheat varieties in the pacific northwest. Northwest Sci. 6: 98–107, illus.

(17) Georgeson, C. C., and Gasser, G. W.
1926. cereal growing in alaska. Alaska Agr. Expt. Sta. Bul. 6, 40 pp., illus.

(18) HALLSTED, A. L., and MATHEWS, O. R.
1936. SOIL MOISTURE AND WINTER WHEAT WITH SUGGESTIONS ON ABANDONMENT. Kans. Agr. Expt. Sta. Bul. 273, 46 pp., illus.

(19) HARRINGTON, J. B.
1936. VARIETAL RESISTANCE OF SMALL GRAINS TO SPRING FROST INJURY. Amer. Soc. Agron. Jour. 28: 374–388.

(20) HOWARD, ALBERT.
1916. THE INFLUENCE OF THE WEATHER ON THE YIELD OF WHEAT. Agr. Jour. India 11: 351–359.

(21) HUNTER, BYRON, SEVERANCE, GEO., and MILLER, R. N.
1925. A REVIEW OF THE AGRICULTURE OF THE BIG BEND COUNTRY. Wash. Agr. Expt. Sta. Bul. 192, 47 pp., illus.

(22) ILJIN, W. S.
1934. THE POINT OF DEATH OF PLANTS AT LOW TEMPERATURE. Zapiski (Bul. Assoc. Russe. Rech. Sci., Prague, Sect. Sci. Nat. et Math.) v. 1 (VI), No. 4, pp. 135–160.

(23) JANSSEN, GEORGE.
1929. EFFECT OF DATE OF SEEDING OF WINTER WHEAT UPON SOME PHYSIOLOGICAL CHANGES OF THE PLANT DURING THE WINTER SEASON. Amer. Soc. Agron. Jour. 21: 168–200, illus.

(24) JASNY, N.
1940. COMPETITION AMONG GRAINS. Stanford Univ., Food Res. Inst. Grain Econ. Ser. No. 2, 606 pp., illus.

(25) JOHNSON, EDW. C.
1932. THE INFLUENCE OF CLIMATE ON WASHINGTON AGRICULTURE. Northwest Sci. 6: 17–24.

(26) JONES, CLARENCE F.
1928. AGRICULTURAL REGIONS OF SOUTH AMERICA. Econ. Geog. 4: [1]–30, illus.

(27) ———
1929. AGRICULTURAL REGIONS OF SOUTH AMERICA. INSTALLMENT V. Econ. Geog. 5: [277]–307, illus.

(28) JONES, JENKIN W., JENKINS, J. MITCHELL, WYCHE, R. H., and NELSON, MARTIN.
1938. RICE CULTURE IN THE SOUTHERN STATES. U. S. Dept. Agr. Farmers' Bul. 1808, 29 pp., illus.

(29) KINCER, J. B.
1922. PRECIPITATION AND HUMIDITY. *In* Atlas of American Agriculture, Part II, Climate, Sect. A. U. S. Dept. Agr. Adv. Sheets 5, 48 pp., illus.

(30) KOSSOWITSCH, P.
1894. ABHÄNGIGKEIT DER BESTOCKUNGSTIEFE DER GETREIDEARTEN VON EINGEN WACHSTHUMSFAKTOREN. Forsch. auf dem Geb. der Agr. Phys. 17: 104–116.

(31) KRASNOSSELSKY-MAXIMOV, T. A.
1931. PHYSIOLOGICAL ANALYSIS OF WINDBURN BY MEANS OF ARTIFICIAL DRY WIND. Trudy Prikl. Bot., Genet., i Selek. (Bul. Appl. Bot., Genet., and Plant Breeding) 25 (3): [3]–44, illus. [In Russian. English summary, pp. [43]–44.]

(32) LAMB, C. A.
1939. FURTHER STUDIES ON ROOT CHARACTERISTICS OF WINTER WHEAT IN RELATION TO WINTER INJURY. Jour. Agr. Res. 59: 667–681, illus.

(33) LAUDE, H. H.
1937. COLD RESISTANCE OF WINTER WHEAT, RYE, BARLEY, AND OATS IN TRANSITION FROM DORMANCY TO ACTIVE GROWTH. Jour. Agr. Res. 54: 899–917, illus.

(34) MALLOCH, J. G., and NEWTON, R.
1934. THE RELATION BETWEEN YIELD AND PROTEIN CONTENT OF WHEAT. Canad. Jour. Res. 10: 774–779.

(35) MARTIN, J. FOSTER.
1932. THE COLD RESISTANCE OF PACIFIC COAST SPRING WHEATS AT VARIOUS STAGES OF GROWTH AS DETERMINED BY ARTIFICIAL REFRIGERATION. Amer. Soc. Agron. Jour. 24: 871–880.

(36) MARTIN, JOHN H.
1927. COMPARATIVE STUDIES OF WINTER HARDINESS IN WHEAT. Jour. Agr. Res. 35: 493–535, illus.

(37) McCall, M. A., and Wanser, H. M.
1924. THE PRINCIPLES OF SUMMER-FALLOW TILLAGE. Wash. Agr. Expt. Sta. Bul. 183, 77 pp., illus.

(38) McCalla, A. G., and Newton, R.
1935. EFFECT OF FROST ON WHEAT AT PROGRESSIVE STAGES OF MATURITY. II. COMPOSITION AND BIOCHEMICAL PROPERTIES OF GRAIN AND FLOUR. Canad. Jour. Res. Sect. C, Bot. Sci. 13: 1–31, illus.

(39) McKinney, H. H., and Sando, W. J.
1935. EARLINESS OF SEXUAL REPRODUCTION IN WHEAT AS INFLUENCED BY TEMPERATURE AND LIGHT IN RELATION TO GROWTH PHASES. Jour. Agr. Res. 51: 621–641, illus.

(40) Newton, R., and McCalla, A. G.
1934. EFFECT OF FROST ON WHEAT AT PROGRESSIVE STAGES OF MATURITY. I. PHYSICAL CHARACTERISTICS OF THE KERNELS. Canad. Jour. Res. 10: 414–429, illus.

(41) Peltier, G. L., and Kiesselbach, T. A.
1934. THE COMPARATIVE COLD RESISTANCE OF SPRING SMALL GRAINS. Amer. Soc. Agron. Jour. 26: 681–687.

(42) Purvis, O. N., and Gregory, F. G.
1937. STUDIES IN VERNALISATION OF CEREALS. I. A COMPARATIVE STUDY OF VERNALISATION OF WINTER RYE BY LOW TEMPERATURE AND SHORT DAYS. Ann. Bot. [London] (n. s.) 1:569–591, illus.

(43) Roterus, Victor.
1934. SPRING AND WINTER WHEAT ON THE COLUMBIA PLATEAU. Econ. Geog. 10: 368–373, illus.

(44) Russell, E. J.
1931. ARTIFICIAL FERTILIZERS IN MODERN AGRICULTURE. [Gt. Brit.] Min. Agr. and Fisheries Bul. 28, 202 pp., illus.

(45) Rutter, Frank R.
1908. CEREAL PRODUCTION OF EUROPE. U. S. Dept. Agr., Bur. Statis. Bul. 68, 100 pp.

(46) Sabashnikov, V.
1932. THE PROBLEM OF WINTER WHEAT IN SIBERIA. Trudy Prikl. Bot., Genet., i Selek. (Bul. Appl. Bot., Genet., and Plant Breeding) Ser. 2, No. 3, pp. [116]–135. [In Russian. English summary, pp. [133]–135.]

(47) Scarth, G. W., and Levitt, J.
1937. THE FROST-HARDENING MECHANISM OF PLANT CELLS. Plant Physiol. 12: 51–78, illus.

(48) Sharp, Paul Francis.
1926. WHEAT AND FLOUR STUDIES, VIII. THE COMPOSITION OF WHEAT AND MILL PRODUCTS FROM FROZEN AND NON-FROZEN WHEAT HARVESTED AT VARIOUS STAGES OF MATURITY. Cereal Chem. 3: 402–410, illus.

(49) Smuts, I. J., Sellschop, J. P. F., and Mackenzie, A. J.
1934. FIELD CROPS IN THE GLEN AREA. Union So. Africa Dept. Agr. Bul. 132, 22 pp., illus.

(50) Suneson, C. A., and Peltier, George L.
1934. COLD RESISTANCE ADJUSTMENTS OF FIELD-HARDENED WINTER WHEATS AS DETERMINED BY ARTIFICIAL FREEZING. Amer. Soc. Agron. Jour. 26: 50–58.

(51) ——— and Peltier, George L.
1938. EFFECT OF WEATHER VARIANTS ON FIELD HARDENING OF WINTER WHEAT. Amer. Soc. Agron. Jour. 30: 769–778, illus.

(52) Taylor, Griffith.
1920. AGRICULTURAL CLIMATOLOGY OF AUSTRALIA. Roy. Met. Soc. [London] Quart. Jour. 46: 331–356, illus.

(53) Timmons, F. L., and Clapp, A. L.
1932. FLORET STERILITY IN WHEAT CAUSED BY A LATE SPRING FREEZE. Amer. Soc. Agron. Jour. 24: 584–585, illus.

(54) Tippett, L. H. C.
1926. ON THE EFFECT OF SUNSHINE ON WHEAT YIELD AT ROTHAMSTED. Jour. Agr. Sci. [England] 16: [159]–165, illus.

298737°—41——23 +

(55) Tumanov, I. I., Borodina, I. N., and Oleinikova, I. V.
1935. THE ROLE OF SNOW COVER IN THE WINTERING OF CROPS. Trudy Prikl. Bot., Genet., i Selek. (Bul. Appl. Bot., Genet., and Plant Breeding) Ser. III, No. 6, pp. 3–57. [In Russian. English summary in Summaries, pp. [1]–4.]

(56) Van Doren, C. A.
1937. BOUND WATER AND ELECTRICAL CONDUCTIVITY AS MEASURES OF COLD RESISTANCE IN WINTER WHEAT. Amer. Soc. Agron. Jour. 29: 392–402, illus.

(57) Waldron, L. R.
1931. FROST INJURY TO SPRING WHEAT WITH A CONSIDERATION OF DROUTH RESISTANCE. Amer. Soc. Agron. Jour. 23: 625–637.

(58) Watson, D. J.
1936. THE EFFECT OF APPLYING A NITROGENOUS FERTILISER TO WHEAT AT DIFFERENT STAGES OF GROWTH. Jour. Agr. Sci. [England] 26: [391]–414, illus.

(59) Whitbeck, R. H., and Finch, V. C.
1930. ECONOMIC GEOGRAPHY. Ed. 2, 565 pp., illus.

(60) Whitcomb, W. O., and Sharp, Paul Francis.
1926. WHEAT AND FLOUR STUDIES, VII. MILLING AND BAKING TESTS OF FROZEN AND NON-FROZEN WHEAT HARVESTED AT VARIOUS STAGES OF MATURITY. Cereal Chem. 3: 301–315, illus.

(61) Worzella, W. W.
1932. ROOT DEVELOPMENT IN HARDY AND NON-HARDY WINTER WHEAT VARIETIES. Amer. Soc. Agron. Jour. 24: 626–637, illus.

(62) Zinzerling, G. D.
1925. NORTHERN LIMITS OF AGRICULTURE. Trudy Prikl. Bot., Genet., i Selek. (Bul. of Appl. Bot., Genet., and Plant Breeding) 15 (3): 1–[144], illus. [In Russian. English summary, pp. [127]–142.]

Climate and Sorghum

By J. H. Martin[1]

SORGHUM HAS proved to be enormously useful to agriculture in areas too hot and dry to grow corn well. In recent years its usefulness has been considerably extended by the production of new varieties and the study of cultural practices. Here are facts that will help in understanding the peculiarities of this crop and in getting the most out of it.

[1] J. H. Martin is Senior Agronomist, in Charge of Sorghum and Broomcorn Investigations, Division of Cereal Crops and Diseases, Bureau of Plant Industry.

SORGHUM is grown largely in parts of Africa, Asia, America, and Australia that are too dry or too hot for successful corn production. It furnishes feed for millions of farm animals. The plant is a native of the Tropics, and, although many varieties now available are adapted to temperate regions, warm weather is required for its successful growth. Grain sorghums (milo, kafir, hegari, etc.) are grown for grain or forage, and sorgos (sweet or "cane") for forage or sirup.

Sorghum is grown throughout almost all of agricultural Africa and in nearly all portions of India except the northern mountainous region. It is an important crop in Manchuria, northern China, and Chosen (Korea) and is grown considerably in Iran (Persia), Arabia, and other parts of the Near East and the Mediterranean regions. The crop occupies about 10 million acres in the United States. Smaller acreages are found in Argentina, Australia, and many other countries. The breeding or introduction of new varieties by agricultural research agencies has aided greatly in extending the region to which sorghums are adapted.

Until recently grain sorghum in the United States (fig. 1) was confined largely to sections having a mean July temperature of 75° F. or higher, an average frost-free period of 160 days or longer, and an average precipitation of 17 to 40 inches (especially those with 17 to 25 inches). Sorgos may be grown farther north than the grain sorghums, since they are used largely for forage and it is therefore not so necessary that they ripen completely. Although well adapted to survive drought, sorghums do not produce satisfactory yields in regions without a summer rainfall, such as the western part of the United States. Under irrigation, however, they are grown successfully in dry sections of California and Arizona.

In recent years, when seasons were warmer and drier than the average, grain-sorghum production has been extended northward and westward into sections formerly restricted largely to sorgo (fig. 2)

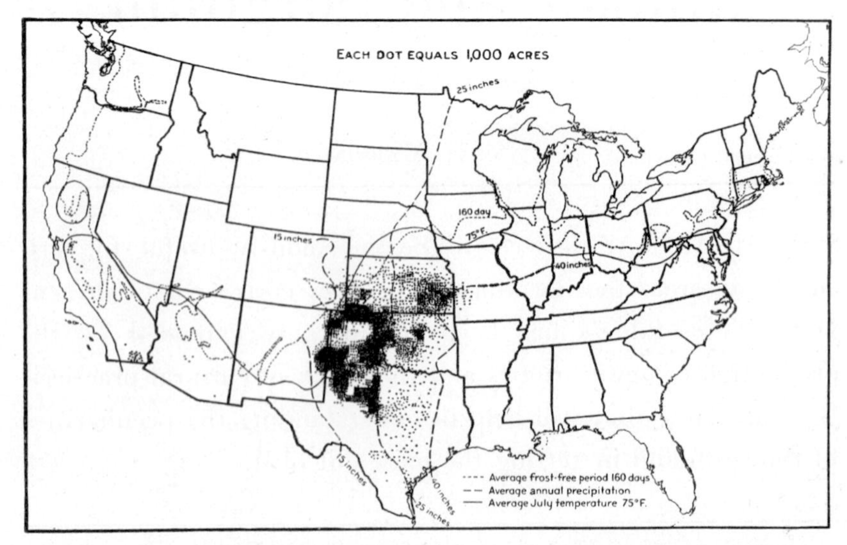

FIGURE 1.—Distribution of grain sorghums in the United States, 1929.

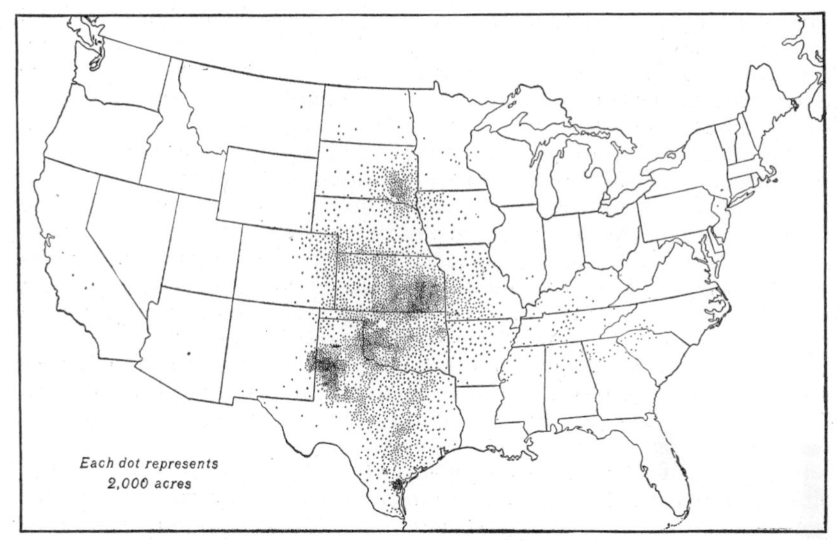

FIGURE 2.—Distribution of sorghum harvested for forage in the United States in 1934.

and corn—a development made possible by new, improved, early-maturing varieties. These new varieties, including Sooner, Colby, Early Kalo, Coes, and Highland, are able to evade many of the ill effects of drought and short seasons. They were developed by the United States Department of Agriculture in cooperation with State agricultural experiment stations to fill an acute need. The limits of production now reach to sections where the average annual precipitation is 15 to 17 inches, the average frost-free period 130 to 140 days, and the long-time mean July temperature 70° F. (though in recent years the latter mean in these sections has approached 75°). There is also a more intensive production of sorgo in South Dakota, Nebraska, and other States in which formerly it was grown only occasionally.

CHARACTERISTICS AND REQUIREMENTS

In the area where sorghums are grown extensively (fig. 1) the acreage exceeds that of corn, largely or entirely because of the greater ability of sorghums to produce a crop under dry, hot conditions. This, in turn, appears to be related to several striking characteristics, including (1) ability to remain dormant during drought and then resume growth, (2) high resistance to desiccation (drying out), (3) low transpiration ratio, (4) large number of fibrous roots, and (5) ability to produce a crop from tillers and branches that develop after rains occur. The relatively impervious, corky epidermis (skin) of sorghum, with its abundant wax covering, retards the drying of the stalks and leaves much as in cactus. The inherent perennial growth characteristic of sorghum enables it to produce new tillers whenever moisture becomes available if drought has not been too prolonged and the plants have not been subjected to freezing. Corn lacks many of these characteristics or possesses them only to a lesser degree.

In those parts of the United States where the yield of corn is as much as two-thirds that of grain sorgum, farmers in general prefer to grow corn because of greater certainty of obtaining a stand in cool soil, less risk of damage in storage, higher feeding and market value, the ability of cornstalks to stand longer after maturity and thus extend the harvest period, and the better adaptability to feeding to some classes of livestock without threshing or grinding.

The minimum temperature for the germination of sorghum seeds is 45° to 50° F. and the minimum for subsequent plant growth about 60°. Well-advanced sorghum plants are killed by temperatures slightly below freezing. Newly emerged seedlings, however, have survived, in part, temperatures as low as 19°. Some young plants, 1 to 3 weeks after emergence, have recovered after freezing at temperatures down to 25°, but they were killed by a temperature of 21° under field conditions.

Sorghums are usually planted after the soil is warm and the danger of frost is over. The advantages of this practice have been demonstrated repeatedly in date-of-planting experiments. The growing season, therefore, is limited by the date of the first fall frost rather than by that of the last in the spring. In the United States the leading sorghum varieties normally require 100 to 120 days to mature, though some of the very early ones may be ripe in 80 days from planting. Since all sorgums normally are not planted until after the average date of the last frost in the spring, the grain types are generally not a successful crop where the frost-free season is less than about 160 days for most varieties, or 130 for the earliest varieties. Damage from fall frosts is minimized by proper choice of varieties and planting dates.

The optimum temperature for the growth of sorghum is not known, but the best yields are secured where the mean July temperature is 80° to 85° F., and high yields are seldom obtained where the mean July temperature is less than 75°. Sorghum plants have survived repeated exposure to air temperatures of 120° to 140° in a greenhouse in summer. Observations suggest, however, that maximum temperatures much above 100° are somewhat detrimental, especially when the plants are approaching the heading stage. The sorghums respond normally to Linsser's "law" regarding heat-unit requirements. According to this law (a modification of Livingston's law, discussed on p. 295), "The heat required to produce a given phase of plant development bears a constant ratio to the total positive heat units in a particular locality." It was found in experiments in three different localities [2] that sorghums ripened when almost exactly 53 percent of the total seasonal heat units above a minimum growing temperature of 50° had accumulated. In response to optimum date of planting sorghums follow Hopkins' bioclimatic law rather closely. Thus when the best date of planting in a particular locality has been established, the corresponding date for some other locality can be calculated by a consideration of altitude, latitude, and longitude.[3]

Sorghums are short-day plants; that is, heading and flowering are hastened by short days and delayed by long days. Most varieties from the Tropics when grown in the United States will not head because the days in summer are too long—14 hours or more of daylight

[2] VINALL, H. N., and REED, H. R. EFFECT OF TEMPREATURE AND OTHER METEOROLOGICAL FACTORS ON THE GROWTH OF SORGHUMS. Jour. Agr. Res. 13: 133–148. 1918.

[3] MARTIN, JOHN H., et al. SPACING AND DATE-OF-SEEDING EXPERIMENTS WITH GRAIN SORGHUMS. U. S. Dept. Agr. Tech. Bul. 131, 47 pp., illus. 1929.

in June. Locally adapted varieties, however, will head and mature grain even with days as long as 16 hours. In southern Florida, sorghums have been planted experimentally in the fall and then subjected to short days and moderate to relatively high temperatures. The result has been greatly restricted vegetative growth. On the other hand, the high temperatures of summer in the Plains States tend to increase the effect of the long days in delaying heading and in increasing vegetative growth. The plants grow taller there, and more leaves are formed. Thus, with favorable growing conditions, early-maturing varieties often grow larger in the North where the days are long than in the South.

The yields of sorghums vary greatly from year to year, depending mostly on temperature and moisture supplies and also on the distribution of moisture during the year. In the southern Great Plains very low yields or failure of grain sorghum may be expected when the precipitation during the crop year is less than 11–12 inches on sandy soils and less than 13–14 inches on heavier loam soils. The frequency of failure to produce grain is reduced by thin planting and wide spacing of rows or by planting drought-escaping varieties. Within certain limits each inch of rainfall above the minimum may result in an average additional production of 2 to 2½ bushels of grain under good cultural conditions.

In northwest Texas and elsewhere under conditions of limited moisture sorghum yields are closely associated with the quantity of water in the soil at planting time. Between planting and the heading period, the total rainfall seldom exceeds the water utilized by the crop plus run-off and evaporation from the soil. During the 5-week period from heading to flowering, sorghum requires a minimum of 0.1 inch of water a day for normal growth and 0.15 inch for high yields. Rainfall during this period is rarely equal to such requirements, so that some water stored in the soil is needed to produce a good crop. An inch of water saved by good cultural practices is nearly as effective as an extra inch of rainfall. Thus adequate tillage, both before and after planting, to destroy water-wasting weeds, often makes the difference between success and failure.

Sorghums respond well to the additional water made available by summer fallow. Milo, particularly, grows well on fallow on the heavier soil types in the southwestern Great Plains, where the grain yields have been increased 50 to 90 percent by fallowing. On very sandy soils or under a higher rainfall, benefits from fallow have been much less or even negligible.

Sorghums also grow well under irrigation in areas where the temperatures are sufficiently high and the growing season sufficiently long.

Climate and Cotton

By C. B. Doyle [1]

COTTON has peculiarities that make it exceptionally sensitive to weather conditions over a long period, and for that reason the effects of weather on production and quality have been studied probably more closely than they have in the case of any other crop. Much of what has been discovered about the hows and whys of this relationship is summed up in this article, which also deals with the broader aspects of climate in relation to cotton production.

[1] C. B. Doyle is Principal Agronomist, Division of Cotton and Other Fiber Crops and Diseases, Bureau of Plant Industry.

COTTON BELONGS to the botanical genus *Gossypium*, a member of the Malvaceae, or mallow family. Among its familiar relatives are the showy-flowered hibiscus, the hollyhock, the marshmallow, and the popular southern vegetable, okra, or gumbo. In its natural habitat cotton is a long-lived perennial, all of the known species being of tropical or subtropical origin. Its natural limits, therefore, are determined by climatic conditions favorable to the perennial habit of growth. With only a few exceptions these conditions are found within a zone extending north and south from the Equator to a line where the mean temperature of the coldest month is about 65° F., corresponding to about 30° north and south latitude. In the New World, wild species of *Gossypium* extend to central Florida and to the northern part of Mexico. Many local species of tropical America are different from those of the Old World.

In the Tropics cotton thrives generally as scattered plants in dooryards and also grows spontaneously in waste places under a wide range of climatic conditions. It is found growing as a perennial from humid seacoast regions to altitudes of 6,000 feet, including extremely dry areas in the more arid regions. Its original home is believed to be in the drier and more open parts of the Tropics, rather than in the forest regions where there is shade and higher humidity. Evidence of this is found in the failure of many efforts to plant cotton on a large scale in humid tropical regions. Such conditions cause excessive vegetative growth at the expense of fruit, and the plants are much more severely attacked by insect pests and diseases than in drier areas. Yields in humid districts usually are too low for profitable production (fig. 1).

Because of the great value of the cotton fiber for domestic uses, efforts were begun centuries ago to cultivate the plant and to extend the limits of production beyond its natural habitat. Through hundreds of years of selection by man, early-maturing forms adapted to

FIGURE 1.—A perennial cotton tree growing along the roadside in tropical Haiti. Cotton production by such plants is negligible.

production as annuals have been developed (fig. 2). Slow and primitive methods of separating the fiber from the seed by hand or by crude roller gins made progress slow at first. After the invention of the saw gin at the end of the eighteenth century, however, cotton cultivation expanded rapidly throughout the world, especially in the United States.

It has long been recognized that freedom from frost for a minimum growing and ripening season, an adequate supply of moisture, and abundant sunshine are the three climatic essentials for successful production. Many investigators have studied the problem of climatic limits for cotton, and the consensus of opinion has been that in general the requirements for successful commercial cultivation are: (1) A mean annual temperature of over 60° F., though where the distribution of rainfall, sunshine, and temperature is favorable, a mean of over 50° F. probably would be sufficient; (2) a frostless season of 180–200 days; (3) a minimum rainfall of 20 inches a year with suitable seasonal distribution—a maximum of 60 inches, or up to 75 inches, would not be excessive if distribution were favorable; (4) open sunny weather; areas recording "half cloudiness" annually have too little sunshine to be safe, and areas over three-fifths cloudy are unsuitable for cotton.

The range of successful production has been extended to areas with shorter seasons by breeding rapid-fruiting, early-maturing varieties, and by the use of improved methods of culture. At the present time cotton is successfully cultivated in the New World from the Equator to about 37° north latitude and to approximately 32° south latitude. The limit of cultivation has been extended in the Old World into the Ukraine to 46° or 47° N. and in Africa and in Australia to about 30° S. (fig. 3). Hundreds of cultivated varieties are now grown throughout the cotton-producing regions of the world. These varieties differ in plant characters as well as in length, strength, abundance, and fineness of fiber.

So widely has cotton become adapted to different climatic conditions in both hemispheres that planting and picking are going on in some part of the world practically every day of the year. In the United States cotton planting extends over a period of about 3 months, from late February or March to April or May. Picking begins in south Texas in June or July and progresses toward the more northern and western sections of the belt until California and Arizona have completed their harvest in January.

The full growing period of the annual types varies considerably. The fine qualities of extra-long staple like that of the sea-island and Egyptian varieties usually require about 6 months to mature, whereas the period for the improved upland varieties is only about 5 months.

The perennial cottons, on the other hand, usually have some open bolls on the plants throughout the entire year, though the bulk of the crop is produced in well-defined periods associated with the seasons.

The approximate dates of cotton planting and picking in the principal producing regions of the world for which data are available are shown in figure 4.

A more detailed discussion of the commercial types of cotton, the principal regions of production, and the soils and climate of the Cotton Belt of the United States is given at the end of this article.

FIGURE 2.—A high-yielding, annual, upland variety of cotton bred and developed in the United States. The leaves have been removed to show the heavy cotton production.

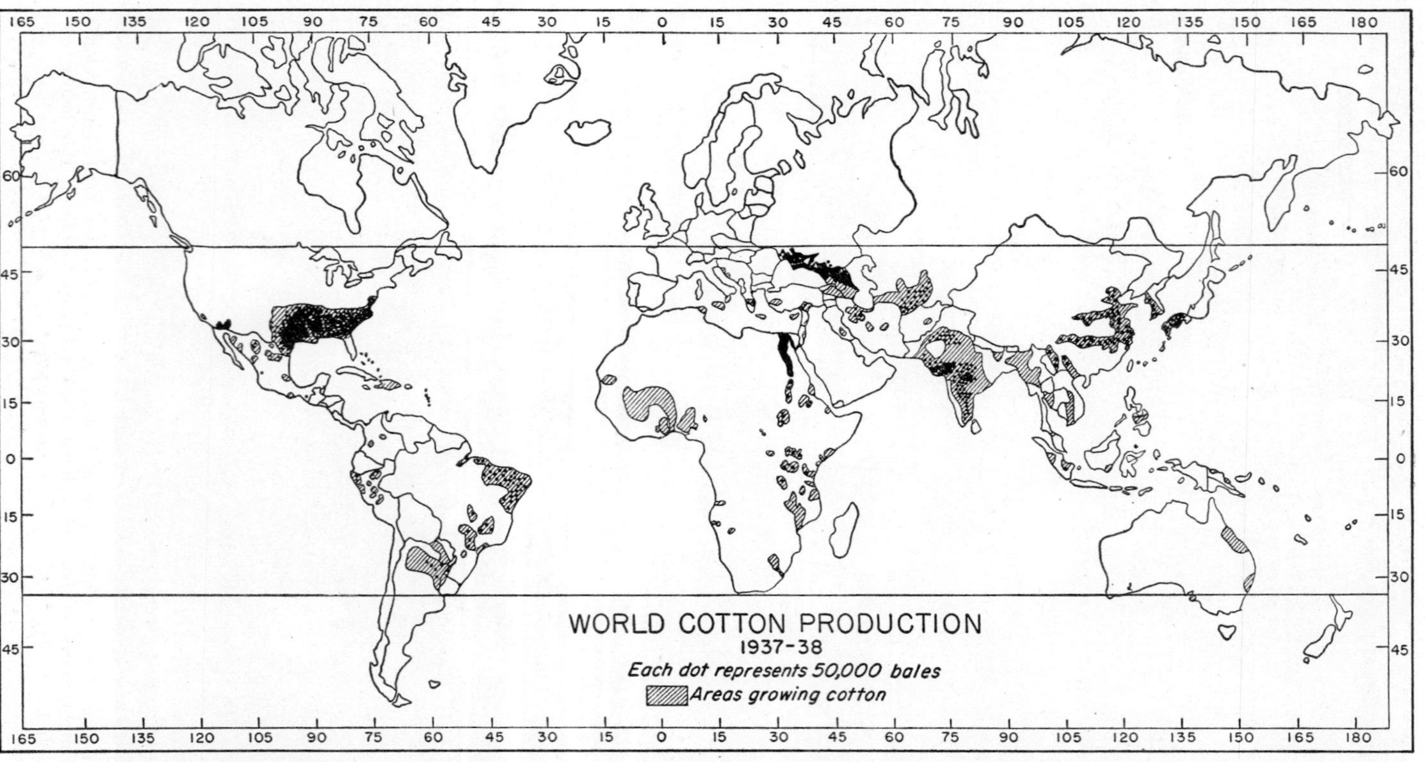

FIGURE 3.—Cotton-producing areas of the world. Horizontal lines indicate the climatic limits of cotton production.

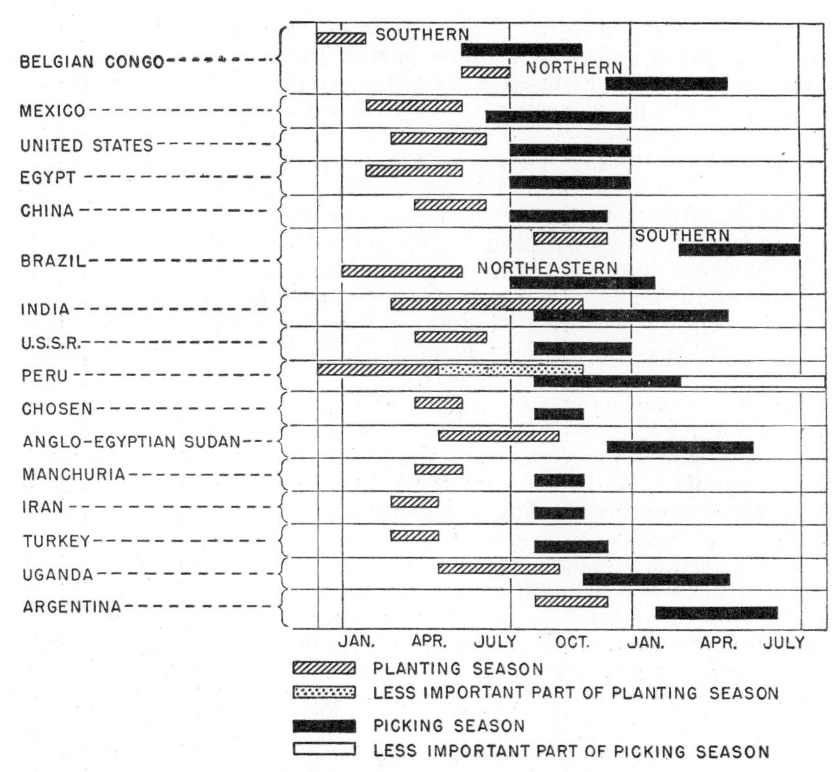

FIGURE 4.—Dates of planting and picking in the principal cotton-producing countries.

WEATHER CONDITIONS FAVORABLE FOR COTTON

In the United States the most favorable conditions for cotton production are a mild spring with light but frequent showers; a moderately moist summer, warm both day and night so as to maintain even and continuous growth and fruiting; and a dry, cool, and prolonged autumn. Cold weather with rain in the spring may rot the seed in the ground, retard the growth of the seedlings, or favor seedling diseases. Too much rain during the growing season causes the development of surface roots at the expense of the deeper roots. This results in wilting and shedding of leaves and bolls if the weather turns very dry in the summer. May and June particularly are critical months during which heavy rainfall, especially if accompanied by low temperatures, is very detrimental, not only interfering with cultivation but promoting the development of diseases and insect pests. A wet summer induces excessive vegetative growth, retards fruiting, and favors rapid increase of the boll weevil, while severe drought often stunts the plants, causes too early maturity, and reduces the yield. Sunshine is especially important when the plants are in bloom. As the cotton matures and the bolls begin to open, rainy weather is detrimental, as it retards maturity, interrupts picking, and discolors or damages the exposed fiber. Moderate rains in early September, followed by warm weather and a late frost, may permit the maturing of a late-season crop on the upper part of the plants. A rather wide daily range in temperature in a dry fall is also favorable to the maturing of the top crop as it checks vegetative growth.

RELATION OF CLIMATIC FACTORS TO YIELD

The literature on the relation of weather to cotton is now extensive, detailed studies having been made and reported by meteorologists, physiologists, botanists, agronomists, and other specialists in the cotton-producing countries. Yield, naturally, has been the important economic problem in these studies, and much has been learned about the effect of seasonal conditions on the factors that affect the growth and fruiting behavior of the plants.

The first essential to maximum yield is a full stand of plants. Heavy soil-packing rains at planting time frequently ruin stands, and in some localities moderate rains that cause the soil to crust result in loss of plants. Hailstorms are especially destructive to the crop at any time during the growing or harvesting season. In some seasons lightning also may be responsible for damage in many local areas, causing considerable loss for the Cotton Belt as a whole. Cold winds frequently devastate large areas of seedlings. Sandstorms or duststorms will "sand off" and kill seedlings in a few hours. These conditions are frequently encountered in the western Cotton Belt, where spring winds are severe.

Weather is also a vital factor in the incidence and severity of many insect invasions as well as of destructive diseases. As a rule these conditions are not general over the Cotton Belt, but they may be of great local or regional importance. In vast areas, lack of rainfall may prevent planting or the germination of the seed after planting. Scant moisture, combined with high winds, may cause the seed to germinate and dry out. Strong winds may also be responsible for extensive physical injury to the plant and may reduce yields. Cold, wet weather in the spring is conducive to the development of cutworm infestations, especially where there is a cover crop or litter on the land. Cold nights and hot days favor the cotton aphid, or cotton louse, which frequently does serious damage to the young plants.

The specialized fruiting habit of the cotton plant causes it to be readily influenced by both favorable and unfavorable weather conditions. This balance between weather and fruiting is so delicate that a relatively small proportion of the floral buds that are formed produce mature bolls. The others are thrown off, and this premature dropping of the "fruit forms" and young bolls is commonly called shedding. This may be better understood when the structural development of the plant and the rates of growth and fruiting are considered.

The plant has two kinds of branches, (1) vegetative branches, or "wood limbs," which normally develop on the lower six or eight main stalk nodes, and (2) the true fruiting branches, which come out immediately above them and bear the fruit. The vegetative branches do not bear bolls directly but function like the main stalk and put out fruiting branches of their own, which in turn form a fruit bud at each node.

The first flowers appear in ascending series on the successive fruiting branches up the main stalk on an average of about every 2½ days, whereas on each fruiting branch successive flowers appear on an average of about every 6 to 7 days. Thus the plant fruits in zones, with the formation of fruiting nodes on the branches up the main stalk about two to three times as fast as the succession of nodes on the fruiting branches.

With a plant as sensitive to changing weather conditions as cotton is during the fruiting period, this habit of progressive fruiting subjects the crop to the influences of seasonal conditions for a long time. The relative abundance of fruit or degree of shedding, the size of bolls, and the staple length and other qualities of the fiber are influenced by the seasonal conditions prevailing during the development of the fruit in each of the zones.

Shedding may occur at any time during the season and may be due to one or more of many causes, some of which are not clearly understood. Among the known causes of shedding are insect pests and diseases; abnormally high temperatures resulting in high transpiration and evaporation and consequent low soil moisture; heavy and continuous rain; abrupt changes in weather conditions from wet to dry, cloudy to clear, cool to hot, or the reverse of these; imperfect pollination due to rainy weather; root injury due to too deep cultivation late in the season, nutritional deficiencies, or other causes. It is recognized that shedding is closely related to the water supply of the plant, and it has been shown that the water requirements of cotton are largest when the plants are setting and maturing a crop. This is also the time when temperatures are highest and soil moisture lowest. Lack of sufficient soil moisture, therefore, probably is the principal cause of shedding. The phenomenally high per acre yields of cotton in the San Joaquin Valley of California and the El Paso-Rio Grande irrigation project in New Mexico and Texas are due chiefly to relatively moderate maximum summer temperatures combined with a controlled soil-moisture supply attained by irrigation.

Temperature and moisture conditions are usually more favorable to vegetative growth during the early part of the season than later. Hence the cotton plant may produce a large weed (rank vegetative growth) and set more flowers than it can maintain during the latter part of the fruiting season, when temperatures are higher and soil moisture is reduced. In many instances readily available plant food is used up when the fruiting activities of the plant make a more exacting demand on the nutrients and water supply. The plant then sheds its buds or young bolls, floral buds, and even leaves, until a point is reached where the remaining bolls can be matured under the prevailing conditions. Since this process of adjustment to changing conditions continues through the season, the amount of shedding varies from time to time and usually increases progressively as the season advances. Experiments have shown that even during seasons when soil and weather conditions are very favorable, a loss of 40 to 60 percent of the bolls by shedding is fairly common.

The advent of the boll weevil very materially shortened the effective fruiting period of the cotton plant and has complicated the effects of season and climate on production. The boll weevil population increases very rapidly as the season advances and the larvae develop in the squares and young bolls from eggs laid by the overwintered adults. The numbers increase so rapidly under favorable conditions during June and July that practically all of the buds developed after the end of July are apt to be destroyed. Because of the work of cotton breeders in developing rapid-fruiting, early-maturing plants, many of the best varieties now produce a reasonably large crop of squares and young bolls in advance of complete boll weevil infestation. Earliness is also favored by close spacing and the other cultural practices that the Department of Agriculture and the State experiment stations have worked out. The improved varieties and these cultural practices have shortened the effective fruiting period of the plants and have resulted in an increase in the average yield per acre in the main Cotton Belt in recent years in spite of the boll weevil.

Detailed cooperative studies designed to measure the comparative influence of geographic locations, soil types, seasonal conditions, and varietal differences on yields, fiber quality, and spinning value of cotton have been in progress. The study in the main Cotton Belt was made on 16 selected varieties grown at 14 separate representative locations, on the same block of land at each place, through 3 consecutive years, from the same stock of seed. In the southwestern irrigated valleys, 7 varieties at 4 locations were also studied in the same manner, 2 of these varieties being represented in all 18 locations.

There is definite evidence from these studies that weather conditions are highly important in determining the yield of cotton and in affecting fiber properties. Information was also obtained indicating that size of boll, lint percentage, and lint index, and the length, fineness, and other characters of the fiber are controlled rather closely by the genetic constitution of the variety, although material modifications in these properties were found under certain weather conditions. Certain other characteristics, including time required for seedling emergence, flowering, opening, proportion of four-lock bolls, yield, acre value, and color and maturity of the fiber, are greatly influenced by weather conditions, despite definite varietal differencies. Chemical analyses show also that the percentages of oil and protein in the seed differed rather widely among varieties but were affected almost equally by weather conditions.

In all of the characteristics studied it was found that varietal differences due to genetic constitution were the most important determining factor, although in certain cases the effects of weather were very great. A detailed examination of the relationships between daily precipitation and maximum and minimum temperatures, on either an average or a cumulative basis by growth periods, indicates clearly that these weather factors do not afford a basis for a critical estimate of yield or fiber quality. The failure to find a close correlation between precipitation and maximum and minimum temperatures with either yield or fiber properties indicates that the usual weather data do not provide adequate evidence for predicting either yield or quality. This is due to the effect of other important variables such as soil moisture, transpiration, and weather changes on shedding and other physiological processes of the plant.

Other studies of weather and cotton have provided information on certain specific relationships in the cotton plant. In Alabama it was found that moisture was the most important factor in determining staple length in a given variety. Detailed studies in North Carolina showed the important relation of length of day, temperature, and sunlight to the development of the cotton fiber in the young bolls.

Because of the great economic value of the cotton crop, changes in the weather during the growing season, and the probable effect of these on production are naturally matters of much concern. Millions of dollars have been spent in assembling detailed meteorological and field data in an effort to develop a dependable system of crop prediction. Much detailed information has been brought together over many years and carefully charted so that current combinations of weather, insect damage, disease, and other factors can be compared with the long-time records of these factors. With few exceptions the seasonal reports and estimates for the Cotton Belt as a whole have been remarkably accurate and only slightly at variance with the final reports at the end of the season. For more specific areas, however, crop predictions are much more difficult and hazardous.

For one thing, the presence of insect pests and diseases materially complicates crop predictions because of the varying amounts of damage done from year to year. Also the specialized habit of the cotton plant of fruiting over a relatively long period adds greatly to the difficulties of forecasting cotton yields from the weather. Varieties of cotton differ also in susceptibility or resistance to seasonal changes. Some are tolerant and show notable resistance to adverse conditions, but all varieties are sensitive to abrupt changes, which may occur in any season over large or small areas. Extreme drought, hot burning winds, or other stress conditions late in the season may turn a favorable crop prospect into almost a crop failure. Or an unusually favorable late season and a delayed frost may turn a prospective failure into a normal yield, or a normal yield into a bumper crop. The many combinations of these factors are so varied and uncertain that a practical method of crop forecasting with cotton, other than for wide areas, is a problem that still offers many difficulties.

EFFECTS OF EXPOSURE AND HARVESTING METHODS

In addition to the effects of weather on cotton yields, another factor of economic importance is the effect of exposure of the matured crop in the field before picking on the grade and market value of the lint. Cotton is bought and sold in the markets of the world on the basis of classification standards prepared and distributed by the United States Department of Agriculture. Grade as applied to cotton refers to the color and luster, or brightness, of the lint, the nature and quantity of foreign material present, such as dirt, leaf trash, etc., and the quality of ginning. If the seed cotton is in proper physical condition, that is, has the proper moisture content, good ginning will not damage the staple and will remove some of the dirt and trash. However, there is no way to improve the color or to restore the luster of the fiber when it has been lost by exposure of the open bolls to sun, wind, and rain for too long a time. Studies made by the Bureau of Agricultural Economics several years ago showed that cotton picked shortly after the opening of the boll is bright and

298737°—41——24

creamy but cotton picked late in the season, after long exposure in the field, is dull and blue. Enormous losses are suffered by American cotton farmers annually as a result of delayed and careless harvesting practices.

It is recognized that in years of bumper crops pickers usually are scarce and wages relatively high. Unfavorable weather during such harvest seasons brings heavy losses in both seed and lint that cannot be avoided. Low grades are more severely penalized and losses are greater in the long-staple cottons than in the short staples. Figures are available to show that over a period of 17 years (1915–16 to 1931–32 inclusive), the difference in central-market price for ⅞-inch staple between commercially high-grade white as compared with dull, grayed, or blue cotton was 3.04 cents a pound, or $15.20 per 500-pound bale. The price difference between the highest commercial grade and the lowest grade of white cotton was 5.13 cents a pound, or $25.65 per 500-pound bale.

Similar studies in Texas showed an average loss of 4 percent in grade after 4 weeks' exposure and a maximum loss of 14 percent in strength of staple. In all cases the cotton became darker and less creamy as the length of exposure increased, deterioration beginning within 3 to 5 weeks after the opening of the bolls. A drop of 4 or 5 grades, a decrease in length of one-sixteenth to three-sixteenths of an inch, and a decrease in price of 150 to 265 points, or $7.50 to more than $13 per 500-pound bale, occurred during exposure.

Excessively long exposure of cotton in the field is often responsible for much damage to the planting quality of the seed as well as for loss of value for milling purposes. The severity of the deterioration depends, of course, on conditions during the exposure. Continuous rains, heavy tropical storms, sudden drought that prevents normal maturity, and unseasonable frost have in some years destroyed or greatly reduced the viability and milling value of hundreds of thousands of tons of seed over wide areas in the Cotton Belt.

Enormous damage to the quality of the seed also occurs each year as a result of picking the cotton while it is green or wet from rain or dew and storing it without drying. Wet seed cotton or seed that is stored with too much moisture will generate heat, and the seed is soon killed or its quality greatly impaired by the stimulated activity of enzymes or of micro-organisms, which multiply rapidly under such conditions. Studies have shown that seed with a moisture content in excess of 12 percent should not be placed in ordinary storage unless provision is made for prompt drying. Air-dried seed probably can be stored safely for 18 months in ordinary dry storage. Experiments have shown that the seed should contain not more than 8 percent of moisture and should be placed in tight containers to prevent absorption of moisture from the atmosphere if they are to be stored for more than 2 years. Seed containing less than 8 percent of moisture may be kept in airtight containers in a cool place for many years without appreciable loss of viability.

If a bale of cotton is allowed to remain on the ground on the farm, in a gin yard, or in some other unprotected place, only a little moisture is required to start damage to the fiber in a few days of high temperatures. The exposed cotton is attacked by fungi, bacteria, and other micro-organisms that damage or destroy the textile utility of the cotton for varying depths in the bale. Investigations made by the Bureau of Agricultural Economics showed damage to the extent of 370 pounds in a 500-pound bale of cotton placed flat on the ground in the open with no covering for a period of 8 months. Another bale, placed on edge and turned over once a week, had 110 pounds damaged. A bale placed on end and not turned had 78 pounds damaged, and a bale placed on timbers off the ground and turned once a week had 49 pounds damaged. In contrast to this, in a bale that was stored in a warehouse during the same period, only 1 pound was damaged.

It has been estimated that losses in the United States to farmers and to the trade due to avoidable weather damage to baled cotton amount to several million dollars for each year's crop.

COMMERCIAL TYPES OF COTTON

The five important commercial types of cotton now produced throughout the world in the order of quality and spinning value of the fiber are sea island (*Gossypium barbadense* L.), Egyptian (*G. barbadense* L.), American upland long staple (*G. hirsutum* L.), American upland short staple (*G. hirsutum* L.), and Asiatic (*G. herbaceum* L., *G. arboreum* L., and other species).

Sea island is the aristocrat of cotton fibers. For more than a hundred years it was grown in the sandy loam soils in a rather well defined region in the humid coastal-plain districts of Florida, Georgia, and South Carolina where the equable climate was believed to impart a silky luster to the fiber not attainable elsewhere in the Cotton Belt. "Crop Lots" and "Fancy" sea islands grown on the islands and along the coast of South Carolina had a fiber 1¾ to 2½ inches long, the most valuable of the world's cottons, surpassing all other types in length, strength, and fineness. Most of the sea-island crop, with a staple of 1½ to 1¾ inches, was grown farther inland in Georgia and Florida and was known commercially as "Floridas" and "Georgias."

The average annual production of sea island in the United States was about 92,000 bales, of which the fancy grades represented about one-tenth. After the invasion of the boll weevil, about 1917, the production of sea island rapidly declined, and by 1922 it was practically abandoned in this country.

Sea island has also been successfully cultivated in the West Indies, and from 1922 to 1934 the production of this cotton was confined almost exclusively to the British West Indies and Puerto Rico. In 1934 recently developed strains of sea island better adapted to production under heavy boll weevil infestation were planted in the areas in the Southeastern States where this crop was formerly grown. During the past 3 years small plantings of these strains have been made also in the Gulf-coast regions of Alabama, Mississippi, Louisiana, and Texas and in other States. In 1939 about 1,700 bales were produced in the continental United States and about 750 bales in Puerto Rico. Including the approximately 4,000 bales produced in the British West Indies and elsewhere, the total world crop of sea-island cotton for 1939 was about 6,500 bales. The 1940 production in the continental United States was about 4,000 bales, with estimates of 1,000 bales in Puerto Rico and 5,100 bales in the British West Indies.

Egyptian cotton is similar to sea island in plant characters, and its fine, silky, strong fiber is second in value only to sea island. The production of Egyptian cotton is confined to the warmer arid regions where there is a long growing season and where irrigation is necessary. Egypt furnishes the bulk of the crop, averaging about 1,700,000 bales annually. Small quantities of Egyptian are also produced elsewhere in North Africa, in India, in the Union of Soviet Socialist Republics, and in Peru. In the United States the cultivation of Egyptian cotton is confined almost entirely to Arizona, where about 39,000 bales were produced in 1940. The staple of the Arizona Egyptian ranges in length from 1½ to 1¾ inches, whereas that of the bulk of the crop grown in Egypt is 1⅛ to about 1½ inches.

American upland long-staple cotton is grown chiefly in the United States and occupies a commercial position between the Egyptian and the upland short staples. The staple ranges in length from 1⅛ to 1½ inches and for some purposes competes with Egyptian. Upland long-staple cotton is produced in the fertile delta soils of the Mississippi Valley, in South Carolina and other Eastern States, in parts of Texas, and in the irrigated valleys of the Southwestern States.

American upland short staple constitutes more than 90 percent of the cotton crop of the United States. Including the production in foreign countries from seed introduced from this country, the American upland type in 1939 represented about 70 percent of the world's crop of 28,800,000 bales. The staple length of upland short staple varies from ⅝ to 1³⁄₃₂ inches, that of the great bulk of the crop—about 83 percent—being ⅞ to 1¹⁄₁₆ inches.

The Asiatic types of cotton are grown chiefly in India and China. The fiber of these cottons is short but strong and of rather coarse or rough texture. The staple is three-eighths to three-fourths of an inch long, with some of the improved strains producing ⅞-inch staple.

A perennial type of long-staple cotton known in the trade as "Tanguis" is grown in the irrigated valleys of Peru. The origin of Tanguis is somewhat obscure, but it is supposed to be a hybrid between one or more of the native Peruvian cottons and upland, Egyptian, or sea island. It produces a strong staple 1⅛ to 1¼ inches long or longer. The type is not well fixed, but the fiber is popular with spinners, and because of its resistance to the verticillium wilt, a fungus disease widespread in Peru, Tanguis now constitutes more than 80 percent of the total annual crop of that country, about 400,000 bales.

A large part of the cotton crop of Brazil comes from long-staple perennial tree cottons known as "Moco" and other kinds grown in the northeastern part of that country. Moco has a strong staple 1¼ to 1⅜ inches in length. Also, in the British West Indies small quantities of an indigenous perennial cotton called "Marie Galente" with a staple up to 1½ inches long or longer are produced annually, and in Haiti about 25,000 bales of cotton with 1⅛- to 1⅜-inch staple are produced annually from perennial plants.

PRINCIPAL REGIONS OF PRODUCTION

In 1939 the six major regions of cotton production in the world and their respective production were: The United States, 11,817,000 bales; India, 4,136,000; Union of Soviet Socialist Republics, 4,000,000; China, 1,900,000; Brazil, 1,996,380; and Egypt, 1,801,000. About 90 percent of the present world crop is produced north of the Equator. In 1939, of the world production of 28,800,000 bales, about 52 percent was produced in the Western Hemisphere, largely in the five countries Argentina, Brazil, Mexico, Peru, and the United States. About 43 percent of the world crop was produced in the United States during the 6-year period 1934 to 1939, inclusive, whereas in the 14-year period 1920 to 1933, inclusive, the United States had produced about 57 percent of the world crop.

Average acre yields in the principal cotton-producing regions vary considerably from year to year. In both Egypt and Peru cotton is grown entirely under irrigation, on fertile soils, and with favorable seasonal conditions. This is reflected in the relatively high average yields of about 500 pounds of lint to the acre. In contrast with this are the extremely low yields of 80–90 pounds per acre in India and in the Belgian Congo and Uganda in Africa. In India impoverished soils and frequent and severe droughts are responsible in large measure for the low yields, whereas excessive rainfall adversely affects yields in the two African regions. Yields range from 165 pounds per acre in Brazil to about 360 pounds in the Union of Soviet Socialist Republics.

Acre yields in the United States increased from a low of 157 pounds in 1930 to 270 pounds in 1937. The yield fell to 236 pounds per acre in 1938 and was 238 pounds in 1939 and 253 pounds in 1940. This increase has been due for the most part to planting on better lands, soil-conservation programs and acreage control, improved cultural practices, crop rotations and fertilizers, and the more general planting of pure seed of improved, high-yielding varieties. The highest State average yields are in the irrigated valleys of the Southwest, in California, Arizona, New Mexico, and adjacent regions in Texas. A bale or more to the acre is a common return. In California the State average was 648 pounds of lint per acre in 1939 and 749 pounds in 1940; yields of two and three bales per acre are common. The highest authenticated yield of cotton in the United States of which there is record was made in 1925 in the Coachella Valley of California, where four full bales of Acala cotton were produced on a measured eleven-twelfths of an acre.

Acreage, production, and average yields per acre of the 15 principal cotton-producing countries for 1937, 1938, and 1939 are shown in table 1.

TABLE 1.—*Cotton: Acreage, production, and acre yields in principal cotton-producing countries, 1937–38, 1938–39, and 1939–40*

Country	Acreage			Production			Acre yields		
	1937–38	1938–39	1939–40	1937–38	1938–39	1939–40	1937–38	1938–39	1939–40
				Bales [1]	*Bales* [1]	*Bales* [1]	*Lbs.*	*Lbs.*	*Lbs.*
United States	33, 623, 000	24, 248, 000	23, 805, 000	18, 946, 000	11, 943, 000	11, 817, 000	269. 9	235. 8	237. 9
Brazil	6, 010, 201	5, 666, 408		2, 074, 727	1, 989, 361	1, 996, 380	165. 0	167. 8	
Argentina	814, 671	840, 750	727, 727	237, 271	326, 959	362, 481	139. 3	185. 9	238. 1
Mexico	829, 342	633, 441	645, 494	340, 041	305, 946	310, 115	196. 0	230. 9	229. 6
Peru	387, 999	395, 000		415, 237	393, 372	413, 514	511. 6	476. 0	
India (excluding Burma)	25, 746, 000	23, 482, 000	21, 356, 000	4, 788, 000	4, 248, 000	4, 136, 000	88. 9	86. 5	92. 6
China (including Manchuria)	9, 300, 000	5, 580, 000		3, 600, 000	2, 300, 000	1, 900, 000	185. 0	197. 0	
Union of Soviet Socialist Republics	5, 163, 000	5, 108, 000	5, 190, 000	3, 700, 000	3, 800, 000	4, 000, 000	342. 6	355. 6	368. 4
Egypt	2, 053, 000	1, 852, 000	1, 687, 000	2, 281, 000	1, 728, 000	1, 801, 000	531. 0	446. 0	510. 3
Uganda	1, 759, 000	1, 530, 000	1, 574, 000	[2] 336, 686	[2] 255, 051	[2] 289, 000	94. 8	79. 0	87. 8
Belgian Congo	951, 335	980, 000		175, 261	161, 000		88. 1	78. 5	
Turkey	792, 541	680, 000		298, 566	306, 000	182, 179	180. 1	215. 1	
Iran (Persia)	636, 283			271, 023	184, 485		203. 6		
Chosen	546, 925	577, 294	620, 482	212, 834	187, 088	188, 948	186. 9	154. 9	145. 6
Anglo-Egyptian Sudan	443, 037	458, 111	426, 452	263, 718	263, 276	234, 106	284. 5	274. 7	262. 4

[1] 478 pounds. [2] Exports.

THE COTTON SOILS OF THE UNITED STATES

Cotton is grown on practically all well-drained types of soil in the Cotton Belt. Boll weevil infestation has altered the relative importance of finer and coarser textured types of soils, particularly in the Southeast. Though less fertile, the fine sandy loams, sandy loams, and loamy sands east of the Mississippi are generally preferred for cotton to the loams, silt loams, and clays because they allow earlier maturity of the plant and consequently avoid a part of the boll weevil damage that occurs on the heavier soils, where the plants tend to more vegetative growth and are later in maturing, especially in wet seasons.

Among the more important soil regions for cotton are: (1) The sandy loams of the Norfolk-Ruston soil associations of the sections of the middle and upper Coastal Plain that extend across the eastern Carolinas, central and southern Georgia, western Florida, and southern Alabama into central Mississippi, Louisiana, and east Texas; (2) the sandy loams and red clay loams of the Cecil-Appling soil associations of the Piedmont Plateau; (3) the alluvial soils of the Mississippi and other river bottoms in Mississippi, Louisiana, Arkansas, Tennessee, Kentucky, and Missouri; (4) the Memphis-Grenada soil associations of silty soils that occur on the loessial uplands or bluffs east of the alluvial valleys, principally in Mississippi and Tennessee; (5) the Houston-Austin-Denton and Wilson soil associations of the Blackland Prairies of Texas; (6) the Grundy-Shelby-Parsons and Summit-Bates soil associations of the eastern Oklahoma prairies; (7) the Houston-Austin-Denton soil associations of the Grand Prairie of Texas; and (8) the Zaneis-Renfrow, Miles-Vernon, and St. Paul-Abilene soil associations of the Red Prairies of western Oklahoma and north-central Texas.

In more recent years cotton production has extended into the High Plains of northwest Texas, where the Greensburg-Pullman-Richfield, Amarillo, and Zita-Pullman soil associations occur. The last 20 years have also seen cotton production extended into the hot, irrigated valleys of California and Arizona and into New Mexico and the adjacent region in west Texas at altitudes approximating 3,800 feet. The principal soils used are those of the alluvial bottoms and the Mohave-Reeves-Anthony associations in California and Arizona, and those of the Reagan-Springer and the Amarillo associations in New Mexico and Texas. (For a detailed description of the soils of the Cotton Belt, see the 1938 Yearbook of Agriculture, Soils and Men.)

THE CLIMATE OF THE COTTON BELT

The average summer temperature in the Cotton Belt of the United States is about 77° F. along the northern boundary. This temperature appears to be the requirement below which commercial production becomes unprofitable. In the southern portion of the belt the average summer temperature is 80° to 85°, and in the hot, dry, irrigated valleys of Arizona it reaches 85° to 90°. Along the northern margin of the belt the last killing frost in spring occurs, on an average, about April 10, and the first killing frost in the fall about October 25, so that the frostless season is about 200 days. In the southern portion of the belt the last killing frost in spring occurs about March 10, and the first killing frost in the fall seldom before November 25, the frostless season being 260 days or more. (See tables and maps in Part 5.)

The development of new, early varieties and improved farming practices have made it possible to extend production into western Oklahoma, west Texas, and the region known as the High Plains in northwest Texas on the cap rock of the so-called Panhandle. The elevation of the High Plains is about 3,200 feet, and the average frostless period is 180 to 200 days. The lands are level and free from stones and trees and are easily cultivated. With the use of power farm machinery, a farmer with the help of members of his family can care for 160 acres of cotton. Because of the limited rainfall a relatively small and uncertain production was expected in this region, but because of the high altitude the light summer rains are sufficient for the production of good crops. Fertilizers have not been required, and insect pests such as the boll weevil give little or no trouble there. The plants usually are small, and much of the crop is gathered by a method more rapid than picking, called "snapping," or pulling the cotton from the plants with the burs. In seasons of extreme drought a method called "sledding" or "stripping" has also been used. Special mechanical devices have been developed for the gins that handle cotton harvested in this manner.

During the period of scarcity following the Civil War, small quantities of cotton were grown as far north as Maryland, Pennsylvania, Delaware, Ohio, and other States, chiefly for homespun. In short seasons, however, the crop did not mature, and with the recovery of the cotton industry in the South, cotton growing in these regions was abandoned. In most seasons a good crop of bolls can be set, but the difficulty of getting the mature bolls dried out and open before frost makes cotton growing in these northern areas too uncertain to be profitable.

The average annual rainfall in the Cotton Belt ranges from 20 inches in western Oklahoma and northwestern Texas to 55 inches in western North and South Carolina and 60 inches in southern Mississippi. Throughout much of the belt it is between 30 and 50 inches. The spring rainfall ranges from 6 inches in western Texas to 16 inches in parts of Arkansas and southern Mississippi, being heavier in the Mississippi Valley States than in Texas or the South Atlantic States. Rainfall is somewhat greater in summer than in the other seasons, especially in the southern and eastern portions of the belt, reaching a maximum of 20 inches in southern Mississippi and parts of North and South Carolina, although in the Black Prairies of Texas the amount received in the summer averages only 8 inches. Autumn is the driest season of the year, practically all of the important cotton regions receiving less than 10 inches of rain during the fall months. This means favorable weather for harvesting the crop.

Climate and Tobacco

By W. W. Garner [1]

THE AUTHOR of this article describes the qualities of various kinds of tobacco leaf in such a way that a smoker can almost taste them. He shows how these qualities are affected by climate and weather, tells what is done to offset certain undesirable conditions, discusses the distribution of tobacco throughout the world, and gives examples of the conditions under which some of the finest tobaccos are produced.

[1] W. W. Garner is Principal Physiologist, in Charge, Division of Tobacco Investigations, Bureau of Plant Industry.

ALTHOUGH TOBACCO is tropical in origin, tobacco culture is world-wide. The plant is grown as far north as central Sweden at approximately 60° north latitude and as far south as southern Australia and New Zealand at about 40° south latitude. Production in Australia and New Zealand is relatively small, but large quantities are grown in various parts of all other continents. Except in Europe, the bulk of the crop north of the Equator, constituting more than 90 percent of the world total, is grown south of 40° N.

Foreign countries each producing 50,000,000 pounds or more annu-

FIGURE 1.—Distribution of culture of the principal commercial types of tobacco in the United States. Several factors are involved in this distribution, but fundamentally the most important are soil and climate in their intimate interrelationships. *A*, Cigar binder, U. S. types 51, 52, 53, 54, 55; *B*, cigar wrapper, U. S. types 61, 62; *C*, cigar filler, U. S. types 41, 42, 43, 44; *D*, southern Maryland, U. S. type 32; *E*, burley, U. S. type 31; *F*, dark air-cured and fire-cured, U. S. types 35, 36, 37, and 21, 22, 23, 24; *G*, flue-cured, U. S. types 11, 12, 13, 14.

ally are the Union of Soviet Socialist Republics, Greece, Italy, France, Germany, and Bulgaria, in Europe; India, China, Turkey, Japan, Chosen, Philippine Islands, Java (and Madura), in Asia; Canada in North America; Cuba in the West Indies; and Brazil in South America. Available statistics indicate that China, India, and the United States each produce roughly 1⅓ billion pounds of leaf and together account for considerably more than half the world output. However, in China and India tobacco is produced to some extent in nearly every province and is grown rather promiscuously under a great variety of climatic and soil conditions. Largely for this reason, the crop, with certain exceptions, lacks uniformity in type and quality, and only a relatively small portion is of commercial importance.

From the standpoint of international trade, only a few small centers of production in other countries are of outstanding importance for the high quality of their products. Striking examples are the east coast of Sumatra, extreme western Cuba, and certain small areas in Turkey and Greece, the products of which are later referred to in more detail. Among other foreign areas producing for export are the State of Bahia in Brazil, the Dominican Republic, southern Bulgaria, and northern Luzon of the Philippine Islands.

In the United States, tobacco culture is highly specialized, and the production of each of several important commercial types is definitely localized (fig. 1), owing primarily to the influences of climate and soil on the properties of the finished leaf.

Thus the tobacco plant can be grown successfully under a very wide range of climatic and soil conditions. On the other hand, the commercial value of the product depends laregly on the environment in which it is produced.[2]

In general, the present producing areas in the United States are easily able to meet commercial requirements for all domestic types of leaf from the standpoint of total output, but in each area there is the important problem of avoiding or minimizing harmful effects on the quality of the tobacco resulting from unfavorable climatic or weather conditions. This problem has been met in some instances by direct modification of climate in the field and in the curing barn, in others indirectly by application of appropriate cultural practices and development of control measures for diseases which are active only under certain weather conditions.

WEATHER AND THE GROWTH OF THE CROP

Much the greater portion of the tobacco grown in the world, including the entire production of the United States, is *Nicotiana tabacum*. In cooler climates this species usually requires a frost-free period of 100 to 120 days from the date of transplanting in the field to full maturity, but with a mean temperature of about 80° F. this period may be shortened to 70 or 80 days or slightly less. *N. rustica*, which is extensively cultivated in India and the Union of Soviet Socialist Republics, and to a lesser extent in China and other countries of Asia and Europe, is a more rapidly growing species and in cool climates can be brought to maturity somewhat in advance of *N. tabacum*.

[2] DUFRÉNOY, J. ECOLOGIE DU TABAC. Rev. de Bot. Appl. et d'Agr. Trop. 13: 114-123. 1933.

Before tobacco seedlings can be set in the field they must be reared to the proper size in coldframes or hotbeds, and this requires a period of 6 to 10 weeks. The seeds are frequently sown well in advance of the arrival of the spring temperatures required for germination. At 50° to 60° F. germination and growth are slow; the optimum temperature is about 75° to 80° and the killing temperature 95° or somewhat higher. Glass or cloth covers are used to protect the young plants in the seedbed.

Relatively early transplanting is generally desirable for several reasons. In northern areas, the normal period for transplanting is May 20 to June 20, and only occasionally are the young plants seriously injured in the field by freezing weather. Late planting may involve danger of serious injury from frost in the fall, to which the crop as it approaches maturity is quite susceptible, and also the crop cannot be properly cured in the barn after the arrival of very cool weather. In the South, unless the crop is set early the soil is likely to become so heated by the sun that the young plants are killed or permanently stunted.

Tobacco in the field grows most rapidly with a mean temperature of about 80°, but the crop eventually will reach full size at considerably lower temperature levels, though the leaf may not ripen normally. Temperatures above 95° on bright days may result in considerable burning of the leaf, especially during periods of drought. As indicated by the data in table 1, taken from United States Weather Bureau records, the range in mean temperature of the growing season from southern Wisconsin and the Connecticut Valley to northern Florida is from about 70° to 77°, and for the major, central belt the general average is about 75°. In the southern producing areas, the principal growing period includes a portion or all of April, May, and June, and a portion or all of July. In the central and northern areas the summer months and part of September constitute the principal growing period. In districts north of Maryland and Kentucky, when for any reason the tobacco is abnormally late in maturing, growers frequently harvest their crop before it is ripe to avoid danger of frost. Frost damage of serious proportions does not very often occur, however.

Frequent rains in the late winter or spring months make the preparation of seedbeds difficult, interfering especially with the process of soil sterilization. The soil of the seedbed needs to be well supplied with moisture at all times during the growth of the seedlings, though excess rainfall and humidity are conducive to damping-off and other diseases. Cool, wet weather greatly favors development of the dreaded blue mold (downy mildew) disease, though effective methods for control—spray and gas treatments—have recently been developed and it may ultimately be possible to produce disease-resistant varieties.

Sufficient rain at transplanting time is especially important. After a good rain transplanting is a comparatively simple operation, but during a drought it is necessary to water each hill by hand or machine. If the drought is severe successful transplanting may be impossible. In the meantime the plants in the seedbed may become so oversized and hardened that they flower prematurely when they are set in the field.

TABLE 1.—*Average monthly, seasonal, and annual temperatures and amounts of precipitation at various points in the tobacco-growing regions of the United States*

Month	Mean temperature					Mean precipitation				
	Hartford, Conn.	Madison, Wis.	Lexington, Ky.	Nashville, N. C.	Bainbridge, Ga.	Hartford, Conn.	Madison, Wis.	Lexington, Ky.	Nashville, N. C.	Bainbridge, Ga.
	°F.	°F.	°F.	°F.	°F.	*Inches*	*Inches*	*Inches*	*Inches*	*Inches*
December	31.0	22.8	35.8	41.6	52.6	3.44	1.72	3.77	3.43	4.00
January	28.3	16.9	32.9	42.8	52.1	3.53	1.63	4.18	3.50	3.89
February	27.0	18.7	35.4	42.4	54.1	3.34	1.50	3.62	3.77	4.57
Winter	28.8	19.5	34.7	42.3	52.9	10.31	4.85	11.57	10.70	12.46
March	37.3	30.4	43.7	51.4	60.8	3.58	2.08	4.32	3.59	4.35
April	47.5	45.6	54.3	59.7	67.6	3.55	2.54	3.50	3.51	3.78
May	58.8	57.6	64.3	69.0	74.8	3.41	3.66	3.91	3.87	3.20
Spring	47.9	44.5	54.1	60.0	67.7	10.54	8.28	11.73	10.97	11.33
June	67.4	67.3	72.2	75.2	80.6	3.13	4.01	4.05	5.56	4.84
July	72.9	72.0	75.9	78.4	81.9	3.57	3.80	3.65	6.57	6.53
August	70.4	69.8	74.5	77.5	81.5	3.84	3.15	3.45	5.17	5.74
Summer	70.2	69.7	74.2	77.0	81.3	10.54	10.96	11.15	17.30	17.11
September	63.9	62.3	68.5	72.0	78.3	3.48	3.08	3.07	3.40	4.09
October	53.4	50.0	57.4	61.3	68.1	2.97	2.32	2.59	2.86	2.32
November	42.0	35.1	44.8	49.9	58.5	3.04	1.76	3.34	2.19	2.23
Fall	53.1	49.1	56.9	61.1	68.3	9.49	7.16	9.00	8.45	8.64
Year	50.0	45.7	55.0	60.1	67.6	40.88	31.25	43.45	47.42	49.54

For normal rapid growth in the field, tobacco requires a liberal, well-distributed rainfall or its equivalent in irrigation water, for the water requirements of the plant are high because of its great expanse of foliage. The plant is very sensitive to defective drainage or waterlogging of the soil, however, and a liberal supply of plant food is essential to sustain the desired rapid growth. Thus injury from excessive rainfall takes the form of depletion of the plant-food supply by leaching on the light soils of the Atlantic Coastal Plain and of drowning of the plants and damage from soil erosion on the heavier inland soils. Severe drought, of course, may cause pronounced stunting of the plants, though most varieties of *Nicotiana tabacum* will successfully withstand drought for a considerable time without prematurely going to seed and, by making very rapid growth when rain comes, may eventually produce a good yield.

The extensive surface and tender nature of the leaves render the crop especially susceptible to serious injury or even destruction by hail and severe wind. With certain types of tobacco, too, a rain and wind storm, if sufficiently prolonged and occurring after the crop has reached an advanced stage, is likely to induce destructive epidemics of the wildfire type of leaf spot disease. A water-soaked condition of the leaf induced by strongly blown rain ordinarily is a controlling factor in susceptibility to the disease. If varieties of tobacco resistant to water soaking can ultimately be obtained, these should be resistant also to wildfire. Susceptibility to water soaking can be partially controlled also by suitable regulation of the nutrition of the plant.

In the tobacco-producing areas of Florida, Georgia, South Carolina, eastern North Carolina, and western Tennessee and Kentucky, the mean annual rainfall is 47 to 51 inches, in southern Wisconsin it is only slightly more than 30 inches, and in most other principal areas it is 40 to 45 inches (table 1). The heavier annual precipitation in the extreme Southeast is due primarily to a summer rainfall of about 17 to 19 inches, whereas in other regions, including southern Wisconsin, the average summer precipitation is about 11 to 14 inches. The western Kentucky and Tennessee district has a relatively heavy spring rainfall of about 14 to 15 inches, as compared with 8 to 12 inches for other tobacco-growing regions. Thus during the principal growing season of approximately 90 days the normal rainfall is about 10 to 13 inches in all principal tobacco-producing areas of the country except the extreme Southeast, where it approximates 15 to 16 inches.

In tobacco culture, very high yields, involving a rank type of growth, are incompatible with good quality. For some types moderately high yields are usually correlated with satisfactory quality, as in the case of cigar tobaccos, but for other types, especially those best adapted to the manufacture of cigarettes, relatively low yields are essential to the production of leaf of the highest quality. In this country the normal weather conditions in themselves are conducive to good yields in practically all the important producing centers, and normal differences in yield between these centers are due chiefly to factors other than climate, more or less correlated with differences in the types of tobacco produced. Seasonal variation in weather in a given locality, however, may greatly affect yield. For the United States as a whole, variations in yield due to weather usually do not exceed 10 percent of the normal yield of about 800 pounds per acre.

There are marked differences in average yields of tobacco among foreign countries, but in most instances these apparently are not due primarily to climatic factors but, as in this country, are related in part to the type of leaf grown. In Europe rather high yields are the rule except where culture of the small-leaved so-called Oriental or Turkish types predominates. In Asia high yields are reported from Japan and moderate yields from India and China. In other principal producing countries in Asia, as well as in Africa and South America, low yields are the rule.

WEATHER AND LEAF QUALITY

From the standpoint of quality of product, tobacco is remarkably sensitive to its environment, and as a rule the major problem of the grower is to obtain a crop of high quality rather than a large yield. The commercial requirements with respect to quality may be quite exacting, and they are also specialized and involve numerous elements. The requirements for one type of leaf often differ radically from those for another; the sort of leaf wanted for plug chewing, for example, is quite different from that desired for cigar wrappers. It is well known that foliage leaves of plants in general are sensitive to the environment in which the plants are grown, and these environmental effects, which would be of no special significance for most crop plants, may largely determine both the type and quality, or grade, of tobacco leaf, including the size, shape, color, venation, elasticity, combustibility, and the details of minute structure and chemical composition.

Within the range that favors reasonably rapid growth and development of the plant, temperature in itself is hardly to be regarded as a factor of major importance in determining quality. At lower temperatures, however, metabolic processes are slowed down and the leaf may fail to reach the stage of full ripeness necessary for the development of some of the properties that determine quality. High temperatures may contribute to development of aroma and to thickening of the leaf by reducing the water content of the plant.

Rainfall and humidity, by influencing the water relations of the plant, have a very important effect on various properties of the leaf contributing to quality. With an optimum water supply insuring full turgidity at all times and with other conditions favorable, a tobacco plant may develop 25 square feet or more of leaf area in a period of 60 days. Under these conditions, with optimum moisture content consistently maintained in the plant, the leaf produced will be relatively very large and broad but extremely thin, with fine veins, and loose, open structure or texture. Such a leaf when cured ordinarily will be elastic, light in color, and of bright luster, weighing perhaps only 2 to 3 grams per square foot of area; it will have a relatively low nicotine content; and when placed in bulk it will ferment very rapidly but develop only a weak aroma and contain little gummy or resinous matter. In addition to favorable rainfall and humidity, other factors contributing to these optimum moisture conditions include partial shade produced by sustained cloudiness or by other means, absence of wind, and soil conditions favoring retention of adequate moisture without impairing soil aeration, which is highly important.

When not too thin and flimsy, this sort of leaf is the ideal cigar-wrapper type, but it is not suited to other purposes. With progressive changes to less favorable moisture conditions there will normally be a tendency toward a corresponding reduction in size and narrowing of the leaf, largely compensated by increased density of structure and weight per unit of area, thickening of veins, decreased elasticity, deeper coloration with duller luster, increased nicotine content, a poorer or at least slower burn, and reduced power to ferment readily but definitely strengthened aroma and more gum and resin. Not all of these characteristics associated with suboptimum moisture relations are desirable in any of the various types of tobacco, but certain combinations of them, in which each is developed to the proper degree, are wanted in the cigar filler, cigarette and pipe-smoking, chewing, and snuff tobaccos. In other words, for best results each commercial type has its own water requirements.

In recent years research has made important advances in the fertilization and management of tobacco soils which serve to minimize the harmful effects of deficient or excessive rainfall on growth and quality of tobacco. It has been found that heavy potash fertilization and the use of limited quantities of chlorides in the fertilizer are both effective in increasing drought resistance. Organic matter in the soil has been shown to be highly important in its bearing on water relations, but it must be of the right kind. Certain weeds and crop plants preceding tobacco in the rotation are decidedly beneficial, while others are definitely injurious.

PRINCIPAL COMMERCIAL TYPES AND WHERE THEY ARE GROWN

To illustrate the correlation of water relations and type of leaf, some of the outstanding commercial types of tobacco and the conditions under which they are grown may be briefly described. It should be kept in mind that, in addition to climate, the variety of seed, the soil, and other factors are of importance in fixing the properties of the product.

On the east coast of Sumatra is grown a cigar wrapper that may be regarded as a world standard of excellence for the various elements of quality already mentioned, as well as for uniformity in grade, wide adaptability, and remarkable wrapping efficiency per unit of weight. The crop is grown on newly cleared soil laden with organic matter so that it has both a high moisture-holding power and ample aeration. The average monthly rainfall during the growing period (spring and early summer) is over 7 inches, and there are about 11 rainy days a month. The mean temperature is about 80° F. and the mean relative humidity 78 percent.[3]

In the Connecticut Valley and in the vicinity of Quincy, Fla., wrapper of the highest grade is also produced, but by means of a unique procedure for modifying the climate—namely, the use of a special type of open-cloth fabric for shading the plants. It has been found that the major function of the cloth tent is to reduce loss of moisture from the soil and the plant by increasing the humidity and reducing air currents.[4] The effect on temperature is negligible, and apparently the reduced light intensity affects the plant only indirectly, that is, by reducing transpiration.

In Pinar del Río Province of western Cuba—especially within an area of about 25 square miles south of the mountains known as Vuelta Abajo—there is produced what is universally conceded to be the world's finest cigar-filler leaf. In fineness and fullness of aroma and the smooth, satisfying property of its smoke, this product has no equal. The crop is grown on sandy loam soils closely resembling in many respects some of the soils of the Southern States. In contrast with the abundant rainfall in Sumatra, the normal monthly rainfall in the growing season (winter) is considerably less than 2 inches. The mean temperature is about 72° F.[5]

In portions of the Macedonia-Thrace region of Greece and in the Smyrna and Baffra-Samsun regions of Turkey the finest grades of the Turkish or oriental types of cigarette leaf are produced. These products possess a very fine, full, quite distinctive aroma, bearing in this respect somewhat the same relation to cigarette tobaccos that the Vuelta Abajo product of Cuba bears to the cigar type. The leaf grown in the Xanthi area of Greece is considered by many to be the very finest of all oriental types. The finest quality of leaf is grown on soil of rather low productivity occupying the slopes of the foothills of the mountains. The outstanding feature of the climate is the

---

[3] KUIJPER, J. METEOROLOGISCHE GEGEVENS OMTRENT DE OOSTKUST VAN SUMATRA IN 1930. Deli Proefsta. te Medan, Meded. (ser. 2), No. 70, 71 pp., illus. 1931.

[4] HASSELBRING, HEINRICH. THE EFFECT OF SHADING ON THE TRANSPIRATION AND ASSIMILATION OF THE TOBACCO PLANT IN CUBA. Bot. Gaz. 57: 257–286, illus. 1914.

[5] FASSIG, OLIVER L. RAINFALL AND TEMPERATURE OF CUBA. Trop. Plant Res. Found. Bul. 1, 32 pp., illus. 1925.

almost complete lack of rain during the last 2 or 3 months of the growing and developmental period of the crop.

The distribution of the various domestic types as shown in figure 1 cannot be explained on the basis of water relations alone, since other important factors, especially the physical and chemical properties of the soil and the variety grown, are involved. The interrelationships of soil and climate are so intimately concerned in the type of leaf produced that they can scarcely be considered as separate factors. However, yearly variation in rainfall, together with the associated conditions in a given locality, is a controlling factor in determining the grade or quality of leaf within a type.[6] In wet years the tendency is toward production of the sort of leaf described as favored by optimum water relations. In dry years the tendency is toward the production of a leaf smaller in size, thicker and more dense in structure, more gummy, more aromatic, less elastic, darker colored, of poorer combustibility, and containing more nicotine. Modifications in cultural practices, especially in the height of topping and in the method of suckering the plants, can be made in part to overcome the adverse effects of unfavorable seasonal weather conditions.

Generally speaking, rapid, uninterrupted growth throughout the season favors production of leaf of high quality. Nevertheless, a limitation of the rainfall during the early stages of growth is often advantageous in promoting root development and conserving the plant-food supply, although if dry conditions persist too long, subsequent rains, by causing extremely rapid growth, may produce an excessively thin, flimsy leaf. Rains following drought which has persisted up to the approach of maturity also may injure the quality of the crop by inducing a so-called second growth, or renewal of vegetative activity in the leaf. In general, only light, infrequent rains are desired during the ripening period. When curing is conducted at ordinary temperatures without the use of artificial heat, prolonged periods of high humidity may cause losses by decay or discoloration of the leaf. Judicious use of artificial heat has been shown to correct this tendency. After the curing is completed, a period of damp weather is required to soften the tobacco so that it can be stripped and graded without breakage.

[6] DARKIS, F. R., DIXON, L. F., and GROSS, P. M. FLUE-CURED TOBACCO. FACTORS DETERMINING TYPE AND SEASONAL DIFFERENCES. Indus. and Engin. Chem., Indus. Ed., 27: 1152–1157, illus. 1935.

Climate and Vegetable Crops

By Victor R. Boswell and Henry A. Jones [1]

THERE ARE probably more ways of getting around climatic handicaps in the case of vegetables than there are with any other crops; yet it is also true that climate is still the boss in vegetable production. This article discusses the general situation and then gives a considerable wealth of interesting and practical details for each of the principal vegetable crops grown in the United States.

[1] Victor R. Boswell is Principal Horticulturist and Henry A. Jones is Principal Olericulturist, Division of Fruit and Vegetable Crops and Diseases, Bureau of Plant Industry.

298737°—41——25 +

Although Mark Twain was doubtless right in saying that everybody talks about the weather, he was not entirely correct in asserting that nobody does anything about it. It is true that man can do nothing to change the weather, but he can do and has done a great deal to adapt himself and his agriculture to the weather of diverse environments. The group of plants loosely called vegetable crops contains many genera and species that are now being profitably grown in regions having weather very different from that in their native habitats. No other group of economic plants—except ornamentals—contains so many species that are being extensively grown out of their natural environment. Despite the fact that the native range of many of these plants appears to have been exceedingly narrow and their climatic requirements rather specific and exacting, their culture may extend over 20 to 25 degrees of latitude, from sea level to 5,000 or 6,000 feet of altitude, and over a considerable range of rainfall.

There are several reasons why most of the vegetable crops are more adaptable to extremes of latitude and altitude than are most field and tree crops.

Most important is the relative ease and cheapness with which seed can be produced in especially favorable locations and shipped any distance to the place where the plants are to be grown for food. The seed of many important vegetable crops cannot be produced successfully and economically in the areas of most extensive culture. Most of the 20,000 acres of spinach in Texas has in the past been planted with seed from Holland and Denmark and the extensive crop of Bermuda onions from seed produced in the Canary Islands and in California.

Again, many plants produce edible crops in such a short time that they can be sown somewhere in this country almost every month in the year and in almost every locality at some season and encounter climatic conditions favorable for food production if not seed production. By following the march of the seasons northward in the spring and southward in the fall, growers have vastly increased the geographic range of useful species. This purposeful and artificial adaptation of comparatively short-season crops to the shifting seasonal weather up and down the country, together with present-day incomparable transportation facilities, makes possible an uninterrupted year-round supply throughout the country of most of the favorite fresh vegetables. Long-season crops, biennials, and perennials are necessarily restricted to areas where the weather remains favorable for many months or throughout a period of years.

Finally, the relatively low cost of bringing most short-season vegetable crops to harvest and the opportunity for speculative operations encourage production in the face of hazards that would be far too great for most long-season and perennial crops. The probability of destruction of perennial crop plants by adverse weather at intervals of a few or even many years will discourage if not prevent planting in hazardous locations. Thus economic forces as well as biological factors play a part in determining the geographic limits of the culture of vegetable crops.

If potatoes, sweetpotatoes, and dry beans (sometimes classed as field crops) are included with other vegetable crop plants, the United States harvests about 8,500,000 acres of vegetables for sale annually, with a farm value in excess of $500,000,000. The portion of the crops moved to market by rail amounts to well over 500,000 carloads. No accurate figures are available on the amount hauled by truck, but it is conservatively estimated as equivalent to 200,000 to 300,000 carloads. In addition the value of vegetables grown in farm gardens for home use is estimated at $300,000,000.

REGIONS OF PRINCIPAL COMMERCIAL PRODUCTION OF VEGETABLES IN THE UNITED STATES

Although at least a few kinds of vegetables can be grown in home and market gardens at some season in every farming region of the country, most of the extensive commercial production has developed in well-defined areas with favorable climate or soil, or access to market, or some combination of these factors. Enormous developments have been made in some areas with very poor sandy soil where the favorable weather permits winter culture of crops of relatively high value. Certain crops, like cauliflower, need the modifying influence of large bodies of water to prevent extreme fluctuations in temperature; others, like the cantaloup, need low atmospheric humidity and an abundance of sunshine. Some other areas with poor sandy soil have become important despite a short growing season because they are close to good markets. Thus climate is only one factor that has determined the distribution of this huge industry, but it is so far the most important one.

Commercial vegetable production is most highly developed in—but not confined to—five major regions.

(1) Atlantic and Gulf region—a belt of variable width from Massachusetts to Texas, extending back from the coast 100 miles or more in the Middle Atlantic and South Atlantic States. This region is generally nonirrigated.

(2) The Great Lakes region—a broad and irregular area extending from upper New York State around the Lakes and up into Minnesota. This also is nonirrigated.

(3) Certain intermountain valleys in Colorado, Utah, and Idaho. These lands are generally irrigated except for dry-land beans and peas.

(4) The Rio Grande Valley of Texas—generally irrigated.

(5) Pacific coast and intermountain valleys of Arizona and California—generally irrigated.

Cool-season crops are grown throughout the Atlantic and Gulf region in suitable seasons. The warm-season crops too, except eggplant, pepper, sweetpotato, and watermelon, are grown very extensively from New York City northward as well as southward. The Great Lakes region is naturally best adapted to the cool- and medium-season crops, some of it being too cool or having too short a growing period for the definitely warm-season crops like sweetpotatoes and watermelons. The intermountain valleys of region 3 lie at such high elevations or latitudes that generally the warm-season crops are not extensively grown. Although the lower Rio Grande Valley, like southern Florida, is far enough south for the warm-season crops even in winter, much of the vegetable acreage is devoted to cool- and medium-season crops grown during periods unfavorable for their production in the North. The coastal areas and valleys of region 5 differ so much in climate, depending on topography and distance from the ocean, that they cannot be characterized by general statements. As almost all types of climate and soil occur in this region practically all crops, including some rather uncommon ones, are grown within it.

RELATION OF CLIMATE TO THE DISTRIBUTION OF VEGETABLE PRODUCTION

A rich sandy loam is considered best for growing most vegetable crops, but even those usually considered rather exacting in soil requirements are successfully grown on a surprisingly wide range of soil classes and types. In the East, for example, root crops are rarely grown on heavy soils, but in some western irrigated valleys carrots and other root crops are grown successfully on heavy silts and silt loams. Such results would doubtless be impossible in nonirrigated regions, but under irrigation a soil-moisture content can be maintained that permits suitable and timely soil preparation and cultivation, assures good stands, promotes continuous growth, and facilitates harvesting. Consequently it appears that the type and native fertility of the soil, while important, do not determine the geographic distribution of vegetable crops of high value. Within limits the suitability of a certain soil is determined largely by the weather and the resultant water supply.

Rainfall

Among vegetable crops only certain beans can be considered as definitely drought-resistant. All others require relatively large amounts of available water in the soil throughout the crop season. Commercial production is therefore confined chiefly to regions having either ample irrigation water or an annual rainfall of between 30 and 40 inches or more. More important than the annual rainfall is the 20 to 25 inches of rainfall required during the 6 months' growing season—a very rough figure since the efficiency of the water supply is dependent upon many factors. Dry lima beans and dry common beans are grown extensively as dry-land crops in certain favorable locations having no more than 15 to 20 inches of annual rainfall. Some of the onions and some spinach are also handled in this manner.

Despite an apparently ample annual rainfall over the central South and much of the Middle West, frequent serious droughts limit extensive commercial production of many vegetables. There is, however, rather widespread and extensive culture of sweetpotatoes, tomatoes, sweet corn, and melons throughout these areas.

Closely associated with rainfall is the factor of atmospheric humidity. Large areas in the Southwest, the Great Plains, and sometimes in the Corn Belt experience such low humidity and such drying winds in summer that normal development and fruitfulness are seriously retarded. Tomatoes, peppers, some kinds of beans, and other vegetable plants grown for their fruits or seeds may be barren for long periods because of damage done to the flowers by the hot, dry air. Even though they are tolerant of high temperatures, such crops must be planted so as to escape this weather as much as possible.

Although there is no deficiency of rainfall for the production of vegetable seeds in the East, seed growing is conducted predominantly under irrigation in the West. Certain seed-borne diseases are far less prevalent on seeds grown in regions of low humidity and with little or no rain during the season. Such regions also provide ideal conditions for pollination and setting of seed. Most important, however, is the absence of rain during harvesting and the ability to cure and thresh seeds in the open.

Temperature

In very few areas of this country is the commercial production of most common vegetables prevented throughout the year by adverse temperatures. The temperatures of the southernmost parts are favorable in the fall, winter, and spring if not in midsummer; and in the northernmost part except at high elevations nearly all vegetables except peppers, eggplant, watermelons, sweetpotatoes, okra, and the late-maturing varieties of squash and pumpkin are grown more or less extensively if other conditions are favorable.

Since the best prices are generally obtained when supplies of a given crop are meager, vegetable growers strive for exceptionally early or late harvests, depending on the time of the year. They try to avoid the peak production of their own or competing areas. Consequently there is a constant effort to push planting and harvest just as close to the limits of normal seasonal temperature levels as possible. Areas characterized by a gradual, consistent temperature rise in the spring and the reverse in the autumn, with a minimum of unseasonable, wide, and sudden fluctuations, are most favorable because there is less danger of early and late crop losses. While this is true for all kinds of farming, it is especially important for vegetable growers, to whom time of harvest is so vital. Regions at high elevations and those far removed from the modifying and equalizing effects of large bodies of water are generally more hazardous than protected valleys and coastal or lake-shore areas. It will be recalled that the greatest market-vegetable plantings are along the seacoasts, in the Great Lakes region, and in protected valleys. Since the time of harvest of crops grown for canning and freezing is generally not so important as good quality, high yield, and cheap production, heavy concentrations of crops for these purposes are found in some regions where very early or late planting designed to catch the highest market prices for fresh products would be too hazardous—as, for example, in the Corn Belt.

Since it is impracticable here to discuss the temperature requirements and responses of all the more than 30 commercially important vegetable crops separately, the following rough grouping is made.

A. Distinctly cool-region crops that prefer 60° to 65° F. and are intolerant of high summer temperatures (above a monthly mean of about 70° to 75°).

1. Very hardy crops that normally may encounter freezing weather in the field without injury.
   - (a) Cabbage and related plants: Cabbage, brussels sprouts, kale, turnips, rutabagas, kohlrabi, collards, sprouting broccoli, horseradish (a perennial).
   - (b) Spinach and beets.
   - (c) Parsnips.
2. Cool-season crops usually damaged by freezing weather.
   - (a) Cauliflower and heading broccoli.
   - (b) Lettuce.
   - (c) Carrots and celery.
   - (d) Peas.
   - (e) Potatoes.

B. Crops adapted to a wide range of temperature but not tolerant to freezing.

1. Crops adapted to monthly means of 55° to 75° and tolerant to frost under certain conditions: Onions, garlic, leeks, shallots.

2. Crops adapted to monthly means of 65° to 80° but not tolerant to frost or prolonged exposure near freezing.

(a) Muskmelons, cucumbers, squash, pumpkins.
(b) Beans, all kinds.
(c) Tomatoes, peppers (some varieties).
(d) Sweet corn.

C. Distinctly warm-region, long-season crops that are intolerant of cool weather (will not thrive below a mean of about 70° F.).

1. Watermelons.
2. Sweetpotatoes.
3. Eggplant, peppers (some varieties).
4. Okra.

D. Perennial crops: Asparagus, globe artichoke, rhubarb.

This article is not intended as a detailed planting calendar for all vegetable crops, and space cannot be devoted here to that subject. The interested reader is referred to Farmers' Bulletin 1673, entitled "The Farm Garden,"[2] which contains maps and tables showing the earliest and latest safe planting dates of the common vegetables all over the United States.

Length of Day

The length of the growing period, type of development, and time of maturity of a few common vegetable crops are profoundly affected by the length of the daylight period during growth. The culture of no species is precluded on account of adverse day length, although certain varieties of a few crops can be grown only in the North and others only in the South. Changes in photoperiod (length of daylight) are closely correlated with changes in temperature, thus confounding the effects of two quite different factors. For the United States as a whole, the periods of longer days are warm and those of the shorter days cool; but at high altitudes and in the far North, the temperature is relatively low despite long days. Conversely, in the lower South, temperatures are relatively high despite short days.

Spinach, onions, potatoes, and cucumbers are sensitive to day length, and the subject will be discussed in connection with these crops.

RELATION OF CLIMATE TO QUALITY

It is well known that, in general, market and eating quality of vegetable products is closely correlated with yield; optimum growth is usually accompanied by the highest quality, while any unfavorable condition that depresses yields is likely to impair quality. The harmful effects of drought and mechanical damage caused by storms are obvious. The direct and indirect effects of temperature and excessive moisture are not so generally appreciated.

Surprising as it may seem to some, it is difficult to grow most vegetables in midsummer in the South. The long season, the frequent rainfall in the humid regions, and the high prevailing temperatures are conducive to the intensive development of insect pests and plant

[2] Obtainable from the Superintendent of Documents, Government Printing Office, Washington, D. C., at 10 cents a copy. Do not send stamps in payment.

diseases. High temperatures speed up growth and maturity, causing the majority of vegetable plants to reach the harvest stage quickly and remain usable for only a short period. Harvesting must be prompt and the harvest period often short lest the products be past their prime and of inferior quality. After harvest, too, deterioration of the fresh product is much faster at high than at low temperatures.

In peas (*3*) [3] and sweet corn (*1*), for example, the maturing processes have been shown to be approximately doubled in rate by an 18° F. rise in temperature. Thus at 82° these products remain in good harvesting condition about half as long as at 64°. The difficulty of obtaining good quality and retaining it in such crops when they mature during hot weather is obvious. Even though they approach harvest in fine condition, a sudden and untimely hot spell can wreak havoc with many of them. Loss of sugars resulting from a high rate of respiration and the development of strong flavors follow even if no visible damage occurs. Lettuce is subject to tipburn (*27*), and other leafy crops such as spinach and cabbage lose their best flavor or become "strong" as well as less attractive at high temperatures. Even some warm-weather crops are subject to damage by excessive heat and sun. Tomatoes scald when exposed to the sun, and even beans may be damaged (*15*). The high summer temperatures of the Middle and Southern States retard optimum color development in tomatoes (*5*) and cause heavy zoning of the interior color of beets (*17*). Rain on ripening tomatoes is conducive to cracking (*11*).

The indirect effects of weather on quality through the ravages of insects and diseases may be even more serious than the direct effects. Defoliation diseases prevent the development of high quality in fruits of the tomato, pepper, muskmelon, cucumber, and bean even if moderate yields are obtained. Yields are usually curtailed or entirely stopped by serious damage by leaf diseases. Fruit and root troubles also take their toll.

In general the present varieties of most vegetables develop their highest quality in the cooler parts of the regions or seasons to which they are adapted. This is true probably because heretofore most of the breeding and selection work has been done in the more northerly part of the country, and consequently varieties have not been developed for southern conditions.

OVERCOMING THE LIMITATIONS OF CLIMATE

It was chiefly because of the great need for vegetable varieties better adapted to the Southeast that the United States Regional Vegetable Breeding Laboratory was established at Charleston, S. C. A comprehensive, cooperative vegetable-breeding program is now being carried on by this laboratory and the experiment stations in the Southeastern States.

In the North, especially in the high-plateau districts of the Rocky Mountains, the number of crops and varieties that can be grown is limited by the short growing season. Quick-maturing varieties of frost-tender plants are needed, and it is chiefly in this phase of the problem that the vegetable breeders at the United States Cheyenne Horticultural Field Station are interested.

[3] Italic numbers in parentheses refer to Literature Cited, p. 397.

Aside from breeding, various other means have been used for a long time to overcome the handicaps imposed by climate. Among these may be mentioned the growing of vegetables in the artificial climates of coldframes, hotbeds, and greenhouses. Starting plants in the field under hot caps or other kinds of protectors to extend the growing season is a common practice in many districts.

Irrigation has probably done more than anything else to extend the frontiers of vegetable production. What were sun-baked deserts at the turn of the century are now our most productive vegetable districts. Irrigation, however, cannot be given all the credit. Most of the irrigated districts are far removed from the large consuming centers. Perishable crops hauled from these production areas to the faraway markets during hot weather were subject to serious losses. Since the development of the modern refrigerator car with its regulated temperature, crop regions and transportation are so finely adjusted that fresh vegetables of all kinds are available to consumers almost everywhere throughout the year.

CLIMATIC REQUIREMENTS OF SPECIFIC CROPS

Since all the vegetable crops except certain beans require an abundance of water during the growing season, they will be discussed mainly from the standpoint of temperature relations, although moisture and other effects will be included whenever they are of special importance.

Very Hardy Cool-Season Crops

Cabbage

Cabbage is grown commercially to some extent in every State. Well-hardened fall cabbage plants will survive winter temperatures in the field as low as 0° F. for short periods if they are of optimum size for wintering-over. To survive such extreme cold, the young plants must be stocky and sturdy and have stems approximately the diameter of a lead pencil. Larger or smaller plants are less hardy, and the larger plants, if they survive, are likely to shoot to seed instead of forming heads in the spring (*4*). When cabbage is in an actively growing condition it is definitely nonhardy and will be damaged by sudden freezing.

Cabbage grows best at monthly means of 60° to 70° F. Grown as a midseason or late crop in the North and as a fall crop in the South, it encounters cooler weather gradually. It will approach the head stage slowly at mean temperatures of 55° to 60° and stand safely for many days at a mean of about 50°, which permits a long harvest period of good-quality cabbage. It will stand frost in the fall or winter in the head stage, but freezing then is generally destructive. When the monthly mean rises above 70°, growth is slow and abnormal, and the quality is usually poor.

Cabbage is a biennial and requires a dormant period at cool temperatures to bolt—initiate the flower stalks and flowers. In its native habitat this cool period comes during the winter after the first summer's growth and is followed by flower and seed production in the second season or year. In plants that have formed heads, exposure to a mean temperature of about 40° F. for 6 to 8 weeks will induce seed stalks (*19*), while in immature plants as little as 2 weeks of such temperatures will suffice if the stems are appreciably larger than a lead pencil. Thus the size of plants to be wintered over must be carefully controlled (*4*).

Spring-planted cabbage sometimes encounters late spells of weather sufficiently cool to induce seed-stalk formation instead of heading. Precautions should be taken therefore to grow strains and varieties less susceptible to bolting and to hold down plant size until danger of cold is past. The Early Jersey Wakefield and Charleston Wakefield varieties bolt less readily than most others, while Copenhagen Market and Golden Acre bolt very readily. If cabbage plants are kept continually at 60° to 70° F. they will remain vegetative for years, producing a succession of heads at the top of an ever-elongating stem that will reach a height of several feet (*19*).

The United States Regional Vegetable Breeding Laboratory is working in cooperation with State experiment stations to develop a high-quality, round-headed variety of cabbage that will stand winter culture in the Southeast without cold injury and will also be resistant to bolting in the spring. The present round varieties are not hardy enough for wintering-over, and they also tend to shoot to seed instead of forming heads after a long cool spell. The hardy, nonbolting varieties now available have pointed heads and are considered less desirable than certain round varieties for market.

Cabbage is much more susceptible to damage by the yellows disease (fusarium wilt) at high than at low temperatures (*29*). The more susceptible varieties are seriously damaged at lower temperatures than are the more resistant sorts. For example, a moderately resistant variety may show only 5 to 10 percent infection after 3 weeks at 59° F., while the same strain will be 100 percent infected in the same time when grown at 77° F. As the temperature rises, the damage is more severe in the infected plant.

Cabbage blackleg, a seed-borne disease, spreads rapidly from centers of infection during rainy weather (*28*). In order to hold blackleg infection to a minimum, most of the cabbage seed grown in America is produced under irrigation in Washington State, in a locality where temperatures are mild and rainfall and humidity are low.

Turnips and Rutabagas

The minimum, optimum, and maximum growth temperatures of turnips and rutabagas, root crops of the cabbage family, are rather similar to those of cabbage, but when immature the plants will tolerate short periods of chilling at a mean of about 40° F. better than cabbage. They are not so likely to shoot to seed prematurely. When they reach marketable size, mild freezing weather is less damaging to them than it is to cabbage.

Though the critical temperatures for these two crops are essentially the same, the distribution of extensive culture is quite different, because it requires about 4 months to produce a crop of rutabagas and only about 3 months for turnips. Since the latter reach market size quickly, they can be sown on either a rising or a falling seasonal change and still escape excessive heat or cold. Rutabagas, however, develop so slowly that they will generally encounter injuriously high temperatures if sown in either spring or late summer in the middle part of the country where the July and August means are above 75° F. Consequently rutabaga is grown chiefly north of the 75° isotherm for August, while turnips are grown in every State. Mean temperatures above 75° cause serious damage to the leaves of both crops, depressing growth or ruining the plants. In rutabaga, high temperatures cause the formation of undesirably long "necks" and poorly shaped roots. When sown in the spring a few varieties of turnip normally produce a few seedstalks by midsummer, but the Shogoin variety is a notoriously premature seeder. Insect pests are also especially severe on these crops during hot, dry weather.

Brussels Sprouts, Kale, and Collards

Brussels sprouts, kale, and collards, all close relatives of cabbage, are also characteristic of the species in that they will not tolerate monthly mean temperatures much above 70° F. Since they are hardy to freezing at the market stage (hardier than cabbage) and cool weather actually improves their eating quality, they are grown chiefly as fall crops. They survive the winter without protection from the Chesapeake Bay area southward and through the Gulf States. Kale and brussels sprouts are grown chiefly along the Middle Atlantic coast, and collards almost entirely in the South.

Sprouting Broccoli

Sprouting broccoli is not to be confused with heading broccoli; the latter is indistinguishable from cauliflower on the market. Sprouting broccoli, as well as some other closely related forms of Brassica, is grown for its large, thick, green, branching flower stalks terminated with massive clusters of flower buds. It is far less exacting than cauliflower and heading broccoli, being grown generally wherever cabbage can be grown. The mean climatic requirements are similar to those of cabbage. Commercial culture of sprouting broccoli is becoming general over the country, but it is produced chiefly in the five principal regions outlined earlier in this article. As the monthly mean temperatures go above 60° F., yields and quality are very seriously reduced.

Spinach

The most extensive plantings of spinach are in Texas, California, Virginia, Maryland, Pennsylvania, New Jersey, Oklahoma, and Louisiana, in approximately the order named. It is grown as a late-fall, a winter, and a spring crop.

Spinach is a cool-season plant that grows well at mean temperatures of only 50° to 60° F. and will tolerate subfreezing temperatures for many weeks after fall sowing. Seed for early spring crops in the Chesapeake Bay area is sometimes sown broadcast in late winter, on frozen, fall-prepared soil. Alternate freezing and thawing covers the seed. Small seedlings and plants approaching full size are distinctly less hardy than those that have developed a few good leaves at the onset of cold weather.

Knott (*14*) has shown that the interrelationships of temperature, length of daylight, and stage of plant development as affecting seedstalk formation and marketable plants are rather complex. Either high temperature or a long daylight period is conducive to seedstalk formation, a condition that makes the plant undesirable for either market or canning. The combination of high temperature and long days is most adverse for vegetative growth. If either factor is low, seeding is delayed. The response to either or both factors at a given time is dependent in part upon the previous history of the plants. For example, high temperature following low temperature during the early stages will have a more disastrous effect than would low temperature following high temperature. Thus sudden warm weather in the spring rather promptly terminates the vegetative growth of spinach wintered over or planted very early. For more detailed discussion of these relationships the reader is referred to the extensive studies of Knott (*14*).

High temperatures (70° to 80° F.) produce a less savoyed (crinkled) and less sturdy type of leaf growth and one of lower market quality than do low temperatures (55° to 65° F.).

Beets

Beets are grown for early (winter) shipping as bunched beets mainly in Texas and Louisiana and for the intermediate season in New Jersey. For canning, the crop is grown in summer, heavily concentrated in the cool districts of New York, Michigan, and Wisconsin.

The beet is normally a biennial, making only vegetative growth and an enlarged storage root in its first uninterrupted season's growth. If this is followed by a cool period of 40° to 50° F. or lower for 3 to 4 weeks, the plants will produce seedstalks upon resuming growth at temperatures of 60° to 70°. Young, immature beet plants that are exposed to more than about 2 weeks of temperatures appreciably below 50° tend strongly to form flower stalks instead of making the desired enlarged root. The plant's response to temperature depends largely upon day length, and the interrelations of these factors, together with the stage of development of the plant, are rather complex. Exposure to temperatures as high as 75° to 80° promptly after chilling tends to prevent seedstalk formation. Day lengths shorter than 12 hours retard seedstalk development, and those longer than 14 hours hasten it markedly, especially if the plants have been kept cool (40° to 50°) for a few weeks. Chroboczek (*7*) has reported extensive studies of these relationships, which space will not permit presenting in detail here.

As monthly mean temperatures rise much above 70° F. they retard growth and affect appearance, color, and texture unfavorably. The long days of the northern beet-growing areas usually do not induce premature seeding because the crops are planted late enough in the spring to escape the long cool spells that help induce it. There is normally little trouble with premature seeding in Texas and Louisiana, because the crop is planted to grow from warmer into cooler weather, the cool weather coming during the short days of late fall and winter which retard seeding. Although the beet withstands mild freezing, the roots cannot be wintered over even when rather small because they shoot to seed later. If the plants reach market size before they encounter cold weather, they will survive frost or mild freezing for some weeks, but they must be harvested before rising temperature causes them to bolt.

This habit of bolting after exposure to low temperatures is used to advantage in the production of the garden-beet seed crop of the west coast. Seed is planted in the nursery in the early fall, and sometime during the winter the stecklings are transplanted to the field. Following a prolonged exposure to low temperatures, practically all of the plants bolt to seed the following spring.

Less Hardy Cool-Season Crops

Peas

The garden pea (*Pisum sativum*), called English pea in the South to distinguish it from edible varieties of the cowpea, is less hardy than the crops discussed in the preceding section. The optimum mean temperatures for peas (about 55° to 65° F.) are probably a little lower than for cabbage, but peas are more seriously damaged by frost. Although the leaves and stems may not be damaged, slight freezing may injure or destroy the blossoms and pods. In most locations, a delay in harvesting resulting from freezing of plants, fruits, or pods will run the crop into still more adverse weather (hot or cold) before a profitable yield can be developed. A temperature as high as 80° for even a day or so is very destructive to cannery peas through its premature ripening effect, lowering the quality and also the yield.

Varietal differences in adaptability are partly the result of differences in the time required to make a crop. The early varieties like Alaska and Surprise develop rapidly and are well along toward harvest before harmful temperatures occur in the less favorable regions, while the late varieties may be so far short of the harvest stage when adverse weather occurs that they fail to make a crop.

There is a further varietal difference in tolerance to high temperature at any given stage of development. The Alaska, which is probably the most heat tolerant of pea varieties, is capable of developing a normal-appearing plant at temperatures that cause a definitely stunted, abnormal growth and low yield in such varieties as Perfection or Laxton Progress.

Although the geographic distribution of the pea and cabbage crops coincides generally, the growing of peas in each of the several regions must be carefully adjusted so as to avoid extremes of weather at either end of the crop season (*3*). Short periods of either heat or cold not damaging to cabbage can be disastrous to peas. The plants are also susceptible to diseases such as root rot, which are much exaggerated by excessive rainfall, and to the ravages of plant lice, which become serious in hot dry weather.

In some of the warmer pea-canning districts, such as parts of Maryland, Illinois, and Ohio, yields are far below those of the cooler pea-growing areas of New York, Wisconsin, Minnesota, and Washington. Even small returns are worth while under such conditions, however, because harvest is early enough to permit the planting of some other crop the same year.

The United States Regional Vegetable Breeding Laboratory has recently selected from certain hybrid lots of peas a few strains that are far more tolerant to cold than any market type now being grown. Although the blossoms and pods are destroyed by mild freezing, the vines are undamaged and will bloom again and yield a delayed crop. These new hardy strains are now (1940) being tested by the laboratory and a number of southern experiment stations to determine their probable value for commercial use.

Potatoes

Climate plays a very important part in potato production. The most successful culture is carried on in the northern tier of States where low temperatures prevail. Smith (*22*) found that regions north of the isotherm of about 70° F. for July produce higher yields than the warmer areas to the South, although good crops of early varieties are grown below the 70° July isotherm in the spring and fall when the temperatures are relatively low.

In no other vegetable crop has the influence of the various environmental factors been given so much study and consideration. Here it will be possible to refer only briefly to a few of the responses of the potato to climatic factors.

Richards (*21*) found slightly different soil temperatures optimum for potato plants at different stages of growth. The young sprouts in the soil made the most rapid development at a constant temperature of about 75° F., but later growth was best at approximately 64°. Soil temperatures above 75° caused excessive branching of the young sprouts, shortening of the internodes, decrease in segmentation of the leaves, and diminution in diameter of the stem.

The progressively lower tuber yields at higher temperatures are due to a reduction in the synthesis of surplus carbohydrate over that consumed in respiration. Under experimental conditions Bushnell (*6*) found a decrease in tuber production at constant temperatures above 68° and complete inhibition at 84° F. He suggests that under field conditions the temperatures giving complete inhibition may be somewhat higher.

The growing of certified potato seed is limited chiefly to the North and to high altitudes, where air temperatures are cool. Under these conditions mosaic symptoms are very distinct, enabling the grower to do effective roguing (removal of diseased plants). Where temperatures of 77° F. or higher prevail, mosaic-infected plants cannot be recognized and therefore are not removed, and the disease continues to spread. Seed produced in such areas will give a high percentage of mosaic plants when used for the commercial crop.

High-temperature injury to the tuber, known as heat necrosis, has been noted, especially on sandy soils where early crops mature during hot weather. It is most prevalent after the vines have died, leaving the soil unshaded.

Freezing injury to the developing potato plant is most common in the South, where the crop is grown during the winter or early spring. It may range from a nipping of the leaves to a killing back of the plant to the surface of the soil. When the latter occurs, new stems form from buds below ground. Varieties differ in their ability to recover from freezing injury; those able to send up new sprouts most quickly are favored if otherwise they are equally good.

In the North the late crop season is often cut short by frosts killing the vines prematurely. Occasional losses also occur from unseasonably hard freezes that injure the tubers in the soil before the crop is harvested, and freezing continues to be a hazard throughout harvest, storage, and transit.

The freezing point of the potato averages about 29° F., ranging from 28.5° to 29.5°. Potatoes exposed for several weeks to temperatures just above freezing turn sweet because of the conversion of starch to sugar, which accumulates. This makes them unpalatable when cooked and also causes an undesirable dark-colored product when the tubers are used for potato chips. The excess sugar, however, can be reduced by storing the potatoes for a time at 60° to 70°; at this temperature the surplus sugar is used up in respiration and by transformation to starch.

Richards (*21*) found that the injury caused by *Rhizoctonia* on the growing points of young potato shoots before they emerge occurs only at temperatures of 70° F. or below, being most serious at 54°. The amount of injury is dependent upon the rate at which the young shoots grow through the soil. Above 70° the rapid development of the growing point, together with the retardation in growth of the fungus, permits the tips of the young shoots to escape injury.

The potato plant also shows a remarkable response to length of daylight. Other growth factors being favorable, there is an increase in aerial stem elongation as the photoperiod increases. This is evident as one proceeds north, as well as under experimental conditions where daylight is supplemented by varying periods of artificial illumination. Werner (*30*) reports that a long day, high temperature, and an abundant external supply of nitrogen favor vegetative growth in all plant parts except tubers. Short days, low temperature, or a deficiency of nitrogen induce early tuberization. Days of intermediate length, low temperature, and an abundant nitrogen supply bring about maximum tuberization. With increase in day length or temperature or both, vegetative growth increased, whereas tuber formation occurred as these factors were decreased. Tubers were produced at temperatures commonly considered too high for tuberization by withholding nitrogen from the nutrient solution, and at even higher temperatures by use of a short—10½-hour—photoperiod.

Flower primordia (groups of cells that will develop into flowers) may be differentiated in well-grown potato plants placed in complete darkness (*12*), and no significant difference occurs in the number differentiated on plants exposed to photoperiods of 2, 4, 6, and 8 hours. Bud and flower drop is common in almost all varieties and is one of the most serious problems in a potato-breeding program because it prevents the production of sufficient quantities of seed. Recent experiments show that if daylight is supplemented by lamplight to get a total day length of 16 or 17 hours, much larger quantities of seed will be produced. This long "day" must be accompanied by cool temperatures and high relative humidity.

Formerly most of the potato pollinations were made in localities that satisfied these conditions, chiefly in northern Maine, northern Minnesota, and at Estes Park, Colo. But even in these most favored places, a few days of cloudy weather or unseasonable temperatures often caused flowers and buds to drop. To avoid these occasional unfavorable seasons, the potato breeders are now making most of their pollinations under greenhouse conditions, where the best temperature, humidity, and photoperiod can be provided.

A practice common among potato growers of western Europe is the exposure of thin layers of seed tubers to subdued light several weeks before planting. Such treatment develops short, tough green sprouts; but exposure of freshly cut seed to the direct rays of the sun at high temperatures for only a few hours may cause damage resulting in a considerable reduction in stand. If table stock is exposed to light sufficiently long to cause greening, a bitter taste develops, rendering the tubers unfit for food.

Potato production does not seem to be greatly influenced by atmospheric humidity except indirectly. The water supply of the soil, however, must be plentiful to provide a uniform and steady tuber growth. An uneven water supply may cause knobbiness, a condition that detracts from the appearance of the tuber and lowers the market value. A check in growth probably "matures" the tuber tissue except in the neighborhood of the eyes; this region proceeds to develop again under favorable growth conditions, causing the knoblike growths.

Poor stands and the accompanying low yields are often the result of decay of the seed piece in the soil. These poor stands can frequently be attributed to unsatisfactory healing (suberization) of the seed piece due to unfavorable climatic conditions at the time of cutting and planting. When the pieces are properly healed, a layer of cork cells is formed at the cut surface, preventing the entrance of various rot organisms. Probably the most common cause of improper healing is the drying out of the seed piece before planting. For instance, if seed is cut and allowed to stand for some time in a strong drying wind, the exposed cells die, the seed piece shrivels, and cork cells do not develop. The cut surface of the seed piece may dry hard and later crack, and when it is planted, parasitic bacteria and fungi may invade and destroy it. Seed pieces planted immediately after cutting will heal before the soil organisms have had an opportunity to invade the tissue, if favorable soil conditions exist. Essential for suberization are the presence of oxygen, high humidity, and a temperature of about 60°–70° F.

Under conditions of extremely high moisture, as in wet soils or very humid storage cellars, enlarged lenticels appear on the surface of the tubers. These detract from their appearance but do not predispose them to decay or impair their food value.

Although potato plants apparently thrive as well under the semiarid conditions of the West as in the more humid East, atmospheric humidity is of importance in that it affects the development of foliage diseases such as late blight and early blight. Of greatest economic importance is late blight, a serious fungus disease of the potato favored by cool moist conditions. This disease caused the Irish potato famine of 1845. Although now world-wide in distribution, the disease is limited within countries by climatic conditions. Martin (*18*) found that both rainfall and temperature are important factors in determining an outbreak of late blight and that for New Jersey July was the most critical month. Epidemics of late blight were experienced every year when the July temperature was below the average of 73.7° F. for the month and the rainfall above the average of 5.02 inches. In years when the July temperature was above and the rainfall below the average for the month, late blight was present in only 1 year out of 10. The variety Sebago, resistant to late blight, has now been introduced and is being increased for distribution. It should find favor in most districts where late blight is a menace.

In the national potato-breeding program, in which the Department of Agriculture and more than 30 States are cooperating, an effort is being made to develop varieties that produce good yields of high-quality potatoes under a somewhat greater range of climatic conditions than is now possible. Consideration is being given to the development of varieties that are drought-resistant, able to survive somewhat higher and lower temperatures than the kinds now grown, and resistant to various insects and diseases. In the South the spread of most of the virus diseases is more rapid than in the North because the climate is congenial to the increase and spread of the insects that transmit the diseases. Varieties resistant to a number of these diseases have been found, and where these are used there is no danger of spread even when climatic conditions favor the increase of the insect carrier.

Cauliflower and Heading Broccoli

Cauliflower is so exacting in its climatic requirements that commercial culture is limited to a few especially favorable areas. Furthermore, it is so sensitive to cultural and nutritional conditions that considerable experience and skill are required in producing it. Like cabbage it requires low mean temperatures (60° to 70° F.), but it is much less tolerant of extremes of heat or cold and other adverse conditions such as strong winds and an arid atmosphere. An appreciable check in the growth of young plants may cause them to "button," or form very small premature heads. The western crops reach maturity during the cooler half of the year with mean temperatures of 50° to 60°. High temperatures cause leafy, ricy, loose, or yellowed curds that are inferior in quality and appearance. Since cauliflower is so sensitive to extremes of both temperature and moisture, its culture is confined mainly to cool, mild, moist areas such as the coastal counties of California and Oregon, Long Island, and high altitudes in Colorado. Direct exposure of the curd to the sun's rays produces an undesirable brown pigment. Varieties of heading broccoli are usually well shaded by the small, incurving inner leaves, but certain varieties of cauliflower must have the large outer leaves pulled together and tied while the curd is still small to give adequate protection.

Carrots

The optimum mean temperatures for carrots are essentially the same as for beets (p. 382), but the distribution of the carrot crop is more localized and is somewhat different from that of beets. The carrot, like the beet, grows best at 60° to 70° F., but in the seedling stage it is more sensitive to extremes of high and low temperatures. Since it requires a longer growing season, it is more confined to areas with longer periods of mild weather and freedom from extremes of either heat or cold. While the beet tolerates repeated mild freezing at the market stage, the tops of the carrot are damaged somewhat, and their attractiveness for market is impaired.

Barnes (*2*) has shown the important relations of soil moisture to the size, shape, and color of carrots. He found the best color and highest carotene content at 50° to 60° (though yields were low) and the poorest at 70° to 80° F.; 40° to 50° was too cool for normal growth, and 70° to 80° too hot. Continuously high soil moisture results in an undesirably short, thick carrot having much lower carotene content and poorer color. Miller et al. (*20*) point out the adverse effect of excessive moisture upon the color of carrots. Other observers have suggested that low temperature was responsible for poor color in the case of fall carrots in the East and winter carrots in Louisiana, but Barnes' work indicates that wet soil is largely responsible.

All the California, Arizona, and Texas carrots, or about 70 percent of the acreage in the United States, are grown under irrigation. By proper water control, good color can be produced. Humid areas are at some disadvantage in this respect, although it should not be inferred that eastern-grown carrots are necessarily of poor color. In recent years considerable progress has been made in the development of strains that maintain good color even in districts where heavy rainfall prevails.

Lettuce

Although nearly every amateur gardener plants lettuce in his early garden, no matter where it is located, it should not be supposed that lettuce can be grown almost anywhere for today's rigid market requirements. Most of the trade demands the so-called Iceberg lettuce almost exclusively. The large, firm, crisp heads marketed as Iceberg appear to be all of the same variety, but in reality they are of a number of strains or varieties with different climatic requirements and tolerances. They have been bred for special adaptation to specific areas and seasons of production, chiefly in the West and Southwest. Although the several strains of New York and Imperial have different growing requirements, they all meet the same exacting specifications on the market and are indistinguishable by the layman.

The greatest proportion of commercial winter lettuce is grown in the Salt River Valley of Arizona and the Imperial Valley of California, with smaller acreages in Florida and adjoining States at temperatures of 50° to 60° F. The chief summer sources are the cool coastal areas of mid-California, Washington, and Oregon; high altitudes of Colorado and Idaho, where mean temperatures are 60° to 65°; and, to a lesser extent, the muck-land areas of upper New York State, at temperatures of 65° to 70°. As compared with that grown in the West, little lettuce is grown in the East except in New York and Florida. Varieties better suited to the temperatures of the East are needed, and considerable progress has been made toward this end in recent years.

The greatest expansion in the lettuce industry occurred after the new lands of the West were brought under irrigation. Cool temperature, low humidity, and irrigation water have each contributed to make the west coast and valleys of the Southwest the most favored places for lettuce production.

Lettuce, especially head lettuce, has a very narrow range of adaptability.[4] Slight differences in mean temperatures and the time a given temperature prevails may spell success or failure. The principal varieties do best at means of 55° to 65° F., although varietal differences exist within this range. Heading is prevented and the plants shoot to seed at temperatures maintained between 70° and 80° (*25*). It has been shown (*27*) that a daily mean as high as 70°, especially with high night temperatures, is conducive to tipburn. Cool nights are essential. Maximum day temperatures as high as 80° for a few hours are not necessarily harmful provided the daily mean is well below 70°. At a constant temperature of 70°, tipburn is serious (*27*). High temperature is also conducive to the development of a bitter flavor.

Small immature plants will tolerate mild freezing, but as they approach maturity, freezing damages the leaves and injures shipping quality.

Celery

Celery growing is one of the most highly specialized, expensive, and difficult of all vegetable enterprises. The very highly localized distribution of the crop is due largely to its particular soil requirements—it is grown chiefly on muck or peat soils except in certain irrigated areas of the West. In addition, celery is among the most exacting of all crops in its temperature and moisture requirements.

Fall-, winter-, and spring-grown celery is produced in important quantities only in California and central Florida. The midseason and late-summer crops are concentrated mainly on the muck soils of New York, Michigan, New Jersey, and Pennsylvania, with smaller acreages on the irrigated lands of Colorado, Oregon, and Washington.

Celery growing is restricted to a few suitable soils and is rather narrowly confined to those regions with a growing season during most of which monthly mean temperatures are between 60° and 70° F. Thompson (*24*) has shown in his extensive studies that chilling celery plants at temperatures of 40° to 50° for 10 days or longer is conducive to seedstalk formation instead of normal development. The older the plants are when chilled, the more promptly and completely they shoot to seed. Long chilling is more effective than short, and the lower the temperature of chilling (not freezing) the more plants will form seedstalks. Freezing the plants is not necessary to induce seeding and in fact is somewhat of a deterrent as compared with long exposure to about 40°.

Chilled plants will form seedstalks rather promptly if the temperature subsequently rises to 55°–70° F., but if higher temperatures (70°–80°) follow chilling, bolting will be prevented. Such high mean temperatures also prevent normal vegetative growth and the development of high quality. Under field conditions where celery is grown commercially, it is very unlikely that temperatures following prolonged chilling will be high enough to prevent bolting.

Thus the response to any specific temperature level depends on the age and condition of the plant, to what temperatures it has been exposed and for how long, and what temperatures it subsequently encounters. There are also marked varietal differences in tendency to bolt prematurely.

---

[4] For further information on specific varietal adaptations, see Farmers' Bulletin 1609, Lettuce Growing, obtainable from the Superintendent of Documents, Government Printing Office, Washington, D. C., at 5 cents a copy.

Crops Adapted to a Wide Range of Temperature and Frost Tolerant

Onions

The onion is grown practically everywhere in the United States at some season of the year, but extensive commercial production is confined to special sections that are particularly suitable. These include portions of the northern tier of States from Connecticut to Minnesota, the west coast, high altitudes of the Rocky Mountain area, and the southern parts of Texas and Louisiana. Fairly cool temperatures should prevail during the early stages of growth, and there must be a good supply of moisture since the soil in contact with the stem plate must be moist to initiate the development of new roots. During bulbing, harvesting, and curing, fairly high temperatures are desirable, and when harvesting and curing begin the humidity should be low.

The heaviest yields, as a rule, are obtained where cool temperatures prevail over a considerable time, permitting an extensive foliage and root development before bulbing starts. Outside the important onion districts the crop does not flourish, chiefly because the requisite cool growing season is too short, the temperatures soon becoming too hot or too cold for the best development of the crop.

Onion varieties are tuned to a rather specific set of climatic conditions. The late-storage varieties of the North, for example, do poorly in the South, and the extra-early varieties commonly grown in the South are ill-suited to the North. Certain varieties, however, may be grown rather widely, provided climatic conditions are similar in the different localities.

The climatic factors most important in determining the adaptability of onion varieties are temperature and length of daylight, or photoperiod. According to Magruder and Allard (*16*), the time when the onion plant will start to bulb is determined by the photoperiod and not by the age of the plant. The minimum photoperiod necessary to initiate bulbing differs among varieties, ranging from 12 hours for the extra-early varieties to about 15 hours for the late types like Sweet Spanish. Early maturity results from the ability of the plant to start bulb formation at short photoperiods and then to develop rapidly. In the North it is almost impossible to obtain good yields of the extra-early varieties by sowing seed directly in the field because seeding is usually done at a date when the photoperiod has already passed the minimum for bulbing. To secure large bulbs of the extra-early varieties in the North, it is necessary to sow seed early in a greenhouse or hotbed to have large plants for transplanting before the minimum photoperiod for bulbing occurs.

An onion variety may mature late because of a long photoperiod requirement, a slow rate of development after bulbing has started, or a combination of the two. These late types usually do poorly in the South because the photoperiod required for bulbing comes during extremely hot weather when sun scald, thrips, and pink rot combine to retard growth. Sweet Spanish, however, is able to produce fair crops because it is somewhat resistant to these troubles.

In central California a considerable acreage of the so-called intermediate crop of onions is grown. During the cool, short days of winter and early spring the plants usually make a large vegetative development. Bulbing does not begin in the spring until the hours of daylight reach the minimum for the varieties in question.

Temperature as well as day length plays an important part in determining the adaptation of varieties, the time of bulbing, and the date of maturity. Thompson and Smith (*26*), found that onion plants of the Ebenezer variety grown under ordinary daylight during winter and spring plus supplementary light till 10 p. m. did not react in the same way under different temperature conditions. The long day was begun December 3; by March 10, plants grown at 50°–60° F. showed no bulbing; those grown at 60°–70° had bulbed, and the tops had fallen but were still green; in those grown at 70°–80° the bulbs had formed and matured, and the tops were dead. However, high temperature alone was not effective in causing bulbing, because plants grown at ordinary day lengths at that season of the year failed to bulb at any of the temperatures noted.

In certain regions, especially in the high altitudes of the West, the photoperiod may be much longer than the minimum requirement, and still bulbing may be delayed because of low temperatures. This enables varieties with short daylight requirements to make considerable foliage development before temperatures are high enough to permit bulbing and explains at least in part why certain extra-early varieties produce well under long days in high altitudes and do poorly at the higher temperatures of the low altitudes under a similar length of day.

The effect of temperature on bolting is very pronounced, and in certain seasons losses to the dry-set and transplant crop may be severe. Thompson and Smith (*26*) found that when medium-sized sets of Ebenezer and Red Wethersfield onions were planted and grown in the greenhouse at 50°–60° F., both varieties bolted 100 percent; at 70°–80° there was no bolting; and at 60°–70° bolting did not exceed 10 percent. Length of daylight had no effect on the percentage of bolters. Some varieties bolt more readily than others; in areas where prevailing temperatures are conducive to bolting, varieties are selected that do not have this tendency.

Climatic factors have localized large-scale onion-seed production almost entirely in the semiarid regions of the West, partly because weather conditions are favorable to pollination and seed setting but chiefly because dry weather during the summer permits the harvesting, curing, and threshing of the seed crop in the open.

Various insect pests and diseases either appear in destructive proportions or are held in check, depending upon climatic conditions. Among the insects, thrips do the most damage. If the spring is warm and dry, the thrips population builds up rapidly and soon causes considerable injury. Relatively cool temperatures retard their development, while driving rains destroy many and help to hold the population low enough to prevent serious damage.

Breeding onions for thrips resistance is a major problem in which the United States Department of Agriculture and several States are cooperating. Plants are selected that have an open habit of growth, which eliminates protected areas between the leaves where thrips can feed and propagate and exposes them to unfavorable weather conditions and to the attack of predatory insects.

Most interesting is the regional limitation of onion smut by the temperature factor. This disease, prevalent in the North, has never been found in the onion-growing districts of Texas and Louisiana. Its absence cannot be explained on the basis of nonintroduction but must be accounted for by the temperature relations of the parasite. Under controlled conditions, a high percentage of plants grown in smut-infested soil (Walker and Jones) became infected at soil temperatures ranging from 50°–77° F., a decided reduction was noted at 80.6°, and there was complete freedom from the disease at 84.2°. In the South, onion seed is sown in late summer or early fall, and during the susceptible period, which coincides with about the first 3 weeks of the plant's life, the temperatures are sufficiently high to inhibit the growth of the parasite. Consequently infection does not occur.

Downy mildew is often very destructive to the onion-bulb crop of the North and to the onion-seed crop of the West. The disease is most prevalent and spreads most rapidly under conditions of moderate temperature and high humidity. The reproductive bodies (conidia) are produced in greatest numbers during rainy periods or when leaves and seedstalks are wet with dew. In breeding onions resistant to downy mildew the progenies are tested in localities that are most congenial for the development of the disease. One such place is in California near the southern end of San Francisco Bay. Here climatic conditions are ideal throughout most of the year for the spread of the disease, and there is very little opportunity for susceptible plants to escape infection. This provides an ideal place for the breeder to eliminate susceptible plants and select only those that are resistant.

Crops Adapted to a Wide Range of Conditions But Not Frost Tolerant

The group of fruit-bearing vegetable crops not tolerant to frost but otherwise widely adapted, of which either the seeds or fleshy fruits are eaten, includes quite diverse species: Beans, cucumbers, muskmelons, squashes, pumpkins, tomatoes, and sweet corn. Neither seeds nor plants of these crops should be planted in the field until all danger of frost is past—unless the grower is willing to take a big risk. Cold, wet weather, even though frost-free, is definitely harmful for all these crops, and they should not be planted until the monthly means have reached 60° to 65° F. A safe rule is to defer planting until the average frost-free date of the locality has been reached. In the humid parts of the country, none of this group thrive at monthly mean temperatures appreciably above 80°, probably

298737°—41——26

largely because of the severity of insect and disease attacks under such conditions. Muskmelons, however, thrive in the dry air of the Imperial Valley up into June, when the monthly mean runs from 80° to 90°.

Beans

The production of dry beans and snap beans will be considered separately because they represent two entirely different types of enterprise, conducted, for the most part, under quite different conditions.

Dry beans.—Practically all extensive dry-bean production is confined to areas of the country having a mean August temperature no higher than 70° F. East of the Mississippi most of this region lies north of the latitude of Boston, but in the Western and Pacific Coast States, high altitude or proximity to the ocean may keep temperatures down to the indicated level as far south as Los Angeles and San Diego. The total dry-bean production is about equally divided between the humid and the dry-land, or irrigated, areas. The dominant varieties grown in the East are different from those of the West, although there is some overlapping. Young (*32*) has presented a well-illustrated discussion of the geography of the dry-bean industry of the country.

Dry beans are usually the only crop grown in a year in a given field, but in California where winters are mild, some winter cover, seed, or forage crop may be grown in addition.

Practically all the dry lima beans, black-eyed peas, cranberry beans, and Pink beans are grown in California; Pintos in Colorado and New Mexico; kidney beans, pea beans, medium beans, and yellow-eyed pea beans in New York and Michigan. Climatic adaptations are largely responsible for this regional distribution of varieties. These several types (except lima beans, which need the highest temperatures) are not far apart in mean-temperature requirement, but they are quite different in water requirements and in tolerance to drought or excessive moisture and to daily maximum temperatures.

In the eastern part of the United States rainy weather at harvesting and curing time is an ever-present hazard. Much rain and damp weather retards proper curing and sometimes causes serious damage to the ripe beans. The western areas usually have favorable dry weather for harvesting and curing.

Snap beans.—Since snap beans for market are harvested long before the seeds or pods are ripe, less time is required to make a crop than for dry beans, and since there is no drying or curing to be done, occasional rains during the harvest period are no disadvantage—in fact, they are necessary to maintain yields through several successive pickings. Thus profitable production of snap beans (except for seed) is possible under many conditions and during short periods definitely unsuited to dry-bean production. "Early" varieties will make a crop in 8 to 10 weeks.

Instead of being highly concentrated in a few principal areas, snap beans are grown for market or canning or both in 25 to 30 States on 1,000 acres or more in each, except in the Great Plains area.

Because of the highly competitive and often speculative character of the late-fall, winter, and early-spring crops in the South, plantings are frequently made so that the crop is subjected for part of the season to temperatures considerably below the probable optimum safe range of 60° to 70° F.

Hot dry winds damage the flowers, reducing the set of pods; and warm wet weather encourages destructive diseases.

The best varieties of snap beans in the Southeast can be grown successfully only within comparatively restricted periods in the spring and fall because of their susceptibility to high temperature and disease. There is a pressing need for varieties with wider adaptability in the South, especially for home use in the summer. The United States Regional Vegetable Breeding Laboratory and cooperating experiment stations of the Southeastern States are working to obtain varieties resistant to heat and to the diseases characteristic of warm regions.

Muskmelons and Cucumbers

Muskmelons and cucumbers have a definitely higher heat requirement than beans. Though early varieties can be grown almost as far north as beans, being adapted to short warm summers, they cannot be grown unprotected in the open as a midwinter crop anywhere in the United States, as beans are grown in southern Florida. While 60° to 70° F. is indicated as the best range for beans, these other vine crops appear better adapted to 65° to 75°. Over most of the country they should be planted in the spring a few days later than beans.

Part of the muskmelon crop is planted in the Imperial Valley about December 1 for harvesting early in May, despite mean December and January temperatures of only 45° to 55° F. in the open. Artificial protection is provided as long as needed by paper covers over the seedlings and by sloping brush and paper barriers on the north sides of the rows. Temperatures under these shelters normally range from 75° to 80° in the daytime down to 40° to 50° at night. Mean temperatures in the open rise above 60° in March, after which no protection is required.

Muskmelons of the small netted type (cantaloups) are grown commercially more or less generally in the Middle and South Atlantic States and the Middle West as well as in Texas, Colorado, Arizona, and California, but the most concentrated acreage is in the irrigated Southwest. There the low relative humidity, high temperatures, and bright days combine to produce fruits with high sugar content, solid flesh, and coarse netting. The fruits mature on dry beds, and because of the absence of rain both foliage and fruit diseases are held to a minimum. In addition the Western States grow thousands of acres of honey ball, honey dew, and related types of melons that can be grown with consistent commercial success only in regions of low atmospheric humidity and rainfall. These types are especially susceptible to diseases that are promoted by high humidity.

Two of the most serious diseases of muskmelon are powdery mildew and downy mildew. The first is especially serious in the hot, dry Imperial Valley, where downy mildew is of no importance. Downy mildew is general and often serious in the coastal area of California and in most of the humid parts of the United States, especially the Atlantic and Gulf States. Muskmelon varieties resistant to powdery mildew have been developed by the Department of Agriculture and the California Agricultural Experiment Station.

The geographic range and total acreage of the cucumber crop are essentially the same as for muskmelons, but since heat is not so necessary the acreage distribution is somewhat different. The heaviest concentration of muskmelons is in the West and Southwest, whereas that of cucumbers is in the East and the Great Lakes States. Economic factors are of some importance, but climate also plays a part. The large slicing cucumbers for market are grown mainly from New York southward through the Atlantic States and westward through the Gulf States to Texas. The bearing season is usually cut short by disease. In the Middle Atlantic and Southern States, high temperatures and humidity appear to so favor the diseases at the expense of the host plant that the bearing season is too short to get generally profitable yields of the small, black-spine, pickling type, but it is long enough to get fairly good yields of the large, white-spine, slicing type. The black-spine varieties are definitely more susceptible to certain diseases and are not well adapted to the South.

The cucumber apparently is not very sensitive to the differences in day lengths and light intensities that occur under field conditions, but varieties show striking differences in response to day length when grown under glass in the late fall, winter, and early spring. Various abnormalities in ratios of pistillate and staminate flowers, unfruitfulness, or abnormal fruits may develop.

Tomatoes

The tomato is grown in every State in the United States and in neighboring Canada and Mexico. Though it will not tolerate frost and requires 5 or 6 months or longer from seed to harvested crop, it is grown successfully in many areas having no more than a 4 months' frost-free period. This is made possible by starting plants early under artificial protection and setting them in the field when danger of frost is past.

Tomatoes are grown unprotected all winter in southern Florida, in the lower Rio Grande Valley, and to a lesser extent in the Imperial Valley and the Yuma district where brush and paper protection is provided. They do best at monthly mean temperatures of 70° to 75° F. but are grown commercially at mean temperatures as low as 65° to 70° and as high as 75° to 80°. The crop is not adapted to monthly mean temperatures above 80° in either the humid or the irrigated regions (*23*).

In humid areas with temperatures above 80° F. disease soon damages the plants seriously, and in arid regions the excessive daily maximum temperatures and the low humidity damage the flowers, in some areas keeping the plants barren for weeks at a time. In the winter-garden area of Texas, spring-grown plants develop to a huge size and remain healthy but barren through the summer. They become fruitful early in the fall upon the return of less extreme daily maximum temperatures.

The crop cannot be grown profitably at mean temperatures that never rise above 65° F. It can be grown in southernmost Florida and Texas in midwinter at December and January means of 60° to 65° only because much of the development of the plants has already been made at temperatures of 65° to 75°. Foster[5] has shown in a striking manner the effects of different mean temperatures on growth and fruitfulness of the tomato. Although mean temperatures of 70° to 75° seem ideal under field conditions, a constant temperature of 75° in the greenhouse in the winter resulted in almost complete barrenness. Under conditions of ample light, a constant temperature of 75° probably would not be so harmful. In the Yuma district, with clear weather nearly every day, winter tomatoes under brush and paper set phenomenally large numbers of fruits at daily ranges of 45° to 80°.

Mean temperatures of 80° F. or above prevent optimum color development in the varieties now grown commercially. Loss of foliage from disease at high temperature and humidity is followed by sunscald of the fruit. Fruit of the best color is produced in the more northerly and the cooler western tomato-growing areas (*5*), although an acceptable color develops in other locations before the mean temperatures rise above 75°.

Very cool weather in the winter tomato sections, or other conditions that interfere with ovule fertilization and seed development in the fruit, commonly causes empty locules or hollow or "puffy" fruits (*10*). This trouble is doubtless related to nutritional conditions too, but it occurs chiefly in Florida, Mississippi, and Texas, where out-of-season tomatoes are so extensively grown.

There are two different wilt diseases of the tomato that are very serious—fusarium wilt and verticillium wilt. Sometimes the two occur together, but generally verticillium is worse in the cooler tomato-growing localities and fusarium in the warmer. Plant breeders of the Department and the State experiment stations have developed a number of varieties resistant to both forms of wilt. Among them are Pan America, Marglobe, and Pritchard (eastern varieties) resistant to fusarium, and Riverside and Essar (western varieties) resistant to verticillium. Work has recently been started to develop varieties resistant to defoliation diseases that are very destructive in the field in the humid parts of the country. Several State experiment stations have developed greenhouse varieties resistant to the fungus *Cladosporium*.

Peppers

Green peppers and pimientos are produced commercially chiefly in the Middle Atlantic, South Atlantic, and Gulf States and in California. Although early varieties are grown to some extent as a local market crop in the North Atlantic and Great Lakes States, the volume of production is small. Over 90 percent of the pimientos are grown in Georgia.

The temperature requirements of sweet peppers are a little higher than those of tomatoes; they are more sensitive to chilly, wet weather in the spring and a little more tolerant of the high summer temperatures of the South. Daily maximum temperatures of 90° F. or higher interfere with fruit setting, especially if the humidity is low. Constant temperatures below 60° or above 90° in the greenhouse during winter resulted in complete barrenness (*8*). Even if fruits set at mean temperatures above 80°, they are likely to be abnormal in size and shape (*8*). Those set at low temperatures (50° to 60°) are likely to be small and seedless.

The hot peppers, such as Tabasco and the various strains of Chili, appear to tolerate higher temperatures than most of the sweet varieties. In this country Tabasco peppers are grown chiefly in Louisiana, and the Chili types are grown almost exclusively in the Southwest, where they are a staple food crop of the Mexicans and Indians. The Chili types do best in a region of low humidity, like the Southwest, especially if they are to be dried.

[5] Data obtained by A. C. Foster, of the Division of Fruit and Vegetable Crops and Diseases, Bureau of Plant Industry.

Sweet Corn

The temperature, moisture, light, and day length required for optimum growth and development of sweet corn are essentially the same as for field corn (see the article by M. T. Jenkins, Influence of Climate and Weather on Growth of Corn, p. 308 in this volume), but a number of indirect climatic influences that are of little or no consequence in field-corn culture and utilization assume primary importance with sweet corn. In fact, they largely determine the distribution of sweet-corn growing and also definitely limit the distribution and utilization of the product after it has been harvested.

Factors that limit distribution.—Few Europeans or peoples of other lands have learned to like sweet corn as it is eaten in the United States; they consider that, like field corn, it is fit only for stock feed.

Despite the fact that temperatures, water supply, and light conditions are suitable, sweet corn is not commonly cultivated in the southern third of the United States, where field corn is grown extensively. Southerners relish "roasting ears" as much as anyone in the country, but few of them know the delights of good sweet corn. Most green corn grown in the South is of nonsweet, or field, varieties. The reason is that the very climatic conditions so favorable for corn are also ideal for the development of various enemies that seriously damage sweet corn but not southern field varieties.

Probably the worst of these enemies is the corn earworm. In the South many broods are produced each season, and there is such an abundance of other plants for it to feed upon that there is nearly always a devastating number of the creatures at hand when sweet corn is growing. Farther north the earworms are less numerous, and in the northern tier of States and New England they are of no importance. The corn earworm prefers sweet corn to other species of plants and to field corn. In the middle and lower South the ears of most sweet-corn varieties become so damaged by worms that they are useless for food. Other insects also are more damaging to sweet corn in the Middle States and the South than in the North.

Plant breeders in the South have made some encouraging progress in developing varieties resistant to the earworm. Experiment station workers in Texas have produced Surcropper Sugar and Honey June, sweet varieties that the earworm generally avoids. The Federal experiment station at Mayaguez, P. R., has produced U. S. D. A. 34, another resistant variety, and the United States Regional Vegetable Breeding Laboratory at Charleston, S. C., among other laboratories, is searching for more high-quality, resistant sweet-corn varieties for the South. The nature of the "resistance" is unknown, but it is believed to be due to some chemical substance in the plant that is repellent to the earworm.

Another factor that seriously limits sweet-corn culture in the warmer parts of the country is disease. Bacterial wilt is practically unknown in the northern tier of States but becomes serious in the Middle and Southern States. Many of the larger, later varieties of sweet corn are more or less resistant to bacterial wilt, but the earlier and higher quality varieties like Golden Bantam are highly susceptible. About 1933 the Bureau of Plant Industry and the Purdue University Agricultural Experiment Station developed Golden Cross Bantam, a rather early, high-quality, yellow hybrid sweet corn that is highly resistant to bacterial wilt. Probably more of Golden Cross Bantam is canned now than any other variety or hybrid.

Many Federal and State research workers have studied the effects of temperature on sweet corn in relation to rate of growth and to quality. There are distinct differences among varieties in their response to specific temperatures, some varieties probably being able to grow actively at a temperature as low as 50° F., while others appear to develop well only at temperatures of about 60° or above. In general, the larger, later kinds require not only a longer season of warm weather to reach the harvest stage than do small, early varieties, but also higher temperatures to make any growth whatever.

The total amount of heat above the minimum growth temperature required to bring any variety of sweet corn to the harvest stage is fairly constant for different plantings and fields in a given region and is characteristic of the variety. The development of the ear from silking to harvest is so closely correlated with prevailing temperature that if the silking date in a locality is known, the day to harvest the corn for highest quality can be predicted with a very high degree of accuracy. The time the ears will remain in good condition for eating or canning can also be predicted, thus enabling canners to be better prepared for handling the crop promptly at the proper stage (*1*).

Relation of climate to quality.—Since sweet corn is always harvested in a green, or immature, stage for food, its handling is subject to serious limitations. The extreme perishability of its eating qualities necessitates using it, or preserving it by canning or freezing, promptly upon attainment of the proper stage.

Formerly it was believed that there was something inherent in southern weather (aside from greater liability of damage by insects and diseases) that made it impossible to grow sweet corn of as good texture and quality as could be grown farther north. It was discovered, however, that the low quality of sweet corn in the South resulted from the difficulty of harvesting it at exactly the right stage of development and from the rapid rate of deterioration after it was harvested because of the high temperatures. The ripening process in the sweet-corn kernel consists chiefly in the conversion of sugar to starch, a chemical process that is very sensitive to temperature. The rate of the conversion is approximately doubled by a rise in temperature of 18° F. Thus in hot weather sweet corn matures so fast that a planting may remain in good usable condition (in the milk stage) for only a day or two, while in a cool region or at a cooler season it may remain equally good for 4 or 5 days.

After sweet corn is harvested the sugars change to starch very rapidly, lowering the eating quality. During hot weather, or if the corn is piled so that the heat of respiration is retained, nearly half the sugar content may be lost in a single day. Refrigeration will of course retard deterioration but is relatively expensive for such a bulky and low-priced crop as green corn. The impracticability of retaining satisfactory quality in fresh sweet corn over a period of several days has helped to prevent the out-of-season shipment of large quantities over long distances, as many other vegetables are shipped. The ravages of the earworm in the South have also worked against the development of large-scale production for shipping to northern markets.

Sweet corn is far more susceptible than field corn to moisture and cold during maturity and the ripening of the seed. It will mold in the husk and be ruined if left in the field to dry as field corn commonly is. Sweet corn for seed must be husked and dried under shelter as soon as it is ripe in order to retain viability and prevent mold.

Warm Region Crops

Watermelon

For best growth and quality, the watermelon requires a long growing season with high temperatures. This crop is not so markedly affected by atmospheric humidity as is the muskmelon. Watermelons with excellent flavor and shipping quality are produced in the humid climate of the Southeast as well as in the arid climate of the Southwest. Under humid conditions, however, foliage diseases are more destructive and cause greater fluctuation in quality and yield per acre. A small acreage in the Southwest is started under hot caps, but this practice is not so extensive as in the case of cantaloups. In a number of districts a strip of barley or rye is grown between the rows of watermelons at a right angle to the strong prevailing winds to prevent erosion of the sandy soil and to help hold a layer of warm air at the soil surface.

Hot weather is needed not only for the growth of the watermelon but also for a large market demand. In the North there is very little demand for watermelons until hot weather arrives.

Sweetpotatoes

The sweetpotato is of tropical origin and will not thrive in cool weather. The least touch of frost will kill the foliage, and prolonged exposure of either the aerial parts of the plant or the roots to temperatures appreciably below 50° F. will result in damage or destruction. The crop is of no commercial importance in regions of mean summer (June through August) temperatures below 70°, and except for the sweetpotatoes produced in the Maryland-Delaware-New Jersey area, most of the country's crop is produced south of the summer isotherm of 75°. No other common crop in the United States will stand more heat, and very few require as much. No farming area of the country is too hot or too hot and moist for it, although there are warm regions of the West to which it is ill-adapted for other reasons.

Sweetpotatoes are not transplanted in the field until the daily mean temperatures approach 70°, which in the eastern half of the country is about 4 weeks after the average date of the last killing frost. If sweetpotatoes are planted near the frost date, even if no frost occurs, the temperatures are too low for normal growth, and many plants die or fail to be productive.

It is notable that very few sweetpotatoes are grown west of the ninety-seventh meridian, which passes through the center of Texas. The crop is not adapted to the deep, heavy, high-nitrogen soils of much of the West, nor is it especially well adapted to culture under irrigation. Most of the sweetpotato acreage west of the Rocky Mountains is concentrated in the San Joaquin Valley. The areas adjacent to the Pacific Ocean are too cool for satisfactory growth, although the growing season is long. Most localities in the United States at elevations of over 2,000 feet have either too low mean temperatures or too short a growing season.

Our climate is so foreign to the sweetpotato that it normally does not flower and until recently was never known to produce viable seed in this country. Seeds of sweetpotato were formerly available only from the Tropics. Our short season, long summer days, and low temperatures prevent flowering and seed formation under normal field conditions. The Louisiana Agricultural Experiment Station has recently developed methods of handling the plants that result in profuse flowering and seed production, thus making possible large-scale plant-breeding work with sweetpotato in this country. In 1939 the Department initiated extensive cooperative breeding and adaptation investigations on sweetpotatoes with half a dozen southern experiment stations.

The sweetpotato has recently assumed new importance as a source of starch. For starch manufacture, the restrictions imposed on the crop by length of growing season and by mean temperatures are much more stringent than for growing for market. Since only low prices can be paid for sweetpotatoes for starch, they can be produced profitably for that purpose only in localities that will give large yields per acre at low cost. It now appears probable that culture for starch will be profitable only in that part of the South below the July-August mean-temperature isotherm of 80° F. Sweetpotato regions north of that not only have too short a season to produce the large yields essential for profit, but on an average the percentage of starch in the roots is a little lower.[6] Preliminary data indicate also that sweetpotatoes with a lower starch content are produced on the heavier types of soil.

Eggplant

Eggplant is a minor crop for which there is little demand in comparison with most crops discussed in this article. The restriction of its extensive commercial culture chiefly to Florida, Louisiana, Texas, New Jersey, and Virginia is probably largely due to economic factors and only in part to climate. This crop has a very high heat requirement, will not tolerate long periods of temperatures near freezing without damage, and is comparatively difficult to grow. It should not be set in the field when mean temperatures are below 65° to 70° F., since serious checking or stunting of the plants by cool weather may result in poor development and low yields for the season. In general its temperature requirements are similar to those of sweetpotato. It is equally sensitive to frost but seems to tolerate temperatures in the 40° to 50° range better than sweetpotato for short periods in the fruiting stage. Most of the growth of the "winter" crop of Florida is made in the fall before cool weather.

Perennial Crops

Asparagus

Asparagus is extensively planted in the hot interior valleys of the west-coast region, the upper Mississippi Valley, and along the Atlantic coast from Massachusetts to South Carolina. Along the shores of the Pacific and in high altitudes the seasons are either too late, too short, or too cool for production of the high yields necessary for profit, and commercial plantings are not found in these regions.

[6] Unpublished data obtained in cooperative investigations of the Mississippi Agricultural Experiment Station and the U. S. Department of Agriculture.

Low temperatures during the cutting season cause the spears to make a slow growth and impair the edible quality. Prolonged periods of low temperatures during growth cause an accumulation of purple or violet pigment in the spear, the color depending upon the variety. This pigmentation is especially undesirable in white asparagus for canning.

Asparagus is not adapted to the far South, according to Kimbrough (*13*), because insufficient reserve food is stored in the fleshy roots to produce a good yield. Instead of being stored, the food produced throughout the long growing season is used in the continual production of new shoots. Even during winter or early spring, a warm spell may produce growth of the shoots, and a later freeze may cause injury. The eating quality of spears produced in the South is excellent, but low yields and small size are the limiting factors in commercial production. High temperatures alone are not a barrier to profitable production. A considerable commercial acreage exists in the Imperial Valley of California. The excessive heat there in July and August seems to inhibit the production of new shoots, but water is applied to keep the tops green, and when temperatures recede somewhat in late summer a new flush of growth appears. After late August or early September irrigation is discontinued so that additional buds will not be forced into growth during the fall and so that the food manufactured in the green "fern" can be stored as reserves in the fleshy roots instead of being used in the production of new shoots. Thus in most irrigated regions the top growth can be controlled by the judicious application of water.

From experimental data, Culpepper and Moon (*9*) have estimated the length of time required for the asparagus shoot to grow in height from 4 to 10 inches at different air temperatures. At a mean daily temperature of 52.5° F. the time required would be 5.3 days; at 57.5° it would be 4.2; at 62.5°, 3.4; at 67.5°, 2.4; at 72.5°, 2.1; and at 77.5°, 1.9. These estimates show in a striking manner why regions with low growing temperatures are not suitable for asparagus production. The rate of elongation, of course, will vary somewhat with the variety, size of spear, soil moisture, soil fertility, and other factors, but temperature is the most important factor.

At exceptionally high temperatures the lateral branches develop early. Working (*31*) found that shoots of a plant growing at temperatures of 95° to 105° F. began branching when only 2 to 3 inches high; at 59° they reached a height of 30 to 40 inches before branching.

Strong drying winds are especially objectionable in regions where green asparagus is to be produced either for market or for canning, since they retard growth on one side of the spear. The resulting crooked spears make packing and bunching difficult and increase the number of culls.

Humidity does not seem to be a factor as far as growth and quality are concerned, for the crop thrives as well in the humid East as in the hot, semiarid valleys of the west coast. Under extreme drought conditions roots may draw moisture from soil levels as deep as 20 feet, which indicates that the plant will adapt itself to long, dry periods by foraging a great distance for water. Fleshy roots and crowns will tolerate submergence in water for a considerable period if the temperatures are fairly low.

In the Sacramento-San Joaquin Delta of California, the garden centipede, which has done considerable damage to the asparagus crop, can be controlled by flooding the beds for a period of 3 to 4 weeks in midwinter.

Besides controlling the centipede, flooding forces the asparagus from 10 days to 2 weeks earlier, and for this reason it has become a general practice on beds that are to be cut for early shipment, even when centipede control is not a problem.

Humidity is an important factor, however, insofar as it influences disease, though the only disease of economic importance is rust. The prevalence of rust is closely related to moisture conditions, a film of moisture on the plant being necessary for the germination of the rust spores. In regions where dew is prevalent throughout the growing season the spread of rust from plant to plant and field to field may be rapid. In the hot interior valleys of California the rust does not spread so rapidly because there is little or no summer rain, dew, or fog; the disease is therefore of minor importance there during most years except on young beds that are not cut and those in which production is discontinued early in the season.

Globe Artichoke

The globe artichoke is probably the most exacting of all vegetable crops with respect to climatic requirements. Commercial production is restricted to a narrow strip of land on the central California coast extending over five counties from Marin in the north to San Luis Obispo in the south. This maritime region, occasionally referred to as the fog belt, is the home of the artichoke industry of the United States and is the only district that produces a high-quality product. Having a cool, humid climate, tempered winter and summer by ocean breezes, it provides almost ideal conditions. Here the buds make the most desirable type of development; the bracts become thick and fleshy and fit together tightly, and floral development is slow, so that large buds of high edible quality are produced. Where adverse climatic conditions such as high temperatures, bright sunshine, and dry atmosphere prevail, the florets develop rapidly, the bracts spread outward, and the best edible stage of the buds is of short duration.

The rootstock tolerates considerable freezing and will survive northern winters, but the aerial portion is injured by temperatures a few degrees below freezing. Commercial production, therefore, must be confined to areas that are relatively frost-free. A light frost does not destroy the edible quality of the buds, but it causes the epidermis of the bracts to blister and peel and detracts from their appearance. Temperatures sufficiently low to kill the buds during the harvest season may delay harvesting for 2 to 6 weeks. If all growth above ground is killed, harvesting may be delayed 6 to 8 weeks.

Rhubarb

Because of climatic limitations rhubarb culture in the United States is definitely restricted to regions north of the Potomac and Ohio Rivers and to the coastal districts of California. The fleshy roots and crown of the rhubarb plant are very resistant to cold and desiccation. In the North they are usually in frozen soil all winter, and in California they may remain inactive in the soil throughout the hot, dry summer. The crop is suited to culture in regions that have alternating warm and cold seasons as in the North, or alternating cool-humid and warm-dry seasons as in California. The plants will not survive the hot, humid summers of the South. Temperatures of 25° to 27° F. will freeze the edible leafstalks and ruin the crop for several pickings. Cool temperatures favor the development of an attractive pink color, while at higher temperatures the green color is more pronounced.

LITERATURE CITED

(1) Appleman, Charles O., and Eaton, S. V.
1921. EVALUATION OF CLIMATIC TEMPERATURE EFFICIENCY FOR THE RIPENING PROCESSES IN SWEETCORN. Jour. Agr. Res. 20: 795–805, illus.

(2) Barnes, W. C.
1936. EFFECTS OF SOME ENVIRONMENTAL FACTORS ON GROWTH AND COLOR OF CARROTS. N. Y. (Cornell) Agr. Expt. Sta. Mem. 186, 36 pp., illus.

(3) Boswell, Victor R.
1929. FACTORS INFLUENCING YIELD AND QUALITY OF PEAS—BIOPHYSICAL AND BIOCHEMICAL STUDIES. Md. Agr. Expt. Sta. Bul. 306, pp. 341–382.

(4) ———
1929. STUDIES OF PREMATURE FLOWER FORMATION IN WINTERED-OVER CABBAGE. Md. Agr. Expt. Sta. Bul. 313, pp. 69–145, illus.

(5) ——— and others.
1933. DESCRIPTIONS OF TYPES OF PRINCIPAL AMERICAN VARIETIES OF TOMATOES. U. S. Dept. Agr. Misc. Pub. 160, 23 pp., illus.

(6) Bushnell, J.
1925. THE RELATION OF TEMPERATURE TO GROWTH AND RESPIRATION IN THE POTATO PLANT. Minn. Agr. Expt. Sta. Tech. Bul. 34, 29 pp., illus.

(7) Chroboczek, Emil.
1934. A STUDY OF SOME ECOLOGICAL FACTORS INFLUENCING SEED-STALK DEVELOPMENT IN BEETS (BETA VULGARIS L.). N. Y. (Cornell) Agr. Expt. Sta. Mem. 154, 84 pp., illus.

(8) Cochran, H. L.
1936. some factors influencihg growth and fruit-setting in the pepper (capsicum frutescens l.). N. Y. (Cornell) Agr. Expt. Sta. Mem. 190, 39 pp., illus.
(9) Culpepper, C. W., and Moon, H. H.
1935. composition of the developing asparagus shoot in relation to its use as a food product and as material for canning. U. S. Dept. Agr. Tech. Bul. 462, 24 pp., illus.
(10) Foster, Arthur C., and Tatman, Everett C.
1937. environmental conditions influencing the development of tomato pockets or puffs. Plant Physiol. 12: 875–880.
(11) Frazier, W. A.
1935. a study of some factors associated with the occurrence of cracks in the tomato fruit. Amer. Soc. Hort. Sci. Proc. (1934) 32: 519–523.
(12) Jones, H. A., and Borthwick, H. A.
1938. influence of photoperiod and other factors on the formation of flower primordia in the potato. Amer. Potato Jour. 15: [331]–336, illus.
(13) Kimbrough, W. D.
1936. asparagus investigations in south louisiana. La. Agr. Expt. Sta. Bul. 270, 11 pp.
(14) Knott, J. E.
1939. the effect of temperature on the photoperiodic response of spinach. N. Y. (Cornell) Agr. Expt. Sta. Mem. 218, 38 pp., illus.
(15) MacMillan, H. G., and Byars, L. P.
1920. heat injury to beans in colorado. Phytopathology 10: [365]–367, illus.
(16) Magruder, Roy, and Allard, H. A.
1937. bulb formation in some american and european varieties of onions as affected by length of day. Jour. Agr. Res. 54: 719–752, illus.
(17) ——— Boswell, V. R., Jones, H. A., and others.
1940. descriptions of types of principal american varieties of red garden beets. U. S. Dept. Agr. Misc. Pub. 374, 60 pp., illus.
(18) Martin, Wm. H.
1923. late blight of potatoes and the weather. N. J. Agr. Expt. Sta. Bul. 384, 23 pp., illus.
(19) Miller, Julian C.
1929. a study of some factors affecting seed-stalk development in cabbage. N. Y. (Cornell) Agr. Expt. Sta. Bul. 488, 46 pp., illus.
(20) ——— Cochran, F. D., and Garrison, O. B.
1935. some factors affecting color in carrots. Amer. Soc. Hort. Sci. Proc. (1934) 32: 583–586.
(21) Richards, B. L.
1921. pathogenicity of corticium vagum on the potato as affected by soil temperature. Jour. Agr. Res. 21: 459–482, illus.
(22) Smith, J. Warren.
1915. the effect of weather upon the yield of potatoes. U. S. Monthly Weather Rev. 43: 222–236, illus.
(23) Smith, Ora.
1932. relation of temperature to anthesis and blossom drop of the tomato, together with a histological study of the pistils. Jour. Agr. Res. 44: 183–190, illus.
(24) Thompson, H. C.
1929. premature seeding of celery. N. Y. (Cornell) Agr. Expt. Sta. Bul. 480, 50 pp., illus.
(25) ——— and Knott, J. E.
1934. the effect of temperature and photoperiod on the growth of lettuce. Amer. Soc. Hort. Sci. Proc. (1933) 30: 507–509.
(26) ——— and Smith, Ora.
1938. seedstalk and bulb development in the onion (allium cepa l.). N. Y. (Cornell) Agr. Expt. Sta. Bul. 708, 21 pp., illus.

(27) Thompson, Ross C.
1926. TIPBURN OF LETTUCE. Colo. Agr. Expt. Sta. Bul. 311, 31 pp., illus.

(28) Walker, J. C.
1922. SEED TREATMENT AND RAINFALL IN RELATION TO THE CONTROL OF CABBAGE BLACK-LEG. U. S. Dept. Agr. Bul. 1029, 27 pp., illus.

(29) ——— and Smith, Rose.
1930. EFFECT OF ENVIRONMENTAL FACTORS UPON THE RESISTANCE OF CABBAGE TO YELLOWS. Jour. Agr. Res. 41: 1–15, illus.

(30) Werner, H. O.
1934. THE EFFECT OF A CONTROLLED NITROGEN SUPPLY WITH DIFFERENT TEMPERATURES AND PHOTOPERIODS UPON THE DEVELOPMENT OF THE POTATO PLANT. Nebr. Agr. Expt. Sta. Res. Bul. 75, 132 pp., illus.

(31) Working, Earl B.
1924. PHYSICAL AND CHEMICAL FACTORS IN THE GROWTH OF ASPARAGUS. Ariz. Agr. Expt. Sta. Tech. Bul. 5, pp. [87]–124, illus.

(32) Young, H. N.
1931. PRODUCTION AND MARKETING OF FIELD BEANS IN NEW YORK. N. Y. (Cornell) Agr. Expt. Sta. Bul. 532, 203 pp., illus.

Climatic Adaptation of Fruit and Nut Crops

By J. R. Magness and H. P. Traub [1]

THIS ARTICLE covers the climatic requirements and the effects of weather for (1) the subtropical fruits—citrus (p. 402), date (p. 404), and fig (p. 406); (2) the deciduous tree fruits (p. 406), including apples, pears, peaches, plums, and apricots; (3) grapes (p. 411); (4) the small fruits—strawberries (p. 412), and raspberries, blackberries, dewberries, currants, gooseberries, cranberries, and blueberries (beginning on p. 413); and, finally, (5) the nut crops (beginning on p. 414), including pecans, walnuts, almonds, filberts, and chestnuts.

---

[1] J. R. Magness, Principal Pomologist, in Charge of Deciduous Fruit Investigations, prepared the parts of the article other than that dealing with subtropical fruits, which was written by H. P. Traub, Principal Horticulturist, in charge of Subtropical Fruit Investigations, Bureau of Plant Industry.

THE DISTRIBUTION of fruit and nut crops in the world is determined almost entirely by climatic factors, the most important of which is temperature. These crops can be classed in three groups, based on their climatic requirements.

(1) The strictly tropical fruits and nuts. This group not only fails to withstand freezing temperatures but may be injured by prolonged exposure to temperatures many degrees above freezing. Thus, the banana is reported to be well adapted only to regions where the temperature never goes below 50° F. The most important fruit crops in the group are bananas, breadfruit, mangoes, papayas, durians, annonas, sapotes, and mangosteens; the most important nut crops are coconuts, Brazil nuts, and cashews. Coffee and cacao, while not horticulturally considered fruits or nuts, are in the same group of plants from the standpoint of climatic requirements. Pineapples are adapted to only slightly cooler conditions than the other fruits listed. Space does not permit a more detailed discussion of the climatic requirement of these crops. None is grown extensively in continental United States. There is a limited production of pineapples and mangoes in Florida.

(2) The subtropical fruits. Plants in this group will endure temperatures slightly below freezing without injury. Included in the group are oranges, grapefruit, lemons, limes, kumquats, cherimoyas, avocados, litchis, jaboticabas, olives, figs, and dates. These fruits will withstand more cold than those in the first group and apparently require some cool weather for proper development—they do not grow well in strictly tropical climates. The trees bearing these fruits, like those of the tropical group, are characteristically evergreen, and none of them are sufficiently hardy to withstand severe freezing. The olive is probably the hardiest, and varieties of olive grown for their fruit are injured by temperatures below 10° F.

(3) The hardy fruits. These are produced on deciduous trees or bushes that during the dormant season go into a rest period, which it takes a period of cold weather to break. Most of them, while dormant, will stand temperatures far below freezing. Because of their requirement of a period of cold in order to develop normally, they are unadapted to tropical climates. The principal fruits of the group include apples, peaches, pears, cherries, plums, and prunes, grapes, apricots, blackberries, and raspberries. Strawberries are evergreen plants, only semihardy, which survive in cold latitudes because of their low growth habit and the protection of snow and other cover.

SUBTROPICAL FRUITS

The climatic belt where subtropical fruits are produced, as the name indicates, is between the true Tropics, where frost never occurs, and the belt in the Temperate Zone where normally the temperature often falls below freezing and stays below for a considerable part of the winter season. This intermediate belt is not confined within exact latitude limits; its boundaries vary owing to other factors that influence climate, such as land elevation, ocean currents, large inland bodies of water, and the protection of mountain ranges. Within this belt are two general types of climate—humid and semiarid. In this brief summary the citrus fruits, the date, and the fig are considered as typical examples of subtropical fruits.

Citrus

The citrus fruits, including the familiar sweet orange, grapefruit, lemon, and lime, are cultivated in both humid and semiarid regions and are interesting from the standpoint of climatic requirements for successful commercial culture.

Temperature Requirements

The reports of Girton (*25*),[2] Fawcett (*21*), and Camp, Mowry, and Loucks (*10*) on temperature requirements of citrus, based mainly on seed-germination or seedling-emergence experiments, indicate that while the so-called zero growth temperature, or vital temperature, for citrus—the lowest temperature at which growth can take place at all—is in the neighborhood of 55° F., and the maximum temperature at which growth can take place is approximately 100°, the optimum for growth ranges between about 73° and 91° for sweet orange, and 79° and 91° for sour orange. On the basis of these results, Webber (*62*) has pointed out that 55° may be considered as the correct zero growth temperature for citrus, with slight differences for individuals, types, species, varieties, and varying physical conditions. Webber has reported average annual indices of heat units available to citrus during the growing period from March to November under California conditions, based on the sum of all the mean daily temperature readings above 55°. He points out that the Washington Navel orange reaches its best development in sections with indices from March to November of 3,000 to 3,500 degree-days, and is less satisfactory in sections with indices as low as 2,500 or as high as 5,000.

Observations by Perry and Frost over a long period in California, as reported by Webber (*62*), indicate that the higher the mean monthly temperatures in February and March, the earlier the midblooming period appears in any year. Apparently the actual temperatures in February and March control flowering to a considerable extent, and the annual variations in this respect will indirectly influence, at least in part, the time of ripening.

Citrus fruit types vary widely with reference to the degree of low temperature they withstand, and this largely determines where they can be most profitably grown. The hardiest of the larger types, the Satsuma orange, can withstand 18° F. without defoliation when in a dormant condition, and thus it can be grown in the northern part of the subtropical belt. On the other hand, limes may be injured at 28° and are consequently confined to the warmest locations. In between are the lemon, sweet orange, grapefruit, and tangerine. In the thoroughly dormant condition the commonly accepted minima for these types are about as follows: Lemon, 26° to 27°; sweet orange and grapefruit, 23° to 24°; and tangerine, 22° to 23°. There is variation within the type, however, as pointed out by Webber et al. (*63*) and Rhoads and DeBusk (*53*). Wright and Taylor (*67*) have established the average freezing point for fruits of the sweet orange, Satsuma orange, and Temple orange at 28.03°, and according to Young (*68*), the freezing point of ripe Washington Navel oranges is from 27° to 28°; that for half ripe, from 28° to 29°; and that for green, from 28.5° to 29.5°.

These minima must be considered in relation to other factors, particularly the condition and relative dormancy of the trees. Trees in good health, well fertilized, and free from disease and insect damage show greater resistance to low temperature than do those that are devitalized by undernourishment, disease, or insect infestation. The degree of damage is also dependent on (1) the location of the trees with reference to air drainage, (2) the minimum temperature, (3) the duration of the low-temperature period, (4) the modifying effects of winds, and (5) the conditions under which the trees thaw out and the after care (*9*, *53*, *63*, *68*).

Since critical low temperatures occur in most areas of the United States where citrus is grown commercially, grove heating is employed during cold periods when it is economically feasible. The method of warming the atmosphere by lighting a large number of small fires throughout the grove area is generally used as a means of frost prevention in the Southwest, where it has been put on a systematic basis (*68*). The temperature is thus made to rise 8° F. or more, which is usually sufficient to prevent damage to trees and fruit. Frost prevention by heating is most efficient when the air near the ground is calm. When frosts are accompanied by winds, heat from the fires is continually carried away, and the fuel consumption

[2] Italic numbers in parentheses refer to Literature Cited, p. 417.

and consequently the cost are relatively greater. In the Southeast, although frosts are often accompanied by high winds, grove heating is gradually increasing.

Trees under 6 years old are more susceptible to low-temperature damage than older ones and are usually mounded with earth well above the bud union during the winter season. If the top is frozen, a new one may be grown from the uninjured scion portion above the bud union. Attempts have been made to select varieties that are relatively hardy. The grapefruit variety Marsh may be cited as an illustration. It is definitely less susceptible to low temperature damage than Duncan and other varieties. Crosses of various citrus types that have been made in attempts to secure greater hardiness in the progeny are described in detail in the 1937 Yearbook of Agriculture.

Another effect of temperature on citrus remains to be noted. In tropical climates the rind of citrus fruits in a great measure retains the green or yellowish-green color even at maturity. By contrast, the rind of citrus in subtropical climates takes on a deep yellow or orange color, depending on the type. Within the subtropical belt a similar though less marked difference in rind color is noted between the warmer and colder areas.

Moisture Supply

It is estimated that 35 inches of water a year is needed for the production of normal citrus crops. In a humid climate like that of Florida, as pointed out by Hume (*32*), there is usually sufficient moisture from rainfall during the growing season from February to November. During the winter season, however, the rainfall is relatively scarce, and the application of irrigation water would be beneficial from "February when trees are in bloom, through June." According to Friend (*24*) the annual rainfall is approximately 23 inches in the semiarid lower Rio Grande Valley, and this deficit must be made up by the application of irrigation water. Fortunately, most of the rainfall occurs during the summer season, when it is most needed. In the semiarid Southwest, citrus trees require irrigation water, in addition to the rainfall. The amount to be supplied depends upon the amount of rainfall, the character of the soil, and the age and type of the trees (*14*, *55*). Vaile (*59*) has shown that in general less water is used and the intervals between irrigations are longer in the cooler coastal districts than in the interior.

Under California conditions, according to Webber (*62*), there is apparently no correlation between rainfall and the date of flowering of citrus trees.

Effects of Humidity and Winds

The work of Hodgson (*31*) indicates that hot, dry winds are the chief cause of June drop of immature Washington Navel orange fruits in southern California. Wager (*61*) reports similar results from South Africa. In the interior valleys of the arid Southwest, abscission of immature fruits, according to Coit and Hodgson (*15*), is due to the daily water deficits in the young developing fruits resulting from high temperature and low relative humidity.

According to Webber (*62*), under California conditions, where there is wide variation in average daily relative humidity—coastal sections 63 to 72 percent, Interior Valley section 50 to 52 percent, and Salton Basin section 37 to 39 percent—"fruits tend to be smoother, thinner skinned, and in general more juicy and richer in quality when grown in an atmosphere of fairly high relative humidity." He also points out that the shape, skin texture, relative development of navel, and depth of color may be affected by the climatic complex, of which the atmospheric humidity is apparently the dominating factor.

Coit and Hodgson (*15*) have shown that within limits the relative humidity can be raised considerably over that of the desert by windbreaks, the trees themselves, and cover crops. Reed and Bartholomew (*52*) have summarized the literature on the effects of desiccating winds on citrus trees and reported their own field observations and experiments. They conclude that desiccating winds cause defoliation, death of twigs, and loss of fruit owing to excessive transpiration during windstorms as well as the mechanical force of the wind.

Light Requirements

According to Palmer (*45*), the earlier ripening of oranges in the northern end of the Central Valley of California, as contrasted with that in the citrus districts 400 miles farther south, is in a great measure due to the longer day during the growing season, although the protection from cool night winds afforded by the surrounding mountains is partly responsible.

After weighing the available evidence from various citrus-producing regions, using as his measure the time of maturity, which is influenced to some extent by the time of flowering, Webber (*62*) concludes that length of day probably has no effect or only a minor one in causing flowering.

Harding et al. (*28*) have reported significantly higher ascorbic acid (vitamin C) values in the juice of oranges picked from outside branches that were well exposed to sunlight as contrasted with fruit from inside, shaded branches.

Effect of Climate on Citrus Diseases and Pests

As an example of the close relationship between climate and the prevalence of diseases, the work of Peltier and Frederich (*46*) with citrus scab may be cited. They found that "any environmental factor or factors inducing a slight spring growth and rapid maturation or late starting, favors scab escape; while any environmental factor or factors inducing a large amount of spring growth and slow maturation favors scab susceptibility." Similar generalizations may be made with reference to citrus diseases caused by other plant pathogens. Fawcett (*22*) points out that certain citrus diseases that have had ample time and opportunity for wide distribution in citrus areas of the world are confined by climatic conditions to definite areas. The various semiarid citrus areas have, in general, the same citrus insect pests, in some cases the same species or different species of the same genus. In general, the important citrus insects in humid climates differ from those of semiarid areas, as pointed out by Quayle (*50*).

Dates

Although the date palm, *Phoenix dactylifera*, will grow in most parts of the subtropical belt, it does not ripen fruit of commercial quality except under certain conditions of temperature and aridity.

Mason (*39*) studied the temperature changes in the interior of the date palm and reported that the temperature at the center of the tree ranged from 26° F. warmer than the surrounding air on the coldest mornings observed to 32° cooler on the hottest day. This stabilization of temperature is apparently due, according to Mason, to the protective insulating leaf bases and the ascending sap current, which has a temperature acquired from the soil; and it would explain at least in part the resistance of the date palm to extremes of temperature.

The date palm can endure lower temperatures than most types of citrus, and when in the dormant condition, according to Swingle (*58*), it is rarely injured at 20° F. and is able to survive in regions where the temperature occasionally falls to 12°. He indicates four different limits: (1) Young palms in active growth would be injured at several degrees below freezing; (2) young palms not in active growth and old palms, if nearly dormant, would be severely injured at 15°; (3) old and dormant palms could withstand temperatures down to 12°; and (4) most date palms would be killed and all would be seriously injured at 10° F., and the culture of dates would be impracticable in regions where such temperatures were experienced more than once in a decade. According to Albert and Hilgeman (*1, 2*) mature palms may be seriously injured at 12° F. in the date-growing region of Arizona, but varieties differ in resistance to low temperature. Young palms will be seriously injured at 20°, and 24° to 26° will cause noticeable injury to lower leaves. According to Nixon and Moore (*44*) leaves of mature palms are injured by prolonged exposure to a temperature of 20°.

According to De Candolle (*11*), temperatures as low as 64.4° F. have no influence on the flowering and fruiting of the date, and Swingle (*58*) reports that this is confirmed by his observations. Although Swingle does not set a maximum at which growth will cease, he does state that the high air temperatures (up to 110° and higher) experienced during the growing season in some semiarid regions where dates are grown commercially are beneficial. Nixon and Moore (*44*) state that in the Coachella Valley of California the air temperature frequently exceeds 110° and has exceeded 122° but that it is not known whether such temperatures are desirable for the date. Albert and Hilgeman (*2*) report that there is no record of injury to date palms by high temperatures in Arizona.

According to Swingle (*58*), at least 3,632 summation heat units during the growing season, with 64.4° F. as zero, are required to ripen a high-quality date such as the Deglet Noor. Later Vinson (*60*) reported that the date palm ceases to grow at 50°. Using this as zero, Albert and Hilgeman (*2*) have classified date varieties on the basis of summation heat units required to reach commercial maturity as (1) early ripening, about 4,000 to 4,200 units; (2) midseason, 4,600 to 4,800 units; and (3) late, 5,200 to 5,300 units.

Mason (*39*) reports that the growth of the date palm may be continuous during the day provided the temperatures are favorable and there is an ample water supply. Even when the minimum air temperature of the day is several degrees below the freezing point, growth may continue provided the maximum temperature during the day is well above the zero growth point, 50° F. Albert and Hilgeman (*2*) report that winter temperatures have a direct influence on the growth of the spathe and the time of blossoming, and that temperatures after blossoming apparently have more effect on the time of ripening than does the date of blossoming.

In the case of the Deglet Noor date, according to Aldrich and his coworkers,[3] it appears that if enough heat units accumulate to cause fruit from inflorescences pollinated in late February or March to ripen during the hot period of late August and September, the fruit is very much inferior to fruit on the same palm maturing during the cooler weather of October or November. The late August and September fruit has a greater shrivel and a darker color at time of picking, or the darker color appears during storage; and it is lacking in flavor as compared with fruit ripening later.

An essential in date culture is a minimum of rainfall and low relative humidity during the fruit-maturing season (*2, 41, 44, 49*). A regular supply of irrigation water must be provided to compensate for the lack of rain. Excessive rainfall or high humidity adversely affects dates by providing conditions favorable for the development of disease and also by causing souring or other spoilage of the fruit. There is a considerable range of resistance to spoilage from rain and humidity among date varieties, and this influences the choice of varieties for specific localities (*2, 44*).

Humid weather during the ripening season favors the growth of several fungi on the fruit and causes spotting, shattering, and rotting of fruits (*23, 44*). Nixon (*42, 43*), Fawcett and Klotz (*23*), Haas and Bliss (*27*), and Albert and Hilgeman (*2*) have reported on water damage to dates. The injuries last named are not due to plant pathogens but to both weather and physiological conditions in the plant. Aldrich and coworkers have classified water injury to date fruits in three general groups: (1) Checking, or blacknose, due to high humidity or light rains when the fruit is changing from light green to the first pink tints (usually between mid-July and mid-August); (2) splitting (also called tearing by Haas and Bliss), which is due to excess rainfall or prolonged wetting of the fruit while it is pink or turning brownish; and (3) excessive hydration, which seems to be related to the loosening of the fruit at the calyx. Whether the entrance of pathogens causes or follows the loosening of the calyx is not known.

Rains in winter may be helpful, but spring precipitation may interfere with date pollination and the fertilization of the flowers.

According to Mason (*40*), who correlated weather conditions with vital activity in date seedlings, "Normal growth, as manifested by the pushing up of the leaves from the growth center, is made chiefly in the time between sunset and sunrise, but also at a reduced rate in daylight, when direct sunlight is cut off by clouds. In full sunlight date palm leaf elongation entirely ceases." With reference to the cause of inhibition of growth, Mason concludes, on the basis of experiments with artificial light, "that the inhibiting of the date-palm leaf growth in intense sunlight of the desert regions is due chiefly to the action of rays of wave length from about 0.57 μ in the yellow to about 0.405 μ in the violet end of the visible spectrum, but invisible ultra-violet rays probably assist in stopping growth." More recent work on other plants seems to indicate that this checking in growth is at least partly due to the inactivation of growth substance by radiation of short wave lengths (*47, 49*).

---

[3] Unpublished results at the United States Date Garden, Indio, Calif.

298737°—41——27 +

Figs

The common cultivated fig, *Ficus carica,* can withstand lower winter temperatures than either citrus or dates. Condit (*16*) reports that the dormant mature fig tree can be expected to withstand winter temperatures of 15° F. without injury; young trees are much more susceptible to low-temperature injury, and in the semiarid Southwest spring frosts cause the most serious damage, though fortunately not frequently. Serious injury may also occur during October and November before the leaves fall. Gould (*26*) points out that in addition, in the southeastern humid region, serious injury may result when low-temperature periods follow exceptionally warm periods of considerable duration that bring trees out of the winter dormant condition.

Figs for preserving or canning are being grown with maximum daily temperatures below 100° F. in humid regions of summer rains (*26, 57*), and also in semiarid areas with similar temperatures and fairly high relative humidity due to rains and fog (*16*). Figs for drying, however, are most successfully produced in regions with long sunny days, maximum daily temperatures around 100° F., and low relative humidity. With temperatures considerably higher than 100°, the fruits ripen prematurely, or the skin is toughened and the proportion of fruits deficient in pulp increased. On the other hand, with a small number of heat units and greater relative humidity, splitting of the fruit and other spoilage troubles are more prevalent (*16, 57*).

In semiarid regions sufficient irrigation water must be supplied to make good any moisture deficiency from lack of natural rainfall, since attempts to grow the fig under dry-land culture have failed. However, rains at the time of caprification (fertilizing of the fig blossoms) are unwelcome, and they are especially serious during the drying season, when figs may be either completely ruined or considerably injured in commercial quality (*16*).

In the semiarid Southwest, some varieties are subject to splitting of immature fresh figs. According to Smith and Hansen (*56*), "this is caused by atmospheric humidity or sudden changes in humidity rather than by soil moisture as was formerly thought." In the humid Southeast, the most common disease is fig rust, *Uredo fici.* It attacks both leaves and fruit, is confined to humid regions, and can be controlled by spraying (*26, 57, 64*). On the Texas Gulf coast, where the Magnolia—a variety that carries the fruits upright on the branches and has a more open eye than some varieties—is chiefly grown, there is a tendency for fruits to sour during damp weather (*57*).

Strong winds at the season of ripening whip the foliage and cause scarring of fruit, especially of such canning varieties as Kadota, thus lowering the grade. Windy weather during the season of caprification may seriously interfere with the normal flight of blastophagas (wasps that fertilize the blossoms) and a poor setting of figs of the Smyrna type may result (*16, 50*).

Since figs ripen very rapidly in the humid sections of the Texas Gulf coast, the fruit must be picked daily to decrease loss from spoilage after picking. To minimize this loss, figs are usually picked before they are soft ripe (*57*).

Condit (*16*) reports that the fruit characters of the fig may be affected by climatic differences. In the hot interior valleys with low relative humidity, second-crop Kadota figs have a very slight neck or none at all, a golden-yellow skin, and an amber pulp, while those grown in moister coastal regions have a distinct neck, green skin, and violet-tinted pulp. Similarly, second-crop Mission figs, in the interior valleys, are smaller, less elongated, and sweeter than those grown along the coast.

DECIDUOUS TREE FRUITS

The climatic adaptation of the group of deciduous tree fruits including apples, pears, peaches, cherries, plums, and apricots is similar for the entire group in that all require a winter dormant period for proper development and fruit production and therefore are limited to temperate regions having sufficient winter cold to break the natural rest period. In their distribution northward they are limited by the duration and intensity of winter cold.

Exposure to 600–900 hours below 45° F. is necessary to fully break the rest period of the commonly grown American peach varieties. Apples apparently require about the same amount of cold as the more slowly responding varieties of peaches, or about 900 to 1,000 hours below 45° (figs. 1 and 2). Pears derived from oriental species have a relatively short cold requirement, while varieties of European origin require about the same amount of cold as peaches.

If the trees are not exposed to sufficient cold, the buds do not open in the spring. With most fruits the blossom buds require slightly less cold than the leaf buds, and frequently in southern latitudes blossom buds will open before the leaf buds begin to grow. Unless the leaf system develops with or shortly after blossom opening, fruit fails to set owing to lack of a food supply from the leaves. Insufficient winter cold to break the rest period is the most important limiting factor in the growing of such fruits as apples in those parts of the United States within 150 miles of the Gulf of Mexico. Peaches can be grown somewhat farther south, while pears derived from Asiatic species are grown even farther south than peaches. Chandler et al. (*13*) have discussed in detail the chilling requirement for these fruits in California.

Low-Temperature Injury

While lack of winter cold prevents the successful culture of these fruits in tropical and subtropical areas, excessive cold is destructive in the colder parts of the world.

The most tender part of the tree during the dormant season is the root system. Experiments indicate that the roots of this group of trees may be injured at any time they reach a temperature below about 20° F. Temperatures ranging from 15° to 20° have been found to injure the roots of apples severely (*12, 37, 48*). It

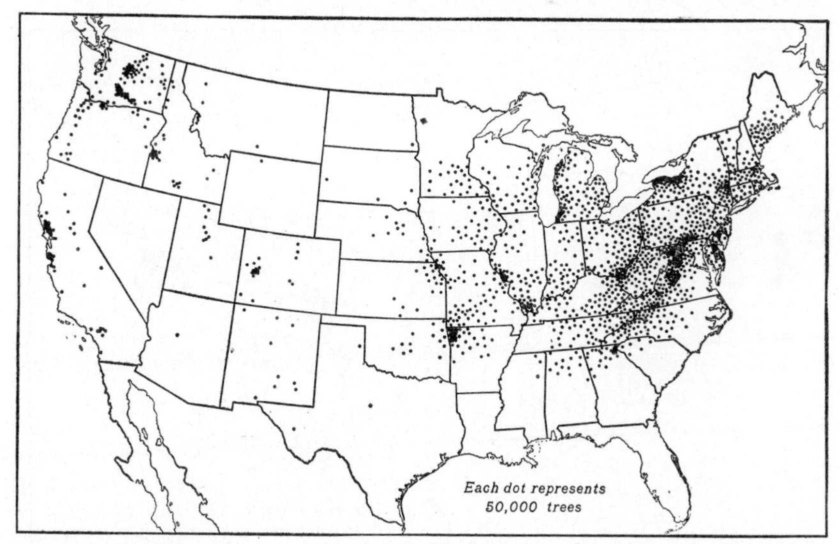

Figure 1.—Apples require considerable winter cold to break the rest period and are not well adapted where summer temperatures are high. Thus few apple trees are grown within 200 miles of the Gulf coast. Principal centers of commercial production are south and east of large bodies of water, as in Michigan and New York, or east of mountain ranges which afford some protection from severe cold. Distribution of apple trees of bearing age as of April 1, 1930, is shown.

is probable that the range of root injury is not greatly different with the other species.

Fortunately the soil protects the root system so that root injury actually occurs less frequently than injury to the tops of trees. A grass sod or a heavy cover crop reduces the rate of cold penetration, and a heavy snow cover is generally sufficient to prevent root injury. In moderately heavy soils that are well supplied with moisture, penetration of cold downward is much less rapid than in more open, drier soils, owing to the release of heat as a result of the freezing of the greater amount of water present. Root injury is most likely to be serious in relatively open soils when prolonged periods of below-zero weather occur with relatively little snow or other cover on the ground. Under these conditions root injury may be severe and may result in the death of the trees even though the tops are not directly injured.

The tenderest of the above-ground portions of the tree is generally the collar, or crown (the portion immediately above the ground line). Very frequently the bark in this region is killed by temperatures that do not injure other portions (*51*). This is likely to occur when sharp freezes follow periods of moderate temperature. Such hardy fruits as apples may be so badly injured as to result in the death of the tree when such sharp freezes occur, although the temperatures do not go below 0° F. Peach trees, particularly in the Southern States, may be injured by temperatures of 15°. Not only is the collar particularly subject to injury, but temperatures are usually lower on the surface of the ground than they are a few feet above.

The fruit buds are usually the next most sensitive. Frequently they are killed by low winter temperatures that do not injure the wood, bark, and leaf buds (*17*, *34*).

Fruits of this group, in common with those of other plants, are more seriously injured if severe freezing weather occurs without a previous period of hardening by moderately cold weather. Thus, Bradford and Cardinell (*6*) state that the greatest injury to fruit trees in Michigan since the establishment of the fruit industry there occurred as the result of a freeze in October 1906, when the temperature remained well above zero. The trees had not been previously exposed to sufficient cold to harden them. Similarly, severe freezes even during midwinter are more damaging if a period of warm weather has preceded the cold.

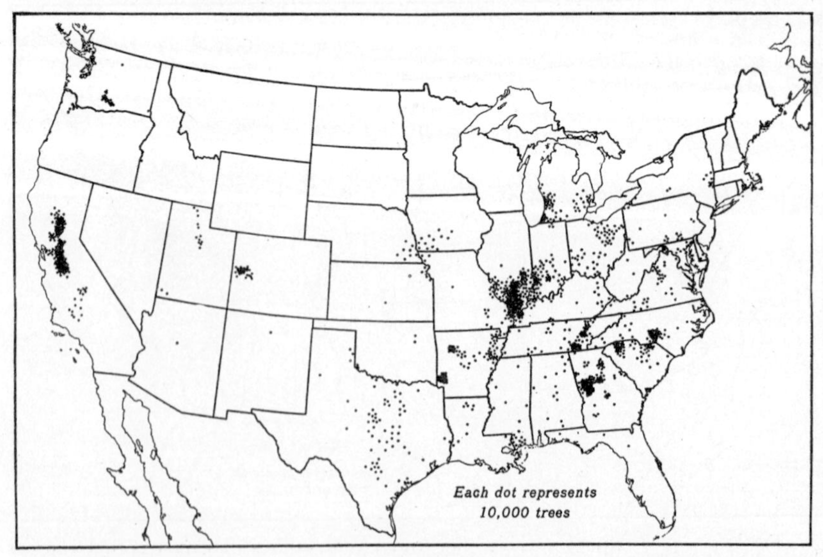

FIGURE 2.—The peach tree thrives well under higher summer temperatures than the apple, requires somewhat less cold to break the rest period, and is more subject to injury from low temperatures. Thus principal centers of peach production are south of the principal centers of apple production. Distribution of peach trees of bearing age as of April 1, 1930, is shown.

While the effects of any freeze will vary greatly, depending on the varieties and preliminary hardening, some generalizations may be made concerning the temperatures that these fruits will normally stand in the colder parts of the country when thoroughly hardened. Thus apples, sour cherries, and American plums under these conditions usually stand temperatures as low as −30° F. without severe injury. Pears, sweet cherries, and Japanese and European plums usually stand −20°. Peaches and apricots are likely to be severely injured by a temperature of −15°. The fruit buds of all of these fruits may be injured at temperatures somewhat above the limits for severe tree injury. Fruit buds of peaches particularly are frequently killed at temperatures of −10°, even in midwinter.

Thus the location of commercial plantings in the northern districts is largely determined by the minimum temperatures the trees will survive. Apples and sour cherries can be grown in the northern part of the Eastern States, particularly in protected locations. Peaches, pears, and European plums are somewhat less hardy and are grown in the northern sections only where protected by large bodies of water or by the topography. None of these fruits thrive in the northern Great Plains, where minimum temperatures below −30° F. are likely to occur.

With the onset of warmer weather and the beginning of growth, all these fruits become less resistant to low temperatures. They differ markedly in the total amount of "growing" weather required to expose the vital flower parts (*5*, *13*). Thus apples brought into greenhouses when dormant but with the rest period broken and maintained at a uniform temperature of about 70° F. require approximately 25 days before the blooms open. Blossoms of most peach varieties under similar conditions will open in 15 to 20 days. With apricots and some varieties of plums an even shorter period is required. This factor is of tremendous importance in determining the susceptibility of these fruits to spring frosts. Because the apricot requires the fewest hours of warm weather to open its flower buds, it is the earliest blooming and consequently the most exposed to killing by frost of the blossoms or young fruits. Certain plum varieties and oriental types of pear are also very early blooming. Peaches, sweet cherries, European plums, sour cherries, and apples follow in that order. Thus the apple, requiring the greatest amount of warm weather to bring it into bloom, is the most likely to escape spring freezing.

The actual temperatures that will cause injury to the blossoms of these fruits are apparently not significantly different. Any temperature sufficiently low to cause appreciable ice formation in the pistil of the blossom, the part that ultimately develops into the fruit, apparently results in killing.

The following data on the relation of stage of development in apple buds to temperatures causing killing of a portion of the blossoms are from Ellison and Close (*20*):

Stage of development of fruit buds:	*Temperatures that result in some flower killing* °*F.*
Buds breaking, "green tip stage"	0–10
Buds packed in cluster, "delayed dormant"	10–20
Buds separated in cluster, "pre-pink"	[1] 24–26
Center bud pink—others no color	
All buds showing color—"pink stage"	
Center bud open, others "balloon stage"	25–27
All buds full open	27–28
Petals fallen	
Small green fruits	

[1] For several hours.

Moisture Requirements

For best growth conditions and production, all of the fruits in this group require ample available moisture in the soil of their root zone throughout the growing season. Since the trees develop large leaf areas, the total water requirement is relatively high. A minimum of 30 inches of precipitation, or a combination of precipitation and irrigation, should be available in any part of the United States where commercial culture is attempted. Somewhat larger quantities of water are essential in the hotter and drier regions (*30*, *35*, *37*).

Under natural rainfall, where prolonged periods of limited rainfall may occur, it is particularly important to select soils that will retain a large amount of available water to carry the trees through periods of drought.

Fruits that ripen early, such as cherries and apricots, apparently can be grown with somewhat less water than late-maturing kinds such as late peaches, apples, and pears. Some of the American-type plums also are highly drought-resistant.

Light Conditions

It is not known that any of the deciduous fruits considered here respond to specific light durations for the initiation of fruitfulness, as is true of many other plant species. All of them appear to develop and function best under conditions of relatively high light intensity. Thus in the Western States, under irrigation and with high light intensities the production of fruits is relatively greater than under eastern conditions. The work of Heinicke and Childers (*29*) has shown that in apple, maximum photosynthesis (manufacture of carbohydrates) is correlated with maximum light intensity—at least under New York conditions. Thus the areas of most intense light, other factors being equal, seem to be preferable for apples and probably for the other fruits of this group.

Summer Temperatures

All these fruits will thrive under widely fluctuating summer temperatures. However, it is possible to make some generalizations concerning the conditions under which the highest production and best quality of fruit are secured.

Sour cherries appear to be adapted to cooler summer temperatures than the other fruits of the group. The main centers of sour cherry production in the United States are where the June, July, and August mean temperatures are about 65° F.

The principal areas for apple production and the areas in which the apple seems to thrive best have mean temperatures for these months of 65° to 75° F. Areas in which the mean temperatures range above 75° appear to be poorly adapted to apple production (*8*). The best pear districts in the Western States appear to have temperatures slightly higher than those found best for apples. With certain varieties of pears, at least, the best dessert and storage quality is secured where the temperatures are relatively high during the growing season.

Peaches, on the whole, seem well adapted to somewhat warmer conditions than apples. Peaches grown where mean summer temperatures are as low as 65° F. usually are not of so high a quality as those grown at warmer temperatures. On the other hand, excellent peach production and quality are secured in some sections having mean summer temperatures above 75°. Most of the present cling peach production in California is in sections having high growing-season temperatures.

Relation of Climatic Conditions to Diseases

The fungus- and bacterial-disease problem is very serious with all of these fruits and is closely correlated with weather conditions. In the parts of the country having wet growing seasons, control of diseases requires expensive spray treatments and in some cases is so difficult as to make the growing of some of the fruits impracticable.

Apple scab, the most serious disease of apples, is a relatively low-temperature fungus that thrives in orchards under conditions of ample precipitation while temperatures are under about 70° F. Thus in the southern apple-growing districts, control of apple scab is primarily a spring and early-summer problem, while in northern districts scab may spread throughout the growing season. Apple scab is practically unknown in the western irrigated districts where little spring or summer rainfall occurs. Other diseases of apples, particularly bitter rot, are high-temperature fungus diseases that are prevalent only in the southern part of the Apple Belt, where temperatures are high and rainfall is likely to be abundant. In pears, the bacterial disease, fire blight, is correlated with both temperature and rainfall conditions. It attacks the trees primarily while they are in an actively growing condition and while spring temperatures are high. In areas where high spring temperatures are coupled with much rainfall, fire blight is so severe that susceptible varieties of pears cannot be grown. Thus in the United States, culture of the more blight-susceptible pear varieties is limited to dry sections in the Western States and to sections in the Eastern States having a very cool spring. The absence of rainfall in the Western States does not prevent blight infection in the trees. but dry conditions tend to reduce the rate of spread.

With peaches, such diseases as brown rot and scab are important only in sections of the country where rainfall is prevalent during the spring or summer. The most serious disease of sour cherries, caused by the leaf-spot fungus, is also dependent upon moisture supply for its spread. Thus in general, in sections having dry summers and water supplied by irrigation instead of rainfall, fungus and bacterial diseases are of minor importance in the growth of these crops, whereas they constitute a major problem in sections having abundant spring and summer rainfall.

GRAPES

Most of the grape production of the world consists of varieties derived from the species *Vitis vinifera*, often spoken of in the United States as Old World grapes or California grapes. In this country the vinifera varieties are grown mainly in California and to a limited extent in other Western States (*33*) (fig. 3).

Since grapes of this species require a short rest period, few are grown within 20° of latitude north or south of the Equator. As they are in general very susceptible to fungus diseases, the principal producing areas are characterized by relatively dry growing seasons. Where grapes are produced for raisins, it is particularly important that the ripening season be dry and relatively hot, to facilitate the drying of the fruit. Most varieties are likely to be injured by temperatures appreciably below 0° F., even during the dormant season, though some varieties selected for hardiness will stand somewhat lower winter temperatures. Spring frosts are a hazard, as with other deciduous fruits, and growth and blossom buds are injured in the spring by about the same temperatures found injurious to peaches. These grapes will thrive well where summer temperatures are frequently above 100°.

In the more humid parts of the United States, varieties developed from native American grapes, either alone or by hybridization with the vinifera varieties, are grown. These in general will withstand lower winter temperatures than vinifera varieties and are less susceptible to fungus diseases. Such varieties as Concord will endure temperatures that kill peach trees; they approach apples in hardiness. The most cold-resistant grapes will stand as low temperatures as will apples.

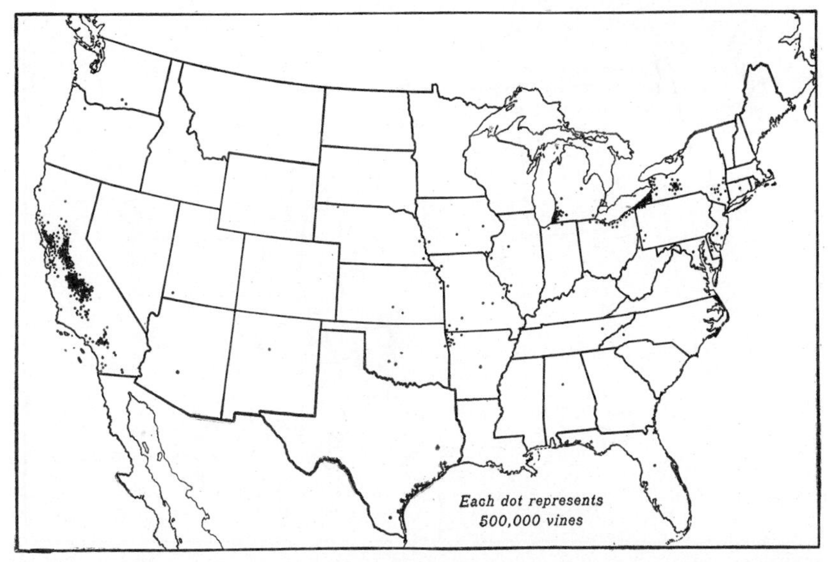

FIGURE 3.—Most of the grapes of the United States are grown in California and are of varieties largely imported from the Old World. These varieties are susceptible to fungus diseases and to winter injury in the colder and more humid parts of the country. In other areas varieties derived wholly or in part from native American species, which are more resistant to cold and to fungus diseases, are grown. Distribution of grapevines of all ages as of April 1, 1930, is shown.

In the Southeastern States, varieties derived from *Vitis rotundifolia*, a native species, are grown extensively. These so-called muscadine varieties are highly resistant to fungus diseases and can be grown with little spraying in very humid climates. They are not very resistant to winter cold and are not grown where temperatures frequently fall below 0° F. They require a long, warm growing season to mature the crop.

All of the grapes are fairly resistant to drought conditions, as compared with most tree fruits. The highest quality of fruit is associated with abundant sunshine during the growing season (7).

SMALL FRUITS

Strawberries

Strawberries are among the most widely adapted of the fruit crops (fig. 4). Varieties have been selected that can be grown in at least the higher elevations in the Tropics, and others are grown in northern latitudes where very severe winter conditions prevail. Notwithstanding the fact that strawberries can be grown as far north as most fruits, they are not truly hardy in the sense that the plant parts withstand very low temperatures. As grown in cold climates, the vital plant parts during the winter season are at or below the ground level, where they receive the maximum protection from snow or other cover. Without such protection, the plants are very susceptible to winter killing. In commercial production, the practice of heavy mulching with straw or similar material is followed in the cold regions to insure protection if the snow cover fails.

In the United States, varieties for the most southern latitudes differ in their growth response from those adapted to severe winters. The principal fruiting in the most southerly regions of strawberry production in the United States occurs during the winter and early spring months. Varieties adapted there must grow, flower, and fruit during the relatively short, cool days of winter. With the Missionary, the principal variety in Florida, fruiting is continuous throughout the winter and spring months. Little if any rest period is required by this variety.

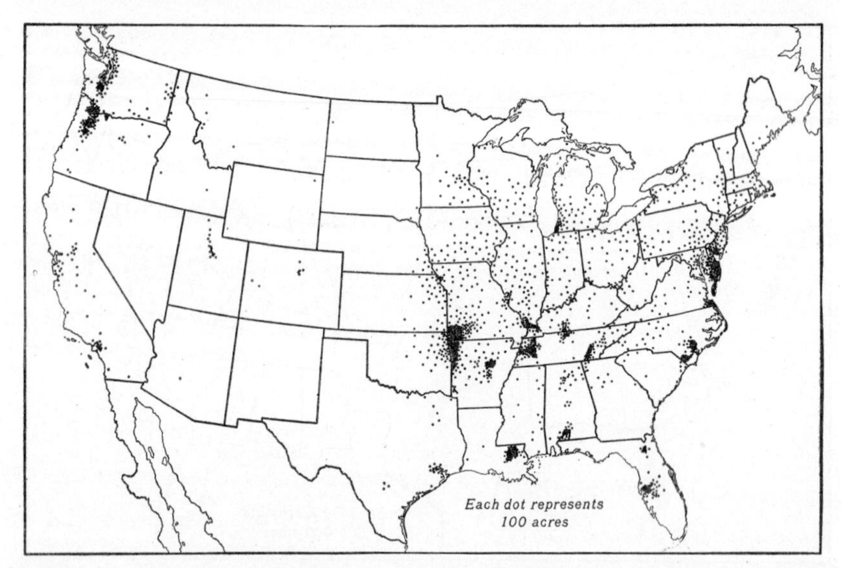

Figure 4.—Although strawberries are grown to a limited extent in every State in the Union, the principal centers of production are in the milder climates of the Southeastern States and along the Pacific coast. North of the Ohio and Potomac Rivers the plants are commonly covered with mulch during the winter months to give added protection, the depth of mulch applied being increased toward the north. Total acreage for 1929 is shown.

Where winters are somewhat more severe, with a period not too cold for plant growth but too cold for fruit production, other varieties are better adapted. Thus, north of the Missionary belt such varieties as Klondike and Blakemore, requiring a slightly longer rest period, are grown.

While relatively hardy varieties are available for still more northern latitudes, protection during the winter months is necessary for successful production. Thus, light mulching with straw or similar material is desirable in the middle latitudes of the United States. The amount of mulch that must be used increases in the more severe climates until the plants are covered several inches deep along the northern borders of the United States. The crown of the strawberry plant, from which the spring growth develops, may be killed or injured in even the hardiest varieties if its temperature falls as low as 10° F. In view of the fact that temperatures at the ground level may be several degrees colder than at a few feet above the ground, the necessity for protection can be readily realized.

Most strawberry varieties are short-day plants in that the fruit buds are initiated while the days are of medium or below-medium length (*18*, *19*). In northern latitudes this occurs in September and early October, and all fruit buds are formed at that season. In southern latitudes also fruit-bud formation takes place in the fall, but growth may be resumed sufficiently early in the spring to have additional fruit-bud formation during the first relatively short days; thus the early crop is produced from fruit buds formed in the fall, while the somewhat later crop is produced from spring-formed buds. This results in a much longer fruit-ripening period in such areas as the Carolinas and Louisiana than in the more northerly latitudes, where spring fruit-bud formation does not occur.

Under the moist humid conditions of the Eastern States, the varieties grown must be resistant to fungus diseases. In the drier regions of the Pacific Coast States, this is less important, and also in this milder climate, winter mulching is not commonly practiced.

In all parts of the country, susceptibility of the blossoms to spring frost injury may result in severe losses. The open blossoms will withstand temperatures only slightly below freezing, and because of the low growth habit of the plant they are very subject to frost injury. Partly grown berries are much more resistant to low temperatures than are the newly opened blossoms.

The strawberry is a relatively shallow-rooted crop and very subject to injury from an insufficient moisture supply. If drought occurs before the crop matures, total production will be seriously curtailed. Dry weather during midsummer interferes with the production of runner plants, but unless it is so severe as to result in the death of the plants or severely restrict runner-plant production, it apparently does not seriously damage the production for the following season. It is extremely important, however, that ample moisture and good growing conditions be present during the fall season, when fruit-bud formation for the following year occurs; otherwise production will be greatly reduced.

A few varieties—the everbearers—have been selected that will develop flower buds and fruit in the relatively long days of midsummer in the more northerly latitudes. If the spring crop is removed by pinching off the blossoms, these varieties will grow and fruit in the long days of midsummer and late summer.

Thus there are strawberry varieties that are adapted to a wide range of climatic conditions, extending from the equable temperature and day length of the Tropics to the extreme cold of the northern latitudes.

Raspberries

Raspberries are best adapted to parts of the United States with relatively cool summers. Under the hot, humid conditions of the Southeastern States, they are subject to leaf and cane diseases, which make commercial production difficult if not impracticable. Although the raspberry apparently requires about as much winter rest as do most of the deciduous tree fruits, it is the prevalence of disease rather than lack of winter cold that limits its production southward in the eastern part of the United States.

Of the two types of raspberries, the red varieties will stand somewhat more severe winter conditions than will the black. Black raspberries are hardy in the Northeastern States but are frequently winter-killed in the upper Mississippi Valley, where some red varieties will survive. Where temperatures are very low, production is made possible by laying down the canes and covering them during the winter months.

Blackberries and Dewberries

The cultivated blackberries and dewberries are derived from a number of different species and consequently they show a wide range of adaptation. Varieties have been selected that thrive satisfactorily under the warm, humid summer conditions of the Gulf States, while others are too susceptible to fungus diseases to be grown in that section. In general the blackberries are less resistant to winter cold than are raspberries. Even the hardiest, such as Eldorado and Snyder, do not endure continued cold much below 0° F., and may be killed by relatively short exposures to temperatures of −20° to −30°. For this reason and because of greater tolerance of warm, humid conditions, the principal blackberry regions of the Eastern States are south of the principal raspberry areas. Many varieties thrive well under the cool and relatively equable climatic conditions of the Pacific Coast States.

Currants and Gooseberries

Currants and gooseberries are very resistant to low winter temperatures but susceptible to leaf and cane diseases under warm, humid summer conditions. They are hardy throughout the northern part of the United States and well into Canada, but are little grown south and west of the Potomac and Ohio Rivers.

Cranberries

The cranberry plant is evergreen, and in common with other evergreen fruit plants it is not truly hardy, although it is grown commercially in such northern districts as Massachusetts and Wisconsin. The plant is a native of swamp areas and stands submergence under water for long periods without injury. These conditions are simulated under commercial culture, the plants being grown on bog fields so arranged that they can be covered with water during the winter months. Although ice may freeze deeply over the fields, the temperatures to which the plants are exposed are not severe. The cranberry thrives best where the summers are relatively cool. Fungus diseases are more serious in the warmer areas. Cranberries are not grown commercially south of New Jersey both because of their poor adaptation to warm conditions and the fact that bog areas are limited in hotter climates.

Blueberries

The common cultivated blueberries are derived chiefly from the high-bush swamp species. Their northern limit is determined by low winter temperatures. They are not hardy in northern Michigan and northern New England, resembling the peach in resistance to winter cold. The range southward is determined by their need for a certain degree of winter cold. Apparently they are poorly adapted south of the Piedmont region in Georgia. They thrive well under relatively cool, moist summer conditions.

The rabbiteye group of high-bush blueberries is native to northern Florida and southern Georgia. Varieties of this species require a very short period of winter cold. They grow vigorously in the hot summers of the Southern States. Their cold hardiness is not well known, but they are probably not hardy north of the Potomac River.

NUT CROPS

Three of the important nut crops of the world—coconut, Brazil nut, and cashew—appear to be strictly tropical in their climatic requirements. The most important of these, the coconut, is believed to have originated in the American Tropics, but it was distributed throughout the tropical regions of the world prior to the exploration of these regions by white men. It appears to be adapted only to regions having a mean yearly temperature above 70° F., with no freezing at any time. An equable temperature throughout the year and at least 40 inches of well-distributed rainfall—except in locations where the roots can reach subterranean water—appears necessary for its best development (*3*). Plantings have been made largely near coasts in practically all tropical countries of the world.

The Brazil nut is native in the river valleys of tropical South America, particularly those of the Amazon and its tributaries. Practically all of the Brazil nuts of commerce come from native trees, and to date the nut has not been cultivated to an appreciable extent either in South America or in other tropical countries. Cultivation would appear possible in regions adapted to the banana, but because of the slowness of the trees to come into production and the rather limited production per tree, the growing of the Brazil nut as a horticultural crop has not been encouraging.

The cashew nut, also native to tropical America, has been grown mainly in the tropical parts of India. In common with the Brazil nut, it is limited to strictly tropical conditions. With improved methods of handling the nut kernels its popularity in world commerce has increased greatly in recent years, although its culture has not yet spread widely through the Tropics, mainly because of difficulty in shelling.

There are no important nut crops that would be considered subtropical in their adaptation. The principal nut crops of the world fall into two classes—tropical and hardy or semihardy.

Deciduous Hardy or Semihardy Nut Crops

The most important nut crops in the deciduous or semihardy group include the walnuts, pecans, chestnuts, almonds, and filberts. All are produced on deciduous trees, in contrast to the evergreens on which tropical nuts are produced, and require some winter cold for the best development. They vary widely both in the amount of winter cold required to break their rest period and in the minimum winter temperature they will endure.

The growth in size of all the nuts is normally completed fairly early in the summer, while the latter part of the growing season is the period of filling, or kernel development. Thus a water shortage in the first half of the season will be reflected in small-sized nuts, and a water shortage, defoliation, or other unfavorable factors during the latter part of the season result in poor filling.

Pecans

The pecan is native to the southern part of the United States and northern Mexico, the native habitat ranging from the Mississippi Valley to west Texas and north to Missouri, southern Illinois, and Indiana. The cultivated varieties have been developed largely from selected seedlings found in the wild or in planted seedling groves. About two-thirds of the present crop in the United States is derived from native seedling trees and about one-third from the improved cultivated varieties. The pecan is not grown commercially outside the United States, though test plantings have been made in several countries. Native nuts are harvested in Mexico.

Most of the pecans in the United States are grown where there is a season of more than 200 frost-free days. A long hot growing season is necessary for maturing the nut. Though the trees appear hardy in such northern latitudes as New York and Michigan, no nuts are matured on trees in these locations.

The pecan apparently requires a smaller amount of winter cold than most deciduous fruits. Thus pecans can be grown successfully along the Gulf coast from northern Florida to Texas. In the regions immediately adjacent to the Gulf, however, spring growth does not start as early as somewhat farther north—an indication that in that area the amount of winter cold is about the minimum required.

The pecan is more resistant to fungus diseases than such other nut trees as the Persian walnut and the filbert. Under the humid conditions prevailing in the Southeastern States, however, fungicide spraying to protect the foliage is generally necessary. In the drier western districts fungus diseases are much less serious. Because of the long growing season and the large foliage system, the pecan is a heavy user of water. In Texas it is normally found along streams where the root system can tap subsurface water supplies. Under cultivation, 40 to 50 inches of water a year in well-distributed rainfall, or a similar amount applied as irrigation, appears desirable for a mature orchard.

Walnuts

Though several types of walnut are used as food in different parts of the world, the Persian, or so-called English, walnut is the type principally cultivated. In the United States, production is mainly in California and Oregon. There is extensive production in practically all of the countries surrounding the Mediterranean Sea. Varieties of the Persian walnut vary greatly in their cold requirement and also in the minimum temperatures they will stand. The hardier varieties, when well hardened, will stand temperatures of −10° to −15° F. Growth starts early in the spring, and spring frosts, where prevalent, are a serious hazard. In humid climates the trees seem very susceptible to fungus diseases, so that the culture of the nut outside of areas having dry summer climates has not been successful.

The Persian walnut requires considerable winter cold to break the rest period (*13, 65*). Certain varieties need as much cold as apples, or even more; others require less cold than peaches. In the coastal districts of southern California production is frequently curtailed because of lack of sufficient winter cold. Varieties requiring the least cold have been planted in the area, and even these sometimes have very late and prolonged blooming seasons.

Very high summer temperatures are likely to be injurious (*4*). The nuts may be sunburned and the meats darkened when they are exposed to temperatures much above 100° F. Thus the crop is best adapted to regions having a moderate-to-cool but dry summer climate. Abundant moisture, however, particularly during the latter part of the growing season, is necessary for the best filling of the nuts.

The black, or American, walnut is a native tree in the United States and apparently is well adapted to all parts of the country except the coldest and the southernmost areas. Though many nuts are gathered, cracked, and sold, commercial culture is negligible.

Almonds

The almond is quite similar to the apricot in its climatic requirements. Only a limited amount of winter cold is necessary to break the rest period. Because of the short rest period and the fact that a relatively low total heat-unit requirement is necessary to bring the trees into bloom, the almond is one of the earliest blooming of the fruit and nut trees. Thus it is extremely subject to damage in sections of the country where moderately late spring frosts are prevalent. This characteristic has limited the commercial production in the United States to California, with a few local plantings in some of the other Western States (*66*). Almonds are extensively grown in the countries surrounding the Mediterranean Sea.

Ample moisture is necessary for the almond as for other nut crops for maximum production and large-sized, well-filled nuts (*66*), but since the trees will survive and produce some nuts with a limited amount of moisture, they have been planted in many areas where water supplies are insufficient for other fruit and nut crops.

Filberts

Commercial filbert production was formerly confined mainly to the Mediterranean countries, although production in Europe occurs northward as far as England. During the past 20 years extensive filbert plantings have been made in western Oregon and western Washington, where conditions are apparently favorable for the European-type filbert (*36*, *54*).

The filbert, in common with the walnut and the almond, seems best adapted to regions having a relatively dry growing season with only moderate summer temperatures. The trees of European varieties will apparently withstand temperatures down to −10° to −15° F. without serious injury. Very severe freezes in the late winter are likely to kill the catkins or the pistillate flowers, which results in poor sets of nuts, but ordinary frosts rarely cause injury. Many of the European varieties are grown as garden plants in the Eastern States, but productiveness has not been sufficiently high to warrant commercial planting. Trees may be injured by severe winter temperatures in the middle latitudes of the East.

Chestnuts

The extensive chestnut forests formerly found in the eastern part of the United States have been largely killed by the fungus disease known as chestnut blight. The European chestnut is widely grown in the Mediterranean countries, where its climatic requirements are apparently similar to those of the Persian walnut. The oriental chestnuts, from China, are being widely tested in the United States. Their climatic requirements appear to be similar to those of the black walnut, except that their range is farther south. Thus they should be adapted to many areas in the Eastern States as well as on the Pacific coast.

LITERATURE CITED

(1) Albert, D. W., and Hilgeman, R. H.
1934. FRUIT GROWTH AND TEMPERATURE RELATIONSHIPS IN THE DATE PALM. Amer. Soc. Hort. Sci. Proc. (1933) 30: 225–228, illus.

(2) ——— and Hilgeman, R. H.
1935. DATE GROWING IN ARIZONA. Ariz. Agr. Expt. Sta. Bul. 149, pp. 229–286, illus.

(3) Bailey, L. H.
1935. THE STANDARD CYCLOPEDIA OF HORTICULTURE . . . New ed., 3 v., illus. New York.

(4) Batchelor, L. D.
1924. WALNUT CULTURE IN CALIFORNIA. Calif. Agr. Expt. Sta. Bul. 379, 91 pp., illus.

(5) Bradford, F. C.
1922. THE RELATION OF TEMPERATURE TO BLOSSOMING IN THE APPLE AND THE PEACH. Mo. Agr. Expt. Sta. Res. Bul. 53, 51 pp., illus.

(6) ——— and Cardinell, H. A.
1926. EIGHTY WINTERS IN MICHIGAN ORCHARDS. Mich. Agr. Expt. Sta. Spec. Bul. 149, 103 pp., illus.

(7) Caldwell, Joseph S.
1925. SOME EFFECTS OF SEASONAL CONDITIONS UPON THE CHEMICAL COMPOSITION OF AMERICAN GRAPE JUICES. Jour. Agr. Res. 30: 1133–1176, illus.

(8) ———
1928. MEAN SUMMER OR "OPTIMUM" TEMPERATURES IN RELATION TO CHEMICAL COMPOSITION IN THE APPLE. Jour. Agr. Res. 36: 367–389.

(9) Camp, A. F.
1935. SOME LESSONS LEARNED IN TWO FREEZES. Fla. State Hort. Soc. Proc. 48: 114–119.

(10) ——— Mowry, Harold, and Loucks, K. W.
1933. THE EFFECT OF SOIL TEMPERATURE ON THE GERMINATION OF CITRUS SEEDS. Amer. Jour. Bot. 20: 348–357.

(11) Candolle, Alphonse de.
1855. GÉOGRAPHIE BOTANIQUE RAISONNÉE . . . 2 v., illus. Paris.

(12) CARRICK, D. B.
1920. RESISTANCE OF THE ROOTS OF SOME FRUIT SPECIES TO LOW TEMPERATURE. N. Y. (Cornell) Agr. Expt. Sta. Mem. 36, pp. 609–661, illus.
(13) CHANDLER, W. H., KIMBALL, M. H., PHILP, G. L., TUFTS, W. P., and WELDON, GEO. P.
1937. CHILLING REQUIREMENTS FOR OPENING OF BUDS ON DECIDUOUS ORCHARD TREES AND SOME OTHER PLANTS IN CALIFORNIA. Calif. Agr. Expt. Sta. Bul. 611, 63 pp., illus.
(14) COIT, J. ELIOT.
1915. CITRUS FRUITS; AN ACCOUNT OF THE CITRUS FRUIT INDUSTRY, WITH SPECIAL REFERENCE TO CALIFORNIA REQUIREMENTS AND PRACTICES AND SIMILAR CONDITIONS. 520 pp., illus. New York. [Rural Sci. Ser.]
(15) ——— and HODGSON, ROBERT W.
1919. AN INVESTIGATION OF THE ABNORMAL SHEDDING OF YOUNG FRUITS OF THE WASHINGTON NAVEL ORANGE. Calif. Univ. Pubs., Agr. Sci. 3: [283]–368, illus.
(16) CONDIT, IRA J.
1933. FIG CULTURE IN CALIFORNIA. Calif. Agr. Col. Ext. Cir. 77, 69 pp., illus.
(17) CRANE, H. L.
1930. PHYSIOLOGICAL INVESTIGATIONS ON THE RESISTANCE OF PEACH BUDS TO FREEZING TEMPERATURES. W. Va. Agr. Expt. Sta. Bul. 236, 80 pp.
(18) DARROW, GEO. M.
1937. INTERRELATION OF TEMPERATURE AND PHOTOPERIODISM IN THE PRODUCTION OF FRUIT-BUDS AND RUNNERS IN THE STRAWBERRY. Amer. Soc. Hort. Sci. Proc. (1936) 34: 360–363.
(19) ——— and WALDO, GEORGE F.
1934. RESPONSES OF STRAWBERRY VARIETIES AND SPECIES TO DURATION OF THE DAILY LIGHT PERIOD. U. S. Dept. Agr. Tech. Bul. 453, 32 pp., illus.
(20) ELLISON, ECKLEY S., and CLOSE, WILBUR L.
1927. CRITICAL SPRING TEMPERATURES FOR APPLES IN THE YAKIMA VALLEY, WASH. U. S. Monthly Weather Rev. 55: 11–18, illus.
(21) FAWCETT, H[OWARD] S.
1929. TEMPERATURE EXPERIMENTS IN GERMINATING ORANGE SEEDS. Calif. Citrog. 14: 515.
(22) ———
1936. CITRUS DISEASES AND THEIR CONTROL. Ed. 2, rev., rewritten, and enl., 656 pp., illus. New York and London.
(23) ——— and KLOTZ, L. J.
1932. DISEASES OF THE DATE PALM, PHOENIX DACTYLIFERA. Calif. Agr. Expt. Sta. Bul. 522, 47 pp., illus.
(24) FRIEND, W. H.
1933. CITRUS ORCHARD MANAGEMENT IN THE LOWER RIO GRANDE VALLEY OF TEXAS. Tex. Agr. Expt. Sta. Cir. 67, 56 pp., illus.
(25) GIRTON, RAYMOND E.
1927. THE GROWTH OF CITRUS SEEDLINGS AS INFLUENCED BY ENVIRONMENTAL FACTORS. Calif. Univ. Pubs., Agr. Sci. 5: 83–117, illus.
(26) GOULD, H. P.
1935. FIG GROWING IN THE SOUTH ATLANTIC AND GULF STATES. U. S. Dept. Agr. Farmers' Bul. 1031, 34 pp., illus. [Revised.]
(27) HAAS, A. R. C., and BLISS, DONALD E.
1935. GROWTH AND COMPOSITION OF DEGLET NOOR DATES IN RELATION TO WATER INJURY. Hilgardia 9: 295–344, illus.
(28) HARDING, PAUL L., WINSTON, J. R., and FISHER, D. F.
1939. SEASONAL CHANGES IN THE ASCORBIC ACID CONTENT OF JUICE OF FLORIDA ORANGES. Amer. Soc. Hort. Sci. Proc. (1938) 36: 358–370.
(29) HEINICKE, A. J., and CHILDERS, N. F.
1937. THE DAILY RATE OF PHOTOSYNTHESIS, DURING THE GROWING SEASON OF 1935, OF A YOUNG APPLE TREE OF BEARING AGE. N. Y. (Cornell) Agr. Expt. Sta. Mem. 201, 52 pp., illus.

(30) Hendrickson, A. H., and Veihmeyer, F. J.
1930. some facts concerning soil moisture of interest to horticulturists. Amer. Soc. Hort. Sci. Proc. (1929) 26: 105–108.
(31) Hodgson, Robert W.
1917. some abnormal water relations in citrus trees of the arid southwest and their possible significance. Calif. Univ. Pubs., Agr. Sci. 3: [37]–54, illus.
(32) Hume, H. Harold.
1926. the cultivation of citrus fruits. 561 pp., illus. New York.
(33) Husmann, George C.
1932. grape districts and varieties in the united states. U. S. Dept. Agr. Farmers' Bul. 1689, 33 pp., illus.
(34) Knowlton, H. E., and Dorsey, M. J.
1927. a study of the hardiness of the fruit buds of the peach. W. Va. Agr. Expt. Sta. Bul. 211, 28 pp., illus.
(35) Lewis, M. R., Work, R. A., and Aldrich, W. W.
1934. studies of the irrigation of pear orchards on heavy soil near medford, oreg. U. S. Dept. Agr. Tech. Bul. 432, 34 pp., illus.
(36) Locklin, H. D.
1927. filbert culture. Wash. Agr. Expt. Sta. Pop. Bul. (n. s.) 6–W, 32 pp., illus.
(37) Magness, J. R.
1929. collar rot of apple trees. Wash. Agr. Expt. Sta. Bul. 236, 19 pp., illus.
(38) ——— Degman, E. S., and Furr, J. R.
1935. soil moisture and irrigation investigations in eastern apple orchards. U. S. Dept. Agr. Tech. Bul. 491, 36 pp., illus.
(39) Mason, Silas C.
1925. partial thermostasy of the growth center of the date palm. Jour. Agr. Res. 31: 415–453, illus.
(40) ———
1925. the inhibitive effect of direct sunlight on the growth of the date palm Jour. Agr. Res. 31: 455–468, illus.
(41) Mortensen, E.
1932. the "winter garden" region of texas. Tex. Agr. Expt. Sta. Cir. 62, 32 pp., illus.
(42) Nixon, Roy W.
1932. observations on the occurrence of blacknose. Date Growers' Inst. Rpt. 9: 3–4.
(43) ———
1933. notes on rain damage to varieties at the u. s. experiment date garden. Date Growers' Inst. Rpt. 10: 13–14.
(44) ——— and Moore, Dewey C.
1939. date growing in the united states. U. S. Dept. Agr. Leaflet 170, 8 pp.
(45) Palmer, Andrew H.
1920. the agricultural significance of sunshine as illustrated in california. U. S. Monthly Weather Rev. 48: 151–154, illus.
(46) Peltier, George L., and Frederich, William J.
1924. relation of environmental factors to citrus scab caused by cladosporium citri massee. Jour. Agr. Res. 28: 241–254, illus.
(47) Popp, H. W., and McIlvaine, H. R. C.
1937. growth substances in relation to the mechanism of the action of radiation on plants. Jour. Agr. Res. 55: 931–936,
(48) Potter, G. F.
1924. experiments on resistance of apple roots to low temperatures. N. H. Agr. Expt. Sta. Tech. Bul. 27, 34 pp., illus.
(49) Potts, A. T.
1924. the lower rio grande valley of texas. Tex. Agr. Expt. Sta. Cir. 34, 13 pp.
(50) Quayle, Henry J.
1938. insects of citrus and other subtropical fruits. 583 pp., Ithaca, N. Y.

(51) Rawlings, C. O., and Potter, G. F.
1937. unusual and severe winter injury to the trunks of Mc intosh apple trees in new hampshire. Amer. Soc. Hort. Sci. Proc. (1936) 34: 44–48, illus.

(52) Reed, H. S., and Bartholomew, E. T.
1930. the effects of desiccating winds on citrus trees. Calif. Agr. Expt. Sta. Bul. 484, 59 pp., illus.

(53) Rhoads, Arthur S., and De Busk, E. F.
1931. diseases of citrus in florida. Fla. Agr. Expt. Sta. Bul. 229, 213 pp., illus.

(54) Schuster, C. E.
1924. filberts. part i. growing filberts in oregon. part ii. experimental data on filbert pollination. Oreg. Agr. Expt. Sta. Bul. 208, 39 pp., illus.

(55) Smith, G. E. P., Kinnison, A. F., and Carns, A. G.
1931. irrigation investigations in young grapefruit orchards on the yuma mesa. Ariz. Agr. Expt. Sta. Tech. Bul. 37, pp. 413–591, illus.

(56) Smith, Ralph E., and Hansen, H. N.
1931. fruit spoilage diseases of figs. Calif. Agr. Expt. Sta. Bul. 506, 84 pp., illus.

(57) Stansel, R. H., and Wyche, R. H.
1932. fig culture in the gulf coast region of texas. Tex. Agr. Expt. Sta. Bul. 466, 28 pp., illus.

(58) Swingle, Walter T.
1904. the date palm and its utilization in the southwestern states. U. S. Dept. Agr., Bur. Plant Indus. Bul. 53, 155 pp., illus.

(59) Vaile, Roland S.
1924. a survey of orchard practices in the citrus industry of southern california. Calif. Agr. Expt. Sta. Bul. 374, 40 pp., illus.

(60) Vinson, A. E.
1914. the effect of climatic conditions on rate of growth of date palms. Bot. Gaz. 57: 324–327, illus.

(61) Wager, Vincent A.
1939. alternaria citri and the november-drop problem of washington navel oranges in the kat river valley. Union So. Africa Dept. Agr. and Forestry Sci. Bul. 193, 18 pp., illus.

(62) Webber, H. J.
1938. influence of environment on citrus. Calif. Citrog. 23: 108, 126, 130.

(63) ——— et al.
1919. a study of the effects of freezes on citrus in california. Calif. Agr. Expt. Sta. Bul. 304, pp. [243]–321, illus.

(64) Weber, George F.
1931. fig rust and its control. Fla. Agr. Expt. Sta. Press Bul. 439, [2] pp.

(65) Wood, Milo N.
1934. pollination and blooming habits of the persian walnut in california. U. S. Dept. Agr. Tech. Bul. 387, 56 pp., illus.

(66) ———
1937. almond culture in california. Calif. Agr. Col. Ext. Cir. 103, 96 pp., illus.

(67) Wright, R. C., and Taylor, George F.
1929. the freezing temperatures of some fruits, vegetables, and cut flowers. U. S. Dept. Agr. Dept. Bul. 1133, 8 pp. [Revised.]

(68) Young, Floyd D.
1929. frost and the prevention of frost damage. U. S. Dept. Agr. Farmers' Bul. 1588, 62 pp., illus.

Climatic Relations of Sugarcane and Sugar Beet

By E. W. Brandes and G. H. Coons [1]

THOUGH it is not possible to change the climate to fit the plant, it is often possible to change the plant to fit the climate. The Indians did this with corn over a period of many thousand years. The plant breeder of today telescopes the process into a few years simply because the systematic and precise methods of modern science enable him to find out quickly just what needs to be done and what material there is to do it with. Nowhere is this more evident than in the breeding work with sugarcane and sugar beet, which has accomplished striking results in recent years.

[1] E. W. Brandes is Head Pathologist in Charge, and G. H. Coons is Principal Pathologist, Division of Sugar Plant Investigations, Bureau of Plant Industry.

In this discussion of the influence of climate upon sugarcane and sugar beet an attempt will be made to deal with these crop plants as dynamic entities, capable of much variation, rather than as static things fixed forever in certain forms. In the field of biological research directional breeding seeks to produce sorts that are improved because they fit the environment instead of succumbing to it. The fruitfulness of specific efforts in this direction may be gaged in advance by taking into account the geographical range, the behavior, and the reactions not only of all the cultivated forms of the species but also of those close botanical allies with which the plant types in question can be made to intercross. In other words, the gene complement of both the species and the genus represents the major entity whose response to climate and other factors must, in the long view, be considered.

Examples will be given for both sugarcane and sugar beet to illustrate how advances may be made within the inherent limits imposed by the species. Apparent obstacles imposed by some phase of climate may be surmounted by revolution in the strains grown. However, there must exist with the stock from which the crop plant arose intercrossable forms suited to the climatic conditions for which adaptation is desired.

The effects of the changing pattern in the crop plants themselves, as well as in their culture, may be far reaching. Conclusions drawn at any one period as to the reaction to climatic factors and the relation of a plant to an environment necessarily will be subject to rather broad revision as the orbits of adaptation of the plants are widened.

SUGARCANE

World Distribution

Setting out on a study trip to visit the numerous parts of the world where sugarcane is produced, a traveler will encounter variations seemingly not much short of extreme in the temperature, moisture, and light conditions in the different countries and also in the natural plant cover. Farmers of all races engage in sugarcane husbandry in more than 50 countries having modern mills for sugar manufacture and in many others where sugarcane is important for food but is not processed into refined sugar. The countries encircle the globe and range from about 40° north latitude to 32° south latitude (fig. 1), encompassing more than half the earth's surface and an even greater proportion of the habitable land surface.

Starting west around the earth at the Equator in the western Pacific islands, without going 10° north or 10° south, the traveler will first find large-scale sugarcane industries in the coastal plain lowland and low valleys of the great Malay Archipelago jutting southeast from Asia. Most of this area may be described as having a tropical rain-forest climate. Cane grows almost everywhere in the entire region, but no large commercial industries are centered there except where there is a brief annual respite from the rains. The same belt in Africa is unimportant for sugar production, although a few cane mills are found in Uganda and Kenya at high elevations and one in the Belgian Congo. In equatorial South America the departure from tropical rain-forest conditions reaches an extreme in

Peru, where cane is grown on the rainless western side of the Andes under irrigation. As compared with the luxuriant rain-forest vegetation of the same latitude in the East Indies, the scanty desert flora of this region suggests anything but the possibility of cane culture; yet, with controlled water supply, conditions for the crop are favorable. Northward in the same belt, sugarcane grows better in some of the high humid valleys of the Andes than in any other part of the New World. Farther north, but still below 10° north latitude, the important sugar industries of the Guianas are located on the seacoast or low-lying lands along the rivers, some even below tidewater.

Having progressed around the world within the narrow confines of what may be considered the deep Tropics and received striking revelations of the great variation in natural conditions under which sugarcane culture is pursued, the traveler meets with more surprises when he turns his attention to the great circles at right angles to the Equator.

Starting again in the western Pacific, but farther south, he encounters sugarcane culture along the coastal rivers of northern New South Wales (28° to 30° S.), where a mild, Temperate Zone, humid climate prevails, with occasional freezes in July and August. Without special remark on the important intervening sugar countries, which include Queensland, the Philippines, southern China, and Formosa, he follows the great circle (approximately 140° east longitude) northward 6,000 miles to the sugarcane industry of the small islands south of Kyushu in the Japanese Archipelago (30° to 32° N.). Distinctive among the climates of important sugarcane countries is that of parts of northern India, with frost in December and January, hot winds in early April, and rains commencing in June. In spite of apparent differences, the sea-level, temperate, rain-forest areas of the southeastern part of the United States (25° to 30° N.), with mild to severe winters, the high tablelands of northwestern Argentina (25° S.), and the undulating coastal areas and acacia-grassland savanna of Natal and Zululand (30° S.), with long, cool winters and marked drought hazard, have a common problem—how to make more efficient use of the winter months. In partial compensation, these countries, together with northern India, New South Wales, and others in similar latitudes, share the advantage of long summer days and accelerated growth, as compared with that in the equatorial zone of 12-hour days. The small sugarcane enterprises of southern Spain and the Azores (38° N.) are believed to be the northernmost commercial industries.

Returning to the Tropics, the traveler perceives that the islands, or groups of islands, lying between 10° and 30°, both north and south of the Equator, and those fringing the outermost limits of the tropical zone have more in common climatically than any other sugarcane countries thus far mentioned. In respect to certain features, principally the amount and distribution of rainfall, there are differences, but in general the light, water supply, and temperature conditions are similar. As a group these islands produce a large proportion of the world's cane sugar. Except at high elevations they are frost-free. Seasonal effects on cane, however, are pronounced, and in particular the combination of short days and temperatures somewhat below optimum for growth in winter results in a long period of stagnation

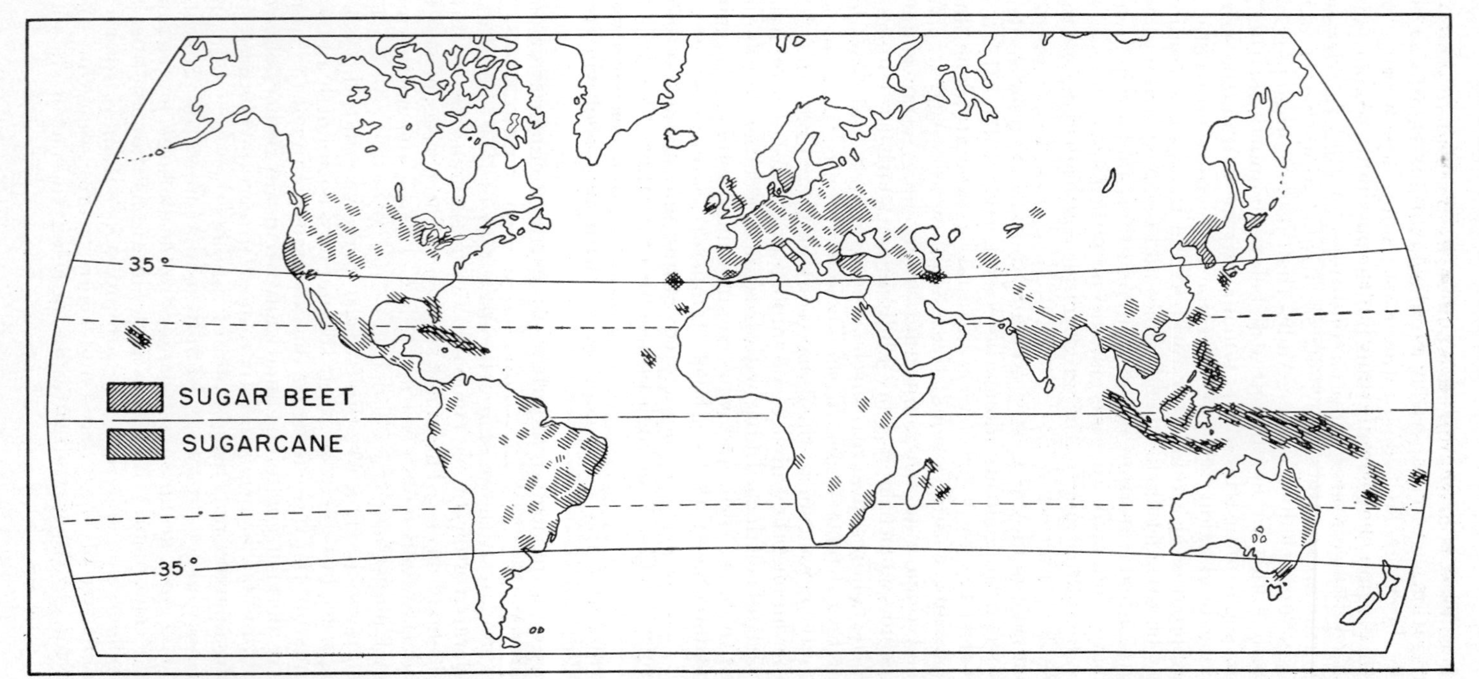

FIGURE 1.—World distribution of sugarcane and sugar beet. Potential areas of production are shown without reference to quantities of sugar produced.

in the development of the varieties now grown. This has long been recognized in some of these countries, including Hawaii, Cuba, Santo Domingo, Puerto Rico, Reunion, Mauritius, Fiji Islands, and others.

Origin and Spread

Until quite recently it has not been possible to consider broadly the climatic and weather requirements of sugarcane in general. Obviously, the potential adaptation of the plant to particular conditions depends on study of its full range of characteristics or, more precisely, on the inherent characteristics of all its ancestral forms. Only in the last few decades has knowledge accumulated as to what these ancestral forms of sugarcane are. Present information indicates that the cultivated kinds are a complex of mixed ancestry (*2*, *3*).[2]

For thousands of years the sugarcane, represented by a relatively few varieties of garden canes developed from several wild species of *Saccharum* by primitive people in Melanesia and British India, has been cultivated. Before historic times sugarcanes started on their migrations eastward and westward from the various Melanesian centers of origin, beginning with the unrecorded voyages of men to the islands of the Pacific and the backwash of migratory races from Melanesia to the Indian Peninsula. The latter movement accounts for the presence in southern India and Malaya of the so-called noble varieties (the varieties of *Saccharum officinarum* are called "noble"), although they are not indigenous there. The indigenous Indian canes found in northern India are very different from these introduced forms in both botanical origins and characteristics.

Within historic times the sugarcane of Melanesian origin, or chiefly of that origin, was carried from India westward to Iran, Mesopotamia, and the Mediterranean countries, including southern Spain. With the discovery of the New World and the increasing demand for sugar in Europe, sugarcane of that type was settled in country after country in America until the center of sugar production for trade rotated westward through 180° of longitude. The varieties of northern India were concerned little, if at all, in this migration.

The few Melanesian varieties that comprised the group of migrants became successively fewer in number as they radiated outward during this long period of time. With such restricted material, very little improvement of sugarcane was possible in the New World, and there is no record of any being made. When, during the past century, shipping facilities permitted more rapid transport, additional varieties of the same general type were brought to the New World. As far as is now known, few varieties were imported, only a small fraction of the range available in the native habitats being represented. It is not surprising, therefore, that the potentialities of sugarcane as a whole in the New World were very insufficiently explored. Reasonably satisfactory performance of sugarcane was all the New World planters asked. The proximity to markets, only a voyage across the Atlantic being required, in contrast with the much longer trip around the Cape of Good Hope, the vast new lands, and slave labor gave the American producer an advantage. Because of this geographical advantage with respect to markets, it was even possible to extend

[2] Italic numbers in parentheses refer to Literature Cited, p. 438.

the range of sugarcane northward and southward, to cover 60° of latitude in the Americas.

Inasmuch as only very restricted plant material was used in these sugarcane enterprises in the Western Hemisphere, which merely "resettled" Old World varieties, the performance of cane in the West Indies and North and South America shows that the plant has considerable adaptability.

With the gradual development of agricultural science and closer scrutiny of the performance of cane—in terms of the increase of recoverable sugar by the month rather than by crop seasons, which may vary greatly in length—it has been possible to measure performance with a much greater degree of refinement. This has permitted evaluation of the different sugar-producing regions by new and more precise methods, taking into consideration climate and other natural conditions. It becomes apparent that some deeply rooted ideas on the relative advantages of sugar-producing regions need revision. The regions where sugarcane is important may owe their rank as producers to considerations among which natural advantage is not paramount.

A comparative analysis of climate in the sugarcane areas of the Eastern and Western Hemispheres reveals certain similarities and also certain striking differences, as the description already given shows. Everything considered—including daily periods of daylight, annual and daily fluctuations in temperature, mean temperature, amount and distribution of rainfall, and soils—the similarities are less impressive than the differences. This is partly due to the different character of the land areas in equivalent latitudes in the two hemispheres.

At zero latitude in the chief sugar-producing part of the Eastern Hemisphere are mountainous islands with tropical island climates characterized by rather abrupt local differences in rainfall but uniform temperatures at equal elevations and surface features favorable for drainage. There is a well-defined east-and-west monsoon, advantageous for ripening. The equivalent land area in the Western Hemisphere is the vast South American continent, mostly low except at the extreme west, where it rises abruptly to the chains of the Andes, with high flat valleys between the ridges. In general the local differences in rainfall are not so pronounced, daily change in temperature is not so great, and the mean temperature (except in the Andes) is somewhat higher than in the Eastern Hemisphere. There is no well-defined monsoon but almost continuous heavy rain broken by periods of less rain in the montaña, or region of the great fan of tributaries in the upper part of the Amazon watershed. Except for length of day, the climates of the Eastern and Western Hemispheres at this latitude are therefore dissimilar. For sugarcane the lack of pronounced temperature change in the montaña is, of course, not unfavorable, but the absence in much of the area of a droughty rest period results in watery juices. These contrasting land conditions are almost the same for a distance of about 10° north and south of the Equator. The principal tropical sugar-producing countries of the Eastern Hemisphere are in this equatorial band.

Between 10° and 20° both north and south latitude the character of land areas important for sugar in the two hemispheres is reversed. North of the Equator, they change from insular to continental in the east, while in the west they change from continental to insular. The two principal tropical sugar-producing countries of the west are in this area.

Between 20° and 30° N., sugar production is continental in both hemispheres, except for the island of Formosa; in the equivalent band south of the Equator it is exclusively continental.

Beyond 30° N. and extending to about 40° wild forms of *Saccharum* have recently been found in the Old World, the outward limits of the range in the Temperate Zone being midcontinental.

Prehistoric and Recent Adjustments

The wide differences in the climates where sugarcane is grown need to be reconciled with the undoubtedly definite requirements of the crop. A part of the explanation lies in the fact that a sexual cycle is not involved in sugarcane culture as it is in that of most staple crops. The commercial product of sugarcane is not fruit or seed but a constituent of the cell sap of the stem, a vegetative part. In general the relationships of light, temperature, moisture, etc., are more exacting for sexual maturity than for vegetative growth. Wherever grown, sugarcane requires about the same units of climate, in whatever pattern they appear, in the course of a year, and takes relatively the same length of time to grow. The total requirement of light, whatever the day length, is large and must synchronize with abundant water and with growth temperatures approaching the optimum during a reasonably long crop season; and during the season there must be at least one rest period, or interruption of rapid growth.

In the Old World long association of the garden forms of cane with wild ancestral forms, with which they freely hybridize, has permitted continuous selection for countless centuries, and there may be found illustrations of distinctly different cultivated or garden forms adapted to widely different climatic conditions. Since in a short space it is not possible to direct attention to more than a few examples, the most diverse forms of cane and the greatest departures in climate will be discussed.

By far the greatest sugar production in India is in the Temperate Zone portions. The cane varieties grown commercially are the garden forms selected by unsung horticulturists ages ago from the local forms of *Saccharum spontaneum*, the wild cane indigenous in northern India. These varieties, slender and free stooling, make tremendous growth in the long days of summer and withstand the cold of winter and the hot dry winds of spring. They are short-cycle forms, completing a sexual generation in 8 to 10 months, and when they bloom the flowers are produced in late autumn. Experimental plantings of varieties of this type in the United States indicate that growth starts at considerably lower temperatures than with varieties of Melanesian origin.

In great contrast with the Temperate Zone climate of northern India is the tropical-island climate of the equatorial belt in the East Indies. In keeping with the climatic requirements the cane varieties are distinctly different from the Indian canes and are of different ancestry. The exemption from extremes of temperature and the almost unvarying light during the year have resulted in the selection of varieties with growth characteristics adapted to these more uniform conditions. It is not surprising that in Java the Melanesian garden canes are the basis of the commercial varieties that give such excellent results there. In the Americas only the more fertile equatorial valleys of the Andes may be compared with the native habitat of the Melanesian garden canes, and even there conditions are not exactly the same.

Sugarcane is not native to the New World. When the West Indies, the Americas, and Africa were colonized, canes originally from the East Indies region, where the climate is relatively stable and always hot, were exclusively used, although climates of that type prevailed in only a relatively few places in the Western Hemisphere, chiefly in small areas in South America. In Cuba and countries equally far from the Equator, where cane of that type is still grown, its relatively poor performance as compared with that in Java is doubtless partly attributable to climatic conditions distinctly different from those of the original habitat. In other parts of the New World where cane was established, climatic conditions departed to an even greater degree—for example, in Louisiana and Argentina, where extremes of temperature prevail. Although sugarcane culture has been important in the Western Hemisphere for centuries, the adaptation of varieties to climate has been imperfect. Only in a few places, most of them of limited area, have the migrants found conditions truly satisfactory.

For most cane-growing countries, distinct opportunities have recently been opened for selection of sugarcane material better fitted to the climate than that now grown. In many parts of the world, particularly in the Western Hemisphere, a gradual transition is taking place in the character of the sugarcanes grown commercially. This transition, which is far reaching and of great economic consequence in many important sugar-producing areas, has lately been much accelerated. It consists chiefly in replacing varieties long in use by hybrid varieties. These hybrids are bred by crossing the old varieties, or varieties of similar character, with wild or primitive types from different and sometimes remote environments (fig. 2). The results of this work have been to double the acre yield of sugar in many instances (*1*) and to focus attention on the relation of the plant to its environment.[3]

In the Old World there is evidence in some places of a greater degree of adjustment to climate by use of a somewhat wider range of sugarcane forms.

Only within the past few years, with study of the wild and garden forms of cane of varied origin, has there been a realization that a very small part of the whole range of sugarcane forms available in the world has been used in the sugarcane "resettlement" enterprises in America. No clear statement of this far-reaching, important conclusion has heretofore been made. Demonstrations on a large scale have indicated that when the climatic requirements are considered and a wider range of plant material is used, great improvement is possible. Only a beginning has been made, centering in the sugarcane-improvement project of the Division of Sugar Plant Investiga-

[3] This varietal revolution is the result of several causes, among which attempts to control the diseases of cane by substituting resistant varieties were important. For example, the prevalence of sereh in the Netherlands East Indies and of mosaic in Puerto Rico and Louisiana resulted in renewed attention to breeding for better adaptation to climate as a sequel to breeding for resistance.

tions of the Department of Agriculture, but results, signalized by the higher acre-yield levels already attained by the completely reconstituted sugar industry of the South, indicate the possibilities. By attention to these principles of climatic requirement, improvement slightly less in degree is possible in the important sugar-producing countries fringing the equatorial belt, where the annual fluctuation of temperature reaches 50° F. or more and the differences between the longest and shortest days are very significant for the growth responses of sugarcane.

The transition in the character of the sugarcanes grown commercially has been somewhat more pronounced in Temperate Zone countries. In Natal, Egypt, Louisiana, and Argentina, all in the Temperate Zone, the first stage of the transition is complete. An analysis of the changes, which were at first brought about largely by laborious cut-and-try methods, demonstrates the practical application of the principles here emphasized. The trend is toward hybrid canes having an admixture of the noble varieties formerly grown and cane types originating in the north Temperate Zone. Without doubt the improvement resulting from this belated concession to the demands of climate can be followed by still further improvement. Conscious selection of breeding material, with attention to the great number of forms assembled during the past 20 years and due consideration of the climatic and other requirements of these forms, will bring nearer the goal of highly efficient sugar production.

FIGURE 2.—Response to climate of different sugarcane varieties in Louisiana. Two commercial varieties, Co. 281 and C. P. 807 (at left and at center), both of which have a strong infusion of Temperate Zone types, grow better in the Louisiana climate than P. O. J. 213 (at right), whose breeding history definitely includes only one such infusion.

Determining Climatic Requirements by Test of Basic Types

In contrast with the large amount of narrowly circumscribed material previously used for test and culture a systematically collected assortment of sugarcane comprising a wide range between extreme forms is now available (*3*). Studies now being carried on by the Division of Sugar Plant Investigations and its cooperators contemplate observations on a large group of wild and "original" garden forms of cane at each of a series of 10 stations spaced at intervals between the Equator and 37° N. The same group is also being studied under controlled conditions of temperature and light. The group comprises forms collected where they are indigenous extending from 40° N. in central Asia to the southern islands of Oceania.

This project, now only in its second year, includes the simultaneous monthly measurement of growth rate and sugar increment throughout the year beginning at the spring solstice. The work is expected to contribute, in the course of time, to a much more precise evaluation of the world's resources of sugarcane germ plasm in varying forms and to the better adjustment of the crop to the climates in present or prospective sugar-producing areas. The attack on this problem has already yielded results indicating that stagnation of growth during the cool months in the outer Tropics and occasional cold injury in the lower latitudes of the Temperate Zone need not be accepted as permanent impairments of farming efficiency. In the collection are wild forms that grow

Figure 3.—Winter-hardy wild sugarcane from Turkestan growing as a perennial at Arlington, Va., where noble canes kill out completely. This wild type arrows (blooms) profusely in August; noble canes flower much later in the Tropics. By taking advantage of the reversed seasons north and south of the Equator and utilizing speedy transport of pollen by airplane, cross breeding has been effected.

rapidly in cool as well as in hot weather and others that tolerate cold (fig. 3). A more discriminating selection for nobilization of basic types (biotypes) adapted to these particular climates is now possible.

SUGAR BEET

World Distribution

In nearly every important country, the production of sugar forms a part of the agricultural economy. Climate determines whether the source of sugar is sugarcane or sugar beet. The sugar beet, a plant of the Temperate Zone, produces one-third of the world's supply. Sugarcane, a perennial grass, requires 8 to 9 months to attain adequate tonnage and satisfactory quality, and its culture is limited to tropical and subtropical climates. The sugar beet, on the other hand, is a relatively cold-hardy plant, grown for sugar production as an annual, which in 160 to 200 days (5½ to 7 months) is capable of producing a large tonnage of roots of high sucrose percentage. Its culture therefore can extend widely north and south; in the Northern Hemisphere the sugar beet is grown from an extreme southern limit of about 35° N. to an extreme northern latitude of about 60°. At Malaga, Spain, sugarcane and sugar beets growing in adjacent fields represent the culture of the two crops at about their respective north and south limits (fig. 1).

As with sugarcane, the potential range of the sugar beet as a crop plant may be predicted from the distribution and attributes of its wild ancestors. Rather general agreement places the center of origin of the genus *Beta* in eastern Asia, possibly Asia Minor or the Caucasus region (*11*). From this general area the distribution of the genus has been westward along the Mediterranean coast, northward and eastward in the arid steppe regions, and as a littoral, or seacoast, plant northward along the Atlantic and North Sea coast lines. The wild relatives of the sugar beet, especially *Beta maritima* L., are cold-hardy, extremely resistant to drought, tolerant of high salt concentrations as evidenced by their growth in situations exposed to ocean spray, and capable of persistence and fair growth even in pauperized soils. Among the types of *B. maritima* adapted to different environments (ecotypes), annuals, winter annuals, biennials, and perennials are found; a northern ecotype, biennial in habit, has been described from Sweden (*8*). Thus the expectations from the genetic complexes encompassed in the genus *Beta* are fulfilled by the establishment of the sugar beet as a crop plant from Spain to Iran in the south and as far north as central Sweden, with production possibilities claimed for the vicinity of Leningrad, Union of Soviet Socialist Republics (*9*); successful culture of the crop on an extremely wide range of soil types, including those highly alkaline or brackish; and the behavior of the plant when subjected to high temperatures, drought, and spring or fall frosts (fig. 1).

As far as temperature is concerned, the sugar beet can grow in any State of the United States. A distinction must be made, however, between mere growth of the plant in reasonably fertile, well-watered soils and the efficient production of sugar-beet roots rich enough in stored sugar to make them satisfactory for sugar fabrication. In general, the sugar beet makes its best and most efficient growth as a crop plant in the United States within a zone lying between the summer-temperature isotherms of 67° and 72° F. In his early studies, Harvey W. Wiley called attention to this relationship and mapped the potential belt of sugar-beet culture in the United States (*12*). Subject to water supply and plant diseases, the localization of the sugar-beet industry in the United States has tallied rather closely with this masterful generalization (fig. 4).

In Europe the approximate course of the July 70° F. isotherm is through north-central France, central Germany, what was formerly Austria about at Vienna, Hungary near Budapest, and thence northward through Kiev, U. S. S. R. The important and highly productive Magdeburg, Czechoslovakian, and Polish regions lie slightly north of this isotherm, and those of Spain, Italy, the Balkan States, Turkey, and Iran, where sugar-beet culture presents more problems, lie to the south, the districts in the last two countries being nearer the July 80° isotherm. The limited sugar-beet culture of the Southern Hemisphere is confined, in the main, to regions crossed by the January 70° isotherm.

Climatic Requirements

The great adaptability of the sugar beet to environment makes it necessary to outline rather broadly the climatic conditions necessary for completion of a crop cycle in which a high level of sugar storage may be attained. As with other plants, temperature and water relations are most decisive. Sugar-beet seed germinates slowly at temperatures only a few degrees above freezing; hence to assure emergence rather than rotting in the soil, air temperatures of 45° to 48° F. or above are required. At the emergence stage, when the bent hypocotyls are pulling the seed leaves above the ground, the sugar beet is

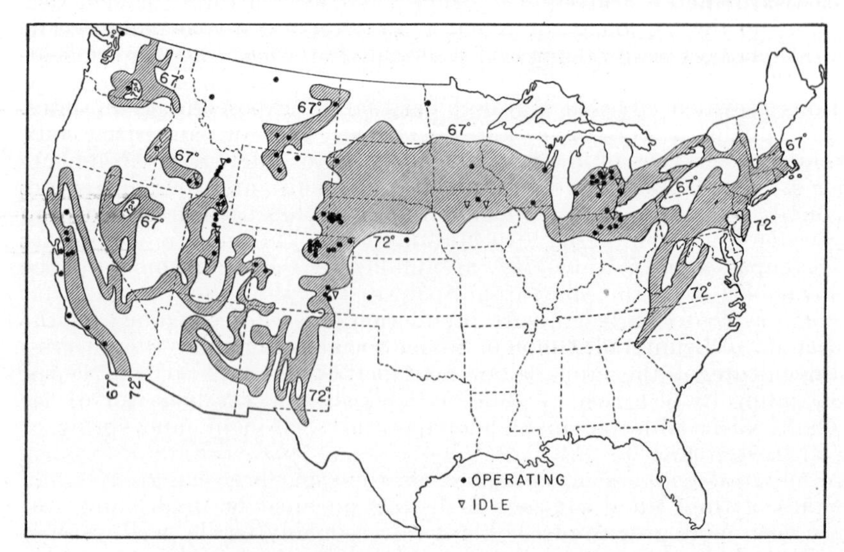

Figure 4.—Location of beet-sugar factories in the United States. The zone between the mean summer isotherms of 67° and 72° F. is shaded.

most sensitive to cold (temperatures of about 27° or below). Once above ground and somewhat conditioned, the plants become very hardy,[4] tolerating without injury cold exposures almost as great as those withstood by small grains. The normal progression of spring temperatures, especially those approaching a daily average of 60°, induces strong growth. Crop growth in late June, July, and August is speeded by mean daily temperatures of 70° or slightly higher, but with extremely high summer temperatures, growth apparently flags.

Within the sugar-beet zone, summer temperatures probably affect production and quality of sugar beets less than does the water supply. Fall temperatures, however, because of their profound effects on sugar storage, are a critical factor. In the humid area and in general in districts in which the crop is grown under irrigation, a sugar-beet plant which has made luxuriant root and top growth usually has attained by September 1 a sucrose percentage of about 12. With the cool days and frosty nights of late September or October, growth is checked, but photosynthetic activity and storage of sugar are augmented (*10*) (fig. 5). Sucrose percentages rise, reaching in mid-October averages of 15 or more; and in November, if injury has not been caused by severe freezing, percentages as high as 18 or even higher may be reached. This relation of sugar storage to cool temperatures is stressed because it explains in a large measure the mediocre or poor performance of the sugar beet in more southern areas which have relatively warm and wet fall weather. Wiley (*13*), found—and abundant tests since have confirmed his findings—that around Washington, D. C., sucrose percentages of sugar beets reach their highest point (about 12 percent) in late August or early September, but fall conditions bring about definite retrogression in these percentages coincident with vigorous growth of the plants.

In apparent contradiction to this course of development and sugar storage under cool, fall conditions is the production in California of extremely high tonnages of sugar beets of a quality not matched in more eastern centers. Sugar beets planted in California in December, January, or February are harvested and processed beginning in late July. Highest sucrose percentages are attained in the hottest months of the year, and sucrose accumulation in the roots takes place at temperatures which in the daytime greatly exceed 100° F. It is common practice there to withhold irrigation water as the harvest period approaches. Probably the high temperatures and decreased water supply operate to check further growth while intensive photosynthetic activity continues, and thus storage of sugar gains to the degree that growth, which consumes foodstuffs, is retarded.

Assuming an accumulation of soil moisture from winter precipitation and normal distribution of moisture throughout the growing season and discounting heavy rains largely lost by run-off, the rainfall requirements in the humid area for average crop production may be placed at 3 to 5 inches for the period from April 15 to June 15, 4 to 6 inches from June 15 to August 15, and 3 to 4 inches from mid-August to October 15, or a total seasonal requirement ranging from 10 to 15 inches. Crops have been grown without irrigation with only 6 inches of effective summer rainfall, but under such conditions production fell

[4] The capacity of the sugar-beet plant, even when small, to recover from hail injury is a very important consideration in many areas where hail damage frequently destroys other leafy crop plants.

FIGURE 5.—Harvesting sugar beets in the humid area of the United States in late fall after cooler weather has checked growth and promoted storage of sugar in the roots.

far below average. With almost garden culture, outstanding yields are obtained in the Sacramento delta region of California under conditions of nearly unlimited water supply, the problem in this district being to keep the water table sufficiently low. In contrast to this are the extreme reductions in yields in other districts, caused by drought periods, and the very noticeable effects of rainless periods of 3 weeks or more. For optimum growth of the crop abundant moisture available throughout the season is necessary so that growth shall not be checked at any stage. In the irrigated sections, where rainfall is either negligible or so small in amount as to be largely lost, and relative air humidities are extremely low, 15 to 24 acre-inches of water are commonly given by a series of applications. Light but frequent irrigations are more efficient than fewer, heavier applications of water. The common fallacy that withholding water from young beets makes deeper rooted plants has been exploded; the practice in reality results in stagnation of plant growth and loss in yield.

The factors of humidity and hours of sunshine operate concomitantly with the major factors mentioned, and their direct effects are difficult to assess. On the other hand, day length may have rather far-reaching effects. The sugar beet is classified as a long-day plant in its fruiting habit. As sugar beets are grown for root production in a season starting in April, the period from April 15 to July 1 is not ordinarily cold enough to cause bolting (sending up seed stalks in the first season of growth) with commercial strains; from midseason on, vegetative growth continues, the shortening hours of daylight operating further to restrict annualism. Thus, in nearly all districts the sugar beet grows entirely vegetatively. Seed production comes about in the second year of growth as a response to fall exposures and winter cold storage.

The excessive and unwanted bolting of ordinary varieties of sugar beet when the crop is grown for sugar production with planting dates advanced to as early as October or November—a practice followed in the coastal areas of southern and central California and in the San Joaquin and Imperial Valleys—presents a serious problem. As high as 25 to 50 percent or more of the plants in the field may go to seed, with consequent loss of sugar. This change from the vegetative to the reproductive phase is associated with conditions during early growth, when temperatures are frequently low enough, combined with adequate light, to induce fruiting, with adverse effects on early plantings. Significant quantitative differences in the cold-exposure periods necessary to induce bolting have been found among varieties and inbred lines. Varieties slow to bolt have been developed by selection, and soon such types will be used almost exclusively for plantings made at advanced dates.

In contrast to beet growing for sugar production, in which the object is to suppress bolting as much as possible, is the correlative activity of the seed-production enterprises, in which maximum seeding of the sugar-beet plants is desired. The responses of the sugar beet to temperature as well as to day length have extremely important relations to seed-production methods, since, within mass-selected varieties, the types vary in their responses, especially to thermal induction of fruiting (seed production brought on by exposures to low temperatures). Selection away from the bolting tendency to obtain varieties which will not go to seed the first season if sown at advanced planting dates has brought up new problems in maintaining these varieties because, within such nonbolting varieties, there remains a certain small proportion of individual plants which still will go to seed readily under mild exposures. If seed production is carried on under mild winter conditions, the individuals which have a tendency to bolt go to seed; those which are slow to bolt do not. Thus, the desired characteristics of the nonbolting sort may be changed drastically in one season of reproduction because of this failure of the desired individuals to go to seed. Certain established sugar-beet seed-growing areas of the United States which have a rather mild winter climate are thus unsuitable for producing seed of the strains refractory to bolting. This seeming impasse in producing seed of nonbolting varieties for growers' use has been overcome by research on the fundamental principles involved. Genetic factors determining bolting proclivities have recently been determined. Studies of thermal induction and photoinduction (fruiting induced by length of day) have been made (7), and it has been found that in the former case duration of exposure below some critical temperature (about 45° F.) is a determining factor for fruiting. There is evidence that the thermal-induction process may be reversible, warm periods nullifying previous effects of cold. An important practical outcome of this research is the recognition that a long exposure to prevailingly cool weather, not necessarily below freezing, causes practically all refractory types to go to seed, thus turning attention away from brief, extreme cold exposures and emphasizing desirability of long-continued low temperatures which still permit some growth. The recent development of the sugar-beet-seed enterprise in the Pacific Northwest stems from these physiological discoveries, and this area has been found suitable for the reproduction of the varieties which could not be grown satisfactorily elsewhere.

Fitting Cropping Practices to Plant and Climatic Requirements

Placing the right plant in the right environment is fundamental in man's conquest of nature. Certain soil types are sought to meet the requirements of a given plant. The obstacle that climate presents in arid, continental regions because of deficits in precipitation is met by utilizing water from distant watersheds or underground sources. Thus the desert is reclaimed. Adjustment of the cropping season so that untoward climatic conditions are avoided likewise assists man in his conquest of the environment.

The recent entrance of sugar-beet culture into the Imperial Valley of California on thousands of acres is an arresting example of such agricultural strategy. In this great fertile expanse, practically rainless and torrid in the summer months, the lack of rainfall has long been met by irrigation. By reversing the sugar-beet season and planting in late September or October, the crop, which has been customarily cataloged as fixed to the spring-summer-fall schedule, has been introduced successfully into a new environment. But even in the Imperial Valley the winter temperatures may induce ordinary varieties to go to seed in the first season. Hence the varieties to be planted must be chosen to fit the climatic situation. U. S. 15, a variety moderately resistant to curly top, obtained in breeding work of the Division of Sugar Plant Investigations, has also the valuable character of being a type slow to bolt under cold exposure. This variety and other selections are coming into wide use for fall and winter plantings. The accomplishment in the Imperial Valley and the possibilities for extension into other regions of mild winter climate hinge therefore on the development and maintenance of nonbolting strains. As such agricultural problems are encountered, emphasis must shift from the more or less fixed factors of the environment to consideration of the right plant for the place and the potentialities within the plant material which may permit better adaptations to the imposed conditions.

Disease Epidemics and Climate

In large areas of the United States within the temperature belt for efficient production, sugar beets are not now grown. Usually some major factor such as lack of an adequate water supply is responsible. In other districts, the reason is economic. There are, however, many areas having adequate soil and water resources where the growing of sugar beets was started, met obstacles, and was abandoned. In the western part of United States, the limiting factor commonly was curly top, a virus disease. Curly top is introduced and spread in the sugar-beet field solely by its insect vector, or carrier, the beet leaf-

FIGURE 6.—Climate, through its influence on the insect-virus relationship, determines the degree of curly top exposure. The susceptible European variety planted here in the center strip has been almost completely destroyed, but the resistant varieties at left and right have made normal growth. (Twin Falls, Idaho, 1938.)

hopper. The prevalence of the disease in any season is a function of the size and movement of the beet leafhopper population. The insect population, in turn, is governed by the kinds and quantities of host plants on the western range lands, which are the breeding grounds of the leafhopper. Thus, in the complicated host-vector relationship of curly top, the effects of climate on the plant successions of western range lands determine curly top epidemics. The recurrent epidemics of curly top at one time seemed to present unconquerable obstacles to sugar-beet culture in the Western States. By the breeding and widespread introduction of curly-top-resistant varieties (*6*), the crop has been restored to the West, and production has been renewed in many districts previously abandoned (fig. 6).

Other areas of the United States are made almost marginal for sugar-beet production by leaf spot (*Cercospora beticola* Sacc.) (*5*). This fungus disease assumes epidemic proportions in warm seasons if rainy periods are frequent in the first half of the growing period. Fundamentally the relationship of epidemics to climate traces to the fungus, whose growth and spore formation are speeded by high temperatures and whose spread and infection require rainy weather. Where climatically induced epidemics have jeopardized production, the newly introduced leaf-spot-resistant varieties have great promise (*4*).

298737°—41——29 +

These plant diseases whose epidemic outbreaks affect the sugar beet as a crop plant are cited because the progress made toward control again turns attention to the plant as an adjustable factor in the environment-plant complex.

LITERATURE CITED

(1) BRANDES, E. W.
1940. RESEARCH ON SUGAR PLANTS AND SOME PRACTICAL ADAPTATIONS. Cong. Rec. App. 86: 3575–3577.

(2) ——— and SARTORIS, G. B.
1936. SUGARCANE: ITS ORIGIN AND IMPROVEMENT. U. S. Dept. Agr. Yearbook 1936: 561–623, illus.

(3) ——— SARTORIS, G. B., and GRASSL, C. O.
1939. ASSEMBLING AND EVALUATING WILD FORMS OF SUGARCANE AND CLOSELY RELATED PLANTS. Internatl. Soc. Sugar Cane Technol. Cong. Proc., Baton Rouge, La., 6: 128–154, illus.

(4) COONS, G. H.
1936. IMPROVEMENT OF THE SUGAR BEET. U. S. Dept. Agr. Yearbook 1936: 625–656, illus.

(5) ——— STEWART, DEWEY, and LARMER, F. G.
1930. THE SUGAR-BEET LEAF-SPOT DISEASE AND ITS CONTROL BY DIRECT MEASURES. U. S. Dept. Agr. Cir. 115, 20 pp., illus.

(6) OWEN, FORREST V., ABEGG, FRED A., MURPHY, ALBERT M., TOLMAN, BION, PRICE, CHARLES, LARMER, FINLEY G., and CARSNER, EUBANKS.
1939. CURLY-TOP-RESISTANT SUGAR-BEET VARIETIES IN 1938. U. S. Dept. Agr. Cir. 513, 10 pp., illus.

(7) ——— CARSNER, EUBANKS, AND STOUT, MYRON.
1940. PHOTOTHERMAL INDUCTION OF FLOWERING IN SUGAR BEETS. Jour. Agr. Res. 61: 101–124, illus.

(8) TJEBBES, K.
1933. THE WILD BEETS OF THE NORTH SEA REGION. Bot. Notiser 1933: 305–315, illus.

(9) [TOLMACHEV, M. I., and ILYINSKY, B. I.]
1934. [ON THE MOVEMENT OF SUGAR-BEET CULTURE NORTHWARD IN U. S. S. R.] Nauch. Zap. Sakh. Promysh. 11: 1–16, illus.

(10) TOTTINGHAM, W. E., LEPKOVSKY, S., SCHULZ, E. R., and LINK, K. P.
1926. CLIMATIC EFFECTS IN THE METABOLISM OF THE SUGAR BEET. Jour. Agr. Res. 33: 59–76, illus.

(11) [VAVILOV, NIKOLAI IVANOVICH.]
1935. [BOTANICAL-GEOGRAPHICAL BASES OF BREEDING.] 60 pp., illus. [In Russian. Summary in French in Rev. de Bot. Appl. et d'Agr. Trop. 16: 124–129, 214–223, 285–293.]

(12) WILEY, H. W.
1901. THE SUGAR BEET: CULTURE, SEED DEVELOPMENT, MANUFACTURE, AND STATISTICS. U. S. Dept. Agr. Farmers' Bul. 52, 48 pp., illus. [2d rev. ed.]

(13) ———
1901. THE INFLUENCE OF ENVIRONMENT UPON THE COMPOSITION OF THE SUGAR BEET. U. S. Bur. Plant Indus. Bul. 64, 32 pp., illus.

Climate and Forage Crops

By O. S. Aamodt [1]

NATURE did a superb job with the grasses and legumes, spreading them over much of the earth, adapting them to an immense range of climates. They would still be there to feed our flocks and herds and to hold and build the soil if there were no other crop plants whatever in the world. This article tells about the adaptability of the grasses and legumes from coast to coast and north to south in the United States—where they came from, what species thrive in different regions and areas, and in general what is being done to make them still more useful in modern agriculture.

[1] O. S. Aamodt is Head Agronomist, in Charge, Division of Forage Crops and Diseases, Bureau of Plant Industry.

In all climates, whatever the degree of latitude or longitude and at almost every altitude from seacoast to alpine heights, grasses and legumes provide the principal source of feed for livestock, at the same time serving to hold the land surface in place against the rush of floodwaters and the force of the wind. Of the many kinds of grasses and legumes, only a few are adapted to any particular climate. Those that thrive on sand dunes along the seacoast would perish on alpine ranges, species found in arid wastes fail in more humid environments, and those common to warm climates succumb to cold, while species hardy in cold climates fail to survive tropical or even subtropical heat.

In the United States, where over half of the land area is covered with grasses and legumes, many of those important on ranges and in pastures and meadows are native species. Many other species, gathered in foreign countries by explorers, sent home by missionaries or other travelers, or brought in by immigrants, have proved valuable supplements to the native plants. Thousands of such introductions fail to find suitable conditions in this country; others react favorably to the environment characterizing one or another part of the country; still others await improvement by selection or breeding or the development of suitable cultural methods. To determine the range of adaptation of introduced species, to develop systems of culture, to bring about improvement by breeding and selection, and to relate these advances to climatic requirements are the objectives of intensive research by the United States Department of Agriculture and the State experiment stations. It is through such research that the United States has acquired and is currently acquiring new and valuable species for agricultural and, as in the case of soybeans, even industrial use, under the different climatic conditions.

The objective of the plant breeder is to develop varieties that are better able to withstand the destructive effects of limiting factors such as climate, unfavorable soil conditions, and pests—weeds, diseases, and insects. The process is one of fitting plants into their environments. Nature has carried on this process over thousands of years with innumerable plant generations. The new environment created by modern agriculture with its destructive tillage operations and intensified outbreaks of plant pests needs new plants adapted to the changed conditions. The breeder is expected to develop these new plants in a relatively short time and within a relatively small number of plant generations. He is able to do this with the aid of scientific knowledge gathered from the fundamental plant sciences and from practical studies and observations. Improved varieties resistant to destructive factors will naturally yield more abundantly than the old and will raise crop values per acre without materially increasing production costs.

ALFALFA

The wide distribution of alfalfa in the world indicates a remarkable adaptability to various climates and soils. Though the crop requires considerable moisture to produce profitable yields, it does best in a relatively dry climate where water is available for irrigation. It will survive a long period of drought but is not productive under such conditions. It is not so well adapted to a humid climate, partly because acid soils are developed under heavy precipitation and partly because diseases are more destructive in humid regions. The rapid extension of alfalfa production in the United States dates from the introduction of Chilean seed into California about 1850. This variety was not resistant to cold, however, and for several years no alfalfa sufficiently hardy to survive the winters of the Northern States was available. Through introduction from other regions where the winters are more severe than they are in Chile, through selection by both nature and man, and through breeding, alfalfas have been made available that are sufficiently hardy to survive with reasonable certainty the winters of any climate in the United States.

Climatic Relationships of Alfalfa

It is generally believed that the native habitat of alfalfa is southwestern Asia. The climate in this region is characterized by cold winters and hot summers. The precipitation, which except at high altitudes is rather limited, occurs mainly in late fall, winter, and early spring. The summers are relatively dry, with low humidity. Historical accounts indicate that it was in this general region that alfalfa was first cultivated. From there it was taken to the Mediterranean countries and to other parts of the world, succeeding best where climatic conditions, particularly humidity, were somewhat similar to those of its native habitat and where sufficient soil moisture was available from subirrigation or surface irrigation. With increased knowledge of other requirements such as those for lime, for inoculation with nitrifying bacteria, and for certain plant-food elements, the culture of the crop has spread to all parts of the world. It is now grown successfully under a wide range of climatic conditions, but it has never been as long-lived in humid as in dry climates. The difficulty in curing the hay in humid areas undoubtedly has had an effect in discouraging interest in alfalfa. Today Argentina with about 20 million acres and the United States with nearly 14 million lead all other countries in production.

Attempts were made as early as 1736 to grow alfalfa in the eastern part of the United States, but it was not until about 1850, when it was introduced into California from Chile, that the crop showed much promise. This is explained by the fact that conditions in California were somewhat similar to those in its native habitat. Alfalfa growing then spread rapidly to other States, but for many years the crop was important only in the West. As knowledge of the requirements of the crop increased, it moved eastward, until some of the Middle Western States now lead all others in acreage cut for hay (fig. 1). The greater part of the seed is still produced in the dry Western States. For some unknown reason seed sets very sparingly under humid conditions. During dry seasons, however, considerable seed is produced in the Eastern States.

Moisture, Temperature, and Other Relationships

Alfalfa has a relatively high water requirement, about 800 pounds of water being required to produce 1 pound of dry matter (*2*).[2] As previously indicated, it succeeds best under conditions of low humidity, provided sufficient soil moisture is available. Under such conditions fields 15 and 20 years old were not uncommon

[2] Italic numbers in parentheses refer to Literature Cited, p. 457.

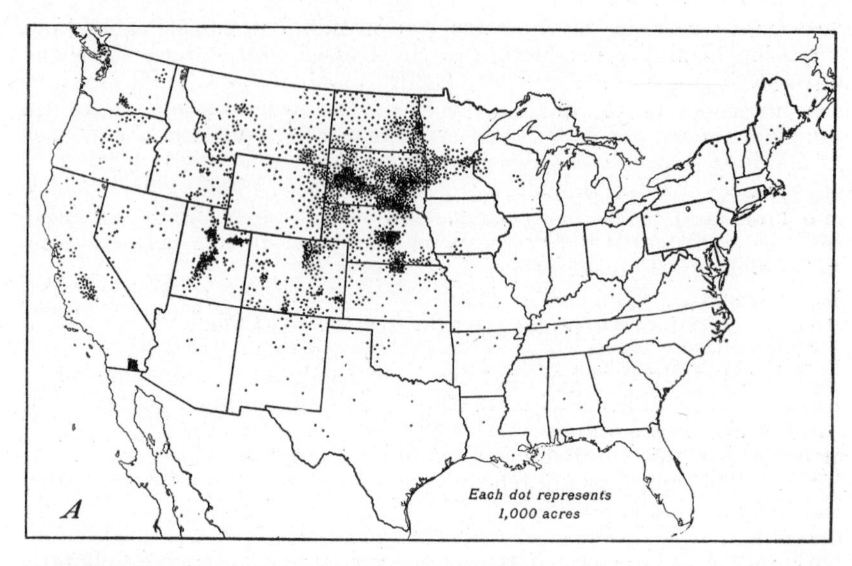

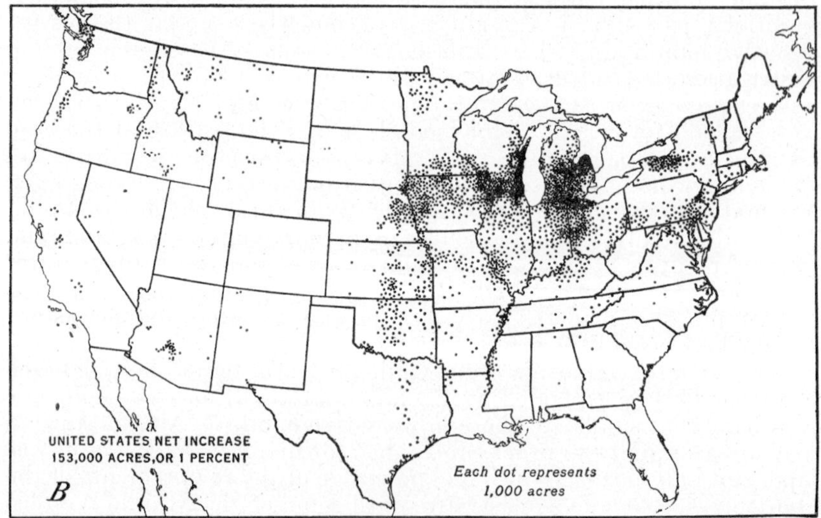

FIGURE 1.—The acreage of alfalfa cut for hay in the United States increased by 153,000 acres between 1929 and 1934. More than balancing the net decrease in the western half of the country (*A*), was the large increase in the eastern half (*B*).

until insects and diseases became increasingly destructive. Exhaustion of certain plant-food elements as a result of growing alfalfa on the same land for many years has tended to reduce productivity and to shorten the life of a stand. Where humidity is high it has seldom been possible to maintain a satisfactory stand for more than 5 or 6 years, partly because of the prevalence of diseases under such conditions. A combination of high humidity, high precipitation, and high temperatures is particularly unfavorable. In some instances where the precipitation is less than 20 inches annually and irrigation is not possible, the high water requirement of alfalfa has resulted in the exhaustion of the subsoil moisture. This has occurred in parts of the Great Plains where good yields were obtained for several years on land sown to alfalfa for the first time. Where it was sown a second time on the same land the yields were far from satisfactory. A careful study showed that in some instances the first seeding had exhausted the subsoil moisture to a depth of 40 feet so that subsequent seedings had to depend upon the annual precipitation, which was not sufficient to meet the requirements for maximum production (*9*, *10*).

Winter killing is often associated with lack of sufficient moisture during the preceding summer and fall by which the vigor of the plants has been reduced to such an extent that they are unable to endure low temperatures.

Heaving from freezing and thawing is responsible for serious losses in some of the Eastern States, usually where the soil is saturated with moisture.

A direct correlation is often shown between soil moisture, whether from precipitation or irrigation, and losses from diseases. Bacterial wilt, for instance, develops more rapidly where soil moisture is abundant and other conditions favor vigorous growth. Certain leaf and stem diseases and yellowing due to the potato leafhopper, *Empoascae fabae* (Harr.), are usually more destructive under humid than under dry conditions.

Alfalfa is more tolerant of extremes of heat and cold than most perennials. The species *Medicago falcata* L. has been reported as growing in Siberia where temperatures as low as −84° F. have been reported (*18*). Other conditions being favorable, certain varieties of alfalfa have been grown successfully where maximum summer temperatures exceed 120°F. Productivity and longevity vary with the species and variety. *M. falcata*, for instance, is usually able to endure a greater degree of cold than *M. sativa* L. or the *M. falcata* × *M. sativa* hybrid, but it is not usually productive or long-lived where the winters are mild and summers long and hot. Certain varieties of *M. sativa*, on the other hand, are not cold resistant and are most productive where the winters are mild and the summers long and warm, but they continue to grow during the winter after the more cold-resistant alfalfas become dormant. Between these extremes are found all gradations that have resulted either from natural selection or natural crossing.

In the United States three broad groups of alfalfas are recognized—hardy, medium hardy, and nonhardy. The regions to which they are adapted are shown in figure 2.

Variation in cold resistance among varieties and strains of alfalfa is illustrated in figure 3.

The response of alfalfas to length of day (photoperiodism) appears to be correlated in some way with their reaction to low temperatures. Under controlled greenhouse tests the nonhardy alfalfas were more vigorous and produced more growth with short days than the hardy alfalfas, while with long days the reverse was true (*19*).

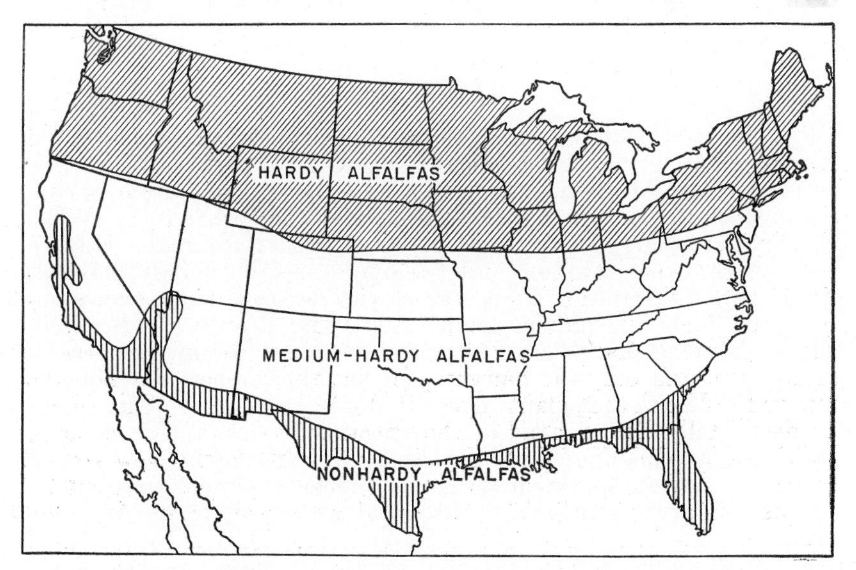

Figure 2.—Adaptation of hardy, medium-hardy, and nonhardy alfalfas.

FIGURE 3.—A demonstration of the difference in cold resistance of different alfalfas. The good stands in the center are Grimm and Canadian Variegated; those on both sides that have been winter-killed are Hairy Peruvian, Spanish, Argentine, and South African alfalfas.

Some recent studies have shown a direct relationship between reserves of food in the roots in the fall and winter killing and productivity the following year (*5*). Where growth is kept down, no opportunity is afforded for the storage of reserves in the roots, and the plants are so weakened that they are unable to endure low temperatures, whereas the same varieties when given an opportunity through proper management to store up reserves survive similar temperatures with little or no injury.

That varieties differ in their ability to survive ice sheets is generally recognized. As might be expected, ice sheets usually are less injurious to hardy than to nonhardy varieties. Some investigations point to the possibility that the injury is due to an accumulation of toxic products of respiration.

CLOVERS

Red clovers are adapted generally to the northern half of the United States, excluding the drier portions of the Great Plains. The various strains have little in common, as far as climatic adaptation is concerned, with the European stocks from which they originated. When red clover was first introduced by the early settlers in the Eastern States it was exposed to low winter temperatures which only the more hardy plants survived. As it was carried westward red clover encountered high midsummer temperatures and drought. The acclimated surviving plants were attacked by a new foe in the form of leafhoppers, and only the hairy types that the hoppers did not like survived. Then the plant diseases took their toll. The plant breeders finally had a hand in the selection process and assisted in evolving new types adapted to the climatic hazards in the New World.

The true clovers, species of the genus *Trifolium*, annual or perennial, are found in every continent of the world, and in all except Australia certain species form a part of the native flora. Only in very limited areas are climatic factors favorable for the continual growth of the perennial species throughout the year. In the cool part of the Temperate Zones the perennials may persist from year to year, but in countries with a more equatorial climate, the winter-annual species are most abundant, and the perennials behave principally as winter annuals. The three most important climatic factors affecting the distribution and development of the true clovers are rainfall, temperature, and light. A copious, uniform supply of soil moisture furnished by precipitation or irrigation and cool temperatures are most favorable for growth. Often a deficiency of light, due to shading by other plants, prevents establishment of seedlings.

Most of the species of agricultural importance appear to have originated in southern Europe and Asia Minor, where the annual rainfall, ranging from 17 inches upward, occurs principally during the winter months when the temperature is relatively cool. Rainfall and temperature are more favorable for clover in northern latitudes than in the Mediterranean regions, but the limitation of light due to the competition of the original tree and shrub growth was critical. Only when man gradually destroyed the tall-growing vegetation, permitting the encroachment of the low-growing species, did the clovers become widely distributed.

The *Melilotus* species, annuals and biennials, appear to have originated in the more arid regions of western Europe and Asia Minor. The early, commonly used name "Bokhara clover" indicates the general region of origin. Once established, the biennial species are tolerant of drought, though a good supply of soil moisture and cool temperatures are necessary for the germination and early growth of the seedling plants. The requirements of the winter-annual species of sweetclovers for moisture and temperature are similar to those of the winter-annual species of the true clovers.

In the United States, climate has had an indirect as well as a direct effect on the distribution and use of clovers. Most of the native North American species of *Trifolium* are found in the Rocky, Sierra Nevada, and Cascade Ranges and are of relatively minor importance though they provide grazing and hay locally. All of the true clovers and sweetclovers of agricultural value are exotic (foreign) plants that were introduced deliberately or by chance and have become established in the environments to which they are best adapted.

Under severe or hazardous conditions the important species of the true clovers—red clover (*Trifolium pratense* L.), white clover (*T. repens* L.), alsike clover (*T. hybridum* L.), strawberry clover (*T. fragiferum* L.)—may behave as annuals and biennials as well as perennials. Crimson clover (*T. incarnatum* L.), low hop clover (*T. procumbens* L.), least hop clover (*T. dubium* Sibth.), Persian clover (*T. resupinatum* L.), cluster clover (*T. glomeratum* L.), subterranean clover (*T. subterraneum* L.) and lappa clover (*T. lappaceum* L.) are principally winter-annual species, although crimson clover is being effectively used as a summer annual in northern Maine.

The principal species of sweetclover (*Melilotus*) are biennial yellow sweetclover (*M. officinalis* Lam.), biennial white sweetclover (*M. alba* Desr.), the winter annual sour or bitter clover (*M. indica* All.), and the summer-annual forms of the biennials. The general distribution is shown in figure 4. General climatic relationships of the regions of distribution may be obtained by comparing this map with the rainfall and temperature maps given in Part 5 of this book.

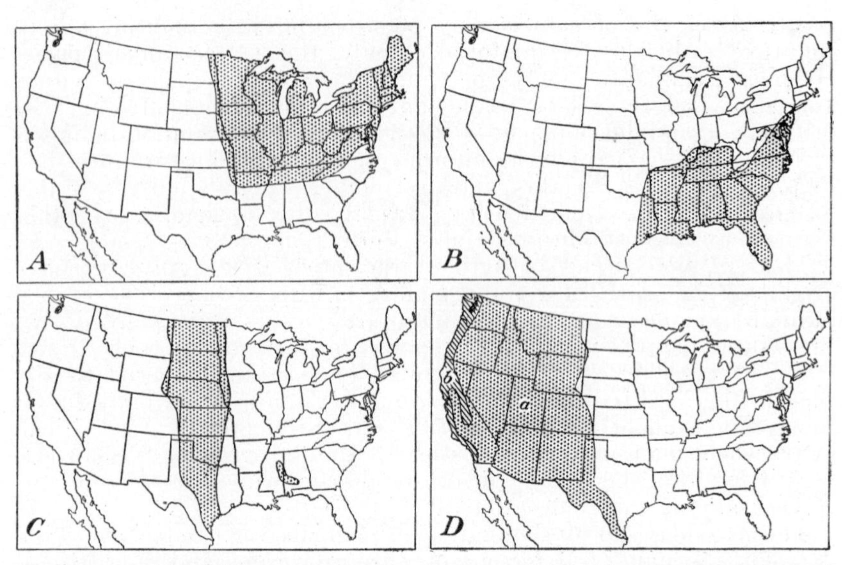

FIGURE 4.—General regional adaptation of clovers: *A*, Red clover, white clover, and alsike clover; *B*, crimson clover, hop clovers, white clover, Persian clover, cluster clover, subterranean clover; *C*, sweetclovers; *D*, *a*, sweetclover, red clover, white clover, alsike clover, strawberry clover; *b*, red clover, sweetclover, winter-annual species of true clovers.

CLIMATIC RELATIONSHIPS OF CLOVERS

Sweetclovers may be grown in any part of the United States where the spring and summer rainfall amounts to 17 inches or more; on acid soils, the application of lime is necessary. Production of sour or bitter clover is confined to the territory bordering the Gulf of Mexico and to southern California, New Mexico, and Arizona; where rainfall is insufficient it may be grown under irrigation. Throughout the Intermountain States, sweetclover and other clovers—principally red clover, white clover, and alsike clover—are widely grown either under irrigation or at high altitudes where rainfall is sufficient. Strawberry clover is particularly well adapted to wet, saline, or alkaline soils of this region. On the Pacific coast, red clover is grown from central Oregon to the Canadian boundary and sweetclovers and the winter-annual species of the true clovers throughout the region where sufficient moisture is available.

Wide differences in the adaptation of varieties and strains of most of the clovers and their direct reaction to temperature, moisture, and length of day exist in all species. Such responses limit the use of any variety for maximum production. In the field the effect of a single climatic factor on plant behavior cannot be distinctly segregated from the interaction of other factors, and interpretations must be tempered accordingly.

Very often red clover stands are lost during the winter months. In part this may be due to low temperatures, to alternating cool and warm temperatures, or to heaving. Unadapted strains, diseased plants, or those that have been closely grazed or cut during the fall months are particularly susceptible to winter hazards (fig. 5). These conditions also affect white clover, alsike clover, and strawberry clover in varying degrees. On the other hand, biennial sweetclover species are normally resistant to low temperatures but are very susceptible to heaving (fig. 6). Winter-killing usually occurs after the first year's growth of sweetclover is cut in the fall, when the plants are making and storing reserves of food in the roots.

Low winter temperatures definitely limit the distribution and adaptation of the winter-annual species of all clovers. Low hop clover and crimson clover appear to be the most tolerant and are the species responsible for extending the winter-annual clover belt as far north as it is shown in figure 4. Sour or bitter clover and berseem clover (*Trifolium alexandrinum* L.) are among the species least tolerant of winter cold. Good fall vegetative growth before the advent of minimum temperatures is the best protection against winter killing.

Wherever clovers are grown in the United States high summer temperatures are not fatal provided soil moisture is abundant and the root systems of the plants are large enough to absorb the moisture required for transpiration. Often, however, even under favorable conditions the removal of a mature companion grain crop from a vigorous growth of red clover, exposing the young plants to the direct rays of the sun, results in the death of many plants. High summer temperatures inhibit the germination of the seed of most of the winter-annual species. The fact that there are different temperature requirements for germination among species contributes to their range of adaptation, since these requirements are related to latitude, soil type, and plant associations (*25*).

For the true clovers rainfall is probably more important than any other climatic factor. All clovers require a moist soil at the time of germination and establishment of seedlings, and a deficiency in soil moisture at this time is probably responsible for more losses than any other factor of climate. Seeds of certain species absorb moisture rapidly (this is a common characteristic of crimson clover), so that when rainfall periods of short duration are followed by dry weather, the young seedlings are killed before the plants are established.

Sweetclovers, when well established, send their extensive taproots to the lower soil levels and persist under drought conditions, though little vegetative growth may be made.

As already noted, when clovers are grown in association with companion crops the limitation of light is often fatal to the seedlings. Even when a stand is established, growth is slow and poor unless the plants get direct light for at least a considerable part of the day (*8*). The clovers are long-day plants, but the species and varieties differ widely in their response to different lengths of exposure to light (fig. 7). Temperature, age, and the carbohydrate-nitrogen balance within the plant appear to affect the response to length of day. The winter-annual species when planted in the spring in the Cotton Belt or the Corn Belt make only a few inches of growth before flowering is induced by the increasing length of day. If the clover is planted in August or later, when day length is

FIGURE 5.—Winter killing of red clover is affected by seed source: A stand of Ohio red clover (*A*) has survived low winter temperatures that left alive only a few plants of French red clover (*B*).

FIGURE 6.—Sweetclover roots heaved out of the soil during late winter.

decreasing, vegetative growth occurs without reproduction. Crimson clover, a true winter annual of the Southeastern States, when planted in May in northern Maine behaves as a summer annual. Growth is rapid with the cool temperatures and adequate rainfall, but blossoming begins in late August. At this time the length of day is rapidly decreasing, and vegetative growth is again stimulated. In the greenhouse true biennial sweetclovers blossom freely a few weeks after planting when subjected to 20 or more hours of illumination. The double-cut or medium forms of red clover blossom freely in the fall in short days provided the plants have made vigorous vegetative growth during the spring and summer months, but the single-cut forms, which require a longer photoperiod, remain in vegetative growth.

FIGURE 7.—Effect of length of day on the blossoming of double and single forms of red clover. All the plants were grown for 4 months with a 14-hour day: *A*, Double-cut red clover; *B*, Single-cut red clover.

The discussion so far has been principally confined to the direct reaction of important climatic factors on clovers. Many indirect relationships exist. The adaptation of red clover in the southern part of the Red Clover Belt is in part dependent upon resistance to southern anthracnose, while in the central and northern part this disease is not troublesome (*15*). The occurrence and development of the causal organism, *Colletotrichum trifolii* S. M. Bain, is stimulated by long periods of warm, moist weather, and thus the effect of climate on the pathogens, or disease organisms, determines the strain of red clover that can be successfully grown. Many of the true clovers and several sweetclovers are self-sterile, depending upon insects—mostly various species of bees—for cross-pollination. Since rainfall and temperature affect the activity of the bees, seed production is favorably or adversely influenced accordingly. In the Corn Belt climate particularly influences seed production of red clover, first by its effect on the activity of honeybees and secondly through the stimulation of growth of other flowering plants competing with red clover as a source of pollen and nectar; the latter cannot usually be obtained from red clover by the honeybee. The desert climate surrounding the irrigated projects of the Intermountain States is unfavorable to other blossoming plants when red clover is in flower, and because of this shortage honeybees are forced to resort to red clover, with resulting large yields of seed (*7*).

In the eastern part of the United States the effect of high rainfall in developing acid soils has indirectly reduced the possibilities of extensive use of sweetclover unless lime is applied, since sweetclover is not tolerant of acid soils.

GRASSES

The grasses that persist naturally in any given region over a long period of time are those that have been successful in adjusting themselves to the factors that limit growth. In order to survive, they have to withstand the extremes of drought, cold, and wind, as well as the diseases and insects of the region, and compete successfully with other plants. The species and varieties that can grow to maturity and reproduce in competition with other plants are the ones selected

Figure 8.—Observational plantings of blue grama at Lincoln, Nebr., produced from seed obtained in: *A*, Oklahoma; *B*, Colorado; *C*, New Mexico; *D*, Nebraska.

by nature's cut-and-try process to cover the land. Darwin has given a vivid picture of this struggle for existence, calling the selective process the "survival of the fittest." Over a period of hundreds of thousands of years nature has produced an adapted vegetation, the distribution of which is governed almost entirely by climate. An example of the variations that result from climate is shown in blue grama grass in figure 8.

The first settlers on our eastern shores destroyed the natural vegetation and substituted for it various kinds of cultivated and grassland crops. This substitution gradually progressed westward until crops replaced the natural vegetation developed by nature on practically all land of any agricultural value. When the farmers brought with them crop seeds from the Old World, they carried on a process of cut and try very much as nature did to find out which crops were best adapted. The only difference was that the farmer took only a few hundred years to make his pattern, whereas nature took many thousands of years in perfecting hers.

The climatic conditions common to the various regions of the United States are essentially the same today as when the first European settlers arrived. The environment, however, has been modified through intensive land use and more complete utilization of the grass. The plant breeder is developing new forms of grasses better adapted to the ever-changing cropping environment and the intensive management practices now in use. In the arid and semiarid regions the native grasses are well adapted to the prevailing climatic conditions and provide an abundance of types that can be fitted into the changing environment and changing management practices.

In the more humid areas of the United States, for example, particularly in the Southeast, emphasis is needed on adaptation to lower levels of soil fertility and use in more intensive cropping systems.

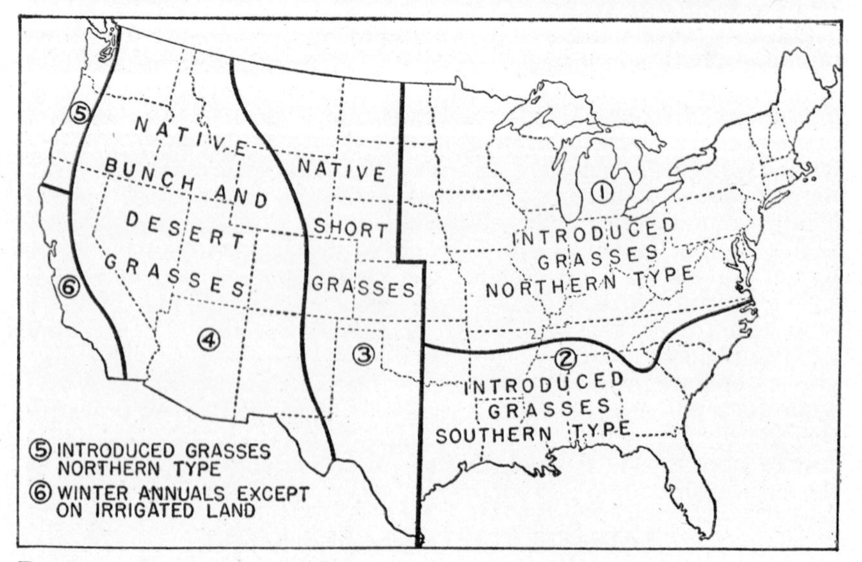

Figure 9.—Grasslands of the United States, showing the dominant type of grasses in each region as determined by the climate.

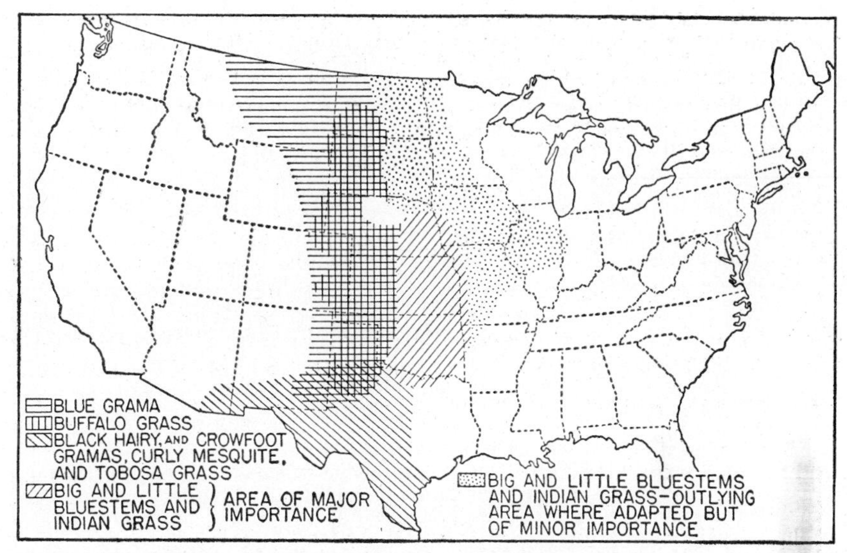

FIGURE 10.—Sections of the United States where native short grasses and prairie grasses are well adapted and are of primary importance.

Introduced species from similar climatic regions in other parts of the world are the best source of improved varieties for this region. The general objectives of the breeder are to produce varieties resistant to drought, disease, and insects, tolerant to temperature extremes and repeated defoliation, adapted for growing in association with other desirable species, palatable, productive, and with growth habits that can take full advantage of the seasonal changes favorable to plant growth.

The distribution in the United States of approximately 1,100 species of grasses, both native and introduced, is largely determined by individual climatic factors and their combination. About 100 of these grasses are of economic importance to agriculture, and this number is divided almost equally between those adapted to humid and to dry-land conditions. Moisture has played an important role in determining the well-defined centers of development of these species. The predominating grasses adapted to arid and semiarid regions are native to the United States; introduced species predominate in the humid regions. Figure 9 shows the general distribution of grasses.

Temperature further limits adaptation, and a striking difference is to be noted between native and introduced species. In the humid regions, regional adaptation is dependent on temperature. The bluegrasses, orchard grass, redtop, timothy, etc., predominate in the North, while Bermuda grass, carpet grass, Dallis grass, and others prevail in the South. In regions of limited rainfall, however, the same native species may extend over a wide range of varying temperatures, as shown in figure 10.

CLIMATIC ADAPTATION OF GRASSES

The work of Brown (*1*), Harrison (*6*), Evans (*3*), and others has shown that temperature and moisture are of equal importance in determining the geographical regions to which the various grasses are adapted. Brown found that the optimum temperature for the production of forage from Kentucky and Canada bluegrass was between 80° and 90° F.; for orchard grass it was 70° F.; while Bermuda grass was more productive at 100° than at any lower temperature. Root and rhizome development were influenced by varying temperatures; 60° was found to be the most favorable temperature for Kentucky bluegrass, 50° for Canada bluegrass, and 70° for orchard grass. Chemical composition was found to be affected by temperature, the crude-fiber content of the herbage increasing as the temperature increased from 40° to 60° whereas the crude-protein content declined slightly.

Grasses are annuals and perennials. Annuals predominate only in a comparatively small area along the southern part of the Pacific slope (region 6 in fig. 9) but perennials carpet vast areas in all parts of the country with green. Because of this wide distribution, the perennial grasses must be able to survive wider ranges of moisture and temperature than such annual crops as the cereals, and they must also be able to produce despite frequent defoliation during periods of limited moisture, high temperatures, or other climatic extremes.

Moisture requirements determine the distribution of grasses not only in broad regions but also within regions. For example, in the humid South, carpet grass and St. Augustine grass are best adapted to moist areas and Bermuda grass and centipede grass to the drier situations. In the humid North, reed canary grass and redtop are considered wet-land grasses, while Canada bluegrass and bromegrass are good examples of grasses adapted to conditions of limited moisture. In the semiarid regions the grama grasses and buffalo grass can endure long periods of limited rainfall, while the bluestems and certain of the wheatgrasses, such as western wheatgrass, require moist situations for survival.

Sudan grass is able to grow vigorously in relatively dry soils at midsummer temperatures. It is well adapted to the prevailing climatic conditions in the central and southern Great Plains. It is also grown extensively as a supplementary pasture and hay crop in the North Central States. This grass appears to be well adapted in the Southeastern States, but the climate is so favorable for the growth of disease organisms parasitic on Sudan grass that the crop is greatly limited. The plant breeder now has promising strains highly resistant to the more common diseases in the region. The indirect effect of climate ir favoring disease on an otherwise well-adapted crop plant is greatly reduced by the production of resistant varieties.

Crested wheatgrass is one of the most cold- and drought-resistant grasses grown commercially in the United States. For this reason it is particularly well suited to the northern Great Plains, where its use for hay and pasture has expanded greatly in recent years. It has also given good results in eastern Washington and Oregon where the moisture is limited, and at altitudes of 5,000 feet or more farther south. It is not adapted to the milder climate of the southern Plains, and under the more favorable moisture conditions of the Eastern States it is not equal to timothy and other adapted grasses.

There has been an erroneous idea that the native dry-land grasses adapted to the Great Plains would be desirable for dry summers in the humid East. Numerous tests with dry-land grasses in the humid sections, however, have shown them to be lower in production than locally adapted species except possibly during short periods of severe drought. Only one grass, bromegrass, originally considered of value mainly for dry-land conditions, has become important in the humid East, where it is of value as a summer drought-resistant grass. Reed canary grass is interesting in that it will make excellent growth with limited moisture—an unusual characteristic for a grass adapted to moist conditions.

Moisture is a factor also in the winter survival of grasses, especially those in the dry northern Plains. The loss of grass stands during the winter months is often ascribed to winter killing or low temperatures when in reality it is due to lack of moisture, or desiccation of plant tissues. No doubt this factor has played a part in determining the grass cover in different areas. In such cases the effects of moisture and temperature are closely related.

In general it can be said that the grasses adapted to the humid regions are more influenced by varying temperatures than are those adapted to the dry lands. Blue grama grass, one of the most widely distributed and desirable species of the Plains, continues to make growth under temperatures varying from 60° to 110° F. Under favorable moisture conditions, summer temperatures have never been high enough to retard the growth of the common summer-growing native species. On the other hand, crested wheatgrass makes little or no growth during periods of high temperature. Its behavior is similar to that of Kentucky bluegrass in the humid regions; both make their maximum growth during the months of medium temperature in spring and fall and become dormant during months of high temperature. In the South lack of cold resistance limits the distribution of many desirable pasture grasses.

The effect of shade or light influences the growth and development of grasses to a lesser degree. Certain grasses have the inherent ability to survive under reduced light, while many others are adversely affected. Development of grasses adapted to growing in partial shade is especially important for lawns. In the North the fescues—red fescue and chewing fescue—and rough stalk bluegrass are the most important, while in the South St. Augustine grass is best adapted to the shade. The latter two, however, require ample moisture for growth, while the fescues will grow with limited moisture. Orchard grass, one of the better pasture grasses, will grow under partial shade. Intensity of light and length of day have a marked influence on leaf and seed development of many native grasses. The effect of shade in retarding the growth of undesirable grasses may be beneficial, as in the control of crabgrass in lawns. Crabgrass requires ample light for growth, and if desirable grasses are allowed to grow tall enough to shade the crabgrass seedlings, they may be materially reduced or eliminated.

Wind helps to determine the rate of evaporation and thus influences the moisture supply. It is also a factor in spreading or retarding fungus-disease attacks, especially in the case of turf grasses.

LESPEDEZA AND OTHER LEGUMES

Lespedeza

In the areas of heavy rainfall in the Southern and Southeastern States, much of the lime-deficient soil is too acid for successful and profitable production of such legumes as red clover and alfalfa. A well-adapted, acid-tolerant, nitrogen-fixing legume in the cropping system of this region was badly needed to keep up the productivity of the soil. Plant explorers and plant breeders finally found such a legume in lespedeza. In the short period of approximately two decades its use has spread to about 20 million acres of land.

The climate of the eastern half of the United States south of the Great Lakes is especially favorable to lespedeza (*20, 21*). West of the one-hundredth meridian in the Great Plains region the crop has not been successful. The relative importance of the various factors of climate in their influence on growth has not been definitely determined, but a high rainfall, well distributed throughout the growing season, together with relatively high humidity and temperature, seems essential for the best results with this very useful crop. The heavy rainfall of the East results in leaching and an acid soil condition which, together with other changes, is detrimental to the growth of many plants, but lespedeza is able to make successful growth under these conditions and to overcome the competition of other plants.

Length of day as determined by latitude also affects the adaptation of varieties of lespedeza. Common lespedeza succeeds best in the southern half of the eastern part of the United States and Korean lespedeza in the central and more northern part. Only the earliest maturing varieties of Korean lespedeza mature seed in the Great Lakes section, and only common lespedeza succeeds in the area bordering the Gulf of Mexico.

While lespedeza is happily at home in this vast area from the Great Lakes to the Gulf of Mexico and from the Atlantic Ocean to the Ozark Mountains, it is only in recent years that the crop has attained

298737°—41——30

major importance. The reason is that Korean lespedeza, the variety best suited to much of this area, was not introduced until December 1919. Since that date, however, it has been planted on millions of acres of farm lands and on eroding fields and roadways and has materially improved the standard of living of many people in the region.

MISCELLANEOUS LEGUMES

Crotalaria (*12*) is also adapted to poor acid soils and a humid climate, but it demands higher temperatures than lespedeza. This limits it to the Southeast, where, on sandy and sandy loam soils, it is an excellent cover and soil-improving crop. Climatic conditions in the western half of the United States do not seem to be favorable to the growth of crotalaria.

Although the area planted to velvetbeans (*22*) each season exceeds 2 million acres, they are limited to the lower Cotton Belt and were extended into Georgia and Alabama only by the use of early-maturing varieties. Velvetbeans like a warm climate with plenty of moisture. The cowpea (*16*) can be grown somewhat farther north, and the total acreage exceeds 6 million. Diseases and parasites that thrive in warm climates have tended to limit the usefulness of this crop and have necessitated the development of resistant varieties. Because cowpeas and velvetbeans are among the few legumes well adapted to the lower South, they are vital in the economic life of the southern farmer.

Climatic factors very largely determine the possible use of cover and green-manure crops for soil improvement. Field peas (*14*), vetches (*13*), bur-clovers (*11*), and crimson clover, which are winter annuals under mild climatic conditions, require comparatively high mean minimum winter temperatures for successful growth. The minimum growth temperature varies with the different crops and this determines which ones can be used most advantageously in a given locality. Since the zero growth point—the minimum temperature at which a plant will make any growth—is directly correlated with its winter hardiness, or its ability to stand low temperatures without being killed, the absolute minimum temperature as well as the mean, or average, minimum is a factor in determining the possible use of certain crops in a given area. Austrian winter field peas, for instance, commonly used as a winter cover crop in the South, have a lower zero

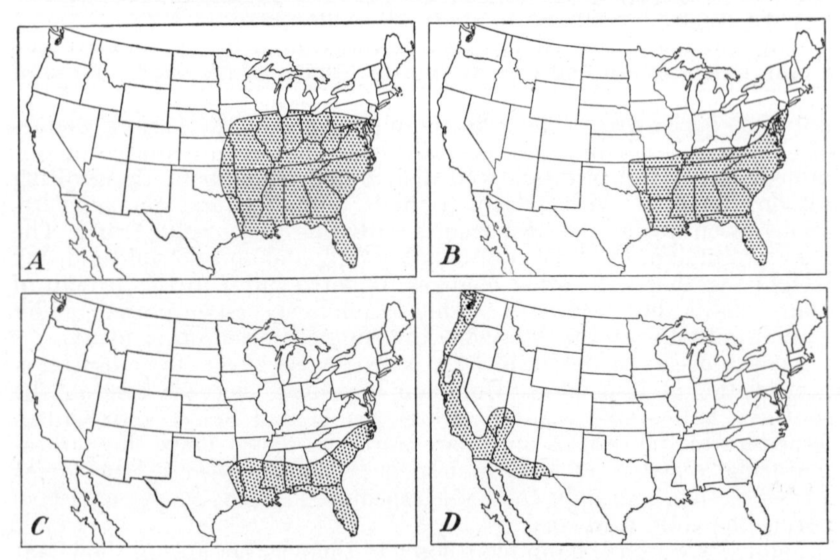

FIGURE 11.—Forage crops adapted to the various climatic regions of the United States. *A*, Lespedeza; *B* and *D*, winter-annual legumes; *C*, velvetbeans and crotalaria.

growth point than hairy vetch; this means that the latter is more winter hardy because it stops growing sooner than the field peas. Thus hairy vetch stands the occasional low temperatures in the South with less injury and can be grown as a winter crop farther north.

When a plant has made succulent or rapid growth by reason of comparatively high temperatures, it will be much more severely injured by a sudden drop in temperature than by a gradual change. The not uncommon sudden winter changes in the Southeastern States and the frequent comparatively high prevailing temperatures limit the use of winter cover crops to the more winter hardy, except in the milder sections, where low temperatures are only occasionally experienced.

In the northern latitudes, where low temperatures preclude the growing of cover crops in the winter, the same crops—field peas, crimson clover, and hairy vetch—used in the South for winter can be grown in the summer.

Climatic factors not only determine the region in which certain cover crops can be used effectively but also the areas in which seed can be produced. It is not possible to produce seed of field peas and hairy vetch economically in the Cotton Belt, principally because of unfavorable light and temperature conditions. In the Pacific coast areas and at northern latitudes farther east, seed production of these crops is possible, and the South is supplied with seed from these areas (fig. 11).

SOYBEANS

Though soybeans are grown in widely separated parts of the world, successful production is largely dependent on climate. Further, their use within a given area is dependent on the adaptation of varieties to local climatic conditions. Through the centuries an almost endless number of varieties, ranging in time required for maturity from 75 to 200 days, have been developed, and though each of these has a rather limited range of adaptation, the large number of varieties with their differing climatic requirements has extended the culture of the crop far beyond the limits that would otherwise have been possible. It is this adaptation of varieties that has made possible the extensive use of soybeans in the United States. Differences in behavior of the same variety in different localities are often so striking as to make it seem to be another variety. The Manchu, Dunfield, Illini, and other varieties used in the North are not suited for the South, while the Mammoth Yellow, Otootan, Laredo, and others adapted to the South do not mature seed in the shorter growing season of the North. Climate has played a major role in developing varieties and determining the limitations of their use through the centuries during which the crop has been grown. Today this same influence is the most prominent factor in directing the course of soybean production in the United States.

Climatic Relationships of Soybeans

The general climatic requirements (*17*) of the soybean (*Soja max* (L.) Piper), which is perhaps one of the earliest crops grown by man, are about the same as for corn. The wild soybean (*Glycine ussuriensis* Regal and Maack), from which the cultivated form is thought to have been derived, occurs throughout China, Manchuria, Japan, Chosen, and southern Siberia. Cultivated soybeans are grown to the greatest extent in China, where they occupy about 9 percent of the total cultivated area. Other countries of the Far East, in order of importance in acreage and production, are Manchuria, Chosen, and Japan.

The wealth of varieties and the antiquity of soybean culture in the Far East indicate that the climatic conditions are naturally favorable to the crop. Manchuria, "the Land of Beans," is about equal in size to the five States of Montana, Wyoming, North and South Dakota, and Nebraska, and has the same geographic latitude. The climate is also somewhat similar. In both regions the summers are warm, the winters extremely cold, and the rainfall averages about the same, though it is more dependable in Manchuria during the growing season. The winters of Manchuria are dry, the drought extending into late spring with only sufficient rainfall in May and early June to start the beans and other crops. The temperature is highest in July and August when the so-called rainy season gives nearly 75 percent of the total annual rainfall. In September and October the rainfall decreases sharply and is followed by weather favorable for the ripening of the beans.

In a study of soybean culture in Germany and of the differences between the climate of that country and Manchuria, Riede (*23*) found that it is quite possible to grow soybeans successfully in any region in which there is a 5-month period of growth with a total heat accumulation of 2,400° C. (4,320° F.) from May to September and an annual precipitation of 12 inches. Lack of sufficient moisture and warmth during the growing season undoubtedly accounts for the poor results obtained in the northwestern part of the United States, which is in the same latitude as Manchuria. In the Philippines (*24*) plantings made during the rainy season produced taller plants with more branches and gave greater yields of seed than those made in the dry season.

The United States now ranks second in acreage and third in production of soybeans. No records of the first introduction of the soybean into the United States are available, but it is mentioned in writings in the early nineteenth century. It was not until the latter part of that century, however, that tests were undertaken by the State experiment stations and the United States Department of Agriculture. In 1939 the acreage for all purposes was 10,006,000 and the production of seed 87,409,000 bushels. The major part of this production is concentrated in the Corn Belt.

Soybeans are sensitive to length of day (*4*), and no one variety is suitable over a wide range of latitude. In the North, where the days are long during the summer, the tall-growing varieties adapted to the Southern States often fail to bloom and will not mature seed. Conversely, a tall, high-seed-yielding, late-maturing northern variety planted in the Southern States grows only a few inches high, blooms within a few weeks after planting, and matures a small crop of seed in midsummer under the relatively short day length (fig. 12).

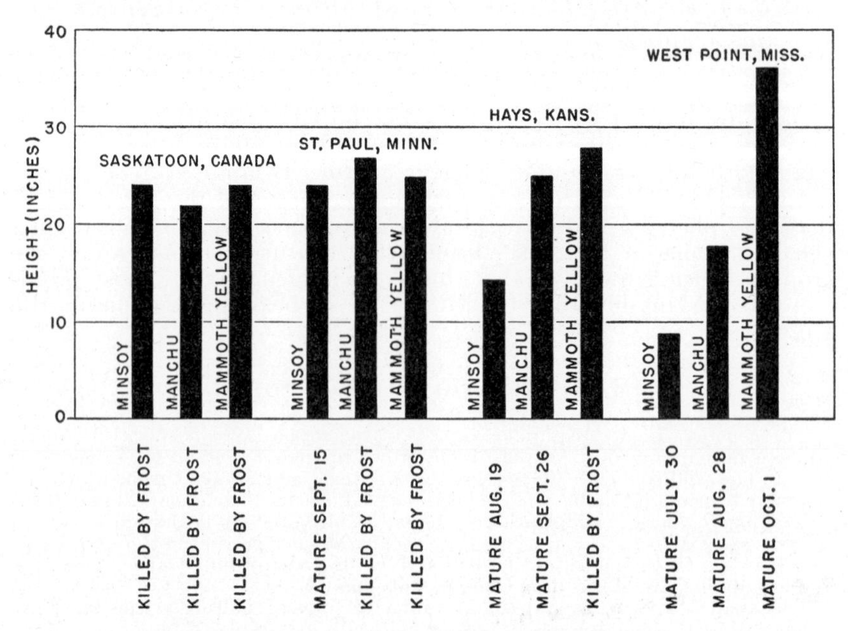

Figure 12.—Heights and dates of maturity of early, medium-early, and late varieties of soybeans grown in four different latitudes in North America in 1930.

In high altitudes in the Western States, where cool nights prevail during the growing season, varieties normally adapted to these latitudes produce abundant vegetative growth but fail to mature seed.

Climate has been found to have a marked influence on the composition of soybean seed; the percentages of oil and protein and the iodine number in any variety vary from season to season on the same type of soil.

The period of germination is the most critical stage for soybeans; excess moisture or prolonged drought at this time is likely to be injurious. When well started, soybeans withstand short periods of drought, and a wet season does not seriously retard growth or decrease yields. They are less susceptible to frost than are cowpeas, field beans, or corn, light frosts having little effect on the plants when young or nearly mature.

LITERATURE CITED

(1) Brown, E. Marion.
1939. SOME EFFECTS OF TEMPERATURE ON THE GROWTH AND CHEMICAL COMPOSITION OF CERTAIN PASTURE GRASSES. Mo. Agr. Expt. Sta. Res. Bul. 299, 76 pp., illus.

(2) Dillman, Arthur C.
1931. THE WATER REQUIREMENT OF CERTAIN CROP PLANTS AND WEEDS IN THE NORTHERN GREAT PLAINS. Jour. Agr. Res. 42: 187–238, illus.

(3) Evans, Morgan W.
1939. RELATION OF LATITUDE TO CERTAIN PHASES OF THE GROWTH OF TIMOTHY. Amer. Jour. Bot. 26: 212–218, illus.

(4) Garner, W. W., and Allard, H. A.
1930. PHOTOPERIODIC RESPONSE OF SOYBEANS IN RELATION TO TEMPERATURE AND OTHER ENVIRONMENTAL FACTORS. Jour. Agr. Res. 41: 719–735, illus.

(5) Grandfield, C. O.
1935. THE TREND OF ORGANIC FOOD RESERVES IN ALFALFA ROOTS AS AFFECTED BY CUTTING PRACTICES. Jour. Agr. Res. 50: 697–709, illus.

(6) Harrison, Carter M.
1934. RESPONSES OF KENTUCKY BLUEGRASS TO VARIATIONS IN TEMPERATURE, LIGHT, CUTTING, AND FERTILIZING. Plant Physiol. 9: [83]–106, illus.

(7) Hollowell, E. A.
1932. RED-CLOVER SEED PRODUCTION IN THE INTERMOUNTAIN STATES. U. S. Dept. Agr. Leaflet 93, 7 pp., illus.

(8) ———
1938. THE ESTABLISHMENT OF LOW HOP CLOVER, TRIFOLIUM PROCUMBENS, AS AFFECTED BY TIME OF SEEDING AND GROWTH OF ASSOCIATED GRASS. Amer. Soc. Agron. Jour. 30: 589–598.

(9) Kiesselbach, T. A., Anderson, Arthur, and Russell, J. C.
1934. SUBSOIL MOISTURE AND CROP SEQUENCE IN RELATION TO ALFALFA PRODUCTION. Amer. Soc. Agron. Jour. 26: 422–442, illus.

(10) ——— Russel, J. C., and Anderson, Arthur.
1929. THE SIGNIFICANCE OF SUBSOIL MOISTURE IN ALFALFA PRODUCTION. Amer. Soc. Agron. Jour. 21: 241–268, illus.

(11) McKee, Roland.
1934. BUR-CLOVER CULTIVATION AND UTILIZATION. U. S. Dept. Agr. Farmers' Bul. 1741, 14 pp., illus.

(12) ——— and Enlow, C. R.
1931. CROTALARIA, A NEW LEGUME FOR THE SOUTH. U. S. Dept. Agr. Cir. 137, 31 pp., illus.

(13) ——— and Schoth, H. A.
1934. VETCH CULTURE AND USES. U. S. Dept. Agr. Farmers' Bul. 1740, 22 pp., illus.

(14) ——— and Schoth, H. A.
1938. CULTURE AND PESTS OF FIELD PEAS. U. S. Dept. Agr. Farmers' Bul. 1803, 16 pp., illus.

(15) MONTEITH, JOHN, JR.
1928. CLOVER ANTHRACNOSE CAUSED BY COLLETOTRICHUM TRIFOLII. U. S. Dept. Agr. Tech. Bul. 28, 27 pp., illus.
(16) MORSE, W. J.
1920. COWPEAS: CULTURE AND VARIETIES. U. S. Dept. Agr. Farmers' Bul. 1148, 26 pp., illus. [Rev. 1924.]
(17) ———
1927. SOYBEANS: CULTURE AND VARIETIES. U. S. Dept. Agr. Farmers' Bul. 1520, 34 pp., illus. [Rev. 1939 by W. J. Morse and J. L. Cartter.]
(18) OAKLEY, R. A., and GARVER, SAMUEL.
1917. MEDICAGO FALCATA, A YELLOW-FLOWERED ALFALFA. U. S. Dept. Agr. Bul. 428, 70 pp., illus.
(19) ——— and WESTOVER, H. L.
1921. EFFECT OF THE LENGTH OF DAY ON SEEDLINGS OF ALFALFA VARIETIES AND THE POSSIBILITY OF UTILIZING THIS AS A PRACTICAL MEANS OF IDENTIFICATION. Jour. Agr. Res. 21: 599–608, illus.
(20) PIETERS, A. J.
1939. LESPEDEZA SERICEA AND OTHER PERENNIAL LESPEDEZAS FOR FORAGE AND SOIL CONSERVATION. U. S. Dept. Agr. Cir. 534, 44 pp., illus.
(21) ———
1939. THE ANNUAL LESPEDEZAS AS FORAGE AND SOIL-CONSERVING CROPS. U. S. Dept. Agr. Cir. 536, 56 pp., illus.
(22) PIPER, C. V., and MORSE, W. J.
[1922.] THE VELVETBEAN. U. S. Dept. Agr. Farmers' Bul. 1276, 27 pp., illus. [Revised in 1938 by W. J. Morse.]
(23) RIEDE, W.
1938. THE GERMAN SOYBEAN PROBLEM. (Translated from German by G. M. Roseveare.) Herbage Rev. 6: 245–258.
(24) RODRIGO, P. A.
1938. ACCLIMATIZATION OF SOYBEAN IN THE PHILIPPINES: I. Philippine Jour. Agr. 9: 223–250.
(25) TOOLE, E. H., and HOLLOWELL, E. A.
1939. EFFECT OF DIFFERENT TEMPERATURES ON THE GERMINATION OF SEVERAL WINTER ANNUAL SPECIES OF TRIFOLIUM. Amer. Soc. Agron. Jour. 31: 604–619, illus.

Climate and Grazing

By W. R. Chapline and C. K. Cooperrider [1]

IN THE WEST, if you could not get along with the Indian, you fought him. The same tactics will not work with the climate. Many people have tried to fight the climate on the range, but in the long run it gets them. On the other hand, it is a pretty good friend if you learn how to get along with it. Here is an article on that subject in relation to the cattle and sheep business. It includes a brief discussion of pastureland in relation to climate, but most of it is about the range.

[1] W. R. Chapline is Principal Inspector of Grazing and Chief of the Division of Range Research, and C. K. Cooperrider is Senior Range Examiner, Southwestern Forest and Range Experiment Station, Forest Service.

THE PROGRESS of settlement in our country in a sense records the influence of climate on forage. Grassy openings in the forests of the Atlantic Coastal Plain supported the few animals of the early colonists. More and larger openings enabled adventurous settlers to move westward. The vast treeless grasslands farther west fed the animals of pack and wagon trains which carried trappers, hunters, traders, and explorers throughout the West. These grasslands enabled the English from the East to set up the commerce of the prairie and to penetrate the Spanish settlements where, long before, the conquistadores had taken advantage of another grassland—the semidesert—to establish the first range industry in what is now our Southwest.

As more and more settlers pushed into all parts of the country, the area of natural grazing grounds was reduced, but at the same time new grazing resources were developed. The best of the former virgin grasslands now grow corn and wheat. Pastures dot areas originally in forest, and spots in desert wastes have been transformed into highly productive feeding grounds through irrigation. Failure to recognize or to heed the limitations climate sets on successful grazing or farming has made for heartaches and disappointments; where such developments have been in harmony with climate, the farmer and stockman have prospered.

Today more than a billion acres, nearly 60 percent of the total land area of the United States, is grazed during at least part of each year. This vast acreage furnishes approximately half the feed for 69 million cattle and 54 million sheep and a considerable part of the feed for 58 million head of swine. These pasture and range lands are the mainstay of the beef-cattle and wool-producing industries and help to support the great dairy industries of the North Central, Northeastern, and northern Pacific Coast States as well as the mohair-producing industry of the Southwest.

Though there is much that is not known about the influence of climate on grazing, experience and research to date indicate many important relationships that justify consideration. Management of cultivated pastures ordinarily aims so to graze the land as to produce as much young green growth as possible. On the western range, because of limited precipitation and uncertainty of regrowth, management must be aimed at utilizing the various forage plants during the periods when they are of the most economic value. Many grasses in the western range area cure on the stalk and furnish desirable forage after maturity.

Most of the tame pastures or grazing resources that have been developed on cultivated lands are in the humid East or in irrigated areas of the West. The natural grazing grounds—the range lands—occur in the semiarid West, in open timber stands of the South, and in the Ozark and similar highlands.

PASTURES ON CULTIVATED LANDS

In general, cultivated pastures have been developed where moisture and soils assure abundant forage growth throughout the grazing season. Grazing is ordinarily postponed at the beginning of the season to permit a vigorous growth to start. By judicious grazing, continuously or in rotation, a maximum of young nutritious growth is kept before the grazing animals. Then growth is rapid. As the temperature rises during the summer months, and especially if the season is very dry, pasture production decreases and stem growth exceeds that of leafage, which results in more crude fiber and less protein. The occasional combination of unusually low rainfall and high temperature in the humid East results in drought conditions that may seriously curtail production in some years. In the South a number of introduced pasture grasses make rapid growth under high temperatures, but they require abundant moisture and fertile soil.

There are two regions of pasture grazing in the East, the northern and the southern, divided roughly by a line from northeastern North Carolina southwest around the point of the Appalachian Mountains in north Georgia and north and west through Tennessee to Oklahoma. In the North, with its warm to cool humid climate, Kentucky and Canada bluegrasses (*Poa pratensis* and *P. compressa*), timothy (*Phleum pratense*), and clovers (*Trifolium* spp.) are among the principal pasture plants; and pastures are largely tame and permanent or are planned to fit in with crop rotations. Grazing capacities are high. Climate restricts grazing to warm weather; hence feeding is required in winter, and the agriculture therefore must include production of hay and grain and harvested forage.

By contrast, in the South pasturage is the main source of livestock feed, and improved pastures may be grazed for most of the year. The more important permanent pasture plants—Bermuda grass (*Cynodon dactylon*), carpet grass (*Axonopus compressus*), Dallis grass (*Paspalum dilatatum*), and lespedeza (*Lespedeza striata*)—afford pasturage in warm weather. The permanent pastures are often supplemented by temporary pastures, in which Napier grass (*Pennisetum purpureum*) and pearl millet (*P. glaucum*) play an important part. Winter pasture is made up chiefly of winter grains and ryegrasses. Extensive use is also made of the natural forage growth of piney woods, hardwood forests, and swampy areas. The abundant forage produced on the wild lands of Florida and along the Gulf coast of Texas has brought about the development of a range-cattle business in those areas. Although many of these native ranges are grazed throughout the year, the low nutritive value of the vegetation in the fall and winter indicates the need for a better seasonal balance between them and cultivated pastures. Many progressive stockmen supplement the native vegetation with concentrated feeds and minerals. The hot humid climate of the South is unusually favorable to parasites, and these have seriously limited livestock production.

Though the West is the home of the range industry, pastures constitute an important part of the grazing resource there. In the humid coastal strip of the Pacific Northwest, pasture conditions are somewhat similar to those in the Northeast, and in addition, because of the mild climate, some winter annuals common to the southern pasture region are successfully grown. The south Pacific area is less humid, summers are hot and dry, rains come in winter, and pasturage, except in irrigated areas, is confined mostly to winter annuals.

In the semiarid range country, particularly north of Arizona, New Mexico, and Texas, natural meadows in low valleys, together with tame pastures and irrigated croplands, are the centers about which most range livestock operations revolve. Although small in area and scattered, they are highly productive sources of winter, spring, and fall feed for the cattle and sheep that graze on the high-mountain range in summer and more or less on lower ranges during the rest of the year. The irrigated pastures of low, warm valleys, such as those in Arizona and California, winter-graze hundreds of thousands of range sheep. They also produce a large share of the winter lambs consumed in the United States and fatten much beef.

Studies of suitable drought-resistant forage plants for dry-farming areas have been carried on by the Bureau of Plant Industry in cooperation with State agricultural experiment stations for the past 30 or 40 years. It is only during the last decade or so, however, that extensive plantings of such drought-resistant plants as crested wheatgrass have been made generally throughout much of the dry-farming area of the West. These plantings, together with studies of the adaptability of numerous native and introduced plants, have clearly shown that local types or strains have developed to meet the special climatic conditions under which they have grown for many years. Plant breeding is now taking advantage of these natural selections in order to develop the most productive strains for adverse farming conditions. Production of forage on the dry-farm pastures varies from year to year with variation in the amount of rainfall and with differences in other climatic factors, but evidence is available to indicate that it does not vary as greatly when adaptable species are used on suitable cultivated lands as it does on the native range.

THE WESTERN RANGE

The western range includes the remaining extensive areas of natural grazing grounds, among which grasslands take a prominent place in size and value. It also includes the shrub-grass areas like those of sagebrush in Idaho and Wyoming and of salt-desert shrub in Nevada and Utah, and the open-stand timberlands of mountains and plateaus. Within the same territory are large and small areas with little forage growth—principally densely timbered lands and low, hot deserts.

The grazing area has shrunk through the years. In some places much of the sod has been turned under, notably in the so-called Dust Bowl of the southern Great Plains; in others, the plow has cut stringers and spots through grass and sagebrush. Because of inadequate precipitation for farming, some of the plowed lands are now coming back to range.

This range area furnishes 65 percent of the forage for the livestock in the territory. From the higher mountain areas, most of which are grazed, comes the water for the extensive irrigation developments, for power, and for municipal water supplies.

There are several distinct range types, the occurrence of each depending largely on climatic factors. These types are briefly described at the end of this article, after the discussion of climate in relation to range conditions in general, and especially to management practices.

INFLUENCE OF CLIMATIC FACTORS ON FORAGE PRODUCTION

The climate of the range territory is not conducive to forage production comparable to that in humid or even subhumid regions. At best it is largely semiarid, and much of it is arid. Moreover, the great fluctuations in weather are a critical factor in range conservation and in sound economic use of range forage for livestock production. Accordingly the influence of the several important climatic factors will be discussed separately.

Precipitation

Annual precipitation on the range averages less than 20 inches, and over most of the area it is less than 15, with vast stretches receiving less than 10. Only in limited mountain areas is annual precipitation greater than 25 inches. In the Plains area rainfall is relatively favorable during the summer growing season, but west of the Rockies, except in Arizona and New Mexico, summer rainfall is light, and at lower elevations in California it is almost negligible.

Fortunately range vegetation is adapted to such low and uncertain precipitation. The principal forage plants are bunchgrasses, or semiturf-forming grasses, which ordinarily cover only 50 to 70 percent of the soil surface even under the most favorable conditions. This permits their roots to draw from the ground between the tufts. Broadly speaking, where the annual rainfall is lower, the more drought-resistant or drought-enduring plants grow in thinner stands. On especially arid areas, the stand often covers less than 10 percent of the soil surface.

Such conditions are reflected to some degree in the grazing capacity of the range. This is also affected, of course, by numerous factors other than precipitation, such as the character of the vegetation, soil, topography, and management. Nevertheless, there are rather definite broad relationships between annual precipitation and relative grazing capacity as determined by recent surveys throughout the West. Table 1 shows these broad relationships expressed in comparable units of acres per cow on the basis of yearlong grazing.

TABLE 1.—*Relative grazing capacity of range land in relation to average annual precipitation*

Average annual precipitation (inches)	Grazing capacity [1] for range in good condition	Approximate present average grazing capacity [1] of large areas	Average annual precipitation (inches)	Grazing capacity [1] for range in good condition	Approximate present average grazing capacity [1] of large areas
	Acres	*Acres*		*Acres*	*Acres*
0–5			20–25	12–35	15–50
5–10	60–200	200 or more	25–30	8–15	10–40
10–15	35–80	70–200	Over 30	3–12	3–20
15–20	25–45	40–120			

[1] Number of acres required to support a cow for a year.

It will be noted in table 1 that there are rather large variations in grazing capacity within most precipitation zones, even when the range is in good condition. This is due to the factors other than precipitation. Variations are greatest in the low-rainfall zones. Grazing capacity of ranges generally is considerably less than that of those in good condition, and thus much of the range area is not now producing the forage it is capable of producing.

The production of forage in any year is also influenced by the character and distribution of the rainfall during the year. The Southwestern Forest and Range Experiment Station has found that rains of less than one-half inch are insufficient to promote growth of perennial range grasses unless they are preceded or followed by more effective rain. Since a high percentage of the precipitation during the growing season falls in storms of less than one-half inch, much of it is not effective or is effective only in a small degree. Moreover, in occasional hard rains a high proportion of the water runs off and is lost to range plants unless the vegetative cover is in a vigorous condition and the surface soil is open and friable so that it can absorb a high proportion of the rainfall.

In studies on the Boise National Forest in Idaho (*3*),[2] for example, rains of approximately 1¾ inches falling in half an hour were almost completely absorbed on slopes of 30- and 40-percent gradient when these slopes were covered with a stand made up largely of perennial wheatgrass having a density of about 35 percent. In contrast to this, on deteriorated range in the same region 34 percent of the rainfall ran off as surface flow from land supporting annual downy chess or cheatgrass, and 64 percent from that supporting annual weeds. This clearly indicates the advisability of maintaining as satisfactory a forage cover as possible.

Drought

Precipitation on the range varies so greatly from year to year that drought may occur in any year or in a series of 2 to 5 or even more years. In southern New Mexico, for example, in each cycle of 8 to 10 years, 3 or 4 consecutive years may occur during which precipitation is enough below its long-time average to cause conditions that are locally considered as drought (*8*). The semidesert range areas in other parts of the Southwest and in the Intermountain region are subject to equally serious drought conditions. On portions of the southern Great Plains conditions are almost as bad. In the less arid and in the northern portion generally of the range territory, however, variations in rainfall are not apt to be so great nor are droughts apt to occur so frequently, but even in those areas extended droughts do occur sufficiently often to disrupt livestock production.

During the last 25 years, precipitation has been lower than during the preceding 30 to 35 years over most of the West, with extreme drought conditions over extensive areas in 1934 and 1936. Gray (*5*), moreover, records a downward trend of 8 inches with a mean of only approximately 29 inches in California during the 80-year period between 1850 and 1930, and Campbell (*1*) has traced this trend through 1934. A similar downward trend has been noted since 1908 by the Northern Rocky Mountain Forest and Range Experiment Station at weather stations in Montana, Idaho, and Washington. (See p. 692 for charts showing precipitation trends in various regions of the United States.)

---

[2] Italic numbers in parentheses refer to Literature Cited, p. 475.

Range plants are adapted to contend with the fluctuating precipitation and have remarkable recuperative powers to offset loss of stand as a result of drought. Adaptations include contraction or breaking up of grass tufts, production of fewer and shorter stems and leaves, the curling or folding of leaves to reduce transpiration, and even dropping of leaves by shrubs if conditions become too severe. When abundant rainfall returns, a large volume of new growth may be produced on the thinned stand if the plants have not been seriously weakened by overgrazing, and this growth in turn renews the weakened root systems and general vigor of the plants.

Alternate declines and recoveries of the black grama stand on the Jornada Experimental Range in southern New Mexico were followed through two extended drought periods which occurred between 1915 and 1927 (*11*). Recovery was rather rapid both under total protection from grazing and under conservative grazing. In fact during the second drought, growth on the conservatively grazed range did not decline so rapidly or so greatly and restoration was more rapid than on the ungrazed areas. Part of this response was doubtless due to the fact that grazing prevented the formation during good years of large tufts which could not be supported in drought years. Growth in height from year to year fluctuated primarily in relation to available moisture from summer rains. Recent studies of these trends by the Southwestern Forest and Range Experiment Station indicate similar or even greater recoveries following the good years and equally serious declines in the drought years.

A number of records also are available from other parts of the West relating to the severe decline in the stand of vegetation as a result of the 1934 drought. For example, 74.8 percent of the plants were killed on overgrazed experimental pastures in western Kansas and 64.6 percent on moderately grazed areas (*13*); 70.9 percent in the northern plains of eastern Montana (*4*); and 40.7 percent in the Snake River Plains of eastern Idaho (*12*). Still further declines have been recorded (*14, 15*) as a result of the 1936 and subsequent droughts, especially in the central and southern Great Plains. The Northern Rocky Mountain Forest and Range Experiment Station measured declines in vegetation of more than 85 and 90 percent on short-grass plains between 1933 and 1937 on experimental range pastures at the Range Livestock Experiment Station of eastern Montana. Recovery was rather remarkable in 1938 and 1939 on these Montana ranges, but the stand is still far below what it was in 1933.

Temperature

In the range territory temperature exerts its greatest influence in limiting early spring forage production. Stockmen are always anxious to move their livestock from feed lots and from the dry and too often scanty forage of winter ranges to lush new growth on spring ranges. Fortunately many of the native plants, such as some of the bluegrasses (*Poa* spp.), produce forage in cool weather and afford early pasturage. Some of the early plants, however, are often of low value, and care must be exercised to avoid use of the important palatable plants before they have made sufficient growth to permit sustained grazing.

In perennial grasses growth processes are proceeding during the winter, even under snow, when plant foods stored in the roots the previous fall are consumed (*9*). Throughout most of the West, active leaf and stem growth of grasses begins sometime in the spring, after average mean daily temperatures are above 40° F. The range is ready for grazing several weeks later—in the mountains of central Utah about a month after snow has disappeared (*2*). On the other hand, certain grasses, such as blue grama, make their growth during the warm months of June, July, and August or, on the warm southwestern ranges, as early in June or July as moisture is favorable. Most perennial grasses have completed their growth and seed production in a period of about 2 or 3 months after active visible growth starts. Browse plants in general start growth in the spring as soon as temperature becomes sufficiently warm, even in the Southwest, where the main production of herbaceous plants occurs after summer rains start in late June or July. Such rapid completion of growth processes by range plants ordinarily enables them to escape damage from early frosts in the fall. Frost injury may lessen the value of some browse foliage, but it makes other browse more palatable.

The Southwest, largely because of its mild climate, is a land of yearlong grazing; it also affords outstanding examples of moving stock with the seasons. Hundreds of thousands of sheep that are summered on timbered ranges in northern Arizona are trailed to southern desert ranges and irrigated pastures in the fall and back to the mountains in the spring. These sheep use designated trails leading from the desert through low to high mountain areas; some flocks travel more than 200 miles.

When the effect of the warm winter rainy season on forage production is over and annual desert herbs begin to dry up, spring is on in the low mountains, and snow will soon be gone on the high summer ranges. It is time for the sheep herder to fold his tent, pack the burros, and start the long trek to the mountains. Sometimes he must move slowly because of little lambs; if the lambs have already been raised and marketed, he goes faster up the trail. In any event, he must travel with the development of the season, not too rapidly, for he does not want to reach the high mountains before the snow is gone, leaving its moisture to start new growth under the stimulus of rising temperature, or before the summer rains begin. But he must travel rapidly enough to leave waning waters and feed and the heat of the desert behind. In October he reverses this practice, dropping lower and lower toward the desert as winter comes. By the time sheep arrive in the desert, lush irrigated pastures await them. Later, if rains are favorable, the desert with its warm daily temperatures puts forth new growth, and sheep may leave the high-cost pastures and graze there, sometimes depending on the succulent plants for water as well as feed.

Other Climatic Factors

No one climatic factor acts alone. Relative humidity, evaporation, and wind all have important relationships to range-plant growth, but primarily as they influence the effectiveness of available precipitation. With high relative humidity, evaporation and transpiration are relatively low; with low humidity, evaporation is high, and so is transpiration if moisture is available.

Evaporation from a free water surface in the northern Great Plains during the growing period from April to September, inclusive, averages about 34 to 38 inches (*6*). It increases toward the south, and in the southern Great Plains from April to September averages 48 to 55 inches. Under the latter conditions, and in most of the drier regions typical of the greater part of the western range area, where evaporation from a free water surface is even greater, evaporation severely restricts the effectiveness of the rainfall available for plant use and thus influences the growth of plants. Approximately 14 inches of rainfall produces good growth of short-grass species in Montana, whereas 21 inches is needed for comparable growth in Texas (*16*) because of the high evaporation rate in the latter State.

Most range plants appear to use much of the moisture that is available for them during their limited growing period, but there is considerable difference in the relative effectiveness with which they utilize an adequate water supply in the production of forage (*10*). The Southwestern Forest and Range Experiment Station has shown experimentally by studies in large plots under range conditions on the Tonto National Forest, that if sufficient water is furnished, range plants will transpire approximately as much water as is evaporated from a free water surface, and this averages approximately 10 inches or more a month during the growing period in that area. But range plants under field conditions do not have as much water as that to transpire. Actually they transpire little more than is evaporated from bare soil of a texture comparable to that on which they are growing.

Wind velocity, air temperature, and relative humidity are all active elements of climate directly influencing evaporation rates and amounts. Accompanying low rainfall in drought years are usually higher temperatures, lower relative humidity, greater evaporation, and occasionally higher wind velocities. All of these tend to accentuate the difficulties of plant production during drought periods. On the Jornada Experimental Range (*11*), for example, loss of as much as 80 percent of the stand of black grama occurred between the fall of 1921 and the fall of 1922 as a result of the extremely severe, hot, drying winds of the spring of 1922, combined with inadequate rainfall in July 1921.

Importance of Range Management in the Solution of Climatic Problems

The range area is so vast and its sound economic use in livestock production is so important to the social welfare of the local communities and the West as a whole that it is vital to determine how management can be adjusted to offset the vagaries of weather. There is still much to learn about the climatic relationships and the conservation and use of the range resource. Research results and practical experience, however, have rather clearly indicated certain broad principles, practices, and basic considerations that should govern continued use of range lands for livestock production.

Recognition of the Submarginal Character of Certain Areas

There are areas in the West that are clearly submarginal for grazing. Other areas, submarginal for agriculture because of limited possibilities for profitable crop production, should remain as range, or if they have been cultivated should be restored to range. While economic and other considerations have a bearing on delimiting such areas, climate alone is a major factor. For example, where the average annual rainfall is below 5 inches, as in southeastern California and southwestern Arizona, the available moisture is too scant and too uncertain to support sufficient palatable vegetation, and the supply of water for livestock is so scarce and so costly that little attempt is made to graze large areas. This desert does furnish occasional winter grazing, but it cannot be depended upon. Such areas are clearly submarginal for grazing.

Even in the zone where rainfall is 5 to 10 inches, drought is so frequent, the forage plants are of a type so susceptible to serious deterioration through overgrazing, and water is often so scarce and costly that some parts of this area also are now submarginal for economical yearlong grazing. Much of the area is now producing so little forage that 200 or more acres are required to support a cow throughout the year. With such low grazing capacity, costs of fencing, furnishing water, and handling are apt to be so high that such land can be utilized to advantage only by the larger livestock outfits which can afford to make major adjustments in their operations during drought and assume the attendant risks.

Good management practices may facilitate restoration of depleted areas and lift them out of a submarginal classification. At the Desert Experimental Range in western Utah notable improvement has been obtained on ranges grazed by sheep where average annual rainfall approximates 7 inches through the application of conservative grazing in winter only, combined with other desirable forms of management.

Dry farming has been attempted on many western range areas where rainfall proved to be insufficient to maintain an agriculture based on the production of cultivated crops without irrigation. It has been estimated that nearly 25 million acres have been plowed, cultivated for a year or so, and then abandoned. Such abandoned fields are found in almost every western State in localities where the average rainfall is less than 15 inches. Soil conditions are now so bad and the possibility of retaining moisture is so uncertain on parts of these abandoned fields that to restore an economically valuable forage cover at a reasonable cost is going to be difficult. Restoration to a suitable range cover, however, is important to make the lands economically valuable again and to reduce wind and water erosion. Research is now pointing the way to adaptable forage plants and low-cost methods of revegetation. Such conditions point definitely to the need for full recognition that there are large areas in the West unsuited to farming which should remain permanently as range and be used primarily for the production of livestock and wildlife.

Conservative Grazing and Forage Reserves

Probably the outstanding requisite of management to meet drought and other adverse influences of climate is conservative grazing. Too often a few good years with increasing forage production encourage the building up of herds. The result is that when drought comes, numbers of livestock may approach a peak. This condition was general in 1934 and far too common in earlier drought years. Even with the Government relief purchases in the summer of 1934, losses on most ranges were great.

Conservative grazing means stocking a range to a point sufficiently below average forage production over the years to provide adequate forage for the livestock in all but severe drought years in order to minimize drought losses, curtail costly supplemental feeding, assure stable livestock production, and maintain the range resource upon which the whole industry is built. If the range is stocked on the basis of average forage production, sufficient forage to carry the livestock satisfactorily will be produced in only about half of the years. Conservative stocking necessitates stocking at somewhere between 15 and 25 percent below average forage production, in a few instances possibly even lower. In the mountains of Utah, stocking 20 percent below the average would have assured adequate forage in three-fourths of the years, and in the other one-fourth any shortage of forage would not have been so excessive but that either provision of supplemental feed or minor adjustments in stocking would have assured stable livestock production and maintenance of the vigor of the vegetation. On national-forest areas in central Utah, where such conservative grazing has been applied, the stand of forage has increased 100 to 200 percent on depleted parts of spring ranges and as much as 400 to 500 percent on summer ranges in 10 to 15 years.

On the other hand, overgrazing—that is, stocking more heavily than average forage production—on range in New Mexico, summerlong or yearlong, caused much greater losses in the stand of forage during drought years than occurred under conservative grazing (*11*). Recovery following drought was also greatly retarded under such heavy grazing. Under continuous excessive use, black grama (*Bouteloua eriopoda*), the most important forage plant, was practically exterminated from extensive range areas during the 1916–18 drought and from additional areas during the 1921–24 drought. Much of this depleted area will require many years of management to bring about restoration. In contrast, conservatively grazed and otherwise well-managed ranges in that area, as previously mentioned, have recovered from drought more rapidly than ungrazed range areas.

Stocking the range on the basis of below-average forage production serves as drought insurance. Although under such use little forage may be carried over on the range from year to year, the cover of vegetation and the sustained vigor of the palatable plants assure maximum production consistent with the amount of rainfall available. It is ordinarily advisable to fence off a portion of the range to be used during the critical period of the year, both to assure fresh forage at that time and to help to define the ability of the range to support the livestock through each year. In the occasional year of extreme drought—usually 1 or 2 in each 10—when production is so low that

298737°—41——31 +

there is insufficient forage for the breeding herd, additional provision must be made in the way of supplemental feed if forced sales and starvation losses are to be avoided. During drought the value of harvested feeds and pasturage increases greatly, and it is not sound business to wait until drought prevails before building up reserves of feed.

If yearlong range-grazing operations are built primarily upon the basis of a breeding herd, it is extremely difficult to allow for fluctuations in stocking from year to year. In areas with rainfall of less than 10 inches, where drought is so frequent and uncertainty of forage production so great, it is best to have part of the herd in steers or other readily salable animals. Then, if the growing season is unfavorable enough to indicate that feed will be short, it is inadvisable to hold such animals in an effort to obtain a better price; rather, steers and calves should be promptly sold so as to retain as much of the range forage as possible for the breeding herd. The breeding herd should also be closely culled, and supplemental feeding should start before serious loss of weight occurs.

Since drought causes decline in the forage-plant cover, and the stand of perennial grasses is less in the year following than during the drought year, care should be exercised in restocking drought-depleted ranges. In 1935 it appeared to the casual observer that the range of eastern Montana had recovered from the 1934 drought. Under the favorable growing conditions of 1935 the thinned stand produced a tall growth. Recovery, however, was more apparent than real, and in the fall or early winter of that year forage on the range rapidly became scarce. By 1938 the density of palatable plants on these drought-stricken ranges was down to one-fourth of the level prior to the droughts of 1934 and 1936. Again, under favorable conditions in 1938, the thinned stand produced a good growth in height; yet those who hoped to obtain forage comparable in animal-months to the predrought production were disappointed. It is necessary, in other words, to avoid overstocking of thinned stands so as to give every advantage possible to rebuilding the density and vigor of the palatable vegetation.

Good Management Pays

There are adequate experimental and practical examples to indicate clearly that sound range management pays. On the plains of eastern Montana, in cooperative studies carried on by the Forest Service, the Bureau of Animal Industry, and the Montana Agricultural Experiment Station, a larger calf crop, greater weaning weight of calves, and greater weight of calves per cow were produced under conservative grazing as compared with approximately 25-percent overstocking. The total cost of forage and feed alone per pound of calf produced approximated 4 cents over a 5-year period for the conservatively grazed area (with hay at $8 a ton and range at 10 cents an acre) in contrast to 5.4 cents per pound of calf on the overgrazed range (*7*).

Conservative grazing and other good management practices on the Jornada and Santa Rita Experimental Ranges in southern New Mexico and Arizona have resulted in calf crops half again as large, losses only a third to a fifth as great as on similar but deteriorated ranges heavily stocked with cattle, and a greater sale value of calves. Such desirable management has made it possible for the ranchers to produce calves at a profit over the years in contrast to the losses sustained where grazing was more or less unrestricted and poorly managed.

Similar beneficial results have been obtained with sheep winter-grazing on the Desert Experimental Range in western Utah. Here two brothers cooperate with the Forest Service. In alternate years, each one uses the open range without paying much attention to good range practices, while the other grazes the experimental pastures where conservative grazing and other desirable management practices are followed. Either band of sheep, when on the experimental range, produces more wool and lambs, does well without any supplemental feed, and has netted $1,000 a year more profit than the band not using the experimental range.

More and more stockmen are taking drought and other adverse climatic factors and the opportunities for recovery in favorable years into account in planning the management of their ranges, with resultant benefits to both themselves and the West generally.

DESCRIPTION OF RANGE TYPES

Grassland Ranges

Tall-Grass Prairie

Almost ideal grassland conditions—favorable moisture and temperature in summer, fine and friable soils, and gently rolling relief—make tall-grass prairie the most productive of the range lands; but the prairie climate is so favorable for farming that only about 19 million of a probable original 250 million acres remain in grazing use. This remnant consists mainly of three areas near the western limit of tall grass, one in North Dakota, one in Nebraska, and another in Kansas and Oklahoma.

Prairie vegetation is characterized by a mixture of tall grasses in which intermingled individuals and spots of shorter grasses and sedges, a great variety of showy flowering herbs, and some half-shrubs complete the stand. It is colorful as well as productive; it has dense, tall slough growth in moist depressions and shorter growth on warm, dry uplands; it comprises spring and summer and late-season growers; and, to a degree, it has the winter-feed characteristics of drier, warmer grasslands, the summer growth of which cures into natural standing hay during the warm, dry days and cool nights of Indian summer.

Short-Grass Plains

In present-day importance, the short-grass range far outranks the prairie. Short grass, like tall grass, originally occupied a vast area, more of which has remained in grazing use because its climate is drier than that of the prairie. Extending eastward from the Rockies, from Canada almost to Mexico, the short-grass plains form a fairly level grassland belt 300 to 600 miles wide. They constituted most of the old cattle empire of early range days; they still hold the lead among range types in total area and number of animals grazed.

Short grasses dominate the vegetation of the plains, although some taller grasses are intermingled with them. The principal grasses such as buffalo grass (*Buchloë dactyloides*) and blue grama (*Bouteloua gracilis*) tend to be more or less sod formers. For one thing, rainfall is low—12 inches or less in some parts toward the north to 22 inches in Texas—most of it falling during the growing season. Consequently, soil moisture penetrates only to shallow depths, grasses consume the moisture, only the upper part of the soil leaches, impervious carbonate hardpan develops near the lower depths of moisture penetration, and the reserves of deeper soil moisture so necessary to tall growth fail to accumulate. Tall plants do occur in depressions where run-off accumulates and sinks to greater than average depths.

Although types of plains vegetation are similar, the plants that compose these types differ widely. The vast extent of the plains—more than 2,500 miles from north to south—makes for differences in climate. Elevation and location with respect to the high face of the Rockies and to the place of origin and paths of storms also affect climate and hence vegetation. Near the plains-prairie border, plants typical of both areas are common, the taller grasses being more conspicuous in a series of wet years. Likewise, near the foothills of the mountains, plants common to drier prairie uplands lend a prairie color to the plains. In the cool northern part, where drought conditions are less acute in early summer and evaporation is moderate, wheatgrasses (*Agropyron* spp.) and needlegrasses (*Stipa* spp.) rise above the blue grama, and here and there sagebrush areas alternate with grassland. In the southern part, as in the Texas Panhandle, the hot rainy season and higher evaporation and transpiration are favorable to buffalo grass. To the west of the area carpeted by this grass, in New Mexido and Colorado, galleta (*Hilaria jamesii*) and gramas (*Bouteloua* spp.) cover the high, cool mesas and interior valleys. Inadequate moisture during spring in that area confines production more or less to the short wet-weather period in summer.

Semidesert-Grass Plains

In the arid and semiarid zone of southern Texas, New Mexico, Arizona, and adjacent Mexico lie grassy plains that resemble the short-grass plains. These low plains are influenced by the climate of intermingled local mountains. Such varying conditions make for short-distance differences in climate and soils and great differences in amount and kind of vegetation.

The principal short grasses of the semidesert range are gramas and curly-mesquite (*Hilaria belangeri*). Tobosa (*Hilaria mutica*) forms a dense bunchlike growth in depressions that become alternately very wet and dry. Sacaton (*Sporobolus wrightii*) grows shoulder high in damp locations; and here and there other tall grasses attain individual prominence in those places that best meet the exacting requirements of the individual species under hot, semiarid conditions.

Scattered through these semidesert grasslands are shurbs and low-branching trees like mesquites, as well as palmlike yuccas and many kinds of cacti. The semidesert grassland bursts forth in a bit of tropical abundance in rainy seasons and shrinks back toward desert when dry. Its plants are peculiarly adapted to resist dry heat and drought and to take advantage of rain when it comes. Good growth in season, retention of feed values in cured forage, and mild winter weather make semidesert grassland among the best of the yearlong breeding ranges.

Pacific Bunchgrass Prairie

In untimbered range and in the open-timbered areas of the northern Rocky Mountains and the Pacific States occur grasses and showy flowering plants that resemble prairie vegetation except that they grow in large, distinct tufts or bunches. The most extensive development of such bunchgrass prairie was in Montana, the Pacific Northwest, and California.

The bunchgrass prairie has undergone great changes; much of the area it occupied has become wheatland and orchard; the bunchgrasses withstood grazing poorly and have disappeared in many places. Deep soil moisture from winter precipitation which encouraged prairie vegetation also allowed the invasion of sagebrush and other deep-rooted plants. Spring and fall moisture accompanied by favorable growing temperatures favored the spread of short-lived annuals. Although still important for grazing, the vegetation on most of the former area of Pacific bunchgrass now resembles that of open-timber, shrub, and annual ranges as much as or more than that of the prairie.

Shrub-Grass Ranges

Outside the grasslands, grasses, or grasses in the larger sense including other herbs, constitute the close-to-the-ground vegetation over millions of acres where shrubs and trees are the more imposing plants. As grasses affect the natural structure, use, and grazing value of grasslands, so too they greatly influence the shrub-grass ranges. Where naturally prominent, grasses are the part of the vegetation that most protects soils, exerts the most influence on what becomes of rain water where it falls, and aids in the absorption of water and the conserving of soil moisture against the ravages of evaporation. They commonly constitute a large part of the feed resources on browse ranges and are necessary to the welfare of most range animals.

Where the vegetation consists of both shrubs and grasses, some peculiar combinations of climatic factors must favor the growth of each at some time during the year, and at other times conditions must not be too adverse to permit their survival. Water must sink deeply enough during some period of the year to support rather deep-rooted plants; there must be rain sometime during the growing season for grasses, or their survival and growth must not be prevented through the drying out of the upper soil layers during critical periods. A common condition is cold winter weather with precipitation enough to sink rather deeply into the ground, a critical annual dry period, and rain sometime during late spring or summer. The more rain in summer, the more prominent are the grasses. Typical shrub-grass ranges are those of sagebrush and salt-desert shrub.

Sagebrush-Grass Range

Areas of sagebrush occur from the Pacific Northwest south to northern New Mexico and Arizona. Sagebrush is also conspicuous in many open-timber areas, particularly the juniper woodlands. The great body of more than 96 million acres of sagebrush range extends from eastern Wyoming west to the Cascades in Oregon and the Sierras in California, through southern Idaho and northern Utah and Nevada. It is typical of dry, cool northern plains and valleys, where much of the annual precipitation occurs in the cool season, and of similar southern areas that are cool because of their elevation but have more summer than winter rainfall.

In some places in the northern part of this region sagebrush forms the spring and fall link between summer and winter grazing grounds. In others it is grazed extensively in winter. Farther south, it also winters many sheep; the otherwise poor sagebrush browse affords emergency feed when snow occasionally covers the grass. The real value of such range is in the herbs and other browse plants that are intermingled with the sagebrush. Too much dependence on sagebrush range for feed results in overuse and decline of the grasses, which gives sagebrush the advantage in the contest for supremacy and lessens the value of the range.

Salt-Desert Shrub

On dry upland plains and flats in Utah, Nevada, southwestern Wyoming, and southern Idaho and in depressions farther south are low shrub growths intermingled with grassland plants. Most of the vegetation is highly resistant to drought and alkali. Some shrubs are good browse, and others almost worthless for feed. Grasses are naturally important; but because of dry conditions, particularly in summer, they form dense stands only in the most favorable locations and are easily killed out through too close grazing.

Other Shrub-Grass Ranges

The southern Arizona and California deserts are shrub deserts. Much of their area is of negligible importance as range. Annual rainfall averages less than 10 inches, in some places less than 3 inches. Water is scarce or lacking, and perennial grasses grow only on a few deep, sandy soils and in depressions watered by run-off. In locations of most favorable winter rainfall, annuals afford winter grazing and forage for lambing for large numbers of sheep. Such operations, however, must be safeguarded through provision for grazing in tame, irrigated pastures, since the desert fails to produce forage in dry years, which are the rule.

Between these deserts and the mountains and on low, dry areas, such as that bordering the lower Rio Grande Valley, are ranges with desert shrubs in places and grassy areas in others. Here also grazing is greatly influenced by the season, whether favorable or unfavorable to growth.

Where extensive mountain masses rise abruptly from the desert plains, as in southern Arizona, desert shrubs extend into the mountains and become associated with low-mountain shrubs; and both give way, in turn, to open-stand chaparral at higher elevations. Such mountain brushlands often naturally have good grass stands and are highly productive forage- and water-yielding areas. Here the average annual precipitation increases to 15, 20, 25, or more inches, probably influenced as much by topography as by elevation. There is also a summer as well as a winter rainy period, with intervening spring and fall dry periods. Summer rainfall is sufficient for abundant growth of grasses, which include typical semidesert and also plains grasses as well as bunchgrasses. Although highly productive in the natural state, these rugged mountain brushlands are easily changed. Too much dependence on browse results in exhausting the grass crop long before all the browse growth is taken and hence in overgrazing of the grass during most of each year. Loss of grass means loss of the better part of the forage and soils, loss of effective moisture through both increasing run-off and evaporation, man-made drought, and deteriorated range and watershed conditions.

Not all mountain brushlands are naturally good range. Chaparral may consist of poor browse plants. Dense brush with little grass is common where winter precipitation is high and summers are long and dry. There are also thickets, such as those common on high mountains, too dense to graze, but sometimes important as sources of winter feed for game.

Timbered Areas

In the range country the mountains have the cooler, more nearly humid climates; they are the timbered lands of the West. Many influences that modify the effects of climate, such as latitude and elevation, make for great differences in the character of forest growth and in grazing uses. Some areas afford range during rather long periods, others for only 2 or 3 months in summer. Some timberlands are too dense to have much forage growth or to permit of the handling of livestock. Others rival the grasslands in importance as range.

These widely distributed and different wooded lands with range values may be roughly divided into woodlands and open-stand saw-timber areas.

Woodlands

Typical woodland ranges are the juniper- and piñon-covered foothills of the southern Rocky Mountain region and the lands with evergreen oaks in the Southwest and in California. The piñon-juniper woodlands form the border zone where mountain forests meet the southern short-grass or semidesert plains or the shrub-grass types. They have a touch of the climate and the vegetation of both types of range. They afford yearlong grazing in parts of the Southwest, and in other parts spring and fall range for some of the yearlong grazing operations that depend on shifting livestock to summer range in the mountains and to valleys and deserts in the winter.

Evergreen-oak woodlands are closely associated with evergreen brush or chaparral, both in location and in character of range growth. In the Southwest the good stands of perennial grasses on areas with scattered oak trees are related to favorable summer rainfall, and the yearlong grazing here is associated with the mild but productive climate. The oak-dotted foothills of California have dry summers but moist, mild winters which make for growth of herbs in winter and spring and provide conditions favorable for cool-season grazing.

Open Forests

The grassy range in open-stand saw timber is largely in pine and pine-fir forests. These ranges also include prairielike parks, alpine areas, and areas with aspen and other trees in open stands. About one-half the 125 million acres of this kind of range is in national forests. Most of it lies at relatively high elevations and is suited to warm-season grazing only. In some places factors such as density of timber and lack of summer moisture result in rather sparse herbaceous growth; in others, grasses grow abundantly. There are shade-loving and sun-loving plants, short and tall grasses, turf and bunchgrasses, grasslike plants, and many nutritious fleshy herbs.

The wide distribution of these timbered ranges, the diverse types of forage on them, and their location with respect to other feed areas account to a large degree for the many different kinds of grazing operations that have developed from Canada to Mexico west of the Great Plains. In the northern, cooler parts of the range country, summering in the mountains affords the opportunity to get livestock off farm pastures and winter ranges during the growing season. This allows a combination of ranging, farming, and feeding and adds materially to the value and size of operations on many farm and pasture areas which are too small and widely scattered to constitute economic units alone and are otherwise unsuited to any but a livestock economy.

In other places, of which Utah is typical, the summer ranges take care of many farm cattle from the thickly settled irrigated valleys. These cattle number only a few to the farm, but in the aggregate they amount to many thousands and are highly important to the individual small farmers. In the same region, mountain meadows and succulent herbs in aspen and other open-timber stands not only afford good summer range for grazing sheep and fattening lambs but also make it possible to use the salt-desert ranges when they are most valuable and to get the flocks off them during critical hot, dry periods.

Timbered ranges are much more than mere seasonal grazing grounds where livestock may be summered. In many instances, herds on winter ranges, pastures, and feed lots are on a maintenance ration by spring, and summer range is depended upon for the growth and conditioning of the animals. In other cases the cool, timbered mountains afford green forage for mother ewes and young lambs and for continued rapid growth of beef stock that comes to the hills in good condition. In the fall such grass-fattened animals are in good shape for rapid finishing in the feed lots or to go direct to market.

LITERATURE CITED

(1) Campbell, R. S.
1936. CLIMATIC FLUCTUATIONS. *In* The Western Range, U. S. Forest Service, 74th Cong., 2d sess., S. Doc. 199, pp. 135–150, illus.

(2) Costello, David F., and Price, Raymond.
1939. WEATHER AND PLANT-DEVELOPMENT DATA AS DETERMINANTS OF GRAZING PERIODS ON MOUNTAIN RANGE. U. S. Dept. Agr. Tech. Bul. 686, 31 pp., illus.

(3) Craddock, George W., and Pearse, C. Kenneth.
1938. SURFACE RUN-OFF AND EROSION ON GRANITIC MOUNTAIN SOILS OF IDAHO AS INFLUENCED BY RANGE COVER, SOIL DISTURBANCE, SLOPE, AND PRECIPITATION INTENSITY. U. S. Dept. Agr. Cir. 482, 24 pp., illus.

(4) Ellison, Lincoln, and Woolfolk, E. J.
1937. EFFECTS OF DROUGHT ON VEGETATION NEAR MILES CITY, MONTANA. Ecology 18: 329–336, illus.

(5) Gray, Leslie G.
1934. LONG-PERIOD FLUCTUATIONS OF SOME METEOROLOGICAL ELEMENTS IN RELATION TO CALIFORNIA FOREST-FIRE PROBLEMS. U. S. Monthly Weather Rev. 62: 231–235, illus.

(6) Horton, Robert E., and Cole, John S.
1934. COMPILATION AND SUMMARY OF THE EVAPORATION RECORDS OF THE BUREAU OF PLANT INDUSTRY, U. S. DEPARTMENT OF AGRICULTURE, 1921–32. U. S. Monthly Weather Rev. 62: 77–89.

(7) Hurtt, Leon C.
1939. OVERGRAZING INCREASES PRODUCTION COSTS BY REDUCING NUMBER AND WEIGHT OF RANGE CALVES. Cattleman 26 (5): 52, illus.

(8) Jardine, James T., and Forsling, Clarence L.
1922. RANGE AND CATTLE MANAGEMENT DURING DROUGHT. U. S. Dept. Agr. Bul. 1031, 83 pp., illus.

(9) McCarty, Edward C.
1938. THE RELATION OF GROWTH TO THE VARYING CARBOHYDRATE CONTENT IN MOUNTAIN BROME. U. S. Dept. Agr. Tech. Bul. 598, 24 pp., illus.

(10) McGinnies, W. G., and Arnold, Joseph F.
1939. RELATIVE WATER REQUIREMENT OF ARIZONA RANGE PLANTS. Ariz. Agr. Expt. Sta. Tech. Bul. 80, 246 pp., illus.

(11) Nelson, Enoch W.
1934. THE INFLUENCE OF PRECIPITATION AND GRAZING UPON BLACK GRAMA GRASS RANGE. U. S. Dept. Agr. Tech. Bul. 409, 32 pp., illus.

(12) Pechanec, J. F., Pickford, G. D., and Stewart, George.
1937. EFFECTS OF THE 1934 DROUGHT ON NATIVE VEGETATION OF THE UPPER SNAKE RIVER PLAINS, IDAHO. Ecology 18: 490–505, illus.

(13) Savage, D. A., and Jacobson, L. A.
1935. THE KILLING EFFECT OF HEAT AND DROUGHT ON BUFFALO GRASS AND BLUE GRAMA GRASS AT HAYS, KANSAS. Amer. Soc. Agron. Jour. 27: 566–582, illus.

(14) Weaver, J. E., and Albertson, F. W.
1939. MAJOR CHANGES IN GRASSLAND AS A RESULT OF CONTINUED DROUGHT. Bot. Gaz. 100: 576–591, illus.

(15) ——— and Albertson, F. W.
1940. DETERIORATION OF MIDWESTERN RANGES. Ecology 21: 216–236, illus.

(16) ——— and Clements, Frederic E.
1938. PLANT ECOLOGY. Ed. 2, 602 pp., illus. New York and London.

Climate and the Nation's Forests

By Raphael Zon [1]

THERE HAS BEEN a good deal of argument about whether forests have any effect on climate. The author of this article holds that they do and makes out a good case. The effects are local and often not of great magnitude, but they may mean much to agriculture in certain areas and with certain crops. More striking are the effects of climate on forests. Modern forest management, the author shows, depends on understanding what climatic variations, big and little, do to trees.

[1] Raphael Zon is Director, Lake States Forest Experiment Station, Forest Service.

Vast forests, large expanses of water, immense stretches of virgin prairie or desert, and fertile soils are all products of the general climate of the earth, over which man has no control, but insofar as they form a part of the environment they may be affected by human activities. The destruction of forests over large areas, the drainage of large swamps, the construction of large-scale irrigation works, and the exhaustion of soil fertility can modify the physical and atmospheric environment of a locality, affecting its suitability for human habitation, for agricultural pursuits, and as a habitat for certain kinds of animal life.

To the extent to which man can destroy or conserve the forests, change water relations, and improve or exhaust soil fertility, he does control climatic factors locally—as history amply proves (*7*)[2]—even though he does not affect the general climate in large regions. Viewed in this light, the forests of the North American Continent assume a much greater historic and social significance than they would have as an exploitable economic resource.

The forests have played an important part in the development of this country in the past. They are destined to play at least an equally important role in the future. The forests of the past were the product of the free play of uncontrolled natural forces; those of the future will be the product of human intelligence based on a scientific knowledge of the natural laws governing their growth and development. Only through arming ourselves with knowledge of how physical and climatic factors affect the forest, on the one hand, and of the biological reactions of the forests to these environmental stimuli, on the other, will we be able to mold the forests of the country to the best interests of the people.

In this article the effects of forests on climate and the relation of climate to forest management will be discussed first. The article will conclude with a brief account of the chief climatic factors that have determined the nature and location of the principal types of forests in the United States.

HOW FORESTS AFFECT LOCAL CLIMATE

Immense forests modify the climate not only over the area they occupy but also over the surrounding country. The reasons for this are clear. Dense forests form a thick mantle covering the ground. They may also be compared to an umbrella with holes in it. These holes may be small or large, many or few, depending on the density of the forest, the size of the individual trees, and whether they are conifers or hardwoods. It is to be expected that such a ground covering must necessarily modify the elements of climate (*17*).

Effect on Air Temperature

A bare surface without impediments receives the full effects of solar radiation, but when the surface is screened by forest cover these effects—heat and light—are greatly modified both quantitatively and qualitatively.

[2] Italic numbers in parentheses refer to Literature Cited, p. 498.

Numerous observations, inside and outside the forest, in different localities and at different times, provide conclusive evidence that, at low elevations in the temperate regions, forests reduce the mean annual temperature by about 1° F. on an average, and at an elevation of about 3,000 feet by 2°. The mean monthly temperature is lower in the forest than in the open for every month of the year, but the difference may reach about 4° F. during the summer, whereas in winter it does not often exceed 0.1°. The mean daily temperature shows a greater degree of difference. During the hottest days of the year the air inside the forest is often more than 5° cooler than that outside, while on the coldest days the difference is only about 2°. The temperature of the air within the forest is therefore not only more moderate but also subject to less fluctuation than that in the open.

Temperature records inside and outside the forest in the northern hardwoods of the Upper Peninsula of Michigan[3] may serve as an example of this influence (fig. 1). In tropical and subtropical regions, the influence of the forest upon the temperature of the air is even greater.

The light intensities within the forest are entirely different from those in the open. If the light intensity in the open under a cloudless sky is designated as 100, then the light intensities in spruce and fir forests will range from 10 to 25 percent, depending upon the density of the cover; in pine forests, from 20 to 40 percent; and in a birch-beech forest, in early spring, from 50 to 75 percent. In other words, a forest cover may intercept and prevent from reaching the ground 50 to 90 percent of the light available.

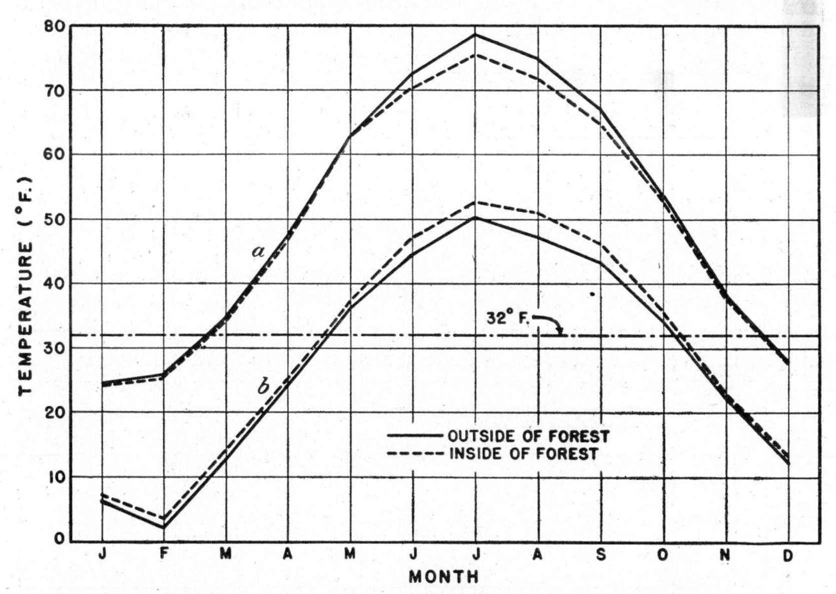

FIGURE 1.—Average daily maximum (*a*) and minimum (*b*) air temperatures inside and outside a birch-beech-maple forest in the Upper Peninsula Experimental Forest, Dukes, Marquette County, Mich., based on 10-year records, 1927–36.

[3] Data taken from climatological summary for the Upper Peninsula Experimental Forest, Dukes, Marquette County, Mich., 1927-36 inclusive, by John R. Neetzel. (Unpublished.)

Effect on Soil Temperature

Forests influence the temperature of the soil in almost the same way as they do that of the air, producing even greater differences. On an average the forest soil is warmer in winter by about 2° F. and cooler in summer by 5° to 9° F. than soil without a forest cover, and this holds true for a depth of as much as 4 feet. In the spring, and especially in the summer, the forest soil is cooler than soil in the open. In the fall and winter it is warmer, but the difference is always less than in summer. The soil under the forest may remain soft when the ground in the open is frozen hard to some depth. If it does freeze, it is to a depth of one-half to less than three-fourths that in the open. Of course this influence varies with the character of the forest.

Figure 2 shows how a northern hardwood forest (birch-beech-maple) affects the march of soil temperatures during the year.

Effect on Moisture

The relative humidity of the air is greater within the forest than outside by 3 to 10 percent on an average. In some cases the difference may be as much as 12 percent. Relative-humidity records from inside and outside a birch-beech-maple forest are presented in figure 3.

Whether the forest actually increases the amount of precipitation is, after 80 years of observations, still a moot question. Though parallel observations carried on in the interior of the forest, on the edge of the forest, and in the open show that the amount of rainfall, as registered by rain gages, is greater inside the forest than on the edge, and on the edge than at some distance from the forest—sometimes by as much

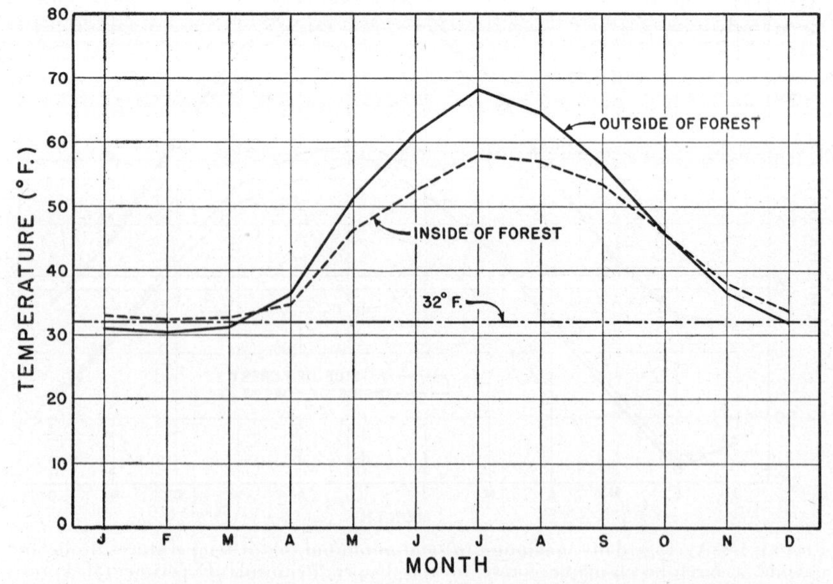

Figure 2.—Average daily soil temperatures, inside and outside a birch-beech-maple forest, to a depth of 6 inches. Upper Peninsula Experimental Forest, Dukes, Marquette County, Mich., 10-year record, 1927–36.

as 25 percent—they do not furnish convincing proof that more rain actually falls over the forest. All that these records indicate is that the rain gages inside the forest, being protected from the wind, may register more water than the rain gages in the open, where they are exposed to the wind. The most that can be said is that the forest may have some effect upon the frequency of precipitation.

The interception of some rainfall by the forest is a well-substantiated fact. Numerous observations in this country and abroad show that the crowns of the trees may intercept as much as 15 to 30 percent of the total precipitation, depending upon the age of the forest and its composition. Only a small part of the precipitation reaches the ground directly through the openings between the leaves and the branches. Another part wets the surface of the leaves and branches and is evaporated back into the air, and still another may run down the trunks to the bases of the trees and into the ground. Coniferous forests, such as spruce and pine, permit a relatively small amount of precipitation to reach the ground, while hardwoods, such as oak and maple intercept comparatively little, especially when the leaves are off. The amount intercepted is equivalent to a considerable reduction in the total precipitation over the area occupied by forest.

During the growing season the temperature of the trunks, branches, and twigs is always lower than that of the surrounding air. This causes the formation of dew on the branches. The difference in the temperature of the air in the forest and that in the open is the cause of air currents between the forest and the fields. These movements facilitate the formation of dew and fogs over fields adjoining forests.

In the spring and fall these fogs save the fields from early frosts and in the summer from damage by hail. Repeatedly and in different countries it has been observed that forests prevent hail from falling over adjoining fields. Coniferous forests have the greatest effect in

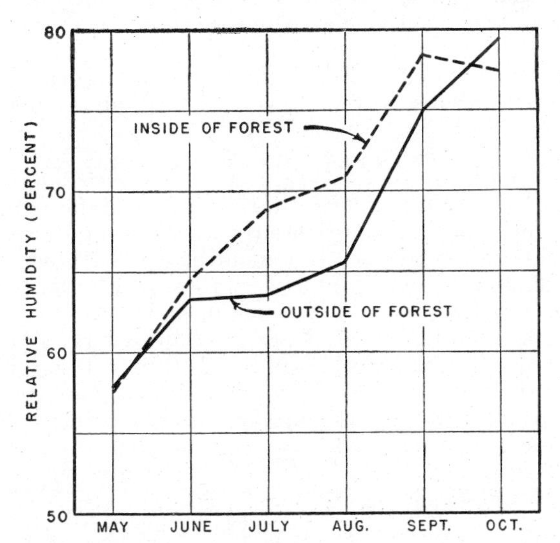

FIGURE 3.—Average daily relative humidity at 5 p. m. inside and outside a birch-beech-maple forest. Upper Peninsula Experimental Forest, Dukes, Marquette County, Mich., 10-year record, 1927–36.

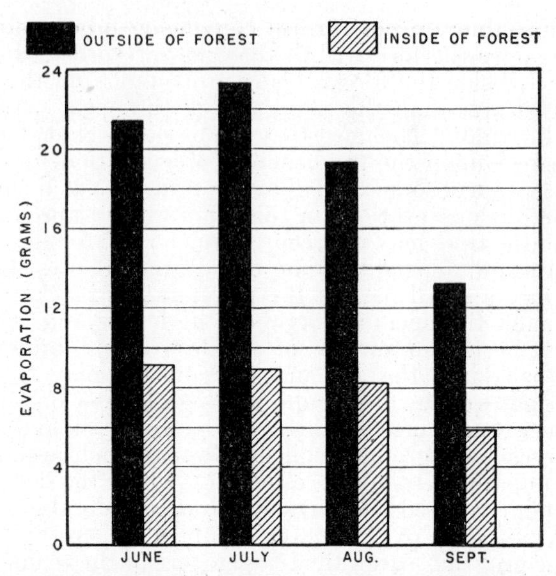

FIGURE 4.—Average daily evaporation in grams inside and outside the forest during the growing season as recorded by Livingston atmometers. Upper Peninsula Experimental Forest, Dukes, Marquette County, Mich., 8-year record, 1928–35.

deflecting hailstorms. Statistics collected for 20 years—1877 to 1897—by a company insuring against hail, confirm the fact that forestless regions are subject to frequent hailstorms while in forested regions hailstorms are of very rare occurrence.

Evaporation from soil protected by the forest is greatly reduced as compared with that in the open. When the soil is protected by a double screen—tree crowns above and a thick layer of dead leaves on the ground—the loss of moisture during the growing season from the forest soil through evaporation may be only one-third to one-half that in the open. This is well illustrated in figure 4 for a northern hardwood forest.

EFFECT ON WIND

Wind loses velocity upon encountering a forest, though at different degrees near the tops of the trees and near the ground. According to some European observations, after wind has penetrated into a dense forest to a distance of some 100 feet, it retains only 60 to 80 percent of its original force, while at a distance of about 200 feet, it has only 50 percent, and at 400 feet, 7 percent. The behavior of wind in a broadleaf forest of maple, birch, and beech (fig. 5) is significantly different during the period when the forest is in leaf and at other times. Even while strong winds are blowing outside, deep in the interior of a dense old forest there may be almost complete calm.

EFFECT ON WATER CONSERVATION

A forest affects the moisture relations of a locality through the manner in which it disposes of the precipitation it receives. By breaking the violence of rain, retarding the melting of snow, increasing the

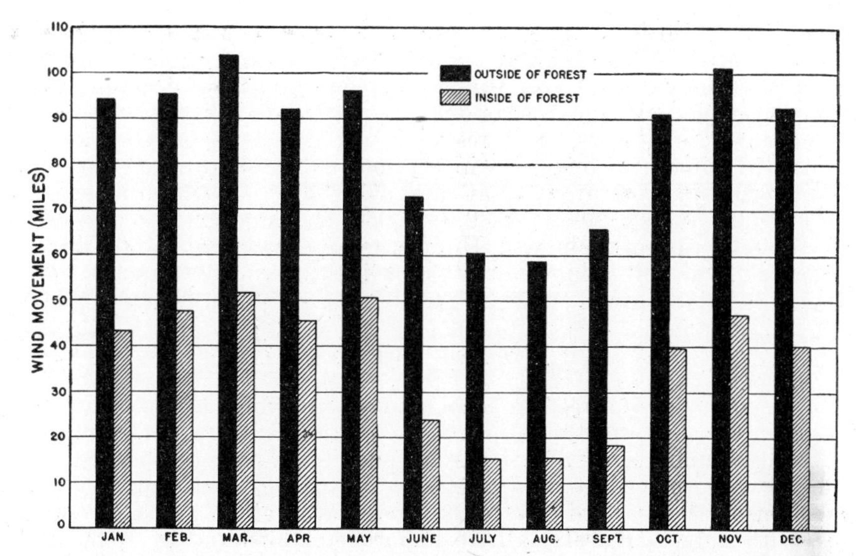

FIGURE 5.—Average daily wind movement 15 feet above the ground inside and outside a maple-birch-beech forest. The greatest difference is in summer, when the trees are in full leaf. Upper Peninsula Experimental Forest, Dukes, Marquette County, Mich., 10-year average, 1927–36.

absorptive capacity of the soil cover, preventing erosion, and checking surface run-off, forests increase underground seepage in general. In this way precipitation, which without the forest cover is rapidly disposed of by surface run-off, is retained in the soil and gradually utilized for tree growth and for maintaining a steady flow of water in streams.

Forest soils have great water-holding capacity. The humus in forest soils holds water equal to twice its weight, whereas sand and clay soils hold only one-quarter to one-half their weights of water respectively. The leaf litter in the forest preserves the porosity of the soil beneath it and thus allows the water to penetrate deeply and be stored as ground water. This storage capacity of the soil under forests depends a great deal, of course, on the character and depth of the soil. A shallow soil underlain near its surface with impermeable rock does not provide for much water storage, but soil that is deep and well protected by a dense forest and leaf litter on the ground forms a vast natural underground reservoir. As H. A. Morgan remarked (*13*), "Dams are good, but if we could raise the underground water table of the Tennessee Valley only 6 inches, that would mean 26 million acre-feet of water—four times as much as the Norris reservoir will hold. Nature would do the storing."

The best aid to nature in storing this water would be well-protected forests on the watershed. There is a great deal of conclusive evidence of the role of forests in water conservation, based on long-time observations—chiefly, it is true, on comparatively small watersheds. A record of more than 100 storms for a period of over 2 years on the Appalachian watersheds indicates that the flow of water during peaks in floods from deforested areas ranges from 10 to 20 times greater than that from forested areas. Small streams are usually continuous from forested areas but often dry up between rains on unforested land.

Forests may not increase the total precipitation, but certainly they help to dispose of it more economically and more fruitfully than does land devoid of forests. In forests the water cycle is retarded, and in this way moisture conditions in the locality are improved.

A record of a recent storm at the LaCrosse, Wis., station illustrates this. On August 20–21, 1939, a 6.05-inch rain fell, continuously, within a period of 24 hours. Under the forest this entire rainfall was stored in the soil, while more than 2 inches ran off from the fields under corn and grain.

The Case of Shelterbelts

The influence of forests on local climate is nowhere better illustrated than in the shelterbelt plantings of the prairie-plains region. Through literally hundreds of varied observations, it has been established that shelterbelts, placed at right angles to prevailing winds, afford a protection on the leeward side to 20 times the height of the trees—that is, with a belt 50 feet high, to a horizontal distance of 1,000 feet. The wind movement does not abruptly return to its initial velocity at this distance, but some measurable reduction has been recorded equal to 50 to 60 times the height of the trees, or 2,500 to 3,000 feet with a 50-foot-high belt. It is clear that some slight effect can be carried from one shelterbelt to another provided the spacing between them does not exceed about 40 times their height. Furthermore, measurements have shown that considerable protection is afforded on the windward side, to a distance of 3 to 5 times the height of the belt. It is, therefore, entirely conceivable that if a large area were protected with shelterbelts at intervals of about two-fifths of a mile, there would be a considerable reduction of the wind movement over the area as a whole.

The retardation of the wind starts a whole chain of favorable climatic influences, such as reduction of evaporation, lowering of temperature, increasing relative humidity of the air, and accumulation of moisture by retaining snow on the fields—all of which result in increase of yield of crops grown under the protective influence of shelterbelts.

This influence of shelterbelts naturally varies with locality, dry and wet years, type of crop, and especially the width, length, density, and height of the shelterbelts, and the intervals at which they are planted.

Aside from their influences on crops, tree belts reduce soil blowing. The ability of wind to move and pick up soil particles varies at least as the second or possibly the third power of the velocity. Consequently, even as little as a 10-percent reduction may mean the difference between considerable soil blowing and very little. A 50-percent reduction in its velocity would practically keep the wind from moving soil particles.

In some localities of western Oklahoma, cottonseed sown on light sandy soils without the protection of shelterbelts is often blown out of the ground, necessitating a second and sometimes a third seeding and delaying the maturing of the cotton in the fall.

In winter, by reducing wind velocity 50 percent and consequently reducing heat losses by radiation and infiltration, shelterbelts may reduce fuel consumption in farmhouses as much as 30 percent. Such results were obtained with test houses, some of which were protected by shelterbelts and others exposed to the wind, the indoor temperatures being maintained at approximately 70° F.

Animals, too, suffer much less in cold weather if protected from wind, and some stock feeders consider a good windbreak almost as valuable as a shed.

Windbreaks play an important role in preventing snow from drifting and causing it to lie and melt evenly and thus water agricultural fields. In areas where windbreaks are not used, a considerable portion of the snow blows into road ditches or swales, where it is of no benefit to crops. By properly designing and locating windbreaks, highway departments find it possible to control snow accumulation and prevent drifts from forming on roads and thus reduce the cost of snow removal.

Effects of Forest Destruction

What the area of the original forests was is a matter of conjecture. It may be safely assumed that the Atlantic forest extended uninterruptedly, except for some swampy treeless areas, over the entire humid eastern part of the United States. This would indicate a forest area of about 800 million acres. The Pacific forest today occupies some 272,500,000 acres and, in spite of considerable encroachment by settlement and logging, largely retains its original boundaries. The original forests, then, must have covered in all about 1,072,500,000 acres.

The area of forest land today, according to the latest Forest Service estimates, is 630,158,000 acres. In the course of the last 150 years, settlement, logging, and fires have reduced the original area by about half, mostly in the East. This, however, does not tell the whole story, because what is now classed as forest land is not all actually covered with forest. Most of it is cut-over land on some of which second-growth forest is coming up and some of which is so depleted by logging and fires that it may be more properly classed as wasteland. There remains today only about 100,832,000 acres of old-growth timber comparable to the original forest—less than one-tenth—and it is still disappearing at a rapid rate.

If forests, as has been shown, tend to modify local climate, particularly in critical areas, by reducing extremes of temperature, increasing humidity, reducing surface-wind velocities, decreasing evaporation, and conserving soil moisture, their disappearance over large areas should have had an adverse effect upon local climate.

Statistical evidence that the climate has changed in some sections of the country as a result of forest destruction is lacking. To begin with, there are no comparable meteorological data upon which to base such conclusions. One often hears that in some sections of the country the growing of certain fruits has been made impossible by the disappearance of the forest. The failure of peaches in the northern part of the Lower Peninsula of Michigan is cited as an example. But it is often difficult to determine whether the trouble was due to the disappearance of the forest or to some other cause.

298737°—41——32

In the humid climate of the East the cutting away of the forest, even if followed by fires, seldom leaves the land absolutely bare. In a few years, shrubs of all kinds and pioneer trees such as aspen, jack pine, pin cherry, and others quickly occupy the ground. While such forests may be of little value economically, they still exert more or less the same climatic influence as forests of greater economic value. It is only in critical areas where forest vegetation is at the limit of its natural occurrence that it fails to reestablish itself naturally if destroyed. Furthermore, where the removal of the forest has been followed by agricultural use and proper handling of the soil, intensive and careful cultivation of crops has to a large extent safeguarded the soil against erosion and rapid run-off.

It is not always easy to find for comparison large contiguous areas similar in every respect except the forest cover. Of particular interest, therefore, are weather observations made during 1933 and 1936 over an area of 7,000 acres in the Copper Basin of eastern Tennessee, which once was heavily forested but now has been completely denuded by smelter fumes (*6*). This denuded forest area is surrounded by a hardwood forest similar to that which originally occupied the basin. The records show that during both winter and summer average daily temperatures were 3° or 4° F. lower in the forest than on the denuded area and did not generally rise as high. Average wind velocity was 7 to 10 times as great on the denuded area in winter, and 34 to 40 times as great in summer; and evaporation was twice as great in winter and 7 times as great in summer. In the winter of 1936 precipitation was 17.5 percent greater in the forest than on the denuded area, and in the winter of 1935 it was 25 percent greater. In both summers it was more than 28 percent greater. The climatic differences, except in precipitation, can be attributed definitely to forest denudation.

In the past, in discussing the calamitous effects of forest denudation, the Old World was drawn upon for examples—the denudation and overgrazing in the Alps and Pyrenees, with resulting disastrous torrents and their destruction of life and property; the deforestation in China and in the Near East and its terrible consequences. Fixation and reforestation of the shifting sand dunes in the Landes region of southern France and the extinction of the Alpine torrents by combined engineering works, sodding, and reforestation were cited as examples of the value of forests in remedying and preventing such disasters.

Today, unfortunately, we do not need to go to the Old World for such lessons. While the effects of the disappearance of the forests of this country have not yet reached the calamitous proportions that they have in some countries of the Old World, there is enough evidence to serve as a warning of what may come if the natural vegetative cover on the land is destroyed. Forest denudation, followed by gross misuse of agricultural land, has already resulted in the loss of millions of tons of soil material washed annually by the Mississippi into the Gulf of Mexico. The productiveness of some 57 million once-fertile acres has been essentially destroyed; that of another 225 million acres has been seriously impaired; and the fertility of 775,678,000 acres more is threatened (*15*). These striking facts have recently attracted the attention of the people.

In many places throughout the country the denudation of the

mountain slopes by cutting, overgrazing, or fires has been followed by disastrous floods. That this damage is caused almost exclusively by the removal of the protective forest cover is shown by a comparison of two watersheds, one of which retains its protective cover and the other is burned. Two such canyons in southern California's chaparral-covered mountains, for instance, were visited during the last days of December 1933 by a general storm. Twelve inches of rain fell on both watersheds. On January 1, 1934, floodwaters swept out of the burned canyon and through a town, destroying 200 homes and taking 34 lives. In the unburned canyon, just a few miles away, this general storm was easily handled by the existing channel, and there was neither flood nor water damage.

That the country is awakening to the danger from extensive removal of the natural vegetative cover, especially the forests, is indicated by the recently enacted legislation for the control of soil erosion and floods at the headwaters of streams, by the adoption of stricter regulations for cutting timber and grazing on public lands, and by voluntary agreements between public agencies and private owners for better use of their agricultural and forest lands.

CLIMATE AND FOREST PRACTICE

Knowledge of the intricate relation between climate and forests forms the scientific basis of forest practice. Such knowledge is essential in developing an effective system of protection against fire, determining the best methods of cutting in different types of forest, securing natural reproduction of the most desirable species, determining the possibilities of reforesting cut-over land, carrying on various cultural operations in young stands, such as thinnings and release cuttings, providing most effective protection of watersheds against rapid surface run-off and erosion, designing shelterbelts in the Great Plains for obtaining the greatest benefit to agriculture and improving living conditions—in fact, in all phases of forest practice.

PROTECTION OF FORESTS AGAINST FIRE

Weather conditions are primarily responsible for the occurrence and the behavior of forest fires, since temperature, precipitation, humidity, and air movement largely determine the dryness, and therefore the inflammability, of the fuel that feeds the fires. Temperature and humidity determine the rate and extent to which inflammable material dries out, while wind movement tends to accelerate drying and to increase the severity of fires by speeding up combustion. Lightning also is important, since in some localities it is one of the chief causes of forest fires.

By correlating the various elements of climate with the inflammability of the leaf litter and dead branches on the ground, it is possible in different localities and seasons to predict the degree of fire hazard for any given day, and thus to be prepared for an emergency. So-called fire-danger meters, now a part of the field equipment of almost every forest ranger, are based on definite relationships between weather and inflammability of forest fuels for any given combination of conditions. These fire-danger meters, together with fire-weather forecasts by local Weather Bureau stations, constitute the first line of defense against fire during the danger season. (*4, 5, 9, 14.*)

By retarding the drying out of the inflammable material and reducing the surface wind velocities, dense forest cover tends to lessen the danger of fire and to prevent its rapid spread. Partial cutting, which means logging only a part of the standing trees at one time, greatly reduces fire hazard in the forest. Clear cutting, on the other hand, increases the fire hazard enormously.

In the Northeast, for example, it has been found that because of higher temperatures, greater wind movement, and greater evaporation, surface duff in the open becomes inflammable approximately 7½ days sooner after a rain than when under forest cover. Fully stocked virgin hardwoods are one of nature's best firebreaks, while removal of the entire forest cover is responsible for our worst fire hazards, because the slash left after logging dries out rapidly without shade or protection against wind and readily catches fire. Instances where fires have stopped at the edge of green timber are common; in fact, one of the earliest methods of fighting fires was to head them into virgin timber, where they could be controlled.

While organization of an effective fire-protective force, fire towers, and equipment for fighting fires are essential, the goal in fire protection is to make the forest as nearly fireproof as possible, and this can be done only when the interrelation between forests and climate is known.

Perpetuation of the Forest Rests Upon Knowledge of Climate

Any forest if left undisturbed for long periods of time will become permanent in character as a result of attaining perfect balance with its environment. This final stage in forest development is usually known as the climax type. Before attaining this climax stage, a forest may have gone through many different stages, each entirely different from the others—somewhat like the evolutionary stages through which an animal goes in embryo before assuming its final form.

For instance, it is generally accepted that the natural evolution of a hardwood forest in the Lake States, after it has been destroyed by fire, begins with aspen. This is the first species to spring up on cut-over and burned-over hardwood land. Because of the short life of the trees, the aspen forest may give way to a white pine forest, and this in turn may change into a hardwood forest. That this is the case is shown by the frequent occurrence in the hardwood forest of a few large white pines which serve as a reminder of an earlier stage in its development. When a mixed forest of white and red pine in the Lake States is cut down, jack pine will probably very largely replace it. If left to itself, this may eventually develop into a red pine or mixed red and white pine forest.

This succession of one type of forest by another is a gradual readjustment of forest vegetation to the changes in local environment brought about by each earlier stage in its development. Jack pine, which springs up readily in the open, creates an environment more favorable for red pine and white pine, which are not so well able to flourish on bare open sites.

By careful use of the ax, or logging, man can perpetuate either the climax type or any of its earlier stages indefinitely. It is not always the final, climax stage that is economically most useful. It may be desirable to perpetuate the stage that produces the most useful products. It is possible, by opening up the forest and letting in more sunshine and moisture to secure reproduction of desirable species, or, by keeping the canopy dense, to prevent undesirable species from coming up. Broadly speaking, forestry is intelligent control of light and shade in the forest, with all the climatic changes they imply.

Experiments carried on in Vermont (*1*) show that in thinning a 20-year-old white pine plantation to about one-half the basal area originally occupied by the trunks of the trees, the total solar radiation for the months of June, July, and August increased in comparison with that in the unthinned plantation 117 percent in the crowns and 164 percent at 8 inches above the ground during the 3 years following thinning. There was also a decrease in the percentage of rainfall intercepted by the crowns to less than 10 percent of the total rainfall. All this perceptibly changed the temperature and moisture conditions of the soil and was reflected in more rapid growth of the trees, both in height and in diameter.

Reforestation

Similar knowledge of climatic conditions is a necessary basis for the successful replanting of denuded land. Small seedlings planted on cut-over and burned-over land are exposed to an environment entirely different from that which prevails within a forest. It is not always possible, therefore, to replant bare land with the same species that occupied the area before the original forest was destroyed.

Records of soil-surface temperatures illustrate the severe climatic conditions with which young trees planted in the open must contend. In 1936, in the sand plains of the northern part of the Lower Peninsula of Michigan, soil-surface temperatures during the warmest part of July reached a maximum of 175° F., and on several occasions temperatures of over 135° F. occurred for periods of 2 hours or more—lethal conditions for young planted trees (*11*). This was an exceptionally hot year, but it indicates the severe atmospheric conditions which young trees must be able to withstand. Records of survival of comparable stock of jack pine, red pine, and white pine on the Huron National Forest, made in the fall of 1936 at the end of the first year of planting, were as follows: Jack pine, 61.2 percent; red pine, 33.3 percent; and white pine, 12.0 percent. It is evident that jack pine had a far better chance to form a successful planting than either red or white pine—especially the latter.

How beneficial even light shade may be under such conditions is shown by the fact that a single clump of scrub oak reduces the soil-surface temperature as much as 30° F. during the hottest part of the day. This is enough to make the difference between lethal and tolerable temperatures for young trees. Plantations 1 to 13 years old in the sand plains of the Lower Peninsula of Michigan consistently show 30 to 40 percent better survival on areas that receive some shade than on those that receive none. Extensive natural openings in these plantations are almost completely denuded of planted trees (*11*).

This is true generally. For instance, in the West it has been shown that the survival of ponderosa pine during the first dry season following field planting was much higher (46 percent) under the brush than in the open, owing to lower evaporation (about one-half), higher relative humidity (about 30 percent), lower soil-surface temperature (51° F.), and greater soil moisture (*16*).

It is only by knowing the atmospheric environment of the land to be planted and the ability of the species to withstand such conditions that an accurate decision can be made as to where to plant and what to plant with any hope of success.

Forests for Protection of Watersheds

Forests, especially at the headwaters of streams, play an important part in flood control. By knowing (1) the factors that contribute toward increasing the infiltration capacity of the soil and reducing the storm run-off from the watershed, and (2) the consumption of water by the forest itself—all of them factors tied up with local climate—it is possible to develop the type of forest that will aid most in conserving water.

This is well substantiated by records based on 4½ years (1935–38) of observation at the Upper Mississippi Soil Erosion Station at LaCrosse, Wis., on the behavior of forested and ungrazed land, forested and grazed land, and cleared pasture land. During this period the ungrazed forested watershed lost only 0.05 inch of precipitation as run-off, while the grazed woods lost 2.16 inches and the open, moderately grazed pasture 0.68 inch. A forested watershed that is ungrazed has a capacity for completely absorbing all summer rainfall and essentially all the melting snow in the spring.

During early August in 1935, southwestern Wisconsin experienced one of the worst summer floods for several decades. Of the total rainfall from May to November of that year, a grazed wood lot under observation yielded 9 percent and an ungrazed wood lot only 0.15 percent in run-off. There are in southwestern Wisconsin some 2 million acres of wood lots similar to those studied. Approximately three-fourths of that area has been burned over, has a sparse timber cover, and is grazed. On the basis of the figures obtained at the LaCrosse Erosion Station for 1935, it is estimated that these latter wood lots during that year contributed some 5,700 million cubic feet (1.05 inches) of run-off to the Mississippi and its tributaries. If these woods were protected from fire and grazing, a great deal of this water would be prevented from getting into the streams in the form of surface run-off.

Many more examples could be cited to show that effective forest practice must rest on thorough knowledge of the relationship between forest vegetation and its environment. This knowledge is especially important in forestry, because the forest is a product of natural forces and must be so dealt with. In agriculture or horticulture, man can employ intensive methods of cultivation and fertilization and produce crops by overcoming certain natural handicaps. In managing a forest or any other wild land, he has to work close to nature and follow its dictates. It is only by knowing the natural laws that have produced the forests in the past and those governing their present development that this great natural resource can be utilized for the best interests of all the people.

HOW CLIMATE AFFECTS FOREST VEGETATION

Oceans—Mothers of Forests

If the entire continent of North America could be seen at once as from an airplane, two broad forest belts would be revealed, one extending from the Atlantic Ocean inland, roughly to the Mississippi River, and the other along the Pacific coast and inland to the Rocky Mountains (*12*). These two forest belts are separated in the central part of the continent by large stretches of grassland and semidesert vegetation (fig. 6). Only in the far north and south of North America do the forest belts come together. North of the fiftieth degree of latitude, in Canada, they merge into one continuous stretch of subarctic forest from the Atlantic to the Pacific Ocean. In the south the two belts are connected by a narrow forest strip on the plateau of northern Mexico.

The two forest belts vary greatly in width. The original forest along the Atlantic coast comprised about 800 million acres, practically all of high economic value, while the Pacific forest, which still largely retains its original boundaries, comprises only about 272,500,000 acres in the Coast Range, the Cascade-Sierras, and the Rocky Mountains, and of this only about 120 million acres is commercially valuable. The location of these two forest belts along the two oceans, their width, and even their general character are readily explained in terms of precipitation combined with the direction of the prevailing winds and the topography.

The region occupied by the Atlantic forest is unbroken by any great mountain ranges, the Appalachian system having only a few high peaks. The prevailing winds during the growing season are from the south, southwest, and southeast. Because of the low, rolling character of the topography, the moisture-laden winds from the Gulf of Mexico sweep to a great distance inland, accounting for the great uninterrupted width of the eastern forest belt.

The region occupied by the Pacific forest is entirely mountainous, broken by major valleys. The winds are largely westerly and northwesterly. They are most frequent in winter and bring the heaviest precipitation in that season. Except along the north coast, therefore, the region is characterized by moist winters and dry summers.

The region occupied by the Atlantic forest is geologically much older than the mountainous West. The processes of weathering and soil formation have been going on in the eastern part of the country for a long time geologically and have resulted in a preponderance of fairly deep, fertile soils. This, together with the favorable distribution of rainfall during the vegetative period, accounts for the overwhelming preponderance of hardwoods, which generally require good soils and ample humidity during the growing season.

The Pacific forest is much younger geologically, and the steep slopes in many parts are still undergoing normal geological erosion. The soils are thin and young. This, together with the low precipitation during the summer, has produced a forest almost exclusively conif-

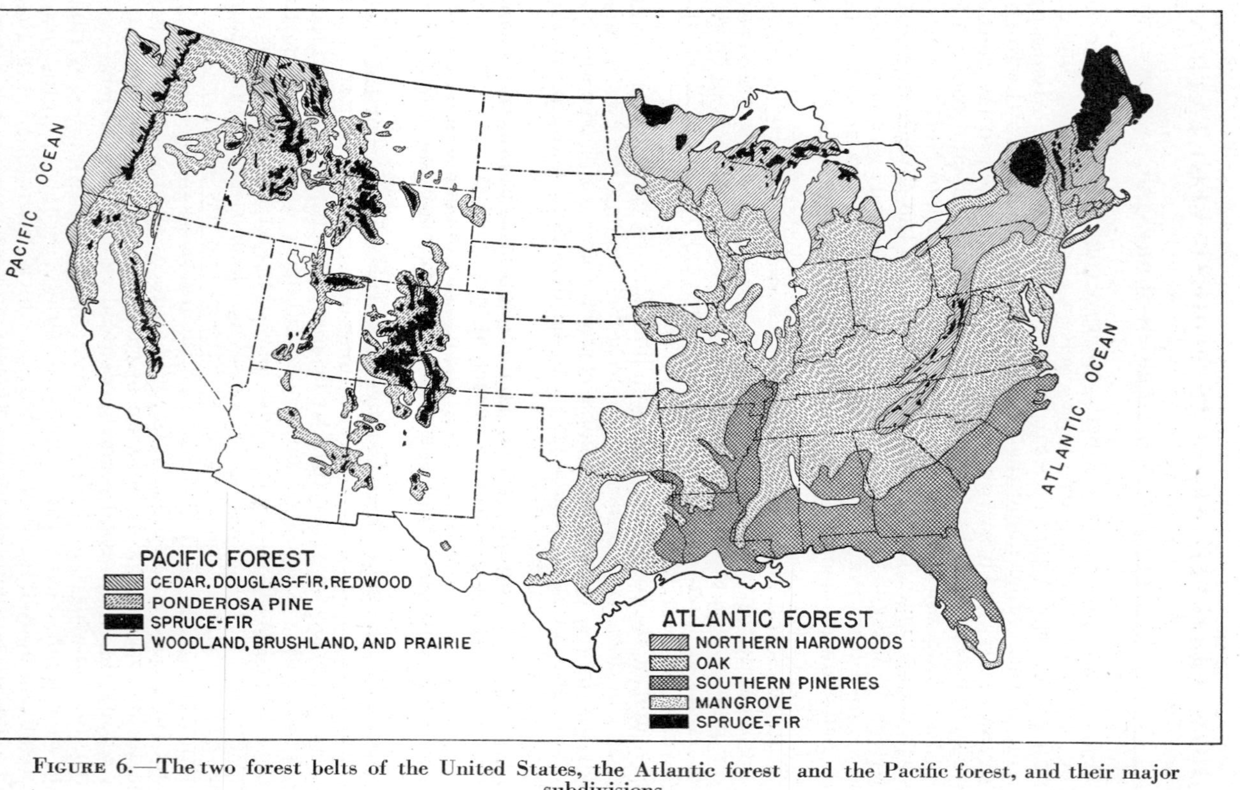

FIGURE 6.—The two forest belts of the United States, the Atlantic forest and the Pacific forest, and their major subdivisions.

erous and confined largely to the western slopes, which are exposed to the moist air currents.

Nowhere is the effect on forests of ocean-fed precipitation combined with topography so strikingly exemplified as in these mountain forests of the West. Here the moist air current encounters three principal parallel mountain ranges, each successively rising to a greater height. A profile along the thirty-ninth parallel of north latitude illustrates this point (fig. 7). Along this parallel, the western air current, fed by the Pacific Ocean, encounters first the Coast Range, which reaches almost to the water's edge. When this air current strikes the mountains and rises, it cools off, releasing heavy precipitation, which sustains a forest of great density and height. After the current has crossed the Coast Range at an elevation of about 2,500 feet, in descending it becomes compressed, hot, and relatively dry. On the east slope of the range precipitation gradually diminishes until it is no longer able to sustain a forest. Brush or grassland, therefore, becomes the dominant vegetation in the valley and extends on the west slope of the second mountain range (the Sierra Nevada) up to an elevation of about 2,500 feet, a level corresponding to the height of the first range over which the air current passes. Above this level, the air current, in ascending, is again cooled and yields precipitation sufficient to sustain forests, which from that point on extend as far as the top of the Sierra Nevadas. On the other side of the Sierra Nevada Range, the air, descending again, becomes dry, causing the replacement of the forest by grass and shrub vegetation for the entire distance between the Sierra Nevadas and the third range—the Rocky Mountains. Dense forest vegetation reappears on the western side of the Rocky Mountains at an elevation of about 8,500 feet, corresponding to the highest level of the Sierra Nevada Range, and extends up the mountains as far as the temperature and exposure to wind permit (the timber line). On the eastern side of the Rocky Mountain range, forest growth thins out because only dry air comes to this region from the west. Whatever forests occur on the east slope of the Rocky Mountains are largely due to the moisture brought from the Gulf of Mexico, in the southeast. This precipitation, however, is scant, and wherever evaporation exceeds precipitation during the growing season, forest growth gives way to sagebrush and grass. Between the Sierras and the Rocky Mountains lie several other smaller ranges or isolated peaks. The elevated plains and peaks that reach into the moist air stream—that is, those that exceed 8,500 feet in elevation—are covered with forest growth. Below this limit is sagebrush and grassland.

The occurrence of forests in the proximity of the Atlantic and Pacific Oceans clearly indicates that the moist winds coming from the oceans give rise to forests. This is true not only of the New World but also of the Old World. The Atlantic Ocean, which gives rise to the eastern forest on the North American Continent, is also responsible for the forest belt bordering the Atlantic Ocean in the Old World. Similarly, the Pacific Ocean makes the existence of two forest areas possible—one in the New World (the western forests of the Americas) and another in the Old World, in eastern Asia. The Indian Ocean gives rise to a forest belt in southern Asia; the northern Arctic Ocean provides moisture for the adjacent countries of the Old and New Worlds and renders the establishment of a forest possible

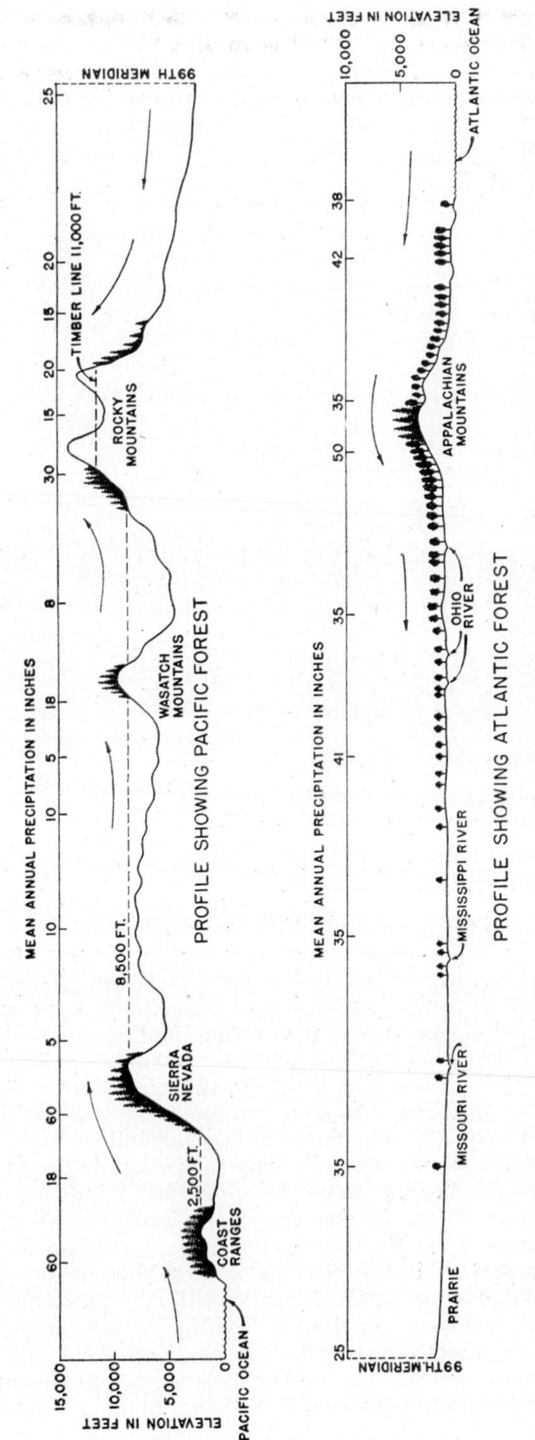

FIGURE 7.—The influence of moist air currents upon the distribution of forests in the West and in the East along the thirty-ninth parallel of north latitude.

wherever the temperature permits. The oceans, therefore, are justly called the "mothers of forests" (*8*).

Great Diversity in Forest Vegetation and Climate

If ocean-fed precipitation, combined with wind movement and topography, explains the general occurrence of forests as distinct from brushland, grassland, or desert, it alone does not explain the great variety of our forests.

Nature has endowed the United States with the richest forests found in any of the Temperate Zones of the world. In the Tropics the forests are richer in species, in Russia there are larger areas of contiguous forests, but nowhere else in the Temperate Zones can be found such a vast area of forests made up of such a variety of types and species. Leaving out of consideration species of semitropical origin found in limited numbers along the coast of southern Florida and those that overlap from the Mexican flora, as well as all species that do not exceed 1 foot in diameter, there are some 700 or more arborescent species within the limits of this country. Of these, not less than 100 are of recognized economic value, and about 200 may be considered in forest management. The richness of the forest flora of this country can best be appreciated in comparison with the temperate forests of Europe, which are made up of not more than a dozen species of economic value.

The Atlantic forest, in its extension from south to north, presents at least five strikingly different types of forests corresponding to differences in climate (fig. 6): (1) Mangrove thickets, (2) the southern pineries, (3) the oak forest, (4) the northern hardwood forest (birch-beech-maple), (5) the spruce-fir forest. The Pacific forest falls roughly into two major subdivisions: (1) Western red cedar, Pacific Douglas-fir, and redwood forests, and (2) the ponderosa pine forest. Even these subdivisions, however, are too broad; they fall far short of presenting the great divergence in types of forest vegetation—natural biological units with which man has to deal as objects of forest management. As a matter of fact, no forest is entirely uniform over any large area, because no large area of the earth is uniform. The smallest difference in elevation (a depression or a hill) or in exposure (north or south slope) is immediately reflected in the character of vegetation, because it means differences in exposure to the sun, in the thawing of the snow, in surface run-off, in the process of weathering of the rock, and therefore in the character of the soil.

Correlating Weather Data and Forest Vegetation

It is largely through studies of clearly defined localized types of forests and their immediate environment that a scientific insight may be gained into the true relationship between vegetation and environment.

The precise nature and quantitative expression of climatic influences is only now beginning to come to light, as, on the one hand, meteorology develops more refined instruments and, on the other, biological sciences reveal more and more the nature of the physiological responses of plants to their environment.

How do the various elements of climate affect forest growth? The ultimate answer invariably is: Through affecting the two most essential conditions of plant life, namely, heat and moisture. Precipitation, temperature, light, relative humidity of the air, and even the soil itself are largely of importance only insofar as they affect the moisture and heat available to plants.

Since most of the heat on the earth comes from the sun and moisture comes from precipitation in its various forms, it would seem that it should be comparatively simple to determine the character of the forest in any locality merely from the available temperature and precipitation data. But the thermometer measures only the temperature of the air and the rain gage the amount of precipitation that falls on the ground. A great part of the living tree is buried deep in the ground, and it is the temperature of the soil, not of the air, that affects the actively functioning roots. It is evident, therefore, that weather data alone cannot be translated directly into terms of vegetational processes.

Furthermore, there is interdependence of climatic factors in their effect upon forests. An average of 15 inches of precipitation a year, for instance, is sufficient to support a forest of ponderosa pine in Montana. To support the same species in New Mexico, a mean annual rainfall of 20 inches or more is needed, to offset the higher temperature and lower atmospheric humidity. When evaporation from the soil, induced by high temperatures, exceeds precipitation, natural forests may entirely disappear. Yet the same amount of precipitation with lower temperatures, and therefore less evaporation, may provide sufficient moisture for sustaining forests.

A good illustration of this interdependence of climatic factors is furnished by ponderosa pine in Arizona and New Mexico (*10*). A 30-year record taken at the Natural Bridge Station in Arizona shows an average annual precipitation of over 23 inches. This is slightly above the precipitation found in a typical ponderosa pine forest. Yet the species occurs here only sparingly and is of subnormal growth. The reason for this is that the temperatures prevalent in this locality are higher than those in typical ponderosa pine forests, which means a higher rate of evaporation and a considerable reduction of the moisture available for plant growth.

The opposite extreme is found in the vicinity of Elizabethtown, N. Mex. There ponderosa pine grows with 2 or 3 inches less than the usual minimum precipitation essential to this type of forest—but the temperature during the growing season is 2° to 3° F. below the average for ponderosa pine.

A decrease in atmospheric humidity tends to reduce the effectiveness of precipitation, while high atmospheric humidity makes it possible for trees to get along with comparatively small amounts of precipitation, as is often the case with forests growing on islands or in a fog belt. Wind, especially when accompanied by low atmospheric humidity, reduces the efficiency of precipitation.

Light—the part of solar radiation visible to the human eye—is an important factor in the life of green plants. Yet in nature, light, heat, and moisture effects are so intimately related that they can be separated only with difficulty. The warmer the climate, for instance, the less the light requirement of trees.

The soil itself affects plant growth chiefly through its water-holding capacity. To determine the net effect of the interacting and compensating climatic factors upon forest vegetation, direct measurements of the temperature and humidity of the soil become essential. Of similar significance are direct measurements of the losses of water from the soil through evaporation or transpiration of the trees themselves.

The correlation between weather data and definite types of forest is still further complicated by the fact that to understand plant life properly it is essential to group all meteorological observations by periods of vegetational growth and rest. During each of these periods, trees, like other plants, require different amounts of heat and moisture. During the winter, trees may withstand extremely low temperatures provided there has been enough heat during the summer period for all the necessary physiological functions. The coldest temperatures on record occur, not near the North Pole, but in the forested regions of Siberia. Yet the Siberian fir, which during its period of rest withstands with impunity the lowest temperatures ever recorded anywhere on the earth's surface, in the spring has its terminal shoots killed at a temperature of 28.5° F.

When the mean air temperature during the four hottest months of the growing season does not exceed 50° F., the forest becomes scrubby in character. A tree may grow in a climate where the temperature during the entire year does not fall below 50° F.; yet if the mean temperature during the growing season does not greatly exceed 50° F., the prolonged mild climate does not benefit its growth.

The same is true of all other climatic factors, except that in the case of precipitation not only the total rainfall during the periods of growth but also its intensity and frequency are of great importance. The total rainfall during the growing season may be sufficient for sustaining forest growth; yet if it comes at frequent intervals and in small quantities, the effect upon vegetation may be negligible, whereas the same amount of precipitation occurring in larger quantities at less frequent intervals may benefit forest growth considerably.

It is evident, therefore, that while weather data for the whole year are important, the records for the growing season are of the greatest significance in interpreting vegetation.

Within recent years several localized studies of the relation between climate and the occurrence of well-recognized, distinct forest types have been made at various forest experiment stations, including those in Colorado (*3*), New Mexico and Arizona (*10*), Idaho and Utah (*2*). Representative of such studies is one conducted by the Southwestern Forest and Range Experiment Station in northern Arizona and northern New Mexico, of four forest types and their environment (*10*). Most of the observations upon which the conclusions are based began in 1908 and were continuous for more than 10 years, while supplementary records were taken at different places for shorter periods.

In this region, altitude far more than latitude determines the character of the climate and vegetation. Forests occur mainly above the 5,000-foot contour, up to 11,500 feet of elevation, which is the upper limit of tree growth. Four well-defined forest types are recognized. These are, in ascending order: (1) The woodland, occupying the zone from 5,000 to 7,000 feet; (2) ponderosa pine, from 7,000 to 8,000 feet; (3) Douglas-fir, from 8,000 to 9,500 feet; and (4) Engelmann spruce, from 9,500 up to about 11,500 feet. These altitudinal zones represent different types of both forest vegetation and climate.

A direct correlation between several climatic factors and the finer subdivisions of forest vegetation is clearly indicated in table 1. This correlation, however, manifests itself only during the growing season. It is further evident that it is not one single climatic factor but the combination of all climatic factors that is responsible for the difference in the types of forest. From this it may be assumed that wherever these climatic factors occur in the same combination as in the four types of forest studied, the same types of forest may be expected. It is also clear that the conditions most affected by the various elements of climate and most crucial to the life of the different species composing the types are heat and moisture. In the ascent from lower to higher altitude, or from warmer to colder climate, heat sets the upper limit for the type. In the descent from higher to lower elevation, or from colder to warmer climate, it is dryness, or moisture deficiency, that sets the lower limit of each type. This relation provides a scientific basis for forest management.

TABLE 1.—*Correlation between climatic zones and forest types in northern Arizona and northern New Mexico* [1]

Forest zone	Summer temperature (June–September)			Moisture			
	Mean	Mean maximum	Mean soil temperature at 1 foot	Annual precipitation	Evaporation (total, June to September)	Available soil moisture at 1 foot	
						Average	Lowest
	° F.	° F.	° F.	*Inches*	*Inches*	*Percent*	*Percent*
Woodland	65–69	79–85	64–75	12–20	30–40	2.6	−0.4
Ponderosa pine	59–63	74–80	56–65	18–25	18–26	3.8	−.5
Douglas-fir	56–58	67–74	52–54	22–34	12–16	13.7	7.6
Engelmann spruce	50–56	58–68	44–50	27–36	10–13	13.7	3.8

[1] Data from G. A. Pearson's Forest Types in the Southwest as Determined by Climate and Soil (*10, p. 120*).

By practicing light or heavy cutting and thus modifying the climatic conditions, the composition of the forest can be controlled and the natural reproduction of the most desirable species encouraged or those kept out which do not hold promise of good development.

LITERATURE CITED

(1) ADAMS, W. R.
1935. EFFECT OF THINNING IN PLANTATIONS ON SOME OF THE PHYSICAL FACTORS OF THE SITE AND ON THE DEVELOPMENT OF YOUNG NORTHERN WHITE PINE (PINUS STROBUS L.) AND SCOTCH PINE (PINUS SILVESTRIS L.). Vt. Agr. Expt. Sta. Bul. 390, 156 pp., illus.

(2) BAKER, F. S., and KORSTIAN, CLARENCE F.
1931. SUITABILITY OF BRUSH LANDS IN THE INTERMOUNTAIN REGION FOR THE GROWTH OF NATURAL OR PLANTED WESTERN YELLOW PINE FORESTS. U. S. Dept. Agr. Tech. Bul. 256, 83 pp., illus.

(3) BATES, CARLOS G.
1924. FOREST TYPES IN THE CENTRAL ROCKY MOUNTAINS AS AFFECTED BY CLIMATE AND SOIL. U. S. Dept. Agr. Bul. 1233, 152 pp., illus.

(4) GISBORNE, H. T.
1928. MEASURING FOREST-FIRE DANGER IN NORTHERN IDAHO. U. S. Dept. Agr. Misc. Pub. 29, 64 pp., illus.

(5) ———
1936. MEASURING FIRE WEATHER AND FOREST INFLAMMABILITY. U. S. Dept. Agr. Cir. 398, 59 pp., illus.

(6) HURSH, C. R., and CONNAUGHTON, C. A.
1938. EFFECTS OF FORESTS UPON LOCAL CLIMATE. Jour. Forestry 36: 864–866.

(7) MARSH, GEORGE P.
1885. THE EARTH AS MODIFIED BY HUMAN ACTION. 629 pp. New York.

(8) MAYR, HEINRICH.
1925. WALDBAU AUF NATURGESETZLICHER GRUNDLAGE. Ed. 2, 568 pp., illus. Berlin.

(9) MITCHELL, J. A.
1929. FOREST FIRE HAZARD AS AFFECTED BY WEATHER CONDITIONS, FOREST TYPE, AND DENSITY OF COVER. Wis. Agr. Expt. Sta. Res. Bul. 91, 26 pp., illus.

(10) PEARSON, G. A.
1931. FOREST TYPES IN THE SOUTHWEST AS DETERMINED BY CLIMATE AND SOIL. U. S. Dept. Agr. Tech. Bul. 247, 144 pp., illus.

(11) RUDOLF, PAUL O.
1939. WHY FOREST PLANTATIONS FAIL. Jour. Forestry 37: 377–383.

(12) SHANTZ, H. L., and ZON, RAPHAEL.
1924. NATURAL VEGETATION. *In* Atlas of American Agriculture, Part I, The Physical Basis of Agriculture, Sect. E. U. S. Dept. Agr. Adv. Sheets 6, 29 pp., illus.

(13) SILCOX, F. A.
1936. FORESTS AND FLOOD CONTROL. Amer. Assoc. Adv. Sci., Occasional Pub. 3: 5–16, illus.

(14) STICKEL, PAUL W.
1931. THE MEASUREMENT AND INTERPRETATION OF FOREST FIRE-WEATHER, IN THE WESTERN ADIRONDACKS. N. Y. State Col. Forestry Syracuse Univ., Tech. Pub. 34, 115 pp., illus.

(15) UTZ, E. J., and KELLOGG, CHARLES E.
1938. THE NATURE AND EXTENT OF SOIL LOSSES. U. S. Dept. Agr. Yearbook 1938: 84–96, illus.

(16) WAHLENBERG, W. G.
1930. EFFECT OF CEANOTHUS BRUSH ON WESTERN YELLOW PINE PLANTATIONS IN THE NORTHERN ROCKY MOUNTAINS. Jour. Agr. Res. 41: 601–612, illus.

(17) ZON, RAPHAEL.
1927. FORESTS AND WATER IN THE LIGHT OF SCIENTIFIC INVESTIGATION. 106 pp., illus. [Reprinted with rev. bibliog. from App. V of Final Rpt., U. S. Natl. Waterways Comn., 1912. S. Doc. 469, 62d Cong., 2d sess., pp. 205–302.]

Climate and Plant Diseases

By Harry B. Humphrey [1]

HERE in brief compass is the dramatic story of the relation of the weather to wheat rust and how this disease is in large part being conquered by plant breeding. Other devastating plant diseases, many of which have caused widespread famines in the past, will undoubtedly be overcome by the same methods.

[1] Harry B. Humphrey is Principal Pathologist, Division of Cereal Crops and Diseases, Bureau of Plant Industry.

Some of the earliest historical records set down by man tell about diseases and pests that took toll of his food resources. More than once the record tells of entire nations threatened with famine from this cause. This has happened throughout history. Less than a century ago, late blight so blasted the potato crop of Ireland as to spread starvation throughout the island. Many Irish-Americans trace their descent to emigrants who were forced to leave the "ould sod" by this disaster. In 1904, 1916, 1935, 1937, and 1938, the United States and Canada experienced rust epidemics in grain that were widespread and devastating in their severity.

Centuries before man recognized the true causes of rusts, smuts, and mildews, he attributed such maladies to the whims of the gods. The Romans believed the god Robigo had the power to protect wheat from rust, and they held sacrificial feasts (Robigalia) to gain his good will. Later, people attributed plant diseases to the vagaries of the weather. Finally, in the middle of the eighteenth century, Tillet proved that wheat bunt is transmitted through its "black dust," which we call spores.

Since Tillet, knowledge in this field has grown enormously, and we now know not only the causes of most of the serious plant diseases but also the true relationship of weather to their incidence, spread, and effects.

Weather influences plant diseases in many different ways. Some require moist, humid conditions for infection and development; others are more serious when it is relatively dry. Some are favored by cool temperatures; others require warm weather. In some cases the principal effect of weather is not on the disease-producing organism itself but on the host plant, or even on an insect carrier of the disease, when such a carrier is necessary to cause infection of the host plant. Many examples of these different relationships might be cited, but only a few can be given here.

The late blight of potato is favored by excessive humidity and moderate temperatures, conditions necessary for the spread of the parasite. Warm, cloudy, moist weather makes the apple and pear more susceptible to bacterial fire blight, gorging tissues with sap so that they are more readily invaded by the organism; hot dry weather checks the progress of the disease. Moisture and moving air are essential in the sporulation (spore formation) and spread of apple scab. The spread of peach brown rot is similarly controlled by rain and wind. Severe drought curbs curly top of sugar beets by killing off certain annuals upon which the leafhopper which carries the curly top virus to the beets depends for summer survival. Scab of wheat and other small grains is always more prevalent when warm, moist weather occurs during the period from heading to maturity.

Among the most important of all the plant diseases affected by weather are the cereal rusts, and their story will be given in more detail.

In observations extending from 1904 to 1925, Stakman and Lambert found that in Minnesota and the Dakotas epidemics of stem rust did not occur in seasons when the average temperature during the critical period was below 61° F. In some seasons, as in 1910, even when the average temperature was relatively high, there was no rust epidemic, largely because of deficient rainfall.

In 1915 the United States produced its record wheat crop—1,009 million bushels. The average summer temperature for that year in Minnesota and the Dakotas ran more than 4° F. below the normal of 62.5°. There was no rust epidemic. The season of 1916 in the spring-wheat States started off even more promisingly than did that of 1915. July 1916, however, was characterized by relatively high temperatures and fairly abundant rainfall. The result was a widespread devastating epidemic of rust. In 1915 the spring-wheat crop had totaled 368 million bushels, with an average yield of 17.8 bushels per acre. In 1916 the total was 178 million bushels, and the average yield was 9.2 bushels. The difference of almost 200 million bushels was principally due to rust, which in turn was made possible by the warm, relatively moist weather of a single month, July 1916.

Humidity is second only to temperature in promoting cereal-rust epidemics. Dew or other free moisture on the wheat plants is necessary for the germination of rust spores. If conditions prevent precipitation of rain or condensation of dew, there need be little fear of an epidemic, even with abundant spores. A succession of overcast nights or of night-long wind movement, which prevents dewfall, synchronized with the critical period for rust infection will prevent the spread of rust, even though the average temperatures are favorable.

The important thing in the development of a rust epidemic is that certain necessary favorable conditions operate at the same time. There must be (1) a favorably warm temperature; (2) abundant moisture with dew or rain; (3) abundant spores to infect the plants; and (4) a susceptible grain or grass host. More than once when the stage has seemed set for a destructive rust epidemic a change in one or another of the essential factors has prevented its culmination. These factors, however, did coincide in the years previously mentioned, when there was widespread rust damage in the Midwestern States.

Weather variations in any one locality are not the only important climatic factors that control epidemics of the cereal rusts in the United States. The climatic weather complex of the entire northern and southern midcontinental area of North America also plays an important role.

In the northern part of the United States and in Canada the grain and grass rusts produce red spores capable of infecting growing grains and wild grasses up to the end of the growing season. At the time of the red-spore stage, grain, both volunteer and fall-sown, has started, and grass has begun to green up in southern Kansas, Oklahoma, and Texas. The spores and grain would seem to be far enough apart so that "never the twain shall meet." Climate and weather, however, bring the two together.

It is characteristic of central North America that successions of cyclonic storms sweep from northern Canada south and east across the United States. Northern winds accompanying such storms may blow for several days at a time from Canada clear down into Texas and farther. These winds pick up the red-rust spores produced in Canada or the northern part of the United States and carry them across the country. As rains occur, the spores are deposited and produce infection on susceptible volunteer and early-sown grain along the way. Spore traps in Texas show heavy showers of red-rust spores following protracted periods of north winds occurring at any time from September into early winter.

Overwintering rust infections in Texas, Mexico, or elsewhere supply spores for new infections on both volunteer and sown grains and on wild grasses as spring growing conditions become favorable. With the right combination of local temperatures and moisture, a general infection may spread from these primary points to start secondary local epidemics, which merge and build up countless billions of spores. These spores are the inoculum for a northward march of infection as the crop comes on successively from south to north in the spring and early summer. A sequence of locally favorable weather conditions, with spore-laden winds driving onward this south-to-north spread of rust, means a rust epidemic sweeping like wildfire through the country's grainfields.

Dependent as it is on climatic and weather forces beyond man's control, the situation at first thought seems insurmountable. Like many other problems, however, it becomes less awe inspiring when reduced to its simplest terms. The four primary elements that must coincide to induce a devastating rust epidemic have been noted. Temperature and moisture, elements of weather, are beyond control; nothing can be done except to talk about them. The amount of inoculum and the acreage of susceptible host plants, on the other hand, are vulnerable and subject to attack. Substantial progress already has been made in curtailing their menace. The stem-rust-resistant spring wheat, Thatcher, bred in cooperative experiments in Minnesota, occupied in 1940 some 17,500,000 acres in the hard red spring wheat area of the United States and Canada. Such an acreage of this variety in 1935, 1937, or 1938 would have prevented the stem-rust epidemics of those years with losses of 100 million bushels and more each year. Soon a new rust-resistant wheat developed by cooperative research in Texas will be distributed to eliminate overwintering infections in the South. This not only will protect the Texas wheat crop but will cut off inoculum from susceptible varieties grown to the north and east. Similarly, new stem- and leaf-rust-resistant varieties of oats and barley are being introduced that will insure these crops against the ravages of rust.

Progress is also being made in the control of other plant diseases by breeding disease-resistant strains. The problem is difficult, and undoubtedly the road to completely successful achievement will be rough. Yet in the end, though we can do nothing about the weather, we may not need to talk about it so far as plant diseases are concerned.

Insects and the Weather

By James A. Hyslop [1]

THE ENTOMOLOGIST studying the lives of insects finds that weather is a constant controlling factor. It has different effects with different species; with each species, certain conditions favor, others discourage migrations and serious outbreaks. The more we learn about this, the better we should be able to combat these enemies and be warned in advance what to expect.

[1] James A. Hyslop is Principal Entomologist in charge of the Division of Insect Pest Survey and Information, Bureau of Entomology and Plant Quarantine.

Insects place a bill against our natural resources and productive capacity of approximately 3 billion dollars a year; they are often the factor determining success or failure in agricultural enterprises. Many of the more important pests are so vitally affected by climatic conditions that they must be considered in any discussion of the effect of climate and weather on agriculture.

The insects have adapted themselves to the normal climatic conditions in the regions where they naturally occur, and it is only when severe departures from these norms occur at a critical period of an insect's life that its numbers increase or decrease materially. The various factors of climate, such as temperature, moisture, and rate of evaporation, affect different insects in varying degrees at different times, and the records generally included in meteorological publications often give rise to misleading conclusions when used in attempting to ascertain the effect of climate on insects.

Each insect has a definite temperature tolerance at each stage of development. Below a certain minimum temperature it dies. Some insects are able to withstand as low temperatures as normally occur in any inhabited part of the world, though in most cases severe cold can be endured only during the hibernating period. Certain Collembola known as snow fleas are often seen to be very active on the little pools of water which form on the surface of ice when the temperature rises slightly above freezing; and larvae of many aquatic insects can be frozen in ice and resume activity immediately after the ice is thawed.

Between the minimum at which life can exist and a temperature known as the threshold of development, the insect remains in a dormant condition. Between the threshold of development and a higher temperature known as the optimum it becomes increasingly active. The optimum is the range of temperatures at which maximum development takes place in the minimum time. It may be a very narrow range or quite a wide one. Temperatures above the optimum retard development. From the upper limit of the optimum to the high temperature that kills the insect, it lives either with reduced activity or in a state of suspended activity known as aestivation. Remarkably high temperatures are tolerated by insects. In certain hot springs, mosquitoes, water bugs, and water beetles live normally in water ranging from 100° to 122° F.

The longer the optimum temperature is maintained, the greater the number of generations an insect may produce at any given place in a single season. The codling moth, an introduced insect very likely brought to this country from Europe by the earliest colonists, is probably the most serious pest of apples. In the Northeastern States, although there is a more or less limited optimum period each year, the codling moth produces one brood, and a comparatively few individuals produce a second brood. In the Shenandoah Valley of Virginia, where there is a more extended optimum period, two more or less complete broods are produced annually, and in the Ozarks the optimum period extends over so long a time that three broods can often be produced. In all regions some individuals produce only one generation despite favorable climatic conditions.

The effects of moisture on insects are like those of temperature—there is a point at which the insect is killed by lack of moisture, an optimum moisture condition, and a condition under which it dies from excessive moisture. Usually moisture and temperature are not independent; the optimum and the extremes are at certain combinations of moisture and temperature. On a graphic chart the optimum weather conditions for an insect would be represented by a series of more or less concentric ovals displaced diagonally when the temperatures are expressed as ordinates and the moisture as abscissas. The central zone would be that series of temperatures and humidities at which the insect's development reaches its maximum speed, and the surrounding zones would indicate areas of successively decreasing activity to the zone of aestivation in one direction and the zone of hibernation in the other. Beyond the latter would be the lethal area for the insect or insect stage. (Some insects do not hibernate or aestivate but remain active throughout the year.) In all cases the lethal zone limits both the general and the periodic distribution of the insect.

Examples are so numerous that only a few of the more outstanding and generally observed responses can be given here.

SPECIFIC RESPONSES TO TEMPERATURE AND MOISTURE

A single drop to the minimum temperature is likely to affect an insect vitally even though the average temperature for a period of a week or a month is decidedly above normal. Twenty degrees below zero in November will destroy all gypsy moth eggs whereas the same temperature late in the winter will allow considerable survival.

The San Jose scale is definitely limited northward by minimum temperatures and does not extend in destructive numbers into the northern Great Plains. In the East Central States its population fluctuates directly with the minimum temperature, other factors being equal.

Cool, delayed springs are very favorable for the development of many species of cutworms; such weather slows up germination of seeds, retards plant development, and gives the worms ample time to devastate truck and field crops. Delayed springs are also very favorable for the seed-corn maggot, an insect that develops on land in which there is a high organic-matter content and thus is particularly troublesome where large quantities of manure or organic fertilizers are used. Hot, dry weather rapidly terminates outbreaks of the seed-corn maggot.

Hot, dry weather in areas under irrigation is very favorable for such insects as the codling moth, which will not lay its eggs when the temperature is below a fixed minimum. For this reason, and because the season is long enough for two or more generations, the codling moth is very destructive in the apple-growing section of the Pacific Northwest, while in such regions as the New England States, where the season is comparatively short and the spring evenings are likely to be too cool for egg laying, it is not a major pest.

The boll weevil, the most important single limiting factor in cotton production, is of minor importance in the northern part of the Cotton Belt owing to the fact that temperatures approaching 0° F. are fatal to it. Over the greater part of the Cotton Belt, however, such temperatures rarely occur. Hot, dry summers are also very detrimental to the development of the insect, and this is probably the greatest factor in limiting boll weevil damage. Wet summers are usually accompanied by heavy boll weevil damage.

Certain tropical and subtropical insects move slowly northward in a series of years having high minimum winter temperatures. Conspicuous among them are the harlequin bug, a pest of cabbage, and the two pickleworms, which attack cucurbits. These insects normally pass the winter in the South Atlantic and Gulf States, where they are indigenous. Following mild winters they move slowly northward, and if a series of such winters occur in succession they may even get into New England and the Lake States. The first severe winter, however, exterminates all except those in their normal habitat. The growing of cucumbers for pickles in the region of normal occurrence of pickleworms is decidedly handicapped by these insects. In the Lake States and New England they occur so rarely that they are not important.

One of the most serious pests of cotton is the cotton leaf worm. This insect is of tropical origin and, so far as present records show, does not pass the winter in North America. In tropical America it apparently breeds continuously throughout the year. As the mild weather extends northward in our summer and southward over the South American continent in our winter, the current generation of moths of the cotton leaf worm flies away from its center of distribution. Apparently the moths enter the United States in the lower Rio Grande section of Texas. The first generation produced in this area moves northward, and if the moths enter this country early enough in the season, succeeding broods eventually may fly into the Lake States and New England, where they often occasion considerable alarm by settling in countless numbers in the larger cities, attracted by the night illumination. This moth is peculiar in being able to obtain its food by rasping the skin of fruits and sucking the juices; most moths do not have any rasping apparatus and cannot do this. When the moth arrives before picking time in the grape region along the Great Lakes, it does considerable damage to the grapes. Less damage is reported for other fruits such as peaches and plums.

The corn earworm, also known as the bollworm and tomato fruitworm, is an insect that normally passes the winter in the soil as far north as southern New Jersey, in the eastern and southern parts of Maryland, and westward throughout southern Missouri to Kansas. In years of mild winters it can survive considerably farther northward, and following such winters it does serious damage to corn and tomatoes early in the season, whereas in normal years little damage is recorded to any but the late crops.

The velvetbean caterpillar is another tropical insect which is decidedly affected by low minimum winter temperatures. It passes the winter successfully in southern Florida almost every year, and in certain winters is able to survive in the Gulf region. Following mild winters it is often a serious pest to velvetbeans, cowpeas, soybeans, and other leguminous crops as far north as the Carolinas.

The serious grasshopper outbreaks of the last few years in the Plains States are a direct result of a series of dry seasons. Drought is particularly favorable to these insects when it occurs at the time the young grasshoppers are hatching.

Dry weather during April and May is very favorable for the development of the chinch bug. Incipient outbreaks of this insect are often frustrated by cool, wet weather at the time the young bugs are leaving their hibernation quarters. If the weather is very cool the insects are not materially affected, but when it is sufficiently warm and humid for the parasitic fungus disease which attacks these insects to develop, yet not warm enough for the bugs to leave hibernation, entire colonies may be wiped out. Even more effective are heavy rains when young bugs are hatched. All the recorded outbreaks of the chinch bug have begun during periods of normal or less than normal rainfall, and it has usually been several years before adverse weather and other natural conditions reduced the number of bugs to the point where they became unimportant.

Long periods of abnormal weather often materially affect insect populations. In years when extended droughts cover large forest areas so that the trees are devitalized, certain bark beetles, such as the southern bark beetle and the hickory bark beetle, become very destructive. Outbreaks of these insects are often terminated by extended periods of abnormally wet weather.

A late, dry fall which retards the germination of wheat seed beyond a certain date will practically eliminate the hessian fly. The fact that this insect is so dependent upon moisture for emergence and for a short period after emergence upon available plants on which to oviposit has led to the very practical control measure of late planting.

The plum curculio, though not in general limited by temperature, is adversely affected by prolonged dry weather at the period when the pupae are in the ground.

Very often the effect of climate on insects is a complicated one. The climate may not directly affect a certain insect but may affect others that prey on it, reducing or increasing their numbers. For example, following a mild winter the green bug will multiply rapidly in a cool, wet spring when temperatures are decidedly below those that allow the parasites of this insect to develop. In such years there are often serious green bug infestations over wide areas from Texas to Minnesota. Under normal temperature conditions numbers of the parasites emerge early enough in the season to keep this insect in check.

The difficulty encountered in the introduction of parasites of the Japanese beetle offers another example of insect-parasite-climate relations. One parasite, a fly, was very effective in parts of Japan but could not adapt itself to the change in the life history of the Japanese beetle produced by the climate of our Middle Atlantic States. Here the Japanese beetles were so delayed in their development that the flies had all emerged and died before the peak of emergence of the beetles, and a very small percentage of the beetles had eggs of the parasite laid upon them.

Another parasite, a wasp, collected in northern Japan, can successfully produce females only when it can lay its eggs on the larger Japanese beetle larvae; when the eggs are laid on the young larvae, only male parasites emerge. In the United States either the development of the beetles was retarded or that of the wasps was accelerated so that when the mass of parasites emerged only very small beetle larvae were available. This necessitated collecting strains of the parasite from southern Japan and China, where climatic conditions had an effect on both the beetle and the parasite more nearly like that in this country.

Climate and Livestock Production

By A. O. Rhoad [1]

IN COMPARISON with our knowledge of animal nutrition and animal diseases, very little is known about the direct effects of climatic factors on livestock production. Yet a surprising number of significant facts have been turned up in scattered investigations, and they are summarized in this article. The author is especially interested in the possibilities of cross breeding as a means of developing types better adapted to regional climatic differences.

[1] A. O. Rhoad is Animal Husbandman, in Charge, Iberia Livestock Experiment Farm, Bureau of Animal Industry, Jeanerette, La.

ALTHOUGH climate primarily affects animals indirectly through its influence on the quantity and quality of the plant products used as feed, it also has direct effects, which are for the most part closely connected with the physiological functions involved in the maintenance of normal body temperature under diverse weather conditions. For most classes of livestock there are optimum climatic conditions under which they will develop and produce best within the limits of their inherent capacity. When farm animals do well in a given region, they are said to be well adapted to the region—that is, to the climate and the local vegetation. The quality and abundance of the latter is, in turn, a direct result of climate acting through the soil.

With few exceptions, all the present types of farm animals in the United States originated in other continents. Vast numbers of breeding stock have been imported from many parts of the Old World and distributed to various regions in this country. For several centuries, through a process of trial and error, adjustment of types and breeds to various environments, nutritional planes, and economic conditions has been going on, until now, though the process still continues, there is evident a certain regional distribution of domestic types and breeds as the areas adapted to each type become better defined.

INDIRECT AND DIRECT EFFECTS OF CLIMATE

A considerable body of scientific information has accumulated on the effect of seasons, as well as of climate in general, on livestock production. Lush and his coworkers (*19*)[2] in the United States and Schutte (*32*) in South Africa have shown with beef cattle on the range that the rate of growth from birth to about 30 months of age is directly influenced by seasonal changes in weather. The variations in live weight of calves in these studies were due, however, not to the direct effects of climate on the animals but to its effects on pasturage. In the case of dairy cattle, Hammond (*15*), reporting on conditions in Jamaica and Trinidad and Rhoad (*27*), on conditions in Minas Gerais, Brazil, have shown that the long period of drought characteristic of many parts of the Tropics materially reduced milk production by greatly reducing the pasturage available and affecting the nutritive value of the grasses. Carneiro (*5*) showed that when dairy cattle were properly fed during the drought season there was no appreciable drop in production. The references given are illustrative of the marked influence of weather on the plane of nutrition of animals and the consequent effects on growth and production.

That climate also influences the production of dairy cows more directly is shown in the analysis by Edwards (*9*) of the butterfat production of Registry of Merit Jersey cows in Maine and Georgia. The fact that the study was made of Registry of Merit records eliminates the nutritional factor, as all cows in this test would be similarly fed on a high plane of nutrition. The differences in production are considered to be due to the direct effect of climate on the cows. There was a midwinter decline in production in Maine that was attributed to the fact that barns were warmed. A somewhat similar study was made by Warren (*34*) on the size of eggs from pullets in different latitudes and at different temperatures within the same

---

[2] Italic numbers in parentheses refer to Literature Cited, p. 514.

latitude. Larger eggs were produced in the northern than in the southern latitudes by pullets of the same breed, and summer eggs were smaller than winter eggs from the same birds (fig. 1). In the Philippines rainfall also influences egg production, as shown by Martin (*21*). On a year-round high plane of nutrition maximum production is attained during the dry season and minimum production during the wet season.

Rainfall is also an important factor in the case of sheep. It is generally recognized that the Merino as a breed is not naturally adaptable to moist conditions. On the other hand, British mutton breeds thrive best in a moist, cool climate. Nichols (*22*) has shown that, apart from their effects on pasturage, temperature and rainfall have a pronounced effect upon the distribution and development of the British breeds of sheep. In England the denser sheep populations are found in areas with 20 to 40 inches of rainfall annually. In South Africa, Bonsma (*2*) has pointed out that the best wool-growing areas have less than 20 inches of rainfall and that the production of fat lambs is possible only in areas with more than 30.

EFFECTS OF SEPARATE CLIMATIC FACTORS

Climate, however, is a complex thing, including such factors as temperature, humidity, atmospheric pressure, wind velocities, and amount of light. Each of these factors affects life processes, but under natural conditions it is seldom possible to determine their effects separately. For this reason, when scientists study the effects of climatic factors they take one at a time and try to hold all the other factors of the environment constant, varying only the one under investigation. Since temperature is perhaps the most important climatic factor in livestock production, and certainly the easiest to control in experiments, considerable work has been done on the effects of temperature on farm animals.

Temperature

With dairy cattle Regan and Richardson (*25*) have shown, under controlled conditions, that as the atmospheric temperature increased

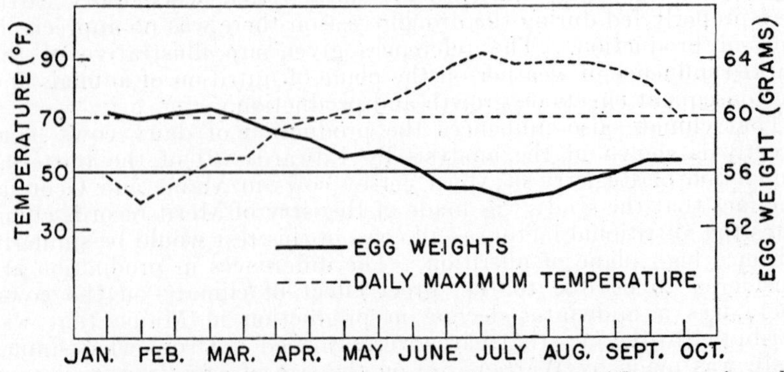

Figure 1.—Mean maximum air temperatures and mean egg weights at semimonthly intervals for 20 White Leghorn hens (second year) at Manhattan, Kans., showing the influence of temperature on annual egg-size curves, 1923–24.

from 40° to 95° F., milk production gradually dropped from 29 to 17 pounds a day. This bears out some of the observations of Rhoad (*26*) in Brazil, who reported that purebred European dairy cattle imported into the Tropics produced, on balanced rations, only 56 percent of their apparent capacity. On the other hand, Kelley and Rupel (*18*) report that winter barn temperatures as low as 45° did not lower the production of milk and suggest that the optimum stable temperature for dairy animals is about 50°. That high-quality dairy cows of the European type produce best under relatively cool conditions is well illustrated in the results reported by Villegas (*33*) with Holstein cows in Singapore in an air-conditioned barn kept at 70°. Cows in this barn produced an average of 24 pounds of milk a day as compared with a production of 9 pounds for a similar group in an open, ventilated barn exposed to tropical temperatures.

Atmospheric temperatures, especially high temperatures, have a profound effect on the reproductive as well as the productive efficiency of livestock. Villegas, in the article just cited, reports that 58 percent of the cows in the air-conditioned barn conceived within 5 months as compared with only 25 percent in the ventilated barn. The breeding efficiency of males in particular is affected by high temperatures. Dawson (*8*), studying the breeding efficiency of proved (aged) sires, found that those used at the southern experiment stations of the United States Department of Agriculture had an average fertility of 36 percent while those in the western and northern stations averaged 49 percent. He attributed this difference to the higher summer temperatures and humidity at the southern stations. Bonsma et al. (*4*) attribute the sterility during the hot months of a large percentage of bulls of the exotic (imported) breeds in South Africa to the high temperature. Phillips and McKenzie (*23*) have experimentally demonstrated that high summer temperatures materially lowered the vitality of the spermatozoa in the ram and, if continued for periods of several weeks, caused degeneration of the reproductive organs, resulting in sterility. These researches explain in part why breeding is seasonal with some classes of livestock, especially sheep. In the United States ewes of the major breeds come in heat and breed during October and November, when the temperatures are considerably below the average of the summer months.

Length of Day and Sunlight

Increasing length of daylight during the spring months also affects the fertility of farm animals, thereby influencing the breeding season. This is best illustrated in poultry. Increased fertility may be brought about by the use of lights, which according to Hammond (*16*) act by stimulating the anterior pituitary gland to increased secretion, which in turn stimulates the ovaries to increased production. The use of lights in poultry houses to stimulate production during the winter months when daylight is limited and egg production is normally low is a common practice on the commercial poultry farm.

That sunlight is an important factor affecting the adaptability of farm animals to the climatic environment has recently been demonstrated by Rhoad (*30*) with beef cattle. When cattle are moved from the shade and exposed to strong sunlight on a summer day, their respiration rate and body temperature rise (fig. 2), indicating increased difficulty in disposing of body heat. This is reflected in grazing habits; less time is spent grazing in an open pasture on a bright, calm summer day than on an overcast day. Cattle grazed more also on bright summer days when there was a gentle breeze than when the air was still. Picó (*24*) states that European types of cattle are adapted to certain areas in Puerto Rico because of the rather constant Caribbean trade winds there.

OVERCOMING CLIMATIC DISADVANTAGES BY BREEDING

That some of the ill effects of high temperature and humidity can be overcome by clipping the animals has been pointed out by Forbes et al. (*11*) and Rhoad (*30*), working with cattle, and by Ritzman and Benedict (*31*), working with sheep. It has been clearly demonstrated in recent years, however, that the lack of adaptability of certain types of animals to tropical climatic conditions, as evidenced by discomfort, low production, and, frequently, degeneration in type (*3*), can best be overcome by breeding. That there are distinct differences between

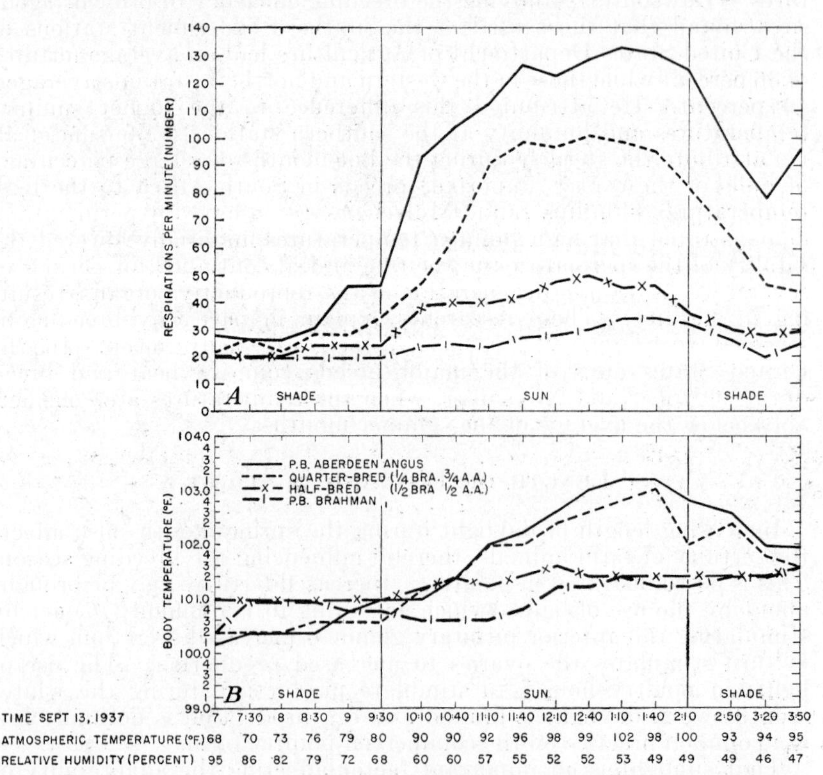

FIGURE 2.—Respiration rate (*A*) and body temperature (*B*) of cattle moved from the shade and exposed to strong sunlight on a summer day. Note the rise in the case of all except the purebred Brahman, which maintained almost a level rate throughout the period of observation.

species and breeds in ability to withstand climatic conditions has been amply demonstrated by Rhoad (*28, 30*) and Carneiro and Rhoad (*6*) in the United States and Brazil, Bisschop (*1*) and Bonsma et al. (*4*) in South Africa, French (*13*) in Tanganyika Territory, Kelley [3] in Australia, and Manresa (*20*) in the Philippines.

The superior adaptability of the Brahman (Zebu) types of cattle to tropical climatic conditions is being utilized in various ways. Edwards (*10*) has shown in Jamaica that when the relatively low milk producing but highly adaptable Montgomery (Sahiwal) type of Zebu was crossed with European dairy cattle, the offspring were frequently much better producers than their parents. Cross breeding had given them a constitution permitting them to express high productive capacity in a tropical environment. Comparable results have been obtained with crossbred beef cattle in South Africa (*1*), Australia,[3] and the Gulf-coast region of the United States.

Cross breeding of Brahman with standard beef breeds for resistance to subtropical climatic conditions has been a general practice in the Gulf-coast region for more than a generation. From one of these crosses, the Shorthorn × Brahman, there has evolved the first strictly American breed of beef cattle, the Santa Gertrudis (fig. 3), developed by the Klebergs of the King Ranch, Kingsville, Tex. In an experimental way the United States Department of Agriculture is developing a new type at the Iberia Livestock Experiment Farm, Jeanerette, La., by crossing the Brahman with the Aberdeen Angus. Other crosses using the Africander breed are also being made for purposes of comparison.

Improved dairy types of cattle adaptable to tropical and subtropical climatic conditions are being developed in India with pure Brahman (Zebu) stock, while in Brazil, Jamaica, and the Philippines new Brahman-European crossbred types are appearing (*29*). That dairy strains of Brahman cattle have not been used in the continental United States to improve the heat-resisting ability of dairy cattle in the South is partly owing to the availability of the Jersey, which Freeborn et al. (*12*) have shown possesses more heat tolerance than some of the other breeds in the United States. Tests at Jeanerette, La., show that this breed has a heat tolerance somewhat superior to the one-quarter Brahman, three-quarters Angus crossbred (unpublished data). The preponderance of Jersey-bred cattle in the Southern States, pointed out by Davidson (*7*) some years ago, may be explained on this basis.

According to Hammond (*17*), the pig under domestication is usually well housed and therefore not subjected to extreme climatic conditions in the Temperate Zone. Hale, however, has shown that in Texas summer temperatures reduce the rate of gain of fattening hogs. In the Philippines (*14*) a new breed, the Berkjala, a cross between the Berkshire and the native Jalajala, is being developed as a lard-type hog to resist tropical climatic conditions.

Farm animals are kept for the most part in an environment that is in many ways artificial, man-created. Much of the success of the livestock industry depends upon our ability to furnish a favorable environment in which livestock can develop and produce to the limit

---

[3] KELLEY, R. B. ZEBU (BRAHMAN) CROSS CATTLE AND THEIR POSSIBILITIES IN NORTH AUSTRALIA. Council Sci. and Indus. Res. Prog. Rpt. 3, 30 pp., illus. 1938. [Mimeographed.]

FIGURE 3.—The bull shown is a Santa Gertrudis, the first breed of cattle to be evolved in the United States to meet specific climatic conditions. It was developed for heat resistance by crossing the Brahman with the beef-type Shorthorn.

of their inherent capacities. To the extent that this cannot be done economically, it is necessary to select and modify breeds to fit the natural environment, of which climate is a major part.

LITERATURE CITED

(1) BISSCHOP, J. H. R.
1938. THE RELATION BETWEEN ENVIRONMENT AND ANIMAL BREEDING WITH SPECIAL REFERENCE TO THE BREEDING OF CATTLE IN THE SEMI-ARID REGIONS OF SOUTH AFRICA. 13th Internatl. Vet. Cong. Papers, Heft 12, pp. [3]–48, illus.

(2) BONSMA, F. N.
1939. FACTORS INFLUENCING THE GROWTH AND DEVELOPMENT OF LAMBS WITH SPECIAL REFERENCE TO CROSS-BREEDING OF MERINO SHEEP FOR FAT-LAMB PRODUCTION IN SOUTH AFRICA. Pretoria Univ. Pub. Ser. 1, Agr. No. 48, 214 pp., illus.

(3) BONSMA, J. C.
1940. THE INFLUENCE OF CLIMATOLOGICAL FACTORS ON CATTLE. OBSERVATIONS ON CATTLE IN TROPICAL REGIONS. Farming in So. Africa 15: 373–385, illus.

(4) ——— SCHOLTZ, G. D. J., and BADENHORST, F. J. G.
1940. THE INFLUENCE OF CLIMATE ON CATTLE. FERTILITY AND HARDINESS OF CERTAIN BREEDS. Farming in So. Africa 15: 7–12, 16, illus.

(5) CARNEIRO, GERALDO G.
1939. ALGUNS FATORES QUE INFLUEM SOBRE A PRODUÇAO DE LEITE DE VACAS MESTIÇAS SIMENTAIS SOB O SISTEMA DE RETIROS. Rev. de Indus. Anim. (n. s.) 2 (1): 28–48, illus.

(6) CARNEIRO, GERALDO G., and RHOAD, ALBERT O.
1936. THE DEVELOPMENT OF CALVES IN THE TROPICS. Trop. Agr. [Trinidad] 8: 177–180, illus.

(7) DAVIDSON, F. A.
1927. RELATION OF TAURINE CATTLE TO CLIMATE. Econ. Geog. 3: [466]–485, illus.

(8) DAWSON, J. R.
1938. THE BREEDING EFFICIENCY OF PROVED (AGED) SIRES. Jour. Dairy Sci. 21: 725–737, illus.

(9) EDWARDS, F. R.
1938. EFFECTS OF CLIMATIC FACTORS ON LIVESTOCK. Amer. Soc. Anim. Prod. Proc. 31: 48–53, illus.

(10) EDWARDS, J.
1932. BREEDING FOR MILK PRODUCTION IN THE TROPICS. Jour. Dairy Res. 3: [281]–293, illus.

(11) FORBES, E. B., and others.
1926. THE INFLUENCE OF THE ENVIRONMENTAL TEMPERATURE ON THE HEAT PRODUCTION OF CATTLE. Jour. Agr. Res. 33: 579–589.

(12) FREEBORN, STANLEY B., REGAN, WILLIAM M., and BERRY, LESTER J.
1934. THE EFFECT OF PETROLEUM OIL FLY SPRAYS ON DAIRY CATTLE. Jour. Econ. Ent. 27: 382–388.

(13) FRENCH, M. H.
1940. CATTLE-BREEDING IN TANGANYIKA TERRITORY AND SOME DEVELOPMENTAL PROBLEMS RELATING THERETO. Empire Jour. Expt. Agr. 8 (29): [11]–22, illus.

(14) GONZALEZ, B. M.
1932. THE ANIMAL IMPROVEMENT PROGRAM OF THE COLLEGE OF AGRICULTURE. Philippine Agr. 21: 1–8, illus.

(15) HAMMOND, JOHN.
1931. TROPICAL DAIRYING PROBLEMS. Trop. Agr. [Trinidad] 8: 311–315, illus.

(16) ———
1934. FERTILITY IN POULTRY. Harper-Adams Util. Poultry Jour. 19: 487–496, illus.

(17) ———
1936. ENVIRONMENTAL CONDITIONS AND LIVESTOCK BREEDING. Problemy Zhivotnovodstva 8: [107]–112.

(18) KELLEY, M. A. R., and RUPEL, I. W.
1937. RELATION OF STABLE ENVIRONMENT TO MILK PRODUCTION. U. S. Dept. Agr. Tech. Bul. 591, 60 pp., illus.

(19) LUSH, JAY L., JONES, J. M., DAMERON, W. H., and CARPENTER, O. L.
1930. NORMAL GROWTH OF RANGE CATTLE. Tex. Agr. Expt. Sta. Bul. 409, 34 pp., illus.

(20) MANRESA, MIGUEL.
1934. A QUARTER CENTURY OF WORK ON ANIMAL IMPROVEMENT. Philippine Agr. 23: 433–443, illus.

(21) MARTIN, RUFINO G.
1940. A STATISTICAL STUDY OF SEASONAL VARIATION IN THE EGG PRODUCTION OF WHITE LEGHORN AND RHODE ISLAND RED CHICKENS. Philippine Jour. Anim. Indus. 7: 45–52, illus.

(22) NICHOLS, J. E.
1933. THE DISTRIBUTION OF BRITISH PURE-BRED FLOCKS OF SHEEP IN RELATION TO ENVIRONMENT. Jour. Anim. Ecol. 2: 1–23, illus.

(23) PHILLIPS, RALPH W., and MCKENZIE, FRED F.
1934. THE THERMO-REGULATORY FUNCTION AND MECHANISM OF THE SCROTUM. Mo. Agr. Expt. Sta. Res. Bul. 217, 73 pp., illus.

(24) PICÓ, FRANK.
1937. EL MEJORAMIENTO DEL GANADO LECHERO EN LOS TROPICOS. Rev. de Agr. de Puerto Rico 29: 269–289, illus.

(25) REGAN, W. M., and RICHARDSON, G. A.
1938. REACTIONS OF THE DAIRY COW TO CHANGES IN ENVIRONMENTAL TEMPERATURE. Jour. Dairy Sci. 21: 73–79.

(26) RHOAD, ALBERT O.
1935. THE DAIRY COW IN THE TROPICS. Amer. Soc. Anim. Prod. Proc. 28: 212–214.

(27) Rhoad, Albert O.
1935. production of brazilian dairy cattle under penkeeping system. Ztschr. f. Zücht., Reihe B, Tierzücht. u. Züchtungsbiol. 33: 105–118, illus.

(28) ———
1936. the influence of environmental temperature on the respiratory rhythm of dairy cattle in the tropics. Jour. Agr. Sci. [England] 26: [36]–44, illus.

(29) ———
1938. mejoramiento del ganado en la america tropical. Pan Amer. Union, Ser. sobre Agr. No. 128, 22 pp., illus.

(30) ———
1938. some observations on the response of purebred bos taurus and bos indicus cattle and their crossbred types to certain conditions of the environment. Amer. Soc. Anim. Prod. Proc. 31: 284–295, illus.

(31) Ritzman, E. G., and Benedict, F. G.
1931. the heat production of sheep under varying conditions. N. H. Agr. Expt. Sta. Tech. Bul. 45, 32 pp.

(32) Schutte, D. J.
1935. factors affecting the growth of range cattle in semi-arid regions. Onderstepoort Jour. Vet. Sci. and Anim. Indus. 5: 535–617, illus.

(33) Villegas, Valente.
1939. livestock industries of cochin china, cambodia, siam, and malaya. Philippine Agr. 27: 693–725, illus.

(34) Warren, D. C.
1939. effect of temperature on size of eggs from pullets in different latitudes. Jour. Agr. Res. 59: 441–452, illus.

Climate in Relation to Worm Parasites of Livestock

By John T. Lucker [1]

THERE ARE many kinds of worms that find their way into the bodies of animals and produce a diseased condition often serious in its effects. The climate of a region has a great deal to do with the type, spread, and intensity of these parasitic diseases; so does the weather from season to season. Exactly what elements in the climate—temperature, moisture, sunlight, and so on—are favorable or unfavorable in each case? Just what effects does each element have, and at what stage in the life cycle of the parasite? The more we know about this, the better we will be prepared to deal with the problem of controlling or preventing the diseases. This article gives some of the evidence that is now available.

[1] John T. Lucker is Associate Zoologist, Zoological Division, Bureau of Animal Industry.

298737°—41——34

In order to understand how climatic factors affect parasitism, it is necessary to understand certain phases of the life cycles of the various kinds of worm parasites and certain differences in the types of life cycles occurring among them.

While they are adults, and in some cases while they are larvae, many kinds of worm parasites live in the bodies of warm-blooded animals such as livestock, and are thus protected from the external environment. Except for a few relatively unimportant species, however, these parasites cannot complete their entire life cycle from egg to adult within the bodies of the final host (called the definitive host by zoologists); ordinarily, a part of their development takes place elsewhere. The microscopic eggs or the larvae of the parasite, which must leave the body of an infested final host by one route or another, are well adapted to survive in the external environment. Almost without exception a parasite in these early stages of development cannot immediately infect a definitive host but must first undergo further development either on the ground or within the body of another organism known as an intermediate host. Most kinds of worm parasites produce enormous numbers of eggs or larvae, some of which ordinarily succeed in completing this necessary development in regions where the parasites are endemic—that is, where they are always present; but even in such favorable regions, climatic factors strongly influence the occurrence and degree of parasitism either directly or indirectly.

With a few exceptions, the eggs or young larvae of the roundworm (nematode) parasites of livestock and, so far as is known, the eggs of all of the tapeworms (cestodes), flukes (trematodes), and thorn-headed worms (Acanthocephala) infesting these animals pass from the definitive host's body onto the ground with the feces or other excreta. For a time, then, they are subjected to the external environment.

The eggs of some of the common and important roundworms (ascarids, trichurids) of livestock undergo a preliminary development and then develop embryos and become infective, while still in the egg stage, to a definitive host. The eggs of others (strongyles, trichostrongyles) hatch after developing embryos and yield larvae which must undergo further development before they become infective (fig. 1). Thus these eggs and larvae are subjected to the external climatic environment for varying periods depending upon the time required for their development and the interval before they are acquired by a definitive host.

In the life cycles of some roundworms (such as some metastrongyles and all spirurids) and of the thorn-headed worms, intermediate hosts are involved. The eggs of these forms are infective for the intermediate hosts, which are invariably invertebrates, without first undergoing any development on the ground; but some time may elapse before they are acquired by the intermediate hosts, and during this period they are directly subjected to environmental influences.

As a rule, the larvae of filarioid nematodes (such as the dog heart worm) are ingested with the blood of the definitive host by biting insects, which act as intermediate hosts; hence they do not come in direct contact with climatic conditions.

Intermediate hosts are also involved in the life cycle of all flukes and tapeworms infecting livestock. The eggs of some flukes have already developed embryos when they are passed in the feces and yield

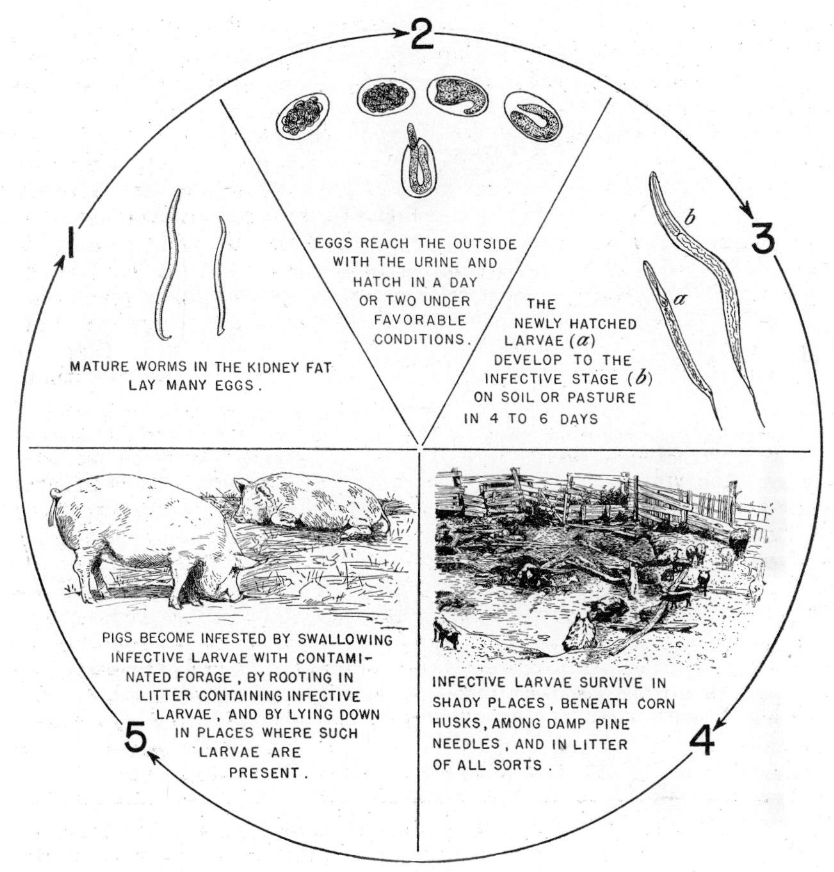

FIGURE 1.—Life cycle of the swine kidney worm.

young ciliated larvae (miricidia) capable of infecting snails when the eggs are ingested by these mollusks. The eggs of most flukes, however, must undergo a period of development before hatching and yielding larvae capable of infecting the snail intermediate host. The survival and hatching of the eggs or the development of the larvae depend on climatic conditions. The larval flukes (cercariae) that develop in the snail in some cases leave its body and encyst (form a tough outer covering) on vegetation, where they must cope with environmental conditions (fig. 2); in other cases, second intermediate hosts—snails, fish, or insects, as a rule—are required for the development of the infective stage of the fluke.

Usually the eggs of tapeworms are infective to intermediate hosts when passed in the excreta of the definitive host. But they may not be ingested by the former for some time and hence may be subjected to climatic conditions. Some of the tapeworms utilize invertebrates as intermediate hosts, while others utilize vertebrates, including domestic animals.

Thus it is apparent not only that climate frequently exerts a direct effect upon eggs and larvae of worm parasites but that it also pro-

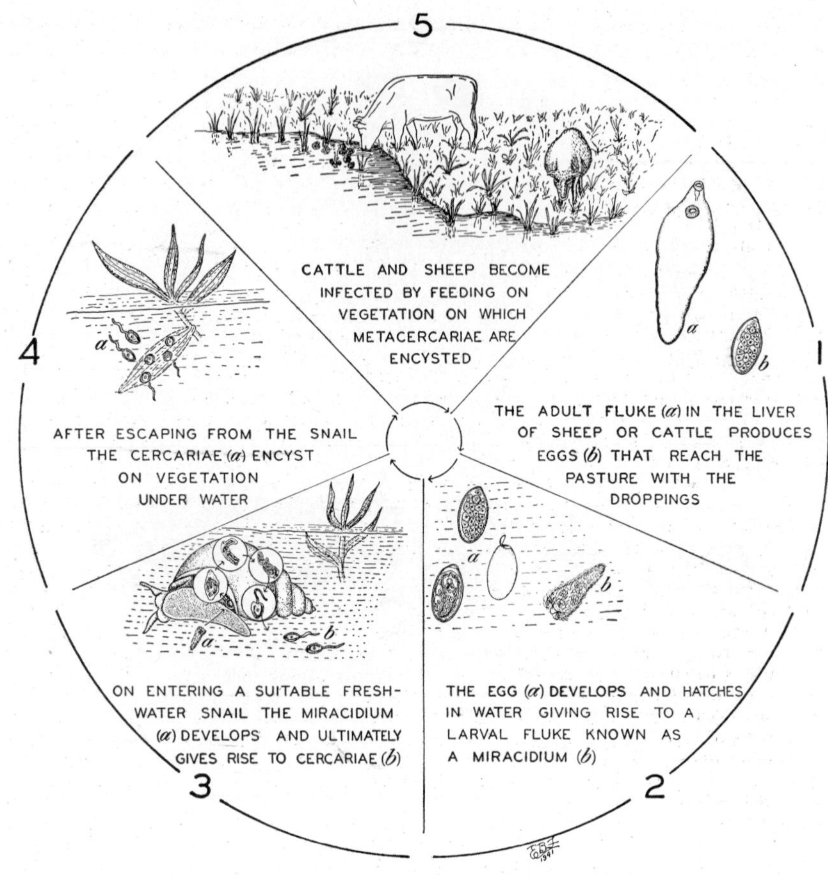

FIGURE 2.—Life cycle of the liver fluke of sheep and cattle.

foundly influences the parasitism of livestock by flukes, tapeworms, thorn-headed worms, and some of the roundworms through its effects on the prevalence and distribution of intermediate hosts.

There is some information available concerning the distribution of the various worm parasites in regions having different climatic conditions, and there are some reports of outbreaks of parasitic disease that have been traced to unusual weather conditions in given regions. But there are few reports of actual field studies of the mutual relationships between preparasitic stages of the parasites and their environments. Experiments on the effects of temperature, moisture, and sunlight on the eggs and larval stages of many of the common worm parasites of livestock and poultry have been reported. In some cases these experiments have clarified the relationships between the climatic conditions prevailing where the parasite occurs and its distribution. To a considerable extent, therefore, statements regarding the effects of climate on parasitism in livestock are based on reasoning from experimental data and known facts concerning distribution. In general the evidence available on the relation between climate and the occurrence and intensity of parasitic infestations is more satisfactory in the case of parasites of man than in the case of parasites of livestock. Because of the similarity of many of the parasites of man to those of domestic animals it is permissible to introduce some of this evidence.

EFFECTS OF MOISTURE

The eggs of roundworms and flukes that undergo development on pastures before they become infective to definitive or intermediate hosts or before larvae hatch from them require a certain amount of moisture. The larvae that hatch from roundworm eggs also cannot develop to the infective stage unless a certain amount of moisture is present, and in this stage their resistance to drying out (desiccation) varies greatly. Hence moisture and rainfall play an extremely important role in the distribution of these parasites.

The large intestinal roundworm of man (*Ascaris lumbricoides*) is probably the commonest and most widely distributed of all human parasites because of the resistance of its eggs to adverse conditions (*6*).[2] This parasite is found in the moist Tropics, in Arctic areas, and in countries that have almost desert conditions. Its occurrence in true desert regions is probably explained by the existence of oases or other local moist areas. It has been reported that the eggs of the human and the pig *Ascaris* seem to be similar in their ability to resist desiccation and to develop in partially dry atmospheres (*16*). After being dried on glass slides, the eggs did not develop embryos in atmospheres less than 80 percent saturated with moisture. Some eggs of the horse ascarid developed embryos in atmospheres 40 to 50 percent saturated with moisture, but practically all pig *Ascaris* eggs perished in 9 days under such conditions. Drying seems to be one of the most important factors in killing eggs of the human *Ascaris*, and there is some evidence that the level of ascarid infestation in man is reduced during a long dry season (*6*).

The eggs of the dog whipworm (*Trichuris vulpis*) require a very high degree of moisture to develop embryos, but less moisture is required by the eggs of one of the large intestinal roundworms of the dog (*Toxocara canis*) (*25*). An important factor influencing the incidence of whipworm and large intestinal roundworm infestations in man in various parts of the world is a difference in the moisture requirements of the eggs; the incidence of large intestinal roundworm infestation has been found to be much greater in drier situations than that of whipworm (*24*). Probably the same explanation applies to these two types of worms in swine, since it has been reported (*28*) that, of 348 hogs, principally from southern Georgia and northern Florida, 74 percent were infested with large intestinal roundworms and 23 percent with whipworms.

The human hookworm, unlike *Ascaris*, is found only in regions of considerable humidity in a zone falling between 36° north latitude and 30° south latitude, since its free-living larval stages require a moist medium and a temperature between 60° and 90° F. for development (*5*). The strongyle nematode parasites of livestock are more or less closely related zoologically to the human hookworms and have the same type of life cycle. But the conditions required for the development and survival of the eggs and larvae in feces and on the ground differ somewhat, and their resistance to climatic conditions varies considerably among the different species.

The several closely related species of strongyles and trichostrongyles occurring in sheep are responsible for a condition frequently called parasitic gastritis. At different times and in different regions one or another species or group of species of these worms appears to be responsible for losses in affected flocks. A study of the prevalence of the gastrointestinal parasites of sheep throughout Queensland, Australia, as indicated by the number of animals infested with worms in various districts, showed that precipitation was the chief climatic determinant. A district with a scanty annual rainfall (about 14 inches) was one of the most worm-free areas. The distribution of the common stomach worm of sheep (*Haemonchus contortus*) throughout Australia and other parts of the world shows that it is primarily dependent on summer rainfall (*19*); in areas of winter rainfall such as England, New Zealand, and South Australia, it is of comparatively little importance. Records available up to 1912 indicated that in the United States the regions where the stomach worm constituted an actual menace to flocks were the Eastern and Middle Western States, and it seemed likely that the dryness of the western plains was the factor that made this parasite of less importance in that

---

[2] Italic numbers in parentheses refer to Literature Cited, p. 525.

region (*9*). This worm is most plentiful in sheep in the South where its abundance is favored by warmth and moisture, but it is also a pest in low wet areas throughout the country (*10*).

In 1934 and again in 1938–39 worms caused trouble in sheep in South Africa because of wet summers, and farmers were warned that since the winter of 1939 had not been as dry as usual, further trouble was to be expected in 1940 (*15*); while it was still spring, reports were being received of lungworms in sheep from regions where these worms had not been a menace in previous years.

A rank growth of feed of low nutritive value during a wet season has been a factor in an outbreak of parasitic gastritis in sheep in New Zealand (*13*). A superabundance of herbage favors the development and survival of infective larvae of sheep strongyles by favoring the retention of moisture in feces on the ground (*32*).

An unusually dry season, however, may sometimes favor an outbreak of parasitism. The occurrence of such an outbreak in sheep in Great Britain during the winter of 1933–34 was explained as due to an unusually dry season (*31*); species of *Trichostrongylus* (commonly referred to as small hairworms) were the primary cause of the disease. Eggs of *Trichostrongylus axei* that have developed embryos are very resistant to drying (*14*), and it was concluded that the outbreak in question was in part due to the storage on pastures of eggs that retained their vitality but could not develop during the dry period (*31*). When wet weather came, a mass development of infective larvae resulted. Poor pasturage during the dry season also resulted in close cropping and an excessive intake of infectious material by the sheep, and undernourishment decreased their resistance to worm infestation.

Another effect of very heavy rainfall may be to cleanse pastures of parasite eggs and larvae. This has been reported to occur in Puerto Rico.[3]

EFFECTS OF TEMPERATURE

When adequate moisture is present, temperature controls the speed of the development of eggs and larvae; in fact, they cannot develop at all except at suitable temperatures. Below a certain temperature, varying somewhat with the species of parasite, development is completely arrested, and still lower temperatures may kill the developing and infectious stages.

The rate of development of eggs of the swine whipworm (*Trichuris suis*) is dependent upon temperature; the lower the temperature, the smaller the percentage of eggs that develop embryos (*1*). At room temperature the eggs of the common liver fluke (*Fasciola hepatica*) hatch in about 18 days; at 36° to 50° F. they may remain viable for more than 2½ years but do not develop embryos (*11*).

The eggs of some nematodes are very resistant to low temperatures. Fresh eggs of the pig *Ascaris* have remained viable at −2° to −16° F. for 40 days (*7*). Many eggs of the common cecal worm of poultry (*Heterakis gallinae*) have survived for 67 to 172 days at 25°; after exposure they were capable of developing embryos and were subsequently infective to poultry (*33*). The eggs of many of the strongyle nematodes, however, are less resistant to low temperatures; those of a number of species of the trichostrongyles infesting sheep were killed by 3 days' exposure at 14° (*8*). Eggs of the swine kidney worm (*Stephanurus dentatus*) were killed in 10 days at 50° (*23*). Those of the common sheep tapeworm (*Moniezia expansa*) survived longest in a moist environment at 36°–37°, although some survived alternate freezing and thawing for considerable periods (*12*). In general it appears that alternate freezing and thawing is more lethal to nematode eggs and larvae than continuous freezing.

Among the infective larvae of the strongyle nematodes of livestock, those of the large (red-worms) and small (cylicostomes) strongyles, which cause the condition in horses known as strongyloidiasis, are noted for their ability to survive for long periods when exposed to subfreezing temperatures. In all regions where horses are raised they may become infested with these worms. It is known that some of the infective larvae can overwinter in very cold regions, and they are also reported to be very resistant to desiccation; nevertheless they are a more serious menace to horses in warm moist regions than elsewhere.

It has been reported that the infective larvae of some of the nematodes of sheep do not survive on pastures over the winter months in eastern Canada (*30*) and that in particular the nodular worm (*Oesophagostomum* sp.) and the stomach

[3] SPINDLER, L. A. THE EFFECTS OF NATURAL FACTORS, RAIN AND SUN, ON SURVIVAL OF EGGS AND LARVAE OF ANIMAL PARASITES UNDER TROPICAL CONDITIONS. Puerto Rico Expt. Sta. Agr. Notes 74, 4 pp. 1936. [Mimeographed.]

worm (*Haemonchus*) are not resistant to winter conditions. Both laboratory and field studies show, according to this report, that in eastern Canada nodular worm larvae are unable to survive from one pasture season to the next.

The swine kidney worm is one of the most serious obstacles to profitable swine production in the South (*22*), but it is not known to be a problem to swine producers in the Northern States. Temperature undoubtedly affects the distribution of this parasite. In Australia the important centers of kidney worm infestation are largely confined to the northeastern coastal belt, mainly because temperatures are lower on the higher tablelands and in the southern coastal areas (*4*). Not only are the eggs of this worm susceptible to freezing and, as already noted, to low temperatures above freezing, but the infective larvae also have been killed by freezing under field conditions in Georgia (*27*). However, moisture also is important as a determinant of kidney worm distribution. In Queensland, Australia, the incidence of this parasite in swine from November 1930 to February 1931 was about 63 percent in an area where the annual rainfall may be as high as 158 inches, 32 percent in an area with a rainfall of 34–45 inches, and 2.5 percent in an area with a rainfall of 27–36 inches (*18*). Both the eggs and the infective larvae of the kidney worm are reported to be extremely susceptible to desiccation in comparison with the same stages of other strongyles (*4*). Data on summer and winter temperatures and rainfall in several parts of Australia showed that the areas where infestations in swine were most common were those in which warm, equable summer temperatures coincide with heavy rainfall (*4*). In regions where summer temperatures were suitable but where summer rainfall was very low the parasite was unknown. One of these regions had a winter rainfall of about 18 inches and winter temperatures not so low as those in a region where the parasite was very common.

The eggs of the human and pig *Ascaris* will develop at temperatures between about 44° and 100° F. and those of the ascarids of dogs and horses within a slightly greater range (*16*). Eggs of two of the swine stomach worms (*Ascarops strongylina* and *Physocephalus sexalatus*) are very resistant to freezing (*1*). Possibly the eggs of other roundworms that require intermediate hosts have a similar resistance to low temperatures.

While low temperatures injure parasite eggs and larvae to a variable degree, high temperatures also kill them, and usually the lethal high temperature is about the same for all species. It has been shown that eggs of the human *Ascaris* are almost instantaneously killed at 158° F. and that a temperature of 122° is lethal to them in about 45 minutes (*16*). In Panama eggs of the human *Ascaris* perished rapidly on the surface of sand when a temperature of 122° was reached (*2*). Under field conditions it is difficult to determine whether the failure of eggs and larvae to survive on bare unshaded ground is due to high soil temperature, to desiccation, or to the action of the rays of the sun.

EFFECT OF SUNLIGHT

It has been demonstrated experimentally that sunlight kills parasite eggs and larvae when temperature and moisture are held within a range that is not deadly. In Puerto Rico both undeveloped and infective eggs of the pig *Ascaris* both in water and in a dried condition, were killed when exposed for a few hours to direct sunlight (*29*). It was also reported that infective swine kidney worm larvae were susceptible to sunlight and were never recovered even from moist soil exposed more than a few hours to the sun (*27*). Neither fresh nor infective eggs of the large roundworm of fowls (*Ascaridia galli*) in a liquid medium survived more than 3 hours' exposure to sunlight (*20*).

Sunlight is essential to nearly all plant life and determines the very existence of the host animals without which parasites could not exist, but it is scarcely as important as other climatic factors in limiting the distribution of parasites, since more or less shade occurs wherever temperature and moisture permit the growth of vegetation. Also, the host animal's feces afford some protection from the sun's rays. Nevertheless, sunlight affects the prevalence of the infectious stages of the parasites locally and within pastures. As already noted, infective kidney worm larvae were not found on moist soil in hog lots exposed to sunlight (*27*), and infective larvae of the swine nodular worms (*Oesophagostomum* sp.) were found on pastures only in situations protected from sunlight and desiccation (*26*). Furthermore, the migrations of infective strongyle larvae in soil and on grass blades are affected by both moisture and sunlight; the larvae of many strongyles avoid intense light. These migrations affect the accessibility of the larvae to grazing livestock.

EFFECT ON DISTRIBUTION OF INTERMEDIATE HOSTS

As an example of the indirect effect of climate on the distribution of parasites through its influence on the distribution of their intermediate hosts, the case may be cited of the nematode *Oxyspirura mansoni*, the eye worm which can cause blindness in poultry. This worm has been known to occur in Florida for many years, and more recently it has spread to Louisiana (*3*). Elsewhere in the United States it is not known to occur, but it is endemic in the tropical belt in both Eastern and Western Hemispheres. The intermediate host of the eye worm is a cockroach, *Pycnoscelus surinamensis*. The distribution of this roach is tropical, extending into subtropical regions. In the United States the roach occurs in Florida, Louisiana, and Texas; elsewhere it has become temporarily established only in greenhouses and places similarly heated during cold weather (*34*). Apparently it is introduced into northern greenhouses with shipments of tropical plants. It has been reported that the roach requires a certain amount of moisture and that in greenhouses it was most plentiful in rooms having a temperature of 60° to 80° F. (*35*). Most of the roaches removed in winter to an unheated room were killed in about a week; during this period temperatures of 36° to 40° were reached. At 24° the roaches were all killed in 14 hours, and at 1° all were killed in 10 minutes. Thus even where adequate rainfall occurs, the distribution of this roach in nature is limited by temperature.

Liver fluke disease (fascioliasis) affords an example of the manner in which unusual climatic conditions affect outbreaks of parasitic disease by affecting the distribution and prevalence of intermediate hosts. In England the disease has occurred in sudden and severe outbreaks lasting 1 or 2 years and separated by long periods during which it is severe only in restricted localities (*17*). There can be no doubt, according to the report cited, that these outbreaks are made possible by a sudden and enormous increase in the numbers of the snail intermediate host (*Limnaea truncatula*) due to particularly favorable climatic conditions. Records show that the disease spreads rapidly following a series of wet years. Wet weather and floods widely disseminate the snail from its usual marshy breeding places. An investigation of the circumstances surrounding an outbreak of liver fluke disease in Germany in 1924–25 showed that the wet summer of 1924 followed two other wet years which had already favored an increase in the snail population, and the floods of 1924 then spread snails over larger areas (*21*).

CLIMATE AND THE CONTROL OF PARASITIC DISEASES

To some extent measures for the control of certain parasitic infestations in livestock take advantage of the destructive effects of climatic factors on eggs and larvae of the parasites. For example, it has been recommended that to avoid kidney worm and nodular worm infestations, pigs should be raised on clean, dry, well-drained soil that receives the maximum of sunlight (*4*); farrowing equipment should be located on such an area at one end of the farrowing field, and this area should be kept free of debris and vegetation (*26, 27*). The drainage of swampy areas serving as breeding places for snails is one of the measures sometimes practicable for the control of liver fluke infestations in cattle and sheep.

It is generally held that parasitic diseases as a whole are more prevalent and cause more damage to livestock in the warm, moist Southern and Southeastern States than in any other large area in the United States. Yet even for this region comprehensive and precise information is not available on the distribution of the various species of parasites or on the effects on the prevalence and intensity of infestations caused by general and local climatic differences or by variations within seasons in different years. There is need for further and more comprehensive investigation of the whole subject of climate in relation to parasitic diseases of livestock before it will be possible to evaluate fully the significance of the subject in relation to the scientific practice of animal husbandry.

LITERATURE CITED

(1) Alicata, Joseph E.
1936. EARLY DEVELOPMENTAL STAGES OF NEMATODES OCCURRING IN SWINE. U. S. Dept. Agr. Tech. Bull. 489, 96 pp., illus.

(2) Brown, Harold W.
1927. STUDIES ON THE RATE OF DEVELOPMENT AND VIABILITY OF THE EGGS OF ASCARIS LUMBRICOIDES AND TRICHURIS TRICHIURA UNDER FIELD CONDITIONS. Jour. Parasitol. 14: 1–15, illus.

(3) Buckley, John S., Bunyea, Hubert, and Cram, Eloise B.
1931. DISEASES AND PARASITES OF POULTRY. U. S. Dept. Agr. Farmers' Bul. 1652, 62 pp., illus.

(4) Clunies Ross, I., and Kauzal, G.
1932. THE LIFE CYCLE OF STEPHANURUS DENTATUS DEISING [SIC], 1839; THE KIDNEY WORM OF PIGS WITH OBSERVATIONS ON ITS ECONOMIC IMPORTANCE IN AUSTRALIA AND SUGGESTIONS FOR ITS CONTROL. Austral. Council Sci. & Indus. Res., Bul. 58, 80 pp., illus.

(5) Cort, William W.
1918. ORIENTAL AND TROPICAL PARASITIC DISEASES. DANGERS TO CALIFORNIA FROM THESE DISEASES. Calif. State Bd. Health Spec. Bul. 28 [29], 12 pp.

(6) ———
1931. RECENT INVESTIGATIONS ON THE EPIDEMIOLOGY OF HUMAN ASCARIASIS. Jour. Parasitol. 17: [121]–144.

(7) Cram, Eloise B.
1924. THE INFLUENCE OF LOW TEMPERATURE AND OF DISINFECTANTS ON THE EGGS OF ASCARIS LUMBRICOIDES. Jour. Agr. Res., 27: 167–175.

(8) Fallis, A. Murray.
1938. A STUDY OF THE HELMINTH PARASITES OF LAMBS IN ONTARIO. Roy. Canad. Inst. Trans. 22: 81–128, illus.

(9) Hall, Maurice C.
1912. OUR PRESENT KNOWLEDGE OF THE DISTRIBUTION AND IMPORTANCE OF SOME PARASITIC DISEASES OF SHEEP AND CATTLE IN THE UNITED STATES. U. S. Dept. Agr. Bur. Anim. Indus. Cir. 193, pp. 419–463, illus.

(10) ———
1940. PARASITES AND PARASITIC DISEASES OF SHEEP. U. S. Dept. Agr. Farmers' Bul. 1330, 49 pp., illus.

(11) Krull, Wendell H.
1934. NOTES ON THE HATCHABILITY AND INFECTIVITY OF REFRIGERATED EGGS OF FASCIOLA HEPATICA LINN. Iowa Acad. Sci. Proc. 41: 309–311.

(12) ———
1940. INVESTIGATIONS ON POSSIBLE INTERMEDIATE HOSTS, OTHER THAN ORIBATID MITES, FOR MONIEZIA EXPANSA. Helminthol. Soc. Wash. Proc. 7: 68–71.

(13) Lyons, J.
1930. LIVESTOCK DIVISION. New Zeal. Dept. Agr. Ann. Rpt. 1929–30: 12–19.

(14) Mönnig, H. O.
1930. STUDIES ON THE BIONOMICS OF THE FREE-LIVING STAGES OF TRICHOSTRONGYLUS SPP. AND OTHER PARASITIC NEMATODES. 16th Union So. Africa Dept. Agr. Dir. Vet. Serv. and Anim. Indus. Rpt. 16: 175–198.

(15) ———
1940. THE DANGER OF WORMS IN SHEEP. Farming in So. Africa 15: 14.

(16) Otto, G. F.
1929. A STUDY OF THE MOISTURE REQUIREMENTS OF THE EGGS OF THE HORSE, THE DOG, HUMAN AND PIG ASCARIDS. Amer. Jour. Hyg. 10: 497–520, illus.

(17) Peters, B. G.
1938. HABITATS OF LIMNAEA TRUNCATULA IN ENGLAND AND WALES DURING DRY SEASONS. Jour. Helminthol. 16: 213–260, illus.

(18) Roberts, F. H. S.
1931. THE KIDNEY WORM OF PIGS. Queensland Dept. Agr. and Stock, Div. Ent. and Plant Pathol., 12 pp., illus.

(19) ———
1936. DISTRIBUTION OF THE GASTRO-INTESTINAL PARASITES OF SHEEP IN QUEENSLAND. Queensland Dept. Agr. and Stock, Anim. Health Sta., Yeerongpilly, Pam. 8, 8 pp.

(20) ———
1937. STUDIES ON THE BIOLOGY AND CONTROL OF THE LARGE ROUNDWORM OF FOWLS ASCARIDIA GALLI (SCHRANK 1788 [SIC]) FREEBORN 1923 [SIC]. Queensland Dept. Agr. and Stock, Anim. Health Sta., Yeerongpilly, Bul. 2, 106 pp., illus.

(21) Schmid, F.
1940. KLIMA UND BODEN IN IHRER WIRKUNG AUF DIE HÄUFIGKEIT PARASITÄRER ERKRANKUNGEN. Deut. Tierärztl. Wchnschr. 48:375–377.

(22) Schwartz, Benjamin.
1934. CONTROLLING KIDNEY WORMS IN SWINE IN THE SOUTHERN STATES. U. S. Dept. Agr. Leaflet 108, 6 pp., illus.

(23) ———
1929. THE LIFE HISTORY OF THE SWINE KIDNEY WORM. Science (n. s.) 70: 613–614.

(24) Spindler, L. A.
1929. THE RELATION OF MOISTURE TO THE DISTRIBUTION OF HUMAN TRICHURIS AND ASCARIS. Amer. Jour. Hyg. 10: 476–496, illus.

(25) ———
1929. A STUDY OF THE TEMPERATURE AND MOISTURE REQUIREMENTS IN THE DEVELOPMENT OF THE EGGS OF THE DOG TRICHURID (TRICHURIS VULPIS). Jour. Parasitol. 16: [41]–46.

(26) ———
1933. FIELD STUDIES OF THE LARVAE OF NODULAR WORMS OF SWINE, WITH SUGGESTIONS FOR CONTROL. North Amer. Vet. 14 (11): 37–44.

(27) ———
1934. FIELD AND LABORATORY STUDIES ON THE BEHAVIOR OF THE LARVAE OF THE SWINE KIDNEY WORM, STEPHANURUS DENTATUS. U. S. Dept. Agr. Tech. Bul. 405, 18 pp.

(28) ———
1934. THE INCIDENCE OF WORM PARASITES IN SWINE IN THE SOUTHERN UNITED STATES. Helmint ol. Soc. Wash. Proc. 1: 40–42.

(29) ———
1940. EFFECT OF TROPICAL SUNLIGHT ON EGGS OF ASCARIS SUIS (NEMATODA), THE LARGE INTESTINAL ROUNDWORM OF SWINE. Jour. Parasitol. 26: 323–331.

(30) Swales, W. E.
1940. THE HELMINTH PARASITES AND PARASITIC DISEASES OF SHEEP IN CANADA. II. NOTES ON THE EFFECT OF WINTER UPON THE FREE-LIVING STAGES OF NEMATODE PARASITES OF SHEEP ON PASTURES IN EASTERN CANADA. Canad. Jour. Compar. Med. 4: 155–161.

(31) Taylor, E. L.
1934. THE EPIDEMIOLOGY OF WINTER OUTBREAKS OF PARASITIC GASTRITIS IN SHEEP, WITH SPECIAL REFERENCE TO OUTBREAKS WHICH OCCURRED DURING THE WINTER OF 1 33–34. Jour. Compar. Path. and Ther. 47: [235]–254.

(32) ———
1935. PARASITIC GASTRITIS: THE CAUSES UNDERLYING ITS DEVELOPMENT IN SHEEP. Vet. Rec. (n. s.) 15: [1339]–1344.

(33) Wickware, A. B.
1940. EFFECTS OF FREEZING TEMPERATURES ON THE EMBRYONATION OF EGGS AND INFECTIVITY OF LARVAE OF HETERAKIS GALLINAE. Canad. Jour. Compar. Med. 4: 110–116.

(34) Zappe, M. P.
1918. A COCKROACH PEST OF GREENHOUSES PYCNOSCELUS (LEUCOPHOEA) SURINAMENSIS LINN. Conn. (State) Agr. Expt. Sta. Bul. 203: 302–313. (17th Rpt. State Entomol. Conn. 1917.)

(35) ———
1919. LIFE HISTORY AND DEVELOPMENT OF THE GREENHOUSE COCKROACH PYCNOSCELUS SURINAMENSIS LINN. Conn. (State) Agr. Expt. Sta. Bul. 211: 311–313. (18th Rpt. State Entomol. Conn. 1918.)

PART FOUR

The Scientific Approach to Weather and Climate

Flood Hazards and Flood Control

THE FACT that as long as man has been on earth floods have plagued him with some of the most dramatic of all disasters is proof enough that they are never likely to be eliminated. But there is also proof that we can add greatly to the flood hazard by the way we use the land. The business of discovering exactly what causes this increased risk, and how to reduce it, is not simple. It is being intensively studied nowadays; some steps toward improvement are being taken; and flood forecasting, which makes it possible to give warning in advance, is also being improved. A number of scientific workers in soil conservation, forestry, and meteorology have contributed to this article on the subject.

THE HYDROLOGIC CYCLE

By Benjamin Holzman [1]

Three-quarters of a century ago George Marsh, the geographer, in discussing the deficiencies of existing climatic data, summarized the problems of hydrology as follows (*24, p. 25*):[2]

> * * * none can tell what percentage of the water they [the lands] receive from the atmosphere is evaporated; what absorbed by the ground and conveyed off by subterranean conduits; what carried down to the sea by superficial channels; what drawn from the earth or the air by a given extent of forest, of short pasture vegetation, or of tall meadow-grass; what given out again by surfaces so covered, or by bare ground of various textures and composition, under different conditions of atmospheric temperature, pressure, and humidity; or what is the amount of evaporation from water, ice, or snow, under the varying exposures to which, in actual nature, they are constantly subjected.

The science of hydrology, which is concerned with the properties and distribution of water and thus with furnishing answers to these questions, has made notable progress during the last two decades. Of basic importance has been the recognition of the fact that the distribution and transport of water in the form of a solid, a liquid, or a vapor obey a fundamental law of equilibrium. This relationship, representing the balance of water that exists between the hydrosphere (oceans, lakes, streams, and underground waters), the lithosphere (the solid part of the earth), and the atmosphere, is called the hydrologic cycle.

Of the total precipitation on continental areas, a portion is returned to the oceans as run-off through rivers and streams, and the remainder is restored to the atmosphere by evaporation and transpiration. At any given time, of course, some water is in storage in the soil, and considerable time may elapse before this water enters the streams through underground flow or is returned to the atmosphere. Although the amount of water held in storage increases with precipitation and diminishes with evaporation, it eventually enters into the hydrologic cycle. Thus the balance between precipitation (P), run-off (R), and evaporation (E) can be expressed as a simple equation, $P=R+E$, and the three components—P, R, and E—may be considered as fundamental variables in the hydrologic cycle.

WATER-CYCLE MEASUREMENTS

In the United States detailed information on the characteristics of rainstorms has been accumulating rapidly. Approximately 2,500 automatic recording and 6,000 nonrecording rain gages distributed throughout the country now supply precipitation measurements. In addition, concentrations of rain gages on selected small plots or watersheds furnish data for research on the relation of precipitation to infiltration and run-off, the variations in rate and duration of rainfall, and other related storm phenomena. Upper-air soundings of temperature, pressure, humidity, and wind have also provided meteorologists with fundamental data from which a better under-

---

[1] Benjamin Holzman is Associate Soil Conservationist, Climatic and Physiographic Division, Office of Research, Soil Conservation Service.

[2] Italic numbers in parentheses refer to Literature Cited, p. 576.

standing of the genesis and nature of storms has been evolved.

Stream gages on all important rivers and on many of their tributaries furnish comprehensive information on the volume of run-off. Supplementing these data, detailed studies of water movement in soils have indicated what portion of the water that seeps into the soil is made available for agriculture, what portion is returned to rivers and streams by underground flow, and how a soil-moisture reservoir may be established.

Until recently evaporation from natural land surfaces has defied measurement. Basic studies in aerodynamics have now yielded information on the structure and characteristics of the atmosphere next to the ground. This knowledge has permitted the development of a technique for measuring evaporation from natural surfaces (*39*). When data on evaporation from the soil from various regions become available, it will be possible for the first time to measure and evaluate accurately all three of the fundamental variables of the hydrologic cycle—rainfall, run-off, and evaporation.

Observations of precipitation on land areas and of run-off from the land have indicated clearly that, on an average, precipitation greatly exceeds run-off. Brückner (*5*), Wüst (*45*), and others have calculated that run-off amounts to approximately 30 percent of the total precipitation falling on land. Although direct evaporation measurements from continental areas are not yet available, the evaporation may be estimated by subtracting the run-off from the rainfall. If approximately 30 percent of continental precipitation runs off, 70 percent must be returned to the atmosphere. These are generalized estimates, it is true, and for any one specific storm or region may be far from the actual values; but they serve to emphasize the great significance of continental evaporation in the hydrologic cycle (*37*).

The realization that continental evaporation constitutes such an important phase of the hydrologic balance has stimulated much speculation regarding the source of moisture for precipitation, in which undue emphasis has been accorded to evaporation as a local source of rainfall. It has been inferred, without adequate basis, that an increase in atmospheric moisture due to evaporation from ponds and lakes or to transpiration from vegetation would result in an increase in local rainfall.

In the United States the belief that if western farmers could be induced to plant trees rainfall would be increased sufficiently to eliminate the climatic hazards to agriculture (*36*) led to the passing of the Timber Culture Act by Congress in 1873. During the period 1875–86, abundant rainfall occurred in the Great Plains, and the idea was frequently advanced that a spread in cultivation changed the hydrologic balance in favor of increased rainfall. It was thought that the soil, after it was broken, acted like a huge sponge, absorbing and storing moisture, so that as cultivation was extended, more and more of the precipitation would be conserved, and increased rainfall would result from the increased evaporation (*20*). Commercial interests found it to their advantage to publicize this hypothesis, which became a factor in the great exploitation of dry-land farms.

The myth that a human agency was responsible for the increased rainfall in the Plains was brusquely shattered by subsequent periods of drought. Failure to recognize that the atmosphere is constantly in

298737°—41——35 +

motion and that moisture may be carried great distances by advancing air masses was directly responsible for the overextension of agriculture in the western part of the United States.

THE AIR-MASS AND WATER CYCLES

In recent years meteorologists have discovered that the atmospheric circulation over the earth consists fundamentally of alternate advances and interactions of huge bodies of air that develop distinctive physical characteristics over various source regions. For example, polar continental air becomes relatively cold and dry through stagnation over the arctic tundra of northern Canada. Tropical maritime air is warm and moist because its source region is located over tropical waters.

In a recent publication of the Department of Agriculture (*14*) the trajectories, or paths, of various air masses have been carefully traced with the aid of upper-air soundings of temperature, pressure, humidity, and wind. The increases and losses of moisture due to evaporation and precipitation were ascertained, and it was shown that the moisture for precipitation in the United States was derived mainly from the oceans and transported by maritime air masses. The analysis of several air-mass migrations demonstrated that the dry polar continental air masses passed off the continent with significant gains in moisture, whereas the tropical maritime air masses, whose moisture was derived primarily from oceanic regions, lost considerable amounts of moisture to the land areas during their poleward migration.

Using average values of the properties of polar continental and tropical maritime air masses, it was found that the total water content of polar continental air in traveling from the Canadian border to the Gulf of Mexico was increased by an amount equivalent to 0.53 inch of rainfall; tropical maritime air, traveling the same distance in the opposite direction, showed a net loss of 0.66 inch of water. Thus, the continental air gained approximately 20 percent less moisture than the maritime air lost. Considered as the portion of continental precipitation returned to the oceans as run-off, this difference is in very close agreement with average run-off estimates.

The air-mass cycle is manifestly an expression of the general circulation of the atmosphere and is closely associated with the balance of water over continental areas, or the hydrologic cycle. In the cycle of air-mass transformation, moist tropical maritime air masses must lose their high water-vapor content before they can ultimately be converted into polar air masses, and similarly polar air masses must gain in moisture before they can be transformed into tropical maritime air masses. Thus two principal classes of air masses can be distinguished—(1) those that are losing their moisture and consequently contribute the major portion of preceipitation to the earth and (2) those that are absorbing moisture and constitute the greatest robbers of moisture from continental areas (*15*).[3]

The operation of the hydrologic cycle according to modern meteor-

[3] Recently the concerted attack of meteorologists on the problem of the general circulation of the atmosphere through isentropic analysis has more than ever emphasized the fact that oceanic areas are the only significant sources of moisture for precipitation on continents (*30*). Great masses of maritime air with high moisture content advance aloft along various thermodynamic surfaces and provide conditions favorable for rainstorms. When the combinations of meteorological variables are not favorable for rainfall, the air-mass cycle continues in operation with the moist air masses losing their moisture to the dry air masses by dissemination through the phenomenon of horizontal turbulence.

ological interpretation is illustrated in figure 1. It should be emphasized that no single diagram can show all the various conditions that could or do occur in nature; thus only the average or most frequent trajectories of water, in either liquid or vapor form, transported between ocean and land are illustrated. The continental air mass is shown to be the agent for transporting land-evaporated moisture out to sea, where it may or may not be precipitated. Ultimately the continental air gains in moisture and is transformed into maritime air. This air reenters the general circulation of the atmosphere and eventually travels poleward, precipitating its moisture over continents or oceans, until finally the air-mass and water cycles are completed.

It is of interest to consider some of the apparent departures from the generalized picture of the hydrologic cycle. Polar continental air masses are frequently checked in their advance southeastward over the United States before passing off the continent, and the resulting reversal of circulation brings about a return flow of modified polar continental air. Occasionally the moisture evaporated from the land and collected during the southerly migration of the polar air may in part be reprecipitated on the land during a returning northerly flow, provided a fresh polar air mass is encountered. Since the moisture content of the returning current of continental air is considerably less than that of the maritime air, the amount of precipitation whose source may be directly traced to evaporation from the land constitutes only a fraction of that supplied by oceanic evaporation.

In summer the average position of the polar front is displaced northward, and the Mississippi Valley and the eastern part of the United States are often inundated by tropical Gulf air. This air-mass type invading the United States by way of the Gulf of Mexico in flowing northward may absorb appreciable quantities of continental moisture. Being characterized by a latent convective instability—a tendency to rise, carrying heat and moisture upward—tropical maritime air masses frequently precipitate moisture in local showers. Thus, for example,

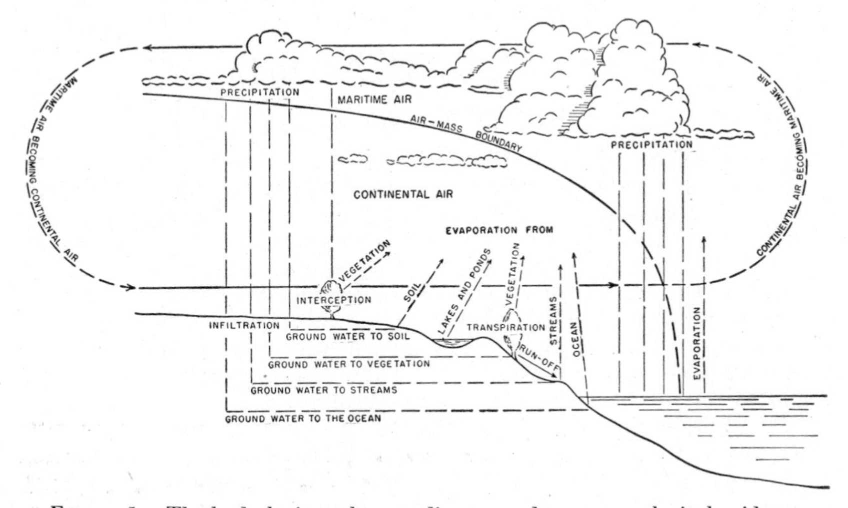

FIGURE 1.—The hydrologic cycle according to modern meteorological evidence.

moisture evaporated from Louisiana and Mississippi into a tropical air mass may constitute a fraction of the supply of moisture for a local summer shower in Pennsylvania. In the diagram of the hydrologic cycle this contintental source of moisture is not shown because of its relative unimportance as compared with the available supply of moisture in tropical maritime air bodies. The details of this interesting summertime operation of the hydrologic cycle are discussed in a recent publication by Bernard (*3*).

POSSIBILITIES OF MANAGEMENT OF HYDROLOGIC FACTORS

From a study of the water cycle we learn that the meteorological forces involved in precipitation are of such magnitude that no human endeavor can ever modify them significantly. Run-off, on the other hand, is highly responsive to human management. Careless and promiscuous denudation of the land inevitably causes accelerated soil erosion and increased run-off, with resultant flood hazards. Careful treatment of the land and the use of appropriate water-conservation and flood-control measures will definitely retard and reduce run-off. Retardation of run-off increases the supply of moisture for evaporation. Any technique which stimulates the evaporation of excessive rainfall does so at the expense of run-off. More significantly, any technique which stimulates land evaporation and exhausts the capillary moisture from the soil helps to reduce run-off from future rains, since some of the water will enter the soil rather than flow off the surface. These procedures are to be identified as important supplemental flood-protection measures. We are limited in our ability to modify the hydrologic balance; we must take our rainfall as it comes, but we can influence run-off and evaporation.

SOME CLIMATIC FACTORS THAT AFFECT RUN-OFF

By G. W. Musgrave [4]

A consideration of the hydrologic cycle indicates the factors that determine the rate and amount of run-off of surface water following storms. For run-off to occur, rainfall must exceed in intensity and volume what the soil, vegetation, and land surface will absorb or retain. Actual measurements show that the amount which may be retained on the canopy of vegetation varies widely in accordance with the vigor and density of the vegetal cover and also with the character of the storm. It is probable that agricultural crops seldom intercept more than 0.5 of an inch of water (*27*), and usually much less than this is held by the plant surfaces above the ground.

The amount of evaporation during a storm ordinarily is also relatively small. The amount of water detained upon the surface of the ground in the form of small, shallow pools is likewise small; it seldom exceeds 0.2 of an inch and more commonly is less than 0.1.

[4] G. W. Musgrave is Principal Soil Conservationist, Division of Research, Soil Conservation Service.

FIGURE 2.—Two samples of Mereta clay loam: *A*, Many years under good grazing practice have left this soil well aggregated and porous and with a high infiltration rate; *B*, dense structure, low porosity, and low infiltration rate are the results of intensive agricultural use.

On the other hand the quantity of water entering the soil may be relatively large—under favorable conditions, 1 or 2 inches an hour or more. Even under adverse conditions the total amount of infiltration during a long storm may be appreciable. Thus with infiltration at 0.1 of an inch an hour during a 20-hour period, 2 inches of water may enter the soil profile—a quantity so large as to justify particular attention to this phase of the hydrologic cycle in all plans for the control of run-off.

SOIL CHARACTERISTICS

The amount and rate of infiltration are primarily dependent on (1) the size of pores, or openings, in the soil, (2) their permanency during a storm, and (3) the total volume of space unoccupied by water or infiltrated soil particles. The size of the pores is largely dependent on the size of the particles comprising the soil profile and their structure or arrangement. Other things being equal, a sandy loam soil will have a higher rate of infiltration than a silt loam because of the larger size of particles and pores. However, the silt loam under favorable management and good land use may have its particles arranged in groups, or aggregated, so that each aggregate, or group, behaves with respect to water movement like a large individual particle. High rates of infiltration are then likely to occur; in many cases higher rates are found in silt loams under such conditions than in sandy loams (*10*).

A porous, well-aggregated Mereta clay loam and a Mereta clay loam of dense structure are shown in figure 2, *A* and *B*. In figure 3 are shown the infiltration rates found in each at a time when both were thoroughly wet. Similar differences are frequently found between soils that have been given good management practices and those that have been intensively cultivated, excessively grazed, or subjected to the burning of surface vegetation.

A soil in which conditions initially favor high infiltration may, during the course of a storm, lose its favorable structure because of

(1) "melting" or slacking of its aggregates, (2) the partial clogging of openings by fine particles deposited by downward-moving water, or (3) partial or complete filling of its pores by water.

Usually soils that have not been intensively cultivated tend not only to have higher infiltration rates at the beginning of a storm period but also to maintain higher rates throughout the storm than do soils whose organic matter has been exhausted and whose structure has been modified by intensive tillage. Lowdermilk (*23*) showed in 1930 that turbid or muddy water applied to soil caused the rate of infiltration to drop to low levels. Run-off water from grassland or well-forested areas commonly is comparatively clear, while that from intensively cultivated areas is ordinarily highly turbid. In the grassland or forested areas the favorable aggregated structure of the soil is more stable and less apt to disintegrate during the course of a storm.

SOIL MOISTURE

In wet soils the infiltration of water ordinarily is less than in dry ones, although this is not invariably true. Soils high in clay and colloids swell when wet, and the pores become smaller, so that when such a soil as the Houston black clay, for example, is thoroughly moist, infiltration is practically zero, although it may be very high in the same soil when dry (*10*). Soils with impermeable subsoils of course have their infiltration rates reduced as the space above becomes filled with water. On the other hand, soils with little clay may have at least as high an infiltration rate when wet as when dry, if not a higher one. This is particularly true when subdrainage is good or the soil is permeable to a considerable depth. For soils in general,

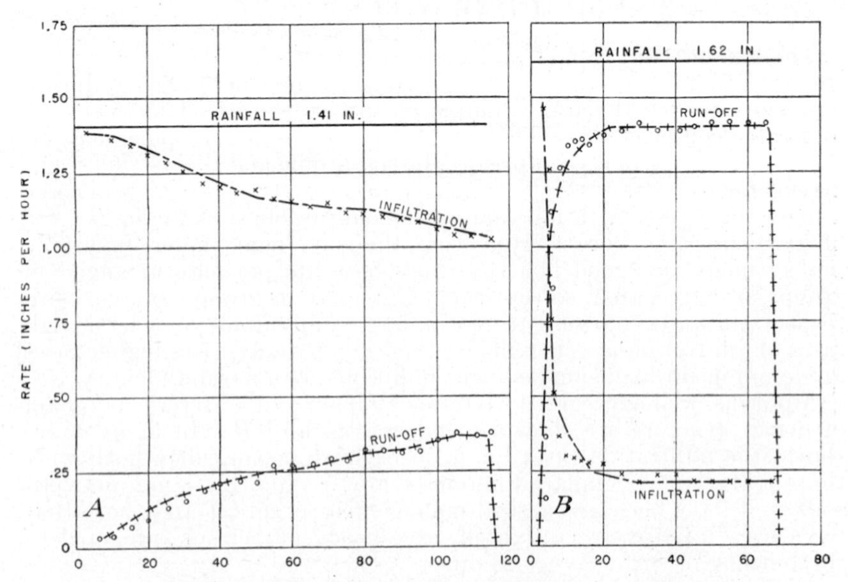

FIGURE 3.—*A*, A rate of infiltration of over 1 inch an hour was found on Mereta clay loam having a good grass cover (fig. 1, *A*); *B*, the infiltration rate was less than 0.25 of an inch an hour on similar soil having poor cover (fig. 1, *B*).

therefore, infiltration has not been found to be proportional to increases or reductions in soil moisture.

Both the levels of soil moisture and temperature have been found to be associated with the rate of infiltration. In field determinations soil moisture was found to be generally low when temperatures of air and soil were high. Under these conditions infiltration rates were higher than when the same soil with the same cover (grass) was moist and the temperature lower. These relationships were found to prevail in general throughout a 2-year period during which successive measurements on the same site were made.[5] To what extent the results are due to temperature and to what extent to soil moisture has not thus far been definitely determined.

TEMPERATURE

Temperature is known to affect the viscosity of water—that is, the resistance of the internal particles to motion—so that at low temperatures it flows somewhat more slowly than at high temperatures. It is to be expected that less water will enter a soil when it is cold than when it is warm; for example, the percentage of precipitation lost as run-off is greater in the winter and late fall than during the spring and summer. Figure 4 shows the average percentage of run-off during an 8-year period at the Bethany, Mo., Soil Conservation Experiment Station.[6]

[5] Borst, H. L., and Musgrave, G. W. SEASONAL VARIATIONS IN INFILTRATION. (Unpublished.)
[6] Smith, D. D. Unpublished data, Bethany, Mo., Soil Conservation Experiment Station.

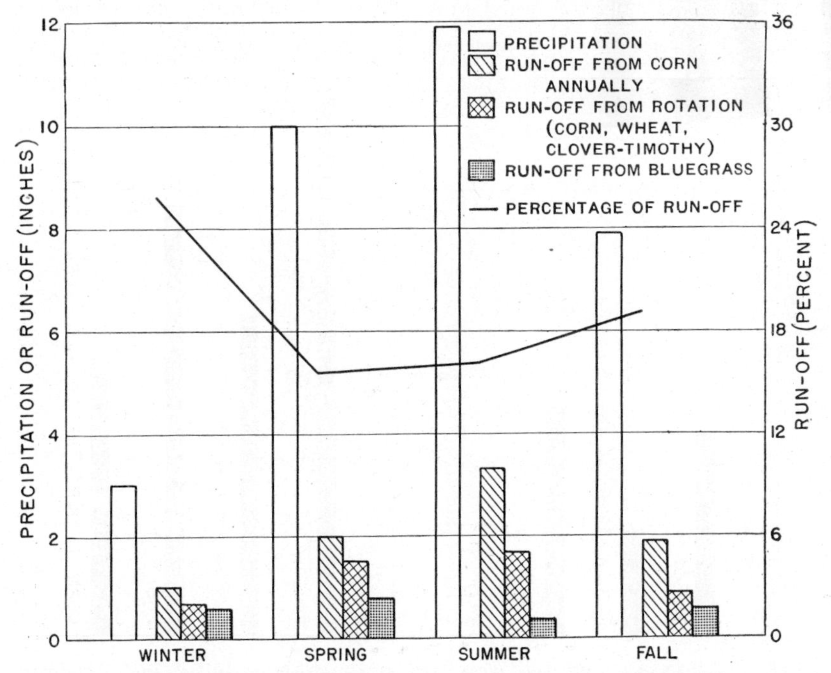

Figure 4.—Precipitation and run-off during an 8-year period (1931–38), by seasons, Soil Conservation Experiment Station, Bethany, Mo.

The effect of temperature on run-off is also illustrated by individual storms. In figure 5 is shown the run-off at the Clarinda, Iowa, Soil Conservation Experiment Station,[7] from plots given different treatment, each in triplicate, from two storms of approximately equal amount and intensity of precipitation, one of which occurred at a relatively low temperature. In the July storm, 0.83 inch of rain fell in 12 hours, maximum intensity 0.70 inch an hour, temperatures 68°–92° F. In December 1936, rainfall was 0.81 inch, maximum intensity 0.60 inch an hour, temperatures 21°–53°. Considerably more run-off occurred in each case when the temperature was low, despite the fact that much more rain had fallen during the 10 days before the summer storm than before the winter one (0.62 inch in July and 0.24 inch in December).

When temperatures are low enough to thoroughly freeze a very wet soil, it is probable that little if any infiltration occurs. On the other hand, it is possible that a frozen soil with a low moisture content may have a high infiltration rate, owing to the formation of frozen aggregates and the flocculation (aggregation) of colloids. In the Midwest particularly, soils are frequently known to enter the winter period with a low moisture content, then to freeze and fluff up to a highly porous condition, and thus be able to absorb water from melting snow, leaving little if any to run off.

SNOW DEPTH AND FROST DEPTH

Snow cover as well as vegetal cover affects the depth of frost penetration. From the Soil Conservation Experiment Station at La

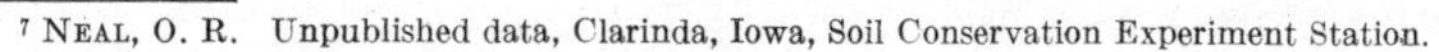

[7] NEAL, O. R. Unpublished data, Clarinda, Iowa, Soil Conservation Experiment Station.

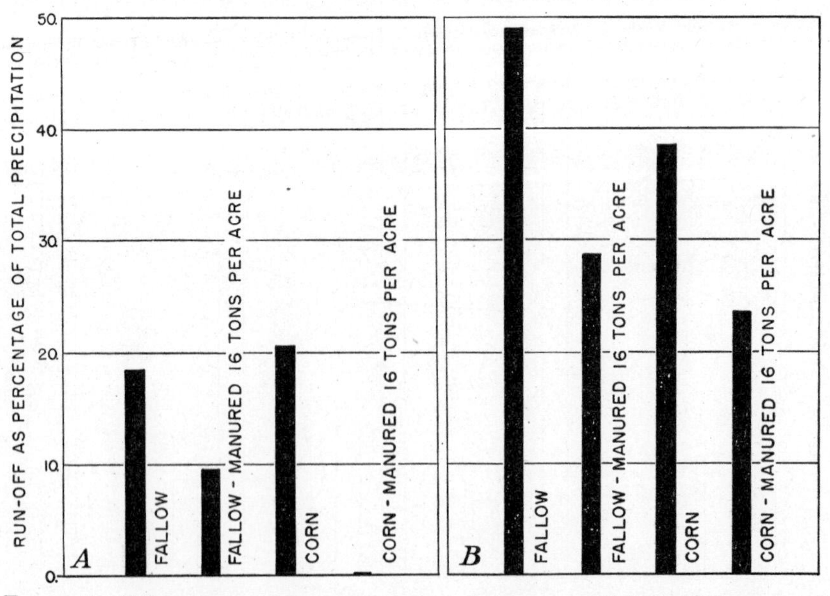

FIGURE 5.—Effect of temperature on run-off. *A*, A storm on July 9, 1935, produced much less run-off under four different conditions of land use than *B*, a similar storm on December 30, 1936, during which the temperatures were much lower.

Crosse, Wis., Atkinson and Bay (*1*) have reported measurements of snow depth and depth of frost penetration for different conditions and kinds of land use. A typical result of their findings is given in figure 6, which shows a greater depth of snow on plots having alfalfa or bluegrass than on adjoining plowed land. For the same period it was found that frost penetrated to a greater depth in the plowed land than in that growing alfalfa or bluegrass. In the spring, however, surface thawing occurred to a greater depth in a given time on the plowed land than under alfalfa or bluegrass, although under all these conditions the thawing began soon after the disappearance of snow.

It is to be expected that the run-off from soil that is frozen deeply will be greater than that from soil frozen only slightly. As an example, figure 7 shows the results for January, February, and March at the La Crosse station for an area in corn and one in bluegrass. During most of this period the ground under the corn was frozen to a much greater depth than that under the bluegrass and the run-off rate was much higher from the deeply frozen corn stubble. But when the frost left this ground in the spring, storms as great as or greater than those which had occurred while the ground was frozen produced no run-off.

At Ithaca, N. Y., run-off from melting snow was high when the ground was frozen, whether the land had a dense cover of grass and clover or was bare, having been planted to potatoes the previous year. There was a marked difference in the amount of erosion, however, the land in grass having no erosion, whereas that which had been in potatoes had severe erosion (table 1). In another series of comparisons, where the soil was not frozen, the amount of run-off from melting snow was slight, although the land had a steeper slope and the snow was deeper.

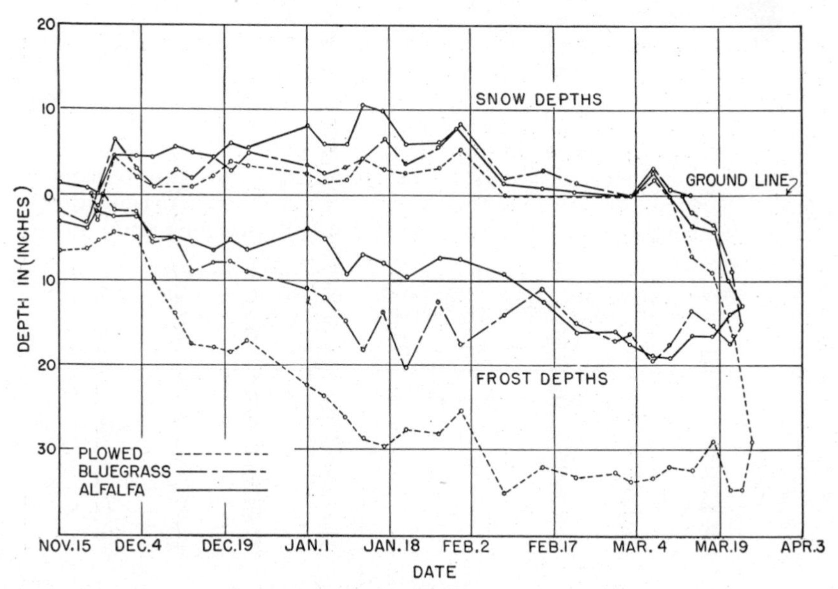

FIGURE 6.—Comparative snow depths and frost depths for land put to different uses, November 19, 1937, to March 25, 1938.

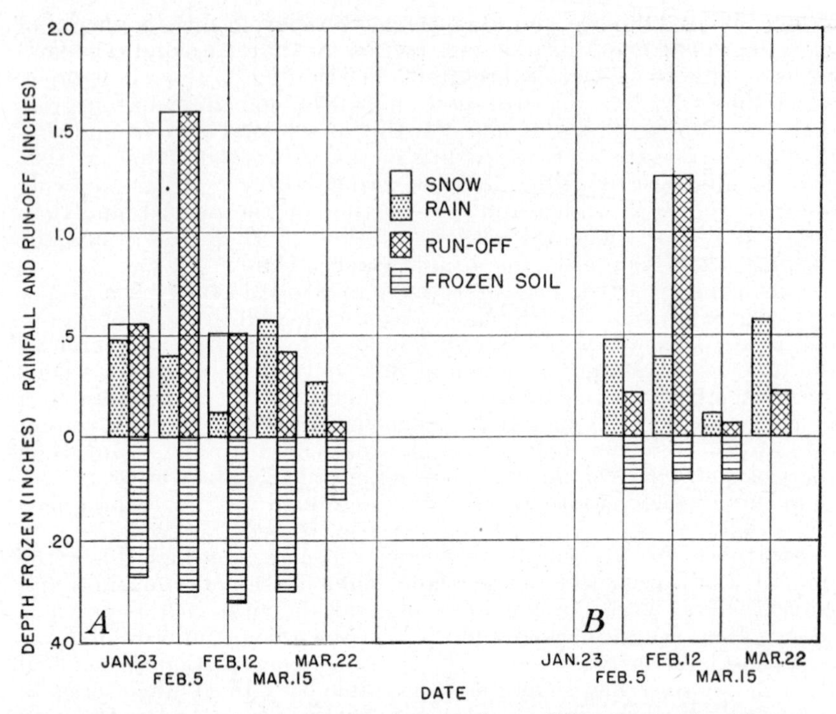

FIGURE 7.—Comparative frost depth, rainfall, and run-off from land with a 16-percent slope under close and under sparse vegetal cover, during January, February, and March at the La Crosse, Wis., Soil Conservation Experiment Station: *A*, Corn annually; *B*, bluegrass.

That the percentage of rainfall lost as run-off is generally greater in northern than in southern climates is seen from the data in table 2, which gives the run-off losses under both clean-tilled crops such as corn and cotton and dense cover such as grass and hay. Under either class of crop more run-off has usually occurred at the northern than at the southern locations. The complexities of climate causing these differences include, for the North: (1) A shorter period during which the ground is covered by vegetation, (2) a longer period during

TABLE 1.—*Influence of snow and vegetative cover on water and soil loss, for the flood period Mar. 10–19, 1936, on Bath flaggy silt loam, Soil Conservation Experiment Station, Ithaca, N. Y.*

[Average precipitation 6.57 inches]

Vegetative cover	Average slope	Snow depth		Run-off	Soil loss per acre
		Mar. 9	Mar. 19		
	Percent	*Inches*	*Inches*	*Inches*	*Pounds*
Soil frozen:					
None (potatoes 1935)	13	13	0	7.87	1,023
Grass and clover	13	13	0	7.87	0
Soil not frozen:					
None (fallow)	20	60	44	.636	0
Grass and clover	20	60	44	.017	0
Woodland	27	19	12	.023	0

which the ground is frozen, (3) lower temperatures of both water and soil, particularly during the fall, winter, and spring, and (4) other factors, such as less biological activity in the soil.

TABLE 2.—*Surface run-off from northern and southern locations, under clean-tilled and dense cover crops, at specified Soil Conservation Experiment Stations*

Location and period of measurement	Average annual rainfall for period	Water loss as percentage of annual precipitation under—		Location and period of measurement	Average annual rainfall for period	Water loss as percentage of annual precipitation under—	
		Clean-tilled crops	Dense cover			Clean-tilled crops	Dense cover
	Inches	*Percent*	*Percent*		*Inches*	*Percent*	*Percent*
Northern locations (less than 180 days between killing frosts):				Southern locations (more than 180 days between killing frosts):			
Beemerville, N. J., 1937–39 [1]	48.12	13.8	5.8	Statesville, N. C., 1932–38	48.20	12.1	0.2
Ithaca, N. Y., 1936–38	42.03	17.6	5.5	Guthrie, Okla., 1930–38	30.63	12.5	1.0
Zanesville, Ohio, 1934–38	38.78	41.9	5.9	Temple, Tex., 1931–38	31.59	12.4	.0
La Crosse, Wis., 1933–38	33.70	28.7	11.2	Temple, Tex., 1933–38	32.72	11.4	.8
La Crosse, Wis., 1934–38	34.51	22.1	9.4	Tyler, Tex., 1933–38	40.41	14.2	.2
Pullman, Wash., 1932–38	20.41	22.5	2.3	Tyler, Tex., 1932–38	40.54	15.5	.4
Hays, Kans., 1930–38	19.58	16.8	6.1	Spur, Tex., 1926–37	20.73	15.5	4.3
Clarinda, Iowa, 1933–38	26.04	13.5	1.0				
Bethany, Mo., 1931–38	30.85	27.9	7.1				

[1] September 1937 to September 1939.

THE CHARACTERISTICS OF THE STORM

The characteristics of each individual storm also determine the amount of surface run-off to a considerable extent. Clearly there is some combination of intensity and amount of rain which produces the maximum run-off. The size of the raindrops, the distance they fall, and the force of their impact upon the ground affect the amount of erosion and run-off. The form of the precipitation—rain, snow, hail—greatly influences the amount and rate of run-off.

A number of attempts have been made to determine the general characteristics of storms and their effects on erosion. Hays [8] at Wisconsin has found that by giving certain weights to the maximum intensity during a 30-minute period, the total amount of rainfall, and the maximum intensity for a 5-minute period, a factor may be developed which will permit an approximate classification of storms according to the degree of erosion they produce. Presumably, a somewhat similar alinement could be established in relation to run-off. Any evidence indicating the effect of storm characteristics on run-off, even though meager, is useful in many ways, particularly in designing protective measures that will have maximum effectiveness during periods when the most damaging storms are expected.

Much less is known about run-off that results from flood-producing storms than about that from ordinary storms, one reason being that the former occur less frequently and therefore provide less opportunity for study. Ordinarily, flood-producing storms are of long duration,

[8] HAYS, O. E. Unpublished report from the La Crosse, Wis., Soil Conservation Experiment Station.

high intensity, or both, and occur at times of the year when temperatures are low, the ground is frozen or covered by snow, and protective conditions in general are at a minimum of effectiveness. Existing evidence indicates, however, that run-off is retarded by the same factors under these conditions as in the case of ordinary storms. Thus, at Zanesville, Ohio, in January 1937,[9] at the time of the Ohio River flood, over 10 inches of rain fell, about 95 percent of which was lost as run-off from land in corn stubble and only about 25 percent from land in good bluegrass (table 3).

TABLE 3.—*Comparative run-off from plots in corn and in bluegrass during flood-producing storm periods, Zanesville, Ohio, January 1937*

Period (1937)	Rainfall (cumulative)	Run-off (cumulative) under—		Period (1937)	Rainfall (cumulative)	Run-off (cumulative) under—	
		Corn	Bluegrass			Corn	Bluegrass
	Inches	*Inches*	*Inches*		*Inches*	*Inches*	*Inches*
Jan. 2	0.29	0.07	0.00	Jan. 22–23	8.08	7.11	1.70
7	.64	.14	.01	24–25	9.98	9.67	2.57
9–10	1.50	.58	.03	31	10.29	9.74	2.57
13–15	3.52	2.59	.65				
17–18	4.48	3.71	.87			*Percent*	*Percent*
20–22	7.24	6.65	1.70	Rainfall lost as run-off		94.65	24.96

The results shown in table 3 occurred on plots 6 by 72 feet on typical Muskingum silt loam. This soil does not swell as much when wet as do many soils, and also it has reasonably good subsurface drainage. Probably the water from successive rains during this period forced entrance into the wet soil by displacing a corresponding volume of water which moved downward through more or less porous substrata. Thus it is not possible to determine from the records exactly how much run-off there would have been on a large watershed where seepage of ground water would be included in the run-off. It is clear, however, that on such small upland areas having dense vegetal cover the run-off even from flood-producing storms may be less than that from land having a sparse vegetal cover. It is also probable that even on a large watershed any subsurface water which does escape to the streams is likely to reach them some time after surface water does. Under these conditions, flood crests may be spread out over longer periods of time.

VEGETAL COVER

Many similar examples show that even under severe storms the amount of run-off is greatly affected by the type of vegetal cover. Table 4, from the records of the La Crosse, Wis., station,[10] gives rainfall and run-off data for the storm of July 5, 1934, the most severe since the installation of recording gages by the Weather Bureau at La Crosse in 1905, and for four storms in 1935 that together caused 60 percent of the total water loss for the year.

[9] BORST, H. L. Unpublished data, Zanesville, Ohio, Soil Conservation Experiment Station.

[10] HAYS, O. E., and PALMER, V. J. SOIL AND WATER CONSERVATION INVESTIGATIONS: PROGRESS REPORT, UPPER MISSISSIPPI VALLEY SOIL AND WATER CONSERVATION EXPERIMENT STATION, LA CROSSE, WIS. Soil Conserv. Serv. ESR-1, [82] pp., illus. 1937. [Mimeographed.]

TABLE 4.—*Rainfall and run-off in storms of high intensity at the La Crosse, Wis., Soil Conservation Experiment Station, 1934 and 1935*

Date of storm	Rainfall				Run-off under—		
	Maximum intensity in period of—			Total	Corn	Clover	Blue-grass
	5 minutes [1]	10 minutes [1]	30 minutes				
	Inches	*Inches*	*Inches*	*Inches*	*Percent*	*Percent*	*Percent*
July 5, 1934	7.92	6.66	[1] 2.93	3.01	54.08	32.58	3.79
July 5, 1935	2.88	2.82	[1] 2.30	1.96	72.88	13.69	.00
Aug. 2, 1935	3.01	2.64	1.78	2.66	59.82	21.87	.00
Aug. 3, 1935	3.12	2.84	2.04	1.06	75.28	25.32	.00
Aug. 5-6, 1935	3.84	3.36	[1] 2.62	2.39	80.03	24.96	.00

[1] Expected frequency, once in more than 100 years.

Although the reduction in the amount of run-off under dense vegetal cover is not so great for these high-intensity storms as it is for the average storm, presumably the causal factors are much the same in both storm types, the difference being merely one of magnitude. In both instances favorable soil structure, fairly high temperatures, and the protecting influences of a dense vegetal canopy tended to reduce run-off, whereas a dense soil structure (often the result of misuse of land), saturated, cold, or frozen soils, or the absence of a good vegetal cover tended greatly to increase run-off.

EVAPORATION AND TRANSPIRATION

BY C. W. THORNTHWAITE AND BENJAMIN HOLZMAN [11]

AMONG the various climatic factors of hydrologic and agricultural significance the return of moisture to the atmosphere from natural land surfaces has resisted measurement most strongly and is consequently least well understood. In precipitation and run-off the water is eventually in the liquid state and can be measured by means of straightforward sampling techniques, but upon evaporating water becomes an invisible gas which mixes with the other gases of the atmosphere and is disseminated through it. Continental evaporation includes evaporation from the soil or ground surface, evaporation from ponds, lakes, streams, reservoirs, and other water bodies, evaporation of moisture intercepted by vegetation during rains, and the transpiration of moisture by vegetation.

For the farmer, the soil is a reservoir to which water is contributed by precipitation and from which it is withdrawn by evaporation and transpiration from the growing crops. During a prolonged period without rain the soil moisture may be drawn upon until the wilting point is approached and plant development and crop yields are adversely affected. A storm may partially or completely replace the moisture that has been lost, but during the period between storms evaporation and transpiration will again deplete the moisture supply. In determining the drought hazard, the measurement of the varying rates of evaporation and transpiration is as essential as information

[11] C. W. Thornthwaite is Chief and Benjamin Holzman is Associate Soil Conservationist, Climatic and Physiographic Division, Office of Research, Soil Conservation Service.

concerning the amount and distribution of rainfall, because they determine the rate at which the water supply is consumed.

NEED FOR METHODS OF MEASURING EVAPORATION AND TRANSPIRATION

Whereas agriculturists are concerned chiefly with the portion of the precipitation that enters the ground and is available to plants, hydrologists are concerned primarily with the portion that runs off. Run-off varies greatly even on small watersheds, largely owing to the variations in field moisture caused by evaporation and transpiration between rains. When the soil is dry, little run-off occurs except in very intense or prolonged rains, because the greater part of the rainfall is used up in replenishing the soil moisture. Only after the soil becomes saturated will water flow off the land as run-off. Thus, in predicting the amount of moisture available for run-off in terms of the observed rainfall, an accurate measure of the rate at which the soil dries out is highly desirable.

Scientists have long recognized the serious need for a method of measuring water losses by evaporation from land surfaces as well as from free water surfaces. In the past significant progress has been made only in the case of the latter. Over bodies of free water, a continuous supply of moisture is available for evaporation, and the actual losses are dependent directly upon climatic and meteorologic factors. Thus it has been possible to develop empirical formulas which permit engineers to compute with reasonable accuracy anticipated water losses from lakes or reservoirs in terms of meteorologic data alone. Expected losses may be estimated approximately from observed losses of water from standard evaporation pans or atmometers (*8*, *29*, *43*).

The rate of emission of water vapor from a natural land surface cannot be determined by such methods. When the surface soil is moist, evaporation may be more rapid than it is from a free water surface, because the soil with its minute irregularities presents a larger evaporating surface. When, however, the surface soil has become wholly or partly dry, evaporation losses are greatly diminished even though the subsoil remains moist. Replacement of surface water from below by capillary action is extremely slow, and the soil moisture can escape to the outer air only as vapor by diffusion through the soil air. Furthermore, as the growing season advances the ground surface becomes shielded by foliage, which causes a progressive diminution in the direct evaporation from the soil even though water losses through transpiration by plants increase.

The physical process of transpiration is not yet completely understood (*22*), but it is recognized that the amount of water lost from an area thereby depends upon the density and character of the vegetation as well as upon atmospheric conditions. Transpiration increases with plant development until maturity is reached, owing largely to the increase in the area of the transpiring surface and in the number of its stomatal openings. With maturity plant activity subsides and transpiration rapidly diminishes. The total removal of water from a field by transpiration depends upon the water requirements of the particular plants and upon their growth, which in turn may be limited by the amount of water available. Consequently evaporation from pans or atmometers cannot supply even a relative measure of water loss from natural land surfaces.

Some information on the amount of transpiration from various species of plants has been obtained through the use of pots, tanks, and lysimeters containing soil and growing plants which can be weighed continuously or at periodic intervals. Because of the necessarily limited surface area and interference by walls, which confine the plant roots and restrict the normal movement of water in the soil, this method creates highly artificial conditions and can yield results only roughly indicative of the magnitude of evaporation and transpiration from natural surfaces.

The lack of a direct measure of evaporation losses from natural surfaces led to the development of the many empirical formulas for expressing the effectiveness of precipitation. Transeau (*40*), one of the earliest to be concerned with the problem, used the quotient of total measured rainfall divided by computed free-water evaporation as a moisture index. Lang's "rain factor" (*21*), de Martonne's "index of aridity" (*25*), Meyer's "N–S quotient" (*26*),[12] and the "hygrometric quotient" of Szymkiewicz (*34*) represent other attempts to determine effective precipitation. The climatic classifications of Köppen (*19*) and Thornthwaite (*35*) both employ means for determining effective precipitation. However, no empirical formula can take the place of actual measurements of evaporation.

Where accurate measurements of precipitation and run-off are available, integrated values of the losses by transpiration and evaporation can be obtained by simple subtraction. Such values provide general information on the average effectiveness of precipitation over long periods of time; they also serve for comparing water losses between regions of different vegetal cover. Kittredge (*18*) has recently made use of available average annual rainfall and run-off data and has prepared a map showing the distribution of the average annual water losses to the atmosphere in the United States. Accurate determination of evaporation losses for short periods of time such as a year or less is not possible, because of the lag in both run-off and evaporation.

A NEW TECHNIQUE FOR MEASURING MOISTURE LOSSES

Fortunately the rapid development of aviation during the last two decades made it necessary to investigate the nature of the lower layers of the atmosphere. Notable advances in our understanding of the mechanics of moisture and heat transfer through these layers have been the result. This knowledge has made possible the development of a technique for direct measurement of evaporation and transpiration from natural surfaces (*39*).

There is a zone in the atmosphere near the earth's surface in which ground friction retards horizontal movement in the lower part of the air column and results in overturning and vertical interchange, or mixing, of air in the column. This is the zone of turbulent mixing, or the

[12] Meyer's N–S (Niederschlag-Sattegungsdefizit) quotient is obtained by dividing precipitation by saturation deficit.

turbulent layer. Within it, the mixing process tends to distribute the moisture evenly and thus to eliminate differences in moisture concentration. So long as there is no addition of moisture to or withdrawal from the layer, its moisture content will be uniformly distributed. On the other hand, if water vapor is emitted from an evaporating surface and is transported upward into the turbulent layer, the moisture concentration will be highest at the base and will diminish with increased elevation. In this way a moisture gradient is established. Such a gradient owes its existence to the continued addition of moisture from below; when evaporation ceases, the moisture will soon be distributed uniformly throughout the turbulent layer, and the gradient will be destroyed. In the same way, abstraction of moisture from the base of the layer by condensation—as when dew "falls"—will create a gradient with minimum moisture concentration at the base, which can be maintained only as long as the removal of moisture continues.

Instruments for measuring the moisture content of the air are available, and when it is measured at two levels the moisture gradient can be determined. In order to determine the rate at which moisture is being evaporated into or condensed from the air, it is necessary to determine only the intensity of turbulent mixing in addition to the moisture gradient. This can be obtained simply by measuring wind velocity at two levels.

The procedure provides a measure not only of evaporation and transpiration but also of condensation and absorption, which in many parts of the world are important sources of moisture for plant growth. The importance of condensation directly into the soil is particularly great in summer on black soils, which have high rates of cooling owing to nocturnal radiation. When moisture concentration is high and radiation at a maximum, as much as 0.05 of an inch of water may be added to the soil by condensation during a single night. The amount of moisture absorbed directly from the air by certain types of vegetation under favorable conditions is not insignificant.

Results of Experimental Measurements

At present the technique for measuring evaporation is being used only on an experimental basis at a few stations, but sufficiently good results have been obtained to warrant the hope that it may find widespread use in the future. One station, situated on the experimental farm at Arlington, Va., has been in continuous operation for more than a year. The moisture content of the air is determined at two levels within 25 feet of the ground by means of hygrothermographs and the rate of turbulent transport by the use of anemometers at the same levels.[13] The instruments are installed over a meadow of perennial grasses which is mowed at various times during the summer.

The observations of precipitation, evaporation, and condensation at Arlington for 1939 are summarized by months in table 5. The data for February and September are missing because of the interruption of the observations by instrumental failure and the installation of new equipment. During the 10 months the total contribution of moisture to the ground by precipitation was 26.34 inches and by con-

[13] For the first few months the observations were made 2 and 28 feet above the ground. Later it was recognized that the upper instruments need not be so high, so they were lowered to 24.5 feet. The lower observations were continued at 2 feet.

densation, 1.77 inches. The total loss by evaporation and transpiration was 11.88 inches. By subtraction, a value of 16.23 inches is obtained for run-off and increase in ground storage.

TABLE 5.—*Exchange of moisture between the ground and the atmosphere, Arlington, Va., 1939*

Month	Precipitation	Condensation	Evaporation	Month	Precipitation	Condensation	Evaporation
	Inches	*Inch*	*Inches*		*Inches*	*Inches*	*Inches*
January	3.41	0.08	0.49	August	2.98	0.16	1.46
February [1]				September [1]			
March	2.81	.03	.92	October	2.38	.25	.78
April	2.93	.31	1.07	November	1.40	.22	.59
May	.20	.11	1.65	December	2.20	.11	.55
June	5.87	.26	2.53				
July	2.16	.28	1.93	Total [2]	26.34	1.81	11.97

[1] Incomplete record.
[2] For the 10 months having complete records.

The losses to the atmosphere were at a minimum in the winter, when evaporation was suppressed by low ground temperatures and there was almost no transpiration. Losses were greatest in June because the vegetation had nearly reached maturity, growth was still active, and transpiration was at its height; they were reduced in July and August by mowing.

Precipitation was very scanty in May, and the soil moisture was reduced nearly 1.5 inches by evaporation and transpiration. However, much of this soil-moisture loss was restored by a rain of 1.17 inches on June 8, and on June 13 there was a rain of 1.88 inches, of which 1.51 inches fell in a single hour.

Relation to Flood Hazard

Water losses to the atmosphere were five times as great in June as in January. In this region, however, precipitation is nearly as great in winter as in summer, and in addition that of the winter may be stored on the ground in the form of snow. Thus the chances for general floods to occur in the colder seasons are greatly enhanced. Actually, the flood hazard is greatest in early spring, when evaporation losses are still quite small and warm rains combined with the melting of accumulated winter snow are most likely to overtax drainage channels.

In central and eastern United States nearly all major flood-producing storms are terminated by the invasion of relatively dry air masses of polar continental origin characterized by a thick turbulent layer and low concentrations of water vapor. These air masses provide conditions most favorable to evaporation and are able to absorb enormous quantities of moisture from the rain-drenched land. Since floods on large watersheds are most frequently due to general storms which must first restore to the soil reservoir water which had previously been lost by evaporation and transpiration, it is evident that land use practices favoring evaporation will accordingly lessen the burden imposed on stream channels by excessive rains, both by retarding immediate run-off and by creating a water-storage capacity in the soil.

298737°—41——36

The losses of moisture from a field in Arlington into continental and maritime air masses during June and July 1939 are shown in table 6. Although the maritime air was considerably warmer than the continental air, its daily rate of intake of moisture from the ground was only 58 percent as great. That evaporation into continental masses is greater than that into maritime has been verified by observation of the change in water content of these masses as they traverse the country.

TABLE 6.—*Exchanges of water vapor between the ground and continental and maritime air masses during June and July 1939 at the Arlington Experiment Station*

Date and air mass type	Days	Average temperature	Total evaporation	Total condensation	Total loss from ground	Average daily loss from ground
	Number	° *F.*	*Inch*	*Inch*	*Inch*	*Inch*
June 1939:						
Continental	10	74.0	0.8887	0.0075	0.8812	0.0881
Maritime	11	76.4	.7182	.1507	.5675	.0516
July 1939:						
Continental	12	72.7	.9740	.0695	.9045	.0754
Maritime	14	79.2	.7878	.1670	.6208	.0443

Intimately associated with the problem of retarding and reducing run-off from the standpoint of flood considerations are questions of climatic risk and of climate-crop relationships. During rainless periods the moisture surface moves downward in the soil profile at rates fundamentally dependent upon the plant complex. This is because transpiration by plants is the chief mechanism whereby water is lost from the soil (*41*). Obviously, then, in those regions where flood-producing rains are common, a vegetal complex having high transpiration values should be favored to create appreciable soil-moisture deficiencies. Conversely, in areas of high drought incidence, plants with small transpiration values should be favored so as to minimize crop failure.

OUTLOOK FOR IMPROVED UNDERSTANDING OF PROBLEMS

Until recently no satisfactory technique for the measurement of actual moisture losses from natural surfaces such as fields or watersheds had been developed. Consequently, lack of pertinent evaporation and transpiration data has delayed the analysis and solution of many climatic and hydrologic problems. It is hoped that in the future evaporation measurements from all types of geographic surfaces, giving information on the moisture requirements of various crops and types of natural vegetation cover and the effectiveness of various moisture-conserving practices, will become available. With the accumulation of this information, the interrelations of climate, hydrology, and agriculture will be more clearly understood.

STORMS AND FLOODS

By Benjamin Holzman and Albert Showalter [14]

Two principal types of storms may produce enough rainfall to cause floods. One type (the thunderstorm) is of short duration, covers a rather small area—rarely producing simultaneous precipitation over more than 1,000 to 2,000 square miles—and has centers of high rainfall intensity with rates occasionally exceeding 5 inches an hour. The other type (the stagnant-cold-front storm) is characterized by considerably longer duration, usually low intensity, and wide extent, and it contributes enormous quantities of water to the land.

These two types of storms represent the extremes of flood types. The first concentrates rainfall in both time and area and produces flash floods on small streams. In the second the rainfall is spread out in time and in area and produces high-water stages on large basins which can usually be predicted in time to provide protection. Combinations or variations of these two types of storms, in addition to simple lifting of warm, moist air masses over mountains, may lead to flood-producing rains over basins of intermediate sizes.

THUNDERSTORMS AND FLASH FLOODS

The high-intensity storm of short duration mainly originates in a warm, moist air mass. Such air masses develop their physical characteristics over tropical waters such as the Gulf of Mexico or ocean waters south of latitude 30°. As a rule these tropical currents are heavily charged with moisture up to about 8,000 feet, but occasionally under unusual conditions their high moisture concentration may extend to altitudes exceeding 16,000 feet. The condensation and precipitation of this abundant moisture causes the excessive rainfall rates associated with local thunderstorms.

The process of convection in the atmosphere brings about the release of the moisture in these tropical maritime air masses. Convection is a turbulent rising of air from lower to higher altitudes; it is excellently illustrated in the formation of cumulus clouds. It may be produced in several ways: Through intense heating of the layer of air next to the ground, causing it to rise because of its lesser density; through the interaction of cold, dense air masses with the warm, moist masses, causing the latter to ascend; through an actual lifting of the moist air as it flows over mountainous terrain; or through a combination of these and other factors.

As the air currents rise they reach elevations of diminishing pressure where they expand and cool. The cooling ultimately causes the water vapor to condense. As the vapor changes to liquid the latent heat of vaporization is added to the air current, which tends to accelerate the turbulent convective process. The condensation then continues at a more rapid rate until nearly all of the moisture in the rising current has been precipitated. Since the motion of the air is mainly vertical and usually attains very high velocities, the rainfall is intense and is generally concentrated over a small area within a few hours. Thunder

[14] Benjamin Holzman is Associate Meteorologist, Soil Conservation Service, and Albert K. Showalter is Associate Meteorologist, Weather Bureau.

and lightning are always associated with the more intense local storms.

A storm of March 12, 1937, observed at the Oklahoma Climatic Research Center,[15] illustrates the rainfall genesis and pattern of local intense storms (*4*). On the morning of that day a great mass of polar continental air occupied the entire Great Plains region. The southern boundary, or cold front, of this extensive mass of cold, dry air extended through Oklahoma and Arkansas and along the southern boundary of Tennessee. At 6:45 p. m., central time, rain began to fall in parts of Kingfisher and Logan Counties, Okla. The rainfall maps in figure 8 show the actual amounts of precipitation by ½-hour intervals. The rain was caused by the interaction of the cold polar air to the north and the warm, moist, tropical Gulf air to the south. As the cold air pushed southward, causing the warm, moist air to ascend, thunderstorms were produced, resulting in several centers of high rainfall intensity. One of these centers moved across the research area. Although the same general meteorological conditions affected the entire area, only the eastern half received any rainfall.

The run-off from such sudden downpours of rain is generally excessive, and frequently the water flowing over the land causes great erosional damage. The rapid concentration of water in the stream channels overtaxes their capacity, and a flash flood results. Because of the local nature of these storms and their characteristically scattered rainfall pattern it is very difficult to give warning of their approach.

PERSISTENT RAIN AND GENERAL FLOODS

Floods on large river systems such as that of the Ohio River are usually produced by periods of persistent warm rainy weather. High water is the result not only of the large total volume of rain but also of the melting of large quantities of snow and ice and of ice jams that back up the water in the river channels.

Most of the rainfall in the United States results from the forced lifting of large masses of moist air which have moved northward from the tropical oceans. As was explained in the discussion of thunderstorms, the moist air is cooled at higher levels to temperatures so low that it can no longer hold its original volume of water vapor. The formation of water droplets on the surface of cold objects illustrates the effect of the cooling of moist air. The lifting is usually accomplished by colder heavier air from snow-covered polar regions which underruns the moist tropical air. The lighter air rises, as oil rises to the top of water or cream to the top of milk.

The hard-driving forces of bitter cold from the northern polar regions are continually trying to force their way southward to tropical oceans and occupy all the area of the United States. The contest between the warm tropical and the cold polar air, which occurs during all seasons but is most evident during the cooler part of the year, may be thought of as a continuous battle of weather along a continually shifting line known in meteorology as the polar front. The attack of the polar army is held close to the ground. When the opposing

[15] In October 1935 the Soil Conservation Service, in cooperation with the Weather Bureau, established with Works Progress Administration funds 200 weather stations, spaced approximately 3 miles apart, in an area of about 1,800 square miles in west-central Oklahoma. Over the entire area simultaneous observations of temperature, relative humidity, wind velocity, and wind direction were made each hour from 7 a. m. to 7 p. m., and during storms rainfall was recorded at 15-minute intervals.

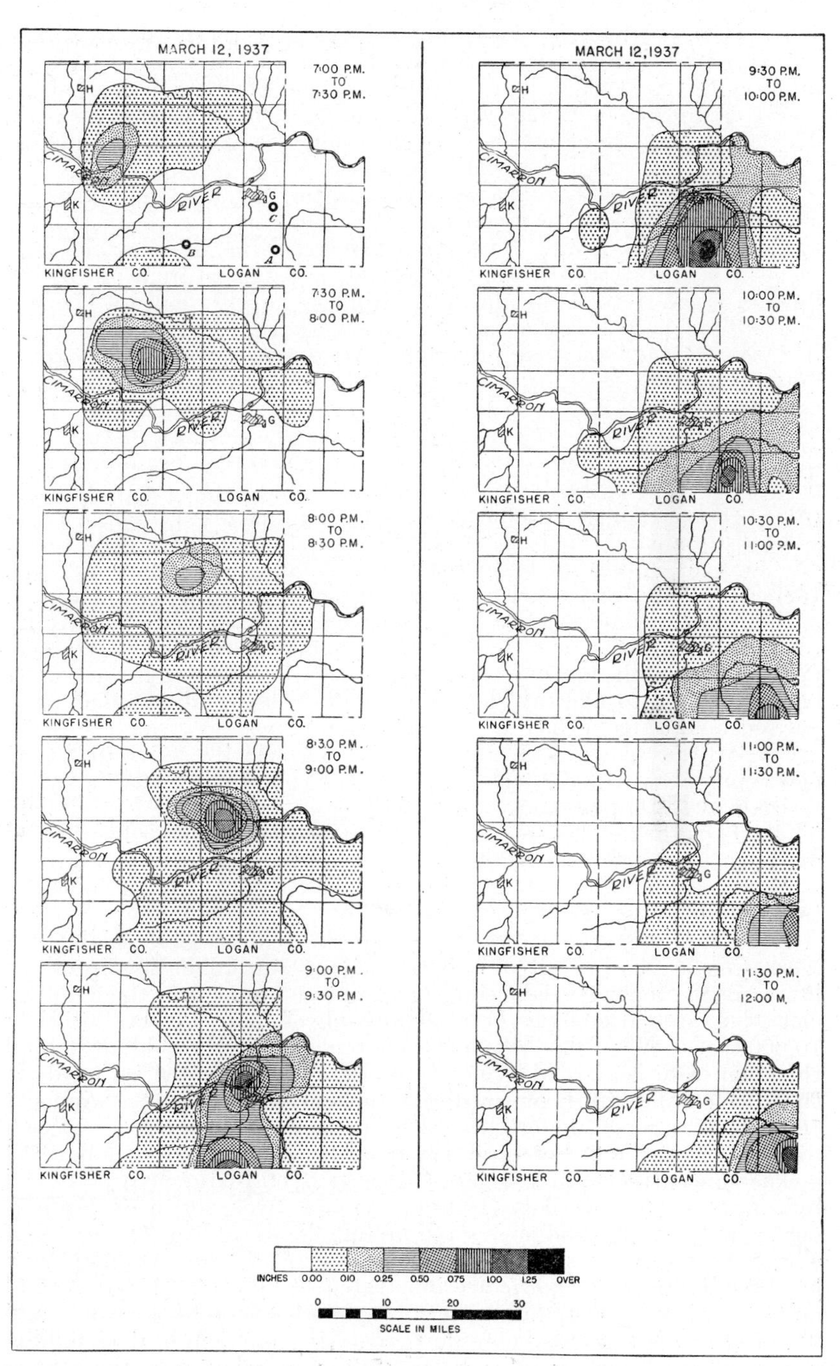

FIGURE 8.—Precipitation at ½-hour intervals in storm of March 12–13, 1937 (*4, p. 6*).

army of tropical breezes, continually trying to reach the Canadian border and bringing warm weather to the United States, finds its infantry forces blocked, it takes to the air and begins to ascend above and overrun the polar mass, thus continuing its northward movement. The battle line therefore becomes not merely a vertical wall but an inclined surface sloping toward the north.

Where the polar forces move southward the line of advance is called a cold front; where the tropical forces move northward the line is known as a warm front. The two armies rarely battle to a standstill; rather, each southward thrust of cold air is balanced by a northward push of warm air. Thus the polar front is not normally a straight line but develops a series of large-scale waves. Because the polar front is in the region of prevailing west-to-east winds, the waves normally move eastward and bring alternating periods of warm and cold weather.

As in an actual battle most of the bloodshed occurs in the front lines, so in the weather battle most of the "rainshed" occurs near the polar front. The areas of rainfall move along with the waves on the front. In certain unusual situations the regular progression of waves is interrupted, and the front becomes stagnant or quasi-stationary over one locality. The battle then rages with more than normal fury. Instead of large waves accompanied by light rains moving along the normal polar front, numerous small waves accompanied by more intense rains move along the quasi-stationary front. This produces persistent rainfall that may eventually accumulate enough water over one watershed to overtax the banks of the river draining that area.

Cold air at the surface is usually accompanied by a high-pressure area, with air blowing spirally outward in a clockwise manner. At elevations above 10,000 feet, however, the cold air is usually characterized by a low-pressure area with counterclockwise circulation. This means that in the cold air mass just behind the polar front there are normally northwest winds at the ground and southwest winds at 10,000 feet. The cold air at all elevations therefore moves generally from west to east, carrying the polar front eastward.

In cases of stagnation when the temperature decreases rapidly with increasing height in the cold air, the change of circulation from the lower to the upper levels becomes more pronounced, and the counterclockwise circulation develops at an altitude of about 5,000 rather than 10,000 feet. When this happens the circulation in the cold air behind the polar front is marked by northeast (instead of northwest) winds at the surface and south or southeast (instead of southwest) winds at 10,000 feet. Since under these conditions the cold air has no push toward the east, a quasi-stationary polar front tends to develop.

The concentration of a series of showers over a large area produced by stagnation of the polar front is typified by a storm of January 1937 (*33*), which produced outstanding floods in the Ohio River. The air trajectories at the surface and at 5,000 meters above sea level for January 20, 1937, are illustrated in figure 9, *A* and *B*, and figure 10 shows the rainfall pattern for the afternoon of the same day.

Considerable study is being devoted to the problem of determining the large-scale abnormalities in the general circulation of the atmosphere that cause the stagnation of the polar front. At present it seems well established that one of the immediate causes is a southward

it is buried too deeply, melting will still occur at the blackened zone, the sunlight passing through the top layer. Blackened thermometers buried in unshaded snow to a depth of 1 foot have recorded higher temperatures than unblackened thermometers at the same level (*6*). Similarly, if the total depth of snow is not too great, melting occurs at the soil surface from absorbed sunlight released as heat.

Contrary to general opinion, rain is not an important factor in snow melt. For example, 5 inches of rain at a temperature of 41° F. can release less than one-third of an inch of snow water. On the other hand, a heavy snow cover, especially when cold, will retain a considerable rainfall and release it only during subsequent thaws.

Warm, moist air, especially when moved by a strong wind, is a major factor in melting snow. When such air is in contact with a snow surface, condensation of moisture takes place, and heat is released. The warmth of the air itself is augmented by this heat of condensation. Fresh sources of heat are constantly available because of the movement of the air, and snow melt progresses rapidly. Melting of snow under these conditions has caused floods in New England, in the northern Lake and Great Plains regions, and in the northern mountains of the West. When rainfall occurs in conjunction with these moist, warm winds optimum conditions for floods prevail. This combination caused the 1936 New England floods,[17] augmented the Ohio River flood of the same year, and is the most frequent cause of floods throughout the snowy portion of the country.

The true chinook wind common to eastern mountain slopes of the West causes rapid removal of a snow cover but seldom if ever results in floods. Though this wind is warm, it is so dry that the melting snow is vaporized, and little of the snow water reaches the soil.

The effect of local topography is illustrated by the fact that snow accumulates most heavily and remains longest on slopes sheltered from wind and sun, partly because it is shifted there from exposed slopes, and partly because rates of evaporation and melting are lower in such locations. On watersheds where the local slope, exposure, and elevation is sufficiently varied, there may be enough difference in the rates of melt in various parts of the watershed to tend to regulate the discharge of snow water.

The sheltering effect of vegetation also tends to regulate melting by introducing a new factor—interception. This suggests the possibility of partial control of snow accumulation and rate of melt through management of the vegetative cover.

FORESTS AND SNOW

Forests, particularly coniferous forests, have a major influence on snow accumulation. Dense coniferous forests retain in their canopy 50 to 90 percent of a heavy fall of snow and thus expose an increased surface to evaporation. Some of this intercepted snow later cascades to the ground, but considerable evaporation takes place if clear, cool weather prevails. Open coniferous forests intercept smaller amounts. Hardwood forests intercept almost no snow and accumulate more on the ground than either coniferous types or open

[17] BALDWIN, HENRY I., and BROOKS, CHARLES F. FORESTS AND FLOODS IN NEW HAMPSHIRE. New England Regional Planning Comn., Pub. 47, 28 pp., illus. 1936. [Processed.]

areas. Herbaceous vegetation has only a minor effect on the disposition of snow.

Thus in general the greatest depths of snow in spring are found in hardwood and open coniferous forests, lesser amounts on cleared areas, and least under dense coniferous forests. Occasionally a very open coniferous forest will hasten the melting of snow through the absorption of sunlight by tree crowns and boles and the reradiation of heat (*16*).

The vegetative cover affects the extent and severity of soil freezing both indirectly through its effect on snow accumulation and more directly through its effect on the character of the soil and the accumulation of litter and humus. Experimental results indicate that soil temperatures in hardwood areas are higher throughout the winter than those in adjacent areas of softwoods. Winter soil temperatures are lower in cleared areas than in any of the forest types. In many cases the hardwood areas will remain unfrozen throughout the winter while the soil in cleared areas and in many of the coniferous areas is frozen solid for long periods.

Forests have an important influence on the rate of snow melt because of their obstruction to wind movement. Wind velocity may be reduced more than 90 percent by a dense coniferous forest (*17*). Even very open coniferous stands and hardwood forests reduce the velocity to some degree. The rate of snow melt is thus reduced in forests during the critical periods of warm, moist winds.

To sum up the effect of forests: Under dense coniferous forests snow accumulation is least, soil freezing is moderate, and snow melt is slowest; under hardwoods and open coniferous forests snow is deepest, soil freezing is prevented or reduced to a minimum, and the rate of snow melt is moderate; in cleared areas snow depths are intermediate, soil freezing is at its maximum, and snow melt is rapid. On a watershed having different types of cover, the varying rates of melting favor lower flood peaks than would occur if one type of cover prevailed.

REDUCING THE FLOOD HAZARD FROM SNOW MELT

Large quantities of accumulated snow, rapid rates of melting during periods of warm, moist winds, and frozen soil or ice layers that interfere with infiltration appear to be the most important factors tending to increase the flood hazard. Since all of these factors are affected by the type of vegetative cover, the flood hazard can be reduced by using an arrangement and distribution of cover types which under local climatic and topographic conditions will tend to regulate the discharge resulting from snow melt.

LAND USE IN FLOOD CONTROL

By ARTHUR C. RINGLAND and OTTO E. GUTHE [18]

PROPER land use can help to reduce the flood hazard. The choice of measures for accomplishing this end is influenced by the frequency and intensity of rainstorms, the length of the growing season, the slope of the land, and the qualities of the soil. One of the first tasks in any upstream program for flood reduction is to evaluate, for individual drainage basins, the adaptability and effectiveness of various recognized land use practices specifically for reducing flood damage, even though the direct agricultural benefits of many of these practices already have been clearly established as practical for soil and water conservation.

Protection from destructive flood flows is now recognized by Congress as a responsibility of the Federal Government in cooperation with State and local public agencies (*31*). Envisaged as a coordinated approach to the problem is the control of whole drainage basins by major engineering works on the arterial channels, by the planning and zoning of the occupied natural flood courses and plains, and by improved land use practices and other conservation measures for control of headwaters. Each large drainage area is made up of numerous component catchment basins with diverse climatic, physiographic, and edaphic conditions which present individual problems. The need for solving these problems is urgent, since Congress has authorized and directed the appraisal of several hundred drainage basins for flood-control purposes.

On a number of these basins the War Department has completed its surveys and is actively engaged in the construction of major engineering works, such as storage reservoirs, flood walls, levees, and channel improvements on arterial rivers and primary tributaries; while as a complement to these downstream works, the Department of Agriculture is preparing to undertake auxiliary measures of minor channel engineering, soil-surface engineering, soil treatment, and land use adjustments in headwater areas (*28*). These measures are designed to protect and further the effectiveness of downstream engineering works, by retarding run-off and decreasing the rates of siltation; to reduce the deposition of erosional debris in river channels and on productive bottom land; and to curb the run-off contributed by tributaries not affected by storage reservoirs.

POSSIBILITIES AND LIMITATIONS OF LAND USE IN FLOOD CONTROL

Although the rates of soil erosion and surface run-off depend in part upon the configuration of the land surface and the nature of the soil, they are also influenced by the ways in which the land is managed, including the uses to which it is put and the cropping, grazing, and forestry practices employed. Vegetative and mechanical measures, designed for the dual purpose of soil and water conservation, increase the amount of storm water that is absorbed by the soil and stored on

[18] Arthur C. Ringland is Special Assistant, Flood Control Coordination, and Otto E. Guthe is Senior Soil Conservationist, Climatic and Physiographic Division, Office of Research, Soil Conservation Service.

the land. These measures include crop rotation, strip cropping, terracing, contour cultivation, contour ridging, contour furrowing, rotation grazing, reforestation, and many others. Experimental evidence has proved each of these measures to be effective under specific climatic or physiographic conditions. An essential feature of all of them is an effective vegetation cover or favorable soil-surface conditions.

The character of the vegetation, as reflected in its composition, height, density, and luxuriance, is governed by soil and weather conditions, method of planting, and field operations. Land uses and cropping practices that give the maximum plant cover within the climatic and physical limitations and the economic requirements of an area are the most effective ones for reducing flood flows. A dense vegetation cover provides a canopy that intercepts a portion of the rainfall and returns it to the air by evaporation without permitting it to reach the ground. This same canopy also breaks the impact of the rain on the ground, thereby retarding soil dispersion and the clogging of the pores in the soil. Stems and fallen leaves of plants obstruct the overland flow of water and in combination with roots furnish an important means of soil stabilization. Furthermore, between storms, vegetative growth tends to deplete the moisture in the soil and so increases its capacity to absorb storm water that would otherwise contribute to stream flow.

Tillage along the contour on slopes will increase the detention of storm water on the land surface, but continued cultivation has the disadvantage of lowering infiltration rates by destroying the soil structure. This can be counteracted in some degree by the addition of organic matter. Any loosening of the surface soil generally makes it more susceptible to erosion when surface run-off does occur and is also conducive to the clogging of soil pores.

The effectiveness of a given set of land use conditions in reducing run-off depends upon the weather sequence prior to a rainstorm and the intensity and duration of the storm itself. The rate at which water can be absorbed is governed not only by the soil texture and structure but also by the amount of water in the soil. Because the noncapillary pores are open to considerable depths after extended dry periods, the storm water has free entry. However, if as a result of previous storms the soil is in a saturated condition at the time of a rain, the intake of water is impeded because the soil pores are filled with water and with soil particles washed in from the surface. Weather conditions during a dry period preceding a storm also have a controlling influence on evaporation and transpiration, both directly by determining the evaporation rates from ground and plant surfaces, and indirectly by regulating plant growth and so controlling the surface area from which transpiration can take place. It is during these periods without appreciable rainfall that soil-moisture deficiencies develop.

Of equal importance is the intensity of rain at any time during the storm. When the intensity of rainfall at the ground exceeds the rate of infiltration into the soil, water begins to collect on the surface and then to run off. Thus direct run-off may occur even from soil with a low moisture content when it has an inherently low infiltration rate or when the rainfall intensity is exceptionally high.

Abundant experimental data clearly show the general relationships of land use practices to surface run-off and soil erosion, but they cannot be used for quantitative comparison until they are analyzed in terms of the storm intensities, soil conditions, and stages and densities of vegetative growth associated with the observations. Since most experiments have been conducted on small plots and catchment areas of less than 1 acre to only a few acres in size, the cumulative effect of the diverse conditions found on large drainage basins is merely suggested by the results obtained.

Land use has definite limitations as a factor in reducing the flood hazard. In common with all control measures, upstream improvement is practical only insofar as the cost does not exceed the value of the individual and social benefits to be attained. In some localities, unfavorable slopes and soils restrict the use of corrective measures. Elsewhere, the resistance of human beings to change may be a barrier to proper land use. Complete cooperation by landowners is seldom attainable, nor can the sustained private maintenance of corrective measures on the land be unconditionally guaranteed. However, experience in areas where such measures have been applied indicates that landowners generally do continue to maintain them.

Occasionally, forces beyond the control of man may combine to create floods of unusual magnitude. General rains caused by moist maritime air flowing over a cold continental air mass and falling without interruption for several days on saturated, frozen, or snow-covered ground may produce major floods. Some of these that were most disastrous to industrial, residential, and rural areas, like the Ohio River flood in 1937, have been the result of such widespread storms. Also, destructive flash floods are sometimes inevitable after sudden rainstorms of high intensity on small drainage basins with pronounced slopes. The value of land use measures would be largely obscured by the overwhelming force of such unusual combinations of flood-producing factors.

At other times, however, proper land use measures may be relied upon with confidence to retard the run-off contributed by numerous small tributaries and so to reduce the concentration of floodwater in the larger streams. The effectiveness of headwaters control has been successfully demonstrated in the Alps of France, Switzerland, Austria, and Italy, where land use treatments and upstream engineering have curbed surface run-off after storms, floodwater velocities of feeder tributaries of steep gradient, riverbank erosion, and the movement of sediment and debris carried by the swollen streams (*9, 32*).[19]

An evaluation of the extent to which readjustments in land use can be counted upon to reduce the flood hazard is beset with difficulties. The distribution, intensity, and duration of precipitation can be measured adequately by a network of recording rain gages or, in regions of heavy snowfall, by snow surveys. Similarly, the relative capacities of different soils to absorb water and of various land treatments to reduce surface run-off and soil erosion are being determined by experimental research. Much of the value of vegetation for head-

[19] See also:

RINGLAND, ARTHUR C. NOTES ON REFORESTATION AND ENGINEERING IN THE FRENCH ALPS. U. S. Forest Serv., Serv. Bul. 17 (23): 3–4. 1933. (Abstract from report, La Restauration des Alpes, of Inspector-General M. P. Mougin to the Ministry of Agriculture of France, 1931.) [Mimeographed.]

RINGLAND, ARTHUR C. NOTES ON SOIL EROSION AND REFORESTATION IN ITALY: SUGGESTIONS FOR AMERICAN APPLICATION. U. S. Forest Serv. 12 pp., illus. 1934. [Mimeographed.]

waters control in humid regions, however, lies in its function of diminishing, or at times even eliminating, storm contributions to run-off. Transpiration preceding rainfall depletes the soil moisture and increases the capacity of the soil to retain storm water. This function of vegetation cannot be correctly evaluated until measurements are available of the amount of moisture returned to the atmosphere from the land surface and from different types of vegetative growth under various climatic conditions. Within the last year notable progress has been made through the development of an inexpensive method, previously described in this article and now in use experimentally, for securing measurements of combined evaporation and transpiration from natural surfaces (*39*).

The study of overland flow and the concentration of excess water from land surfaces into tributary drainageways and subsequently into trunk streams has progressed slowly because of the complexity of the problem. Within a single drainage basin there may be great variations in rainfall intensity, soil condition, slope, vegetation or land use, and drainage-pattern density—that is, the number of streams in a given area. Lack of information on the interrelation of these variables makes it difficult to apply experimental data showing the relations of different land use practices to run-off from small areas to the calculation of the volume of surface run-off from large drainage basins.[20]

SURVEYS AND RESEARCH UNDER WAY

At present the Department of Agriculture is conducting surveys in many flood-producing areas of the United States for the purpose of securing estimates of the probable reductions in flood flows and sedimentation which could be effected through improved land use practices and minor engineering works. The techniques utilized for making such estimates and for determining benefits therefrom have varied with the surveys.

Basically, the procedures have had much in common. First, an analysis is made of the flood-producing storms that have been experienced on or near the drainage area. The drainage basin is then divided into minor drainage units for which land treatments, readjustments in use, and minor engineering works suitable for recommendation are planned. Run-off and erosion values for the existing and proposed practices are secured from detailed measurements in the field and at experiment stations having similar physical conditions. These values, however, must be adjusted on the basis of past experience to allow for the modifying influence of overland flow. Only then can they be used in association with theoretical storm occurrences for calculating the probable reductions in flood crests and sedimentation. To estimate the benefits to be secured downstream from upstream corrective measures, studies are made of the damage resulting from overflow and deposition of debris and silt from floods of different magnitudes. After the effectiveness of the various proposed upstream improvements has been determined on the basis of the survey findings, they are considered in relation to the downstream investigations or

[20] Bernard (*2*) has developed a method which, in theory, combines and routes the flow from each of the many component units of a watershed, each unit being assigned the hydrograph secured by experimentation on identical site conditions. He thereby secures a hydrograph of flow at the outlet of the watershed.

construction plans of the War Department to determine the most satisfactory control program for the project as a whole.

Although these surveys represent a concerted attempt to evaluate existing and recommended land use practices as measures for reducing the flood hazard, the complexity of the problem and the lack of precedent for solving it call for additional research which will result in a clearer understanding of the ways in which the many conditioning factors of a single drainage basin combine to regulate the flow of water from the area.

In time, improved land use management will not only become progressively more effective as a supplement to engineering works in reducing flood hazards but also will greatly help to maintain agriculture in a more stable condition. It should be noted that downstream flood-control measures likewise serve multiple purposes. Major engineering works may be designed to permit navigation, irrigation, or the production of power; while zoning of flood plains to prevent unwise occupancy may release areas for forestry, wildlife, or recreational use.

FLOOD FORECASTING

By Merrill Bernard [21]

At 10 a. m. on January 27, 1937, floodwaters marked the highest stage in the 65 years of record on the Ohio River at Louisville, Ky., submerging the gage on the riverbank to a little more than the 57-foot mark, 29 feet above flood stage. A view of Louisville on January 25 is shown in figure 11. Immediate concern was centered upon the reported water levels upstream at Cincinnati, Parkersburg, and Pittsburgh; but in fact the first scene of the impending flood had

[21] Merrill Bernard is Supervising Hydrologist, Weather Bureau.

Figure 11.—Louisville, Ky., under floodwaters, January 25, 1937.

298737°—41——37 +

been laid more than a month before in remote tropical and polar source regions of warm-damp and cold-dry air masses.

What circumstances combined to bring the river to the particular stage of 57.15 feet at Louisville? The forecaster's answer had to be a quantitative evaluation of the immediately determinable forces that transported inland, precipitated, and finally concentrated the myriad of water particles within the narrow dimensions of the Ohio River flood channel during the nearly 30 days of almost continuous rainfall from December 28, 1936, to January 25, 1937.

CAUSES AND RESULTS OF FLOODS

A flood is the temporary unbalance in nature that results when more water is supplied to the land in the form of precipitation than can be absorbed by the land itself and its vegetation or retained in natural reservoirs and man-made works for providing storage. The localized effect is the rapid rise of the water to and above the in-bank capacity of the channel reach, often with accompanying inundation of fertile and highly developed valley areas.

The cost of a flood to a community includes these principal items: (1) Loss of human life; (2) danger to the public health; (3) damage to movable property; (4) damage to immovable property; and (5) intangible losses, such as disruption of business and transportation. An accurate and timely forecast of an impending flood should eliminate the first, materially reduce the second and third, to some extent reduce the fourth by providing an opportunity to protect the less vulnerable areas, and help to decrease the fifth class of damage.

White (*44*) has presented graphically estimates of flood losses in the United States. In figure 12, the distribution of loss is shown geographically. It is seen that the greatest loss is confined to the Mississippi Valley, with the Atlantic and Gulf coasts also suffering appreciable damage. In figure 13 the flood loss is shown by class and regional division. By far the greatest of the losses subject to classification are those of property—largely buildings, highways, and railroads.

THE PROBLEM OF FLOOD FORECASTING

Facts contradicting the prevailing idea that the occurrence of floods is confined to a well-defined "flood season" are shown in table 7. Of the 168 months in the period 1924 to 1937, inclusive, only 15 did not bring to some locality a flood of damaging proportions.

TABLE 7.—*Loss of life and property from floods in the United States, 1924–37, inclusive*

Month	Property loss	Lives lost	Month	Property loss	Lives lost
	Dollars	*Number*		*Dollars*	*Number*
January	429,579,704	192	September	29,017,359	40
February	11,668,111	6	October	29,295,960	6
March	182,037,019	81	November	51,816,720	94
April	421,758,397	359	December	22,759,787	27
May	62,428,287	170			
June	106,685,176	158	Monthly average	8,515,000	7
July	56,678,606	104			
August	26,821,341	28	Annual average	102,182,000	90

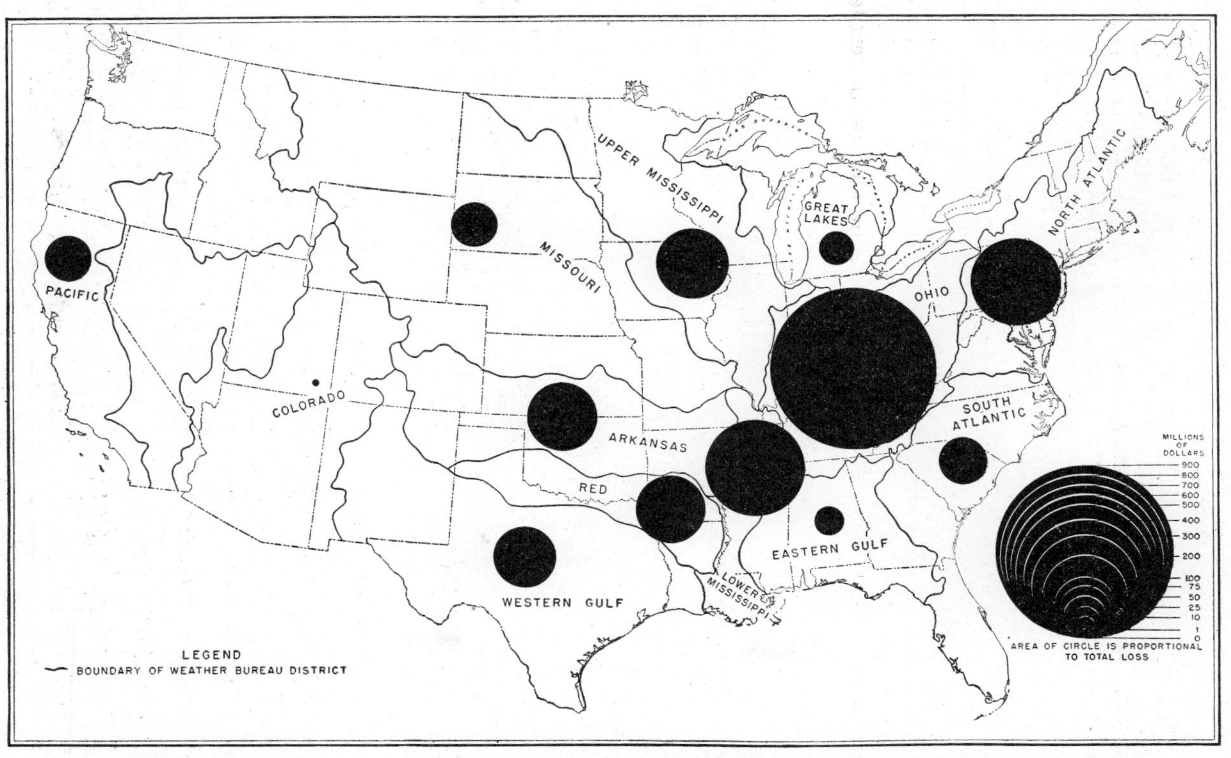

FIGURE 12.—Distribution of estimated flood losses in the United States, by regional divisions, July 1, 1902, to December 31, 1937.

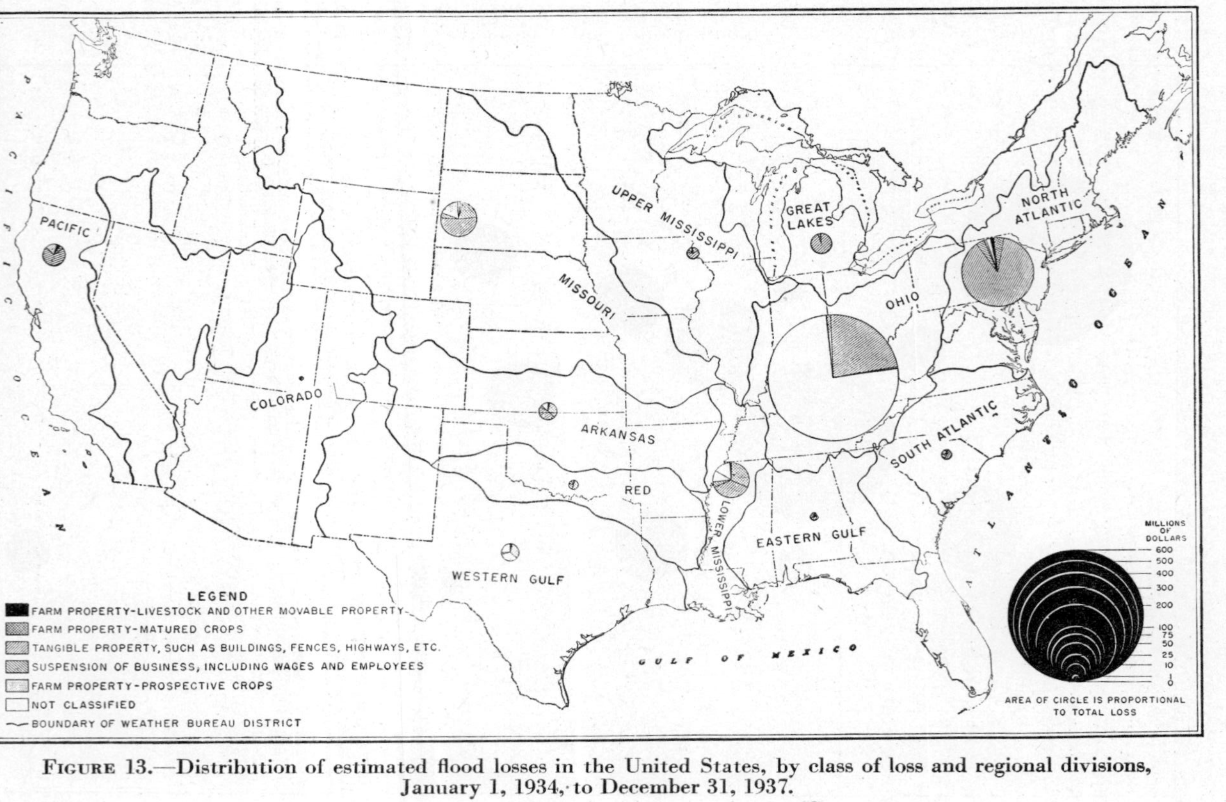

FIGURE 13.—Distribution of estimated flood losses in the United States, by class of loss and regional divisions, January 1, 1934, to December 31, 1937.

The complexity of the problem of forecasting the individual flood is seen in figure 14, *A*, in which the principal factors and their relationships are shown diagrammatically. To observe, record, transmit, receive, tabulate, and analyze the data representing them demands a closely organized service characterized by unremitting alertness, dependability of communications, simplicity of method, and the fortified judgment of trained and experienced personnel. The functional outline of such a service is shown in figure 14, *B*.

The flood forecast, to be effective, must be accurate and timely. Accuracy will depend on the adequacy of the data and the flexibility of the method of forecasting, which should provide for the use of the greatest number of determinable factors. The period of forecast (the interval between the time of issuance and the time of arrival of the forecast stage or flood crest) will depend upon the promptness with which data are assembled, organized, and translated into terms of

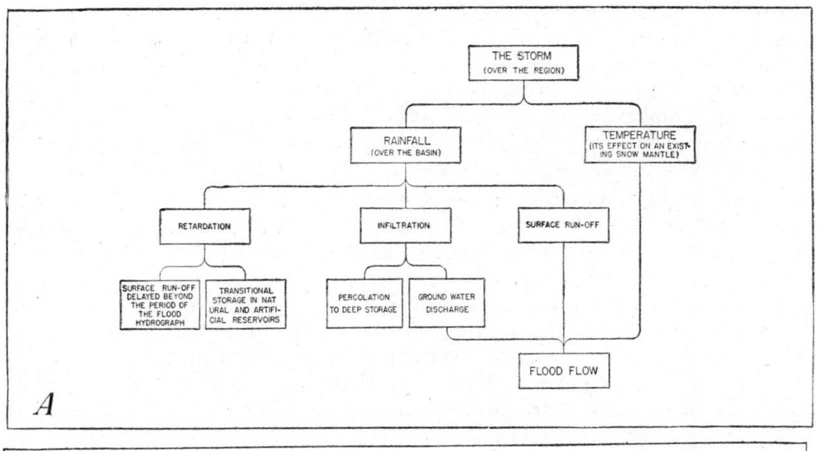

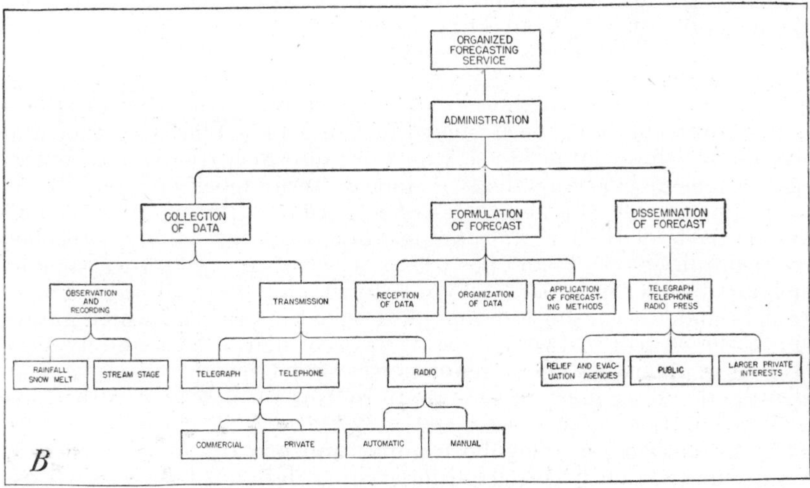

FIGURE 14.—*A*, Factors involved in flood forecasting; *B*, functional outline of a forecasting service.

flood discharge and stage. A 6-hour reporting period is proving to be of workable length on river systems of intermediate size. This allows 2 to 3 hours for the reception of data and 3 to 4 hours for the formulation and dissemination of the forecasts. Rainfall reports are so organized that the distribution of average depth for each 6-hour period over the principal tributary basins can be determined rapidly by mechanical and graphical methods. River-stage reports, received periodically, serve as indices of run-off conditions and also aid in progressively plotting the flood hydrograph as it develops.

THE FLOOD-FORECASTING SERVICE AND HOW IT OPERATES

In the United States the flood-forecasting service to the public is conducted by the Weather Bureau. This service has been continuous on the larger rivers since 1892. The work is administered and the service rendered through 73 river forecasting districts serving nearly 1,000 cities, towns, and communities. It is hoped that the service can ultimately group the river districts by major river basins in order more effectively to coordinate the forecasting procedure between districts.

The service, conducted so long as an established function of the Weather Bureau, is not spectacular in character and is taken by the public as a matter of course. Its difficulties are not generally realized. Inadequate facilities for gathering data on rainfall and stream flow impose an undue dependence upon the personal judgment of the forecaster; failure of communications with outlying reporting stations in critical periods immeasurably increases the difficulties of accurate prediction. With a staff designed only to meet the routine needs of the city, the Weather Bureau Office in Pittsburgh, during the peak of the flood of March 1936, answered nearly 8,000 telephone inquires in 1 day. The task of handling such inquiries, together with tremendous pressure for advance information from public agencies and private industrial interests, creates a situation far from conducive to efficient forecasting.

The factors involved in the typical headwater or tributary forecasting problem have been shown in figure 14. The collection and assembly of these data require a network of observational and reporting stations of varying density and pattern depending largely on the physiographic characteristics of the region. In the more mountainous parts of the country the network is limited to points reached by telegraph or telephone lines where observer-reporters are available. Such an observer is usually a layman to whom a nominal wage is paid. He acts under a carefully prepared, detailed instruction which guides him in the care of instruments and the recording of data and fixes the interval of reporting, the circumstances under which reporting shall begin, and the primary and alternate routing of messages to the forecasting center.

Communication systems, both public and private, must be utilized to the fullest in gathering flood-forecasting data. The organized use of radio amateurs has provided security against wire-line failure. Service-operated radio networks, including both automatic and manual transmission types, are demonstrating their effectiveness and dependability in several parts of the country.

The simplest method of forecasting is that based upon stage relations, an estimated future river stage at any point being reflected more or less consistently by the prevailing stage at a point upstream. This method meets conditions on the lower reaches of the larger rivers where stage relations are usually stable and distances are sufficiently great to provide time for action after the forecasts have been issued. The limitations of the method when applied to tributary or headwater streams are obvious. Among them are the increasing instability of stream flow with steepening slope; the impossibility of accurately combining converging flows expressed in terms of stage; the relatively short concentration period characteristic of headwater streams; and the difficulty of correcting for lateral inflow between river stations.

Under headwater conditions the forecast, to be at all effective, must be projected from the time of falling rain. In northern latitudes and in the West, run-off from melting snow must be taken into account. Seasonal, day-by-day, and even hourly changes in ground surface conditions, as they affect the infiltration capacity of the soil, must be evaluated.

In formulating the forecast, there is need, as figure 14 indicates, to anticipate progressively throughout the course of a flood-producing storm the amount, duration, and sequence of a number of meteorologic and hydrologic factors and their combinations. These embrace the hydrologic cycle from the embryo storm, in the form of converging air masses of critical character and proportions, through rainfall and run-off, to stream flow. With limited sources of data and equally limited knowledge of the formation and character of storms, rainfall cannot now be forecast quantitatively with great accuracy or consistency. Full use can, however, be made of existing meteorological and aerological services as outposts against the unheralded approach of flood-producing storms.

The stage is set for a flood during the period preceding that of heaviest rainfall, when conditions develop that establish the degree of imperviousness of the ground surface. This period varies with locality, season, and the nature of soil and cover. During the summer months, relatively high rates of evaporation and transpiration result in near-maximum infiltration capacities of the soil. The flow in the smaller streams is reduced to that wholly supplied from groundwater sources. Under these conditions, considerable quantities of rain can fall without creating flows of flood proportions.

Preparing for the Danger Season

In contrast are the conditions of late winter and early spring. A snow mantle of high water content may cover the basin, or moderate but prolonged rains may have reduced the infiltration capacity of the soil to a minimum. Evaporation is usually negligible and the demands of vegetation low. Under these conditions, the initial flow in the streams, being fed more rapidly from the raised water table, may be relatively high.

These considerations suggest that flows from selected subbasins can be used as run-off indices to evaluate surface conditions and to determine the amounts of rainfall that will be absorbed by the land through infiltration. A successful forecasting procedure therefore should include a systematic means of assembling at the forecasting center throughout the possible flood season a day-by-day evaluation of surface conditions in terms of stream discharge from watersheds selected as typical of the basin.

As winter draws to a close, indications of the approaching flood season become apparent. A heavy snow mantle may envelop the upper portions of the more critical flood-producing tributary basins and show a tendency to release large quantities of run-off water with the gradually rising temperature typical of the season. Or abnormally persistent late-winter rains may have fallen to build up the ground-water table and reduce to a minimum the absorptive capacity of the soil.

At the forecasting center located on one of the larger rivers, these developments will manifest themselves in a gradually rising water level which is registered at the gaging station located on the bank of the river. Advices received from the forecasters at stations upstream will become the basis for the forecast of the flood crest. Because of the tendency for floods to travel more slowly in the larger rivers, the downstream forecaster will have opportunity to predetermine his flood peak with timeliness and precision.

The forecaster at the headwater station, however, does not enjoy the same degree of security to be found at the lower river station. At the former there are only a comparatively few hours between the time when the flood crest is discernible in the upper reaches of the stream and its arrival at the city or town for which the forecasting service is rendered. To provide adequate preparation for an impending flood, the headwater forecaster must go beyond upstream river stage and resort to rainfall as the basis for his forecast. To fortify himself he must keep in close touch with the weather forecaster, who will inform him of changing weather conditions and will advise him of the amounts of rain to be expected. The observers attending rainfall-reporting stations have been instructed to acquaint themselves with conditions of snow mantle and ground surface over the basin. With the beginning of heavy rainfall these observers report by telegraph or telephone the amount of rain that has fallen every 6 hours. The forecaster then applies his forecasting techniques, which take into account not only the rainfall but the infiltration capacity of the soil, the run-off to be expected from melting snow, and the physiographic characteristics of his basin, which have much to do with the shape of the flood hydrograph (graph showing the height of water as it varies with time) and the rapidity with which it will reach a peak.

An Example of Headwater Forecasting

Consider as an example the forecast center that has the responsibility of issuing forecasts for Millville, W. Va., on the Shenandoah River. Figure 15 shows graphically the sequence of events associated with the storm and flood of January 29–February 3, 1939.

Previously determined rainfall and stream-flow relations for the basin indicate an initial run-off coefficient of about 10 percent (that is, 10 percent of the rainfall ran off into the stream). The increase in value of this factor as the storm progressed is shown in the figures. In the latter stages of the storm 75 percent of the rain that fell reached the stream as surface run-off.

The situation as portrayed in the weather map for 7:30 a. m., January 28, pointed to an outbreak of precipitation in the west Gulf area moving northeastward toward the Appalachian region.

At 7:30 p. m. on the 28th there were indications of a rapid northeastward movement of a well-defined tongue of moist air accompanied by copious rainfall.

Another area of cyclonic action becoming evident at that time lay off the south Atlantic coast and was producing rainfall in the Carolinas and on the Georgia coast.

At 7:30 a. m., January 29, the principal area of precipitation had entered the Appalachian region. Rains continued along the south Atlantic coast. The outlook then indicated the threat of flood and the necessity for preparedness at the forecasting center.

Weather conditions at 7:30 p. m. confirmed the forecaster's judgment as to the seriousness of the situation, warranted a call for general reporting from rainfall stations throughout the basin, and justified the issuance of cautionary warnings. An estimate was made of rainfall to be expected in the next 6-hour period, and this was used in the preliminary computation of flood flow.

The material in the hands of the forecaster, period by period, is given in figure 15. From rainfall up to 7:30 a. m. of the 30th it was possible to formulate an approximate forecast of the peak stage. This was modified from data received at the end of the rainfall period, 1:30 a. m., January 31. However, at 7:30 a. m., January 31, the situation was complicated by a region of cyclonic action which was developing over the Great Basin and the far Southwest.

At 7:30 p. m. of January 31 the further development and movement of this secondary disturbance presented a potential threat to the Appalachian region, particularly since it followed so closely an appreciable rise in the Shenandoah.

The rains anticipated on January 31 had materialized over the basin by the morning of February 2, the greatest amount falling between 7:30 a. m. and 1:30 p. m. of the 3d.

It can be seen that a forecast of the peak stage was possible at 1:30 p. m., February 3, approximately 40 hours in advance of the arrival of the crest at Millville. Six hours later, at 7:30 p. m., February 3, after rainfall had stopped, this forecast was confirmed and refined as shown in figure 15, affording reasonable opportunity for the evacuation and protection of low-lying areas in the vicinity of Millville.

COMMUNITY RESPONSIBILITY IN FLOOD PREPAREDNESS

It is the community's task through concerted public action to maintain an alert awareness of the flood hazard and to educate the public to the advantages and economies of flood preparedness. It is also the community's responsibility to develop well-organized plans for action during floods, and this is best accomplished through prearranged cooperation with the American Red Cross and the Corps of Engineers of the United States Army.

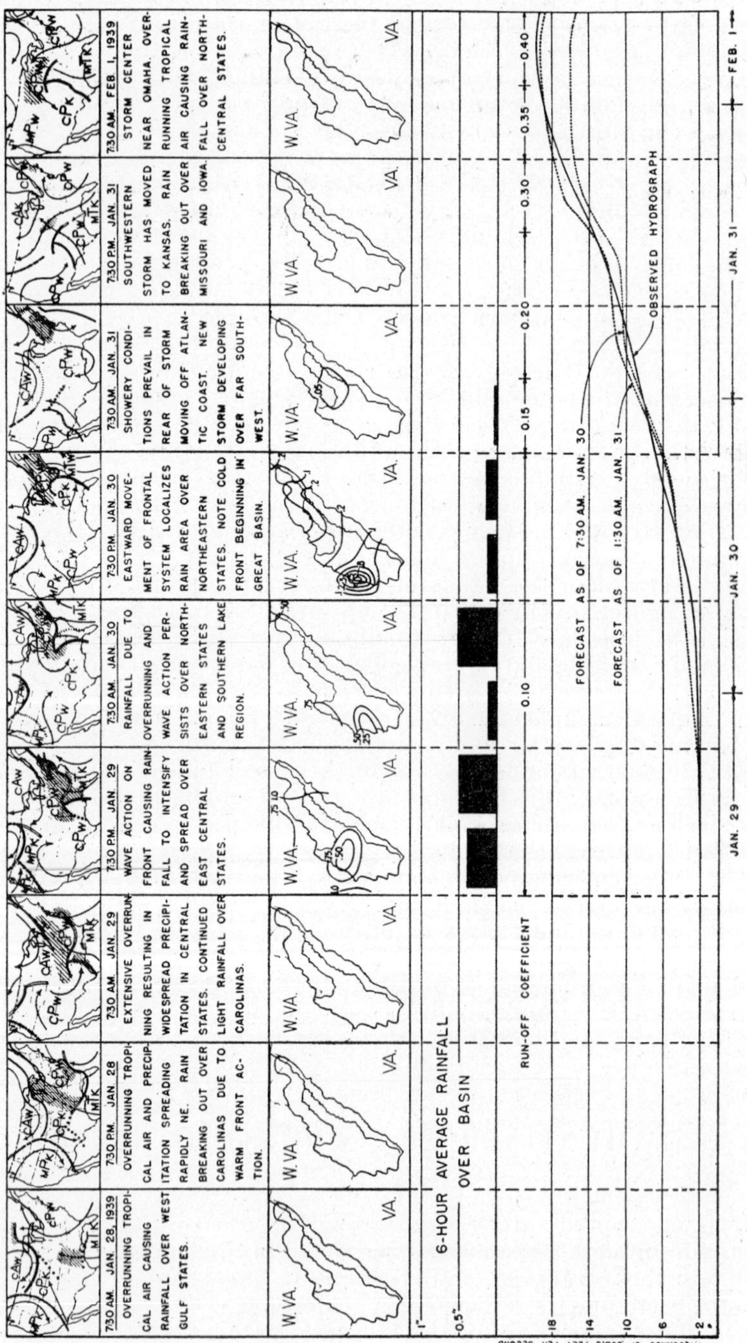

7:30 A.M. JAN. 28, 1939
OVERRUNNING TROPICAL AIR CAUSING RAINFALL OVER WEST GULF STATES.

7:30 P.M. JAN. 28
OVERRUNNING TROPICAL AIR AND PRECIPITATION SPREADING RAPIDLY NE. RAIN BREAKING OUT OVER CAROLINAS DUE TO WARM FRONT ACTION.

7:30 A.M. JAN. 29
EXTENSIVE OVERRUNNING RESULTING IN WIDESPREAD PRECIPITATION IN CENTRAL STATES. CONTINUED LIGHT RAINFALL OVER CAROLINAS.

7:30 P.M. JAN. 29
WAVE ACTION ON FRONT CAUSING RAINFALL TO INTENSIFY AND SPREAD OVER EAST CENTRAL STATES.

7:30 A.M. JAN. 30
RAINFALL DUE TO OVERRUNNING AND WAVE ACTION PERSISTS OVER NORTHEASTERN STATES AND SOUTHERN LAKE REGION.

7:30 P.M. JAN. 30
EASTWARD MOVEMENT OF FRONTAL SYSTEM LOCALIZES RAIN AREA OVER NORTHEASTERN STATES. NOTE COLD FRONT BEGINNING IN GREAT BASIN.

7:30 A.M. JAN. 31
SHOWERY CONDITIONS PREVAIL IN REAR OF STORM MOVING OFF ATLANTIC COAST. NEW STORM DEVELOPING OVER FAR SOUTHWEST.

7:30 P.M. JAN. 31
SOUTHWESTERN STORM HAS MOVED TO KANSAS. RAIN BREAKING OUT OVER MISSOURI AND IOWA.

7:30 A.M. FEB. 1, 1939
STORM CENTER NEAR OMAHA. OVERRUNNING TROPICAL AIR CAUSING RAINFALL OVER NORTH-CENTRAL STATES.

W. VA. VA.

6-HOUR AVERAGE RAINFALL OVER BASIN

1" 0.5"

RUN-OFF COEFFICIENT 0.10 0.15 0.20 0.30 0.35 0.40

THOUSANDS OF CUBIC FEET PER SECOND

18 14 10 6 2

FORECAST AS OF 7:30 A.M. JAN. 30

FORECAST AS OF 1:30 A.M. JAN. 31

OBSERVED HYDROGRAPH

JAN. 29 JAN. 30 JAN. 31 FEB. 1

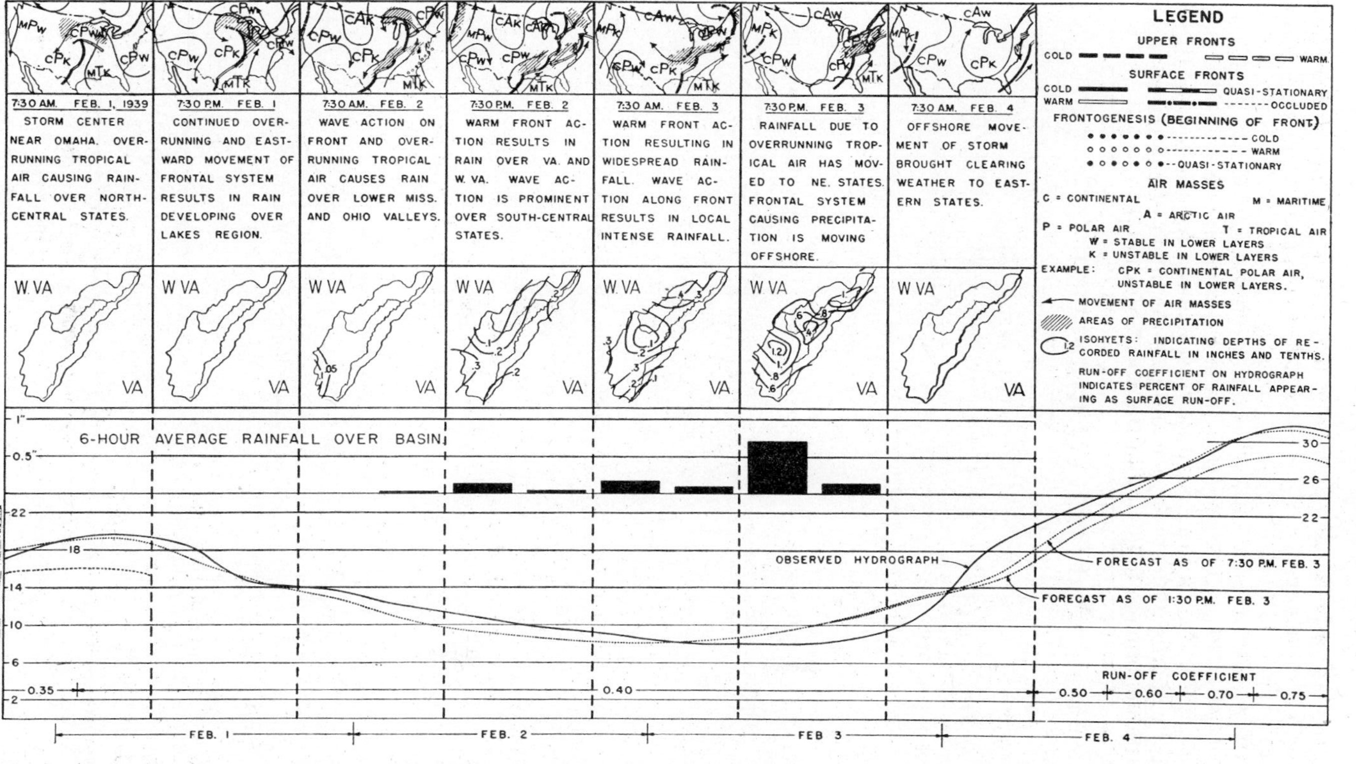

FIGURE 15.—Illustration of an improved method of headwater forecasting. Under the weather maps at the top are given the weather reports received by the forecaster every 12 hours. The river valley maps show amounts of rainfall every 12 hours. Below the maps, the hydrograph of the Shenandoah River at Millville, W. Va., shows the forecasts of river conditions compared with the actual conditions as they occurred.

"If we had only known in time . . ." "If we had only taken advantage of the warning . . ." are heard as a mournful echo after each disastrous flood.

The Weather Bureau, with a real appreciation of the limitations of its present facilities, has set about to so improve its river- and flood-forecasting service as to remove the justification for the first of these excuses, which is admittedly accountable for much of the misery and preventable damage following in the wake of a flood.

LITERATURE CITED

(1) Atkinson, H. B., and Bay, Clyde E.
1940. SOME FACTORS AFFECTING FROST PENETRATION: A SUMMARY. Amer. Geophys. Union Trans. 1940, pt. 1, p. 121. (Original paper presented by J. E. Church at the Western Interstate Snow-Survey Conference, Palo Alto, Calif., 9 pp., illus.)

(2) Bernard, Merrill.
1937. GIVING AREAL SIGNIFICANCE TO HYDROLOGIC RESEARCH ON SMALL AREAS. *In* Headwaters Control and Use, Upstream Engin. Conf., 1936, pp. 50–75, illus.

(3) ———
1938. HYDROMETEOROLOGY—A COORDINATION OF METEOROLOGY AND HYDROLOGY. Amer. Geophys. Union Trans. 19 (2): 598–602, illus.

(4) Blumenstock, David I.
1939. RAINFALL CHARACTERISTICS AS RELATED TO SOIL EROSION. U. S. Dept. Agr. Tech. Bul. 698, 44 pp., illus.

(5) Brückner, Ed.
1905. DIE BILANZ DES KREISLAUFS DES WASSERS AUF DER ERDE. Geog. Ztschr. 11: 436–445.

(6) Church, J. E., Jr.
1912. THE CONSERVATION OF SNOW. ITS DEPENDENCE ON FORESTS AND MOUNTAINS. Sci. Amer. Sup. 74: 152–155, illus.

(7) Clyde, George D.
1931. SNOW-MELTING CHARACTERISTICS. Utah Agr. Expt. Sta. Tech. Bul. 231, 47 pp., illus.

(8) Follansbee, Robert.
1934. EVAPORATION FROM RESERVOIR SURFACES. Amer. Soc. Civ. Engin. Trans. 99: 704–715.

(9) [France] Direction des Eaux et Forêts.
1911. RESTAURATION ET CONSERVATION DES TERRAINS EN MONTAGNE. 3 v., illus. Paris.

(10) Free, G. R., Browning. G. M., and Musgrave, G. W.
1940. RELATIVE INFILTRATION AND RELATED PHYSICAL CHARACTERISTICS OF CEETAIN SOILS. U. S. Dept. Agr. Tech. Bul. 729, 52 pp., illus.

(11) Grover, Nathan C.
1937. THE FLOODS OF MARCH 1936. PART 1. NEW ENGLAND RIVERS. U. S. Geol. Survey, Water-Supply Paper 798, 466 pp., illus.

(12) ———
1937. THE FLOODS OF MARCH 1936. PART 2. HUDSON RIVER TO SUSQUEHANNA RIVER REGION. U. S. Geol. Survey, Water-Supply Paper 799, 380 pp., illus.

(13) ——— and Lichtblau, Stephen.
1937. THE FLOODS OF MARCH 1936. PART 3. POTOMAC, JAMES, AND UPPER OHIO RIVERS. U. S. Geol. Survey, Water-Supply Paper 800, 351 pp., illus.

(14) Holzman, Benjamin.
1937. SOURCES OF MOISTURE FOR PRECIPITATION IN THE UNITED STATES. U. S. Dept. Agr. Tech. Bul. 589, 42 pp., illus.

(15) ———
1937. USE OF AEROLOGICAL SOUNDINGS IN DETERMINING THE SOURCES OF MOISTURE FOR PRECIPITATION. Amer. Geophys. Union Trans. 18 (2): 488–489.

(16) JAENICKE, ALEXANDER J., and FOESTER, MAX H.
1915. THE INFLUENCE OF A WESTERN YELLOW PINE FOREST ON THE ACCUMULATION AND MELTING OF SNOW. U. S. Monthly Weather Rev. 43: 115–124, illus.

(17) JEMISON, G. M.
1934. THE SIGNIFICANCE OF THE EFFECT OF STAND DENSITY UPON THE WEATHER BENEATH THE CANOPY. Jour. Forestry 32: 446–451.

(18) KITTREDGE, JOSEPH, Jr.
1938. THE MAGNITUDE AND REGIONAL DISTRIBUTION OF WATER LOSSES INFLUENCED BY VEGETATION. Jour. Forestry 36: 775–778, illus.

(19) KÖPPEN, W.
1900. VERSUCH EINER KLASSIFIKATION DER KLIMATE, VORZUGSWEISE NACH IHREN BEZIEHUNGEN ZUR PFLANZENWELT. Geog. Ztschr. 6: 593–611, 657–679.

(20) KOLLMORGEN, WALTER.
1935. RAINMAKERS ON THE PLAINS. Sci. Monthly 40: 146–152.

(21) LANG, R.
1920. VERWITTERUNG UND BODENBILDUNG ALS EINFÜHRUNG IN DIE BODENKUNDE. 188 pp., illus. Stuttgart.

(22) LIVINGSTON, BURTON E.
1938. INFLUENCES THAT AFFECT TRANSPIRATION FROM PLANT LEAVES. Sigma Xi Quart. 26: 88–101, illus.

(23) LOWDERMILK, W. C.
1930. INFLUENCE OF FOREST LITTER ON RUN-OFF, PERCOLATION, AND EROSION. Jour. Forestry 28: 474–491, illus.

(24) MARSH, GEORGE P.
1869. MAN AND NATURE; OR, PHYSICAL GEOGRAPHY AS MODIFIED BY HUMAN ACTION. 577 pp. New York.

(25) MARTONNE, EM. DE.
1926. ARÉISME ET INDICE D'ARIDITÉ. [Paris] Acad. des Sci. Compt. Rend. 182: 1395–1398.

(26) MEYER, ALFRED.
1926. ÜBER EINIGE ZUSAMMENHÄNGE ZWISCHEN KLIMA UND BODEN IN EUROPA. Chem. der Erde 2: [209]–347, illus.

(27) MUSGRAVE, G. W., and NORTON, R. A.
1937. SOIL AND WATER CONSERVATION INVESTIGATIONS AT THE SOIL CONSERVATION EXPERIMENT STATION, MISSOURI VALLEY LOESS REGION, CLARINDA, IOWA. U. S. Dept. Agr. Tech. Bul. 558, 182 pp., illus.

(28) RINGLAND, ARTHUR C.
1939. RELATION OF HEADWATERS-CONTROL TO THE NATIONAL PROGRAM OF FLOOD PROTECTION. Amer. Geophys. Union Trans. 20 (2): 203–204.

(29) ROHWER, CARL.
1934. EVAPORATION FROM DIFFERENT TYPES OF PANS. Amer. Soc. Civ. Engin. Trans. 99: 673–703, illus.

(30) ROSSBY, CARL-GUSTAF, NAMIAS, JEROME, and SIMMERS, RITCHIE G.
1938. FLUID MECHANICS APPLIED TO THE STUDY OF ATMOSPHERIC CIRCULATIONS. PART I. A STUDY OF FLOW PATTERNS WITH THE AID OF ISENTROPIC ANALYSIS. Mass. Inst. Technol. and Woods Hole Oceanographic Inst. Papers, Phys. Oceanography and Met., v. 7, No. 1, 125 pp., illus.

(31) SAVILLE, THORNDIKE.
1936. TRENDS IN A NATIONAL POLICY OF STREAM-MANAGEMENT. Amer. Geophys. Union Trans. 20: 143–154.

(32) STRELE, G.
1936. FÜNFZIG JAHRE ERFAHRUNGEN BEI DER WILDBACHVERBAUUNG IN OESTERREICH. Wasserkr. u. Wasserwirtsch. 31: 61–65, 77–80, illus.

(33) SWENSON, BENNETT.
1938. THE OHIO AND MISSISSIPPI RIVER FLOODS OF JANUARY-FEBRUARY 1937. U. S. Monthly Weather Rev. Sup. 37, 55 pp. illus.

(34) SZYMKIEWICZ, DEZYDERY.
1925. ÉTUDES CLIMATOLOGIQUE. V. COMMENT CARACTÉRISER L'HUMIDITÉ D'UN CLIMAT? Soc. Bot. Poloniae Acta 2: [239]–264, illus.

(35) Thornthwaite, C. Warren.
1931. THE CLIMATES OF NORTH AMERICA ACCORDING TO A NEW CLASSIFICATION. Geog. Rev. 21: 633–655, illus.

(36) ———
1936. THE GREAT PLAINS. *In* Goodrich, Carter, Allin, Bushrod W., Thornthwaite, C. Warren, and others, Migration and Economic Opportunity, the Report of the Study of Population Redistribution, pp. 202–250, illus. Philadelphia and London.

(37) ———
1937. THE HYDROLOGIC CYCLE REEXAMINED. U. S. Soil Conserv. Serv., Soil Conserv. 3: 85–91, illus.

(38) ———
1937. THE RELIABILITY OF RAINFALL INTENSITY-FREQUENCY DETERMINATIONS. Amer. Geophys. Union Trans. 18 (2): 476–484, illus.

(39) ——— and Holzman, Benjamin.
1939. THE DETERMINATION OF EVAPORATION FROM LAND AND WATER SURFACES. U. S. Monthly Weather Rev. 67: 4–11, illus.

(40) Transeau, Edgar N.
1905. FOREST CENTERS OF EASTERN AMERICA. Amer. Nat. 39: 875–889, illus.

(41) Veihmeyer, F. J.
1938. EVAPORATION FROM SOILS AND TRANSPIRATION. Amer. Geophys. Union Trans. 19: 612–619, illus.

(42) Ward, Robert De Courcy.
[1925.] THE CLIMATES OF THE UNITED STATES. 518 pp., illus. Boston, New York, [etc.].

(43) Welton, F. A., and Wilson, J. D.
1938. COMPARATIVE RATES OF WATER LOSS FROM SOIL, TURF, AND WATER SURFACES. Ohio Agr. Expt. Sta. Bimo. Bul. 23: 13–16.

(44) White, Gilbert F.
1939. ECONOMIC ASPECTS OF FLOOD-FORECASTING. Amer. Geophys. Union Trans. 20 (2): 218–233, illus.

(45) Wüst, Georg.
1922. VERDUNSTUNG UND NIEDERSCHLAG AUF DER ERDE. [Berlin] Gesell. f. Erdk. Ztschr. 1922 (1–2): 35–43.

How the Daily Forecast is Made

By C. L. Mitchell and H. Wexler [1]

MAKING the daily weather forecast is a highly expert job. Gradually the guesswork and the art have been reduced, and the process has become more and more scientific. To show how it is done, this article takes a single forecast made on a day in March 1939, gives some of the data the forecaster had available, and tells how he used it to predict what the weather would be during the next day over an area covering 16 States. This particular example was chosen because it was an "easy" one, though it may not seem so to the general reader.

[1] C. L. Mitchell is Principal Meteorologist and Forecaster and H. Wexler is Associate Meteorologist, Weather Bureau.

The forecasts of the weather to be expected during the next few days, issued daily by the Weather Bureau of the United States and the meteorological services of other countries, are made on the basis of the fact that existing weather conditions travel constantly, changing more or less as they move. By making observations of the weather simultaneously at a large number of places distributed over as large a part of the earth's surface as possible, transmitting them immediately to a central station, and there preparing from them a map showing the existing weather over a particular region, it is possible to estimate how these existing conditions will move and change and hence what weather will be experienced in different areas in the immediate future.

For this purpose the United States Weather Bureau maintains about 350 stations distributed over the country. Observations from which to prepare maps and diagrams of many different kinds are taken simultaneously at these stations, and in addition reports are received from many places in Canada, Mexico, Central America, and the West Indies, from scores of ships at sea, from islands in the Pacific and Atlantic Oceans, and from the continents of Europe, Asia, and Africa. The data that are collected and charted include not only information about temperature, barometric pressure, wind, rain, and other conditions at the surface of the earth, but also reports obtained from soundings of the atmosphere up to altitudes of several miles at a large number of stations.

This organization has grown from small beginnings more than 70 years ago, when the Signal Corps of the United States Army inaugurated a meteorological service in response to the demand created by the success of pioneer efforts on the part of Cleveland Abbe to conduct such a service at the Cincinnati Observatory. The fact that weather conditions travel over the surface of the earth had been indicated more than a hundred years earlier by Benjamin Franklin's discovery in 1743 that a storm experienced at Philadelphia in September of that year moved eastward across the country and was confirmed by subsequent studies on the part of many investigators during the eighteenth and nineteenth centuries.

After the invention of the electric telegraph, many saw the possibility of forecasting the weather by the obvious and simple process of telegraphing ahead what was coming. The synoptic map prepared from observations taken simultaneously at a network of stations over a large region, showing the weather conditions over this region at the time of the observations, was introduced early in the nineteenth century. Daily telegraphic maps were first issued in the United States by the Smithsonian Institution beginning in 1850, only 5 years after the opening of the first commercial telegraph line. France first issued daily telegraphic charts regularly in 1863, and other countries followed with similar maps in steady succession.

DEVELOPMENT OF UPPER-AIR OBSERVATIONS

During recent years the observing network has been enlarged, and the completeness and frequency of the observations have steadily increased; in particular upper-air data from aerological soundings have become more complete and more quickly available for current daily use. Long before weather forecasting was undertaken, upper-air exploration had begun. In 1749 Alexander Wilson, of Glasgow, was raising thermometers on kites.[2] In 1784 John Jeffries and the aeronaut Blanchard made the first balloon ascents for meteorological purposes. Thereafter progress was slow until 1852, when John Welsh, of Kew Observatory, England, made balloon ascents to 7,000 meters (over 4 miles), taking observations of temperature, pressure, and humidity. Between 1862 and 1866 James Glaisher carried out meteorological observations in a series of historic balloon ascents.

In the seventies in the United States the Signal Corps of the Army established the first high-mountaintop weather observatories on Mount Washington, N. H. (6,300 feet), and on Pikes Peak, Colo. (14,100 feet). The continuous observations at these stations when compared with similar observations at nearby lowland or valley stations threw a good deal of light on the upper-air structure of storms, which had previously been studied from surface conditions alone. The observations were studied more zealously by the European meteorologists than by the American, and their valuable results led to the establishment of a large number of mountain observatories in Europe. Attempts to use the daily telegraphed reports from the mountain stations in making daily forecasts were unsuccessful, for the reasons that an adequate working hypothesis as to the relation of upper-air conditions to surface weather was lacking and the mountaintop observations were not truly representative of the free atmosphere, owing to the disturbing influence of the mountain itself. The mountain observatories in this country were therefore closed, but active work on other methods of procuring upper-air data was continued.

As an indirect means of determining upper-air motions, classification of the forms of clouds and observations of their movements were industriously carried out by many observers, beginning in the early nineteenth century. The French naturalist, Lamarck, in 1801, was the first to attempt a classification, but the credit of classifying the clouds in a scientific manner belongs to Luke Howard. In 1803 he named the main classes—cirrus, stratus, cumulus, and nimbus. Many investigators used cloud observations in determining the courses of air currents aloft and the relation between cloud type and ensuing rain. Clement Ley's cloud studies in England (1865–78) gave the first adequate description of the upper windflow in cyclones and anticyclones. In this country the most elaborate summary of cloud observations was made by Clayton in his review of data of the Blue Hill Observatory of Harvard University, in Massachusetts.[3] Clayton found that while cloud types gave definite warning of precipitation in the next few hours, they were of very little help for longer intervals.

In 1893 the first recording instruments, or meteorographs, were sent up on small free balloons by Hermite and Besançon in France. A year later instruments were sent up in box kites by Rotch and Fergusson in the United States. Pressure, temperature, and humidity were recorded by pens tracing curves on a sheet of paper fastened to a drum rotated by a clock. The record was evaluated after the meteorograph was recovered. Important investigations with the

[2] SHAW, NAPIER. METEOROLOGY IN HISTORY. *In* Manual of Meteorology, v. 1, illus. Cambridge, England. 1926.

[3] CLAYTON, H. HELM. DISCUSSION OF CLOUD OBSERVATIONS AT BLUE HILL OBSERVATORY. Harvard Univ. Astron. Observ. Ann. 30: [271]-500, illus. 1896.

298737°—41——38

use of balloons or kites were made later by Teisserenc de Bort in France, Assmann in Germany, Dines in Scotland, and Clayton in the United States.

In 1909 Rotch, at Blue Hill Observatory, made the first upper-wind observations by means of a theodolite (a telescope mounted so as to measure horizontal and vertical angles) with which he observed at regular intervals the elevation and horizontal (azimuthal) angles of a small balloon, called a pilot balloon. Knowing the rate of climb of the balloon, its horizontal path could be plotted and the wind direction and velocities at various heights found. Pilot-balloon observations are now taken several times daily at more than 100 stations in the United States.

So extensively had the program of upper-air research developed before the World War that 18 countries were actively participating in this type of work. However, for various reasons the data obtained were not available for current use in forecasting. The sounding balloon, while easy to use and capable of reaching great heights, suffered from the disadvantage that the record often could not be recovered until weeks and even months after the release. The kite could be released only under certain favorable wind and weather conditions, and usually reached a height of only a mile, while the sounding took several hours and required a mass of cumbersome equipment and the work of several men. Hence the upper-air data served only for statistical investigations.

The rapid development of the airplane during the World War resulted in a quick and easy means of obtaining observations up to 2 or 3 miles; and, what was just as important, the detailed-forecast requirements for aircraft operations served as a stimulus to the use of the upper-air data in forecasting.

After the war the airplane sounding was adopted in many countries. In the United States the Navy had already made such soundings as far back as 1917, and the Weather Bureau in cooperation with the Army made test soundings in 1918. Airplane soundings were made frequently at most of the Naval Air Stations in the 1920's. It was not until 1931, however, that the Weather Bureau began to replace the kite stations, which had at no time numbered more than six, by airplane stations. Four such stations were established in the summer of 1931, and together with soundings made by the Navy and one by the Massachusetts Institute of Technology the total number available was about a dozen. In July 1934, following the recommendations of the President's Science Advisory Board, Congress authorized an increase in the number of Weather Bureau airplane stations and the use of Army planes at other stations, so that the total number of airplane soundings—Weather Bureau, Navy, Army, and Massachusetts Institute of Technology—available for daily use was over 20. The number was gradually increased to about 30 in 1937.

Despite their advantages over the balloon and the kite soundings, the airplane soundings were expensive, and it was often impossible to take them during periods of disturbed weather, when they would have been most valuable. The latter objection applied also to the pilot-balloon soundings. Consequently, at about the time that the extended network of airplane stations was being established in the United States, research was being actively conducted both in this country and abroad to develop a radio-meteorograph—radiosonde—consisting of a lightweight meteorograph and radio transmitter attached to a small balloon. Each of the three meteorological elements, pressure, temperature, and relative humidity, is measured by the meteorograph and indicated by radio signals, which are intercepted at the ground by a radio receiver. The radiosonde observations, besides being collected at the ground without loss of time, have the added value of being less expensive than airplane soundings and independent of bad flying weather, and they can be obtained at far greater heights.

The first successful radiosonde ascent was made before 1930 by the Russian meteorologist Moltchanoff at Sloutsk, near Leningrad. The first one in this country was made by Lange, of Blue Hill Observatory, in 1935. Bureau of Standards scientists devised a radiosonde that was first used by the Navy at Washington, D. C., in 1936 and then at Fairbanks, Alaska, during some special investigations of polar weather in 1937–38. In July 1938, 6 airplane stations of the Weather Bureau network changed over to radiosondes. Finally, in July 1939, all of the Weather Bureau and 3 of the 9 Navy airplane stations were replaced by radiosonde stations, making a total of about 30 in all.

Meanwhile the purely empirical methods, based on experience alone, to which weather forecasting, as developed in the nineteenth century, was at first limited, have in recent years been supplemented to an increasing extent by methods based on an understanding and an explicit application of the physical laws to which atmospheric phenomena conform. For this the development of the polar-front theory, described elsewhere in this volume (Rossby, p. 599; Reichelderfer, p. 128), has been largely responsible.

MAKING THE DAILY FORECAST

The object in weather forecasting is to provide the farmer, the city dweller, the shipper of perishable goods, the railroads, the public utilities such as gas, electric, and street-transportation companies, the aviator, and the owners and masters of all types of vessels from fishing and pleasure craft up to the largest passenger liner, and all others interested in the weather, with as accurate weather information as possible and with forecasts as far ahead as practicable. In order to do this it is necessary for the forecaster to know intimately what changes have taken place in the weather situation for the last day or two. When he has become well acquainted with the sequence of events and weather phenomena as shown on the principal weather chart and all the auxiliary charts and graphs that are prepared regularly, he is ready to project the present conditions into the future to the best of his ability with the aid of every scrap of information that will give a hint as to what will take place within the next 12, 24, 36, and even 48 hours.

There are now available every 6 hours detailed observations at the surface of the earth from hundreds of places in the United States, including Alaska, and Canada, and from Bermuda and scores of ships at sea; and every hour from most of the stations in the United States and southern Canada via the telegraphic typewriter, or teletype. In addition, twice-daily reports are received from parts of Mexico, Central America, the West Indies, Greenland, the Azores, Europe, northern Africa, China, Japan, Siberia, the Philippines, Honolulu, and Midway, Wake, and a few other islands between Honolulu and the Philippines.

The data from a large number of stations in the United States, southern Canada, Mexico, Central America, the West Indies, and Bermuda and reports from ships in the adjacent waters are plotted on a single sheet—the principal weather chart—containing an outline map of this area. The rest of the reports are entered on a chart of the Northern Hemisphere and are utilized largely in the preparation of semiweekly weather outlooks. In preparing the daily forecasts, the surface observations are supplemented, as previously described, with pilot-balloon observations now made at nearly 100 stations in the United States and at a few stations in Alaska and southern Canada and with the observations from 35 to 40 radiosonde and airplane stations fairly well distributed over the United States and 2 in Alaska.[4]

The Principal Weather Chart

The data entered on the principal weather chart enable the forecaster to locate all the areas of low barometric pressure (lows) and of high pressure (highs), and at least the principal fronts (dividing lines between air masses of different origin, density, and water-vapor content), as well as the directions and rates of movement of the centers of the highs and lows and of the fronts since they first made their appearance on the weather chart. He sees not only these important features of the map but also the type of weather produced by them at all reporting stations. The principal items that indicate the current condition are the temperature and the dewpoint (the temperature at which the water vapor in the air would begin to condense if the air were cooled), the proportion of sky covered by clouds, and the occurrence or nonoccurrence of precipitation at each station. To obtain an idea of the changes or movements, the 3-hour pressure change entered for each station on the principal chart must be utilized. Other data and information entered on a 12-hour pressure-change chart prove extremely helpful on many occasions.

It is of great importance in forecasting to know in as much detail as possible the vertical structure of the atmosphere, especially through the first 2 or 3 miles above the surface. Attention is given to the direction and velocity of the wind at the different stations at several levels up to 14,000 feet above sea level, as plotted on the pilot-balloon charts, and to the individual plottings of both airplane and radiosonde observations, especially those in areas (as shown on the principal weather chart) where important developments are occurring or are likely to occur. Meanwhile, specialists in interpretation of upper-air data have drawn cross sections of the atmosphere to a height of 5 kilometers (about 3 miles) or more and charts and diagrams showing the physical state of the atmosphere.

Close attention is also given to cloud observations from a very large number of stations, as entered on a cloud chart (not here reproduced). Lower clouds (such as stratus, strato-cumulus, cumulus, and cumulo-nimbus), the intermediate clouds (alto-stratus, alto-cumulus,

[4] The number in Alaska was increased to 7 late in 1940; and on April 1, 1941, all radiosonde stations in the United States began making 2 observations each day, at 1 a. m. and 1 p. m., eastern standard time.

and cirro-cumulus), and the high clouds (cirrus and cirro-stratus) are entered so as to indicate the direction of movement and the amount of sky covered by each type. The low clouds are entered in blue pencil and the intermediate and high clouds in red pencil. Of all types of cloud the alto-stratus, intermediate in height, is by far the most important, because this type indicates the so-called warm front (or up-glide) action of moist air that has reached the condensation level, and from these clouds all of our long-continued light-to-moderate precipitation comes.

Conclusions are drawn from careful consideration of the several charts and diagrams referred to and are checked and rechecked with each other; and if there appears to be a conflict between the determinations from different charts, a quick decision must be made as to which will be accepted. Having accomplished all of this in as systematic and complete a manner as possible in the short time available for the purpose and having made computations as to the rate and direction of movement of the fronts and the troughs of low pressure, the forecaster is ready to begin dictating State forecasts, forecasts for coastal waters, and a general forecast, and in addition a summary of weather conditions during the past 24 hours. In the forecasts an attempt is made to indicate the state of the sky as to amount of cloudiness (fair, increasing cloudiness, mostly cloudy, etc.); the occurrence of precipitation (rain, snow, showers, etc.); and any changes of importance in temperature (warmer, colder, much colder, etc.; if no material change in temperature is likely, the terms "little change in temperature" or "not much change in temperature" are used).

An Example of a Daily Forecast

In order to show, in as much detail as practicable, the various steps leading up to the actual making of weather forecasts from synoptic charts and the type of reasoning involved in making the forecasts, the weather situation at 7:30 a. m., eastern standard time, on March 29, 1939, has been selected. Most of the charts and diagrams, actually made and utilized in analysis and prognosis (forecasting) are here reproduced.

The map selected is one without important complications; it is what is called an "easy" map from which to make forecasts that will verify well. It should not be inferred that map analysis and prognosis can be accomplished quickly and satisfactorily in all cases even by an experienced forecaster; the actions and interactions of the air masses are so complicated and the changes that occur in them over very large areas are so involved that the weather for a small area such as a State cannot now (and probably never will) be predicted with 100-percent accuracy in complicated weather situations for more than a few hours ahead. But very complicated weather situations would not be suitable for illustration and explanation to those who are not trained synoptic meteorologists.

All weather reports received by telegraph, radio, or cable are in code. Formerly a word code was used, but now they are mostly in a numeral code, each message consisting of several groups of five figures each. Reports received by teletype are either in numeral code or in symbols and figures. As the reports are received at the district forecast center they are immediately translated by a man who is an expert in such work, and a "chart man" enters on each chart the data required. Translation begins about 7:40 a. m. and 7:40 p. m. and is usually stopped about 9:15, so that the forecaster can complete his analysis of the map and prepare to begin forecasting at 9:30 or shortly thereafter. The forecasts are completed and dictated within a few minutes and are immediately telegraphed to the Weather Bureau stations in the States for which they have been made. Copies are furnished to press associations and newspapers without delay.

Description of Charts

The Principal (Surface) Weather Map.—The principal weather chart for 7:30 a. m., March 29, 1939, is reproduced in figure 1; it shows weather conditions at the surface. No names of places are printed on the base map for the United States; the chart men must be able to enter data instantly for each station, which is identified only by a circle at the proper location. Since July 1, 1939, the stations have been identified either by a group of three figures or by a two- or three-letter designation, both in the coded reports and on the maps. The following data for each station are entered on this chart, but not all are reproduced in figure 1:

1. State of weather (amount of cloudiness, rain, snow, etc.).
2. Direction and force of wind (Beaufort scale).
3. Temperature and dew point.
4. The barometric pressure reduced to the value it would have at sea level (in millibars[5] and tenths).
5. Pressure tendency and amount of change during last 3 hours.
6. Amount of rain or melted snow in inches and hundredths during last 12 hours.
7. Miscellaneous data, such as thunderstorms, fog, and frost.

Long before the translation of all the reports is completed, the forecaster begins to analyze the map; he draws as many isobars—lines connecting places of equal pressure—as possible with the incomplete entry of data, finishing this work after the translation has been completed or stopped. In order to analyze a weather map correctly and without loss of time, it is necessary to refer to the completely analyzed maps of 6 or 12 hours before; with the air masses properly identified and the fronts properly placed on these previous maps, the analysis of the current map is greatly facilitated

There are two important sets of lines in figure 1. The lines in black pencil on the original chart are the isobars, which are drawn for each 3 millibars, or approximately 0.09 of an inch, difference in pressure. The lines separating air masses are the fronts; on the original chart the cold fronts are drawn in blue pencil, the warm fronts in red, and the occluded fronts in purple. When the movements of the air currents are such that colder air is advancing over regions occupied by warmer air, the front, or discontinuity, between the two air masses is called a cold front; if warmer air is advancing into regions

[5] A millibar is 1/1000 of the pressure that would be exerted per unit area by a column of mercury 29.531 inches high at 32° F. in latitude 45°; it is a force of 1,000 dynes per square centimeter.

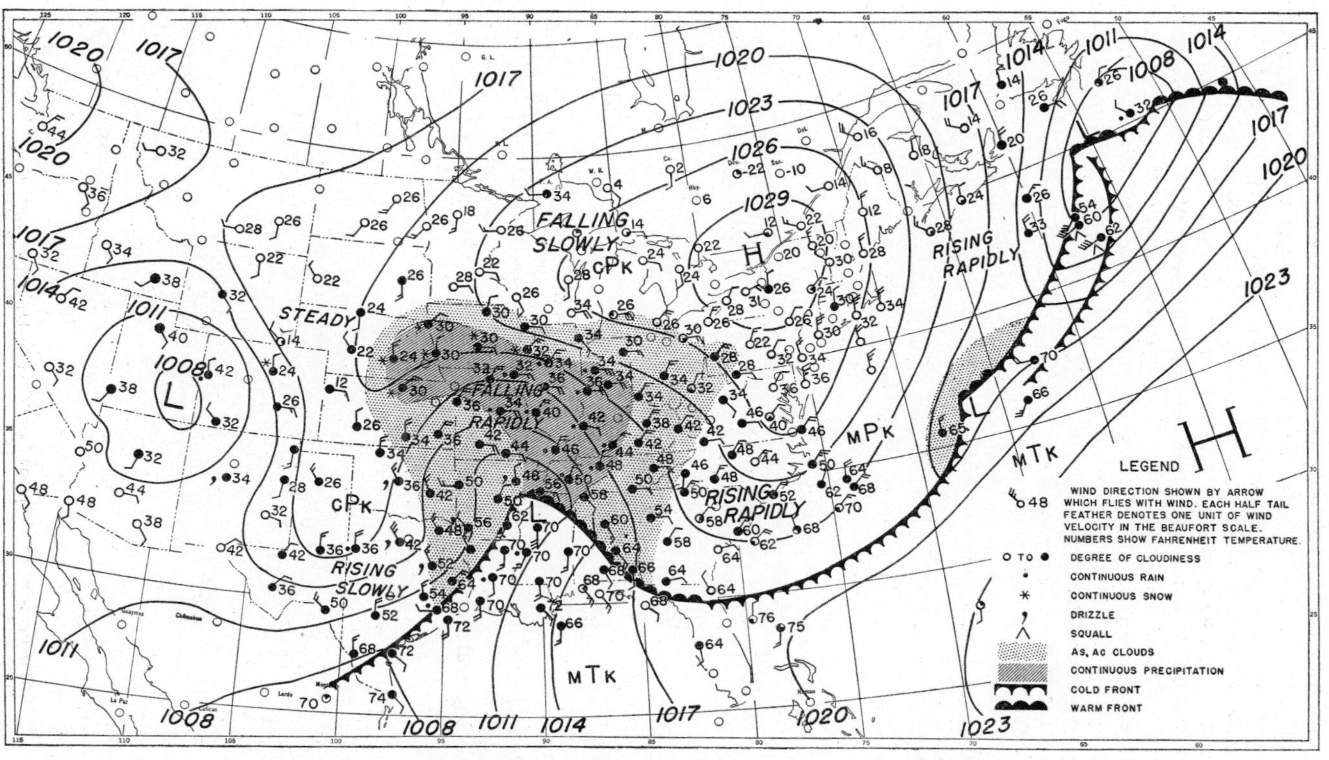

FIGURE 1.—The principal weather chart for 7:30 a. m., March 29, 1939.

occupied by colder air, the discontinuity is called a warm front; the discontinuity formed when a cold front overtakes a warm front and displaces the warm air formerly between them to a higher level is known as an occluded front. The air masses are classified into tropical and polar, according to their place of origin. Each of these is further subdivided into continental and maritime, according to whether the source region was over land or ocean, and still further subdivided according to whether they are warmer or colder than the surface over which they are flowing. These characteristics are indicated by symbols to designate the different types; thus the symbol mTk means air of maritime (m) tropical (T) origin and colder (k) than the surface over which it is moving; cPk is air of continental (c) polar (P) origin, colder (k) than the surface over which it is moving; and mPk is air of maritime polar origin, colder than the surface over which it is moving.

The portion of the front on this map that extends from near the mouth of the Rio Grande to eastern Arkansas is a cold front, and it separates the air of tropical origin, labeled mTk, from the air of continental polar origin, labeled cPk. Examination of the temperature and wind data for the stations in the tropical air shows temperatures of 66° to 72° F., and dew-point temperatures of 64° to 70°, with winds from a southerly direction. This air must have moved over a body of warm water for a considerable period of time in order to have picked up sufficient moisture to raise the temperature of the dew point to these high values. Immediately to the west of this front both the air temperature and the dew point rapidly fall off through the 50's and 40's with a temperature reading of 36° reported from Oklahoma City. Since this air mass to the west has undoubtedly come originally from a far-northern region, it is called polar air, and having moved southward from northern Canada, as its previous history showed, it is labeled cPk. As long as the cold air advances (usually in a southerly or easterly direction), the boundary, or line of discontinuity, between it and the warmer air ahead is called a cold front.

Attention is now turned to the part of the frontal system that extends from the center of the wave disturbance over Arkansas southeastward to the extreme southern portion of Georgia, thence eastward for about 500 miles, and thereafter northeastward over the Atlantic Ocean. As is usually the case with a cold front of great length, wave disturbances have developed. One is here shown northwest of the island of Bermuda, and another and more important one south of Newfoundland. It will be noted that the entire air mass south of this front is labeled mTk, being of tropical or subtropical origin, and the air masses to the north of the front are labeled cPk and mPk, both being of polar origin but the latter having a trajectory, or path of movement, that took it over the ocean for several hundred miles, where the air gradually became warmer and more moist.

The entire front is called a cold front, except the portion extending from Arkansas to extreme southwestern Georgia and other portions over the ocean to the northeast or east of the wave disturbances; these parts of the front are called warm fronts because the warm air to the south is advancing northward at the surface while the cold air is retreating. The area within the "wave" portion of the front is called the warm sector. The waves move along the front, usually developing into wave disturbances with closed isobars—that is, into systems in which a wind circulation has been set up around a center. As a rule the cold front to the southwest or west of a disturbance moves faster than the warm front and eventually overtakes it east or southeast of the center. When this happens the disturbance becomes occluded, and the warm sector gradually disappears, the warm air being forced upward over the colder air. When the supply of moist air is greatly lessened, or even cut off, by the occlusion process, there is much less condensation and lighter precipitation, and hence less energy for maintaining the disturbance; in most cases it moves more slowly and loses intensity.

Ordinarily, fair weather with little or no cloudiness is expected at and around the center of a high-pressure area (H), especially to the east of a line drawn north-south through its center, because over this area the air is of polar origin and not only was rather dry originally but is further dried because it is descending and becoming warmer by compression. The opposite process is involved ahead of moving disturbances (lows or cyclones) and behind moving highs (anticyclones). There, air is ascending, as it usually moves up the warm-front surface. Near the low a more violent upward motion occurs, caused by the advancing cold front. In its ascent the air is cooled because of expansion due to gradually lessened pressure. As soon as the condensation level is reached, the formerly invisible water vapor begins to condense into visible droplets, and clouds begin to form. When there is sufficient moisture in the air and the lifting of the air mass continues, especially if it is of tropical origin, precipitation occurs, and rain or snow will reach the ground unless the precipitation is light and the air sufficiently dry to cause it to evaporate before it reaches the ground.

On the surface map of 7:30 a. m., March 29, 1939, the weather is clear or is characterized by scattered high clouds of the cirrus type at most stations not only near and east of the north-south axis of the high centered near Lake Ontario but also west of the high center over the northern border States. Cloudiness has already set in over Ohio, southwestern Pennsylvania, and the western portions of Maryland and Virginia. Here the clouds observed are alto-cumulus and alto-stratus; and from these States to the center of the disturbance over Arkansas the sky is completely overcast with alto-stratus clouds from which precipitation is beginning to occur in Indiana and Kentucky, where also low clouds of the stratus type are observed. To the rear of the cold front the sky is overcast with low clouds over Texas and Oklahoma, and some light or drizzling rain is falling.

The Upper-Air Maps.—Turning to the upper-air data, one of the first things to be noted in looking at the 10,000-foot (3-kilometer) pilot-balloon map for the morning of March 29, 1939 (fig. 2), is the change in wind circulation as compared with the sea level map and the displacement or disappearance of the centers of high pressure and low pressure. The arrows on the chart fly with the wind, and the number of half feathers represents the wind velocity in the Beaufort scale, which uses numbers from 0 to 12; the temperature (centigrade) and the pressure in millibars are entered for airplane or radiosonde stations on the 6,000-, 10,000-, and 14,000-foot maps. (Of these three, only the 10,000-foot map is given here.) In addition, pressures for stations at high elevations in the West are entered on the 6,000-foot

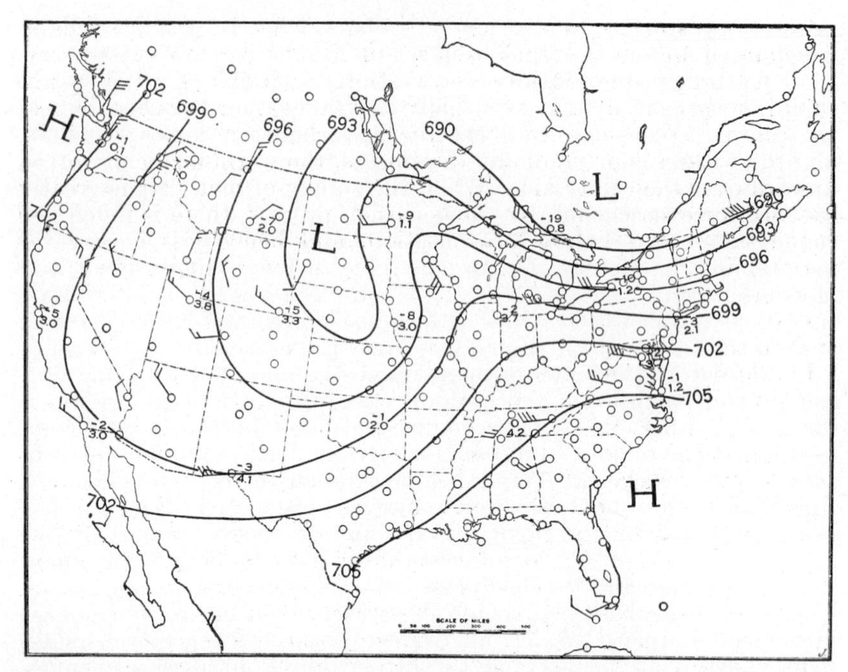

Figure 2.—Chart showing upper-air data at 10,000 feet above sea level as gathered by pilot balloon for the morning of March 29, 1939.

map. Pressures for 5,000 feet above sea level, entered on the 6,000-foot map, range from 842 to 850 millibars, and those for 10,000 feet range from 690 to 705 millibars. On the principal map (fig. 1) they range from 1005.1 to 1031.5 millibars. Isobars on upper-air maps are drawn for the same interval (3 millibars) as on the surface map. In the free air the wind blows very nearly parallel to the isobars, so that if changes in the pressure field 24 hours ahead can be roughly approximated, both the direction and speed of the air movement aloft can be estimated with sufficient accuracy to be of much value in forecasting.

It will be noted that the low center at the surface in Arkansas is displaced to the northwest at higher levels. On the 6,000-foot map it is some distance northwest of the surface center; and the 10,000- and 14,000-foot maps show a further displacement northwestward. When a disturbance is moving eastward or northeastward at a more or less normal rate, the coldest average temperature of the air column in the lower layers is usually northwest of the low center; since this air is more dense and therefore heavier than the surrounding air, there is a more rapid decrease in pressure with altitude than over adjacent areas, so that the lowest pressure at, say, 5,000 feet above sea level is over this dense air to the northwest of the surface center. This pressure effect is still evident in many cases at 10,000 feet or higher, usually being manifest, not as a distinct cyclonic center, but as a trough in the isobaric pattern farther to the west and northwest than the center, either at the surface or at 6,000 feet. In old occluded lows, however, the cold air moves around the center even up to high levels, the warm sector having disappeared altogether, so that the lowest pressure and more or less circular isobars are found over approximately the same area up to 4 miles or more above sea level.

As for highs, they rapidly disappear with height when they are moving cold highs, as in this case, and a short distance aloft the westerlies appear. The dome of polar air accompanying this high is subsiding, resulting in descent of air from aloft and a marked temperature inversion (increase of temperature with height) near the ground above the thin layer of air cooled excessively at night by radiation; in many instances the temperature actually rises many degrees in the first few hundred feet of ascent. Winds blow from some westerly direction, as a rule, when well above these highs; and the highest pressure aloft may be found far to the south, as is indicated on the 14,000-foot map of March 29.

In addition to the air temperature and dew point at each reporting station, we now have a fairly good picture of the distribution of pressure and of wind direction and velocity up to 14,000 feet above sea level, from the surface map and the upper-air maps. Also entered, on the cloud chart (not shown) for each station, are the types and directions of movement of clouds observed; the heavily shaded areas on the principal weather chart show where active precipitation is occurring at the time of observation, and the lightly shaded areas show the extent of the alto-stratus cloud.

The Isentropic Chart.—One of the auxiliary charts most recently developed is known as an insentropic chart. Instead of showing meteorological conditions over a surface at a given height above sea level, it shows conditions at each point at a height where the so-called potential temperature has a given selected value. The potenital temperature is the temperature to which air would come, as a result of compression or expansion, if the pressure were changed from its actual value to 1,000 millibars without any heat being communicated to the air or lost by the air. A surface over which the potential temperature has the same value everywhere is called an isentropic surface; and the isentropic chart is a map of conditions over such a surface. In meteorological work the potential temperature is measured on a thermometric scale in which the freezing point of water under standard conditions is marked 273° (instead of 32° as on the Fahrenheit scale, or 0° as on the centigrade scale) and the boiling point is marked 373°; this scale is called the absolute temperature scale.[6] Figure 3 is a map of the meteorological conditions on the isentropic surface over which the potential temperature is everywhere 301° Abs.

The observations from which figure 3 was drawn were obtained 3½ hours before those used in the surface map. Along the front over the Atlantic Ocean, the contour lines of the height of the isentropic surface, as well as the moisture lines, show a maximum gradient, or rate of decrease, as would be expected in the neighborhood of a front. Southeast of Newfoundland, where the first disturbance (area of low pressure) is located, there is a northward bulge of the moisture lines relative to the contour line, and a similar picture exists for the minor wave disturbance east of the Virginia Capes. In both disturbances condensation areas are indicated by the lines intersecting the isobars, and the surface reports indicate precipitation at these localities.

[6] Absolute zero—the complete absence of heat—is −273° F.

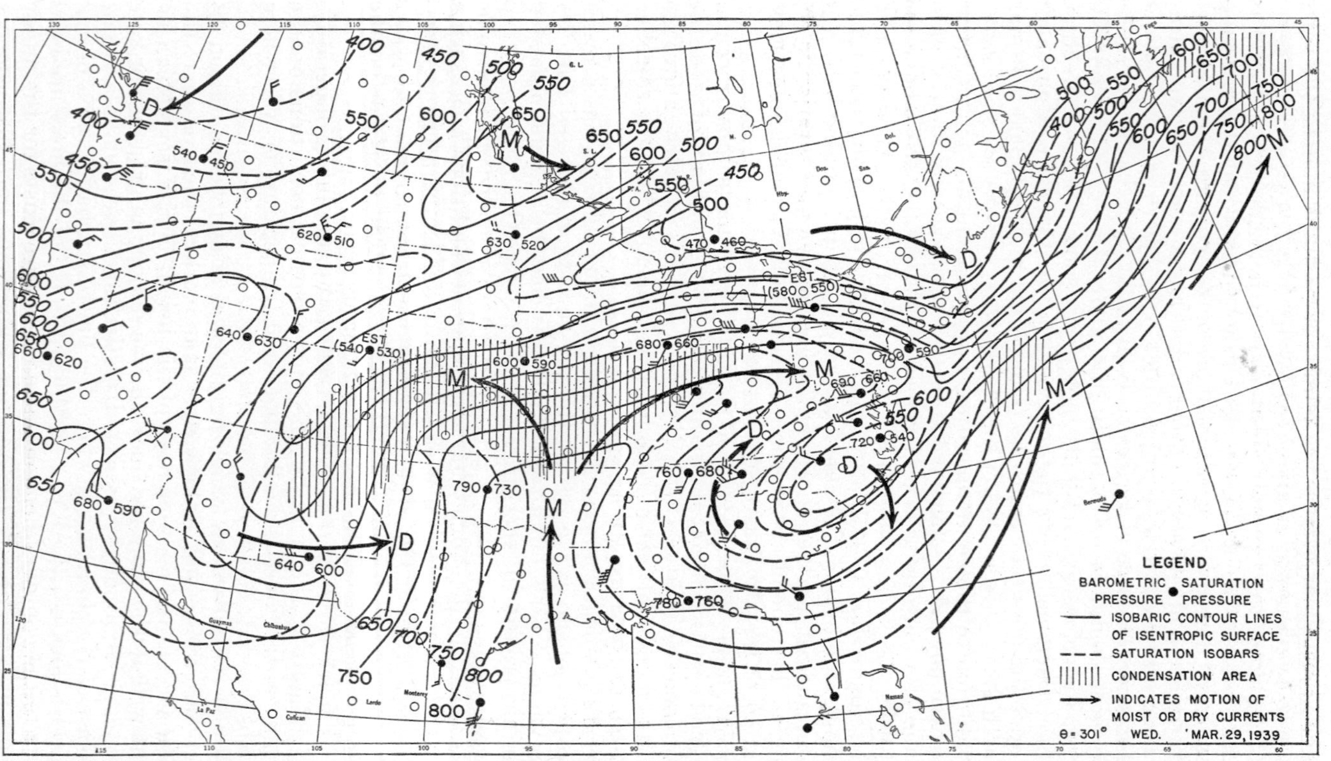

FIGURE 3.—The flow pattern for an isentropic surface corresponding to a potential temperature of 301° Abs. for March 29, 1939.

Over the Southeastern States there is seen an "island" of dry air which has been cut off from its northern source by a moist current. Clear weather is associated with this dry island, and a portion of it is moving toward the southeast, evidently with down-slope motion, while another portion is flowing to the northeast and merging with the moist current moving up the Mississippi Valley; this latter (moist) current branches, that is, splits into two currents, one moving to the east in the form of a narrow tongue and the other to the west. Owing to the high moisture content of this air and the steep northerly slope of the surface, condensation is soon reached and is indicated by the shaded region. Note how this corresponds to the alto-stratus cloud and precipitation areas on the sea level map (fig. 1). In the west over Texas is shown a dry current cutting into the moist current, and this is responsible for the ending of the significant precipitation over Texas and Oklahoma. The drizzle occurring over these States is falling out of low-lying stratus clouds, as the Oklahoma City sounding shows.

The Cross-Section Charts.—In figures 4 and 5 are shown two cross sections through the disturbance over the Midwest. One (fig. 4) is a north-south section from Sault Ste. Marie, Mich., to Pensacola, Fla., showing very clearly the section of the sloping warm front that is found at the surface south of Nashville, Tenn.; the front is located about 500 meters (1,500 feet) above the ground at this station, as shown by the change in the wind from easterly at the ground to southerly above, and by the increase in temperature from 9° to 13° C. and in specific humidity (weight of water vapor in unit weight of the air) from 61. to 8.6 grams of water per kilogram of air. At Chicago this front is identified by similar changes in the vertical distribution of temperature and humidity, and this is true to a less marked degree at Sault Ste. Marie. Note how at all three stations the front is characterized by a constant potential temperature of about 293° Abs.

The second section (fig. 5) goes from El Paso, Tex., to Lakehurst, N. J., and passes just north of the center of the low. No tropical air is found at the ground in this section, but the trough of low pressure in the frontal surface coincides with the position of the surface cyclone. The slope of the warm front from Nashville to Lakehurst is much less steep than that in the north-south section, and this is one factor responsible for the lack of precipitation in this area.

The Pressure-Change Chart.—On the 12-hour pressure-change chart (not here reproduced) the sea level pressure is entered below the circle representing a station, and above this entry is written the change in pressure during the last 12 hours, corrected for the normal daily range. Except for some stations located along the coast, the barometer normally reads from 1 to 3 millibars higher at 7:30 a. m. than at 7:30 p. m., and this normal change, having nothing to do with weather conditions, is eliminated; the remainder of the changes are due to the horizontal movement (advection) of air masses of differing density and to other physical or dynamical processes that increase or decrease the total weight of the air column up to the upper limits of the atmosphere. There is also entered for each station the net amount of the change (increase or decrease) in atmospheric pressure during the 3 hours preceding the observation taken from the barograph, together

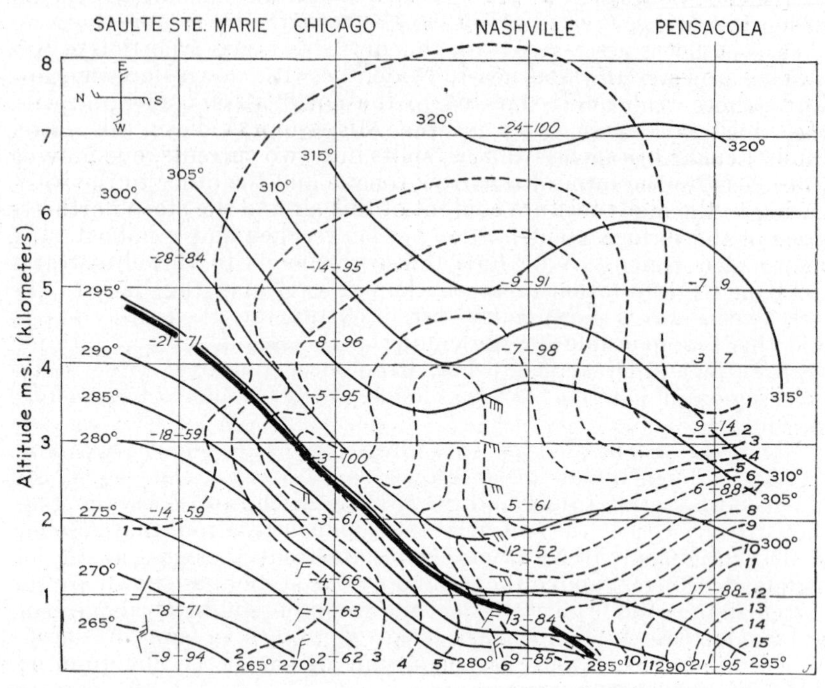

FIGURE 4.—Cross section through the disturbance over the Midwest, March 29, 1939, from Sault Ste. Marie, Mich., to Pensacola, Fla.

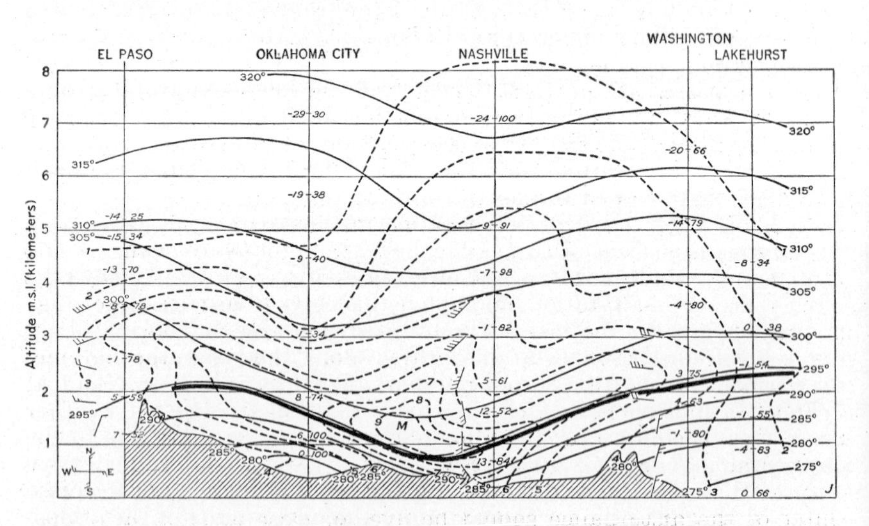

FIGURE 5.—Cross section through the storm of March 29, 1939, from El Paso, Tex., to Lakehurst, N. J.

with a slanting line indicating the slope of the trace on the barograph during this period.

The actual pressure and the amounts of abnormal change are entered in pencil on this chart, while for purposes of quick appraisal, the upward tendencies and slants are in red pencil and the downward tendencies and slants in blue pencil. Heavy blue lines are drawn separating areas on the map showing 12-hour increases in pressure from areas showing decreases. If these increases or decreases amount to 3 millibars or more, lighter lines are drawn (in red for increase and in blue for decrease) for each 3 millibars. On this particular map the greatest change both upward and downward is 9 millibars; therefore two light lines surround the station or stations with a change of 9 millibars, and the amount of this greatest change is entered in large figures in the appropriate color and preceded by a minus or plus sign, making this important feature stand out for quick inspection and appraisal. Where the 3-hour pressure tendency exceeds 1.5 millibars, a green dashed line is drawn around the area with 1.5 millibars or more change, and other dashed lines for multiples of 1.5 (3.0, 4.5, 6.0, etc.). These dashed green lines are called isallobars and the areas within them are often called isallobaric lows or isallobaric highs, as the case may be. An area of 12-hour pressure fall is called a katallobar, while an area of 12-hour pressure rise is called an anallobar. These isallobaric lows and highs, as well as katallobars and anallobars, are all very important in projecting weather into the future, and especially in predicting the pattern of the weather maps 12, 24, 36, and even 48 hours ahead. If the forecaster knows what the pressure distribution will be on future maps he will be able to forecast with a high degree of accuracy, provided he has made a correct analysis of the current map and upper-air data.

Preparing the Forecast

After the analysis of surface maps and upper-air maps and diagrams has been completed, the preparation of forecasts is begun. The first and one of the principal preliminary steps is the determination, as accurately as the data permit, of the location 24 hours hence of the centers of the highs and lows, the positions of the fronts (especially the cold fronts), and of the troughs of low pressure without fronts. In many cases a fairly satisfactory estimate of the direction and rate of movement may be made by simply measuring the movement during the last 12 or 24 hours and then extrapolating, or extending, this movement into the future. Several years ago, however, the Norwegian meteorologist Sverre Pettersen developed more refined extrapolation methods which have proved very helpful to the synoptic meteorologist in estimating these movements. Applying them to the center of the Arkansas low and to the trough containing a cold front that extends thence southwestward to southern Texas on the 7:30 a. m. map of March 29, 1939 (fig. 1), we find that after 24 hours the center of the disturbance should be over or close to Ohio, with the trough and cold front extending south-southwestward to the vicinity of Pensacola, Fla., while the movement of the high should take its center eastward to a position a short distance east of Nova Scotia.

These calculations were actually completed before the forecasts were made on the map of March 29; by extrapolation the same information was available for an additional 12 hours ahead. The map for 7:30 a. m., March 30, 1939 (not here reproduced) shows a close agreement with the calculations. On the basis of this estimate of the future locations of the fronts and other features, it was comparatively easy to estimate the advance of the precipitation area; and from our knowledge of the arrangement of surface air masses with respect to fronts, troughs, wedges, and centers, the forecaster was then able to predict quite well the wind directions and approximate rate of air movements, and the resultant changes in temperature, in the several States comprising his district.

In the making of the precipitation forecasts, the upper-air data are of prime importance. If the radiosonde or airplane observations show that stable air with little moisture (dry air) is likely to be over a particular locality during the forecast period, there is little likelihood of precipitation or even much cloudiness. In this case, however, the upper-air picture was very different. The individual plottings of radiosonde and airplane observations, as well as the isentropic chart and the cross sections, showed quite plainly the reason for so much cloudiness and active precipitation. The moist tongue on the isentropic chart (fig. 3) represents only a skin layer on a single selected equal potential-temperature, or isentropic, surface (in this case 301° Abs.); but the cross sections and plots of data for individual stations showed that this moist tongue was of considerable depth. Moreover, the wind data plotted on the isentropic chart indicated up-slope motion, and the air was so close to the condensation level that not much lifting was required to produce condensation, clouds, and precipitation.

The surface and cloud observations substantiated the conclusions reached by consideration of upper-air data. The 10,000-foot chart (fig. 2) indicated that there would be a further turning of the wind over the Lake region and the Atlantic States from westerly to a more southerly direction; and that air at this level and also for a considerable distance above and below would move from the vicinity of the lower Mississippi Valley, where the moisture content of the air was greatest, northeastward at an average rate of about 30 miles per hour. The expected movements of the centers of the low and the high and the trough containing the cold front over the west Gulf States, as well as the 12-hour and 3-hour pressure changes, all supported the indications of this comparatively rapid movement.

The official State forecasts issued on the morning of March 29, 1939, called for the extension of the rain area northeastward to Massachusetts and New Hampshire by 7:30 a. m. of the 30th, and the ending of the rain by the same hour in western Kentucky and western and southern Tennessee because of the passage of the cold front and the arrival of dry polar air. No rain was predicted for northern Michigan and northern Wisconsin because the wind at intermediate and higher levels was expected to continue to blow from west to east, preventing the moist air from the South from reaching that area; furthermore, inspection of the isentropic chart shows that the westerly wind was not up slope over the northern Lake region. These forecasts, together with those for changes in temperature, were well verified.

Forecasting Procedure

The forecaster begins his forecasting day about 8:15 a. m. by studying the circulation in the free air as shown by the pilot-balloon charts and drawing the isobars on the 6,000-, 10,000-, and 14,000-foot maps. This provides him with a fairly complete picture of the direction and rate of movement of the various air masses, information that is invaluable not only in his forecast later on, but also in his analysis of the surface synoptic weather map, which is begun between 8:30 and 8:45 a. m., at least a half hour before translation is finished.

Analysis, including the drawing of fronts and isobars, continues through translation and continuous entry of observations on the map upon which the forecaster is working. He sketches all or a part of a front or an isobar here and there over the map as entry of data progresses, gradually completing the lines in the East, while the chart man concentrates on entering data from western stations, then changing positions while data are entered for eastern stations and map construction shifts to the West. A lull in reports comes for the forecaster for a few minutes while those for Alaska, Greenland, and northern Canada are being translated and entered on a separate section of the map covering these areas; he is then able for the first time to survey and work on the entire main synoptic map and can refer to previous maps underneath the current one. The chart man soon returns for entry of late reports on the main map, while the forecaster at least partly constructs the chart for the northern areas.

Returning to the job of finishing the principal synoptic chart, the forecaster usually is compelled to call a halt on the translation and entry of late land and vessel reports in order to spend a few minutes in computations and in correlation of the conclusions (sometimes contradictory) reached from his brief study of the several charts and cross sections, before beginning dictation of the forecasts at or shortly after 9:30 a. m. All regular State forecasts, special forecasts, and weather synopses are completed by or shortly after 10 a. m. As soon as a State forecast is completed, it is telegraphed immediately, and by 10 a. m. all the Weather Bureau stations in the forecast district have received their State forecasts.

The actual time consumed in formulating and dictating the forecasts for the Washington forecast district, comprising 16 States and the District of Columbia, is seldom more than 15 to 20 minutes. The time-consuming work is the translation of the data and their entry on the several charts; at least 1½ hours is required for the translation and map drawing. The decoding and plotting of data from pilot balloon, radiosonde, and airplane observations begins much earlier than the translation of synoptic reports. This work, together with the drawing of isentropic charts and cross sections, requires much time, but when enough trained and experienced men are available it is usually well along or completed by 9:15 a. m.

WHAT A NEWSPAPER WEATHER MAP SHOWS

The daily newspaper weather map is a simplified form of the forecaster's principal chart. Wind, temperature, state of weather, and pressure (isobars) are shown for selected cities. On this ele-

298737°—41——39 +

mentary chart, highs and lows and their movements from day to day are related in a useful way to the major changes in the weather in any locality, but especially in the northern part of the country. By a study of the map, the newspaper reader can get a fairly good idea of the wind, rain, snow, clouds, and temperature changes as related to the forms of isobars.

Ordinarily during a period of cold winter weather the low is preceded by cloudiness, rising temperature, easterly or southerly winds, and rain or snow and is followed by colder winds from west to north and the cessation of precipitation; the high is then in control, with fine, cold weather which persists until the influence of the next low is felt. But the march of weather has many variations from this simple sequence; these changes are shown in much greater detail on the forecaster's chart. The newspaper reader who watches the map in connection with changes in his own locality may acquire a certain proficiency in anticipating the outstanding changes in the weather. The map enables him to develop a better appreciation of the reasons for the Weather Bureau forecasts, helps him to understand the weather data in the table near the map, and assists him in applying the forecasts and data to his individual needs.

Newspaper maps are prepared in Weather Bureau field offices for publication locally. The New York office makes the map used for distribution by wirephoto.

The Scientific Basis of Modern Meteorology

By C. G. Rossby [1]

IN SEVERAL SCIENCES on which agriculture is closely dependent there have been striking developments in recent decades, and these have resulted in rapid progress of great benefit to mankind. Genetics, soil science, and nutrition have all made great strides based on important fundamental discoveries. Latest to join this group is meteorology. Here is a semitechnical presentation of the physical basis of this science as it has been developed since the last great war.

[1] C. G. Rossby is Assistant Director of the Weather Bureau.

THE SCIENCE of meteorology does not yet have a universally accepted, coherent picture of the mechanics of the general circulation of the atmosphere. This is partly because observational data from the upper atmosphere still are very incomplete, but at least as much because our theoretical tools for the analysis of atmospheric motions are inadequate. Meteorology, like physics, is a natural science and may indeed be regarded as a branch of the latter; but whereas in ordinary laboratory physics it is always possible to set up an experiment, vary one factor at a time, and study the consequences, meteorologists have to contend with such variations as nature may offer, and these variations are seldom so clean-cut as to permit the establishment of well-defined relationships between cause and effect.

Under these conditions theoretical considerations become more important than ever. The atmosphere may be considered as a turbulent fluid subjected to strong thermal influences and moving over a rough, rotating surface. As yet no fully satisfactory theoretical or experimental technique exists for the study of such fluid motions; yet it is safe to say that until the proper theoretical tools are available, no adequate progress will be made either with the problem of long-range forecasting or with the interpretation of past climatic fluctuations.

Certain phases of the admittedly oversimplified analysis of the circulation of the atmosphere presented in this article may be traced as far back as 1888, to the German physicist Von Helmholtz, but other parts are the result of recent research and should, to some extent, be considered as the author's personal view. The combination of these various elements into a still fairly crude bird's-eye view of the atmosphere and its circulation was undertaken during the last 4 or 5 years as a byproduct of an intensive study of Northern Hemisphere weather, with which the author had the good fortune to be associated. This study was conducted as a cooperative project between the United States Department of Agriculture and the Massachusetts Institute of Technology and was to a large extent supported by Bankhead-Jones funds. A brief historical outline of the development of the theory will be found at the end of the article.

CONVECTIVE CIRCULATION

The energy that drives the atmosphere is obtained from the sun's radiation. Just outside the atmosphere an area exposed at right angles to the sun's rays would receive radiant energy at the rate of about 2 gram-calories per square centimeter per minute. The earth is approximately spherical, and its surface area is therefore four times as large as the cross-section area intercepting the sun's rays; it follows that on an average each square centimeter at the outer boundary of the atmosphere receives about one-half of a gram-calorie per minute. Part of this radiation is reflected back to space from the upper surface of clouds in the atmosphere, and part is lost through diffuse scattering of the solar radiation by air molecules and dust. It is estimated that a total of about 40 percent on an average is lost through these processes. (It is this reflection that determines the whiteness, or albedo, of the earth as a planet, and thus the earth is said to have an albedo of about 40 percent.) The remaining radiation passes through the atmosphere without much absorption and finally reaches the surface of the earth, where it is absorbed, generally without much loss through reflection. Snow surfaces furnish an important exception, since they may reflect as much as 80 percent of the incident solar radiation.

Since the mean temperature of the earth does not change appreciably, it follows that the heat gained from the sun must be sent back to space. In the surface of the earth the solar radiation is transformed into heat, and this heat is returned as "long"—infrared—radiation toward space. The rate at which the ground sends out such radiation is very nearly proportional to the fourth power of the absolute temperature. Thus, at 10° C. the heat loss of the ground through radiation is about 15 percent greater than at freezing, and it follows that the surface temperature of the earth must increase if the incident solar radiation increases, to maintain equilibrium between radiation income and loss. The ground is very nearly a perfect radiator, that is, it sends back to the atmosphere and to space the maximum amount obtainable from any surface at a particular temperature.

All the invisible radiation from the ground cannot escape to space; the larger part of it is absorbed in the atmosphere, principally by the water vapor in the lower layers, but also to some extent by small amounts of ozone present in the upper atmosphere. The atmosphere in turn emits infrared (heat) radiation upward and downward. The radiation emitted in either direction increases with the mean temperature of the atmospheric column but is always less than the radiation emitted by a perfect radiator of the same temperature. The more perfectly the atmospheric column absorbs the ground radiation from below, the more perfectly it radiates. It is evident that if radiative processes alone controlled the behavior of the atmosphere it would have to emit as much as it absorbs. Since it emits in two directions but absorbs appreciably only from the ascending ground radiation, it follows that the mean temperature of the atmosphere must be lower than that of the ground. Also, since the ground receives not only solar radiation but also infrared radiation from the atmosphere, the ground temperature must be higher than might be expected from the intensity of the incident solar radiation alone.

The preceding analysis shows that the atmosphere serves as a protective covering which raises the mean temperature of the surface of the earth. This is often referred to as the "greenhouse" effect of the atmosphere. The analysis also shows that the atmosphere as a whole must be colder than the ground. The reasoning may be refined by considering the atmosphere as consisting of a number of superimposed horizontal layers, and it may then be shown that the mean temperature must decrease upward from layer to layer, fairly rapidly near the ground, then more and more slowly. At great heights (above 10 kilometers, or 6 miles) the temperature becomes very nearly constant. This layer is called the stratosphere.

Up to this point our analysis has been based on the assumption that no appreciable direct absorption of solar radiation occurs in the atmosphere. This is approximately correct as far as the lowest 20 kilometers (12 miles) of the atmosphere are concerned. However, between approximately 20 to 50 kilometers (12 to 30 miles) above the ground the atmosphere contains a certain amount of ozone, increasing from the Equator to high latitudes, and this ozone is capable of directly absorbing some of the radiation emitted by the sun and also, to a somewhat lesser extent, part of the long-wave radiation from below. As a result, in the upper portions of this ozone layer the air temperature appears to exceed the mean air temperature next to the ground. It is this ozone layer which protects us from the extreme ultraviolet rays in the sun's radiation.

At still higher levels the oxygen and the nitrogen in the earth's atmosphere are capable of intense direct absorption of solar radiation. For this and other reasons, it is now generally believed that the temperature again rises to values which may be as high as 500° to 1,000° Abs. above 150 kilometers (93 miles) above sea level.

This uppermost region of high temperature is located at a height where the air density is so small that no appreciable direct dynamic effect on air circulation in the lower layers of the atmosphere can be expected. It is necessary to admit, however, that temperature variations and resulting circulation at the ozone level may be significant so far as weather and wind in the lowest strata are concerned. No existing theory suggests a definite mechanism for control of sea level circulation and weather by an ozone layer. On the other hand, circulation in the lowest 20 kilometers of the atmosphere has definitely been shown to produce redistributions of the ozone aloft, and hence atmospheric ozone has of late become an element of decided interest even to practical meteorologists, as a means of tracing air movements in the stratosphere.

Until our knowledge of the absorption and emission of radiation by water vapor increases, it is not possible to state what the final decrease of temperature with elevation would be in case of purely radiative equilibrium, but it is probable that in the lowest portion of the atmosphere it would be far steeper than the decrease actually observed (about 6° C. in 1 kilometer, or 17° F. in a mile). As a result of evaporation, the lowest layers would be very nearly saturated with water vapor. It can be demonstrated that a saturated atmosphere in which the decrease in temperature with elevation is more rapid than the value just indicated must be mechanically unstable or, allowing for its compressibility, top-heavy, and thus must tend to turn over. Violent vertical currents (convection) would result, which would carry water vapor and heat from the earth's surface to higher levels.

At these upper levels the water vapor would condense as the result of expansion cooling, and from there the heat realized through the condensation processes would be sent out to space through infrared radiation. In this way the free atmosphere would actually give off more heat by radiation than it would absorb, and the loss would be balanced by convective transport of latent heat upward. Thus an atmosphere heated uniformly from below in all latitudes and longitudes—that is, the atmosphere of a uniformly heated nonrotating globe—would show no sign of organized circulation between different latitudes but would be characterized by violent convection somewhat like that in a kettle of water which is being heated from below.

Rising bodies of air expand with decreasing air pressure and cool as the result of the expansion. In the convectively unstable atmosphere here described, the ascending currents would acquire their momentum in the overheated layers next to the ground and rise beyond the level where they reach temperature equilibrium with the

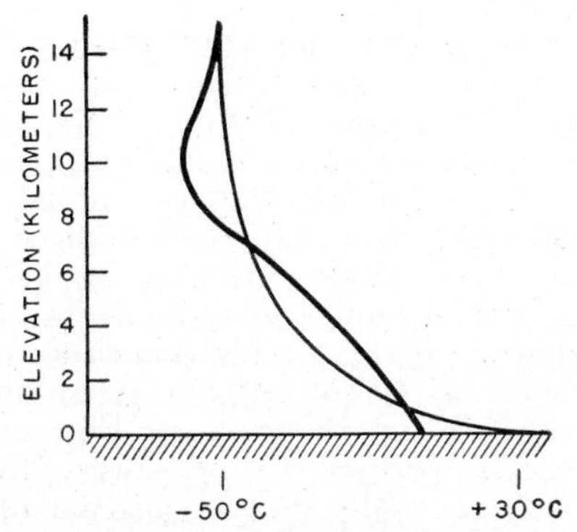

FIGURE 1.—The thin line shows how the temperature would drop with height if radiation alone controlled the state of the atmosphere. This is an unstable arrangement resulting in violent overturning. The heavy line shows the result—cooling next to the ground, a moderate temperature drop with elevation in the lower atmosphere (troposphere), then a marked temperature minimum (tropopause), and above that an almost constant temperature.

environment. As a result of this overshooting, a layer of minimum temperature would be created at the top of the lower, convective portion of the atmosphere (the troposphere). It follows that troposphere and stratosphere would be separated by a narrow transition zone (tropopause) of rapid temperature increase upward. The effect of convection on an unstable temperature distribution assumed to have been established by radiation is shown in figure 1. Figure 2, *A*, shows the convective circulation of the troposphere on a uniformly heated nonrotating globe, as described.

MERIDIONAL (NORTH-AND-SOUTH) CIRCULATION

Into this chaotic state a certain order is brought through the fact that the incoming solar radiation is far from uniformly distributed over the surface of the earth. Because of the low angle of incidence of solar radiation in polar regions, a given horizontal area in high lati-

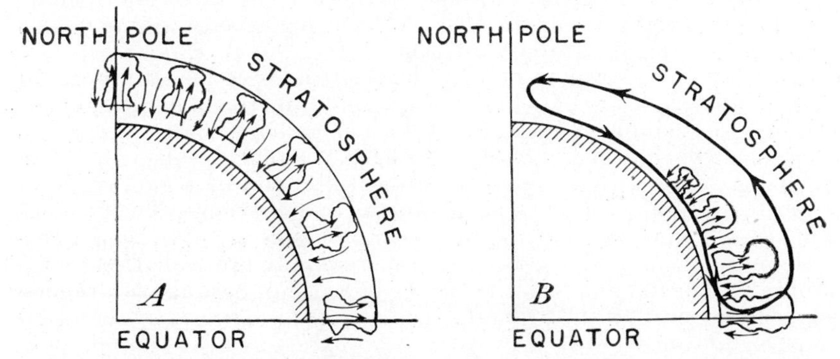

FIGURE 2.—Schematic diagrams illustrating *A*, the heavy, irregular convective activity, accompanied by cumulus and thunderstorm clouds, that would characterize the atmosphere if the sun's heat were applied uniformly everywhere and the earth did not rotate; *B*, concentration of convection in the vicinity of the Equator, north winds near the ground and south winds aloft, which would result on a nonrotating earth with the sun's heat applied mainly in low latitudes, as it actually is on the rotating earth.

tudes receives far less solar radiation than an equal area closer to the Equator. To determine the consequences of this concentration of heat income in equatorial regions, it is advisable for a moment again to disregard the rotation of the earth and investigate what would happen if the earth stood still but the sun followed its normal path across our sky. In response to the greater heat income in low latitudes, the temperature there would rise until the increased temperature of the atmosphere in this region would result in increased infrared radiation toward space, capable of reestablishing complete balance with the heat received from the sun. Such an equilibrium corresponds to a far greater increase from Pole toward Equator in surface temperature or in the temperature of the lower atmosphere than is actually observed. As a result of this heating of the atmosphere in low latitudes, the air there would expand vertically, while the cooling in high latitudes would result in a vertical shrinking.

Thus, at a fixed level of, say, 5 kilometers (3 miles) above sea level, a greater portion of the total atmospheric air column would be found overhead near the Equator than near the Poles. Since the air pressure always measures the weight of the superimposed air column, it follows that higher pressure would prevail at the 5-kilometer level near the Equator than near the Poles. Air, like any fluid, tends to move from high to low pressure, and thus the upper atmosphere would be set in motion from the Equator polewards. This motion obviously would raise the sea level pressure near the Poles and reduce it near the Equator, and as a result the surface air would move from Poles toward Equator.

Considering the Northern Hemisphere only, it is thus evident that the inequality in heat income between latitudes produces, on a nonrotating globe, south winds aloft and north winds below. This circulation scheme is illustrated in figure 2, *B*. Relatively warm air is carried northward aloft and relatively cold air is carried southward near the ground. As a result, it is no longer necessary for the ground and the sea surface in low latitudes to reradiate all the local radiation income to space, but part of this heat is used up in evaporation and is transported northward and upward in the form of latent and realized heat. It is finally returned to space from higher latitudes or higher elevations through infrared radiation.

Thus a vertical column of air in high latitudes no longer absorbs as much radiation as it emits but is continually suffering a net loss of heat through the combined effects of the various radiative processes. This loss is balanced by a gain of heat (realized or latent) resulting from the exchange of air with more southerly latitudes and by a gain resulting from realization of latent heat through condensation. Even though our present knowledge of the radiative processes in the atmosphere is still very incomplete, it is becoming increasingly probable that everywhere in high and middle latitudes the free atmosphere above a shallow layer of air next to the ground is constantly losing heat by radiation. The significance of water vapor as a carrier of heat (latent) poleward and upward is, for the same reason, becoming more and more appreciated.

As a result of the net transport of heat poleward the temperature contrast between Pole and Equator is reduced.

The poleward flow of warm air aloft and the transport toward the Equator of relatively cold air next to the ground has the further effect of bringing about a reduction in the vertical temperature decrease. Thus instability is cut down and vertical convection reduced in middle and high latitudes.

The picture thus obtained, that of an atmosphere heated from below and rising near the Equator, chilled and sinking in higher latitudes, requires a few additional comments to eliminate possible misunderstandings. Even in high latitudes the temperature decreases upward. Thus, if the air in these regions is steadily sinking, the individual air particles must be getting warmer, which would hardly seem to be in accord with the idea that the air in this region is losing heat through radiation. It must be remembered, however, that air is highly compressible. As the air sinks it comes under the influence of higher pressure. Owing to the compression its temperature rises, just as the temperature of a gas in a cylinder rises with compression. In the atmosphere, the rate at which the temperature of a sinking particle would rise as a result of compression is about 10° C. in 1 kilometer. Thus, if the temperature of a sinking air particle rises only 6° C. in 1 kilometer, it means that the particle has given off heat corresponding to a temperature drop of about 4° C. Dry air, rising through the atmosphere, cools through expansion at the same rate, 10° C. in 1 kilometer. Thus if a rising current shows a temperature drop of only 6° C. per kilometer, heat must have been added, corresponding roughly to a temperature increase of 4° C. per kilometer. If this additional amount of heat is not available, the temperature at fixed upper levels would obviously drop.

In saturated air, rising through the lower atmosphere, a certain amount of heat is made available through the condensation of the water vapor carried along by the current. Thus the expansion cooling of saturated air is less intense than the expansion cooling of dry air. The actual rate of cooling varies, but it amounts to about 6° C. per kilometer in the lower atmosphere for temperatures around freezing.

The circulation described above between a heat source in low latitudes and at low elevations and a cold source in middle and higher latitudes but distributed over all elevations works on the same principle as a simple heat engine. In such an engine the difference between the heat received at the heat source and the heat given off at the cold source is converted into work. Here it appears as kinetic energy of the wind system. Unless brakes are applied, the wind must constantly increase in speed. Such brakes are provided by the friction between the winds and the ground (or sea surface). Since no appreciable changes are wrought in the surface of the earth, the energy of the winds is steadily converted into heat, which ultimately must be radiated back to space. Thus, in the final analysis, the total amounts of radiation received and given off by the planet Earth must equal each other.

The scheme just outlined differs sharply from the true situation observed in the atmosphere, and this discrepancy depends mainly on two factors completely neglected up to the present time. The first of these is the rotation of the earth; the second the distribution of continents and oceans. The effect of the rotation will be discussed first, the earth's surface still being considered as uniform.

INFLUENCE OF THE EARTH'S ROTATION

The earth does not appreciably change its speed of rotation, and thus it may be assumed that on an average it neither receives momentum from nor gives off momentum to the atmosphere. The rotation, however, does profoundly affect the character of the flow patterns observed in the atmosphere.

To understand the influence of the earth's rotation, consider first this simple experiment: If a marble attached to a piece of string is placed on top of a smooth table and swung around the free end of the string and if then the length of the string is shortened, it will be found that the speed of the marble increases. If the string is shortened to one-half its original length, the speed of the marble is doubled; if the string is reduced to one-third its original length, the speed of the marble is tripled. Thus the product of speed and radius of rotation remains constant during the experiment. This product is usually referred to as the angular momentum (per unit mass) of the marble.

A ring of air extending around the earth at the Equator, at rest relative to the surface of the earth, spins around the polar axis with a speed equal to that of the earth itself at the Equator. If somehow this ring is pushed northward over the surface of the earth, its radius is correspondingly reduced; and it follows from the principle set forth that the absolute speed of the ring from west to east increases. Since the speed of the surface of the earth itself from west to east decreases northward, it follows that the moving ring, in addition to its northward velocity, must acquire a rapidly increasing speed from west to east relative to the earth's surface.

The principle itself may be illustrated very simply by an extreme and absurd case. The eastward speed of the earth itself at the Equator is about 465 meters (509 yards) per second. A ring of air displaced from this latitude to latitude 60, where the distance from the axis of the earth is only half that at the Equator, would appear in its new position with double the original absolute velocity, or 930 meters (1,017 yards) per second. Since the speed of the earth itself at this latitude is only half what it is at the Equator, or 232 meters (254 yards) per second, it follows that a ring of air thus displaced would move eastward over the surface of the earth with a relative speed of 698 meters per second (about 1,560 miles per hour). Obviously such wind speeds never occur in the atmosphere, one reason being the effect of frictional forces, another the fact that large-scale atmospheric displacements never are symmetric around the earth's axis or as large as those indicated.

It is apparent, however, that this tendency toward the establishment of west winds in northward-moving rings of air and of east winds in southward-moving rings must modify the previously described meridional (north-south) circulation scheme considerably. This is best seen if one assumes that the meridional circulation scheme characteristic of a nonrotating earth (fig. 2, *B*) is suddenly set in operation on a rotating earth in which the atmosphere previously was at rest relative to the ground. The moment the circulation begins, west winds (relative to the earth) would begin to develop in the upper atmosphere, with a slight component northward, and east winds in the lower atmosphere, with a slight component southward.

In this scheme ground friction plays a basic role, since it prevents the development of excessive east winds in the surface layers. The upper atmosphere, in which west winds prevail, is not in direct contact with the earth's surface; however, mixing of air between the upper and lower strata must reduce the west winds aloft as well as the east winds below. Since the momentum of the east winds also is reduced from below, through the effect of ground friction, it is apparent that the mass of the west winds aloft would far exceed the mass of the easterlies near the surface. Figure 3, *A*, illustrates what the velocity distribution would be a short time after the rotation began.

Certain features of this picture agree well with observed conditions. Above 4 or 5 kilometers (2½ to 3 miles), westerly winds prevail in all latitudes. At sea level, easterly wind components are normally observed between latitude 30° N. and 30° S. Other belts of easterly wind components are observed in the polar regions, north of latitude 60° N. and south of latitude 60° S. Unexplained, however, is the fact that in each hemisphere westerly winds prevail also at sea level within a broad belt between latitudes 30° and 60°, approximately.

It is fairly easy to see that the theoretical model in figure 3, *A*, characterized by east winds everywhere in the surface layers, is physi-

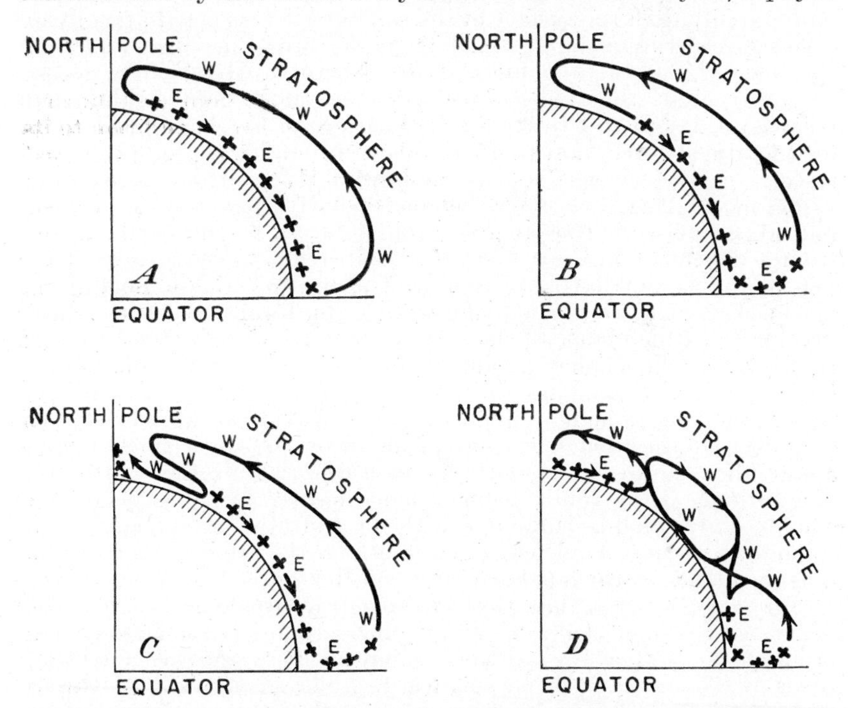

FIGURE 3.—Why the earth's rotation leads to a break-down into several cells of the simple meridional (north-south) circulation represented in figure 2, *B*. *A*, A short time after the meridional circulation indicated by the arrows is set in operation, west winds appear aloft, east winds below. *B*, Gradually the upper west winds are brought down to the ground near the Pole, and the east winds rise near the Equator. *C*, The west winds are retarded by friction and seek their way northward, but cooling and sinking continue next to the Pole. Finally, *D*, a complete three-cell circulation system develops.

cally impossible as a steady state. If east winds prevailed in all latitudes, friction between the atmosphere and the solid earth would constantly tend to reduce the rotation of the earth. On the other hand, the atmosphere would constantly gain momentum from the earth. Sooner or later a state of equilibrium would be established in which the atmosphere would neither gain nor lose momentum through contact with the earth—an equilibrium which is known to prevail, since the rotation of the earth for practical purposes can be regarded as constant. Such an equilibrium requires that the retarding influence of the east winds must be offset by the accelerating influence of a belt or belts of west winds, also in the surface layers. It is clear, however, that this argument is incapable of determining the number, width, and strength of the required west-wind belts. It is the purpose of the four diagrams in figure 3 to explain why the initial meridional circulation, under the influence of the earth's rotation, necessarily must break down into at least three separate cells on each hemisphere.

In order to understand the successive stages of development indicated in figure 3, it is first necessary to discuss, in some detail, the effect of the rotation of the earth on the relative motion of air over its surface. Wherever a ring of air parallel to a latitude circle is rotating more rapidly than the surface of the earth itself, it is acted upon by an excess of centrifugal force which tends to throw the ring away from the axis of the earth, which in the Northern Hemisphere means southward.[2] If the ring rotates with the same speed as the earth (that is, if it is at rest relative to the surface of the earth) this excess of centrifugal force vanishes. If this were not the case, any object resting on the surface of the earth would be thrown toward the Equator. A ring of air rotating more slowly than the earth itself, and hence appearing as an east wind relative to the earth, suffers from a deficiency in centrifugal force and tends to move toward the axis of the earth, that is, in this hemisphere, toward the north. To keep a west-wind belt from being thrown southward, the atmospheric pressure must be higher to the south than to the north of the ring (in the Northern Hemisphere), thus producing a force directed northward and capable of balancing the excess centrifugal force. If no such pressure force (gradient) is available, the ring will be displaced slightly southward until enough air has piled up on its south side to bring about the required cross-current pressure rise to the south and equilibrium. The total displacement needed for this purpose is usually quite small as compared with the width of the current.

To keep an east-wind belt in equilibrium, the atmospheric pressure must be higher on the north side than on the south side (in the Northern Hemisphere), so that the resulting pressure force balances the deficiency in centrifugal force acting on the ring. It has already been brought out that in the Northern Hemisphere air moving northward tends to acquire a velocity eastward, while air moving southward tends to acquire velocity westward. To offset this tendency toward deflection eastward,[3] a north-bound current of limited width piles up

[2] That part of the centrifugal force (per unit mass) which corresponds to the earth's own rotation is balanced by a component of the earth's gravitational attraction. The resultant of this component of the centrifugal force and of the earth's total true gravitational attraction is perpendicular to the earth's surface and constitutes what is normally referred to as gravity.

[3] The method of compensation here described is obviously impossible for circumpolar rings of air. Hence rings of air displaced northward acquire west-wind tendencies, south-bound rings east-wind tendencies, as brought out previously.

air to the east and creates higher pressure to the east than to the west, while the reverse applies to a south-bound current.

All these results may be generalized so as to apply to any wind direction. It is thus found that in the Northern Hemisphere steady winds always blow in such a fashion that the air pressure drops from right to left across the current for an observer facing downstream. The stronger the current flows, the steeper the drop in cross-current pressure. If, in any horizontal plane, lines of constant air pressure (isobars) are drawn, it may be seen that the air follows the isobars and moves counterclockwise around regions of low pressure (cyclones) and clockwise around regions of high pressure (anticyclones). In the Southern Hemisphere, the direction of motion around highs and lows is reversed.

It is apparent from the preceding reasoning that the relationship between wind and horizontal pressure distribution is truly mutual; a prescribed pressure distribution will gradually set the air in motion in accordance with the law set forth; likewise, if somehow a system of horizontal currents has been set up in the atmosphere, the individual current branches will very quickly be displaced slightly to the right (in the Northern Hemisphere) until everywhere the proper cross-current pressure drop from right to left has been established. Owing to the ease with which the atmosphere thus builds up the cross-current pressure drop required for equilibrium flow, the reasoning just outlined merely helps in understanding why the pressure in the Northern Hemisphere always rises from left to right for an observer looking downstream but does not by itself indicate that one current pattern is more likely to be established than another. To establish the character of the current patterns, either the pressure distribution must be known, or additional physical principles must be utilized.

It is now possible to return to a discussion of the circulation development in figure 3. In an axially symmetric atmosphere, such as the one here discussed, the absolute angular momentum of individual parcels of air does not change except through the influence of frictional forces. Under these conditions it is evident that the meridional (north-south) movements indicated in figure 3, *A*, must gradually redistribute the absolute angular momentum so as to create west winds next to the ground in the polar regions, and east winds aloft over the Equator. This is the state illustrated in figure 3, *B*. If the meridional circulation is slow, the pressure distribution in the atmosphere must constantly adjust itself fairly closely to the prevailing zonal winds. Thus, in figure 3, *B*, there would be a sea-level-pressure maximum at the transition point between the east winds in low latitudes and the west winds farther north. This latter belt of west winds can continue its southward displacement only as long as it is acted upon by an excess of centrifugal force. However, part of the air in this west-wind belt must steadily lose momentum through frictional contact with the ground. Under the influence of the resulting deficiency in centrifugal force this shallow portion of the belt next to the earth's surface must seek its way northward, as indicated in figure 3, *C*. Since air continues to cool and sink next to the Pole, it follows that the retarded west winds, for purely dynamic reasons, are forced to escape aloft some distance from the Pole. Finally a cellular state develops, as indicated in figure 3, *D*.

The Three Hemispheric Circulation Cells

Up to this point the break-down of the original simple meridional circulation scheme has been treated as a purely dynamic effect. It now becomes necessary to investigate whether the final mean circulation scheme is compatible with the thermal processes of the atmosphere. For this purpose we must fall back upon our as yet very incomplete knowledge of radiative processes in the atmosphere.

It was stated previously that practically everywhere above a shallow layer next to the ground the free atmosphere suffers heat losses through the combined effects of the various radiative processes to which it is subjected. In middle latitudes at 2 or 3 kilometers above sea level, these losses would produce a cooling at fixed levels of the order of magnitude of perhaps 1° or 2° C. per day.

Thus, with the possible exception of equatorial regions, the free atmosphere everywhere serves as a cold source (condenser) for the circulation engine. Heat sources are located at the earth's surface and above the surface layers in those regions where latent heat is released through condensation. The release of latent heat through scattered, unorganized convective action is of little consequence for the atmospheric heat engine, but those regions where there is organized ascending mass motion with attending condensation and release of latent heat become important heat sources capable of driving the atmospheric circulation. It follows that the atmosphere itself to a considerable extent has the power to regulate the distribution of its heat sources and also, through dynamically produced temperature changes, to modify the intensity of its cold sources.[4] The latter effect follows from the fact that a temperature change modifies the emission, but not the absorption, of a given parcel of air.

It follows from the preceding discussion that the air ascending in the equatorial belt and spreading polewards at upper levels must lose heat fairly quickly and that parts of it must reach ground again when it is in the horse latitudes (in the neighborhood of 30° N. or S.). A branch of the descending air spreads polewards; another branch equatorwards. The poleward branch will appear as a west or southwest wind, and must eventually meet the cold air seeping equatorwards from the Pole. Forced ascent results, requiring a heat source which is provided through the release of latent heat in the ascending air.

Thus the original single meridional circulation cell characteristic of each hemisphere in the original scheme breaks up in such a fashion that one cell extends from the Equator to the horse latitudes, another from about latitude 60° polewards. The resulting scheme of circulation is illustrated in figure 4. In both extreme cells the heat sources are found at low levels, the cold sources well distributed along the vertical. Looking eastward at a meridional vertical section through the Northern Hemisphere, one would observe counterclockwise circulation in each of these extreme cells. These circulations are direct in the sense that they carry heat from heat source to cold source, all the while transforming a small fraction of the heat energy received into kinetic energy. The direct cell to the south may be called the trade-wind cell, since the southward-moving lower branch of this cell

[4] This would become significant in an atmosphere free from water vapor.

is responsible for the steady northeast trade winds just north of the Equator. For reasons which will appear, the northern cell will be referred to under the name "polar-front cell."

It now seems possible to offer an explanation also for the circulation in middle latitudes. In the two direct circulation cells to the north and to the south, strong westerly winds are continually being created at high levels. Along their boundaries with the middle cell, these strong westerly winds generate eddies with approximately vertical axes. Through the action of these eddies the momentum of the westerlies in the upper branches of the two direct cells is diffused toward middle latitudes, and the upper air in these regions is thus dragged along eastward. The westerlies observed in middle latitudes are thus frictionally driven by the surrounding direct cells. The excess of centrifugal force acting on these upper west winds of middle latitudes forces the air southward, but equilibrium is never reached, since the air still farther to the south, instead of piling up and thus permitting the establishment of an adequate cross-current pressure drop, cools through radiation and sinks to lower levels.

It has already been pointed out that the air which sinks in the horse latitudes spreads both polewards and equatorwards. The poleward branch must obviously appear as a west wind accompanied by a cross-current pressure drop northward. It continues to move northward, since the retarding influence of ground friction continually keeps the surface westerlies below the intensity required for equilibrium. Aloft the situation is reversed, since there the frictionally driven winds always remain slightly in excess of the value required to balance the cross-current pressure drop. The result is a motion northward near the surface, a slight motion southward aloft.

Thus, to an observer looking eastward, the meridional circulation in middle latitudes is clockwise and opposite to the direct counterclockwise circulations to the north and south. This middle cell serves as a necessary brake on the general circulation driven by the direct-working heat engines farther to the north and to the south. It has already

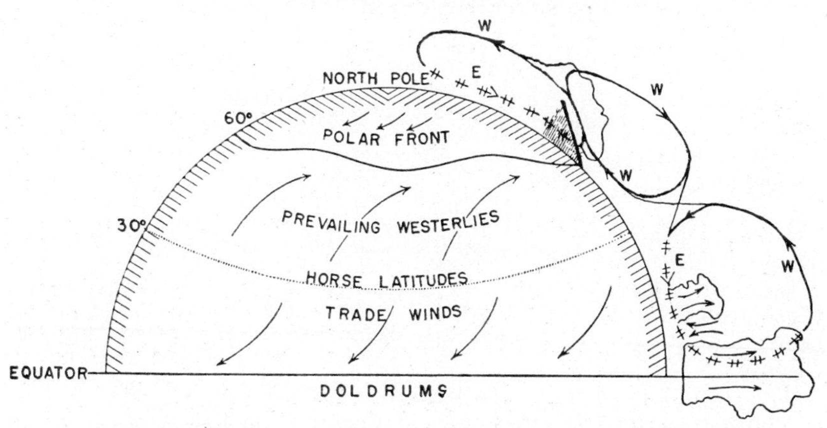

FIGURE 4.—The final cellular meridional circulation on a rotating earth: Convection near the Equator, a clear zone of descending air motion north of it (about latitude 30° N.), and heavy slanting cloud masses with accompanying precipitation in the polar-front zone (55°–60° N.).

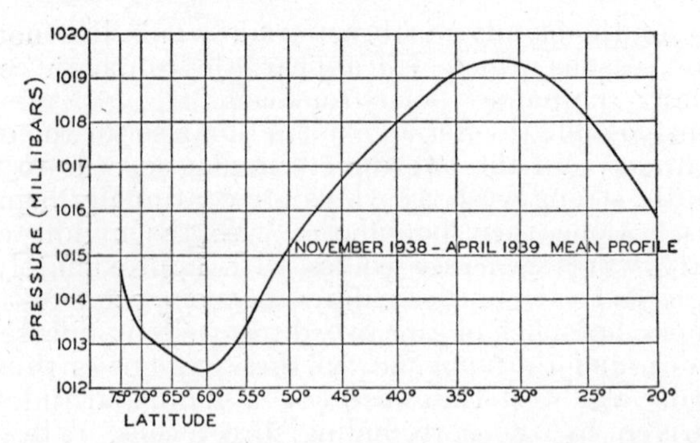

FIGURE 5.—Pressure profile for the Northern Hemisphere. (From (*2*).)[5]

been stressed that part of the (relative) momentum eastward generated aloft in the direct cells to the north and south spills over into the middle cell (through large-scale horizontal friction), where it is destroyed through slow southward displacement. The surface westerlies established in this middle cell serve the additional purpose of balancing the retarding force exerted on the earth itself by the easterlies farther south and north.

It follows from the previously established rule for the relation between wind and pressure that the sea level pressure must drop from the Pole southward to about 60° N., then rise to about 30° N., and finally drop from there on toward the Equator. At higher levels, where the wind is everywhere westerly, the pressure rises steadily from the Pole toward the Equator. Thus at sea level a trough of low pressure is established in latitude 60° and a ridge of high pressure in the vicinity of 30° N. The observed mean pressure as a function of latitude for the winter 1938–39, shown in figure 5, is in good agreement with the result of the previous analysis.

Climatic Zones

By this time it becomes possible to talk of climatic zones. The ascending motion in the equatorial region will obviously be attended by a great deal of convective activity, violent because of the extreme instability of the vertical temperature drop. Owing to the absence of horizontal contrasts, this convective activity will follow the sun with a great deal of regularity and produce the heavy afternoon showers characteristic of this climatic zone. The air descending in the horse latitudes will have lost a great deal of its moisture, and the descending motion leads to warming by compression at intermediate levels. Thus, in spite of relatively high surface temperatures, the vertical temperature drop is fairly weak and the air itself so dry as to prevent convection. This region, then, will be characterized by an arid, or semiarid, climate.

The region of ascending motion around 55° or 60° N. will obviously be characterized by a great deal of precipitation from the ascending air. It also is evident that this precipitation will be of an entirely

[5] Italic numbers in parentheses refer to Literature Cited, p. 654.

different nature from that observed in the Tropics. Because of the southward movement of cold polar air along the ground and the northward movement of warm and relatively moist subtropical air aloft, the vertical temperature drop in this region will be too weak to permit violent convection, and the precipitation must be associated with the orderly ascent of moist, warm air over the wedgelike tongues of polar air which extend southward. In this region, cold polar air and moist subtropical air converge next to the earth's surface. This, then, must be a region in which the surface isotherms, or lines of equal temperature, are constantly being crowded together and where abrupt transitions from subtropical to polar air conditions may be observed.

This transition zone, incessantly regenerated and incessantly destroyed, is in modern meteorology referred to as the polar-front zone. Here cold and warm air masses are in constant battle. This battle expresses itself through the formation of quasi-horizontal waves which normally progress from west to east along the front. The length of individual waves varies between 1,000 and 5,000 kilometers (about 600–3,000 miles). Because of the constant battle of air masses the polar-front region is characterized by strong temperature contrasts and a rapid succession of dry and wet spells.

The polar regions, characterized in the main by the descent of air which has lost most of its moisture in the ascent over the polar front, are characterized by cold arid or semiarid climate.

PLANETARY FLOW PATTERNS AND THE STABILITY OF ZONAL CIRCULATION

The preceding analysis indicates that the polar front tends to occupy a mean position parallel to a latitude circle. The Southern Hemisphere, with its practically uniform water cover, is probably to a very large extent characterized by such a zonal arrangement of the different wind belts and of the polar front. Thus it is fairly well established that the storms (polar-front waves) of high southerly latitudes move with far greater regularity from west to east than the storms of the Northern Hemisphere. This difference in behavior results from the influence of the nonzonal distribution of oceans and continents in the Northern Hemisphere, which leads to a break-down of the polar front. The break-down is reflected also in the sea-level-pressure distribution.

Figure 6 shows the practically zonal normal pressure distribution observed in the Southern Hemisphere, while figure 7 shows the extremely asymmetric normal pressure distribution characteristic of the Northern Hemisphere. Both figures refer to winter conditions. It is evident that particularly in the Northern Hemisphere the belts of high and low pressure have broken down into separate closed centers of high and low pressure. These centers are usually referred to by the somewhat misleading name "centers of action." During the winter season, at least five such centers may be observed in our hemisphere—the Icelandic and Aleutian lows, the Pacific high, the Bermuda or Azores high, and the Asiatic high. The daily synoptic weather charts for the Northern Hemisphere show a great many more moving high- and low-pressure systems, associated with the battle between cold and warm air masses along the polar front. The construction of mean charts permits the elimination of these moving

298737°—41——40

disturbances and brings out clearly the quasi-permanent character of the centers of action listed above.

Of late such mean pressure charts for periods of a week, a month, or a season have received a great deal of attention. When a sequence of weekly mean charts is studied it is found that the centers of action may move very slowly, eastward or westward, several weeks in succession. Frequently one or several of these centers of action may break up into several parts. With the breaking up of the zonal pressure distribution into separate centers of action or cells goes a breaking up of the mean polar front into two, three, or four separate portions, usually extending from southwest to northeast. The position of these separate mean fronts is determined by the size, development, and position of the individual centers of action. Since, on the other hand, most of the storms which control weather in our latitudes move along the frontal zones thus established, it is easy to see why it is imperative to understand the factors which lead to the break-down of the ideal zonal circulation into individual centers of action. As a

FIGURE 6.—Normal sea-level-pressure distribution (millibars) over the Southern Hemisphere in July. (From (*21*).) Compare this with figure 7 and note the great regularity and symmetry of the pressure distribution in the Southern Hemisphere, due, presumably, to the absence of large land masses.

first step it is necessary to discuss briefly the possible types of nonzonal steady flow patterns that can exist on the earth.

It is a well-known fact in mechanics that a rotating rigid body will not change its rate of rotation unless it is subjected to a force which produces a moment (torque) around the axis of rotation. If the body does not rotate initially, a torque is needed to set it in rotation. This simple principle can be applied to vertical columns of air as they move over the surface of the earth, but in so doing one must keep in mind that the earth itself is everywhere in a state of rotation around the vertical. To demonstrate this rotation it is sufficient to refer to the case of an ordinary freely suspended pendulum, which swings back and forth in a vertical plane. If a pointer is attached to the pendulum weight and permitted to trace the path of the pendulum in a sand bed just below, it will be found that the plane of the pendulum slowly turns clockwise (in the Northern Hemisphere). At the Pole the plane of oscillation would make one complete turn (360°) in 24 hours; in latitude

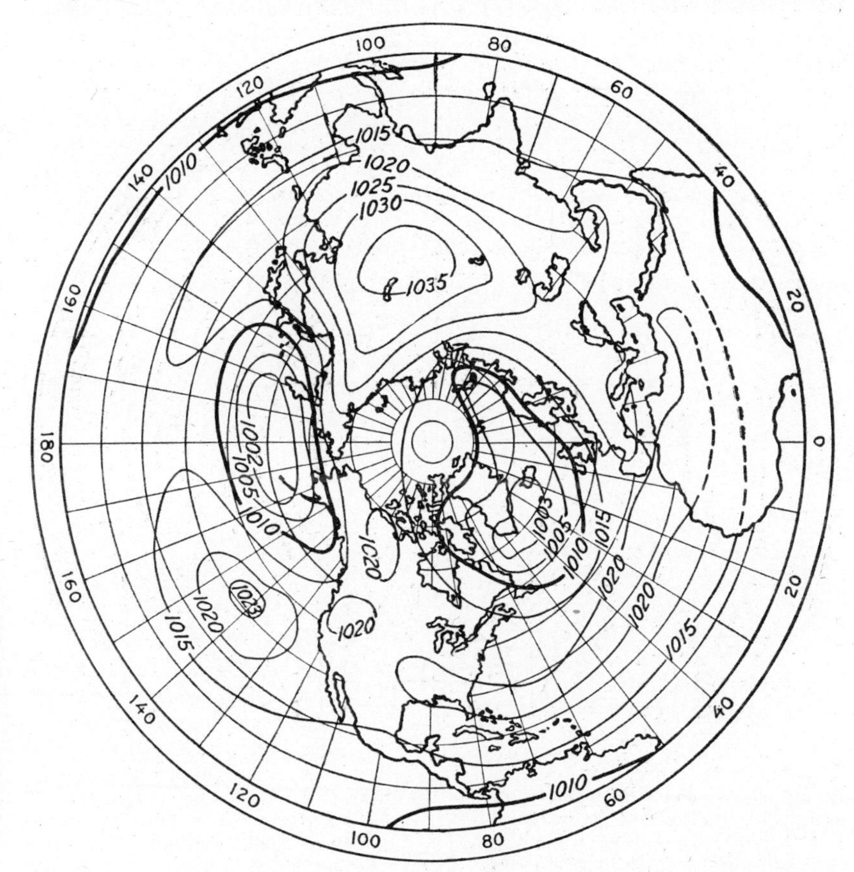

FIGURE 7.—Normal sea-level-pressure distribution (millibars) over the Northern Hemisphere in January. (From (*21*).) Note the great irregularity of the pressure distribution in the Northern Hemisphere as compared with that in the Southern (fig. 6), the two deep cyclonic (low-pressure) centers over the northernmost oceans, and the well-developed anticyclone (high pressure center) over Asia.

30° it turns more slowly, making one complete turn in 48 hours. It is well known that the time of rotation of the pendulum plane may be obtained by dividing 24 by the sine of the latitude.

It is obvious that this rotation of the plane of oscillation simply means that below our feet the earth rotates counterclockwise (clockwise in the Southern Hemisphere), rapidly at the Poles and more and more slowly as we approach the Equator. Vertical air columns which move from one latitude to another tend to take their rotation with them. Thus, a current of air originating in high northerly latitudes, where the cyclonic (counterclockwise) rotation of the earth is strong, and moving southward to a latitude where the cyclonic rotation of the earth is weak, will possess an excess cyclonic rotation around the vertical over that of the earth itself when it arrives at its destination. This excess rotation can express itself in two different ways or in a combination of both, as illustrated in figure 8.

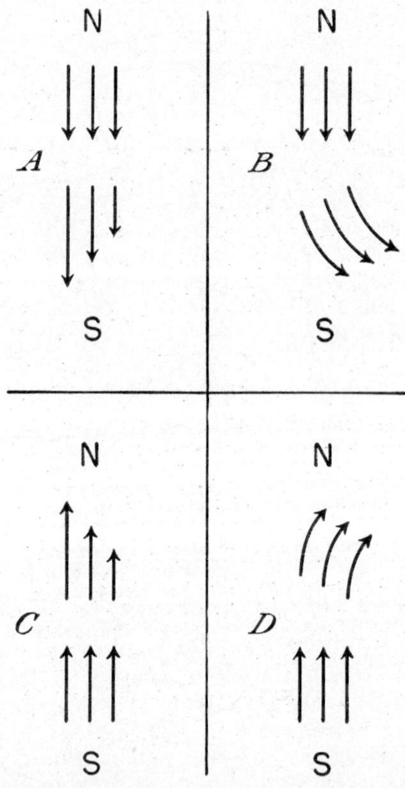

FIGURE 8.—Changes in current structure resulting from southward and northward movements in the Northern Hemisphere: *A*, A narrow current moving southward would, if forced to follow a straight path, acquire a strong cyclonic (counterclockwise) shear; *B*, if free to seek its own path, it would curve around cyclonically; *C*, a narrow current moving northward would, if forced to follow a straight path, acquire a strong anticyclonic (clockwise) shear; *D*, if free to seek its own path, it would curve around anticyclonically. In all cases the current would pile up air on the right-hand side looking downstream, but the slight deflections needed to bring this about would not materially affect the flow patterns illustrated.

The current can follow a straight path but develop a shear so that the right edge of the current (looking downstream) moves faster than the left edge (fig. 8, *A*). In the atmosphere there are several influences at work that normally prevent the development of strong shear zones and lead to the establishment of currents of fairly uniform velocity cross-stream. In that case the current is forced to bend around cyclonically, as indicated in figure 8, *B*. Figures 8, *C*, and 8, *D*, illustrate the corresponding effects in a north-bound current developing anticyclonic (clockwise) rotation.

When the mean zonal circulation was discussed, a uniform seeping southward of cold air from high latitudes was assumed. In that case there is, of course, no possibility for the establishment of cyclonically curved stream lines, and the excess of cyclonic rotation in the southward-moving belt of cold air should therefore lead to strong cyclonic shear in the northern belt of easterlies. Likewise, in the free atmosphere, where rings of air are displaced northward toward regions where the earth itself rotates more rapidly counterclockwise (cyclonically) around the vertical, the resulting deficiency in rotation of the displaced air columns must express itself in the form of anticyclonic shear. However, in both cases it can be said that the statistical mean northward and southward velocities associated with the general circulation between latitudes are so weak that frictional forces of all kinds have ample time to prevent the establishment of sharp shear zones. The situation is different in the case of air currents that for some reason or other are definitely deflected from their east-west motion. In these currents latitude changes occur so quickly that the frictional forces have inadequate time to act. In such currents, the excesses or deficiencies in rotation have a tendency to produce curved flow patterns. Initially straight currents from the north curve around cyclonically, currents from the south curve around anticyclonically.

It is particularly interesting to apply these results to a study of the stability of west-wind or east-wind belts of limited width. If a current from the west at some point in its path is subjected to a cyclonic torque which gives it a slight deflection northward, it follows that the current from then on will head toward higher latitudes, where the rotation of the earth itself around a vertical becomes stronger and stronger. Thus the relative cyclonic rotation (curvature) which the current acquired at the initial point of deflection will decrease and eventually, after sufficient displacement northward, change into an anticyclonic curvature. The current will then finally bend back toward its equilibrium position. As it moves southward it will pick up cyclonic relative rotation (curvature), and the net effect will be a sinusoidal, or wavelike, oscillation of the west-wind belt around a certain mean latitude, such that the current will form a series of standing waves downstream from the point at which it was disturbed initially.

The amplitude of these waves depends upon the intensity of the initial disturbance, but the wave length depends principally on the strength of the west-wind belt. The stronger the wind, the longer the wave length. For the wind velocities prevailing in the upper troposphere in our middle latitudes in wintertime, this wave length is of the order of magnitude of 5,000 kilometers (3,000 miles). These

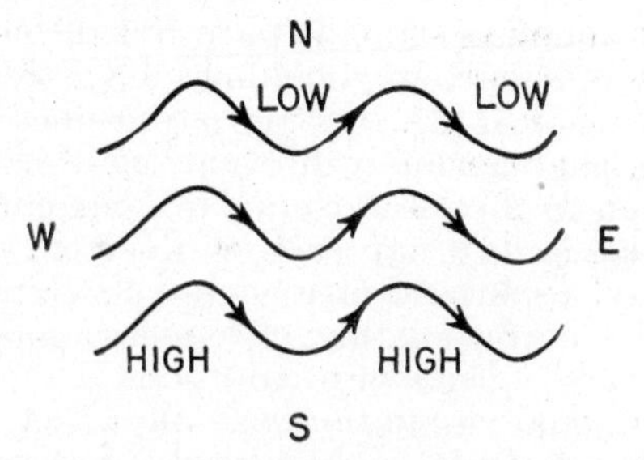

FIGURE 9.—Diagram of waves on a broad west-wind belt, showing troughs of low pressure and ridges of high pressure.

"resonance" waves give us a length scale for the large semipermanent centers of action into which the previously described symmetric zonal circulation actually breaks up.

If the same type of reasoning is now applied to a narrow current from the east, which at a given point in its path is given a slight cyclonic rotation (cyclonic curvature), it follows that the current from then on moves slightly southward. However, the farther south it moves, the stronger will be the cylonic rotation of the current, since it is constantly moving toward latitudes where the earth's own cylonic rotation around the vertical becomes weaker and weaker. Thus the current is deflected farther and farther away from its equilibrium latitude. Finally it will have turned around completely and will then appear as a west wind, but with sufficiently strong cylonic curvature to return to its original path. If the current had originally been deflected northward it would describe a complete anticyclonic circuit. This may be of importance in connection with the breaking up of the high-pressure belt around latitude 30°. It is fairly evident that the cold easterly winds to the north, because of the large body of cold air over the Arctic, are constrained to break up into cyclonic vortices.

The analysis shows that easterly winds are unstable and tend to break up into large cyclonic or anticyclonic eddies. The dimensions of the eddies thus formed increase with the velocity of the east wind itself, and they agree reasonably well with the dimensions of the cy-

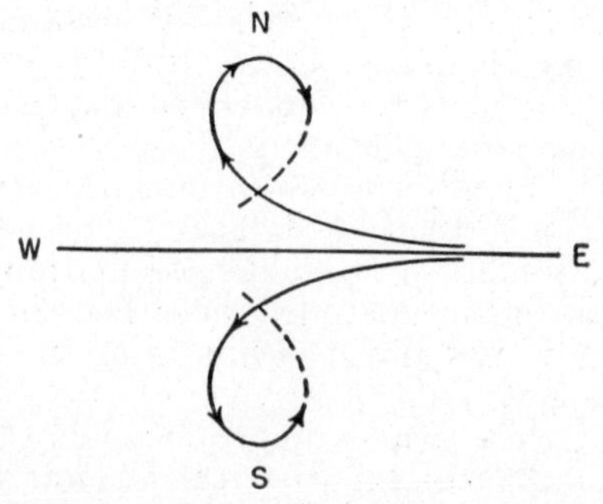

FIGURE 10.—The upper curve represents the path of a narrow east-wind belt which has received a small initial deflection northward. The lower curve represents the path of a current which has received an initial deflection southward. Since a current in a state of steady motion cannot intersect itself, the analysis suggests that narrow east-wind belts are unstable, resulting in the intermittent formation of large vortices.

clonic centers of action referred to above. Figure 9 illustrates a steady resonance wave on a broad west-wind belt and figure 10 the trajectory of a deflected east-wind belt of narrow width.

To completely understand the behavior of cold currents from the north a further reference should be made to the spinning-marble experiment discussed earlier. It was pointed out that by a shortening of the string the marble could be made to spin faster and by a lengthening of the string to spin more slowly. In the same way, the outer edge, or periphery, of a rotating column of air which is stretched vertically and shrunk horizontally will spin around more rapidly; if the column shrinks vertically and stretches horizontally it will spin more slowly. In applying this result to vertical columns in the atmosphere it is necessary to consider the absolute rotation. It thus follows that air columns which stretch vertically must acquire an excess (cyclonic) rotation relative to the earth, while air columns which shrink vertically acquire a deficient (anticyclonic) rotation relative to the surface of the earth.

It is a well-established fact that cold currents from the north gradually sink and spread out next to the surface of the earth. This sinking is most marked along the right-hand edge of the cold current (for an observer facing downstream). Thus the left-hand branch of the current curves around cyclonically as a result of the decrease in latitude, but the right-hand branch, in which strong sinking occurs, curves around anticyclonically. As a result the deflected cold current spreads south in a fanlike fashion.

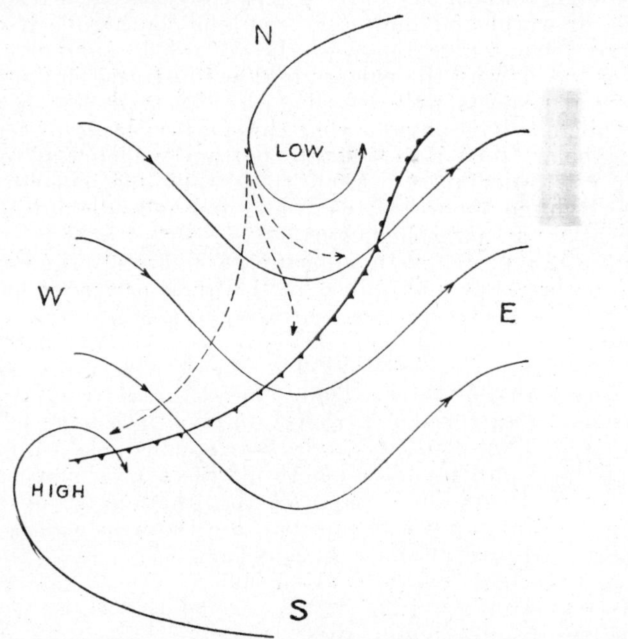

FIGURE 11.—Break-down of the zonal polar front and establishment of a typical branch front through the injection of polar air into a trough in the westerlies. Subsiding, undercutting branches of the polar air take on anticyclonic curvature (broken lines); nonsubsiding branches will curve around cyclonically and form the left edge of the cold wave. The polar front is indicated by a barbed line.

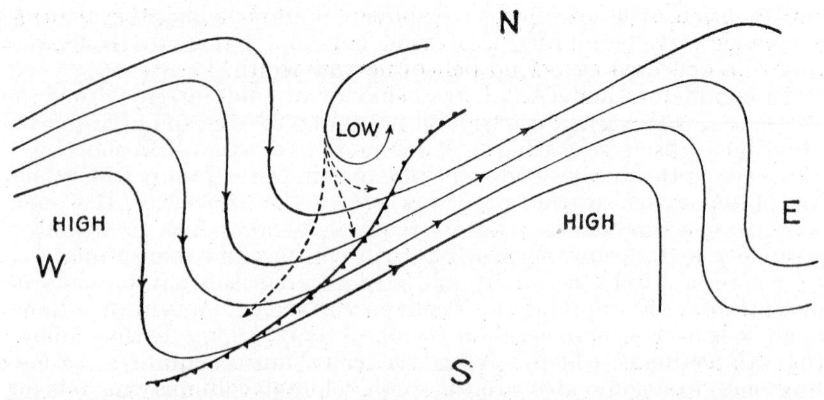

Figure 12.—Injection of polar air into a slanting trough of the westerlies. Such troughs may easily form as a result of thermal perturbations of the westerlies set up along the slanting eastern coast lines of Asia and North America-Greenland.

If for some reason the westerlies of middle latitudes are disturbed and a quasi-stationary wave pattern is established, the pressure will drop wherever a wave trough is being established. Cold air from the north will be pulled into these low-pressure troughs. Hence intermittent outbreaks of cold polar air from the previously undisturbed east-wind belt to the north are likely to occur wherever there is a trough toward the south in the westerlies. Corresponding outbreaks of warm and moist air from the southern belt of easterlies tend to occur where the westerlies are deflected northward. One obtains in this way the pattern of flow illustrated in figure 11, which in several respects well describes the observed flow pattern in the atmosphere. It is obvious that this pattern leads to a breaking up of the polar front into separate portions which run roughly from southwest to northeast. Along these individual polar fronts, waves form which move northeastward and gradually die out in the central low-pressure areas to the north.

Figure 12 represents a modification of figure 11 obtained by assuming that the crests and valleys of the quasi-permanent waves in the west-wind zone extend from southwest to northeast, parallel to three of the four principal boundaries between oceans and continents in the Northern Hemisphere. This theoretical picture agrees remarkably well with the observed mean pressure and frontal distribution in any one of the principal frontal zones of the Northern Hemisphere.

To each speed of the westerlies corresponds one definite resonance wave length, and this wave length increases with increasing strength of the westerlies. Thus it appears that the number of points where polar air is simultaneously injected into the west-wind zone depends upon the strength of the westerlies and decreases as the westerlies increase. In the Southern Hemisphere, where land masses are relatively insignificant or, in the case of the Antarctic Continent, symmetrically distributed, these injection points may occur in any longitude and thus the mean wind and pressure distributions should appear fairly uniform around the globe. In the Northern Hemisphere, on the other hand, preferential injection points are established, and the final mean pressure distribution is thus far from symmetric around the axis of the earth.

INTENSITY FLUCTUATIONS IN ZONAL CIRCULATION AND THE CIRCULATION INDEX

In view of the fact that the dimensions and positions of the circulation patterns associated with strong and weak circulation differ in a characteristic fashion, it is evidently important to develop a simple index to the intensity of the zonal circulation. It has been pointed out previously that the surface westerlies in middle latitudes form a part of a reverse meridional circulation cell which is driven by the direct cells to the north (polar-front cell) and to the south (trade-wind cell). Because of this frictional drive it is reasonable to assume that these surface west winds, at least qualitatively, furnish a good measure for the variations in the general zonal circulation of the atmosphere. A simple measure of the intensity of these sea level westerly winds may be obtained by taking the difference between the mean pressure observed in latitude 35° N., near the center of the subtropical high, and the mean pressure observed in latitude 55° N., just south of the pressure trough normally prevailing in the vicinity of latitude 60° N. This mean-pressure difference is very nearly proportional to the mean wind component from the west prevailing within this zone, if surface frictional forces are disregarded. In view of the variations in the difference between the mean temperature of an air column in latitude 35° N. and another air column in latitude 55° N., it is, unfortunately, impossible to use the same mean-pressure difference as a quantitative measure of the mean west-wind component at higher levels within the same zone, but it should at least serve as a qualitative index to the variations in circulation intensity at higher levels.

Mean weekly values of this circulation index have been computed since 1936 and show amazingly strong fluctuations from week to week in the circulation intensity. During the winter season these fluctuations range from an index value of about 15 millibars to one of about −5 millibars, the latter value indicating an actual reversal of flow in the surface layers (east wind). These fluctuations are well illustrated by the curve in figure 13. The variations in circulation intensity are obviously fairly irregular, but it is also evident that trends persisting through 3 or 4 weeks are fairly common during the winter. The irregularity of the variations in circulation intensity is sufficiently pronounced to effectively eliminate all possibility of long-range forecasting on the basis of periodicities, but the persistence tendency in the index curve is sufficiently high to permit judicious extension (extrapolation) of a trend for a week at a time. During the summer the fluctuations in circulation intensity are somewhat smaller and also more irregular. It is hard to see how adequate short-term long-range weather forecasts can be developed until there is an adequate understanding of these amazing fluctuations in the zonal circulation intensity.

It has already been mentioned that the energy of the westerlies depends upon the meridional circulation between heat sources and cold sources in the two direct meridional cells, to the north and to the south of the westerlies. It would, therefore, seem probable that a

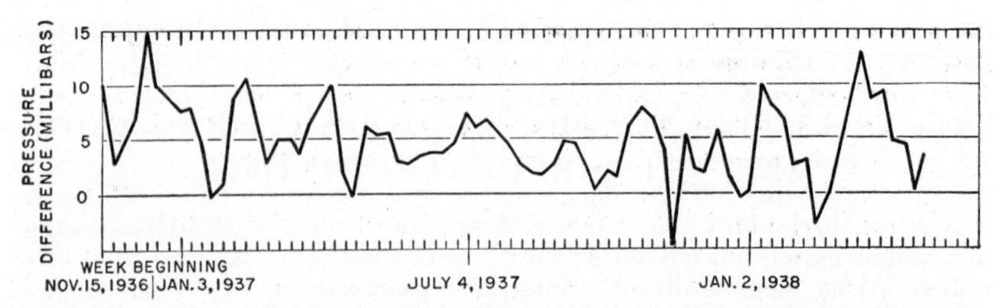

Figure 13.—Zonal circulation variations during the period November 1936–May 1938. (Adapted from (*2*).) This index to the zonal circulation is computed weekly as the difference between the mean pressure at latitude 35° and the mean pressure at latitude 55°. The greater this index is, the stronger the prevailing west wind in middle latitudes. Note the large amplitude of fluctuations in winter, particularly the occurrence of long trends downward or upward through several weeks in succession.

satisfactory understanding of the variations in the zonal circulation intensity cannot be reached until fairly complete temperature and humidity data from the upper atmosphere over the entire Northern Hemisphere are available in the form of daily routine measurements. No adequate physical theory is available at the present time from which the fluctuations in circulation intensity may be computed, but recent studies suggest that these fluctuations may be associated with the intermittent establishment of a direct inflow of deep, moist air from the equatorial trade-wind belt into the westerlies of middle latitudes. There is good reason to hope that the problem of the circulation fluctuations will be brought much closer to its solution within the next few years.

INFLUENCE OF LAND MASSES AND OCEANS ON THE CIRCULATION PATTERN

In older writings it is sometimes stated that the difference between land climate and sea climate is caused by the difference in specific heat between water and solid rock. It is more correct to emphasize that the upper layers of the ocean are nearly always in a state of violent stirring whereby heat losses or heat gains occurring at the sea surface are distributed throughout large volumes of water. This mixing process sharply reduces the temperature contrasts between day and night and between winter and summer.

In the ground, there is no turbulent redistribution of heat, and the effect of molecular heat conduction is very slight. Thus violent contrasts between seasons and between day and night are created in the interior of continents. During the winter the snow cover which extends over large portions of the northern continents reflects back toward space a large part of the sparse incident solar radiation. For these various reasons the northern continents serve as efficient manufacturing plants for dry polar air. The polar air cap is no longer symmetric but is displaced far to the south, particularly over the interior of Asia. This in turn means that the mean polar-front zone is deformed and tends to follow the boundaries of the northern continents, extending northeastward along the Pacific coast of Asia, then southeastward along the Rockies, and finally northeastward along our Atlantic coast toward Iceland. Our knowledge of the upper westerlies at high levels is still very incomplete, but it appears that they, too, are displaced southward over the Asiatic Continent.

The polar air which is being steadily manufactured over the interior of Asia generates a polar front which in the main follows the Pacific coast line of that continent. Just as pure easterly winds are established behind the mean polar front on a symmetric globe, northeasterly winds will be established to the north and west of the Asiatic polar front and southwesterly winds south and east of the same front. This arrangement of currents is, however, highly unstable. It has already been brought out that currents from the north tend to assume cyclonic curvature unless they have an opportunity to sink and spread out. The cold currents from the north behind the Asiatic polar front cannot spread out toward the interior where still deeper masses of cold air are stored. Hence they must stream south over the Pacific, and these intermittent outbursts help to maintain a deep cyclonic vortex off the Pacific coast of Asia.

The air masses which are found south and east of the Asiatic frontal zone and at higher levels stream toward the Aleutian Islands. As they move northward they must gradually curve around anticyclonically (clockwise). It has already been pointed out that the wave length of such an oscillating west-wind belt increases with increasing wind velocity. Hence, if the southwest or west-southwest winds off the coast of Asia are sufficiently strong they will follow the boundaries of the north Pacific Ocean, curving around anticyclonically as a result of their northward displacement. In this case a single frontal zone is established, along which storms move rapidly in an eastward direction, crossing the Pacific coast of North America in fairly high latitudes (British Columbia, Washington, Oregon).

On the other hand, as the southwesterly winds off the coast of China grow weaker, they tend to curve around anticyclonically much more sharply. A trough of low pressure may then be created in the middle or eastern part of the Pacific, and thus another injection point for polar air may be established. A new polar front, extending across the mid-Pacific from southwest to northeast, may thus be established by purely dynamic means, whenever the general circulation slows down. Storms (waves) traveling northeastward along this polar front bring moist, southerly winds to California. These moist air masses are trapped between the Pacific polar front on the one hand and the mountains and the cold air masses over the continent on the other. They are therefore forced to ascend, and in so doing they probably produce a large portion of the winter rains in southern and central California.

As a result of the production of polar air over Greenland and the North American continent, another polar-front zone is established over the Eastern States, extending from the lower Mississippi Valley over New England, Newfoundland, and the northern North Atlantic toward northern Norway. When the circulation in middle latitudes is very weak, a second Atlantic polar front may be established over western Europe. This doubling of the Atlantic polar front appears to be a more infrequent phenomenon than the doubling of the Pacific polar front.

Figures 14 and 15 represent an attempt at a comparison of the observed pressure distribution during a period of very weak zonal movement in middle latitudes with the computed air trajectories during a period of weak circulation. The observed pressure distribution (fig. 14) shows that the Aleutian low has split into two separate centers, one off Kamchatka and one in the Gulf of Alaska. Likewise, the Icelandic low has split up, with one center over Labrador and a second center in the form of a long trough extending southwestward from Spitzbergen to a point off Ireland. The center positions of these observed cyclonic whirls agree fairly well with the computed circulation centers in figure 15.

In computing this last circulation diagram it was assumed that the easterlies to the north have a mean velocity of 8.9 meters per second, the westerlies in middle latitudes a mean velocity of 15.5 meters per second, and the easterlies still farther to the south a mean velocity of about 13.3 meters per second. These velocities were chosen so as to give a proper wave length for the westerlies and the proper dimensions for the cyclonic and anticyclonic eddies to the north and

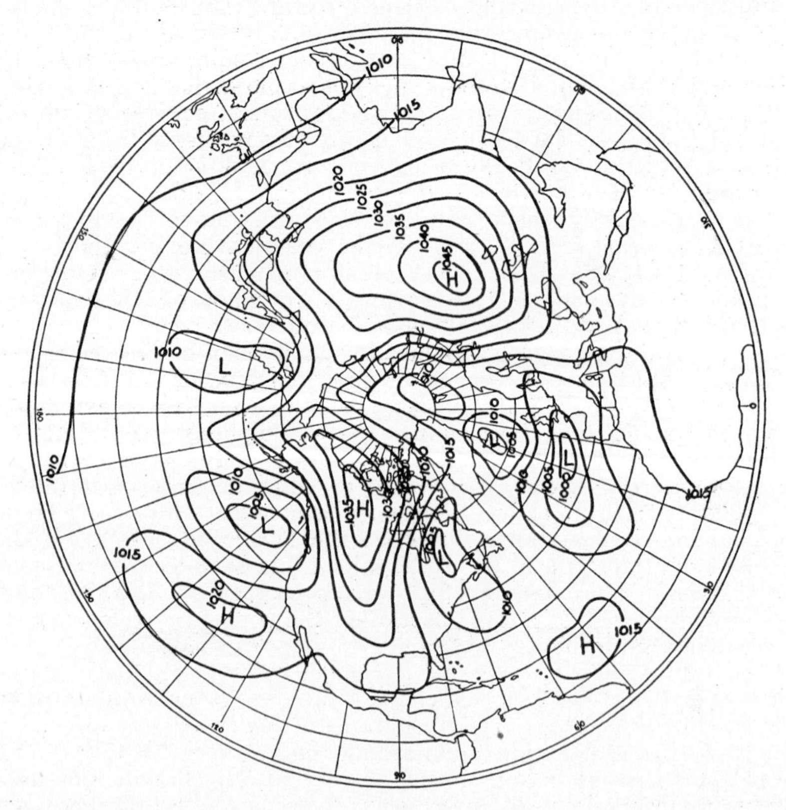

FIGURE 14.—Mean sea-level-pressure distribution (millibars) during a week of slow zonal circulation, November 14–20, 1937. (From (2).) Note two separate low-pressure centers in the Pacific, a well-developed continental high in North America, the split character of the Icelandic low, and the displacement toward Europe of the Asiatic high.

south. Thus the only claim that can be made for this theoretical analysis is that with reasonable values for the prevailing zonal winds it leads to flow patterns of a high degree of verisimilitude. In view of the disturbing influence on the mean zonal pressure distribution of the relatively shallow, cold anticyclones over Asia and North America, it is impossible to start the analysis from the observed zonal pressure distribution.

It is fairly apparent that both the theoretical and the observed circulation imply the existence of double polar fronts both in the Pacific and in the Atlantic. The positions of these mean fronts have been indicated by broken lines in figure 15.

During periods of strong circulation the theoretical resonance wave length analyzed previously becomes too large for the development of two frontal zones either in the Pacific or in the Atlantic. The resonance wave pattern is no longer free to develop, and the circulation pattern is probably mainly a function of the distribution of continents and oceans.

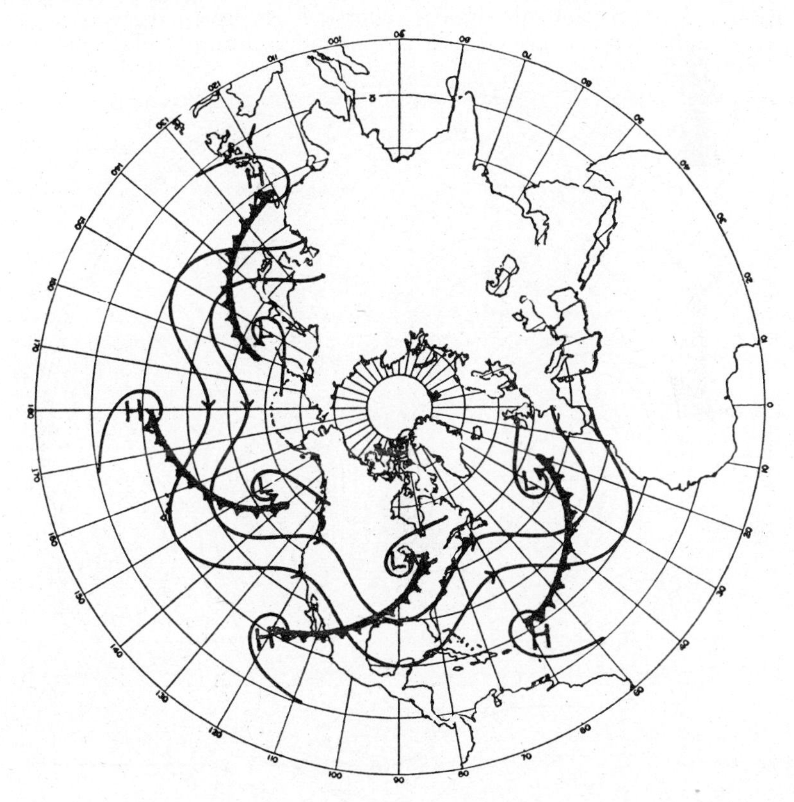

FIGURE 15.—An example of the theoretical planetary flow pattern for weak zonal circulation. Compare this diagram with figure 14 and note the presence in both of a split Aleutian low and a split Icelandic low, with one branch centered over eastern North America. In comparing the two diagrams it should be remembered that the wave pattern of the westerlies indicated here is in reality (fig. 14) obscured by shallow cold-air anticyclones but that it would appear clearly on a corresponding chart for the 3-kilometer level.

Figure 16 is typical of the mean pressure distribution during periods of strong circulation. A comparison between figures 14 and 16 reveals certain marked contrasts which appear to be typical.

During periods of strong circulation both the Aleutian and the Icelandic lows are characterized by single, well-developed centers and by large dimensions. The Aleutian low is then normally located near the Alaskan Peninsula and the Icelandic low in the vicinity of Iceland or even east and north of it.

During periods of weak circulation one or the other or even both of these centers split into two separate cells of smaller dimensions than normal. One part of the Aleutian low may be found near Kamchatka; one in the Gulf of Alaska. At the same time the Icelandic low is frequently displaced westward and southward, or it may, as in figure 14, split into two cells.

During periods of strong circulation, a fairly well developed high-pressure area, often referred to as the Great Basin high, is usually found over the southern portion of the Rocky Mountain States. This is really a part of the subtropical (warm) high-pressure area. North of this high-pressure area there is a rapid inflow of relatively mild

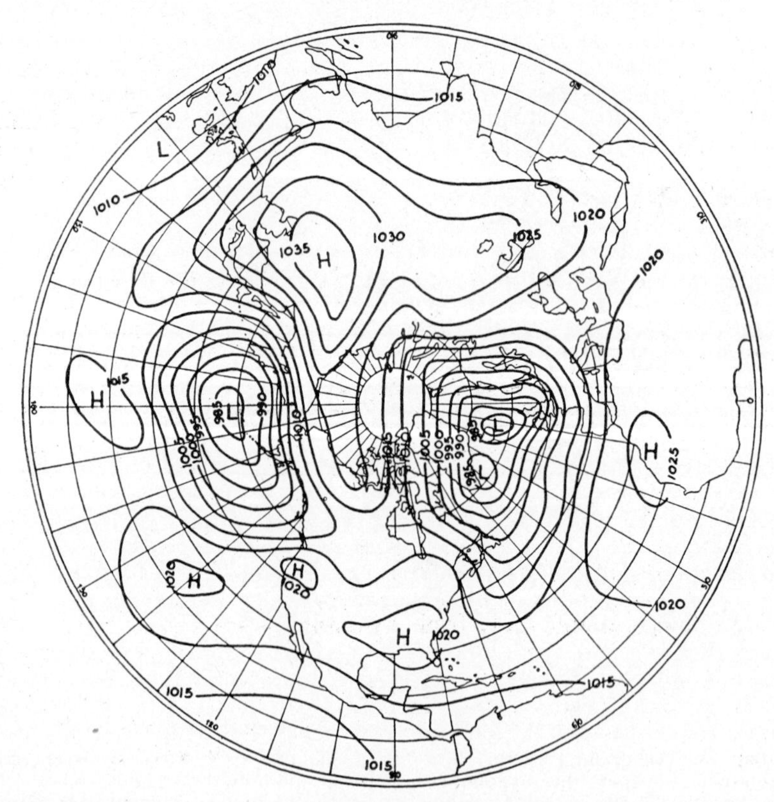

Figure 16.—Mean sea-level-pressure distribution (millibars) during a week of strong zonal circulation (January 9–15, 1938). (From (*2*).) Note the presence of a single strong Aleutian low, a single Icelandic low, and the displacement toward the Pacific of the Asiatic high.

Pacific air masses over the United States, and rapid air motion eastward prevails over the Northern States. There are very few indications of the development of a cold continental anticyclone over the interior of this continent.

During such periods of strong circulation, maritime inflow from the southwest characterizes weather conditions in northwestern Europe. Both our Pacific Northwest and northwestern Europe are then dominated by a rapid succession of wave cyclones—warm, moist, subtropical air masses alternating with relatively mild, maritime polar air masses moving in from the west or northwest. Rainfall on the Pacific coast occurs mainly far to the north, in British Columbia or Washington and Oregon.

Finally, during such periods of strong circulation, the Asiatic high appears to be displaced toward the Pacific side of Eurasia.

On the other hand, as the zonal circulation of middle latitudes weakens and finally reaches a minimum value, there is a marked tendency for the Great Basin anticyclone to disappear and for a strong continental anticyclone to develop over the interior of North America. The center of this anticyclone is located far to the north, in Canada, and a wedge of high pressure extends southward into the United States. Thus, in the surface layers, there is very little air movement from west to east across North America. At the same time, the Asiatic anticyclone is usually displaced westward, toward Europe. The effects of these pressure changes on weather conditions are profound. There will now be an outflow of cold continental air from the east over Alaska and even over British Columbia, and another outflow from the southeast of extremely cold continental air from Asia over northwestern Europe.

The polar-front cyclones, which move up over the Pacific toward that portion of the Aleutian low which during periods of weak circulation is located in the Gulf of Alaska, are quite apt to bring with them warm, moist air masses from the southwest. It has already been brought out that these moist currents are frequently trapped between the polar air masses which come down over the Pacific to the west and the mountains and continental air masses to the east. Thus forced to ascend, the moist air yields heavy rainfall fairly far south on the Pacific coast.

During periods of weak circulation, the theoretical sea-level-pressure distribution is so disturbed through the development of continental anticyclones that it may become unrecognizable. For this reason it is of some interest to look at the pressure distribution at higher levels, say 3 kilometers (about 2 miles), as determined with the aid of upper-air data now available daily from a number of stations in the United States (figs. 17 and 18). In figure 18, corresponding to a period of weak circulation, there are good indications of low-pressure troughs off the Pacific coast and east of the Atlantic coast. Figure 17, corresponding to a case of strong circulation, shows a single well-marked trough, probably an extension of the Icelandic low, extending southwestward through the Mississippi Valley.

During periods of strong circulation, characterized by strong west-to-east movements in middle latitudes, the belt of westerlies is usually displaced somewhat to the north of its normal position. Because of the prevailing strong winds, intense lateral mixing and turbulence

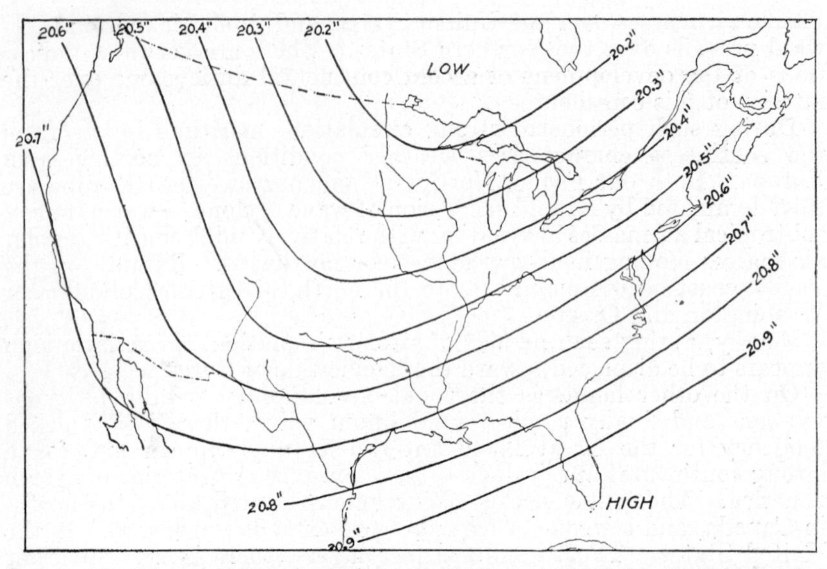

Figure 17.—Mean pressure (inches) at the 3-kilometer level for the 5-day period February 26–March 2, 1939. This map corresponds to a period of strong circulation. (From (*2*).) Notice the general trend of the isobars from west-southwest to east-northeast in the eastern half of the country, indicating a general west-southwestern wind. This type of wind distribution aloft in the eastern part of the United States corresponds to temperatures well above normal.

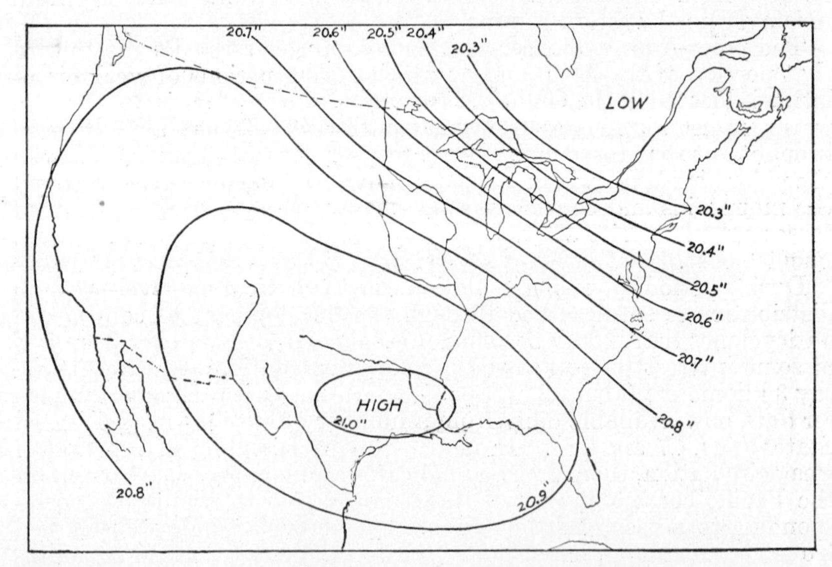

Figure 18.—Mean pressure (inches) at the 3-kilometer level for the 5-day period March 19–23, 1939. This map corresponds to a period of weak circulation. (From (*2*).) Notice the west-northwest winds over the Middle West and the East, corresponding to temperatures well below normal in these sections. This pressure distribution suggests two troughs, one over the Atlantic coast and another over the Pacific just off the California coast.

develop in middle latitudes. This mixing process transports heat northward and creates positive temperature anomalies in middle latitudes and presumably negative ones farther south. During periods of weak circulation, the west-east components decrease in intensity, and there is a pronounced tendency toward the development of large-scale north-south current systems. At such times regions of positive and negative temperature anomalies will appear side by side, but their position will not always be the same, as may be inferred from the previous discussion of the relation between the size of the stationary flow patterns and the prevailing zonal-circulation intensity. The four anomaly charts, figures 19–22, are intended to bring out these differences between periods of strong and weak circulation.

The value of the relationship described above between the observed circulation pattern and the intensity of the zonal circulation lies in the fact that it reduces the number of variables to be considered in any discussion of weather types by establishing two idealized world pressure patterns, for periods of maximum and minimum circulation intensity. Given the values of the zonal circulation index during a few consecutive weeks (during the winter season) it is probably possible, from these values alone, to give a description of the mean pressure distribution at the end of the period that will be decidedly better than a pure guess, although definitely subject to a considerable margin of uncertainty. Until it becomes possible to predict the fluctuations in the zonal-circulation index, it is of course impossible to utilize this knowledge with full effectiveness in forecasting.

The preceding discussion suggests another important application.

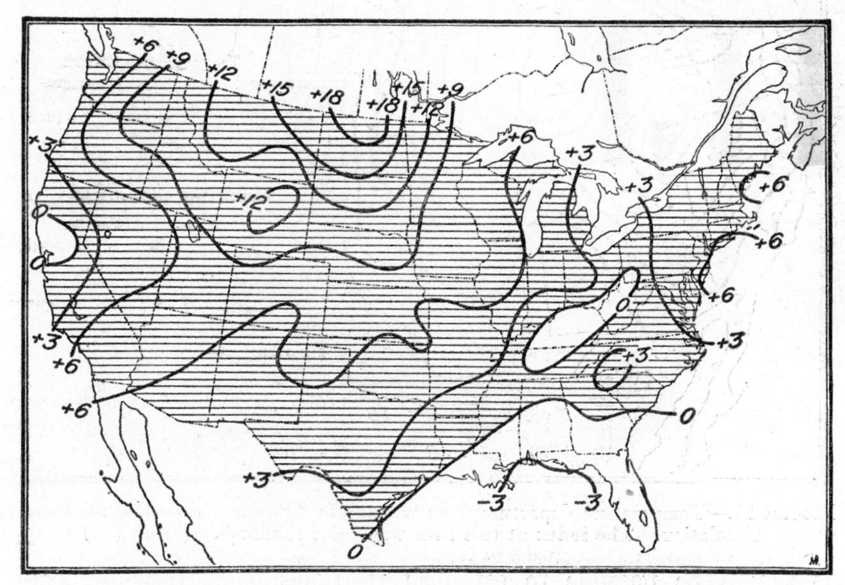

FIGURE 19.—Temperature departure from normal, in ° F., for a period of maximum circulation. The index at this time was 13.2 millibars. (From (2).)

298737°—41——41 +

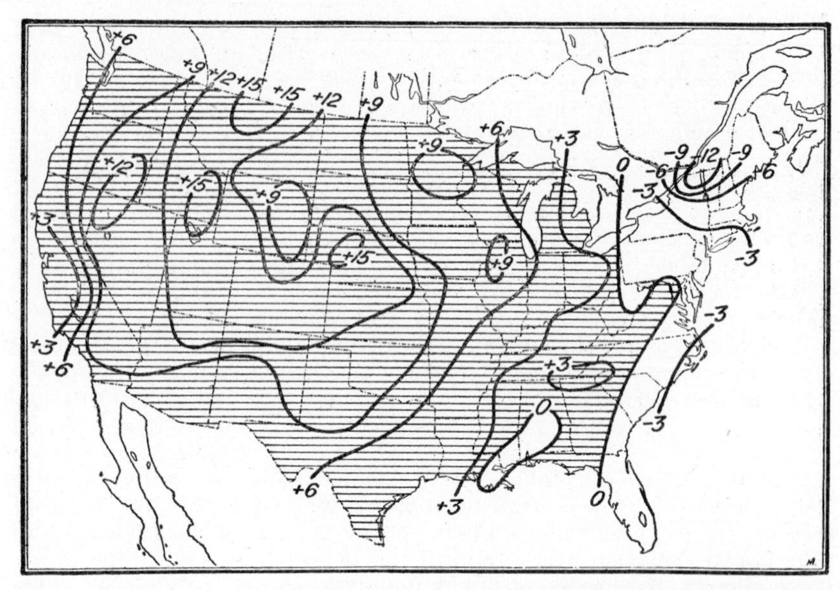

FIGURE 20.—Temperature departure from normal, in ° F., for a period of maximum circulation. The index at this time was 12.5 millibars. (From (*2*).)

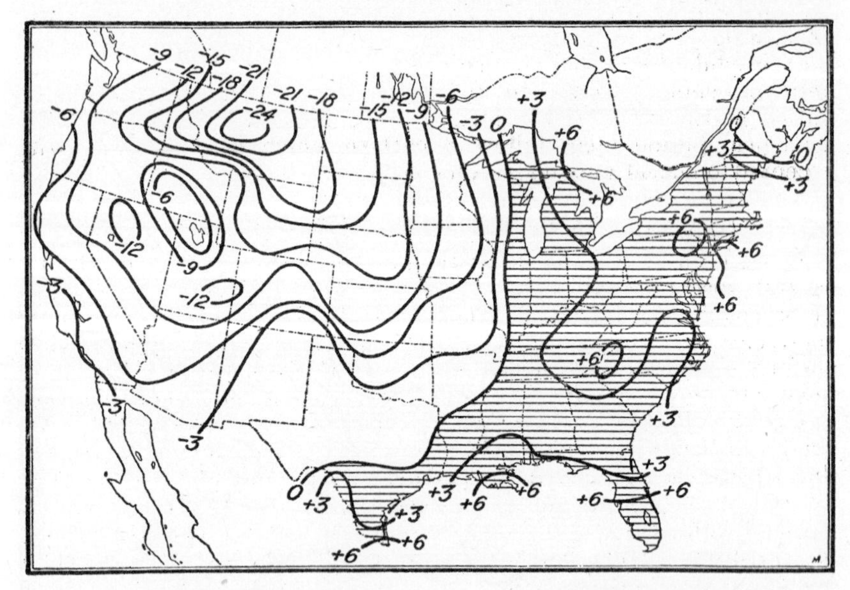

FIGURE 21.—Temperature departure from normal, in ° F., for a period of minimum circulation. The index at this time was −1.4 millibars. (From (*2*).)

It should be possible to establish relationships corresponding to (but not necessarily identical with) the ones described above, between mean zonal-index values and mean circulation patterns for longer periods (months or years). The establishment of such climatic patterns, having a physical background, should be of great value in

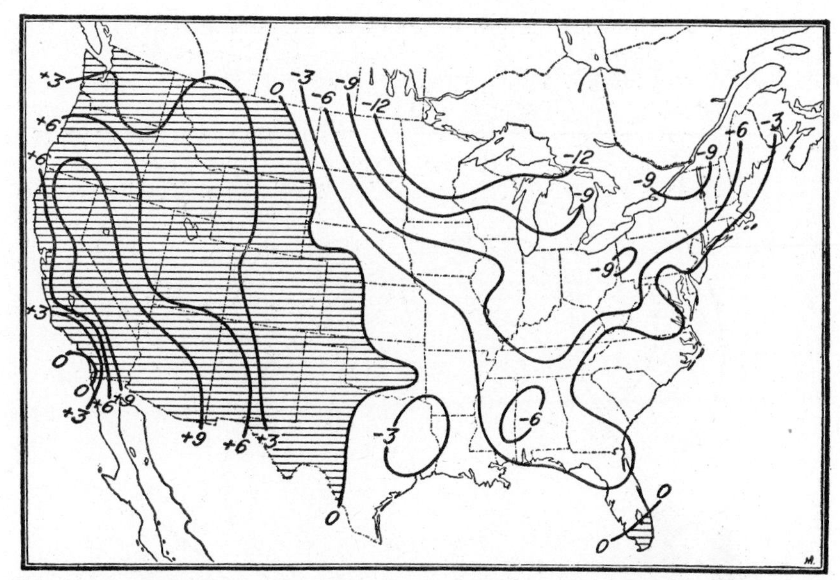

FIGURE 22.—Temperature departure from normal, in ° F., for a period of minimum circulation. The index at this time was 0 millibars. (From (*2*).)

the analysis of past climatic fluctuations and should serve to emphasize the need for restraint in this field of research, by bringing out the self-evident fact that the sequence of past climatic events can vary only very slightly from point to point. Hence, the geographic distribution of the climates assumed to have prevailed during a certain geological period must follow a pattern which is compatible with accepted physical and meteorological principles.

POLAR-FRONT WAVES

It has been brought out that the polar front must break down into several disconnected parts extending normally in a southwest-northeast direction. Under steady conditions each such front would represent the intersection with the ground of a sloping boundary surface, ascending toward the northwest and separating a wedge of polar air moving southwestward from a warm and moist current moving northeastward above and to the southeast of the front. Actually this front is never in stable equilibrium, but along it waves will develop which normally move northeastward while at the same time often increasing in horizontal and vertical amplitude. It is the interaction of cold and warm air masses in these waves that is responsible for the storms which control the day-by-day changes in weather so characteristic of our latitudes.

An idealized picture of such a wave is given in figure 23. The center portion of this diagram gives a horizontal projection of the wave, as observed at the ground. The polar front itself, indicated by a broken line, extends northward into the domain of the cold air. The instantaneous direction of motion of the warm air is indicated by the arrows on the double lines, while the direction of motion of the cold air is indicated by heavily drawn single lines.

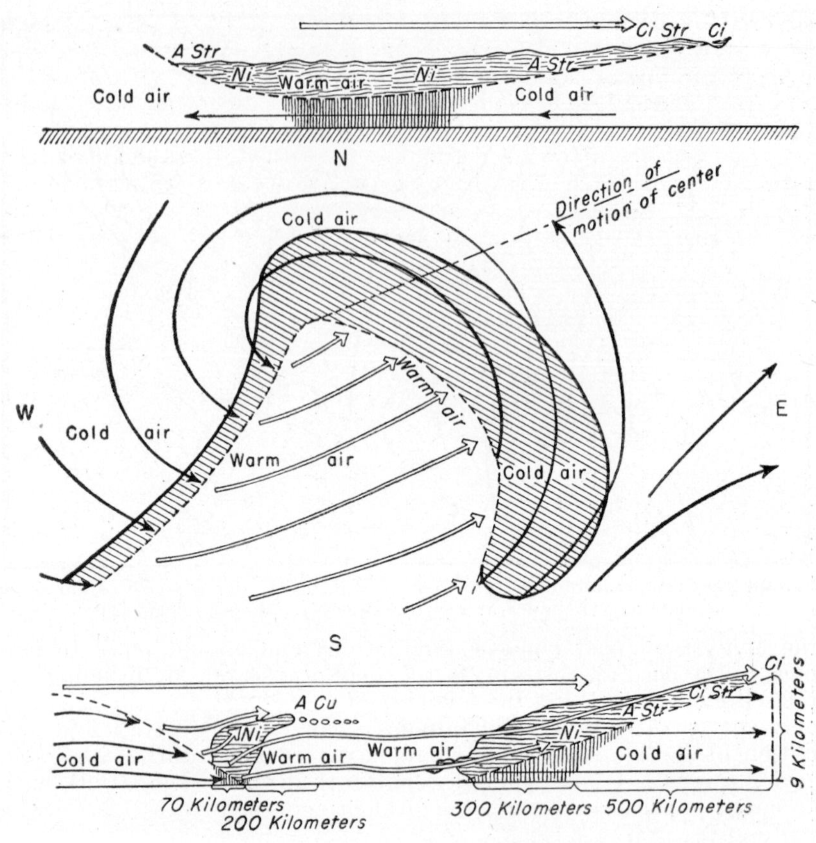

FIGURE 23.—Idealized polar-front wave. (From Haynes (*10*).) In the center is a horizontal view of the distribution of air masses at the ground. The broken line is the boundary (polar front) at the ground between a warm current from the west-southwest (white arrows), displacing to the east a wedge of cold air (black arrows) returning northward from a brief sojourn in southern latitudes. Along the boundary of the receding cold air (warm front) the warm air rises, and its moisture condenses and produces a broad area of rain or snow (shaded area). The upper part of the diagram represents a vertical west-east section north of the center, the lower part a similar section south of the center. (A Str means alto-stratus clouds; Ni, nimbus; Ci Str, cirro-stratus; Ci, cirrus; A Cu, alto-cumulus. Figures in the lower diagram are approximate.)

Along its advancing edge the warm air is forced to rise over the cold air. Because of the resulting expansion under decreased pressure, the warm air cools, condensation results, and rain must fall within the hatched area indicated in the diagram. In the rear of the warm current, cold air advances from the northwest; the sinking cold air moves more rapidly than the retreating warm air and forces the latter upward, again producing condensation and precipitation.

That portion of the polar front along which warm air replaces cold is referred to as a warm front, while the portion along which cold air replaces warm is called a cold front. Because of frictional retardation along the ground, the shallow wedge of cold air ahead of the warm front moves fairly slowly. At the cold front, cold surface air is retarded by friction, but the upper layers are free to move at high speed, so that the cold front may advance rapidly through the development of a rolling or overturning motion within the cold air. Thus the cold front normally moves faster than the warm front and eventually overtakes it.

Above and below the horizontal view in figure 23 are two idealized vertical sections of a polar-front wave, one (above) extending from west to east, north of the wave center, and the other (below) from west to east south of the wave center. These sections give a good

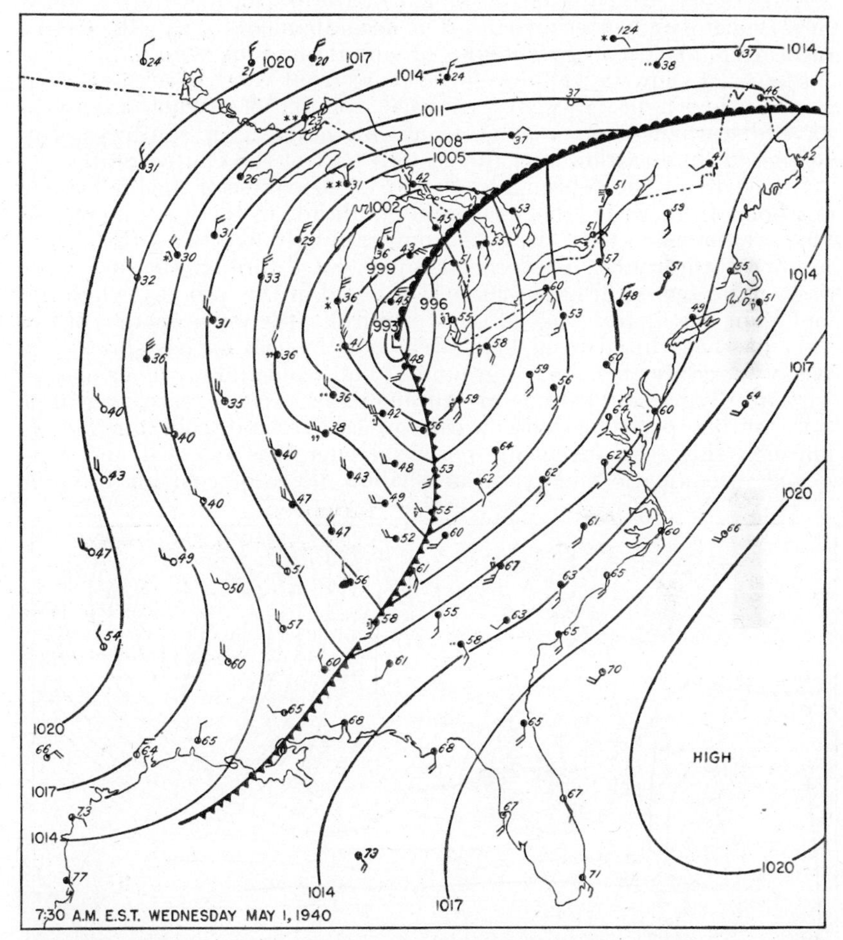

FIGURE 24.—An example of a polar-front wave over the United States. (From (*10*).) The cold front is indicated by the barbed line, the warm front by the line with filled half circles. The eastern part of the country is located within the warm air, and the western part and the upper Great Lakes region are in the cold air. This may be seen from the temperatures (in °F.) at each station. The wind direction is shown by arrows, attached to the circles representing the stations, which point in the direction toward which the wind is blowing, and wind velocity is indicated by cross bars on the arrows, one full bar denoting approximately 5 miles per hour. The degree of cloudiness is indicated by the extent to which the station ring is filled. Note the counterclockwise wind circulation around the low-pressure center east of Lake Michigan.

indication of the typical cloud decks that develop along the boundary between the two air masses in such a polar-front wave.

The ascent of warm air at the warm front is usually steady, and the rainfall has the character of steady rain. If the warm air is unstable, however, this instability may be released through forced ascent, and the steady warm-front rain may then be intensified in spots into violent convective rain. This occurs fairly frequently in the warm-front rains in the southern part of the United States but it is quite uncommon in northwestern Europe.

At the cold front the forced ascent of the warm, moist air is much more violent and intermittent; it is accompanied by squally winds, and the clouds are of the cumulus or cumulo-nimbus type.

Figure 24 shows a well-developed polar-front wave over the United States, while figure 25 gives a typical example of a whole family of wave disturbances on a polar front extending in a southwesterly-northeasterly direction over the eastern part of the United States.

It has already been brought out that in the course of the life history of a polar-front wave, the horizontal amplitude of the wave increases, while at the same time the cold front gradually overtakes the slower moving warm front. This process is illustrated through the successive stages represented in figure 26. At the end of this process, when the cold front has finally reached the warm front, the warm section of the wave has been lifted to higher levels, and the cold air has spread out over a larger area next to the ground. Thus cold and warm air masses originally lying side by side are through this process rearranged in a more stable position, with warm air above and cold air below. Through this rearrangement, potential energy is released and converted into kinetic energy. The shallow layer of cold air brought

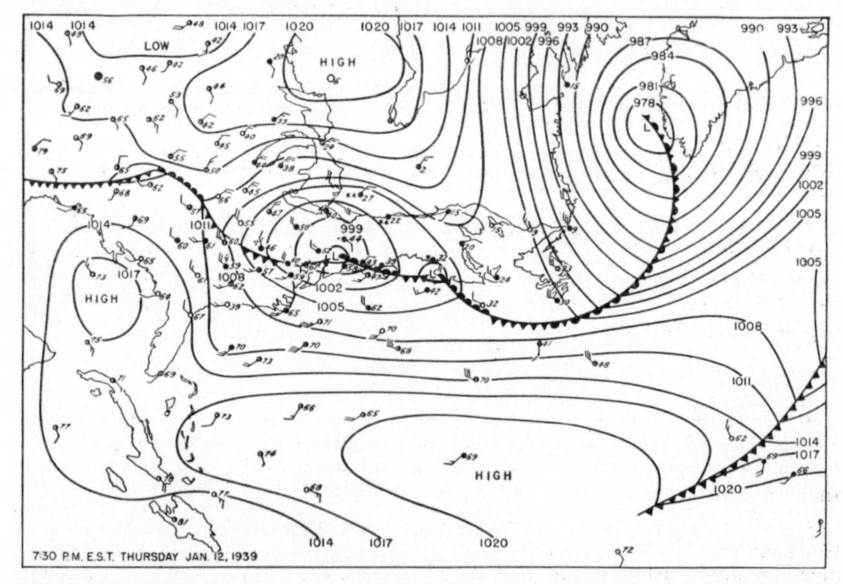

FIGURE 25.—An example of a family of waves on a frontal zone extending from the Gulf of Mexico to Greenland during a period of weak circulation. The symbols used are the same as those in figure 24. (From (*10*).)

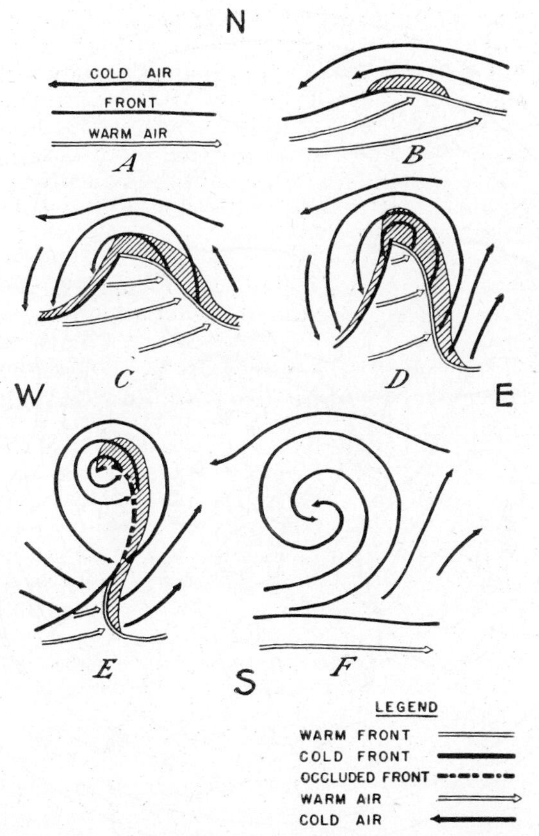

FIGURE 26.—Schematic horizontal representation of the gradual development and ultimate occlusion of a polar-front wave. (From (*10*).)

southward and eastward through this process is eventually warmed and transformed into subtropical air, capable of rising over the next outbreak of cold polar air.

A polar-front wave is said to occlude when its cold front finally completely overtakes the warm front, and the process itself is referred to as an occlusion. The occluded waves have a tendency to gravitate into the large-scale semipermanent cyclonic centers of action, such as the Aleutian and Icelandic lows.

SUMMER CIRCULATION PATTERNS

As has been shown, the northern polar front during the winter season tends to bulge southward over the continents, in response to the intense production of cold air over the large snow-covered land masses in high latitudes. In summer the situation is to some extent reversed. Over the major portion of these land areas the snow cover disappears, and the temperature rises above that prevailing over the ocean areas. Because of the high elevation of the sun and the long days in high latitudes, the rate of production of polar air falls off, and

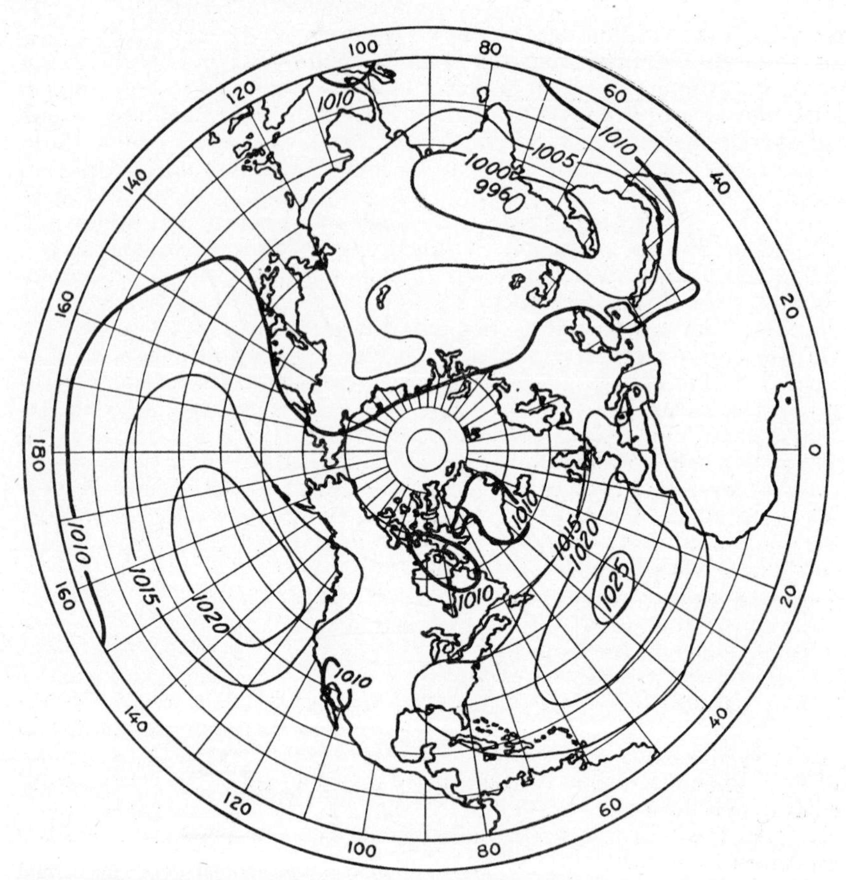

FIGURE 27.—Normal sea-level-pressure distribution (millibars) over the Northern Hemisphere in July. (From (*21*).) Compare this with figure 7 and note the complete disappearance of the Aleutian low. The Icelandic low is now very weak, and the Asiatic high has been replaced by relatively low pressure. Note the well-developed oceanic highs characteristic of the summer season.

the temperature contrast between high and low latitudes diminishes. Thus the contrast between air masses also diminishes, and the polar front recedes northward. There is now a tendency for the polar front to bulge northward over the continents and southward over the oceans.

During the winter the meridional temperature contrast dominates and determines the broad features of the circulation pattern. The winter temperature contrast between land and ocean serves, in the main, to accentuate this meridional contrast. During the summer season, on the other hand, the meridional temperature gradient is so weakened that the temperature contrast between land and ocean areas tends to become the dominating factor, to a considerable extent opposing the normal meridional temperature contrast. As a result, widespread but slow-functioning plants for cold-air production are established over the northern oceans.

Just as the cold air produced in polar regions during the winter season spreads southward and in so doing acquires an anticyclonic rotation (east wind) around the polar air dome, so the slowly spreading air from the summer maritime cold-air plants assumes a clockwise rotation around the ocean basins. Since pressure and wind always tend toward a mutual adjustment, it follows that the northern oceans will be dominated by large high-pressure areas (fig. 27). Above these high-pressure areas there must be a compensating inflow from the continents.

It is not possible at present to apply successfully the previously developed concept of planetary flow patterns to the summer circulation problem. Because of the reduced temperature contrasts characteristic of this season and the resulting weaker winds it is probable that weather then is much more completely dominated by local factors. For these reasons the following discussion will be restricted to the circulation over the North American Continent during the warm season.

The meridional temperature contrast over this continent practically disappears south of latitude 45°. The principal polar front normally extends west-east somewhere in the vicinity of the Great Lakes. Apart from occasional inundations with rapidly warming polar air, the United States is covered with a blanket of tropical air and its weather is consequently to a large extent dominated by processes occurring within this air mass.

The prevailing motion in the warm air over the United States and south of the polar front consists in a drift eastward, strong in the north and decreasing in intensity southward, until it practically vanishes at about latitude 30°. This wind distribution is strongly suggestive of the frictional mechanism for the maintenance of the westerlies in middle latitudes discussed previously. It thus appears that the eastward drift of the air over the United States may be explained as the result of drag exerted by the somewhat stronger west winds prevailing over the polar front farther to the north, an explanation which is strengthened by the fact that the absence of horizontal temperature contrasts indicates that there are no wind-energy sources to be found in the central and southern parts of this country.

The wind energy brought in from the north must undergo an incessant decay and dissipation. Such a decay must be associated with a breaking up of the wind currents into eddies of varying diameters. It will be shown later that this is actually the case and that the lower troposphere is characterized by the frequent formation of clockwise (anticyclonic) vortices which tend to remain stagnant or to drift slowly eastward across the continent. These quasi-horizontal eddies are not so clearly established next to the ground, and thus it becomes necessary to make use of the upper-air data for their study.

It has been brought out previously that the free atmosphere everywhere is losing heat by radiation. This loss is, however, small and widespread, probably of the order of magnitude of 1° or 2° C. a day. Thus, if one wants to follow an individual parcel of air over short periods of time it is permissible to assume that its movement takes place without change in realized heat content (barring condensation of water vapor). A good way of expressing the heat content of a parcel of air is to indicate the temperature that this parcel would have if it were compressed, without gain or loss of heat, to a standard (sea level) pressure. This temperature is called the potential temperature of the air. It is possible to compute the potential temperature of any air parcel the actual temperature and pressure of which are known. When this is done it is found that the potential temperature normally increases upward in the atmosphere (about 4° to 5° C. per kilometer in the lower troposphere; somewhat more rapidly higher up). It follows from the definition of potential temperature that for a constant pressure it increases with the actual temperature. Thus the potential temperature normally increases southward.

If one now plots, for a number of points in the United States, the height above sea level where a certain potential temperature is found, it becomes possible to construct a topographic chart for a surface of constant potential temperature in the atmosphere. Such a surface (also called an isentropic surface) is normally found to slant downward from north to south. Since potential temperature normally increases upward along the vertical, it follows that the higher isentropic surfaces are characterized by a higher potential temperature than the lower ones. If, for a given occasion, a set of such charts is prepared for different surfaces, it is possible to prepare a vertical cross section through the atmosphere to describe the potential temperature distribution. A mean cross section of this type is given in figure 28, in which the broken lines (isentropic lines) indicate the intersection with the individual isentropic surfaces. This diagram brings out the fact that

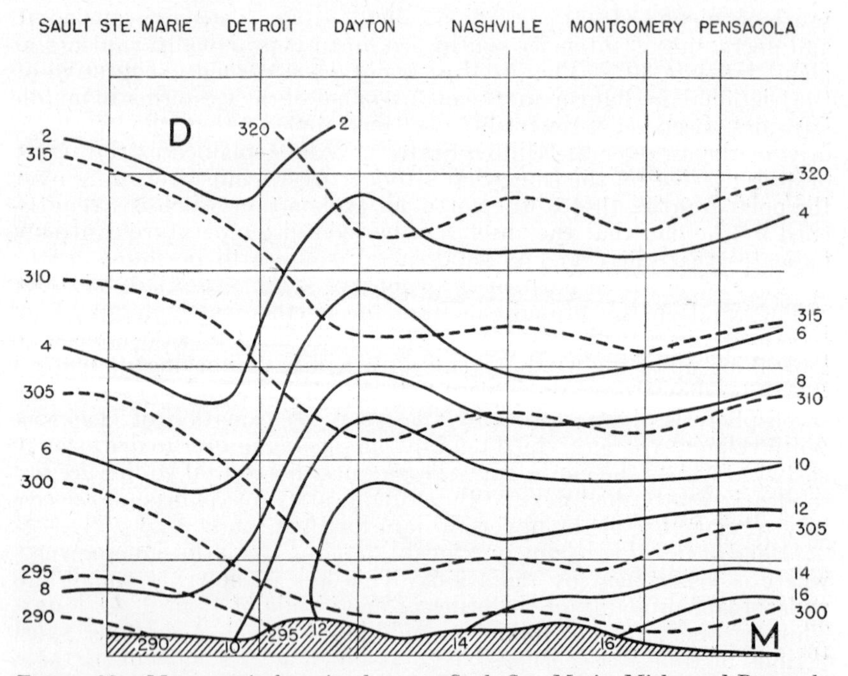

FIGURE 28.—Mean vertical section between Sault Ste. Marie, Mich., and Pensacola, Fla., August 1936. Horizontal lines are drawn for intervals of 1 kilometer, broken lines represent potential temperature (in °C. Abs.), and full lines specific humidity (in grams of water vapor per kilogram of moist air). (From (*19*).) Note constancy of potential temperature (and hence ordinary temperature) from Dayton southward. (D indicates dry air; M, moist air.)

during the summer, when the temperature itself does not vary greatly from north to south, the isentropic lines (and surfaces) are fairly horizontal, except far to the north.

The significance of the isentropic surfaces lies in the following:

As long as parcels of air move without appreciable change in heat content, they must remain within one and the same isentropic surface. Thus, to the extent that this assumption is fulfilled, it can be said that by studying charts of the same isentropic surface for 2 consecutive days, it is reasonably sure that the same parcels of air are being dealt with. This would not be the case if charts for fixed upper levels were studied, since air may rise or sink through a fixed horizontal plane.

To identify the individual parcels of air in a given isentropic surface, use can be made of their moisture content, expressed as a weight ratio between water vapor and air per unit mass of moist air. This ratio (specific humidity) does not change except as the result of condensation or evaporation, or as the result of mixing with air of a different specific humidity. By drawing lines of constant specific humidity in a surface of constant potential temperature, a method of "tagging" and identification of air parcels is reached.

It is important to know whether air is moving up slope or down slope in the isentropic surface. Up-slope motion may lead to condensation, and in that case the realized heat content increases so that the air must climb toward a surface of higher heat content (higher potential temperature). To study the motion in a given isentropic surface, one may plot on the chart for that particular surface wind directions and wind velocities as obtained by interpolation from pilot-balloon observations and compare the resulting pattern of motion with the pattern of the contour lines. The final isentropic chart should thus contain specific-humidity lines, contour lines, and winds.

A study of daily isentropic charts for the summer season reveals that the free air circulation over North America is dominated to a very large extent by large anticyclonic vortices. The accompanying chart for June 27, 1937, furnishes a beautiful illustration (fig. 29).

In this case, strong westerly to northwesterly winds prevail from the Great Lakes eastward. Possibly as a result of frictional drag from this strong wind system a tongue of moist air has been brought in over the United States, extending from Arizona toward Illinois and Indiana, from then on curving anticyclonically southward and finally southwestward toward the Gulf coast. A tongue of dry air is sliding southward and downhill from New England, winding itself clockwise around the moist air. The movement of this dry air must be accompanied by a certain amount of vertical shrinking and horizontal stretching to permit it to assume the clockwise trajectory indicated on the chart. Practically all isentropic charts for the summer months contain examples of such spiraling interaction between moist and dry tongues, and normally the spiraling motion has a clockwise direction. As might be expected the moist tongues form troughs and the dry tongues ridges in the contour patterns.

Thunderstorms and convective activity are most likely to occur in the moist tongues where the supply of water vapor is adequate, particularly on the left side of the axes of the moist currents (facing downstream). Convective vertical currents may, of course, develop anywhere as a result of intense surface heating, but in those regions where the convective towers shoot up into an overlying dry stratum, lateral mixing processes will soon deplete the cloud masses of their moisture, whereas the development can proceed unhindered in regions where the moisture content aloft is high. Figure 30 shows the path of the center of maximum thunderstorm activity during the same general period from which figure 29 was taken. This path shows a characteristic anticyclonic trajectory very similar to the one suggested by successive isentropic charts for the entire period, and it emphasizes the significance of isentropic charts for summertime rainfall forecasting.

The clockwise eddies referred to above are so characteristic of our summer circulation and so slowly changing that they may be found also in mean isentropic charts for longer periods. Figure 31, *A* and *B*, gives the mean insentropic charts for the months of August 1935 and August 1936. It is seen that both charts indicate the presence of large anticyclonic eddies; that for 1935, which probably comes fairly close to normal conditions, is characterized by two eddies—one moist tongue entering the United States from the southwest over Arizona and a second entering from the south over western Florida. In 1936 there was only one large eddy, with a large dry

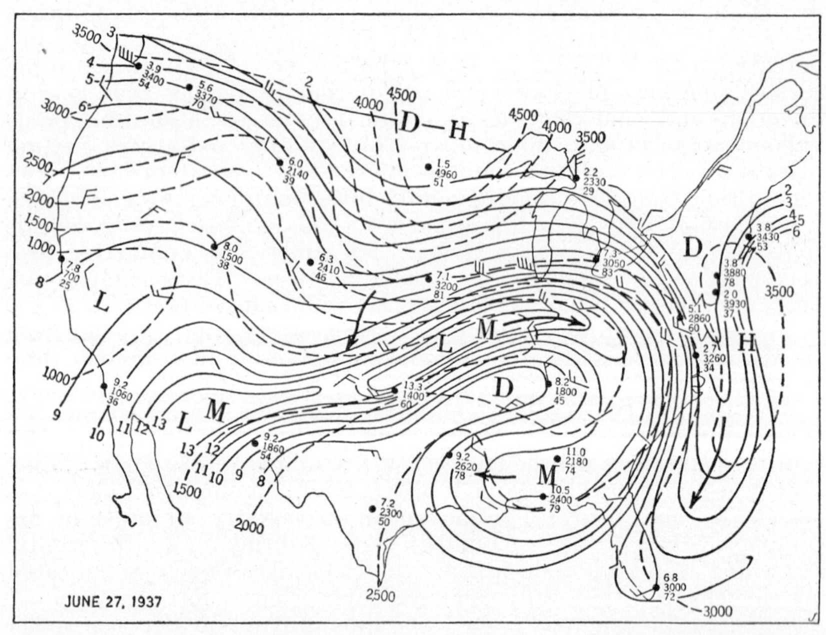

FIGURE 29.—Typical anticyclonic eddy formation of a moist tongue in an isentropic surface. This chart is drawn for a potential temperature of 310° Abs. Broken lines represent contour lines (height above sea level) and indicate 500-meter intervals. Constant specific-humidity lines (full lines) represent intervals of 1 gram of water vapor per kilogram of moist air. To the right of the station dot are figures indicating the observed specific humidity (top), the height of the surface (center, in meters), and the relative humidity (bottom). Winds are entered in the same manner as in figure 24. M represents a tongue of moist air; D, of dry air. H indicates high level of isentropic surface; L, low level. Arrows show directions in which the different tongues have been moving during the last 24 hours. (From (*17*).)

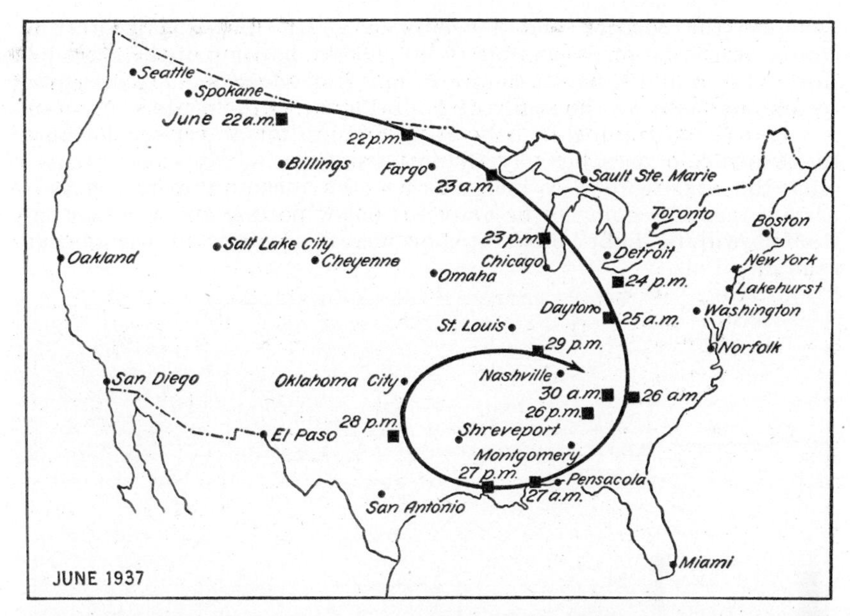

Figure 30.—Trajectory of the center of maximum thunderstorm activity following the invasion of a tongue of moist air aloft and positions of upper-air sounding stations used in this analysis (dots). The black squares mark the successive positions of the center of thunderstorm activity for the 12-hour periods preceding the dates (in June 1937) entered beside them; these were fixed with the aid of thunderstorm reports and 12-hourly amounts of precipitation. (From (*14*).)

current sweeping downhill from the north over the Great Lakes region. The persistence of this large dry tongue aloft is associated with the severe drought of that year in a large part of the Middle West.

APPLICATIONS TO LONG-RANGE FORECASTING

It is, of course, impossible to utilize effectively the results set forth above as long as the mechanics and thermodynamics of the changes in circulation intensity which cause, or are associated with, the observed changes in the mean circulation patterns are not understood. These changes are generally fairly slow; it has already been pointed out that in winter the normal time interval between two consecutive peaks of circulation intensity is about 6 weeks. Thus the circulation-intensity trend is likely to persist from one week to the next, and this persistence tendency has a definite forecasting value. The same applies to the persistence which may be observed in the gradual displacements of the centers of action. It should not be forgotten that so far even our daily forecasts are obtained through a technique which essentially makes use of persistence tendencies of various kinds rather than of thoroughly understood dynamic and thermodynamic calculations. Modern daily forecasting terminology often suggests an intimacy with the physical processes of weather which sometimes is more wishful than real.

If it is possible to predict with some degree of success, 1 week in advance, the position and development of the principal centers of action, it also becomes possible to predict the position of the principal frontal zones and hence of the prevailing storm tracks. A forecasting technique based on the study of the behavior of the centers of action is obviously not going to help in predicting, for any given locality, the sequence of weather day by day a week in advance, but it does offer the opportunity to tell whether the mean temperature in a certain region is going to be above or below normal and whether the rainfall will be light, moderate, or heavy in terms of the normal rainfall intensity.

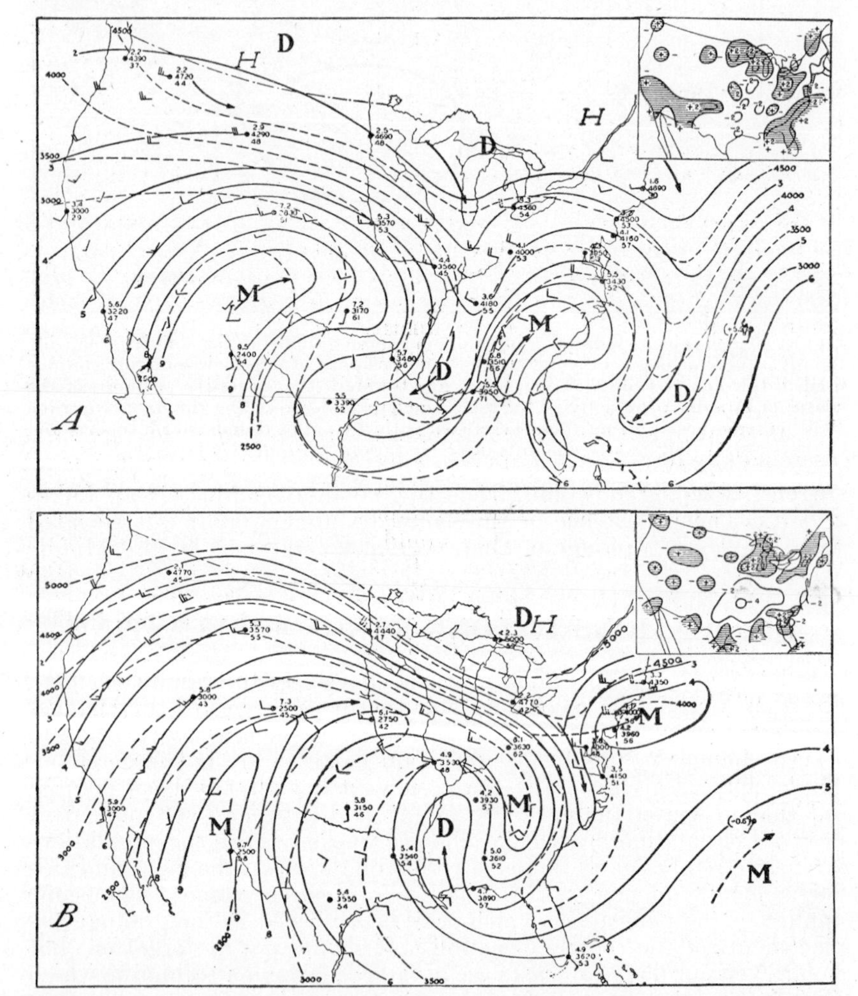

FIGURE 31.—*A*, Mean isentropic chart for August 1935. Symbols and notations are the same as in figure 29. *B*, Mean isentropic chart for August 1936. Note precipitation deficiency in the Middle West under the dry portion of an anticyclonic eddy. (Insets, departures of precipitation from normal, expressed in inches.) (From (*24*).)

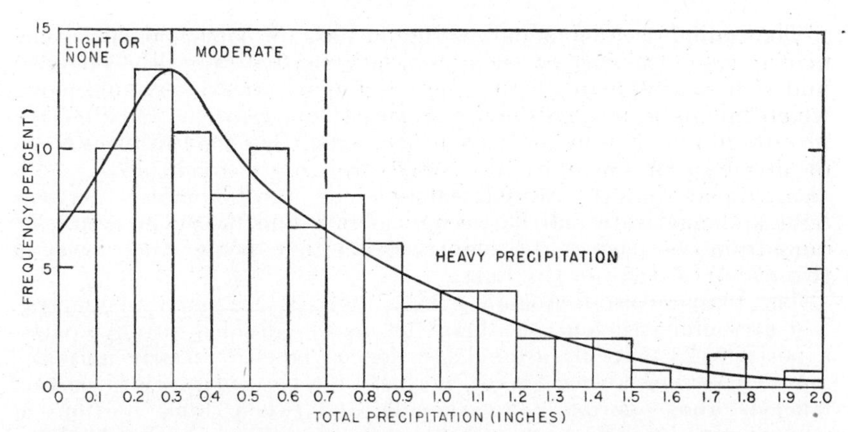

FIGURE 32.—Normal frequency distribution of accumulated 5-day rainfall for Iowa in August. Areas of light, moderate, and heavy precipitation are of equal size.

An experiment in 5-day forecasting of temperature and rainfall anomalies, based on such studies of the behavior of the centers of action in the atmosphere, has recently been organized as a joint undertaking between the Department of Agriculture, the Weather Bureau, and the Massachusetts Institute of Technology. In view of the fact that the technique employed will probably find increased applicability during the next few years, it seems appropriate to devote some space to a description of this project.

The project leaders are well aware of the fact that the technique used in daily forecasting cannot very well be extended to periods much in excess of 2 or possibly 3 days. Even if the forecaster should have a perfectly correct concept of the anticipated weather sequence, a slight error in his timing of the events would soon throw the forecast out of line with the observed weather. It is therefore necessary to treat the 5-day forecast problem as a statistical one, particularly in view of the fact that a statistical technique based on the ideas set forth above might perhaps eventually be extended to cover even longer forecast periods (two, or as a possible upper limit, three weekly or 5-day intervals), which obviously would be impossible on the basis of the technique used in daily forecasting.

As a first step in this development, a statistical study has been made of the normal character of the 5-day mean temperatures and accumulated 5-day rainfall intensities in the United States, and the results have been expressed graphically in the form of frequency curves. These curves represent, specifically, for a given region and a given season (month), the frequency of different departures from normal of the 5-day mean temperature, and likewise the frequency distribution of accumulated 5-day rainfall amounts for different regions and seasons. Both types of curves are prepared, not from records of a single station, but from State averages, and they are based on roughly 50 years of data. These curves are probably adequately representative of a State as a whole in open country such as the Mississippi Valley, but they are definitely inadequate in the mountainous regions, where the climatic characteristics vary sharply from point to point.

The rainfall-frequency curves (fig. 32) are, of course, highly asymmetric, since there is no such thing as negative rainfall. The area under the curve in this figure may be divided into three equal parts, which might be labeled "none or light," "moderate," and "heavy" precipitation. It is evident from these definitions that all three types of precipitation have equal chance probability (one-third). It is also evident that the rainfall values giving the boundaries between light and moderate and between moderate and heavy precipitation vary from one part of the country to another, being much lower in the arid West than in the East.

The temperature-frequency curves (fig. 33) are fairly symmetric. The area under the curve in figure 33 may be divided into five parts, a portion (25 percent) around the normal labeled "nearly normal," another portion labeled "below normal" (25 percent), a third portion labeled "above normal" (25 percent), and two extreme portions of 12.5 percent each named "much below normal" and "much above normal," respectively. Also here the numerical values of the various demarkation lines vary from region to region, since the frequency curve has a small spread in a maritime climate and a large spread in a continental climate. The normal 5-day mean temperature itself varies of course from station to station and from day to day throughout the month, but there is good reason to believe that the frequency distribution of departures from normal in climatologically homogeneous regions changes only slowly from point to point and from day to day.

Through the statistical analysis just described it is possible to incorporate, in the definitions and terminology used in the 5-day forecasts, the climatological characteristics of each particular district in the United States. The forecaster's problem is reduced to the task

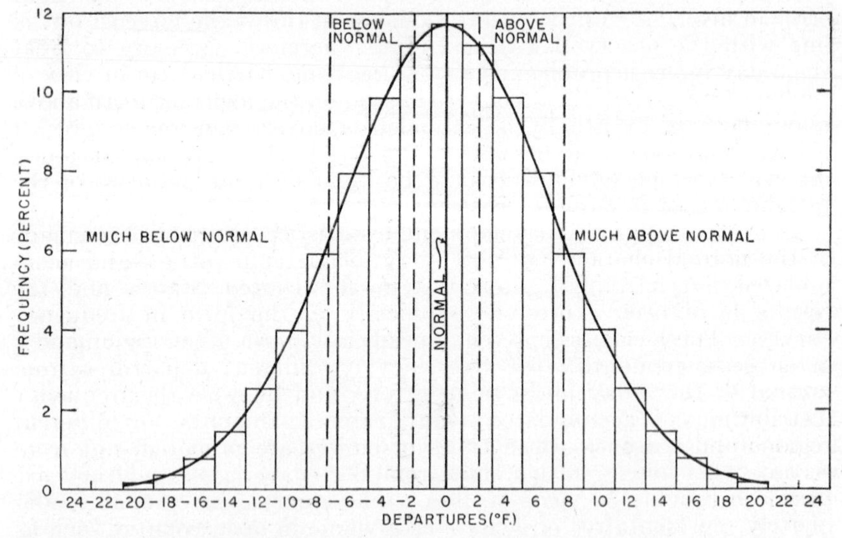

FIGURE 33.—Normal frequency distribution of different departures from normal of 5-day mean temperatures for Iowa in August. Areas marked below normal, normal, and above normal are of equal size (each one-fourth of total), and the two extreme areas are likewise equal (each one-eighth of total).

of determining from the current weather charts and for each 5-day period the regions in which the rainfall will be light, moderate, or heavy and the regions in which the temperatures will be much below normal, above normal, etc. Through the choice of definitions introduced he has been spared the necessity of keeping in mind the climatic characteristics of each portion of the country. If desirable, it is of course possible, once the forecast has been completed, to translate the predicted anomaly distributions roughly into actual degrees of departure from normal and into actual amounts of precipitation.

On the basis of the definitions introduced, it is evident that in a long series of charts of the observed 5-day anomaly distribution, areas of light, moderate, and heavy rainfall should be equal, and similar considerations apply to the areas of different observed temperature departures.

The actual forecasting technique is based entirely on the use of prognostic charts. The first step consists in the construction of a mean sea-level-pressure chart for the United States for the coming 5-day interval. In the construction of this chart, the principal guidance is furnished by the past behavior of the circulation index and of the large centers of action. The main problem is to decide whether the circulation intensity is going to increase or decrease; as yet this question has to be answered largely on the basis of persistence tendencies.

The next step is to construct a prognostic pressure chart for the 3-kilometer level over the United States.

Because of the lack of upper-air data from the surrounding oceans, it is not generally possible to base the preparation of this chart on continuity of trends, and other cruder guiding signs have to be used. With increasing circulation, the north-south amplitudes of the isobars at 3 kilometers tend to decrease; with decreasing circulation they increase. Furthermore, there are certain characteristic 3-kilometer-pressure patterns which normally occur with maximum and minimum circulation (figs. 17 and 18). This part of the procedure is as yet extremely uncertain and awaits additional upper-air data from the oceans before substantial improvements can be expected.

Quite recently a procedure has been developed which permits determination by extrapolation of the pressure at the 3-kilometer level from the observed pressure and temperature at sea level. The procedure is applicable only over the oceans and specifically only in those regions where strong winds or shower activity give indications of intense vertical stirring, so that the vertical temperature-lapse rate may be estimated. Through this procedure it is now possible to draw reasonably adequate 3-kilometer-pressure charts for the entire region between 30° and 170° west longitude, thus including large portions of the Atlantic and the Pacific. With the aid of consecutive-mean charts of the observed pressure distribution over this large area the problem of drawing prognostic mean 3-kilometer-pressure charts for the United States has come much closer to being a practical routine operation than before.

During the warm half of the year a prognostic mean isentropic chart is constructed, mainly on the basis of the slowness of and continuity in the evolution of the isentropic flow patterns.

The three charts obtained thus far are not independent of each

298737°—41——42

other. If the pressure distributions at sea level and at 3 kilometers are known, the mean temperature between these two levels is prescribed. The resulting horizontal distribution of the 5-day mean temperature for the lowest 3 kilometers must not depart too much from the normal north-south temperature contrast in the atmosphere and must be compatible with the prognostic isentropic chart, since temperature and moisture content are fairly intimately correlated. These considerations and other similar cross checks of the prognostic charts serve the extremely important purpose of insuring internal consistency in the anticipated mean state of the atmosphere, and therein lies the principal scientific achievement of this forecasting project. The prognostic charts are modified until such consistency is obtained.

It then becomes possible to draw prognostic charts of temperature and rainfall anomalies for the coming period; in this work full use is made of the locations and movements of the principal frontal zones as indicated by the prognostic pressure-distribution charts and of indications concerning the availability of moisture furnished by the prognostic isentropic chart.

Figures 34–38 contain the prognostic and verification charts for one of the first periods treated by this technique. Real difficulties are encountered when the rainfall is of a convective character and hence very spotty in its occurrence. The particular forecast illustrated in figure 37 is satisfactory over the major part of the country, but it exhibits two definite errors, one of them the extension into Montana of the heavy rainfall forecast and the other the omission to forecast the heavy rainfall which actually occurred over a small portion of the middle Atlantic coast. More intense stress on the need for consistency between the various prognostic charts would have reduced the magnitude of these errors.

It should be added that mistakes in timing might easily affect this type of forecasting also. If an error is made in the timing of the displacement of the centers of action, the anticipated rainfall or temperature patterns may be correct in their general character but incorrectly placed on the map, resulting, obviously, in a failure of the forecast in certain regions.

The principal advantage of the procedure outlined above lies in the fact that it helps to insure consistency and permits the forecaster to incorporate into his picture of the coming atmosphere, step by step, every prognostic indication at his disposal. The human mind has a limited capacity, and as long as forecasting is done in the head, from inspection of a great and bewildering mass of data, it is more than likely that for each new indication considered, an earlier indication is dropped and forgotten. This danger is reduced through the introduction of the engineering procedure outlined above.

For agriculture, flood control, water supply, and many other interests, quantitative forecasts are of tremendous potential value. The technique outlined above represents a crude first step toward such quantitative forecasting, and it is therefore certain to be further developed in the years to come.

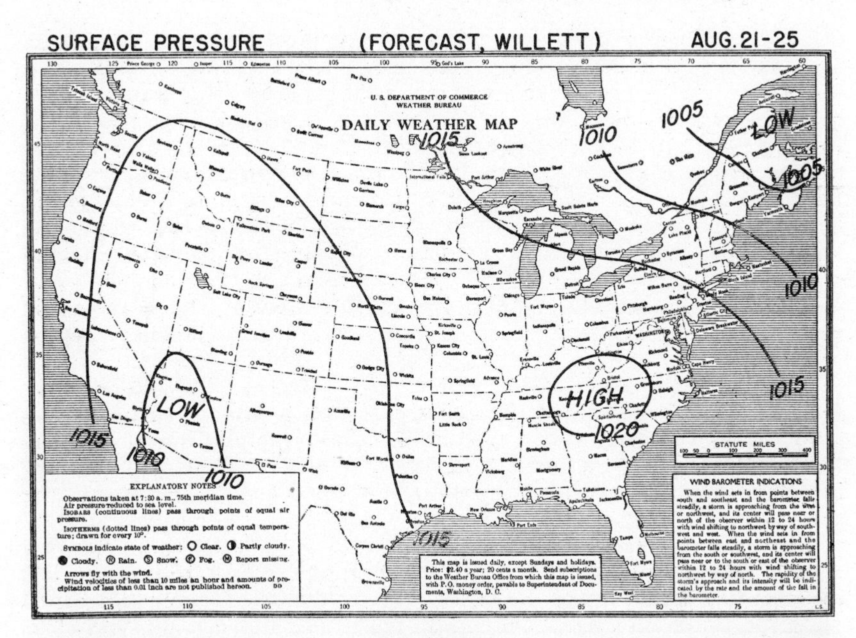

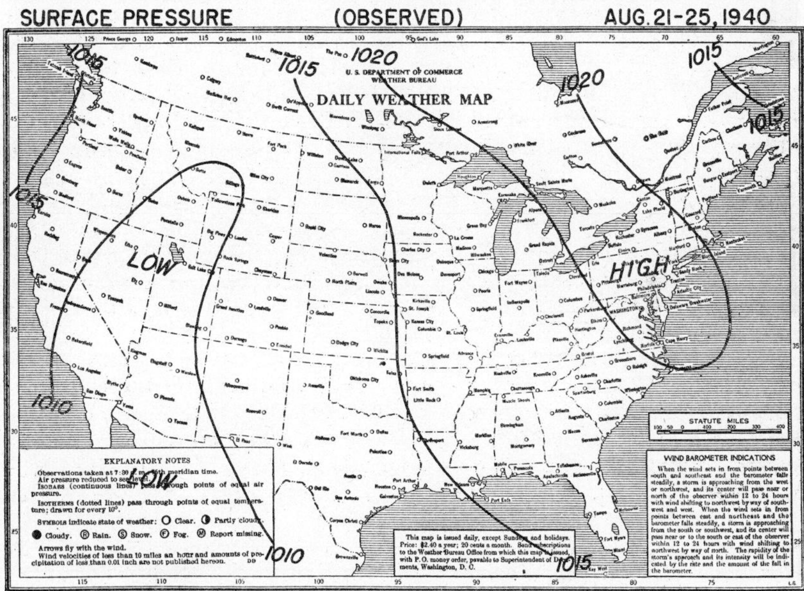

FIGURE 34.—Forecast and verification charts of mean sea-level-pressure distribution (millibars) over the United States for the period August 21–25, 1940, prepared on daily-weather-map forms.

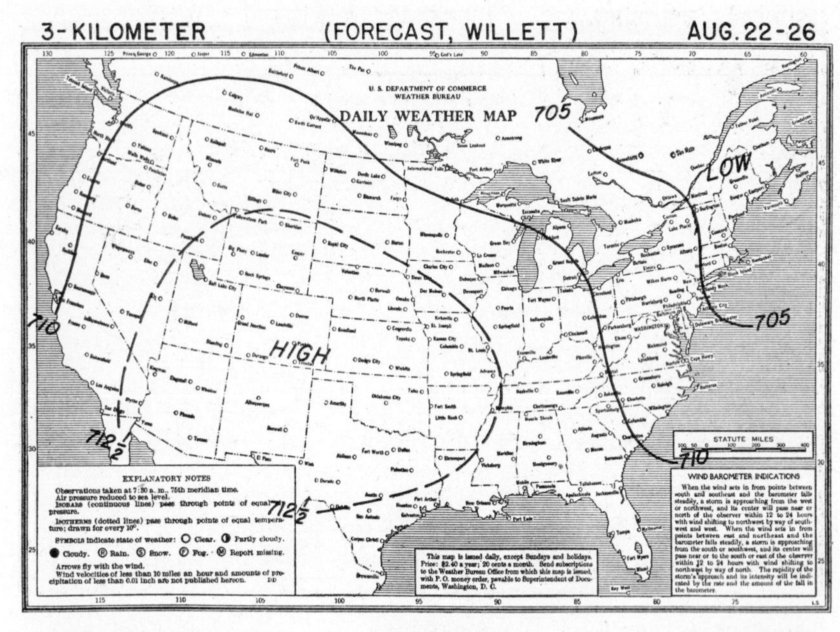

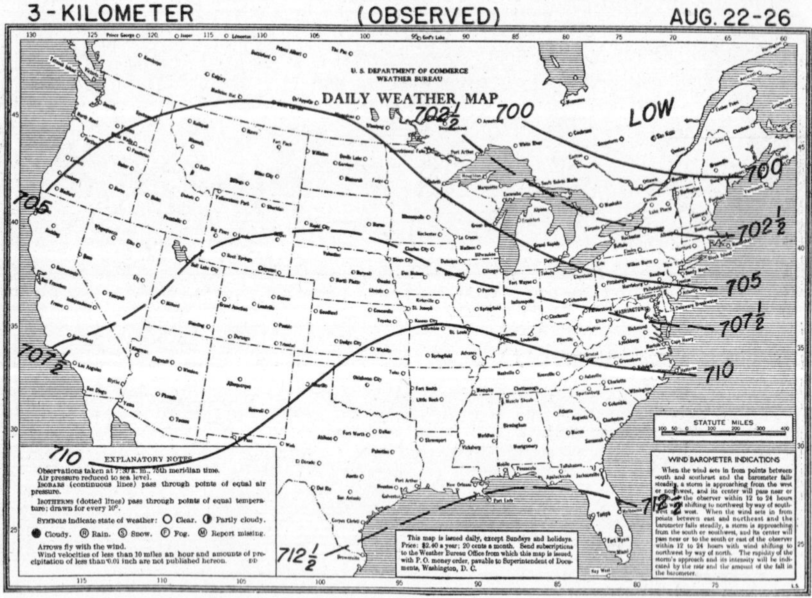

FIGURE 35.—Forecast and verification charts of mean 3-kilometer-pressure distribution (millibars) over the United States for the period August 21–25, 1940.

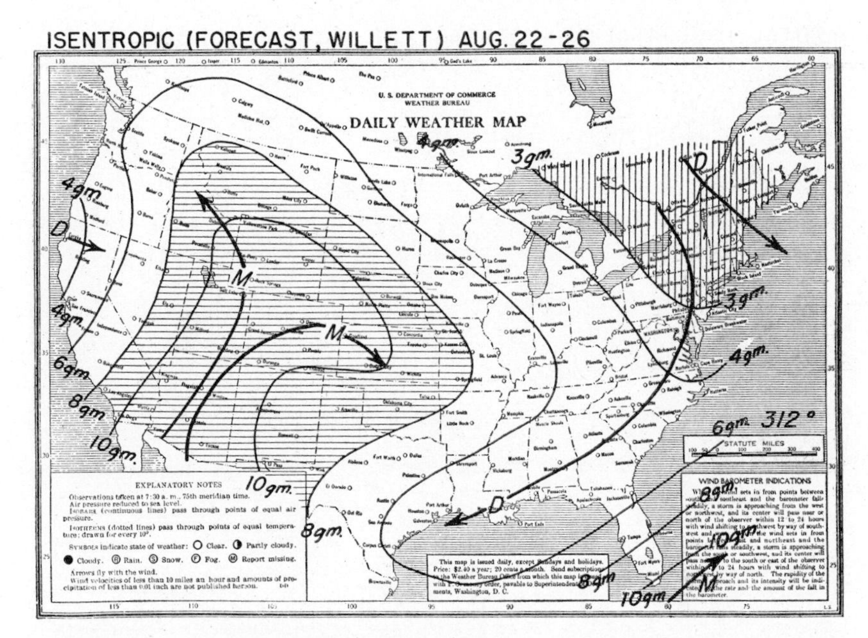

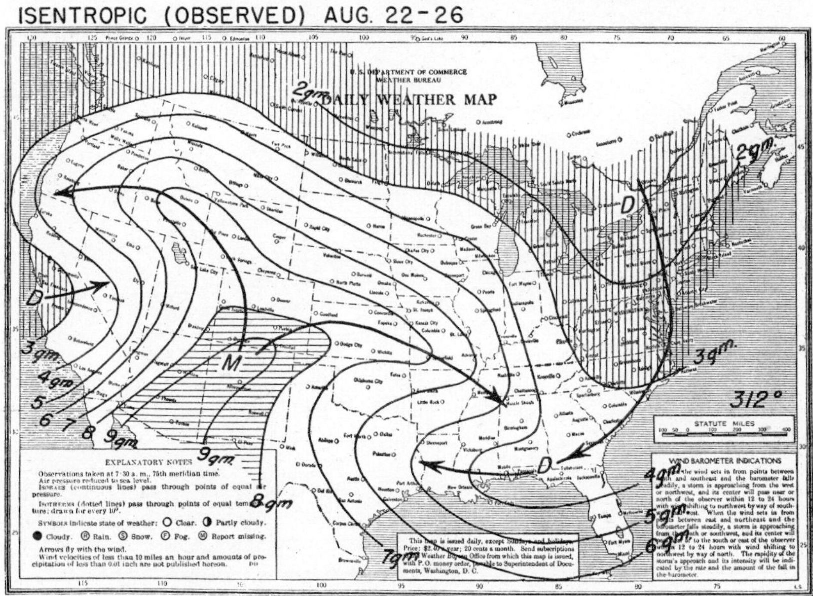

FIGURE 36.—Forecast and verification charts of the mean isentropic-moisture distribution over the United States for the period August 21–25, 1940.

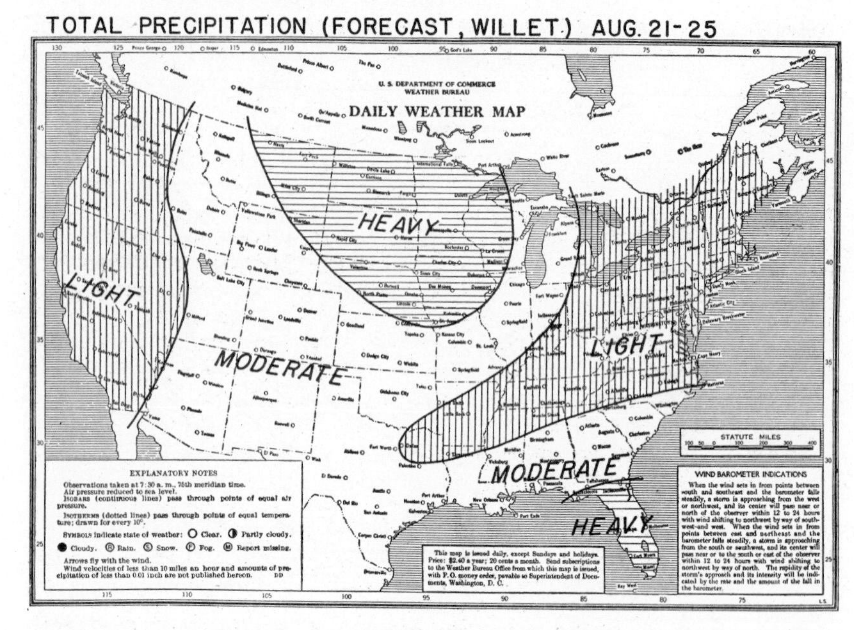

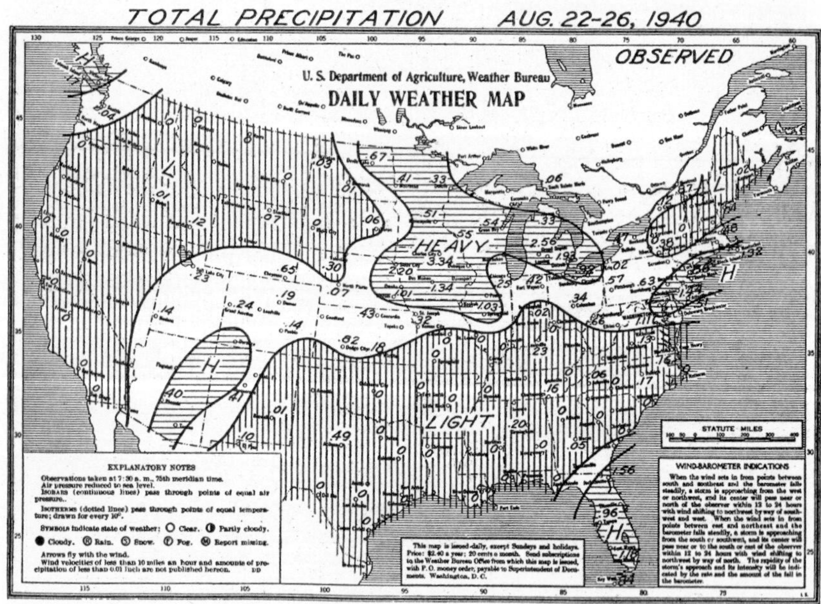

FIGURE 37.—Forecast and verification charts of accumulated-rainfall distribution for the period August 21–25, 1940.

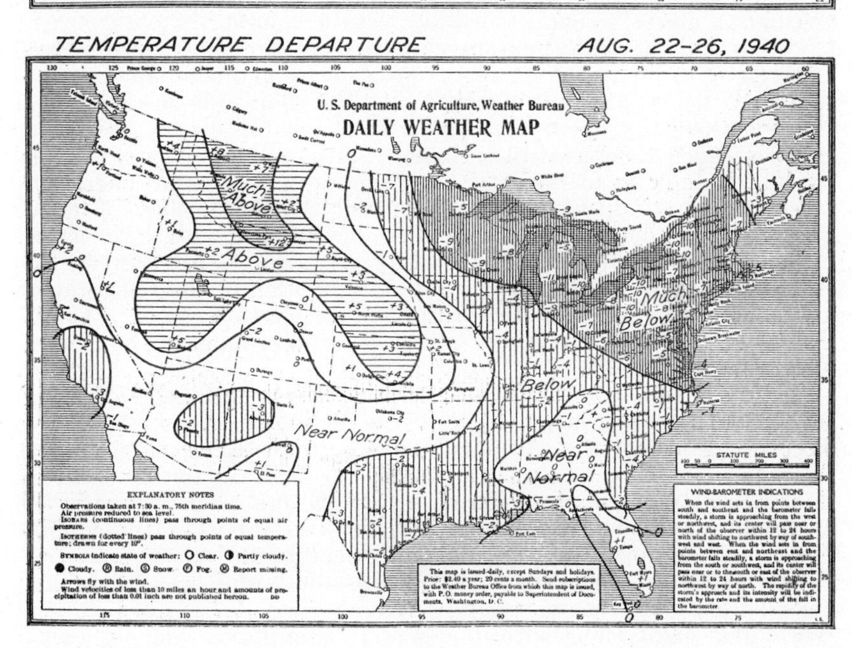

FIGURE 38.—Forecast and verification charts of mean temperature anomalies for the period August 21–25, 1940.

HISTORICAL NOTES

The brief notes given below do not in any sense constitute an attempt to trace the history of the growth of our knowledge concerning the atmosphere, as may be seen from the fact that there are a number of basic meteorological discoveries to which no reference is made. The single purpose of these notes is to attempt to trace the origin of the principal ideas which the writer has sought to weave into a coherent picture of the atmosphere as a mechanical and thermodynamic machine that responds in a predictable fashion to specific external influences.

The German physicist Von Helmholtz took a great deal of interest in meteorological problems. His two papers in 1888 on atmospheric motions, translated into English and published by Cleveland Abbe (*1*), contain a remarkably modern picture of the circulation of the atmosphere. In his analysis, Von Helmholtz considered the atmosphere as consisting of a number of flywheels, or rings of air, spinning around the earth's axis in different latitudes. He realized that the energy of this flywheel motion comes from superimposed slow meridional circulations set up as a result of the inequality in solar radiation income between low and high latitudes. He also recognized that frictional forces, both along the earth's surface and in the free atmosphere, are needed if the thermally driven meridional circulation and the flywheel circulation are to be maintained at a constant speed.

Von Helmholtz was apparently aware of the important role played by surfaces of discontinuity in the atmosphere and gave an elaborate dynamic theory for the intermittent generation and destruction of the polar front, without actually introducing this term. His polar front extended along a latitude circle. Considerable time was devoted by Von Helmholtz to the study of wave motions in atmospheric surfaces of discontinuity, but the waves analyzed by him have a length of up to a few kilometers and should not be confused with the observed cyclonic polar-front waves. He also derived an expression for the equilibrium slope of the polar front as a function of the temperature and wind discontinuity between the two air masses separated by the front. He may be regarded as a very early forerunner of the modern meteorological school.

In Von Helmholtz's day, the synoptic charts contained so few and such scattered observations that it was obviously impossible to give direct evidence for the existence of discontinuities in either wind or temperature. Nevertheless, the theory for such discontinuities continued to attract the attention of theoretical meteorologists, and the Austrian meteorologist Margules (*12*) finally established the equilibrium condition for a front of arbitrary orientation.

The squall line (nowadays called the cold front) was fairly well known from observations at an early stage, but it was not until the World War came along with its demand for improved meteorological service that the Norwegian meteorological school, headed by V. Bjerknes, actually had at its disposal a network of stations sufficiently dense (though of very limited extent) to permit the discovery of both cold front and warm front as elements of the ideal cyclone model (*4*). From then on a rapid development took place. The life history of cyclones culminating in the occlusion process and the characteristic properties of the different air masses interacting in a polar-front wave were discovered by the Norwegian meteorologists, J. Bjerknes and H. Solberg, and by the Swede, Bergeron (*5*). It is very difficult to separate their individual contributions since they worked in close harmony. This theory now serves as the principal basis for daily forecasting.

The break-down of the symmetrical polar front into branches extending generally from southwest to northeast was clearly indicated as an empirical fact fairly early in the writings of the Norwegian school (*6*). Bergeron (*3*) likewise recognized as an empirical fact the existence of a reverse cell in the meridional circulation of the atmosphere, without being able to offer any explanation. The recognition that such a cell must exist to serve as a necessary brake on the general circulation of the atmosphere came from the Massachusetts Institute of Technology school of meteorologists, where also the first attempts were made to compute physically reasonable models for the statistical mean meridional circulation (*17*). In these attempts the role of large-scale lateral mixing processes in diffusing momentum northward or southward was first recognized in modern times, although Von Helmholtz's papers actually contain references to the possible significance of such processes.

Sir Napier Shaw (*20*) was the first to advocate the use of isentropic charts, but the first synoptic isentropic charts were drawn at the Massachusetts Institute of Technology (*16*), and it was there that specific humidity was introduced as a quasi-conservative element useful for tagging and identifying air masses. These isentropic-humidity charts in time led to the analysis of the free-air, anticyclonic eddy patterns which dominate our summer weather, and to the development of a dynamic theory of the maintenance of the eddies (*19*).

The break-down of the zonal circulation into horizontal cells or centers of action has, of course, been known as long as world-wide synoptic charts have been available. The dynamic theory for the large-scale planetary flow patterns was developed at the Massachusetts Institute of Technology (*18*), where the relation between the size of these patterns and the zonal circulation intensity was discovered.

The first systematic attempts to utilize the circulation model presented in this paper in the preparation of 5-day forecasts were made by Willett and his collaborators (*2*). The principal advocate of the introduction of engineering techniques in forecasting is the Norwegian meteorologist Petterssen (*15*), whose work along that line has led to the development of several important aids to our synoptic forecasting technique. In this country the use of prognostic charts as a tool in forecasting has been strongly advocated by Prof. H. Byers, of the University of Chicago. The systematic procedure described in this article for the construction of reasonably complete three-dimensional prognostic models of the atmosphere was developed at the Massachusetts Institute of Technology and is still in its infancy.

Our knowledge of the atmospheric radiation processes is of a later date. Taking into account the fact that the atmospheric water vapor is practically transparent to solar radiation but nearly opaque to the long heat radiation from the ground, Emden (*8*), through theoretical studies, made it plausible that radiation alone would produce a highly unstable lower troposphere characterized by a rapid vertical temperature drop upward, and a nearly isothermal stratosphere. Before him, Humphreys (*11*) and Gold (*9*) had given fairly reasonable explanations for the temperature of the stratosphere. Simpson (*22*, *23*) was the first to compute the vertical transfer of radiation in the atmosphere under actually observed temperature conditions, taking into account the selective character of water-vapor absorption. A German meteorologist, Möller (*13*), was the first to state clearly that the free atmosphere practically everywhere must be considered as a cold source with respect to purely radiative processes, a conclusion which necessitated a thorough revision of certain earlier theories for the general circulation of the atmosphere. The principal work on the determination of the absorption coefficients of water vapor is now carried on at the California Institute of Technology by Elsasser (*7*). Until these coefficients have been carefully determined, our ideas concerning the general circulation must remain fairly speculative.

LITERATURE CITED

(1) ABBE, CLEVELAND.
1893. THE MECHANICS OF THE EARTH'S ATMOSPHERE. Smithsn. Inst. Misc. Collect. 34 (843): 31–129. [Translations of papers by Hermann von Helmholtz on atmospheric motions.]

(2) ALLEN, R. A., FLETCHER, R., HOLMBOE, J., NAMIAS, J., and WILLETT, H. C.
1940. REPORT ON AN EXPERIMENT IN 5-DAY WEATHER FORECASTING. Mass. Inst. Technol., Woods Hole, Phys. Oceanog. and Met. Papers, v. 8, No. 3, 94 pp., illus. [Edited by H. C. Willett.]

(3) BERGERON, TOR.
1928. ÜBER DIE DREIDIMENSIONAL VERKNÜPFENDE WETTERANALYSE. Geofys. Pub., v. 5, No. 6, 111 pp., illus.

(4) BJERKNES, J.
1919. ON THE STRUCTURE OF MOVING CYCLONES. Geofys. Pub., v. 1, No. 2, 8 pp., illus.

(5) ——— and SOLBERG, H.
1922. LIFE CYCLES OF CYCLONES AND THE POLAR FRONT THEORY OF ATMOSPHERIC CIRCULATION. Geofys. Pub., v. 3, No. 1, 18 pp., illus.

(6) BJERKNES, V.
1923. ON THE DYNAMICS OF THE CIRCULAR VORTEX WITH APPLICATIONS TO THE ATMOSPHERE AND THE ATMOSPHERIC VORTEX AND WAVE MOTIONS. Geofys. Pub., v. 2, No. 4, 88 pp., illus.

(7) ELSASSER, WALTER M.
1938. NEW VALUES FOR THE INFRARED ABSORPTION COEFFICIENT OF ATMOSPHERIC WATER VAPOR. U. S. Monthly Weather Rev. 66: 175–178, illus.

(8) EMDEN, R.
1913. ÜBER STRAHLUNGSGLEICHGEWICHT UND ATMOSPHÄRISCHE STRAHLUNG. Bayer. Akad. der Wiss., Math.-Phys. Kl. Sitsber. 1913: 55–142, illus.

(9) GOLD, E.
1909. THE ISOTHERMAL LAYER OF THE ATMOSPHERE AND ATMOSPHERIC RADIATION. Roy. Soc. London Proc., Ser. A, 82: 43–70.

(10) HAYNES, B. C.
1940. METEOROLOGY FOR PILOTS. U. S. Dept. Com., U. S. Civil Aeronaut. Adm., Civil Aeronaut. Bul. 25, 167 pp., illus.

(11) HUMPHREYS, W. J.
1909. VERTICAL TEMPERATURE-GRADIENTS OF THE ATMOSPHERE, ESPECIALLY IN THE REGION OF THE UPPER INVERSION. Astrophys. Jour. 29: 14–32, illus.

(12) MARGULES, M.
1906. ÜBER TEMPERATURSCHICHTUNG IN STATIONÄR BEWEGTER UND IN RUHENDER LUFT. Hann-Band Met. Ztschr. 1906, p. 293.
(13) MÖLLER, FRITZ.
1935. DIE WÄRMEQUELLEN IN DER FREIEN ATMOSPHÄRE. Met. Ztschr. [Brauschweig] 52: 408–412, illus.
(14) NAMIAS, JEROME.
1938. THUNDERSTORM FORECASTING WITH THE AID OF ISENTROPIC CHARTS. Amer. Met. Soc. Bul. 19: [1]–14, illus.
(15) PETTERSSEN, SVERRE.
1940. WEATHER ANALYSIS AND FORECASTING; A TEXTBOOK ON SYNOPTIC METEOROLOGY. 505 pp., illus. New York and London.
(16) ROSSBY, C[ARL]-G[USTAF], and collaborators.
1937. ISENTROPIC ANALYSIS. Amer. Met. Soc. Bul. 18: 201–209, illus.
(17) ——— and collaborators.
1939. ON THE ROLE OF ISENTROPIC MIXING IN THE GENERAL CIRCULATION OF THE ATMOSPHERE. 5th Internatl. Cong. Appl. Mech. Proc. 1939: 373–378.
(18) ———, and collaborators.
1939. RELATION BETWEEN VARIATIONS IN THE INTENSITY OF THE ZONAL CIRCULATION OF THE ATMOSPHERE AND THE DISPLACEMENTS OF THE SEMIPERMANENT CENTERS OF ACTION. Yale Jour. Mar. Res., v. 2, No. 1, pp. 38–55, illus.
(19) ——— NAMIAS, JEROME, and SIMMERS, RITCHIE G.
1938. FLUID MECHANICS APPLIED TO THE STUDY OF ATMOSPHERIC CIRCULATIONS, PART I. A STUDY OF FLOW PATTERNS WITH THE AID OF ISENTROPIC ANALYSIS. Mass. Inst. Technol., Woods Hole, Phys. Oceanog. and Met. Papers, v. 7, No. 1, 125 pp., illus.
(20) SHAW, NAPIER.
1930. MANUAL OF METEOROLOGY, V. III. THE PHYSICAL PROCESSES OF WEATHER. 445 pp. Cambridge, England.
(21) ———
1936. MANUAL OF METEOROLOGY. V. II. COMPARATIVE METEOROLOGY. 472 pp. Cambridge, England.
(22) SIMPSON, G. C.
1928. SOME STUDIES IN TERRESTRIAL RADIATION. Roy. Met. Soc. [London], Mem. 2: [69]–95, illus.
(23) ———
1928. FURTHER STUDIES IN TERRESTRIAL RADIATION. Roy. Met. Soc. [London], Mem. 3: [1]–26, illus.
(24) WEXLER, H., and NAMIAS, J.
1938. MEAN MONTHLY ISENTROPIC CHARTS AND THEIR RELATION TO DEPARTURES OF SUMMER RAINFALL. Amer. Geophys. Union Trans. 19: 164–170, illus.

Amateur Forecasting From Cloud Formations

By C. G. Rossby [1]

[1] C. G. Rossby is Assistant Director of the Weather Bureau.

A FARMER OR sailor who has made himself thoroughly familiar with the characteristics of a typical polar-front storm can often do a creditable job of short-term weather forecasting merely from local observations, based on the fact that there is a definite, orderly sequence of events during the passage of such a storm. A brief description of such a sequence is given here, illustrated by photographs taken from various storms.

If an observer somewhere in the Mississippi Valley is located far to the northeast of the approaching storm and the storm moves northeastward in such a fashion that the low-pressure center passes north and west of him, he will first experience fine weather, possibly with some fine-weather cumulus clouds (fig. 1, *A*) and gentle variable winds. Feathery cirrus clouds (fig. 1, *B*) will gradually move up over the sky from the west or northwest. The barometer will begin to drop, and a gentle wind from the southeast will set in. The cirrus clouds will gradually merge into a thin cirro-stratus cloud veil (fig. 2) through which it is still possible to make out the sun. Often a halo can be seen around the sun at about 22° from its center.

The lower convective cumulus clouds will now begin to dissolve, and the wind will pick up. The cloud deck will gradually get lower and change into a dense, uniform alto-stratus cloud layer (fig. 3) moving from the west or southwest, while the wind at the ground continues to blow from the southeast. Eventually rain will begin to fall, at first in fine drops, then as a moderately heavy, steady fall. The wind will increase and veer somewhat to the south. The temperature will rise, since the returning polar air just in advance of the warm front has had a fairly long southern sojourn. With the passage of the warm front, the wind may swing from southeast or south to southwest, the clouds will break, and the barometer will stop falling. Sometimes the warm-front rain is interspersed with heavy showers resulting from convection in the unstable warm air sliding up over the wedge of cold air in advance of the passage of the warm front.

In the warm sector itself southwest winds prevail, and the barometer, at least to begin with, is fairly steady. In summer, heavy convective showers may occur in this part of the polar-front wave (fig. 4), particularly near the cold front, since the initial instability of the warm moist air from the Gulf of Mexico is heightened through heating over land and the most genuinely tropical air is found just in advance of the cold front.

In winter the ground may have been thoroughly chilled by the preceding warm-front rain, so that, particularly if the wind is light, the moist tropical air is chilled as it moves inland over the cold ground, and fog results.

As the cold front approaches, the barometer again begins to drop, the wind backs slightly (from southwest to south-southwest), and towering cumulo-nimbus clouds appear in the west (fig. 5). A well-developed cold front is often accompanied by a dark squall cloud parallel to the front. In figure 6, the cloud extends north and south. In such a squall cloud there are often signs of violent overturning, or rolling, of the air. The passage of the cold front is accompanied by heavy rain squalls and an abrupt drop in temperature. The wind veers fairly abruptly from south to southwest, west, or even northwest, the barometer rises quickly, and the clouds break.

FIGURE 1.—*A*, Typical fine-weather cumulus clouds. *B*, Cirrus clouds, heralding the advent of warm air at very high levels above the receding wedge of cold air. These clouds consist of ice crystals and form at levels of 3 to 5½ miles above sea level.

The problem of short-term weather forecasting from local observations is of considerable interest not only to farmers and seamen but also to the military services. Nowadays military operations are planned in such a fashion as to take full advantage of the weather. This applies to aircraft operations, to chemical warfare, and to naval operations where visibility becomes a meteorological element of supreme importance. Military meteorologists, however, must be able to operate even when the communication systems on which the meteorological services normally depend for their data break down or when the radio is silenced for fear vital meteorological information might fall into the hands of the enemy. In these cases the ability to make short-term predictions from local readings and observations becomes supremely important.

FIGURE 2.—The warm air, coming closer, now penetrates to somewhat lower levels. The cirrus clouds have merged into a cirro-stratus veil. Sunlight passing through the ice crystals gives rise to a halo.

FIGURE 3.—As the cold wedge recedes and the warm air advances, a layer of alto stratus clouds forms in the boundary between the two air masses. This cloud consist of water droplets and forms at a height of about 2½ miles above sea level.

FIGURE 4.—Violent cumulo-nimbus (thunderstorm) clouds in the warm air. Such clouds do not develop unless the convective currents rise well above the level of freezing temperature.

FIGURE 5.—The cold front approaches, and the thunderstorm clouds announcing its arrival in the west are brightly illuminated by the morning sun. There is haze and dust, characteristic of the warm air after it has moved for a considerable distance over land.

FIGURE 6.—Some well-developed cold fronts are marked by a long squall cloud parallel to the front, clearly indicative of a rolling motion in the advancing cold air.

298737°—41——43 +

PART FIVE

Climatic Data, With Special Reference to Agriculture in the United States

World Extremes of Weather

LOWEST temperature of record in the United States, −66° F. at Riverside Ranger Station, Wyo., in Yellowstone Park, February 9, 1933.

Lowest in Alaska, −78° F. at Fort Yukon, January 14, 1934.

Highest for the United States, 134° F. at Greenland Ranch, Death Valley, Calif., July 10, 1913.

Highest and lowest temperatures recorded anywhere on the earth are: 136° F. at Azizia, Libya, North Africa, September 13, 1922; −90° at Verkhoyansk, Siberia, February 5 and 7, 1892. High and low mean annual temperatures: 86° at Massawa, Eritrea, Africa; −14° at Framheim in the Antarctic. The estimated mean temperature at the South Pole, elevation 8,000 feet, is considerably below −22°.

Average annual precipitation for the United States, approximately 29 inches.

Wettest State, Louisiana, with an annual average rainfall of 55.11 inches.

Driest State, Nevada, averaging 8.81 inches annually.

Highest local average annual rainfall in the United States, 150.73 inches at Wynoochee Oxbow, Wash., based on a 13-year record.

Greatest 24-hour rainfall in the United States, 23.22 inches at New Smyrna, Fla., October 10–11, 1924.

Extreme minimum rainfall records in the United States include a total fall of only 3.93 inches at Bagdad, Calif., for a period of 5 years, 1909–13, and an annual average of 1.35 inches at Greenland Ranch, Calif.

In the Philippines, 46 inches of rainfall was reported in a 24-hour period, July 14–15, 1911, at Baguio, Luzon. This is believed to be the world's record for a 24-hour rainfall.

An authenticated rainfall record of 241 inches in 1 month—August 1841—was reported at Cherrapunji, India, with more than 150 inches in a period of 5 consecutive days. Average annual rainfall at Cherrapunji is 426 inches.

Heavy snowfall records include 60 inches at Giant Forest, Calif., in 1 day; 42 inches at Angola, N. Y., in 2 days; 54 inches at The Dalles, Oreg., in 3 days; and 96 inches at Vanceboro, Maine, in 4 days.

Greatest seasonal snowfall, 884 inches, more than 73 feet, at Tamarack, Calif., during the winter of 1906–7.

The largest hailstone definitely recorded fell at Potter, Nebr., July 6, 1928. It was weighed, measured, and photographed immediately after falling. The weight was 1½ pounds. There have been reports of much larger stones, but they undoubtedly refer to masses of ice resulting from the freezing together of two or more separate stones coming in contact with one another on the ground after falling.

The Climates of the World

By Wesley W. Reed [1]

ON PAGES 672–684 the author gives data on mean and extreme temperatures and monthly and yearly precipitation for 387 representative stations throughout the world, exclusive of the United States. Preceding this information he discusses the principal features of climates over the Eastern and Western Hemispheres. The chief characteristics of the world's climates are illustrated by maps.

[1] Wesley W. Reed is Meteorologist and Assistant Chief, Division of Climate and Crop Weather, Weather Bureau.

TEMPERATURE DISTRIBUTION

THE DISTRIBUTION of temperature over the world and its variations through the year depend primarily on the amount and distribution of the radiant energy received from the sun in different regions. This in turn depends mainly on latitude but is greatly modified by the distribution of continents and oceans, prevailing winds, oceanic circulation, topography, and other factors.

Maps showing average temperatures over the surface of the earth for January and for July are given in figures 1 and 2.

In the winter of the Northern Hemisphere, it will be noted, the poleward temperature gradient (that is, the rate of fall in temperature) north of latitude 15° is very steep over the interior of North America. This is shown by the fact that the lines indicating changes in temperature come very close together. The temperature gradient is also steep toward the cold pole over Asia—the area marked −60°. In western Europe, to the east of the Atlantic Ocean and the North Atlantic Drift, and in the region of prevailing westerly winds, the temperature gradient is much more gradual, as indicated by the fact that the isotherms, or lines of equal temperature, are far apart. In the winter of the Southern Hemisphere, as shown on the map for July (a winter month south of the Equator), the temperature gradient toward the South Pole is very gradual, and the isothermal deflections from the east-west direction (that is, the dipping of the isothermal lines) are of minor importance because continental effects are largely absent.

In the summers of the two hemispheres—July in the north and January in the south—the temperature gradients poleward are very much diminished as compared with those during the winter. This is especially marked over middle and higher northern latitudes because of the greater warming of the extensive interiors of North America

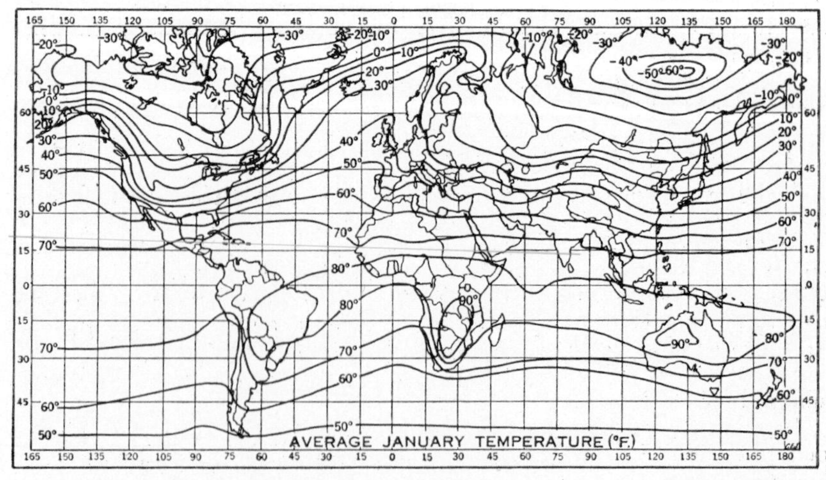

FIGURE 1.—January isotherms (lines of equal temperature) around the earth.

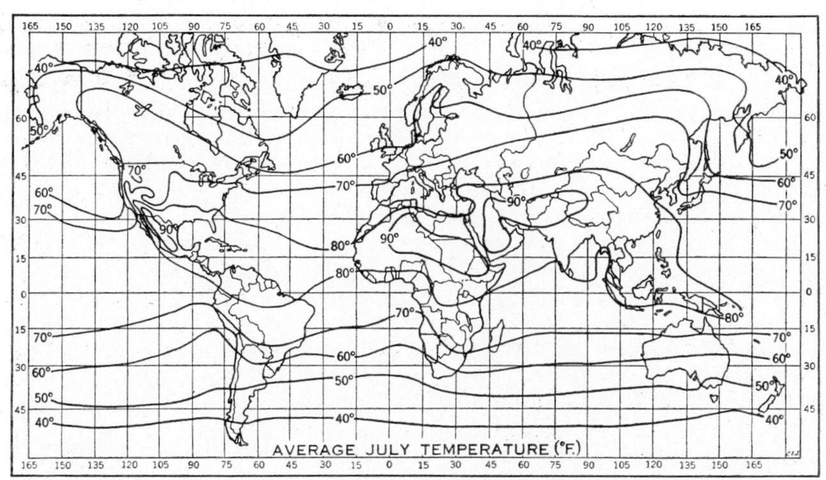

Figure 2.—July isotherms (lines of equal temperature) around the earth.

and Eurasia than of the smaller land areas in middle and higher southern latitudes.

DISTRIBUTION OF PRECIPITATION

Whether precipitation (see the map, fig. 3) occurs as rain or snow or in the rarer forms of hail or sleet depends largely on the temperature climate, which may be influenced more by elevation than by latitude, as in the case of the perpetually snow-capped mountain peaks and glaciers on the Equator in both South America and Africa.

The quantity of precipitation is governed by the amount of water vapor in the air and the nature of the process that leads to its condensation into liquid or solid form through cooling. Air may ascend to great elevations through local convection, as in thunderstorms and in tropical regions generally; it may be forced up over topographical elevations across the prevailing wind direction, as on the southern or windward slopes of the Himalayas in the path of the southwest monsoon of India; or it may ascend more or less gradually in migratory low-pressure formations such as those that govern the main features of weather in the United States.

The areas of heaviest precipitation on the map (fig. 3) are generally located, as would be expected, in tropical regions, where because of the high temperature the greatest amount of water vapor may be present in the atmosphere and the greatest evaporation takes place—although only where conditions favor condensation can rainfall occur. Outstanding exceptions are certain regions in high latitudes, such as southern Alaska, western Norway, and southern Chile, where relatively warm, moist winds from the sea undergo forced ascent over considerable elevations.

In marked contrast to the rainy regions just named are the dry polar regions, where the water-vapor content of the air is always very low because of the low temperature and very limited evaporation. The dry areas in the subtropical belts of high atmospheric pressure (in the vicinity of latitude 30° on all continents, and especially from

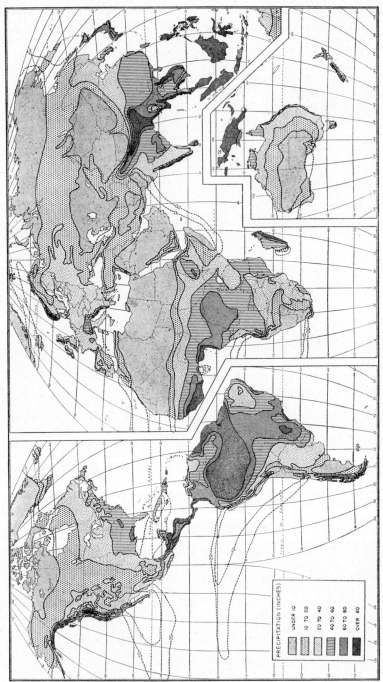

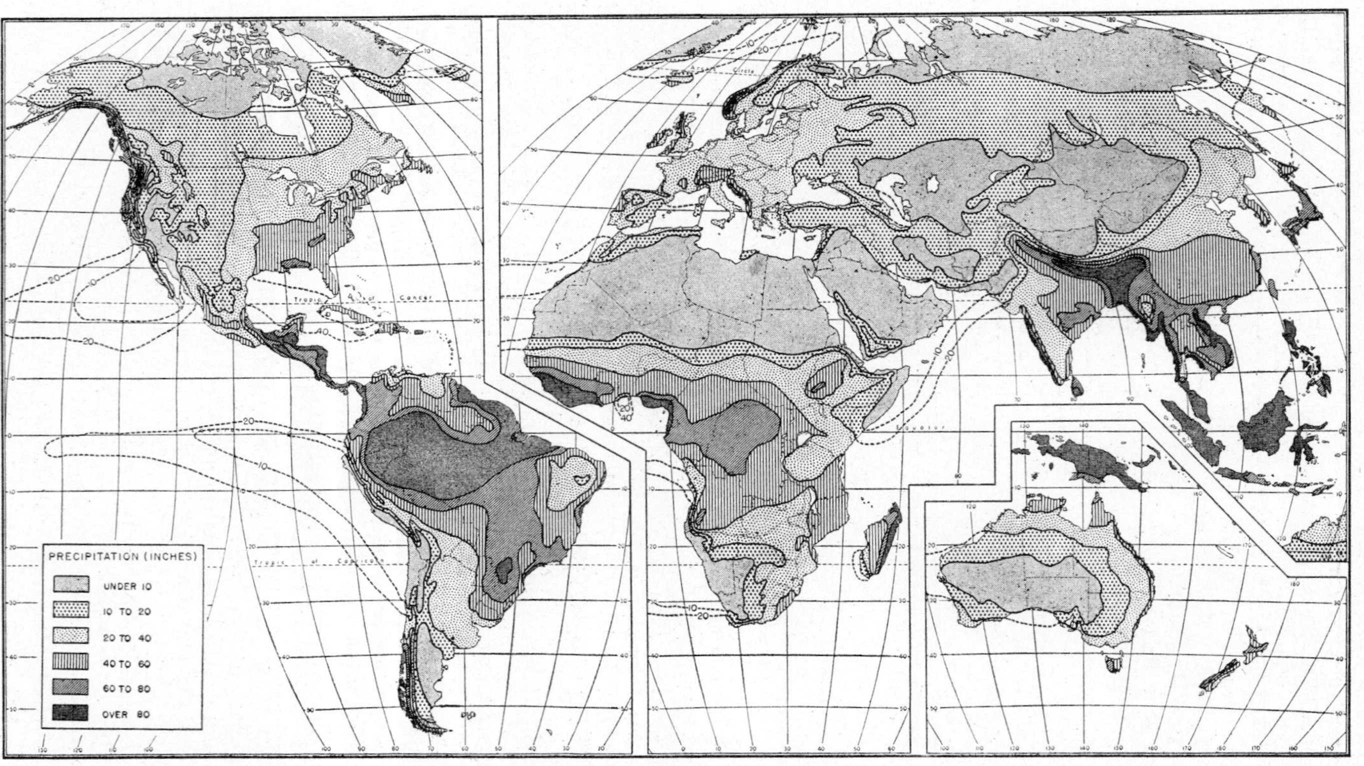

FIGURE 3.—Distribution of precipitation over the earth.

the extreme western Sahara over a broad, somewhat broken belt to the Desert of Gobi), and the arid strips on the lee sides of mountains on whose windward slopes precipitation is heavy to excessive, are caused by conditions which, even though the temperature may be high, are unfavorable to the condensation of whatever water vapor may be present in the atmosphere.

In the table following are data on mean temperatures for January, April, July, and October, with extremes recorded in the period of record, and monthly and annual precipitation for about 500 selected stations well distributed over the earth.

NORTH AMERICA

North America is nearly all within middle and northern latitudes. Consequently it has a large central area in which the continental type of climate with marked seasonal temperature extremes is to be found.

Along the coasts of northern Alaska, western Canada, and the northwestern part of the United States, moderate midsummer temperatures are in marked contrast to those prevailing in the interior east of the mountains. (Note, for example, the great southward dip of the 60° isotherm along the west coast in fig. 2.) Again, the mild midwinter temperatures in the coastal areas stand out against the severe conditions to be found from the Great Lakes region northward and northwestward (fig. 1).

In the West Indian region, temperature conditions are subtropical; and in Mexico and Central America, climatic zones depend on elevation, ranging from subtropical to temperate in the higher levels.

The prevailing westerly wind movement carries the continental type of climate eastward over the United States, so that the region of maritime climate along the Atlantic Ocean is very narrow.

The northern areas are, of course, very cold; but the midwinter low temperatures fall far short of the records set in the cold-pole area of northeastern Siberia, where the vast extent of land becomes much colder than the partly ice-covered area of northern Canada.

From the Aleutian Peninsula to northern California west of the crests of the mountains, there is a narrow strip where annual precipitation is over 40 inches; it exceeds 100 inches locally on the coast of British Columbia (see fig. 3). East of this belt there is an abrupt falling-off in precipitation to less than 20 inches annually over the western half of the continent from lower California northward, and to even less than 5 inches in parts of what used to be called the "Great American Desert," in the southwestern part of the United States.

In the eastern part of the continent—that is, from the southeastern part of the United States northeastward to Newfoundland—the average annual precipitation is more than 40 inches. Rainfall in the West Indies, southern Mexico, and Central America is generally abundant. It is very spotty, however, varying widely even within short distances, especially from the windward to the leeward sides of the mountains.

SOUTH AMERICA

A large part of South America lies within the Tropics and has a characteristically tropical climate. The remaining rather narrow southern portion is not subject to the extremes of heat and cold that are found where wide land areas give full sway to the continental type of climate with its hot summers and cold winters, as in North America and Asia. Temperature anomalies unusual for a given latitude are to be found mainly at the elevated levels of the Andean region stretching from the Isthmus of Panama to Cape Horn.

The Antarctic Current and its cool Humboldt branch skirting the western shores northward to the Equator, together with the prevailing on-shore winds, exert a strong cooling influence over the coastal regions of all the western countries of South America except Colombia. On the east the southerly moving Brazilian current from tropical waters has the opposite, or warming, effect except along southern Argentina.

In the northern countries of South America the sharply contrasted dry and wet seasons are related to the regime of the trade winds. In the dry season (corresponding to winter in the Northern Hemisphere) these winds sweep the entire region, while in the wet season (corresponding to summer in the Northern Hemisphere) calms and variable winds prevail. In the basin of the Amazon River the rainfall is related to the equatorial belt of low pressure and to the trade winds, which give the maximum amounts of rainfall in the extreme west, where they ascend the Andean slopes.

The desert areas on the west coast of South America, extending from the Equator southward to the latitude of Santiago, are due primarily to the cold Humboldt or Peruvian Current and upwelling cold coastal water. The moist, cool ocean air is warmed in passing in over the land, with a consequent decrease in relative humidity, so that the dew point is not reached and condensation of vapor does not occur until the incoming air has reached high elevations in the Andes, where temperatures are very much lower than along the coast.

In southern Chile the summer season has moderate rainfall, and winters are excessively wet. The conditions that prevail farther north are not present here, and condensation of moisture from the ocean progresses from the shores up to the crests of the Andes. By the time the air passes these elevations, however, the moisture has been so depleted that the winds on the leeward slopes are dry, becoming more and more so as they are warmed on reaching lower levels. The mountains can be looked upon as casting a great "rain shadow"—an area of little rain—over southern Argentina.

EUROPE

In Europe there is no extensive north-south mountain system such as is found in both of the Americas, and the general east-west direction of the ranges in the south allows the conditions in the maritime west to change rather gradually toward Asia. Generally rainfall is heaviest on the western coasts, where locally it exceeds 60 inches annually, and diminishes toward the east—except in the elevated Alpine and Caucasus regions—to less than 20 inches in eastern Russia. There is a well-defined rain shadow in Scandinavia, with over 60 inches of rain in western Norway and less than 20 inches in eastern Sweden.

Over much of Europe rainfall is both abundant and rather evenly distributed throughout the year. The chief feature of seasonal distribution of precipitation is the marked winter maximum and the extremely dry, even droughty, summers in most of the Mediterranean lands.

Isothermal lines have the general direction of the parallels of latitude except in winter, when the waters of the western ocean, warmed by the Gulf Stream, give them a north-south trend. Generally there are no marked dips in isotherms due to elevation and continental type of climate such as are found in North America. In Scandinavia, however, the winter map shows an abrupt fall in temperature from the western coast of Norway to the eastern coast of Sweden and thence a continued fall eastward, under a type of exposure more and more continental in contrast to the oceanic exposure on the west.

ASIA

The vast extent of Asia gives full opportunity for continental conditions to develop a cold area of high barometric pressure in winter and a low-pressure, hot area in summer, the former northeast of the Himalayas and the latter stretching widely from west to east in the latitude of northern India. (See the area marked 90° on the map, fig. 2.) These distributions of pressure give to India the well-known monsoon seasons, during which the wind comes from one direction for several months, and also affect the yearly distribution of rainfall over eastern Asia.

In winter the air circulation is outward over the land from the cold pole, and precipitation is very light over the entire continent. In summer, on the contrary, there is an inflow of air from the oceans; even the southeast trade winds flow across the Equator and merge into the southwest monsoon which crosses India. This usually produces abundant rain over most of that country, with excessively heavy amounts when the air is forced to rise, even to moderate elevations, in its passage over the land. At Cherrapunji (4,455 feet), on the southern side of the Khasi Hills, in Assam, the average rainfall in a winter month is about 1 inch, while in both June and July it is approximately 100 inches. However, this heavy summer rainfall meets an impassable barrier in the Himalaya

Mountains, while the much lighter summer monsoon rainfall over Japan and eastern Asia does not extend far into China because of lesser elevations. Consequently, while the southeast quadrant of Asia, including the East Indies, also with monsoon winds, has heavy to excessive annual rainfall, the remainder of the continent is dry, with vast areas receiving less than 10 inches annually.

North of the Himalayas the low plains are excessively cold in winter and temperatures rise rather high in summer. At Verkhoyansk in the cold-pole area, and north of the Arctic Circle, the mean temperature in January is about −59° F. and in July approximately 60°; the extreme records are a maximum of 94°, from readings at 1 p. m., and a minimum of −90°.

In southwestern Asia the winter temperature control is still the interior high-pressure area, and temperatures are generally low, especially at high elevations; in summer at low elevations excessively high maxima are recorded, as, for example' in the Tigris-Euphrates Valley.

AFRICA

Africa, like South America, lies very largely within the Tropics; and there, too, temperature distribution is determined mainly by altitude. Moreover, along the southern portion of the western coast the cool Benguela Current moves northward, and on the eastern coast are the warm tropical currents of the Indian Ocean, which create conditions closely paralleling those found around the South American Continent. In the strictly tropical areas of Africa conditions are characterized by prevailing low barometric pressure, with convectional rainfall and alternate northward and southward movement of the heat equator, while in both the north and the south the ruling influences are the belts of high barometric pressure.

Except in the Atlas Mountains in the northwest, where the considerable elevations set up a barrier in the path of the trade winds and produce moderate rainfall, the desert conditions typified by the Sahara extend from the Atlantic to the Red Sea and from the Mediterranean southward well beyond the northern Tropic to about the latitude of southern Arabia.

South of the Sahara, rainfall increases rapidly, becoming abundant to heavy from the west coast to the central lakes, with annual maxima of over 80 inches in the regions bordering the eastern and western extremes of the Guinea coast. This marked increase in precipitation does not extend to the eastern portion of the middle region of the continent, where the annual amounts received are below 40 inches and decrease to less than 10 inches on the coasts of Somaliland. Also to the south of the central rainy area there is a rapid fall in precipitation toward the arid regions of Southwest Africa, where conditions are similar to those in Somaliland.

The heavy rainfall over sections of Ethiopia from June to October, when more than 40 inches fall and bring the overflowing of the otherwise arid Nile valley, is one of the earth's outstanding features of seasonal distribution of rainfall.

Moist equatorial climate is typified by conditions in the Belgian Congo; arid torrid climate by those of Egypt and the Sahara; and moderate plateau climate by those found in parts of Ethiopia and the British possessions to the southward.

AUSTRALIA

In the southern winter the high-pressure belt crosses the interior of Australia, and all except the southernmost parts of the continent are dry. In summer, on the other hand, this pressure belt has moved south of the continent, still giving dry conditions over the southern and western areas. Thus the total annual precipitation is less than 20 inches except in the extreme southwest and in a strip circling from southeast to northwest. The average annual precipitation is even less than 10 inches in a large south-central area.

In the south the winter precipitation is of the cyclonic type; the heavy summer rains of the north are of monsoon origin; and those of the eastern borders are in large part orographic, owing to the presence of the highlands in the immediate vicinity of the coasts. In the outer or seaward border of the rainfall strip along the coastal region, the mean annual rainfall is over 40 inches and in many localities over 60 inches. This is true also for the monsoon rains in the north.

Because of the location of Australia, on both sides of the southern Tropic, temperatures far below freezing are to be found only in a small part of the continent, in the south at high elevations. In the arid interior extreme maximum temperatures are very high, ranking with those of the hottest regions of the earth.

TEMPERATURE AND PRECIPITATION DATA FOR REPRESENTATIVE STATIONS ON A WORLD-WIDE DISTRIBUTION

NORTH AMERICA

Country and station	Latitude	Longitude	Elevation	Temperature: Mean: Length of record	Mean: January	Mean: April	Mean: July	Mean: October	Extreme: Length of record	Extreme: Maximum	Extreme: Minimum	Average precipitation: Length of record	January	February	March	April	May	June	July	August	September	October	November	December	Year
	° ′	° ′	Ft.	Yr.	°F.	°F.	°F.	°F.	Yr.	°F.	°F.	Yr.	In.	In.	In.	In.	In.	In.	In.	In.	In.	In.	In.	In.	In.
Alaska:																									
Allakaket	66 34 N.	152 44 W.	600	24	−20.3	17.0	57.7	20.2	24	90	−70	25	0.77	0.84	0.70	0.36	0.65	1.32	2.11	2.02	1.55	1.11	0.83	0.84	13.10
Anchorage	61 13 N.	149 52 W.	111	22	11.2	34.9	57.0	36.4	22	92	−36	22	.85	.69	.57	.39	.48	.58	1.65	2.64	2.49	2.08	1.06	.84	14.32
Barrow	71 23 N.	156 17 W.	13	25	−17.0	−0.9	40.2	16.4	25	78	−56	23	.15	.20	.14	.13	.15	.26	.93	.74	.46	.59	.32	.27	4.34
Cordova	60 32 N.	145 42 W.	83	26	27.2	37.7	54.8	42.1	26	87	−19	27	9.49	10.70	8.49	8.69	9.09	6.03	8.51	13.24	19.96	22.94	15.51	12.78	145.43
Dillingham	59 03 N.	158 27 W.	20	22	16.1	29.8	55.6	36.3	22	89	−41	21	1.87	1.34	1.78	1.29	1.63	1.70	2.71	3.91	3.93	2.78	1.73	1.45	26.12
Dutch Harbor	53 53 N.	166 32 W.	13	22	32.2	35.9	51.3	42.2	22	80	8	18	5.80	5.24	5.01	4.02	4.41	2.74	1.92	2.35	5.21	7.33	5.71	7.03	56.77
Fairbanks	64 51 N.	147 43 W.	440	34	−11.6	28.7	60.0	26.8	34	99	−66	34	.97	.49	.70	.29	.57	1.30	1.92	2.10	1.31	.85	.74	.63	11.87
Fort Yukon	66 34 N.	145 18 W.	417	23	−21.6	20.5	61.2	20.7	23	100	−78	23	.40	.41	.26	.27	.49	.80	1.07	1.27	.65	.60	.35	.31	6.88
Holy Cross	62 16 N.	159 50 W.	50	35	−0.4	25.9	56.5	29.7	35	93	−58	29	1.49	.97	1.29	.66	.67	1.31	2.70	3.78	2.91	1.67	1.29	1.32	20.06
Juneau	58 18 N.	134 24 W.	72	43	27.5	40.6	56.6	43.3	43	89	−15	45	7.18	5.63	5.41	5.46	5.22	3.95	5.03	7.33	10.15	11.18	9.10	7.61	83.25
Ketchikan	55 21 N.	131 39 W.	17	28	32.6	42.2	57.5	46.4	28	96	−8	28	13.71	11.63	12.20	10.79	8.31	6.55	8.24	11.51	12.14	20.13	19.74	15.94	150.89
Kodiak	57 48 N.	152 24 W.	152	36	29.8	36.7	54.3	42.4	36	85	−12	46	4.66	4.73	3.83	3.93	6.03	4.91	3.60	5.00	5.43	7.55	5.72	6.09	61.48
Kotzebue	66 55 N.	162 32 W.	11	14	−9.2	13.1	52.4	24.2	14	81	−58	6	.94	.24	.26	.50	.09	.57	1.05	.89	.73	.37	.36	.32	6.32
Matanuska	61 30 N.	149 15 W.	152	19	12.6	36.3	57.7	36.9	19	91	−36	19	.94	.80	.61	.47	.62	1.06	1.87	2.88	2.39	1.84	1.05	1.08	15.61
Nome	64 30 N.	165 24 W.	14	32	3.4	18.8	49.8	29.3	32	84	−47	32	1.16	.83	.88	.64	.66	1.21	2.55	3.36	2.77	1.61	1.00	1.15	17.82
Nulato	64 43 N.	158 04 W.	153	13	−7.5	21.1	57.5	27.0	13	90	−62	13	1.40	.96	1.26	.38	.58	.83	2.41	2.64	2.10	1.87	1.21	.86	16.50
Sitka	57 03 N.	135 20 W.	15	56	32.4	41.4	54.9	46.0	56	87	−5	77	7.84	6.78	5.97	5.58	4.15	3.36	4.29	7.02	10.33	12.64	10.07	9.10	87.13
Canada:																									
Atlin	59 35 N.	133 38 W.	2,240	14	−1.6	30.9	52.7	35.6	22	86	−58	18	.93	.87	.62	.31	.41	.81	1.04	.93	1.25	1.25	1.28	1.24	10.94
Banff	51 10 N.	115 34 W.	4,521	20	13.4	36.5	56.8	38.7	33	93	−10	23	1.43	.79	1.27	1.16	2.38	3.02	2.48	2.39	1.71	1.19	1.80	1.06	20.68
Chesterfield Inlet	63 45 N.	91 50 W.	48	8	−26.5	2.5	47.2	22.0	8	84	−17														
Edmonton	53 33 N.	113 30 W.	2,158	30	5.9	40.8	61.2	41.8	46	98	29	38	.87	.64	.67	.82	1.81	3.13	3.39	2.40	1.39	.73	.69	.77	17.31
Fort Chipewyan	58 52 N.	111 10 W.	714	43	−12.7	26.6	59.4	32.5	43	93	−58	43	.68	.54	.68	.69	.83	1.36	2.31	1.63	1.22	.91	.94	.80	12.59
Fort Good Hope	66 25 N.	128 53 W.	214	12	−22.9	13.6	59.6	21.0	31	95	−79	21	.48	.52	.60	.54	.66	1.22	1.39	1.63	1.11	1.04	.73	.53	10.45
Halifax	44 39 N.	63 36 W.	88	50	23.0	39.4	64.8	48.7	53	99	−21	50	5.59	4.52	5.02	4.50	4.17	3.70	3.90	4.53	3.55	5.25	5.40	5.39	55.52
Hebron	58 12 N.	62 21 W.	60	18	−5.7	18.3	47.1	31.2	18	84	−42	15	.95	.67	.86	1.10	1.56	2.15	2.70	2.71	3.34	1.56	1.10	.60	19.30
Massett	53 58 N.	132 09 W.	30	17	35.8	42.6	58.1	46.6	27	84	−2	23	5.79	4.04	3.42	4.97	3.99	2.46	2.80	2.65	3.88	6.18	7.37	6.37	53.92
Montreal	45 30 N.	73 35 W.	187	50	13.0	41.3	69.5	46.6	43	96	−27	50	3.75	3.17	3.52	2.51	3.03	3.48	3.70	3.46	3.54	3.28	3.47	3.74	40.65
Moose Factory	51 14 N.	80 30 W.	30	33	−4.4	28.0	61.2	39.2	38	97	−54	33	1.26	.91	1.14	1.03	1.76	2.22	2.39	3.27	2.89	1.80	1.11	1.17	20.95
Port Nelson	57 0 N.	92 51 W.	49	19	−18.8	21.5	55.7	28.4	13	92	−55	19	.84	.46	.88	1.07	.94	1.92	1.96	2.60	2.08	1.19	1.08	1.13	16.15
Prince Albert	53 10 N.	105 38 W.	1,432	30	−5.9	36.2	62.0	38.3	43	96	−70	41	.76	.60	.86	.88	1.48	2.67	2.17	2.27	1.39	.79	.87	.66	15.40
Quebec	46 48 N.	71 13 W.	296	50	9.7	36.4	66.7	43.5	52	97	−34	50	3.75	3.14	3.22	2.40	3.16	3.94	4.07	3.92	4.01	3.47	3.55	3.43	42.06
St. Johns	45 17 N.	66 04 W.	125	50	23.4	35.0	59.1	45.3	52	92	−21	50	5.38	5.07	4.51	4.24	3.56	3.55	3.73	3.58	3.77	5.40	6.06	4.92	53.77
Toronto	43 40 N.	79 24 W.	379	80	22.2	41.8	68.7	47.8	87	103	−28	80	2.72	2.48	2.53	2.46	2.92	2.81	2.88	2.80	2.96	2.43	2.76	2.58	32.33

Vancouver	49 17 N.	123 05 W.	136	28	35.6	47.6	63.3	49.4	29	92	2	26	8.40	6.03	4.98	3.29	2.99	2.57	1.23	1.70	4.07	5.65	9.52	8.22	58.65
White River	48 35 N.	85 16 W.	1,244	30	0.4	34.2	60.5	36.4	42	97	−60	30	1.63	1.25	1.46	1.52	2.14	2.47	3.12	3.00	2.88	2.44	2.39	1.86	26.16
Winnipeg	49 53 N.	97 07 W.	760	40	−3.4	37.8	66.6	40.9	43	103	−46	40	.74	.79	1.08	1.50	2.23	3.27	3.04	2.38	1.97	1.48	.96	.93	20.37
Canal Zone:																									
Balboa Heights	8 58 N.	79 33 W.	118	20	80.0	82.0	80.0	79.0	20	97	63	29	.91	.79	.63	2.72	7.91	7.99	7.28	8.07	7.87	10.31	10.08	4.17	68.73
Colon	9 22 N.	79 55 W.	25	20	75.2	81.2	80.4	80.0	20	95	66	56	3.74	1.62	1.58	4.30	12.37	13.29	16.00	14.75	12.50	15.13	20.70	11.37	127.35
Central America:																									
Belize	17 29 N.	88 14 W.	7	5	76.1	80.8	82.4	80.4	22	99	46	24	7.44	3.22	2.47	2.23	4.91	7.86	8.23	8.27	9.38	10.58	13.29	6.65	84.53
Guatemala	14 37 N.	90 31 W.	4,855	6	63.0	70.0	69.2	67.8	13	90	41	29	.30	.13	.47	1.22	6.00	10.84	7.98	7.77	9.11	6.76	.94	.32	51.84
San Jose	9 56 N.	84 07 W.	3,760	5	67.3	70.5	69.1	68.4	12	94	47	34	.60	.18	.77	1.76	9.04	9.53	8.27	9.53	12.04	11.78	5.75	1.59	70.84
San Salvador	13 42 N.	89 12 W.	2,155	14	72.5	77.1	75.4	74.8	5	103	45	23	.17	.21	.50	1.96	6.69	11.13	12.11	11.72	11.03	10.37	1.79	.59	68.27
Greenland:																									
Angmagssalik	65 36 N.	37 34 W.	104	25	16.9	23.5	43.9	29.8	24	77	−23	22	3.46	1.73	2.20	2.40	2.76	2.09	2.13	2.48	4.06	6.26	3.42	2.68	35.67
Godthaab	64 10 N.	51 44 W.	66	44	14.4	24.6	43.9	30.6		76	−20	35	1.46	1.81	1.77	1.10	1.65	1.30	2.32	3.11	3.27	2.48	1.89	1.57	23.73
Ivigtut	61 12 N.	48 10 W.	82	42	18.5	30.9	49.8	33.8	48	86	−20	45	3.27	2.72	3.39	2.44	3.58	3.03	3.27	3.78	6.02	5.87	4.41	3.07	44.85
Jakobshavn	69 13 N.	51 02 W.	102	47	−0.4	14.5	45.9	25.3		71	−46	48	.35	.28	.47	.47	.55	.83	1.22	1.42	1.38	.94	.67	.51	9.09
Upernivik	72 47 N.	56 07 W.	62	46	−7.6	5.9	41.0	24.8		69	−44	45	.43	.51	.67	.59	.55	.51	.91	1.10	1.06	1.10	1.06	.51	9.00
Iceland:																									
Vestmanno	63 26 N.	20 15 W.	23	40	34.5	39.6	52.5	42.1	34	71	−6	34	5.47	4.61	4.45	3.70	3.11	3.31	3.07	2.99	5.79	5.59	5.23	5.59	52.91
Mexico:																									
Chihuahua	28 38 N.	106 4 W.	4,669	10	55.2	65.0	76.2	64.0	12	103	11	22	.20	.35	.32	.24	.24	1.65	3.58	3.70	3.27	.94	.51	.39	15.39
Guadalajara	20 41 N.	103 20 W.	5,184	24	59.2	69.0	69.5	66.6	29	99	24	33	.43	.24	.24	.16	1.10	8.82	9.41	8.54	7.17	2.20	.75	.67	39.73
Guaymas	27 55 N.	110 53 W.	30	6	64.2	72.3	86.7	81.1				5	.20	.00	.32	.16	.20	.08	1.69	3.58	2.40	.35	.63	1.50	11.11
La Paz	24 10 N.	110 21 W.	59	10	63.3	71.6	84.6	79.9	11	114	35	13	.20	.08	.04	.00	.00	.20	.43	1.22	1.42	.59	.47	1.06	5.71
Lerdo	25 30 N.	103 32 W.	3,740	11	58.7	71.5	79.4	69.8	13	105	23	14	.39	.07	.20	.28	.83	1.54	1.54	1.34	1.97	.79	.75	.51	10.21
Manzanillo	21 7 N.	101 41 W.	13	5	74.7	75.2	81.7	80.1				10	.04	.24	.00	.00	.00	4.02	5.12	5.75	13.11	4.53	.51	2.95	36.27
Mazatlan	23 11 N.	106 25 W.	256	42	68.4	71.8	82.6	80.4	30	95	42	47	.79	.51	.24	.08	.12	1.46	5.94	8.27	7.99	2.60	.87	1.26	30.13
Mexico City	19 24 N.	99 12 W.	7,575	15	54.2	63.5	62.7	59.6	18	92	24	17	.46	.22	.35	.81	2.10	4.68	6.69	6.00	5.08	2.04	.65	.30	29.38
Monterrey	25 40 N.	100 18 W.	1,732	17	57.6	74.2	80.8	71.7	24	118	21	33	.55	.71	.83	1.30	1.34	3.03	2.28	2.36	5.16	2.95	1.50	.79	22.80
Progreso	21 17 N.	89 40 W.	46	12	69.6	81.8	80.0	79.4	12	102	53	12	.77	.64	.58	.69	1.29	2.74	1.71	3.06	2.61	2.89	1.23	.73	18.94
Salina Cruz	16 12 N.	95 12 W.	184	20	76.3	81.3	81.9	80.2				23	.04	.39	.63	.47	3.27	11.89	4.48	5.51	7.05	4.02	.94	.12	38.81
Tampico	22 13 N.	97 51 W.	59	11	65.8	76.0	82.0	77.8				15	1.53	1.18	1.02	1.53	1.85	8.70	4.88	4.84	10.78	5.00	2.01	1.61	44.93
Vera Cruz	19 12 N.	96 8 W.	52	12	70.6	76.4	79.8	78.8	12	96	49	12	.74	.50	.37	.75	1.83	10.21	13.44	11.84	14.14	5.80	3.19	.93	63.74
Zacatecas	22 47 N.	102 34 W.	8,570	15	48.8	58.6	57.8	55.4	15	84	21	35	.51	.31	.39	.24	.87	4.06	4.09	3.42	3.46	1.61	.63	.54	20.13
West Indies:																									
Bridgetown	13 6 N.	59 37 W.	181	10	76.3	78.4	80.0	79.3	18	91	61	19	2.06	1.70	1.64	1.67	1.82	4.36	4.84	6.81	6.60	6.03	4.58	3.47	45.58
Camaguey	21 19 N.	77 55 W.	344	13	71.6	78.0	81.6	78.6	13	102	45	20	1.54	1.40	2.43	3.64	7.62	10.52	5.60	5.54	7.26	5.44	3.12	1.96	56.07
Havana	23 8 N.	82 21 W.	161	21	69.8	74.3	79.2	77.2	21	95	50	63	2.84	1.84	1.92	2.28	4.45	6.46	4.87	5.48	5.78	6.57	3.15	2.44	48.08
Kingston	18 1 N.	76 48 W.	24	16	76.9	78.7	81.9	80.8	16	98	57	53	.92	.67	.96	1.18	4.16	4.00	1.53	3.37	4.42	6.96	2.80	1.55	32.52
Port au Prince	18 33 N.	72 20 W.	121	20	78.0	80.2	84.0	80.8	25	100	59	44	1.15	2.41	3.73	6.65	9.42	4.17	2.86	5.30	7.52	6.89	3.61	1.31	55.02
San Juan	18 29 N.	66 7 W.	100	39	74.8	76.7	80.0	79.9	39	94	62	39	4.45	2.68	2.88	4.01	5.87	5.28	5.80	6.07	6.35	5.60	6.97	5.38	61.34

TEMPERATURE AND PRECIPITATION DATA FOR REPRESENTATIVE STATIONS ON A WORLD-WIDE DISTRIBUTION—Continued

SOUTH AMERICA

Country and station	Latitude	Longitude	Elevation	Temperature								Average precipitation													
				Mean					Extreme																
				Length of record	January	April	July	October	Length of record	Maximum	Minimum	Length of record	January	February	March	April	May	June	July	August	September	October	November	December	Year
	° ′	° ′	Ft.	Yr.	°F.	°F.	°F.	°F.	Yr.	°F.	°F.	Yr.	In.	In.	In.	In.	In.	In.	In.	In.	In.	In.	In.	In.	In.
Argentina:																									
Bahia Blanca	38 45 S.	62 15 W.	82	42	74.8	60.6	48.0	59.2	50	108	18	20	2.20	2.24	2.24	3.46	1.14	0.63	0.91	0.71	1.65	2.48	1.81	2.05	21.52
Buenos Aires	34 36 S.	58 22 W.	82	10	74.4	63.3	51.2	61.2	50	103	28	20	3.11	2.60	3.94	4.72	2.83	2.01	2.16	2.24	2.87	3.35	3.94	4.09	37.86
Cipolletti	38 56 S.	68 08 W.	889	9	72.6	55.7	41.8	56.8	17	106	9	20	.43	.43	.75	.43	.55	.94	.51	.43	.39	.83	.55	.47	6.71
Colonia Sarmiento	45 30 S.	69 00 W.	899	8	64.8	51.9	37.4	52.6	13	99	−27	20	.16	.32	.39	.47	.79	.51	.83	.35	.47	.24	.24	.16	4.93
Cordoba	31 25 S.	64 12 W.	1,388	41	73.8	62.7	51.7	63.6	49	114	13	20	4.17	4.32	3.50	1.68	.99	.28	.33	.51	.90	2.38	4.02	4.65	27.73
Deseado	47 46 S.	65 55 W.	20	8	61.4	50.4	39.0	50.7	8	102	1	8	.59	.51	.28	.71	1.61	.59	1.30	.51	.12	.32	.16	.47	7.17
La Quiaca	22 10 S.	65 31 W.	11,358	11	55.3	50.2	37.8	51.6	19	90	0	20	3.27	2.36	2.01	.28	.00	.00	.04	.00	.00	.20	1.06	2.13	11.35
Mendoza	32 53 S.	68 49 W.	2,477	23	75.2	60.1	47.2	63.0	31	109	15	20	.87	1.18	1.10	.47	.39	.35	.24	.32	.51	.75	.71	.75	7.64
Puerto Madryn	42 49 S.	64 58 W.	46	8	68.8	58.6	44.5	55.0	8	102	11	20	.50	.59	.47	.63	.67	.63	.47	.26	.35	.55	.32	.43	5.87
Salta	24 46 S.	65 28 W.	3,865	10	70.8	63.0	54.6	66.4	18	101	15	20	6.50	6.22	4.02	1.26	.39	.12	.04	.20	.35	1.22	2.44	5.20	27.96
Santiago	27 47 S.	64 15 W.	613	28	82.6	70.5	56.6	72.6	36	115	24	20	3.42	2.80	2.99	1.26	.55	.32	.20	.24	.51	1.46	2.44	4.21	20.40
Victorica	36 10 S.	65 21 W.	1,027	9	75.9	60.0	46.9	60.8	17	113	4	20	2.95	2.99	2.95	1.61	.91	.43	.35	.51	1.18	2.56	2.01	2.20	20.65
Bolivia:																									
La Paz	16 30 S.	68 9 W.	12,001	6	53.2	50.4	45.3	52.5	4	75	27	5	3.86	4.53	2.60	1.46	.47	.08	.16	1.10	.79	1.30	1.54	4.29	22.18
Sucre	19 03 S.	65 16 W.	9,344	5	55.4	54.2	49.3	55.6	6	82	25	32	6.34	4.68	3.74	1.77	.28	.08	.16	.16	.79	1.42	2.40	4.37	26.19
Brazil:																									
Bahia	13 00 S.	38 31 W.	154	22	79.9	79.2	74.2	77.2	22	95	62	11	3.24	4.83	5.46	9.66	10.20	9.55	7.38	4.85	3.30	4.68	4.71	6.00	73.86
Barra do Cordo	5 30 S.	45 16 W.	266	18	79.6	79.8	77.0	82.3	17	103	54	11	6.98	7.07	7.17	4.28	2.74	.73	.43	.45	1.12	1.61	3.46	4.67	40.71
Belem	1 27 S.	48 29 W.	42	18	79.4	79.9	80.2	80.2	18	95	64	29	11.56	12.94	14.88	12.13	9.44	6.73	6.15	4.45	3.47	2.80	2.61	6.03	93.19
Bella Vista	22 06 S.	56 22 W.	528	10	81.0	75.6	64.5	74.8	10	108	28	5	8.58	4.86	5.39	3.60	3.18	3.89	1.44	1.98	2.55	5.75	5.91	4.07	51.20
Caetite	14 3 S.	42 37 W.	2,953	22	73.4	72.2	66.6	72.6	22	99	46	11	5.48	3.34	3.15	2.63	.56	.43	.37	.24	.94	2.81	5.12	5.92	30.99
Corumba	18 59 S.	57 39 W.	381	8	83.1	82.4	74.2	81.6	8	106	33	11	7.32	5.92	5.11	4.59	2.93	1.86	.34	1.17	2.58	3.95	5.64	7.07	48.48
Cuyaba	15 36 S.	56 06 W.	541	9	81.4	80.8	75.6	82.8	9	99	50	25	9.83	8.31	8.31	4.00	2.07	.27	.22	1.14	2.00	4.49	5.94	8.07	54.65
Goyaz	15 55 S.	50 08 W.	1,706	12	74.6	76.0	71.9	77.8	12	104	36	6	12.11	10.87	11.57	4.90	.42	.50	.01	.44	1.72	4.86	8.63	10.41	66.44
Manaos	3 08 S.	60 01 W.	147	14	81.2	80.6	81.0	83.6	14	101	66	15	9.52	8.80	9.22	9.17	6.75	4.36	2.72	1.20	1.94	4.55	5.12	8.29	71.64
Morro do Chapeo	11 33 S.	41 14 W.	3,543	10	69.4	68.9	62.2	68.8	10	91	44	13	3.98	4.03	4.09	3.44	1.84	1.96	2.00	1.56	1.04	2.09	3.88	4.06	33.97
Passo Fundo	28 16 S.	52 24 W.	2,198	18	73.2	66.2	56.3	63.0	17	101	21	10	5.41	3.50	4.32	3.44	5.40	6.87	4.24	4.68	7.21	4.61	3.72	4.27	57.67
Pirapora	17 21 S.	44 57 W.	1,548	16	77.1	75.6	68.2	78.0	16	100	37	8	13.26	6.57	6.72	3.87	.53	.11	.15	.65	1.20	4.32	5.97	9.49	52.84
Porto Alegre	30 01 S.	51 13 W.	37	21	76.9	69.2	57.0	65.5	21	105	28	15	4.19	3.28	3.67	4.50	3.96	4.87	4.28	5.10	4.52	3.04	3.10	4.00	48.51
Porto Nacional	10 39 S.	48 20 W.	778	9	79.2	79.2	75.6	81.0	9	104	50	7	11.92	11.73	12.34	8.35	2.01	.02	.19	.30	1.46	6.54	10.57	9.94	75.37
Quixeramobim	5 16 S.	39 15 W.	679	24	84.1	81.2	80.0	84.2	35	99	64	25	3.08	3.45	5.76	4.86	3.67	1.55	.84	.44	.08	.05	.17	1.13	25.08

Recife	8 04 S.	34 52 W.	97	11	82.3	81.2	76.6	80.4	11	94	67	48	2.05	3.27	6.46	8.50	11.02	11.02	10.47	6.38	2.64	1.02	1.06	1.18	65.07
Riberaio Preto	21 10 S.	47 48 W.	1,824	17	75.4	72.0	64.6	73.4	17	104	29	17	9.35	7.28	6.63	3.20	1.77	1.58	.60	1.25	2.45	4.55	6.64	9.82	55.12
Rio de Janeiro	22 54 S.	43 10 W.	210	49	78.4	74.6	68.4	71.2	49	102	52	75	4.97	4.50	5.32	4.18	3.18	2.26	1.68	1.76	2.59	3.27	4.06	5.48	43.25
Sao Paulo	23 33 S.	46 38 W.	2,690	14	70.6	66.6	59.4	64.8	31	101	28	31	9.09	8.54	6.18	2.95	2.91	2.24	1.34	2.05	3.39	4.49	5.24	7.60	56.02
Taperinha	2 30 S.	54 20 W.	66	11	78.4	78.2	78.4	81.3	11	96	65	9	6.50	10.82	11.39	11.87	10.68	6.52	4.25	1.97	1.48	1.04	1.95	4.70	73.17
Therezina	5 05 S.	42 49 W.	230	11	80.0	79.6	78.4	83.3	12	102	57	7	9.14	6.28	10.32	9.65	3.98	.84	.32	.81	.42	.72	1.57	4.55	48.60
Uruguayana	29 45 S.	57 5 W.	1,230	15	80.0	68.9	57.0	66.1	15	108	27	7	3.76	3.96	6.66	6.88	6.04	3.86	3.13	2.93	4.03	4.11	4.37	3.46	53.19
British Guiana:																									
Dadanawa	2 48 N.	59 26 W.		9	82.2	82.7	81.0	84.6	4	103	66	9	1.34	2.00	2.26	5.56	7.84	13.61	10.44	8.14	2.56	1.65	1.06	2.05	58.51
Georgetown	6 50 N.	58 12 W.		41	79.0	80.2	79.8	81.2	17	92	68	46	8.50	5.95	6.77	6.35	11.25	11.87	10.00	6.47	3.05	2.54	5.88	11.75	90.38
Chile:																									
Caldera	27 3 S.	70 53 W.	92	13	66.1	60.8	54.7	58.9	24	86	39	25	.01	[1]T	[1]T	[1]T	.14	.13	.15	.08	.03	.02	.02	.01	.59
Evanjelistas	52 24 S.	75 6 W.	180	11	47.0	44.7	39.3	42.2		60	24	26	11.78	9.59	11.43	11.16	9.61	9.31	9.56	8.59	9.35	8.88	9.91	10.16	119.33
Iquique	20 12 S.	70 11 W.	30	13	69.4	64.5	59.4	63.2	25	92	43	25	[1]T	[1]T	[1]T	[1]T	[1]T	[1]T	.03	.01	.01	[1]T	[1]T	.00	.05
Melinka	43 54 S.	73 46 W.	16	11	56.3	50.9	45.5	49.4	11	76	29	11	5.99	6.62	8.54	10.63	13.76	14.48	15.06	12.80	10.11	7.54	9.72	9.68	124.93
Ovalle	30 36 S.	71 12 W.	820	12	69.4	62.0	53.6	61.4	12	97	33	12	[1]T.	[1]T.	[1]T.	.01	1.40	1.31	1.02	.59	.47	.02	.08	[1]T	4.90
Punta Angeles	33 01 S.	71 38 W.	134	14	64.4	59.2	53.1	57.5	25	94	36	32	.01	.01	.37	.50	4.29	5.70	4.00	2.70	1.22	.44	.33	.11	19.68
Punta Arenas	53 10 S.	70 54 W.	92	14	52.6	43.6	35.4	45.3				20	1.26	1.02	1.59	2.03	2.59	1.78	2.13	1.51	1.50	.85	1.28	1.32	18.86
Punta Dungeness	52 24 S.	68 26 W.	16	13	53.0	45.7	37.4	44.6		80	19	21	1.05	.69	.84	1.00	.78	.67	.80	.59	.43	.38	.45	1.05	8.73
Santiago	33 27 S.	70 42 W.	1,706	14	69.3	59.2	48.1	58.3	21	99	24	58	.03	.06	.19	.57	2.44	3.29	3.11	2.17	1.23	.54	.26	.20	14.09
Temuco	38 45 S.	72 38 W.	367	8	63.5	54.6	46.6	54.4	9	98	21	12	1.09	1.14	2.94	4.93	9.68	6.50	7.50	5.98	3.35	2.38	3.28	2.38	51.15
Valdivia	39 48 S.	73 14 W.	30	11	62.3	53.8	46.2	53.0	11	95	25	52	2.46	2.80	5.63	9.17	15.53	16.94	16.63	13.38	8.22	5.28	4.88	4.21	105.13
Colombia:																									
Bogota	4 36 N.	74 5 W.	8,678	2	57.6	57.8	56.1	56.8				31	2.22	2.28	3.67	5.24	4.23	2.10	1.80	1.93	2.34	5.49	5.13	3.10	39.53
Buenaventura	3 53 N.	77 10 W.	39									7	17.90	12.33	11.34	25.60	28.40	23.76	22.35	26.66	27.93	34.66	28.08	21.64	280.65
Cartagena	10 28 N.	75 34 W.	16									12	.00	.01	.07	.55	3.39	5.06	2.80	4.96	5.20	8.78	4.46	.36	35.64
Ecuador:																									
Quito	0 14 S.	78 30 W.	9,350	7	57.2	57.1	56.6	58.0	4	79	35	14	4.16	3.36	5.23	7.25	5.00	1.57	.81	1.24	2 .6	6 3.9	1 4.0	1 3.8	843.08
French Guiana:																									
Cayenne	4 56 N.	52 21 W.	20	23	79.2	80.0	80.2	82.7	23	97	65	51	14.37	12.28	15.83	18.86	21.89	15.51	6.93	2.76	1.22	1.34	4.61	10.71	126.31
Paraguay:																									
Asuncion	25 21 S.	57 37 W.	305	20	82.0	73.2	65.6	73.8	20	109	33	40	5.92	4.93	5.27	5.74	4.85	2.88	2.38	1.63	3.40	5.87	5.63	6.11	54.61
Peru:																									
Arequipa	16 22 S.	71 33 W.	8,040	13	58.0	58.0	57.2	57.8	13	82	36	34	1.21	1.71	.60	.15	.02	.01	.03	.01	.00	.02	.03	.37	4.16
Cailloma	15 8 S.	71 52 W.	12,992	17	43.8	40.8	33.4	41.2	17	82	−10	17	5.31	5.98	5.33	1.62	.37	.20	.06	.22	.58	1.10	1.09	4.23	26.09
Cuzco	13 31 S.	72 3 W.	11,319	4	54.2	52.4	48.1	54.3	14	80	28	12	6.49	5.44	4.41	1.96	.56	.20	.15	.43	.97	2.67	2.90	5.48	31.66
Lima	12 3 S.	77 3 W.	512	10	73.4	70.2	61.2	63.0	6	90	40	18	.02	.01	.02	.03	.10	.24	.35	.41	.39	.19	.10	.04	1.90
Mollendo	17 5 S.	72 2 W.	80	10	72.6	69.2	62.0	64.4	10	90	50	10	.04	.07	[1]T	.03	.07	.05	.04	.18	.19	.10	.06	.02	.85
Uruguay:																									
Montevideo	34 52 S.	58 32 W.	82	10	72.4	62.8	50.0	58.6	20	109	25	20	2.77	2.82	3.21	4.62	3.84	2.72	2.52	3.06	3.36	2.46	3.21	3.40	37.99
Venezuela:																									
Caracas	10 30 N.	66 55 W.	3,420	16	65.8	69.4	68.9	69.6	16	91	45	35	.84	.35	.61	1.50	2.83	4.24	4.25	4.32	4.03	4.04	3.40	1.74	32.15
Ciudad Bolivar	8 9 N.	63 33 W.	125	5	79.2	82.8	80.6	83.0	7	97	66	9	.49	.21	.22	.96	2.69	5.45	6.33	7.00	3.02	3.46	3.35	1.97	35.15
Maracaibo	10 38 N.	71 36 W.	20	9	81.4	84.0	85.3	82.4	9	102	68	11	.02	.02	.25	.61	2.39	2.11	1.87	2.09	3.03	4.94	3.12	.46	20.91
Merida	8 36 N.	71 9 W.	5,384	9	64.8	67.8	67.9	67.2	9	85	52	11	2.75	1.63	3.66	6.90	10.95	7.20	4.62	6.20	6.17	10.44	8.26	3.05	71.83

See footnotes on p. 677.

TEMPERATURE AND PRECIPITATION DATA FOR REPRESENTATIVE STATIONS ON A WORLD-WIDE DISTRIBUTION—Continued

EUROPE

Country and station	Latitude	Longitude	Elevation	Temperature: Mean: Length fo record	Temperature: Mean: January	Temperature: Mean: April	Temperature: Mean: July	Temperature: Mean: October	Temperature: Extreme: Length of record	Temperature: Extreme: Maximum	Temperature: Extreme: Minimum	Average precipitation: Length of record	Janury	February	March	April	May	June	July	August	September	October	November	December	Year
	° ′	° ′	Ft.	Yr.	°F.	°F.	°F.	°F.	Yr.	°F.	°F.	Yr.	In.	In.	In.	In.	In.	In.	In.	In.	In.	In.	In.	In.	In.
Austria:																									
Vienna	48 15 N.	16 22 E.	666	20	31.9	48.8	65.8	48.8	54	97	−4	70	1.46	1.30	1.81	2.05	2.80	2.72	3.11	2.72	1.97	1.85	1.77	1.81	25.37
British Isles:																									
Dublin	53 21 N.	6 16 W.	155	35	40.2	45.2	58.4	48.3	41	85	4	35	2.29	1.89	1.94	1.90	2.05	1.95	2.56	3.04	1.92	2.68	2.67	2.48	27.37
Glasgow	55 53 N.	4 18 W.	180	35	38.6	45.0	58.0	47.4	50	85	7	35	3.27	2.88	2.67	2.08	2.59	2.52	3.09	3.91	2.98	3.40	3.64	4.15	37.18
London	51 30 N.	0 8 W.	149	35	38.5	47.6	63.5	50.2	90	100	4	35	1.86	1.67	1.83	1.54	1.76	2.02	2.38	2.21	1.82	2.63	2.36	2.39	24.47
Valencia	51 56 N.	10 15 W.	30	35	44.4	48.0	58.8	51.5	58	81	20	35	5.49	5.20	4.54	3.67	3.17	3.20	3.78	4.79	4.14	5.57	5.46	6.64	55.65
Bulgaria:																									
Sofia	42 42 N.	23 20 E.	1,804	25	28.4	50.2	69.1	52.8	37	102	−24	20	1.26	1.18	1.54	1.97	2.95	3.07	2.56	2.05	2.40	2.09	2.13	1.10	24.30
Czechoslovakia:																									
Prague	50 5 N.	14 25 E.	646	17	30.0	47.6	66.6	48.7	43	95	−14	70	.87	.83	1.10	1.54	2.36	2.76	2.56	2.24	1.65	1.22	1.18	.94	19.25
Denmark:																									
Copenhagen	55 41 N.	12 33 E.	43	33	30.5	42.2	61.8	46.5	70	90	−13	40	1.30	1.30	1.46	1.30	1.46	1.77	2.32	2.56	1.77	2.09	1.65	1.77	20.75
Vestervig	56 47 N.	8 19 E.	63	20	34.0	42.4	60.2	47.0	55	93	−4	40	1.77	1.61	1.77	1.46	1.61	1.61	2.44	3.27	2.56	3.38	2.76	2.72	26.96
Finland:																									
Helsingfors	60 12 N.	24 55 E.	38	20	21.4	36.8	63.8	40.6	44	88	−23	30	2.15	1.87	1.87	1.53	1.85	1.91	2.48	3.26	2.81	2.71	2.74	2.57	27.75
France:																									
Bordeaux	44 50 N.	0 42 W.	242	20	41.1	53.5	69.5	57.0	48	107	3	39	2.48	2.01	2.28	2.52	2.80	2.76	1.89	1.97	2.60	3.62	3.15	2.68	30.76
Brest	48 23 N.	4 30 W.	213	20	44.9	50.6	64.2	55.6	63	100	12	45	3.27	2.64	2.05	2.09	1.81	1.97	1.97	2.16	2.80	3.86	3.62	3.39	31.63
Lyon	45 41 N.	4 47 E.	981	20	35.4	51.2	69.4	53.4	78	101	−4	32	1.46	1.46	1.93	2.40	3.31	3.31	2.95	3.23	2.99	3.94	2.60	1.69	31.27
Marseilles	43 18 N.	5 23 E.	246	20	44.2	55.1	72.0	59.2	68	100	12	44	1.93	1.42	1.61	1.69	1.89	1.02	.55	.94	2.36	4.02	3.11	2.05	22.59
Paris	48 48 N.	2 30 E.	162	20	37.8	50.2	65.6	51.9	78	101	−14	38	1.54	1.22	1.61	1.65	2.09	2.32	2.20	2.16	1.97	2.32	1.81	1.73	22.62
Toulouse	43 37 N.	1 27 E.	636	20	40.2	52.4	70.2	56.6	78	106	−3	37	1.85	1.61	1.89	2.64	3.15	3.19	1.54	1.93	2.13	2.36	1.97	1.73	25.99
Germany:																									
Berlin	52 31 N.	13 22 E.	131	30	30.2	45.8	64.4	48.3	82	99	−15	50	1.54	1.44	1.71	1.43	1.94	2.54	3.03	2.25	1.65	1.82	1.68	1.85	22.88
Danzig	54 24 N.	18 40 E.	16	30	28.8	42.5	63.6	47.6	51	96	−16	25	1.16	.92	1.38	1.34	2.08	2.29	2.92	2.61	2.03	2.17	1.52	1.31	21.73
Frankfort on the Main	50 7 N.	8 39 E.	341	30	32.4	49.6	66.4	49.6	51	100	−7	50	1.70	1.30	1.55	1.39	2.01	2.77	3.07	2.35	1.81	2.26	1.94	1.95	24.10
Hamburg	53 33 N.	9 58 E.	85	30	31.7	44.8	62.6	48.6	54	92	−6	25	1.88	1.86	2.11	1.64	2.02	2.90	3.60	3.00	2.44	2.97	1.88	2.28	28.58
Munich	48 9 N.	11 34 E.	1,722	30	28.2	46.0	64.2	47.3	54	97	−14	40	1.82	1.41	2.04	2.79	3.67	4.68	5.02	4.17	3.70	2.52	1.85	2.22	35.89
Greece:																									
Athens	37 58 N.	23 43 E.	351	46	47.6	59.8	81.3	67.1	70	109	20	54	2.17	1.49	1.39	.86	.81	.58	.30	.39	.57	1.65	2.79	2.48	15.48
Corfu	39 37 N.	19 57 E.	105	20	49.9	58.9	76.6	65.6	36	102	23	38	7.72	6.11	4.18	3.70	2.45	1.05	.28	.56	2.82	5.02	7.05	9.54	50.48
Hungary:																									
Budapest	47 31 N.	19 1 E.	426	20	31.6	51.8	70.4	52.0	27	102	−2	35	1.46	1.22	1.77	2.28	2.91	2.91	2.09	1.97	2.01	2.60	2.09	1.89	25.20

Italy:																									
Cagliari	39 14 N.	9 6 E.	246	9	50.4	58.4	76.4	65.0	17	102	25	25	1.68	1.35	2.14	1.63	1.03	.91	.08	.22	1.15	2.10	3.96	2.79	19.04
Palermo	38 6 N.	13 20 E.	233	18	50.8	58.6	76.0	67.0	36	114	29	25	4.02	3.10	2.83	2.61	1.38	.63	.31	.56	1.47	3.98	3.90	4.69	29.48
Rome	41 53 N.	12 29 E.	167	50	45.0	57.0	76.1	62.4	73	104	21	25	3.61	2.74	3.08	3.07	2.37	1.78	.83	1.04	3.02	5.32	4.52	4.12	35.50
Turin	45 4 N.	7 41 E.	902	35	33.2	53.7	72.8	54.0	46	96	4	25	2.28	1.48	2.38	4.41	4.91	4.19	2.40	2.73	2.83	3.68	2.57	1.63	35.49
Venice	45 26 N.	12 20 E.	69	16	35.8	55.0	75.3	57.0	56	97	14	25	1.44	1.60	2.16	2.24	2.90	2.90	1.92	2.04	2.54	2.75	2.18	1.61	26.28
Latvia:																									
Riga	56 57 N.	24 6 E.	23	20	24.3	41.2	64.8	44.6	25	92	−20	25	1.38	1.34	1.22	1.46	1.54	2.48	3.58	3.42	2.05	2.05	1.97	1.69	24.18
Netherlands:																									
Amsterdam	52 23 N.	4 55 E.	5	20	37.5	47.1	63.0	51.4	37	91	4	25	2.01	1.50	1.93	1.57	1.93	2.01	2.91	3.19	2.48	3.38	2.32	2.72	27.95
Norway:																									
Bergen	60 24 N.	5 19 E.	146	50	34.2	42.1	57.9	45.1	55	89	5	40	8.54	6.42	5.94	4.13	4.49	3.78	5.79	7.52	8.66	8.94	8.27	8.54	81.02
Oslo	59 55 N.	10 43 E.	82	50	24.1	39.9	62.6	41.9	55	95	−26	40	1.06	1.06	1.34	1.34	1.69	1.85	2.87	3.54	2.32	2.56	1.85	1.73	23.21
Tromso	69 39 N.	18 57 E.	376	50	26.6	31.5	51.8	36.0	55	[2] 82	−1	40	4.61	4.13	3.23	2.44	1.97	2.13	2.48	2.83	4.57	4.61	4.37	3.98	41.35
Trondhjem	63 26 N.	10 25 E.	194	50	27.3	37.9	57.2	41.2	45	95	−15	50	3.42	2.87	2.24	1.81	1.50	1.73	2.24	2.95	3.27	3.39	3.11	2.56	31.09
Vardo	70 22 N.	31 8 E.	39	50	21.9	28.8	47.5	34.7	55	[2] 78	−11	50	2.64	2.83	2.09	1.65	1.38	1.57	1.73	2.01	2.40	2.48	2.52	2.56	25.86
Poland:																									
Lemberg	49 50 N.	24 1 E.	978	20	25.2	46.1	66.2	48.6	46	99	−28	35	1.26	1.50	1.81	1.97	2.83	3.66	4.09	3.11	2.40	2.09	1.81	1.65	28.18
Warsaw	52 13 N.	21 3 E.	361	25	25.7	45.7	65.4	47.2	44	98	−28	100	1.26	1.06	1.34	1.46	2.05	2.60	3.07	2.95	1.85	1.65	1.50	1.42	22.21
Portugal:																									
Lisbon	38 43 N.	9 9 W.	312	20	50.9	58.6	71.2	63.2	53	103	30	20	3.47	3.78	2.92	1.99	1.81	.87	.26	.26	1.60	3.10	4.75	4.06	28.87
Rumania:																									
Bucharest	44 25 N.	26 6 E.	276	20	26.6	51.8	73.0	53.8	48	105	−23	60	1.34	1.09	1.65	1.73	2.47	3.46	2.68	2.00	1.56	1.70	1.90	1.59	23.17
Jassy	47 10 N.	27 37 E.	328	20	25.8	49.4	70.4	51.0	31	104	−20	12	.94	.94	1.34	1.73	2.20	2.72	2.40	1.65	1.34	1.34	1.34	.83	18.77
Spain:																									
Madrid	40 24 N.	3 41 W.	2,188	20	40.4	52.4	73.8	56.0	64	112	10	30	1.34	1.10	1.77	1.85	1.77	1.18	.47	.47	1.30	1.77	1.85	1.61	16.48
Oviedo	43 23 N.	5 49 W.	801	20	44.3	50.2	63.7	56.4	56	100	13	30	2.83	2.80	4.41	3.70	2.72	2.64	2.05	1.61	2.87	3.58	3.70	3.90	36.81
Seville	37 23 N.	5 59 W.	98	20	49.6	61.5	81.8	67.0	57	124	22	30	2.13	1.85	2.48	1.85	1.69	.55	.04	.16	.75	1.93	2.40	2.72	18.55
Valencia	39 28 N.	0 23 W.	59	19	49.8	57.8	74.6	64.2	55	109	18	30	1.34	1.22	1.54	1.54	1.69	.83	.47	.35	2.99	3.31	1.97	1.89	19.14
Spitzbergen:																									
Green Harbor	78 2 N.	14 14 W.	13	14	2.7	7.3	41.7	21.6	17	61	−57	14	1.31	1.24	1.06	.93	.48	.47	.68	.83	.92	1.20	.99	1.57	11.68
Sweden:																									
Haparanda	65 50 N.	24 9 E.	30	33	11.4	27.8	58.1	33.8	57	91	−40	51	1.52	1.08	1.04	.93	1.13	1.32	1.80	2.11	2.17	2.20	1.85	1.26	18.41
Stensele	65 4 N.	17 10 E.	1,078	20	8.7	28.8	54.5	31.1	44	84	−49	51	.98	.71	.71	.78	1.27	1.66	2.67	2.91	1.99	1.60	1.10	.94	17.32
Stockholm	59 21 N.	18 4 E.	146	33	26.6	38.1	62.6	43.0	57	92	−22	51	.98	.91	1.08	1.07	1.44	1.63	2.37	2.59	1.75	1.98	1.53	1.31	18.64
Switzerland:																									
Santis	47 15 N.	9 20 E.	8,202	20	16.4	22.6	40.4	29.8	-----	66	−26	16	5.67	6.69	6.73	8.11	7.83	11.18	12.32	10.83	8.27	7.20	4.80	6.10	95.73
Zurich	47 23 N.	8 33 E.	1,542	20	31.5	47.8	64.8	48.8	-----	98	−11	37	1.93	2.24	2.91	3.78	4.49	5.28	5.20	5.24	4.33	4.06	2.80	2.91	45.17
Turkey:																									
Istanbul	41 2 N.	28 47 E.	246	47	42.4	53.0	74.5	62.6	28	100	17	48	3.43	2.72	2.44	1.65	1.18	1.34	1.06	1.65	2.05	2.52	4.02	4.80	28.86
Union of Soviet Socialist Republics: [3]																									
Archangel	64 34 N.	40 33 E.	20	35	8.1	30.0	59.5	33.8	-----	94	−49	35	.89	.74	.82	.72	1.24	1.86	2.52	2.47	2.16	1.66	1.18	.95	17.21
Astrakhan	46 21 N.	48 2 E.	−46	35	19.2	47.8	77.4	49.5	-----	110	−22	35	.49	.43	.39	.65	.71	.78	.48	.53	.54	.47	.54	.59	6.60
Baku	40 21 N.	49 50 E.	−43	35	38.1	50.9	77.4	61.9	-----	99	-----	-----	1.15	.78	.90	.74	.55	.27	.20	.25	.68	1.11	1.20	1.13	8.96
Kharkov	50 0 N.	36 14 E.	381	35	18.1	44.6	69.1	44.4	-----	99	−34	25	1.18	1.18	1.10	1.57	1.89	2.72	2.56	2.01	1.26	1.69	1.46	1.30	19.92
Kiev	50 27 N.	30 30 E.	600	35	21.2	44.2	66.7	45.1	-----	95	−22	35	1.37	1.16	1.74	1.72	2.00	2.94	3.18	2.23	1.81	1.93	1.62	1.55	23.25
Leningrad	59 56 N.	30 16 E.	20	35	18.3	37.0	63.5	40.5	-----	97	−39	40	1.07	.99	.92	1.23	1.62	2.14	2.33	3.25	2.37	1.81	1.43	1.28	20.44
Minsk	53 54 N.	27 33 E.	738	29	19.8	40.8	63.5	41.7	-----	91	−27	25	1.46	1.42	1.34	1.61	2.01	3.23	3.42	2.99	1.77	1.65	1.73	1.54	24.17

[1] Trace.
[2] Maximum at 2 p. m.
[3] Mean temperatures determined from observations taken at 7 a. m., 1 p. m., and 9 p. m.; maximum temperature taken ascribed to readings taken at 1 p. m.

TEMPERATURE AND PRECIPITATION DATA FOR REPRESENTATIVE STATIONS ON A WORLD-WIDE DISTRIBUTION—Continued

EUROPE—Continued

Country and station	Latitude	Longitude	Elevation	Temperature: Mean: Length of record	Mean: January	Mean: April	Mean: July	Mean: October	Extreme: Length of record	Extreme: Maximum	Extreme: Minimum	Average precipitation: Length of record	January	February	March	April	May	June	July	August	September	October	November	December	Year
Union of Soviet Socialist Republics—Con.	° ′	° ′	Ft.	Yr.	°F.	°F.	°F.	°F.	Yr.	°F.	°F.	Yr.	In.	In.	In.	In.	In.	In.	In.	In.	In.	In.	In.	In.	In.
Moscow	55 50 N.	37 33 E.	525	35	12.6	38.1	64.4	38.9	----	100	−43	36	1.33	1.21	1.38	1.37	1.78	2.65	3.18	3.06	2.15	2.07	1.73	1.58	23.49
Odessa	46 26 N.	30 46 E.	213	35	26.4	47.1	72.7	52.3	----	95	15	35	1.15	.88	1.05	.93	1.14	2.24	1.74	1.39	1.21	1.47	1.06	1.17	15.43
Orenburg	51 45 N.	55 6 E.	374	30	4.3	39.2	71.6	39.6	----	105	−44	32	1.24	.75	.92	.85	1.31	1.65	1.39	1.29	.98	1.18	1.47	1.39	14.42
Rostov	47 12 N.	39 41 E.	157	30	21.0	48.2	74.7	49.6	----	102	−19	25	1.30	1.50	1.22	1.46	1.65	2.36	2.09	.94	1.02	1.30	1.61	1.46	17.91
Ust Zylma	65 27 N.	52 10 E.	82	25	−0.8	26.6	57.9	28.8	----	89	−61	20	.78	.66	.65	.63	1.31	2.00	2.64	2.37	2.11	1.34	1.06	.83	16.38
Vologda	59 15 N.	39 50 E.	400	32	10.4	35.8	63.7	36.5	----	93	−42	25	.98	.87	.87	1.10	2.01	2.68	2.68	2.80	2.24	1.61	1.14	1.06	20.04
Vyatka	58 36 N.	49 40 E.	538	35	4.8	34.9	64.6	34.0	----	92	−43	25	1.30	1.26	1.02	1.06	1.93	2.48	2.44	2.80	2.28	2.05	1.77	1.46	21.85
Zlatoust	55 10 N.	59 41 E.	1,503	35	3.6	33.3	60.8	32.2	----	93	−51	25	.59	.47	.47	.87	2.01	3.15	3.50	2.95	2.13	1.57	1.22	.83	19.76
Yugoslavia:																									
Belgrade	44 48 N.	20 27 E.	453	8	33.0	53.4	72.2	53.6	8	107	−9	33	1.31	1.19	1.61	2.39	2.76	3.00	2.59	1.92	1.71	2.36	1.92	1.61	24.37

ASIA

Country and station	Latitude	Longitude	Elevation	Temperature: Mean: Length of record	Mean: January	Mean: April	Mean: July	Mean: October	Extreme: Length of record	Extreme: Maximum	Extreme: Minimum	Average precipitation: Length of record	January	February	March	April	May	June	July	August	September	October	November	December	Year
Afghanistan:																									
Kabul	34 41 N.	69 9 E.	7,280	24	31.8	56.7	76.9	59.6	21	112	−7	----	1.21	1.43	4.05	3.67	0.78	0.21	0.13	0.14	0.03	0.56	0.82	0.43	13.46
Arabia:																									
Aden	12 45 N.	45 03 E.	94	25	76.2	83.1	88.1	83.8	33	109	61	39	.32	.19	.48	.18	.12	.06	.03	.12	.15	.09	.08	.11	1.93
Muscat	23 37 N.	58 35 E.	20	28	70.6	83.3	91.0	85.4	34	114	53	27	1.16	.84	.59	.40	.01	.11	.02	.03	.00	.09	.33	.59	4.17
Baluchistan:																									
Quetta	30 13 N.	67 01 E.	5,502	43	39.8	59.6	79.0	57.1	51	104	3	43	1.88	1.81	1.88	1.01	.37	.15	.36	.42	.07	.13	.32	.93	9.33
China:																									
Chungking	29 34 N.	106 31 E.	755	25	48.4	67.4	84.0	67.0	25	111	29	26	.67	.89	1.30	3.98	5.34	7.41	5.78	4.87	5.72	4.59	1.92	.89	43.36
Foochow	25 59 N.	119 27 E.	66	14	53.0	64.4	84.2	72.8	14	102	29	26	1.74	3.70	5.19	5.06	6.42	8.72	6.99	7.81	8.90	2.43	1.67	2.25	60.88
Hankow	30 35 N.	114 17 E.	118	29	40.1	61.9	85.4	66.6	29	106	13	26	1.72	1.66	3.70	5.80	6.15	8.69	7.74	3.88	2.66	3.11	2.17	.93	48.21
Hongkong	22 18 N.	114 10 E.	105	35	60.2	70.8	82.5	76.8	41	97	32	37	1.32	1.63	2.72	5.36	11.65	15.93	13.83	14.12	9.84	4.88	1.85	1.14	84.27
Lanchow	36 2 N.	103 50 E.	328	5	20.0	53.0	73.0	49.8	5	100	−6	----	----	----	----	----	----	----	----	----	----	----	----	----	----
Shanghai	31 12 N.	121 26 E.	23	23	39.8	57.8	82.2	65.3	53	103	10	53	1.97	2.33	3.43	3.64	3.66	7.28	5.91	5.64	4.72	3.06	2.01	1.30	44.95
Tengueh	24 45 N.	98 14 E.	5,358	10	47.0	60.4	68.6	62.2	10	85	22	13	.53	1.23	1.65	2.91	5.19	9.50	11.97	11.16	6.88	6.92	1.52	.80	60.26
Tientsin	39 9 N.	117 11 E.	16	20	24.8	56.6	81.2	58.0	21	109	−3	19	.15	.11	.47	.61	1.21	2.72	6.98	5.57	1.83	.67	.45	.11	20.88
Yunnanfu	25 2 N.	102 41 E.	6,371	13	49.6	64.4	71.1	62.7	10	91	24	23	.36	.53	.65	.75	4.57	6.52	9.02	8.56	5.41	3.29	1.96	.58	42.20
Chosen:																									
Keijo	37 34 N.	126 59 E.	97	18	23.8	51.4	76.6	56.1	22	100	−10	17	1.07	.83	1.62	3.16	3.13	5.35	12.61	10.34	4.36	1.47	1.86	.80	46.60

East Indies:																								
Batavia	6 11 S.	106 50 E.	26	55	78.7	80.4	79.4	80.6	62	96	66	44	12.28	12.68	8.07	5.47	4.25	3.82	2.80	1.69	2.95	4.57	5.79	7.76	72.13
Koepang	10 16 S.	123 34 E.	7	14	80.8	80.8	78.4	81.8	14	101	60	44	15.79	15.04	8.82	2.60	1.26	.43	.20	.12	.12	.79	3.46	9.96	58.59
Manokwari	0 52 S.	134 20 E.	62	4	79.5	79.8	79.7	80.4	4	91	70	22	10.71	9.92	13.23	10.67	8.42	7.99	6.30	5.59	4.84	4.06	5.75	11.10	98.58
Port Moresby	9 29 S.	147 09 E.	128	19	82.2	81.2	78.0	80.2	6	98	68	28	7.48	9.25	6.81	3.31	2.99	.79	.98	.75	1.38	.83	2.05	4.21	40.83
Sandakan	5 50 N.	118 07 E.	10	14	80.0	82.2	82.2	81.6	14	97	69	33	18.46	9.61	8.11	4.17	5.98	7.28	6.54	8.07	9.41	10.00	14.68	17.68	119.99
East Turkestan:																								
Kashgar	39 30 N.	75 53 E.	4,255	27	22.6	59.2	79.8	56.8	35	110	−8	-----	.30	.00	.20	.20	.80	.40	.30	.70	.30	.00	.00	.20	3.40
French Indo-China:																								
Hanoi	21 02 N.	105 51 E.	46	20	63.0	75.0	84.6	78.8	35	109	41	25	.79	1.09	2.01	3.48	7.89	8.89	12.08	12.20	11.04	4.47	1.96	.89	66.79
Luang Prabang	19 50 N.	102 4 E.	1,148	15	68.7	82.9	82.9	80.2	18	113	33	25	.52	.48	1.11	4.06	5.80	6.10	9.24	11.21	6.93	3.67	1.16	.48	50.76
Saigon	10 47 N.	106 42 E.	37	19	79.3	85.6	81.3	81.0	30	104	59	30	.76	.11	.54	2.07	8.45	12.98	11.92	10.70	14.30	10.61	4.76	2.17	79.37
India:																								
Benares	25 30 N.	83 0 E.	250	43	61.1	86.8	86.0	79.2	51	120	30	47	.71	.59	.29	.23	.50	4.80	11.72	11.43	6.70	2.18	.20	.19	39.54
Bombay	18 54 N.	72 49 E.	37	43	75.5	83.0	81.4	82.4	51	100	56	39	.09	.03	.02	.06	.71	18.48	25.17	14.19	10.84	1.84	.38	.07	71.88
Calcutta	23 36 N.	88 23 E.	21	43	66.6	85.6	83.6	81.0	51	111	44	33	.41	1.15	1.25	1.75	5.74	11.43	12.89	12.16	10.35	3.91	.56	.21	61.81
Cherrapunji	25 15 N.	91 42 E.										40	.69	2.02	12.12	33.07	43.84	95.72	99.52	76.09	47.41	13.83	1.45	.20	425.96
Colombo	6 54 N.	79 53 E.	24	32	79.5	82.7	81.3	80.6	25	97	62	12	3.29	1.83	4.14	7.07	13.13	7.31	6.11	2.78	5.56	13.34	10.77	4.71	80.04
Delhi	28 39 N.	77 17 E.	718	43	59.0	85.4	88.0	80.0	51	118	32	33	1.07	.66	.47	.38	.63	3.10	8.06	7.88	4.40	.29	.10	.48	27.52
Hyderabad	17 20 N.	78 30 E.	1,719	29	72.0	88.7	80.4	78.9	37	112	47	42	.18	.13	.46	.84	.87	4.18	6.13	6.64	6.91	3.21	1.10	.38	31.03
Karachi	24 53 N.	66 57 E.	13	41	67.1	79.8	84.6	80.6	51	118	39	32	.62	.41	.22	.16	.06	.98	3.12	1.59	.44	.00	.05	.13	7.78
Lahore	31 34 N.	74 20 E.	702	43	55.0	80.2	90.6	77.6	51	120	29	44	.92	1.00	.71	.43	.64	1.52	4.92	4.47	2.40	.26	.06	.40	17.73
Leh	34 10 N.	77 42 E.	11,530	43	19.2	42.9	63.5	44.7	51	93	−19	32	.37	.34	.30	.22	.21	.17	.47	.52	.28	.17	.04	.17	3.26
Madras	13 4 N.	80 14 E.	22	43	76.2	85.3	87.4	82.3	58	113	57	98	.96	.31	.35	.67	1.92	1.98	3.87	4.64	4.89	10.94	13.05	5.44	49.02
Rangoon	16 43 N.	96 13 E.	18	43	76.8	87.0	80.6	81.7	51	107	55	40	.09	.25	.32	1.60	12.41	18.09	21.17	19.52	15.65	6.97	2.47	.12	98.66
Simla	31 7 N.	77 8 E.	7,232	29	41.2	57.8	64.6	57.0	37	94	17	33	2.64	3.31	2.44	1.75	2.68	6.91	16.95	18.16	5.71	.87	.45	1.24	63.11
Iran:																								
Kerman	30 30 N.	57 0 E.	6,100	7	44.9	61.4	81.4	63.4	7	112	7	5	.50	.89	.85	.74	.14	.18	.00	.00	.05	.06	.51	1.44	5.36
Meshed	36 16 N.	59 35 E.	3,104	14	34.3	56.8	77.5	56.8	19	112	−8	26	.82	1.00	2.24	1.84	1.23	.33	.06	.03	.02	.39	.60	.66	9.22
Teheran	35 41 N.	51 25 E.	4,002	22	36.0	59.7	85.4	64.4	27	109	−4	25	1.65	1.14	1.96	1.37	.60	.08	.16	.04	.08	.34	.88	1.23	9.53
Iraq:																								
Bagdad	33 21 N.	44 28 E.	120	27	48.6	70.4	94.4	77.6	34	123	19	32	1.17	1.32	1.34	.93	.23	.00	.00	.03	.01	.08	.74	1.23	7.08
Basra	30 25 N.	47 50 E.	10	18	51.8	74.4	92.9	78.0	20	122	24	20	1.37	1.15	1.06	.48	.29	.00	.00	.00	.09	.05	.73	1.20	6.42
Japan:																								
Hakodate	41 47 N.	104 43 E.	13	30	25.5	42.8	66.0	50.4	52	92	−7	25	2.23	2.16	2.55	2.83	3.18	3.62	5.02	5.16	6.68	4.59	3.70	2.96	44.68
Kanazawa	36 32 N.	136 39 E.	94	20	36.8	52.4	75.6	60.6	42	101	15	20	10.79	6.82	6.17	6.74	6.07	6.69	8.18	7.07	8.78	7.48	10.45	14.40	99.64
Nagasaki	32 44 N.	129 52 E.	436	25	42.8	58.2	78.8	65.2	47	98	22	25	3.07	3.06	5.24	8.87	8.12	13.09	9.94	7.95	7.12	5.18	3.45	3.46	78.55
Tokyo	35 41 N.	139 46 E.	19	30	37.9	54.2	76.0	61.2	52	98	15	25	2.06	2.56	4.28	5.28	5.88	6.31	5.57	4.59	7.49	7.24	4.31	2.27	57.84
Malay States:																								
Singapore	1 18 N.	103 51 E.	8	20	79.8	81.6	81.4	81.2	26	97	66	52	9.88	6.61	7.40	7.64	6.65	6.85	6.77	7.95	6.77	8.07	9.92	10.55	95.06
Manchukuo:																								
Hailar	49 14 N.	119 43 E.	1,997	19	−18.7	32.4	69.2	32.4	19	104	−57	13	.17	.15	.15	.41	.65	2.37	3.04	2.73	1.56	.40	.20	.16	11.99
Harbin	45 46 N.	126 50 E.	494	20	−4.2	42.2	74.2	42.2	26	102	−40	19	.15	.17	.27	.90	1.60	4.07	5.65	4.11	2.16	1.11	.35	.17	20.71
Moukden	41 48 N.	123 23 E.	144	20	8.8	47.6	77.2	49.6	22	103	−27	18	.17	.26	.35	1.11	2.30	3.46	6.11	6.14	3.29	1.52	1.02	.24	25.97
Nepal:																								
Katmandu	27 43 N.	85 21 E.	4,388	20	50.4	68.0	76.0	67.8	26	99	27	29	.99	.86	1.09	1.94	4.01	9.22	14.91	14.66	7.35	2.29	.15	.31	57.78
Palestine:																								
Jerusalem	31 47 N.	35 13 E.	2,200	20	44.6	60.4	75.9	69.6	20	108	25	54	6.38	5.06	3.56	1.69	.27	.01	.00	.00	.04	.41	2.29	5.50	25.21
Philippine Islands:																								
Iloilo	10 42 N.	122 34 E.	21	16	79.2	83.2	80.7	81.0	27	98	64	36	2.23	1.82	1.13	1.44	5.75	10.33	14.98	13.66	12.51	10.72	7.43	5.02	87.02
Manila	14 35 N.	120 59 E.	47	16	77.2	82.8	81.2	80.6	49	101	58	16	.82	.42	.83	1.28	4.45	9.23	17.28	16.00	14.30	6.71	5.24	3.05	79.61
Siam:																								
Bangkok	13 43 N.	100 25 E.	14	12	79.2	86.6	83.8	82.6	12	106	52	19	.33	.58	1.77	1.65	6.30	5.49	6.24	6.98	11.73	8.32	2.67	.30	52.36

TEMPERATURE AND PRECIPITATION DATA FOR REPRESENTATIVE STATIONS ON A WORLD-WIDE DISTRIBUTION—Continued

ASIA—Continued

Country and station	Latitude	Longitude	Elevation	Temperature: Mean: Length of record	Mean: January	Mean: April	Mean: July	Mean: October	Extreme: Length of record	Extreme: Maximum	Extreme: Minimum	Average precipitation: Length of record	January	February	March	April	May	June	July	August	September	October	November	December	Year
	° ′	° ′	Ft.	Yr.	°F.	°F.	°F.	°F.	Yr.	°F.	°F.	Yr.	In.	In.	In.	In.	In.	In.	In.	In.	In.	In.	In.	In.	In.
Syria:																									
Beirut	33 45 N.	35 28 E.	125	25	55.4	64.9	80.2	74.8	30	102	30	45	7.33	5.75	3.92	2.23	.84	.14	.02	.03	.30	2.10	5.28	7.54	35.48
Tibet:																									
Gyantse	28 55 N.	89 33 E.	13,110	12	24.4	41.5	58.0	46.0	9	85	−20														
Turkey:																									
Sivas	39 44 N.	37 0 E.	4,330	10	23.8	49.4	67.3	51.2	10	104	−22	8	2.05	1.32	1.28	1.73	3.05	1.20	.36	.11	.64	.93	1.52	1.01	15.20
Smyrna	38 27 N.	27 15 E.	33	8	47.0	60.4	81.3	65.9	26	111	12	20	4.13	2.94	3.35	1.77	1.26	.49	.21	.13	.91	1.79	4.24	4.43	25.65
Trebizond	41 0 N.	39 44 E.	92	5	44.0	53.2	74.1	64.4	9	95	25	10	2.87	1.89	2.83	2.75	1.96	2.63	1.73	2.32	3.03	3.34	4.17	4.88	34.40
Union of Soviet Socialist Republics:[4]																									
Akmolinsk	51 12 N.	71 23 E.	1,148	18	.3	33.3	70.0	36.0	28	99	−56	32	.59	.51	.51	.55	.98	1.81	1.38	1.50	1.06	1.06	.67	.59	11.21
Barnaul	53 20 N.	83 47 E.	535	33	−0.6	33.6	68.0	35.8		96	−61	75	.75	.51	.55	.59	1.26	1.73	2.13	1.77	1.14	1.26	1.06	1.02	13.77
Bulun	70 45 N.	127 47 E.	66	7	−40.0	4.6	52.7	11.3	7	85	−75	8	.27	.26	.26	.53	.59	.92	1.32	1.54	1.40	1.00	.38	.28	8.75
Dudinka	69 07 N.	87 00 E.	56	17	−20.7	3.9	56.3	16.2	17	83	−70	17	.20	.22	.18	.29	.43	1.17	1.26	1.70	1.66	.72	.33	.24	8.40
Guriev	47 7 N.	51 55 E.	−60	27	12.4	46.4	78.4	47.5	26	105	−34	22	.43	.30	.34	.48	.67	.82	.65	.48	.57	.38	.60	.63	6.35
Irkutsk	52 17 N.	104 20 E.	1,532	34	−6.2	33.3	64.4	32.0	34	94	−52	38	.51	.35	.32	.59	1.30	2.16	3.15	2.80	1.69	.71	.63	.71	14.92
Kazalinsk	45 46 N.	62 07 E.	220	53	12.2	50.7	79.9	47.7		108	−27	53	.41	.37	.49	.43	.48	.35	.25	.26	.30	.53	.48	.50	4.85
Krasnovodsk	40 0 N.	52 59 E.	−56	44	37.4	57.7	84.0	63.3		108	1	50	.55	.44	.75	.78	.23	.23	.10	.14	.13	.20	.42	.52	4.49
Nikolaievsk	53 8 N.	140 43 E.	108	63	−10.5	27.3	61.7	28.6		92	−51	51	.59	.48	.67	1.15	1.31	1.55	2.06	3.07	2.67	1.99	1.24	.80	17.58
Nizhne Kolymsk	68 32 N.	160 59 E.	16	6	−40.0	3.6	53.8	8.2	5	82	−57	6	.47	.25	.18	.22	.20	.66	1.48	1.20	.85	.50	.42	.29	6.72
Novo Mariinski Post	64 45 N.	177 33 E.	16	16	−10.5	5.9	51.6	23.0	16	75	−50	15	.32	.26	.24	.19	.39	.95	1.28	1.52	1.13	.53	.25	.39	7.45
Okhotsk	59 21 N.	143 17 E.	20	32	−10.5	21.0	54.3	26.6		77	−50	18	.08	.09	.17	.35	.80	1.69	2.31	2.42	2.10	.95	.15	.11	11.22
Olekminsk	60 22 N.	120 26 E.	663	25	−31.9	23.2	66.9	23.0		95	−76	24	.32	.23	.22	.30	.80	1.51	1.49	1.91	1.14	.59	.57	.39	9.47
Pamir Post	38 11 N.	74 02 E.	11,942	26	0.0	30.9	57.0	31.8		87	−52	26	.20	.17	.12	.25	.24	.42	.50	.22	.08	.06	.02	.04	2.32
Petropavlovsk	53 0 N.	158 39 E.	289	15	12.7	29.8	53.4	39.6		84	−25	16	1.22	2.28	2.33	2.05	2.21	2.54	3.61	3.92	3.77	4.91	3.36	2.32	34.52
Tashkent	41 20 N.	69 18 E.	1,568	56	31.5	58.6	81.3	54.3		109	−19	56	1.79	1.44	2.48	2.01	1.13	.46	.13	.05	.18	1.03	1.34	1.67	13.71
Tobolsk	58 12 N.	68 14 E.	355	22	−4.4	32.9	65.3	32.7		95	−51	35	.63	.55	.63	.67	1.54	2.32	2.87	2.68	1.73	1.34	1.06	.91	16.93
Verkhoyansk	67 33 N.	133 34 E.	328	38	−58.2	9.3	59.9	5.7		94	−90	27	.16	.13	.10	.16	.26	.88	1.05	1.04	.51	.33	.28	.15	5.05
Vladivostok	43 7 N.	131 55 E.	55	35	7.3	40.1	64.6	48.7		96	−22	49	.28	.35	.63	1.22	1.97	2.76	3.03	4.33	4.41	1.81	1.14	.51	22.44
Yeniseisk	58 27 N.	92 10 E.	279	34	−8.5	29.8	67.3	30.4	34	96	−65	41	.79	.55	.47	.71	1.30	2.44	2.44	2.64	1.57	1.54	1.22	1.14	16.81

See footnotes on p. 683.

AFRICA

Algeria:																								
Algiers	36 37 N.	3 4 E.	126	19	55.5	62.0	77.2	70.4	36	112	28	27	4.02	2.62	3.32	2.06	1.73	0.74	0.13	0.12	1.17	3.41	4.11	4.00	27.43
Biskra	34 51 N.	5 44 E.	407	17	51.6	67.1	90.7	71.9	18	119	28	18	.68	.56	.69	.50	.55	.22	.15	.11	.56	.48	.46	.90	5.86
El Golea	30 33 N.	3 42 E.	1,247	15	49.4	70.6	93.6	73.0	19	124	22	12	.52	.14	.12	.11	.06	.01	.00	.01	.01	.05	.11	.55	1.69
Geryville	33 41 N.	1 0 E.	4,298	15	38.6	53.4	78.9	58.6	28	108	1	17	1.06	.79	.91	1.73	1.81	1.30	.35	.47	1.38	1.10	1.10	1.57	13.57
In Salah	27 17 N.	2 27 E.	919	13	55.4	73.8	98.4	79.5	14	133	25	4	-	-	-	-	-	-	-	-	-	-	-	-	.12
Anglo-Egyptian Sudan:																								
El Fasher	13 32 N.	25 18 E.	2,395	5	69.4	82.4	82.4	80.6	5	113	33	13	[1] T	.00	.02	.02	.39	.59	4.59	5.63	1.29	.26	.00	.00	12.79
Gallabat	12 48 N.	36 10 E.	2,502	16	78.2	85.9	74.4	78.2	16	111	43	18	.00	.04	.12	.39	2.44	5.87	7.87	9.65	6.30	1.73	.16	.00	34.57
Khartoum	15 37 N.	32 33 E.	1,280	21	72.0	86.6	90.2	88.5	21	117	41	22	[1] T	[1] T	[1] T	[1] T	.12	.32	1.57	2.20	.71	.20	.00	.00	5.12
Mongalla	5 11 N.	31 47 E.	1,440	18	82.4	83.6	78.2	80.8	18	110	52	18	.08	.75	1.54	4.17	5.39	4.61	5.20	5.83	4.88	4.29	1.81	.32	38.87
Wadi Halfa	21 55 N.	31 19 E.	421	19	60.8	80.0	89.6	82.0	19	126	28	(5)	(5)	(5)	(5)	(5)	(5)	(5)	(5)	(5)	(5)	(5)	(5)	(5)	(5)
Angola:																								
Huambo	12 45 S.	15 40 E.	5,771	4	67.8	67.2	64.8	70.6	4	90	33	4	8.71	9.38	8.70	5.85	1.20	.00	.00	.11	.73	3.80	9.12	8.93	56.53
Loando	8 49 S.	13 13 E.	167	15	77.6	79.2	68.2	74.1	24	91	57	42	1.06	1.18	2.56	4.61	.51	.01	[1] T	.02	.08	.28	1.22	.87	12.40
Mossamedes	15 12 S.	12 9 E.	66	-	72.3	73.8	64.4	66.9	-	-	-	10	.09	.15	.36	.63	[1] T	.00	.00	[1] T	[1] T	.09	.08	.07	1.47
Ashanti:																								
Accra	5 33 N.	0 12 W.	60	25	80.6	81.1	76.9	77.8	4	95	59	32	.65	1.00	1.83	3.70	5.65	7.00	1.70	.61	.98	1.94	1.49	.69	27.24
Belgian Congo:																								
Elisabethville	11 39 S.	27 28 E.	4,055	13	72.0	69.2	61.0	74.6	9	97	34	14	9.01	9.54	8.74	1.81	.23	.00	[1] T	.01	.14	1.18	4.42	10.11	45.19
Usumbura	3 23 S.	29 20 E.	2,625	8	74.0	74.5	72.6	75.4	8	94	54	11	3.69	4.04	4.71	6.51	2.41	.23	.13	.11	1.23	2.77	3.89	3.84	33.56
British Somaliland:																								
Berbera	10 27 N.	45 02 E.	31	9	76.8	82.8	98.0	84.3	15	117	52	12	.12	.31	.73	.49	.39	.00	.11	.05	.03	.05	.03	.07	2.38
Egypt:																								
Alexandria	31 12 N.	29 53 E.	105	20	57.8	66.4	79.0	75.2	20	111	37	30	2.09	.94	.51	.16	.04	T	T	T	.04	.28	1.34	2.64	8.04
Aswan	24 2 N.	32 53 E.	327	20	62.0	80.6	92.6	84.0	20	124	36	20	(5)	(5)	(5)	(5)	(5)	(5)	(5)	(5)	(5)	(5)	(5)	(5)	(5)
Cairo	30 3 N.	31 15 E.	98	20	55.0	69.6	82.8	73.8	34	113	31	34	.35	.20	.16	.12	.04	T	.00	.00	T	.08	.12	.20	1.27
Eritrea:																								
Massaua	15 37 N.	39 27 E.	63	16	78.7	84.6	95.4	87.4	8	112	65	21	1.61	.67	.63	.51	.43	.00	.12	.24	.16	.32	.87	1.85	7.41
Ethiopia:																								
Adis Ababa	9 02 N.	38 45 E.	8,005	9	59.9	64.4	62.0	61.8	9	93	32	23	.59	1.89	2.76	3.42	2.95	5.75	10.98	12.09	7.56	.79	.55	.24	49.57
Gambela	8 15 N.	34 35 E.	1,345	12	81.5	85.2	78.4	79.8	12	111	47	16	.28	.39	1.42	3.11	5.98	7.13	8.23	9.33	7.44	3.39	1.57	.51	48.78
French Equatorial Africa:																								
Brazzaville	4 17 S.	15 16 E.	951	16	78.8	80.4	72.2	79.2	16	101	53	13	4.21	5.20	6.18	8.94	5.47	.28	.04	.12	.91	5.04	7.05	5.79	49.23
Fort Lamy	12 7 N.	15 0 E.	886	8	76.8	90.7	84.3	85.0	8	118	46	9	.00	.00	.09	.34	3.15	2.96	6.33	7.89	2.92	.86	.00	.00	24.54
Libreville	0 23 N.	9 26 E.	115	22	80.0	80.7	75.8	78.5	22	99	60	20	9.84	9.33	13.19	13.42	9.61	.51	.08	.71	4.09	13.58	14.72	9.80	98.88
French West Africa:																								
Bobo Dioulasso	11 10 N.	4 19 W.	1,509	6	75.6	85.8	78.1	81.2	6	107	46	7	.00	.13	1.70	1.61	4.29	4.87	8.02	10.60	7.00	1.87	.70	.04	40.83
Dakar	14 40 N.	17 25 W.	98	18	70.4	73.6	82.3	82.8	15	104	55	18	.04	.06	.02	T	.06	.45	3.18	8.93	4.67	1.77	.07	.35	19.60
Kayes	14 26 N.	11 26 W.	164	16	77.0	93.8	83.8	86.1	15	118	48	18	T.	.01	.04	.10	.67	3.75	7.26	8.42	5.52	1.59	.04	.07	27.47
Port Etienne	20 54 N.	17 3 W.	90	6	67.6	70.2	74.9	77.4	6	107	46	3	.10	.09	.66	.00	.01	.00	.18	.57	.29	.00	.00	.09	1.99
Timbuctu	16 46 N.	3 2 W.	886	11	71.2	89.4	90 9	89.2	12	122	41	17	.00	.01	.04	[1] T	.21	.88	2.69	2.70	1.01	.14	[1] T	.00	7.68
Italian Somaliland:																								
Mogadiscio	2 5 N.	45 25 E.	59	2	77.4	81.7	74.8	76.4	2	93	61	8	T	.02	.02	3.66	3.15	2.59	1.67	1.41	.44	2.42	1.73	.17	17.28
Kenya:																								
Eldama Ravine	0 3 S.	35 30 E.	7,239	6	61.6	63.2	59.4	61.0	6	90	37	21	1.08	2.12	3.81	6.48	6.33	4.88	4.57	5.19	2.73	2.61	.17	.27	40.24
Nairobi	1 18 S.	36 50 E.	5,450	8	64.5	65.6	60.2	66.2	8	89	36	20	1.39	2.41	5.17	9.24	5.79	1.69	.60	.96	.98	2.10	5.11	2.63	38.07

See footnotes on pp. 677 and 683.

TEMPERATURE AND PRECIPITATION DATA FOR REPRESENTATIVE STATIONS ON A WORLD-WIDE DISTRIBUTION—Continued

AFRICA—Continued

Country and station	Latitude	Longitude	Elevation	Temperature								Average precipitation													
				Mean					Extreme																
				Length fo record	January	April	July	October	Length of record	Maximum	Minimum	Length of record	January	February	March	April	May	June	July	August	September	October	November	December	Year
	° ′	° ′	Ft.	Yr.	°F.	°F.	°F.	°F.	Yr.	°F.	°F.	Yr.	In.	In.	In.	In.	In.	In.	In.	In.	In.	In.	Ih.	In.	In.
Libya:																									
Bengazi	32 6 N.	20 4 E.	82	20	56.8	66.1	78.0	74.6	7	109	38	30	2.74	1.50	.70	.14	.10	.02	[1] T	[1] T	.13	.67	2.02	2.54	10.56
Tripoli	32 54 N.	13 11 E.	59	25	54.0	64.3	78.7	73.4	20	113	35	29	3.24	1.91	.96	.48	.27	.06	.02	.05	.40	1.53	2.91	3.96	15.79
Madagascar:																									
Tamatave	18 9 S.	49 26 E.	13	15	80.5	78.0	70.5	75.5	15	100	55	14	14.13	14.13	17.74	10.94	9.01	12.06	12.87	7.13	6.77	5.39	4.44	10.66	125.27
Tananarivo	18 55 S.	47 33 E.	4,593	15	70.2	66.8	57.6	67.2	24	93	35	34	12.01	11.50	7.40	2.01	.55	.28	.24	.32	.59	2.52	5.08	11.26	53.76
Morocco:																									
Agadir	30 28 N.	9 39 W.	705	8	59.0	62.4	71.8	69.5	8	119	35	6	2.80	1.01	.91	.36	.17	.00	.00	.00	.00	.23	1.33	1.78	8.59
Bekrit	33 10 N.	4 50 W.	6,266	7	38.0	46.5	69.6	52.7	5	100	5	6	1.70	3.52	2.68	2.78	1.08	1.82	.06	.78	.64	2.47	3.72	2.04	23.29
Marrakech	31 38 N.	7 59 W.	1,509	11	51.3	62.8	81.5	67.1	10	118	24	14	1.31	.95	1.73	1.37	.76	.37	.06	.06	.13	.93	1.94	1.21	10.82
Rabat	34 0 N.	6 20 W.	210	12	52.9	58.6	71.0	64.8	10	115	34	6	3.48	2.38	3.59	1.48	.87	.17	.07	.01	.28	1.28	4.03	3.14	20.78
Mozambique:																									
Beira	19 50 S.	34 51 E.	30	8	81.2	76.8	69.4	76.9	20	108	48	15	9.85	9.74	10.59	4.28	2.63	.92	.66	1.20	.62	1.54	5.89	8.17	56.09
Lourenco Marques	25 58 S.	32 36 E.	194	14	78.4	74.2	65.6	72.8	18	112	46	25	5.99	6.20	3.30	1.59	1.38	.54	.52	.60	.88	2.03	3.09	4.22	30.34
Nigeria:																									
Calabar	4 58 N.	8 19 E.	33	18	80.0	81.1	78.0	78.1	16	100	59	18	1.14	2.24	5.67	9.02	12.32	17.09	21.06	20.24	16.54	11.85	7.44	1.97	126.58
Debundja	4 5 N.	8 59 E.	16	2	78.8	79.7	75.4	76.8	2	92	64	14	7.91	11.26	16.06	18.11	25.43	58.35	63.03	54.21	61.42	46.34	24.06	13.39	399.57
Lokoja	7 48 N.	6 44 E.	320	18	79.6	84.1	78.6	79.7	16	103	52	13	.55	.47	1.54	4.88	6.02	5.51	7.52	6.93	10.16	4.25	.35	.28	48.46
Sokoto	13 2 N.	5 15 E.	1,160	19	74.2	90.8	81.4	83.8	18	114	45	8	.00	.00	.20	.20	1.69	4.25	6.77	7.99	3.74	.39	.00	.00	25.23
Northern Rhodesia:																									
Livingstone	17 51 S.	25 51 E.	3,000	8	75.7	72.8	64.6	80.8	4	103	37	12	8.40	6.84	5.32	.68	.32	.00	.00	.00	.00	.88	2.92	8.42	33.78
Nyassaland:																									
Zomba	15 22 S.	35 18 E.	3,100	25	72.4	69.2	61.8	74.1	28	102	41	25	10.60	10.59	8.92	3.71	1.08	.50	.33	.38	.35	1.55	5.29	10.73	54.03
Sierra Leone:																									
Freetown	8 30 N.	13 14 W.	224	40	81.5	82.8	79.0	80.1	34	101	61	46	.41	.30	1.16	4.06	11.47	20.04	35.58	36.57	28.48	12.62	5.12	1.42	157.23
Southern Rhodesia:																									
Bulawayo	20 9 S.	28 36 E.	4,440	24	71.2	65.7	56.8	71.7	24	99	25	27	5.81	4.05	3.03	.65	.29	.03	.04	.03	.12	.91	3.31	5.18	23.45
Salisbury	17 48 S.	31 5 E.	4,865	22	69.8	66.6	56.2	70.2	28	102	30	27	7.35	7.22	4.52	.95	.57	.06	.03	.08	.27	1.20	3.60	5.88	31.73
Southwest Africa:																									
Swakopmund	22 41 S.	14 31 E.	26	10	64.0	60.4	56.6	57.1	10	104	34	14	.10	.06	.10	.03	.04	.02	.01	.02	.02	.04	.02	.14	.60
Windhuk	22 34 S.	17 5 E.	5,463	15	74.0	66.2	56.0	70.0	15	95	26	23	3.66	2.90	3.07	1.59	.24	.03	.06	.09	.06	.36	.81	1.97	14.84

Tanganyika:																								
Dar es Salaam	6 49 S.	39 18 E.	26	17	81.8	79.0	74.2	76.6	17	95	60	21	3.15	2.13	5.24	12.16	7.32	1.06	1.61	1.06	1.14	1.22	2.83	3.86	42.78
Tabora	5 1 S.	32 49 E.	4,058	10	73.2	73.2	71.0	78.2	10	98	49	15	5.28	4.76	6.06	5.83	.71	.12	.00	[1] T	.28	.47	3.54	5.63	32.68
Tandala	9 23 S.	34 14 E.	6,629	5	61.4	59.6	53.2	63.4	5	86	31	5	9.62	8.99	13.98	8.04	2.15	.06	.04	.32	.53	.42	3.97	9.22	57.34
Tunisia:																								
Tunis	36 48 N.	10 10 E.	105	16	50.6	59.5	79.5	68.9	42	122	28	10	2.36	2.09	1.61	1.30	.91	.47	.08	.16	1.06	1.54	2.68	1.54	15.80
Uganda:																								
Entebbe	0 4 N.	32 28 E.	3,846	19	71.6	71.0	69.4	71.3	16	92	51	17	2.48	3.66	6.68	9.75	10.62	4.78	2.80	3.13	2.96	3.70	4.82	4.59	59.97
Fort Portal	0 40 N.	30 17 E.	5,229	11	68.2	67.8	66.2	66.6	2	86	50	15	.93	2.31	5.45	7.49	5.74	3.16	1.80	4.24	7.68	8.51	6.83	2.62	56.76
Union of South Africa:																								
Cape Town	33 56 S.	18 29 E.	40	28	69.5	63.0	54.6	60.9	48	104	31	64	.60	.52	.85	1.87	3.80	4.47	3.83	3.35	2.17	1.64	1.03	.88	25.01
Durban	29 52 S.	31 3 E.	260	10	74.7	69.8	62.0	68.2	50	111	41	29	4.39	5.31	5.75	3.79	2.60	1.13	1.32	1.71	2.86	5.79	5.09	5.13	44.87
East London	33 1 S.	27 54 E.	150	26	70.0	65.6	59.1	63.4	38	102	34	40	3.30	3.24	3.69	2.68	2.26	1.36	1.37	1.82	2.95	3.45	3.36	3.31	32.79
Grahamstown	33 18 S.	26 32 E.	1,700	10	68.4	63.7	54.6	60.8	25	110	25	47	2.56	2.73	3.20	2.36	2.04	1.44	1.22	1.50	2.41	2.95	3.25	2.55	28.21
Johannesburg	26 11 S.	28 3 E.	5,750	20	66.4	59.8	50.5	62.8	20	90	23	37	6.19	5.21	4.51	1.81	.79	.14	.33	.50	.97	2.54	4.94	5.38	33.31
Kimberley	28 44 S.	24 46 E.	4,042	22	77.6	65.5	52.2	69.2	31	107	21	41	2.26	2.61	3.04	1.41	.69	.26	.27	.26	.53	1.04	1.53	1.96	15.86
Port Nolloth	29 14 S.	28 12 E.	25	14	59.9	58.6	54.4	57.2	14	104	32	40	.06	.06	.15	.23	.41	.42	.33	.33	.19	.12	.07	.09	2.46

[4] Mean temperature values determined from observations taken at 7 a. m., 1 p. m., and 9 p. m.; maximum values based on observations at 1 p. m.
[5] Wadi Halfa, Anglo-Egyptian Sudan, and Aswan, Egypt, are in the "rainless" area; exact values on precipitation are not available.

AUSTRALASIA

Australia:																								
Adelaide	34 56 S.	138 35 E.	140	75	73.7	64.0	51.8	61.9	75	116	32	88	0.72	0.72	1.03	1.75	2.78	3.12	2.64	2.51	2.06	1.74	1.15	1.00	21.22
Alice Springs	23 38 S.	133 37 E.	1,926	15	81.8	68.8	53.2	72.4	46	117	23	42	1.74	1.62	1.20	.85	.68	.53	.43	.37	.38	.68	.92	1.31	10.71
Bourke	30 13 S.	145 58 E.	361	15	83.3	68.4	52.6	69.8	49	127	25	41	1.62	1.83	1.44	1.26	1.05	1.14	.86	.89	.84	1.03	1.29	1.22	14.47
Brisbane	27 28 S.	153 2 E.	137	45	77.2	70.3	58.5	69.8	45	109	36	75	6.29	6.19	5.75	3.56	2.85	2.77	2.30	2.10	2.05	2.52	3.73	4.96	45.07
Darwin	12 28 S.	130 51 E.	97	15	83.4	83.8	77.8	85.0	43	104	56	46	15.64	12.69	9.80	4.28	.74	.15	.07	.10	.47	2.08	5.03	10.32	61.37
Derby	17 18 S.	123 40 E.	53	15	86.1	83.4	71.5	84.4	28	114	42	40	7.20	5.89	4.24	1.40	.71	.52	.18	.10	.01	.07	1.05	4.33	25.70
Eucla	31 46 S.	128 50 E.	15	15	70.0	65.3	54.8	62.0	47	123	28	40	.63	.60	.92	1.13	1.23	1.10	.90	.94	.75	.66	.71	.39	9.96
Georgetown	18 22 S.	143 32 E.	991	15	82.7	77.9	67.4	81.2	15	108	33	41	8.53	8.15	5.14	1.58	.34	.46	.29	.15	.32	.82	1.86	5.94	33.58
Halls Creek	18 13 S.	127 46 E.	1,224	15	86.6	77.9	64.4	83.3	26	112	32	20	5.64	4.81	3.03	.98	.45	.26	.28	.13	.16	.58	1.42	3.32	21.06
Laverton	28 40 S.	122 23 E.	1,529	15	83.6	69.2	53.2	68.6	24	115	24	11	1.19	.88	1.09	1.11	1.32	1.12	.62	.65	.54	.31	.49	.55	9.87
Mein	13 13 S.	142 47 E.	400	15	81.6	78.8	73.4	80.9	15	104	43	25	13.57	11.04	9.12	3.35	.38	.24	.08	.11	.06	.60	2.57	6.25	47.37
Melbourne	37 49 S.	144 58 E.	115	76	67.4	59.4	48.7	57.7	76	111	27	71	1.91	1.72	2.19	2.19	2.17	2.07	1.85	1.87	2.45	2.63	2.24	2.29	25.58
Mitchell	26 32 S.	147 52 E.	1,102	15	80.0	67.1	52.2	68.8	15	111	19	29	3.42	3.01	3.49	1.46	1.55	1.75	1.54	1.00	1.36	1.47	2.11	2.42	24.58
Onslow	21 43 S.	114 57 E.	14	15	85.9	79.8	65.0	75.5	28	117	38	25	.88	.68	.85	1.06	1.76	1.83	1.16	.43	.06	.00	.02	.17	8.90
Perth	31 57 S.	115 50 E.	197	35	73.8	66.8	55.2	60.8	35	108	34	51	.34	.45	.79	1.65	4.97	6.92	6.57	5.63	3.41	2.21	.81	.57	34.32
Rockhampton	23 24 S.	150 30 E.	37	15	80.8	74.6	62.7	74.8	15	112	35	42	7.89	8.13	5.20	2.34	1.79	2.39	1.70	.84	1.40	1.73	2.32	4.36	40.09
Sydney	33 52 S.	151 12 E.	138	73	71.6	64.7	52.8	63.6	73	108	36	68	3.67	4.25	4.99	5.33	5.23	4.75	4.86	3.01	2.85	2.84	2.81	2.87	47.46
New Zealand:																								
Auckland	36 50 S.	174 50 E.	152	56	66.5	61.2	51.8	57.3	50	90	32	74	2.67	3.05	.02	3.43	4.63	4.92	4.95	4.22	3.64	3.69	3.32	2.90	44.44
Dunedin	45 52 S.	170 31 E.	300	59	58.0	51.7	42.4	51.0	65	94	23	70	3.34	2.75	2.96	2.78	3.26	3.15	2.99	3.14	2.75	3.13	3.28	3.53	37.06
Wellington	41 16 S.	174 46 E.	10	56	62.5	57.0	47.7	54.3	65	88	29	69	3.30	3.19	3.29	3.80	4.76	4.87	5.55	4.43	3.99	4.19	3.44	3.30	48.11
Oceania:																								
Apia, Samoan Islands	13 48 S.	171 46 W.	16	20	79.6	79.4	77.2	78.7	29	96	61	21	18.90	16.65	14.96	11.26	5.63	5.75	2.60	3.78	5.83	7.05	11.26	14.80	118.47
Fanning Island	3 54 N.	159 23 W.	17	10	81.8	81.8	82.4	82.8	8	100	69	13	10.77	9.72	12.54	17.04	13.99	11.49	11.24	5.71	3.99	4.98	3.76	12.99	118.22
Guam, Ladrone Islands	13 24 N.	144 38 E.	67	17	79.0	81.2	81.0	80.5	17	93	64	17	2.42	2.86	3.19	2.18	4.07	5.65	14.24	15.70	16.14	12.61	7.20	4.80	91.06
Hilo, Hawaii	19 44 N.	155 3 W.	40	35	70.0	71.2	74.6	74.5	35	91	51	35	11.77	10.82	15.08	13.06	9.21	7.40	9.89	11.81	10.84	10.97	13.80	12.47	137.12

TEMPERATURE AND PRECIPITATION DATA FOR REPRESENTATIVE STATIONS ON A WORLD-WIDE DISTRIBUTION—Continued

AUSTRALASIA—Contintinued

Country and station	Latitude	Longitude	Elevation	Temperature								Average precipitation													
				Mean					Extreme																
				Length of record	January	April	July	October	Length of record	Maximum	Minimum	Length of record	January	February	March	April	May	June	July	August	September	October	November	December	Year
	° ′	° ′	Ft.	Yr.	°F.	°F.	°F.	°F.	Yr.	°F.	°F.	Yr.	In.	In.	In.	In.	In.	In.	In.	In.	In.	In.	In.	In.	In.
Oceania—Continued.																									
Honolulu, Hawaii	21 19 N.	157 52 W.	13	55	71.1	73.0	77.7	77.0	48	90	52	61	3.54	3.72	3.18	2.06	1.43	.83	1.04	1.20	1.40	1.97	3.30	4.07	27.74
Noumea, New Caledonia	22 16 S.	166 27 E.	30	10	79.0	76.4	68.7	72.4	24	99	52	54	3.79	4.77	5.81	5.13	4.50	3.63	3.69	2.69	2.46	2.06	2.35	2.64	43.52
Ocean Island, Gilbert Islands	0 52 S.	169 35 E.	85	12	82.2	82.2	82.0	82.4	12	96	68	12	12.88	9.03	8.43	8.49	6.07	5.13	5.67	2.67	3.90	4.80	5.74	8.03	80.84
Papeiti, Society Islands	17 32 S.	149 34 W.	20	15	80.2	80.2	76.3	78.4	8	93	61	35	8.21	7.44	6.94	4.34	3.33	2.72	1.91	1.63	2.29	3.52	5.18	8.01	55.52
Suva, Fiji Islands	18 8 S.	178 26 E.	44	33	79.9	78.6	73.6	76.0	33	98	57	34	10.72	10.13	14.70	11.28	10.16	6.15	4.60	8.24	6.98	7.80	9.51	12.11	112.38
Tulagi, Solomon Islands	9 5 S.	160 8 E.	7	9	82.7	82.4	81.0	81.6	9	97	70	21	13.44	16.18	16.45	8.24	7.50	5.66	6.26	6.86	7.74	7.91	8.48	10.65	115.37
Volcano Observatory, Hawaii	19 26 N.	155 16 W.	3,984	27	57.6	59.2	63.0	63.0	27	86	40	27	11.75	7.32	10.76	8.87	5.81	4.29	6.20	6.48	6.93	6.42	10.04	10.53	95.40
Waialeale, Hawaii	22 4 N.	159 30 W.	5,075									20													460.20

OCEANS

Country and station	Latitude	Longitude	Elevation	Temp. mean: Length of record	January	April	July	October	Extreme: Length of record	Maximum	Minimum	Precip.: Length of record	January	February	March	April	May	June	July	August	September	October	November	December	Year
Atlantic Ocean, North:																									
Bermuda	32 18 N.	64 46 W.	151	24	62.6	64.6	78.4	73.8	32	94	39	55	4.48	4.60	4.74	4.10	4.54	4.49	4.53	5.40	5.19	5.95	5.01	4.78	57.81
Las Palmas, Canary Islands	28 07 N.	15 26 W.	39	34	64.0	66.0	72.0	72.0	34	99	46	35	1.54	1.06	.90	.55	.16	.04	.08	.08	.16	1.06	2.24	1.69	9.56
Ponta Delgada, Azores	37 44 N.	25 40 W.	72	30	58.0	60.0	71.0	66.0	32	82	42	30	2.83	3.07	2.28	2.01	2.20	1.34	.79	1.46	2.44	3.27	3.58	3.07	28.34
Santiago, Cape Verde Island	14 54 N.	23 31 W.	111	16	72.0	74.0	78.0	80.0	16	92	56	22	.32	.08	.08	.04	.00	.00	.24	3.42	3.46	1.06	.47	.24	9.41
Atlantic Ocean, South:																									
Falkland Islands	51 41 S.	57 42 W.	70	10	49.8	43.6	36.4	42.2	10	75	19	22	2.74	2.35	2.30	2.34	2.82	2.22	2.14	1.89	1.35	1.50	1.98	2.71	26.34
South Georgia	54 13 S.	36 33 W.	13	10	42.8	37.2	27.8	35.8	15	80	−3	20	3.35	4.14	5.06	5.28	5.54	4.96	5.49	5.06	3.44	2.59	3.38	2.94	51.23
South Orkneys	60 44 S.	44 39 W.	23	8	32.6	26.3	10.2	25.2	13	51	−40	18	1.48	1.54	1.82	1.73	1.32	1.16	1.20	1.38	.98	1.01	1.37	.89	15.88

ANTARCTICA

Country and station	Latitude	Longitude	Elevation	Temp. mean: Length of record	January	April	July	October	Extreme: Length of record	Maximum	Minimum	Precip.: Length of record	January	February	March	April	May	June	July	August	September	October	November	December	Year
Little America	78 34 S.	163 56 W.	50	2	20.9	−22.8	−40.5	−17.2	2	38	−72														

Climate and Weather Data for the United States

By J. B. Kincer [1]

THE FOLLOWING PAGES of the Yearbook contain data on climate and weather in the United States of interest in connection with agriculture. Practically every county in every State is included, so that farmers everywhere may find facts that are of value in their own locality. Beginning with page 689, this article discusses the material included in the tables and maps. Before taking up this discussion, the author gives some general background on the collection of climatic and weather data in the United States so the reader may know the sources of the material used.

[1] J. B. Kincer is Principal Meteorologist and Chief of the Division of Climate and Crop Weather, Weather Bureau.

WEATHER OBSERVATIONS IN THE UNITED STATES

Early weather observations and weather studies in this country were made in a spasmodic manner by several uncoordinated agencies. So far as is known, the first records on the American Continent were kept by the Reverend John Campanius at Swedes Fort, near Wilmington, Del., in 1664, but there followed more than a century for which only fragmentary historical references to the subject are available. These very early records were necessarily of a descriptive, noninstrumental nature.

The first systematic instrumental records in the United States were made by John Lining at Charleston, S. C., beginning in 1738. Some of the other older available records were made at New Haven, Conn., beginning in 1780; Baltimore, Md., 1817; and Philadelphia, Pa., 1825. In the Midwest there are a few century-long records. Those at St. Paul, Minn. (including early records made at Fort Snelling), and Leavenworth, Kans., were begun in 1836 and those at St. Louis, Mo., in 1837. Some of the longer records on the Pacific coast are those of Sacramento and San Francisco, Calif., begun in 1849, and San Diego, Calif., in 1850.

About the middle of the nineteenth century official interest in meteorology was awakened, and the Smithsonian Institution entered the field of observational work, supplementing records that had previously been made by the Army. In the early period of observations, records were made only of the fundamental aspects of the weather, such as temperature at certain hours of the day and precipitation, which, however, provide basic data for climatic investigations. Later, after 1830 and especially from 1850 on, increasing attention was given to the theoretical aspects of meteorology, although most of the records were continued on substantially the same basis as at the beginning.

Historically, the early climatic observations in this country may be classed as follows: Records made at military posts by the Medical Department and the Signal Service of the Army from the early part of the nineteenth century up to about 1890. In 1840 the data thus collected were published by Samuel Forry under the title "The Climate of the United States and Its Endemic Influences." At this time the study of meteorological data was largely prosecuted to ascertain the mechanism of storms, their mode of progression, and their relation to weather characteristics and sequences. Nevertheless, the data collected were admirably suited also to fundamental climatic studies.

In 1857 Blodgett's Climatology of the United States, a volume of over 500 pages, was published, and 3 years later a report was issued by the Surgeon General of the Army bringing available records up to 1860 and covering 40 years at many of the stations maintained by the War Department. By that time the Smithsonian Institution had entered the field of meteorology. The institution began making systematic observations in 1849 and continued actively in the work for more than 20 years. The data collected were published in the Smithsonian Contributions to Knowledge, which includes Tables of Rain and Snow in the United States.

In 1847, Joseph Henry, Secretary of the Smithsonian Institution, submitted a program of organization and work for that institution, including a system of meteorological observations entitled "Solving the Problem of American Storms." In 1865 the Honorable Isaac Newton, United States Commissioner of Agriculture, endorsed a recommendation of Professor Henry's that a more extensive weather service be established for the benefit of agriculture. Five years later, in 1870, the Congress of the United States acted favorably on this recommendation by enacting a joint resolution which assigned to the Army the responsibility of taking meteorological observations at all military posts. The Smithsonian Institution relinquished its meteorological work, and in 1874 transferred its observers to the Signal Service of the Army, then under Gen. Albert J. Myer.

The Signal Service, however, concerned itself mainly with the issue of weather forecasts (then called weather probabilities) with the result that purely climatological work practically ceased. Under the new set-up, many of the former cooperative observers of the Smithsonian Institution became disinterested and ceased their observational work altogether, so that by the middle eighties this corps of observers had dwindled to a mere skeleton of the original number. Under the administration of Gen. A. W. Greely, 1887–91, there was a marked revival of interest in climatic work, with volunteer observers in all parts of the country grouped in climate and crop services for the several States. During the succeeding decade this sytem was continued and enlarged by the Weather Bureau in its early years.

From the standpoint of homogeneity the observations made by the Army Medical Department stand first, but unfortunately the geographic distribution of stations was so irregular and the distances between them in many cases so great that, standing alone, the data were of limited value for climatic records. Those of the Smithsonian Institution were, as a rule, carefully made and quite complete with respect to climatic fundamentals, but the number of observing stations was limited, varying from less than 100 about 1850 to a maximum of about 350 when the work was taken over by the Signal Corps of the Army. Like the Army posts, Smithsonian stations also were unbalanced in geographic distribution from a national standpoint, almost all of them being located in the eastern half of the country. The collection of data that were adequate in reliability, geographic distribution, and homogeneity was not really begun until the latter part of the nineteenth century.

Contribution of Cooperative Observers

In 1890 Congress established the Weather Bureau as a Bureau in the Department of Agriculture and, by legislation, transferred all official meteorological work to it. This act went into effect July 1, 1891, and provided, among other things, for the "taking of such meteorological observations as may be necessary to establish and record climatic conditions in the United States."

In giving the direction for collecting "sufficient records to establish the climatic characteristics of the United States," the Congress probably did not realize the magnitude of the undertaking. Literally thousands of stations were necessary, and the funds available for the inauguration of the work were wholly inadequate to finance the project, especially if the observers were to be compensated for taking observations and rendering reports; moreover, only a limited number of meteorological instruments could be provided. Under these conditions, the Bureau inaugurated an extensive system of cooperative observation stations which has developed into one of the most extraordinary official services known anywhere and probably nets the public more per dollar expended than any other government service in the world. The system includes literally thousands of unpaid cooperative observers to whom the Bureau furnishes thermometers, thermometer shelters, and rain gages.

It is a remarkable fact that thousands of people in all parts of the country freely give their time to make the necessary observations and reports, every day in the year, year after year, without a break in the records. The Bureau now has approximately 5,000 of these observers who serve without compensation; this means that if for each there is required an average, of say, 20 minutes a day to take and record the observations, answer questions about local weather, and make the regular monthly reports, the total time contributed to the Government for the entire service would amount to 75,000 8-hour days of work each year. There is no other Government cooperative enterprise that even remotely compares with this—that is, in which a considerable part of the time of those cooperating is required every day in the year, including Sundays and holidays, for long periods. Some 300 of the Bureau's cooperative observers have served for 25 years or more, and during this time have made daily observations and rendered monthly reports to the Bureau. Elwood Kirkwood, observer at Mauzy, Ind. (post office, Rushville), has to his credit the longest continuous service, 59 years; some 70 others have taken observations regularly for more than 40 years.

In assuming the obligations of a cooperative observer of the Weather Bureau, a person undertakes to perform certain exacting duties every day in the year during most of his life. What impels people to make this work practically a lifetime job? This question was eloquently answered a few years ago by Judge A. S. Peacock, of Wakeeney, Kans., who, at the beginning of his thirty-first year as cooperative observer said, in a sketch entitled "Keeping Weather Records," published in the Western Kansas World:

"Is the making of these weather records considered worth while? It would seem so * * * if we may judge by the number of inquiries for weather facts. Within the past 10,957 days[2] we have answered at least that many questions concerning the weather. And that would be a rather low average—only one question per day. If the weather be extra cold or unusually hot; drought or deluge—look out for a flood of inquiries, 15 to 40 in 1 day, occasionally. Think of the work of merely taking the phone receiver down 10,000 times! And right here our envious friend is prone to feel that any man would be foolish to work 30 years on any kind of a job without pay. He is too small and narrow to be able to conceive that any man or woman would work for mere personal satisfaction; the pleasure of neighbors, or the benefit of generations that are yet to come and take possession of the land.

[2] This was written on August 1, 1935. Subsequently, of course, Judge Peacock has added many more days to his record.

"Yes, it is a lot of work and daily bother, but we like it. After 30 years of the habit there is a sort of unexplainable attraction or fascination about it. Yes, we like to answer questions about the weather, though occasionally some of them are called in at very inopportune times. But let 'em come! We are here to be useful, and nothing affords us greater pleasure than to add in some small degree to the pleasure and satisfaction of others."

After the transfer of official meteorological work to the Weather Bureau in 1891, the expansion of the cooperative climatological service was pushed vigorously. At the time of transfer, 1,745 stations were in operation, and at the time of publishing the first edition of Weather Bureau Bulletin W, containing extensive climatic summaries, there were available for inclusion some 2,200 records, covering 10 years or more up to 1908. Thereafter further expansion was effected, so that in compiling records for the preparation of Sections A, B, and I, entitled "Climate," of the Atlas of American Agriculture, some 1,600 were found covering the 20-year period from 1895 to 1914, and about 2,000 additional records of 5 to 19 years.

This Yearbook contains summaries of 4,900 records of 10 years or more, about 1,400 for the full 40 years, 1899 to 1938, and nearly 2,000 for at least 35 years within this period; lack of space prevented the inclusion of several hundred comparatively short records from additional stations in counties where longer records were available. The locations of the stations whose records have been used are shown on the map on page 702.

DATA USED IN MAPS AND TABLES

For many years the Weather Bureau has maintained some 200 observing stations known as stations of the first order, manned by professional meteorologists, at which complete meteorological observations are made, including automatic, continuous instrumental records of many weather elements. Since these stations are not spaced closely enough to provide data adequate for climatic purposes, a large number of cooperative stations, already described, are maintained to obtain the necessary basic data.

The instrumental equipment at the latter includes maximum and minimum thermometers, thermometer support, instrument shelter, and rain gage. No automatic recording instruments are provided. In addition to observations of temperature and precipitation, however, cooperative observers record various other weather aspects, such as character and time of beginning and ending of precipitation, state of the sky, prevailing wind direction, occurrence of storms, hail, sleet, frost, and any other noteworthy weather features.

Of the maps beginning on page 702, those showing wet-bulb temperature, days with snow cover, dense fog, thunderstorms, and hail, and the relative humidity and sunshine maps represent data from first-order stations only; in all other cases, records of some 5,000 cooperative stations were considered in preparing the maps. The State tables, beginning on page 751, are based primarily on records from cooperative stations.

Temperature Data

For depicting the basic climatic characteristics of a locality the most important temperature data required are: Average daily temperature; average daily range and average daily variability; average monthly temperature; average monthly range and absolute monthly extremes; seasonal temperature, especially the average for the summer (June through August) and for the winter (December through February); average annual temperature and average annual range; and the frequency of occurrence and duration of certain significant temperatures.

The true average daily temperature corresponds closely to the average of 24 hourly observations, but as several other combinations of hourly values give averages that differ little from the true daily average, some one of these is generally used to reduce computational work. The combination

$$\frac{(7 \text{ a. m.} + 2 \text{ p. m.} + 9 \text{ p. m.} + 9 \text{ p. m.})}{4}$$

gives a value which differs only slightly from the true daily average; and

$$\frac{(\text{sunrise} + 2 \text{ p. m.} + 9 \text{ p. m.})}{3}$$

also gives fairly accurate results. The formula

$$\frac{(\text{maximum} + \text{minimum})}{2}$$

is easy of application and very satisfactory when dependable maximum and minimum thermometers are used and properly exposed, as at official Weather Bureau stations. The mean of the daily extremes is, as a rule, slightly too high, but it usually does not vary more than half a degree from the true daily average. This is the combination employed by the Weather Bureau to obtain the average daily temperature.

The mean daily temperature is the basic climatic unit. The mean monthly temperature is the average of the daily values for the month and, in practice, the average annual temperature is the mean of the 12 monthly mean values.

The meteorological seasons differ somewhat from the astronomical seasons because the temperature lags considerably behind the apparent alternating annual north and south march of the sun. For example, in northern latitudes, the sun's altitude is lowest about December 22, nearly a month before the average coldest weather of winter, which occurs about the middle of January. The year is divided into four seasons of 3 months each, and the coldest consecutive 3 months are, on an average, December, January, and February. This period therefore comprises the meteorological winter. Similar conditions obtain for the other seasons. March–May comprises the meterological spring; June–August, summer; and September–November, fall. Seasonal averages are averages for the 3 months of the meteorological season.

The average winter and average summer temperatures are especially important because in the northern portions of the United States and at higher altitudes in the West the 3 summer months coincide more or less with the growing season for potatoes and corn, while the winter temperature shows many interesting correlations with the northern limit of winter wheat and several tree fruits. Just as the mean daily temperature is approximately the average of the maximum and minimum, so the annual mean is represented very closely by the average of the extreme months, January and July. The difference between this and the mean for the 12 separate monthly means in most sections of the country is only a fraction of a degree. The accompanying tables and maps include data showing the mean January temperature, the mean July temperature, temperature extremes, and other related data.

Temperature and Planting Dates

Though the time of lowest or highest temperature for individual years may vary considerably from year to year, the normals, or long-time averages, show a uniform march from the low of winter, about January 15, to the high of summer, about July 15, and then a recession back to the winter low. The spring rise in the annual temperature march has some interesting relations to agricultural operations. For example, the usual date of the beginning of spring-wheat seeding is the time when the normal daily temperature rises to 37° F. in the locality where seeding is to be done; spring oats, 43°; early potatoes, 45°; corn, 55°; and cotton, 62°. Incidentally, 55°, the corn-planting temperature, comes at the time of the average date of the last killing frost in spring, and 62°, the cotton-planting temperature, after the last killing frost.

Precipitation Data

Moisture falls from the clouds in either liquid or solid form as rain, snow, hail, sleet; "precipitation" is a general term used to embrace any and all of these forms and includes, in addition to actual rainfall, the water equivalent of snow, hail, etc., expressed in inches and hundredths of inches of water depth. For example, 1 inch of rain means that if the amount falling should be retained on a flat surface without any run-off or seepage, the layer of water deposited would be 1 inch deep.

The moisture equivalent of snow varies greatly, ranging from 5 or 6 inches of very wet, heavy snow to an inch of water, to 15 or more inches of very light, fluffy snow to an inch. In observational procedure the snow is either weighed or melted and then measured as water. Where this is not practicable, the arbitrary rule that 10 inches of snow will equal approximately 1 inch of water is sometimes employed. This is fairly accurate for snow of about average density.

Basic Precipitation Data

The basic precipitation data are the average annual amounts. However, the annual values are insufficient for an adequate appraisal of moisture conditions, especially as they affect crops, produce floods, etc. The seasonal distribution, that is, whether or not the rain falls at a time of year when it will be most beneficial to growing crops, must be known, as well as the intensity of the rainfall, which determines whether the amounts falling are absorbed largely by the soil or mainly lost into streams and rivers, possibly producing floods; the frequency of droughts; and many other aspects of precipitation that cannot be determined from the annual, or even monthly, totals. In recent years the importance of microclimatic observations has become more and more apparent. Precipitation stations for making these observations are much closer together than those in a general climatological system such as that represented by the data in the accompanying maps and tables. The more detailed records are most valuable in studying the geographic variations and differences in intensity of rainfall from place to place for contiguous localities.

Precipitation Tables and Maps

The accompanying maps and tabular data show the average annual, average monthly, and average seasonal rainfall. A number of auxiliary maps show variations from the average amounts, including the percentage of years with less than 20 and 15 inches, respectively, of rain. Others show the maximum precipitation in 1 month, in 24 hours, and in 1 hour; the average snowfall; average number of days with snow cover, thunderstorms, and hail, as well as somewhat related phenomena, such as humidity, fog, etc. In addition a special tabulation at the foot of each State table gives the year-by-year State averages from the earliest date of record to 1939.

Precipitation Characteristics and Trends

No aspect of climate has greater economic significance than the comparatively long-time trends in precipitation.

With regard to characteristics of precipitation from year to year and trend tendencies from decade to decade, the United States may be divided into three broad west-to-east divisions as follows: Area 1, all States from the Rocky Mountains westward; area 2, all States between the Rocky Mountains and the Mississippi River, including Montana; and area 3, all States east of the Mississippi River. With such a division, areas 1 and 2 show quite similar trend characteristics, although the average annual precipitation in area 1 (17.9 inches) is much smaller than that in area 2 (28 inches). The average for the eastern division, area 3, is 43.5 inches.

Figure 1, *A*, shows the weighted average precipitation, in percentage departures from normal, for these three divisions, year by year, from 1886 to 1940, and also for the United States as a whole. Figure 1, *B*, shows the general trend tendencies for the respective areas by 10-year moving averages of percentages of normal.

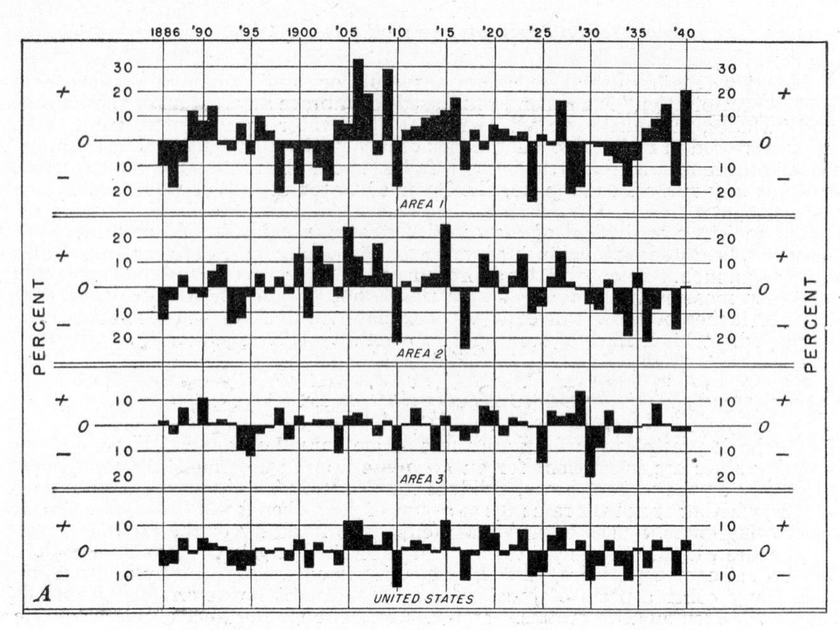

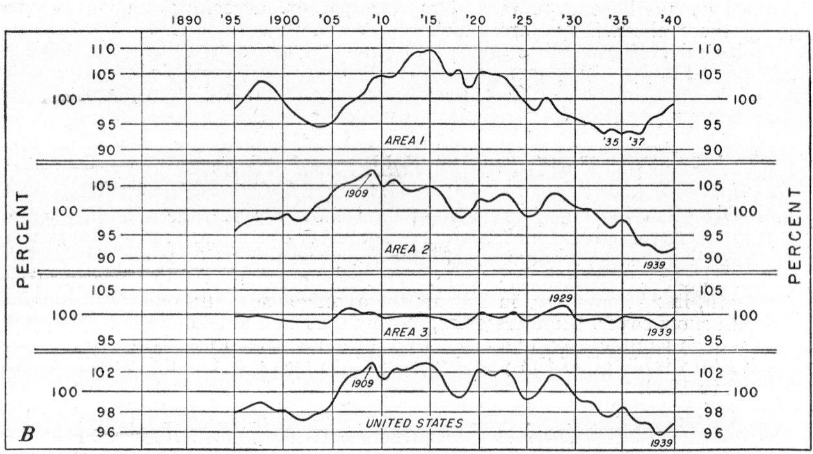

FIGURE 1.—No aspect of climate has greater economic significance than the comparatively long-time trends in precipitation. *A*, Year-by-year weighted average precipitation, 1886 to 1940, in percentage departures above or below normal, in three broad divisions of the United States and the country as a whole. Area 1 comprises the western part of the country to the Rocky Mountains; normal precipitation, 17.9 inches. Area 2, from the Rocky Mountains to the Mississippi River; normal precipitation, 28 inches. Area 3, from the Mississippi to the Atlantic coast; precipitation, 43.5 inches. Normal precipitation for the United States (weighted State averages) is 29 inches. *B*, General-trend tendencies; each point represents a 10-year average, expressed in percentage of normal rainfall, up to and including the date under which the point appears.

An examination of these graphs discloses some interesting and important precipitation characteristics.

In area 1 (fig. 1, *A*) the period 1889–97 had mostly above-normal rainfall, followed by 6 years of marked deficiencies. Then, beginning with 1904, the general tendency was toward markedly above normal up to 1916, with another extremely dry period from 1928 to 1935. The wettest year was 1906, with 33 percent above normal, and the driest 1924 with 25 percent below normal, while all but one of the last 5 years had above-normal precipitation. On the trend graphs (fig. 1, *B*) each point represents a 10-year average up to and including the respective dates. While 4 of the last 5 years in this area had above normal precipitation, the accumulated excesses for these were not quite sufficient to bring the trend curve, representing decade averages, up to normal, but a definite recovery tendency is shown for these recent years. It might be added that in 1941 (up to April 15) this area had abnormally heavy precipitation.

The outstanding features of area 2 (fig. 1, *A*) are the tendency for subnormal amounts of precipitation during the first decade beginning in 1886, followed, beginning with 1900, by mostly above normal, except for a few extremely dry years, through the decade ending with 1925, and marked deficiencies during the last 10 years. The wettest year in this area was 1915, with precipitation 25 percent above normal, and the driest, just 2 years later, 1917, with 25 percent below normal. An outstanding feature of the record for this area, which includes the Great Plains States, is the prolonged drought period of the 1930's. This decade reached a lower average precipitation than any like period since 1886, but here also there is a fairly definite suggestion of recovery. Available records show that these precipitation trends come in long swings of above and below normal, and the period covered by this summary is a comparatively short one (only about five decades). However, data available from a few long records within the area strengthen this suggestion of a general recovery, and also the probability that the 1940 decade will have much better moisture conditions.

Area 3 (fig. 1, *A*) is characterized by small variations from year to year, frequent alternations of above and below normal, and comparative absence of prolonged drought periods. The wettest year was 1929, with 14 percent above normal, and the driest the following year, 1930, with 20 percent below normal. Thus the maximum range on either side of normal is 35 percent, against 50 in area 2 and 58 in area 1.

The trend graphs (fig. 1, *B*) show that, on a basis of 10-year overlapping averages, the wettest decade in area 1 was that ending with 1915, and the driest period centered in 1935. In area 2 the wettest decade was that ending with 1909 and the driest that ending with 1939. In area 3 the wettest 10 years covered the period from 1920 to 1929 and the driest the decade 1930–39.

Sunshine Data

The time from sunrise to sunset represents the total possible number of hours of sunshine for any particular day. At first-order Weather Bureau stations automatic instrumental recorders determine the number of hours and minutes that the sun actually shines on any day, and, with the possible amount as a base, the percentage of the possible is computed. Sunshine data are recorded for both values—hours of actual amount and percentage of the possible. Maps of the United States beginning on page 702 show both the average number of hours of sunshine and the percentage of the possible amounts (daily averages) for the winter and the summer seasons; also, the average annual number of clear and of cloudy days.

The possible amount of daily sunshine varies on December 22, the shortest day of the year, from 10 hours and 35 minutes at latitude 25° N., the latitude of the southern end of Florida, to 8 hours and 10 minutes at latitude 49° N., the northern boundary of the United States from Minnesota westward. Farther north it decreases with the latitude, until north of the Arctic Circle the sun does not rise above the horizon at this time.

At the time of the longest day of summer, June 21, the possible amount varies from 13 hours and 41 minutes at latitude 25° N. to 16 hours and 19 minutes at latitude 49° N. At this time north of the Arctic Circle the sun does not set. Thus, on a clear day in early summer the most northern States receive about 2 hours more of sunshine than is possible in the extreme south, but in early winter the reverse is true. In northern localities where the growing season is short,

298737°—41——45

this greater amount of sunshine in summer is important in hastening the maturing of crops so that they escape early fall frosts.

The foregoing figures relate to the total possible amount of sunshine which would be experienced with a continuously clear sky. However, the amount of cloudiness varies greatly in different parts of the country, and the actual amount of sunshine received depends on the frequency of cloudy weather. In midwinter—January—the amount of sunshine actually received on an average ranges from a minimum of 2 or 3 hours a day in the Pacific Northwest and the region of the Great Lakes, to more than 7.5 hours in the far Southwest, southwestern New Mexico, southern Arizona, and southern California; much of the Florida Peninsula and the Rio Grande Valley of Texas receive an average of more than 6 hours.

In midsummer—July—the averages range from 7 or 8 hours a day along the northern Pacific coast and in eastern Gulf localities to about 13.5 hours in much of the Great Valley of California. During the 3 summer months in southwestern Arizona and much of California the sun shines, on an average, during more than 90 percent of the total number of hours from sunrise to sunset.

Killing Frost and the Growing Season

The growing season of crops susceptible to frost damage—the so-called warm-weather crops—is restricted by the number of days between the last killing frost in the spring and the first in the fall. Maps and tabular data show for the country as a whole, and for individual States, the average dates of the last killing frost in the spring and the first in the fall, together with the average length of the period between these dates, usually referred to as the growing season.

On some of the Florida Keys freezing temperatures have never occurred, and consequently the frostless season covers the whole year. However, these are the only localities in the United States definitely frost-free. Throughout most of Florida, along the coast of the Gulf of Mexico, and in favored localities in Arizona and California, the average growing season is more than 260 days. Along the northern margin of the Cotton Belt it is about 200 days, and in the northern part of the Corn Belt from 140 to 150 days. In northern Maine and northern Minnesota, where hay, potatoes, oats, and barley are the principal crops, it is about 100 days, and in the higher altitudes in the West less than 90 days.

There is very little agriculture, except wild hay production and grazing, where the average season between spring and fall killing frosts is less than 90 days. In such regions frosts are likely to occur in any of the summer months. The length of the season without killing frost varies year by year, as indicated by records for selected stations for the several States.

Seasonal Progress of the Weather

The following brief summaries of weather in the United States, month by month, refer to the normal, or long-time, average conditions, and should not be considered as a forecast for any particular month or year. While the weather for individual years may differ considerably from these summaries, they nevertheless afford a broad picture of the seasonal progress of temperature, variations in precipitation, occurrence of frost, etc., that is approximated when conditions are about normal.

January

January is the coldest month of the year, although on an average the temperature is only slightly below that of February. In the extreme north-central portion of the country the monthly average of temperature is near 0° F., while a mean in excess of 43°, the critical vegetative temperature, obtains over about one-tenth of the country, mainly Florida and the Gulf sections, as well as the lower elevations of Arizona and California. In the extreme upper Great Plains cold waves occasionally bring temperatures of −50° or lower, while the extreme subzero line extends to the northern portion of the Gulf States.

In Tennessee and Mississippi and parts of adjoining States, the average January precipitation is more than 4 inches, but over considerable western areas, especially in the Plains States, the average is less than 1 inch, occurring mostly in the form of snow. In upper Michigan and central New York snowfall for this month averages about 30 inches, but it decreases gradually southward to about 1 inch in the northern portions of the Gulf States.

While January is considered a between-season month in the Southern States, preparation of soil for spring planting is usually possible, and some seeding of oats and hardy forage crops is carried on. In the warmer portions, planting of potatoes and hardy truck crops can usually be accomplished. In the northern half of the country most crops are dormant.

February

The mean February temperature usually is only slightly higher than that of January, ranging from less than 10° F. in North Dakota to about 45° in the Gulf States. Although February is not the coldest month of the year in the South, some severely cold weather has occurred there during February. The memorable cold wave in February 1899 carried subzero temperatures into the northernmost part of Florida. Frost occurs at rare intervals in southern Florida; the average date of the last killing frost in the vicinity of latitude 29° is about the middle of February.

In most of the central and eastern cotton States February precipitation averages over 4 inches, and it exceeds 6 inches in parts of Alabama and Georgia. From these areas the amounts decrease to about 1 inch in central and western Oklahoma and the cotton districts of western Texas. Precipitation is still light in the Great Plains, and the rainy season continues in the Pacific Coast States.

During this month vegetation remains practically dormant in the northern half of the country, except on the Pacific coast. In the most southern sections hardy truck crops are planted and grown in the open, protected from the severest cold weather. The seeding of early truck is accomplished in the southern tier of States; the planting of corn normally begins in southernmost Texas early in the month.

March

In March the spring rise in temperature becomes rather pronounced, especially in the Central and Northern States. In the most northern north-central districts the monthly average is about 20° F., or about 15° higher than that of February. In a considerable belt along the Gulf Coast temperatures average above 60°, about 10° higher than in the preceding month. Occasionally very warm weather is experienced in March, with the temperature reaching 90° or over in the interior of the country; above 80° has been recorded in all sections except the higher elevations of the West. In an average year killing frost does not occur along the immediate Gulf coast after March 1, nor after the close of the month south of South Carolina and the most northerly portions of Georgia and Alabama, central Arkansas, and central Oklahoma.

Precipitation averages from 4 to 6 inches in the central and eastern cotton States, and about 2 inches in much of the western Cotton Belt. With the seasonal rise in temperature there is a noticeable increase in rainfall in the northern Great Plains, but in central and southern portions of the area the rainy season does not set in until later. Rainfall continues heavy along the Pacific coast. Thunderstorms become more frequent, especially in the lower Ohio Valley and the central and southern part of the Mississippi Valley.

Vegetation usually continues dormant during much of March in the northern tier of States, but growth becomes rapid in southern sections, with such spring crops as oats and corn usually appearing above the ground. By the middle of the month the temperature rise is normally sufficient to permit corn planting northward to southeastern South Carolina, north-central Georgia, central Alabama, and southern Arkansas, and for early spring-wheat seeding in the southern portion of the Spring Wheat Belt. Seeding of spring oats begins as far northward as the central portions of the country.

April

Normally April brings a marked rise in temperature, especially in the Central and Northern States. The monthly averages are about 40° F. in the extreme north, some 20° higher than for March, and in most of the Gulf area they range from 65° to 70°. Temperatures as high as 90° or above have been recorded in this month in nearly all sections of the country, while extremes of 100° or over have occurred in the Southwest. South of the Ohio and central Mississippi Valleys temperatures seldom fall below 20° in April.

Killing frost may be expected to occur in half the years during the first 10 days of April as far south as central South Carolina, northern Georgia and Alabama, central Arkansas, and central Oklahoma, but by the close of the month the normal frost line has receded to the northern Ohio Valley, southern Iowa, and southeastern Nebraska. However, during the first half of the month killing frost may be expected in 1 year in 10 on an average as far south as the southern parts of Georgia, Alabama, and Mississippi, and the central portions of Louisiana and Texas.

In April it is usually still too cold for vegetation to develop in extreme northern sections of the country. In central districts, however, winter grains, grass, and pastures frequently make considerable growth, while early planted potatoes begin to mature in Texas. Early fruit and berries bloom as far north as Maryland, Virginia, and the Ohio Valley.

This is a month of intense farm activity in most sections of the country. In the Southern States the planting of commercial crops is nearing completion, with cultivation begun. Cotton planting begins about April 1 in the central parts of the Gulf States and extends to the northern limits of the cotton area about the end of the month. Corn planting begins about the first of the month as far north as southern Virginia, Kentucky, Missouri, and Kansas, and by the end of the month usually as far north as southern Pennsylvania, central Ohio, Indiana, Illinois, and Iowa.

May

Normally, temperatures continue to rise rather rapidly in May, the average for the month ranging from about 50° F. in the extreme upper Lake region and the interior of the Northeast to 75° along the Gulf coast. The normal killing frost line recedes northward to the northern limits of the country, except very locally. After the end of May frost occurs on an average in only a few localities of the extreme Northeast and the upper Lake region, but in extensive elevated areas west of the Great Plains the average date is later than May 31. However, temperatures as low as freezing may be expected as often as 1 year in 10 in early May as far south as New Jersey, the central portions of Maryland and Virginia, the most western part of North Carolina, central Kentucky, and the southernmost parts of Indiana, Illinois, and Missouri.

An outstanding characteristic of the normal rainfall of May is the marked increase over the Great Plains, with the monthly averages ranging from about 3 inches over the eastern part of the area to about 2 inches in the west. May rainfall averages more than 3 inches practically everywhere east of the one-hundredth meridian. East of the Rocky Mountains the heaviest falls, more than 4 inches, occur in the Ozark region, including eastern Oklahoma. In Pacific coast sections the dry season is approaching, and the decrease in rainfall is pronounced, especially in California.

Farm work is carried on actively during May in all parts of the country, with corn planting beginning during the first 10 days of the month as far north as about the northern limits of the Corn Belt.

June

The average temperature for June ranges from 60° to 70° F. in the Northern States, is lower at high western elevations, and rises to about 80° in the extreme South. While freezing temperatures are sometimes experienced in the more Northern States, killing frost occurs there as late as the first 10 days of June only about 1 year in 10.

In the far West the dry season becomes well established, but in the Great Plains States June is one of the wettest months of the year. It is noteworthy that a large percentage of the total annual rainfall in the Great Plains region, particularly in the northern part, comes during the spring and early summer months when it is of greatest value to growing crops.

June is an important month in crop development and farm work. Cotton usually is blooming and fruiting in southern and central parts of the Cotton Belt and forming squares farther north; corn is silking and tasseling as far north as Virginia and Kansas by the close of the month. Winter grains are usually maturing as far north as central Pennsylvania and Nebraska and heading and blooming in more northern States. The planting of corn is usually completed in the later districts early in the month, and the planting of late potatoes and truck crops is under way in the North.

July

July, as a rule, is the warmest month of the year except along the Pacific coast, where the highest temperatures usually come later. The average temperature for the month ranges from 65° F. (lower in the higher elevations of the West and locally east of the Rocky Mountains in the extreme north) to more than 80° over the lower Great Plains and most of the Gulf area. It will be noted that the annual range of temperature, that is, the difference between the average for the coldest and that for the warmest month, is much greater in the North than in the South. For example, at Bismarck, N. Dak., the seasonal rise is from a minimum of about 8° in January to 70° in July, or 62°, while at New Orleans it is from 54° in January to 82° in July, or 28°, less than half as much. There is, of course, a corresponding difference in the July–January recession. Notwithstanding the general warmth in July, at times unseasonably low temperatures bring frost and freezing weather to parts of the Northern States. In fact subfreezing temperatures have occurred in July locally as far south as southwestern Virginia. The lowest July temperature of record is 10°, occurring in both Colorado and Wyoming, and the highest 134° in Death Valley, Calif.

In much of the Great Plains there is, on the average, more rainfall in July than in June, the amounts ranging mostly from 2 to 3 inches. The scanty rainfall in Pacific coast sections is in contrast to the normally heavy amounts in the Southeastern States where the maximum, 8 to 10 inches, occurs in Florida. July rainfall results largely from local thunderstorms, this being the month of their maximum activity. The greatest average number—20 during the month—occurs in the southern Rocky Mountain area and the east Gulf sections.

July is a month of great activity on farms. The harvesting and threshing of many of the small-grain crops are accomplished, with best results while fair weather persists. Ample moisture is required for the development of corn; in many areas it is the most critical month for the corn crop. Winter-wheat harvest usually becomes general by the first of the month as far north as the Ohio Valley, northern Missouri, and northern Kansas, and by the 20th in more northern sections. Spring-wheat harvest normally begins in the southern portions of the Spring Wheat Belt about July 10. Cultivation of cotton is mostly completed during this month, with plants blooming and fruiting to the northern limits of the belt and picking begun in southern portions. Corn is coming into tassel or into silk in northern producing sections. Early potatoes are dug as far north as New Jersey and the Ohio Valley.

August

The normal August temperatures do not differ greatly from those for July, although as a rule August is a degree or two cooler, except in the Pacific Coast States, where the reverse is true. The mean monthly temperatures range from about 65° F. in the most northern part of the United States (somewhat lower in the elevated western sections) to more than 80° in most of the South.

Rainfall still results largely from local thunderstorms, with the heaviest falls, 8 to 10 inches, along the eastern Gulf coast. There is a noticeable falling off of precipitation in the Great Plains, and the dry season continues in the Pacific Coast States. In the far Southwest July and August largely comprise the rainy season; New Mexico and Arizona usually have much more rainfall then than in any of the other months.

In the higher elevations of the more Western States, winter-wheat harvest becomes general in August, while the harvest of spring wheat continues in the north-central portions of the country. Corn usually requires ample moisture until at least the middle of the month. In the upper Mississippi Valley the crop usually reaches the roasting-ear stage about the middle of August, or a little later; in Southern States early corn matures the latter part of the month. Cotton picking begins in the southern Cotton Belt during the first 10 days of August and advances by the latter part of the month to southern North Carolina, northern Alabama, and southern Oklahoma.

September

In September the recession of temperature becomes quite noticeable, amounting to 10° F. in the northern portion of the country; in the extreme South, however, September is only about 3° cooler than August. Because of this rapid fall in temperatures, killing frost occurs, on an average, early in the month in a few far northern sections of the country and over considerable areas at higher elevations in the West.

In the Great Plains States the dry season is approaching, with a monthly average of less than 2 inches of rainfall over much of the area. The heaviest average September rainfall is in the extreme Southeast, where the monthly amounts range from 6 to 8 inches. The rainy season also begins in the North Pacific area, some localities having an average of 4 to 6 inches.

Farm activities have to do largely with the harvesting of spring-planted crops and the preparation of soil for the seeding of winter grains. In the Winter Wheat Belt, especially the western sections, generous rains are desired to condition seedbeds properly. Seeding winter wheat begins in the extreme northern portion of the country during the first week in September, but the bulk of the crop is not sown until after the 10th of the month. In the South, cotton is being picked, and fortunately, except for heavy rainfall in the extreme Southeast, the fall season is the driest of the year in the Cotton Belt.

October

The midfall recession of temperatures in October is rapid, corresponding to the April, or midspring, rise. The October averages range from less than 45° F. in northern sections of the country to about 70° along the Gulf coast, or an average of about 13° cooler than September in the North and about 8° cooler in the South.

In an average year, killing frost may be expected by the first of October as far south as western Maryland, central Wisconsin, southern Minnesota, and central Nebraska, and by the close of the month in southern North Carolina, north-central Georgia and Alabama, central Mississippi, and south-central Oklahoma.

The average October rainfall is greatest in southern Florida and along the north Pacific coast, where the amounts range locally up to 10 inches. Occasional tropical storms, with attending excessive precipitation, account for the high monthly average in southeastern Florida, while the definite establishment of the rainy season results in heavy rainfall along the north Pacific coast. Over the Great Plains region there is a marked falling off in precipitation, much of the area having monthly averages of less than an inch.

The more important farm activities during October are the seeding of winter grains, the husking or picking of corn, and the harvesting of cotton and fruit. The threshing of spring grains is usually completed during the month, and also the seeding of winter wheat, rye, and oats in most sections. The bulk of the cotton crop is usually picked by the last of the month. Livestock remain on the range in most western districts but are frequently moved to lower levels, while in some localities cattle and sheep are driven to ranches.

November

East of the Rocky Mountains the average temperature for November ranges from about 25° F. in the North to 60° along the Gulf coast. Cold waves of considerable severity sometimes overspread the North Central States but usually lose energy rapidly in their eastward and southward progress and are seldom of long duration. Zero temperatures have never been recorded in November at a first-order Weather Bureau station south of the Ohio River, but freezing has occurred as far south as Tampa, Fla.

By November 1 killing frost occurs, on an average, nearly to the central portions of the eastern Gulf States, Arkansas, and Oklahoma, and by the end of the month to northern Florida and most of the immediate Gulf coast. In parts of the far Southwest and along the California coast, as well as in most of the Great Valley of California, killing frost does not occur, as a rule, during November.

East of the Rocky Mountains the heaviest rainfall occurs in the central and lower Mississippi Valley, where the normals for limited areas are slightly more than 4 inches. The Great Plains States, as a rule, have less than an inch of precipitation, but in the Pacific coast area the rainy season becomes fully established, with some northern localities having an average of about 20 inches for the month. In the southern end of the Great Valley of California, however, rainfall continues light, the normal being less than an inch. This is the month of maximum rainfall in some north Pacific sections.

The more important farm activities in November are gathering corn, picking and ginning cotton, and marketing potatoes and fall truck crops. In southern sections the seeding of winter grains and the planting of fall and winter gardens continue. The digging of sugar beets is still in progress in the Rocky Mountain and plateau districts, and by the close of the month the bulk of the crop has been delivered to factories. In most of the western-range sections livestock are usually moved from the higher levels to the lower plains or to feed lots. In the north Pacific area pastures usually are greatly improved because of the increased rainfall.

December

The recession in temperature is not so rapid in December as in the preceding fall months, although it is rather marked in the Northern States. The December means range from about 10° F. in the most northern north-central districts to about 55° along the Gulf coast and 70° in the most southern part of Florida. Cold waves usually become more frequent and severe in the interior of the country, and very low temperatures occur occasionally. Readings of −50° have been recorded in some northwestern sections, and subzero weather has occurred as far south as Kansas, Missouri, Tennessee, and North Carolina. Along the central and east Gulf coast the average date of the first killing frost in the fall is about December 1, some 3 months later than in localities of the most northern part of the United States.

East of the Rocky Mountains, heavy precipitation occurs in the lower Mississippi Valley and southern Appalachian Mountain districts. In Florida, however, the dry season is on, while in some of the Great Plains States the monthly average is only about one-half of an inch. Rainfall is heavy in the north Pacific area and in northern Rocky Mountain sections. Heavy snows frequently occur in the elevated regions of the more western States, with occasional heavy falls in Michigan and the interior of the Northeast. December has the fewest thunderstorms of any month of the year.

Throughout the central and northern sections of the country there is, as a rule, little farm activity during December. The marketing of farm products continues active, and, when the weather permits, some shock corn husking is accomplished. Much citrus fruit is usually harvested in Florida, and the harvesting of oranges, olives, and winter truck goes forward in California. This is a critical frost month in the citrus districts of Florida, Texas, and California.

Climates of the United States

(46 MAPS)

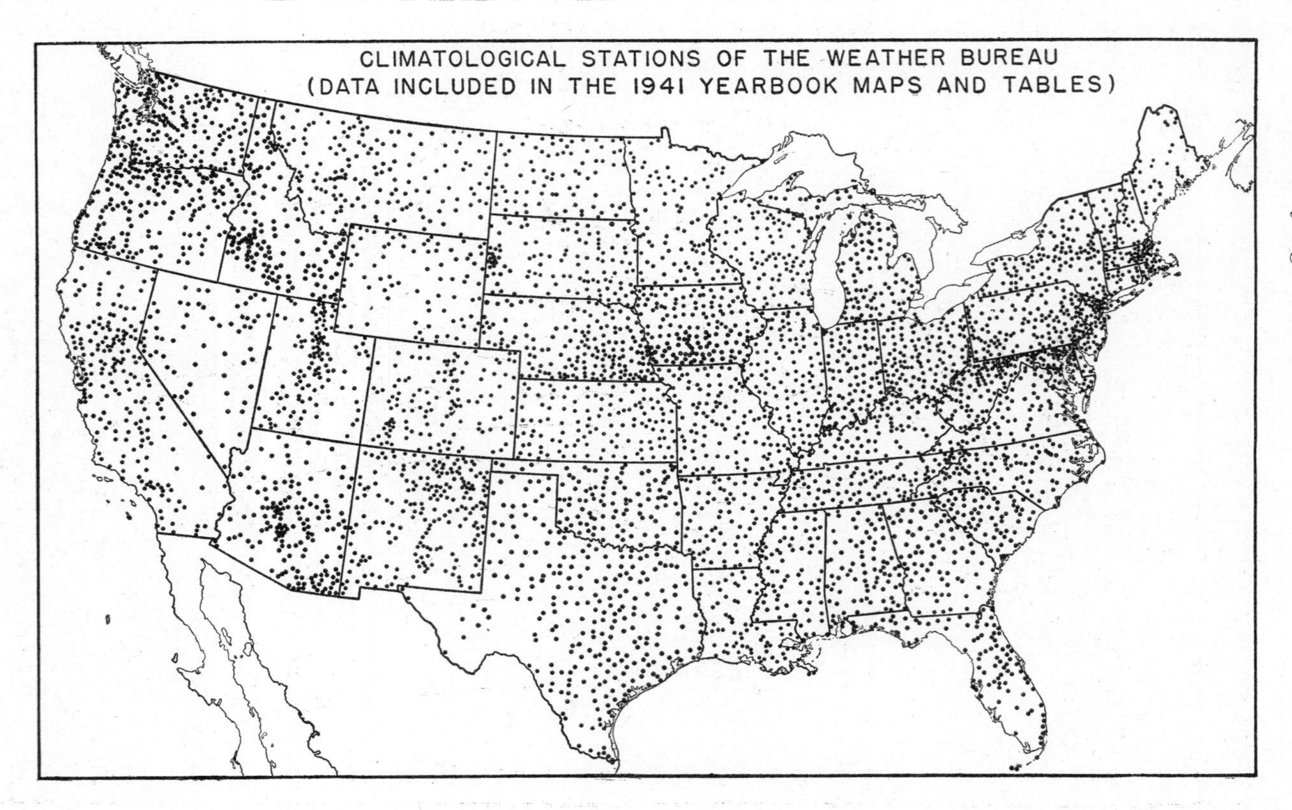
CLIMATOLOGICAL STATIONS OF THE WEATHER BUREAU
(DATA INCLUDED IN THE 1941 YEARBOOK MAPS AND TABLES)

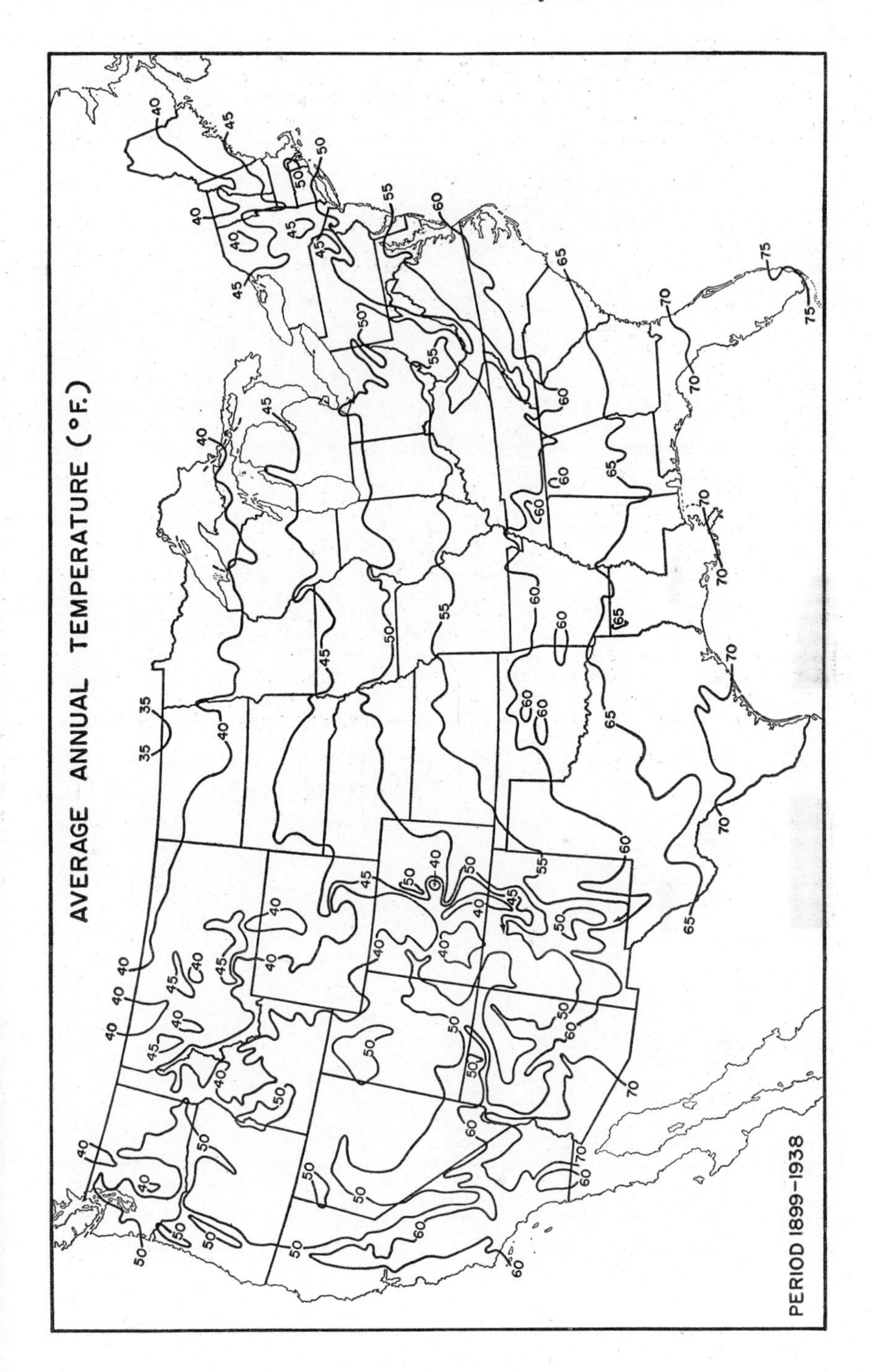
AVERAGE ANNUAL TEMPERATURE (°F.)
PERIOD 1899–1938

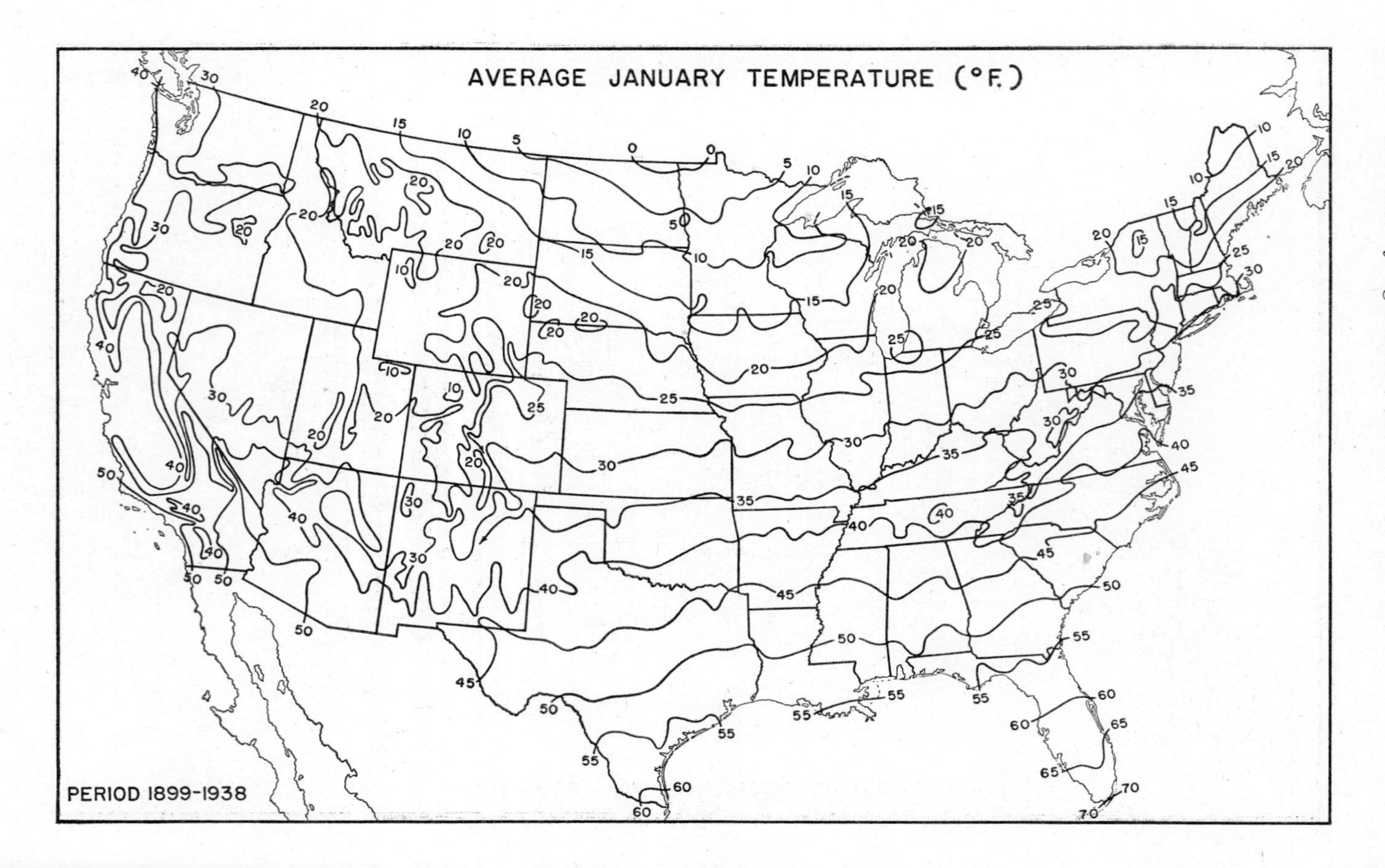
AVERAGE JANUARY TEMPERATURE (°F.)
PERIOD 1899-1938

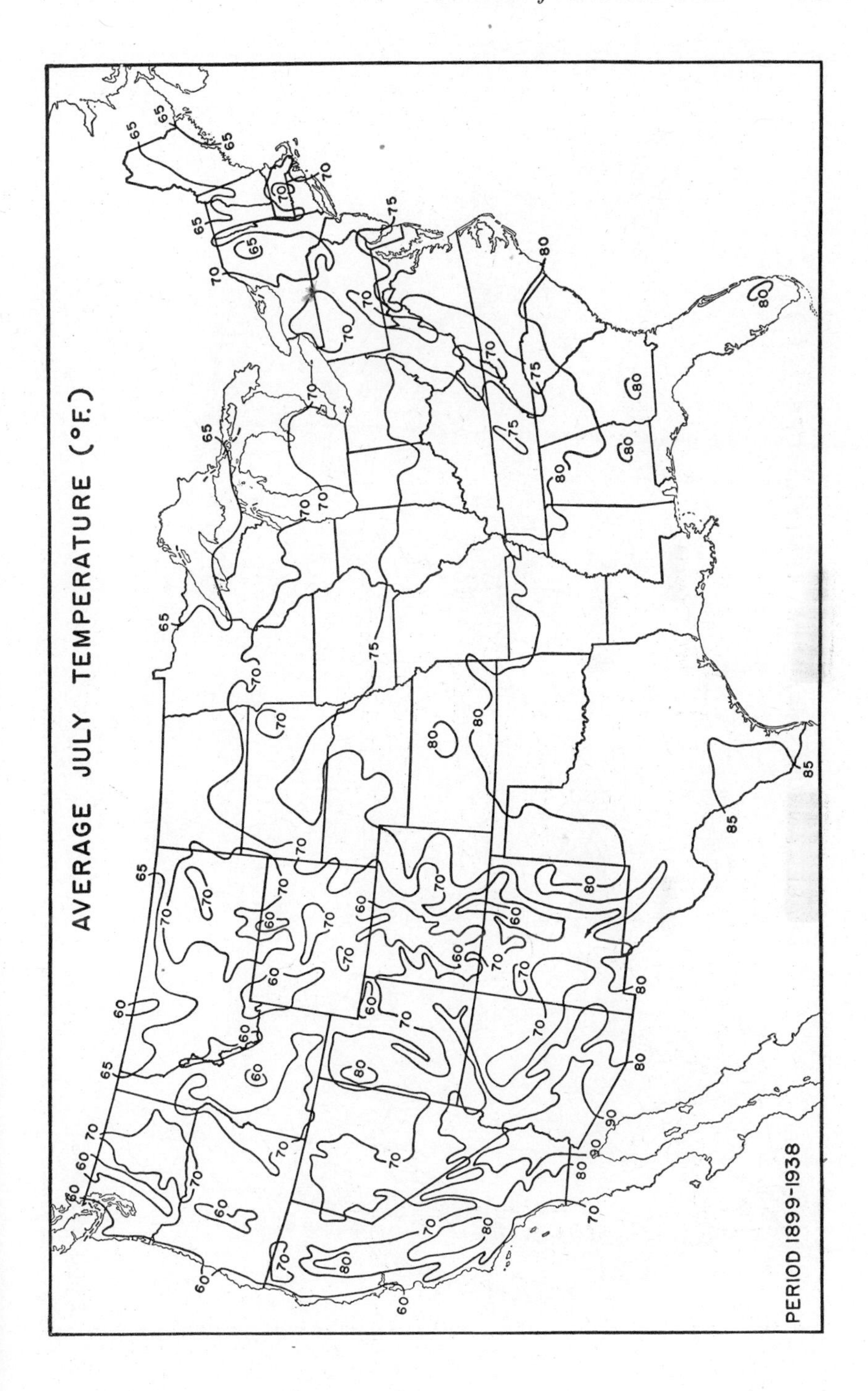
AVERAGE JULY TEMPERATURE (°F.)
PERIOD 1899-1938

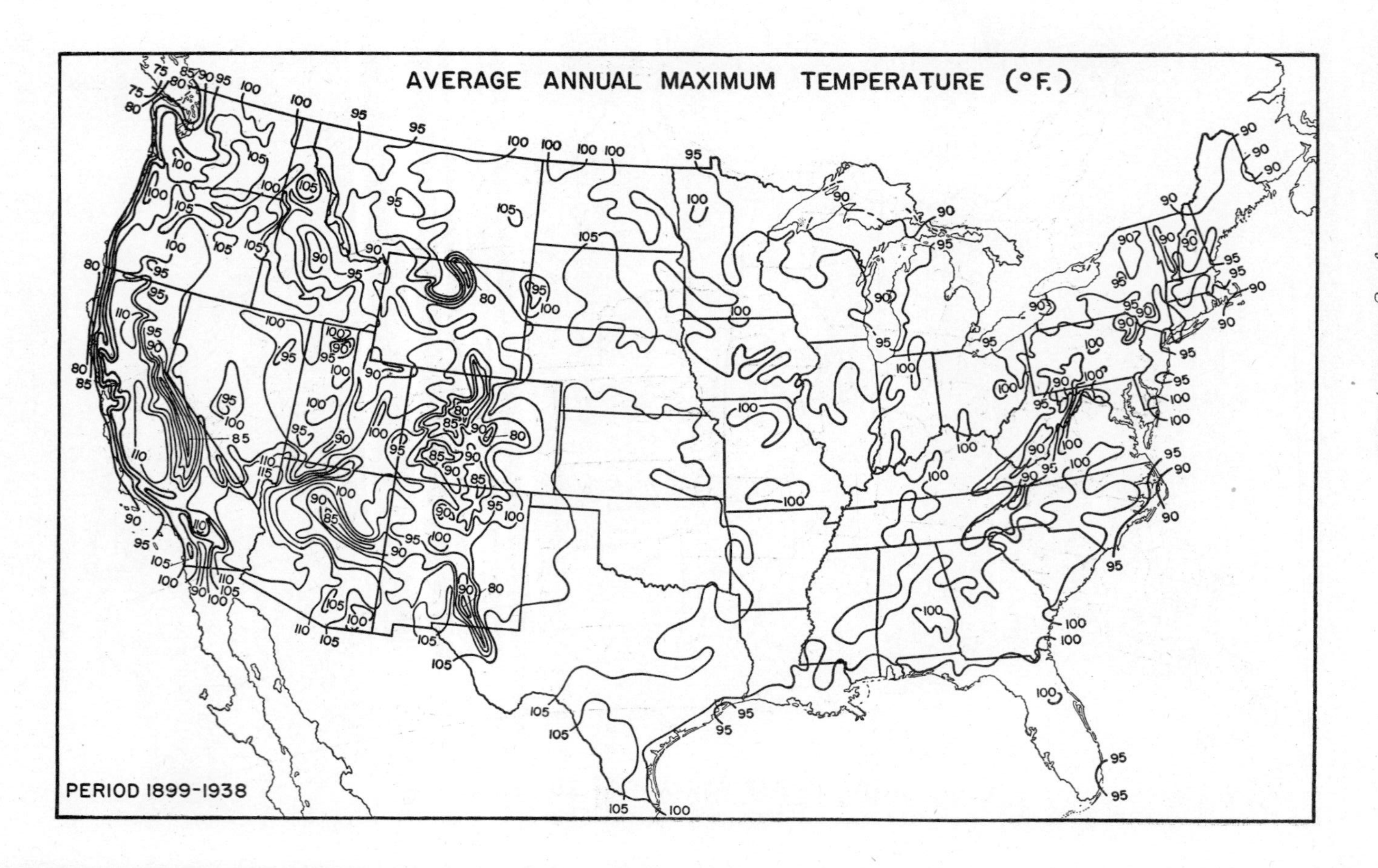
AVERAGE ANNUAL MAXIMUM TEMPERATURE (°F.)
PERIOD 1899-1938

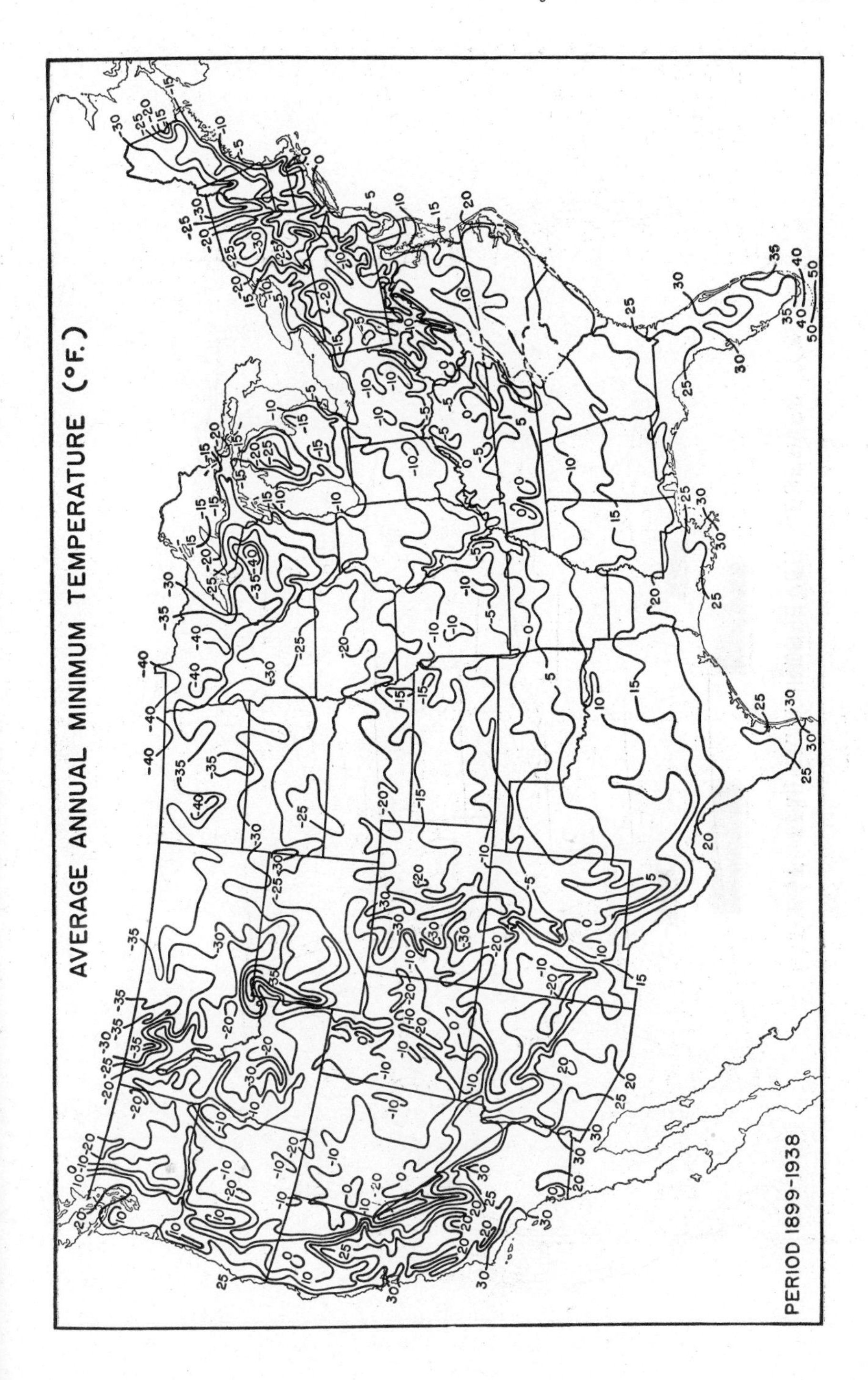
AVERAGE ANNUAL MINIMUM TEMPERATURE (°F.)
PERIOD 1899-1938

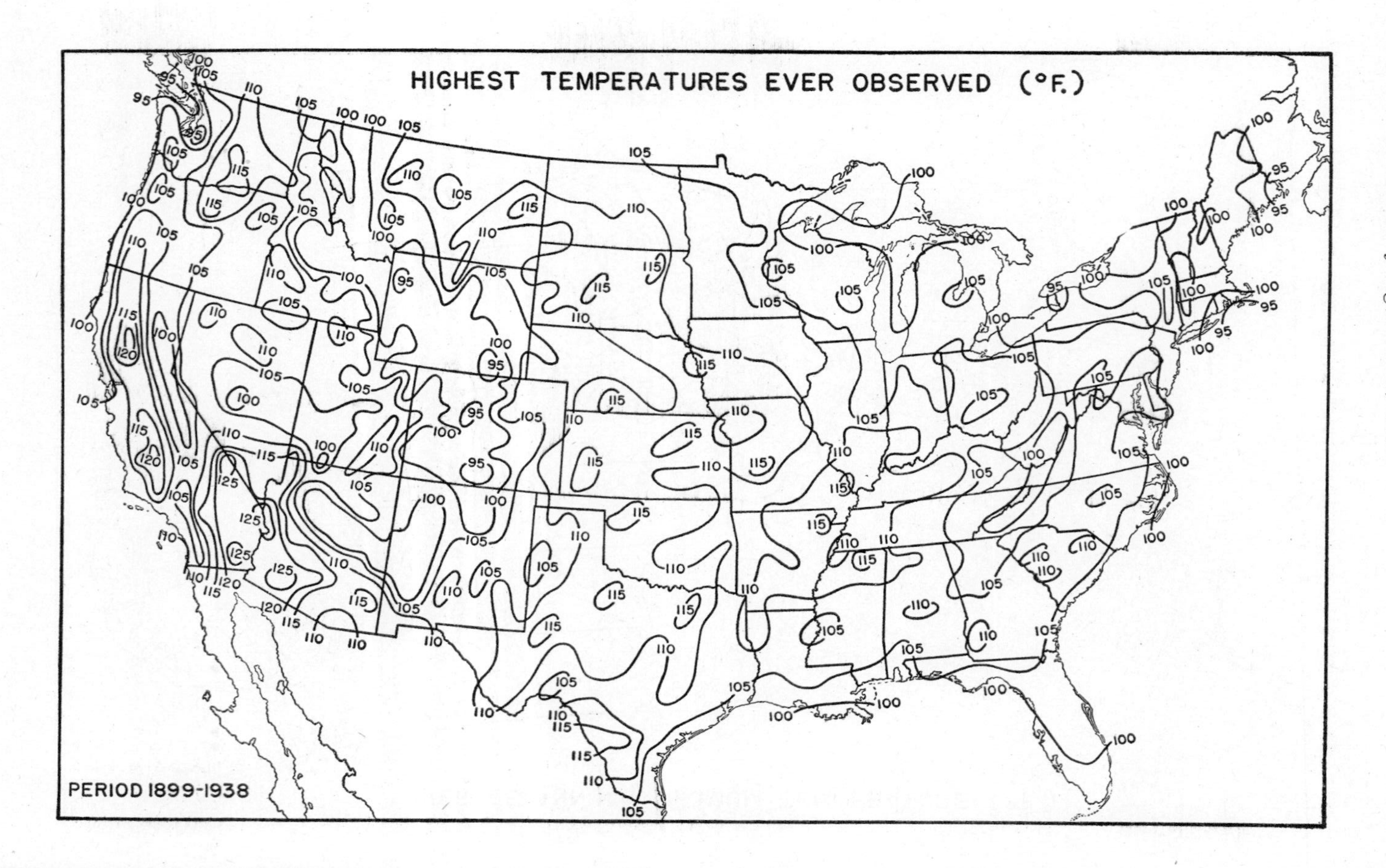
HIGHEST TEMPERATURES EVER OBSERVED (°F.)
PERIOD 1899-1938

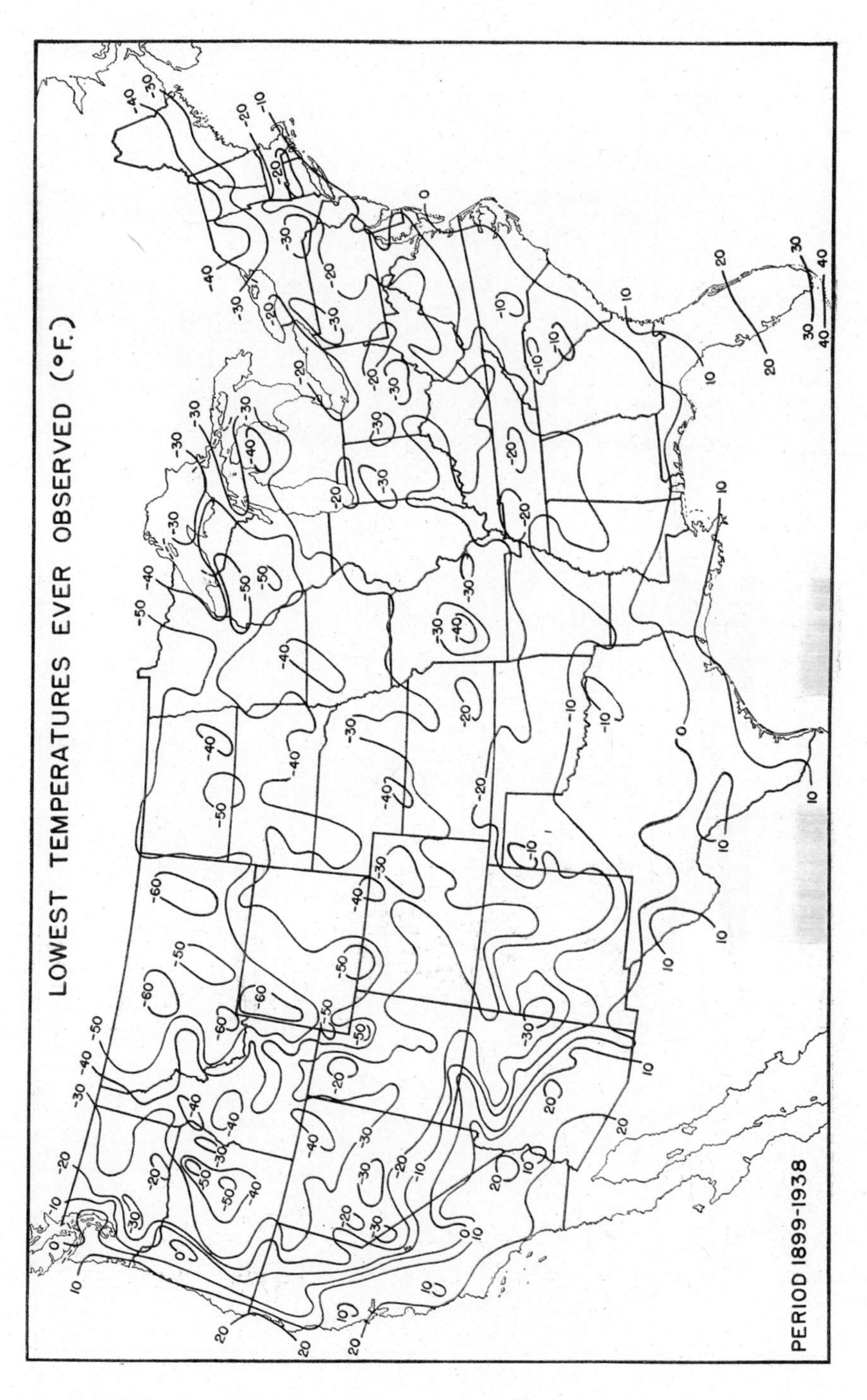
LOWEST TEMPERATURES EVER OBSERVED (°F.)
PERIOD 1899-1938

298737°—41——46

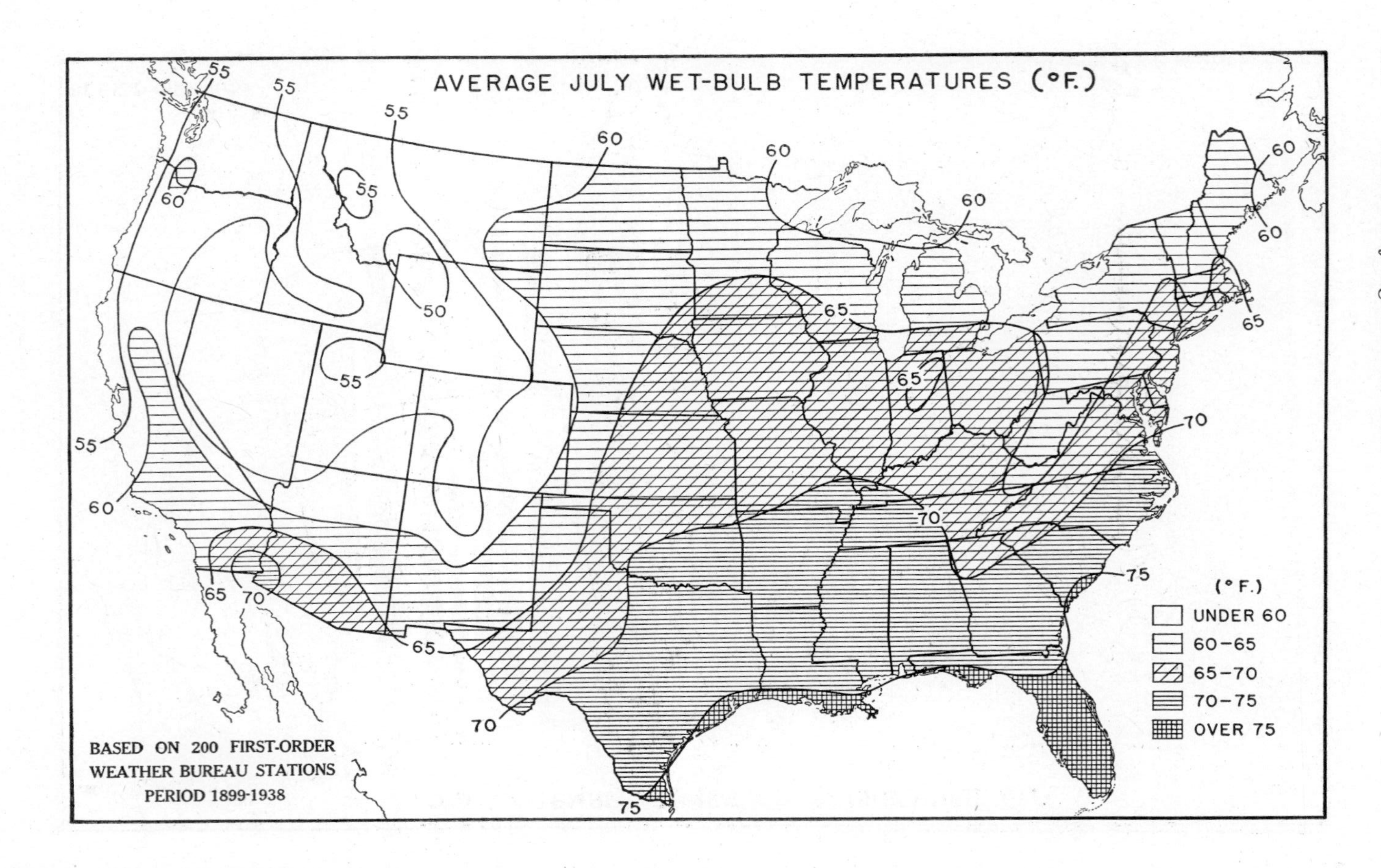
AVERAGE JULY WET-BULB TEMPERATURES (°F.)
(°F.)
UNDER 60
60–65
65–70
70–75
OVER 75
BASED ON 200 FIRST-ORDER
WEATHER BUREAU STATIONS
PERIOD 1899-1938

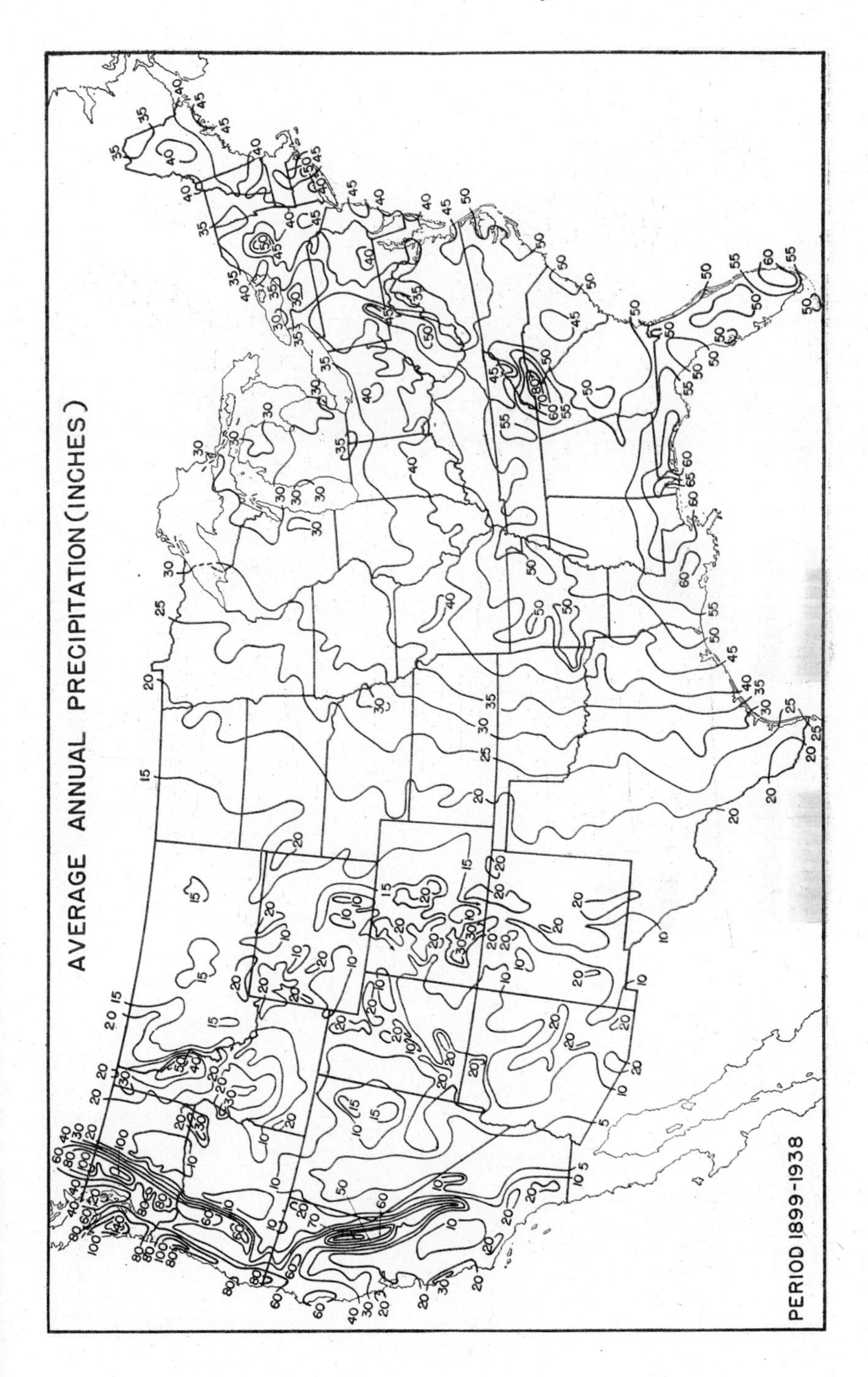
AVERAGE ANNUAL PRECIPITATION (INCHES)
PERIOD 1899-1938

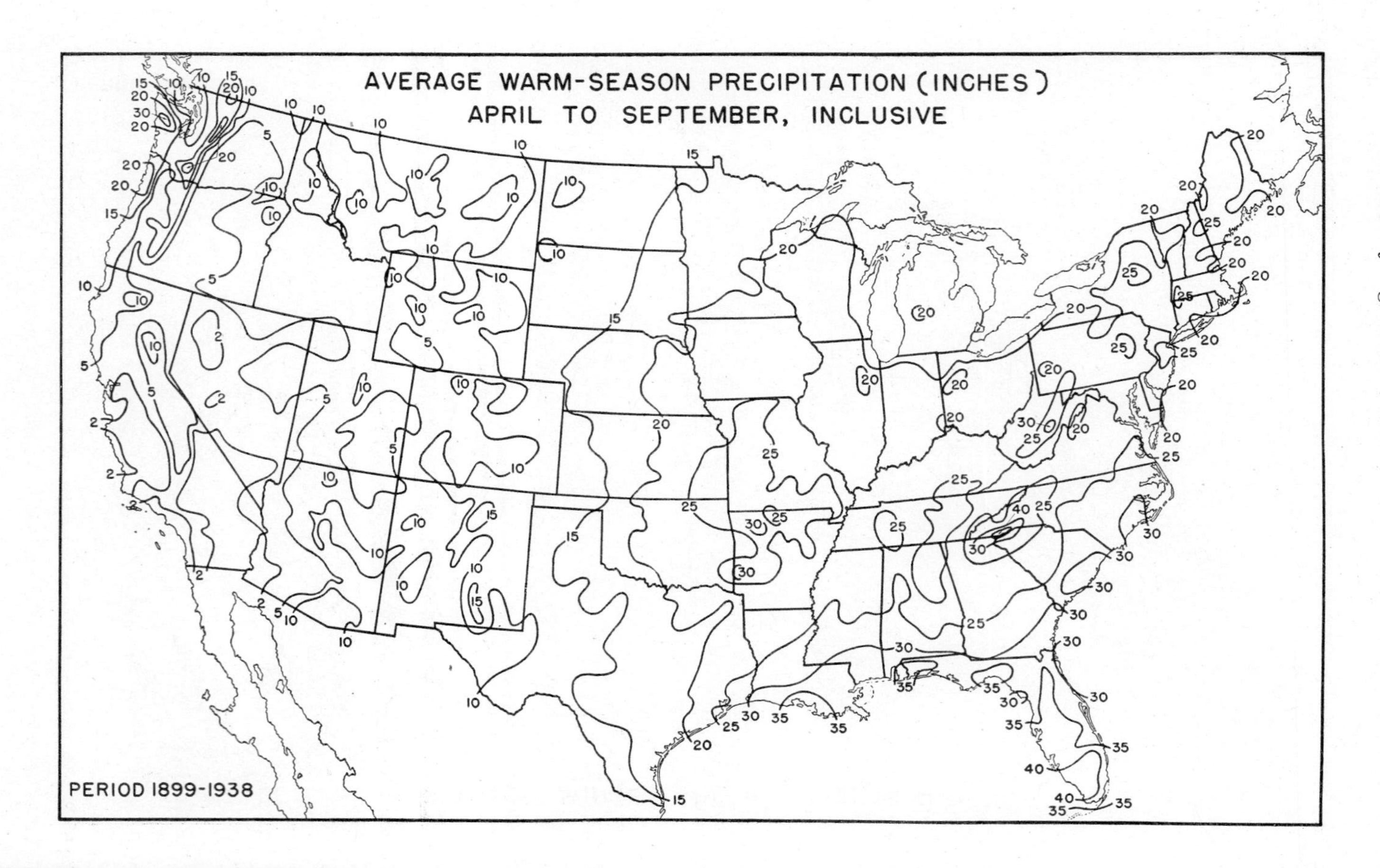
AVERAGE WARM-SEASON PRECIPITATION (INCHES)
APRIL TO SEPTEMBER, INCLUSIVE
PERIOD 1899-1938

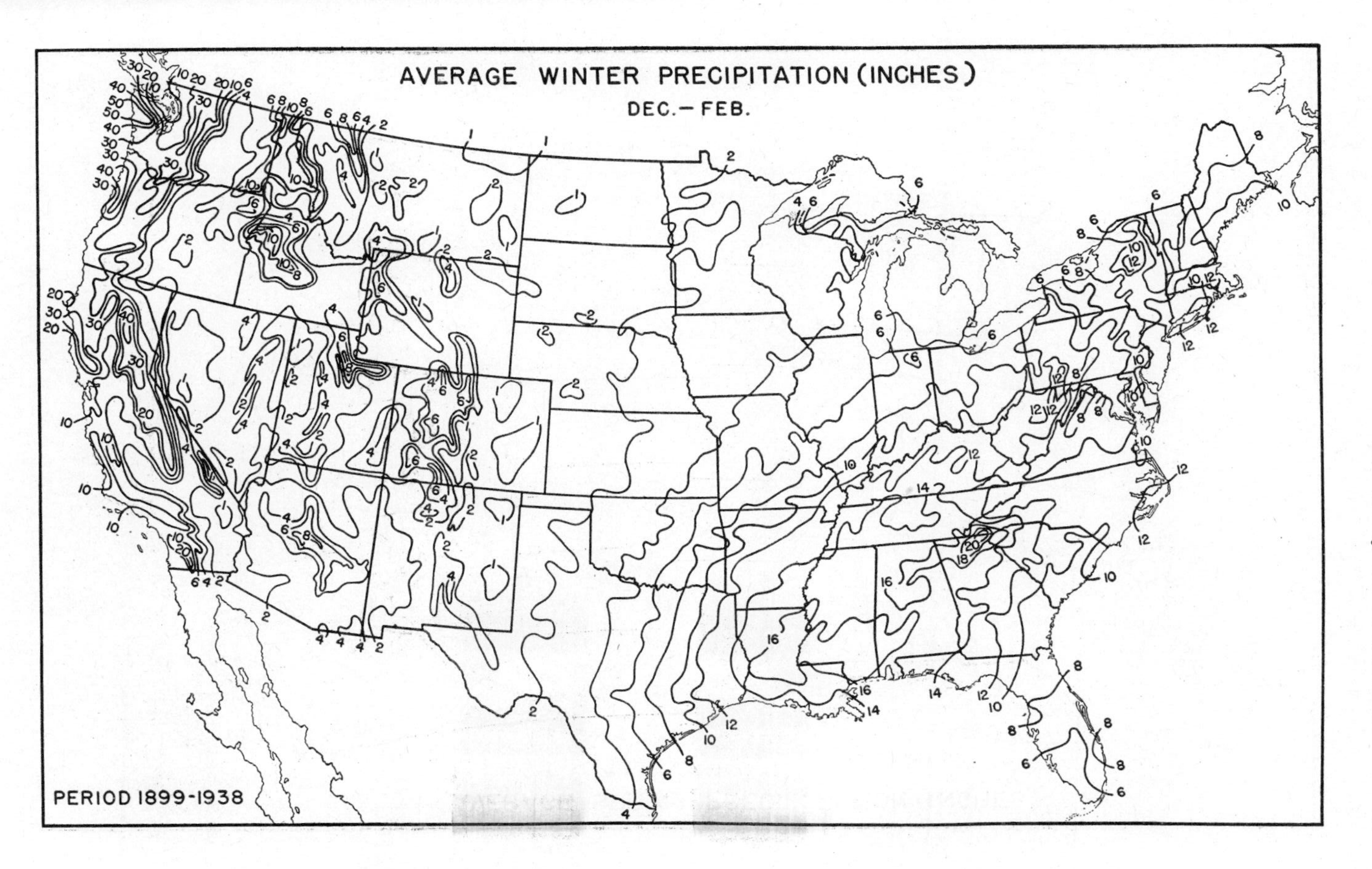
AVERAGE WINTER PRECIPITATION (INCHES)
DEC.–FEB.
PERIOD 1899-1938

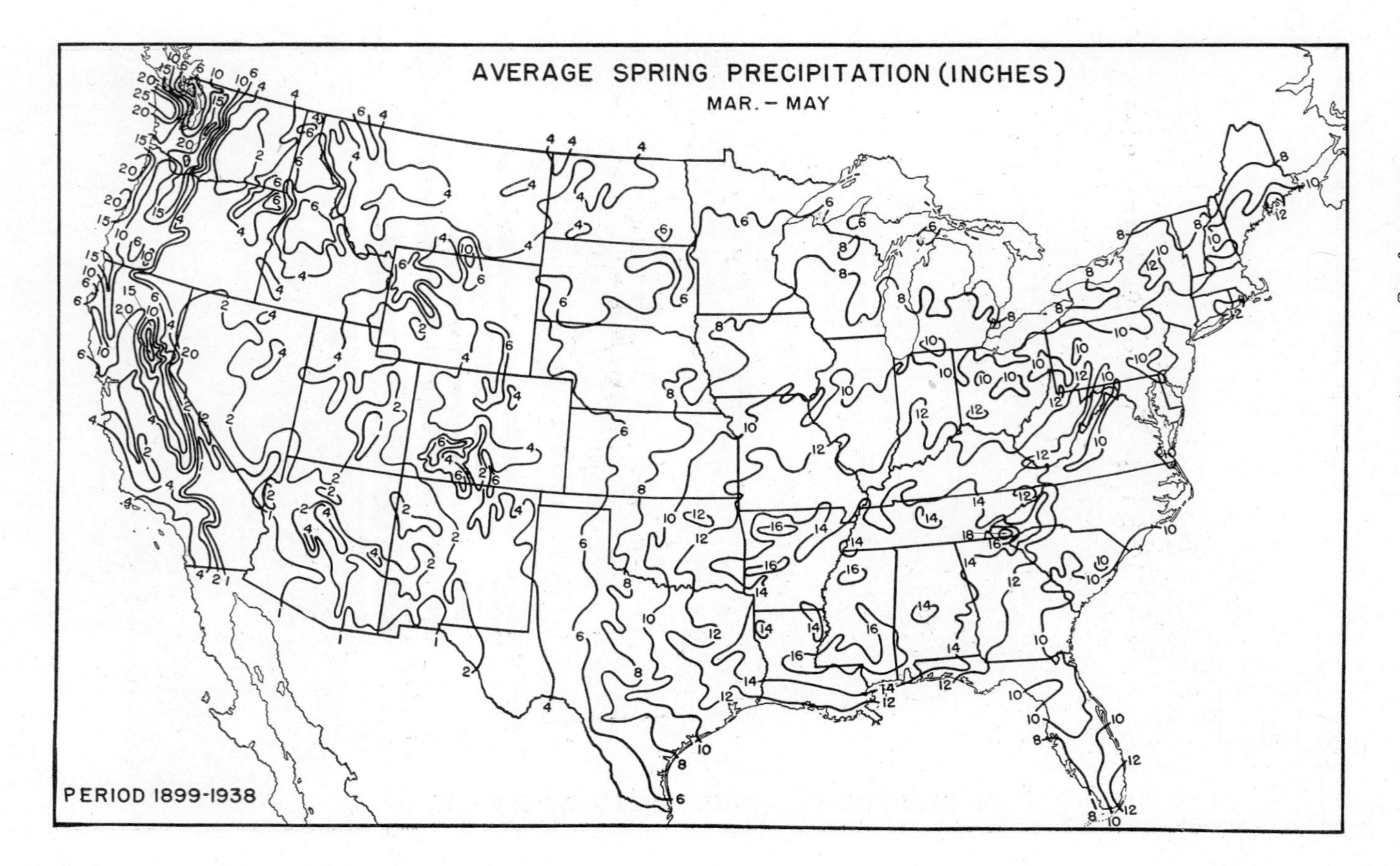
AVERAGE SPRING PRECIPITATION (INCHES)
MAR. – MAY
PERIOD 1899-1938

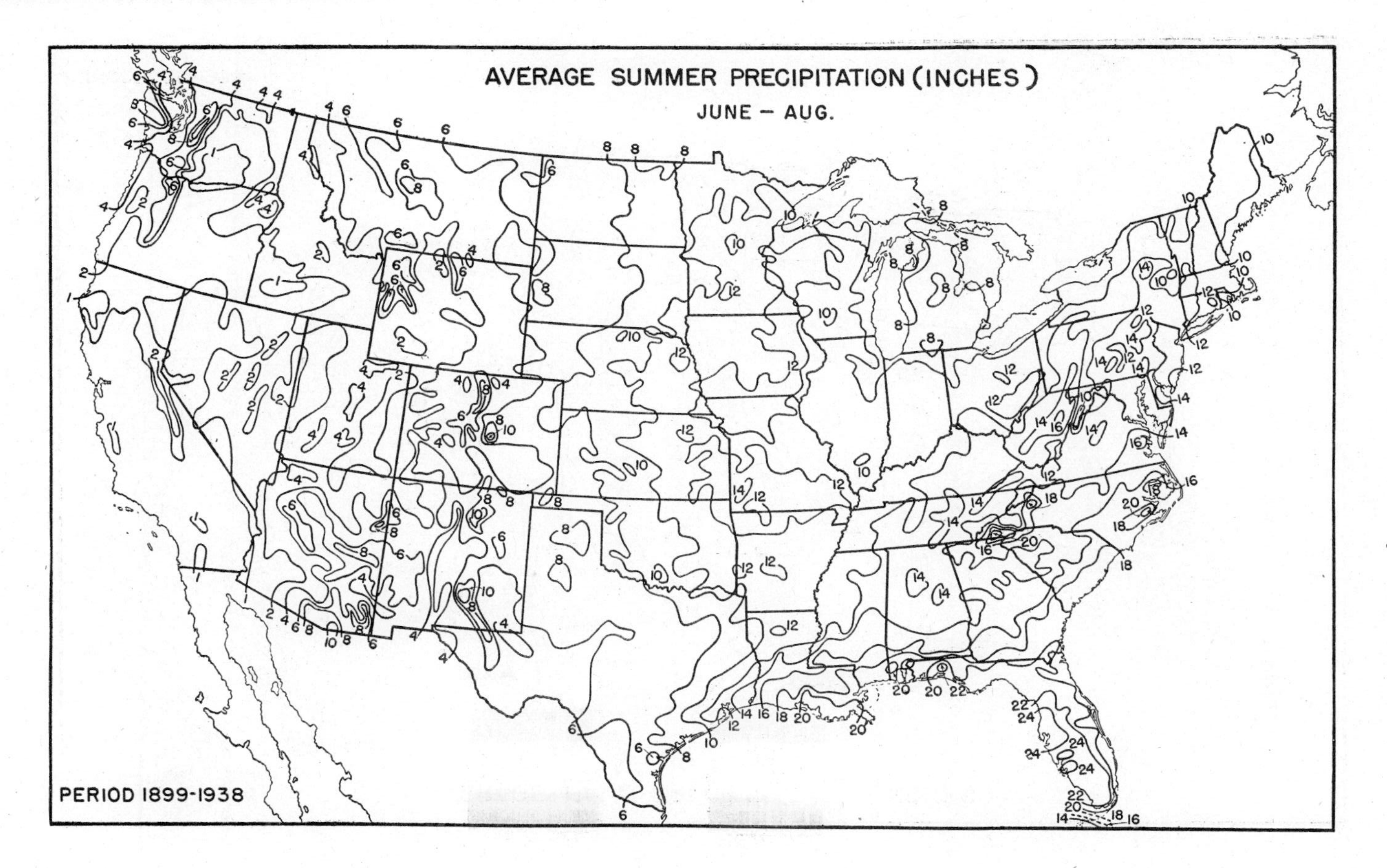
AVERAGE SUMMER PRECIPITATION (INCHES)
JUNE – AUG.
PERIOD 1899-1938

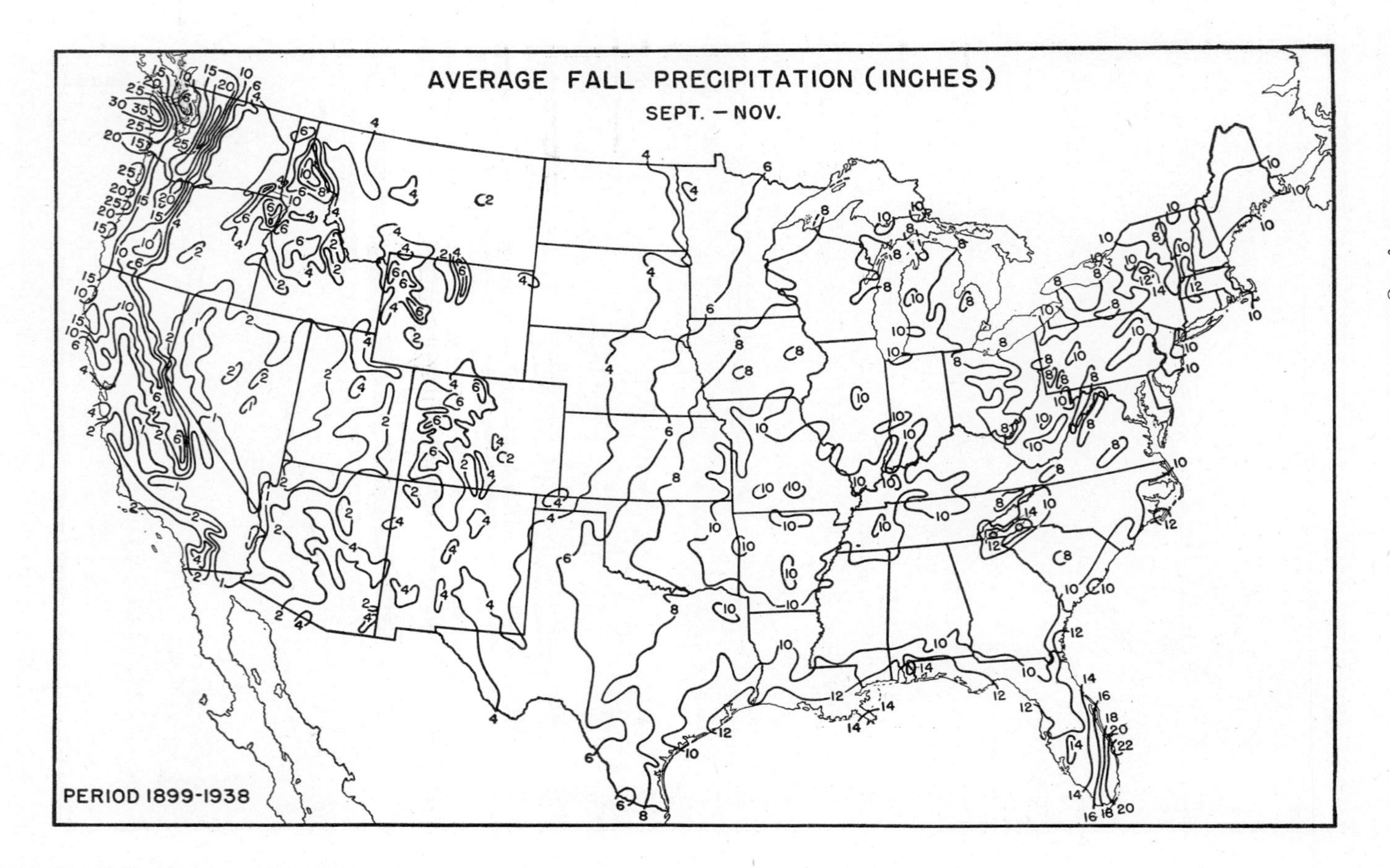
AVERAGE FALL PRECIPITATION (INCHES)
SEPT. – NOV.
PERIOD 1899-1938

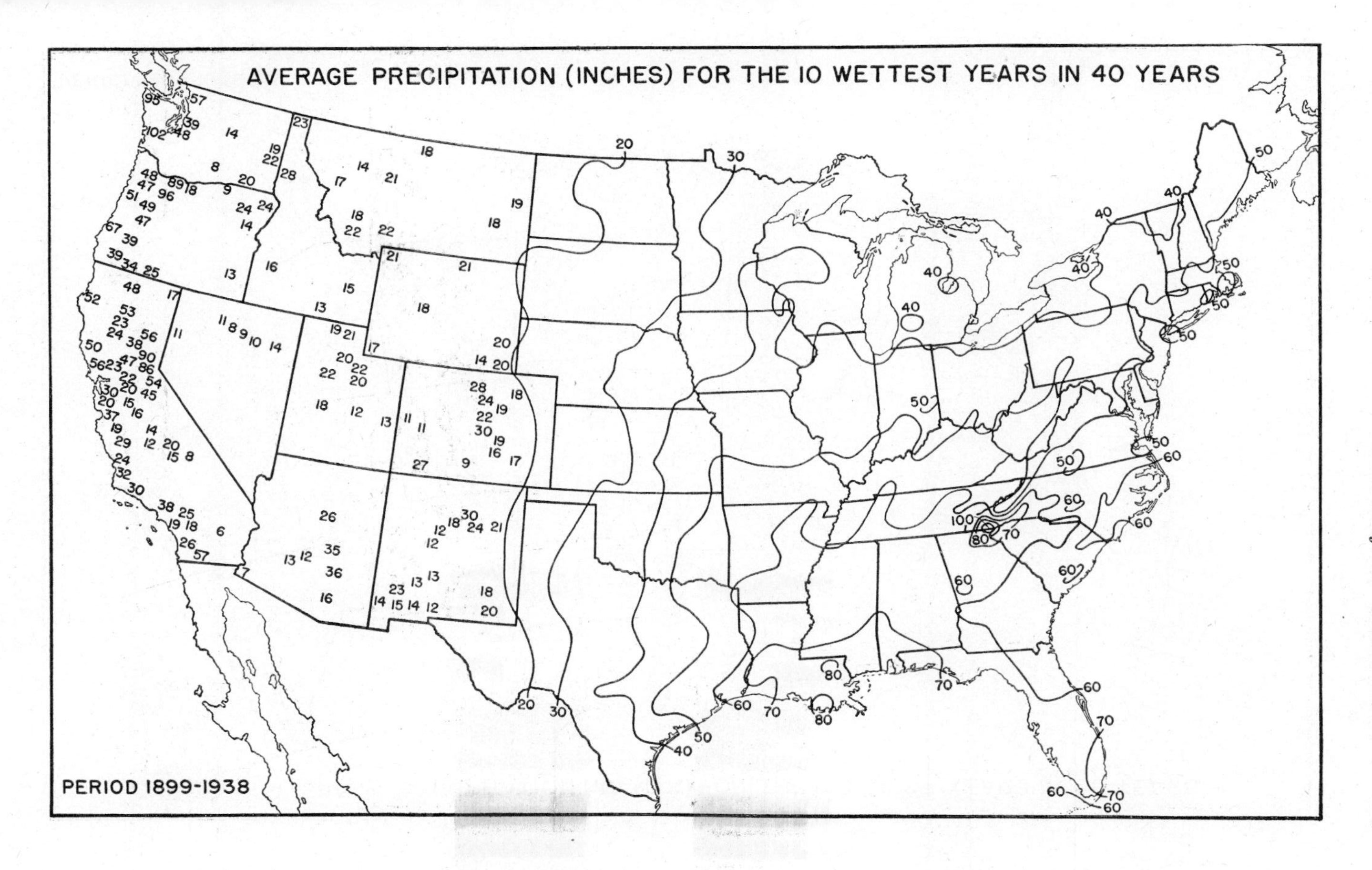
AVERAGE PRECIPITATION (INCHES) FOR THE 10 WETTEST YEARS IN 40 YEARS
PERIOD 1899-1938

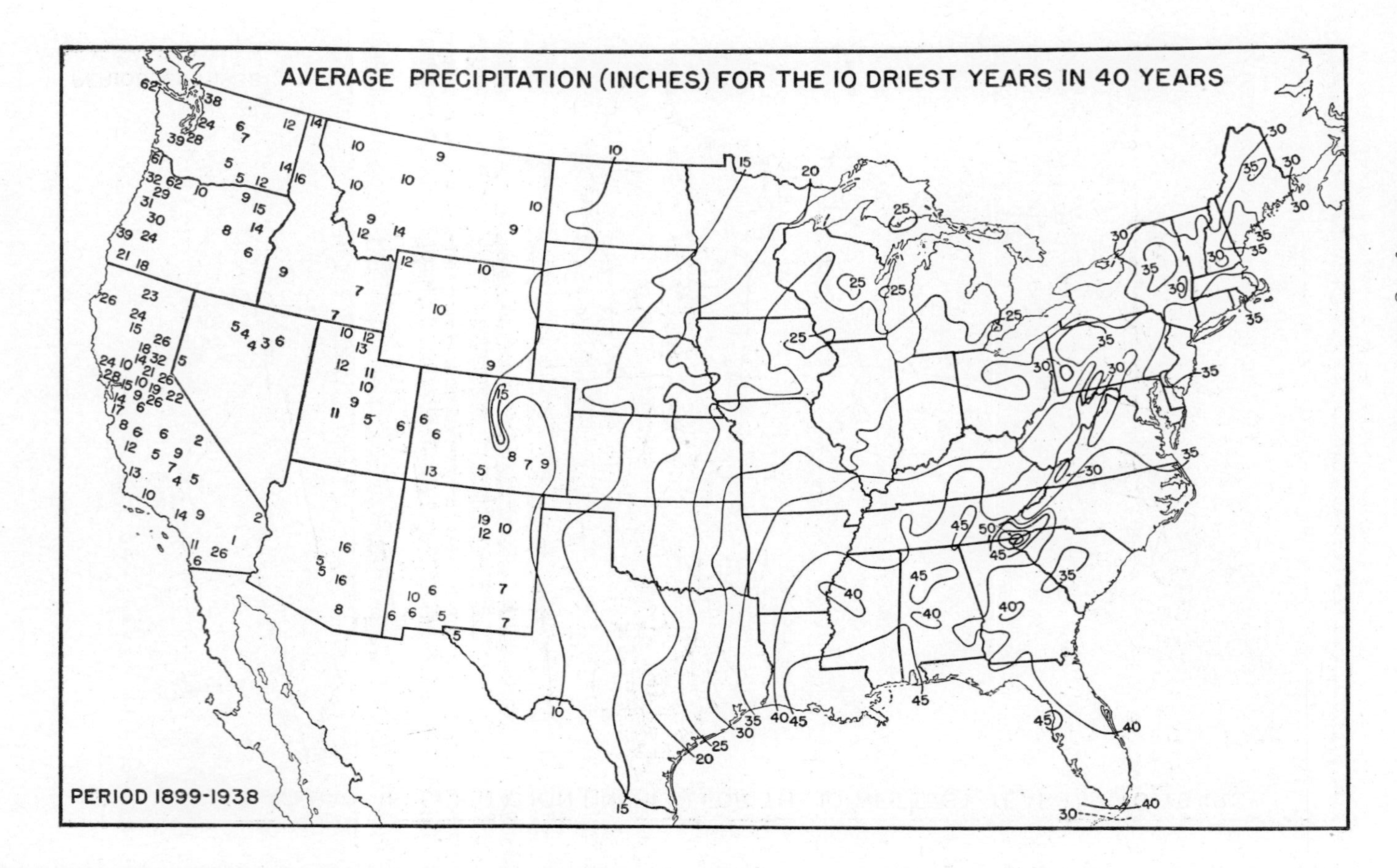
AVERAGE PRECIPITATION (INCHES) FOR THE 10 DRIEST YEARS IN 40 YEARS
PERIOD 1899-1938

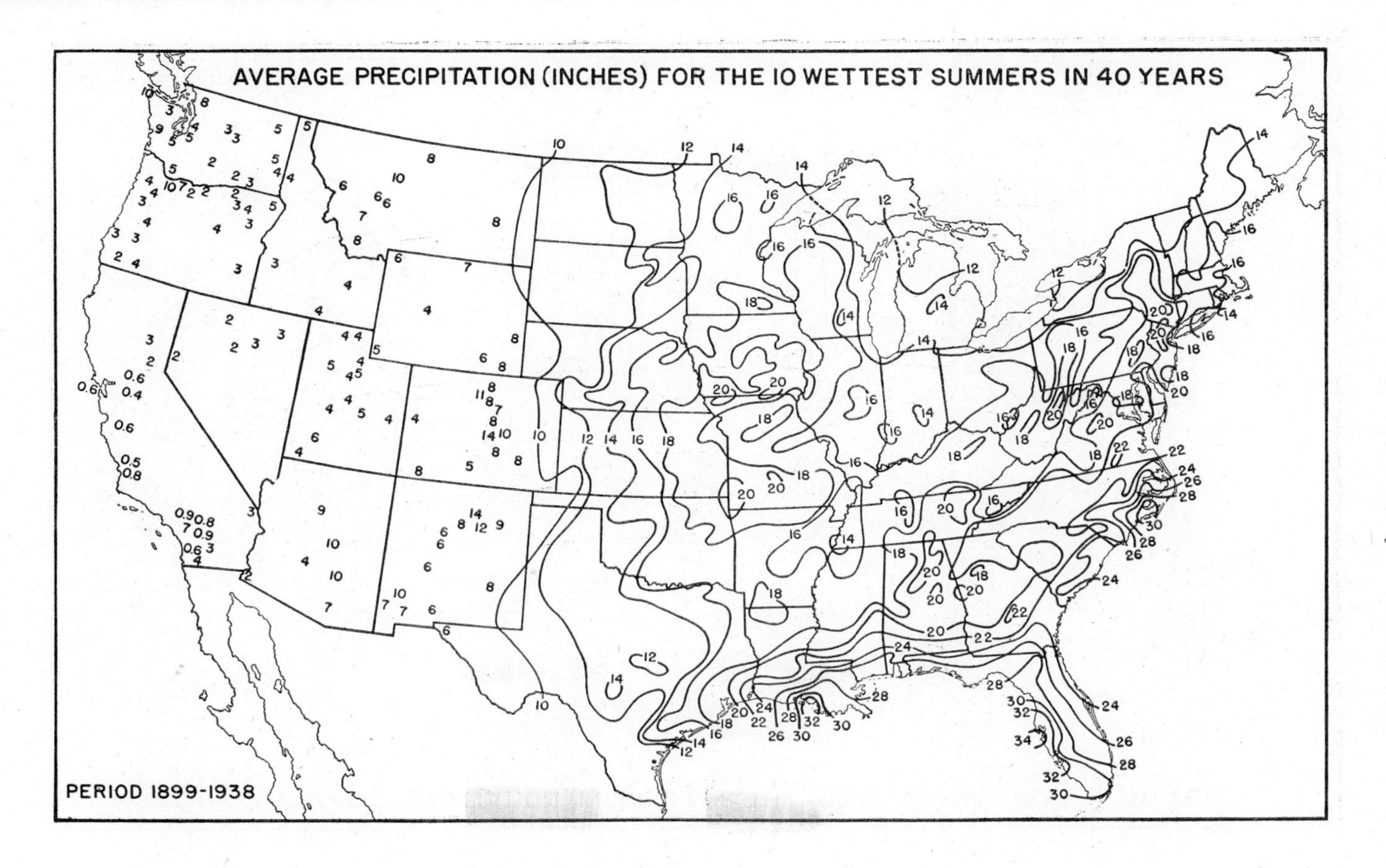
AVERAGE PRECIPITATION (INCHES) FOR THE 10 WETTEST SUMMERS IN 40 YEARS
PERIOD 1899-1938

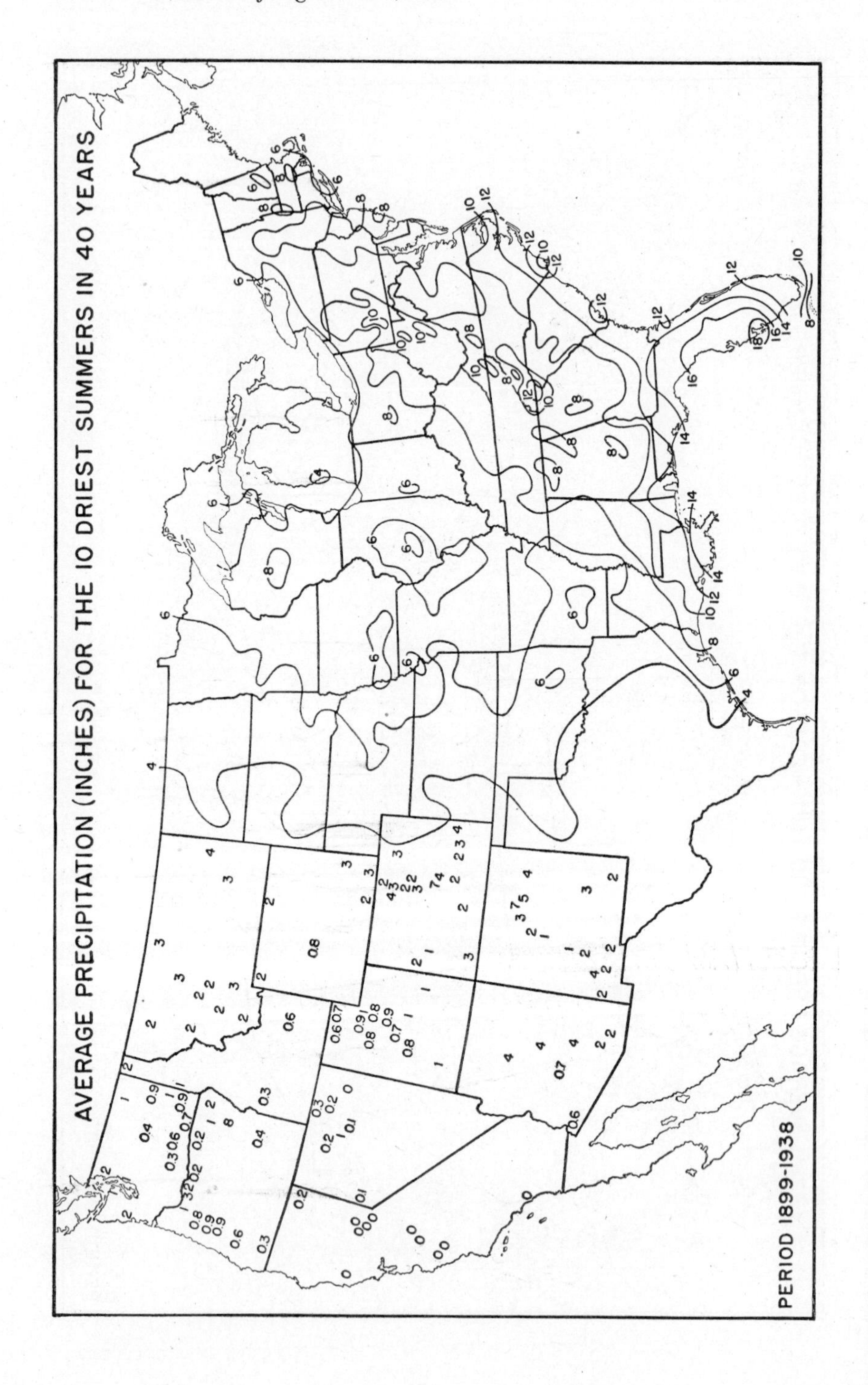
AVERAGE PRECIPITATION (INCHES) FOR THE 10 DRIEST SUMMERS IN 40 YEARS
PERIOD 1899-1938

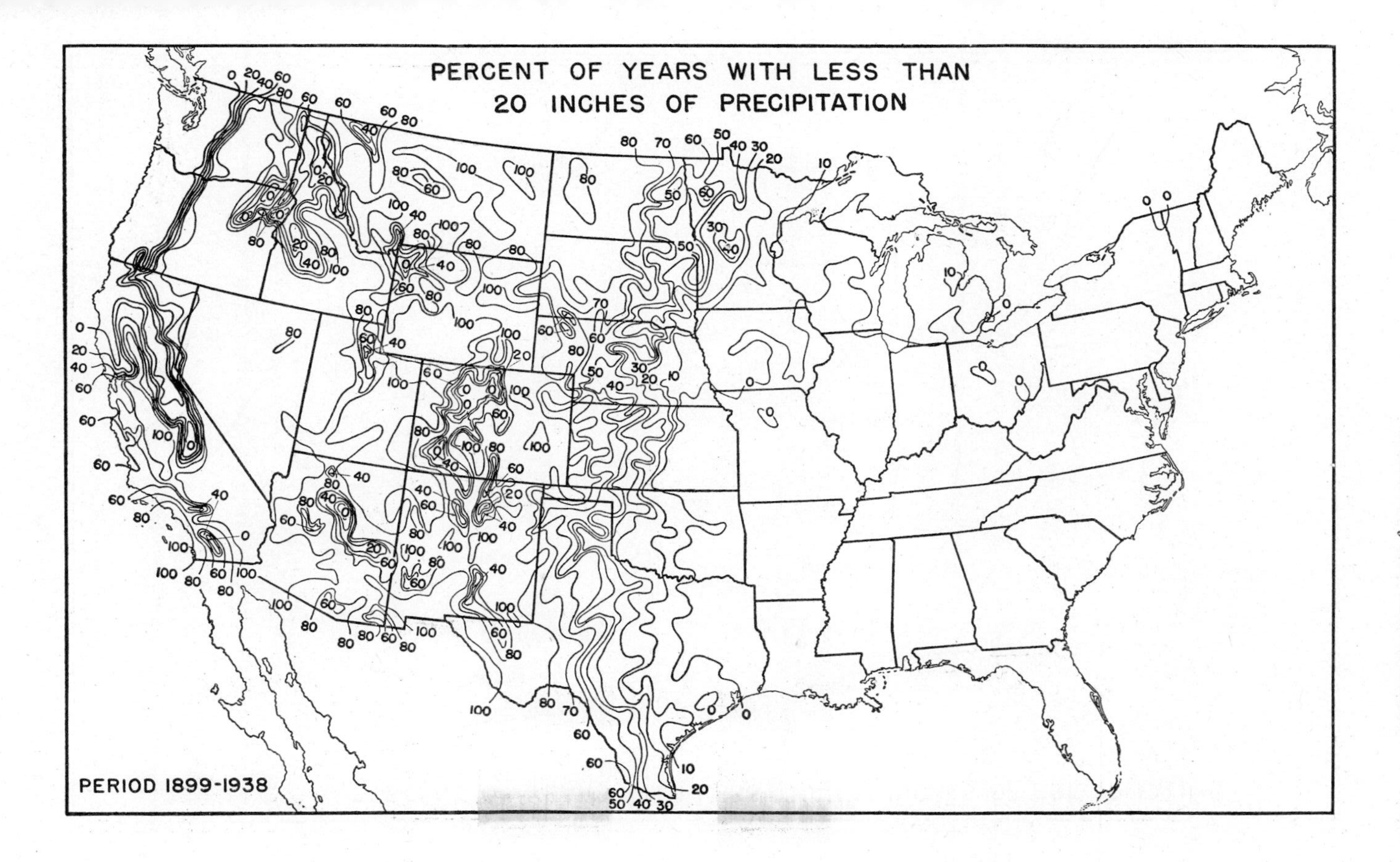
PERCENT OF YEARS WITH LESS THAN
20 INCHES OF PRECIPITATION
PERIOD 1899-1938

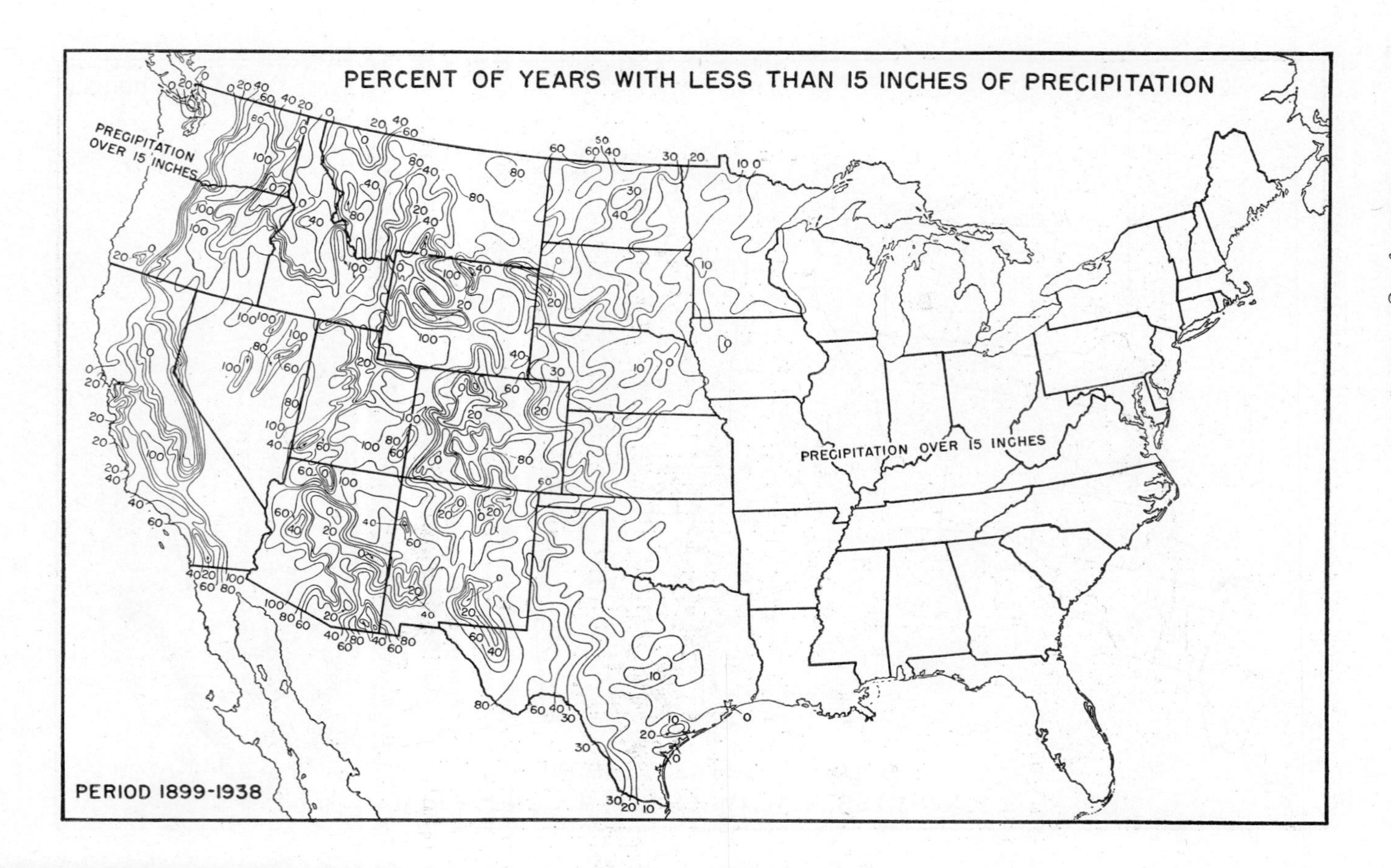
PERCENT OF YEARS WITH LESS THAN 15 INCHES OF PRECIPITATION
PRECIPITATION OVER 15 INCHES
PRECIPITATION OVER 15 INCHES
PERIOD 1899-1938

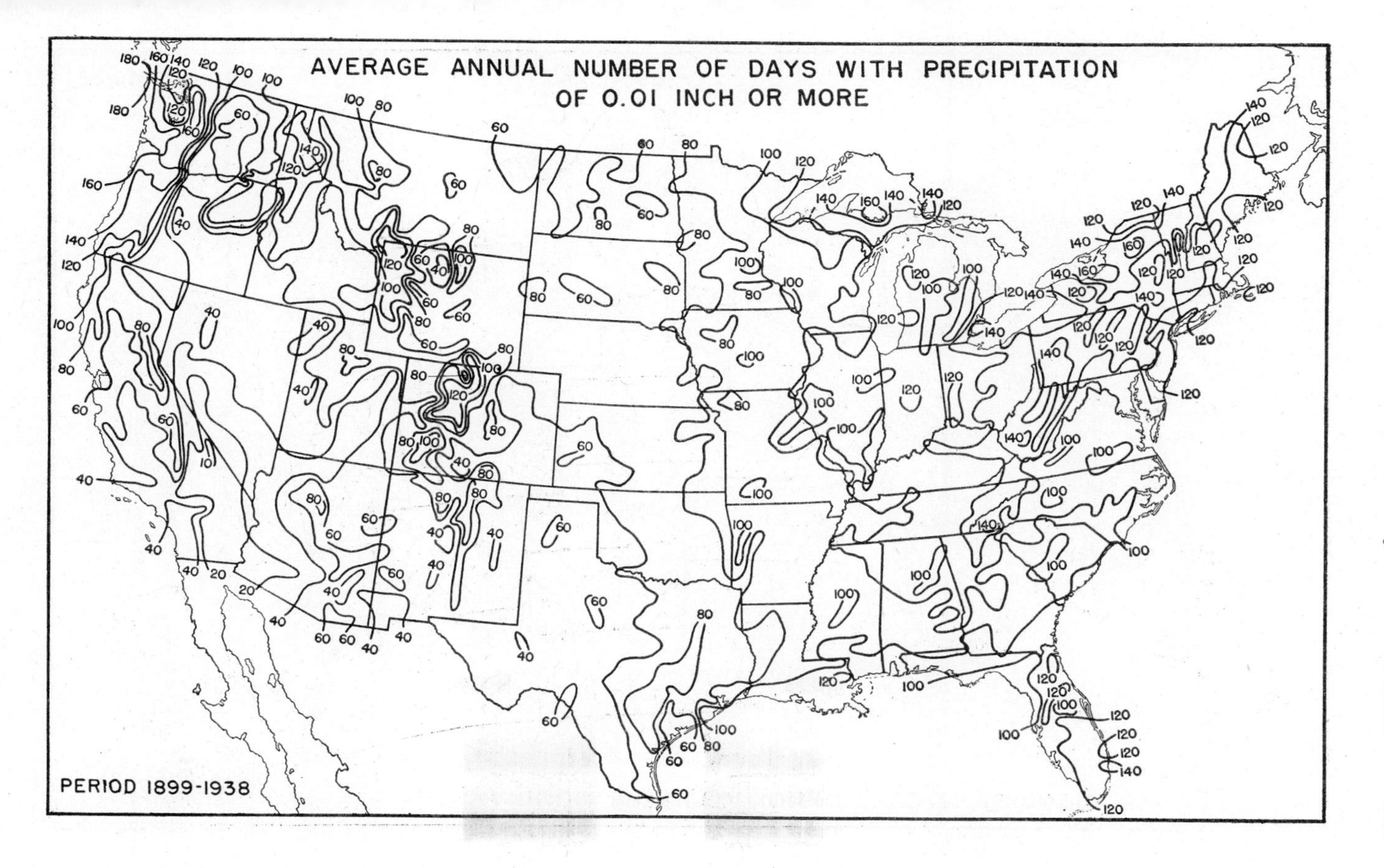
AVERAGE ANNUAL NUMBER OF DAYS WITH PRECIPITATION
OF 0.01 INCH OR MORE
PERIOD 1899-1938

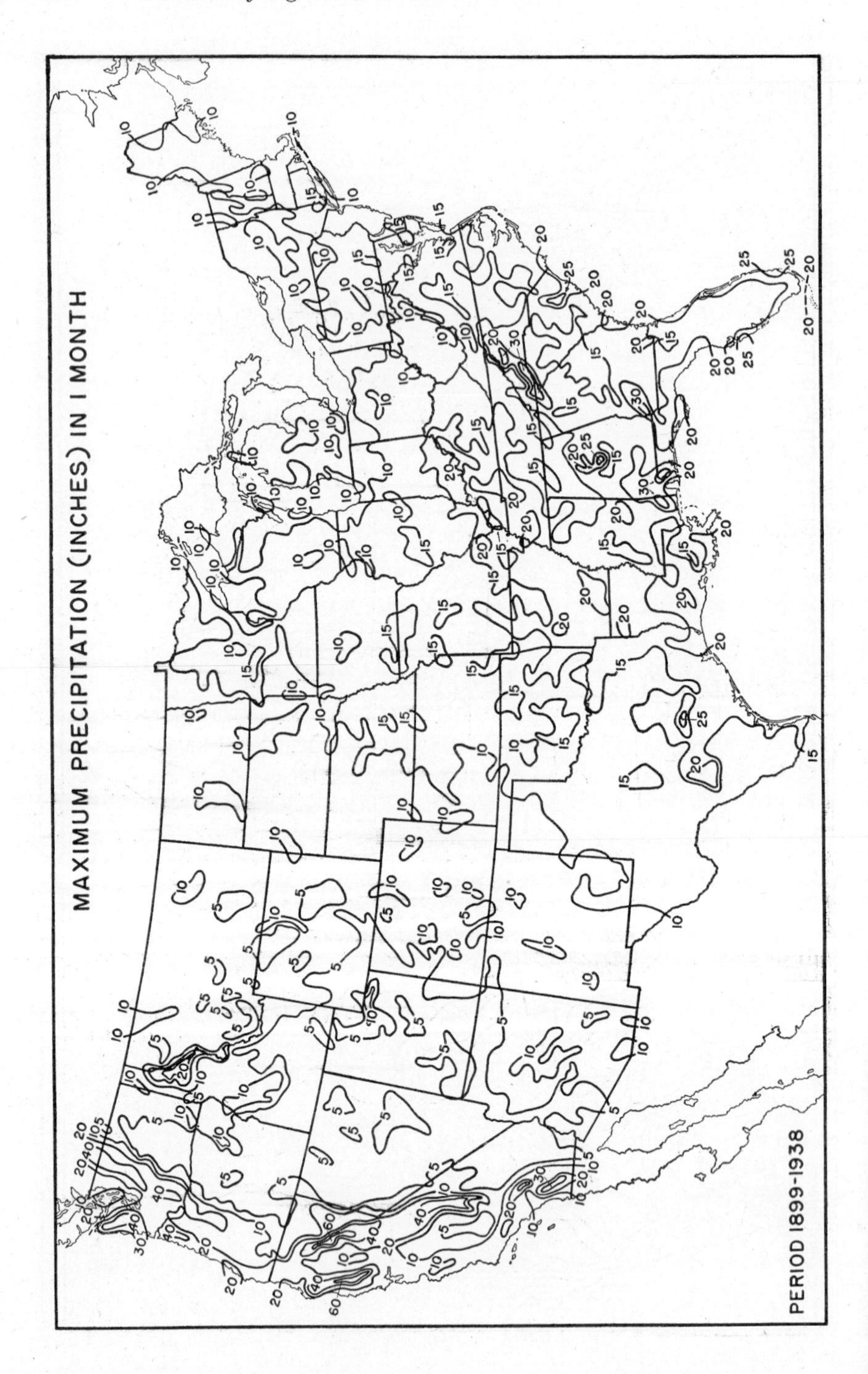
MAXIMUM PRECIPITATION (INCHES) IN 1 MONTH
PERIOD 1899-1938

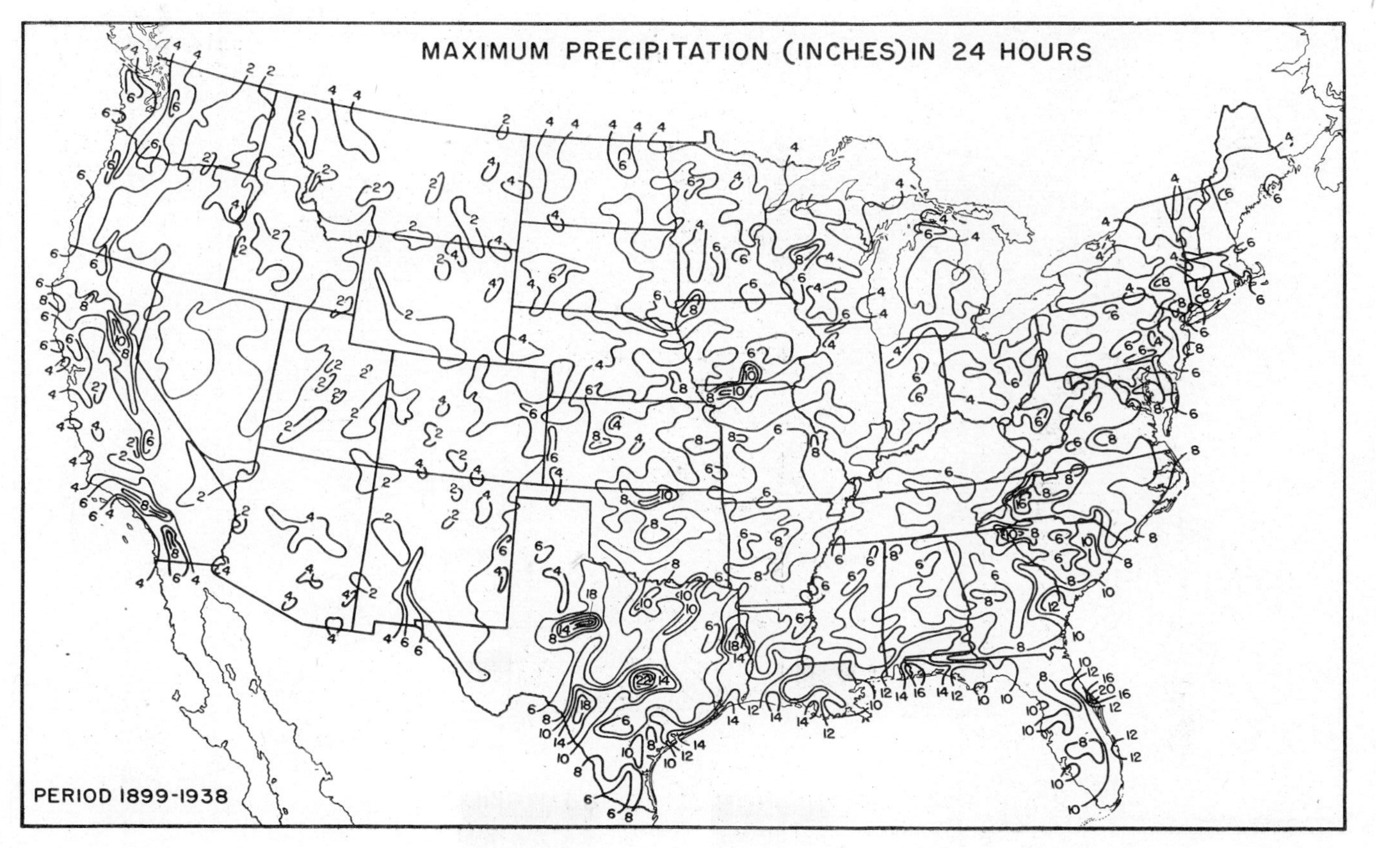
MAXIMUM PRECIPITATION (INCHES) IN 24 HOURS
PERIOD 1899-1938

298737°—41——47

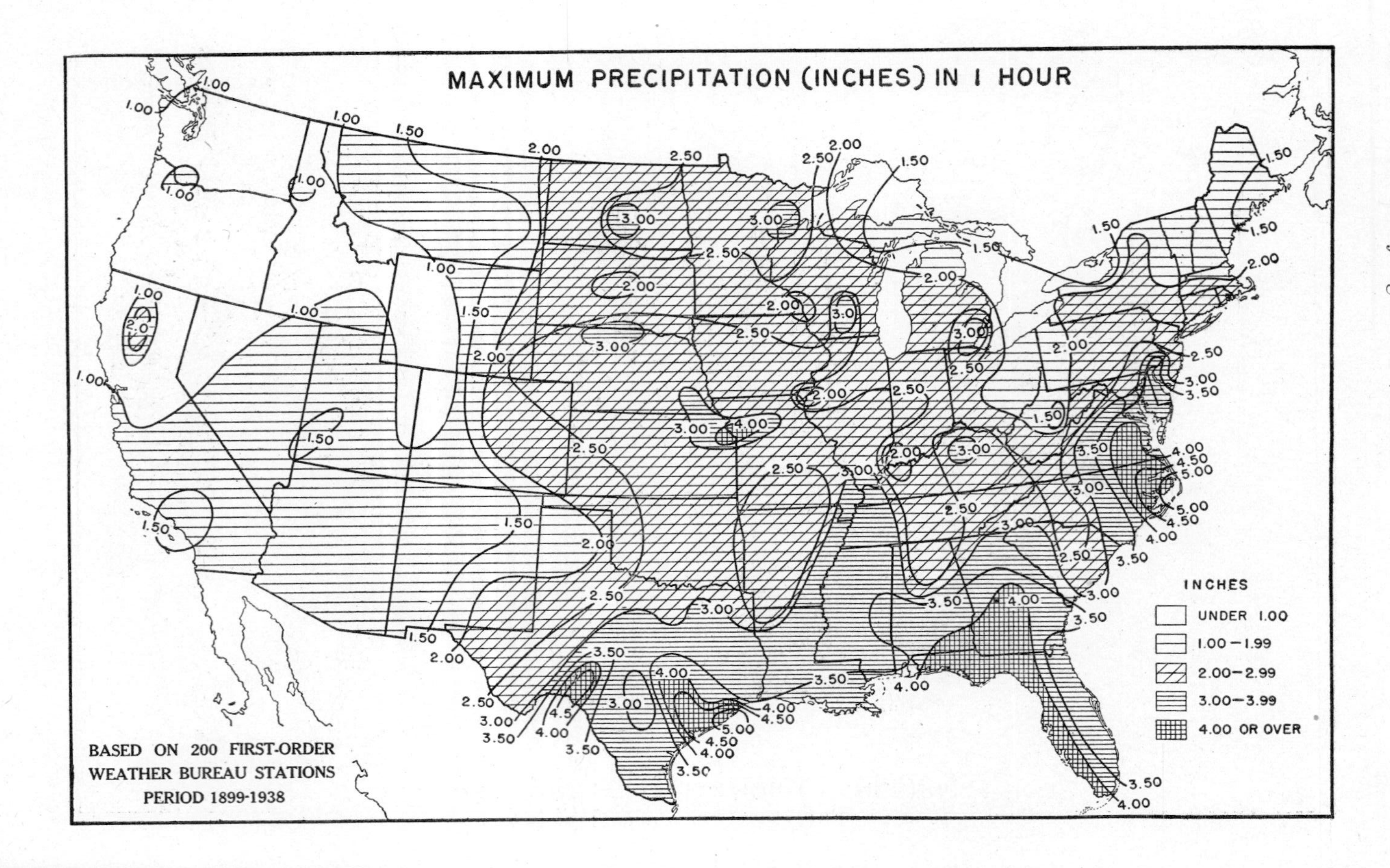
MAXIMUM PRECIPITATION (INCHES) IN 1 HOUR
INCHES
UNDER 1.00
1.00 – 1.99
2.00 – 2.99
3.00 – 3.99
4.00 OR OVER
BASED ON 200 FIRST-ORDER
WEATHER BUREAU STATIONS
PERIOD 1899-1938

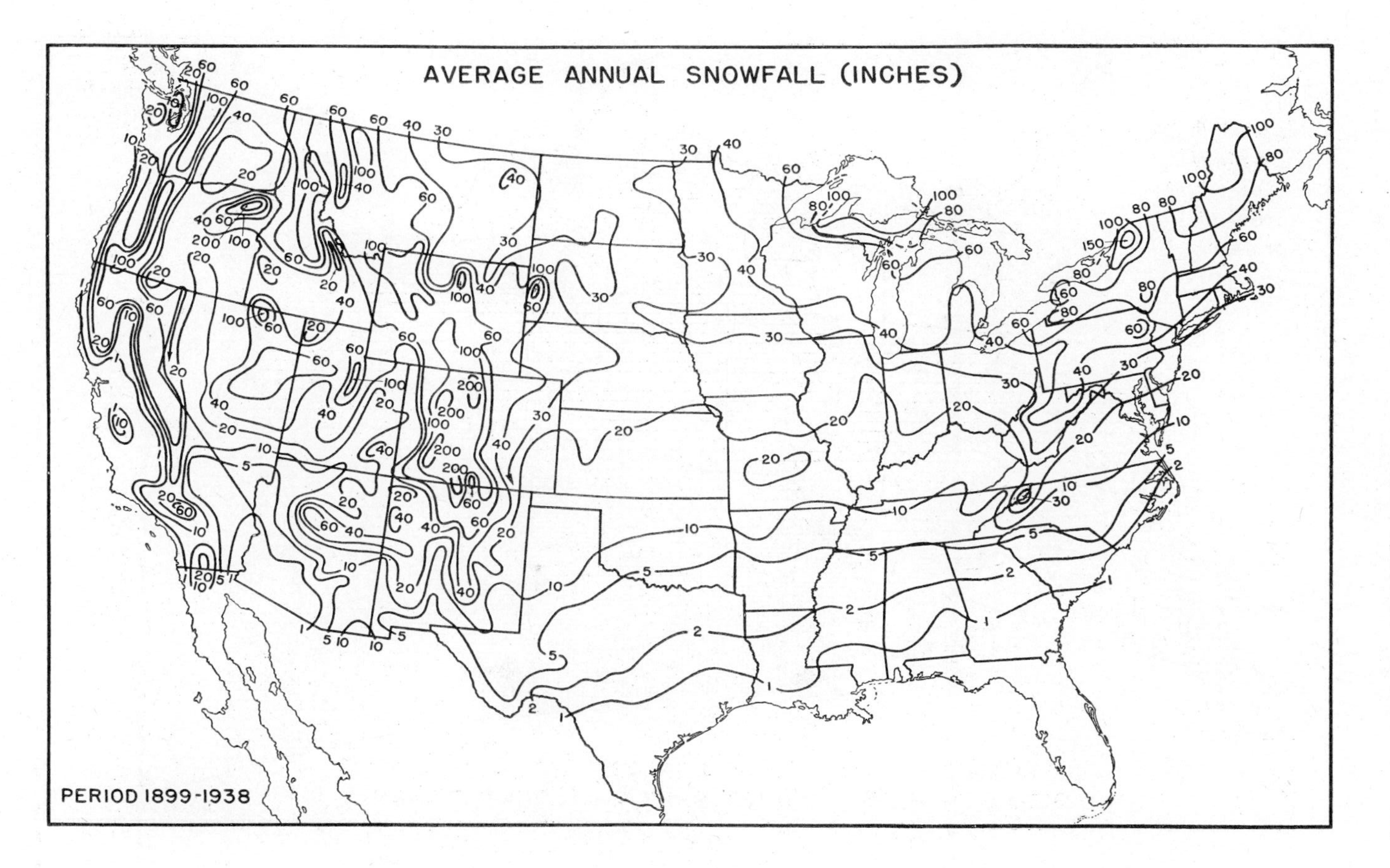
AVERAGE ANNUAL SNOWFALL (INCHES)
PERIOD 1899-1938

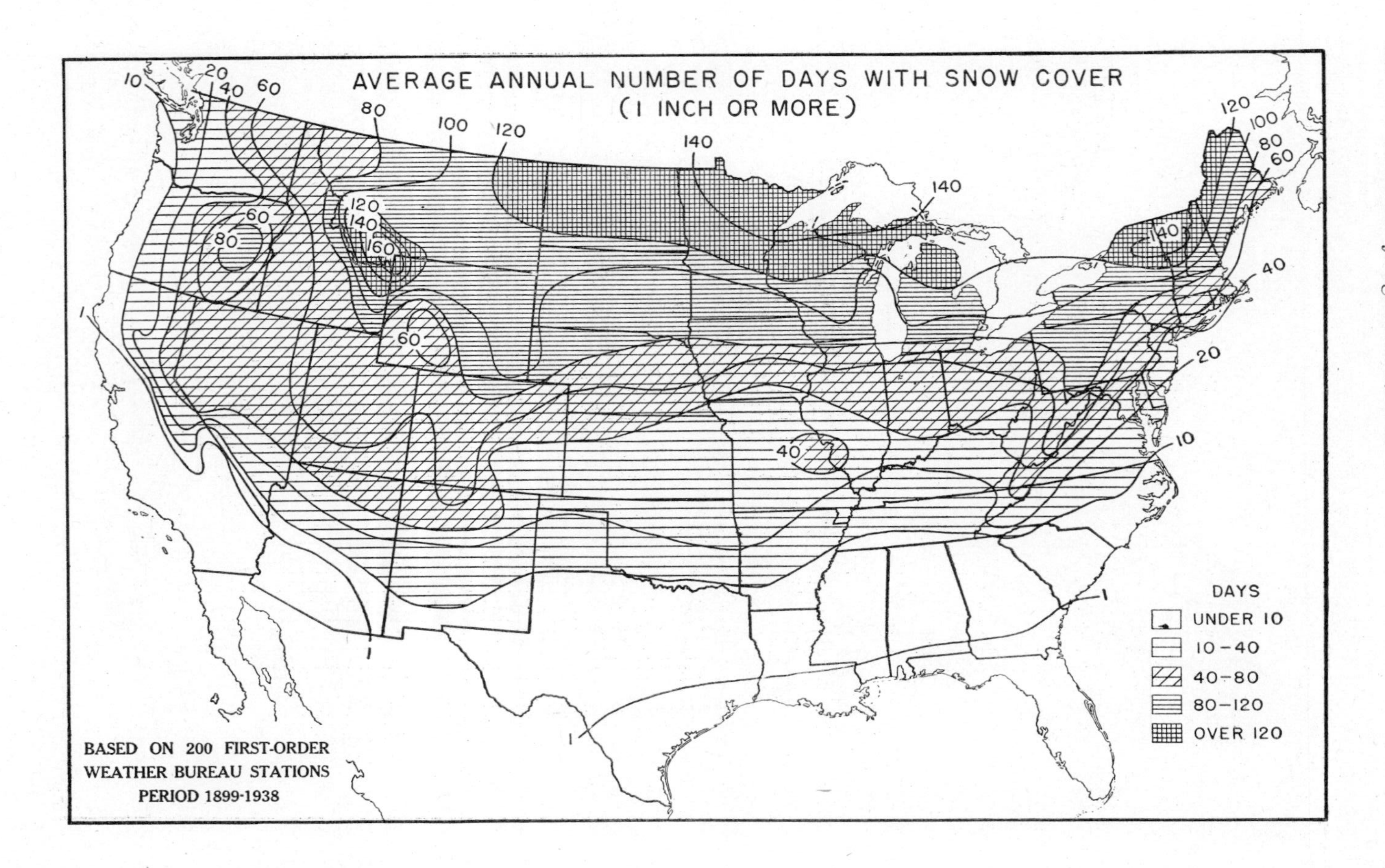
AVERAGE ANNUAL NUMBER OF DAYS WITH SNOW COVER
(1 INCH OR MORE)
DAYS
UNDER 10
10–40
40–80
80–120
OVER 120
BASED ON 200 FIRST-ORDER
WEATHER BUREAU STATIONS
PERIOD 1899-1938

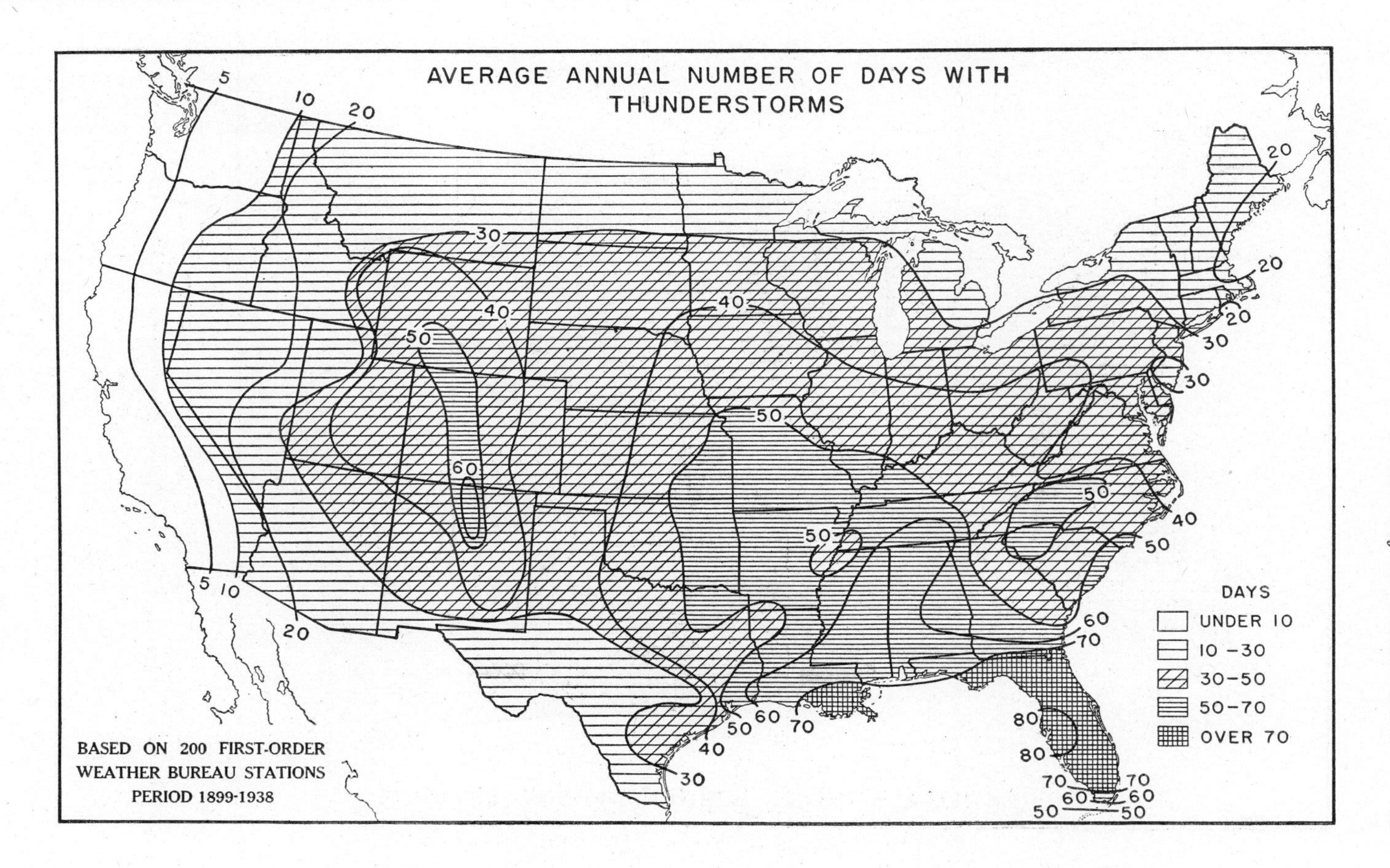
AVERAGE ANNUAL NUMBER OF DAYS WITH
THUNDERSTORMS
DAYS
UNDER 10
10 –30
30–50
50–70
OVER 70
BASED ON 200 FIRST-ORDER
WEATHER BUREAU STATIONS
PERIOD 1899-1938

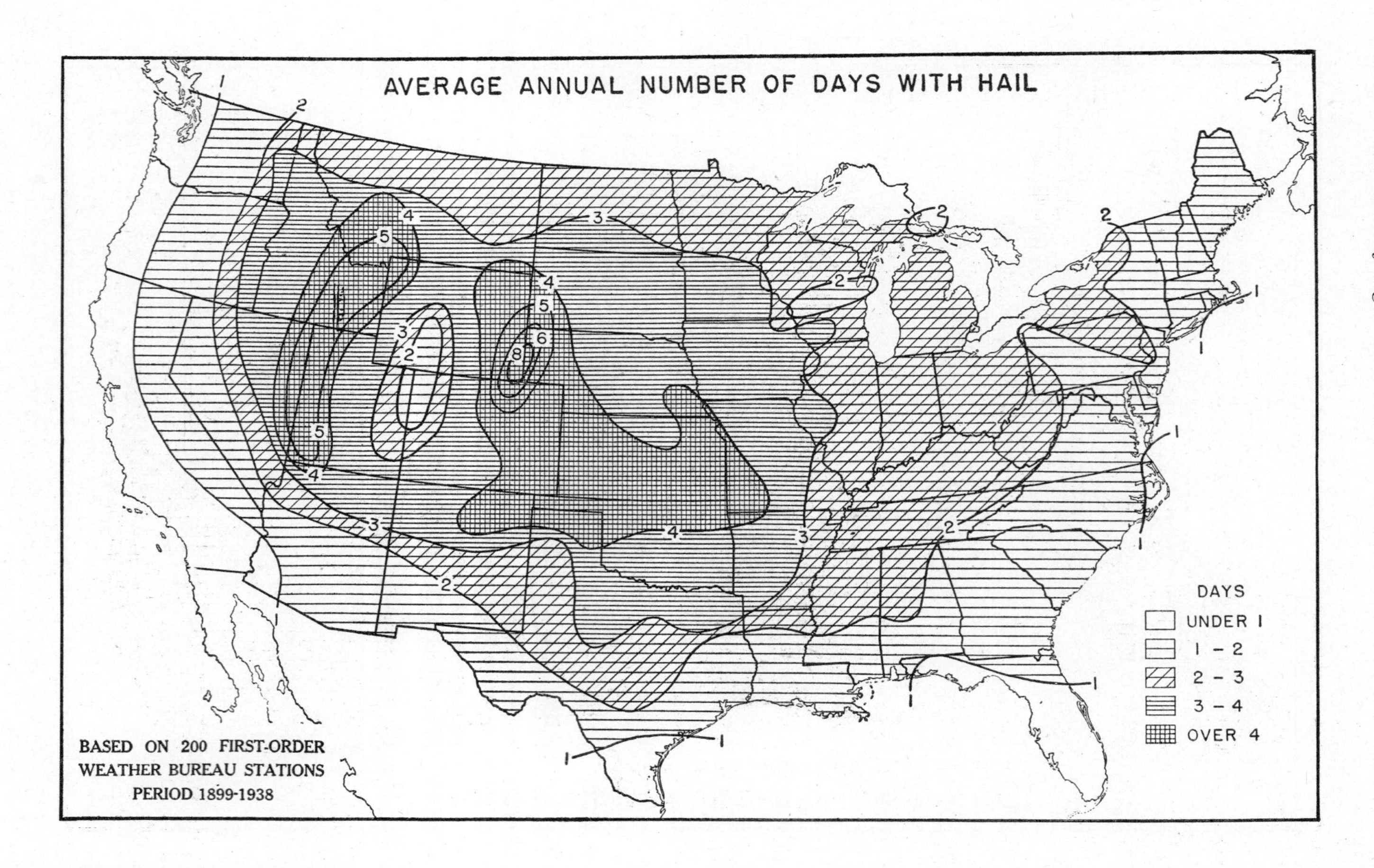
AVERAGE ANNUAL NUMBER OF DAYS WITH HAIL
DAYS
UNDER 1
1 — 2
2 — 3
3 — 4
OVER 4
BASED ON 200 FIRST-ORDER
WEATHER BUREAU STATIONS
PERIOD 1899-1938

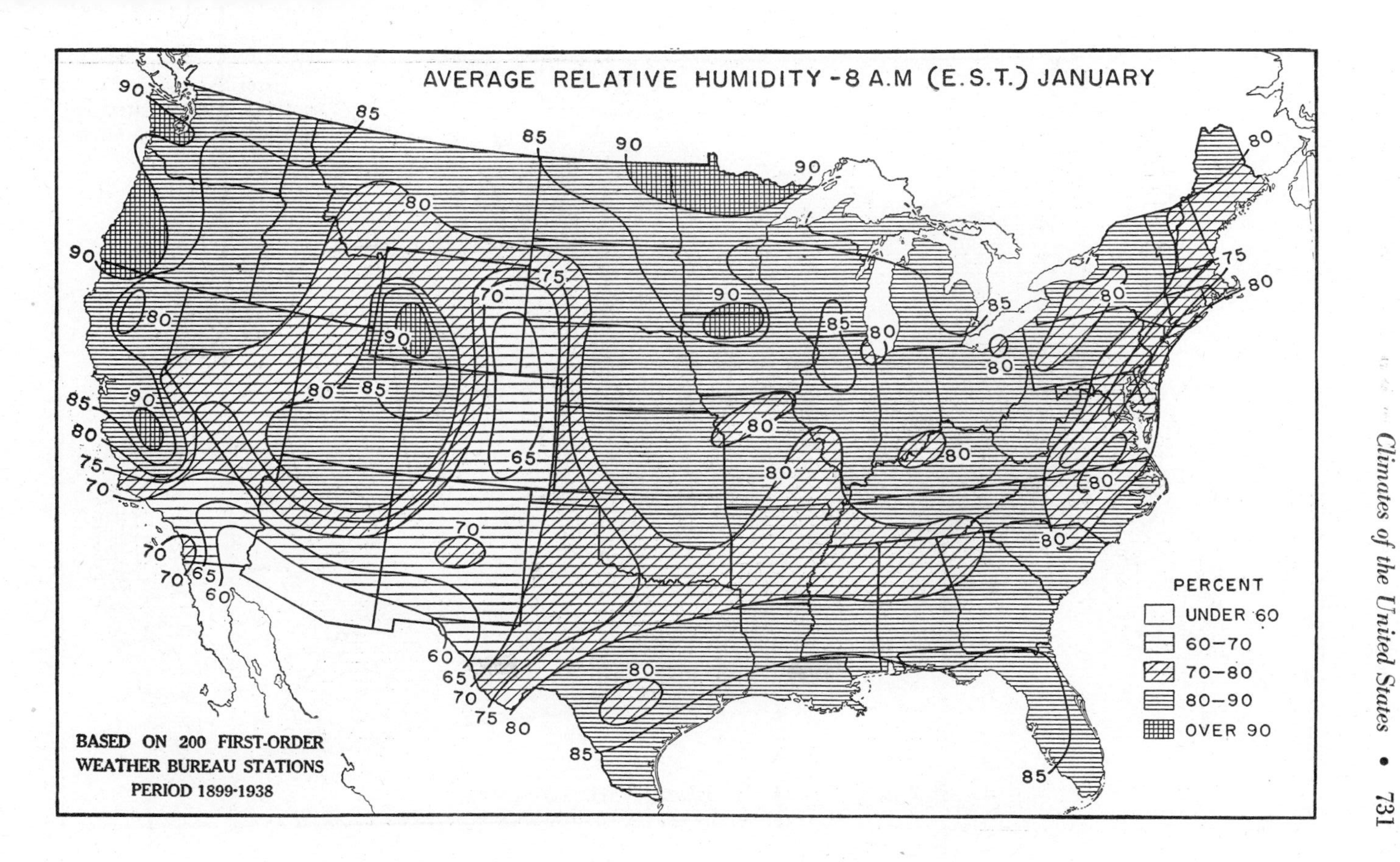
AVERAGE RELATIVE HUMIDITY - 8 A.M (E.S.T.) JANUARY
PERCENT
UNDER 60
60–70
70–80
80–90
OVER 90
BASED ON 200 FIRST-ORDER
WEATHER BUREAU STATIONS
PERIOD 1899-1938

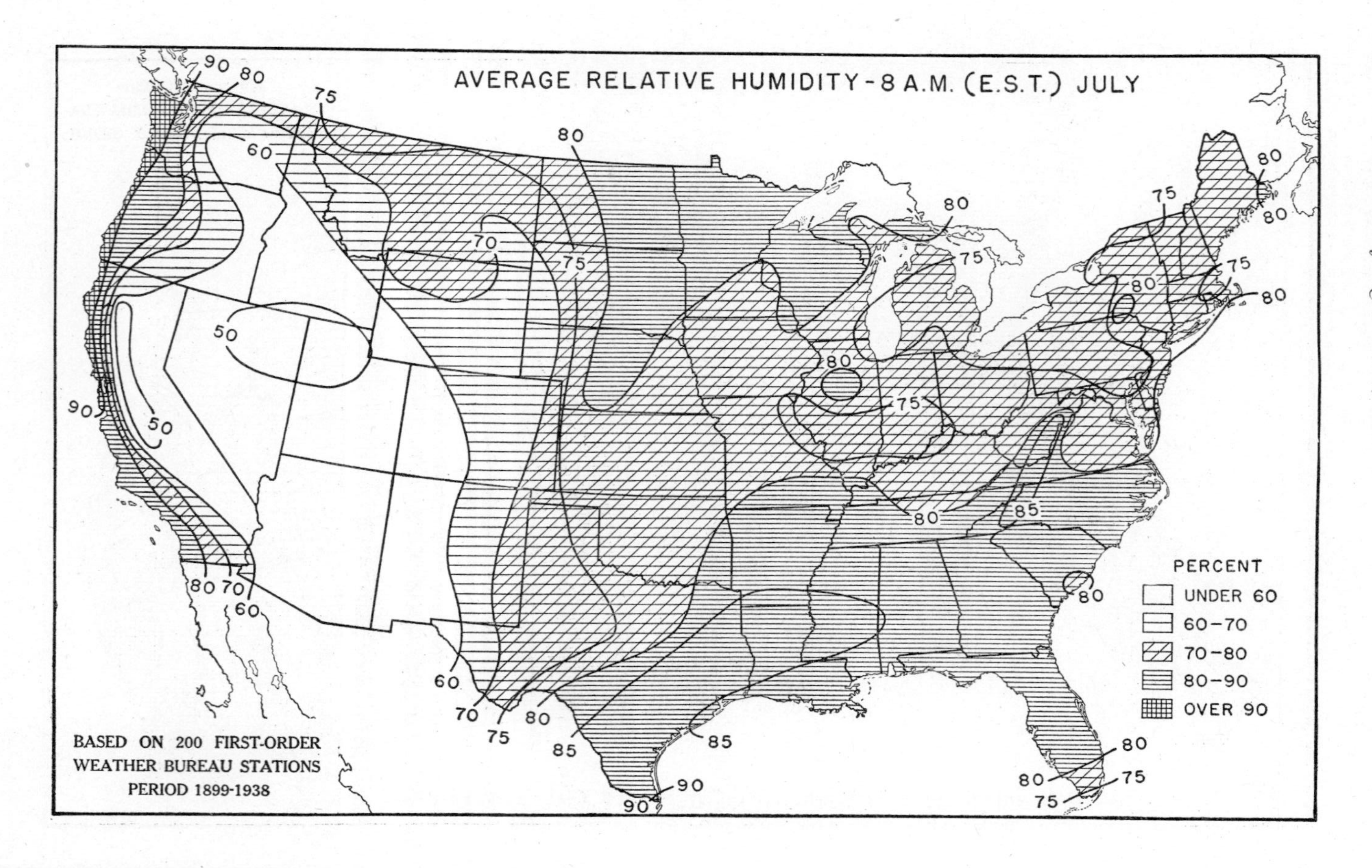
AVERAGE RELATIVE HUMIDITY - 8 A.M. (E.S.T.) JULY
PERCENT
UNDER 60
60-70
70-80
80-90
OVER 90
BASED ON 200 FIRST-ORDER
WEATHER BUREAU STATIONS
PERIOD 1899-1938

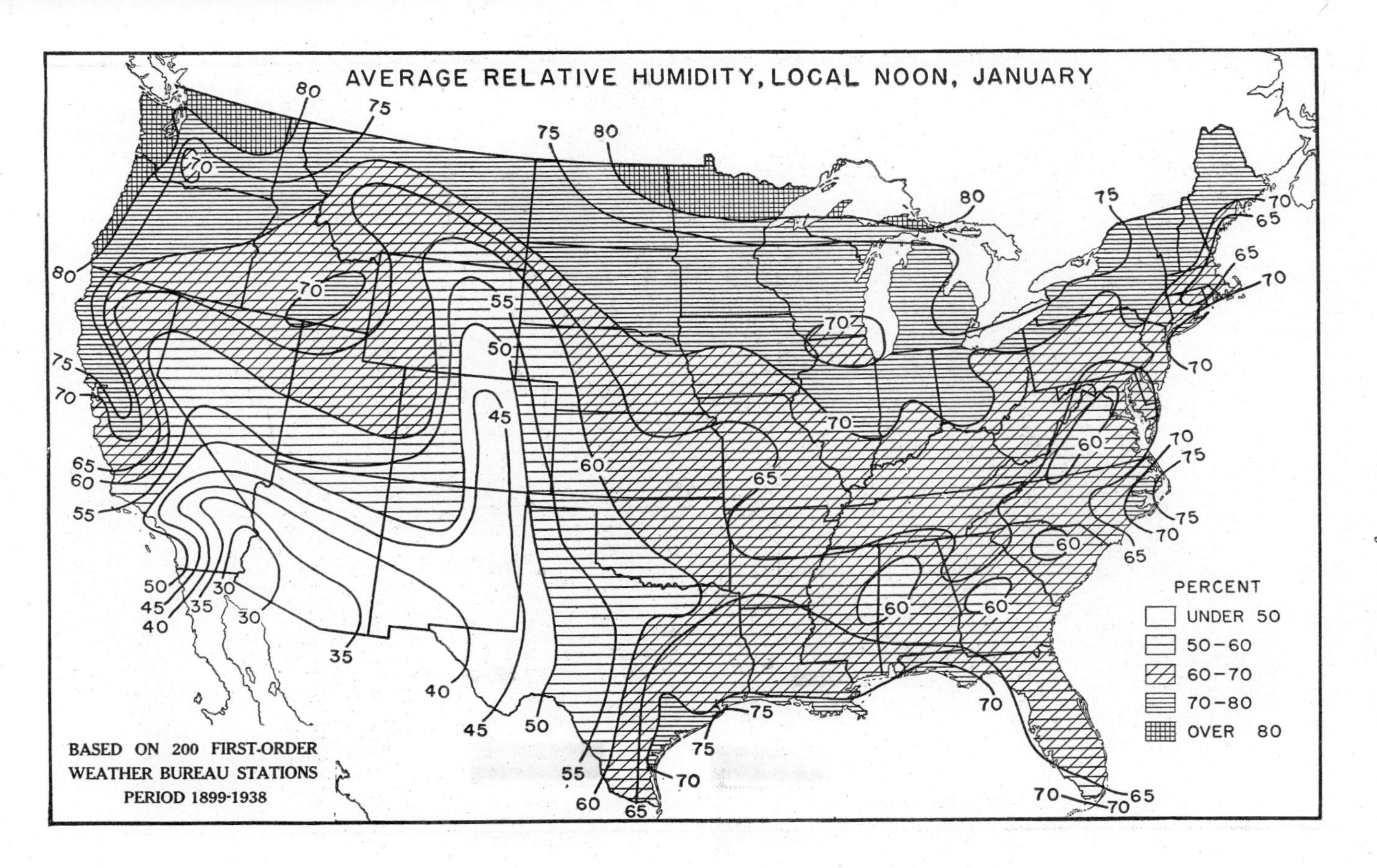
AVERAGE RELATIVE HUMIDITY, LOCAL NOON, JANUARY
PERCENT
UNDER 50
50-60
60-70
70-80
OVER 80
BASED ON 200 FIRST-ORDER
WEATHER BUREAU STATIONS
PERIOD 1899-1938

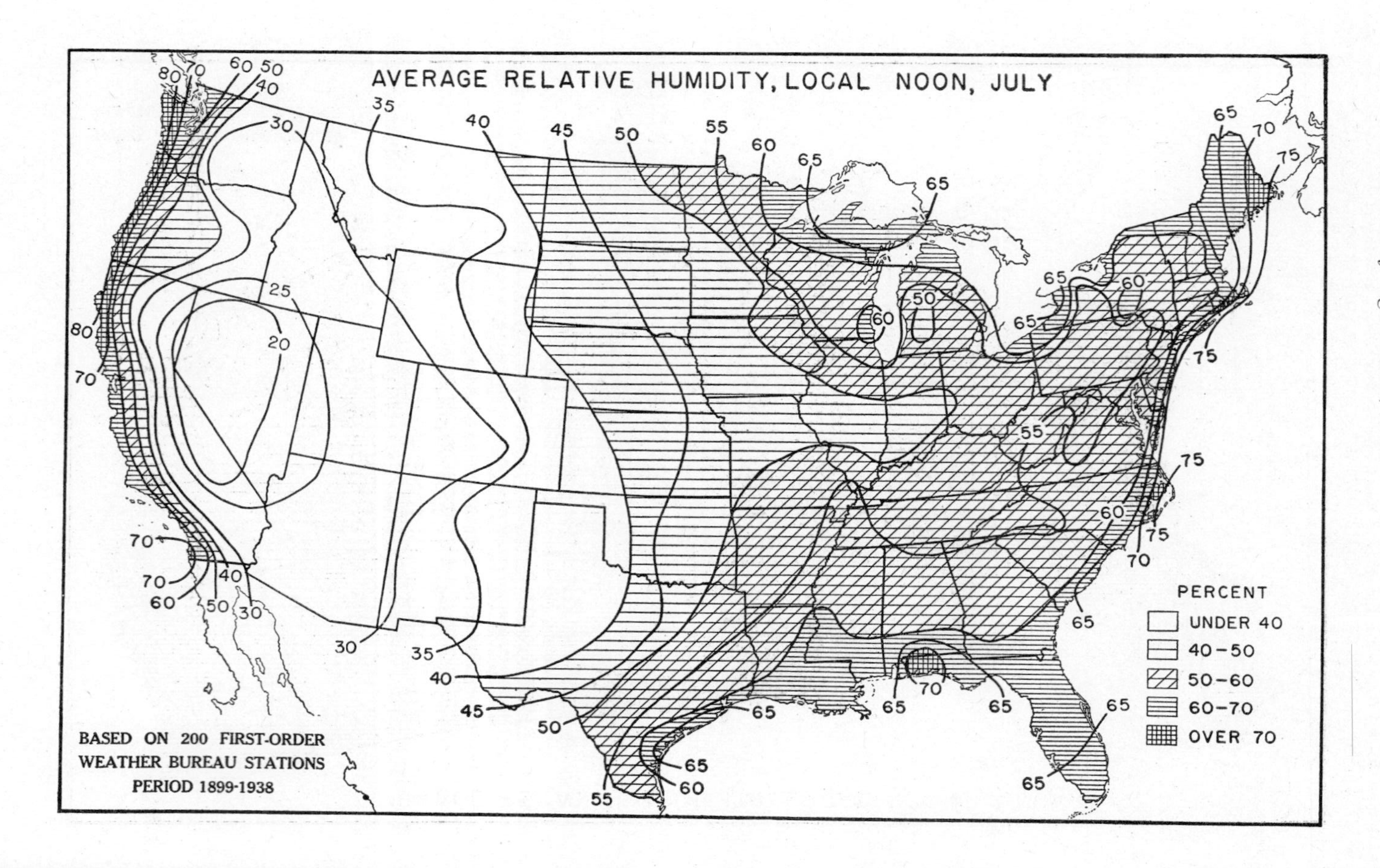
AVERAGE RELATIVE HUMIDITY, LOCAL NOON, JULY
PERCENT
UNDER 40
40–50
50–60
60–70
OVER 70
BASED ON 200 FIRST-ORDER
WEATHER BUREAU STATIONS
PERIOD 1899-1938

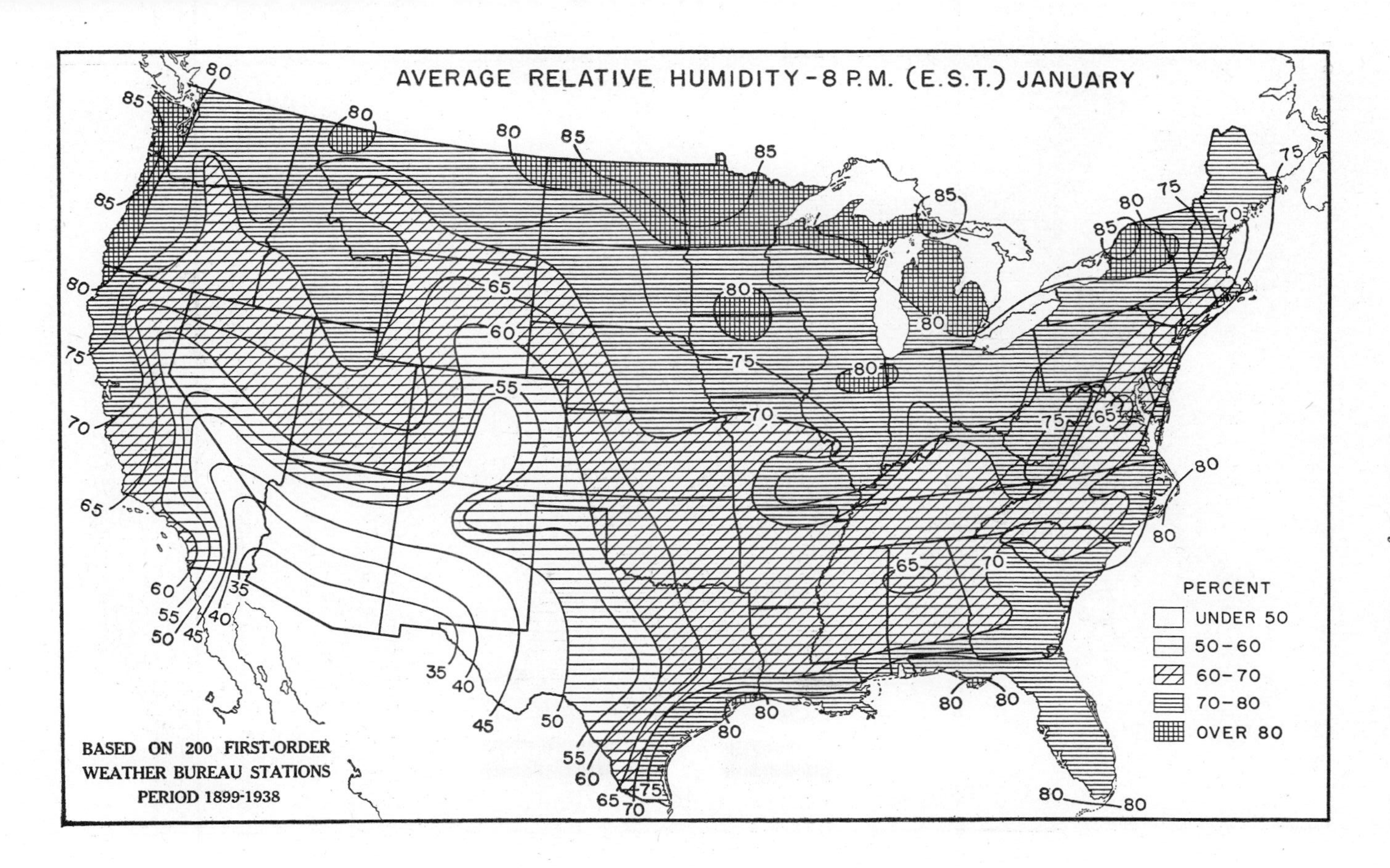
AVERAGE RELATIVE HUMIDITY - 8 P.M. (E.S.T.) JANUARY
PERCENT
UNDER 50
50 - 60
60 - 70
70 - 80
OVER 80
BASED ON 200 FIRST-ORDER
WEATHER BUREAU STATIONS
PERIOD 1899-1938

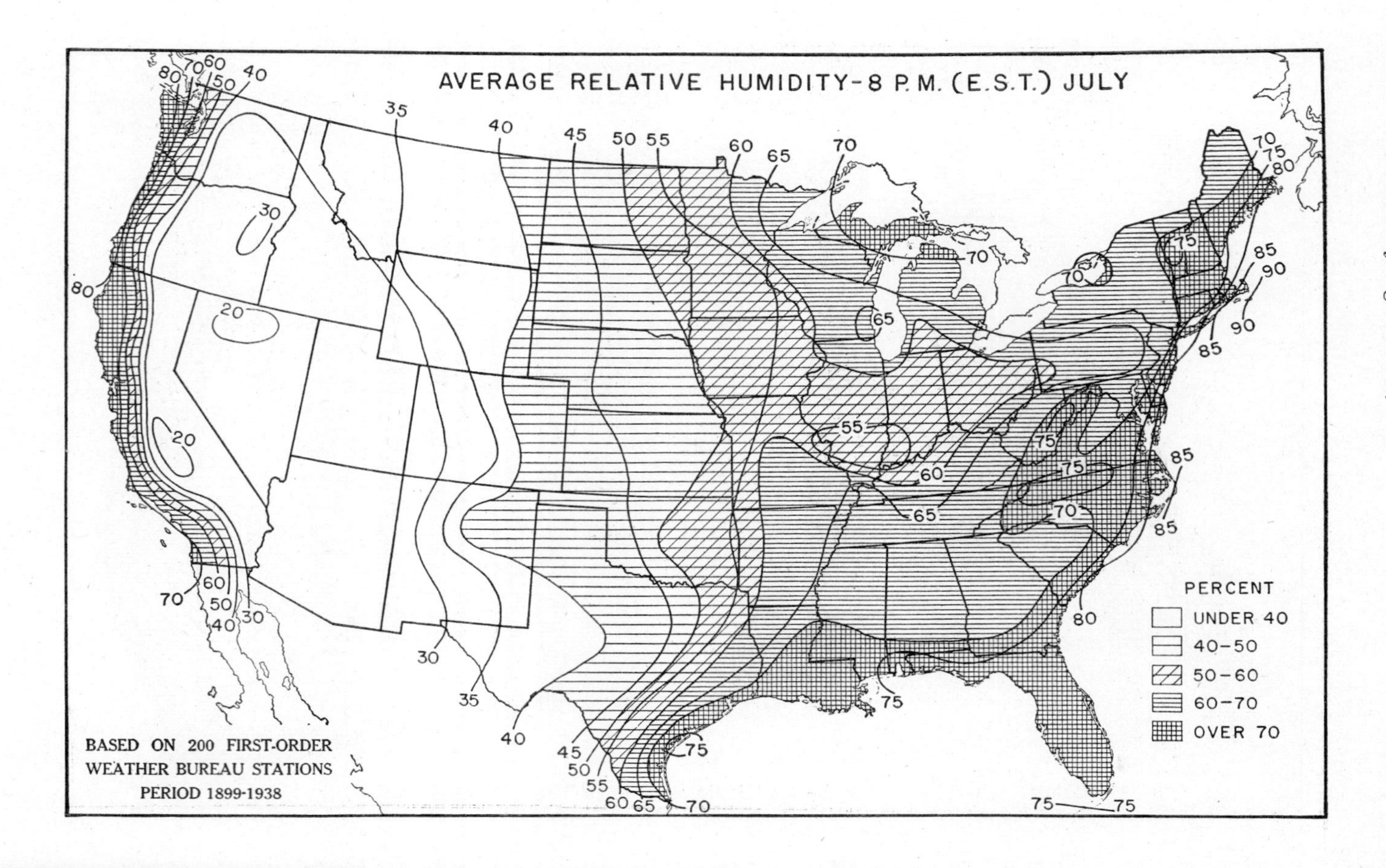
AVERAGE RELATIVE HUMIDITY-8 P.M. (E.S.T.) JULY
PERCENT
UNDER 40
40–50
50–60
60–70
OVER 70
BASED ON 200 FIRST-ORDER
WEATHER BUREAU STATIONS
PERIOD 1899-1938

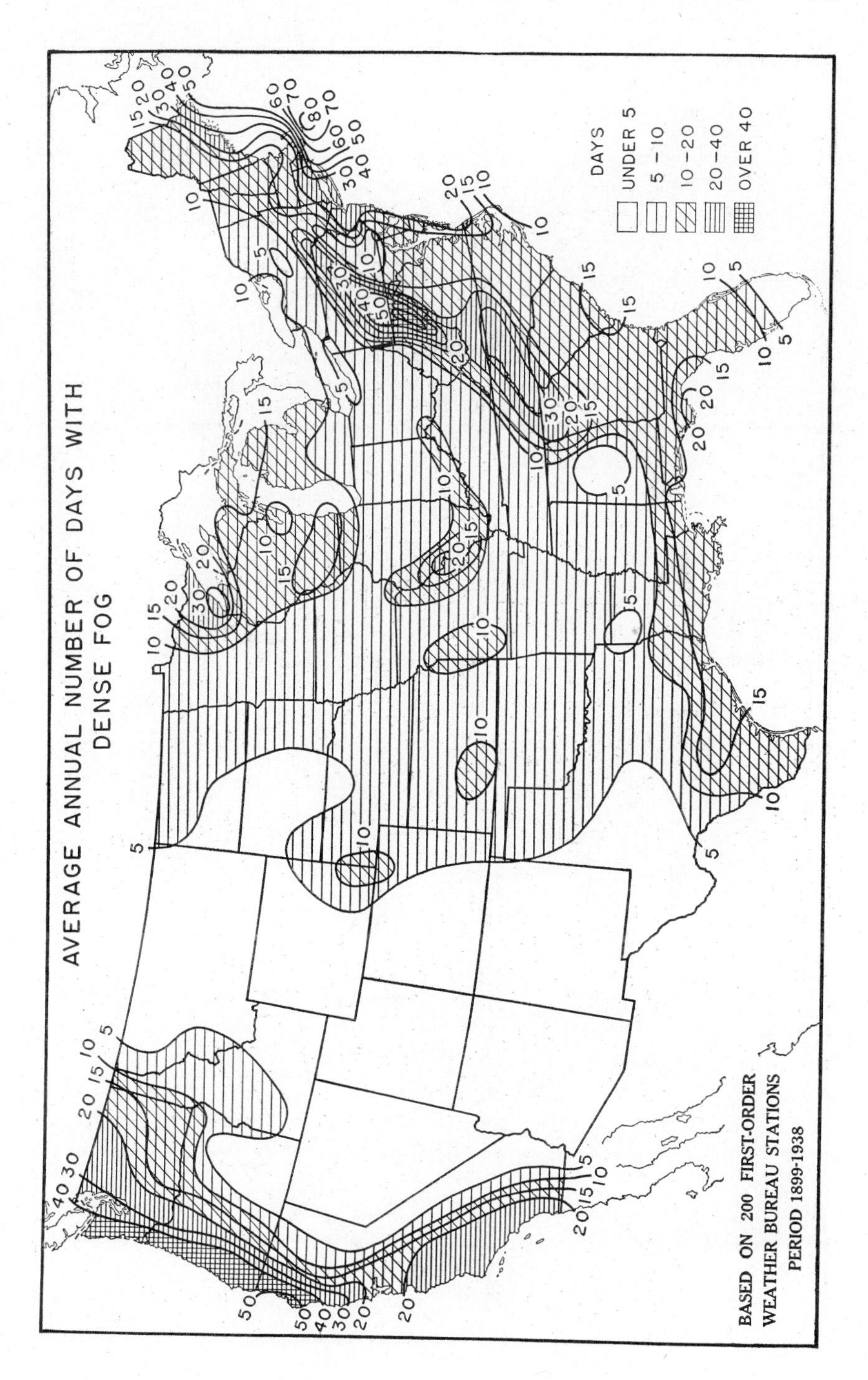
AVERAGE ANNUAL NUMBER OF DAYS WITH
DENSE FOG
DAYS
UNDER 5
5 – 10
10 – 20
20 – 40
OVER 40
BASED ON 200 FIRST-ORDER
WEATHER BUREAU STATIONS
PERIOD 1899-1938

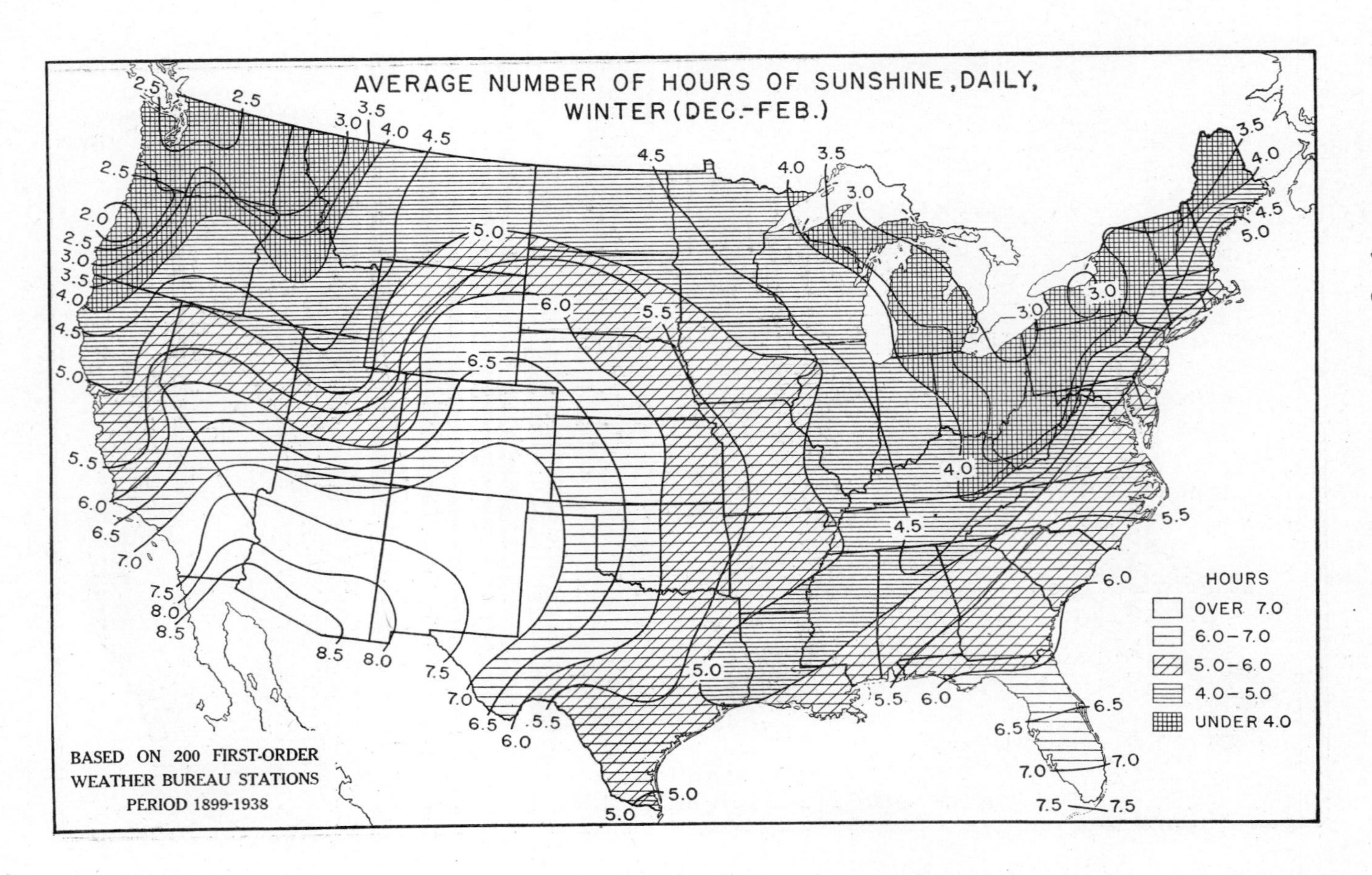
AVERAGE NUMBER OF HOURS OF SUNSHINE, DAILY, WINTER (DEC.-FEB.)
HOURS
OVER 7.0
6.0 – 7.0
5.0 – 6.0
4.0 – 5.0
UNDER 4.0
BASED ON 200 FIRST-ORDER WEATHER BUREAU STATIONS PERIOD 1899-1938

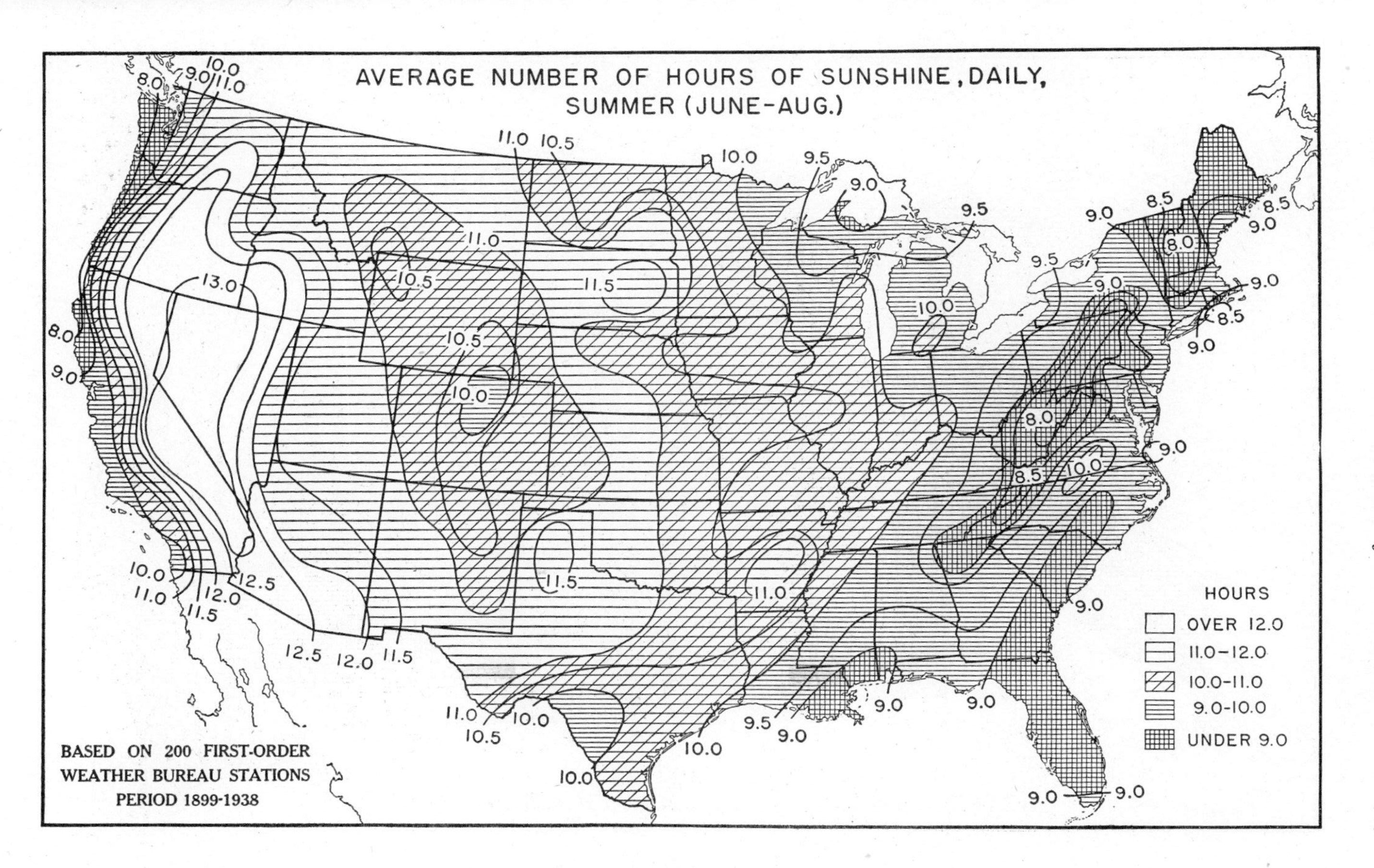
AVERAGE NUMBER OF HOURS OF SUNSHINE, DAILY,
SUMMER (JUNE-AUG.)
HOURS
OVER 12.0
11.0–12.0
10.0–11.0
9.0–10.0
UNDER 9.0
BASED ON 200 FIRST-ORDER
WEATHER BUREAU STATIONS
PERIOD 1899-1938

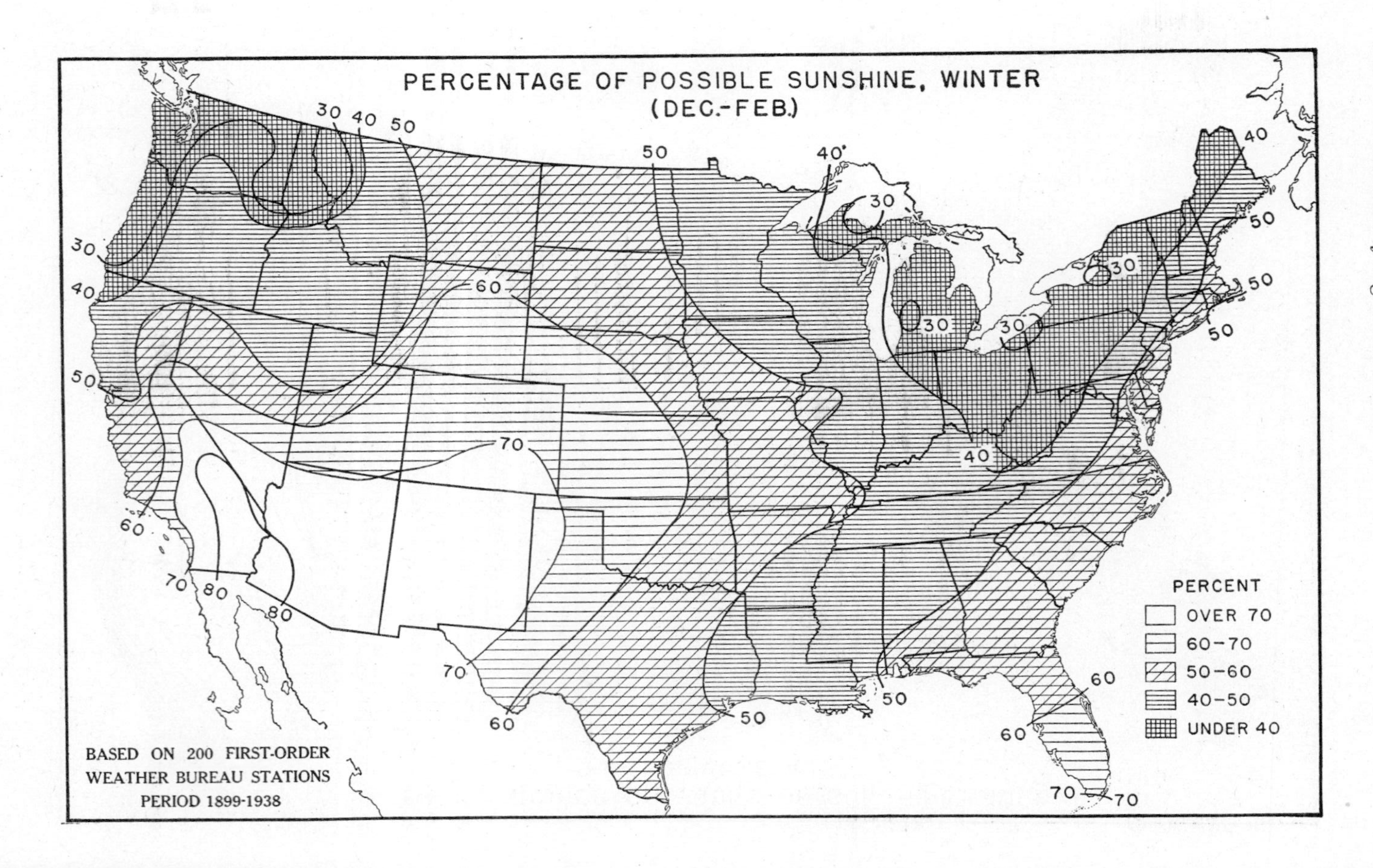
PERCENTAGE OF POSSIBLE SUNSHINE, WINTER
(DEC.-FEB.)
PERCENT
OVER 70
60–70
50–60
40–50
UNDER 40
BASED ON 200 FIRST-ORDER
WEATHER BUREAU STATIONS
PERIOD 1899-1938

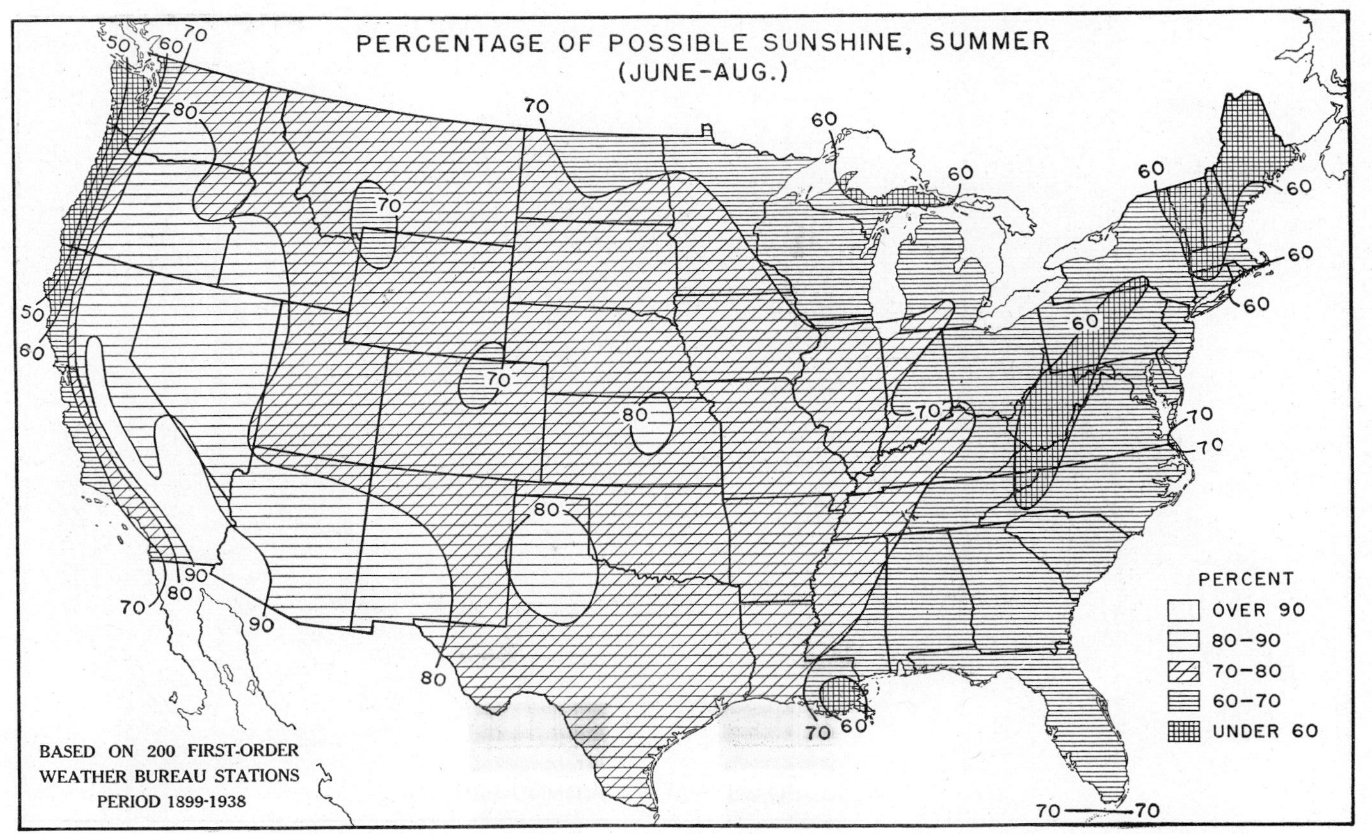
PERCENTAGE OF POSSIBLE SUNSHINE, SUMMER
(JUNE-AUG.)
PERCENT
OVER 90
80–90
70–80
60–70
UNDER 60
BASED ON 200 FIRST-ORDER
WEATHER BUREAU STATIONS
PERIOD 1899-1938

298737°—41——48

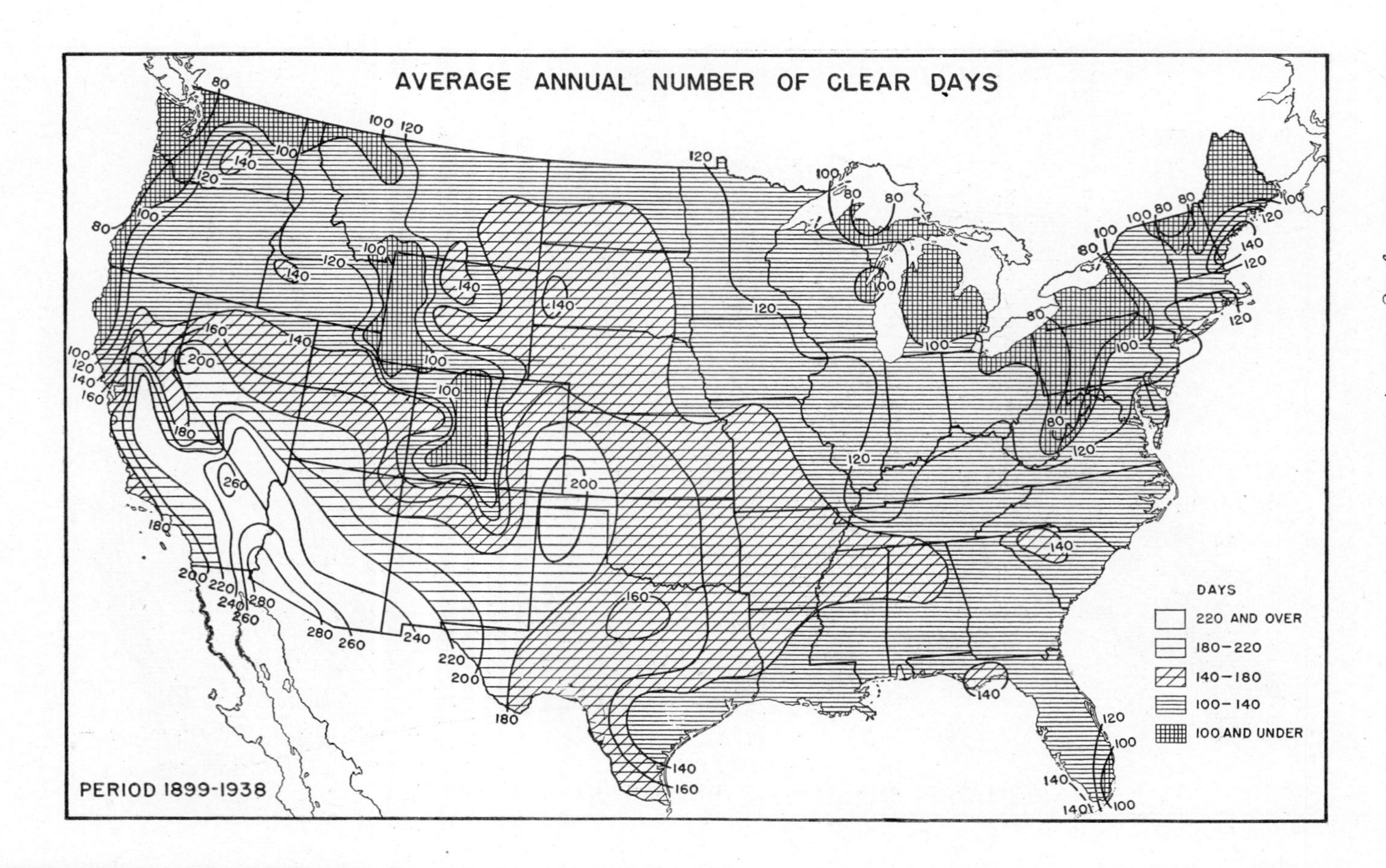
AVERAGE ANNUAL NUMBER OF CLEAR DAYS
DAYS
220 AND OVER
180–220
140–180
100–140
100 AND UNDER
PERIOD 1899-1938

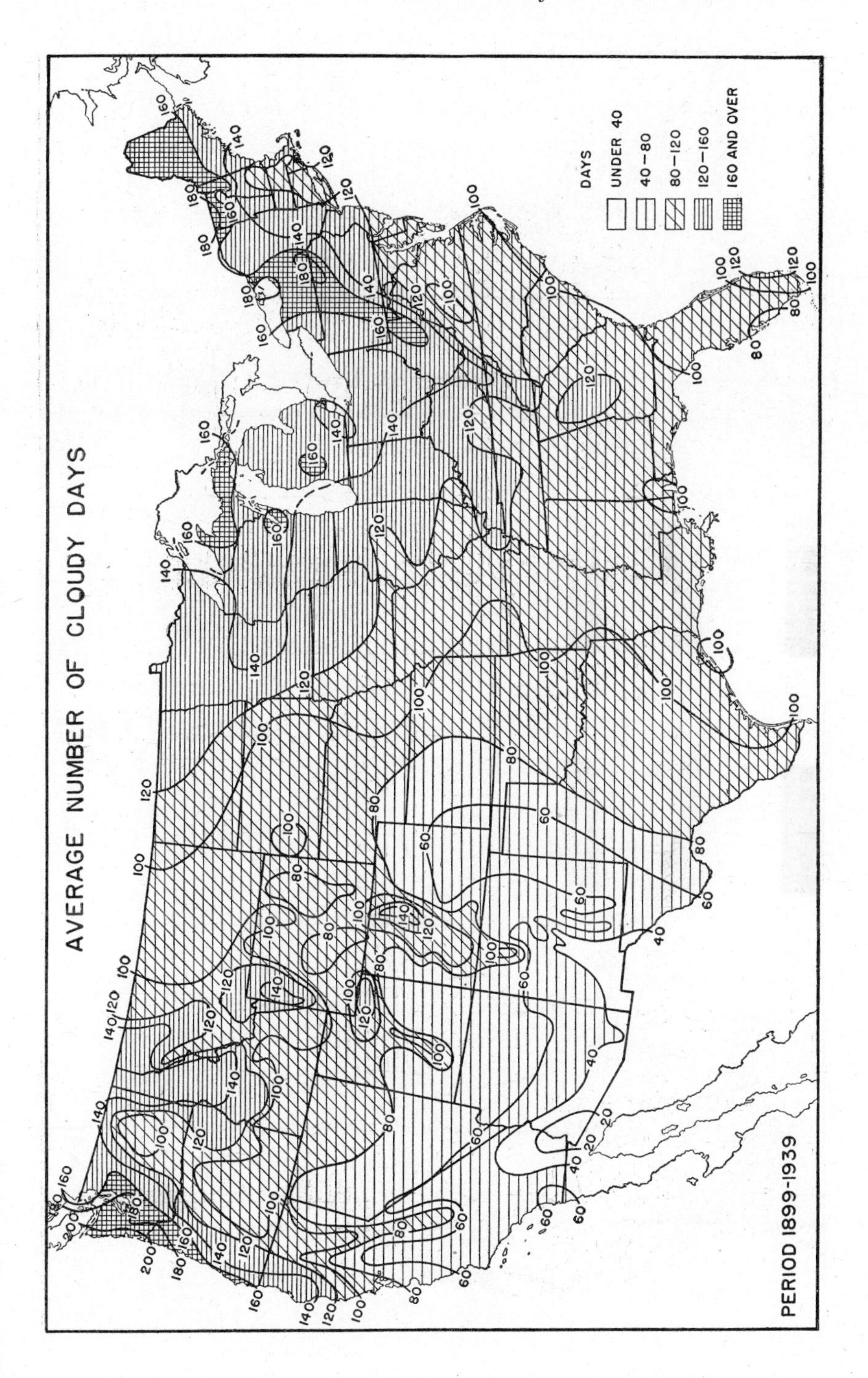
AVERAGE NUMBER OF CLOUDY DAYS
DAYS
UNDER 40
40–80
80–120
120–160
160 AND OVER
PERIOD 1899-1939

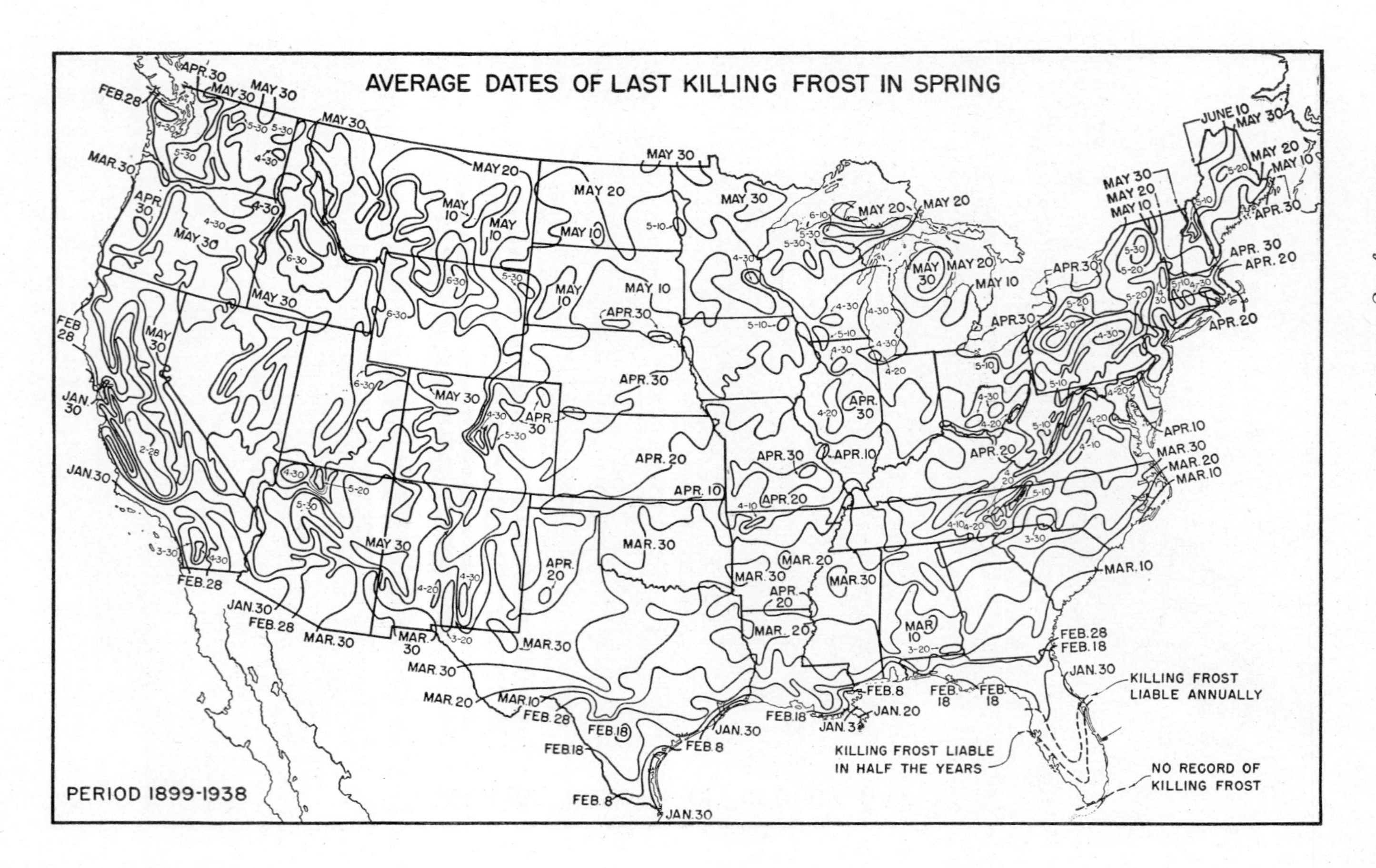
AVERAGE DATES OF LAST KILLING FROST IN SPRING
PERIOD 1899-1938
KILLING FROST LIABLE ANNUALLY
KILLING FROST LIABLE IN HALF THE YEARS
NO RECORD OF KILLING FROST

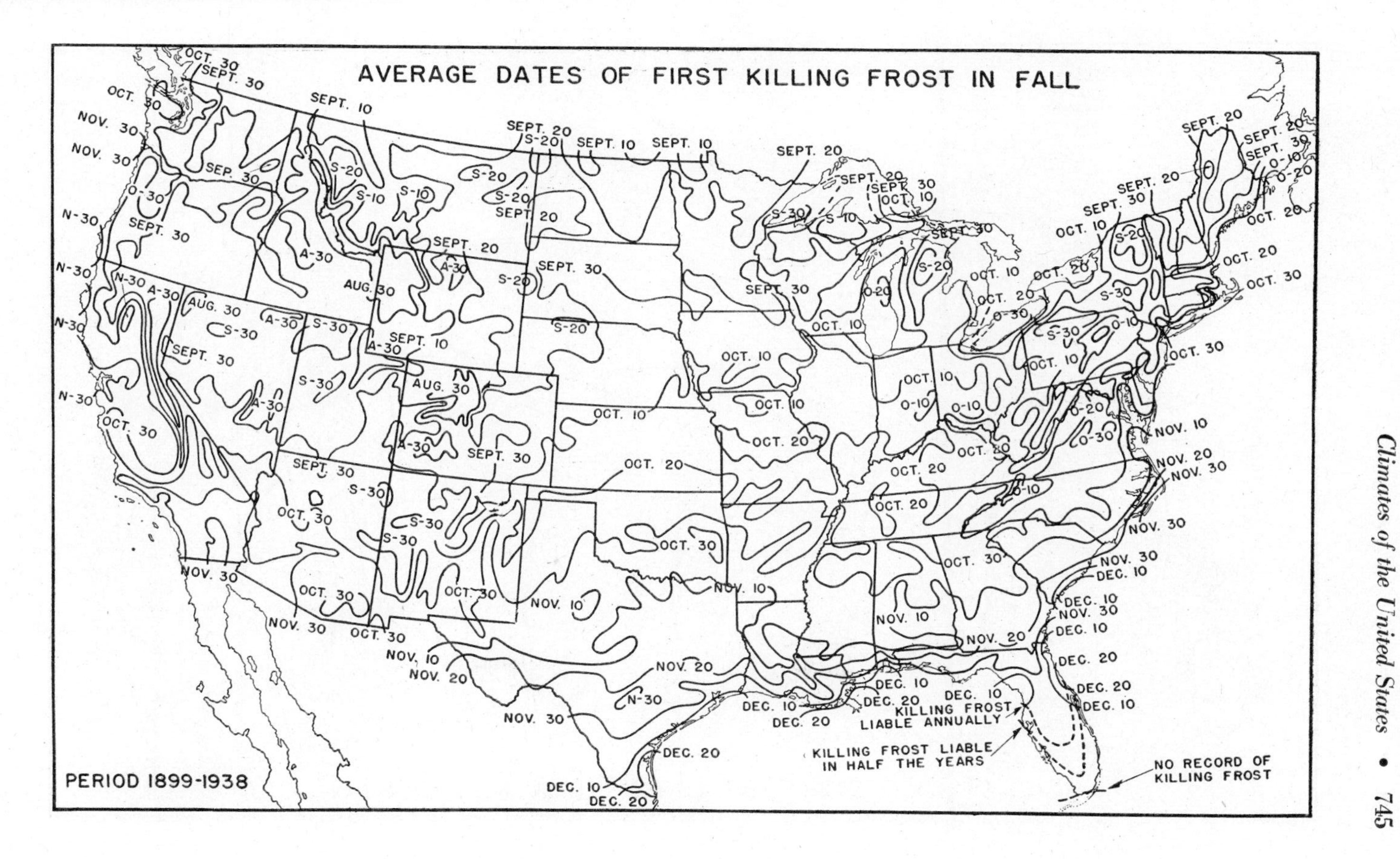
AVERAGE DATES OF FIRST KILLING FROST IN FALL
PERIOD 1899-1938
KILLING FROST LIABLE ANNUALLY
KILLING FROST LIABLE IN HALF THE YEARS
NO RECORD OF KILLING FROST

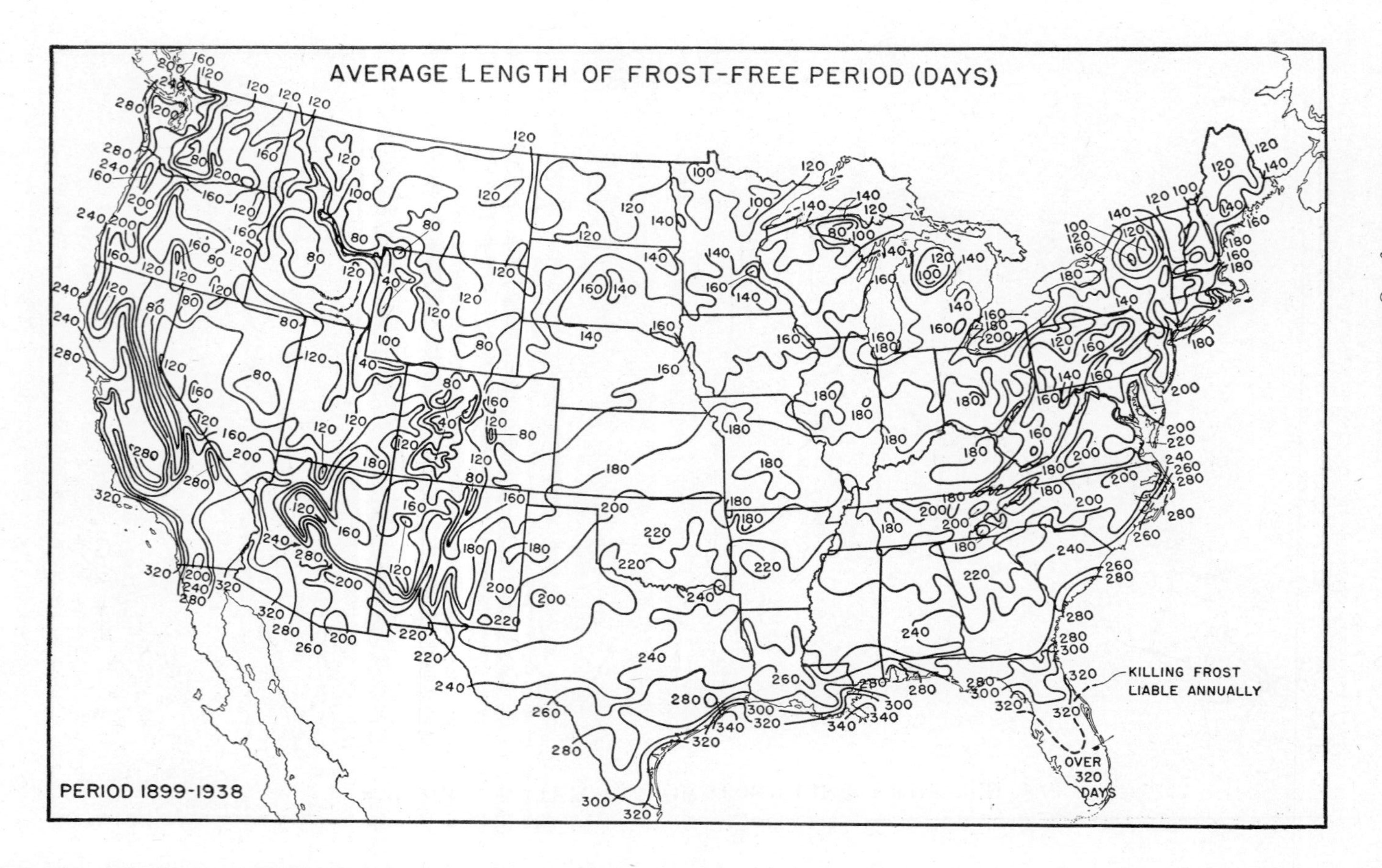
AVERAGE LENGTH OF FROST-FREE PERIOD (DAYS)
KILLING FROST LIABLE ANNUALLY
OVER 320 DAYS
PERIOD 1899-1938

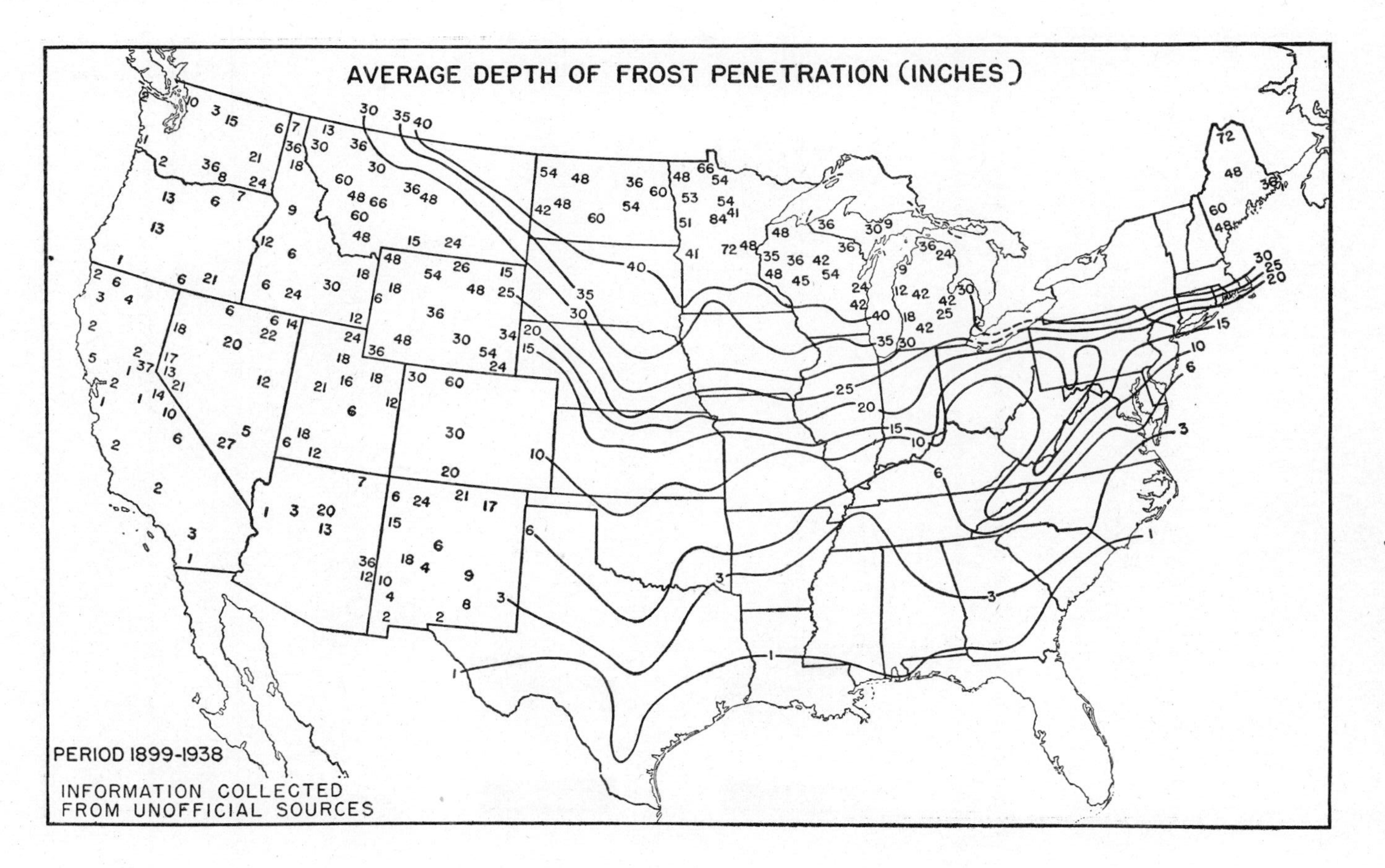
AVERAGE DEPTH OF FROST PENETRATION (INCHES)
PERIOD 1899-1938
INFORMATION COLLECTED FROM UNOFFICIAL SOURCES

Climates of the States

Including for each State: Climatic summary tables, precipitation and temperature tables, special frost tables, 7 maps, and supplementary climatic notes.

ALABAMA

Climatic summary

County[1]	Station	Temperature: Length of record	January average	July average	Maximum	Minimum	Killing frost average dates: Length of record	Last in spring	First in fall	Growing season[2]	Average precipitation: Length of record	January	February	March	April	May	June	July	August	September	October	November	December	Annual
		Yr.	*°F.*	*°F.*	*°F.*	*°F.*	*Yr.*			*Days*	*Yr.*	*In.*	*In.*	*In.*	*In.*	*In.*	*In.*	*In.*	*In.*	*In.*	*In.*	*In.*	*In.*	*In.*
Autauga	Prattville	38	48.5	80.1	106	8	38	Mar 21	Nov. 7	231	37	5.04	5.28	5.87	4.59	3.51	3.77	5.10	4.55	3.30	2.68	3.35	4.94	51.98
Baldwin	Bay Minette	18	53.1	81.0	106	11					23	5.21	5.44	5.52	4.81	4.61	5.09	8.40	5.92	5.70	4.37	3.19	4.97	63.23
	Daphne	17	53.1	80.7	105	0	18	Mar. 4	Nov. 22	263	20	3.55	5.09	5.04	4.67	4.16	4.57	7.99	6.38	7.82	3.50	3.24	5.41	61.42
	Robertsdale										27	5.28	4.82	5.05	4.79	5.19	5.54	9.03	7.03	6.58	4.76	3.57	5.03	66.67
	Silver Hill	18	53.8	80.9	105	13	21	Mar. 2	Nov. 25	268	21	4.92	4.53	4.96	5.19	4.93	5.45	7.56	6.77	5.22	4.81	3.29	4.95	62.58
	Fairhope										5	5.48	2.85	4.31	7.89	6.56	4.49	7.54	7.45	3.97	3.64	2.60	3.50	60.28
Barbour	Clayton										10	6.35	5.32	6.98	5.65	3.84	3.38	8.00	5.99	4.55	3.46	4.03	4.28	61.83
	Eufaula	40	48.3	80.6	106	−4	40	Mar. 13	Nov. 13	245	40	4.54	5.52	5.50	4.51	3.68	4.04	6.10	4.93	3.54	2.64	2.70	4.84	52.54
Bibb	Centerville	22	47.0	80.8	112	−1	22	Mar. 24	Nov. 10	231	22	6.19	5.22	6.45	5.80	4.05	4.18	5.21	4.43	2.98	3.16	3.80	5.74	57.21
Blount	Oneonta	22	43.0	77.2	104	−15	22	Apr. 11	Oct. 27	199	33	5.43	5.46	6.18	5.27	4.98	4.52	6.53	5.13	3.18	3.05	3.12	5.66	58.51
Bullock	Union Springs	39	48.9	81.2	106	−6	40	Mar. 10	Nov. 17	252	40	4.66	6.00	6.22	4.92	3.70	3.89	5.33	4.69	2.88	3.12	2.98	4.65	53.04
Butler	Greenville	11	52.3	82.1	106	7	11	Mar. 7	Nov. 21	259	38	4.67	5.46	5.82	4.86	4.13	4.05	5.66	4.96	3.40	2.72	3.24	5.04	54.01
	McKenzie										8	3.77	5.71	8.35	4.13	2.59	5.39	5.17	3.93	4.94	3.62	4.46	5.19	57.25
Calhoun	Anniston	40	45.1	78.2	105	−10	36	Mar. 28	Nov. 3	220	40	4.95	5.26	5.77	4.93	3.83	4.02	5.45	4.17	3.16	2.80	3.30	5.44	53.08
Chambers	Milltown										13	4.10	5.54	6.60	5.82	2.93	4.18	5.48	4.03	2.68	2.97	3.16	5.22	52.71
Cherokee	Maple Grove	25	42.2	78.9	109	−9	26	Apr. 7	Oct. 25	201	40	5.23	5.38	6.29	4.82	4.03	4.01	5.01	3.92	2.99	3.27	3.43	5.85	54.23
Chilton	Clanton	38	46.9	80.1	110	−9	40	Mar. 27	Nov. 5	223	40	5.44	5.74	5.78	4.86	3.99	3.87	5.46	4.23	3.07	2.74	3.32	5.43	53.93
Choctaw	Lock 2										5	6.22	5.69	4.94	7.15	3.61	2.65	8.43	4.50	1.63	2.69	4.07	5.26	56.84
	Lock 3										5	5.81	4.92	5.07	6.58	3.33	2.33	6.73	3.30	2.04	2.18	3.63	5.21	51.13
	Pushmataha	38	49.1	80.5	108	−7	38	Mar. 25	Nov. 7	227	40	5.76	5.90	5.53	5.25	4.74	4.66	5.70	4.53	3.66	2.75	3.73	5.87	58.08
Clarke	Lock 1										5	5.63	5.36	5.07	6.03	4.75	3.37	5.61	4.44	2.06	2.43	3.92	4.62	53.29
	Thomasville	38	49.2	81.0	109	−5	38	Mar. 18	Nov. 10	237	40	5.19	5.43	5.62	4.48	4.32	4.07	5.97	4.74	3.34	2.66	3.42	4.91	54.15
Coffee	Elba						1	Mar. 19	Nov. 6	232	9	6.07	7.92	8.74	6.02	3.87	5.59	8.35	5.37	4.62	3.63	3.84	3.25	67.27
Colbert	Riverton	38	41.4	78.7	109	−11	39	Apr. 9	Oct. 26	200	39	4.71	4.53	5.76	4.83	4.52	4.01	4.29	4.01	3.25	3.49	3.73	5.54	52.67
	Tuscumbia	38	42.4	80.5	107	−8	37	Mar. 27	Nov. 1	219	40	4.65	4.50	5.60	4.92	4.24	4.05	4.18	3.88	2.85	3.25	3.32	5.14	50.58
Conecuh	Evergreen	36	51.6	81.3	107	0	40	Mar. 18	Nov. 14	241	40	4.61	5.48	5.81	4.91	4.15	4.14	6.12	4.57	3.70	3.01	3.04	4.80	54.34
Coosa	Goodwater	40	45.7	79.8	107	−8	40	Mar. 30	Nov. 4	219	40	5.47	5.74	5.63	4.78	3.82	4.13	6.07	5.22	2.82	2.98	3.31	5.40	55.37
Covington	River Falls										10	6.10	5.78	7.36	4.96	3.89	3.40	6.83	5.28	3.81	3.74	3.64	4.06	58.85
Crenshaw	Highland Home	40	50.7	79.9	105	−4	40	Mar. 10	Nov. 21	256	40	4.77	5.53	6.07	4.53	3.69	4.06	5.65	4.48	3.22	2.77	3.40	5.02	53.19
Cullman	St. Bernard	31	43.6	78.3	107	−17	32	Apr. 8	Oct. 24	199	32	5.57	4.70	5.88	5.39	5.05	4.37	5.12	4.41	2.61	3.82	3.89	5.76	56.57
Dale	Newton										14	5.29	6.07	6.38	5.39	3.74	4.36	5.55	5.56	5.70	2.91	2.88	4.49	58.32
	Ozark	33	51.9	80.6	109	8	34	Mar. 7	Nov. 19	257	40	4.61	5.68	5.53	4.38	3.43	4.33	6.19	5.14	4.26	2.77	2.84	4.65	53.81
Dallas	Selma	38	49.9	81.7	106	−5	40	Mar. 12	Nov. 15	248	40	4.85	5.27	5.41	4.59	3.88	3.54	5.11	4.04	2.85	2.49	3.00	5.26	50.29
De Kalb	Mentone						14	Apr. 16	Oct. 24	191	27	5.09	5.12	5.93	5.32	4.62	4.26	5.23	4.55	2.99	3.64	3.55	6.13	56.43
	Valley Head	38	41.7	77.8	106	−18	38	Apr. 12	Oct. 27	198	40	5.00	4.85	5.80	5.34	4.47	4.35	4.99	4.42	2.53	3.43	3.30	5.06	53.54
Elmore	Tallassee										40	4.81	5.45	5.99	4.59	3.55	3.69	5.21	4.56	2.86	2.72	2.98	5.37	51.78
	Wetumpka	40	49.0	81.6	108	−7	40	Mar. 17	Nov. 8	236	40	4.64	5.55	5.88	4.56	3.68	4.06	4.68	4.23	3.05	2.83	3.20	5.29	51.65

See footnotes at end of table.

ALABAMA—Continued

Climatic summary—Continued

County[1]	Station	Temperature: Length of record	Temperature: January average	Temperature: July average	Temperature: Maximum	Temperature: Minimum	Killing frost average dates: Length of record	Killing frost average dates: Last in spring	Killing frost average dates: First in fall	Killing frost average dates: Growing season[2]	Average precipitation: Length of record	January	February	March	April	May	June	July	August	September	October	November	December	Annual
		Yr.	°F.	°F.	°F.	°F.	Yr.			Days	Yr.	In.	In.	In.	In.	In.	In.	In.	In.	In.	In.	In.	In.	In.
Escambia	Brewton (near)	25	51.3	81.5	109	9	13	Mar. 21	Nov. 7	231	15	5.06	5.60	6.47	4.78	4.03	5.75	7.21	6.16	4.67	4.16	3.35	4.62	61.86
Etowah	Gadsden	39	44.4	80.3	108	−13	40	Apr. 1	Nov. 2	215	40	5.26	5.41	6.41	4.95	4.31	4.06	4.88	4.51	2.86	3.28	3.31	5.60	54.84
Fayette	Fayette						7	Mar. 23	Oct. 27	218	11	5.29	4.26	7.81	5.57	4.76	4.58	4.60	4.14	2.96	3.28	5.44	4.93	57.62
Geneva	Coffee Springs										15	5.57	5.21	5.54	4.92	3.19	4.70	6.55	4.53	5.31	2.87	3.02	4.69	56.10
	Geneva										10	4.54	4.68	6.02	4.83	3.58	3.37	6.53	4.86	4.31	2.35	3.06	3.14	51.27
Hale	Greensboro	39	48.2	80.9	106	−5	40	Mar. 12	Nov. 13	246	40	5.12	5.11	5.60	4.94	4.57	3.45	5.17	4.10	3.03	2.74	3.16	5.61	52.60
Houston	Alaga										32	4.46	4.73	4.49	4.49	3.80	4.75	6.85	5.30	4.59	2.70	2.67	4.77	53.60
	Dothan										20	5.11	5.09	6.20	4.13	2.66	4.39	5.59	5.07	5.53	2.43	3.28	4.37	53.85
Jackson	Bridgeport										40	4.82	4.84	6.15	4.86	4.42	4.25	4.95	4.13	2.60	3.42	3.42	5.46	53.32
	Scottsboro	36	43.7	78.4	109	−16	37	Apr. 8	Oct. 30	205	40	4.91	4.80	5.96	4.99	4.22	4.26	4.93	4.13	2.93	3.33	3.35	5.50	53.31
Jefferson	Birmingham	40	46.5	80.0	107	−10	40	Mar. 16	Nov. 11	240	40	5.01	4.78	6.00	4.90	4.28	4.22	5.51	4.38	3.20	2.98	3.50	5.32	54.08
	Leeds										22	5.89	5.22	6.41	5.29	4.16	4.03	4.82	4.16	2.82	3.67	4.12	5.84	56.43
Lauderdale	Florence	40	42.3	79.7	108	−13	40	Apr. 5	Oct. 29	207	40	4.92	4.55	5.84	4.73	4.33	4.48	4.61	3.86	3.01	3.33	3.53	5.30	52.49
Lee	Auburn	33	49.8	80.2	108	4	32	Mar. 22	Nov. 14	237	40	4.68	5.53	5.78	4.59	3.71	3.96	5.32	4.61	3.15	2.82	3.12	5.40	52.67
	Opelika	19	45.9	79.6	104	−7	20	Mar. 23	Nov. 8	230	19	4.50	5.95	5.90	4.22	3.41	4.05	5.01	4.31	3.37	3.04	2.94	5.61	52.31
Lowndes	Benton										33	5.29	5.95	6.61	4.43	4.40	3.41	5.26	3.98	3.40	2.56	3.23	5.22	53.74
	Fort Deposit	26	47.8	81.1	107	−6	24	Mar. 9	Nov. 17	253	28	4.78	5.79	5.23	4.40	3.76	3.70	5.08	4.09	3.35	2.73	3.10	5.07	51.08
Macon	Milstead										36	5.00	5.40	5.59	4.64	3.96	3.46	5.45	4.36	3.03	2.90	3.16	5.35	52.30
	Tuskegee	39	49.4	81.0	107	6	39	Mar. 14	Nov. 15	246	39	4.34	5.17	5.47	4.13	3.07	2.94	4.64	3.89	2.55	2.41	2.97	4.96	46.54
Madison	Madison	38	43.4	80.1	111	−10	40	Apr. 5	Oct. 31	209	40	4.65	4.51	5.77	5.01	4.22	4.41	4.53	3.73	3.12	3.45	3.63	5.44	52.47
Marengo	Demopolis										40	5.17	5.42	5.65	4.87	4.16	3.82	4.70	3.71	3.09	2.59	2.94	5.45	51.57
Marion	Hamilton	17	43.2	78.8	105	−16	19	Apr. 4	Oct. 21	200	20	4.70	4.80	5.98	4.50	4.07	3.88	4.68	4.06	2.90	2.33	3.00	5.23	50.13
Marshall	Albertville	12	45.2	79.2	107	−6	12	Mar. 3	Nov. 6	248	13	5.35	4.75	6.92	5.23	4.41	4.50	5.18	4.07	2.92	3.57	4.34	4.92	56.16
	Guntersville										34	4.99	4.81	5.47	5.11	4.79	4.09	5.20	3.97	3.28	3.37	3.37	5.21	53.66
Mobile	Citronelle	40	53.0	81.1	107	−2	39	Mar. 8	Nov. 23	260	40	5.20	6.10	6.52	5.65	5.03	5.20	7.43	6.20	4.58	3.56	3.28	5.51	64.26
	Mobile	40	52.8	81.6	103	−1	40	Feb. 17	Dec. 12	298	40	4.75	5.22	5.63	5.06	4.57	4.96	7.22	6.11	4.64	3.82	3.48	5.21	60.67
	Seven Hills	12	54.9	81.3	104	15	13	Mar. 13	Nov. 23	255	13	4.72	5.38	6.72	5.44	5.49	4.91	8.04	6.37	4.43	3.37	4.34	5.32	64.53
	Spring Hill	18	52.4	80.8	104	11	24	Feb. 24	Dec. 19	298	25	4.45	5.38	5.82	4.95	5.32	5.45	8.19	7.59	5.67	4.18	3.81	5.36	66.17
Monroe	Bermuda	18	49.9	80.2	108	−4	21	Mar. 25	Nov. 6	226	21	4.34	6.30	6.24	4.66	4.44	4.20	6.53	5.57	5.26	2.62	3.30	5.52	58.98
Montgomery	Montgomery	40	49.5	81.3	107	−5	40	Mar. 3	Nov. 19	261	40	4.90	5.54	6.03	4.77	3.73	3.70	4.88	3.80	3.32	2.58	3.25	4.94	51.44
	Primrose Farm										17	4.97	4.93	5.70	4.57	3.51	4.04	5.01	3.85	3.16	2.54	2.84	4.27	49.39
Morgan	Decatur	40	43.1	80.6	108	−12	40	Mar. 26	Nov. 5	224	40	4.61	4.38	5.72	4.63	4.09	3.89	4.29	3.93	2.36	3.12	3.35	5.12	49.49
Perry	Marion										30	5.54	5.52	5.47	4.29	3.91	3.09	4.73	4.05	2.65	2.80	2.98	5.12	50.15
	Uniontown	29	48.3	80.7	109	−6	29	Mar. 21	Nov. 5	229	29	5.18	5.32	4.92	4.09	3.81	3.29	5.11	3.96	2.78	2.27	2.80	5.31	48.84
Pickens	Cochrane										19	5.80	4.11	5.40	5.73	3.91	3.22	4.66	4.01	3.03	2.39	3.21	5.47	50.94
	Dancy										33	4.81	4.36	5.47	5.08	4.57	3.78	4.59	3.51	2.78	2.61	3.41	5.21	50.18
Pike	Troy	28	51.5	80.7	108	8	31	Mar. 16	Nov. 17	246	31	5.24	5.08	6.18	5.05	3.51	3.73	5.93	4.83	4.22	2.67	3.38	4.44	54.26

Russell	Seale										14	4.44	4.74	5.82	4.39	2.18	3.38	5.85	4.67	2.64	3.36	2.71	4.21	48.39
St. Clair	Ashville	20	43.9	78.6	105	−12	20	Apr. 3	Oct. 27	207	22	5.17	5.25	6.27	4.93	4.43	4.39	5.37	4.74	3.84	2.94	2.75	5.50	55.58
Shelby	Calera										38	5.12	5.18	6.25	4.52	3.71	3.88	5.40	4.51	3.28	3.07	3.31	5.13	53.36
	Helena										25	5.67	5.63	6.55	5.26	3.94	4.01	4.28	4.48	2.85	3.32	4.00	5.56	55.55
Sumter	Livingston	18	45.5	81.0	105	−5	21	Mar. 25	Nov. 1	221	22	4.30	4.74	4.93	5.05	4.03	4.59	5.32	3.34	2.84	2.52	2.56	4.90	49.12
Talladega	Lock 4	40	45.5	80.1	109	−9	40	Mar. 26	Nov. 5	224	40	5.50	5.72	6.15	4.96	4.16	3.92	5.05	4.54	3.00	3.17	3.50	5.89	55.56
	Talladega	37	46.5	80.1	109	−10	38	Apr. 2	Nov. 2	214	40	5.16	5.55	6.09	4.81	4.06	4.58	5.20	4.45	3.17	2.98	3.40	5.38	54.83
Tallapoosa	Camp Hill	32	47.9	79.8	109	−4	38	Mar. 24	Nov. 11	232	38	4.67	5.01	5.83	4.64	3.62	3.73	5.32	4.39	2.96	2.46	2.94	4.95	50.52
	Dadeville										34	4.89	5.12	6.15	4.79	3.50	3.99	5.23	4.61	2.73	2.86	3.17	5.20	52.24
	Martin Dam										14	5.10	4.87	5.64	4.66	2.83	3.52	5.29	4.22	2.97	3.02	3.43	4.55	50.10
Tuscaloosa	Tuscaloosa	40	45.8	81.5	108	−7	40	Mar. 23	Nov. 9	231	40	5.20	4.98	5.99	5.18	4.37	3.86	5.24	4.03	2.80	3.00	3.70	5.72	54.07
Walker	Cordova	15	46.1	79.4	105	−5	16	Apr. 2	Oct. 25	206	27	5.34	5.13	5.46	4.96	3.99	4.07	6.06	4.24	2.91	3.33	2.97	5.19	53.65
Washington	Millry										31	5.84	5.45	5.96	5.45	4.13	3.99	6.01	4.66	3.46	2.96	3.45	5.68	57.04

[1] The following counties, for which no records are available, are best represented by the stations indicated: Clay—Talladega; Cleburne—Anniston; Franklin—Tuscumbia; Greene—Greensboro; Henry—Ozark; Lamar—Hamilton; Lawrence—Decatur; Limestone—Madison; Randolph—Camp Hill; Wilcox—Greenville; Winston—St. Bernard.

[2] Length of growing season between average dates of last killing frost in spring and first in fall.

Precipitation and temperature—State unit values

[This tabulation gives the mean annual, mean monthly, and average seasonal precipitation, 1886–1938, and the mean annual temperatures, 1902–38, for Alabama]

Precipitation		Precipitation		Precipitation		Precipitation		Temperature		Temperature	
Year	Mean	Year	Mean	Year	Mean	Month	Mean	Year	Mean	Year	Mean
	In.		*In.*		*In.*		*In.*		°*F.*		°*F.*
1886	55.33	1907	54.98	1928	55.51	May	3.88	1902	63.7	1921	66.2
1887	47.55	1908	48.01	1929	76.48	June	4.23	1903	62.2	1922	65.7
1888	57.42	1909	58.32	1930	46.17	July	5.49	1904	63.1	1923	64.1
1889	43.30	1910	45.20	1931	42.78	August	4.62	1905	63.1	1924	63.0
1890	49.99	1911	52.54	1932	63.76	September	3.28	1906	63.9	1925	65.8
1891	52.85	1912	66.45	1933	48.27	October	2.79	1907	64.2	1926	63.7
1892	56.81	1913	52.06	1934	55.18	November	3.24	1908	64.3	1927	66.4
1893	50.11	1914	44.90	1935	49.17	December	4.90	1909	64.2	1928	63.2
1894	47.42	1915	53.75	1936	60.65			1910	63.0	1929	64.0
1895	49.92	1916	53.21	1937	58.38	Annual	53.00	1911	65.7	1930	64.0
1896	45.25	1917	53.74	1938	48.35			1912	62.5	1931	64.9
1897	47.30	1918	56.22					1913	64.0	1932	65.0
1898	49.09	1919	65.14			Season	Average	1914	63.2	1933	66.0
1899	47.84	1920	64.20	Month	Mean			1915	63.7	1934	64.7
1900	66.16	1921	45.34					1916	64.0	1935	65.0
1901	55.61	1922	58.78					1917	62.2	1936	65.1
1902	49.27	1923	60.87		*In.*		*In.*	1918	64.2	1937	64.5
1903	49.96	1924	47.23	January	4.98	Winter	15.12	1919	64.4	1938	65.8
1904	39.21	1925	45.20	February	5.24	Spring	14.23	1920	62.7		
1905	55.03	1926	60.79	March	5.86	Summer	14.34				
1906	55.93	1927	45.48	April	4.49	Fall	9.31				

ALABAMA—Continued

Dates of last killing frost in spring and first in fall, with length of growing season

Year	Decatur			Gadsden			Tuscaloosa		
	Last in spring	First in fall	Growing season [1]	Last in spring	First in fall	Growing season [1]	Last in spring	First in fall	Growing season [1]
			Days			*Days*			*Days*
1899	Apr. 2	Nov. 4	216	Apr. 9	Sept. 27	171	Apr. 9	Nov. 3	208
1900	Apr. 1	Nov. 9	222	Apr. 13	Nov. 9	210	Apr. 2	Nov. 9	221
1901	Mar. 21	Nov. 6	230	Mar. 23	Nov. 6	228	Mar. 22	Nov. 6	229
1902	Mar. 19	Nov. 28	254	Apr. 2	Oct. 30	211	Mar. 20	Nov. 28	253
1903	Feb. 22	Oct. 25	245	Apr. 5	Oct. 25	203	Mar. 26	Oct. 25	213
1904	Apr. 4	Oct. 21	200	Apr. 4	Oct. 24	203	Apr. 5	Oct. 24	202
1905	Apr. 17	Nov. 2	199	Apr. 18	Nov. 11	207	Apr. 18		
1906	Mar. 22	Oct. 11	203	Mar. 21	Oct. 11	204	Apr. 1	Oct. 29	211
1907	Apr. 14	Nov. 7	207	Apr. 14	Oct. 29	198	Apr. 15	Nov. 13	212
1908	Apr. 4	Oct. 25	204	Apr. 4	Nov. 6	216	Mar. 23	Nov. 6	228
1909	Mar. 27	Oct. 13	200	Mar. 26	Oct. 25	213	Mar. 17	Nov. 18	246
1910	Apr. 26	Oct. 29	186	Apr. 25	Oct. 29	187	Apr. 25	Oct. 29	187
1911	Mar. 31	Nov. 13	227	Mar. 17	Nov. 13	241	Mar. 18	Nov. 13	240
1912	Mar. 10	Nov. 2	237	Mar. 10	Nov. 3	238	Mar. 11	Nov. 3	237
1913		Oct. 21		Mar. 28	Oct. 21	207	Mar. 28	Oct. 21	207
1914	Apr. 10	Oct. 28	201	Apr. 10	Oct. 28	201	Apr. 11	Oct. 28	200
1915	Apr. 4	Nov. 16	226	Apr. 4	Nov. 16	226	Apr. 5	Nov. 16	225
1916	Mar. 17	Nov. 15	243	Mar. 18	Nov. 15	242	Apr. 10	Oct. 22	195
1917	Mar. 19	Oct. 13	208	Mar. 19	Oct. 25	220	Mar. 19	Oct. 24	219
1918	Feb. 23	Nov. 13	263	Feb. 24	Nov. 25	274	Feb. 24	Dec. 1	280
1919	Apr. 2	Nov. 14	226	Apr. 1	Nov. 17	230	Apr. 2	Nov. 14	226
1920	Mar. 9	Nov. 12	248	Apr. 6	Nov. 13	221	Mar. 15	Nov. 13	243
1921	Mar. 29	Nov. 11	227	Mar. 29	Nov. 3	219	Mar. 4	Nov. 11	252
1922	Mar. 21	Nov. 21	245	Mar. 23	Nov. 21	243	Mar. 9	Nov. 23	259
1923	Apr. 1	Nov. 1	214	Apr. 1	Oct. 25	207	Apr. 1	Oct. 24	206
1924	Apr. 2	Nov. 19	231	Apr. 3	Oct. 23	203	Mar. 16	Nov. 19	248
1925	Mar. 15	Oct. 28	227	Mar. 20	Oct. 20	214	Mar. 3	Oct. 29	240
1926	Apr. 2	Oct. 25	206	Apr. 1	Oct. 27	209	Apr. 2	Nov. 3	215
1927	Mar. 23	Oct. 15	206	Apr. 22			Mar. 23	Nov. 20	242
1928	Apr. 16	Nov. 11	209	Apr. 17	Nov. 5	202	Mar. 18	Nov. 11	238
1929	Mar. 11	Nov. 5	239	Mar. 18	Nov. 6	233	Feb. 25	Nov. 30	278
1930	Mar. 29	Oct. 31	216	Mar. 30	Oct. 26	210	Mar. 6	Oct. 31	239
1931	Mar. 18	Nov. 7	234	Apr. 2	Nov. 2	214	Mar. 18	Nov. 7	234
1932	Mar. 16	Nov. 12	241	Mar. 24	Nov. 10	231	Mar. 16	Nov. 12	241
1933	Mar. 22	Nov. 10	233	Mar. 22	Nov. 8	231	Mar. 27	Nov. 9	227
1934	Mar. 20	Nov. 12	237	Apr. 13	Nov. 2	203	Mar. 20	Nov. 12	237
1935	Mar. 13	Nov. 23	255	Apr. 14	Nov. 21	221	Mar. 1	Nov. 23	267

Year	Thomasville			Ozark			Citronelle		
	Last in spring	First in fall	Growing season [1]	Last in spring	First in fall	Growing season [1]	Last in spring	First in fall	Growing season [1]
			Days			*Days*			*Days*
1899	Mar. 29						Mar. 8	Dec. 5	272
1900	Mar. 17	Nov. 9	237				Feb. 19	Dec. 9	293
1901	Mar. 7	Nov. 16	254				Mar. 7	Nov. 16	254
1902	Mar. 19	Nov. 28	254		Nov. 28		Mar. 18	Nov. 28	255
1903	Feb. 23	Oct. 25	244	Feb. 22	Oct. 25	245	Feb. 18	Nov. 18	273
1904	Mar. 5	Nov. 15	255	Mar. 4	Nov. 28	269	Mar. 4	Dec. 13	284
1905	Feb. 17	Nov. 30	286	Feb. 18	Dec. 4	289	Feb. 16	Dec. 4	291
1906	Mar. 20	Nov. 13	238	Apr. 2	Oct. 29	210	Mar. 21	Nov. 13	237
1907	Feb. 16	Nov. 13	270		Nov. 13		Feb. 15	Nov. 13	271
1908	Feb. 29	Nov. 15	260		Nov. 15		Feb. 21	Nov. 15	267
1909	Mar. 17	Oct. 25	222	Feb. 26	Oct. 25	241	Feb. 17	Nov. 19	275
1910	Apr. 26	Oct. 29	186	Apr. 26	Oct. 29	186	Mar. 16	Oct. 29	227
1911	Mar. 16	Nov. 13	242		Nov. 13		Mar. 17	Nov. 13	241
1912	Mar. 16	Nov. 3	232	Mar. 10	Nov. 27	262	Mar. 10	Nov. 3	238
1913	Mar. 28	Oct. 21	207	Mar. 29	Oct. 22	207	Mar. 28	Nov. 10	227
1914	Apr. 10	Oct. 28	201	Mar. 2	Nov. 20	263	Mar. 23	Oct. 28	219
1915	Mar. 25	Nov. 16	236	Apr. 5			Mar. 24	Nov. 16	237
1916	Apr. 10	Nov. 15	219		Nov. 16		Mar. 17	Nov. 15	243
1917	Mar. 19	Oct. 24	219	Mar. 6	Oct. 25	233	Mar. 6	Oct. 24	232
1918	Apr. 13	Dec. 2	233	Feb. 6	Dec. 26	323	Apr. 12	Dec. 26	258
1919	Apr. 2	Nov. 14	226	Feb. 17	Dec. 28	314	Jan. 11	Dec. 17	340
1920	Mar. 12	Oct. 31	233	Mar. 9	Nov. 17	253	Mar. 9	Nov. 17	253
1921	Feb. 26	Nov. 11	258	None	Nov. 5	309	Jan. 10	Dec. 5	329
1922		Nov. 29		Mar. 5	Nov. 26	266	Mar. 5		
1923	Apr. 1	Nov. 1	214	Mar. 20	None	287	Apr. 1		
1924	Feb. 28	Nov. 26	272	Mar. 22	Nov. 25	248	Mar. 22	Nov. 19	242
1925	Feb. 13	Oct. 20	249	Mar. 4	Nov. 23	264	Mar. 3	Nov. 23	265
1926	Mar. 31	Nov. 6	220		Nov. 11		Mar. 16	Nov. 11	240
1927	Mar. 22	Nov. 19	242	Mar. 4	Nov. 19	260	Mar. 4	Nov. 19	260
1928	Mar. 18	Nov. 13	240	Mar. 18	Nov. 21	248	Mar. 18	Nov. 21	248
1929	Mar. 11			Feb. 23	Nov. 30	280	Feb. 23	Nov. 30	280
1930		Oct. 31		Mar. 5	Nov. 1	241	Mar. 4	Nov. 1	242
1931	Mar. 18	Nov. 1	228	Mar. 10	None	297	Mar. 10	None	297
1932	Mar. 15	Nov. 12	242	Mar. 16	Nov. 12	241	Mar. 15	Nov. 12	242
1933	Mar. 11	Nov. 8	242	Mar. 5	Nov. 9	249	Mar. 21	Dec. 27	281
1934	Mar. 28	Nov. 12	229	Mar. 20	Nov. 13	238	Mar. 11	Dec. 8	272
1935	Mar. 13	Nov. 22	254	Mar. 1	Nov. 23	267	Mar. 13	Nov. 18	250

1936	Apr. 3	Nov. 16	227	Mar. 21	Nov. 16	240	Mar. 18	Nov. 16	243	Apr. 3	Nov. 17	228	Feb. 19	Nov. 26	280	Mar. 19	Nov. 26	252
1937	Mar. 29	Oct. 24	209	Apr. 10	Oct. 24	197	Mar. 29	Oct. 24	209	Mar. 29	Oct. 24	209	Mar. 29	Oct. 24	209	Mar. 28	Nov. 18	235
1938	Mar. 7	Nov. 24	262	Apr. 10	Oct. 25	198	Mar. 7	Nov. 25	263	Mar. 7	Nov. 9	247	Feb. 26	Nov. 25	272	Feb. 20	Nov. 25	278
Mean	Mar. 26	Nov. 5	224	Apr. 1	Nov. 2	215	Mar. 23	Nov. 9	231	Mar. 18	Nov. 10	237	Mar. 7	Nov. 19	257	Mar. 8	Nov. 23	260
Extremes	Feb. 22[2]	Oct. 11[4]	[6] 186	Feb. 24[2]	Sept. 27[4]	[6] 171	Feb. 24[2]	Oct. 21[4]	[6] 187	Feb. 13[2]	Oct. 20[4]	[6] 186	None[2]	Oct. 22[4]	[6] 186	Jan. 10[2]	Oct. 24[4]	[6] 219
	Apr. 26[3]	Nov. 28[5]	[7] 263	Apr. 25[3]	Nov. 25[5]	[7] 274	Apr. 25[3]	Dec. 1[5]	[7] 280	Apr. 26[3]	Dec. 2[5]	[7] 286	Apr. 26[3]	None[5]	[7] 323	Apr. 12[3]	None[5]	[7] 340

[1] Number of days between last killing frost in spring and first in fall.
[2] Earliest date in spring.
[3] Latest date in spring.
[4] Earliest date in fall.
[5] Latest date in fall.
[6] Shortest growing season.
[7] Longest growing season.

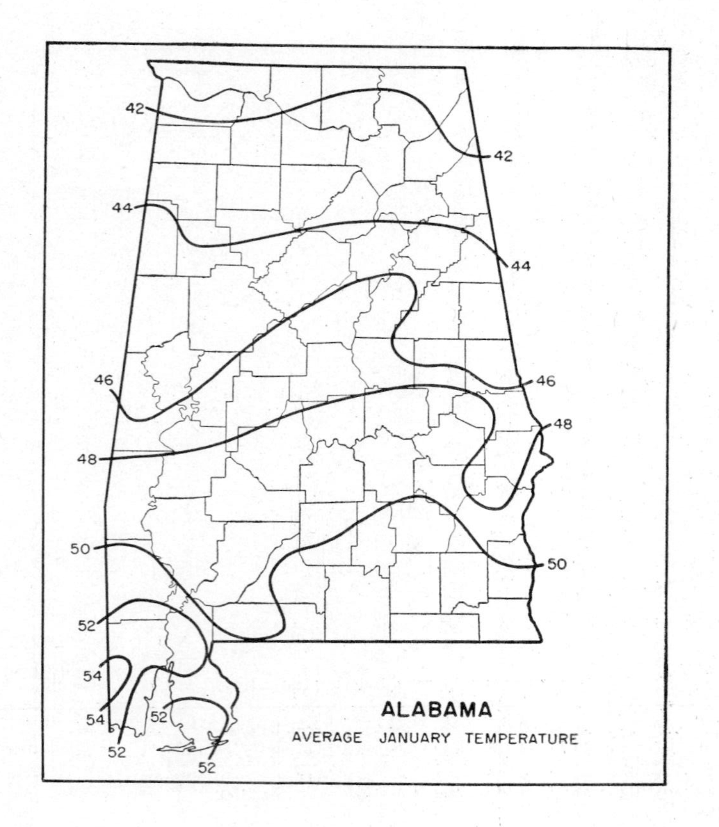
42
42
44
44
46
46
48
48
50
50
52
54
54
52
52
52
ALABAMA
AVERAGE JANUARY TEMPERATURE

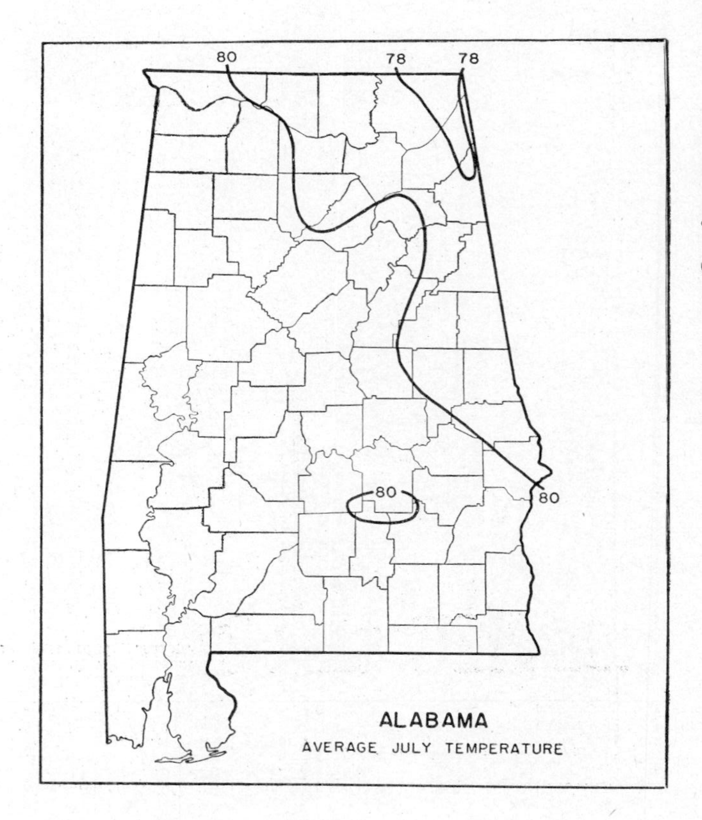
80
78
78
80
80
ALABAMA
AVERAGE JULY TEMPERATURE

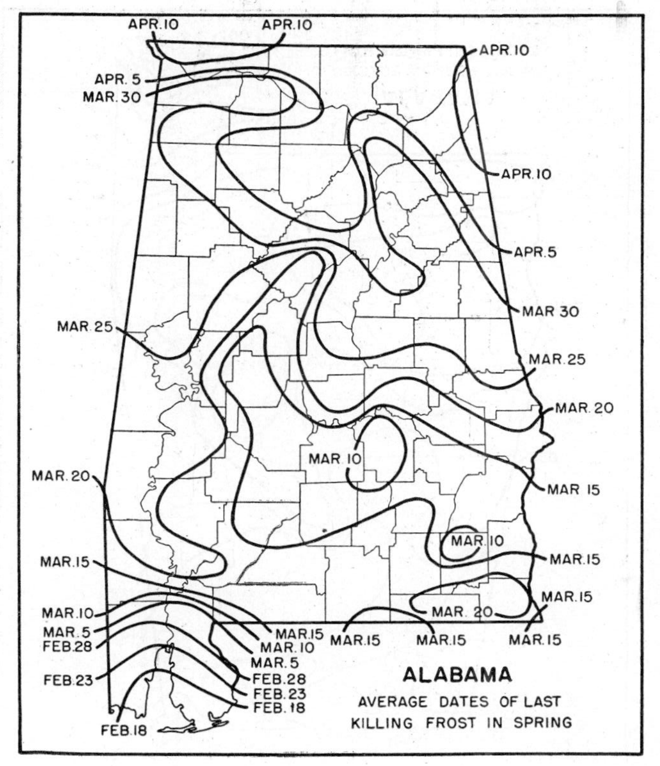
ALABAMA
AVERAGE DATES OF LAST
KILLING FROST IN SPRING
APR. 10
APR. 5
MAR. 30
MAR. 25
MAR. 20
MAR. 15
MAR. 10
MAR. 5
FEB. 28
FEB. 23
FEB. 18

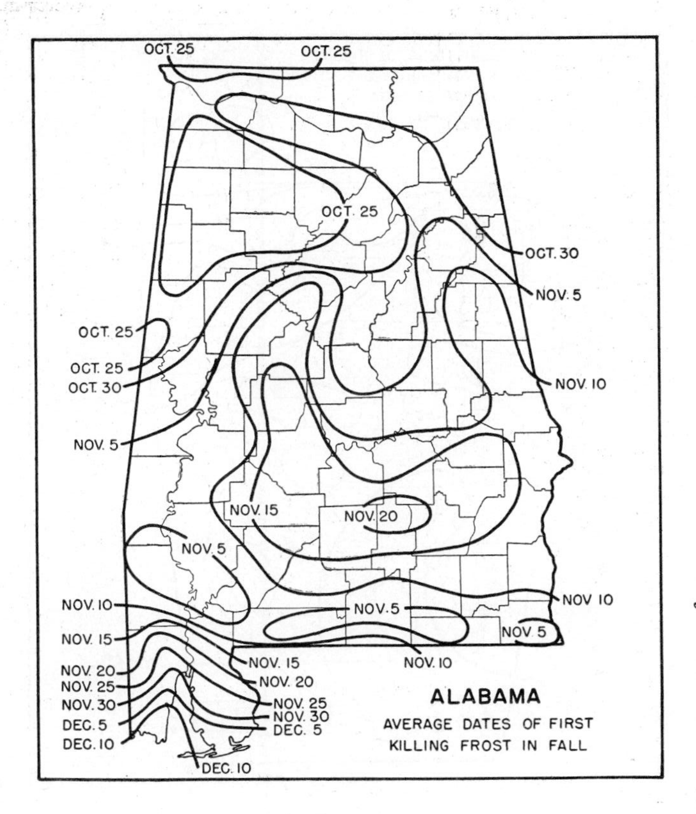
ALABAMA
AVERAGE DATES OF FIRST
KILLING FROST IN FALL
OCT. 25
OCT. 30
NOV. 5
NOV. 10
NOV. 15
NOV. 20
NOV. 25
NOV. 30
DEC. 5
DEC. 10

298737°—41——49 +

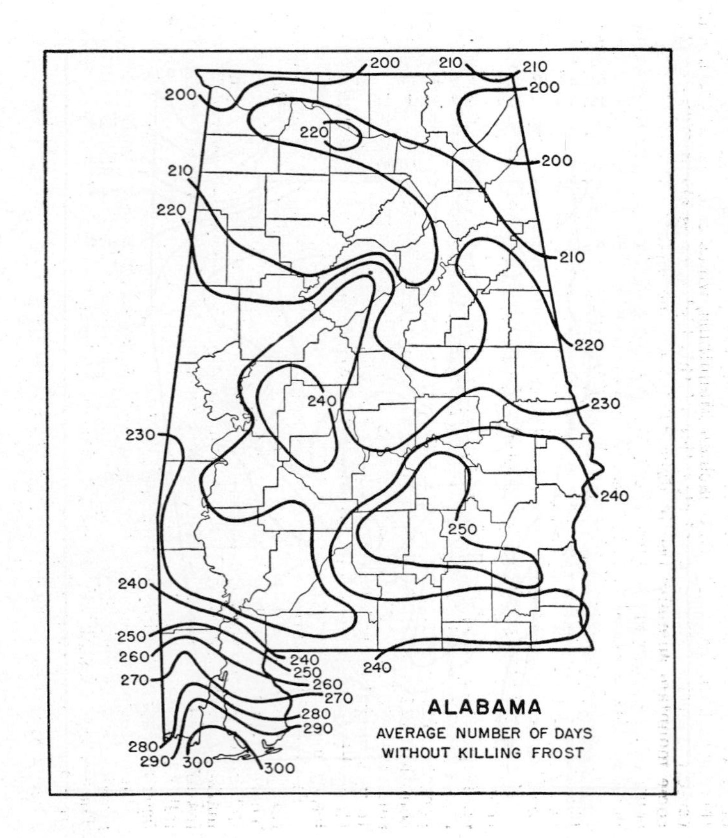
ALABAMA
AVERAGE NUMBER OF DAYS
WITHOUT KILLING FROST

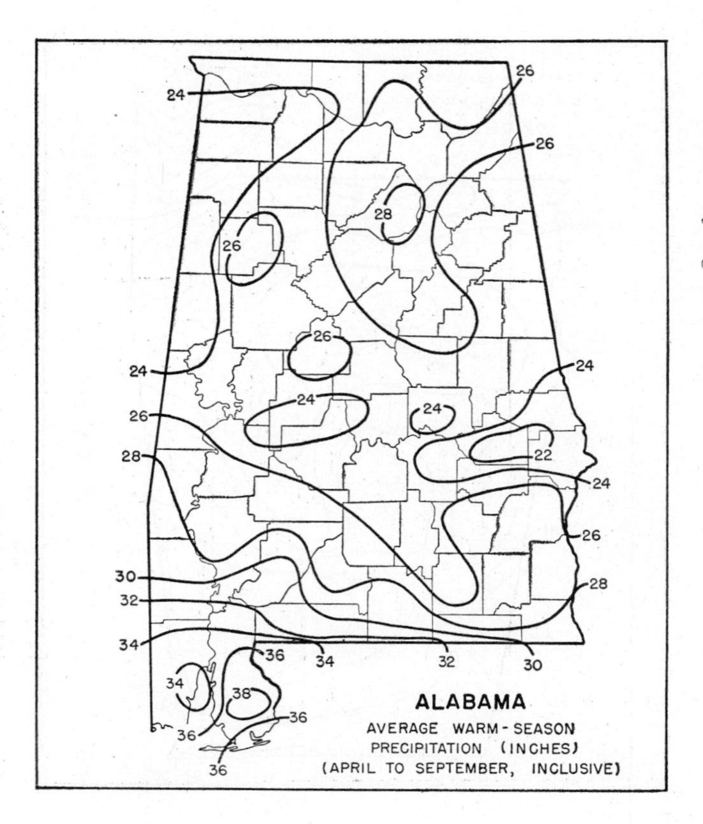
ALABAMA
AVERAGE WARM-SEASON
PRECIPITATION (INCHES)
(APRIL TO SEPTEMBER, INCLUSIVE)

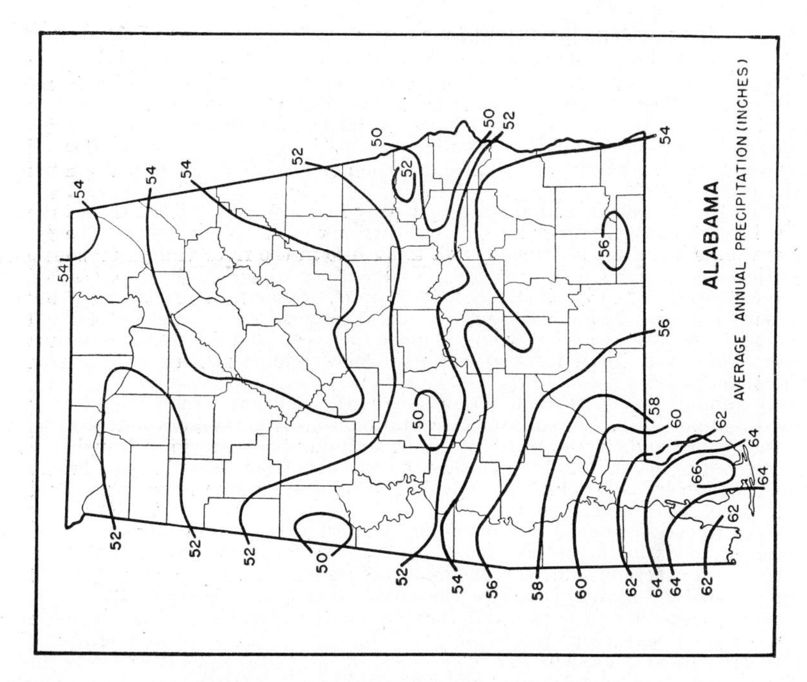

SUPPLEMENTARY CLIMATIC NOTES FOR ALABAMA

The surface of Alabama rises as an undulating plain from the level of the Gulf of Mexico in the southwest to foothills in the central part of the State. Thence there is a sharp rise to the Appalachian Mountains, which extend into the northeastern counties. The general elevation of this high area is about 800 feet, but some mountain summits rise to over 2,000 feet, the highest, Mount Cheaha in southwestern Cleburne County, being 2,407 feet high. In every direction except northeast there are downward slopes from these highlands into river valleys.

The northern part of the State is drained by the Tennessee River; the middle part by the Tombigbee, Black Warrior, Coosa, Tallapoosa, and middle Chattahoochee; and the southern part by the Tombigbee, Alabama, Conecuh, Escambia, Choctawhatchee, and Chattahoochee Rivers.

The geographic position, topography, and prevailing winds of Alabama all contribute to a temperate climate. The summers, while warm, are not very oppressive, and heat prostrations rarely occur. In these southern latitudes summer days are shorter and the nights considerably longer than in the north, which compensates somewhat for the more southerly geographic location. In the northern counties higher altitudes also help make the nights comfortable. While the summers are long, the daytime temperatures are not as a rule excessively high. In fact, considerably higher temperatures have occurred in the extreme northern Great Plains than were ever experienced in Alabama, and 27 of the States have higher maxima.

Severely cold weather seldom occurs, and freezing temperatures usually do not continue longer than 48 consecutive hours, even in the northern part of the State. There is usually an abundance of sunshine during the crop-growing months and well into the harvest season, but the winter and early spring are sometimes marked by prolonged periods of cloudiness and heavy to excessive rains. A feature of the Alabama climate is the relatively dry, sunny weather during the fall, or crop-harvesting season; the coldest weather of winter and spring, also, is usually accompanied by clear skies.

Precipitation is normally adequate for all agricultural needs, while the long growing season permits two, sometimes three, crops a year on the same land. The heaviest rainfall usually occurs when a West Indian hurricane passes inland from the eastern Gulf of Mexico.

There are three climatic divisions in Alabama. The northern lies north of latitude 33°, where the climate is controlled largely by alternating cyclonic disturbances and anticyclones, the paths of the centers of which are usually north of the State. The southern division lies roughly south of latitude 31°30′. It is not entirely free from influences peculiar to the Temperate Zone, but the climate is largely subtropical and is markedly influenced by the Gulf of Mexico. The climate of the middle division is a combination of those of the other two in modified form.

Owing to the flow of cold air into relatively low places and down river valleys, there is considerable irregularity in the distribution of killing frosts. The growing season is definitely shortened from this cause in the river valleys of southern counties.

Precipitation is nearly all in the form of rain. Snow rarely falls except in the northern counties where it occurs on an average of twice each winter. The average fall in this area is only about 3 inches per year, and this includes unusually heavy snows in a few individual winters. Snow seldom remains on the ground more than 2 days.

July rainfall in Alabama, as elsewhere in the Southeastern States, is of the greatest importance. Adequate precipitation to sustain vegetation already in good growing condition or to revive crops suffering from previous droughts may be expected to occur in July. During the 55 years from 1884 through 1938, the State means were below 4 inches only 8 times in July, compared with 29 times in April, 35 in May, and 28 in June.

Heavy to excessive general rains of late winter or early spring sometimes cause damaging floods in the streams of Alabama. Although it is possible for floods to occur at any season, March is the month of their greatest frequency. Tropical storms sometimes cause floods in the summer and fall but are very unusual. Extensive areas of rich bottom land are inundated in times of flood, sometimes with much damage to crops, though the land may benefit by alluvial deposits where currents are not swift.

Severe general droughts are practically unknown in Alabama. Few months have ever passed without beneficial rains in some part of the State, and in only a few localities has an entire month been without precipitation. Relatively brief periods of droughty conditions sometimes prevail, usually in the fall months but occasionally in other seasons. Yield of crops is occasionally reduced, but a complete general crop failure attributable to drought has never occurred.

Destructive West Indian storms visit the coastal area on an average about once every 7 years, between July and November.

During the passage of cyclonic disturbances over and to the north of Alabama there are occasionally destructive local windstorms, some of which develop into tornadoes. Tornadoes have been experienced in Alabama in every month of the year and in every county, but they occur mostly in the spring.

Thunderstorms are most frequent in summer but have occurred in all months. They are not often severe and are only occasionally accompanied by hail; destructive local thunderstorms are rare.

Dense fogs are rare and most likely to occur from November to February.

The prevailing direction of the wind for the year is from the south; in winter from the north; in spring, south; in summer, southwest; in September, east; in October and November, north. The highest recorded velocity in the State was 82 miles an hour, from the east, at Mobile on October 18, 1916.

Eugene D. Emigh, *Associate Meteorologist and Climatic Section Director for Alabama, Weather Bureau, Montgomery.*

ARIZONA

Climatic summary

County	Station	Temperature					Killing frost average dates				Average precipitation													
		Length of record	January average	July average	Maximum	Minimum	Length of record	Last in spring	First in fall	Growing season[1]	Length of record	January	February	March	April	May	June	July	August	September	October	November	December	Annual
		Yr.	*°F.*	*°F.*	*°F.*	*°F.*	*Yr.*			*Days*	*Yr.*	*In.*	*In.*	*In.*	*In.*	*In.*	*In.*	*In.*	*In.*	*In.*	*In.*	*In.*	*In.*	*In.*
Apache	Alpine	15	27.3	60.6	96	−27	21	June 17	Sept. 21	96	23	1.40	1.97	1.71	1.10	0.70	0.86	4.25	3.54	2.51	1.96	1.37	1.78	23.15
	Chinle	21	27.9	74.0	103	−32	22	May 23	Oct. 5	135	21	.41	.60	.53	.41	.30	.46	1.70	1.36	1.07	.76	.39	.61	8.60
	Fort Defiance	17	25.6	68.5	98	−30	15	May 26	Sept. 30	127	16	.78	1.27	.83	.75	.64	.82	1.53	2.08	1.33	.51	.85	.73	12.12
	Greer	----	----	----	----	----	13	June 9	Sept. 16	99	17	1.49	1.52	1.83	.98	.71	.95	4.46	4.31	1.49	1.43	1.07	1.69	21.93
	Henry's Camp	22	33.2	70.6	104	−20	22	May 22	Oct. 7	138	22	2.03	2.79	2.13	1.30	.92	.93	4.05	4.17	2.58	1.24	1.42	1.95	25.51
	Saint Johns	30	31.1	72.9	104	−22	32	May 5	Oct. 11	159	31	.72	.65	.79	.59	.55	.58	2.38	2.31	1.36	.68	.58	.79	11.98
	Saint Michaels	20	27.6	69.5	106	−25	21	May 21	Oct. 1	133	21	.96	.98	.95	.51	.38	.43	2.44	2.39	1.32	1.11	.68	1.01	13.16
	Springerville	25	31.1	66.3	96	−28	26	May 28	Oct. 2	127	28	.58	.60	.56	.48	.49	.60	3.14	3.22	1.52	.77	.58	.60	13.14
Cochise	Benson	38	46.4	81.1	113	5	38	Mar. 28	Nov. 8	225	39	.63	.89	.54	.23	.12	.33	2.53	2.65	1.35	.50	.72	.69	11.18
	Bisbee	40	46.4	76.3	106	8	37	Mar. 28	Nov. 22	239	39	1.10	1.44	.98	.53	.27	.65	4.22	4.67	2.09	1.00	1.09	1.49	19.53
	Bowie	36	46.1	83.1	116	10	35	Mar. 26	Nov. 8	227	37	.72	.91	.64	.23	.22	.28	2.16	2.11	.95	.69	.74	.84	10.49
	Cochise	25	43.8	79.7	114	−4	22	Apr. 1	Nov. 7	220	25	.74	.90	.68	.22	.22	.27	2.79	2.17	1.21	.58	.82	.80	11.40
	Douglas	35	45.3	79.8	111	−7	35	Apr. 8	Nov. 6	212	35	.63	.75	.47	.27	.21	.45	3.18	2.96	1.29	.78	.80	.99	12.78
	Fairbank	----	----	----	----	----	16	Apr. 21	Oct. 25	187	29	.56	.65	.44	.20	.17	.62	3.75	2.70	1.19	.48	.62	.68	12.06
	Fort Huachuca	22	45.9	76.6	105	0	19	Mar. 30	Nov. 17	232	20	1.46	1.34	1.00	.34	.37	.59	3.83	3.80	1.59	.66	1.06	1.27	17.31
	Leslie Canyon	----	----	----	----	----	18	Apr. 7	Oct. 31	207	23	.62	.77	.58	.29	.31	.57	3.09	2.95	1.39	.75	.77	.81	12.90
	Lewis Springs	----	----	----	----	----	22	Apr. 12	Oct. 21	192	23	.51	.68	.35	.13	.12	.58	3.32	2.68	1.08	.51	.60	.59	11.15
	Naco	----	----	----	----	----	21	Mar. 25	Nov. 11	231	24	.75	.79	.59	.26	.16	.54	4.12	2.87	1.61	.82	.78	1.02	14.31
	Paradise	31	38.4	72.6	104	−6	30	Apr. 24	Oct. 20	179	31	1.16	1.30	1.13	.63	.40	.60	4.23	3.51	2.08	1.08	1.29	1.58	18.99
	Portal	----	----	----	----	----	----	----	----	----	24	1.03	1.22	.89	.55	.37	.60	3.51	3.79	2.19	1.20	1.50	1.55	18.40
	Rucker Canyon	----	----	----	----	----	18	Apr. 24	Oct. 22	181	27	1.40	1.59	1.23	.58	.47	.72	4.59	4.01	2.16	1.38	1.23	1.71	21.07
	San Simon	18	43.8	81.5	111	−5	26	Apr. 4	Nov. 10	220	28	.64	.71	.79	.29	.22	.22	1.75	1.91	.83	.42	.55	1.03	9.36
	Tombstone	38	47.0	78.9	110	9	36	Mar. 28	Nov. 19	236	38	.80	.94	.68	.28	.24	.49	3.64	3.59	1.60	.68	.77	.96	14.67
	Willcox (near)	40	41.2	77.7	110	2	37	Apr. 28	Oct. 28	183	38	.93	1.02	.81	.23	.26	.28	2.44	2.60	1.18	.67	.83	.98	12.23
Coconino	Big Springs	7	----	65.6	97	----	12	June 6	Oct. 1	117	11	.93	1.41	1.69	2.14	.85	.31	1.77	2.57	1.27	1.77	.75	1.91	17.37
	Bly Ranger Station	----	----	----	----	----	----	----	----	----	7	2.31	1.67	2.03	1.81	.48	.52	2.89	2.73	1.99	1.51	1.55	2.85	22.34
	Bright Angel Ranger Station.	12	21.0	61.6	91	−25	14	June 14	Sept. 15	93	13	2.94	4.63	2.89	1.57	1.39	.88	2.08	2.46	2.28	1.28	1.57	2.91	26.88
	Flagstaff	40	27.2	65.2	99	−30	40	June 3	Sept. 29	118	40	1.95	2.12	1.99	1.28	.74	.52	3.11	3.03	1.69	1.48	1.34	1.67	20.92
	Fort Valley	30	24.7	62.3	94	−33	30	June 16	Sept. 18	94	30	2.24	2.46	2.19	1.34	.89	.65	3.37	3.39	1.92	1.53	1.20	2.07	23.25
	Grand Canyon	33	28.9	68.8	103	−22	32	May 19	Oct. 7	141	33	1.33	1.81	1.32	.79	.77	.36	2.18	2.43	1.55	1.24	1.07	1.65	16.50
	Lees Ferry	16	35.0	87.0	114	2	18	Mar. 23	Nov. 5	227	19	.35	.62	.46	.41	.37	.16	.70	1.18	.50	.50	.44	.53	6.22
	Mormon Lake	21	----	65.1	92	----	17	May 30	Oct. 4	127	21	----	----	----	1.56	.84	.62	2.77	2.98	2.23	1.78	----	----	----
	Supai	21	41.6	83.0	115	−2	22	Mar. 6	Nov. 15	254	22	.73	1.08	.60	.66	.32	.39	.96	1.54	.68	.91	.42	1.00	9.29
	Tuba City	36	31.9	77.4	108	−15	33	Apr. 23	Oct. 19	179	34	.55	.57	.40	.52	.25	.33	.88	.83	.68	.62	.52	.57	6.72

[1] Length of growing season between average dates of last killing frost in spring and first in fall.

ARIZONA—Continued

Climatic summary—Continued

County	Station	Temperature					Killing frost average dates				Average precipitation													
		Length of record	January average	July average	Maximum	Minimum	Length of record	Last in spring	First in fall	Growing season	Length of record	January	February	March	April	May	June	July	August	September	October	November	December	Annual
		Yr.	°*F.*	°*F.*	°*F.*	°*F.*	*Yr.*			*Days*	*Yr.*	*In.*	*In.*	*In.*	*In.*	*In.*	*In.*	*In.*	*In.*	*In.*	*In.*	*In.*	*In.*	*In.*
Coconino—Contd.	Wallace Ranger Station.										13	1.58	1.97	.87	1.13	.44	.58	3.05	2.77	1.98	1.42	.83	1.00	17.62
	Williams	35	30.2	67.1	102	−25	35	June 2	Sept. 26	116	35	2.19	2.63	2.08	1.54	.80	.45	3.44	3.19	1.50	1.37	1.25	2.23	22.67
Gila	Alamo Ranger Station.						20	Apr. 9	Nov. 4	209	22	1.49	1.78	1.13	.86	.28	.41	2.48	2.15	1.35	.83	1.07	1.46	15.29
	Gisela						16	Apr. 20	Nov. 2	196	18	1.99	2.22	1.69	1.01	.51	.40	2.42	2.12	1.78	.92	1.78	1.64	18.48
	Globe	36	44.1	82.3	110	10	36	Mar. 29	Nov. 13	229	34	1.53	1.61	1.28	.71	.40	.44	2.82	2.60	1.31	.91	1.20	1.69	16.50
	Intake						14	Mar. 24	Nov. 23	244	29	1.24	1.50	1.08	.64	.29	.30	2.19	2.13	1.02	.69	.96	1.52	13.56
	Miami	24	44.8	83.1	110	13	24	Mar. 17	Nov. 22	250	25	2.20	2.28	1.66	.95	.52	.52	2.95	3.00	1.60	.94	1.39	2.35	20.36
	Natural Bridge	24	40.5	76.0	101	2	32	Apr. 15	Nov. 8	207	40	2.45	3.24	2.54	1.56	.57	.50	3.14	3.19	1.93	1.58	1.94	2.48	25.12
	Payson	26	35.7	72.7	104	−18	26	May 23	Oct. 11	141	28	2.22	2.64	2.02	1.22	.31	.56	2.81	3.05	1.83	1.49	1.73	2.09	21.97
	Reno Ranger Station	30	45.1	84.5	115	11	30	Mar. 31	Nov. 9	223	28	2.16	2.54	2.06	1.11	.32	.39	2.18	2.52	1.30	1.05	1.61	2.59	19.83
	Roosevelt	30	47.3	88.4	115	18	30	Feb. 9	Dec. 7	301	32	2.03	2.36	1.83	.96	.31	.46	1.70	2.20	1.12	.99	1.34	2.04	17.34
	San Carlos	29	45.5	85.4	115	1	28	Mar. 26	Nov. 9	228	33	1.24	1.51	1.04	.55	.27	.29	1.84	1.96	.93	.57	1.02	1.42	12.64
	Young						22	May 7	Oct. 14	160	24	2.15	2.38	2.32	1.33	.45	.72	3.21	3.33	1.86	1.10	1.63	2.04	22.52
Graham	Fort Grant						22	Apr. 6	Nov. 11	219	34	1.14	1.11	.79	.43	.27	.26	2.63	2.45	1.33	.63	.84	1.20	13.08
	Thatcher	35	43.9	82.8	116	7	33	Apr. 10	Nov. 1	205	37	.62	.81	.63	.30	.17	.28	1.79	1.83	1.03	.65	.79	.75	9.65
Greenlee	Blue						24	May 5	Oct. 14	162	26	1.38	1.42	1.38	.82	.52	.62	4.09	3.27	1.89	1.63	1.42	1.45	19.89
	Clifton	30	45.5	85.4	114	13	30	Mar. 2	Nov. 24	267	38	.90	1.19	.84	.39	.32	.44	2.33	2.51	1.53	.91	.71	1.10	13.17
	Eagle Creek						10	Apr. 17	Oct. 22	188	17	1.69	1.67	.95	.56	.65	.69	3.74	3.23	2.16	.88	1.08	1.18	18.48
Maricopa	Agua Caliente	11	51.5	92.0	121	19	10	Mar. 3	Nov. 18	260	11	.60	.19	.12	.02	.04	.04	.34	.82	.32	.13	.08	.28	2.98
	Aguila						15	Mar. 14	Nov. 29	260	15	.83	1.49	.80	.67	.10	.15	.95	2.04	.88	.43	.44	1.42	10.20
	Ashdale Ranger Station.						16	Apr. 3	Nov. 8	219	22	2.82	2.92	2.30	1.44	.38	.34	2.40	3.02	1.79	1.16	1.56	2.99	23.12
	Buckeye	40	50.1	89.2	121	11	38	Mar. 9	Nov. 19	255	39	.84	.89	.69	.36	.09	.09	1.03	.92	.67	.42	.68	.95	7.63
	Chandler	21	48.4	89.1	120	9	21	Mar. 19	Nov. 18	244	21	.85	.85	.69	.47	.18	.09	.98	1.09	.87	.47	.70	.92	8.16
	Gila Bend	35	52.7	92.6	123	11	34	Feb. 16	Nov. 30	287	36	.60	.53	.61	.18	.10	.07	.74	.92	.45	.34	.52	.72	5.78
	Goodyear	13	49.6	90.3	118	18	14	Mar. 16	Nov. 15	244	14	.51	.90	.79	.31	.13	.15	1.30	1.02	.72	.52	.72	.95	8.02
	Goulds Ranch	23	50.4	89.4	116	19	24	Feb. 18	Nov. 26	281	24	.87	.88	.62	.36	.12	.07	.81	1.10	.70	.34	.61	1.04	7.52
	Granite Reef Dam	37	52.4	89.6	121	12	37	Feb. 14	Dec. 4	293	37	1.12	1.14	.91	.54	.16	.16	1.17	1.18	.74	.50	.86	1.11	9.59
	Litchfield Park	16	50.3	91.0	117	17	22	Mar. 3	Nov. 22	264	22	.80	.94	.76	.33	.17	.12	.78	1.48	.60	.29	.70	1.07	8.04
	Marinette	24	50.3	90.9	120	17	21	Mar. 3	Nov. 27	269	22	.82	.81	.58	.47	.13	.16	.78	1.02	.56	.31	.67	1.29	7.60
	Mesa Experiment Farm.	38	50.0	87.6	119	15	38	Mar. 7	Nov. 19	257	40	.82	1.00	.83	.42	.12	.13	1.05	1.14	.75	.40	.78	1.06	8.50
	Mormon Flat	14	52.0	93.1	118	20	8	Feb. 15	Dec. 29	317	14	1.14	1.84	1.39	.82	.19	.43	1.15	2.21	1.23	.42	1.02	1.69	13.53
	Phoenix	40	51.8	90.3	118	16	40	Feb. 5	Dec. 6	304	40	.77	.89	.67	.43	.12	.08	1.00	.93	.71	.44	.71	.87	7.62

	Sentinel	19	53.9	94.1	124	18	21	Feb. 11	Dec. 15	307	19	.53	.50	.36	.26	.03	.12	.58	.81	.20	.29	.35	.51	4.54
	Tempe Date Orchard	34	48.5	88.0	119	12	32	Mar. 8	Nov. 21	258	34	.90	1.06	.85	.42	.15	.12	1.16	1.16	.77	.51	.71	1.15	8.96
	Wickenburg	31	47.3	86.1	115	11	31	Apr. 2	Nov. 16	228	31	1.37	1.16	.66	.53	.13	.12	1.47	1.81	.93	.64	.65	1.42	10.89
	Wittman	9	49.7	91.2	116	16	14	Feb. 27	Dec. 7	283	10	1.12	1.51	.69	.30	.28	.06	.87	1.99	1.10	.31	.45	1.05	9.73
Mohave	Fort Mohave	16	51.0	93.0	127	14	13	Feb. 18	Dec. 5	290	18	.44	1.07	.42	.17	.06	.07	.21	.92	.32	.37	.26	.45	4.76
	Kingman	35	43.3	82.3	117	6	33	Apr. 12	Nov. 10	212	35	1.22	1.58	1.11	.58	.31	.16	1.01	1.53	.77	.70	.60	1.37	10.94
	Mount Trumbull						13	Apr. 21	Oct. 12	174	16	.87	1.55	1.00	.70	.76	.44	1.79	2.26	.63	1.19	.49	1.17	12.85
	Truxton	22	39.1	79.9	110	−3	20	Apr. 18	Nov. 6	202	24	1.10	1.19	.77	.53	.43	.23	1.41	1.76	.86	.64	.41	1.12	10.45
	Wickieup						12	Mar. 31	Nov. 8	222	14	.79	2.40	.86	.75	.09	.26	.99	1.49	.54	.51	.32	1.51	10.51
Navajo	Fort Apache	34	36.6	72.6	105	−15	32	May 10	Oct. 14	157	33	1.52	1.48	1.55	1.08	.50	.49	3.02	2.75	1.72	1.07	1.33	1.32	17.83
	Holbrook	38	32.2	76.5	106	−21	38	Apr. 30	Oct. 18	171	36	.55	.67	.57	.57	.29	.46	1.88	1.47	.97	.66	.66	.57	9.32
	Kayenta	22	27.5	75.7	104	−17	22	Apr. 28	Oct. 13	168	22	.56	.65	.70	.46	.39	.34	1.30	1.46	.82	.80	.56	.60	8.64
	Jeddito	21	29.8	71.8	104	−30	21	May 16	Oct. 4	141	22	1.17	.98	.98	.68	.45	.31	2.27	1.96	.92	1.05	.61	1.32	12.70
	Lakeside	15	27.4	66.8	105	−24	18	May 24	Oct. 2	131	18	1.93	1.98	1.98	1.36	.60	.58	4.36	2.98	1.78	1.77	1.53	1.79	22.64
	Pinedale	22	28.9	69.2	99	−29	22	May 29	Oct. 8	132	26	1.53	1.77	1.44	1.21	.54	.73	3.37	2.67	1.72	1.53	1.53	1.70	19.74
	Snowflake	35	30.8	72.2	102	−30	31	May 22	Oct. 5	136	35	.70	.82	.81	.69	.57	.58	2.34	2.58	1.42	.91	.65	.65	12.72
	Winslow	30	31.2	77.2	107	−19	29	May 2	Oct. 17	168	29	.55	.48	.45	.49	.29	.31	1.53	1.72	.89	.52	.49	.62	8.34
Pima	Ajo	24	52.0	89.4	115	17	22	Jan. 27	Dec. 16	323	25	.89	.72	.70	.31	.12	.11	1.58	1.78	.74	.47	.68	1.04	9.14
	Fresnal Ranch School.	14	48.2	82.0	113	13	16	Mar. 16	Nov. 21	250	15	1.04	1.81	1.44	.35	.22	.65	3.54	3.93	1.83	.58	1.38	1.56	18.33
	Helvetia (near)	20	47.0	78.9	108	10	20	Mar. 25	Nov. 21	241	21	1.42	1.94	1.34	.48	.36	.81	4.45	4.06	1.96	.49	1.32	1.50	20.13
	Rosemont						6	Apr. 9	Nov. 22	227	17	1.29	1.37	1.19	.62	.22	.61	4.02	3.52	1.64	.66	1.09	1.68	17.91
	Santa Marguerite						8	Mar. 14	Nov. 19	250	21	1.09	1.33	.90	.34	.19	.57	4.24	4.01	2.29	.48	1.32	.94	17.70
	Tucson, University of Arizona.	40	49.6	85.1	111	6	40	Mar. 19	Nov. 19	245	40	.81	.89	.76	.40	.20	.32	2.15	2.02	1.14	.53	.92	1.02	11.16
Pinal	Casa Grande	30	50.0	91.6	122	17	26	Mar. 9	Nov. 19	255	33	.72	.89	.71	.26	.07	.22	1.28	1.30	.77	.23	.85	.95	8.25
	Casa Grande Ruins	15	49.3	89.1	117	8	16	Mar. 23	Nov. 14	236	15	1.01	.94	.80	.34	.09	.29	1.37	1.40	.53	.59	.92	1.45	9.73
	Dudleyville	26	48.5	82.4	114	9	24	Mar. 28	Nov. 12	229	25	1.54	1.44	1.02	.73	.35	.31	2.51	2.70	1.25	.68	1.07	1.63	15.23
	Florence	22	50.6	90.0	117	11	24	Mar. 12	Nov. 17	250	25	1.09	.91	1.00	.40	.18	.16	1.43	1.58	.87	.36	.85	1.48	10.31
	Maricopa	38	49.3	92.0	126	8	39	Mar. 4	Nov. 24	265	37	.67	.72	.56	.29	.12	.14	1.27	1.39	.76	.41	.67	.94	7.94
	Oracle	34	46.0	79.6	108	2	33	Mar. 21	Nov. 20	244	35	2.15	2.04	1.65	.85	.36	.46	2.97	3.26	1.46	.75	1.57	2.19	19.71
	Pinal Ranch						33	May 2	Oct. 16	167	40	2.95	3.38	2.56	1.12	.46	.51	2.95	3.31	2.11	1.23	2.03	3.00	25.61
	Red Rock	10	50.6	90.0	118	14	16	Mar. 4	Nov. 25	266	25	.82	.70	.70	.34	.14	.24	1.53	1.42	1.21	.36	.93	1.18	9.57
	Sacaton	31	49.3	88.3	117	9	30	Mar. 11	Nov. 13	247	31	.87	.83	.90	.32	.18	.13	1.65	1.67	.81	.38	.73	1.24	9.71
	Superior						8	Apr. 6	Nov. 15	223	19	1.56	2.28	1.79	.97	.30	.36	2.39	2.89	1.37	.99	1.35	2.16	18.41
Santa Cruz	Canille	16	40.0	73.2	109	−3	23	May 2	Oct. 17	168	27	1.25	1.50	.99	.42	.27	.95	5.22	4.15	1.88	.74	1.09	1.47	19.93
	Elgin (near)						14	Apr. 29	Oct. 25	179	26	1.09	1.12	.66	.30	.23	.72	4.10	3.72	1.69	.62	.84	1.07	16.16
	Nogales	30	46.3	79.8	109	11	31	Mar. 30	Nov. 14	229	31	1.07	.95	.74	.31	.16	.55	3.91	4.02	1.76	.68	.87	1.10	16.12
	Patagonia						16	Apr. 14	Oct. 25	194	17	.92	1.13	.98	.35	.21	.69	4.14	4.19	1.72	.64	.98	1.36	17.31
	San Rafael						14	Apr. 13	Oct. 29	199	16	.99	1.20	.96	.37	.17	.91	4.88	4.11	1.95	.74	1.14	1.40	18.82
Yavapai	Ash Fork	23	35.1	74.1	105	−17	25	May 7	Oct. 15	161	26	1.13	1.34	1.06	.90	.46	.59	2.06	2.16	1.07	.78	.54	1.21	13.30
	Bagdad	10	44.2	83.8	114	10	14	Mar. 31	Nov. 14	228	14	1.35	2.69	1.04	.70	.38	.47	1.08	2.36	1.16	.76	.57	1.78	14.34
	Cedar Glade						20	Apr. 26	Oct. 17	174	23	1.38	1.66	1.00	.63	.54	.41	1.76	2.27	1.16	1.01	.72	1.51	14.05
	Childs	20	45.0	84.8	117	2	23	Mar. 23	Nov. 12	234	23	1.92	2.06	1.54	1.06	.42	.38	2.14	2.59	1.74	.94	1.08	2.10	17.97
	Clemenceau	16	44.3	84.0	110	9	16	Mar. 25	Nov. 9	229	16	.95	1.12	.66	.72	.27	.24	1.38	1.80	1.70	.61	.77	1.07	11.29
	Columbia	14	51.8	87.6	114	16	14	Mar. 3	Dec. 5	277	14	1.97	2.55	1.54	.77	.22	.22	2.57	2.02	.56	.94	1.42	1.78	16.56
	Crown King						18	Apr. 29	Oct. 18	172	23	3.09	3.24	2.46	2.00	.63	.54	3.71	4.12	1.92	1.58	1.33	3.64	28.26
	Jerome	39	42.3	78.8	105	7	39	Apr. 1	Nov. 22	235	39	1.86	2.11	1.70	.98	.51	.36	2.79	2.93	1.42	1.13	1.33	1.67	18.79
	Prescott	40	35.0	72.5	105	−21	40	May 17	Oct. 7	143	39	2.01	2.39	2.03	1.13	.50	.39	3.02	3.32	1.63	1.09	1.40	1.80	20.71
	Prescott Dry Farm	16	36.9	74.1	104	−1	16	Apr. 23	Oct. 21	181	17	1.13	1.15	.94	.79	.44	.33	2.76	2.54	1.31	1.09	.68	1.18	14.34
	Seligman	29	35.0	72.2	110	−18	32	May 15	Oct. 6	144	30	.89	1.00	.92	.48	.31	.26	2.06	2.01	.93	.79	.66	1.00	11.31

ARIZONA—Continued

Climatic summary—Continued

County	Station	Temperature					Killing frost average dates				Average precipitation													
		Length of record	January average	July average	Maximum	Minimum	Length of record	Last in spring	First in fall	Growing season	Length of record	January	February	March	April	May	June	July	August	September	October	November	December	Annual
		Yr.	*°F.*	*°F.*	*°F.*	*°F.*	*Yr.*			*Days*	*Yr.*	*In.*	*In.*	*In.*	*In.*	*In.*	*In.*	*In.*	*In.*	*In.*	*In.*	*In.*	*In.*	*In.*
Yavapai—Con.	Sycamore Ranger Station.						12	Apr. 20	Nov. 3	197	18	1.41	2.52	1.51	1.03	0.21	0.27	2.34	3.11	1.75	1.22	1.08	1.74	18.19
	Tonto Ranger Station.						21	May 2	Oct. 18	169	26	1.80	1.38	1.26	1.09	.53	.29	2.45	2.77	1.56	1.02	1.28	1.59	17.02
	Walnut Creek Ranger Station.						21	May 23	Sept. 29	129	23	1.87	2.02	1.35	.94	.49	.60	2.64	2.90	1.61	.88	.55	1.96	17.81
	Walnut Grove						20	Apr. 26	Oct. 28	185	40	1.82	2.16	1.49	.88	.29	.32	2.57	2.48	1.33	1.13	1.41	1.82	17.70
	Yaeger Canyon						10	Apr. 18	Oct. 31	196	20	1.32	1.85	1.39	1.04	.52	.48	3.24	3.19	1.58	1.05	1.04	1.64	18.34
	Yarnell						9	Apr. 9	Oct. 24	198	16	1.87	2.57	2.19	1.11	.36	.33	2.55	3.03	1.36	.89	1.88	1.86	20.00
Yuma	Aztec	22	53.5	94.2	125	15	22	Feb. 7	Dec. 11	307	22	.66	.57	.46	.23	.04	.06	.43	.48	.35	.25	.71	.57	4.81
	Mohawk	34	54.3	94.6	126	16	36	Jan. 19	Dec. 20	335	40	.38	.47	.32	.15	.03	.06	.38	.85	.27	.25	.26	.61	4.03
	Parker	38	49.1	91.5	127	9	38	Mar. 2	Nov. 15	258	37	.70	.74	.43	.21	.09	.05	.45	.68	.32	.31	.39	.71	5.08
	Quartzsite	24	49.7	94.0	124	9	24	Mar. 12	Nov. 21	254	25	.42	.85	.35	.22	.06	.16	.69	1.08	.46	.38	.37	.75	5.79
	Salome (near)	30	48.1	87.8	118	15	30	Mar. 12	Nov. 21	254	30	.97	1.10	.67	.30	.07	.16	1.19	1.56	.51	.46	.42	1.06	8.47
	Wellton	15	50.6	91.5	120	16	14	Mar. 9	Nov. 17	253	15	.42	.55	.35	.14	.06	.01	.43	.79	.39	.33	.17	.75	4.39
	Yuma	40	54.6	91.0	120	22	40	Jan. 12	Dec. 26	348	40	.35	.42	.35	.14	.03	.02	.22	.55	.49	.28	.23	.50	3.58

ARIZONA—Continued

Precipitation and temperature—State unit values

[This tabulation gives the mean annual, mean monthly, and average seasonal precipitation, 1886–1938, and the mean annual temperatures, 1895–1938, for Arizona]

Precipitation		Precipitation		Precipitation		Precipitation		Temperature		Temperature	
Year	Mean	Year	Mean	Year	Mean	Month	Mean	Year	Mean	Year	Mean
	In.		*In.*		*In.*		*In.*		°*F.*		°*F.*
1886	9.89	1908	16.16	1930	15.55	July	2.13	1895	62.1	1917	58.7
1887	11.42	1909	14.48	1931	19.60	August	2.28	1896	64.9	1918	58.5
1888	12.30	1910	10.08	1932	13.64	September	1.20	1897	62.0	1919	58.2
1889	13.29	1911	16.29	1933	11.90	October	.81	1898	61.8	1920	58.6
1890	15.49	1912	13.10	1934	10.47	November	.93	1899	62.2	1921	60.3
1891	8.28	1913	12.52	1935	15.45	December	1.23	1900	63.7	1922	59.3
1892	9.85	1914	17.06	1936	14.33			1901	63.4	1923	58.3
1893	10.41	1915	16.39	1937	13.01	Annual	13.45	1902	62.3	1924	59.2
1894	11.09	1916	17.24	1938	12.90			1903	61.4	1925	59.6
1895	13.19	1917	13.04					1904	61.7	1926	60.2
1896	12.88	1918	15.18			Season	Average	1905	60.6	1927	61.1
1897	12.47	1919	20.70	Month	Mean			1906	60.5	1928	60.8
1898	12.20	1920	13.65					1907	61.2	1929	59.7
1899	8.61	1921	15.17					1908	60.4	1930	59.5
1900	7.83	1922	13.16					1909	59.7	1931	60.3
1901	10.65	1923	17.80		*In.*		*In.*	1910	62.5	1932	59.6
1902	10.23	1924	9.12	January	1.26	Winter	3.82	1911	59.6	1933	60.1
1903	8.93	1925	13.33	February	1.33	Spring	1.95	1912	57.9	1934	62.9
1904	9.45	1926	16.55	March	1.06	Summer	4.74	1913	58.1	1935	60.0
1905	27.83	1927	16.64	April	.57	Fall	2.94	1914	60.4	1936	61.4
1906	16.48	1928	9.91	May	.32			1915	58.7	1937	60.1
1907	15.41	1929	11.29	June	.33			1916	59.2	1938	60.2

ARIZONA—Continued

Dates of last killing frost in spring and first in fall, with length of growing season

Year	Flagstaff			Holbrook			Parker			Phoenix			Tucson			Yuma		
	Last in spring	First in fall	Growing season[1]	Last in spring	First in fall	Growing season[1]	Last in spring	First in fall	Growing season[1]	Last in spring	First in fall	Growing season[1]	Last in spring	First in fall	Growing season[1]	Last in spring	First in fall	Growing season[1]
			Days			*Days*			*Days*			*Days*			*Days*			*Days*
1899	June 2	Oct. 6	126	May 5	Oct. 15	163	Mar. 17	Dec. 6	264	Mar. 11	Dec. 11	275	Mar. 19	Dec. 5	261	Feb. 7	None	328
1900	May 13	Sept. 19	129	Apr. 11	Oct. 16	188	Feb. 8	Dec. 13	308	Feb. 9	Dec. 23	317	Feb. 24	Oct. 30	248	None	do	365
1901	June 15	Sept. 25	102				Feb. 2	Dec. 9	310	Jan. 12	Dec. 13	335	Apr. 5	Dec. 8	247	Jan. 11	Dec. 14	337
1902	June 4	Sept. 29	117				Mar. 4			Feb. 1	Nov. 28	300	Mar. 4	Nov. 28	269	None	None	365
1903	May 18	Sept. 15	120		Oct. 16		Mar. 7	Dec. 5	273	Feb. 18	Dec. 23	308	Mar. 23	Dec. 4	256	Feb. 4	do	331
1904	June 8	Sept. 27	111	May 9	Oct. 13	157	Feb. 13	Nov. 12	272	Jan. 31	Dec. 27	331	Mar. 13	Dec. 13	275	None	do	366
1905	June 16	Sept. 18	94	May 11	Sept. 30	142	Feb. 14	Nov. 9	268	Feb. 14	Dec. 2	291	Feb. 14	Nov. 29	288	do	do	365
1906	June 3	Sept. 16	105	May 1	Oct. 6	158	Mar. 31	Nov. 20	234	Mar. 2	Nov. 20	263	Mar. 3	Oct. 23	234	Jan. 2	Nov. 30	332
1907	June 16	Sept. 19	95	May 24	Nov. 5	165	Mar. 28	Nov. 23	240	Jan. 20	Dec. 19	333	Mar. 29	Nov. 22	238	None	None	365
1908	June 8	Sept. 26	110	May 11	Sept. 27	139	Feb. 15			Feb. 15	Dec. 1	200	Mar. 23	Oct. 19	210	Feb. 14	Nov. 30	290
1909	do	Sept. 22	105	May 12	Oct. 9	150	Feb. 16	Nov. 16	273	Feb. 10	Nov. 16	279	Apr. 7	Nov. 11	218	None	Dec. 4	337
1910	May 7	Sept. 28	144	May 5	Oct. 19	167	Feb. 18	Nov. 19	274	Feb. 18	Dec. 23	308	Feb. 22	Nov. 28	279	Feb. 18	Dec. 31	316
1911	June 3	Oct. 3	122	May 18	do	154	Feb. 28	Nov. 13	258	Feb. 17	Nov. 26	282	Feb. 17	Nov. 18	274	Jan. 3	Dec. 15	346
1912	June 17	Sept. 22	97	May 14	Oct. 4	143	do	Oct. 26	240	Jan. 29	Dec. 19	325	Mar. 12	Dec. 5	268	None	Dec. 25	359
1913	June 30	Sept. 24	86	Apr. 13	Nov. 1	202	Mar. 27	Dec. 1	249	Mar. 1	Dec. 5	279	Mar. 27	do	253	Jan. 22	Dec. 5	317
1914	May 26	Oct. 5	132	May 4	Oct. 27	176	Feb. 6	Nov. 18	285	Feb. 7	Dec. 8	304	Feb. 28	Dec. 7	282	None	None	365
1915	June 15	Sept. 14	91	May 8	Oct. 4	149	Jan. 21	Nov. 13	296	Mar. 3	Nov. 13	255	Mar. 7	Nov. 11	249	do	Dec. 17	350
1916	May 28	Sept. 24	119	May 26	Oct. 24	151	Feb. 3	Nov. 8	278	Feb. 2	do	285	Mar. 25	Nov. 8	228	Jan. 12	Dec. 9	332
1917	June 2	Sept. 26	116	May 4	Oct. 12	161	Mar. 22	Oct. 29	221	Mar. 4	Dec. 8	279	Apr. 2	Nov. 17	229	None	None	365
1918	May 30	Sept. 24	117	Apr. 27	Oct. 26	182	Mar. 8	Nov. 7	244	Feb. 20	Nov. 8	261	Feb. 20	Nov. 8	261	do	Dec. 31	364
1919	May 6	Oct. 4	151	Apr. 11	Oct. 19	191	Mar. 9	Oct. 26	231	Mar. 1	Nov. 29	273	Mar. 10	Nov. 9	244	Jan. 1	None	365
1920	May 15	Sept. 26	134	May 5	Oct. 24	172	Mar. 19	Nov. 9	235	Jan. 12	Dec. 13	336	Mar. 29	Nov. 26	242	None	do	366
1921	June 18	Oct. 18	122	May 20	Oct. 27	160	Feb. 19	Nov. 8	262	Feb. 8	Nov. 19	284	Apr. 6	Nov. 19	227	Jan. 12	do	354
1922	June 2	Oct. 13	133	May 12	Oct. 29	170	Mar. 4	Nov. 3	244	Feb. 5	Nov. 5	273	Apr. 10	Oct. 31	204	Feb. 4	do	331
1923	June 17	Sept. 24	99	May 1	Oct. 19	171	Feb. 12	Nov. 29	290	Feb. 6	Dec. 12	309	Mar. 23	Nov. 28	250	Feb. 11	do	324
1924	June 9	Oct. 3	116	Apr. 18	Sept. 27	162	Mar. 16	Oct. 11	209	Jan. 20	Dec. 19	334	Apr. 17	Nov. 7	204	Jan. 3	do	364
1925	May 2	Sept. 30	151	Apr. 23	Oct. 16	176	Mar. 13	Nov. 5	237	Jan. 18	Dec. 4	320	Apr. 2	do	219	Jan. 13	do	353
1926	May 25	Oct. 12	140	Mar. 30	Oct. 24	208	Mar. 30	Nov. 3	218	Jan. 29	Dec. 15	320	Mar. 30	Nov. 15	230	None	Dec. 25	358
1927	May 29	Sept. 27	121	Apr. 21	Oct. 2	164	Mar. 16	Nov. 18	247	Jan. 1	Dec. 8	341	Mar. 22	Dec. 1	254	do	None	365
1928	June 13	Oct. 2	111	Apr. 22	Oct. 17	178	Mar. 30	Nov. 8	223	Jan. 26	Dec. 19	328	Mar. 16	Nov. 17	246	do	do	366
1929	June 3	Oct. 11	130	May 2	Oct. 22	173	Apr. 12	Nov. 14	216	Feb. 10	Nov. 26	289	Mar. 26	Oct. 30	218	Jan. 27	do	339
1930	do	Sept. 25	114	May 10	Oct. 12	155	Mar. 1	Nov. 19	263	Jan. 23	Nov. 20	301	Mar. 1	Nov. 19	263	Jan. 9	Dec. 27	352
1931	May 27	Sept. 21	117	Apr. 21	Oct. 30	192	Jan. 28	do	295	Jan. 20	Nov. 23	307	Mar. 27	Nov. 20	238	None	Nov. 23	326
1932	June 8	Oct. 6	120	Apr. 28	Oct. 5	160	Mar. 4	Dec. 6	277	Feb. 4	Dec. 16	316	Mar. 5	Nov. 23	263	Jan. 29	None	337
1933	June 6	Oct. 18	134	May 12	Nov. 3	175	Feb. 19	Nov. 29	283	Feb. 20	Dec. 17	300	Mar. 6	Nov. 6	245	Feb. 9	do	325
1934	June 8	Sept. 25	109	Apr. 4	Oct. 21	200	Jan. 26	Nov. 20	298	None	Nov. 30	333	Apr. 4	Nov. 21	231	None	do	365

1935	June 1	Sept. 28	119	May 5	Oct. 24	172	Mar. 20	Nov. 1	226	Jan. 22	Dec. 16	328	Mar. 11	Nov. 4	238	do	do	365
1936	June 5	do	115	Apr. 7	Oct. 27	203	Mar. 23	Nov. 5	227	Jan. 21	None	346	Apr. 6	Nov. 3	211	Feb. 6	Dec. 30	328
1937	June 4	Oct. 8	126	May 1	Oct. 19	171	Feb. 27			Feb. 9	do	326	Mar. 27	Dec. 19	267	Feb. 2	None	332
1938	June 19	do	111	Apr. 1	Oct. 17	199	Feb. 18	Nov. 7	262	Jan. 25	Nov. 13	292	Mar. 31	Nov. 13	227	None	do	365
Mean	June 3	Sept. 29	118	Apr. 30	Oct. 18	171	Mar. 2	Nov. 15	258	Feb. 5	Dec. 6	304	Mar. 19	Nov. 19	245	Jan. 12	Dec. 26	348
Extremes	May 2[2]	Sept. 14[4]	[6] 86	Mar. 30[2]	Sept. 27[4]	[6] 139	Jan. 21[2]	Oct. 11[4]	[6] 209	None[2]	Nov. 5[4]	[6] 255	Feb. 14[2]	Oct. 19[4]	[6] 204	None[2]	Nov. 23[4]	[6] 290
	June 30[3]	Oct. 18[5]	[7] 151	May 26[3]	Nov. 5[5]	[7] 208	Apr. 12[3]	Dec. 13[5]	[7] 310	Mar. 11[3]	None[5]	[7] 346	Apr. 17[3]	Dec. 19[5]	[7] 288	Feb. 18[3]	None[5]	366

[1] Number of days between last killing frost in spring and first in fall.
[2] Earliest date in spring.
[3] Latest date in spring.
[4] Earliest date in fall.
[5] Latest date in fall.
[6] Shortest growing season.
[7] Longest growing season

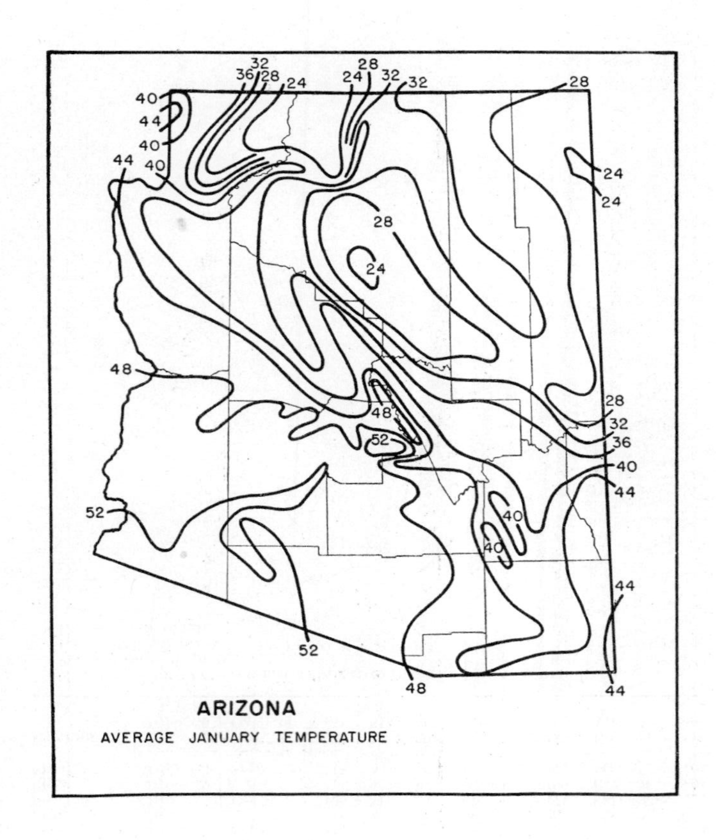
ARIZONA
AVERAGE JANUARY TEMPERATURE

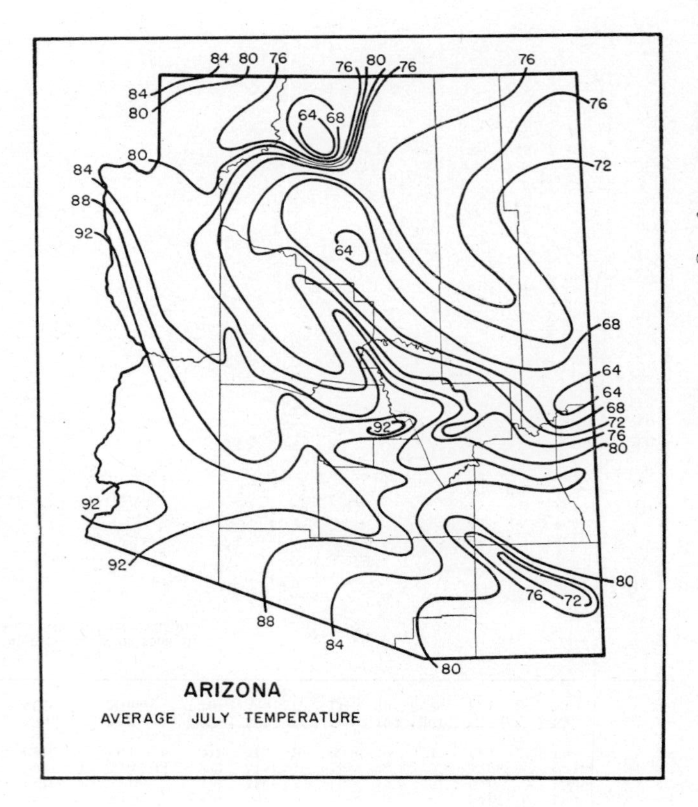
ARIZONA
AVERAGE JULY TEMPERATURE

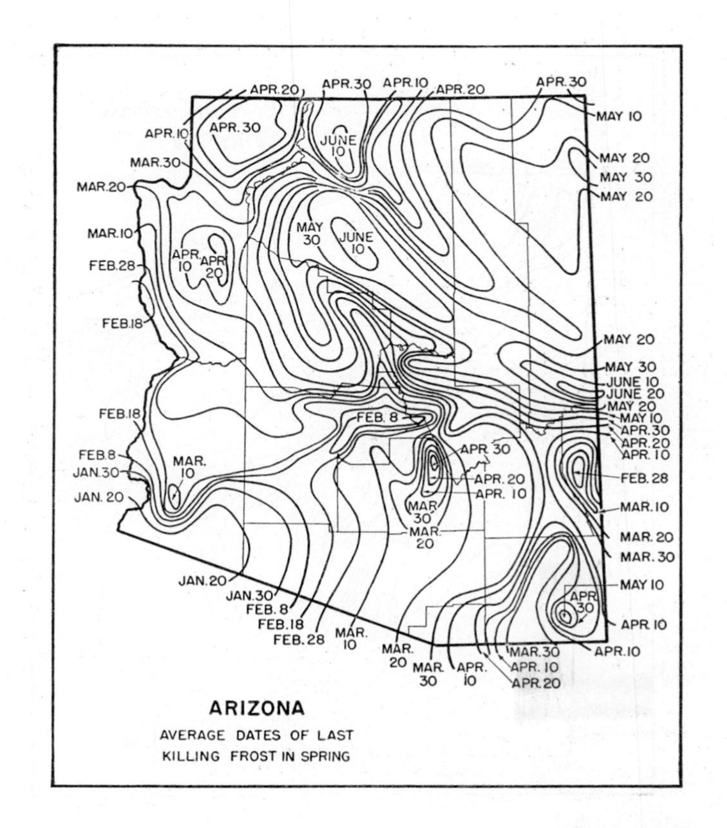

ARIZONA
AVERAGE DATES OF LAST KILLING FROST IN SPRING

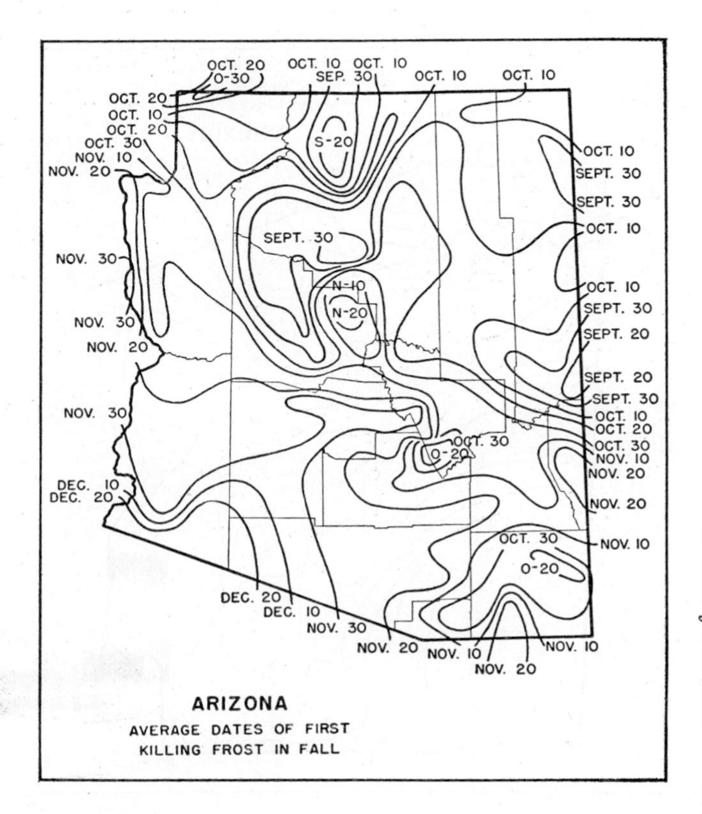

ARIZONA
AVERAGE DATES OF FIRST KILLING FROST IN FALL

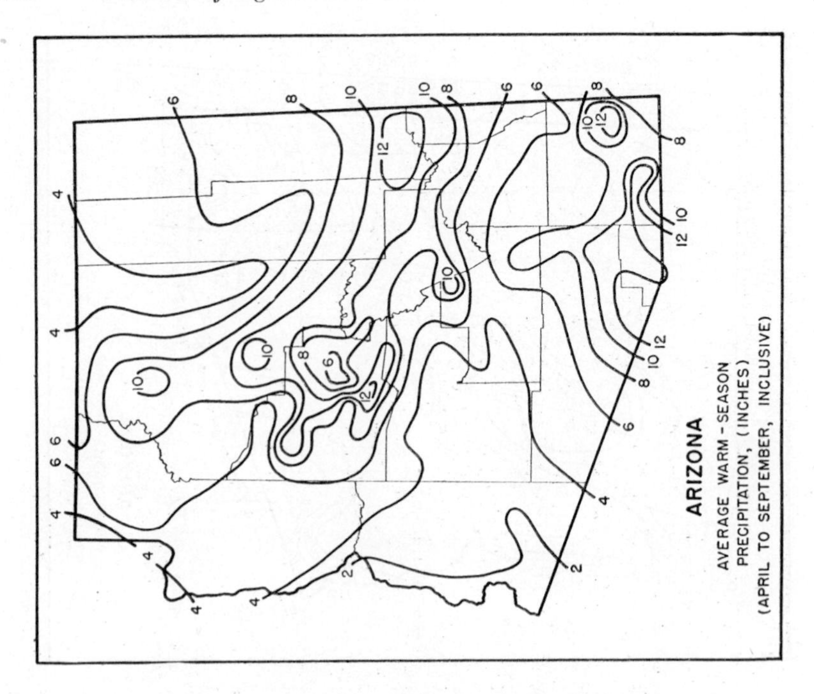

ARIZONA

AVERAGE WARM-SEASON PRECIPITATION, (INCHES)
(APRIL TO SEPTEMBER, INCLUSIVE)

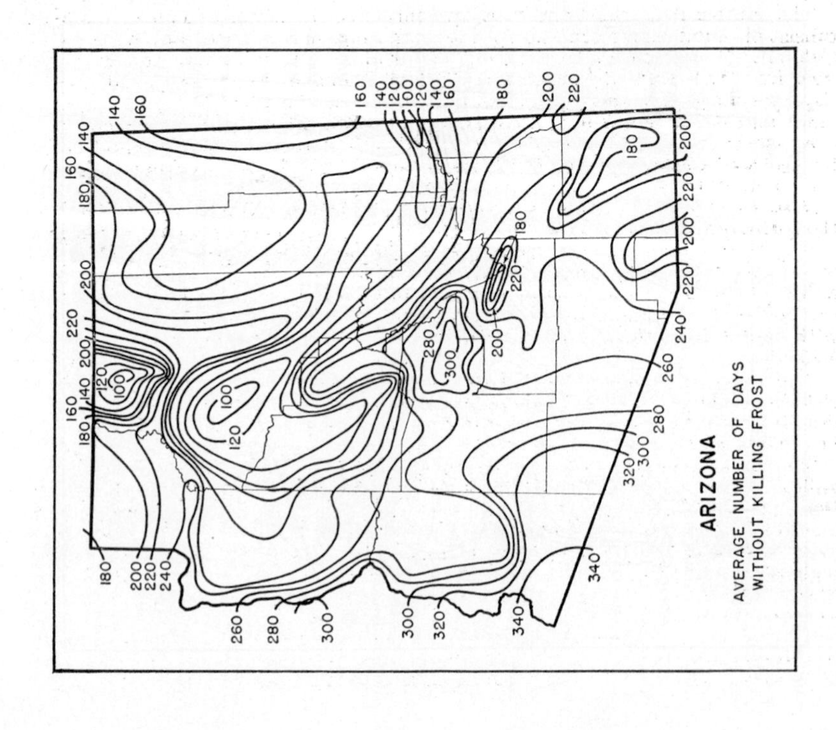

ARIZONA

AVERAGE NUMBER OF DAYS WITHOUT KILLING FROST

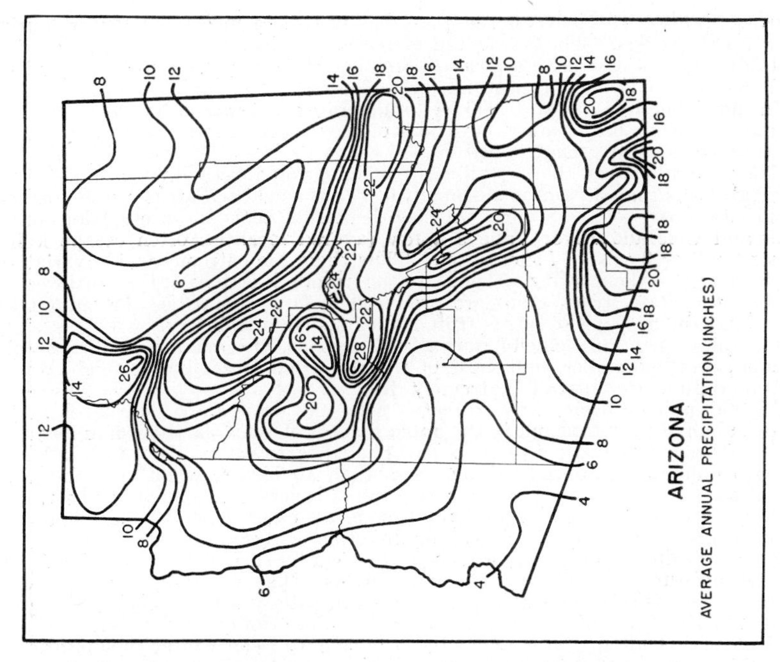

SUPPLEMENTARY CLIMATIC NOTES FOR ARIZONA

Arizona comprises 113,956 square miles, of which there are 146 square miles of water surface. Only two States, Connecticut and New Mexico, have a smaller water area.

The southeastern third and fully two-thirds of the northern half of the State consist of undulating plains, steep ridges, and high peaks, extending north of the Colorado River across the Shivwits and Kaibab Plateaus, and south of that river from the Hualpai Mountains in central Mohave County eastward through the Bradshaw and San Francisco Mountains to the great Mogollon Plateau uplift and on to the White Mountains in east-central Arizona. The mountain-peak elevations range from 3,500 to 12,600 feet, and contours in general deflect toward the southwest into the Sonoran Desert and toward the northeast into the Painted Desert.

Virtually the entire State is in the drainage basin of the Colorado River, and the entire drainage is into the Gulf of California. Stupendous canyons have been cut by the Colorado and its tributaries. The principal gorge of the Colorado is in Arizona—the world-famed Grand Canyon, which varies in width from 4 to 18 miles. It begins at the junction of the Little Colorado with the main stream and extends westward and southwestward for about 217 miles into Mohave County, with depths from the rim of the canyon to the river bed ranging from 2,700 to 5,700 feet.

The range of temperature between day and night is extreme, especially at elevations above 5,000 feet, where the nights are usually cool and comfortable, despite the intense heat registered during the summer days. At low elevations hot nights may occur from the end of June to early September.

Throughout the lower sections, mainly in southwestern Arizona, including the valleys of the lower Salt, Gila, and Colorado Rivers, where elevations are less than 3,000 feet above sea level, readings above 100° F. in the shade occur frequently during the long summer, which lasts from April to November. However, because of the dry atmosphere, temperatures in the high 90's in these desert regions are more comfortable than those of 80° in the Atlantic and Gulf Coast States, where the principal cause of discomfort during periods of hot weather is excessive humidity rather than high temperature.

The southern section of Arizona enjoys a delightful winter season, being located in the belt of maximum sunshine and minimum relative humidity for the entire

United States. This part of the State has become a mecca for winter tourists and health seekers. The scenic and recreational areas in the mountain sections of the north and east have a pleasant summer climate, with cool, bracing nights and frequent showers that sustain vegetation.

In the higher areas, above 7,000 feet, temperatures average as low as in southern Minnesota, while in the lower elevations of the western and southern parts of the State conditions are semitropical.

The period between the last killing frost in spring and the first in fall is short, averaging less than 3 months in some places in the elevated areas of the northern and eastern parts of the State. On the other hand, in the lower elevations of the Gila and Colorado River Valleys a few favored localities often escape killing frosts for 2 or 3 years in succession. Thus there are extremely wide variations in the length of the growing season. In the irrigated sections of the southwestern part of the State, truck crops are produced in large quantities throughout the year, and the growing of citrus fruit is an important industry.

Precipitation occurs chiefly during two seasons, the maximum during July, August, and September, and most of the rest from December through March. May and June are normally extremely dry.

Annual precipitation varies directly with elevation above sea level in the western half of the State and to the upper reaches of the Gila River and its tributaries. From the Little Colorado River northeastward to the Utah and New Mexico boundaries rainfall averages less than 10 inches, while over the lower elevations of southwestern Arizona the annual average is generally less than 5 inches. The distribution of precipitation in all cases depends somewhat upon location with relation to the prevailing direction of the winds.

Summer rains occur mostly as showers caused by solar heating and the forced flow of moisture-laden air over elevated regions. The water vapor necessary for these showers is transported by the deep southeasterly wind current forming the western part of one of the large anticyclonic eddies found aloft in summer over the southern United States and adjacent regions. The winter precipitation is less of the showery type and results largely from activity on the Pacific polar front, which in winter is at times found as far south as 35° N.

Snowfall is of rare occurrence in the low elevations of the southern and western parts of the State, but in the mountains and higher plateaus of the north-central sections annual amounts in excess of 100 inches are frequently recorded. The gradual melting of this snow later in the year serves to maintain a moderate supply of water in most of the streams until the appearance of the normally heavy rains of late summer.

The principal storage reservoirs are Lake Mead, formed by water impounded by Boulder Dam on the Colorado River; the Roosevelt, Horse Mesa, Mormon Flat, and Stewart Mountain Reservoirs on the Salt River; the San Carlos on the Gila; and Bartlett Reservoir on the Verde River.

The evaporation rate in Arizona is high, owing to low humidity and high temperatures. The annual average amounts from a free water surface at stations where records have been kept long enough to give comparable values are (in inches): Yuma Citrus, 120; University of Arizona at Tucson, 91; Willcox, 89; Roosevelt, 77; and Mesa Experiment Farm, 78.

The average annual number of clear days for the State is 222, partly cloudy 85, and cloudy 58. In some parts of the southern section the average number of clear days in the year is 280.

One of the most striking climatic features of Arizona is the bright sunshine, which averages 90 percent of the possible amount at Yuma and 84 percent at Phoenix, the only stations where sunshine records are available.

The relative humidity is unusually low, averaging 55 percent at 6 a. m. and 27 percent at 6 p. m. for the combined records at Phoenix, Yuma, and Tucson. Afternoon readings much lower than these averages are frequently recorded.

Wind velocities are generally light, and the direction of movement is variable. The prevailing direction for the State as a whole is from the southwest. At Phoenix the prevailing direction is from the east, with an average velocity of 5.8 miles an hour, while at Yuma it is north, averaging 5.9 miles an hour. At times, more often during the warm season, frequent duststorms occur. Tornadoes are rarely seen in Arizona.

GERSHOM K. GREENING, *Associate Meteorologist and Climatic Section Director for Arizona, Weather Bureau, Phoenix.*

ARKANSAS

Climatic summary

County [1]	Station	Temperature: Length of record	Temperature: January average	Temperature: July average	Temperature: Maximum	Temperature: Minimum	Killing frost average dates: Length of record	Killing frost average dates: Last in spring	Killing frost average dates: First in fall	Killing frost average dates: Growing season [2]	Average precipitation: Length of record [2]	January	February	March	April	May	June	July	August	September	October	November	December	Annual
		Yr.	°F.	°F.	°F.	°F.	Yr.			Days	Yr.	In.	In.	In.	In.	In.	In.	In.	In.	In.	In.	In.	In.	In.
Arkansas	Stuttgart	40	43.4	81.4	112	−10	40	Mar. 28	Oct. 30	216	40	5.18	3.94	5.06	4.84	4.88	3.73	3.61	3.44	3.26	3.28	3.92	5.23	50.37
Ashley	Crossett	20	45.2	81.7	113	−14	21	Mar. 29	Nov. 11	227	23	5.80	3.45	4.74	4.97	4.34	3.73	4.96	3.01	2.37	3.67	4.29	5.64	50.97
	Portland	32	47.0	81.8	110	−4	30	Mar. 22	Nov. 5	228	33	4.82	4.11	5.06	4.82	4.86	3.25	3.92	3.17	2.63	2.86	4.22	5.95	49.67
Baxter	Mountain Home	22	38.1	79.2	114	−16	25	Apr. 8	Oct. 23	198	25	3.12	2.55	3.93	4.55	5.43	4.59	3.88	3.76	4.06	4.08	3.12	3.59	46.66
Benton	Bentonville	33	36.8	78.2	111	−17	32	Apr. 6	Oct. 26	203	33	2.86	2.20	3.62	4.50	4.98	5.08	3.68	3.92	4.34	3.63	3.29	2.43	44.53
	Gravette	40	36.6	78.1	114	−29	40	Apr. 19	Oct. 22	186	40	2.79	2.06	3.56	4.47	5.25	5.48	3.65	3.97	4.23	3.69	3.21	2.35	44.71
	Rogers	40	38.0	78.1	112	−24	40	Apr. 10	Oct. 25	198	40	2.64	1.94	3.26	4.34	4.95	4.98	4.01	3.80	4.24	3.20	3.06	2.37	42.79
Boone	Harrison	36	36.9	77.8	112	−24	38	Apr. 17	Oct. 21	187	37	3.13	2.57	3.21	4.59	5.28	4.55	3.67	3.50	4.21	3.14	2.86	2.58	43.29
	Lead Hill	15	37.7	80.9	116	−28	14	Apr. 8	Oct. 29	204	15	3.04	2.59	2.92	3.63	5.00	4.34	2.30	2.87	3.18	3.11	3.30	2.66	38.94
Bradley	Warren	40	45.1	82.3	111	−8	38	Mar. 27	Nov. 7	225	39	4.87	4.34	5.30	5.09	4.53	3.80	3.96	3.35	3.68	3.23	4.20	6.02	52.37
Carroll	Eureka Springs	36	38.4	78.9	112	−17	36	Apr. 9	Oct. 27	201	37	3.33	2.55	3.99	4.87	5.73	5.47	3.79	4.75	4.56	3.57	3.19	2.86	48.66
Clark	Amity	36	43.3	81.2	115	−12	36	Apr. 2	Nov. 4	216	36	4.67	3.47	4.36	4.99	5.12	4.58	3.34	3.47	3.35	3.28	3.67	4.44	48.74
	Arkadelphia	13	45.2	80.9	112	0	29	Mar. 25	Nov. 7	227	38	4.86	3.61	4.57	4.85	4.96	4.58	3.63	3.49	2.95	3.36	3.73	5.00	49.59
Clay	Corning	32	38.5	80.2	113	−25	36	Apr. 2	Oct. 24	205	39	4.68	3.27	4.53	5.00	4.32	4.17	3.68	3.71	3.53	3.54	3.65	3.84	47.92
Clebourne	Higden	----	----	----	----	----	17	Mar. 31	Nov. 4	218	19	4.74	2.81	5.36	5.12	6.04	4.46	3.33	3.67	3.85	4.17	3.89	4.26	51.70
Cleveland	Rison	22	45.7	82.1	115	−11	24	Mar. 30	Nov. 2	217	28	5.12	3.81	5.14	4.54	4.24	3.68	3.92	3.18	2.98	3.16	3.57	5.22	48.56
Columbia	Magnolia	21	47.0	82.4	112	−5	21	Mar. 24	Nov. 15	236	21	5.11	3.69	4.63	4.55	4.58	3.19	4.13	2.54	2.10	2.99	4.76	5.64	47.91
Conway	Morrilton	16	41.4	82.9	114	−6	17	Mar. 23	Nov. 10	232	19	4.21	2.81	4.34	4.57	4.65	3.89	2.56	2.65	2.81	3.78	4.01	3.97	44.25
Craighead	Jonesboro	40	40.4	81.4	116	−18	38	Apr. 1	Nov. 4	217	40	5.10	3.57	4.76	4.57	4.21	3.80	3.32	3.29	3.53	3.32	3.46	4.50	47.43
Crittenden	Memphis, Tenn	40	42.3	80.9	106	−9	40	Mar. 17	Nov. 10	238	40	4.71	3.58	4.90	4.46	4.00	3.10	3.16	2.98	2.68	3.01	3.89	4.82	45.29
Cross	Wynne	30	41.2	81.0	110	−18	30	Mar. 29	Oct. 30	215	30	5.46	3.49	5.35	5.33	4.47	3.86	3.75	3.71	3.53	3.76	3.93	4.97	51.61
Dallas	Princeton	13	44.7	80.8	114	−4	24	Apr. 1	Nov. 4	217	26	4.71	3.55	5.04	5.06	5.07	3.97	4.06	2.78	3.29	3.14	3.74	5.20	49.61
Desha	Arkansas City	----	----	----	----	----	21	Mar. 26	Nov. 5	224	40	4.71	4.28	5.29	5.13	4.68	3.60	3.60	3.70	2.86	2.63	4.00	5.83	50.31
	Dumas	28	44.6	82.1	112	−6	30	Mar. 21	Nov. 4	228	34	5.18	3.98	5.83	4.65	4.74	3.66	4.02	3.34	3.04	3.26	4.38	6.25	52.33
	Yancopin	----	----	----	----	----	12	Mar. 21	Nov. 10	234	14	5.37	3.88	5.28	3.82	4.22	3.28	4.08	2.70	2.57	3.56	5.33	6.65	50.74
Faulkner	Conway	40	42.0	81.9	115	−13	40	Mar. 25	Nov. 3	223	40	4.90	3.51	4.51	4.99	5.19	3.89	3.65	3.36	3.51	3.42	3.82	4.37	49.12
Franklin	Ozark	34	40.4	82.2	120	−16	34	Mar. 27	Nov. 7	225	36	3.31	2.70	3.55	4.51	5.42	4.36	3.19	3.86	3.47	3.54	3.11	3.36	44.38
Fulton	Mammoth Springs	34	37.7	78.8	109	−23	33	Apr. 8	Oct. 22	197	34	3.79	2.68	3.75	4.90	4.45	4.33	3.71	3.98	3.77	3.37	3.47	3.40	45.60
Garland	Hemp Wallace	20	41.8	80.0	111	−12	20	Apr. 10	Oct. 23	196	20	4.56	3.64	4.60	6.20	5.61	4.28	4.96	4.68	3.50	3.25	4.00	4.60	53.88
	Hot Springs	32	44.2	82.3	115	−12	33	Mar. 30	Nov. 6	221	35	5.19	3.49	4.48	6.13	5.54	4.49	3.85	3.68	3.50	3.40	4.07	4.77	52.59
Greene	Paragould	----	----	----	----	----	12	Mar. 28	Nov. 4	221	13	6.27	3.67	5.64	4.84	4.69	3.73	3.39	3.90	3.33	3.44	3.57	4.57	51.04
Hempstead	Fulton	----	----	----	----	----	18	Mar. 29	Nov. 3	219	40	4.90	3.42	4.36	4.64	4.57	4.12	3.75	2.91	2.63	2.82	3.69	4.34	46.15
	Hope	33	45.3	82.0	115	−10	33	Mar. 21	Nov. 7	231	33	5.34	3.53	4.61	4.75	5.12	3.67	4.47	2.68	3.23	3.02	4.40	4.68	49.50
Hot Spring	Malvern	35	43.3	81.2	114	−11	36	Mar. 29	Nov. 1	217	36	5.41	3.85	5.00	5.47	4.81	4.51	4.21	3.63	3.50	3.32	4.00	5.06	52.77

[1] The following counties, for which no records are available, are best represented by the stations indicated: Calhoun—Camden; Chicot—Portland; Crawford—Fort Smith; Drew—Warren; Grant—Malvern; Lincoln—Dumas; Prairie—Stuttgart; Saline—Little Rock; Sevier—Grannis; St. Francis—Wynne.

[2] Length of growing season between average dates of last killing frost in spring and first in fall.

298737°—41——50

ARKANSAS—Continued

Climatic summary—Continued

County	Station	Temperature					Killing frost average dates				Average precipitation													
		Length of record	January average	July average	Maximum	Minimum	Length of record	Last in spring	First in fall	Growing season	Length of record	January	February	March	April	May	June	July	August	September	October	November	December	Annual
		Yr.	°F.	°F.	°F.	°F.	Yr.			Days	Yr.	In.	In.	In.	In.	In.	In.	In.	In.	In.	In.	In.	In.	In.
Howard	Center Point	32	46.0	82.3	112	−10	33	Mar. 29	Nov. 11	227	34	3.99	3.34	4.42	5.14	5.97	4.22	3.92	2.76	3.53	3.10	3.68	4.74	48.81
Independence	Batesville	31	38.2	80.0	111	−18	34	Apr. 6	Oct. 28	205	39	4.57	3.32	4.54	4.73	4.95	3.98	3.53	4.13	3.70	3.31	3.43	3.94	48.13
Izard	Calico Rock	22	37.0	80.8	114	−20	24	Apr. 4	Oct. 30	209	34	3.62	2.62	3.72	4.54	4.70	3.79	3.59	4.53	3.54	3.19	3.10	3.36	44.30
Jackson	Newport	40	40.2	81.8	114	−14	40	Mar. 26	Oct. 31	219	40	5.26	3.19	4.69	4.79	4.35	4.00	3.10	3.65	3.61	3.41	3.65	4.19	47.89
Jefferson	Lake Farm	16	43.8	80.3	106	−10	15	Mar. 30	Oct. 27	211	14	4.69	4.54	4.63	4.77	3.78	4.17	3.95	2.75	4.06	2.67	3.37	5.38	48.76
	Pine Bluff	40	44.2	82.3	110	−6	40	Mar. 25	Nov. 8	228	40	5.22	3.93	5.26	5.39	4.59	3.75	3.73	3.16	3.36	3.18	4.13	5.61	51.31
Johnson	Lutherville	40	40.2	80.1	116	−17	40	Apr. 3	Oct. 31	211	39	4.14	3.16	4.25	4.75	5.38	4.55	3.61	3.70	4.13	4.03	3.55	4.15	49.40
Lafayette	Lewisville	14	47.0	82.4	110	−8	15	Mar. 23	Nov. 1	223	16	3.86	3.64	3.88	5.19	5.48	4.30	3.84	2.99	2.78	2.38	2.84	4.70	45.88
Lawrence	Alicia	12	38.9	79.1	105	−14	14	Mar. 31	Oct. 19	202	14	4.45	3.49	4.50	6.65	5.83	4.11	4.40	5.16	4.30	3.02	4.01	4.32	54.24
	Black Rock						20	Apr. 1	Nov. 4	217	34	4.68	3.11	4.68	5.10	4.74	3.68	3.77	3.91	4.07	3.47	3.96	3.90	49.07
Lee	Marianna	26	42.5	81.2	109	−11	27	Mar. 23	Nov. 2	224	27	4.98	3.65	4.89	4.13	4.06	3.57	3.37	2.79	2.79	3.37	3.46	4.67	45.73
Little River	Index						12	Mar. 28	Nov. 10	227	21	4.66	2.78	4.16	4.47	4.15	2.94	3.22	2.73	2.88	3.14	3.64	4.03	42.80
	White Cliffs						19	Mar. 27	Nov. 8	226	33	4.12	3.23	4.27	5.16	4.51	3.45	2.80	2.77	2.58	3.13	3.28	4.38	43.68
Logan	Booneville	23	41.7	82.6	118	−18	21	Apr. 2	Nov. 1	213	25	4.11	2.45	3.77	4.55	5.41	4.44	3.24	3.39	3.52	3.44	3.40	3.32	45.04
	Subiaco	40	42.0	82.2	117	−17	40	Mar. 25	Nov. 5	225	40	3.69	2.83	3.78	4.41	5.10	4.04	3.21	3.55	3.45	3.47	3.28	3.40	44.21
Lonoke	England	31	43.3	86.1	112	−13	30	Mar. 23	Nov. 2	224	32	5.05	3.75	4.98	5.34	4.53	3.55	2.98	3.50	3.14	3.21	3.80	4.95	48.78
Madison	Dutton	32	35.9	75.5	109	−23	33	Apr. 22	Oct. 19	180	34	3.96	2.76	4.14	5.68	6.14	5.64	4.03	3.89	5.33	4.00	3.51	3.74	52.82
Marion	Dodd City	20	37.0	77.3	106	−25	20	Apr. 20	Oct. 21	184	21	3.16	2.62	3.35	4.43	4.84	4.08	4.27	4.66	3.83	2.72	2.18	2.70	42.84
Miller	Spring Bank						17	Mar. 27	Nov. 27	245	29	4.48	3.55	4.41	5.65	4.59	3.77	3.61	3.25	2.86	3.02	4.06	5.58	48.83
	Texarkana	40	46.3	82.7	117	−9	40	Mar. 21	Nov. 9	233	40	4.48	3.37	4.30	4.94	4.52	3.71	4.11	3.37	2.67	3.41	3.67	4.61	47.16
Mississippi	Blytheville	13	41.1	81.4	108	−8	13	Mar. 28	Oct. 31	217	13	6.55	2.77	4.76	4.39	3.83	3.92	3.74	3.96	3.70	3.66	3.87	4.22	49.37
	Osceola	23	40.9	81.3	110	−17	24	Mar. 29	Nov. 4	220	27	4.79	3.07	5.04	4.64	4.91	3.38	3.31	3.30	2.96	3.24	4.05	4.43	47.12
Monroe	Brinkley	40	42.5	81.4	111	−12	40	Mar. 28	Nov. 2	219	40	5.25	4.10	5.30	5.24	5.20	3.69	4.20	3.45	3.82	3.36	4.05	5.16	52.82
	Clarendon						24	Mar. 26	Nov. 1	220	34	4.90	3.80	5.08	5.38	4.73	3.50	3.45	3.59	3.45	3.17	4.10	5.18	50.33
Montgomery	Mount Ida	24	41.2	80.0	116	−15	24	Apr. 8	Oct. 27	202	24	4.93	3.23	4.47	5.35	5.25	4.10	3.28	3.49	3.64	4.03	4.54	4.21	50.52
Nevada	Prescott	40	44.8	82.3	112	−7	40	Mar. 23	Nov. 7	229	40	4.93	3.71	4.54	4.81	4.91	4.16	4.07	3.16	3.19	2.93	3.84	4.74	48.99
Newton	Nail	24	36.3	75.4	105	−22	24	Apr. 10	Oct. 26	199	26	3.63	2.87	4.13	5.43	6.35	4.88	4.49	3.96	4.32	3.44	3.39	3.66	50.55
Ouachita	Camden	40	45.1	81.4	115	−10	40	Mar. 25	Nov. 4	224	40	4.68	3.85	4.76	4.74	4.64	4.00	4.08	3.03	3.04	2.96	4.20	5.50	49.48
Perry	Thornburg	16	40.4	79.9	113	−15	17	Apr. 3	Oct. 29	209	18	4.81	3.40	4.36	4.56	5.75	4.85	4.43	3.28	3.77	3.98	3.88	4.26	51.33
Phillips	Helena	29	43.9	81.3	111	−9	35	Mar. 25	Nov. 1	221	40	5.33	3.90	5.75	5.03	4.66	3.41	3.85	3.63	2.96	2.97	4.51	5.35	51.35
Pike	Murfreesboro	9	47.1	83.7	116	0	12	Mar. 23	Nov. 12	234	19	5.13	3.18	4.24	4.64	4.26	4.16	3.05	2.99	2.94	3.14	3.98	4.58	46.29
Poinsett	Marked Tree	22	39.3	81.1	109	−13	24	Mar. 26	Oct. 31	219	34	5.73	3.49	5.11	5.19	4.75	3.26	3.66	3.55	3.03	3.96	4.24	4.57	50.54
Polk	Mena	40	41.8	80.2	112	−15	40	Mar. 26	Nov. 8	227	39	4.13	3.27	4.28	5.49	5.95	4.95	3.58	4.13	4.10	3.92	3.69	4.01	51.50
	Grannis	18	41.7	79.3	110	−14	18	Mar. 31	Nov. 4	218	19	5.42	3.97	4.51	5.25	5.84	4.82	4.48	3.05	4.75	4.38	4.77	5.04	56.28
Pope	Russellville	14	39.6	81.2	109	−15	13	Apr. 6	Oct. 28	205	13	4.10	3.25	3.61	3.72	6.38	4.21	4.18	3.48	3.77	3.13	3.78	3.29	46.90
	Turnpike						14	Apr. 9	Oct. 27	201	14	4.73	3.20	4.20	4.95	5.54	4.77	3.52	3.57	5.42	5.00	3.99	4.30	53.19
Pulaski	Little Rock	40	42.6	81.2	110	−12	40	Mar. 17	Nov. 13	241	40	4.87	3.21	4.25	5.06	4.41	3.41	3.31	3.35	2.99	2.85	3.61	4.80	46.12
Randolph	Pocahontas	40	39.0	80.7	112	−22	40	Apr. 2	Nov. 2	214	40	4.49	3.32	4.51	4.85	4.82	4.43	4.03	4.51	3.56	3.51	3.62	3.99	49.64

Scott	Waldron						18	Mar. 29	Nov. 6	222	18	4.34	3.41	4.05	5.22	5.65	4.48	3.35	2.78	3.47	3.83	3.67	3.58	47.83
Searcy	Gilbert						14	Apr. 8	Oct. 29	204	13	3.83	2.73	2.92	5.07	4.64	3.81	3.40	3.73	4.12	4.39	2.81	3.27	44.72
	Marshall	20	39.5	79.2	110	−24	20	Apr. 3	Oct. 26	206	21	3.42	2.43	4.16	6.05	6.64	4.79	3.90	5.19	4.26	3.92	3.65	3.72	52.13
Sebastian	Fort Smith	40	40.6	82.2	113	−15	40	Mar. 21	Nov. 10	234	40	2.62	2.23	2.75	3.65	4.61	3.58	2.78	2.89	3.16	3.22	2.60	2.61	36.70
Sharp	Hardy	22	38.3	79.4	112	−19	23	Apr. 8	Oct. 28	203	23	4.04	3.02	3.87	4.69	4.96	4.37	3.79	4.47	3.60	2.82	3.50	3.70	46.83
Stone	Arlberg						12	Mar. 31	Nov. 1	215	13	4.67	3.14	4.81	5.50	5.48	4.78	3.59	4.97	4.01	4.30	3.60	4.30	53.15
Union	El Dorado	35	46.7	82.4	112	−4	35	Mar. 19	Nov. 15	241	34	4.63	3.93	5.11	5.32	4.79	3.44	4.22	3.10	2.90	3.17	4.42	6.35	51.38
	Huttig	21	48.4	82.8	107	−2	20	Mar. 22	Nov. 7	230	21	4.21	3.99	5.79	5.70	5.50	3.90	3.69	4.08	2.76	3.22	3.72	5.15	51.71
	Junction City	30	46.1	82.1	111	−15	31	Mar. 29	Nov. 4	220	33	3.60	3.64	4.86	5.01	5.10	3.82	4.27	3.26	2.44	2.78	3.34	4.85	46.97
Van Buren	Bee Branch	38	41.5	81.0	114	−19	38	Apr. 4	Oct. 29	208	40	4.54	3.04	4.60	4.75	5.19	4.44	3.43	3.72	3.21	3.56	3.71	4.22	48.41
	Clinton						18	Mar. 30	Oct. 31	215	17	4.57	3.19	5.26	4.69	5.33	3.84	2.72	3.57	4.04	4.26	4.24	4.49	50.20
Washington	Fayetteville	40	38.5	78.9	110	−24	40	Apr. 6	Oct. 25	202	40	3.00	2.29	3.46	4.49	5.14	4.63	3.62	3.93	4.02	3.60	3.05	2.67	43.90
White	Searcy	22	40.7	81.4	115	−20	24	Mar. 29	Nov. 3	219	23	5.41	2.92	4.81	4.20	4.27	4.11	2.97	3.68	3.22	3.41	4.07	4.32	47.39
Woodruff	Georgetown						21	Mar. 25	Nov. 2	222	26	5.80	3.41	5.18	4.91	4.44	4.12	3.30	3.40	3.78	3.53	3.81	4.52	50.20
Yell	Danville						22	Mar. 30	Nov. 1	216	22	4.30	2.69	4.31	4.85	4.97	4.06	3.21	3.16	3.49	3.96	3.64	3.71	46.35
	Dardanelle	29	41.3	82.1	113	−11	29	Mar. 29	Nov. 4	220	40	3.76	2.97	4.19	4.13	5.12	3.66	3.17	3.49	3.30	3.35	3.34	3.69	44.17

Precipitation and temperature—State unit values

[This tabulation gives the mean annual, mean monthly, and average seasonal precipitation, 1886–1938, and the mean annual temperatures, 1902–38, for Arkansas]

Precipitation		Precipitation		Precipitation	
Year	Mean	Year	Mean	Year	Mean
	In.		*In.*		*In.*
1886	42.55	1907	49.73	1928	50.50
1887	37.29	1908	48.88	1929	46.10
1888	45.67	1909	44.05	1930	46.62
1889	45.61	1910	45.21	1931	46.98
1890	61.58	1911	49.54	1932	51.11
1891	44.43	1912	45.83	1933	49.07
1892	57.75	1913	54.01	1934	42.47
1893	47.91	1914	42.85	1935	57.02
1894	49.05	1915	53.08	1936	34.15
1895	44.69	1916	42.18	1937	55.20
1896	37.72	1917	40.72	1938	49.05
1897	46.13	1918	44.64		
1898	56.82	1919	54,52	**Month**	**Mean**
1899	41.49	1920	54.28		
1900	49.03	1921	47.46		
1901	35.27	1922	46.50		
1902	51.70	1923	59.85		*In.*
1903	44.62	1924	37.03	January	4.44
1904	43.45	1925	42.19	February	3.40
1905	62.17	1926	49.24	March	4.74
1906	55.99	1927	65.85	April	4.73

Precipitation	
Month	Mean
	In.
May	4.87
June	4.04
July	3.75
August	3.56
September	3.42
October	3.06
November	3.91
December	4.14
Annual	48.06
Season	**Average**
	In.
Winter	11.98
Spring	14.34
Summer	11.35
Fall	10.39

Temperature		Temperature	
Year	Mean	Year	Mean
	°*F.*		°*F.*
1902	60.5	1921	64.2
1903	59.3	1922	62.7
1904	60.5	1923	61.6
1905	59.6	1924	60.1
1906	60.3	1925	63.0
1907	61.9	1926	61.3
1908	62.1	1927	63.1
1909	62.1	1928	61.1
1910	61.0	1929	60.5
1911	62.8	1930	61.7
1912	59.8	1931	62.5
1913	61.6	1932	62.0
1914	61.4	1933	63.2
1915	60.6	1934	62.8
1916	61.9	1935	61.4
1917	59.2	1936	62.0
1918	61.4	1937	61.1
1919	61.6	1938	63.6
1920	60.7		

ARKANSAS—Continued

Dates of last killing frost in spring and first in fall, with length of growing season

Year	Fort Smith			Hope			Jonesboro			Little Rock			Rogers			Warren		
	Last in spring	First in fall	Growing season[1]	Last in spring	First in fall	Growing season[1]	Last in spring	First in fall	Growing season[1]	Last in spring	First in fall	Growing season[1]	Last in spring	First in fall	Growing season[1]	Last in spring	First in fall	Growing season[1]
			Days			*Days*			*Days*			*Days*			*Days*			*Days*
1899	Apr. 1	Nov. 3	216	Mar. 29	Nov. 3	219	Apr. 8	Oct. 31	206	Apr. 1	Nov. 3	216	Apr. 9	Oct. 29	203	Mar. 29	Nov. 3	219
1900	Mar. 31	Nov. 9	223	Apr. 1	Nov. 11	224	Apr. 12	Nov. 9	211	Mar. 21	Nov. 9	233	Apr. 13	Nov. 1	202	Apr. 1	Nov. 9	222
1901	Mar. 21	Nov. 16	240	Apr. 3	Nov. 16	227	Mar. 21	Dec. 14	268	do	Nov. 16	240	Apr. 19	Oct. 14	178	Apr. 3	Nov. 15	226
1902	Mar. 17	Nov. 27	255	Mar. 18	Nov. 27	254	Mar. 19	Oct. 29	224	Mar. 18	Dec. 5	262	Mar. 31	Nov. 15	229	Mar. 20	Oct. 19	213
1903	Mar. 24	Nov. 17	238	Apr. 4	Nov. 18	228	Mar. 25	Oct. 25	214	Mar. 1	Nov. 18	262	May 1	Oct. 18	170	Apr. 5	do	197
1904	Mar. 28	Nov. 13	230	Mar. 13	Nov. 11	243	Mar. 28	Nov. 13	230	Mar. 28	Nov. 13	230	Apr. 10	Oct. 23	196	Mar. 28	Oct. 24	210
1905	Feb. 28	Nov. 29	274	Feb. 22	do	262	Apr. 17	Oct. 12	178	Feb. 21	Nov. 30	282	Mar. 21	Oct. 21	214	Mar. 14	Oct. 22	222
1906	Mar. 1	Oct. 31	244	Mar. 21	Oct. 10	203	Apr. 1	Oct. 11	193	Mar. 29	Nov. 22	238	Mar. 24	Oct. 10	200	Apr. 1	Oct. 11	193
1907	Mar. 2	Nov. 11	254	Mar. 15	Oct. 14	213	Apr. 14			Feb. 22	Nov. 12	263	Apr. 13	Oct. 13	183	Apr. 2	Oct. 14	195
1908	Feb. 22	Nov. 12	265	Feb. 20						do	do	264	Apr. 30	Sept. 28	151	Mar. 21	Nov. 14	238
1909	Mar. 15	Nov. 17	247				May 2	Oct. 13	164	Mar. 15	Nov. 18	248	May 2	Oct. 12	163	Apr. 9	Nov. 18	223
1910	Feb. 25	Oct. 29	246				Apr. 25	Oct. 28	186	Apr. 26	Oct. 29	186	Apr. 26	Oct. 28	185	Apr. 26	Oct. 29	186
1911	Mar. 16	Nov. 2	231				Mar. 24	Oct. 25	215	Mar. 16	Nov. 2	231	Mar. 29	Oct. 22	207	Mar. 16	Nov. 3	232
1912	Mar. 25	do	222				Mar. 25	Nov. 3	223	Mar. 25	Nov. 3	223	Apr. 8	Oct. 23	198	Mar. 25	Nov. 2	222
1913	Mar. 28	Oct. 30	216				Mar. 29	Oct. 21	206	Mar. 16	Oct. 30	228	Apr. 5	Oct. 20	198	Mar. 28	Oct. 31	207
1914	Apr. 9	Nov. 17	222				Apr. 10	Oct. 28	201	Mar. 22	Nov. 17	240	Apr. 12	Oct. 27	198	Apr. 10	Oct. 28	201
1915	Mar. 31	Nov. 15	229		Nov. 15		Apr. 4	Nov. 15	225	do	Nov. 15	238	Apr. 3	Oct. 9	189	Apr. 4	Nov. 15	225
1916	Apr. 9	Oct. 21	195	Mar. 4	Oct. 21	231	Apr. 9	Nov. 14	219	Mar. 16	Nov. 14	243	Apr. 9	Oct. 20	194	Mar. 16	Oct. 20	218
1917	Mar. 8	Oct. 9	215	Mar. 5	Oct. 23	232	Apr. 10	Oct. 9	182	Mar. 5	Oct. 24	233	do	Oct. 9	183	Apr. 10	do	193
1918	Mar. 10	Nov. 1	236	Feb. 21	Nov. 24	276	Apr. 12	Nov. 1	203	Feb. 22	Nov. 23	274	do	Nov. 1	206	Apr. 12	Nov. 24	226
1919	Mar. 6	Nov. 13	252	Mar. 1	Nov. 13	257	Apr. 2	Nov. 14	226	Mar. 6	Nov. 13	252	Apr. 12	Nov. 11	213	Mar. 6	Nov. 14	253
1920	Apr. 5	Nov. 3	212	Apr. 5	Nov. 3	212	Apr. 5	Nov. 12	221	Apr. 5	Nov. 12	221	Apr. 14	Oct. 28	197	Apr. 5	Nov. 12	221
1921	Apr. 17	Nov. 10	207	Apr. 17	Nov. 10	207	Apr. 18	do	208	Mar. 29	do	228	May 3	Oct. 12	162	Mar. 29	Nov. 20	236
1922	Mar. 4	Nov. 26	267	Mar. 4	Nov. 21	262	Mar. 8	Nov. 21	258	Mar. 4	Nov. 24	265	Apr. 1	Oct. 18	200	Mar. 4	Dec. 19	290
1923	Mar. 31	Nov. 29	243	Apr. 1	Oct. 24	206	Mar. 31	Oct. 22	205	Apr. 1	Nov. 30	243	May 9	Oct. 21	165	Apr. 1	Oct. 20	202
1924	Apr. 1	Nov. 24	237	Apr. 2	Oct. 25	206	Apr. 2	Nov. 19	231	do	Nov. 25	238	Apr. 2	Oct. 24	205		Nov. 20	
1925	Mar. 15	Oct. 28	227	Mar. 15	Oct. 31	230	Mar. 3	Oct. 30	241	Mar. 15	Oct. 30	229	May 1	Oct. 20	172	Mar. 15	Oct. 31	230
1926	Apr. 1	Nov. 5	218	Apr. 1	Nov. 5	218	Apr. 1	Oct. 25	207	Mar. 27	Nov. 3	221	Apr. 1	Oct. 25	207	Apr. 1	Nov. 5	218
1927	Mar. 22	Nov. 16	239	Mar. 22	Nov. 17	240	Apr. 22	Nov. 6	198	Mar. 22	Nov. 17	240	Apr. 22	Nov. 17	209	Mar. 22	Nov. 16	239
1928	Apr. 15	Nov. 20	219	Apr. 16	Nov. 20	218	Apr. 16	Oct. 31	198	Feb. 26	Nov. 20	268	Apr. 16	Oct. 31	198	Apr. 15	Nov. 20	219
1929	Mar. 10	Nov. 5	240	Mar. 10	Nov. 5	240	Mar. 10	Nov. 5	240	Mar. 10	Nov. 5	240	Mar. 18	Oct. 24	220	Mar. 10	Nov. 5	240
1930	Mar. 30	Oct. 31	215	Mar. 30	Oct. 31	215	do	Oct. 31	215	Mar. 26	Nov. 25	244	Mar. 31	Oct. 29	212	Mar. 26	Oct. 31	219
1931	Mar. 29	Dec. 2	248	Apr. 22	Nov. 1	193	Mar. 17	Dec. 2	260	Mar. 10	Dec. 2	267	Apr. 22	Nov. 1	193	Mar. 10	None	297
1932	Mar. 14	Nov. 11	242	Mar. 14	Nov. 11	242	Mar. 15	Nov. 12	242	Mar. 14	Nov. 11	242	Mar. 31	do	215	Mar. 13	Nov. 12	244
1933	Mar. 21	Nov. 10	234	Mar. 21	Nov. 8	232	Mar. 21	Nov. 8	232	Mar. 21	Nov. 8	232	Mar. 26	Nov. 8	227	Mar. 21	Dec. 7	261
1934	Mar. 19	Nov. 23	249	Mar. 19	Nov. 23	249	Mar. 28	Nov. 12	229	Mar. 19	Nov. 23	249	Mar. 28	Nov. 12	229	Mar. 19	Nov. 12	238
1935	Mar. 7	Nov. 20	258	Feb. 28	do	268	Mar. 17	Nov. 18	246	Feb. 28	Nov. 23	268	Mar. 17	Nov. 5	233	Feb. 28	Nov. 23	268

1936	Apr. 3	Nov. 4	215	Apr. 3	Nov. 4	215	Apr. 3	Nov. 4	215	Apr. 3	Nov. 4	215	Apr. 7	Nov. 3	210	Apr. 3	----------	------
1937	Mar. 29	Oct. 23	208	Apr. 6	Oct. 23	200	Mar. 29	Oct. 23	208	Mar. 28	Oct. 23	209	Apr. 10	Oct. 23	196	----------	Oct. 23	------
1938	Mar. 7	Oct. 24	231	Apr. 3	Oct. 24	204	Apr. 10	Oct. 24	197	Feb. 25	Nov. 8	256	Apr. 2	do	204	Apr. 3	Nov. 8	219
Mean	Mar. 21	Nov. 10	234	Mar. 21	Nov. 7	231	Apr. 1	Nov. 4	217	Mar. 17	Nov. 13	241	Apr. 10	Oct. 25	198	Mar. 27	Nov. 7	225
Extremes	Feb. 22[2] Apr. 17[3]	Oct. 9[4] Dec. 2[5]	[6] 195 [7] 274	Feb. 20[2] Apr. 22[3]	Oct. 10[4] Nov. 27[5]	[6] 193 [7] 276	Mar. 3[2] May 2[3]	Oct. 9[4] Dec. 14[5]	[6] 164 [7] 268	Feb. 21[2] Apr. 26[3]	Oct. 23[4] Dec. 5[5]	[6] 186 [7] 282	Mar. 17[2] May 9[3]	Sept. 28[4] Nov. 17[5]	[6] 151 [7] 233	Feb. 28[2] Apr. 26[3]	Oct. 11[4] None[5]	[6] 186 [7] 299

[1] Number of days between last killing frost in spring and first in fall.
[2] Earliest date in spring.
[3] Latest date in spring.
[4] Earliest date in fall.
[5] Latest date in fall.
[6] Shortest growing season.
[7] Longest growing season.

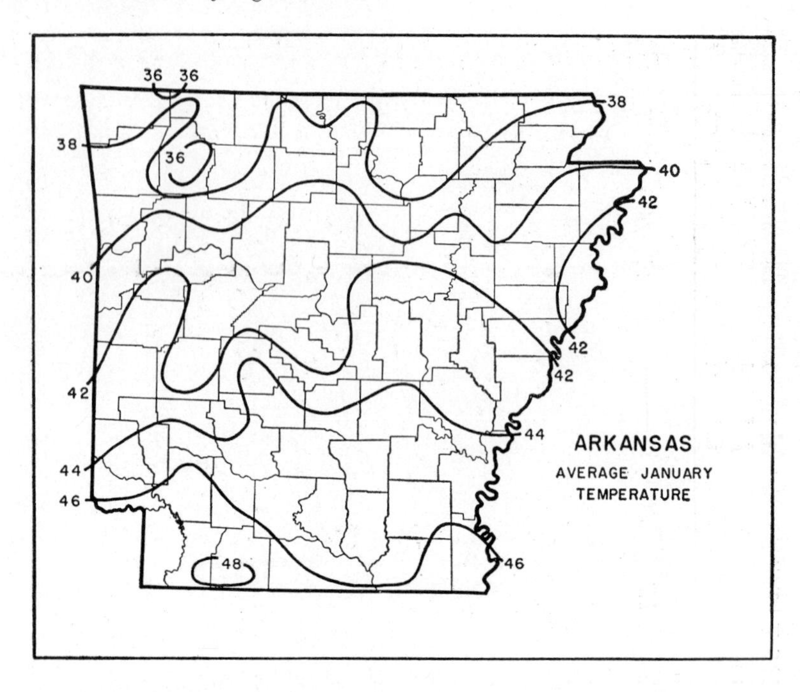
36
36
38
36
40
42
38
40
42
42
42
42
44
44
46
48
46
ARKANSAS
AVERAGE JANUARY
TEMPERATURE

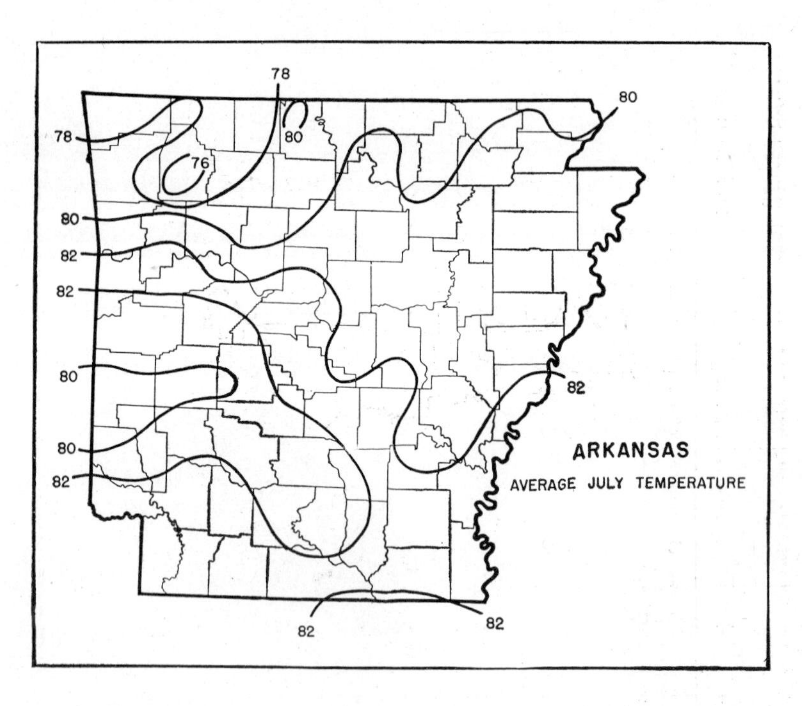
78
80
78
80
76
80
82
82
80
82
80
82
82
82
ARKANSAS
AVERAGE JULY TEMPERATURE

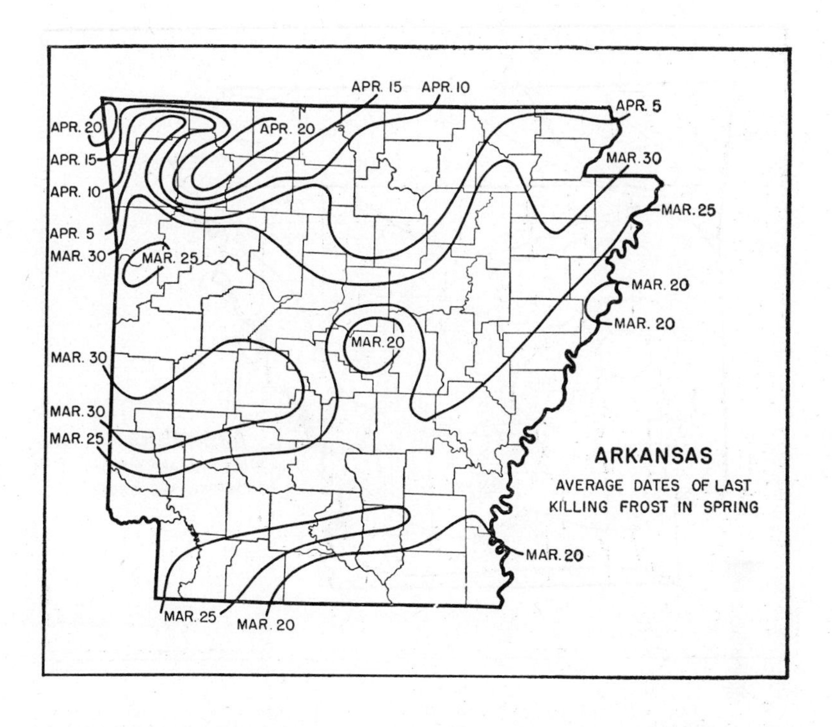

APR. 15
APR. 10
APR. 5
APR. 20
APR. 20
APR. 15
APR. 10
MAR. 30
MAR. 25
APR. 5
MAR. 30
MAR. 25
MAR. 20
MAR. 20
MAR. 20
MAR. 30
MAR. 30
MAR. 25
ARKANSAS
AVERAGE DATES OF LAST KILLING FROST IN SPRING
MAR. 20
MAR. 25
MAR. 20

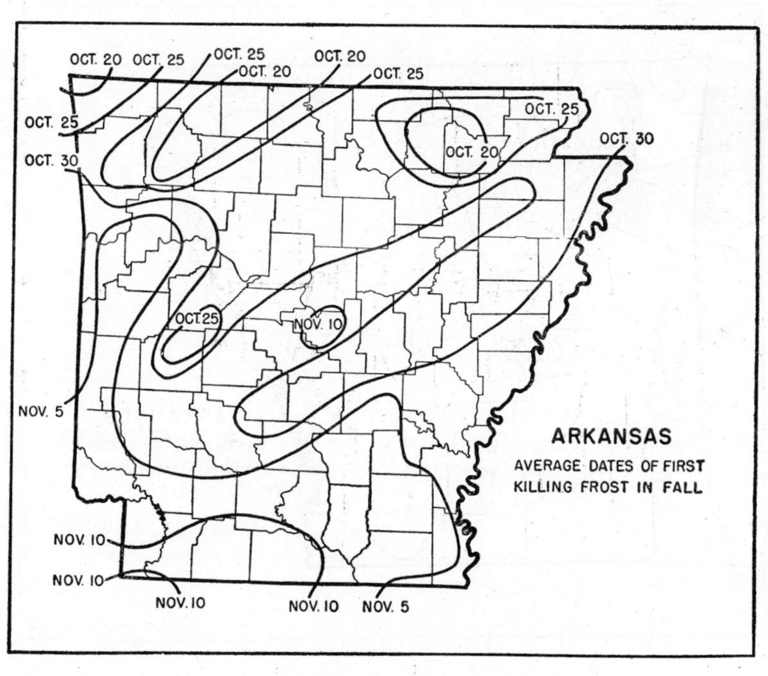

OCT. 20
OCT. 25
OCT. 25
OCT. 20
OCT. 20
OCT. 25
OCT. 25
OCT. 25
OCT. 30
OCT. 30
OCT. 20
OCT25
NOV. 10
NOV. 5
ARKANSAS
AVERAGE DATES OF FIRST KILLING FROST IN FALL
NOV. 10
NOV. 10
NOV. 10
NOV. 10
NOV. 5

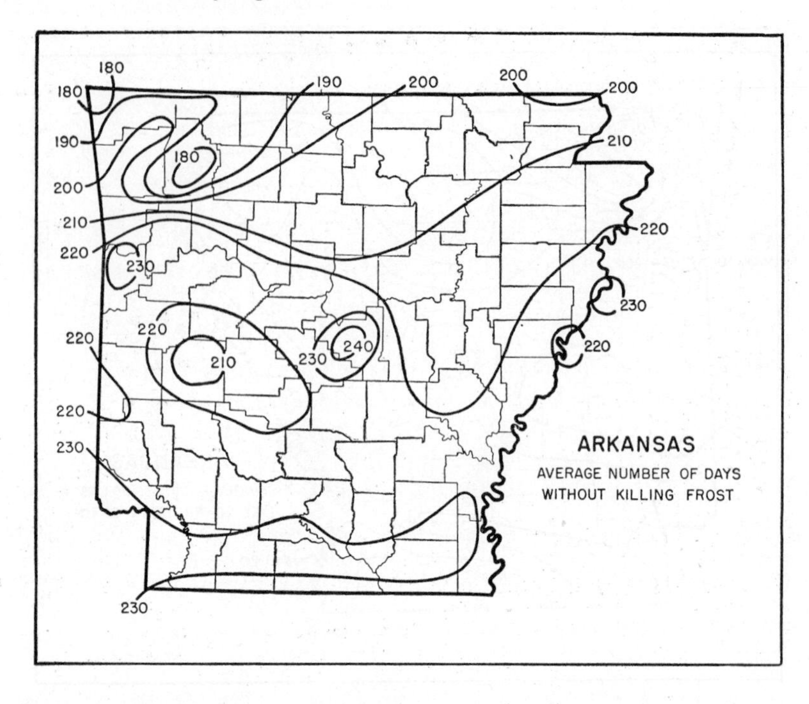

ARKANSAS

AVERAGE NUMBER OF DAYS WITHOUT KILLING FROST

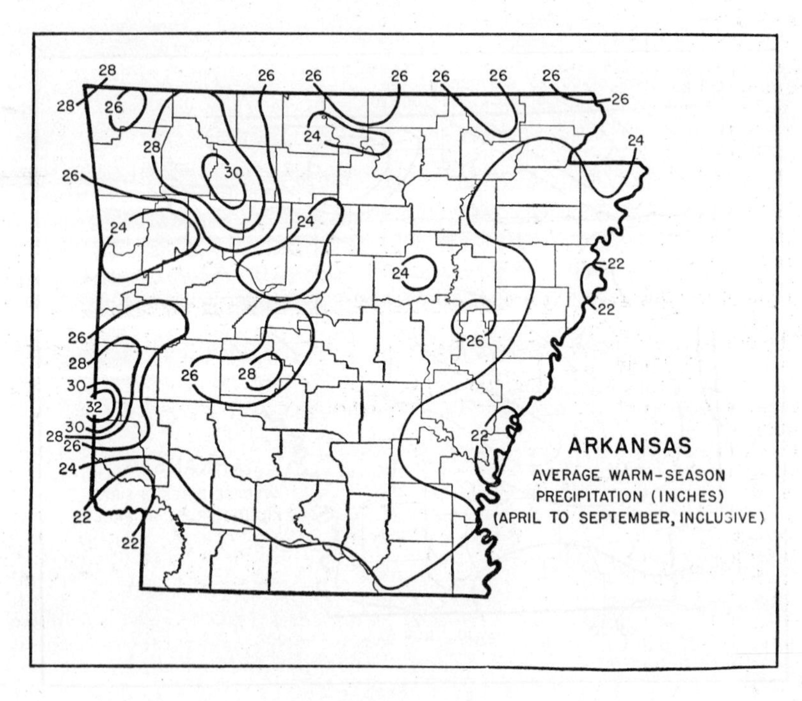

ARKANSAS

AVERAGE WARM-SEASON PRECIPITATION (INCHES) (APRIL TO SEPTEMBER, INCLUSIVE)

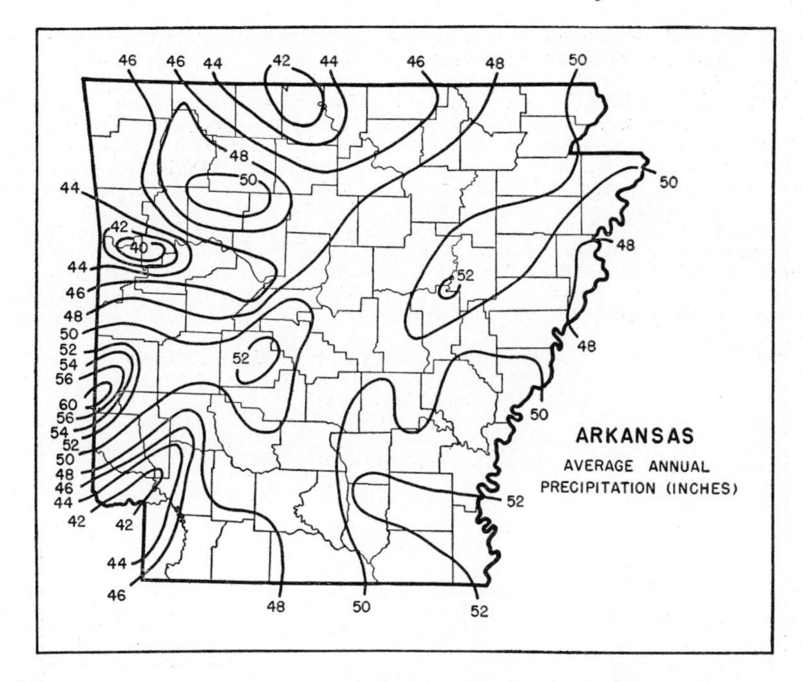

SUPPLEMENTARY CLIMATIC NOTES FOR ARKANSAS

Arkansas covers an area of approximately 53,850 square miles, extending from latitude 34° to 36°30′ N. and longitude 90° to 94°30′ W. The Missouri Pacific Railroad, crossing the State from southwest to northeast, skirts the foothills of the mountains. The section east of the Missouri Pacific, with the exception of Crowleys Ridge, is lowland, while that to the west is generally mountainous. The elevation varies from 58.9 feet above sea level, at a point where the Ouachita River crosses the Arkansas-Louisiana line, to the two highest points in the State, Mount Magazine, in Logan County, 2,823 feet, and Rich Mountain in Polk County, which is perhaps a little higher and is one of the highest points between the Rocky and the Appalachian Mountains.

The entire State slopes to the south and east, and practically all the drainage reaches the Mississippi River through the St. Francis, White, Arkansas, Ouachita, and Red Rivers—the White, Arkansas, and Ouachita draining most of the State. The soil of the lowlands is a rich alluvial deposit that is very fertile, but in many places that of the uplands is badly eroded and has lost its fertility.

The climate of Arkansas is agreeable and favors a diversified agriculture. For the State as a whole, the summers are moderately long and hot, with day temperatures sometimes exceeding 100° F. in July and August. In a few northern counties and in the Ouachita Mountain highland, day temperatures are not quite so high.

The winters are short and moderately cold. In the northern counties zero temperatures are of frequent occurrence in January and February, and zero has been recorded to the southern border.

Rainfall for the State as a whole is rather evenly distributed through the year, being ample under normal conditions for agricultural purposes. The highland sections are well adapted to raising corn, hay, grains, and fruit, while the lowlands are best suited for cotton and rice farming. The growing of spinach has become an important industry in Sebastian and Crawford Counties.

Most of the precipitation is in the form of rain, but snow occurs in the mountainous sections and frequently covers the ground for 2 or 3 weeks. Snowfall in the southern counties is generally light and snow remains on the ground only a few days.

Owing to the character of the soil and the steepness of the land surface in the mountainous areas, hot dry summers are much more damaging to crops there than in the east and southeast. If it were possible to hold all rainfall in the locality where it falls until it soaks into the ground, droughts in Arkansas would be less severe.

Cotton and strawberries are damaged by late spring frosts in some years, but as a rule all crops mature in the fall before the first killing frost.

Generally speaking, precipitation increases from the northwest to the southeast. The heaviest rainfall usually occurs in March, April, and May, while the driest months are August, September, and October. May, with a State average of 4.87 inches, is the wettest month, and October, with 3.06 inches, the driest.

At most stations in Arkansas the prevailing wind direction is from the south and southwest during the warmer months, and in winter from the north or northwest. There are rather frequent east or northeast winds in late summer and early fall. In recent years dust from dry regions farther west has been brought into Arkansas during drought periods by west and southwest winds, a new phenomenon for the State.

WALTER C. HICKMON, *Assistant Meteorologist and Climatic Section Director for Arkansas, Weather Bureau, Little Rock.*

CALIFORNIA

Climatic summary

County	Station	Temperature: Length of record	Temperature: January average	Temperature: July average	Temperature: Maximum	Temperature: Minimum	Killing frost average dates: Length of record	Killing frost: Last in spring	Killing frost: First in fall	Killing frost: Growing season[1]	Average precipitation: Length of record	January	February	March	April	May	June	July	August	September	October	November	December	Annual
		Yr.	°F.	°F.	°F.	°F.	Yr.			Days	Yr.	In.	In.	In.	In.	In.	In.	In.	In.	In.	In.	In.	In.	In.
Alameda	Berkeley	40	48.5	61.5	106	25	34	Jan. 14	Dec. 27	347	40	4.95	4.45	3.61	1.33	0.83	0.21	0.02	0.03	0.41	1.13	2.32	3.81	23.10
	Livermore	39	47.1	70.3	113	19	36	Mar. 16	Nov. 26	255	40	3.13	2.48	2.28	.84	.50	.11	.01	.01	.30	.58	1.33	2.43	14.00
	Oakland	40	48.0	62.6	100	25	37	Jan. 11	Dec. 28	351	40	4.62	4.39	3.46	1.26	.71	.22	.01	.04	.43	1.06	2.33	3.69	22.22
Alpine	Markleeville										19	4.03	3.59	1.84	1.17	.75	.50	.51	.32	.50	.90	1.98	2.70	18.79
	Tamarack	22	25.7	57.9	88	−29	20	June 28	Aug. 13	46	26	10.14	6.91	6.82	2.94	2.36	1.20	.72	.51	1.07	2.67	4.90	6.51	46.75
	Twin Lakes	13	24.1	58.4	91	−26	12	July 2	Aug. 11	40	20	7.64	7.45	5.81	3.90	1.54	1.39	.50	.30	.72	1.90	3.15	6.72	41.02
Amador	Electra	34	46.0	78.0	114	15	32	Mar. 12	Nov. 21	254	35	6.09	6.04	5.22	2.38	1.10	.39	.01	.01	.50	1.41	2.50	4.84	30.49
	Kennedy Mine	33	44.1	76.2	110	14	33	Mar. 19	Nov. 25	251	40	5.49	5.38	4.85	2.31	1.05	.34	.00	.01	.55	1.54	2.84	4.42	28.78
	Tiger Creek	32	40.1	70.3	110	6	32	Apr. 26	Oct. 30	187	32	8.79	8.37	6.73	3.52	1.67	.76	.03	.05	.67	2.10	3.94	6.86	43.49
Butte	Biggs	18	47.1	80.1	118	17					18	5.63	3.50	3.41	.90	.94	.42	.01	.01	.54	1.10	2.35	3.29	22.10
	Chico	40	45.2	79.1	117	11	36	Mar. 28	Nov. 17	234	40	4.95	4.50	3.40	1.62	.93	.48	.02	.01	.55	1.18	2.88	4.27	24.79
	De Sabla	32	40.2	72.5	112	−2	33	May 5	Oct. 24	172	35	12.32	11.63	8.82	4.16	2.40	.94	.02	.01	.95	2.82	6.16	9.80	60.03
	Inskip	31	36.1	69.4	103	2	24	May 15	do.	162	31	15.76	14.42	10.27	5.57	2.83	1.18	.09	.08	1.18	3.55	7.50	11.71	74.14
	Las Plumas	25	46.4	82.4	118	19	25	Feb. 20	Dec. 11	294	25	8.18	9.49	5.31	3.49	1.43	.65	.02	.01	.41	1.82	4.72	7.91	43.44
	Oroville	40	45.0	79.1	119	13	36	Mar. 17	Nov. 26	254	40	5.37	4.85	3.92	1.71	1.07	.42	.01	.01	.51	1.34	3.08	4.78	27.07
	West Branch	31	38.0	67.5	106	−3	32	May 19	Oct. 1	135	32	14.19	12.97	8.86	5.06	2.76	1.09	.08	.11	1.11	3.35	7.72	10.82	68.12
Calaveras	Jenny Lind	7	44.2	77.1	115	10	8	Apr. 8	Nov. 7	213	32	4.22	3.71	3.04	1.22	.51	.18	.00	.02	.25	.76	1.46	3.16	18.53
	Milton (near)	26	46.4	78.2	113	20	27	Feb. 17	Dec. 11	297	30	4.08	3.81	3.87	1.38	.84	.16	.00	.03	.43	.87	2.03	3.24	20.74
	Mokelumne Hill	28	44.8	76.3	109	18	28	Mar. 19	Nov. 28	254	29	6.01	5.57	5.40	2.19	1.12	.25	.00	.02	.68	1.65	3.22	4.51	30.62
	West Point										40	7.16	7.27	6.77	3.22	1.63	.56	.02	.04	.72	2.05	3.88	5.77	39.09
Colusa	Colusa	34	44.9	77.5	114	14	34	Feb. 25	Nov. 21	269	36	3.11	2.89	2.23	.83	.41	.24	.00	.01	.37	.56	1.65	2.86	15.16
	East Park	28	42.8	76.5	112	3	28	Apr. 16	Oct. 23	190	28	3.58	3.43	1.92	.96	.56	.24	.02	.02	.41	.64	1.76	3.57	17.11
Contra Costa	Antioch	39	47.1	76.5	114	14	32	Feb. 18	Nov. 28	283	40	2.70	2.37	1.85	.63	.37	.10	.01	.02	.31	.54	1.16	2.19	12.25
	Crockett	21	47.4	66.6	104	19	21	Jan. 22	Dec. 24	336	21	2.65	3.49	2.00	1.26	.36	.20	.00	.02	.26	.91	1.71	2.92	15.78
Del Norte	Crescent City (near)	35	45.9	59.3	102	19	35	Apr. 2	Nov. 18	230	36	12.51	11.53	9.86	6.20	3.48	1.85	.33	.39	2.35	5.28	10.84	11.25	75.87
El dorado	Pilot Creek						10	Apr. 27	Oct. 18	174	16	16.31	9.88	13.37	4.45	3.15	1.04	.07	.08	1.30	3.74	7.07	8.93	69.39
	Placerville	40	41.3	72.1	114	8	36	Apr. 23	Oct. 24	184	40	7.44	7.27	6.44	2.84	1.44	.57	.02	.02	.68	2.04	3.82	5.96	38.54
Fresno	Auberry	22	43.2	79.7	114	11	22	Apr. 25	Nov. 7	196	24	3.97	5.25	4.24	1.98	.81	.15	.03	.02	.37	1.04	2.06	3.95	23.87
	Big Creek	24	39.8	72.3	102	1	24	Apr. 30	Oct. 31	184	23	4.50	6.27	4.80	2.92	1.44	.50	.07	.15	.55	1.50	2.53	4.82	30.05
	Cliff Camp	11	34.5	66.4	102	−10	12	May 28	Sept. 23	118	16	6.13	7.72	5.49	3.95	1.29	.66	.23	.15	.38	1.67	3.66	7.25	38.58
	Coalinga	27	45.5	82.6	120	11	27	Mar. 21	Nov. 15	239	27	1.37	1.61	1.09	.56	.26	.10	.08	.00	.07	.22	.51	1.19	7.06
	Fresno	40	45.5	81.3	115	17	40	Feb. 9	Dec. 1	295	40	1.85	1.60	1.68	.80	.39	.08	.01	.01	.15	.61	.88	1.37	9.43
	Friant										38	3.01	2.40	2.35	1.01	.48	.08	.00	.01	.13	.59	1.26	1.94	13.26
	Huntington Lake	23	29.5	61.4	100	−18	23	June 9	Oct. 1	114	24	4.42	6.25	4.49	2.69	1.43	.53	.10	.20	.58	1.49	2.41	4.73	29.32
	Reedley	21	48.0	80.6	116	17	20	Mar. 8	Nov. 26	263	24	2.47	2.00	2.13	.90	.70	.02	.02	.02	.30	.59	1.04	1.74	11.93

[1] Length of growing season between average dates of last killing frost in spring and first in fall.

CALIFORNIA—Continued

Climatic summary—Continued

County	Station	Temperature: Length of record	Temperature: January average	Temperature: July average	Temperature: Maximum	Temperature: Minimum	Killing frost average dates: Length of record	Killing frost average dates: Last in spring	Killing frost average dates: First in fall	Killing frost average dates: Growing season	Average precipitation: Length of record	January	February	March	April	May	June	July	August	September	October	November	December	Annual
		Yr.	*°F.*	*°F.*	*°F.*	*°F.*	*Yr.*			*Days*	*Yr.*	*In.*	*In.*	*In.*	*In.*	*In.*	*In.*	*In.*	*In.*	*In.*	*In.*	*In.*	*In.*	*In.*
Glenn	Monroeville										18	4.05	3.34	1.70	.95	.46	.14	.03	.02	.38	.64	2.33	3.47	17.51
	Orland	40	45.4	81.9	120	17	35	Mar. 4	Nov. 25	266	40	3.58	3.31	2.47	1.10	.60	.32	.02	.01	.43	.93	2.02	3.09	17.88
	Willows	40	45.4	79.2	116	15	36	Mar. 10	Nov. 22	257	40	3.50	3.16	2.35	.89	.55	.27	.01	.02	.40	.79	1.96	3.02	16.92
Humboldt	China Flat	30	41.7	72.7	113	9	30	Mar. 8	Nov. 12	249	29	8.42	7.02	4.70	3.22	1.45	.62	.09	.08	.94	2.32	6.81	7.80	43.47
	Eureka	40	47.3	56.1	85	20	40	Jan. 26	Dec. 20	328	40	6.73	6.15	5.09	2.91	1.43	.66	.11	.18	.88	2.34	5.44	5.66	37.58
	Orleans	35	43.6	74.6	117	8	34	Mar. 23	Nov. 11	233	36	8.70	7.53	5.55	3.29	1.56	.90	.23	.16	1.10	2.91	7.41	7.92	47.26
	Upper Mattole						13	Mar. 9	Nov. 10	246	39	15.14	13.25	9.98	5.18	2.54	1.03	.06	.13	1.29	4.93	12.14	12.60	78.27
Imperial	Amos	32	54.7	93.0	130	21	22	Jan. 29	Dec. 18	323	33	.27	.45	.30	.15	.06	.06	.20	.55	.18	.13	.14	.34	2.83
	Brawley	28	52.7	91.1	121	19	28	Feb. 5	Dec. 5	303	30	.35	.41	.20	.15	.06	.01	.06	.16	.08	.27	.12	.56	2.43
	Calexico	21	53.2	89.8	117	21	19	Feb. 1	Dec. 9	311	20	.49	.52	.29	.08	.06	.01	.09	.57	.24	.17	.29	.37	3.18
	Imperial	21	53.6	91.9	124	16	18	Jan. 29	do	311	21	.26	.89	.19	.18	.03	.00	.12	.29	.22	.26	.13	.78	3.35
Inyo	Bishop	17	37.6	73.1	109	−15	8	May 11	Oct. 10	152	19	2.45	1.07	1.12	.30	.26	.12	.09	.17	.30	.33	.41	.87	7.49
	Bishop Creek	28	28.3	60.6	88	−13	29	June 19	Sept. 9	82	28	2.55	3.32	1.92	.95	.76	.64	.43	.67	.38	.94	1.40	2.24	16.20
	Greenland Ranch	27	51.6	102.0	134	15	27	Jan. 28	Dec. 6	312	28	.25	.26	.16	.05	.06	.03	.12	.09	.09	.09	.13	.16	1.49
	Haiwee	15	39.5	81.9	107	4	14	Mar. 28	Nov. 9	226	16	.54	.87	.63	.35	.17	.28	.08	.22	.18	.32	.43	.80	4.87
	Independence	40	39.0	78.3	109	−5	40	Apr. 11	Oct. 28	200	40	1.06	.77	.46	.18	.20	.09	.14	.16	.16	.32	.30	.65	4.49
	South Lake	14	24.9	57.5	90	−22	14	June 18	Sept. 10	84	14	2.10	3.56	1.83	1.59	.87	.82	.88	1.06	.50	.98	1.37	2.59	18.15
Kern	Bakersfield	38	47.0	83.5	118	13	36	Feb. 21	Nov. 25	277	40	1.06	1.08	1.06	.59	.42	.07	.01	.01	.11	.33	.54	.84	6.12
	Dudley	26	46.3	85.4	118	16	26	Mar. 13	do	257	27	1.33	1.42	1.16	.46	.40	.08	.02	.03	.06	.31	.54	1.04	6.85
	Edison (near)	31	50.0	87.3	115	24	31	Jan. 14	Dec. 28	348	35	1.89	1.66	2.08	1.08	.65	.11	.01	.05	.13	.49	.80	1.59	10.54
	Glennville (near)	28	40.5	72.6	104	4	28	May 1	Oct. 31	183	30	3.47	3.34	3.21	2.22	.96	.21	.05	.10	.19	.75	1.73	3.41	19.64
	Kernville										40	2.18	2.13	1.57	.60	.32	.07	.09	.12	.17	.32	.77	1.60	9.94
	Maricopa	27	46.7	85.5	117	17	28	Feb. 10	Dec. 5	298	27	1.01	1.00	.97	.51	.38	.13	.01	.02	.11	.29	.35	.91	5.69
	Middlewater	26	46.2	84.6	120	12	27	Feb. 27	Nov. 28	274	28	1.01	1.13	.89	.39	.26	.07	.01	.01	.08	.33	.36	.81	5.35
	Tehachapi	24	40.5	75.0	105	−4	16	Apr. 26	Oct. 16	173	27	1.63	2.15	1.69	.95	.47	.14	.09	.21	.30	.50	.94	1.35	10.42
	Tejon Rancho	35	48.1	81.4	110	20	24	Jan. 30	Dec. 17	321	38	1.92	2.02	2.09	1.26	.60	.12	.03	.01	.11	.50	1.07	1.66	11.39
	Wasco	38	45.5	82.7	116	12	34	Mar. 15	Nov. 16	246	39	1.18	1.20	1.16	.59	.35	.05	.00	.02	.15	.29	.45	.87	6.31
Kings	Hanford	40	45.2	80.9	116	14	38	Mar. 3	Nov. 14	256	40	1.72	1.52	1.64	.64	.35	.10	.00	.01	.22	.34	.73	1.18	8.45
Lake	Helen Mine										22	20.53	16.80	11.92	4.87	2.96	.71	.07	.01	1.38	3.92	10.20	12.94	86.31
	Hullville	30	40.7	71.3	112	5	30	May 7	Oct. 11	157	31	10.29	8.19	4.84	3.00	1.44	.61	.05	.05	.65	2.04	5.55	8.77	45.48
	Lakeport										37	6.20	5.54	3.70	1.61	.74	.29	.01	.01	.40	1.28	3.19	4.90	27.87
Lassen	Doyle	16	30.7	71.6	111	−25	16	June 11	Sept. 15	96	16	1.13	1.58	1.09	.70	.56	.56	.15	.18	.37	.82	1.11	1.54	9.79
	Madeline	19	23.2	63.9	105	−36	20	June 22	Aug. 26	65	22	2.26	1.57	1.20	.70	.96	.70	.45	.27	.57	.85	.91	1.67	12.11
	Susanville	30	30.7	69.5	106	−17	28	May 18	Oct. 7	142	31	3.64	2.66	2.64	1.05	.84	.51	.22	.19	.50	1.01	1.77	2.77	17.80
	Westwood	18	27.8	65.0	100	−17	17	June 5	Aug. 28	84	18	3.19	3.79	2.26	1.67	1.06	.75	.08	.22	.60	1.45	2.83	3.73	21.63
Los Angeles	Avalon	28	54.8	66.6	100	33	28	None	None	365	28	2.35	3.11	2.02	.80	.30	.07	.00	.05	.08	.58	.73	2.70	12.79
	Claremont	39	51.2	73.8	114	19	34	Mar. 6	Dec. 5	274	39	3.84	3.83	3.45	1.55	.74	.12	.02	.06	.21	.88	1.23	2.60	18.53
	Fairmont	17	43.7	80.5	109	11	18	Mar. 20	Nov. 23	248	30	3.46	3.41	2.43	.87	.39	.07	.02	.16	.21	.46	.72	2.83	15.03

	Los Angeles	40	54.2	70.5	109	28	40	Jan. 3	Dec. 28	359	40	3.17	3.26	2.63	.97	.38	.09	.00	.01	.20	.54	1.06	2.45	14.76
	Mount Wilson	22	42.5	73.7	101	7	23	May 6	Oct. 29	176	35	6.40	7.66	5.88	2.56	1.01	.18	.02	.08	.45	1.34	1.81	5.49	32.88
	Newhall	16	48.4	77.6	113	10	7	Mar. 12	Nov. 8	241	17	4.33	4.32	4.51	.88	.65	.05	.01	.04	.21	.64	1.14	2.49	19.27
	Pasadena	34	52.3	73.1	113	21	30	Feb. 3	Dec. 13	313	34	4.28	4.43	3.17	1.45	.63	.12	03	.01	.31	.84	1.38	3.35	20.00
	San Fernando	20	53.5	74.0	113	23	21	Feb. 27	Dec. 11	287	38	3.56	3.60	2.86	1.16	.53	.10	.02	.01	.21	.58	1.19	2.72	16.54
	Sierra Madre	30	54.0	73.2	110	28	22	Jan. 4	Dec. 30	360	40	5.04	5.10	4.52	2.07	.99	.23	.03	.03	.36	1.06	1.64	3.72	24.79
Madera	Madera	40	44.3	78.9	115	10	36	Mar. 19	Nov. 17	243	39	1.95	1.94	1.74	.78	.35	.06	.01	.01	.09	.48	.94	1.46	9.81
	North Fork	30	41.9	76.7	111	4	32	May 1	Oct. 31	183	35	7.12	6.50	5.88	2.56	1.40	.26	.05	.05	.54	1.33	2.43	5.08	33.20
Marin	Kentfield	30	45.8	65.5	112	17	35	Mar. 13	Nov. 20	252	40	9.84	8.90	6.38	2.59	1.45	.36	.02	.02	.63	2.23	5.04	7.62	45.08
	Point Reyes	40	49.8	53.7	98	27	39	Jan. 2	Dec. 30	362	40	3.63	2.96	2.44	1.09	.64	.27	.05	.05	.47	1.17	2.17	3.03	17.97
Mariposa	Dudley's	30	38.8	68.0	107	−10	30	May 18	Oct. 6	141	30	8.14	7.70	5.53	2.95	1.13	.32	.02	.02	.44	1.66	3.14	5.88	36.93
	Mariposa										29	6.17	6.09	4.53	2.20	.86	.24	.03	.01	.31	1.35	2.36	4.12	28.27
	Yosemite	33	34.3	70.1	110	−6	30	May 19	Sept. 29	133	35	6.35	6.39	5.26	2.84	1.40	.73	.23	.21	.87	1.84	2.71	5.07	33.90
Mendocino	Branscomb	21	43.0	66.2	104	16	23	May 6	Oct. 26	173	24	17.29	14.48	9.52	5.27	2.57	1.15	.11	.03	1.33	4.14	12.42	12.77	81.08
	Fort Bragg						16	Feb. 24	Nov. 30	279	39	7.71	6.31	4.91	2.45	1.30	.47	.08	.03	.71	2.08	5.01	6.13	37.19
	Ukiah	40	45.2	72.5	114	12	38	Apr. 9	Nov. 3	208	40	7.87	6.57	4.64	2.02	1.01	.38	.02	.01	.44	1.76	4.31	6.43	35.46
Merced	Le Grand	38	45.6	80.0	117	11	35	Mar. 19	Nov. 18	244	39	2.50	2.36	2.21	.91	.46	.06	.01	.00	.18	.69	1.25	1.91	12.54
	Los Banos	24	49.4	78.5	116	17	16	Feb. 11	Nov. 26	288	40	1.89	1.48	1.48	.63	.40	.05	.00	.01	.11	.35	.86	1.41	8.67
	Merced	40	45.1	79.1	116	16	37	Mar. 9	Nov. 20	256	40	2.42	2.10	2.12	.93	.44	.09	.01	.02	.17	.53	1.20	1.78	11.81
Modoc	Alturas	22	27.3	67.3	105	−32	24	June 13	Aug. 29	77	23	2.07	1.40	1.49	1.20	1.06	.64	.50	.21	.57	.83	1.10	1.53	12.60
	Cedarville	40	30.1	71.8	111	−20	40	May 24	Sept. 27	126	40	1.82	1.54	1.53	.97	.88	.64	.21	.14	.52	1.03	1.44	1.51	12.23
	Fort Bidwell	28	27.8	69.9	106	−21	27	May 26	Sept. 25	122	27	2.04	1.74	1.45	1.19	.83	.69	.21	.18	.61	.95	1.78	1.67	13.34
	Steele Swamp										16	.94	1.01	1.08	1.44	.92	.88	.22	.11	.63	1.09	1.45	1.17	10.94
Mono	Ellery Lake	14	22.6	55.0	83	−25	14	June 28	Sept. 3	67	14	4.59	5.87	4.07	3.19	1.46	1.38	.74	.75	.48	1.37	2.39	4.92	31.21
	Gem Lake	14	26.0	60.3	91	−20	14	June 19	Sept. 13	86	14	4.09	5.30	3.27	2.34	1.00	.76	.61	.56	.41	1.35	1.56	3.88	25.13
	Lundy Lake	13	26.2	62.9	90	−34	14	June 7	Sept. 20	105	14	1.93	3.50	1.72	1.00	.68	.85	.57	.48	.27	.75	.99	2.15	14.89
	Shield's Ranch										29	1.91	2.03	1.13	.75	.68	.61	.58	.44	.31	.56	.91	1.50	11.41
Monterey	Abbott's										23	3.90	5.73	2.98	1.44	.47	.17	.02	.05	.31	.49	1.90	3.40	20.86
	Del Monte	23	49.3	61.2	94	20	23	Feb. 11	Dec. 4	296	28	3.48	2.97	2.17	.91	.38	.14	.00	.02	.34	.41	1.15	3.16	15.13
	King City	32	48.4	67.1	113	17	32	Apr. 10	Nov. 7	211	40	2.48	2.01	1.90	.62	.28	.07	.01	.01	.17	.32	.94	1.45	10.26
	Parkfield (near)										31	3.64	2.86	2.24	.95	.42	.14	.02	.03	.13	.55	1.04	2.38	14.40
	Priest Valley										40	4.51	3.95	3.57	1.24	.67	.09	.00	.05	.21	.86	1.57	3.10	19.82
	Salinas	40	49.7	63.3	110	18	32	Mar. 17	Nov. 22	250	40	3.01	2.33	2.22	.89	.45	.10	.02	.03	.29	.43	1.18	2.42	13.37
	Spreckels	31	48.6	61.3	107	18	28	Mar. 25	Oct. 31	220	34	3.02	2.24	2.14	.81	.49	.12	.01	.02	.27	.38	1.01	2.41	12.92
Napa	Mount St. Helena										12	14.40	12.04	10.33	3.36	2.11	.55	.02	.01	1.40	2.30	6.07	6.88	59.47
	Napa	37	47.1	66.1	110	17	38	Mar. 12	Nov. 26	259	39	4.81	4.42	3.24	1.31	.66	.20	.01	.03	.39	1.22	2.49	3.93	22.71
	St. Helena	31	45.5	69.8	115	11	32	Mar. 29	Nov. 4	220	31	7.57	6.62	3.63	1.89	.85	.31	.01	.04	.39	1.19	3.26	6.14	31.90
Nevada	Bowman Dam	13	35.6	67.8	102	−2	17	May 12	Oct. 15	156	29	12.78	12.09	11.97	5.07	3.60	1.62	.13	.13	.97	4.33	7.68	9.20	69.57
	Deer Creek	32	35.5	66.0	103	−5	32	May 23	Sept. 28	128	32	13.10	12.27	9.19	4.90	2.67	1.08	.04	.05	.89	3.20	6.54	10.41	64.35
	Lake Spaulding	31	34.4	64.5	102	−11	32	June 5	Sept. 24	111	40	11.86	11.91	10.55	5.16	3.06	1.27	.08	.14	1.11	3.93	6.92	9.41	65.40
	Nevada City	40	40.9	70.1	111	−1	40	May 19	Oct. 7	141	40	9.39	9.00	7.73	3.73	1.93	.64	.04	.05	.74	2.62	5.03	7.76	48.66
	Soda Springs	40	27.2	60.1	90	−28	33	June 20	Aug. 27	68	8	7.65	8.62	5.76	4.01	1.95	1.60	.18	.16	.54	3.05	4.12	8.00	45.64
	Truckee	26	25.9	61.0	101	−28	19	June 23	Aug. 21	59	27	6.02	5.27	4.86	1.42	.80	.36	.20	.18	.43	1.11	1.93	3.55	26.13
Orange	Tustin (near)	26	52.9	71.7	111	18	32	Feb. 7	Dec. 7	303	40	2.59	2.71	2.15	.86	.42	.07	.00	.02	.14	.65	1.03	2.01	12.65
Placer	Auburn	40	45.1	77.2	112	12	36	Mar. 10	Nov. 27	262	40	6.51	6.43	5.19	2.50	1.03	.40	.00	.01	.43	1.80	3.26	5.08	32.64
	Blue Canyon	40	38.0	66.1	100	−5	32	May 24	Oct. 12	141	40	11.00	10.61	8.86	4.35	2.65	1.02	.05	.08	.95	3.23	6.32	8.44	57.56
	Cisco	17	32.7	65.2							18	12.35	9.01	9.88	2.73	2.32	.73	.18	.10	1.08	3.19	5.72	7.49	54.78
	Colfax	40	43.4	76.1	110	8	36	Apr. 11	Nov. 17	220	40	8.86	8.88	7.43	3.55	1.87	.68	.05	.02	.77	2.58	4.93	6.90	46.52
	Tahoe	29	26.3	60.6	94	−15	24	June 22	Sept. 2	72	29	5.84	5.85	3.72	2.18	.95	.70	.25	.16	.50	1.37	2.76	5.07	29.35
	Rocklin	38	46.2	76.8	118	14	33	Mar. 17	Nov. 11	239	38	4.78	4.46	3.70	1.64	.79	.28	.00	.01	.33	1.12	2.20	3.76	23.07
Plumas	Chester										28	5.25	4.64	3.61	2.17	1.28	.76	.13	.15	.74	1.40	3.42	4.50	28.05
	Portola	22	28.3	63.1	110	−28	22	July 4	July 27	23	24	2.72	3.04	2.14	1.19	.68	.40	.07	.05	.26	.84	1.51	2.34	15.24
	Quincy	40	34.0	66.1	105	−28	38	June 9	Aug. 30	82	40	7.38	6.48	5.84	2.61	1.74	.77	.08	.37	1.08	2.46	4.69	5.83	39.33

CALIFORNIA—Continued

Climatic summary—Continued

County	Station	Temperature: Length of record	January average	July average	Maximum	Minimum	Killing frost average dates: Length of record	Last in spring	First in fall	Growing season	Average precipitation: Length of record	January	February	March	April	May	June	July	August	September	October	November	December	Annual
		Yr.	°F.	°F.	°F.	°F.	Yr.			Days	Yr.	In.	In.	In.	In.	In.	In.	In.	In.	In.	In.	In.	In.	In.
Riverside	Aguanga (near)										31	2.61	2.78	2.08	1.05	.36	.06	.21	.46	.25	.76	.65	2.05	13.32
	Blythe	28	50.4	91.1	122	5	24	Feb. 25	Nov. 18	266	30	.48	.52	.39	.12	.03	.11	.29	.41	.44	.28	.32	.72	4.11
	Indio	39	54.2	92.5	125	13	32	Feb. 6	Dec. 2	299	40	.57	.57	.30	.14	.05	.02	.11	.24	.23	.29	.19	.54	3.25
	Palm Springs	33	55.0	90.6	122	18	16	Jan. 18	Dec. 18	334	34	.89	1.54	.61	.24	.08	.02	.16	.22	.11	.42	.28	1.03	5.60
	Riverside	40	52.0	75.6	118	21	38	Mar. 6	Nov. 26	265	40	2.22	2.34	2.15	.85	.46	.04	.01	.16	.19	.68	.71	1.72	11.53
	San Jacinto	38	50.2	77.6	120	7	36	Mar. 16	Nov. 19	248	40	2.44	2.72	2.38	1.24	.49	.07	.09	.20	.17	.73	.97	1.98	13.48
Sacramento	Folsom	38	46.0	79.1	119	15	36	Feb. 26	Dec. 2	279	40	4.92	4.50	3.69	1.72	.83	.23	.01	.01	.37	1.21	2.31	3.87	23.67
	Sacramento	40	45.6	73.9	114	17	40	Feb. 6	Dec. 10	307	40	3.31	3.08	2.41	1.04	.54	.16	.00	.00	.30	.80	1.55	2.69	15.88
San Benito	Hollister	40	47.4	65.6	112	15	38	Mar. 8	Nov. 20	257	40	2.80	2.34	2.25	.92	.44	.11	.04	.01	.23	.45	1.26	2.25	13.10
	Indria	18	46.5	81.3	113	14	18	Mar. 23	Nov. 29	251	21	2.53	3.68	2.47	.96	.56	.09	.02	.07	.10	.63	1.31	2.42	14.84
San Bernardino	Bagdad	23	52.2	95.0	119	10	17	Jan. 18	Dec. 21	337	24	.29	.26	.23	.15	.16	.02	.17	.33	.06	.24	.14	.19	2.24
	Barstow	18	46.1	83.8	114	12	14	Mar. 8	Nov. 8	245	19	.88	.60	.80	.20	.15	.19	.25	.15	.27	.40	.27	.35	4.51
	Bear Valley Dam										18	9.34	6.62	8.96	2.19	1.17	.20	.33	.75	.57	1.36	2.36	3.81	37.66
	Kingston										14	.48	.59	.38	.16	.14	.12	.33	.52	.13	.17	.21	.51	3.74
	Needles	38	51.3	93.2	125	18	31	Feb. 5	Dec. 3	301	40	.47	.65	.41	.20	.08	.08	.35	.75	.32	.30	.36	.65	4.62
	Redlands	40	50.9	76.5	115	18	37	Feb. 27	Dec. 6	282	40	2.65	2.84	2.61	1.30	.72	.12	.04	.14	.23	.91	.98	2.06	14.60
	San Bernardino (near)	40	51.6	77.0	116	17	38	Mar. 15	Nov. 23	253	40	3.19	3.45	2.99	1.48	.66	.12	.04	.14	.25	.90	1.10	2.54	16.86
	Seven Oaks	29	38.4	63.9	93	−9	28	June 15	Sept. 17	94	29	5.17	5.99	4.68	2.35	.89	.26	.60	.85	.50	1.36	1.55	4.10	28.30
	Trona	19	43.1	88.8	118	10	19	Mar. 16	Nov. 13	242	19	.64	.94	.44	.21	.25	.12	.04	.14	.08	.26	.29	.80	4.21
San Diego	Campo										39	3.52	4.16	3.09	1.51	.67	.08	.70	.58	.25	.67	1.33	2.66	19.22
	Cuyamaca	39	38.2	69.9	113	−1	38	May 6	Oct. 30	177	40	6.85	8.07	7.22	3.49	1.68	.35	.46	.68	.53	1.73	2.61	5.69	39.36
	El Cajon	39	52.4	73.0	113	19	36	Feb. 25	Nov. 25	273	40	2.70	3.04	2.40	1.07	.54	.10	.07	.09	.11	.71	1.00	2.29	14.12
	Escondido	40	50.8	71.9	113	13	36	Mar. 9	Nov. 25	261	40	3.43	3.74	2.87	1.33	.67	.09	.04	.10	.11	.83	1.19	2.71	17.11
	Nellie						10	May 11	Oct. 20	162	20	10.82	8.65	10.67	2.87	2.24	.18	.55	.60	.50	1.91	3.25	5.95	48.19
	San Diego	40	55.1	67.5	110	25	40	None	None	365	40	1.97	2.22	1.59	.71	.31	.05	.04	.05	.09	.52	.72	1.84	10.11
San Francisco	San Francisco	40	49.8	58.9	101	27	40	Jan. 7	Dec. 29	356	40	4.41	3.99	2.96	1.08	.61	.17	.01	.02	.37	.95	2.10	3.56	20.23
San Joaquin	Benson's Ferry										26	2.90	3.08	1.92	1.09	.51	.14	.00	.00	.28	.62	1.40	2.68	14.62
	Lathrop										24	2.06	2.15	1.32	.76	.43	.09	.01	.00	.28	.46	1.10	1.97	10.63
	Lodi	22	45.4	72.7	110	13	23	Mar. 13	Nov. 15	247	27	3.54	3.10	3.27	1.17	.65	.20	.00	.02	.23	.86	1.56	2.50	17.10
	Stockton	40	44.8	74.0	110	17	34	Feb. 14	Nov. 28	287	40	2.98	2.52	2.25	.92	.58	.12	.00	.01	.29	.64	1.38	2.42	14.11
San Luis Obispo	Paso Robles	40	46.0	71.2	117	0	37	Apr. 11	Nov. 2	205	40	3.82	3.56	2.90	.91	.45	.10	.01	.03	.21	.60	1.23	2.57	16.39
	San Luis Obispo	40	51.9	64.4	110	20	40	Jan. 30	Dec. 16	320	40	5.21	4.56	3.56	1.25	.65	.17	.01	.05	.26	.81	1.65	3.68	21.86
San Mateo	San Mateo	22	50.8	68.4	104	23	10	Feb. 8	Dec. 24	319	21	5.69	4.09	4.21	1.10	.63	.17	.01	.01	.32	.93	2.00	2.93	22.09
Santa Barbara	Los Alamos										30	3.64	3.51	2.73	.96	.39	.08	.00	.06	.20	.55	.99	2.73	15.84
	Santa Barbara	40	53.3	66.4	115	23	31	Jan. 22	Dec. 19	331	40	4.25	4.16	3.34	1.04	.51	.11	.02	.06	.44	.76	1.27	2.94	18.90
	Santa Maria	35	51.2	63.4	109	24	32	Feb. 26	Nov. 25	272	35	2.98	2.77	2.81	.98	.48	.11	.00	.04	.20	.72	1.07	1.95	14.11
Santa Clara	Lick Observatory	40	41.0	70.7	100	9	36	May 13	Nov. 11	182	40	5.85	5.11	4.69	1.97	1.03	.24	.01	.02	.39	1.20	2.47	4.49	27.47
	Los Gatos	40	47.6	68.2	109	21	32	Feb. 3	Dec. 16	316	40	7.03	6.07	4.85	1.64	.74	.13	.00	.02	.50	1.03	2.51	5.10	29.62

	Palo Alto	16	46.5	65.5	105	20	16	Feb. 18	Nov. 28	283	28	3.45	3.05	2.00	.90	.46	.16	.00	.02	.32	.65	1.35	2.81	15.17
	San Jose	32	48.2	67.2	106	18	37	Feb. 10	Dec. 6	299	40	2.97	2.58	2.34	.89	.51	.11	.00	.02	.33	.61	1.27	2.30	13.93
	Santa Clara	40	48.2	66.0	111	19	39	Mar. 13	Nov. 22	254	40	3.29	2.78	2.53	.88	.51	.13	.01	.02	.37	.63	1.35	2.52	15.02
Santa Cruz	Boulder Creek	----	----	----	----	----	----	----	----	----	18	16.00	8.91	9.93	2.23	1.84	.36	.01	.02	.86	2.34	4.43	6.89	53.82
	Santa Cruz	40	49.9	62.7	108	20	39	Mar. 2	Nov. 28	271	40	5.88	5.21	4.04	1.54	.87	.25	.04	.04	.51	1.31	2.56	4.80	27.05
	Watsonville	36	49.8	62.7	110	15	34	Mar. 23	Nov. 10	232	38	4.51	3.77	3.44	1.10	.66	.16	.02	.03	.39	.85	1.85	4.31	21.09
Shasta	Delta	16	44.1	77.6	114	15	12	Mar. 19	Nov. 19	245	18	16.15	12.85	11.09	4.11	2.98	1.07	.10	.06	1.20	4.52	7.36	9.19	70.68
	Fall River Mills (near).	16	31.5	69.7	106	−18	16	May 19	Sept. 22	126	16	2.23	2.62	2.30	1.70	1.13	.67	.14	.07	.59	1.28	2.10	2.31	17.14
	Hot Creek	16	34.3	70.9	113	−17	16	May 24	Sept. 29	128	18	2.27	2.65	1.82	1.50	1.18	.73	.12	.11	.42	1.13	1.77	2.34	16.04
	Kennett	14	43.9	81.0	115	15	14	Apr. 7	Nov. 15	222	32	12.19	11.23	7.12	4.30	2.34	1.31	.13	.08	.89	2.87	7.53	9.58	59.57
	Redding	40	45.3	82.0	113	17	39	Feb. 28	Dec. 3	278	40	7.13	6.93	4.96	2.74	1.44	.86	.10	.04	.82	2.15	4.52	5.85	37.54
Sierra	Downieville	19	37.5	68.4	105	1	21	May 25	Oct. 3	131	22	12.72	11.22	7.69	4.97	2.44	.92	.12	.10	1.15	2.68	6.87	9.90	60.78
	Sierraville	28	26.4	62.7	104	−34	28	July 1	July 31	30	29	4.37	4.17	2.61	1.66	.80	.54	.35	.18	.49	1.12	2.24	3.67	22.20
Siskiyou	Happy Camp	20	37.8	71.9	113	6	20	May 4	Oct. 10	159	23	7.55	6.86	4.96	2.61	1.30	.64	.19	.14	.63	2.58	6.20	7.72	41.38
	Montague	37	33.8	72.7	110	−15	34	May 14	Oct. 2	141	38	1.74	1.50	1.24	.78	.70	.66	.44	.25	.48	.91	1.83	1.76	12.29
	Mount Shasta	40	33.1	65.7	108	−9	34	May 31	Sept. 27	119	40	6.46	5.53	4.97	2.46	1.46	.88	.14	.30	.83	2.12	4.28	4.83	34.26
	Scott Bar	----	----	----	----	----	----	----	----	----	15	4.31	3.65	2.26	1.71	1.05	.64	.12	.20	.52	2.05	3.71	4.56	24.78
Solano	Vacaville	36	46.0	74.6	115	14	38	Mar. 21	Nov. 15	239	40	5.33	4.75	3.56	1.34	.66	.15	.00	.02	.30	.99	2.53	4.38	24.01
Sonoma	Cloverdale	37	47.1	71.7	115	17	36	Mar. 7	Nov. 26	264	37	8.58	7.24	5.35	2.06	1.24	.41	.03	.02	.49	1.66	4.03	6.44	37.55
	Healdsburg	40	46.8	69.1	116	17	38	Mar. 17	Nov. 13	241	40	8.69	7.36	5.34	2.15	1.17	.36	.03	.02	.45	1.76	4.70	6.86	38.89
	Santa Rosa	40	46.6	65.6	112	15	34	Apr. 10	Nov. 3	207	40	6.06	5.43	4.04	1.85	1.02	.30	.02	.02	.47	1.45	3.43	5.02	29.11
Stanislaus	Denair	40	43.4	76.7	116	15	37	Mar. 10	Nov. 19	254	40	2.08	1.83	1.96	.89	.46	.09	.00	.01	.10	.45	1.06	1.87	10.80
	Newman	40	45.9	78.0	115	17	34	Mar. 5	Nov. 22	262	40	2.21	1.76	1.75	.65	.40	.05	.00	.01	.18	.35	1.01	1.69	10.06
	Oakdale (near)	38	44.5	77.6	114	12	26	Mar. 18	Nov. 23	250	38	2.74	2.47	2.52	1.06	.52	.16	.00	.01	.21	.64	1.47	2.28	14.08
Sutter	Nicolaus	----	----	----	----	----	----	----	----	----	19	2.71	3.59	2.19	1.57	.47	.29	.01	.01	.07	.97	2.06	3.62	17.56
Tehama	Mineral	12	29.8	65.4	100	−13	13	June 20	Sept. 10	82	14	7.07	7.16	6.84	4.13	2.05	1.29	.09	.07	.68	2.76	4.57	8.56	45.27
	Red Bluff	40	45.3	81.6	115	17	40	Mar. 6	Dec. 5	274	40	4.56	3.85	3.22	1.43	.91	.48	.03	.04	.72	1.32	2.63	3.91	23.10
Trinity	Forest Glen	19	37.3	68.4	107	−2	17	May 29	Sept. 30	124	27	9.43	8.84	5.80	3.71	1.57	.91	.20	.10	.92	2.94	7.31	9.27	51.00
	Hayfork	20	37.5	68.7	111	−6	20	June 3	Sept. 8	97	19	4.81	5.10	2.71	1.85	.87	.43	.13	.10	.52	1.32	4.45	5.44	27.73
	Weaverville	26	37.8	71.4	116	−5	24	May 25	Sept. 20	118	27	6.06	5.55	3.33	2.64	1.03	.83	.10	.13	.70	1.82	5.07	5.60	32.86
Tulare	Angiola	40	44.2	81.0	118	5	38	Mar. 21	Nov. 11	235	39	1.47	1.37	1.29	.62	.36	.05	.01	.01	.17	.35	.54	1.08	7.32
	Hot Springs	30	41.4	74.5	104	6	30	Apr. 23	Nov. 9	200	17	5.73	9.19	5.41	5.08	1.69	.93	.17	.08	.32	1.59	3.60	7.07	40.86
	Giant Forest	18	33.1	65.7	94	−5	18	June 2	Oct. 4	124	31	4.89	4.26	3.81	2.45	1.01	.27	.04	.07	.22	.98	1.90	4.02	23.92
	Lemon Cove	40	46.9	82.0	118	18	36	Feb. 27	Nov. 29	275	40	2.61	2.66	2.63	1.47	.76	.17	.01	.03	.17	.63	1.23	1.97	14.34
	Lindsay	25	45.4	81.0	115	18	25	Mar. 19	Nov. 14	240	25	2.14	2.10	1.80	.94	.50	.15	.00	.00	.06	.46	.75	1.77	10.67
	Porterville	40	46.9	81.4	114	18	38	Mar. 9	Nov. 25	261	40	2.04	1.87	1.89	1.05	.61	.10	.01	.01	.14	.48	.82	1.56	10.58
	Springville (near)	31	38.3	69.9	104	−2	31	May 13	Oct. 17	157	31	7.00	6.70	5.25	3.38	1.55	.46	.11	.22	.37	1.50	2.69	5.38	34.61
	Visalia	39	46.4	80.3	115	13	36	Mar 9	Nov. 28	264	40	1.96	1.80	1.70	.87	.45	.07	.00	.01	.12	.41	.77	1.43	9.59
Tuolumne	Hetch Hetchy	28	36.0	71.9	106	−3	24	May 4	Oct. 23	172	27	6.11	6.20	4.88	3.25	1.83	.84	.21	.13	.64	1.90	2.73	4.89	33.61
	Lake Eleanor	29	35.8	70.8	103	−7	28	May 21	Oct. 13	145	29	7.98	7.88	5.63	3.54	1.76	.77	.12	.23	.64	1.95	3.40	6.03	39.93
	Sonora	33	44.1	78.0	110	14	30	Mar. 29	Nov. 22	238	40	6.52	5.97	5.84	2.58	1.23	.35	.01	.02	.36	1.67	2.98	4.63	32.16
Ventura	Ojai	33	50.6	73.0	119	13	33	Mar. 29	Nov. 16	232	34	5.17	4.91	3.70	1.28	.54	.07	.01	.05	.36	.73	1.25	3.54	21.61
	Ozena	----	----	----	----	----	----	----	----	----	35	3.01	3.20	2.69	.69	.38	.08	.08	.17	.36	.46	.70	2.11	13.93
	Ventura	----	----	----	----	----	----	----	----	----	28	3.36	3.15	2.72	.92	.31	.08	.00	.02	.20	.71	1.15	2.67	15.29
Yolo	Brooks	18	44.6	80.8	119	9	18	Mar. 25	Nov. 15	235	18	3.06	4.68	2.21	1.51	.38	.23	.00	.01	.11	.90	2.13	3.74	18.96
	Davis	40	45.4	75.3	116	12	34	Mar. 17	Nov. 14	242	40	3.65	3.22	2.50	.96	.48	.15	.00	.01	.29	.68	1.58	2.91	16.43
	Woodland	23	46.3	78.0	114	15	17	Mar. 1	Nov. 24	268	31	3.95	3.13	2.65	1.00	.59	.25	.00	.01	.21	.80	1.83	2.82	17.24
Yuba	Camptonville (near)	28	41.1	73.8	112	8	28	May 1	Nov. 2	185	30	13.47	10.73	8.14	4.83	2.60	.93	.04	.04	.97	2.85	6.51	10.80	61.91
	Dobbins (near)	24	46.5	78.6	113	16	33	Mar. 10	Dec. 2	267	35	8.12	7.47	5.94	2.87	1.84	.71	.02	.02	.63	1.85	4.17	6.78	40.42
	Marysville	40	45.9	78.3	118	16	34	Feb. 21	Nov. 21	273	40	4.18	3.74	3.05	1.28	.74	.00	.27	.02	.35	1.02	2.38	3.66	20.69

CALIFORNIA—Continued

Precipitation and temperature—State unit values

Precipitation

Year	Mean
	In.
1886	19.48
1887	18.59
1888	21.35
1889	33.25
1890	25.29
1891	22.23
1892	25.98
1893	23.24
1894	25.84
1895	22.24
1896	28.59
1897	18.99
1898	10.35
1899	22.47
1900	19.84
1901	22.12
1902	24.22
1903	20.69
1904	30.39
1905	21.59
1906	38.70
1907	32.49
1908	18.78
1909	42.13
1910	16.77
1911	29.39
1912	22.27
1913	25.20
1914	31.13
1915	33.82
1916	34.84
1917	16.48
1918	24.47
1919	21.29
1920	26.71
1921	25.89
1922	28.96
1923	14.13
1924	17.05
1925	21.13
1926	27.06

Precipitation

Year	Mean
	In.
1927	27.50
1928	18.64
1929	15.00
1930	18.38
1931	24.37
1932	15.60
1933	20.18
1934	18.01
1935	22.06
1936	26.20
1937	29.06
1938	30.06

Month	Mean
	In.
January	4.80
February	4.29
March	3.66
April	1.73
May	1.01
June	.31
July	.07
August	.10
September	.44
October	1.21
November	2.36
December	4.01
Annual	23.99

Season	Average
	In.
Winter	13.10
Spring	6.40
Summer	.48
Fall	4.01

Winter precipitation (in percent of normal)

Year[1]	Percent
1886	87
1887	89
1888	84
1889	49
1890	187
1891	101
1892	81
1893	102
1894	92
1895	163
1896	83
1897	92
1898	44
1899	40
1900	55
1901	99
1902	84
1903	71
1904	82
1905	89
1906	109
1907	153
1908	107
1909	202
1910	108
1911	140
1912	49
1913	66
1914	196
1915	173
1916	112
1917	113
1918	67
1919	94
1920	57
1921	113
1922	143
1923	91
1924	37
1925	89
1926	85

Winter precipitation (in percent of normal)

Year[1]	Percent
1927	112
1928	57
1929	57
1930	98
1931	55
1932	120
1933	78
1934	89
1935	85
1936	130
1937	123
1938	140

Spring precipitation (in percent of normal)

Year	Percent
1886	122
1887	63
1888	69
1889	158
1890	111
1891	86
1892	127
1893	142
1894	57
1895	81
1896	151
1897	73
1898	41
1899	116
1900	92
1901	66
1902	95
1903	113
1904	171
1905	137
1906	220
1907	193
1908	59

Spring precipitation (in percent of normal)

Year	Percent
1909	61
1910	63
1911	135
1912	159
1913	71
1914	62
1915	130
1916	70
1917	67
1918	129
1919	72
1920	134
1921	86
1922	91
1923	76
1924	59
1925	114
1926	96
1927	87
1928	115
1929	70
1930	99
1931	59
1932	60
1933	76
1934	32
1935	138
1936	64
1937	112
1938	168

Temperature

Year	Mean
	°F.
1902	58.8
1903	59.2
1904	60.3
1905	59.5
1906	59.6
1907	58.7
1908	58.3
1909	57.9
1910	59.4
1911	56.9
1912	57.4
1913	58.2
1914	58.5
1915	58.1
1916	56.5
1917	58.0
1918	58.4
1919	58.0
1920	58.0
1921	59.1
1922	57.7
1923	58.1
1924	58.7
1925	58.8
1926	60.5
1927	58.1
1928	58.7
1929	57.7
1930	57.4
1931	58.8
1932	57.3
1933	57.0
1934	59.9
1935	57.2
1936	59.0
1937	57.6
1938	57.7

[1] Includes December of preceding year.

Dates of last killing frost in spring and first in fall, with length of growing season

Year	Bakersfield			Brawley			Fresno			Napa			Paso Robles			Red Bluff		
	Last in spring	First in fall	Growing season[1]	Last in spring	First in fall	Growing season[1]	Last in spring	First in fall	Growing season[1]	Last in spring	First in fall	Growing season[1]	Last in spring	First in fall	Growing season[1]	Last in spring	First in fall	Growing season[1]
			Days			*Days*			*Days*			*Days*			*Days*			*Days*
1899							Feb. 7	None	328	Mar. 13	Dec. 19	281	Apr. 23	Dec. 20	241	Mar. 13	Dec. 19	281
1900							Feb. 8	Dec. 31	326	Feb. 6	Dec. 30	327	Apr. 26	Oct. 30	187	Jan. 26	Dec. 29	337
1901	Feb. 2	Dec. 8	309				Jan. 10	Dec. 11	335	Feb. 10	Dec. 14	307	Apr. 10			Apr. 4	Dec. 14	254
1902							Feb. 1	Dec. 14	316	Jan. 31	Dec. 28	331	Apr. 26	Oct. 30	187	Mar. 14	Dec. 29	290
1903		Dec. 25					Feb. 16	Dec. 5	292	Feb. 18	Dec. 5	290				Mar. 9	Dec. 7	273
1904		Dec. 5					Feb. 10	Dec. 6	299	Mar. 25	do	255				Mar. 21	Dec. 6	260
1905	Feb. 14	Dec. 23	312				Mar. 31	Nov. 22	236	Mar. 30	Nov. 20	235	Mar. 31			Feb. 13	Nov. 28	288
1906	Mar. 1	Oct. 21	234				Jan. 5	Nov. 19	318	Jan. 7	Nov. 24	321	Apr. 2			Mar. 15	Nov. 24	254
1907	Mar. 30	Nov. 1	216				Mar. 13	Dec. 29	291	Jan. 18	None	348	Mar. 27	Nov. 18	236	Mar. 14	Dec. 29	290
1908	Mar. 31	Nov. 7	221		Dec. 20		Jan. 8	Nov. 29	326	Mar. 6	Dec. 17	286	Feb. 2	Nov. 29	301	Mar. 26	Nov. 29	248
1909	None	Dec. 3	336	Feb. 22	Dec. 4	285	None	Dec 3	336	Jan. 10	Dec. 3	327	None	Oct. 26	299	Jan. 11	Nov. 16	309
1910	Feb. 6	Dec. 29	326	Feb. 18	Dec. 17	302	Feb. 16	Dec. 26	313	Feb. 5	Dec. 24	322	May 5	Nov. 14	193	Jan. 18	Dec. 31	347
1911	Mar. 26	Dec. 26	275	Feb. 17	Nov. 28	284	Apr. 13	Nov. 11	212	Apr. 12	Nov. 12	214	May 15	Sept. 26	134	Apr. 12	Nov. 11	213
1912	Feb. 28	Oct. 24	239	Feb. 23	Dec. 21	302	Feb. 25	Nov. 22	271	Jan. 5	None	361	May 22	Oct. 6	137	Mar. 16	Dec. 1	260
1913	Mar. 26	Dec. 6	255	Mar. 1			Feb. 20	Dec. 5	288	May 8	Dec. 4	210	May 4	Oct. 5	154	Mar. 25	Nov. 23	243
1914	Jan. 21	Nov. 30	313	Feb. 8	Dec. 15	310	None	Nov. 30	333	Mar. 30	Nov. 27	242	Mar. 28	Oct. 22	208	Feb. 4	Dec. 13	312
1915	Feb. 6	Nov. 12	279		Nov. 15		Jan. 19	Nov. 12	297				May 2	Sept. 29	150	Feb. 21	Dec. 29	311
1916	Feb. 2	do	284	Feb. 3	do	286	Feb. 1	Nov. 13	286				May 20	Oct. 26	159	Mar. 2	Nov. 14	257
1917	Apr. 1	Dec. 4	247	Mar. 4	Nov. 30	271	Mar. 23	Dec. 8	260	Apr. 19	Oct. 30	194	May 26	Oct. 19	146	Apr. 16	Dec. 14	242
1918	Feb. 17	Nov. 12	268	Feb. 5	do	298	Apr. 4	Nov. 26	236	May 26	Nov. 7	165	do	Oct. 26	153	Apr. 4	Nov. 8	218
1919	Feb. 25	Nov. 1	249	Feb. 26	Nov. 29	276	Jan. 9	Oct. 31	295	Mar. 12	Oct. 26	228	Apr. 19	Oct. 17	181	Feb. 3	Nov. 27	297
1920	Feb. 11	Nov. 29	292	None	Dec. 4	338	Jan. 14	Dec. 5	326	Apr. 22	Dec. 12	234	Apr. 24	Oct. 20	179	Mar. 26	Dec. 12	261
1921	Feb. 16	Nov. 17	274	Feb. 17	Nov. 19	275	Apr. 4	Nov. 18	228	Apr. 15	Nov. 16	215	Apr. 15	Nov. 17	216	Apr. 15	Nov. 18	217
1922	Mar. 17	Nov. 4	232	Feb. 4		231	Apr. 9	Nov. 5	210	do	Nov. 14	213	May 10	Oct. 30	173	May 9	Nov. 30	205
1923	Mar. 5	Dec. 3	273	Mar. 5	Dec. 12	282	Feb. 4	Dec. 2	301	Mar. 30	Dec. 2	247	Mar. 24	Nov. 28	249	Feb. 14	Dec. 4	293
1924	Jan. 24	Nov. 13	294	Jan. 26	Nov. 25	304	Jan. 22	Dec. 18	331	Mar. 21	Dec. 6	260	Apr. 16	Oct. 10	177	Apr. 15	Dec. 6	235
1925	Jan. 21	Dec. 14	327	Jan. 18			Mar. 11	Nov. 7	241	Mar. 17	Nov. 6	234	Apr. 21	Nov. 4	197	Mar. 10	Nov. 5	240
1926	Jan. 27	Dec. 13	320	Jan. 29	Dec. 17	322	Jan. 27	Dec. 13	320	Jan. 25	Dec. 13	322	Jan. 27	Dec. 13	320	Feb. 20	Dec. 14	297
1927	Mar. 16	Nov. 25	254	Jan. 25	Dec. 8	317	None	Dec. 7	340	Apr. 16	Nov. 23	221	Apr. 11	Nov. 23	226	Feb. 12	Nov. 22	283
1928	Feb. 17	Nov. 21	278	Feb. 15	Nov. 19	278	Feb. 16	Dec. 15	303	Mar. 31	Nov. 16	230	Feb. 12	Oct. 4	229	Feb. 22	Dec. 11	293
1929	Apr. 7	Nov. 12	219	Feb. 16	Nov. 23	280	Apr. 7	Nov. 13	220	Apr. 23	Nov. 14	205	Apr. 10	Oct. 27	200	Apr. 7	Dec. 28	265
1930	Mar. 1	Nov. 20	264	Feb. 4	Nov. 20	289	Jan. 3	Nov. 20	321	Mar. 1	do	258	Mar. 1	Nov. 14	258	Mar. 1	Dec. 21	295
1931	Jan. 20	Nov. 23	307	Jan. 20	Nov. 23	307	None	Nov. 22	325	Jan. 17	Nov. 9	296	Mar. 27	Nov. 12	230	None	Dec. 12	345
1932	Feb. 18	Dec. 4	290	Feb. 3	Dec. 12	313	Feb. 3	Dec. 12	313	Apr. 22	Oct. 12	173	Apr. 23	Oct. 20	180	Feb. 2	Dec. 8	310
1933	Feb. 20	Nov. 30	283		Dec. 18		Feb. 10	Dec. 1	294		Nov. 30		May 10	Nov. 5	179	Feb. 18	Dec. 16	301
1934	Feb. 11	Dec. 2	294	Jan. 9	Nov. 28	323	Jan. 8	Dec. 3	329	Jan. 9	Dec. 3	328	Apr. 5	Nov. 28	237	Jan. 11	Dec. 1	324
1935	Mar. 23	Nov. 1	223	Jan. 22	None	344	Jan. 20	Oct. 31	284	Mar. 24	Oct. 29	219	Apr. 10	Oct. 23	196	Apr. 9	Oct. 30	204

[1] Number of days between last killing frost in spring and first in fall.

298737°—41——51 +

CALIFORNIA—Continued

Dates of last killing frost in spring and first in fall, with length of growing season—Continued

Year	Bakersfield			Brawley			Fresno			Napa			Paso Robles			Red Bluff		
	Last in spring	First in fall	Growing season[1]	Last in spring	First in fall	Growing season[1]	Last in spring	First in fall	Growing season[1]	Last in spring	First in fall	Growing season[1]	Last in spring	First in fall	Growing season[1]	Last in spring	First in fall	Growing season[1]
			Days			*Days*			*Days*			*Days*			*Days*			*Days*
1936	Feb. 7	Dec. 1	298	None	Dec. 2	337	Mar. 23	Dec. 2	254	Apr. 2	Nov. 2	214	Apr. 7	Nov. 4	211	Apr. 1	Nov. 10	223
1937	Feb. 10	Dec. 21	314	Feb. 14	Dec. 22	311	Jan. 31	Dec. 24	327	Mar. 22	Dec. 21	274	Apr. 30	Nov. 8	192	Feb. 15	Dec. 23	311
1938	Feb. 17	Nov. 12	268	Jan. 22	Nov. 24	306	None	Nov. 12	315	Mar. 31	Nov. 11	225	Apr. 1	Nov. 7	220	Mar. 21	Nov. 11	235
Mean	Feb. 21	Nov. 25	277	Feb. 5	Dec. 5	303	Feb. 9	Dec. 1	295	Mar. 12	Nov. 26	259	Apr. 11	Nov. 2	205	Mar. 6	Dec. 5	274
Extremes	None[2] Apr. 7[3]	Oct 21[4] Dec. 29[5]	[6] 216 [7] 237	None[2] Mar. 5[3]	Nov. 15[4] None[5]	[6] 271 [7] 344	None[2] Apr. 13[3]	Oct. 31[4] None[5]	[6] 210 [7] 340	Jan. 5[2] May 26[3]	Oct. 12[4] None[5]	[6] 165 [7] 361	None[2] May 26[3]	Sept 26[4] Dec. 20[5]	[6] 134 [7] 320	None[2] May 9[3]	Oct. 30[4] Dec. 31[5]	[6] 204 [7] 347

Year	Redlands			Sacramento			San Jose			Santa Barbara			Tustin (near)			Ukiah		
	Last in spring	First in fall	Growing season[1]	Last in spring	First in fall	Growing season[1]	Last in spring	First in fall	Growing season[1]	Last in spring	First in fall	Growing season[1]	Last in spring	First in fall	Growing season[1]	Last in spring	First in fall	Growing season[1]
			Days			*Days*			*Days*			*Days*			*Days*			*Days*
1899	Feb. 5			Feb. 5	Dec. 18	316										Feb. 5	Dec. 13	311
1900	Apr. 9	Dec. 31.	266	None	Dec. 31	365										Apr. 9	Dec. 28	263
1901	Feb. 2	Dec. 12	313	Feb. 11	Dec. 11	303	Feb. 10	Dec. 13	306							Apr. 26	Dec. 7	225
1902	Jan. 31	Nov. 24	297	Feb. 1	Nov. 25	297	Jan. 27	Nov. 28	305							May 2	Nov. 28	210
1903	Feb. 14			Feb. 19	Dec. 6	290	Feb. 18											
1904	Feb. 6			Feb. 9	do	301	Jan. 28										Dec. 3	
1905		Dec. 1		Jan. 4	Dec. 24	354	Feb. 13	Dec. 12	302							Feb. 14		
1906	Apr. 2	Nov. 19	231	Jan. 22	Dec. 2	314		Nov. 24			Nov. 30		None	None	366	Apr. 2	Oct. 21	202
1907	Feb. 27	None	308	Jan. 15	None	351	Mar. 13	None	294	None	None	365	do	do	366	Apr. 3	Nov. 18	229
1908	Mar. 14	Nov. 24	255	None	Nov. 29	334	Mar. 8	Nov. 27	264	do	Dec. 16	351	do	do	367	Apr. 22	Oct. 21	182
1909	Mar. 12	Dec. 4	267	do	Nov. 27	331	Jan. 10	Dec. 4	328	do	Dec. 4	338	do	do	366	Apr. 5	Nov. 7	216
1910	Feb. 18	None	317	Jan. 5	Dec. 30	359	Feb. 5	Dec. 26	324	Feb. 3	Nov. 28	298	Jan. 6	do	360	Mar. 25	Nov. 13	233
1911	Feb. 28	Nov. 29	274	Feb. 26	Nov. 11	258	Feb. 16	Nov. 12	269	Feb. 18	None	317	Feb. 16	do	319	Apr. 15	Nov. 11	210
1912	Feb. 26	Dec. 6	284	Jan. 5	Dec. 1	331	Jan. 5	Dec. 23	353	None	Dec. 6	341	None	do	366	Apr. 12	Nov. 10	212
1913	Mar. 25			Mar. 25	Dec. 4	254	Mar. 26	Nov. 24	243	Mar. 15			Jan. 8	do	358	May 13	Oct. 5	145

[1] Number of days between last killing frost in spring and first in fall.
[2] Earliest date in spring.
[3] Latest date in spring.
[4] Earliest date in fall.
[5] Latest date in fall.
[6] Shortest growing season.
[7] Longest growing season.

1914	------	Dec. 14	------	Jan. 10	Dec. 8	332	Feb. 7	Dec. 13	309	------	Dec. 14	------	None	do	366	Mar. 2	Nov. 14	257
1915	Feb. 21	Nov. 14	266	Jan. 23	Dec. 27	338	Jan. 19	Nov. 14	299		------		Jan. 15	Nov. 12	301	Mar. 13	Oct. 23	224
1916	Jan. 31	Nov. 13	287	May 7	Nov. 13	190	Jan. 31	do	288	Feb. 2	Nov. 7	279	Jan. 30	Nov. 21	296	May 7	Oct. 2	148
1917	Mar. 16	None	291	Apr. 16	Dec. 6	234	Mar. 31	Dec. 10	254	Mar. 15	None	292	Mar. 23	Dec. 11	263	May 16	Oct. 18	155
1918	Feb. 19	Dec. 23	307	Mar. 6	Nov. 29	268	Feb. 16	do	297	None	Dec. 24	358	Feb. 8	Nov. 24	289	Apr. 15	Oct. 25	193
1919	Feb. 26	Nov. 27	274	Jan. 8	Nov. 28	324	Jan. 29	Dec. 9	314	Jan. 1	Nov. 28	331	Mar. 15	Nov. 8	238	May 31	Oct. 17	139
1920	Mar. 27	Dec. 5	253	Mar. 26	Dec. 20	269	Feb. 21	Dec. 13	296	Jan. 10	None	357	Mar. 27	Dec. 4	252	May 24	Oct. 20	149
1921	Apr. 14	Nov. 18	218	Apr. 14	Nov. 18	218	Feb. 15	Nov. 18	276	Feb. 16	do	319	Apr. 15	Nov. 18	217	Apr. 16	Oct. 24	191
1922	Apr. 6	Nov. 4	212	Feb. 4	Dec. 4	303	Feb. 3	Nov. 29	299	Feb. 3	do	332	Apr. 13	Nov. 3	204	Apr. 19	Oct. 29	193
1923	Mar. 5	Dec. 22	292	Feb. 2	Dec. 11	312	Feb. 14	Dec. 11	300	Feb. 10	Dec. 11	304	Mar. 15	Dec. 11	271	Apr. 25	Oct. 24	182
1924	Mar. 22	Dec. 18	271	Mar. 21	Dec. 17	271	Jan. 22	Dec. 17	330	Jan. 3	Dec. 18	350	Jan. 18	Oct. 11	267	May 6	------	------
1925	Jan. 17	Dec. 15	332	Jan. 9	None	357	Mar. 11	Dec. 14	278	Jan. 8	None	358	Jan. 14	Nov. 5	295	Mar. 13	Nov. 3	235
1926	Jan. 28	Dec. 14	320	Jan. 15	Dec. 14	333	Jan. 21	do	327	None	Dec. 28	362	Jan. 26	Dec. 15	323	Mar. 10	Sept. 30	204
1927	Jan. 25	Dec. 9	318	Jan. 23	Dec. 7	318	Feb. 11	Dec. 7	299	do	None	365	------	Nov. 23	327	Apr. 17	Nov. 1	198
1928	Feb. 24	Nov. 19	269	Jan. 16	None	351	Jan. 20	Dec. 15	330	Jan. 20	do	347	Jan. 18	Dec. 18	335	Apr. 4	Oct. 13	192
1929	Apr. 7	None	269	Apr. 9	do	267	Apr. 7	Dec. 28	265	Feb. 11	do	324	Mar. 25	Dec. 22	272	Apr. 12	Oct. 30	201
1930	Jan. 8	Nov. 19	315	Jan. 13	Dec. 22	343	Jan. 10	Dec. 21	345	None	Dec. 22	356	Feb. 23	Nov. 19	269	May 17	Oct. 11	147
1931	Feb. 21	Nov. 16	268	None	Nov. 23	327	None	Nov. 24	328	do	Nov. 23	327	------	Nov. 22	326	Apr. 2	Nov. 11	223
1932	Feb. 19	Dec. 11	296	Feb. 2	Dec. 9	311	Feb. 18	Dec. 12	298	Feb. 3	Dec. 29	330	Feb. 3	Dec. 24	325	Apr. 21	Oct. 24	186
1933	Mar. 24	Nov. 29	250	Feb. 10	None	325	Feb. 10	Nov. 17	280	Feb. 10	Dec. 17	310	Mar. 23	Nov. 28	250	Apr. 18	Nov. 6	202
1934	Jan. 9	Dec. 3	328	None	do	365	None	None	365	None	None	365	None	None	365	Feb. 13	Nov. 26	286
1935	Mar. 10	Nov. 4	239	Jan. 20	Nov. 4	288	Mar. 10	Nov. 4	239	Mar. 22	Dec. 17	270	None	Oct. 30	303	Apr. 9	Oct. 22	196
1936	Mar. 27	Dec. 30	278	Mar. 25	Nov. 30	250	Feb. 4	Dec. 4	304	None	None	367	Mar. 27	Dec. 1	249	Apr. 5	Nov. 2	211
1937	Feb. 27	Dec. 25	301	Jan. 25	None	341	Feb. 9	Dec. 27	321	Feb. 9	do	326	Mar. 6	None	301	Feb. 20	Nov. 7	260
1938	Feb. 17	Nov. 12	268	Jan. 24	Nov. 13	293	Feb. 17	Nov. 13	269	None	Nov. 12	216	Mar. 30	Nov. 11	226	Mar. 31	Nov. 6	220
Mean	Feb. 27	Dec. 6	282	Feb. 6	Dec. 10	307	Feb. 10	Dec. 6	299	Jan. 22	Dec. 19	331	Feb. 7	Dec. 7	303	Apr. 9	Nov. 3	208
Extremes	Jan. 8[2]	Nov. 4[4]	[6] 212	None[2]	Nov. 4[4]	[6] 190	------	Nov. 4[4]	[6] 239	------	Nov. 7[4]	[6] 270	None[2]	Oct. 11[4]	[6] 204	Feb. 5[2]	Sept. 30[4]	[6] 139
	Apr. 14[3]	None[5]	[7] 332	May 7[3]	None[5]	[7] 366	Apr. 7[3]	None[5]	[7] 365	Mar. 22[3]	None[5]	[7] 366	Apr. 15[3]	None[5]	[7] 366	May 31[3]	Dec. 28[5]	[7] 311

[2] Earliest date in spring.
[3] Latest date in spring.
[4] Earliest date in fall.
[5] Latest date in fall.
[6] Shortest growing season.
[7] Longest growing season.

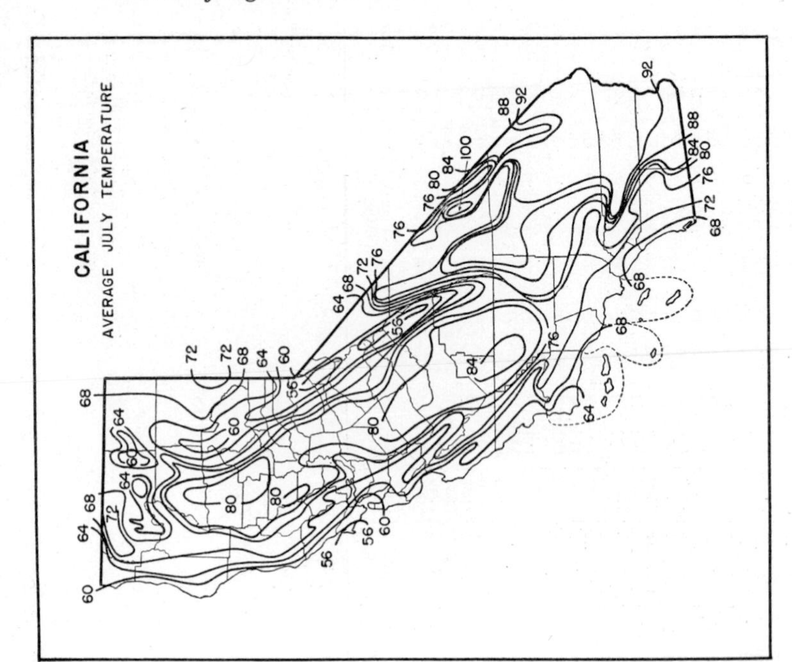
CALIFORNIA
AVERAGE JULY TEMPERATURE

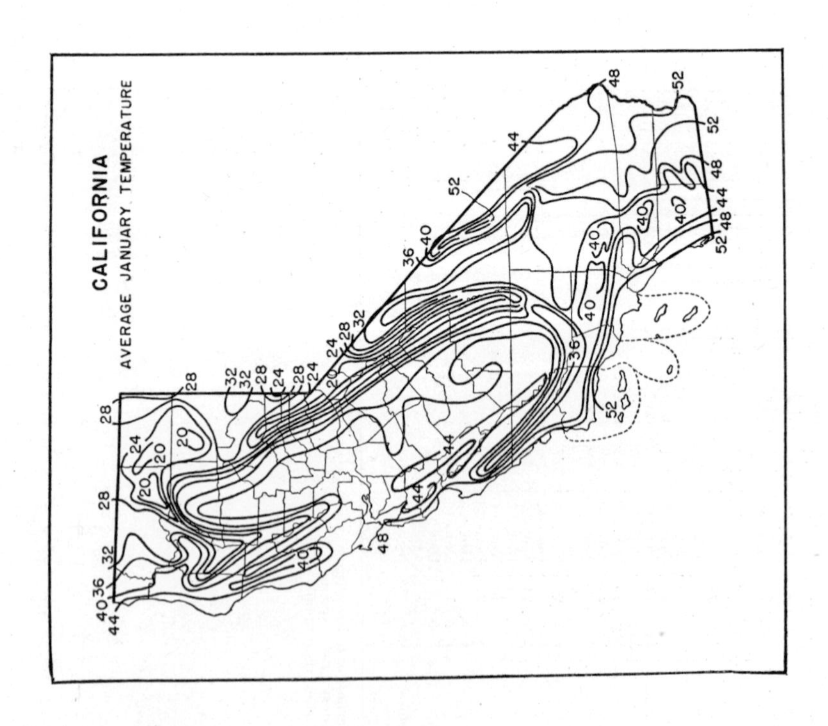
CALIFORNIA
AVERAGE JANUARY TEMPERATURE

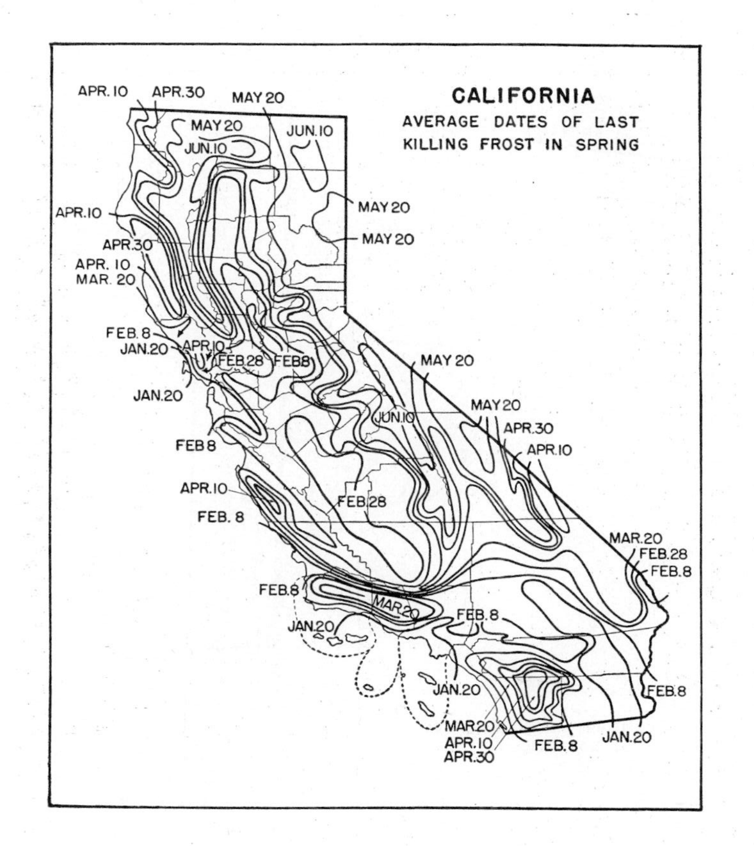
CALIFORNIA
AVERAGE DATES OF LAST
KILLING FROST IN SPRING
APR. 10
APR. 30
MAY 20
MAY 20
JUN. 10
JUN. 10
MAY 20
MAY 20
APR. 10
APR. 30
APR. 10
MAR. 20
FEB. 8
JAN. 20
APR. 10
FEB. 28
FEB. 8
JAN. 20
MAY 20
JUN. 10
MAY 20
APR. 30
APR. 10
FEB 8
APR. 10
FEB. 28
FEB. 8
MAR. 20
FEB. 28
FEB. 8
FEB. 8
MAR. 20
JAN. 20
FEB. 8
JAN. 20
MAR. 20
APR. 10
APR. 30
FEB. 8
JAN. 20
FEB. 8

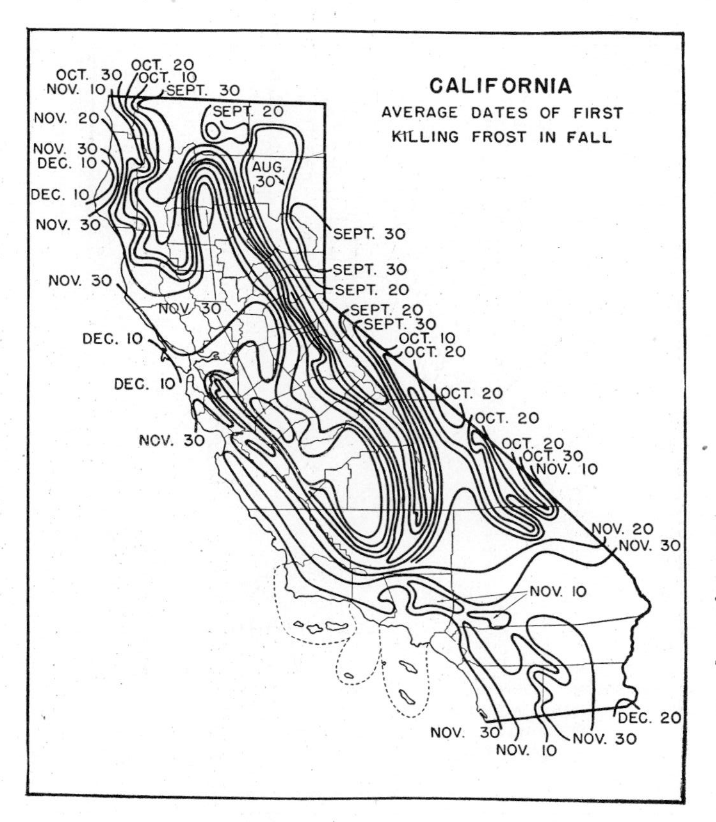
CALIFORNIA
AVERAGE DATES OF FIRST
KILLING FROST IN FALL
OCT. 30
NOV. 10
OCT. 20
OCT. 10
SEPT. 30
SEPT. 20
NOV. 20
NOV. 30
DEC. 10
AUG. 30
DEC. 10
NOV. 30
SEPT. 30
SEPT. 30
SEPT. 20
NOV. 30
NOV. 30
SEPT. 20
SEPT. 30
OCT. 10
OCT. 20
DEC. 10
DEC. 10
OCT. 20
OCT. 20
NOV. 30
OCT. 20
OCT. 30
NOV. 10
NOV. 20
NOV. 30
NOV. 10
DEC. 20
NOV. 30
NOV. 10
NOV. 30

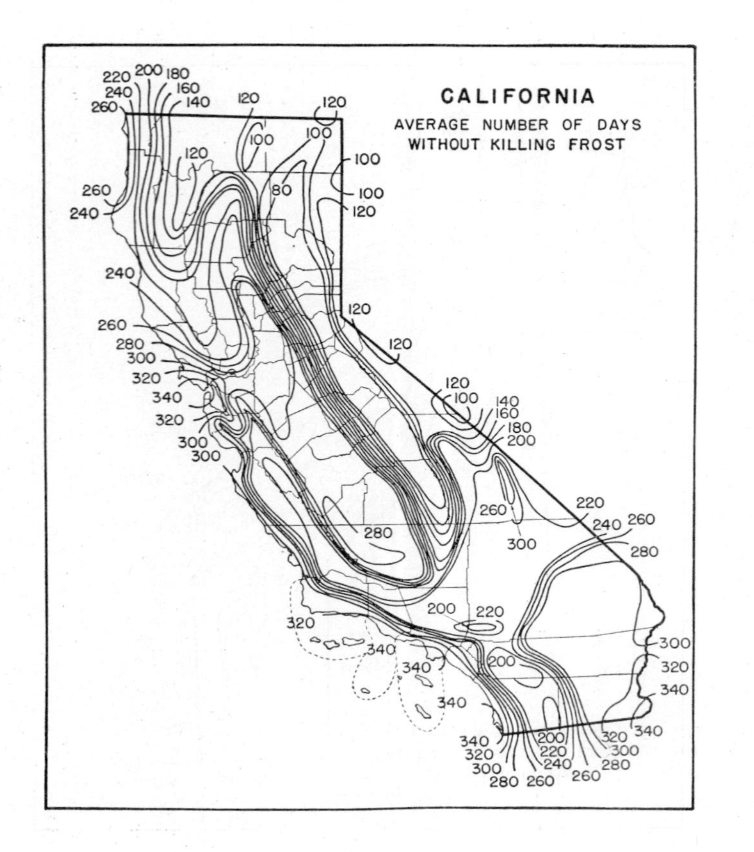
CALIFORNIA
AVERAGE NUMBER OF DAYS
WITHOUT KILLING FROST

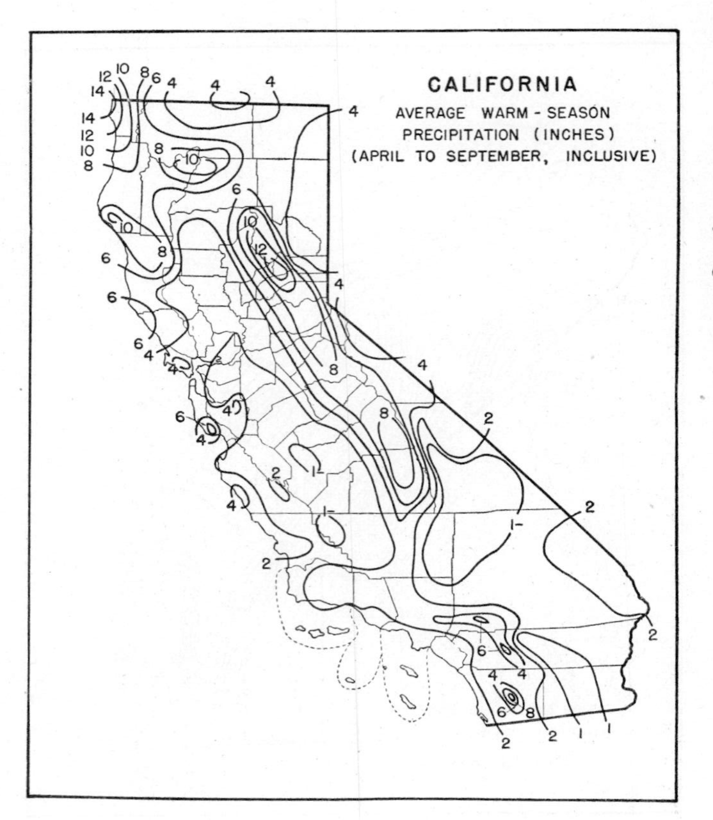
CALIFORNIA
AVERAGE WARM - SEASON
PRECIPITATION (INCHES)
(APRIL TO SEPTEMBER, INCLUSIVE)

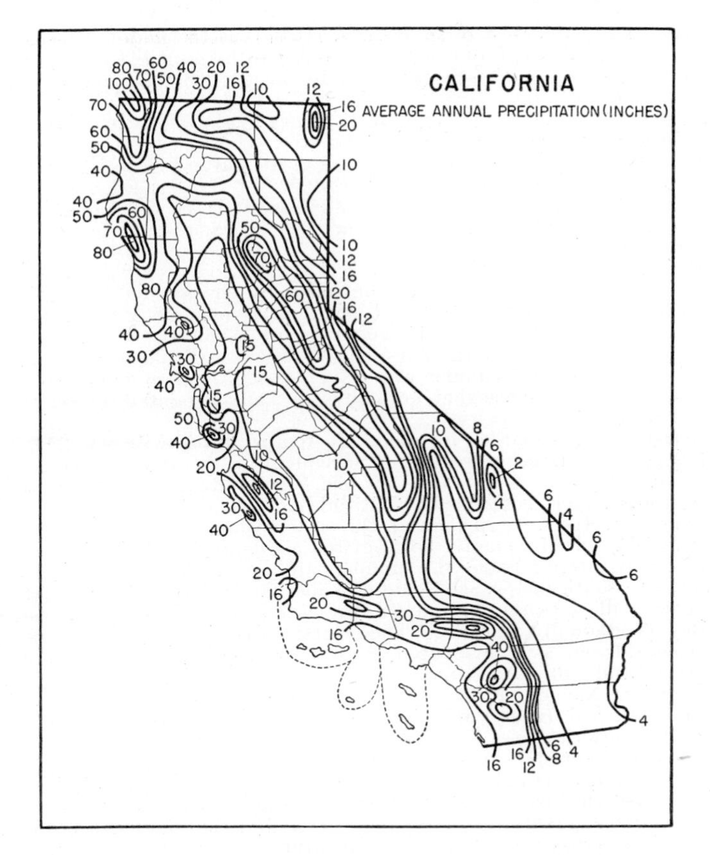

SUPPLEMENTARY CLIMATIC NOTES FOR CALIFORNIA

The topography of California is more diversified than that of any other State. Elevations range from 276 feet below sea level in parts of Death Valley to 14,495 feet above at the top of Mount Whitney—the lowest and the highest points, respectively, in the United States.

The more outstanding physical features of California are: The Great Interior Valley, drained by the Sacramento and San Joaquin River systems, one of the most important agricultural sections of the State; the Sierra Nevada on the east and the Coast Range on the west; the San Francisco Bay area, with its adjacent small fertile valleys; the Golden Gate, through which the Sacramento and San Joaquin Rivers flow to the sea and much low-lying marine air enters the interior; the mountain ranges of southwestern California, which increase precipitation on their westward and southwestward slopes, act as a barrier to the cold air from the north, and cause dynamic heating of air from the interior plateau as it descends the slopes to the fertile southwestern plains; and the extensive desert regions in the southeastern part of the State.

A number of rivers flow into the Pacific through the Coast Range Valleys, the more important of which are the Klamath, Eel, Russian, Pajaro, Salinas, Santa Inez, and Santa Clara. The many eastern tributaries of the Sacramento and San Joaquin collect a vast amount of water from the gently rising western slopes of the Sierra Nevada, but the abrupt eastern slopes have little run-off, and none of the precipitation that falls east of the Sierras or in the desert regions to the southeast reaches the sea.

Climatic factors have an unusually wide range in California, largely owing to the influence of mountains. There are several different climates, and marked differences in climatic conditions occur within short distances because of the local topography. In most other regions, latitude is the major determinant of temperature, but not in California. Here the isotherms have mostly a north-south instead of the usual east-west trend, following topographic contours rather than parallels of latitude.

The Pacific Ocean, in connection with prevailing westerly winds, gives the immediate coastal area a true marine climate. The Coast Range, acting as a barrier, nearly nullifies this water influence on its eastern sides, except in areas opposite breaks in the barrier; hence most of the interior has either a continental or a mountain climate. While the prevailing westerly wind is greatly modified by topography, it increases precipitation and has an equalizing effect on temperature over a large part of the State.

Nearly all parts of the State have a wet season and a dry season. This distribution of precipitation is largely controlled by the anticyclonic cell that is normally found off the California coast, particularly in summer when the rainfall is at a minimum. Precipitation in winter occurs usually when this anticyclone either is absent or is far south of its usual position. Owing to conservation of winter precipitation, the summer water supply is now more dependable in this State than in many regions that normally have ample rainfall during the crop-growing season.

The coastal area is marked by moderate temperatures, with small daily and annual ranges, and freezing weather is infrequent on the immediate coast to the northern boundary of the State. In the Coast Range mountain districts, temperature is largely controlled by altitude and local topography and is much more equable on the western than on the eastern slopes. In the coastal valleys the summer days are frequently hot, but the nights are cool.

In the Great Interior Valley the summers are hot, day temperatures increasing from north to south in the San Joaquin Valley and from south to north in the Sacramento Valley, as the marine air that enters these valleys from San Francisco Bay is gradually warmed. The winters are mild throughout this area, latitude considered, as is evidenced by the growing of citrus fruit northward nearly to latitude 40°.

In the Sierra Nevada, altitude is the important temperature control, and the daily and seasonal ranges are large, somewhat more marked on the eastern than on the western slopes. At the high elevations freezing temperatures may occur in midsummer and subzero readings in winter.

Owing to the marine influence on the west and to the mountain barrier on the north and east, the coastal area between Los Angeles and San Diego has one of the most equable climates in the United States, but the southern coastal valleys sometimes have large daily ranges of temperature.

The normal length of the growing season in California ranges from the entire year, 365 days, on the extreme southern coast, to less than 100 days in interior mountain districts above the 6,000-foot level.

The average amount of precipitation is influenced by the distance from the ocean, the altitude, the shape and steepness of mountain slopes, and the direction of the slopes in relation to the moisture-bearing winds. As a rule, precipitation increases from south to north and is much heavier on southern and western than on northern and eastern mountain slopes. Drought damage is rarely severe because of the extensive use of irrigation. Drought in the spring may curtail the grain crop and cause a shortage of range feed, while the late starting of fall rains may unfavorably affect winter pastures, grain, and cover crops.

The average annual precipitation for different localities ranges from less than 2 inches in Death Valley to over 109 inches in parts of Del Norte County. At some desert stations entire years have been without precipitation, while the greatest annual amount is 153.54 inches at Monumental, Del Norte County.

Rains of 10 inches or more in 24 hours have occurred at a number of mountain stations. Such downpours are most frequent over the mountains of southern California. Desert stations also occasionally receive very heavy rains. Torrential rains over the mountains of southern California have caused major floods, with great property loss in that area.

The average seasonal snowfall ranges from a trace or none at all along the middle and southern coast, to 449 inches at Tamarack, Alpine County. The western slopes of the northern and middle Sierras include several localities where the mean seasonal fall approaches the record for the United States. However, the seasonal snowfall from year to year in mountain districts varies greatly, ranging from 23 percent to 215 percent of the normal.

Fog is most frequent in coastal and nearby foothill districts, and generally increases with increase in latitude and altitude, although Point Reyes on the immediate middle coast has the greatest number of days with fog. Near the coast it is more frequent in summer than in winter and also on the windward than on the leeward mountain slopes. Fog is common over a considerable part of the Great Valley in winter.

On the coast and the windward slopes of the nearby mountains, the relative humidity is high throughout the year, generally increasing from south to north and from winter to summer. In interior lowland districts it is very low in summer and relatively high in winter.

In general, sunshine increases with increased distance from the coast and decreases with increase in latitude and altitude.

Along the coast the most frequent wind direction is northwest. Elsewhere the surface winds are greatly influenced by mountain barriers and local topography. Tornadoes rarely occur in California. The most destructive local winds are caused by the flow of air down mountain slopes and valleys, as in the "Santa Ana" winds of southern California, and the desiccating northerly and northeasterly winds of foehn, or chinook, character that sometimes flow down into the Sacramento and San Joaquin Valleys.

MALCOLM SPRAGUE, *Associate Meteorologist and Climatologist for California, Weather Bureau, San Francisco.*

COLORADO

Climatic summary

County [1]	Station	Temperature: Length of record	Temperature: January average	Temperature: July average	Temperature: Maximum	Temperature: Minimum	Killing frost average dates: Length of record	Killing frost: Last in spring	Killing frost: First in fall	Growing season [2]	Average precipitation: Length of record	January	February	March	April	May	June	July	August	September	October	November	December	Annual
		Yr.	°F.	°F.	°F.	°F.	Yr.			Days	Yr.	In.	In.	In.	In.	In.	In.	In.	In.	In.	In.	In.	In.	In.
Adams	Simpson										13	0.28	0.48	1.05	2.07	2.26	1.96	2.31	1.85	0.90	0.98	0.63	0.59	15.36
Alamosa	Garnett	36	17.1	62.5	92	−41	39	June 8	Sept. 12	96	40	.13	.19	.37	.58	.61	.68	1.21	1.30	.83	.57	.30	.20	6.97
Baca	Springfield										24	.37	.65	1.16	1.82	2.28	1.95	2.10	1.73	1.42	1.07	.71	.50	15.76
	Two Buttes	35	31.1	76.6	111	−26	34	May 1	Oct. 17	169	36	.22	.53	.64	1.55	1.98	2.10	1.94	1.62	1.29	.78	.48	.49	13.62
	Utleyville										18	.21	.35	.64	1.26	2.34	1.88	2.42	1.60	1.30	1.15	.42	.34	13.91
Bent	Las Animas	39	28.0	75.9	114	−32	40	Apr. 29	Oct. 9	163	40	.12	.45	.58	1.66	2.06	1.55	2.27	1.45	.99	.76	.48	.40	12.77
Boulder	Boulder	40	32.7	71.0	102	−33	40	May 3	Oct. 11	161	40	.36	.80	1.55	2.77	2.90	1.55	1.91	1.53	1.51	1.61	.83	.86	18.18
	Hawthorne										30	.41	1.04	1.88	3.26	3.35	1.90	2.22	1.80	1.86	2.01	1.13	1.12	21.98
	Longmont	29	26.7	71.0	104	−38	29	May 7	Oct. 2	148	29	.23	.51	.74	1.79	2.32	1.59	1.75	1.18	1.30	1.11	.56	.56	13.64
	Silver Lake										29	2.16	2.93	3.42	4.11	2.73	2.51	3.89	2.37	2.17	1.85	1.65	1.92	31.71
Chaffee	Buena Vista	31	22.3	60.2	105	−37	30	June 5	Sept. 21	108	39	.35	.59	.72	.88	.81	.55	1.92	1.44	.76	.57	.47	.39	9.45
	Garfield										25	1.53	2.04	2.20	1.96	1.63	1.44	2.78	2.64	1.67	1.55	1.43	1.68	22.55
	Salida	31	27.6	65.1	100	−35	30	May 29	Sept. 19	113	31	.39	.77	.72	1.43	.94	.96	1.74	1.57	1.10	.80	.67	.62	11.71
Cheyenne	Cheyenne Wells	39	28.8	74.9	110	−31	40	May 6	Oct. 7	154	40	.26	.50	.72	1.82	2.07	2.49	2.52	2.42	1.25	.89	.44	.48	15.86
Clear Creek	Idaho Springs	34	27.0	62.5	91	−29	33	May 23	Sept. 25	125	36	.28	.54	.91	2.09	1.76	1.33	2.73	2.11	1.43	1.22	.53	.51	15.44
Conejos	Cumbres										29	3.75	4.59	4.62	2.48	1.73	.98	2.61	2.82	2.22	1.90	2.41	2.92	33.03
	Manassa	32	19.8	62.6	92	−33	32	June 5	Sept. 13	100	33	.13	.25	.40	.56	.70	.54	1.08	1.39	.70	.69	.29	.23	6.96
Costilla	Blanca	11	20.2	62.6	90	−30	10	June 10	Sept. 18	100	11	.10	.25	.17	1.09	.87	.56	2.20	2.05	.73	.82	.19	.17	9.20
	La Veta Pass										30	1.13	1.73	2.54	2.39	1.78	1.09	2.19	2.13	1.27	1.44	1.69	1.60	20.98
	San Luis	24	21.7	62.2	98	−34	24	June 5	Sept. 21	108	24	.37	.37	.51	.94	.95	.77	2.09	1.63	1.04	.96	.41	.40	10.44
Crowley	Ordway										23	.14	.29	.65	1.04	1.81	1.51	1.56	1.72	.84	.63	.49	.35	11.03
Custer	Westcliffe	30	24.8	61.6	95	−54	29	June 7	Sept. 14	99	30	.58	.75	1.24	2.15	1.83	1.56	2.46	2.26	1.42	1.19	.84	.77	17.05
Delta	Cedaredge	30	26.4	70.5	101	−23	31	May 11	Oct. 4	146	30	.70	.88	1.01	1.17	1.18	.75	.91	1.11	1.28	1.22	.70	.74	11.65
	Columbine Ranch										25	2.35	2.06	2.18	2.00	1.80	1.11	2.13	2.57	2.27	2.05	1.76	2.17	24.45
	Delta	38	24.6	73.9	109	−36	38	May 8	Oct. 2	147	40	.60	.42	.62	.65	.91	.39	.68	1.01	.99	.85	.52	.53	8.17
	Paonia	34	25.4	71.0	100	−28	34	May 4	Oct. 13	162	39	1.24	1.31	1.56	1.55	1.51	.65	1.03	1.35	1.43	1.49	1.18	1.29	15.59
Denver	Denver	40	32.0	72.5	105	−29	40	Apr. 26	Oct. 14	171	40	.31	.55	1.13	2.11	2.01	1.29	1.58	1.46	1.20	1.04	.61	.70	13.99
Dolores	Rico										29	2.32	2.40	2.59	1.74	1.47	1.42	3.08	2.90	2.75	1.74	1.50	1.86	25.77
Douglas	Castle Rock	25	28.8	67.0	99	−37	26	May 17	Sept. 25	131	27	.36	.57	1.33	2.32	2.22	1.79	2.74	1.91	1.20	1.22	.56	.82	17.04
Elbert	Hamps	21	27.0	67.7	99	−31	21	May 16	Sept. 27	134	21	.26	.49	.92	2.45	1.76	1.81	2.55	2.15	1.13	.62	.31	.51	14.96
	Limon (near)	28	25.6	69.3	101	−30	29	May 14	Oct. 3	142	29	.17	.34	.65	1.58	2.08	1.91	2.37	2.00	1.15	.77	.44	.58	14.04
El Paso	Calhan	32	26.9	68.6	98	−30	32	May 16	Oct. 1	138	32	.32	.49	.81	1.77	2.14	1.65	2.73	3.05	1.28	.69	.52	.63	16.08

[1] The following counties, for which no data are available, are best represented by the stations indicated: Arapahoe—Simpson; Archuleta—Wolf Creek Pass; Eagle—Nast; Gilpin—Idaho Springs.

[2] Length of growing season between average dates of last killing frost in spring and first in fall.

	Colorado Springs	40	30.2	68.2	98	−27	40	May 8	Oct. 3	148	40	.22	.41	.73	1.54	2.18	1.67	2.61	2.34	1.21	.59	.35	.34	14.19
	Fremont Express Station.	26	24.6	57.8	84	−29	26	June 2	Sept. 17	107	26	.37	.76	1.41	2.30	2.77	2.42	3.93	3.58	1.36	1.12	.75	.76	21.53
	Lake Moraine	40	20.3	53.6	85	−34	40	June 22	Sept. 5	75	40	.59	.89	1.76	3.03	2.75	2.57	4.36	3.96	1.81	1.40	.91	.84	24.87
	Momument	28	26.9	65.7	99	−40	28	May 25	Sept. 21	119	28	.40	.76	1.33	2.49	2.52	1.79	3.02	2.98	1.47	1.07	.80	.78	19.41
Fremont	Canon City	39	36.4	74.0	104	−30	39	Apr. 28	Oct. 13	168	40	.29	.51	.84	1.46	1.56	1.10	1.82	2.16	1.19	.77	.59	.53	12.82
	Penrose (near)										15	.18	.40	.62	.85	1.67	1.14	1.49	2.06	1.21	.53	.53	.39	11.07
Garfield	Glenwood Springs	33	23.3	67.3	100	−38	33	May 24	Sept. 24	123	36	1.39	1.29	1.45	1.42	1.30	.87	1.46	1.68	1.49	1.17	.98	1.20	15.70
	Rifle	33	23.0	71.0	104	−34	24	May 12	Sept. 30	141	24	.82	.60	.88	1.00	1.02	.40	1.17	1.07	1.19	1.13	.75	.87	10.90
	Shoshone						8	May 5	Oct. 6	154	29	1.41	1.47	1.38	1.44	1.32	1.09	1.53	1.79	1.65	1.34	1.15	1.21	16.78
Grand	Fraser	28	11.4	53.6	86	−50	28	July 16	Aug. 2	17	28	1.55	1.81	1.85	2.16	1.82	1.28	2.35	1.66	1.50	1.39	1.16	1.42	19.95
Gunnison	Crested Butte	27	12.6	56.9	91	−42	28	July 2	Aug. 22	51	29	2.36	2.25	2.11	1.66	1.58	1.34	2.28	2.26	2.40	1.21	1.31	1.97	22.73
	Gunnison	38	7.6	61.5	105	−47	40	June 21	Aug. 31	71	39	.71	.76	.66	.70	.85	.75	1.65	1.45	1.01	.68	.48	.70	10.40
	Pitkin										29	1.13	1.29	1.32	1.26	1.20	1.09	2.48	1.97	1.55	1.06	.87	1.18	16.40
	Sapinero (near)	34	17.1	59.3	88	−29	34	June 12	Sept. 18	98	38	1.79	2.09	2.41	2.03	1.73	.94	1.59	1.89	1.71	1.50	1.35	1.83	20.86
Hinsdale	Cathedral	13	13.0	57.0	86	−34	13	July 2	Aug. 25	54	17	.33	.62	.84	.81	1.01	.92	2.58	2.17	1.22	.76	.76	.34	12.36
Huerfano	Cuchara Camps										27	.75	1.57	2.16	2.89	2.27	1.54	3.64	2.68	1.65	1.81	1.50	1.27	23.73
	Huerfano (near)	16	28.9	70.3	105	−42	15	May 21	Sept. 29	131	17	.45	.76	1.25	1.78	1.34	1.21	2.27	2.27	.86	.94	1.03	.77	14.93
Jackson	Pearl										17	2.17	2.21	2.06	1.86	1.62	1.10	1.60	1.64	1.59	1.49	1.33	1.23	19.90
	Spicer	26	17.4	58.8	91	−49	26	June 29	Aug. 28	60	29	.70	.82	.91	1.06	.98	.72	1.27	1.23	1.17	1.17	.83	.78	11.64
Jefferson	Cheesman	36	29.0	66.8	99	−35	36	May 16	Sept. 30	137	36	.23	.52	.92	1.95	1.86	1.49	2.87	2.51	1.37	1.00	.55	.60	15.87
	Edgewater	30	30.2	71.4	106	−30	29	May 7	do	146	31	.37	.71	1.11	1.95	2.43	1.39	1.73	2.11	1.31	1.29	.81	.96	16.17
	Kassler	25	31.8	73.0	103	−32	25	May 6	Oct. 5	152	40	.42	.75	1.33	2.63	2.36	1.64	1.91	1.81	1.51	1.36	.75	.87	17.34
Kiowa	Eads	26	28.2	75.8	106	−24	20	May 7	Oct. 9	155	27	.15	.37	.53	1.14	2.32	2.14	2.50	1.73	1.17	.98	.35	.28	13.66
	Haswell										16	.14	.24	.41	.83	2.14	1.93	2.00	1.52	.88	.71	.65	.23	11.68
Kit Carson	Burlington	34	28.5	74.6	107	−23	33	May 4	Oct. 7	156	40	.15	.41	.64	1.94	2.11	2.83	2.58	2.72	1.57	.96	.46	.51	16.88
Lake	Leadville	33	17.6	56.2	86	−31	37	June 17	Sept. 5	80	37	1.26	1.50	1.62	1.72	1.36	1.31	3.43	2.64	1.50	1.20	.90	1.13	19.57
La Plata	Durango	40	24.8	67.0	99	−27	39	May 28	Sept. 26	121	40	1.47	1.77	1.90	1.48	1.10	.87	2.15	2.31	1.88	1.73	1.30	1.58	19.54
	Fort Lewis	21	22.3	64.5	99	−32	21	June 6	Sept. 22	108	27	1.12	1.81	1.66	1.14	1.04	.83	2.42	2.39	2.03	1.63	.95	1.27	18.29
	Ignacio	25	21.8	67.5	101	−38	25	do	do	108	25	1.11	1.26	1.44	1.16	.95	.85	2.20	2.17	1.68	1.26	.98	1.04	16.10
	Tacoma										25	1.96	1.89	1.86	1.66	1.21	1.14	2.58	2.46	2.48	1.97	1.65	1.65	22.51
	Terminal Dam										25	2.40	2.46	2.28	1.99	1.33	1.14	2.97	2.61	2.70	2.29	1.74	2.25	26.16
Larimer	Estes Park (near)	22	25.1	61.7	98	−35	23	June 9	Sept. 15	98	30	.47	.89	1.30	2.30	2.09	1.42	2.75	2.17	1.57	1.33	.86	.79	17.94
	Fort Collins	40	26.0	68.9	102	−38	40	May 7	Sept. 29	145	40	.27	.64	1.08	2.13	2.82	1.56	1.64	1.32	1.52	1.17	.49	.56	15.20
	La Porte										27	.36	.77	1.14	2.43	2.62	1.45	1.91	1.43	1.41	1.28	.54	.61	15.95
	Longs Peak	40	22.5	55.5	94	−41	40	July 2	Aug. 30	59	40	.71	1.29	2.00	2.92	2.44	1.68	3.48	2.27	1.87	1.52	.83	.96	21.97
	Moraine	12	25.1	59.1	96	−42	12	June 14	Sept. 10	88	17	.75	.93	1.38	2.26	1.61	1.41	2.32	1.39	1.48	1.23	.50	.75	16.01
	Waterdale	34	28.2	67.3	102	−41	34	May 13	Sept. 29	139	40	.22	.64	1.17	2.19	2.62	1.64	1.81	1.63	1.58	1.23	.50	.57	15.80
Las Animas	Hoehne	21	32.7	71.5	110	−32	20	May 17	Oct. 6	142	22	.31	.68	.74	1.99	1.65	1.40	2.22	1.74	1.18	.95	.55	.61	14.02
	North Lake										36	.71	1.19	1.76	2.24	1.99	1.81	3.85	3.15	1.72	1.22	.88	.82	21.34
	Trinidad	35	33.9	71.9	99	−26	34	May 2	Oct. 16	167	39	.43	.78	1.02	1.90	1.89	1.73	2.36	2.10	1.34	1.20	.76	.69	16.20
Lincoln	Arriba	22	27.5	72.0	105	−30	22	May 16	Oct. 5	142	23	.10	.49	.72	1.73	2.20	1.93	2.31	2.23	1.45	.91	.46	.58	15.11
	Long Branch	19	26.3	72.5	104	−31	19	May 7	Oct. 1	147	19	.16	.35	.63	1.29	2.07	1.71	1.94	2.18	1.06	.67	.40	.26	12.72
Logan	Le Roy	35	26.3	73.0	107	−29	38	May 5	Oct. 5	153	40	.24	.49	1.00	2.53	2.70	2.40	2.33	2.37	1.35	1.10	.50	.67	17.68
	Sterling	29	23.8	72.4	105	−33	29	May 7	Sept. 30	146	29	.24	.39	.75	1.92	2.71	2.09	1.72	2.06	1.36	.95	.44	.52	15.15
Mesa	Collbran	37	21.9	68.7	100	−36	37	May 22	Sept. 28	129	40	1.15	1.10	1.57	1.69	1.53	.81	1.27	1.51	1.64	1.49	1.04	1.12	15.92
	Fruita	36	22.5	75.3	108	−34	36	May 6	Oct. 7	154	36	.85	.73	.96	.80	.84	.44	.85	1.00	1.13	1.05	.73	.79	10.17
	Grand Junction	40	25.0	77.9	105	−21	40	Apr. 16	Oct. 24	191	40	.57	.58	.75	.77	.79	.45	.70	1.11	.94	.88	.57	.65	8.76
	Palisade	25	25.3	77.7	107	−23	25	Apr. 22	Oct. 19	180	26	.63	.45	.85	1.02	.97	.54	.93	1.07	1.26	1.17	.75	.68	10.32
Mineral	Hermit (near)	27	11.6	54.8	89	−41	27	July 11	Aug 12	32	31	.91	.90	1.27	1.15	1.08	1.19	2.64	2.61	2.07	1.74	1.03	.85	17.44
	Wagon Wheel Gap Experiment Station	16	15.0	56.2	82	−24	16	June 10	Sept. 11	93	16	1.00	.96	1.52	1.45	1.20	1.20	3.02	2.25	1.51	1.72	1.34	1.12	18.29
	Wolf Creek Pass										16	2.94	3.30	3.27	1.99	1.43	1.01	3.07	3.56	2.36	2.61	2.10	2.20	29.84

COLORADO—Continued

Climatic summary—Continued

County	Station	Temperature					Killing frost average dates				Average precipitation													
		Length of record	January average	July average	Maximum	Minimum	Length of record	Last in spring	First in fall	Growing season	Length of record	January	February	March	April	May	June	July	August	September	October	November	December	Annual
		Yr.	*°F.*	*°F.*	*°F.*	*°F.*	*Yr.*			*Days*	*Yr.*	*In.*	*In.*	*In.*	*In.*	*In.*	*In.*	*In.*	*In.*	*In.*	*In.*	*In.*	*In.*	*In.*
Moffat	Lay	36	17.6	66.7	102	-47	38	June 23	Sept. 3	72	36	1.16	1.08	1.38	1.43	1.44	.75	.97	1.09	1.42	1.34	.85	1.16	14.07
Montezuma	Mancos	19	25.6	66.2	96	-26	18	June 6	Sept. 24	110	21	1.32	1.50	2.06	1.78	1.26	.88	1.89	2.06	1.61	1.62	1.17	1.22	18.37
	Mesa Verde Park	16	28.6	72.2	102	-15	16	May 2	Oct. 16	167	17	1.25	2.16	2.05	1.36	1.13	.76	2.17	2.23	2.10	1.16	1.20	1.52	19.09
Montrose	Crawford (near)	13	25.4	68.1	93	-24	14	May 21	Oct. 4	136	14	.77	.51	.55	.87	.89	.81	1.25	1.20	1.16	1.11	.87	.81	10.80
	Montrose	36	24.0	71.2	103	-27	35	May 10	do	147	39	.55	.51	.74	.86	.95	.47	.84	1.31	1.09	.96	.52	.72	9.52
Morgan	Fort Morgan	39	23.5	72.8	109	-36	39	May 9	Oct. 1	145	40	.17	.33	.63	1.94	2.28	1.78	2.28	1.60	1.24	.80	.34	.36	13.75
Otero	La Junta										18	.23	.49	.68	1.64	2.06	1.96	2.39	2.12	.69	.89	.51	.62	14.28
	Rocky Ford	40	29.9	75.5	106	-32	39	Apr. 28	Oct. 9	164	40	.14	.29	.52	1.50	1.91	1.40	2.07	1.47	.84	.77	.47	.34	11.72
Ouray	Ironton										11	2.18	2.14	2.25	2.42	1.26	1.24	3.30	2.37	2.32	2.28	1.60	1.69	25.05
Park	Hartsel										30	.19	.25	.36	.67	.83	1.10	3.02	2.26	1.18	.48	.30	.26	10.90
Phillips	Haxtun										18	.12	.24	.60	2.00	2.66	2.45	2.32	1.78	1.09	1.05	.46	.38	15.15
	Holyoke	28	26.9	73.7	110	-36	30	May 9	Oct. 1	145	34	.18	.37	.92	2.26	2.74	3.12	2.66	2.64	1.44	.89	.40	.54	18.16
Pitkin	Ashcroft	20	16.8	55.2	89	-31	20	June 28	Sept. 1	65	22	1.58	1.58	2.32	2.14	1.77	1.48	2.06	2.24	1.87	1.60	1.20	1.29	21.13
	Nast	16	16.0	57.3	91	-36	19	June 25	Sept. 3	70	22	1.60	1.67	1.56	1.35	1.12	1.04	2.31	1.73	1.31	1.14	1.32	1.71	17.86
Prowers	Holly	37	30.8	77.0	109	-23	37	Apr. 27	Oct. 11	167	39	.18	.54	.62	1.64	1.98	2.04	2.33	2.25	1.28	.81	.53	.38	14.58
	Lamar	40	31.3	78.8	111	-30	39	Apr. 26	Oct. 10	167	40	.22	.59	.77	1.61	2.25	2.14	2.49	1.99	1.22	.94	.52	.55	15.29
Pueblo	Pueblo	40	31.6	74.8	104	-27	40	Apr. 23	Oct. 14	174	40	.26	.52	.66	1.37	1.51	1.29	1.87	1.73	.86	.60	.40	.47	11.54
Rio Blanco	Meeker	29	20.6	64.6	103	-43	28	June 15	Sept. 10	87	28	.97	.86	1.31	1.59	1.44	.98	1.40	1.75	1.68	1.52	1.03	1.03	15.56
	Rangely	9	17.5	69.1	106	-37	8	May 27	Sept. 15	111	11	.59	.86	.85	.58	.78	.60	.57	1.54	1.37	1.25	.64	.73	10.36
Rio Grande	Del Norte	17	20.2	62.4	88	-26	17	May 30	Sept. 25	118	17	.26	.28	.58	.51	.75	.49	1.40	1.69	.93	.58	.60	.25	8.32
Routt	Columbine										29	1.98	2.44	2.43	2.05	2.00	1.15	1.97	1.82	1.91	1.72	1.47	2.18	23.12
	Hayden	21	16.8	66.3	102	-44	18	June 10	Sept. 15	97	22	1.37	1.23	1.38	1.48	1.57	.98	1.49	1.59	1.86	1.44	1.01	1.36	16.76
	Steamboat Springs	27	13.8	61.2	99	-54	30	June 28	Aug. 24	57	29	2.37	2.49	2.36	2.14	2.03	1.24	1.80	1.77	1.91	2.12	1.70	2.33	24.26
Saguache	Marshall Pass										13	1.74	1.89	1.83	1.40	.97	1.30	1.72	1.32	.98	.99	1.11	1.92	17.17
	Saguache	37	19.7	64.7	102	-27	33	May 30	Sept. 26	119	34	.20	.35	.43	.65	.80	.84	1.69	1.75	.94	.73	.31	.30	8.99
San Juan	Cascade										32	2.77	3.02	3.34	2.14	1.39	1.29	2.95	2.93	2.80	2.52	1.86	2.49	29.50
	Silverton	34	16.8	55.4	96	-33	32	July 6	Aug. 19	44	33	1.87	2.01	2.82	1.68	1.38	1.63	2.97	3.24	2.85	2.34	1.39	1.84	26.02
San Miguel	Ames										25	1.60	2.21	2.61	2.27	1.87	1.07	2.67	2.83	2.21	1.91	1.39	1.77	24.41
	Savage Basin										18	3.34	4.01	4.32	4.42	2.60	.77	3.02	3.19	2.77	2.93	2.93	3.11	37.41
	Telluride	30	20.7	58.4	96	-36	31	June 27	Aug. 31	65	30	1.40	1.88	2.44	2.26	1.79	1.13	2.67	3.25	1.88	1.66	1.46	1.34	23.16
	Trout Lake										25	1.86	2.66	3.15	2.55	2.18	1.31	3.31	3.14	2.62	2.09	1.65	2.05	28.57
Sedgwick	Julesburg	22	25.4	74.7	108	-38	22	May 15	Oct. 2	140	27	.21	.35	.75	2.17	2.70	2.63	2.54	2.59	1.27	.99	.50	.44	17.14
	Sedgwick	27	24.6	75.1	112	-40	26	May 9	do	146	28	.22	.31	.78	2.14	2.70	2.88	2.44	2.47	1.57	1.10	.43	.49	17.53
Summit	Dillon	28	12.7	55.1	87	-46	28	July 14	Aug. 10	27	29	1.21	1.43	1.88	1.93	1.51	.97	2.12	1.88	1.41	1.40	1.03	1.39	18.16
Teller	Auldhurst										23	.35	.71	1.00	2.13	1.69	1.84	3.69	3.11	1.67	.77	.61	.75	18.32
	Victor	27	24.8	58.0	92	-25	27	June 10	Sept. 15	97	27	.31	.50	1.20	1.19	1.74	1.77	4.92	4.14	1.48	.84	.61	.56	19.26

Washington	Akron	10	24.7	73.7	102	−28	11	May 14	Oct. 4	143	19	.30	.44	1.05	2.61	2.78	2.37	2.65	2.12	1.54	1.13	.60	.66	18.25
	Cope	10	28.2	71.7	103	−32	8	May 12	Oct. 6	147	30	.21	.55	1.30	1.97	2.52	2.85	2.65	2.70	1.40	.88	.66	.59	18.28
Weld	Fort Lupton	20	26.5	73.7	106	−31	20	May 5	Oct. 2	150	28	.17	.37	.53	1.39	2.38	1.55	1.54	1.33	1.16	1.01	.43	.48	12.34
	Greeley	38	24.9	72.2	107	−45	38	May 5	Sept. 30	148	39	.21	.42	.75	1.52	2.28	1.57	1.69	1.15	1.13	.98	.41	.49	12.60
	Grover (near)	27	25.2	70.4	105	−37	27	May 20	Sept. 24	127	36	.21	.53	.54	1.52	2.26	1.70	2.32	1.68	1.33	.65	.34	.49	13.57
Yuma	Wray	36	28.5	74.8	110	−32	36	May 7	Oct. 3	149	37	.20	.53	.82	2.26	2.74	2.77	2.78	2.55	1.34	1.00	.51	.48	17.98
	Yuma										40	.21	.48	.98	2.08	2.48	2.67	2.66	2.60	1.06	.96	.44	.49	17.11

Precipitation and temperature—State unit values

[This tabulation gives the mean annual, mean monthly, and average seasonal precipitation, 1886–1938, and the mean annual temperatures, 1896–1938, for Colorado]

Precipitation		Precipitation		Precipitation		Precipitation		Temperature		Temperature	
Year	Mean	Year	Mean	Year	Mean	Month	Mean	Year	Mean	Year	Mean
	In.		In.		In.		In.		°F.		°F.
1886	17.58	1908	17.09	1930	17.32	June	1.41	1896	46.5	1918	44.5
1887	14.21	1909	20.96	1931	14.03	July	2.23	1897	44.8	1919	43.9
1888	12.00	1910	14.35	1932	14.17	August	1.98	1898	44.0	1920	43.5
1889	13.73	1911	19.24	1933	15.16	September	1.34	1899	44.8	1921	46.7
1890	11.97	1912	18.84	1934	10.89	October	1.14	1900	47.4	1922	44.6
1891	19.88	1913	17.78	1935	15.81	November	.79	1901	47.2	1923	43.7
1892	15.56	1914	19.26	1936	16.06	December	.91	1902	46.3	1924	43.6
1893	12.89	1915	19.44	1937	14.59			1903	44.6	1925	45.3
1894	14.37	1916	18.70	1938	19.35	Annual	16.49	1904	45.4	1926	45.0
1895	18.33	1917	14.74					1905	44.4	1927	45.2
1896	15.07	1918	18.75					1906	45.0	1928	44.7
1897	19.46	1919	17.22	Month	Mean	Season	Average	1907	45.7	1929	43.8
1898	15.61	1920	17.75					1908	44.0	1930	44.6
1899	14.67	1921	19.37					1909	44.2	1931	46.2
1900	14.43	1922	15.60					1910	46.5	1932	45.0
1901	14.14	1923	21.23		In.			1911	44.6	1933	46.8
1902	13.88	1924	13.75	January	0.77		In.	1912	42.2	1934	49.5
1903	13.80	1925	16.96	February	.96	Winter	2.64	1913	43.3	1935	46.6
1904	16.30	1926	16.98	March	1.30	Spring	4.96	1914	45.3	1936	46.9
1905	18.09	1927	20.32	April	1.80	Summer	5.62	1915	44.1	1937	45.9
1906	19.71	1928	17.05	May	1.86	Fall	3.27	1916	44.1	1938	46.6
1907	16.33	1929	18.16					1917	43.6		

COLORADO—Continued

Dates of last killing frost in spring and first in fall, with length of growing season

Year	Denver			Pueblo			Le Roy			Las Animas			Grand Junction			Garnett		
	Last in spring	First in fall	Growing season [1]	Last in spring	First in fall	Growing season [1]	Last in spring	First in fall	Growing season [1]	Last in spring	First in fall	Growing season [1]	Last in spring	First in fall	Growing season [1]	Last in spring	First in fall	Growing season [1]
			Days			Days			Days			Days			Days			Days
1899	May 4	Oct. 16	165	May 4	Oct. 5	154	May 4	Sept. 28	147	May 1	Oct. 16	168	Apr. 20	Oct. 16	179	June 10	Aug. 20	71
1900	Apr. 29	Oct. 7	161	Apr. 17	Oct. 7	173	Apr. 18	Oct. 7	172	Apr. 14	Oct. 7	176	Mar. 28	Oct. 21	207	May 27		
1901	Apr. 17	Oct. 13	179	Apr. 18	Oct. 13	178	Apr. 17	Oct. 13	179	Apr. 18	Oct. 13	178	Apr. 17	Nov. 2	199			
1902	Apr. 22	Sept. 12	143	Apr. 26	Sept. 12	139	Apr. 26	Sept. 12	139	Apr. 24	Sept. 11	140	Apr. 1	do	215	July 6	Sept. 12	68
1903	Apr. 30	Sept. 15	138	May 3	Oct. 8	158	May 3	Sept. 15	135	Apr 30	Sept. 17	140	Apr. 13	Oct. 31	201	May 31	Sept. 8	100
1904	Apr. 17	Oct. 19	185	Apr. 25	Oct. 19	177	May 9	Sept. 14	128	May 9	Oct. 19	163	Apr. 8	Nov. 5	211	June 5	Sept. 11	98
1905	May 5	Oct. 10	158	do	Oct. 11	169	May 6	Oct. 10	157	Apr. 21	Oct. 11	173	May 11	Oct. 9	151	May 30	Aug. 13	75
1906	do	Oct. 19	167	Apr. 14	Oct. 21	190	do	Oct 5	152	Apr. 14	Oct. 21	190	Apr. 3	Oct. 18	198	June 8	Sept. 13	97
1907	May 3	Apr. 26	176	May 4	do	170	May 27	Oct. 12	138	May 4	Oct. 8	157	May 14	Nov. 6	176	June 10	Sept. 22	104
1908	May 6	Sept. 27	144	Apr. 29	Sept. 27	151	May 21	Sept. 27	129	Apr. 30	Sept. 28	151	Apr. 29	Sept. 27	151	July 7	Sept. 18	73
1909	do	Oct. 9	156	May 2	Oct. 9	160	May 9	Oct. 9	153	May 6	Oct. 23	170	May 1	Oct. 9	161	May 30	Sept. 14	107
1910	Apr. 16	Oct. 20	187	Apr. 16	Oct. 6	173	May 17	Aug. 25	100	Apr. 16	Oct. 6	173	Apr. 17	Oct. 20	186	May 22	Sept. 6	107
1911	do	do	187	May 2	Oct. 16	167	Apr. 21	Oct. 19	181	do	Oct. 19	186	do	Oct. 17	183	May 28	Oct. 4	129
1912	May 14	Sept. 25	134	Apr. 22	Sept. 21	152		Sept. 21		Apr. 20	Sept. 24	157	Apr. 14	Oct. 6	175	June 16	Sept. 10	86
1913	Apr. 25	Oct. 16	174	Apr. 24	Oct. 11	170				Apr. 13	Oct. 10	180	Apr. 24	Oct. 26	185	May 30	Sept. 17	110
1914	Apr. 19	Oct. 14	178	Apr. 19	Oct. 14	178				Apr. 25	Oct. 13	171	Mar. 23	Nov. 11	233	May 24	Sept. 14	113
1915	May 7	Oct. 8	154	May 7	Oct. 9	155	May 21	Oct. 7	139	May 20	Oct. 4	137	May 2	Nov. 10	192	May 20	do	117
1916	Apr. 14	Oct. 5	174	Apr. 9	Oct. 19	193	May 16	Sept. 28	135	May 2	Oct. 18	169	Apr. 20	Oct. 19	182	June 3	Sept. 11	100
1917	May 4	Oct. 18	167	May 6	Oct. 10	165	May 8	Oct. 8	153	May 6	Oct. 11	158	Apr. 30	Oct. 18	171	do	Sept. 26	115
1918	Apr. 24	Oct. 27	186	Apr. 30	Oct. 26	179	May 11	Oct. 24	166	May 11	Oct. 25	167	May 12	Oct. 26	167	May 27	Oct. 8	134
1919	June 2	Oct. 11	131	June 2	Oct. 11	131	Apr. 29	Oct. 5	159	June 1	Oct. 10	131	Apr. 10	Oct. 5	178	June 6	Sept. 22	108
1920	Apr. 13	Oct. 22	192	Apr. 27	Oct. 15	171	May 15	Sept. 26	134	Apr. 29	Sept. 26	150	Apr. 26	Oct. 21	178	May 19	Sept. 6	110
1921	Apr. 18	Oct. 28	193	Apr. 28	Oct. 8	163	May 2	Oct. 3	154	Apr. 26	Sept. 21	148	Apr. 8	Oct. 26	201	June 1	do	97
1922	Apr. 19	Oct. 17	181	Apr. 18	Oct. 17	182	Apr. 28	Oct. 8	163	May 15	Oct. 6	144	Apr. 18	Oct. 22	187	June 3	Sept. 12	101
1923	May 16	Oct. 13	150	Apr. 15	Oct. 14	182	May 15	Oct. 13	151	do	Sept. 28	136	Apr. 4	Oct. 15	194	June 17	Sept. 2	77
1924	Apr. 27	Nov. 6	193	Apr. 28	Sept. 28	153	do	Oct. 5	143	do	Sept. 21	129	Apr. 18	Oct. 12	177	June 20	Sept. 12	84
1925	Apr. 29	Oct. 17	171	Apr. 7	Oct. 18	194	May 5	Oct. 8	156	May 1	Oct. 16	168	Mar. 19	Oct. 19	214	June 13	do	91
1926	Apr. 9	Sept. 24	168	Apr. 3	Sept. 25	175	Apr. 25	Sept. 24	152	Apr. 25	Sept. 24	152	Apr. 1	Oct. 30	212	June 23	Aug. 19	57
1927	Apr. 21	Oct. 12	174	Apr. 21	Nov. 2	195	May 10	Sept. 20	133	Apr. 22	Sept. 28	159	Apr. 15	Nov. 5	204	June 2	Sept. 28	118
1928	Apr. 26	Oct. 17	174	Apr. 14	Oct. 22	191	Apr. 27	Oct. 21	177	Apr. 24	Oct. 16	175	Apr. 9	Nov. 3	208	June 21	Sept. 4	75
1929	May 1	Oct. 22	174	May 2	Oct. 24	175	May 6	Oct. 22	169	May 3	Oct. 21	171	Apr. 11	Oct. 23	195	June 20	Sept. 9	81
1930	May 18	Oct. 17	152	Apr. 1	Oct. 17	199	May 18	Oct. 16	151	May 23	Oct. 16	146	May 10	Oct. 17	160	June 23	Sept. 13	82
1931	Apr. 21	Oct. 30	192	Apr. 22	Oct. 30	191	May 22	Oct. 27	158	Apr. 29	Oct. 21	175	Apr. 4	Oct. 27	206	May 30	Aug. 29	91
1932	Mar. 30	Oct. 18	202	Apr. 28	Oct. 25	180	Apr. 26	Oct. 5	162	May 1	Oct. 3	155	Mar. 31	Oct. 19	202	June 8	Sept. 8	92
1933	Apr. 14	Nov. 4	204	Apr. 14	Oct. 22	191	Apr. 15	Oct. 16	184	Apr. 21	Oct. 1	163	Apr. 14	Nov. 2	202	do	Sept. 16	100
1934	Apr. 6	Sept. 26	173	Apr. 7	Oct. 28	204	Apr. 20	Sept. 15	148	Mar. 23	Nov. 2	224	May 19	Oct. 24	158	June 25	Sept. 3	70

1935	Apr. 26	Oct. 22	179	Mar. 21	Oct. 25	218	May 4	Oct. 5	154		Oct. 26		Apr. 11	Oct. 17	189	July 4	Sept. 7	65
1936	Apr. 6	Oct. 21	198	Apr. 6	Oct. 7	184	Apr. 22	Oct. 7	168	Apr. 30	Oct. 7	160	Apr. 7	Oct. 25	201	June 9	do	90
1937	Apr. 25	Oct. 13	171	Apr. 25	Oct. 19	177	Apr. 30	Oct. 13	166	Apr. 27	do	163	Mar. 30	Nov. 8	223	June 15	Sept. 24	101
1938	May 7	Oct. 19	165	May 8	Oct. 23	168	Apr. 20	Oct. 18	181	Apr. 11	Oct. 20	192	Apr. 7	Nov. 3	210	May 24	Sept. 30	129
Mean	Apr. 26	Oct. 14	171	Apr. 23	Oct. 14	174	May 5	Oct. 5	153	Apr. 29	Oct. 9	163	Apr. 16	Oct. 24	193	June 8	Sept. 12	96
Extremes	Mar. 30 [2]	Sept. 12 [4]	131 [6]	Mar. 21 [2]	Sept. 12 [4]	[6] 131	Apr. 15 [2]	Aug. 25 [4]	[6] 100	Mar. 23 [2]	Sept. 11 [4]	[6] 129	Mar. 19 [2]	Sept. 27 [4]	[6] 151	May 19 [2]	Aug. 13 [4]	[6] 57
	June 2 [3]	Nov. 6 [5]	204 [7]	June 2 [3]	Nov. 2 [5]	[7] 218	May 27 [3]	Oct. 27 [5]	[7] 184	June 1 [3]	Nov. 2 [5]	[7] 224	May 19 [3]	Nov. 11 [5]	[7] 233	July 6 [3]	Oct. 8 [5]	[7] 134

[1] Number of days between last killing frost in spring and first in fall.
[2] Earliest date in spring.
[3] Latest date in spring.
[4] Earliest date in fall.
[5] Latest date in fall.
[6] Shortest growing season.
[7] Longest growing season.

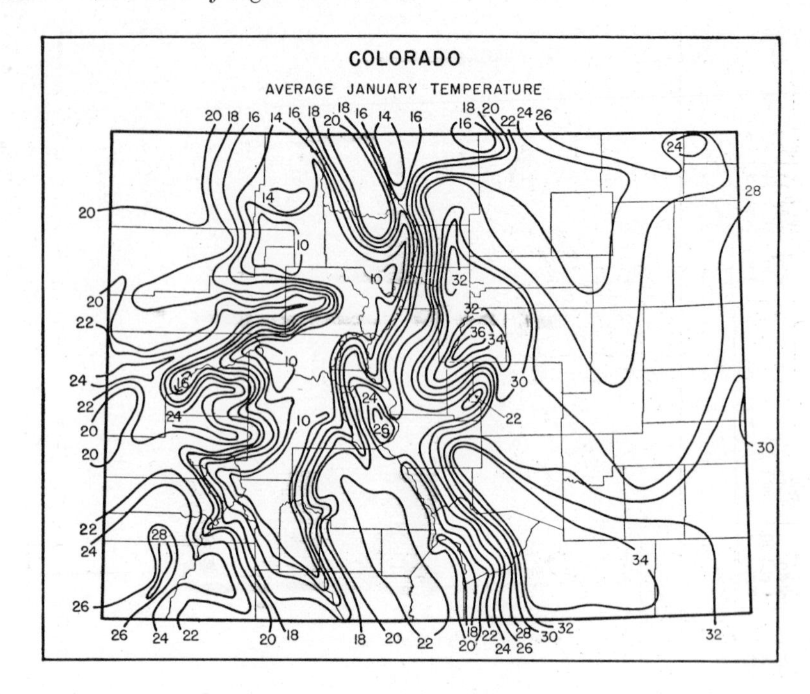
COLORADO
AVERAGE JANUARY TEMPERATURE

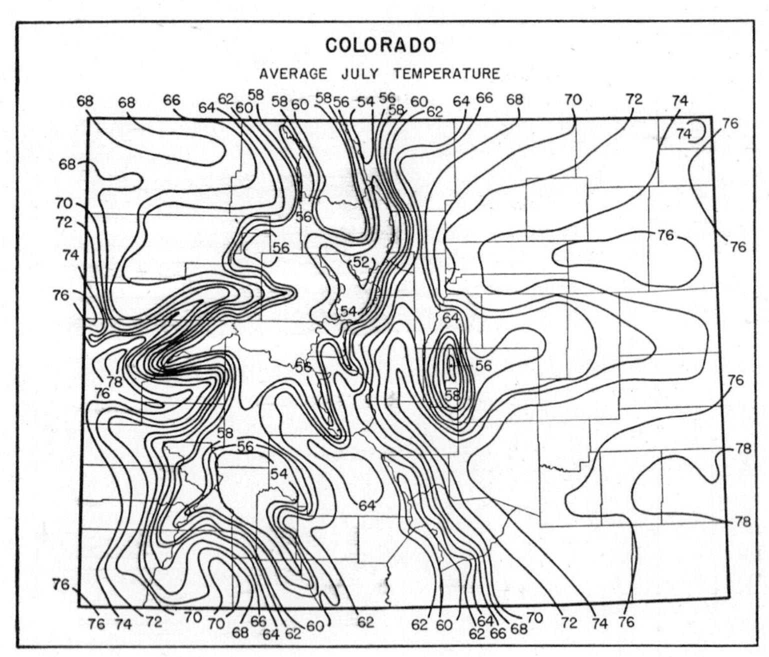
COLORADO
AVERAGE JULY TEMPERATURE

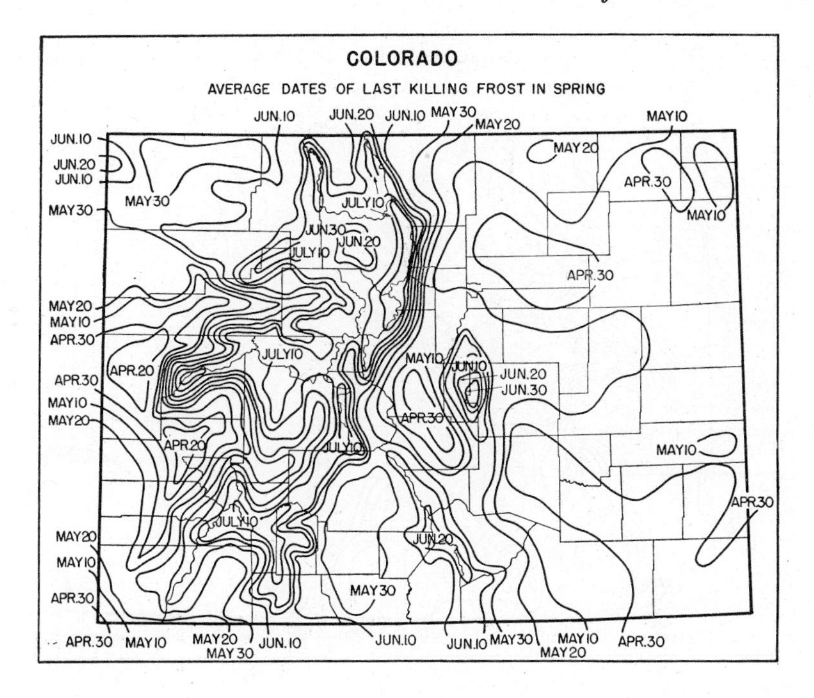
COLORADO
AVERAGE DATES OF LAST KILLING FROST IN SPRING
JUN.10
JUN.20
JUN.10
MAY 30
MAY 20
MAY 10
JUN.10
JUN.20
JUN.10
MAY 30
MAY30
JULY10
JUN.30
JUN.20
JULY10
APR.30
APR.30
MAY20
MAY10
APR.30
JULY10
MAY10
JUN10
JUN.20
JUN.30
APR.20
APR.30
MAY10
MAY20
APR.30
APR20
JULY10
MAY10
APR.30
JULY10
JUN.20
MAY20
MAY10
APR.30
MAY 30
APR.30
MAY10
MAY20
MAY 30
JUN.10
JUN.10
JUN.10
MAY30
MAY 10
MAY20
APR.30

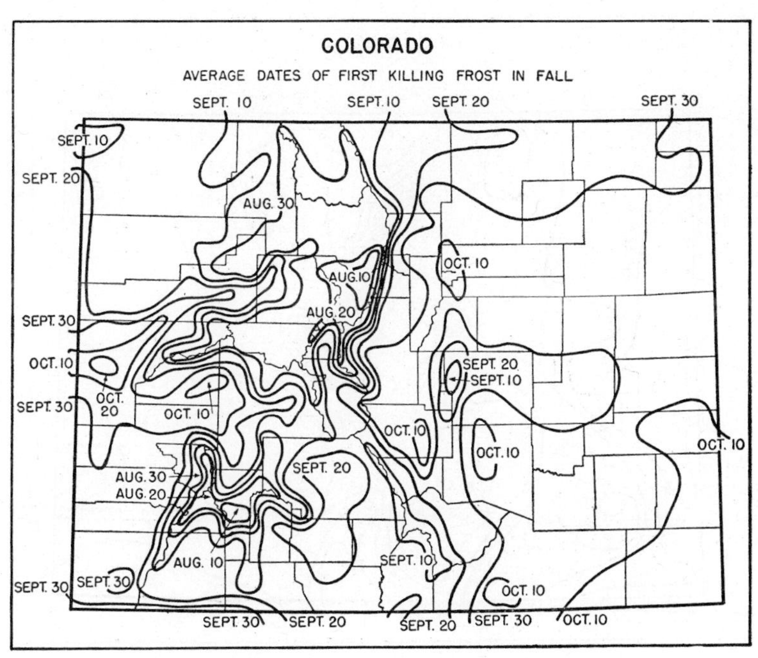
COLORADO
AVERAGE DATES OF FIRST KILLING FROST IN FALL
SEPT. 10
SEPT.10
SEPT. 20
SEPT. 30
SEPT. 10
SEPT. 20
AUG. 30
OCT. 10
AUG.10
AUG. 20
SEPT. 30
OCT. 10
SEPT. 20
SEPT. 10
SEPT. 30
OCT. 20
OCT. 10
OCT. 10
OCT. 10
OCT. 10
SEPT. 20
AUG. 30
AUG. 20
AUG. 10
SEPT. 10
SEPT. 30
SEPT. 30
OCT. 10
SEPT. 30
SEPT. 20
SEPT. 20
SEPT. 30
OCT. 10

298737°—41——52

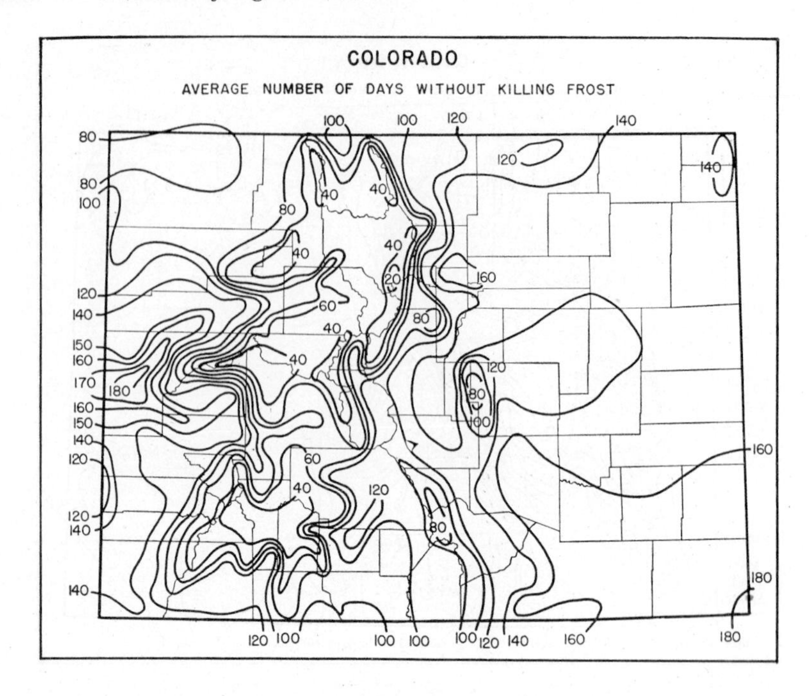
COLORADO
AVERAGE NUMBER OF DAYS WITHOUT KILLING FROST

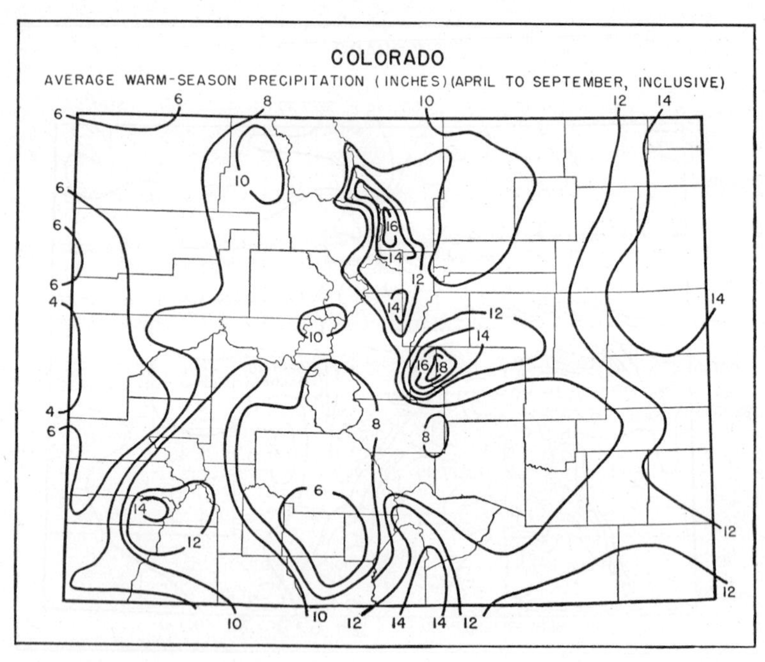
COLORADO
AVERAGE WARM-SEASON PRECIPITATION (INCHES)(APRIL TO SEPTEMBER, INCLUSIVE)

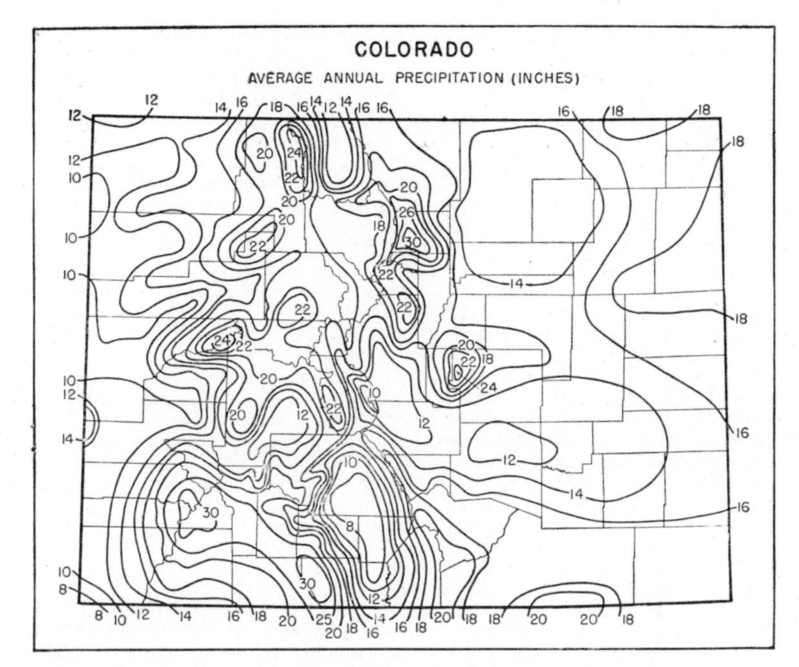

SUPPLEMENTARY CLIMATIC NOTES FOR COLORADO

Nearly half of Colorado is mountainous; the rest is plains and high mesas. About 40 percent of the area of the State is above 7,000 feet in elevation. The northeastern section, with a total area of 32,000 square miles, consists of high, rolling plains with a general slope to the north and east.

By far the greatest part of the northeastern section is drained by the South Platte River and its tributaries. These numerous tributaries, which rise in the mountains, are of great importance as the source of water supply for extensive irrigated districts. Much of the mountain area drained by the South Platte is in a protected location, south of the usual paths of storms, and it does not in general receive heavy snowfall. Therefore the regular flow of the stream is inadequate to irrigate all the lands easily susceptible of irrigation. An area of nearly 30,000 square miles lies in the drainage basin of the Arkansas River, the northern slope of which is characterized by gently undulating plains; on the southern slope similar plains occur east of the Purgatoire River, but the topography is generally more rugged. Agriculture in this valley is almost wholly dependent on irrigation.

The Continental Divide approximately bisects the State from north to south. From the main range, numerous secondary ranges and spurs run in all directions in the western part, forming many mesas and narrow fertile valleys and three large upland parks, called North, Middle, and South Parks. The San Luis Valley is an immense flat basin. The greatest part of the western section is drained by tributaries of the Colorado. Most of the streams in Colorado are perennial, but the volume of water they carry fluctuates greatly, depending on the amount of snow stored in the mountains. Of the principal streams from which a considerable amount of water is diverted for irrigation, the Uncompahgre alone lacks sufficient volume to supply the land dependent on it.

Because of the diversified topography of the State, there is a remarkable variety of climates, great differences often occurring within short distances. Lamar and the summit of Pikes Peak differ by 35° F. in mean temperature—a difference equal to that between southern Florida and Iceland. The average annual snowfall at Cumbres is 264 inches, while at Manassa, less than 30 miles away, it is only 18 inches.

The climate of the plains is distinctly continental. Its general features are low relative humidity; a large amount of sunshine; light rainfall, confined largely to the warmer half of the year; moderately high wind movement; a large daily range in temperature; high day temperatures in summer; and generally in the winter a few protracted cold spells. The climate of the foothills differs from that of the plains in having diminished wind movement, less severe changes in temperature from day to day, and a narrower annual temperature range, with the winter months notably warmer. The distinct climatic feature of the western section, especially of its lower valleys, is the comparative uniformity of the weather from day to day. Severe cold waves, common on the eastern plains, are comparatively rare in the western part of the State.

The decrease in temperature from the eastern boundary westward to the foothills is less than might be expected, owing to the occurrence of mountain and valley winds and the greater frequency of the chinook. The extreme maximum temperatures, on the contrary, are very closely related to the elevation. Below 5,000 feet, day temperatures of 100° F. are not infrequent during summer, but above that elevation readings as high as 100° are very rare. The day temperatures in winter are lower on the western slope than at like elevations east of the mountains. This seems to be due to the comparative rarity of chinook winds on the western slope.

There is a tendency for a high-pressure area to form in western Colorado in winter and to remain stationary for several days. When such a pressure distribution controls the weather, the sky is clear, the day temperatures are moderately high and uniform, and the nights are cold, though seldom excessively so except when the ground is covered with snow and where the air drainage is poor. Night temperatures depend largely on the topography, air drainage exerting a greater control than does the actual elevation. The lowest readings, from —40° to —54° F. are observed in the mountain valleys and parks, where the air tends to become stagnant. In such localities there is almost always an inversion of temperature during cold spells, the greatest cold generally being confined to the lower strata of air whose upper limits do not always reach the higher altitudes.

The mildest weather during cold spells is found below, or near the mouths of, the larger canyons. The comparative freedom from frost in such regions has led to the development of an extensive fruit-growing industry. Above 9,000 feet frost may be expected every month of the year.

Precipitation over the plains decreases from east to west. An important feature is the proportionately large amount of rain that falls in the growing season.

In western sections of the State the most important part of the precipitation occurs in winter and early spring; January, February, and March are the months of heaviest snowfall. There is a substantial increase in precipitation with increase in altitude.

In southwestern counties there is a marked tendency toward drought in late spring and early summer; June is practically rainless. The eastern plains also are visited occasionally by dry spells lasting for several weeks.

The average relative humidity is about 52 percent in the lower western valleys and along the eastern foothills, but it increases to 70 percent near the eastern boundary. The prevailing lack of moisture in the air is favorable to increased intensity of the direct rays of the sun, but the dry atmosphere also facilitates rapid cooling by evaporation, so that even the warmest days are comfortable in the shade and are succeeded by cool nights.

In the lower western valleys the amount of sunshine is great, especially during the summer months, and an abundance of sunshine is received east of the mountains.

The prevailing winds of the plains are from the north or northwest in winter and from the south or southeast in summer. On account of the comparatively level and treeless character of the country, high velocities often occur. At the lower levels of the western slope the wind movement is light and commonly of the mountain-and-valley type. At the summits of the mountains, the winds are generally from the west and are frequently very strong in winter and spring. High winds often interrupt traffic for considerable periods, and their action in drifting and packing the snow is very important. The wind movement is lowest near the foot of the mountains; over the plains it increases toward the east. The velocities are greatest in spring and least in late summer and fall. Below the Royal Gorge, in Fremont County, the mountain-and-valley winds are strong enough to modify materially the climate of a considerable area. The descending current of air is generally sufficient to prevent the stratification necessary for the occurrence of excessive cold. As a consequence, the winter climate is milder there than elsewhere in the State.

Edwin B. Gittings, *Principal Meteorologist and Climatic Section Director for Colorado, Weather Bureau, Denver.*

FLORIDA

Climatic summary

County [1]	Station	Temperature: Length of record	Temperature: January average	Temperature: July average	Temperature: Maximum	Temperature: Minimum	Killing frost average dates [2]: Length of record	Killing frost: Last in spring	Killing frost: First in fall	Killing frost: Growing season [3]	Average precipitation: Length of record	January	February	March	April	May	June	July	August	September	October	November	December	Annual
		Yr.	°F.	°F.	°F.	°F.	Yr.			Days	Yr.	In.	In.	In.	In.	In.	In.	In.	In.	In.	In.	In.	In.	In.
Alachua	Archer	20	56.2	80.8	104	10	20	Mar. 7	Nov. 22	260	19	3.35	3.34	3.09	1.96	3.23	7.56	7.91	7.84	5.92	2.97	2.02	3.98	53.17
	Gainesville	40	57.6	80.7	103	6	40	Feb. 22	Dec. 4	285	40	3.10	3.07	3.27	2.63	3.30	6.79	7.12	6.72	5.39	3.10	1.68	2.93	49.10
Baker	Glen St. Mary	40	55.3	80.9	104	8	40	Mar. 9	Nov. 19	255	39	2.93	3.49	3.86	3.00	4.03	6.70	7.25	6.38	5.33	3.20	1.56	2.88	50.61
Bay	Panama City	39	54.1	81.7	105	4	40	Mar. 1	Nov. 28	272	39	4.03	4.35	3.79	3.80	3.68	4.34	7.39	7.78	6.50	3.81	3.16	4.74	57.37
Brevard	Malabar	25	63.3	81.4	101	21	26	Jan. 21	Dec. 25	338	28	2.67	2.44	2.38	2.28	3.92	5.55	5.87	5.60	6.71	7.35	2.34	2.41	49.52
	Merritts Island	40	62.3	81.2	99	22	39	(11)	(6)		40	2.64	2.63	2.91	2.46	4.00	6.49	6.40	5.36	7.10	6.46	2.48	2.27	51.20
	Titusville	36	61.3	81.5	102	18	36	Jan. 26	Nov. 30	308	38	2.28	2.74	2.84	2.31	4.91	6.76	7.13	6.28	6.87	5.48	2.35	2.36	52.31
Broward	Davie	24	66.3	79.4	99	21	23	Feb. 11	Dec. 22	314	25	2.44	2.16	3.17	4.12	6.23	9.08	7.23	7.32	9.55	8.77	3.34	1.61	65.02
	Fort Lauderdale	26	68.9	81.4	99	28	26	(6)	(2)		25	2.62	1.98	2.99	4.53	6.38	7.99	6.15	6.49	8.43	9.61	3.77	2.04	62.98
Calhoun	Blountstown	21	53.6	81.5	105	12	26	Feb. 28	Nov. 19	264	22	4.12	4.21	3.88	4.94	3.87	6.48	7.74	7.98	5.28	2.39	2.97	4.00	57.86
Charlotte	Punta Gorda	23	64.6	81.5	98	27	24	(3)	(5)		25	1.96	2.23	2.25	2.42	3.86	6.50	7.84	7.36	8.51	3.78	1.76	1.51	49.98
Citrus	Inverness	38	58.5	80.9	102	14	36	Feb. 12	Dec. 9	300	40	2.42	2.72	3.30	2.71	4.12	7.29	8.87	7.70	6.07	2.85	1.82	2.67	52.54
Clay	Middleburg	28	55.3	81.1	107	12	30	Mar. 1	Nov. 27	271	28	2.69	3.28	3.56	2.99	4.86	7.03	7.50	6.54	6.08	4.13	1.58	3.18	53.42
Collier	Everglades	12	67.4	81.8	100	28	12	(2)	(1)		12	1.30	1.20	2.71	1.44	5.93	9.58	8.78	8.31	9.96	3.91	1.17	.76	55.05
Columbia	Lake City	40	55.8	81.0	106	6	40	Mar. 4	Nov. 25	266	40	2.84	3.59	3.74	2.77	3.58	6.78	7.48	6.52	4.92	2.60	1.61	3.17	49.60
Dade	Homestead	27	66.8	80.5	98	26	23	(6)	(4)		23	1.94	1.72	2.17	3.47	7.34	8.22	7.08	8.29	9.18	9.14	2.13	1.20	61.88
	Miami	40	68.0	81.7	96	27	40	(10)	(3)		40	2.45	1.95	2.35	3.38	7.11	7.41	5.29	6.37	8.87	8.98	3.28	1.74	59.18
De Soto	Arcadia	28	63.8	81.5	103	20	30	Feb. 4	Dec. 18	317	39	1.95	2.40	2.63	2.39	4.17	7.08	7.76	8.13	6.95	3.63	1.45	1.76	50.30
Duval	Jacksonville	40	56.8	81.4	104	10	40	Feb. 15	Dec. 11	299	40	2.53	2.88	3.03	2.56	4.30	6.14	6.70	5.68	5.93	4.17	1.58	2.71	48.21
Escambia	Cottage Hill	34	53.0	79.9	108	13	34	Mar. 4	Nov. 18	259	17	5.69	5.14	5.33	4.93	4.85	6.90	8.54	6.55	5.04	5.66	3.12	4.53	66.28
	Molino	16	52.6	79.6	105	13	17	Feb. 27	Nov. 16	262	16	4.67	5.77	5.47	4.84	5.12	5.50	8.20	7.10	7.79	3.40	3.42	6.10	67.38
	Pensacola	40	53.6	80.6	103	7	40	Feb. 16	Dec. 13	300	40	4.27	4.32	4.23	4.62	3.77	4.03	6.61	7.50	5.55	4.84	3.35	4.72	57.81
Franklin	Apalachicola	35	55.4	81.5	104	19	36	Feb. 11	do	305	35	3.78	3.73	3.92	3.57	3.38	4.92	7.42	7.77	8.13	3.24	2.64	4.50	57.00
	Carrabelle	38	54.3	81.4	103	7	39	Feb. 21	Dec. 6	288	38	3.34	3.64	3.79	3.36	2.86	5.35	7.38	7.10	7.64	3.14	2.46	4.12	54.18
Gadsden	Mt. Pleasant	32	54.4	80.3	106	11	34	Mar. 4	Nov. 24	265	33	3.99	4.50	3.98	4.00	3.72	5.24	6.73	6.53	5.57	2.53	2.28	4.13	53.20
	Quincy	24	53.8	80.5	105	12	26	Mar. 10	Nov. 21	256	24	4.31	4.53	4.49	3.98	4.08	5.62	6.28	6.03	4.86	2.66	2.69	4.00	53.53
Glades	Moore Haven	20	64.4	80.6	103	23	20	Feb. 13	Dec. 21	311	21	1.47	1.85	2.25	2.86	4.81	8.12	7.15	7.15	7.07	4.26	1.79	.74	49.52
Hamilton	Jasper	20	53.4	81.1	103	5	22	Feb. 23	Nov. 29	279	20	3.19	4.13	3.67	2.82	4.08	6.46	6.27	6.91	4.41	2.46	2.07	3.57	50.04
Hernando	Brooksville	38	60.4	81.1	104	16	38	Feb. 13	Dec. 9	299	40	2.63	3.01	3.16	2.99	4.16	8.18	9.75	8.10	6.50	3.33	2.02	2.63	56.46
Highlands	Avon Park	37	63.6	81.5	102	21	36	Jan. 12	Dec. 25	347	37	2.18	2.49	2.25	2.56	4.58	8.12	8.06	7.60	6.78	3.97	1.70	1.83	52.12
Hillsborough	Plant City	36	61.3	81.0	104	15	36	Feb. 12	Dec. 10	301	35	2.51	3.09	3.13	2.54	4.57	8.66	8.15	8.40	6.55	2.95	1.56	2.13	54.24
	Tampa	40	61.8	81.6	98	19	39	Jan. 13	Dec. 27	348	40	2.30	2.76	2.58	2.25	3.42	7.01	7.88	7.62	6.28	2.84	1.44	1.97	48.35

[1] The following counties, for which no records are available, are best represented by the stations indicated: Bradford—Raiford; Dixie—Perry; Flagler—Crescent City; Gulf—Apalachicola; Gilchrist—Archer; Hardee—Avon Park; Hendry—Fort Myers; Lafayette—Perry; Liberty—Blountstown; Martin—Fort Pierce; Santa Rosa—Pensacola; Sarasota—Bradenton; Sumter—Brooksville; Suwannee—Lake City; Wakulla—Carrabelle.

[2] Figures in parentheses denote the frequency of observed killing frosts during period indicated.

[3] Length of growing season between average dates of last killing frost in spring and and first in fall.

FLORIDA—Continued

Climatic summary—Continued

County	Station	Temperature: Length of record	Temperature: January average	Temperature: July average	Temperature: Maximum	Temperature: Minimum	Killing frost average dates: Length of record	Killing frost average dates: Last in spring	Killing frost average dates: First in fall	Killing frost average dates: Growing season	Average precipitation: Length of record	January	February	March	April	May	June	July	August	September	October	November	December	Annual
		Yr.	°F.	°F.	°F.	°F.	Yr.			Days	Yr.	In.	In.	In.	In.	In.	In.	In.	In.	In.	In.	In.	In.	In.
Holmes	Bonifay	26	53.3	81.2	107	13	27	Feb. 28	Nov. 26	271	26	4.66	4.97	4.44	4.92	3.76	5.13	7.62	5.53	4.96	2.94	3.44	5.03	57.40
Indian River	Fellsmere	25	63.7	81.0	101	24	25	Jan. 24	Dec. 23	333	27	2.38	2.37	2.42	3.32	4.92	7.00	6.84	6.95	8.92	6.58	2.31	1.74	55.75
Jackson	Marianna	38	52.8	81.0	106	13	37	Mar. 3	Nov. 22	264	39	4.12	4.69	4.42	4.09	3.83	4.92	7.03	5.94	5.30	2.72	2.83	4.62	54.51
Jefferson	Monticello	35	54.0	80.6	109	14	33	Feb. 28	Nov. 25	270	34	4.09	4.21	3.76	3.69	4.15	6.18	6.97	7.30	5.84	2.69	2.46	4.34	55.68
Lake	Clermont	39	61.7	82.7	104	18	38	Jan. 20	Dec. 17	331	40	2.26	2.79	2.84	2.81	4.49	7.21	7.32	6.98	6.60	3.22	1.57	2.11	50.20
	Eustis	40	60.3	82.5	104	16	40	Feb. 7	Dec. 18	314	40	2.54	2.58	2.97	2.73	4.32	6.39	7.43	6.16	5.86	3.45	1.92	2.18	48.53
Lee	Fort Myers	40	64.5	81.1	98	24	40	(7)	(5)		40	1.72	2.26	1.91	1.98	4.14	9.28	8.21	8.35	7.23	4.27	1.31	1.40	52.06
Leon	Tallahassee	40	54.5	80.8	104	−2	40	Feb. 25	Dec. 4	282	40	3.98	4.58	4.06	3.77	3.73	6.55	6.94	6.78	5.40	2.45	2.48	4.17	54.89
Levy	Cedar Key	34	58.4	81.8	101	15	36	Feb. 4	Dec. 15	314	38	2.84	2.74	3.06	2.19	2.55	5.00	7.99	8.43	5.64	2.69	1.73	2.92	47.78
Madison	Madison	36	55.2	81.3	104	14	36	Feb. 25	Dec. 7	285	36	3.28	4.16	3.45	3.28	3.61	5.87	6.98	6.88	5.25	2.52	2.21	3.77	51.26
Manatee	Bradenton	40	62.0	80.7	100	19	38	Jan. 20	Dec. 22	336	40	2.62	2.98	2.38	2.40	3.11	6.66	9.66	9.06	7.62	3.50	1.84	2.17	54.00
Marion	Ocala	39	58.0	81.1	105	12	40	Feb. 18	Dec. 5	290	38	2.55	3.39	3.34	3.28	4.32	7.39	7.98	7.68	5.98	2.89	1.67	2.86	53.33
	Rockwell	19	57.8	82.0	103	18	14	Feb. 21	Dec. 10	292	19	2.77	2.83	2.78	1.90	3.61	6.89	8.85	8.62	5.56	2.60	2.15	2.98	51.54
Monroe	Key West	40	69.9	83.2	100	41	40	None	None		40	1.78	1.48	1.54	1.32	3.83	4.74	3.32	4.48	5.93	6.16	2.08	1.70	38.36
	Long Key	20	70.2	84.2	99	37	20	do	do		20	1.57	1.33	1.52	1.90	3.92	3.46	4.13	6.02	8.04	8.43	2.42	1.71	44.45
Nassau	Fernandina	37	55.8	81.3	103	16	37	Feb. 9	Dec. 17	311	36	2.65	2.99	3.21	2.91	3.59	5.62	5.80	5.23	6.76	4.35	2.14	2.87	48.12
	Hilliard	28	55.1	80.8	105	15	30	Feb. 28	Dec. 1	276	28	2.42	3.09	3.64	2.80	3.92	6.22	8.53	7.32	5.54	3.49	1.66	2.73	51.36
Okaloosa	Garniers	25	53.8	80.6	106	13	26	Mar. 13	Nov. 21	253	25	4.76	4.75	4.81	4.48	3.78	4.19	8.22	7.82	5.52	4.55	3.52	4.82	61.22
Okeechobee	Okeechobee	22	63.7	80.9	99	23	20	Feb. 12	Dec. 21	312	21	1.44	1.89	2.37	3.64	3.94	7.22	6.57	5.98	7.41	4.92	1.99	1.24	48.61
Orange	Isleworth										23	1.79	2.46	3.02	2.92	5.07	7.36	7.15	6.61	6.29	3.28	1.87	1.87	49.69
	McDonald	22	59.8	81.2	102	17	24	Feb. 10	Dec. 15	308	16	2.29	2.07	2.47	2.43	4.75	6.72	7.14	6.02	5.52	4.62	2.41	2.27	48.71
	Orlando	40	61.4	82.0	103	18	39	Feb. 3	Dec. 14	314	40	2.39	2.52	3.05	2.65	4.57	7.35	7.88	6.74	6.97	4.47	1.68	2.18	52.45
Osceola	Kissimmee	36	61.7	81.7	102	19					40	2.31	2.88	3.10	2.62	4.68	6.74	7.63	6.74	5.62	3.93	1.89	2.10	50.24
	St. Cloud	18	62.1	82.0	102	21	19	Jan. 25	Dec. 24	333	20	2.17	2.64	2.92	2.28	4.59	6.07	6.69	6.97	5.99	3.73	2.07	2.42	48.54
Palm Beach	Belle Glade	14	64.1	79.9	100	25	14	Feb. 4	Dec. 23	322	15	1.65	1.70	3.30	3.41	4.14	9.58	7.19	8.12	9.36	4.49	2.75	1.01	56.70
	Hypoluxo	39	67.8	81.2	100	26	36	(7)	(8)		39	3.05	2.92	2.94	3.49	5.03	7.67	5.34	5.51	8.13	9.04	3.63	2.00	58.75
	Jupiter	20	66.4	81.0	99	24	20	(2)	(2)		20	3.76	2.40	3.70	2.81	4.32	6.52	6.03	6.77	8.48	11.16	3.00	2.32	61.27
	Ritta	18	65.0	80.5	98	29	18	(8)	(4)		18	1.42	1.55	2.32	2.56	4.78	5.82	6.44	6.31	6.90	4.76	1.19	1.18	45.23
Pasco	St. Leo	40	60.6	80.7	102	19	39	Feb. 7	Dec. 13	309	40	2.82	3.09	3.23	2.53	4.35	8.47	8.58	8.18	6.92	3.56	2.00	2.39	56.12
Pinellas	Pinellas Park	26	62.1	81.1	100	25	26	(12)	(10)		25	2.48	2.94	2.87	2.67	3.93	6.28	9.04	9.09	8.25	3.76	1.85	2.38	55.54
	St. Petersburg	24	64.1	82.8	98	28	24	(6)	(4)		25	2.25	2.97	2.62	2.83	3.36	4.98	8.63	7.80	7.72	3.66	1.86	2.22	50.90
	Tarpon Springs	40	61.2	81.4	100	19	39	Jan. 30	Dec. 18	322	40	2.41	3.07	2.80	2.34	3.11	5.86	8.66	8.53	6.76	3.36	1.90	2.38	51.18
Polk	Bartow	40	61.8	81.6	102	18	39	Feb. 5	Dec. 13	311	40	2.61	2.94	3.08	2.77	4.92	8.69	8.37	7.63	7.59	3.48	1.64	2.06	55.78
	Davenport	15	63.5	82.2	103	22	16	Jan. 29	Dec. 16	321	16	1.85	2.39	3.48	2.77	4.77	7.08	7.14	6.92	7.25	2.99	1.59	1.40	49.63
	Fort Meade	22	61.1	81.3	102	14	21	Feb. 14	Dec. 14	303	22	3.06	2.99	3.04	2.39	4.59	9.50	9.56	10.15	8.03	4.44	1.78	2.31	61.84
	Lake Alfred	22	62.9	82.4	103	23	22	Jan. 20	Dec. 20	334	14	2.10	2.58	3.10	3.17	4.80	8.17	7.58	7.16	6.99	2.60	1.37	1.52	51.14
	Lakeland	22	63.4	81.5	100	24					24	2.20	2.72	3.46	3.00	5.40	7.78	7.81	7.45	6.62	2.72	1.75	1.79	52.70
	Lake Wales	14	62.9	81.9	104	23					15	2.11	1.70	2.93	2.85	5.46	8.13	7.92	7.91	6.57	2.91	1.05	2.09	51.63

Putnam	Crescent City	37	59.0	81.7	103	13	38	Feb. 13	Dec. 15	305	37	2.44	3.19	3.35	2.76	4.72	7.26	6.74	6.59	5.98	3.94	1.73	2.66	51.36
	Federal Point	40	58.2	81.9	106	13	40	Feb. 9	Dec. 20	314	40	2.53	3.22	3.29	2.81	4.29	6.84	6.89	6.17	6.44	4.70	1.75	2.84	51.77
	Palatka	15	59.4	82.2	103	20	14	Feb. 2	Dec. 16	317	14	2.58	3.12	3.88	3.75	4.74	7.15	7.21	6.10	6.81	3.99	1.67	2.02	53.02
	Satsuma Heights	14	57.7	81.3	103	18	14	Feb. 13	do	306	14	2.24	2.92	2.38	1.99	4.65	6.08	6.89	7.17	4.94	4.47	2.09	3.58	49.40
St. Johns	Hastings	14	58.7	81.0	102	20	15	Feb. 22	Dec. 5	286	15	2.29	2.93	3.13	3.79	3.88	6.81	7.08	6.35	7.29	4.43	1.78	2.23	51.99
	St. Augustine	38	58.0	80.7	104	13	40	Feb. 10	Dec. 19	312	40	2.49	3.46	3.15	2.79	3.50	5.62	5.92	4.97	6.35	5.25	2.11	2.87	48.48
	Switzerland	24	56.1	80.6	102	12	23	Feb. 12	Dec. 16	307	26	2.54	2.99	3.27	2.76	4.14	6.14	7.16	6.42	6.66	4.32	1.64	2.76	50.80
St. Lucie	Fort Pierce	37	65.2	81.5	100	24	38	(11)	(6)		38	2.58	2.28	2.74	3.12	4.36	5.93	5.50	5.12	7.39	7.12	3.03	1.89	51.06
Seminole	Sanford	25	61.6	81.9	102	21	25	Jan. 28	Dec. 23	329	26	2.09	2.35	2.95	2.66	4.29	6.68	7.53	6.35	5.87	4.60	2.06	2.16	49.59
Taylor	Perry	22	54.9	81.7	103	15	24	Feb. 24	Nov. 26	275	9	2.85	3.56	4.20	2.86	3.74	6.16	9.55	7.43	6.66	2.46	3.65	2.20	55.32
Union	Raiford	37	55.9	81.2	104	6	37	Feb. 28	do	271	39	2.77	3.44	3.38	2.87	3.85	6.37	7.20	6.21	5.36	3.06	1.47	3.24	49.22
Volusia	Daytona Beach	15	61.0	80.5	100	24	16	Jan. 21	Dec. 24	337	16	2.00	2.48	3.33	2.64	4.02	6.39	5.76	4.49	5.29	5.39	2.50	2.28	46.57
	DeLand	38	59.7	81.3	102	15	39	Feb. 21	Dec. 9	291	32	2.23	2.77	3.27	2.78	4.75	8.06	7.83	6.68	6.11	4.86	2.12	2.30	53.76
	New Smyrna	38	59.9	80.3	103	16	40	Feb. 5	Dec. 22	320	39	2.55	2.97	3.13	2.19	4.00	6.20	6.01	5.35	6.28	5.81	2.20	2.29	48.98
	Orange City	20	59.2	81.6	103	15	21	Feb. 24	Dec. 6	285	22	2.69	2.91	2.84	2.22	3.92	6.76	6.57	6.86	6.01	4.15	1.96	1.93	48.82
Walton	DeFuniak Springs	36	53.1	80.9	107	0	38	Mar. 2	Nov. 24	267	37	4.61	5.61	5.45	4.69	4.73	6.09	8.64	7.38	5.57	3.42	3.33	4.91	64.43
Washington	Vernon	36	52.8	81.3	107	2	15	Mar. 7	Nov. 17	255	36	4.32	4.67	4.97	4.48	4.60	5.54	7.70	6.55	5.44	2.98	2.96	4.89	59.10

Precipitation and temperature—State unit values

[This tabulation gives the mean annual, mean monthly, and average seasonal precipitation, 1886–1938, and the mean annual temperatures, 1902–38, for Florida]

Precipitation		Precipitation		Precipitation		Precipitation		Temperature		Temperature	
Year	Mean	Year	Mean	Year	Mean	Month	Mean	Year	Mean	Year	Mean
	In.		*In.*		*In.*		*In.*		°*F.*		°*F.*
1886	54.30	1907	48.90	1928	60.25	May	4.02	1902	68.9	1921	70.0
1887	51.72	1908	47.59	1929	59.19	June	6.68	1903	67.8	1922	70.0
1888	54.62	1909	48.37	1930	59.85	July	7.35	1904	68.1	1923	69.0
1889	50.69	1910	51.60	1931	43.36	August	6.91	1905	68.7	1924	68.0
1890	53.62	1911	47.82	1932	52.98	September	6.69	1906	68.8	1925	69.5
1891	47.60	1912	65.27	1933	55.39	October	4.24	1907	69.6	1926	68.0
1892	48.53	1913	48.22	1934	52.94	November	2.23	1908	69.4	1927	70.2
1893	54.24	1914	49.24	1935	52.38	December	2.75	1909	69.2	1928	68.0
1894	53.24	1915	56.15	1936	57.60			1910	67.6	1929	69.3
1895	48.18	1916	47.44	1937	58.52	Annual	52.76	1911	70.7	1930	68.0
1896	50.92	1917	41.33	1938	43.17			1912	68.8	1931	69.2
1897	55.75	1918	50.31					1913	69.2	1932	70.2
1898	49.52	1919	57.50			Season	Average	1914	68.3	1933	70.3
1899	52.65	1920	57.74	Month	Mean			1915	68.9	1934	68.9
1900	60.58	1921	44.91					1916	69.1	1935	69.0
1901	59.00	1922	57.23					1917	67.9	1936	68.9
1902	51.33	1923	50.22		*In.*		*In.*	1918	69.1	1937	68.6
1903	55.57	1924	61.89	January	2.79	Winter	8.65	1919	69.6	1938	69.2
1904	47.99	1925	51.83	February	3.11	Spring	10.01	1920	67.7		
1905	60.45	1926	59.95	March	3.17	Summer	20.94				
1906	53.98	1927	40.78	April	2.82	Fall	13.16				

FLORIDA—Continued

Dates of last killing frost in spring and first in fall, with length of growing season

Year	Pensacola			DeFuniak Springs			Apalachicola			Tallahassee			Gainesville			Jacksonville		
	Last in spring	First in fall	Growing season[1]	Last in spring	First in fall	Growing season[1]	Last in spring	First in fall	Growing season[1]	Last in spring	First in fall	Growing season[1]	Last in spring	First in fall	Growing season[1]	Last in spring	First in fall	Growing season[1]
			Days			*Days*			*Days*			*Days*			*Days*			*Days*
1899	Mar. 8	Dec. 5	272	Mar. 29	Dec. 4	250				Mar. 8	Dec. 5	272	Feb. 15	Dec. 30	318	Mar. 8	Dec. 30	297
1900	Feb. 19	None	316	Mar. 2	Nov. 13	256				Feb. 26	None	309	Feb. 19	None	316	Feb. 25	None	310
1901	Mar. 6	Dec. 15	284	Mar. 17	Nov. 16	244				Mar. 17	Dec. 15	273	Mar. 17	Nov. 17	245	Mar. 7	Dec. 16	284
1902	Feb. 18	Dec. 27	312	Mar. 19	Nov. 28	254				Feb. 18	Dec. 27	312	Feb. 19	Dec. 27	311	Feb. 18	Dec. 26	311
1903	do	Nov. 19	274	Feb. 20	Nov. 19	272		Nov. 19		do	Nov. 19	274	do	Nov. 19	273	do	Nov. 19	274
1904	Feb. 12	Dec. 18	310	Feb. 23	Nov. 16	267	Jan. 30	Dec. 20	325	Mar. 16	Dec. 29	288	Feb. 2	Dec. 16	218	Feb. 12	Dec. 29	321
1905	Feb. 16	Dec. 5	292	Feb. 27	Dec. 4	280	Feb. 16	Dec. 5	292	Feb. 16	Dec. 5	292	Feb. 16	Dec. 11	298	Feb. 16	None	319
1906	Jan. 24	Dec. 23	333	Mar. 21	Nov. 13	237	Jan. 24	Nov. 13	293	Mar. 21	Nov. 13	237	Mar. 21	Nov. 13	237	None	Nov. 13	316
1907	None	Dec. 5	338	Feb. 16	Nov. 14	271	None	Dec. 5	338	Feb. 7	Dec. 5	301	Feb. 9	Dec. 5	299	Feb. 9	Dec. 5	299
1908	Feb. 21	None	315	Feb. 23	Nov. 15	266	Feb. 20	None	316	Feb. 21	None	315	Feb. 22	Dec. 27	209	Feb. 21	None	315
1909	Feb. 1	Dec. 21	323	Feb. 17	Dec. 30	316	Feb. 1	Dec. 23	325	Feb. 1	Dec. 10	312	Feb. 3	Dec. 23	323	Feb. 1	Dec. 10	312
1910	Feb. 19	Dec. 1	285	Feb. 19			Feb. 14	Dec. 2	291	Feb. 19	Dec. 1	285	Mar. 16	Dec. 2	261	Feb. 14	Dec. 2	291
1911	Feb. 23	Nov. 25	275	Feb. 25	Nov. 13	261	Feb. 23	Nov. 25	275	Feb. 24	Nov. 13	262	Feb. 23	Nov. 25	275	Feb. 24	Nov. 25	274
1912	Feb. 22	Nov. 28	280	Feb. 22	Nov. 28	280	Feb. 5	None	331	Feb. 12	Nov. 28	290	Feb. 8	Nov. 26	292	Feb. 5	None	331
1913	Feb. 14	None	321	Jan. 28	Nov. 10	286	Feb. 16	Dec. 9	296	None	Nov. 10	313	Feb. 16	Nov. 10	267	None	Dec. 9	342
1914	Mar. 13	Nov. 20	252	Mar. 23	Nov. 18	240	Mar. 2	Nov. 20	263	Mar. 9	Nov. 20	256	Mar. 23	Nov. 20	242	Mar. 3	Nov. 20	262
1915	Mar. 22	Dec. 3	256	do	Nov. 30	252	Mar. 23	Nov. 30	252	Mar. 23	Dec. 21	273	do	Nov. 30	252	Mar. 23	Nov. 30	252
1916	Feb. 15	Nov. 16	275	Mar. 17	Nov. 16	244	Mar. 17	Nov. 16	244	Feb. 16	Nov. 16	274	Mar. 17	Nov. 16	244	Apr. 10	Nov. 17	221
1917	Feb. 3	Dec. 9	209		Nov. 24		Mar. 6	Nov. 24	263	Mar. 6	Nov. 25	264	Mar. 6	Nov. 24	263	Mar. 6	Nov. 25	264
1918	Jan. 23	Dec. 26	337	Feb. 6			Feb. 24	Dec. 3	282	Feb. 5	Dec. 26	324	Feb. 5	Dec. 29	327	Feb. 6	Dec. 29	326
1919	Feb. 10	Dec. 15	308		Dec. 15		Feb. 11	Dec. 15	307	Feb. 17	Dec. 15	301	Feb. 17	Dec. 16	302	Feb. 17	Dec. 16	302
1920	Mar. 7	Nov. 17	255	Mar. 14	Nov. 13	244	Mar. 8	Nov. 17	254	Mar. 8	Nov. 18	255	Mar. 8	Dec. 29	296	Mar. 8	Nov. 18	255
1921	None	None	365	Apr. 12	Nov. 11	213	None	None	365	None	None	365	None	None	365	None	None	365
1922	Feb. 8	do	327	Mar. 5	Nov. 29	269	Feb. 8	do	327	Feb. 17	do	318	Feb. 8	Nov. 27	292	Feb. 9	do	326
1923	Feb. 19	do	316	Mar. 20			Feb. 19	do	316	Mar. 20	do	287	Feb. 20	Nov. 18	271	Feb. 20	Nov. 18	271
1924	Jan. 14	Dec. 26	347	Mar. 22	Nov. 25	248	Jan. 22	do	344	Mar. 15	Nov. 30	260	Mar. 15	Nov. 26	256	Mar. 16	Nov. 26	255
1925	Mar. 3	Dec. 23	295	Jan. 31	Nov. 23	296	Feb. 12	Dec. 23	314	Mar. 3	Nov. 24	266	Feb. 13	Nov. 24	284	Mar. 3	Nov. 17	259
1926	Mar. 14	None	293	Mar. 14	Nov. 11	242	Mar. 14	Dec. 30	291	Feb. 28	Nov. 11	256	Mar. 15	Nov. 20	250	Mar. 14	Dec. 31	292
1927	Jan. 16	Dec. 9	327	Jan. 17	Dec. 9	326	Jan. 17	Dec. 9	326	Mar. 4	Nov. 19	260	Mar. 4	Dec. 9	280	Mar. 3	Dec. 9	281
1928	Feb. 19	Nov. 26	281	Feb. 20	Nov. 21	275	Feb. 19	do	294	Feb. 20	Nov. 21	275	Feb. 19	Nov. 21	276	Feb. 19	Nov. 27	282
1929	Jan. 7	Dec. 3	330	Feb. 12	Nov. 30	291	Jan. 7	Dec. 20	347	Feb. 12	Nov. 30	291	Jan. 13	Nov. 30	321	None	Nov. 30	333
1930	Jan. 30	Dec. 23	327	Mar. 4	Nov. 1	242	Jan. 24	Dec. 24	334	Mar. 4	Nov. 27	268	Mar. 4	Nov. 27	268	do	None	365
1931	Jan. 20	None	346	Feb. 11	None	324	Jan. 15	None	351	Mar. 10	None	297	Mar. 10	None	297	Jan. 15	do	351
1932	Mar. 13	Dec. 17	279	Mar. 14	Nov. 13	244	Mar. 10	do	297	Mar. 15	Nov. 14	244	Mar. 14	Nov. 13	244	Mar. 14	do	293
1933	Feb. 12	None	323	Feb. 12	Nov. 17	278	Feb. 9	do	326	Feb. 12	None	323	Feb. 9	None	326	Feb. 9	do	326
1934	Mar. 11	Dec. 8	272	Mar. 12	Dec. 8	271	Mar. 11	Dec. 11	275	Mar. 12	Nov. 13	246	Mar. 11	Nov. 13	247	Mar. 11	Dec. 8	272
1935	Feb. 28	Nov. 23	268	Mar. 1	Nov. 23	267	Feb. 28	Dec. 21	296	Mar. 1	Nov. 23	267	Mar. 1	Dec. 3	277	Mar. 1	Dec. 3	277

1936	Feb. 19	None	317	Mar. 19	Nov. 17	243	Feb. 11	None	325	Feb. 19	Nov. 27	282	Feb. 11	Nov. 17	280	Feb. 11	Nov. 28	291
1937	Mar. 16	Nov. 18	247	Mar. 29	Nov. 18	234	None	Nov. 18	321	Mar. 16	Nov. 18	247	None	Nov. 21	324	None	Nov. 21	324
1938	Apr. 10	Nov. 25	229	Feb. 1	Nov. 25	297	Jan. 28	Nov. 25	301	Feb. 26	Nov. 25	272	Feb. 26	Nov. 25	272	Jan. 29	Nov. 28	303
Mean	Feb. 16	Dec. 13	300	Mar. 2	Nov. 24	267	Feb. 11	Dec. 13	305	Feb. 25	Dec. 4	282	Feb. 22	Dec. 4	285	Feb. 15	Dec. 11	299
Extremes	None [2]	Nov. 16 [4]	[6] 229	Jan. 17 [2]	Nov. 1 [4]	[6] 213	None [2]	Nov. 13 [4]	[6] 244	None [2]	Nov. 10 [4]	[6] 237	None [2]	Nov. 10 [4]	[6] 237	None [2]	Nov. 13 [4]	[6] 221
	Apr. 10 [3]	None [5]	[7] 365	Apr. 12 [3]	None [5]	[7] 326	Mar. 23 [3]	None [5]	[7] 365	Mar. 23 [3]	None [5]	[7] 365	Mar. 23 [3]	None [5]	[7] 365	Apr. 10 [3]	None [5]	[7] 365

[1] Number of days between last killing frost in spring and first in fall.
[2] Earliest date in spring.
[3] Latest date in spring.
[4] Earliest date in fall.
[5] Latest date in fall.
[6] Shortest growing season.
[7] Longest growing season.

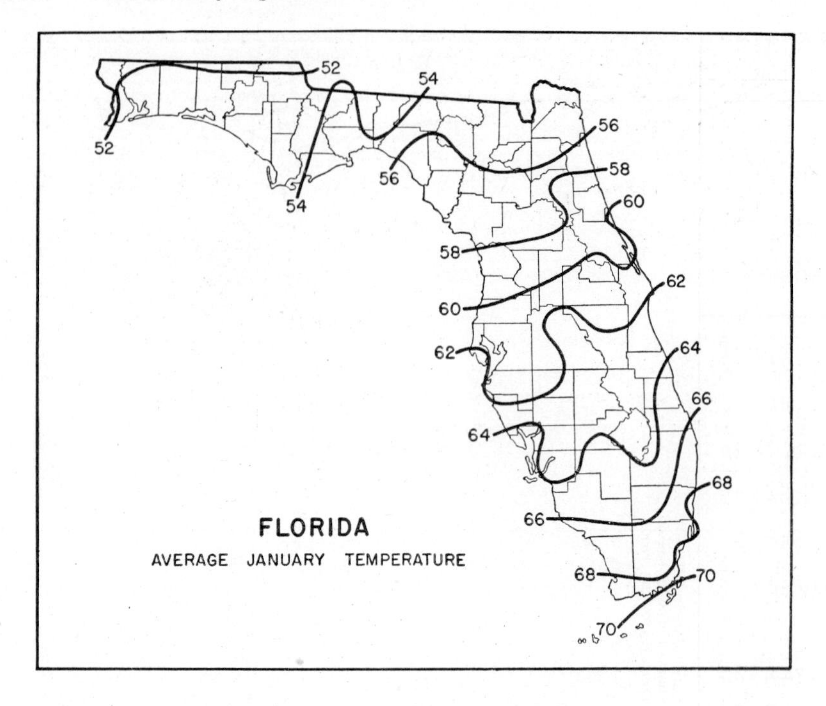
52
52
54
54
56
56
58
58
60
60
62
62
64
64
66
66
68
68
70
70
FLORIDA
AVERAGE JANUARY TEMPERATURE

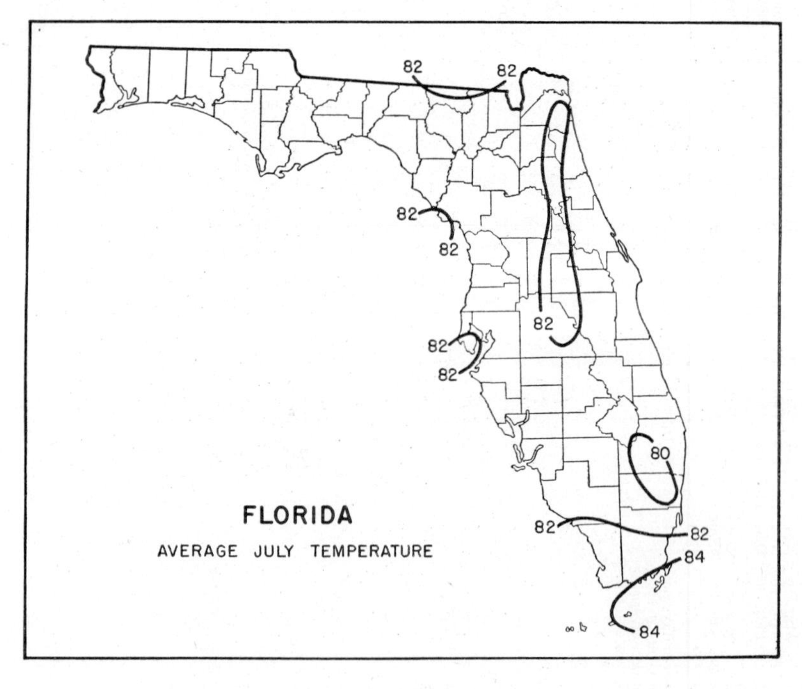
82
82
82
82
82
82
82
82
80
82
84
84
FLORIDA
AVERAGE JULY TEMPERATURE

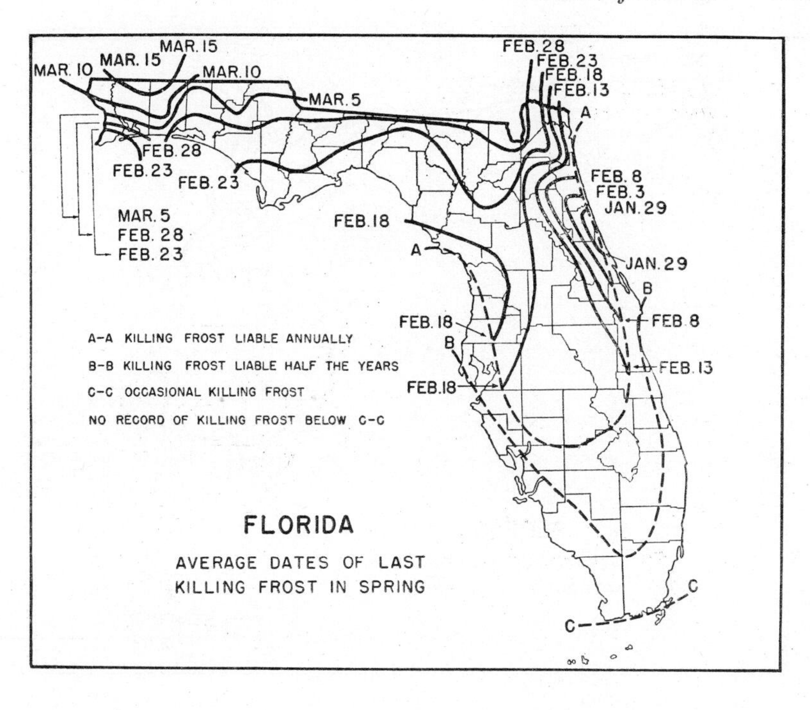
MAR. 10
MAR. 15
MAR. 15
MAR. 10
MAR. 5
FEB. 28
FEB. 23
FEB. 18
FEB. 13
A
FEB. 28
FEB. 23
FEB. 23
FEB. 8
FEB. 3
JAN. 29
MAR. 5
FEB. 28
FEB. 23
FEB. 18
A
JAN. 29
B
FEB. 18
FEB. 8
B
FEB. 13
FEB. 18
A-A KILLING FROST LIABLE ANNUALLY
B-B KILLING FROST LIABLE HALF THE YEARS
C-C OCCASIONAL KILLING FROST
NO RECORD OF KILLING FROST BELOW C-C
FLORIDA
AVERAGE DATES OF LAST
KILLING FROST IN SPRING
C
C

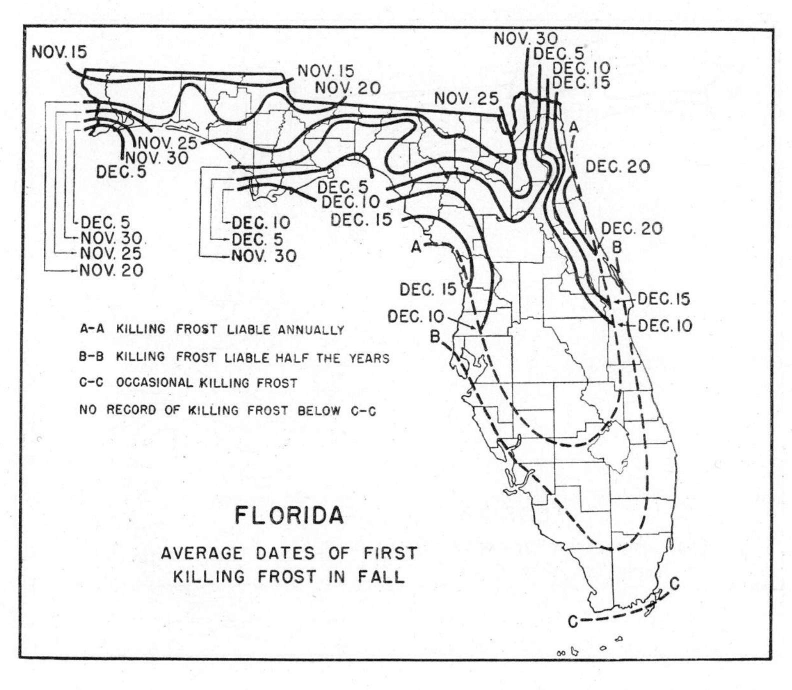
NOV. 15
NOV. 30
DEC. 5
DEC. 10
DEC. 15
NOV. 15
NOV. 20
NOV. 25
A
NOV. 25
NOV. 30
DEC. 5
DEC. 20
DEC. 5
DEC. 10
DEC. 15
DEC. 5
NOV. 30
NOV. 25
NOV. 20
DEC. 10
DEC. 5
NOV. 30
A
DEC. 20
B
DEC. 15
DEC. 15
DEC. 10
DEC. 10
B
A-A KILLING FROST LIABLE ANNUALLY
B-B KILLING FROST LIABLE HALF THE YEARS
C-C OCCASIONAL KILLING FROST
NO RECORD OF KILLING FROST BELOW C-C
FLORIDA
AVERAGE DATES OF FIRST
KILLING FROST IN FALL
C
C

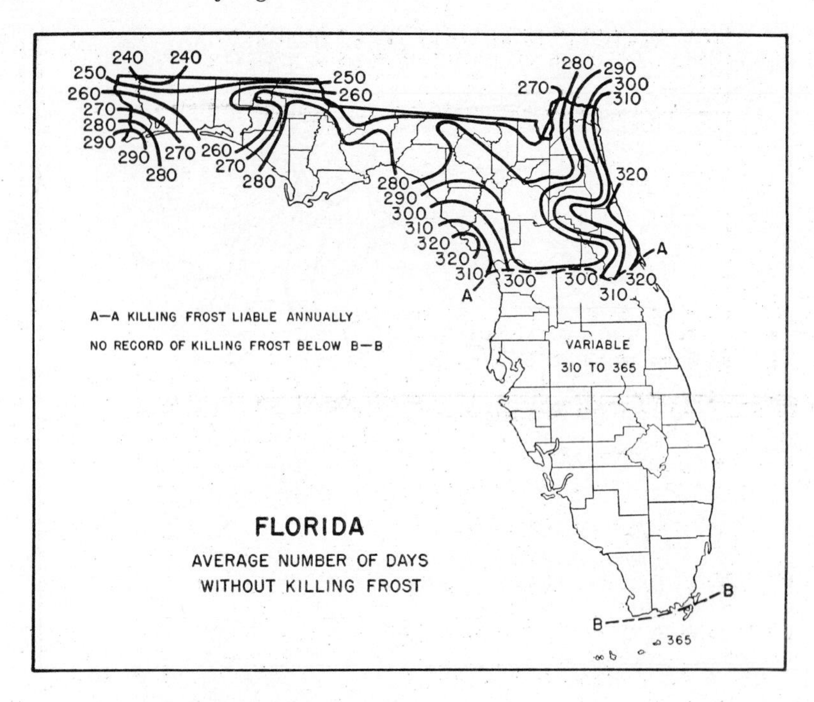
A—A KILLING FROST LIABLE ANNUALLY
NO RECORD OF KILLING FROST BELOW B—B
VARIABLE
310 TO 365
FLORIDA
AVERAGE NUMBER OF DAYS
WITHOUT KILLING FROST

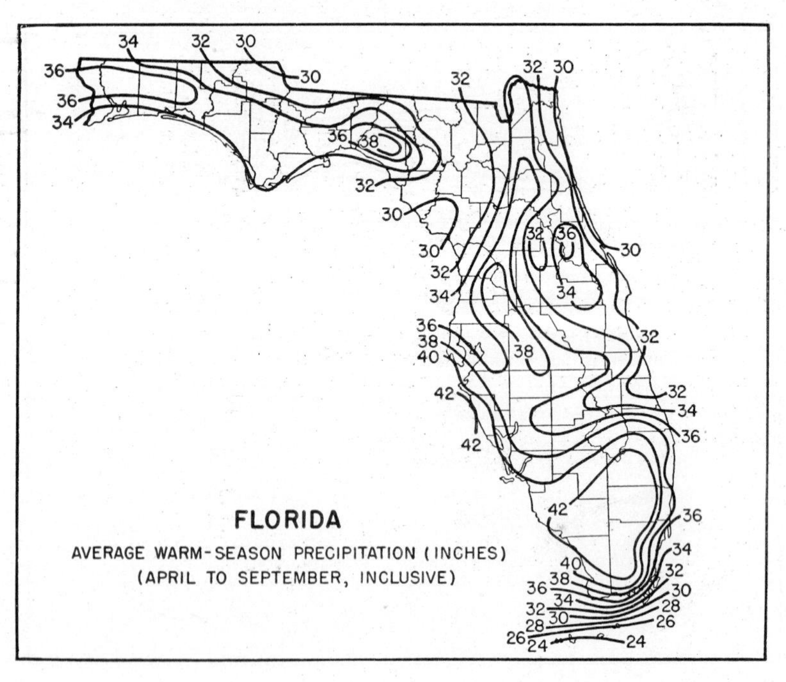
FLORIDA
AVERAGE WARM-SEASON PRECIPITATION (INCHES)
(APRIL TO SEPTEMBER, INCLUSIVE)

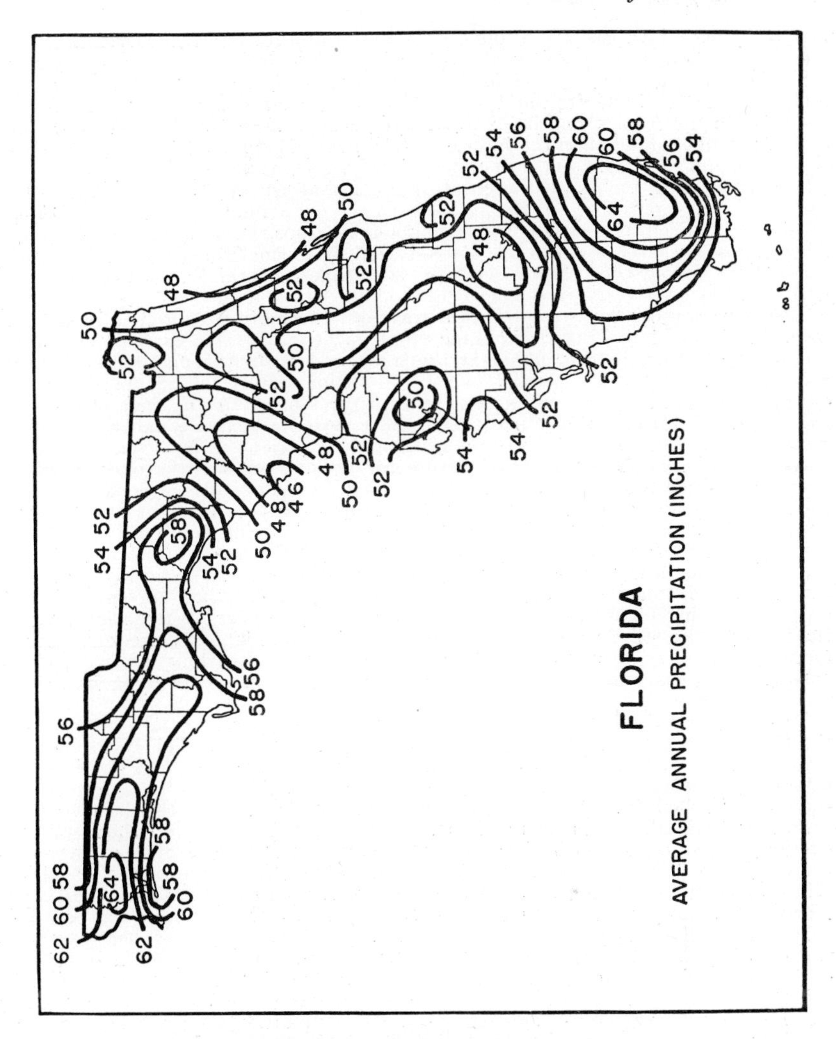

SUPPLEMENTARY CLIMATIC NOTES FOR FLORIDA

Florida is a low-lying subtropical peninsula comprising about 55,000 square miles of land area and surrounded, except on the north, by the waters of the Atlantic Ocean and the Gulf of Mexico. It has some 3,700 miles of indented coast line, the longest of any State, and no point in the State is more than 60 miles from salt water. The highest point in the State is only 325 feet above sea level, and most of the interior ranges in elevation from 50 to about 100 feet. The coastal areas are low and flat and indented by many bays and marshy inlets, while most of the extreme southern part is composed of low swamplands known as the Everglades.

Numerous sluggish streams drain into the Gulf and the Atlantic from an ill-defined divide of relatively low, rolling hills, which extends roughly north and south near the middle of the peninsula. There are numerous shallow lakes throughout the interior, the largest being Lake Okeechobee. Many varieties of soil are found, ranging from the sandy pinelands and marshes of the coastal areas to the darker and more fertile soils of the interior. The reclaimed muck soils of the Everglades and similar soils found locally elsewhere are very fertile.

Citrus and other tropical fruits, many varieties of truck crops, and sugarcane are the principal agricultural products of Florida. The State ranks among the greatest producing areas of the country for winter and spring vegetables and truck crops, although the production of citrus and tropical fruits is by far the largest single agricultural industry. Some kinds of commercial crops are grown in every month of the year. Cotton and tobacco are important in northern counties.

Owing to the tropical marine exposure, the coastal areas are warmer in winter and cooler in summer than the interior. The heat of summer is tempered by sea breezes, while the warm water modifies winter temperatures. It is only occasionally that freezing occurs on the coast of south and central Florida. Afternoon thundershowers prevent the frequent occurrence of extremely high temperatures in summer. From the standpoint of commercial crops the occasional cold waves in winter are of greatest concern, for it is mainly during the winter season that these crops are grown. Many winters—sometimes several in succession—pass without frost or freezing in southern Florida.

The majority of the occasional cold waves of the more severe type in winter bring minimum temperatures ranging from 15° to 20° F. in extreme northern sections to 32° or slightly higher at the southern end of the mainland. These cold spells, however, are usually of short duration, rarely lasting more than 3 days, and even in the coldest periods temperatures nearly always rise above the freezing point during the daytime. Unusually severe cold waves and widespread disaster to fruits and vegetables are occasionally experienced, however.

As the average minimum temperature for the coldest months over most of southern Florida is about 50° F., it requires an active importation of cold air from the Northwest to cause subfreezing temperatures. This is brought about most effectively by an extensive mass of cold polar air moving southeastward over the Plains and eastern Gulf States in conjunction with a mass of moist, tropical air moving north-northeastward along the Atlantic coast. On the night of the arrival of the polar air there is frequently considerable wind movement, and on the following night, when the wind subsides, loss of heat by radiation lowers the temperature still further. Consequently the second night of a freeze is often more damaging to vegetation than the first. On such occasions marked differences in temperatures may occur in places not far apart, depending upon air drainage.

The seasonal distribution of rainfall shows two high points and two low for the year. The principal high point occurs in summer and a slightly secondary high occurs in winter. The minima occur in April and November. There is considerable variation in rainfall from year to year, and stations with long records show that in the wetter years the totals may be double those for the drier years.

Summer rainfall comes mostly in the form of thundershowers, which, on an average, occur on about half the days at any given station. These showers, while usually heavy, frequently last only an hour or two; thus in the so-called rainy season the duration of rainfall is only about 6 to 7 percent of the time. During the remainder of the year rain occurs, on an average, about 1 day in 4.

In practically every part of Florida there are occasional very heavy rains, nearly always associated with tropical disturbances. On the other hand, there have been periods of a month or more with no rainfall at all. These droughts usually occur in spring and autumn at about the time of the annual minimum of rainfall. They may delay or damage crops, but fortunately are of rare occurrence.

Winds of high velocity occur occasionally at all seasons of the year in connection with thunderstorms, but these are of short duration and local in character. Tornadoes also occur, averaging about two a year, but they are usually limited in extent and do very little damage. Tropical storms produce the principal winds of high velocity and destructiveness experienced in Florida, but while, on an average, one of these storms visits some part of the State annually, damage is usually confined to paths averaging 40 to 75 miles wide. It will be seen, therefore, that in any given section of the State many years may go by between such visitations.

As would be expected from the heavy rainfall and proximity to the sea, the relative humidity is high. Days with dense fog average only 12 to 14 a year, and fog is confined almost exclusively to the early mornings in the colder season.

Florida is sunny. The percentage of the possible amount of sunshine is high, and in southern Florida the abundance of sunshine in winter and spring contributes largely to making this section popular as a winter resort.

GRADY NORTON, *Meteorologist and Acting Climatic Section Director for Florida, Weather Bureau, Jacksonville.*

GEORGIA

Climatic summary

County [1]	Station	Temperature: Length of record	Temperature: January average	Temperature: July average	Temperature: Maximum	Temperature: Minimum	Killing frost average dates: Length of record	Killing frost average dates: Last in spring	Killing frost average dates: First in fall	Killing frost average dates: Growing season [2]	Average precipitation: Length of record	January	February	March	April	May	June	July	August	September	October	November	December	Annual
		Yr.	°F.	°F.	°F.	°F.	Yr.			Days	Yr.	In.	In.	In.	In.	In.	In.	In.	In.	In.	In.	In.	In.	In.
Baldwin	Milledgeville	38	47.1	81.5	110	−4	38	Mar. 20	Nov. 8	233	38	4.09	4.47	4.64	3.97	3.20	4.00	5.95	4.59	3.48	2.66	2.38	3.89	47.32
Bartow	Adairsville	26	41.8	78.1	104	−8	25	Apr. 7	Oct. 30	206	25	4.52	5.82	5.53	3.82	4.20	4.02	5.23	4.53	2.95	2.70	2.75	5.27	51.34
Ben Hill	Fitzgerald	21	51.1	82.0	106	−1	21	Mar. 11	Nov. 12	246	22	3.46	4.03	4.49	3.60	3.28	3.86	5.96	5.19	3.89	2.03	1.84	3.01	44.64
Berrien	Alapaha	40	51.2	81.5	107	0	39	Mar. 10	Nov. 17	252	40	3.83	4.31	4.04	3.52	3.35	4.87	5.74	5.39	4.14	2.05	1.87	3.41	46.52
Bibb	Macon	40	46.8	81.2	105	−4	40	Mar. 16	Nov. 11	240	40	3.79	4.45	4.49	3.72	2.85	3.68	5.00	4.34	3.08	2.54	2.36	3.72	44.02
Brooks	Quitman	40	53.6	81.5	108	2	40	Mar. 7	Nov. 15	253	40	3.79	4.43	4.04	3.52	3.89	5.75	7.29	6.65	5.29	2.24	2.14	4.08	53.11
Bulloch	Brooklet	39	50.0	82.0	107	2	39	Mar. 15	do	245	39	2.99	3.61	3.72	3.23	3.64	6.34	5.86	5.73	4.86	2.22	2.22	3.04	47.46
Burke	Waynesboro	23	48.0	80.3	107	−1	23	Mar. 27	Nov. 8	226	23	2.95	4.10	3.68	2.96	2.93	5.03	5.51	4.94	3.22	2.41	2.24	3.16	43.13
Calhoun	Morgan	13	48.2	81.2	104	−2	12	Mar. 12	Nov. 9	242	13	3.98	5.80	5.10	4.14	3.46	4.16	5.46	4.94	3.65	2.15	2.55	4.04	49.43
Camden	St. Marys	11	53.7	81.3	106	16	11	Mar. 2	Nov. 23	266	11	2.73	2.97	2.94	2.55	5.11	4.99	7.29	6.01	7.85	5.17	1.63	3.07	52.31
Charlton	St. George	23	55.5	81.1	108	15	23	Mar. 6	Nov. 24	263	23	2.65	3.02	3.14	2.52	3.68	6.53	7.26	7.63	5.41	2.70	1.70	3.12	49.36
Chatham	Savannah	40	52.7	81.2	105	8	40	Feb. 28	Nov. 28	273	40	2.53	3.27	2.92	2.40	3.21	4.77	6.64	6.55	5.72	2.48	1.80	2.38	44.67
Chattooga	Gore	15	42.0	77.7	104	−10	15	Apr. 13	Oct. 22	192	15	3.95	6.23	6.90	4.50	4.37	4.68	5.04	4.75	3.40	3.07	2.91	6.02	55.82
Cherokee	Canton										40	4.94	5.40	5.47	4.59	3.85	4.02	5.44	4.76	2.79	3.30	3.14	5.87	53.57
Clarke	Athens	40	44.1	79.9	108	−3	40	Apr. 2	Nov. 5	217	40	4.47	5.16	4.94	4.20	3.47	4.13	5.01	4.61	3.16	3.27	2.53	4.90	49.85
Clay	Fort Gaines	40	50.2	81.0	106	−2	40	Mar. 12	Nov. 14	247	40	4.61	5.22	4.78	4.25	3.62	4.43	6.06	5.41	3.59	2.53	2.75	4.71	51.96
Clinch	Fargo	11	56.0	82.3	106	13	11	Mar. 4	Nov. 12	253	11	3.31	3.62	4.03	3.46	3.38	6.42	6.60	5.70	6.66	1.91	1.97	2.51	49.57
Cobb	Lost Mountain	20	43.0	78.2	102	0	20	Apr. 6	Oct. 30	207	19	4.43	5.11	5.25	3.86	3.92	4.13	4.94	4.63	2.97	3.18	2.78	5.39	50.59
Colquitt	Moultrie	13	55.1	82.0	104	15	13	Mar. 1	Nov. 24	268	13	3.26	3.63	4.46	3.64	2.29	4.50	6.45	6.55	4.53	2.25	2.17	2.96	46.69
Coweta	Newnan	40	45.2	79.9	108	−9	39	Mar. 26	Nov. 9	228	40	4.84	5.50	5.75	4.23	3.61	4.11	4.75	4.56	2.82	2.90	2.93	5.14	51.14
Decatur	Bainbridge	40	52.4	81.8	109	1	38	Mar. 10	Nov. 15	250	40	3.94	4.49	4.26	3.75	3.65	4.87	6.15	6.09	4.62	2.33	2.27	4.02	50.44
Dodge	Eastman	40	51.4	82.2	109	−2	37	Mar. 13	Nov. 14	246	40	4.01	4.67	4.77	3.49	3.28	4.21	6.20	4.93	3.86	2.66	2.44	3.55	48.07
Dougherty	Albany	40	51.5	82.2	106	−2	39	Mar. 12	Nov. 16	249	40	4.23	4.83	4.69	4.02	3.94	4.49	6.16	5.77	3.64	2.34	2.27	3.87	50.25
Early	Blakely	40	51.7	81.1	110	−1	40	Mar. 15	Nov. 14	244	38	4.47	5.37	5.00	4.49	3.61	4.36	6.88	5.64	4.03	2.52	2.84	4.60	53.81
Elbert	Elberton	17	44.6	79.8	109	−2	17	Apr. 2	Oct. 30	211	16	3.80	6.26	5.07	3.75	3.29	4.93	4.80	5.16	3.67	2.98	2.53	4.93	51.17
Emanuel	Stillmore	15	52.0	81.2	106	11	15	Mar. 9	Nov. 15	251	14	3.09	3.54	4.43	3.87	3.34	4.94	7.43	5.08	4.67	2.38	2.01	2.79	47.57
Fannin	Blue Ridge	12	40.4	74.0	101	−5	11	Apr. 19	Oct. 20	184	15	4.83	4.93	7.01	5.57	4.52	4.35	5.20	4.63	2.92	2.63	3.51	6.11	56.21

[1] The following counties, for which no records are available, are best represented by the stations indicated: Appling, Montgomery, Toombs, and Wheeler—Hazlehurst; Atkinson and Cook—Alapaha; Bacon, Brantley, and Pierce—Waycross; Baker, Lee, and Terrell—Albany; Banks, Forsyth, Franklin, and Jackson—Gainesville; Barrow, Morgan, Oconee, and Oglethorpe—Athens; Bleckley, Johnson, Treutlen, and Wilkinson—Dublin; Bryan—Savanah; Butts—Monticello; Candler and Screven—Miller; Carroll—Tallapoosa; Catoosa, Dade, Polk, Walker, and Whitfield—Rome; Chattahoochee—Columbus; Clayton, De Kalb, Douglas, Henry, and Paulding—Atlanta; Coffee, Crisp, Irwin, and Turner—Fitzgerald Columbia and McDuffie—Augusta; Crawford, Houston, Jones, and Twiggs—Macon; Dawson, Pickens, Union, and White—Dahlonega; Dooly, Schley, and Webster—Americus; Echols and Lanier—Valdosta; Effingham—Brooklet; Evans, Liberty, and Long—Glennville; Fayette and Heard—Newman; Glascock and Hancock—Warrenton; Grady and Mitchell—Thomasville; Miller and Seminole—Bainbridge; Quitman and Randolph—Ft. Gaines; Rockdale and Walton—Covington; Taliaferro—Greensboro; Towns—Clayton; Upson—Fairview.

[2] Length of growing season between average dates of last killing frost in spring and first in fall.

GEORGIA—Continued

Climatic summary—Continued

County	Station	Temperature					Killing frost average dates				Average precipitation													
		Length of record	January average	July average	Maximum	Minimum	Length of record	Last in spring	First in fall	Growing season	Length of record	January	February	March	April	May	June	July	August	September	October	November	December	Annual
		Yr.	*°F.*	*°F.*	*°F.*	*°F.*	*Yr.*			*Days*	*Yr.*	*In.*	*In.*	*In.*	*In.*	*In.*	*In.*	*In.*	*In.*	*In.*	*In.*	*In.*	*In.*	*In.*
Floyd	Rome	40	43.4	79.9	107	−7	40	Mar. 31	Nov. 3	217	40	5.06	5.56	5.87	4.67	4.13	4.49	4.96	4.55	2.83	3.18	3.26	5.65	54.21
Fulton	Atlanta	40	44.0	78.5	103	−8	40	Mar. 23	Nov. 9	231	40	4.47	4.83	5.12	4.00	3.62	3.63	4.40	3.99	2.89	2.90	2.80	4.93	47.58
Gilmer	Diamond	15	40.4	74.5	100	−12	15	Apr. 11	Oct. 22	194	15	5.19	6.90	7.21	5.12	5.18	6.21	5.74	6.11	4.25	3.00	3.17	6.43	64.51
Glynn	Brunswick	30	54.0	81.8	103	13	25	Mar. 2	Dec. 3	276	30	2.66	3.54	3.11	2.93	3.56	5.59	7.68	6.29	7.00	3.44	1.74	2.59	50.13
Gordon	Resaca							Apr. 13	Oct. 26	196	40	5.06	5.49	5.83	4.85	3.88	4.09	5.17	4.23	2.64	3.28	3.36	5.76	53.64
Greene	Greensboro	37	45.1	79.8	107	5	37	Mar. 30	Nov. 4	219	37	4.24	4.57	4.51	4.09	3.29	4.07	5.18	4.87	3.42	2.91	2.54	4.16	47.85
Gwinnett	Norcross										23	5.02	4.97	5.10	3.93	4.05	3.82	5.66	4.17	2.67	3.26	3.05	5.76	51.46
Habersham	Cornelia	20	43.0	77.2	103	0	20	Apr. 4	Nov. 4	214	20	5.90	5.29	5.35	5.45	4.80	3.44	5.91	4.49	4.16	3.59	4.19	6.67	59.24
Hall	Gainesville	40	41.7	77.3	106	−6	40	Apr. 1	Oct. 31	213	40	4.87	5.38	5.52	4.23	3.94	4.14	5.38	4.46	3.48	3.24	3.05	5.27	52.96
Haralson	Tallapoosa	40	43.3	77.9	107	−12	40	Apr. 8	do	206	40	4.67	5.22	5.35	4.82	3.77	4.06	5.16	4.52	3.38	2.92	3.05	5.38	52.30
Harris	Goat Rock										26	4.18	4.20	4.83	4.11	2.65	2.76	5.45	3.75	2.15	2.44	2.65	4.25	43.42
Hart	Hartwell	38	44.1	79.5	109	3	38	Apr. 2	Nov. 2	214	38	4.22	4.77	4.51	3.96	3.55	3.77	4.81	4.73	3.30	3.16	2.62	4.89	48.29
Jasper	Monticello	39	45.9	80.5	109	3	39	Mar. 23	Nov. 10	232	39	4.42	5.33	5.22	4.34	3.47	4.88	5.22	4.84	3.43	3.12	2.59	4.55	51.41
Jeff Davis	Hazlehurst	20	52.0	81.6	107	14	20	Mar. 8	Nov. 18	255	20	3.69	4.00	4.15	3.24	3.43	5.48	7.29	6.02	5.05	1.98	1.97	3.16	49.46
Jefferson	Louisville	36	47.8	80.8	105	−2	36	Mar. 18	Nov. 8	235	35	3.34	4.25	3.95	3.70	3.57	4.22	5.43	4.69	2.82	2.69	2.30	3.31	44.27
Jenkins	Millen	40	49.3	81.9	108	2	40	Mar. 22	Nov. 10	233	40	3.39	3.98	3.80	3.32	3.18	4.90	6.18	4.53	3.66	2.31	2.05	3.42	44.72
Lamar	Fairview	24	47.8	79.6	104	5	30	do	do	233	24	4.48	4.43	5.25	4.22	3.31	3.79	5.40	4.20	3.04	2.65	2.41	4.09	47.27
Laurens	Dublin	27	49.7	81.1	108	8	27	Mar. 17	do	238	40	4.10	4.48	4.46	3.43	3.54	4.89	5.67	4.91	3.91	2.47	2.49	3.81	48.16
Lincoln	Lisbon	26	46.0	80.2	110	7	21	Apr. 4	Oct. 29	208	26	3.96	4.46	4.43	3.09	3.40	3.85	5.03	4.23	3.36	2.32	2.22	4.10	44.45
Lowndes	Valdosta	24	54.0	81.4	105	12	24	Mar. 14	Nov. 16	247	24	3.52	4.02	3.59	3.56	3.65	5.45	6.32	6.25	4.64	2.09	1.95	4.19	49.23
Lumpkin	Dahlonega	40	42.0	76.0	102	−11	40	Apr. 8	Oct. 30	205	40	5.64	5.86	5.92	4.89	4.85	4.63	5.48	5.12	3.89	3.80	3.58	6.85	60.51
Macon	Marshallville	37	48.8	81.4	107	−3	37	Mar. 18	Nov. 9	236	37	4.90	5.31	5.22	3.93	3.62	4.34	5.90	4.69	3.51	2.90	2.97	4.46	51.75
Madison	Carlton Bridge	40	44.1	79.2	109	−4	39	Apr. 3	Nov. 1	212	39	4.88	5.36	5.18	4.12	3.59	4.60	4.67	4.69	3.81	3.29	3.25	5.19	52.63
Marion	Putnam	19	48.4	80.9	107	−3	19	Mar. 27	Nov. 3	221	19	3.67	5.72	5.00	3.70	3.09	3.67	5.05	4.63	3.63	2.49	2.39	4.08	47.12
McIntosh	Valona	15	51.6	81.2	105	5	15	Mar. 7	Nov. 19	257	15	2.81	3.53	3.42	2.66	3.80	5.07	6.32	7.61	5.76	4.06	2.13	2.71	49.88
Meriwether	Woodbury	9	43.5	78.9	103	5	12	Mar. 29	Nov. 3	219	38	4.14	5.00	5.51	4.06	3.28	4.25	5.77	4.17	3.08	2.63	2.42	4.41	48.72
Monroe	Forsyth	10	45.6	80.6	106	6	10	Mar. 25	do	223	10	2.93	5.73	5.24	3.96	3.87	5.08	4.38	5.06	3.86	2.43	2.65	5.31	50.50
Murray	Ramhurst	23	43.4	76.6	104	−10	23	Apr. 15	Oct. 24	192	23	4.50	5.76	5.68	4.13	3.99	5.25	5.22	5.17	3.19	3.05	3.10	5.41	54.45
Muscogee	Columbus	40	48.9	82.1	106	− 3	40	Mar. 12	Nov. 16	249	40	4.35	5.34	5.41	4.14	3.16	3.61	5.72	4.32	2.60	2.81	2.51	4.70	48.67
Newton	Covington	25	44.5	80.0	107	−10	22	Mar. 31	Nov. 4	218	40	4.49	5.40	5.06	4.22	3.71	4.24	4.91	4.25	2.93	3.01	2.70	4.85	49.77
Peach	Ft. Valley	18	48.7	80.8	107	7	18	Mar. 15	Nov. 15	245	18	4.61	4.15	5.22	4.31	3.47	4.48	5.48	4.75	3.23	2.88	2.58	3.85	49.01
Pike	Concord	6	47.0	78.7	103	5	6	Apr. 2	Nov. 5	217	26	4.77	4.64	6.21	4.20	3.24	4.08	6.04	4.34	2.90	2.80	2.57	4.54	50.33
Pulaski	Hawkinsville	40	49.2	81.6	110	−3	40	Mar. 12	Nov. 11	244	40	4.29	4.44	4.65	3.37	3.25	4.34	5.44	4.63	3.46	2.44	2.30	3.51	46.12
Putnam	Eatonton	23	45.9	79.7	106	2	23	Apr. 2	Nov. 5	217	23	4.24	4.67	4.90	3.70	3.77	3.97	4.72	4.67	3.36	2.82	2.24	4.11	47.17
Rabun	Clayton	39	40.9	73.6	102	−9	39	Apr. 15	Oct. 23	191	38	6.35	6.16	7.06	5.79	5.03	5.86	6.79	6.42	5.22	4.46	4.26	7.56	70.96
Richmond	Augusta	40	48.1	81.3	106	3	40	Mar. 16	Nov. 13	242	40	3.49	4.18	3.81	3.34	3.07	4.40	4.82	4.67	3.22	2.62	2.24	3.34	43.20
Spalding	Griffin	40	46.6	79.7	108	−7	38	Mar. 28	Nov. 9	226	40	4.37	5.32	5.40	4.20	3.11	3.90	5.04	4.57	3.11	2.75	2.54	4.70	49.01

Stephens	Toccoa	40	43.2	78.2	107	−2	40	Apr. 5	Nov. 3	212	40	5.20	5.55	5.73	4.67	4.01	4.37	5.41	5.65	3.98	4.17	3.32	6.20	58.26
Stewart	Lumpkin	20	48.4	80.6	106	−5	20	Mar. 21	Nov. 9	233	20	4.24	5.64	4.84	4.48	3.12	3.34	4.56	4.66	3.02	2.39	2.70	4.68	47.67
Sumter	Americus	40	48.5	81.2	111	−6	40	Mar. 17	Nov. 15	243	40	4.49	5.19	5.11	3.74	3.69	3.91	5.47	5.17	3.44	2.54	2.62	3.94	49.31
Talbot	Talbotton	39	48.1	80.2	110	−6	39	Mar. 24	Nov. 9	230	39	4.25	5.37	5.67	4.32	3.65	4.20	5.22	4.21	3.20	2.91	2.82	4.73	50.55
Tattnall	Glennville	34	52.5	81.5	106	11	34	Mar. 6	Nov. 19	258	34	2.77	3.43	3.27	2.76	3.21	5.16	6.46	6.20	5.54	2.22	1.98	3.02	46.02
Taylor	Butler										31	4.22	5.05	5.10	4.17	3.73	4.67	6.08	5.18	3.91	2.68	2.78	4.34	51.91
Telfair	Lumber City										30	3.88	3.93	4.12	3.11	3.02	5.10	6.42	5.82	4.13	2.17	2.15	2.97	46.82
Thomas	Thomasville	40	53.4	80.8	106	2	39	Mar. 6	Nov. 20	259	40	3.93	4.53	4.16	3.46	3.63	5.49	6.94	5.76	5.32	2.47	2.22	4.03	51.94
Tift	Tifton	18	52.4	80.9	106	12	17	do	Nov. 17	256	22	4.55	3.85	4.59	3.75	3.32	4.46	6.45	5.43	3.73	2.46	1.99	3.75	48.33
Troup	West Point	40	45.8	80.6	106	−5	39	Mar. 25	Nov. 8	228	40	4.41	5.47	5.72	4.60	3.75	4.27	5.40	4.75	2.85	2.72	2.89	5.24	52.07
Ware	Waycross	40	53.4	81.9	106	4	39	Mar. 9	Nov. 18	254	40	3.06	4.06	3.37	2.87	3.79	6.22	6.95	5.68	4.58	2.54	2.02	2.84	47.98
Warren	Warrenton	40	47.0	80.5	108	−2	38	Mar. 24	Nov. 10	231	40	4.09	4.79	4.40	3.85	3.03	4.04	4.94	4.39	3.74	2.92	2.59	3.82	46.60
Washington	Harrison	17	47.4	80.6	103	−2	17	Mar. 29	Nov. 3	219	17	3.37	5.22	4.43	3.33	3.27	5.45	4.47	5.02	3.25	2.84	2.69	3.98	47.32
Wayne	Jesup	10	50.9	82.1	104	1	10	Mar. 14	Nov. 13	244	10	3.45	4.95	3.46	2.29	4.56	5.60	6.07	6.71	3.23	2.87	1.89	3.35	48.43
Wilcox	Abbeville										36	3.85	4.19	3.96	3.41	3.45	3.90	6.72	4.76	3.96	2.03	2.37	3.27	45.87
Wilkes	Washington	40	45.5	80.5	109	−4	38	Mar. 28	Nov. 8	225	40	4.25	5.03	4.56	4.10	3.27	4.24	5.34	4.35	3.86	3.00	2.46	4.21	48.67
Worth	Poulan	18	50.3	80.2	108	−1	18	Mar. 16	Nov. 10	239	18	3.80	4.84	4.44	3.47	3.50	4.46	7.10	6.39	3.26	2.61	1.86	3.74	49.47

Precipitation and temperature—State unit values

[This tabulation gives the mean annual, mean monthly, and average seasonal precipitation, 1886–1938, and the mean annual temperatures, 1902–38, for Georgia]

Precipitation		Precipitation		Precipitation		Precipitation		Temperature		Temperature	
Year	Mean	Year	Mean	Year	Mean	Month	Mean	Year	Mean	Year	Mean
	In.		*In.*		*In.*		*In.*		°*F.*		°*F.*
1886	52.85	1907	48.67	1928	59.56	May	3.51	1902	63.6	1921	66.1
1887	50.11	1908	50.25	1929	70.37	June	4.47	1903	62.6	1922	65.6
1888	58.93	1909	48.62	1930	45.68	July	5.86	1904	62.7	1923	64.3
1889	48.68	1910	43.86	1931	37.39	August	5.22	1905	63.3	1924	62.8
1890	47.46	1911	47.43	1932	58.32	September	3.76	1906	63.6	1925	65.6
1891	50.30	1912	63.21	1933	41.72	October	2.79	1907	64.2	1926	63.6
1892	51.39	1913	46.67	1934	48.36	November	2.66	1908	64.4	1927	65.9
1893	46.83	1914	45.70	1935	44.64	December	4.16	1909	64.0	1928	63.2
1894	49.55	1915	49.58	1936	58.87			1910	63.0	1929	64.1
1895	51.60	1916	43.67	1937	52.52	Annual	50.16	1911	65.6	1930	63.5
1896	44.73	1917	47.54	1938	42.06			1912	62.9	1931	64.9
1897	49.15	1918	49.31					1913	64.1	1932	65.1
1898	54.54	1919	55.27	Month	Mean	Season	Average	1914	63.3	1933	65.6
1899	44.75	1920	60.14					1915	63.7	1934	64.0
1900	57.56	1921	41.08					1916	64.1	1935	64.3
1901	57.55	1922	55.26					1917	62.4	1936	64.4
1902	50.14	1923	52.72		*In.*		*In.*	1918	64.3	1937	63.9
1903	53.79	1924	54.15	January	4.31	Winter	13.29	1919	65.0	1938	65.0
1904	36.84	1925	41.01	February	4.82	Spring	12.11	1920	62.9		
1905	50.47	1926	50.43	March	4.94	Summer	15.55				
1906	54.79	1927	40.79	April	3.66	Fall	9.21				

298737°—41——53 +

GEORGIA—Continued

Dates of last killing frost in spring and first in fall, with length of growing season

Year	Toccoa			Atlanta			Millen			Americus			Waycross			Thomasville		
	Last in spring	First in fall	Growing season [1]	Last in spring	First in fall	Growing season [1]	Last in spring	First in fall	Growing season [1]	Last in spring	First in fall	Growing season [1]	Last in spring	First in fall	Growing season [1]	Last in spring	First in fall	Growing season [1]
			Days			*Days*			*Days*			*Days*			*Days*			*Days*
1899	Apr. 10	Nov. 3	207	Apr. 10	Nov. 3	207	Apr. 10	Nov. 4	208	Apr. 10	Nov. 4	208	Mar. 9			Mar. 8	Nov. 4	241
1900	Apr. 14	Nov. 9	209	Apr. 1	Nov. 10	223	Apr. 1	Nov. 9	222	Apr. 1	Nov. 9	222	Mar. 17	Nov. 10	238	Feb. 26	Nov. 10	257
1901	Mar. 22	Nov. 6	229	Mar. 17	Nov. 7	235	Mar. 22	Nov. 16	239	Mar. 22	Nov. 16	239	Mar. 22	Nov. 16	239	Mar. 22	Nov. 16	239
1902	Apr. 9	Nov. 28	233	Mar. 19	Nov. 28	254	Mar. 20	Nov. 28	253	Mar. 20	Nov. 28	253	Mar. 20	Nov. 28	253	Mar. 19	Nov. 28	254
1903	Apr. 24	Oct. 25	184	Mar. 2	Oct. 25	237	Feb. 23	Oct. 25	244	Feb. 22	Oct. 25	245	Feb. 23	Nov. 19	269	Feb. 23	Nov. 19	269
1904	Apr. 13	Oct. 24	194	Apr. 4	Nov. 7	217	Apr. 5	Nov. 14	223	Mar. 4	Nov. 14	255	Feb. 18	Nov. 14	270	do	Nov. 14	265
1905	Apr. 18	Oct. 22	187	Apr. 17	Oct. 22	188	Apr. 17	Nov. 12	209	Apr. 17	Nov. 12	209	Feb. 27	Dec. 4	380	Feb. 27	Dec. 4	280
1906	Apr. 1	Oct. 11	193	Mar. 21	Oct. 11	204	Mar. 21	Oct. 29	222	Mar. 21	Oct. 29	222	Mar. 21	Nov. 13	237	Mar. 21	Nov. 13	237
1907	Apr. 15	Oct. 14	182	Apr. 15	Oct. 14	182	Apr. 15	do	197	Apr. 15	Nov. 14	213	Apr. 15	Nov. 14	213	Apr. 15	Nov. 14	213
1908	Apr. 4	Nov. 6	216	Mar. 21	Nov. 6	230	Feb. 28	Nov. 6	252	Feb. 28	Nov. 6	252	Feb. 28	Nov. 6	252	Feb. 28	Nov. 6	252
1909	Apr. 10	Oct. 13	186	Mar. 16	Oct. 25	223	Mar. 16	Oct. 25	223	Feb. 26	Oct. 25	241	Feb. 26	Nov. 19	266	Feb. 26	Oct. 25	241
1910	Apr. 24	Oct. 29	188	do	Oct. 29	227	Apr. 26	Oct. 29	186	Apr. 26	Oct. 29	186	Apr. 26	Oct. 30	187	Apr. 26	Oct. 29	186
1911	Mar. 31	Nov. 3	217	do	Nov. 13	242	Mar. 17	Nov. 13	241	Mar. 17	Nov. 13	241	Mar. 17	Nov. 13	241	Mar. 17	Nov. 13	241
1912	Mar. 26	Oct. 24	212	Mar. 10	Nov. 3	238	Mar. 10	Nov. 3	238	Mar. 10	Nov. 3	238	Feb. 23	Nov. 16	267	Feb. 23	Nov. 16	267
1913	Mar. 29	Oct. 21	206	Mar. 28	Oct. 21	207	Mar. 28	Oct. 21	207	Mar. 28	Oct. 21	207	Mar. 28	Oct. 21	207	Mar. 28	Oct. 21	207
1914	Apr. 21	Oct. 28	190	Apr. 10	Oct. 28	201	Mar. 24	Oct. 28	218	Mar. 23	Nov. 17	239	Mar. 23	Nov. 20	242	Mar. 23	Nov. 18	240
1915	Apr. 4	Nov. 16	226	Apr. 4	Nov. 16	226	Apr. 4	Nov. 16	226	Apr. 4	Nov. 16	226	Apr. 1	Nov. 16	229	Apr. 4	Nov. 16	226
1916	Apr. 10	Oct. 22	195	Mar. 17	Nov. 15	243	Apr. 10	do	220	Apr. 10	do	220	Apr. 10	do	220	Apr. 10	do	220
1917	do	Oct. 13	186	Mar. 19	Oct. 20	215	Mar. 19	Oct. 25	220	Mar. 19	Oct. 24	219	Mar. 6	Oct. 25	233	Mar. 6	Oct. 25	233
1918	Apr. 12	Nov. 13	215	Apr. 11	Dec. 26	259	Feb. 23	Nov. 13	263	Feb. 6	Dec. 26	323	Feb. 6	Dec. 26	323	Feb. 6	Dec. 26	323
1919	Apr. 2	Nov. 14	226	Apr. 1	Nov. 14	227	Apr. 2	Nov. 15	227	Feb. 17	Nov. 15	271	Feb. 17	Dec. 17	301	Feb. 17	Dec. 15	301
1920	Apr. 14	Oct. 29	198	Apr. 14	Nov. 13	213	Apr. 6	Oct. 30	207	Apr. 7	Nov. 18	226	Mar. 9	Nov. 18	254	Mar. 9	Nov. 18	254
1921	Apr. 18	Nov. 11	207	Apr. 12	Nov. 11	213	Apr. 12	Nov. 13	215	Feb. 26	Nov. 13	260	Jan. 27			None	Nov. 13	317
1922	Mar. 22	Nov. 21	244	Mar. 5	Nov. 21	261	Mar. 5	Nov. 23	263	Mar. 5	Nov. 27	267	Feb. 17			Mar. 5	Nov. 29	269
1923	Apr. 2	Nov. 1	213	Apr. 1	Nov. 9	222	Mar. 20	Nov. 9	234	Mar. 20	Nov. 20	245	Mar. 20	Nov. 10	235	Mar. 20	Nov. 10	235
1924	Mar. 22	Nov. 19	242	Apr. 2	Nov. 25	237	Mar. 22	Nov. 19	242	Mar. 17	do	248	Mar. 17	Nov. 26	254	Mar. 16	Nov. 26	255
1925	Apr. 1	Oct. 29	211	Mar. 4	Oct. 29	239	Apr. 1	Nov. 17	230	Mar. 4	Nov. 23	264	Mar. 4	Nov. 17	258	Mar. 3	Nov. 24	266
1926	Apr. 20	Nov. 5	199	Apr. 1	Nov. 3	216	Mar. 18	Nov. 6	233	Mar. 16	Nov. 6	235	Mar. 16	Nov. 11	240	Mar. 15	Nov. 11	241
1927	Mar. 5	Nov. 7	247	Mar. 4	Nov. 19	260	Mar. 5	Nov. 21	261	Mar. 5	Nov. 19	259	Mar. 5	Nov. 21	261	Mar. 4	Dec. 9	280
1928	Mar. 31	Nov. 13	227	Mar. 20	Nov. 21	246	Feb. 26	do	269	Feb. 29	Nov. 21	266	Feb. 20	do	275	Feb. 20	Nov. 21	275
1929	Mar. 18	Nov. 5	232	Mar. 18	Nov. 29	256	Feb. 23	Nov. 30	280	Feb. 23	Nov. 30	280	Feb. 12	Nov. 30	291	Feb. 12	Nov. 30	291
1930	Mar. 31	Nov. 1	215	Mar. 4	Nov. 1	242	Mar. 4	Nov. 1	242	Mar. 5	Oct. 31	240	Mar. 5	Nov. 15	255	Mar. 4	Nov. 27	268
1931	Mar. 30	Nov. 2	217	Mar. 17	Dec. 8	266	Mar. 18	do	228	Mar. 18	None	289	do	Nov. 2	242	Mar. 5	None	302
1932	Mar. 25	Nov. 13	233	Mar. 15	Nov. 12	242	Mar. 16	Nov. 12	241	Mar. 15	Nov. 12	242	Mar. 11	Nov. 20	254	Feb. 15	Nov. 13	272
1933	Mar. 27	Nov. 8	226	Mar. 5	Nov. 9	249	Mar. 5	Nov. 9	249	Mar. 5	Dec. 8	278	Mar. 5	Nov. 17	257	Feb. 12	None	323
1934	Apr. 13	Oct. 29	199	Mar. 15	Oct. 29	228	Mar. 16	Nov. 13	242	Mar. 21	Nov. 16	240	Mar. 16	Nov. 13	242	Mar. 11	Nov. 13	247
1935	Mar. 13	Nov. 20	252	Mar. 13	Nov. 23	255	Mar. 1	Nov. 22	266	Mar. 13	Nov. 23	255	Mar. 2	Nov. 24	267	Mar. 1	Nov. 24	268
1936	Apr. 4	Nov. 17	227	Apr. 4	Nov. 16	226	Apr. 4	Nov. 16	226	Apr. 4	Nov. 17	227	Feb. 19	Nov. 16	271	Feb. 12	Nov. 28	290

Year																		
1937	Mar. 29	Oct. 24	209	Mar. 29	Oct. 24	209	Mar. 29	Oct. 24	209	Mar. 29	Oct. 24	209	Mar. 17	Nov. 21	249	Mar. 16	Nov. 18	247
1938	Apr. 11	Nov. 9	212	Mar. 7	Nov. 9	247	Apr. 4	Nov. 25	235	Feb. 26	Nov. 25	272	Feb. 26	Nov. 25	272	Feb. 26	Nov. 25	272
Mean	Apr. 5	Nov. 3	212	Mar. 23	do	231	Mar. 22	Nov. 10	233	Mar. 17	Nov. 15	243	Mar. 9	Nov. 18	254	Mar. 6	Nov. 20	259
Extremes	Mar. 5[2] Apr. 24[3]	Oct. 11[4] Nov. 28[5]	[6] 182 [7] 252	Mar. 2[2] Apr. 17[3]	Oct. 11[4] Dec. 26[5]	[6] 182 [7] 266	Feb. 23[2] Apr. 26[3]	Oct. 21[4] Nov. 30[5]	[6] 186 [7] 280	Feb. 6[2] Apr. 26[3]	Oct. 21[4] None[5]	[6] 186 [7] 323	Jan. 27[2] Apr. 26[3]	Oct. 21[4] Dec. 26[5]	[6] 187 [7] 323	None[2] Apr. 26[3]	Oct. 21[4] None[5]	[6] 186 [7] 323

[1] Number of days between last killing frost in spring and first in fall.
[2] Earliest date in spring.
[3] Latest date in spring.
[4] Earliest date in fall.
[5] Latest date in fall.
[6] Shortest growing season.
[7] Longest growing season.

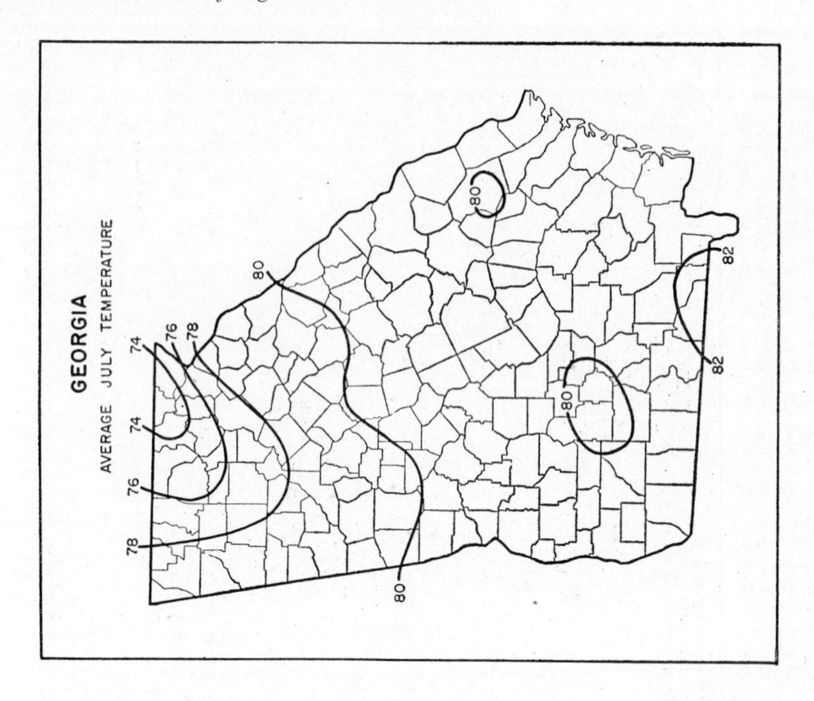
GEORGIA
AVERAGE JULY TEMPERATURE
74
76
78
80
82

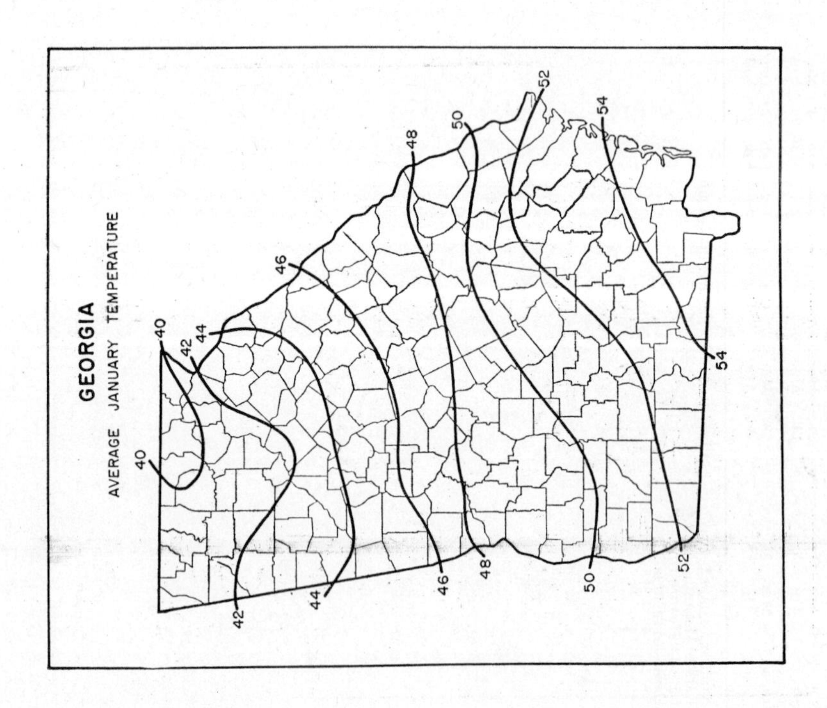
GEORGIA
AVERAGE JANUARY TEMPERATURE
40
42
44
46
48
50
52
54

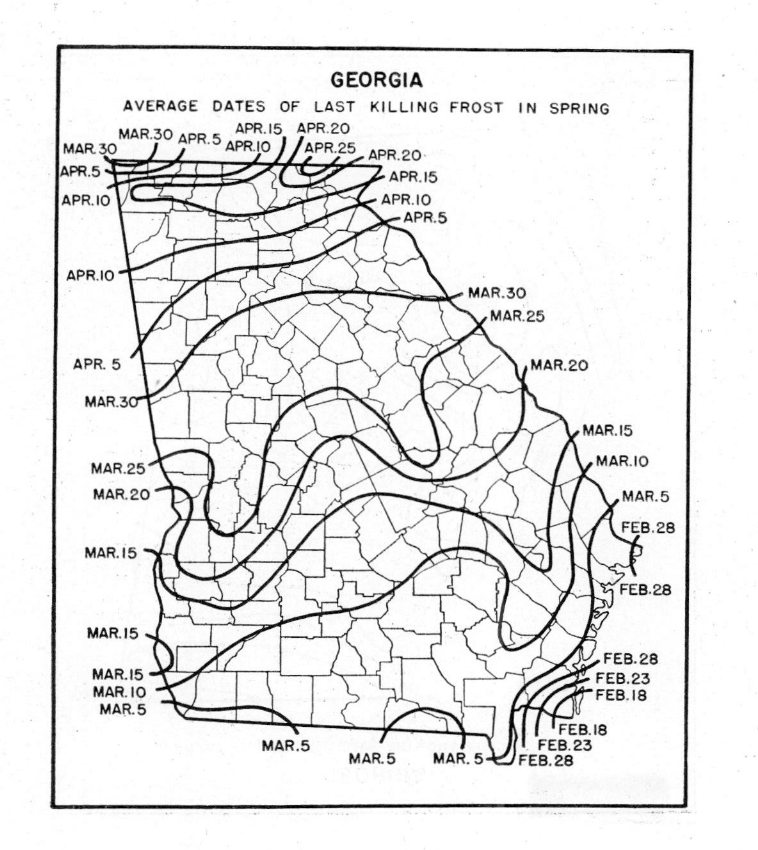
GEORGIA
AVERAGE DATES OF LAST KILLING FROST IN SPRING
MAR.30
MAR.30
APR.5
APR.15
APR.10
APR.20
APR.25
APR.20
APR.5
APR.15
APR.10
APR.10
APR.5
APR.10
MAR.30
MAR.25
APR. 5
MAR.20
MAR.30
MAR.15
MAR.10
MAR.25
MAR.20
MAR.5
FEB.28
MAR.15
FEB.28
MAR.15
FEB.28
FEB.23
MAR.15
MAR.10
FEB.18
MAR.5
FEB.18
FEB.23
MAR.5
MAR.5
MAR. 5
FEB.28

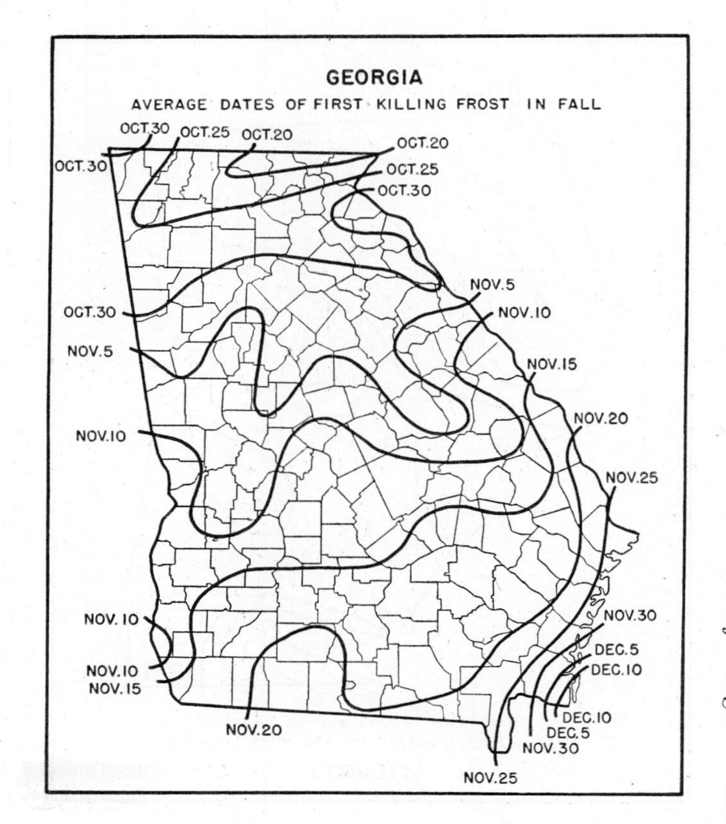
GEORGIA
AVERAGE DATES OF FIRST KILLING FROST IN FALL
OCT.30
OCT.25
OCT.20
OCT.20
OCT.30
OCT.25
OCT.30
NOV.5
OCT.30
NOV.10
NOV.5
NOV.15
NOV.20
NOV.10
NOV.25
NOV.30
NOV. 10
DEC.5
DEC.10
NOV.10
NOV.15
DEC.10
NOV.20
DEC.5
NOV.30
NOV.25

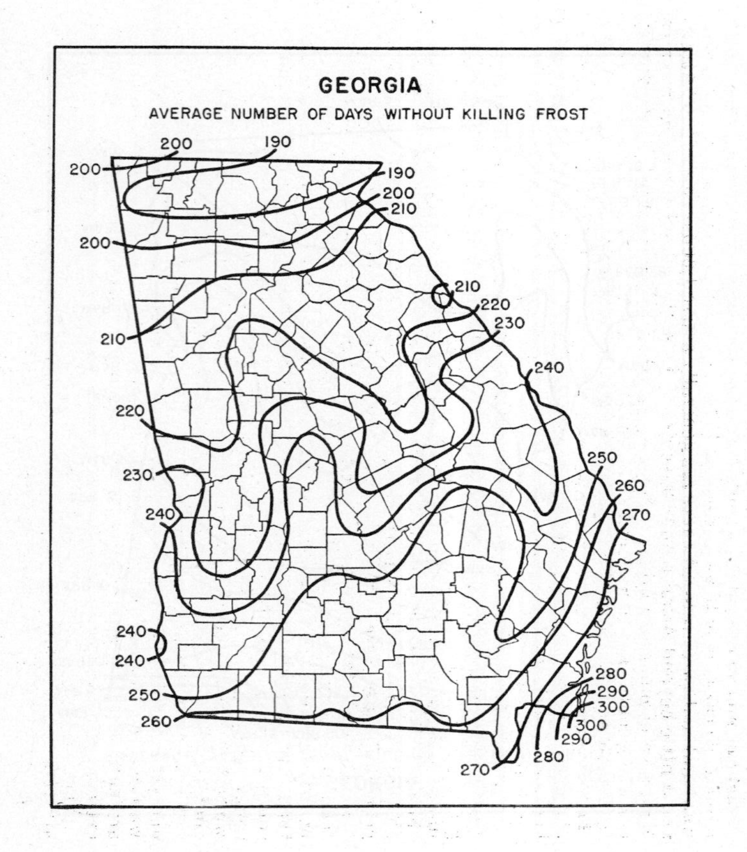
GEORGIA
AVERAGE NUMBER OF DAYS WITHOUT KILLING FROST
190
200
210
220
230
240
250
260
270
280
290
300

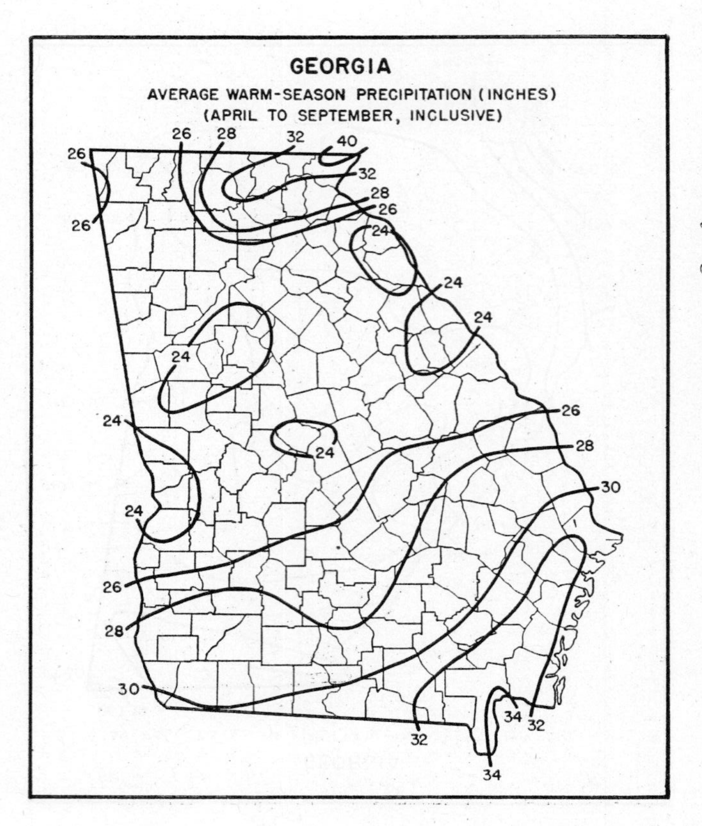
GEORGIA
AVERAGE WARM-SEASON PRECIPITATION (INCHES)
(APRIL TO SEPTEMBER, INCLUSIVE)
24
26
28
30
32
34
40

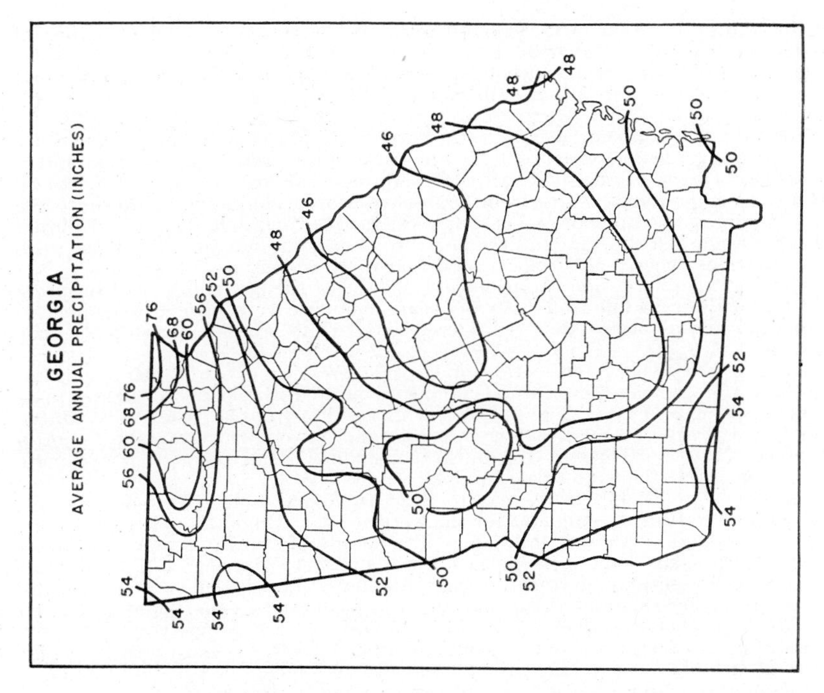

SUPPLEMENTARY CLIMATIC NOTES FOR GEORGIA

Eight or nine northeastern counties of Georgia are decidedly mountainous, with numerous peaks rising to an altitude of 4,000 feet or more. From this area southward and southwestward altitudes are generally above 1,000 feet nearly to Athens and a little beyond Atlanta and Carrollton. Directly west of the mountain area is an area of numerous broad valleys separated by ranges of hills. The country extending southward to less than 30 miles from Augusta and Columbus and nearly to Macon and Milledgeville is mostly rough. Over this upland section outside the mountain area altitudes range generally from about 600 to 1,800 feet, except along the rivers. Still farther south some hills are found, but they gradually become smaller and more widely separated until an extensive low, flat plain is reached, extending inland from the coast for 50 to 75 miles.

The chief factors that control the climate of Georgia are its proximity to the Atlantic Ocean and the Gulf of Mexico, its latitude, and its altitude. The geographical position of the State, well south in the Temperate Zone, and its proximity to large bodies of semitropical water naturally indicate a warm, moist climate. While this is true for the central and southern sections, the higher altitudes of the northern part have a rather marked modifying effect on the general climate there, especially from Atlanta to the Tennessee border.

As in other States of the deep South, the range between summer and winter temperatures is small in comparison with that in regions farther north. The normal midwinter (January) temperature for Georgia is only about 30° F. lower than that for midsummer (July), whereas the annual range is as much as 60° in some of the more northern States. However, the temperature changes between summer and winter are often very pronounced, because the prevailing winds in winter are from the continental interior and modify the effect of the ocean and the Gulf, imposing the continental type of climate characteristic of the interior States.

The soil and climate of Georgia are suitable for the production of cotton, corn, and the cereals. The State is noted for its excellent peaches, and the Georgia watermelon has a national reputation. Grapes grow well in most sections, figs are cultivated as far north as Atlanta without winter protection, and in the extreme southeastern part a few oranges and bananas are grown.

Very changeable temperature conditions prevail in winter. The daily maxima are very rarely below 32° F., and there are frequent periods of striking warmth in the winter months. Unseasonably cold or unseasonably warm weather in winter has caused the average temperature in the warmest January to be as much as 20° F. higher than that of the coldest January at many places in Georgia where the record covers 50 years or more. This is true also for the other winter months.

Normally the temperature rises rather rapidly in March and April. The State average temperature exceeds 70° F. for all months from May to September, inclusive. Owing to its high altitude, however, a large section of northern Georgia is comparatively free from oppressive heat, including, in addition to the mountain area, the upland section southwestward beyond Atlanta and Carrollton. There is a marked constancy in temperature during the summer in contrast with the variations experienced from year to year in other seasons.

Although there are wide variations in the dates of the last killing frost in spring and the earliest in fall from year to year, comparatively little frost injury to staple field crops occurs, but truck crops and fruits occasionally suffer serious damage.

Rainfall in the northern section of Georgia presents two well-marked peaks, one in winter and the other in midsummer, separated by a period of lighter rains in both spring and fall. The fall season is the driest of the year. The March and July averages are related to the October and November averages in the ratio of about 5 to 3. Toward the south the summer peak becomes increasingly prominent, while the winter peak is much reduced.

Variations in rainfall from year to year are remarkable. At most stations having long records, the amount for the wettest year is about double that for the driest. About half the rainfall comes in amounts of 1 inch or more within 24 hours. Dry spells sometimes cause heavy damage to growing crops and result in more or less serious shortage of water supplies. These conditions are usually limited to rather small areas, so that any selected locality is not likely to have a serious drought oftener than once in 10 to 15 years.

Snowfall in Georgia is light—inconsequential, in fact—in many winters as far north as Atlanta. An average annual snowfall of 5 inches or more is found only in the mountain area.

The percentage of relative humidity is highest in winter, with a secondary peak in midsummer. Spring and fall have the relatively driest atmosphere, conforming to the principal pattern of seasonal distribution of rainfall.

Property damage and loss of life due to lightning, wash-outs, hailstorms, and tornadoes are no more serious in Georgia than in most other States in which moderate to abundant rainfall occurs.

George W. Mindling, *Senior Meteorologist and Climatic Section Director for Georgia, Weather Bureau, Atlanta.*

IDAHO

Climatic summary

County	Station	Temperature: Length of record	Temperature: January average	Temperature: July average	Temperature: Maximum	Temperature: Minimum	Killing frost average dates: Length of record	Killing frost average dates: Last in spring	Killing frost average dates: First in fall	Killing frost average dates: Growing season[1]	Average precipitation: Length of record	January	February	March	April	May	June	July	August	September	October	November	December	Annual
		Yr.	°*F.*	°*F.*	°*F.*	°*F.*	*Yr.*			*Days*	*Yr.*	*In.*	*In.*	*In.*	*In.*	*In.*	*In.*	*In.*	*In.*	*In.*	*In.*	*In.*	*In.*	*In.*
Ada	Boise	40	30.4	74.2	121	−28	40	Apr. 23	Oct. 17	177	40	1.55	1.39	1.43	1.21	1.22	0.86	0.30	0.19	0.50	1.15	1.37	1.30	12.47
	Kuna	31	27.9	73.5	111	−28	31	May 10	Oct. 1	144	31	1.20	.89	1.09	1.02	1.11	.74	.37	.22	.50	.96	1.27	1.05	10.42
	Meridian	27	28.3	72.8	110	−30	28	May 3	Sept. 30	150	28	1.48	1.22	1.26	1.13	1.11	.82	.30	.23	.50	1.01	1.32	1.27	11.65
Adams	Council	28	23.2	71.9	109	−23	27	May 6	Oct. 1	148	27	3.59	2.95	2.63	2.28	1.58	1.45	.49	.44	.82	1.60	3.20	3.62	24.65
	Cuprum	24	23.7	64.1	106	−44	24	June 20	Sept. 10	82	25	4.56	3.23	2.76	2.38	2.92	2.04	.73	.77	1.29	2.47	3.78	3.97	31.30
	New Meadows	33	19.2	62.6	104	−49	34	June 27	Aug. 27	61	34	3.03	2.35	2.03	1.64	1.56	1.53	.58	.56	1.00	1.68	2.65	2.91	21.52
Bannock	Chesterfield	18	18.4	62.1	99	−48	21	June 23	Aug. 19	57	21	1.38	1.14	1.37	1.11	1.78	1.39	.88	1.09	.91	1.14	.96	1.18	14.33
	Grace	30	20.2	67.7	103	−40	31	May 29	Sept. 15	119	32	1.18	1.10	1.15	1.36	1.53	1.09	1.05	1.02	.96	1.34	1.06	1.03	13.87
	Pocatello	38	25.5	72.2	105	−28	40	Apr. 28	Oct. 6	161	39	1.33	1.14	1.35	1.48	1.43	1.00	.80	.78	.85	1.14	.92	1.12	13.34
Bear Lake	Geneva						16	June 27	Aug. 31	65	20	1.38	1.37	1.17	1.11	.98	.66	.81	.54	1.21	1.09	1.34	.95	12.61
	Lifton	19	17.3	67.5	99	−38	19	May 20	Sept. 20	123	19	.61	.73	.87	1.23	.87	.63	.75	.74	.80	1.14	.56	.70	9.63
	Montpelier	21	16.7	66.9	102	−34	23	June 9	Sept. 9	92	23	1.00	1.44	1.25	1.60	1.17	.94	.94	.93	1.03	1.28	.88	1.03	13.49
	Paris	14	19.9	62.8	97	−35	12	June 14	Sept. 7	85	16	1.72	1.39	1.10	1.17	.89	.99	.63	.89	.91	1.14	.99	.80	12.63
Benewah	St. Maries	38	28.1	67.2	106	−26	37	May 9	Sept. 23	137	37	3.44	2.30	2.59	1.74	1.85	1.46	.68	.76	1.20	2.12	3.34	3.67	25.15
Bingham	Aberdeen	24	19.8	69.9	104	−42	25	June 2	Sept. 12	102	25	.64	.67	.69	1.00	1.06	.72	.56	.47	.59	.95	.69	.64	8.68
	Blackfoot	40	20.7	68.7	108	−40	36	May 22	Sept. 17	118	40	1.04	.84	.96	.94	1.24	.85	.68	.58	.79	1.01	.73	.92	10.58
	Fort Hall	24	20.4	70.6	104	−42	24	May 24	Sept. 19	118	24	.74	.72	.88	1.19	1.08	.70	.62	.66	.69	1.02	.68	.68	9.66
	Springfield	29	19.5	70.1	106	−45	29	June 1	Sept. 12	103	30	.98	.83	.65	1.10	1.12	.77	.61	.54	.73	1.07	.89	.85	10.14
Blaine	Hailey	34	19.2	67.9	109	−36	33	June 2	Sept. 19	109	33	2.16	1.98	1.32	1.10	1.40	.90	.57	.49	.62	1.14	1.40	2.02	15.10
Boise	Bogus Creek						12	June 12	Sept. 13	93	23	2.79	2.83	2.54	2.59	2.22	1.47	.63	.51	1.22	2.08	3.40	2.41	24.69
	Garden Valley	19	23.4	70.1	110	−32	22	May 25	Sept. 14	112	25	3.22	2.55	2.37	1.63	1.24	1.01	.27	.50	.83	1.28	3.22	3.15	21.27
	Grimes Pass						6	May 16	Sept. 19	126	29	3.80	3.12	2.78	2.07	1.90	1.45	.51	.60	1.02	1.71	3.64	3.63	26.23
	Idaho City	25	24.2	67.6	109	−38	26	June 20	Aug. 31	72	31	3.22	2.99	2.12	1.41	1.34	.90	.38	.42	.64	1.48	2.89	3.21	21.00
	Kirkham	19	21.5	66.3	107	−35	27	June 27	Aug. 29	63	29	3.37	2.52	2.23	1.57	1.67	1.39	.55	.57	.95	1.50	3.14	3.34	22.80
	Pyle Creek						25	June 6	Sept. 5	91	29	4.05	3.20	2.69	1.76	1.38	1.13	.41	.43	.80	1.52	3.88	3.70	24.95
	Sheep Hill						24	May 28	Sept. 19	114	30	4.41	3.59	2.65	1.61	1.48	1.14	.49	.31	.66	1.39	3.83	3.69	25.25
Bonner	Lakeview	17	28.5	65.2	98	−11	17	May 10	Oct. 8	151	18	3.50	2.69	2.44	1.76	2.59	2.12	1.18	1.03	1.80	2.48	4.54	3.17	29.30
	Priest River Experiment Station.	27	23.3	64.2	102	−30	34	June 7	Sept. 12	97	27	3.98	2.81	2.52	1.94	1.84	1.80	.85	1.03	1.70	2.51	3.66	4.31	28.95
	Standpoint	28	25.0	65.3	104	−35	28	May 20	Sept. 18	121	28	3.82	2.79	2.60	1.86	1.84	1.72	.70	1.02	1.65	2.45	3.99	4.35	28.79
Bonneville	Gray's Lake	17	17.8	63.6	103	−45	20	June 26	Sept. 3	69	20	1.59	1.56	1.60	1.59	1.81	1.24	1.07	1.14	.99	1.51	1.15	1.37	16.62
	Idaho Falls	34	20.4	69.0	104	−37	34	May 15	Sept. 19	127	35	1.20	.85	.93	.85	1.34	1.18	.69	.67	.82	1.06	.67	1.01	11.27
	Irwin	32	19.0	64.8	102	−45	31	June 15	Sept. 4	81	32	1.39	1.15	1.07	.95	1.40	1.24	.92	.87	1.10	1.24	.99	1.19	13.51
Boundary	Bonners Ferry	11	21.7	65.3	102	−26	11	May 5	Sept. 25	143	16	3.05	1.59	1.53	.99	1.39	1.59	1.06	.82	1.58	1.87	2.93	3.07	21.47
	Porthill	38	23.6	65.8	102	−29	39	May 11	Sept. 29	141	40	2.30	1.53	1.44	.93	1.53	1.48	.91	.92	1.22	1.60	2.36	2.07	18.29

[1] Length of growing season between average date of last killing frost in Spring and first in Fall.

IDAHO—Continued

Climatic summary—Continued

County	Station	Temperature: Length of record	Temperature: January average	Temperature: July average	Temperature: Maximum	Temperature: Minimum	Killing frost average dates: Length of record	Killing frost average dates: Last in spring	Killing frost average dates: First in fall	Killing frost average dates: Growing season [1]	Average precipitation: Length of record	January	February	March	April	May	June	July	August	September	October	November	December	Annual
		Yr.	°*F.*	°*F.*	°*F.*	°*F.*	*Yr.*			*Days*	*Yr.*	*In.*	*In.*	*In.*	*In.*	*In.*	*In.*	*In.*	*In.*	*In.*	*In.*	*In.*	*In.*	*In.*
Butte	Arco	29	15.5	66.4	102	−46	30	June 5	Sept. 10	97	32	.93	.65	.83	.75	1.23	1.15	.52	.60	.51	.70	.56	.95	9.38
Camas	Big Smoky Ranger Station.										16	1.81				.44	.76	.41	.70	.57	2.41			
	Hill City	17	14.9	66.1	102	−44	20	June 15	Aug. 30	76	19	2.20	1.82	1.40	.98	1.11	.68	.30	.41	.45	1.07	1.53	2.12	14.07
	Soldier Creek Ranger Station.	28	19.9	64.7	100	−34	37	June 22	Sept. 11	81	29	3.63	3.11	1.99	1.66	1.41	1.03	.67	.61	.76	1.60	2.77	3.51	22.75
Canyon	Caldwell	34	28.2	73.5	107	−34	34	May 7	Oct. 3	149	34	1.25	1.05	1.03	.91	.96	.72	.34	.24	.44	.75	1.11	1.07	9.87
	Deer Flat	20	26.0	73.6	105	−28	18	May 2	Oct. 1	152	21	.99	.68	.94	.74	.73	.61	.16	.19	.34	.65	.91	.94	7.88
	Parma	15	27.4	75.0	109	−35	16	Apr. 30	Sept. 26	149	16	1.07	.76	.73	.82	.63	.73	.13	.19	.32	.67	.93	.98	7.96
Caribou	Blackfoot Dam	17	15.2	63.0	96	−42	19	June 21	Aug. 22	62	19	1.66	1.60	1.22	1.21	1.64	1.60	1.03	.97	1.31	1.37	1.27	1.39	16.27
Cassia	Albion	12	29.1	66.4	106	−24	12	May 31	Sept. 12	104	11	1.20	1.35	1.18	1.28	1.60	1.09	.64	.40	.71	1.58	1.48	1.29	13.80
	Bostetter Ranger Station.	17		58.3	93		16	July 9	Aug. 11	33	18						1.58	.88	1.04	1.15	1.42			
	Burley	21	25.4	73.2	106	−35	21	May 16	Sept. 23	130	21	.95	.89	.73	1.18	.95	.74	.39	.60	.47	.91	.84	.91	9.56
	Oakley	40	27.9	70.8	108	−27	39	May 18	do	128	40	.77	.80	.82	1.17	1.33	1.10	.65	.63	.67	1.00	.71	.68	10.33
Clark	Dubois	16	16.9	70.3	102	−28	16	May 20	Sept. 22	125	18	.87	.65	.61	.89	1.09	1.16	.89	.86	.73	1.05	.56	.90	10.26
	Spencer	16	14.4	64.4	97	−38	16	June 5	Sept. 9	96	20	1.43	1.48	1.45	1.45	2.28	1.39	1.24	.94	1.03	1.43	1.16	1.72	17.00
Clearwater	Bungalow Ranger Station.	10	28.1	70.7	111	−20	13	May 18	Sept. 29	134	13	6.03	3.51	4.57	3.65	2.00	2.70	.70	.90	1.65	4.07	5.85	6.16	41.79
	Orofino	33	29.3	73.0	118	−24	34	Apr. 30	Oct. 12	165	34	3.03	2.65	2.99	2.08	2.25	1.97	.64	.66	1.48	2.10	3.50	3.06	26.41
	Pierce	12	23.0	65.1	107	−44	21	June 23	Sept. 1	70	7	4.83	4.35	5.44	3.17	2.31	2.41	.64	.42	1.13	3.07	4.35	6.62	38.74
Custer	Challis	27	18.6	67.6	101	−32	26	May 29	Sept. 17	111	26	.42	.50	.41	.52	1.02	.94	.52	.53	.68	.58	.38	.63	7.13
	Loon Creek	12	19.0	60.0	96	−38	12	July 3	Aug. 29	57	13	1.67	1.40	1.33	1.19	1.61	1.55	.96	.85	1.66	.87	1.96	1.45	16.50
	Mackay	30	16.7	66.6	104	−27	30	June 1	Sept. 17	108	31	.82	.77	.54	.66	1.09	1.06	.89	.81	.76	.66	.48	.72	9.26
	Obsidian	27	13.9	57.5	93	−44					28	2.15	1.74	1.46	1.23	1.38	1.24	.65	.74	.90	1.22	1.69	1.87	16.27
	Stanley	10	11.8	55.4	91	−50					10	1.76	1.65	1.70	1.41	1.49	1.18	.68	.97	1.07	1.13	1.94	1.49	16.47
Elmore	Arrowrock	26	24.5	74.7	112	−32	27	May 4	Oct. 7	156	27	2.77	2.28	2.02	1.53	1.23	.89	.44	.27	.50	1.18	2.53	2.35	17.99
	Atlanta	21	20.3	62.3	106	−34					22	3.50	3.33	2.39	1.48	1.38	1.15	.69	.74	.95	1.84	2.69	3.36	23.50
	Garnet	17	33.8	78.5	113	−5	16	Apr. 14	Oct. 22	191	16	.78	.91	.81	.82	.79	.88	.38	.07	.41	.81	.69	.68	8.03
	Glenns Ferry	29	28.6	78.0	115	−31	29	May 6	Oct. 3	150	29	1.20	.99	.74	.80	.92	.59	.30	.11	.33	.63	1.30	1.10	9.01
	Little Camas						15	June 17	Sept. 5	80	17	3.09	2.48	1.40	1.27	1.38	1.05	.57	.36	1.02	1.71	2.69	2.49	19.51
	Mountain Home	32	27.5	72.3	107	−36	33	May 16	Sept. 18	125	33	1.24	1.10	1.04	.85	.89	.63	.39	.16	.47	.96	1.21	1.10	10.04
	Pine						20	June 4	Sept. 10	98	27	3.73	2.85	1.98	1.30	1.27	.74	.35	.36	.69	1.48	2.99	3.14	20.88
	Prairie	16	20.2	68.4	104	−39	23	June 12	Sept. 9	89	24	2.62	2.15	1.88	1.33	1.49	.92	.33	.36	.70	1.36	2.83	2.65	18.62
	Rattlesnake						6	June 4	Sept. 8	96	10	3.09	2.59	1.97	1.88	1.61	.60	.54	.27	.86	1.24	4.42	2.64	21.71
	Sunnyside	11	27.8	72.8	105	−18	10	May 17	Oct. 1	137	11	1.42	1.23	1.05	1.14	1.25	.88	.60	.16	.71	.88	1.51	1.20	12.03

Franklin	Preston	17	19.7	70.0	105	−36	15	May 27	Sept. 23	119	17	1.35	1.39	1.68	1.91	1.40	1.02	1.17	.97	.84	1.20	1.39	1.67	15.99
	Weston	18	24.7	68.0	104	−25	18	May 31	Sept. 13	105	18	1.70	1.19	1.82	1.48	1.99	1.16	.63	.95	.93	1.24	1.24	1.04	15.37
Fremont	Ashton	38	18.1	65.5	100	−37	35	June 5	Sept. 10	97	38	1.86	1.32	1.21	1.16	1.84	1.51	.93	.76	1.11	1.29	1.23	1.57	15.79
	Big Springs						8	June 29	Aug. 26	58	8	2.23	2.65	3.62	2.65	2.14	1.56	1.49	1.53	2.19	2.10	2.92	2.20	27.28
	Lake	12	14.9	59.0	92	−42	12	June 22	Aug. 29	68	13	2.11	1.95	2.28	1.71	1.63	1.93	1.03	1.04	.75	1.12	1.11	1.77	18.43
	Rice	7	17.1	63.5	96	−32	9	June 17	Sept. 8	83	10	2.80	2.02	1.55	1.80	2.11	1.09	1.23	.70	1.25	1.44	1.20	2.34	19.53
Gem	Emmett	32	28.9	75.1	111	−27	33	Apr. 24	Oct. 9	168	32	1.35	1.08	1.16	1.00	1.01	.84	.31	.24	.53	.86	1.26	1.28	10.92
	Tripod Mountain						24	May 28	Sept. 21	116	29	2.87	2.32	2.27	1.87	1.58	1.44	.43	.46	.82	1.48	2.73	2.58	20.85
Gooding	Bliss	19	26.4	75.1	111	−35	19	June 3	Sept. 24	113	21	1.21	.94	.89	.84	.95	.36	.21	.21	.39	.76	1.17	.91	8.84
	Gooding	28	23.1	71.9	110	−34	29	May 21	Sept. 21	123	29	1.31	1.07	.79	.94	.81	.55	.32	.23	.41	.84	1.33	.96	9.56
	Wendell	16	27.0	73.6	109	−26	18	do	Sept. 25	127	19	1.46	1.15	.66	.99	.93	.74	.26	.21	.51	1.19	1.41	.86	10.37
Idaho	Cottonwood	23	26.5	67.0	106	−34	23	June 4	Sept. 27	115	23	2.22	1.82	2.12	2.12	2.48	2.48	.93	.95	1.46	1.76	2.24	1.92	22.50
	Fenn Ranger Station	22	29.2	71.6	113	−25	22	Apr. 27	Oct. 12	168														
	Grangeville	15	28.0	67.8	108	−24	17	May 13	Sept. 24	134	21	1.76	1.73	2.56	2.56	3.01	2.98	.74	.80	1.58	2.23	1.99	1.70	23.64
	Kooskia	28	28.7	72.2	116	−30	29	May 4	Oct. 3	152	30	2.22	1.74	2.45	2.52	2.67	2.03	.77	.69	1.43	2.02	2.45	1.99	22.98
	Riggins										22	1.06	1.35	1.53	1.53	1.83	1.72	.51	.58	.91	1.07	1.05	1.49	14.63
	Warren	10	19.4	57.7	100	−45	8	July 21	Aug. 7	17	11	2.43	2.13	1.75	1.70	1.40	1.82	.76	1.10	1.22	1.78	1.94	3.26	21.29
Jefferson	Mud Lake	14	12.3	68.0	100	−42	16	June 3	Sept. 8	97	15	.56	.40	.48	.63	1.02	.90	.48	.72	.55	.62	.32	.70	7.38
Jerome	Hazelton	21	25.7	75.2	111	−34	21	May 16	Sept. 21	128	22	1.23	1.16	1.03	1.18	1.08	.63	.23	.40	.42	.90	1.08	1.09	10.43
	Jerome	22	26.2	74.5	108	−25	21	May 8	Oct. 4	149	23	1.09	.97	.83	.94	.84	.43	.19	.25	.28	.71	.88	.85	8.26
Kootenai	Coeur d'Alene	28	27.1	69.1	108	−34	26	do	Oct. 6	151	14	3.57	2.49	2.17	1.71	1.65	1.44	.76	.80	1.11	1.52	2.57	3.01	22.80
Latah	Moscow	40	28.0	67.1	105	−30	40	May 6	Oct. 6	153	40	3.04	2.10	2.24	1.57	1.71	1.45	.55	.64	1.13	1.69	2.85	2.84	21.81
	Potlatch	24	26.7	64.8	104	−42	23	June 4	Sept. 11	99	21	3.03	2.38	2.67	1.98	1.70	1.65	.45	.56	1.24	1.60	2.81	2.88	22.95
Lemhi	Forney	12	20.8	60.8	100	−33	12	July 5	Aug. 12	38	13	1.64	1.64	1.73	1.25	1.92	1.94	1.08	.62	1.07	1.07	1.48	1.72	17.16
	Lemhi	11	17.4	64.0	101	−35	9	June 10	Sept. 10	92	11	.56	.48	.71	1.20	1.52	1.30	.75	.79	.79	.65	.36	.83	9.94
	Salmon	30	17.8	68.3	106	−37	32	May 23	Sept. 9	109	31	.69	.39	.51	.68	.99	1.31	.78	.61	.77	.65	.58	.66	8.62
Lewis	Kamiah						16	May 19	Sept. 27	131	22	1.96	1.45	2.24	2.21	2.03	1.85	.43	.66	1.28	1.70	2.18	2.02	20.01
	Nezperce	29	26.4	65.4	105	−39	29	May 25	Sept. 20	118	29	1.68	1.27	1.77	2.05	2.45	2.07	.72	.72	1.20	1.71	1.86	1.46	18.96
Lincoln	Richfield	24	19.7	70.0	105	−40	24	June 5	Sept. 13	100	25	1.31	.96	.75	.90	1.01	.64	.28	.24	.46	.85	1.03	1.11	9.54
	Shoshone	29	23.0	71.9	106	−36	30	May 25	Sept. 20	118	31	1.45	1.13	.80	.93	1.01	.56	.22	.31	.43	.87	1.28	1.02	10.01
Madison	Hawley Gulch Ranger Station.										9	1.71				2.54	2.03	1.37	1.40	1.75	2.26	1.61	3.20	
	Sugar	30	16.3	66.9	104	−44	31	June 1	Sept. 15	106	31	1.15	.85	.67	.78	1.37	1.09	.67	.51	.92	1.10	.64	1.05	10.80
Minidoka	Rupert	31	24.4	71.8	105	−34	32	May 17	Sept. 21	127	32	1.11	.96	.81	1.02	1.10	.83	.47	.46	.58	1.01	1.31	1.00	10.66
Nez Perce	Lapwai	22	31.5	72.9	116	−26	19	May 7	Sept. 30	146	20	2.17	1.58	2.04	1.64	1.27	1.52	.41	.62	1.83	1.53	2.06	2.01	17.68
	Lewiston	39	33.4	75.9	117	−23	40	Apr. 5	Oct. 26	204	40	1.29	1.13	1.28	1.06	1.34	1.28	.47	.56	.87	1.15	1.56	1.28	13.27
Oneida	Malad	23	21.3	70.2	108	−25	24	May 28	Sept. 19	114	25	1.40	1.33	1.40	1.61	1.28	.91	1.12	.99	1.05	1.36	1.14	1.27	14.86
Owyhee	Grandview	22	28.9	75.3	115	−34	23	Apr. 28	do	144	24	.73	.72	.72	.85	.89	.58	.28	.18	.40	.87	.65	.75	7.62
	Hot Springs	13	32.0	74.7	107	−11	12	May 22	Oct. 7	138	12	1.04	.86	.64	.87	.72	.89	.50	.16	.55	.78	.84	.75	8.60
	Indian Cove	14	28.0	76.8	112	−35	13	do	Sept. 24	125	16	1.04	.83	.71	.75	1.02	.63	.47	.26	.40	.66	.78	.89	8.44
	Silver City										10	3.60	2.85	1.62	1.95	2.19	1.70	.92	.34	.69	1.40	2.80	3.10	23.16
Payette	Payette	35	27.1	73.9	113	−33	36	May 9	Oct. 1	145	37	1.55	1.18	1.08	.76	.91	.75	.29	.15	.38	.89	1.08	1.41	10.43
Power	American Falls	30	24.4	70.2	106	−33	30	May 26	Sept. 16	113	33	1.49	1.16	1.33	1.34	1.52	.99	.66	.57	.64	1.30	1.17	1.06	13.23
Shoshone	Avery	23	26.4	67.1	108	−25	24	June 2	Sept. 22	112	25	4.18	3.10	3.83	2.55	2.08	2.02	.87	.89	1.69	2.77	3.61	4.10	31.69
	Burke	9	21.9	59.9	95	−21	9	June 6	Aug. 31	86	9	5.99	5.12	4.78	2.50	3.09	2.61	1.68	1.03	2.62	3.49	5.78	5.26	43.95
	Kellogg	33	26.6	67.2	109	−27	34	May 19	Sept. 24	128	34	3.68	2.70	3.12	2.16	2.42	2.03	.86	.99	1.71	2.68	3.66	3.65	29.66
	Mullan	17	25.3	65.1	102	−28	18	May 31	Sept. 14	106	18	4.42	3.67	3.90	2.38	2.13	2.34	.69	.95	1.58	2.91	4.16	5.17	34.30
	Prichard						12	June 3	Sept. 4	93	24	4.68	3.88	3.97	2.27	2.29	2.07	.79	.93	1.71	3.08	4.53	5.62	35.82
	Roland	18	22.8	62.9	96	−27	18	June 1	Sept. 9	100	18	7.91	5.87	5.49	3.22	2.12	2.50	.73	1.31	2.21	4.06	5.84	8.36	49.62
	Wallace	29	26.4	66.6	107	−24	30	May 11	Oct. 2	144	30	5.16	3.73	4.06	2.51	2.54	2.29	.92	1.09	1.98	3.31	5.38	5.78	38.75
Teton	Driggs	23	16.2	62.2	97	−50	25	June 16	Aug. 29	74	29	1.85	1.26	1.16	1.18	1.96	1.70	1.34	1.29	1.34	1.18	1.16	1.42	16.84
	Felt	14	13.6	61.5	98	−50	14	July 3	Aug. 28	56	13	1.09	.84	.75	1.02	1.38	1.21	.96	1.31	1.35	1.02	.83	1.16	12.92

IDAHO—Continued

Climatic summary—Continued

County	Station	Temperature					Killing frost average dates				Average precipitation													
		Length of record	January average	July average	Maximum	Minimum	Length of record	Last in spring	First in fall	Growing season	Length of record	January	February	March	April	May	June	July	August	September	October	November	December	Annual
		Yr.	°*F.*	°*F.*	°*F.*	°*F.*	*Yr.*			*Days*	*Yr.*	*In.*	*In.*	*In.*	*In.*	*In.*	*In.*	*In.*	*In.*	*In.*	*In.*	*In.*	*In.*	*In.*
Twin Falls	Buhl	32	27.2	73.0	107	−29	31	May 11	Oct. 12	154	32	1.04	.92	.71	.88	1.08	.89	.38	.31	.42	.93	.97	.79	9.32
	Hollister	25	26.5	71.8	108	−35	27	May 23	Sept. 23	123	27	.84	.85	.70	1.09	1.14	.83	.39	.43	.44	.91	.81	.72	9.15
	Milner Dam	22	25.7	72.9	108	−30	23	May 16	Sept. 29	136	23	1.25	.92	.85	.91	1.08	.98	.32	.29	.43	.85	1.08	.81	9.77
	Murtaugh	20	24.4	69.3	101	−31	20	do	Sept. 24	131	21	1.30	1.07	.80	1.06	1.07	.93	.28	.41	.66	.90	1.13	.86	10.47
	Twin Falls	32	26.5	73.4	105	−30	33	May 18	Sept. 26	131	33	1.15	.92	.93	1.03	1.06	.72	.35	.24	.52	.93	1.07	.88	9.80
Valley	Alpha	17	18.5	61.7	100	−47	(2)	(2)	(2)	(2)	17	3.49	2.65	2.96	2.30	1.72	1.61	.48	.60	.78	1.84	3.44	3.62	25.49
	Deadwood	9	14.6	61.5	98	−48	(2)	(2)	(2)	(2)	9	5.35	4.25	4.10	2.02	1.48	1.73	.99	.60	.68	1.90	2.68	6.77	32.55
	McCall	27	17.9	63.1	104	−34	27	June 20	Sept. 3	75	28	3.57	3.05	2.56	1.91	1.72	1.59	.48	.61	.99	1.86	2.77	3.58	24.69
Washington	Cambridge	34	21.5	73.8	117	−35	34	May 17	Sept. 25	131	38	2.95	2.25	1.82	1.46	1.10	1.05	.40	.34	.56	1.11	2.47	2.67	18.18
	Weiser	27	25.7	77.0	115	−28	27	May 3	Oct. 5	155	27	1.77	1.34	1.03	1.03	.77	.86	.19	.25	.37	.78	1.26	1.50	11.15

[2] Freezing temperatures common in all months.

Precipitation and temperature—State unit values

[This tabulation gives the mean annual, mean monthly, and average seasonal precipitation, 1886–1938, and the mean annual temperatures, 1896–1938, for Idaho]

Precipitation		Precipitation		Precipitation		Precipitation		Temperature		Temperature	
Year	Mean	Year	Mean	Year	Mean	Month	Mean	Year	Mean	Year	Mean
	In.		*In.*		*In.*		*In.*		°*F.*		°*F.*
1886	16.70	1908	16.97	1930	17.03	July	0.64	1896	45.6	1918	46.5
1887	16.03	1909	22.83	1931	15.02	August	.62	1897	45.7	1919	45.2
1888	16.41	1910	17.62	1932	19.71	September	.98	1898	44.4	1920	45.0
1889	14.76	1911	18.15	1933	18.67	October	1.44	1899	44.7	1921	46.6
1890	19.03	1912	22.19	1934	16.10	November	1.97	1900	47.6	1922	44.1
1891	15.93	1913	20.44	1935	12.40	December	2.11	1901	46.8	1923	45.1
1892	19.99	1914	17.13	1936	16.49			1902	45.4	1924	45.1
1893	20.13	1915	19.35	1937	20.03	Annual	17.91	1903	44.5	1925	47.3
1894	20.01	1916	21.02	1938	19.57			1904	46.8	1926	47.3
1895	13.89	1917	19.67					1905	45.8	1927	45.2
1896	20.91	1918	17.46					1906	46.0	1928	45.8
1897	20.19	1919	15.96	Month	Mean	Season	Average	1907	46.1	1929	44.2
1898	14.92	1920	19.20					1908	45.1	1930	44.9
1899	18.96	1921	18.93					1909	45.5	1931	45.9
1900	16.39	1922	16.01					1910	46.8	1932	44.1
1901	15.13	1923	19.33		*In.*		*In.*	1911	44.2	1933	45.1
1902	16.96	1924	13.49	January	2.22	Winter	6.03	1912	44.5	1934	49.9
1903	17.58	1925	19.51	February	1.70	Spring	4.88	1913	44.4	1935	45.0
1904	17.74	1926	18.24	March	1.80	Summer	2.61	1914	46.2	1936	45.8
1905	15.63	1927	24.04	April	1.44	Fall	4.39	1915	46.2	1937	44.8
1906	21.01	1928	13.90	May	1.64			1916	43.3	1938	46.5
1907	20.63	1929	13.94	June	1.35			1917	44.2		

IDAHO—Continued

Dates of last killing frost in spring and first in fall, with length of growing season

Year	Boise			Mackay			Moscow			New Meadows			Pocatello			Twin Falls		
	Last in spring	First in fall	Growing season [1]	Last in spring	First in fall	Growing season [1]	Last in spring	First in fall	Growing season [1]	Last in spring	First in fall	Growing season [1]	Last in spring	First in fall	Growing season [1]	Last in spring	First in fall	Growing season [1]
			Days			*Days*			*Days*			*Days*			*Days*			*Days*
1899	May 1	Oct. 2	154				May 14	Oct. 1	140					Oct. 2				
1900	Apr. 8	Oct. 23	198				May 7	Oct. 27	173				Mar. 28	Sept. 27	183			
1901	June 5	Nov. 2	150				Apr. 27	Nov. 2	189				Apr. 1	Nov. 2	215			
1902	Apr. 13	Nov. 1	202				May 30	Sept. 28	121				Apr. 10	Sept. 26	169			
1903	Apr. 29	Oct. 30	184				May 21	Nov. 7	170		Sept. 9		May 2	Oct. 15	166			
1904	May 5	Nov. 12	191				May 25	Nov. 5	164	June 25	Sept. 11	78	May 8	Oct. 18	163			
1905	Apr. 11	Oct. 10	182				May 18	Oct. 13	148	May 24	Aug. 16	84	May 10	Oct. 10	153		Oct. 10	
1906	Apr. 12	Oct. 18	189				Apr. 12	Oct. 20	191	June 22	Sept. 10	80	Apr. 13	Oct. 13	183	May 5	Sept. 26	144
1907	Apr. 29	Nov. 3	188				Apr. 29	Nov. 3	188	May 21	Aug. 19	90	May 5	Nov. 4	183	May 21	Sept. 20	122
1908	Apr. 26	Sept. 24	151	June 22	Sept. 24	94	Apr. 26	Sept. 25	152	June 20	Aug. 26	67	May 9	Sept. 26	140	May 17	Sept. 26	132
1909	May 12	Oct. 8	149	May 19	Sept. 18	122	Apr. 30	Oct. 8	161	May 19	Sept. 18	122	May 6	Oct. 8	155	do	Oct. 8	144
1910	Apr. 15	Oct. 27	195	May 3	Aug. 25	114	Apr. 15	Sept. 25	163	June 8	Aug. 30	83	May 2	Oct. 5	156	do	Sept. 26	132
1911	Apr. 14	Oct. 19	188	June 23	Sept. 6	75	May 23	Sept. 23	123				May 7	Oct. 19	165	May 7	Oct. 7	153
1912	Mar. 31	Oct. 9	193	May 23	Sept. 15	115	Apr. 15	Oct. 7	175				May 13	Sept. 15	125	May 14	Sept. 5	114
1913	Apr. 23	Oct. 10	170	May 16	Sept. 24	131	Apr. 23	Sept. 23	153	July 14	Aug. 19	36	Apr. 23	Sept. 25	155	July 14	Sept. 24	72
1914	Apr. 28	Nov. 7	193	June 9	Sept. 13	96	Apr. 28	Oct. 20	175	July 22	Aug. 10	19	May 5	Sept. 12	130	June 6	Sept. 15	101
1915	Mar. 19	Oct. 11	206	June 27	Sept. 9	74	Apr. 21	Sept. 12	144	July 19	Sept. 5	48	do	Sept. 14	132	May 4	Sept. 14	133
1916	May 12	Oct. 5	146	June 21	Sept. 10	81	May 13	Oct. 2	142	June 10	Aug. 19	70	May 15	Sept. 28	136	May 16	Oct. 4	141
1917	May 2	Oct. 18	169	May 17	Oct. 17	153	May 15	Oct. 16	154	July 30	Aug. 1	2	Apr. 29	Oct. 18	172		Oct. 17	
1918	May 25	Oct. 23	151	June 2	Oct. 6	126	May 25	Oct. 21	149	June 30	Oct. 23	115	Apr. 27	Oct. 26	182	May 22	Oct. 24	155
1919	May 4	Oct. 9	158	do	Oct. 22	142	May 3	Sept. 20	140	June 8	Sept. 22	106	May 6	Oct. 10	157	June 1	Oct. 10	131
1920	Apr. 24	Oct. 19	178	June 11	Aug. 28	78	May 30	Oct. 13	136	June 24	Aug. 20	57	June 1	Oct. 16	137	do	Oct. 16	137
1921	Apr. 30	Sept. 13	136	May 12	Sept. 4	115	Apr. 30	Sept. 10	133	May 12	Sept. 12	123	Apr. 24	Sept. 29	158	May 12	Sept. 12	123
1922	May 9	Oct. 30	174	May 28	Sept. 7	102	May 22	Oct. 21	152	May 11	Sept. 8	120	May 27	Oct. 14	140	May 27	Sept. 29	125
1923	Apr. 13	Oct. 19	189	June 14	Sept. 18	96	Apr. 30	Oct. 23	176	June 14	Sept. 5	83	Apr. 25	Oct. 12	170	do	Oct. 13	139
1924	Apr. 16	Sept. 26	163	June 7	Sept. 20	105	Apr. 27	Oct. 5	161	July 24	Aug. 30	37	May 6	Sept. 20	137	May 6	Sept. 21	138
1925	Apr. 25	Oct. 24	182	May 16	Aug. 15	91	May 3	Sept. 20	140	June 14	Sept. 10	88	Apr. 28	Oct. 9	164	May 9	Sept. 30	144
1926	Apr. 23	Sept. 23	153	May 7	Sept. 15	131	May 30	Sept. 23	116	July 21	Sept. 24	65	Apr. 2	Sept. 24	175	do	Sept. 18	132
1927	Apr. 20	Oct. 6	169	May 31	Sept. 1	93	May 6	Oct. 7	154	July 16	Aug. 31	46	Apr. 21	Oct. 6	168	June 1	Sept. 15	106
1928	Apr. 21	Oct. 21	183	do	Sept. 14	106	May 3	Sept. 20	140	June 7	Aug. 20	74	do	Oct. 11	173	May 5	Sept. 21	139
1929	May 10	Oct. 11	154	June 3	Sept. 10	99	May 1	Sept. 28	150	July 28	Aug. 10	13	May 6	Sept. 8	125	June 3	Sept. 7	96
1930	Mar. 31	do	194	do			May 7	Oct. 10	156	July 20	Aug. 21	32	Apr. 1	Oct. 16	198	May 23	Sept. 24	124
1931	Apr. 20	Nov. 9	203	May 21	Sept. 22	124	May 8	do	155	do	Aug. 9	20	May 8	Oct. 30	175	May 11	Sept. 25	137
1932	Apr. 6	Oct. 19	196	May 24	Aug. 30	98	May 26	Oct. 9	136	do	Aug. 2	13	Apr. 9	Oct. 4	178	Apr. 15	Aug. 31	138
1933	May 10	Oct. 21	164	June 7	Sept. 16	101	May 12	Sept. 24	135	July 31	Aug. 6	6	May 9	Sept. 26	140	May 9	Sept. 16	130
1934	Apr. 4	Sept. 26	175	June 3	Sept. 24	113	Apr. 15	do	162	June 20	Aug. 1	42	Apr. 3	Sept. 27	177	Apr. 18	Sept. 15	150

1935	Mar. 27	Oct. 20	207	June 2	Sept. 29	119	May 25	Aug. 16	83	July 30	Aug. 16	17	Apr. 25	Oct. 23	181	May 11	Sept. 28	140
1936	Apr. 6	Oct. 22	199	June 9	Sept. 12	95	Apr. 6	Oct. 15	192	June 19	Aug. 19	61	Apr. 9	Sept. 16	160	May 21	Sept. 15	117
1937	Apr. 24	Oct. 5	164	June 5	Sept. 25	112	May 6	Sept. 24	141	June 25	Aug. 2	38	Apr. 24	Sept. 25	154	May 30	Sept. 24	117
1938	May 6	Nov. 6	184	June 19	Oct. 13	116	Apr. 19	Oct. 17	181	June 10	Aug. 20	71	May 6	Oct. 18	165	May 18	Oct. 19	154
Mean	Apr. 23	Oct. 17	177	June 1	Sept. 17	108	May 6	Oct. 6	153	June 27	Aug. 27	61	Apr. 28	Oct. 6	161	do	Sept. 26	131
Extremes	Mar. 19[2]	Sept. 13[4]	[6] 136	May 3[2]	Aug. 15[4]	[6] 74	Apr. 6[2]	Aug. 16[4]	[6] 83	May 19[2]	Aug. 1[4]	[6] 2	Mar. 28[2]	Sept. 8[4]	[6] 125	Apr. 15[2]	Aug. 31[4]	[6] 72
	June 5[3]	Nov. 12[5]	[7] 207	June 27[3]	Oct. 22[5]	[7] 153	May 30[3]	Nov. 7[5]	[7] 192	July 31[3]	Oct. 23[5]	[7] 123	June 1[3]	Nov. 4[5]	[7] 215	July 14[3]	Oct. 24[5]	[7] 155

[1] Number of days between last killing frostl n spring and first in fall.
[2] Earliest date in spring.
[3] Latest date in spring.
[4] Earliest date in fall.
[5] Latest date in fall.
[6] Shortest growing season.
[7] Longest growing season.

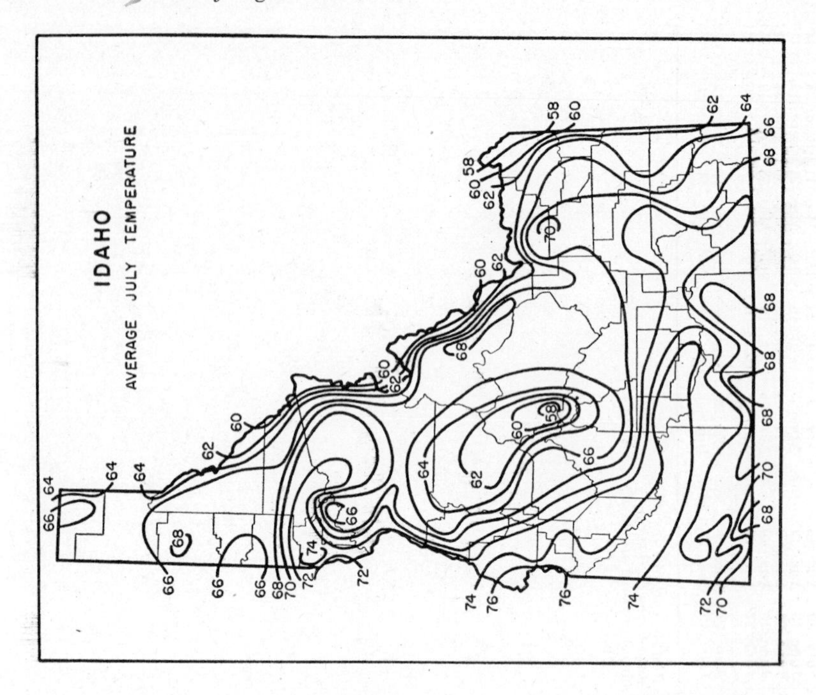
IDAHO
AVERAGE JULY TEMPERATURE

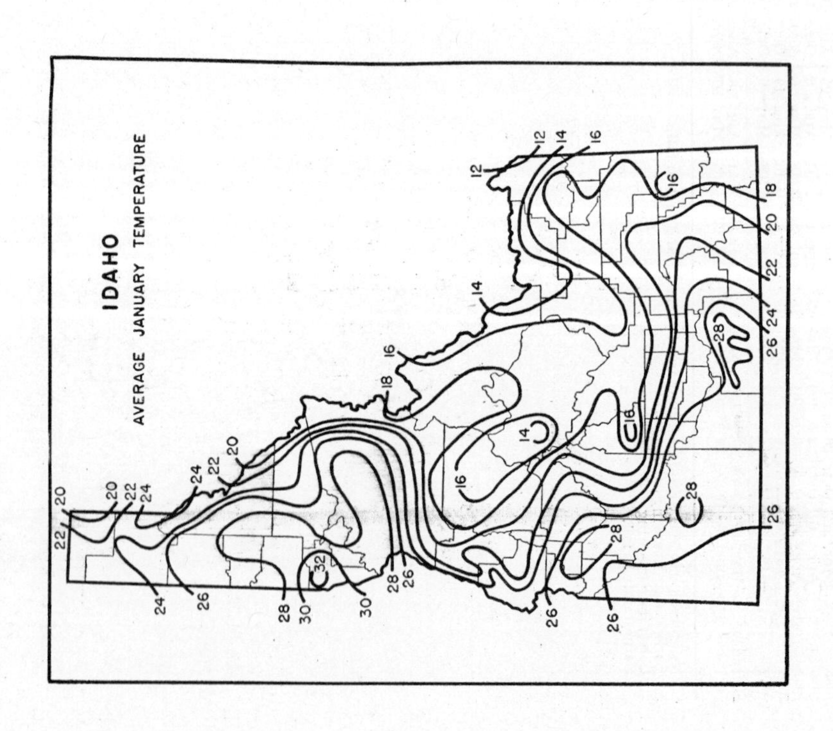
IDAHO
AVERAGE JANUARY TEMPERATURE

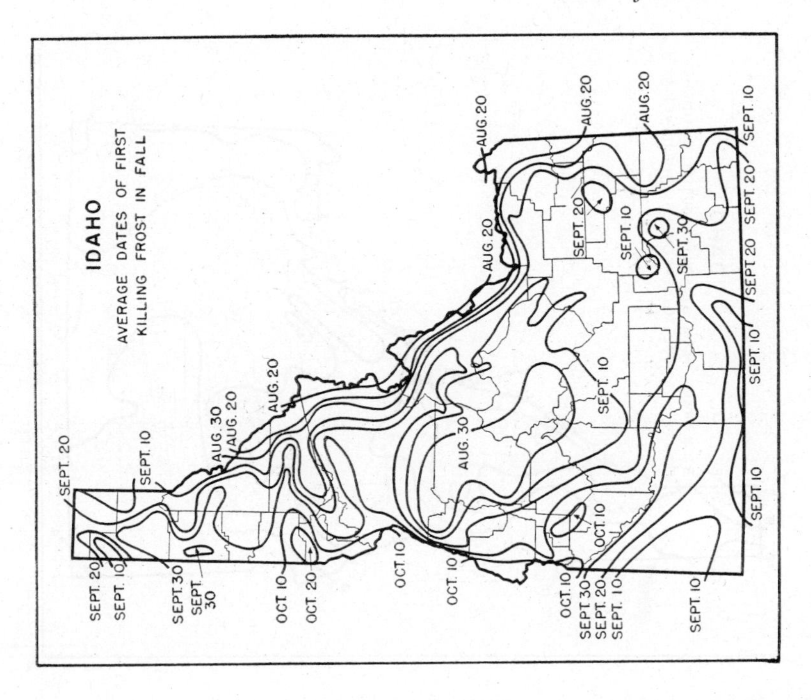
IDAHO
AVERAGE DATES OF FIRST
KILLING FROST IN FALL

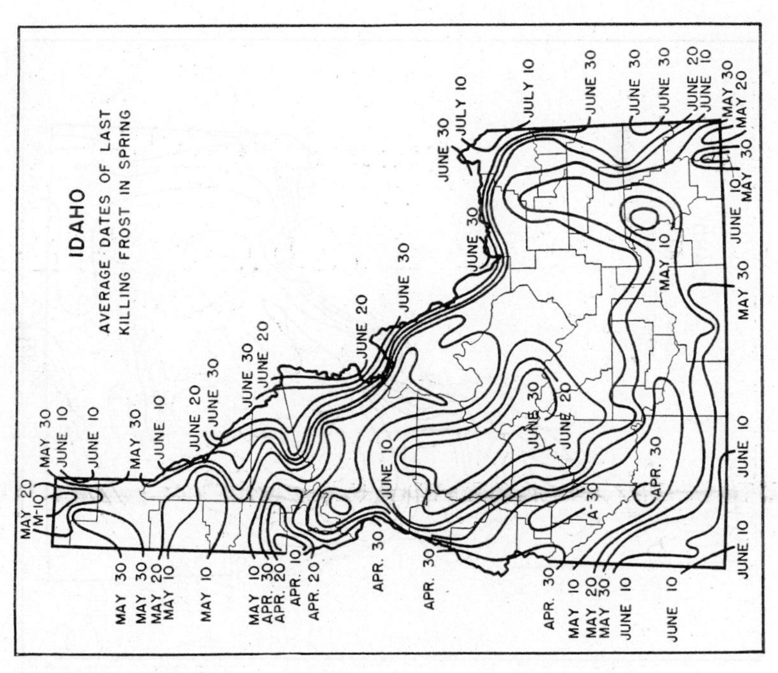
IDAHO
AVERAGE DATES OF LAST
KILLING FROST IN SPRING

298737°—41——54

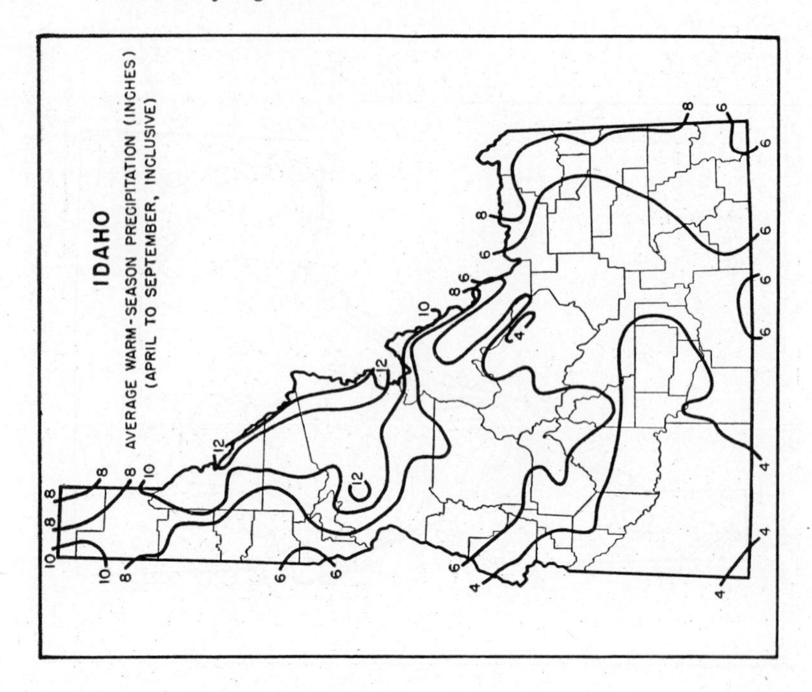
IDAHO
AVERAGE WARM-SEASON PRECIPITATION (INCHES)
(APRIL TO SEPTEMBER, INCLUSIVE)

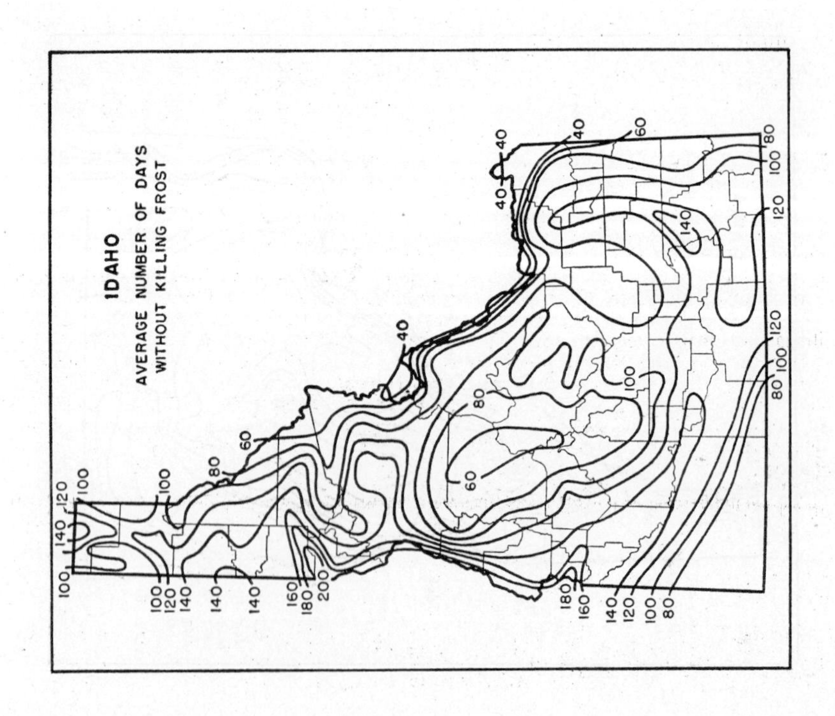
IDAHO
AVERAGE NUMBER OF DAYS
WITHOUT KILLING FROST

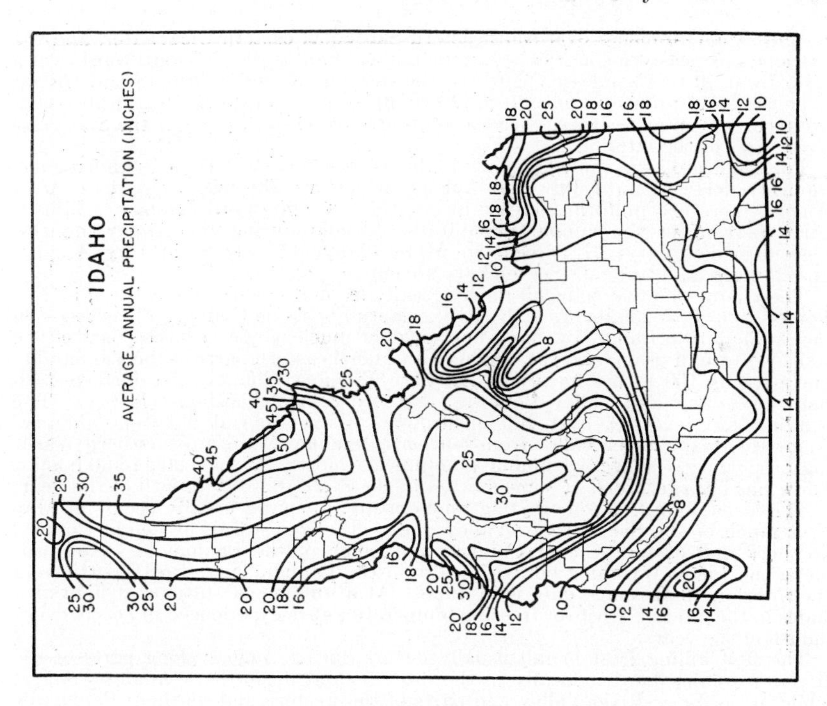

SUPPLEMENTARY CLIMATIC NOTES FOR IDAHO

Much of Idaho has a rugged surface, with numerous ridges and spurs projecting from the main mountain ranges. There are, however, considerable areas of fairly level or rolling prairie land between the mountains, and smaller valleys between the minor ranges. Elevations range from 783 feet at the confluence of the Clearwater and Snake Rivers in Nez Perce County to 12,665 feet at the top of Mount Borah, in eastern Custer County. Considerable areas lie between 2,500 and 6,000 feet above sea level. In the southern part are the Snake River plains, an extensive area with a comparatively flat surface. These plains increase in elevation from 2,114 feet at Weiser, at the extreme western edge, to 5,000 feet in the extreme east, not far from Yellowstone Park.

So far as temperature and precipitation are concerned, altitude is in general a more potent factor of control than latitude in the climate of Idaho. The entire State lies within the region of prevailing westerly winds and is affected in a marked degree by the ameliorating influence of the Pacific Ocean, so that the climate is milder than its latitude and altitude would indicate. It is considerably milder than that of the States lying in the same latitude east of the Continental Divide, the lofty ranges of which frequently serve as a barrier against the cold waves and blizzards that occasionally sweep down from the Canadian Northwest.

Because of intervening north-south mountains to the west of the State—especially the Cascade Range—which rob the eastward-moving winds of much of their moisture, precipitation is light except at the higher elevations. There are alternating mountain ranges and lower, comparatively flat intervening areas from the coast of Washington to northern Idaho. In the Olympic Mountains, in western Washington, the average annual precipitation is considerably in excess of 100 inches, while to the leeward, in the Puget Sound area, this is reduced to 40 or 50 inches. The amount of precipitation rises again in the Cascades of Washington to more than 80 inches, but decreases in the Columbia Basin to 10 or 15 inches, while still another rise in the Bitter Root Mountains of Idaho brings the annual average up to more than 40 inches. These variations afford perhaps the most outstanding examples of topographic influence on precipitation to be found anywhere in the world.

The annual average precipitation in Idaho itself ranges locally from 10 inches or less over the Snake River plains and northward into Lemhi and Custer Counties to more than 40 inches over southeastern Shoshone, eastern Clearwater, and the extreme northeastern counties. In much of the Panhandle and southward over a strip from 50 to 75 miles in width to the northern parts of Elmore and Camas Counties, precipitation ranges from 20 to 30 inches. Between 10 and 20 inches are received, on an average, over the southern and eastern parts of the State and over parts of the interior.

For the State as a whole, January is the wettest month. There is an irregular monthly decrease until July and August, which are the driest months. After August there is a uniform increase in monthly amounts until January. Thirty-three percent of the annual precipitation occurs during the winter months, December–February; 27 percent in March–May; 15 percent in June–August; and 25 percent in the fall, September–November.

The average annual snowfall ranges locally from 16 inches at Lewiston, in Nez Perce County, to 230 inches at Roland, eastern Shoshone County. It exceeds 60 inches along the Idaho-Wyoming border, over much of the northern part of the southwestern division, and the northern and northeastern parts of the Panhandle, and exceeds 100 inches locally in northern Fremont County, the northwestern parts of Adams and Valley Counties, and east-central Shoshone County. The heaviest fall reported, over 200 inches, was in east-central Shoshone County. Along the Snake River Valley from southern Bingham County to southern Washington County, the average annual amounts are mostly between 20 and 30 inches. Snow has been recorded at some station in the State in every month of the year.

The last killing frost, or freezing temperature, in spring usually occurs in May over much of the Snake River Valley and to the southward, in Lemhi County, northern and eastern Custer County, and much of the Panhandle. However, along the Idaho-Wyoming border, locally in the Panhandle, and over portions of the interior, the average date is in June. At a number of stations at high altitudes in the interior, frosts or freezing temperatures are experienced in nearly every month of the year.

The first killing frost in fall usually occurs during August along parts of the Idaho-Wyoming border, locally in the interior, and in northern Adams County, while in the Boise River Valley and parts of the western and southern Panhandle it is usually deferred until October. Over much of the remainder of the State the first killing frost is usually recorded some time in September.

The average length of the growing, or frost-free, season ranges from less than 70 days over much of Caribou County, parts of southern Valley County, the northeastern parts of Boise, Elmore, and Adams Counties, and southern Custer and south-central Clearwater Counties, to more than 160 days over the northwestern parts of Bannock and Nez Perce Counties, southern Gem, northeastern Ada, and southwestern Clearwater Counties, and locally in northern Idaho County. Over parts of the Panhandle and much of the western Snake River plains it exceeds 125 days, and in some localities in these areas even 150 days.

For the State as a whole, there is an average of 167 clear days during the year, ranging from 9 in January to 21 in July; 94 partly cloudy days, ranging from 7 days a month during the late fall and winter to 10 in May; 104 cloudy days, ranging from 3 each in July and August to 15 in January.

The wind movement averages 6 miles an hour at Boise and 9.2 miles at Pocatello. The highest wind velocities are recorded during late winter or early spring, and the lowest during late summer or autumn.

Hail falls occasionally over the agricultural sections of Idaho, but usually it is not of sufficient intensity to cause serious damage to crops. While thunderstorms occur over the mountains, they are not frequent in the lower country and when they do occur they are relatively mild. Typical tornadoes are of rare occurrence.

HARRY G. CARTER, *Associate Meteorologist and Climatic Section Director for Idaho, Weather Bureau, Boise.*

ILLINOIS

Climatic summary

County [1]	Station	Temperature: Length of record	Temperature: January average	Temperature: July average	Temperature: Maximum	Temperature: Minimum	Killing frost average dates: Length of record	Killing frost average dates: Last in spring	Killing frost average dates: First in fall	Killing frost average dates: Growing season [2]	Average precipitation: Length of record	January	February	March	April	May	June	July	August	September	October	November	December	Annual
		Yr.	*°F.*	*°F.*	*°F.*	*°F.*	*Yr.*			*Days*	*Yr.*	*In.*	*In.*	*In.*	*In.*	*In.*	*In.*	*In.*	*In.*	*In.*	*In.*	*In.*	*In.*	*In.*
Adams	Coatsburg	14	26.2	76.5	111	−29	11	Apr. 25	Oct. 20	178	14	1.89	1.90	2.24	3.56	4.16	4.35	3.64	3.18	4.50	2.11	1.90	1.54	34.97
	Golden										26	1.69	1.33	2.80	3.02	4.52	4.43	3.16	2.86	4.48	2.54	2.34	1.64	34.81
	Quincy	27	28.4	80.7	114	−20	27	Apr. 13	Oct. 19	189	33	1.85	1.56	2.41	3.12	4.29	4.45	3.26	3.27	4.62	2.29	2.33	1.61	35.06
Alexander	Cairo	40	36.8	79.7	106	−16	40	Mar. 29	Nov. 1	217	40	4.25	2.66	4.12	3.60	3.42	3.59	2.97	3.14	3.12	2.86	3.24	3.49	40.46
Bond	Greenville	40	30.8	78.4	115	−21	40	Apr. 17	Oct. 24	190	40	2.51	2.03	3.49	3.79	4.08	4.00	3.00	3.55	3.63	3.19	2.49	2.39	38.15
Bureau	Tiskilwa	12	23.5	73.6	108	−28	15	Apr. 28	Oct. 15	170	40	1.64	1.60	2.73	3.14	4.03	3.63	3.28	3.49	3.97	2.59	2.26	1.58	33.94
	Walnut	40	23.5	75.9	111	−26	40	Apr. 30	Oct. 14	167	40	1.62	1.57	2.47	2.80	4.01	3.80	3.42	3.76	4.55	2.56	2.10	1.51	34.17
Carroll	Mount Carroll	40	20.7	73.6	108	−35	40	May 9	Oct. 4	148	40	1.43	1.28	2.13	2.77	4.12	4.39	3.56	3.96	4.30	2.64	2.30	1.55	34.43
	Zion	12	18.9	72.6	106	−30	13	May 2	Oct. 12	163	12	1.27	1.39	1.93	2.91	3.94	3.84	4.13	4.19	3.40	2.01	2.10	1.63	32.74
Cass	Beardstown										23	1.83	1.16	2.87	3.28	4.43	3.95	2.83	3.23	4.09	2.69	2.43	1.61	34.40
Champaign	Philo	15	26.9	75.1	105	−26	14	Apr. 29	Oct. 11	165	17	2.53	2.32	2.80	3.11	3.75	3.55	4.20	3.32	2.95	2.53	2.44	2.14	35.64
	Rantoul	14	26.9	75.1	106	−24	14	do	do	165	15	2.45	2.04	3.17	3.61	4.37	4.08	3.90	4.05	3.47	2.32	2.33	2.02	37.81
	Urbana	36	26.7	75.5	108	−25	36	Apr. 21	Oct. 18	180	36	2.23	1.74	3.23	3.75	3.86	3.39	3.11	3.47	3.58	2.63	2.37	2.18	35.54
Christian	Morrisonville	39	28.8	76.4	111	−29	40	Apr. 25	Oct. 15	173	40	2.17	1.72	3.04	3.42	3.87	4.07	3.20	3.34	3.54	2.79	2.34	2.03	35.53
	Pana	40	29.4	77.3	110	−25	40	Apr. 24	Oct. 19	178	40	2.33	1.99	3.17	3.40	4.07	4.07	3.14	3.73	3.61	2.99	2.38	2.35	37.23
Clark	Casey	10	30.9	75.7	102	−22	12	Apr. 27	Oct. 17	173	30	2.64	1.93	3.72	3.32	4.37	3.61	2.94	3.91	3.92	3.35	2.85	2.74	39.30
Clay	Flora	40	31.6	77.9	111	−25	38	Apr. 18	Oct. 18	183	40	3.07	2.03	3.61	3.61	4.03	3.69	3.29	3.65	3.67	3.30	2.89	2.88	39.72
Clinton	Carlyle										16	2.59	2.57	3.67	4.03	3.64	4.13	3.54	3.10	3.78	3.07	2.66	2.25	39.03
Coles	Charleston	40	29.5	77.2	110	−24	40	Apr. 26	Oct. 16	173	40	2.50	1.98	3.59	3.41	4.18	3.66	3.69	3.57	3.84	3.17	2.63	2.61	38.83
Cook	Chicago (University)	40	25.7	73.9	105	−23	40	Apr. 13	Oct. 26	196	40	1.75	1.63	2.73	2.64	3.39	3.39	3.07	3.33	3.50	2.44	2.13	1.85	31.85
	Chicago Airport	11	25.3	75.5	109	−20	11	do	Oct. 28	198	13	1.89	1.29	2.78	2.22	3.06	4.14	2.90	3.09	3.75	2.47	2.19	1.78	31.56
	LaGrange	16	23.6	73.1	104	−22	18	Apr. 29	Oct. 13	167	18	1.69	1.84	2.34	2.37	4.10	3.49	3.90	3.79	3.66	2.08	1.90	1.61	32.77
Crawford	Palestine	40	31.6	78.2	112	−21	40	Apr. 19	Oct. 20	184	40	3.27	2.09	3.98	3.32	4.27	3.79	3.37	3.87	3.55	3.21	2.80	3.09	40.61
	Robinson	12	31.8	76.3	108	−18	12	do	Oct. 18	182	13	2.95	3.11	3.93	3.47	4.30	4.19	4.64	3.40	3.76	2.95	2.84	3.27	42.81
De Kalb	Sycamore	40	22.3	73.3	109	−26	40	May 8	Oct. 6	151	40	1.47	1.42	2.59	2.86	3.88	4.00	3.18	3.77	4.10	2.81	2.15	1.63	33.86
De Witt	Clinton	24	26.9	76.0	105	−25	27	May 1	Oct. 15	167	29	2.04	1.43	3.38	3.87	4.20	4.12	3.47	3.79	4.42	3.41	2.72	2.14	38.99
Douglas	Tuscola	14	26.8	75.5	110	−25	16	do	Oct. 16	168	40	2.36	1.92	3.38	3.62	4.12	3.90	3.33	3.79	3.78	2.95	2.44	2.36	37.95
Edgar	Paris	40	28.3	76.5	109	−23	40	Apr. 26	Oct. 23	180	40	2.63	1.84	3.65	3.45	4.04	3.93	3.36	3.43	3.79	2.96	2.67	2.55	38.30
Edwards	Albion	18	32.4	78.4	109	−21	16	Apr. 13	do	193	19	3.99	2.76	4.20	3.32	3.51	4.22	3.53	3.39	3.18	2.67	2.80	3.09	40.66
Effingham	Effingham	34	29.9	77.6	111	−29	33	Apr. 22	Oct. 17	178	35	2.61	1.94	3.68	3.37	4.25	4.18	3.08	4.00	3.63	3.26	2.83	2.73	39.56
Fayette	Vandalia										13	1.98	1.66	3.78	3.08	3.98	4.11	3.98	3.52	3.46	2.80	2.24	2.32	36.91
Ford	Roberts										28	1.65	1.37	2.80	3.35	3.75	3.19	3.10	3.15	3.79	2.82	2.33	1.83	33.13
Franklin	Benton	8	34.7	78.3	102	−14	12	Apr. 18	Oct. 19	184	26	3.76	1.82	3.55	3.50	4.09	3.51	2.18	3.58	3.70	3.39	3.12	3.18	39.38

[1] The following counties, for which no records are available, are best represented by the stations indicated: Boone—Marengo; Brown—Rushville; Calhoun—Grafton; Cumberland—Casey; Du Page—Aurora; Hardin—Golconda; Henderson—Monmouth; Lawrence—Mount Carmel; Menard—Springfield; Putnam—Henry; Rock Island—Geneseo Scott—White Hall; Stark—Galva; Tazewell—Bloomington.

[2] Length of growing season between average dates of last killing frost in spring and first in fall.

ILLINOIS—Continued

Climatic summary—Continued

County	Station	Temperature					Killing frost average dates				Average precipitation													
		Length of record	January average	July average	Maximum	Minimum	Length of record	Last in spring	First in fall	Growing season	Length of record	January	February	March	April	May	June	July	August	September	October	November	December	Annual
		Yr.	*°F.*	*°F.*	*°F.*	*°F.*	*Yr.*			*Days*	*Yr.*	*In.*	*In.*	*In.*	*In.*	*In.*	*In.*	*In.*	*In.*	*In.*	*In.*	*In.*	*In.*	*In.*
Fulton	Astoria	16	26.4	74.1	108	−25	15	Apr. 26	Oct. 12	169	32	1.98	1.97	2.91	3.53	3.90	4.36	3.32	3.13	4.34	2.31	2.19	1.74	35.68
	Fairview										27	1.64	1.38	2.52	3.03	3.89	4.11	3.32	3.03	4.07	2.58	2.36	1.51	33.44
Gallatin	Shawneetown										27	4.81	2.46	4.57	4.03	4.21	3.83	2.94	3.76	3.68	3.15	3.43	3.64	44.51
Greene	White Hall	36	29.2	76.5	113	−26	36	Apr. 22	Oct. 18	179	37	2.09	1.71	3.04	3.63	4.21	3.83	3.20	3.55	4.41	3.13	2.57	1.95	37.32
Grundy	Morris	27	24.0	75.4	109	−26	27	May 3	Oct. 10	160	27	1.61	1.18	2.46	2.99	3.55	3.48	2.54	2.91	3.60	2.60	2.46	1.67	31.05
Hamilton	McLeansboro	40	33.6	78.9	113	−23	40	Apr. 16	Oct. 21	188	40	3.81	2.45	3.95	3.84	4.00	3.55	3.04	3.39	3.90	2.94	3.04	3.49	41.40
Hancock	LaHarpe	40	25.5	76.1	113	−30	40	Apr. 26	Oct. 13	170	40	1.96	1.53	2.65	3.00	4.43	4.76	3.75	3.11	4.36	2.25	2.18	1.57	35.55
	Warsaw										24	1.93	1.53	2.04	2.96	4.33	4.92	3.27	2.78	4.09	2.48	2.53	1.59	34.45
Henry	Galva	40	23.1	75.6	111	−29	39	Apr. 29	Oct. 15	169	40	1.54	1.51	2.60	3.03	4.08	3.69	3.56	3.42	4.04	2.37	2.16	1.46	33.46
	Geneseo	10	24.0	74.1	107	−25	13	Apr. 27	Oct. 14	170	26	1.63	1.65	2.35	2.95	3.94	4.01	3.97	3.93	4.41	2.36	2.41	1.43	35.04
Iroquois	Watseka	17	25.9	74.2	106	−23	21	Apr. 28	Oct. 9	164	36	2.02	1.58	2.98	3.23	4.33	3.61	3.33	3.62	3.89	2.54	2.41	2.19	35.73
Jackson	Carbondale	31	35.3	80.0	113	−24	34	Apr. 13	Oct. 20	190	34	3.46	2.24	3.65	3.95	4.36	4.35	3.20	4.03	3.95	3.74	3.22	3.12	43.27
Jasper	Newton										18	3.76	1.91	3.92	3.22	4.43	3.83	3.11	3.89	3.34	2.81	3.08	2.53	39.83
Jefferson	Mount Vernon	40	32.5	78.6	114	−22	40	Apr. 16	Oct. 21	188	40	3.24	2.35	3.80	3.70	4.18	4.13	2.80	3.79	3.75	3.27	2.89	3.07	40.97
Jersey	Grafton										40	2.31	1.94	3.28	3.86	4.04	3.81	2.72	3.49	3.83	3.12	2.59	2.24	37.23
Jo Daviess	Galena										15	1.38	1.11	1.74	2.24	3.72	3.98	3.28	3.28	3.80	2.81	2.63	1.46	31.43
Johnson	New Burnside	40	34.9	78.4	112	−26	38	Apr. 17	Oct. 21	187	40	4.36	2.71	4.33	4.31	4.04	4.21	3.26	3.49	3.75	3.53	3.52	3.74	45.25
Kane	Aurora	40	23.0	73.5	111	−25	40	May 5	Oct. 11	159	40	1.68	1.50	2.55	2.78	3.89	4.15	3.16	3.49	4.11	2.67	2.26	1.69	33.93
	Elgin	18	22.3	73.8	103	−20	20	May 2	Oct. 14	165	32	1.75	1.47	2.31	2.82	3.70	3.97	2.97	3.06	4.22	2.92	2.29	1.49	32.97
	St. Charles	15	22.8	73.6	106	−21	14	May 5	Oct. 11	159	14	1.67	2.22	3.03	3.03	4.68	3.22	4.45	3.82	4.37	2.29	2.13	1.70	36.61
Kankakee	Kankakee	24	25.3	75.4	109	−24	23	Apr. 30	Oct. 14	167	28	1.77	1.34	2.65	3.20	3.92	3.56	2.84	3.28	3.45	2.83	2.38	1.87	33.09
Kendall	Yorkville	15	22.7	73.8	106	−26	14	May 4	Oct. 11	160	17	1.26	1.62	2.15	2.65	4.66	3.98	3.72	3.80	4.48	2.26	1.75	1.35	33.68
Knox	Galesburg	10	24.0	73.0	108	−28	16	Apr. 29	Oct. 14	168	23	1.90	1.69	2.69	3.89	4.30	3.86	4.29	3.34	3.83	2.31	2.60	1.73	36.43
La Salle	LaSalle	34	25.2	76.4	113	−24	34	Apr. 30	Oct. 18	171	38	1.60	1.42	2.39	2.93	3.55	3.64	2.84	3.72	4.13	2.30	2.00	1.57	32.09
	Ottawa	39	24.9	75.8	112	−26	38	do	Oct. 12	165	39	1.65	1.60	2.44	2.99	3.92	3.25	3.02	3.77	3.91	2.24	2.20	1.61	32.60
	Streator	20	24.1	74.9	108	−26	24	do	Oct. 13	166	30	1.92	1.64	2.48	2.92	3.86	3.29	3.26	3.23	3.71	2.31	2.15	1.69	32.46
Lake	Antioch	20	20.4	72.5	105	−25	19	May 4	do	162	21	1.80	1.56	2.40	3.14	3.95	3.17	3.55	2.95	4.04	2.94	1.99	1.71	33.20
	Waukegon	16	23.6	72.0	108	−24	16	May 10	Oct. 15	158	16	1.52	1.11	1.87	2.83	3.21	3.77	3.09	3.08	4.18	2.74	2.43	1.61	31.44
Lee	Ashton	11	22.3	72.0	108	−32	10	Apr. 27	Oct. 11	167	11	1.47	1.93	2.77	2.68	5.02	3.65	4.16	3.87	3.32	2.07	1.74	1.69	34.37
	Dixon	40	21.9	74.4	110	−27	40	May 2	Oct. 13	164	40	1.48	1.33	2.40	2.79	4.07	4.13	3.89	3.51	4.12	2.78	2.08	1.53	34.11
	Paw Paw										26	1.64	1.25	2.57	2.78	3.45	4.23	2.60	2.97	4.40	3.05	2.33	1.56	32.83
Livingston	Dwight	26	24.8	74.9	106	−25	26	May 2	Oct. 17	168	33	1.81	1.72	2.64	3.16	3.77	3.59	2.96	3.37	3.74	2.31	2.35	1.84	33.26
	Pontiac	36	26.2	76.9	108	−24	36	Apr. 26	Oct. 15	172	36	2.11	1.66	2.68	3.54	3.83	3.04	2.77	2.93	3.86	2.44	2.23	1.91	33.00
Logan	Lincoln	40	27.4	76.6	113	−34	40	Apr. 29	do	169	40	2.01	1.65	2.98	3.45	4.29	3.78	3.10	3.39	4.29	2.65	2.31	2.02	35.92
McDonough	Macomb	7	26.0	74.5	99	−28	10	Apr. 26	Oct. 17	174	34	1.91	1.48	2.60	2.99	4.02	4.46	3.84	3.20	4.05	2.48	2.22	1.51	34.76
McHenry	Marengo	40	20.9	73.1	109	−27	40	May 4	Oct. 11	160	40	1.49	1.32	2.24	2.73	3.52	3.99	3.13	3.46	4.12	2.62	2.05	1.53	32.20
McLean	Bloomington	40	26.4	76.7	114	−24	40	Apr. 27	Oct. 16	172	40	2.01	1.72	3.12	3.51	4.07	4.09	3.07	3.42	4.13	2.63	2.57	2.01	36.35

Macon	Decatur	40	28.1	77.2	110	−25	40	Apr. 25	Oct. 17	175	40	2.27	1.89	3.36	3.65	4.17	3.58	3.31	3.54	4.11	2.96	2.37	2.33	37.54
Macoupin	Carlinville	40	29.8	77.7	113	−23	39	Apr. 23	Oct. 18	178	40	2.26	1.90	3.25	3.96	4.16	3.93	3.32	3.45	3.90	3.12	2.56	2.26	38.07
Madison	Edwardsville										29	2.36	1.79	3.29	4.08	4.54	3.81	2.85	3.74	4.18	3.31	2.46	2.26	38.67
Marion	Salem										24	3.07	1.78	3.63	3.88	4.74	3.78	3.27	4.16	3.38	3.62	2.86	3.14	41.31
Marshall	Henry	40	25.3	76.2	113	−27	39	Apr. 28	Oct. 14	169	40	1.75	1.60	2.71	3.12	3.82	3.74	3.11	3.34	4.03	2.42	2.21	1.62	33.47
Mason	Havana	40	26.4	77.7	113	−26	36	Apr. 23	Oct. 19	179	39	1.92	1.55	2.66	3.14	3.73	3.70	3.66	3.06	4.02	2.34	2.13	1.63	33.54
Massac	Brookport										10	5.81	3.16	4.85	3.97	3.40	3.88	3.80	2.99	4.60	2.70	3.45	3.05	45.66
Mercer	Aledo	38	23.6	75.8	113	−30	37	Apr. 27	Oct. 15	171	38	1.48	1.30	2.31	2.97	4.16	4.50	3.53	3.31	4.55	2.41	2.20	1.43	34.15
Monroe	Waterloo										27	2.70	1.78	3.20	4.10	4.39	3.99	2.77	3.82	3.62	3.53	2.95	2.53	39.38
Montgomery	Hillsboro	40	30.3	77.9	112	−22	39	Apr. 23	Oct. 17	177	40	2.36	1.93	3.32	3.77	4.32	4.02	2.95	3.67	3.74	3.21	2.46	2.25	38.00
Morgan	Jacksonville	40	28.1	76.8	112	−28	40	Apr. 24	Oct. 15	174	40	1.87	1.52	2.82	3.24	4.21	3.90	2.89	3.63	4.32	2.76	2.27	1.74	35.17
	Waverly										18	2.14	1.96	2.31	3.18	4.54	3.46	2.94	3.16	4.00	2.34	2.34	1.77	34.14
Moultrie	Sullivan	15	28.8	76.2	111	−24	15	Apr. 24	Oct. 16	175	15	2.59	2.22	2.91	3.97	4.27	3.97	3.28	3.29	3.51	2.49	2.59	1.95	37.04
Ogle	Oregon										30	1.43	1.25	2.13	3.06	3.52	4.38	2.82	3.49	4.07	2.82	2.30	1.69	32.96
	Rochelle										15	1.61	1.25	1.85	2.94	3.33	5.24	3.55	3.57	4.71	2.56	2.45	1.36	34.42
Peoria	Peoria	40	25.6	76.4	113	−27	40	Apr. 15	Oct. 20	188	40	1.82	1.77	2.78	3.23	4.08	3.78	3.63	3.24	4.27	2.41	2.29	1.71	35.01
	Princeville										10	1.78	1.49	2.53	2.83	4.08	3.15	3.20	2.95	3.52	2.04	2.31	1.51	31.39
Perry	Du Quoin	40	34.0	79.2	113	−22	40	Apr. 16	Oct. 15	182	40	3.17	2.28	3.71	3.65	3.90	3.97	3.52	3.71	3.67	2.94	2.91	3.06	40.49
Piatt	Bement										10	2.61	2.06	2.70	3.94	4.61	2.78	3.65	2.78	3.54	1.90	2.02	1.98	34.57
Pike	Griggsville	40	28.7	78.0	113	−25	40	Apr. 16	Oct. 20	187	40	1.90	1.58	2.71	3.42	4.24	4.20	2.96	3.45	4.93	2.76	2.33	1.70	36.18
	Pearl										17	1.49	1.15	3.00	3.74	3.52	3.38	2.40	3.21	4.10	3.84	2.28	1.68	33.79
Pope	Golconda	18	35.4	79.2	108	−16	17	Apr. 12	Oct. 21	192	33	5.02	3.38	4.53	4.15	3.60	4.09	3.51	3.64	3.72	3.39	3.61	3.88	46.52
Pulaski	Grand Chain										15	5.15	2.51	4.57	3.79	3.99	4.48	3.02	3.39	4.00	3.24	3.77	3.46	45.37
Randolph	Chester										40	3.20	2.25	3.73	4.14	4.03	4.03	3.23	3.89	3.72	3.06	2.83	2.79	40.90
	Sparta	40	33.1	79.1	114	−23	40	Apr. 13	Oct. 20	190	40	2.99	2.03	3.46	4.05	4.15	3.50	3.11	3.86	3.46	3.36	2.80	2.68	39.45
Richland	Olney	40	32.1	78.2	112	−21	40	Apr. 18	do	185	40	3.47	2.18	3.87	3.51	4.13	3.73	3.34	3.78	3.78	3.04	2.99	2.99	40.81
St. Clair	Mascoutah	40	32.1	78.9	113	−20	36	do	Oct. 22	187	40	2.65	2.16	3.35	4.04	4.28	3.78	2.99	3.80	3.72	3.16	2.80	2.46	39.19
Saline	Harrisburg	40	35.7	79.7	113	−22	39	Apr. 13	do	192	40	4.19	2.63	4.12	3.94	3.84	3.90	3.55	3.89	3.63	3.39	3.13	3.46	43.67
Sangamon	Springfield	40	28.2	78.0	110	−24	40	Apr. 11	do	194	40	1.99	1.75	3.13	3.13	4.24	3.87	2.88	3.30	3.71	2.48	2.26	1.85	34.59
Schuyler	Rushville	38	27.2	76.9	113	−26	38	Apr. 23	Oct. 20	180	40	1.77	1.42	2.71	3.21	4.26	3.87	3.10	3.21	4.39	2.16	2.14	1.72	33.96
Shelby	Windsor	35	28.9	76.5	111	−26	35	Apr. 27	Oct. 16	172	35	2.53	1.98	3.69	3.82	4.61	3.89	3.56	3.52	4.14	2.88	2.57	2.54	39.73
Stephenson	Freeport	30	20.0	73.7	112	−27	30	May 8	Oct. 6	151	30	1.38	1.20	2.05	2.85	3.58	4.51	3.33	3.77	4.31	2.88	2.32	1.49	33.67
Union	Anna	40	35.1	79.5	112	−20	39	Apr. 9	Oct. 26	200	40	3.92	2.79	4.22	4.50	4.28	4.12	3.35	3.73	4.06	3.45	3.58	3.58	45.58
Vermilion	Danville	33	27.8	76.4	112	−23	30	Apr. 24	Oct. 16	175	35	2.47	1.63	3.13	3.35	3.76	3.48	3.06	3.46	3.64	2.88	2.49	2.28	35.63
	Hoopeston	36	26.9	75.7	111	−25	34	May 1	Oct. 14	166	36	2.53	1.97	3.16	3.71	3.92	3.67	3.54	3.57	3.91	2.72	2.64	2.35	37.69
Wabash	Mount Carmel	36	33.0	78.6	112	−17	37	Apr. 15	Oct. 23	191	40	4.07	2.65	4.31	2.74	3.92	4.10	3.23	3.42	3.66	3.50	3.25	3.73	42.58
Warren	Monmouth	40	24.2	75.9	110	−27	40	Apr. 27	Oct. 14	170	40	1.73	1.56	2.54	3.09	3.93	4.48	3.88	3.13	4.46	2.44	2.32	1.53	35.09
Washington	Nashville										35	2.87	1.82	3.58	3.56	3.89	3.72	2.91	3.91	3.14	3.45	2.59	2.65	38.09
Wayne	Fairfield	40	33.3	79.0	113	−22	40	Apr. 13	Oct. 22	192	40	3.26	2.22	3.75	3.54	4.05	3.89	3.08	3.74	3.72	3.14	2.84	3.11	40.34
White	Carmi										16	4.20	2.00	3.71	3.41	4.33	3.41	2.93	3.32	4.88	3.36	3.25	3.05	41.85
Whiteside	Morrison	40	22.2	74.7	112	−30	38	May 1	Oct. 12	164	40	1.50	1.47	2.38	2.95	4.26	4.22	3.74	3.70	4.10	2.59	2.11	1.51	34.53
Will	Joliet	40	24.2	74.0	109	−25	40	May 3	do	162	40	1.74	1.53	2.56	2.98	3.76	3.69	3.07	3.29	3.76	2.53	2.25	1.80	32.96
Williamson	Halfway	11	34.3	78.4	110	−18	10	Apr. 15	Oct. 20	188	11	3.38	2.80	3.58	3.58	3.34	3.64	3.83	2.95	3.41	3.01	2.64	3.51	39.67
Winnebago	Kishwaukee	12	20.7	72.8	108	−26	14	May 5	Oct. 9	157	14	1.38	1.61	2.52	3.14	4.27	3.19	3.76	4.52	3.94	2.14	2.08	1.35	33.90
	Rockford	40	21.4	74.1	112	−26	40	May 6	Oct. 10	157	40	1.59	1.50	2.54	2.77	3.84	3.99	3.48	3.65	4.02	2.74	2.21	1.57	33.90
	Winnebago	16	20.7	72.8	110	−26	15	May 7	Oct. 9	155	15	1.53	1.75	2.80	3.43	4.74	3.60	4.25	4.66	3.73	2.42	2.25	1.78	36.94
Woodford	Minonk	40	24.8	75.6	111	−28	39	Apr. 29	Oct. 12	166	40	1.62	1.54	2.53	3.00	3.73	3.54	3.10	3.45	3.75	2.43	2.14	1.67	32.50

ILLINOIS—Continued

Precipitation and temperature—State unit values

[This tabulation gives the mean annual, mean monthly, and average seasonal precipitation, 1886–1938, and the mean annual temperatures, 1902–38, for Illinois]

Precipitation		Precipitation		Precipitation		Precipitation		Temperature		Temperature	
Year	Mean	Year	Mean	Year	Mean	Month	Mean	Year	Mean	Year	Mean
	In.		In.		In.		In.		°F.		°F.
1886	34.57	1907	40.98	1928	37.27	May	4.08	1902	52.1	1921	56.6
1887	33.62	1908	35.75	1929	41.97	June	3.91	1903	51.5	1922	54.5
1888	39.30	1909	43.69	1930	27.75	July	3.25	1904	50.2	1923	53.2
1889	35.71	1910	32.37	1931	37.86	August	3.31	1905	51.5	1924	50.7
1890	37.62	1911	39.14	1932	36.39	September	3.73	1906	52.8	1925	53.2
1891	33.16	1912	35.66	1933	34.99	October	2.54	1907	51.9	1926	51.9
1892	41.35	1913	35.21	1934	33.06	November	2.68	1908	53.8	1927	53.5
1893	34.34	1914	28.44	1935	41.89	December	2.19	1909	52.4	1928	52.9
1894	29.35	1915	41.96	1936	30.27			1910	52.2	1929	51.4
1895	31.58	1916	37.04	1937	36.82	Annual	36.61	1911	54.0	1930	54.0
1896	37.24	1917	32.30	1938	40.61			1912	50.7	1931	56.3
1897	36.50	1918	37.78					1913	54.1	1932	53.5
1898	47.31	1919	37.44	Month	Mean	Season	Average	1914	53.2	1933	55.1
1899	33.29	1920	32.63					1915	52.2	1934	54.6
1900	35.61	1921	40.63					1916	52.5	1935	52.7
1901	26.25	1922	34.03					1917	49.7	1936	53.3
1902	41.99	1923	37.66		In.		In.	1918	52.7	1937	52.0
1903	34.86	1924	35.92	January	2.39	Winter	6.53	1919	53.6	1938	55.5
1904	37.87	1925	32.62	February	1.95	Spring	10.66	1920	52.3		
1905	36.83	1926	43.25	March	3.18	Summer	10.47				
1906	37.72	1927	49.39	April	3.40	Fall	8.95				

Dates of last killing frost in spring and first in fall, with length of growing season

Year	Chicago			Mount Carroll			Peoria			Springfield			Mount Vernon			Cairo		
	Last in spring	First in fall	Growing season[1]	Last in spring	First in fall	Growing season[1]	Last in spring	First in fall	Growing season[1]	Last in spring	First in fall	Growing season[1]	Last in spring	First in fall	Growing season[1]	Last in spring	First in fall	Growing season[1]
			Days			*Days*			*Days*			*Days*			*Days*			*Days*
1899	Apr. 2	Sept. 30	181	Apr. 19	Sept. 27	161	Apr. 9	Sept. 30	174	Apr. 9	Sept. 29	173	Apr. 8	Sept. 27	172	Apr. 2	Sept. 30	181
1900	Apr. 13	Nov. 6	207	May 5	Oct. 17	165	Apr. 14	Nov. 6	206	Apr. 12	Nov. 8	210	Apr. 14	Oct. 18	187	Mar. 31	Nov. 9	223
1901	Apr. 19	Oct. 17	181	June 8	Sept. 19	103	Apr. 21	Oct. 5	167	Apr. 20	Nov. 4	198	Apr. 21	do	180	Mar. 27	Nov. 4	222
1902	Apr. 8	Nov. 23	229	Apr. 27	Sept. 12	138	Apr. 9	Oct. 14	188	Apr. 15	Nov. 23	222	Apr. 15	Sept. 15	153	Apr. 8	Nov. 27	233
1903	Apr. 5	Oct. 27	205	June 7	Sept. 18	103	Apr. 14	Oct. 24	193	Apr. 4	Oct. 24	203	May 1	Oct. 24	176	Mar. 3	Nov. 7	249
1904	Apr. 21	Oct. 28	190	May 16	Sept. 15	122	Apr. 21	Oct. 23	185	Apr. 21	Oct. 26	188	Apr. 21	Oct. 26	188	Mar. 27	Nov. 13	231
1905	Apr. 7	Oct. 21	197	Apr. 22	Oct. 11	172	Apr. 22	Oct. 21	182	Apr. 16	Oct. 12	179	Apr. 22	Oct. 12	173	Apr. 17	Nov. 11	208
1906	Mar. 31	Oct. 10	193	May 10	Oct. 10	153	May 7	Oct. 10	156	Apr. 2	Oct. 10	191	May 7	Oct. 10	156	Apr. 1	Oct. 11	193
1907	May 4	Oct. 14	163	May 28	Sept. 25	120	May 4	Oct. 13	162	Apr. 17	Oct. 19	185	May 1	Oct. 11	163	Apr. 14	Oct. 28	197
1908	Apr. 3	Oct. 12	192	May 3	Sept. 29	149	Apr. 12	Oct. 9	180	Apr. 3	Oct. 31	211	Apr. 3	Nov. 5	216	Apr. 3	Nov. 5	216
1909	May 2	Oct. 14	165	May 4	Sept. 27	146	Apr. 23	Oct. 12	172	Apr. 10	Oct. 12	185	May 2	Oct. 12	163	Apr. 9	Oct. 13	187
1910	Apr. 24	Oct. 29	188	May 14	Oct. 22	161	Apr. 24	Oct. 23	182	Apr. 24	Oct. 29	188	Apr. 25	Oct. 28	186	Apr. 24	Oct. 28	187
1911	Apr. 7	Oct. 24	200	May 5	do	170	Apr. 9	Oct. 24	198	Apr. 7	Nov. 1	208	Apr. 9	Oct. 24	198	Mar. 16	Nov. 2	231
1912	Apr. 18	do	189	May 14	Sept. 29	138	Apr. 19	Oct. 23	187	Apr. 3	Nov. 2	213	Apr. 8	Oct. 23	198	Mar. 25	do	222
1913	Apr. 7	Oct. 20	196	June 8	Sept. 22	106	Mar. 28	Oct. 21	207	Mar. 28	Oct. 21	207	Apr. 5	Oct. 22	200	Mar. 28	Oct. 31	217
1914	Apr. 10	Oct. 27	200	Apr. 20	Oct. 25	188	Apr. 12	Oct. 26	197	Apr. 9	Oct. 27	201	Apr. 12	Oct. 27	198	Apr. 9	Oct. 27	201
1915	Apr. 4	Oct. 9	188	Apr. 17	Oct. 9	175	Apr. 4	Oct. 9	188	Apr. 3	Oct. 9	189	Apr. 13	Oct. 9	179	Apr. 3	Nov. 15	226
1916	Apr. 9	Oct. 22	196	May 2	Sept. 16	137	Apr. 9	Oct. 11	185	Apr. 9	Oct. 11	185	Apr. 9	Oct. 22	196	Mar. 23	Nov. 13	235
1917	May 23	Oct. 8	138	May 23	Oct. 1	131	Apr. 15	Oct. 8	176	Apr. 13	Oct. 6	176	Apr. 14	Oct. 9	178	Mar. 6	Oct. 13	221
1918	Apr. 19	Nov. 2	197	May 1	do	153	May 1	Nov. 1	184	Apr. 10	Nov. 1	205	Apr. 13	Nov. 1	202	Apr. 10	Nov. 11	215
1919	Apr. 25	Oct. 29	187	Apr. 26	Oct. 11	168	Apr. 26	Oct. 17	174	Apr. 1	Nov. 2	215	Apr. 26	Nov. 5	193	Apr. 1	Nov. 12	225
1920	Apr. 13	do	199	May 14	Oct. 1	140	Apr. 13	Oct. 29	199	Apr. 14	Oct. 29	198	Apr. 14	Oct. 29	198	Apr. 13	Oct. 29	199
1921	Apr. 17	Nov. 10	207	May 16	Oct. 8	145	Apr. 18	Nov. 2	198	Apr. 17	Nov. 2	199	Apr. 18	Nov. 10	206	Mar. 29	Nov. 12	228
1922	Apr. 1	Nov. 15	228	Apr. 29	Oct. 15	169	Apr. 1	Oct. 17	199	Mar. 22	Oct. 18	210	Apr. 20	Oct. 18	181	Mar. 8	Nov. 16	253
1923	May 9	Oct. 30	174	May 13	Sept 14	124	Apr. 17	Oct. 21	187	Apr. 9	Oct. 21	195	Apr. 18	Oct. 20	185	Apr. 1	Oct. 31	213
1924	Apr. 2	Nov. 9	221	May 20	Sept. 30	133	Apr. 2	Oct. 23	204	Apr. 2	Oct. 23	204	Apr. 2	Oct. 23	204	Apr. 2	Oct. 24	205
1925	Mar. 20	Oct. 10	204	May 25	Oct. 10	138	Apr. 5	Oct. 10	188	May 25	Oct. 10	138	Apr. 1	Oct. 19	201	Mar. 15	Oct. 20	219
1926	Apr. 19	Oct. 26	190	May 15	Sept. 26	134	Apr. 26	Oct. 31	188	Apr. 19	Oct. 25	189	Apr. 20	Nov. 2	196	Apr. 1	Nov. 2	215
1927	Apr. 23	Nov. 4	195	Apr. 24	Oct. 14	173	Apr. 24	Nov. 5	195	Apr. 23	Oct. 14	174	Apr. 25	Nov. 5	194	Mar. 4	Nov. 3	244
1928	Apr. 16	Sept. 26	163	May 13	Sept. 24	134	Apr. 28	Sept. 26	151	Apr. 15	Sept. 26	164	Apr. 28	Sept. 24	149	Apr. 16	Oct. 31	198
1929	Apr. 1	Nov. 5	218	May 21	Oct. 4	136	Apr. 1	Oct. 25	207	Apr. 1	Oct. 25	207	Mar. 20	Oct. 25	219	Mar. 10	Nov. 5	240
1930	Apr. 2	Oct. 18	199	May 17	Oct. 1	137	Mar. 30	Oct. 20	204	Mar. 30	Oct. 18	202	Apr. 25	Oct. 18	176	Mar. 29	Oct. 24	209
1931	do	Nov. 24	236	May 23	Oct. 18	148	Apr. 6	Nov. 6	214	Apr. 6	Nov. 6	214	Apr. 7	Nov. 6	213	Mar. 20	Nov. 6	231
1932	Apr. 13	Nov. 11	212	Apr. 28	Sept. 30	155	Apr. 13	Oct. 30	200	Apr. 14	Oct. 11	180	Apr. 15	Oct. 28	196	Mar. 18	Nov. 2	229
1933	Mar. 26	Oct. 25	213	Apr. 27	Oct. 13	169	Mar. 28	Oct. 25	211	Mar. 22	Nov. 8	231	Mar. 26	Nov. 8	227	Mar. 22	Nov. 8	231
1934	Apr. 13	Oct. 28	198	Apr. 28	Oct. 28	183	Apr. 25	Oct. 28	186	Apr. 25	Oct. 28	186	Apr. 25	Oct. 28	186	Mar. 28	Nov. 12	229
1935	Apr. 17	Nov. 5	202	May 4	Oct. 4	153	Apr. 16	Oct. 4	171	Apr. 16	Oct. 4	171	Apr. 16	Oct. 4	171	Mar. 9	Oct. 7	212
1936	Apr. 23	Nov. 4	195	May 14	Oct. 2	141	Apr. 23	Oct. 23	183	Apr. 22	Oct. 24	185	Apr. 23	Oct. 24	184	Apr. 7	Oct. 28	204

[1] Number of days between last killing frost in spring and first in fall.

ILLINOIS—Continued

Dates of last killing frost in spring and first in fall, with length of growing season—Continued

Year	Chicago			Mount Carroll			Peoria			Springfield			Mount Vernon			Cairo		
	Last in spring	First in fall	Growing season [1]	Last in spring	First in fall	Growing season [1]	Last in spring	First in fall	Growing season [1]	Last in spring	First in fall	Growing season [1]	Last in spring	First in fall	Growing season [1]	Last in spring	First in fall	Growing season [1]
			Days			*Days*			*Days*			*Days*			*Days*			*Days*
1937	Apr. 16	Oct. 14	181	Apr. 11	Oct. 8	180	Apr. 11	Oct. 14	186	Apr. 11	Oct. 14	186	Apr. 11	Oct. 14	186	Mar. 29	Oct. 24	209
1938	Apr. 8	Nov. 8	214	May 12	Oct. 25	166	Apr. 10	Oct. 24	197	Apr. 9	Oct. 24	198	Apr. 10	Oct. 24	197	Apr. 3	do	204
Mean	Apr. 13	Oct. 26	196	May 9	Oct. 4	148	Apr. 15	Oct. 20	188	Apr. 11	Oct. 22	194	Apr. 16	Oct. 21	188	Mar. 29	Nov. 1	217
Extremes	Mar. 20 [2]	Sept. 26 [4]	[6] 138	Apr. 11 [2]	Sept. 12 [4]	[6] 103	Mar. 28 [2]	Sept. 26 [4]	[6] 151	Mar. 22 [2]	Sept. 21 [4]	[6] 138	Mar. 20 [2]	Sept. 15 [4]	[6] 153	Mar. 3 [2]	Sept. 30 [4]	[6] 181
	May 23 [3]	Nov. 24 [5]	[7] 236	June 8 [3]	Oct. 28 [5]	[7] 188	May 7 [3]	Nov. 6 [5]	[7] 214	May 25 [3]	Nov. 23 [5]	[7] 231	May 7 [3]	Nov. 10 [5]	[7] 227	Apr. 24 [3]	Nov. 27 [5]	[7] 253

[2] Earliest date in spring.
[3] Latest date in spring.
[4] Earliest date in fall.
[5] Latest date in fall.
[6] Shortest growing season.
[7] Longest growing season.

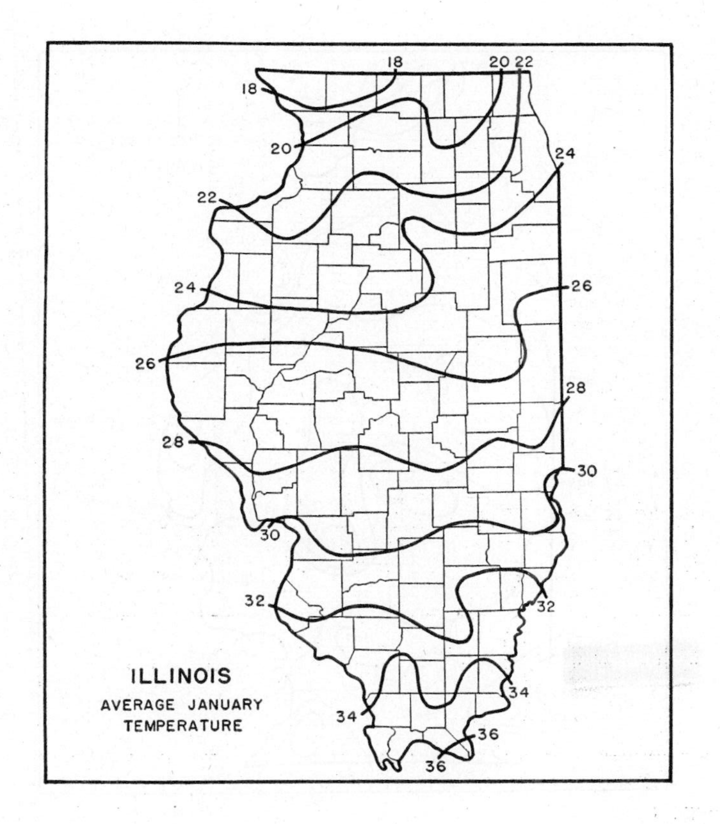
ILLINOIS
AVERAGE JANUARY TEMPERATURE
18
20
22
24
26
28
30
32
34
36

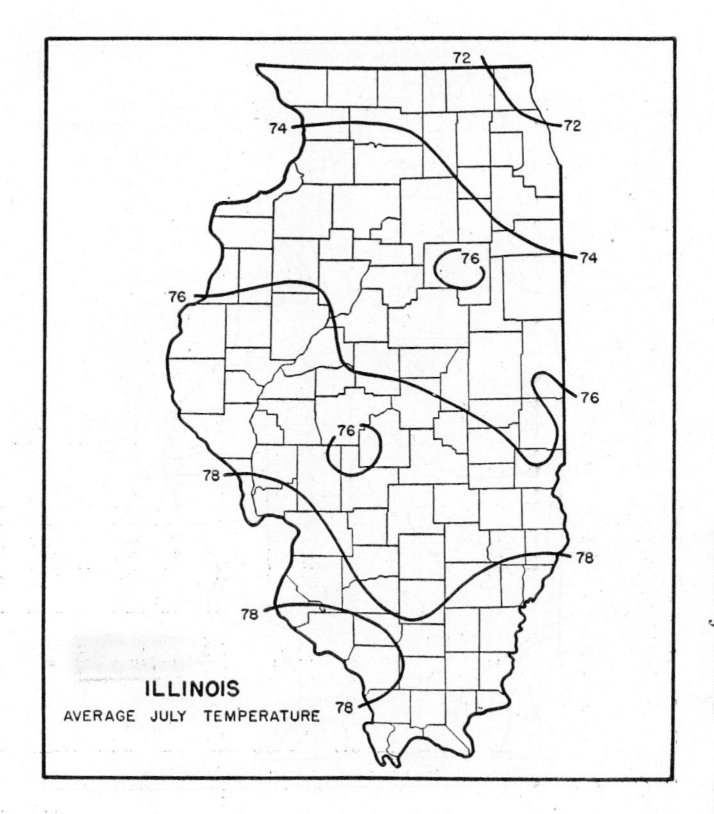
ILLINOIS
AVERAGE JULY TEMPERATURE
72
74
76
78

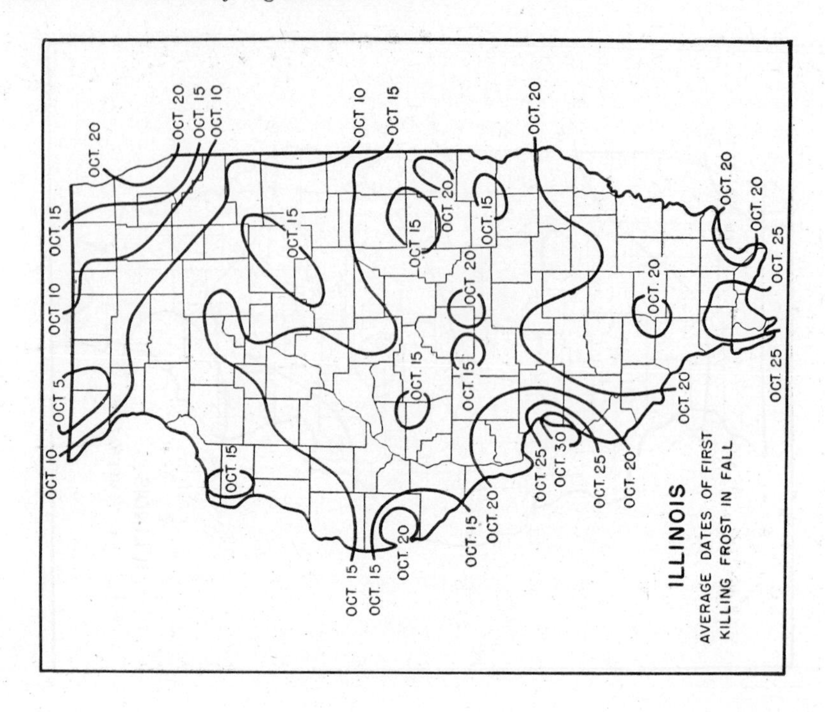
ILLINOIS
AVERAGE DATES OF FIRST
KILLING FROST IN FALL

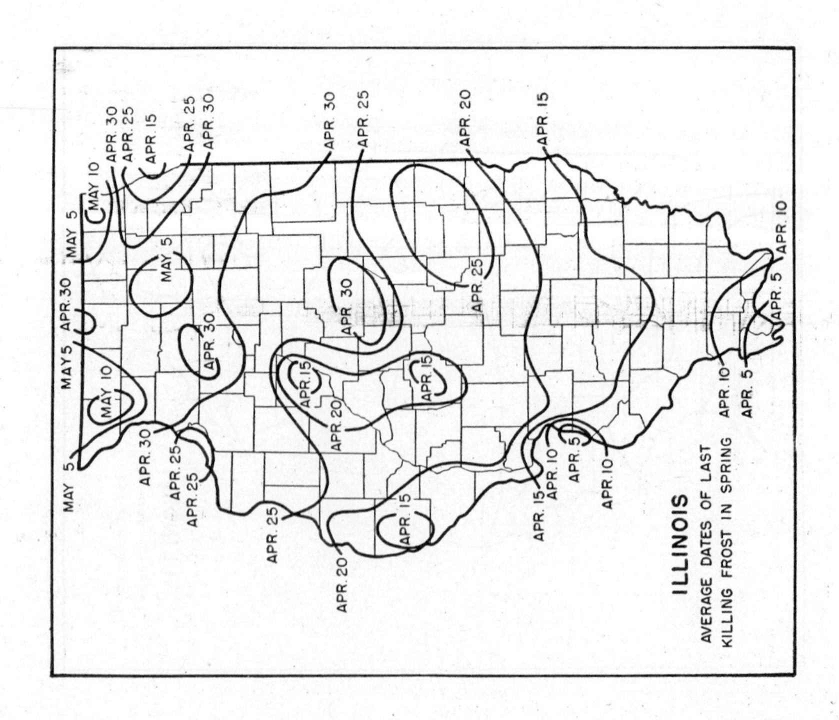
ILLINOIS
AVERAGE DATES OF LAST
KILLING FROST IN SPRING

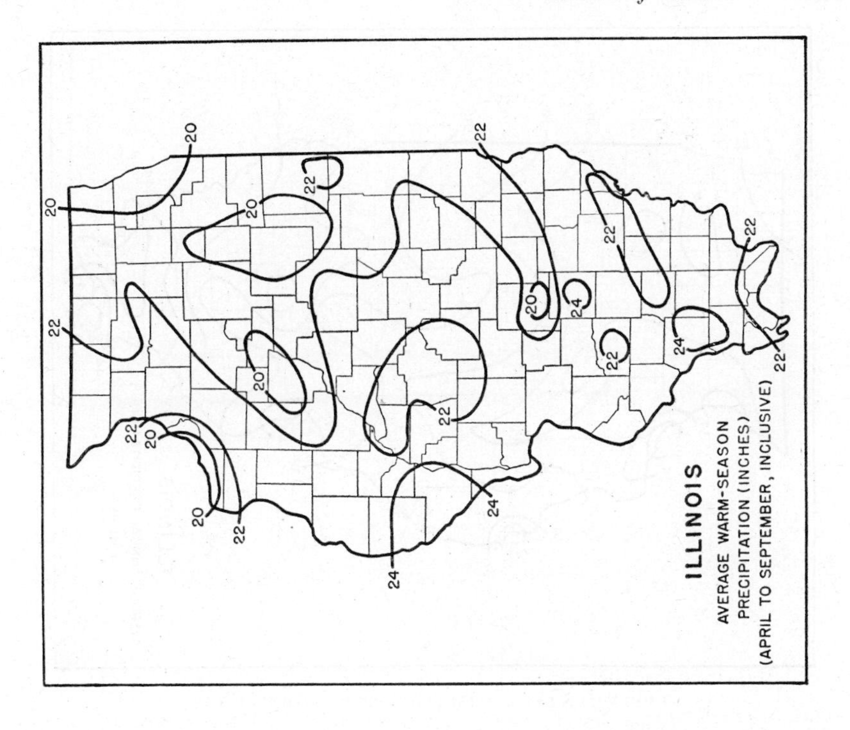
ILLINOIS
AVERAGE WARM-SEASON
PRECIPITATION (INCHES)
(APRIL TO SEPTEMBER, INCLUSIVE)

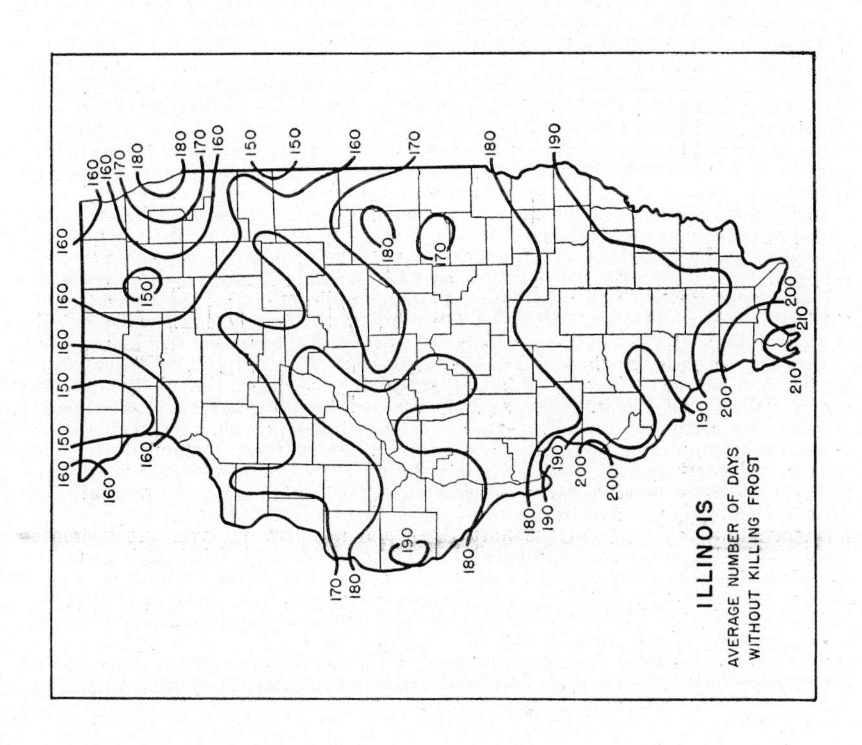
ILLINOIS
AVERAGE NUMBER OF DAYS
WITHOUT KILLING FROST

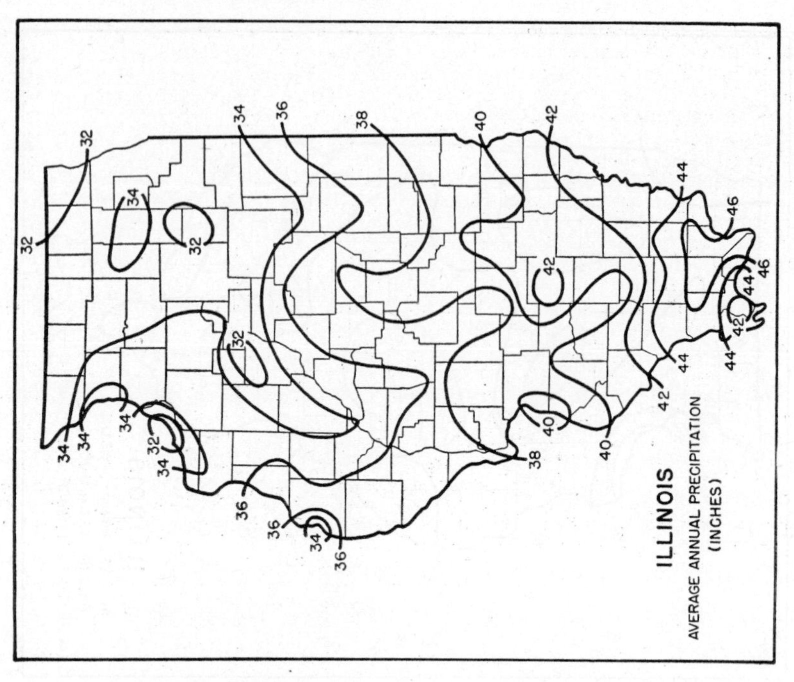

SUPPLEMENTARY CLIMATIC NOTES FOR ILLINOIS

Illinois lies in the great central plain of North America and covers an area of 56,665 square miles. It has a gentle slope from north to south with an average elevation for the State of about 600 feet above sea level. Several of the northern counties and small areas in the central part have elevations generally above 800 feet. Charles Mound in Jo Daviess County, with an elevation of 1,241 feet, is the highest point in the State; the lowest point, 269 feet, is at the junction of the Mississippi and Ohio Rivers. The Illinois, the most important river within the State, is formed by the junction of the Des Plaines and the Kankakee Rivers in the northeastern part of Grundy County and crosses the north-central and western parts of the State.

Because of its length from north to south, Illinois presents a rather wide variation in climatic conditions. It lies within the principal storm tracks that cross the country and as a consequence experiences marked weather changes, especially in winter. In the northern part, the climate is most pronouncedly of the continental type, with warm summers and cold winters; in the central part, the summers are likewise warm and the winters moderately cold; while in the southern part of the State the summers are warm and the winters still less severe.

Progressively toward the south the summer heat is interrupted by fewer intervening cool periods. In the area adjacent to Lake Michigan, that body of water exerts some modifying influences. The summer rainfall is largely of the local-shower type; although droughty conditions sometimes prevail, the precipitation is ordinarily ample for the needs of vegetation. In southern sections during the winter and early spring, heavy rainfall results from low atmospheric pressure systems (cyclonic depressions) that originate in the Southwestern States and pass up the Ohio Valley. A considerable part of the winter's precipitation is in the form of snow, especially in the north. In general, snowfall averages decrease southward; deep snow, accompanied by strong winds and drifting, is not uncommon in northern Illinois and may occasionally occur in the extreme south.

It is seldom that a summer passes without temperatures exceeding 100° F., either locally or over the whole State. Zero temperatures are experienced every winter, at least in the northern half of the State.

The average date of the last killing frost in the spring is about May 10 in extreme northern Illinois, mid-April in central and most of the southern parts of the State, and about the close of March at Cairo in the extreme south. In general, the first killing frost in fall occurs in October, the first or second week of that month in the northern part, the second or third week in the central part, and during the last 10 days in the south. The average length of the growing season ranges from approximately 150 days in extreme northern Illinois to more than 200 days in the extreme south, a difference of nearly 2 months.

Available records show that the northern part of the State receives 28 percent of its annual rainfall in the spring months, 32 in the summer, and 26 in the fall; the central part, 30 percent in spring, 29 in summer, and 24 in the fall; and the southern part, 30 percent in spring, 26 in summer, and 23 in the fall.

Illinois has had several major droughts in the past half century—in 1887, 1901, 1914, 1930, 1934, and 1936.

Relative humidity ranges between 72 and 75 percent in the winter months and 64 and 68 percent in the summer. Sunshine during the year averages approximately 60 percent of the possible amount. For the State as a whole, measurable precipitation normally occurs on 100 days of the year; the weather averages clear on 160 days, partly cloudy on 94 days, and cloudy on 111 days.

The prevailing winds are mostly from the southwest or south. The wind-velocity records at first-order Weather Bureau stations in and near the State show the greatest movement in March, with an average hourly velocity of 10 to 14 miles an hour, and the least in August, with averages approximately two-thirds those of March. The highest wind of record, covering a 5-minute period, was 65 miles an hour from the northeast, observed at Cairo on June 21, 1891, and at Chicago on February 12, 1894. Local wind squalls and tornadoes sometimes cause destruction over limited areas.

Elward W. Holcomb, *Meteorologist and Climatic Section Director for Illinois, Weather Bureau, Springfield.*

INDIANA

Climatic summary

County [1]	Station	Temperature: Length of record	Temperature: January average	Temperature: July average	Temperature: Maximum	Temperature: Minimum	Killing frost average dates: Length of record	Killing frost average dates: Last in spring	Killing frost average dates: First in fall	Growing season [2]	Average precipitation: Length of record	January	February	March	April	May	June	July	August	September	October	November	December	Annual
		Yr.	°F.	°F.	°F.	°F.	Yr.			Days	Yr.	In.	In.	In.	In.	In.	In.	In.	In.	In.	In.	In.	In.	In.
Adams	Berne	29	27.1	74.7	107	−22	29	May 1	Oct. 14	166	29	2.62	1.49	3.54	3.32	3.77	3.52	3.64	3.25	3.71	2.69	2.45	2.51	36.51
Allen	Fort Wayne	40	26.7	74.1	106	−24	39	Apr. 23	Oct. 16	176	39	2.38	1.82	3.31	3.04	3.46	3.33	3.34	2.98	3.20	2.56	2.33	2.38	34.13
Bartholomew	Columbus	40	31.1	76.5	111	−27	39	Apr. 28	Oct. 13	168	40	3.66	2.37	3.96	3.68	3.58	3.49	2.85	3.68	3.70	3.12	2.73	3.13	39.95
Benton	Fowler	8	29.9	78.3	111	−21	8	Apr. 26	Oct. 17	174	11	2.30	1.56	2.54	2.93	3.73	3.59	3.23	2.82	4.15	2.66	2.97	1.99	34.47
Boone	Whitestown	40	27.5	75.0	112	−24	40	Apr. 30	Oct. 9	162	40	2.91	1.93	4.03	3.55	4.13	3.62	3.51	3.35	3.64	2.86	2.58	2.75	38.86
Brown	Hickory Hill	26	31.7	76.7	110	−20	26	Apr. 24	Oct. 21	180	26	3.71	1.84	3.87	3.35	4.07	3.88	3.12	3.87	4.42	3.07	3.14	3.12	41.46
Carroll	Delphi	40	26.7	75.8	112	−26	39	May 3	Oct. 6	156	40	2.75	1.98	3.30	3.44	4.11	3.91	3.48	3.47	3.73	2.81	2.66	2.61	38.25
Cass	Logansport	20	26.0	75.4	106	−25	20	May 1	Oct. 12	164	36	2.64	1.82	2.95	3.23	3.86	3.62	3.57	3.50	4.01	2.64	2.57	2.39	36.80
	Jeffersonville	40	34.9	78.8	111	−13	40	Apr. 12	Oct. 22	193	40	4.34	2.86	4.37	3.84	4.02	3.58	3.48	3.39	2.78	2.83	3.03	3.82	42.34
Clark	Forest Reserve	26	33.5	77.3	111	−22	26	Apr. 26	Oct. 15	172	27	4.71	2.30	4.31	3.88	3.84	3.80	3.47	4.03	3.40	3.02	2.93	3.68	43.37
Clinton	Frankfort	25	28.2	75.3	108	−23	25	Apr. 27	Oct. 13	169	25	2.82	1.72	3.55	3.47	4.54	4.09	3.99	3.46	4.06	3.08	2.56	2.71	40.05
Crawford	Marengo	40	32.3	75.9	110	−30	39	Apr. 30	Oct. 9	162	39	4.48	3.09	4.82	3.94	4.64	4.08	3.71	3.80	3.56	3.28	3.20	3.96	46.56
Daviess	Washington	40	32.4	77.8	113	−19	40	Apr. 17	Oct. 23	189	39	3.90	2.41	4.27	3.53	4.16	4.36	3.30	4.07	3.65	3.36	2.93	3.47	43.41
Dearborn	Moores Hill	37	31.2	75.8	108	−21	37	Apr. 25	Oct. 16	174	37	3.90	2.51	4.06	3.62	4.02	3.46	3.26	3.51	3.36	3.02	2.88	3.13	40.73
Decatur	Greensburg	40	29.5	75.8	106	−24	37	Apr. 24	Oct. 17	176	38	3.61	2.45	4.06	3.35	3.80	3.66	3.60	3.30	3.52	3.11	2.67	3.10	40.23
De Kalb	Auburn	24	24.5	72.2	105	−22	23	May 10	Oct. 6	149	24	2.25	2.08	2.56	2.75	3.74	3.38	2.86	3.24	2.67	2.64	2.18	2.11	32.46
Delaware	Muncie						14	Apr. 27	Oct. 18	174	19	2.97	1.79	4.02	3.86	4.08	4.63	3.38	3.86	4.13	2.52	2.70	2.95	40.89
Dubois	Huntingburg	30	35.5	77.9	108	−20	30	Apr. 23	Oct. 17	177	30	4.65	2.64	4.32	4.12	4.46	4.15	3.81	3.98	4.21	3.83	3.34	4.10	47.61
Elkhart	Goshen	24	24.7	73.5	111	−25	24	May 10	Oct. 10	153	24	1.81	1.31	2.59	3.27	3.59	3.27	2.43	2.83	3.50	2.94	2.36	2.15	32.05
Fayette	Connersville	25	29.3	75.1	107	−23	25	May 3	Oct. 7	157	25	3.05	1.98	3.93	3.47	3.37	3.35	3.27	3.54	3.01	3.25	2.21	2.73	37.16
Fountain	Veedersburg	39	28.7	75.9	112	−27	40	May 2	Oct. 11	162	38	2.65	1.86	3.15	3.34	4.17	3.95	3.67	3.59	3.62	2.96	2.45	2.49	37.90
Franklin	Brookville	14	32.1	75.6	108	−22	13	May 1	do	163	14	3.47	2.04	3.25	2.99	3.76	3.76	3.51	3.26	4.88	3.39	2.90	2.53	39.74
Fulton	Rochester	24	27.0	75.1	109	−30	24	do	Oct. 9	161	25	2.56	1.88	2.59	3.22	3.96	3.78	3.33	3.86	4.09	2.21	2.84	2.29	36.61
Gibson	Princeton	40	33.6	78.7	113	−20	40	Apr. 18	Oct. 19	184	39	4.12	2.69	4.23	3.65	4.02	3.90	3.15	3.58	3.62	3.02	2.89	3.58	42.45
Grant	Marion	40	27.7	74.8	108	−25	40	May 6	Oct. 6	153	40	3.03	1.97	3.73	3.53	3.71	3.88	3.20	3.41	3.91	2.71	2.53	2.90	38.51
Greene	Worthington	19	31.1	76.5	109	−24	18	Apr. 22	Oct. 11	172	20	3.83	2.65	4.24	3.55	4.60	4.10	3.88	3.21	3.15	3.53	2.66	3.37	42.77
	Elliston	40	31.0	77.3	112	−24	40	do	Oct. 13	174	25	3.62	1.89	3.83	3.39	4.77	3.93	2.31	3.78	3.77	3.08	2.97	3.35	40.69
Hamilton	Noblesville										25	2.83	1.63	3.57	3.72	3.86	4.13	3.47	3.15	4.24	2.64	2.83	2.74	38.81
Hancock	Greenfield	34	29.4	75.4	109	−21	34	Apr. 25	Oct. 16	174	35	2.83	1.85	3.96	3.65	3.98	3.78	3.78	3.73	3.78	2.61	2.87	2.38	39.20
Harrison	Evans Landing										16	5.25	2.89	3.98	3.92	4.14	3.81	3.35	3.36	3.18	3.11	2.87	3.45	43.31
Howard	Kokomo	40	28.0	76.3	110	−22	40	Apr. 29	Oct. 11	165	40	3.00	1.92	3.50	3.63	4.05	3.68	3.31	3.79	3.82	2.90	2.76	2.63	38.99
Huntington	Huntington	40	26.6	74.6	110	−20	40	May 4	do	160	39	2.68	2.02	3.30	3.10	3.86	3.84	3.30	3.54	3.19	2.92	2.59	2.48	36.82
	Markle	12	27.4	72.7	101	−22	12	May 8	Oct. 2	147	12	2.52	2.16	3.58	3.01	3.74	4.54	3.33	3.11	3.10	2.74	2.47	2.61	36.91
Jackson	Seymour	40	32.8	77.0	111	−22	39	Apr. 24	Oct. 15	174	40	3.71	2.67	4.09	3.65	4.06	3.63	3.12	3.72	3.50	3.18	2.70	3.36	41.39
Jasper	Wheatfield	22	25.2	74.5	112	−25	22	May 8	Oct. 6	151	22	1.84	1.38	2.65	3.74	3.32	3.54	2.77	3.64	4.01	2.94	2.46	2.44	34.73
	Collegeville	38	25.1	75.2	116	−27	38	May 3	Oct. 10	160	38	2.06	1.64	2.94	3.54	4.19	3.38	3.62	3.42	3.56	2.80	2.46	2.20	35.81
Jay	Salamonia	32	27.8	73.8	112	−25	32	May 9	Oct. 7	151	38	3.17	2.15	4.07	3.88	3.51	3.82	3.79	3.19	3.56	2.47	2.70	2.87	39.18
Jefferson	Madison	40	34.2	78.0	110	−20	39	Apr. 22	Oct. 21	182	39	4.29	2.67	4.34	3.93	4.21	4.06	3.59	3.74	3.38	3.08	2.91	3.55	43.75
Jennings	Butlerville	40	32.1	76.4	110	−26	40	Apr. 27	Oct. 17	173	39	4.56	2.78	4.59	4.20	4.60	4.22	3.54	3.99	3.45	3.50	3.09	3.65	46.17

Johnson	Vincennes	40	32.3	79.2	111	−19	40	Apr. 13	Oct. 23	193	40	3.96	2.40	4.34	3.83	4.34	4.51	3.48	3.80	3.93	3.53	3.16	3.61	44.89
Knox	Edwardsport	10	32.6	80.8	112	−16	14	Apr. 19	Oct. 21	185	15	3.88	2.04	3.32	3.15	4.19	3.66	2.84	3.74	3.93	3.00	2.93	2.82	39.50
	Decker										21	3.67	2.15	3.73	3.36	4.01	4.14	2.49	3.87	3.51	3.48	2.61	3.88	40.90
Kosciusko	Winona Lake	30	26.2	74.7	116	−23	31	May 3	Oct. 13	163	31	2.39	1.89	2.93	3.39	3.83	3.54	3.18	3.44	3.65	2.82	2.68	2.29	36.03
Lagrange	Howe	32	24.5	74.1	111	−23	32	May 10	Oct. 7	150	32	2.20	1.87	2.74	3.48	3.97	3.78	3.31	2.97	3.39	2.98	2.87	2.55	36.11
Lake	Whiting	29	25.6	75.0	106	−19	28	Apr. 21	Oct. 20	182	29	1.85	1.36	2.55	2.94	3.71	3.52	2.78	3.51	3.44	2.95	2.33	1.96	32.90
	Hobart	19	25.6	75.0	109	−20	20	May 5	Oct. 18	166	20	1.83	1.35	2.84	3.26	3.26	3.47	2.85	3.45	4.03	3.15	2.84	2.04	34.37
La Porte	LaPorte	40	24.1	73.7	110	−25	40	May 7	Oct. 11	157	39	2.44	2.18	3.23	3.33	4.21	3.81	3.28	3.50	3.87	3.27	2.98	2.67	38.77
Lawrence	Williams										18	4.03	2.34	4.02	3.36	4.11	3.23	2.94	3.67	4.48	3.00	3.11	3.59	41.88
	Bedford	28	32.8	77.8	111	−18	26	Apr. 22	Oct. 20	181	25	3.88	2.36	4.50	3.51	4.30	3.88	2.59	3.80	4.05	3.69	3.30	3.70	43.56
Madison	Anderson	40	29.1	74.9	105	−20	40	May 1	Oct. 16	168	40	2.72	1.72	3.59	3.48	4.11	4.03	3.55	3.62	3.71	2.71	2.67	2.58	38.49
Marion	Indianapolis	40	29.5	76.3	106	−25	40	Apr. 15	Oct. 24	192	40	3.01	2.03	3.93	3.47	3.62	3.59	3.48	3.38	3.44	2.71	2.72	2.88	38.26
Marshall	Plymouth	33	25.6	73.2	109	−23	32	May 7	Oct. 9	155	32	2.04	1.66	2.87	3.04	4.15	3.47	3.01	3.58	3.57	2.91	2.61	2.29	35.20
Martin	Shoals	26	32.1	76.8	114	−22	26	Apr. 24	Oct. 17	176	28	4.15	2.08	4.27	3.57	4.39	3.68	3.02	4.03	3.91	3.36	2.81	3.33	42.60
Monroe	Bloomington	40	30.9	76.7	110	−20	40	Apr. 22	Oct. 21	182	40	4.19	2.82	4.67	3.88	4.43	3.77	3.42	3.89	3.81	3.47	3.08	3.68	45.11
Montgomery	Crawfordsville	36	28.7	76.6	110	−22	35	May 1	Oct. 12	164	34	2.64	1.75	3.66	3.44	3.98	3.57	3.36	3.92	4.22	3.04	2.61	2.73	38.92
Morgan	Martinsville										16	3.45	2.21	3.81	3.39	4.14	4.07	3.46	3.86	4.47	2.93	2.77	2.88	41.44
Noble	Albion	22	24.8	73.4	111	−21	21	May 6	Oct. 11	158	22	1.83	1.23	2.52	2.74	2.98	3.33	2.57	2.81	3.53	2.68	2.48	2.20	30.90
Orange	Paoli	40	32.8	76.6	111	−28	40	Apr. 25	Oct. 16	174	40	3.91	2.47	4.23	3.69	4.39	3.71	3.34	4.10	3.49	3.30	2.98	3.61	43.22
Parke	Rockville	40	29.1	76.2	109	−22	40	Apr. 23	Oct. 15	175	40	2.80	1.90	3.67	3.61	4.32	3.99	3.35	3.58	3.81	3.04	2.79	2.79	39.65
Perry	Rome	35	36.2	78.7	110	−19	36	Apr. 17	Oct. 20	186	35	5.14	3.06	4.69	4.38	4.17	3.92	4.07	3.50	3.28	3.35	3.33	3.98	46.87
Porter	Valparaiso	32	24.6	73.3	105	−22	24	May 2	Oct. 16	167	31	1.95	1.76	3.10	3.28	3.95	3.66	3.19	3.53	3.73	2.97	2.48	2.23	35.83
Posey	Mount Vernon	40	34.1	78.5	109	−21	40	Apr. 14	Oct. 21	190	40	4.30	2.61	4.26	3.74	3.88	3.67	3.39	3.18	3.49	3.18	3.08	3.56	42.34
Pulaski	Winamac	28	26.6	74.3	109	−25	28	May 3	Oct. 9	159	27	1.77	1.68	3.15	3.39	3.83	3.70	3.13	3.24	4.00	3.18	2.73	2.43	36.23
Putnam	Greencastle	31	28.8	76.4	108	−21	31	Apr. 28	Oct. 21	176	31	2.50	1.91	4.12	3.83	4.51	4.48	3.43	4.13	4.03	3.10	2.83	3.19	42.06
Randolph	Farmland	40	28.6	74.4	110	−24	40	Apr. 30	Oct. 14	167	40	2.80	1.93	3.85	3.51	3.67	4.24	3.51	3.55	3.72	2.54	2.34	2.62	38.28
Rush	Mauzy	40	28.7	74.0	108	−26	40	May 3	Oct. 7	157	40	3.48	2.28	4.18	3.63	3.99	3.52	3.47	3.44	3.68	3.18	2.67	3.06	40.58
St. Joseph	South Bend	39	25.2	73.7	109	−20	40	May 7	Oct. 15	167	39	2.15	1.67	2.81	3.03	3.89	3.38	2.97	3.39	3.48	3.01	2.66	2.39	34.83
	Notre Dame	27	26.1	74.2	105	−21	27	Apr. 28	Oct. 20	175	26	2.06	1.38	2.63	2.93	3.79	3.36	2.83	2.93	3.36	2.90	2.38	2.17	32.72
Scott	Scottsburg	40	33.5	77.7	109	−26	40	Apr. 19	Oct. 19	183	40	4.05	2.51	4.21	3.86	3.91	3.79	3.41	3.66	2.94	3.10	2.89	3.52	41.85
Shelby	Shelbyville	34	30.2	76.1	108	−24	34	Apr. 28	Oct. 12	161	37	3.42	2.21	4.05	3.63	4.01	3.94	3.67	3.40	3.61	3.14	2.79	2.92	40.79
Starke	Knox	12	25.9	73.0	100	−20	12	May 6	Oct. 5	152	12	2.82	2.08	2.85	3.53	5.25	3.67	3.80	4.38	3.31	2.71	2.62	2.19	39.21
Steuben	Angola	28	25.3	73.1	106	−20	27	May 4	Oct. 18	167	27	2.26	1.95	3.16	3.14	3.39	3.78	3.50	3.11	3.53	2.71	2.67	2.56	35.76
Sullivan	Farmersburg	39	30.6	76.6	111	−24	40	Apr. 19	Oct. 16	180	39	2.59	1.77	3.49	3.03	4.35	3.59	3.00	3.52	3.79	3.03	2.55	2.51	37.22
Switzerland	Vevay	40	34.1	77.3	109	−24	39	Apr. 24	Oct. 21	180	39	4.20	2.76	4.26	3.51	4.22	4.20	3.74	4.11	3.28	2.71	2.70	3.54	43.23
	Dam No. 39	18	34.6	76.3	109	−12					18	4.08	2.25	4.13	3.46	3.53	3.97	3.38	4.32	3.31	2.16	2.80	3.34	40.73
Tippecanoe	Lafayette	40	27.5	76.2	111	−33	40	Apr. 27	Oct. 12	168	40	2.64	2.04	3.18	3.40	3.94	3.65	3.71	3.59	3.71	2.88	2.63	2.63	38.00
Vanderburgh	Evansville	40	34.8	79.6	108	−16	40	Apr. 2	Oct. 30	211	40	3.99	2.49	3.84	3.48	3.66	3.73	3.11	3.13	3.38	3.02	2.82	3.54	40.19
Vigo	Terre Haute	40	30.7	77.9	110	−18	40	Apr. 13	Oct. 24	194	40	3.01	2.09	3.90	3.49	3.99	3.76	3.09	3.61	3.93	2.98	2.76	2.86	39.47
Wabash	Wabash	14	27.7	75.0	109	−18	14	May 3	Oct. 13	163	16	2.54	1.76	3.04	3.41	3.44	3.99	3.62	3.84	3.82	2.55	2.66	2.55	37.22
Warren	Judyville	11	27.5	74.7	104	−23	10	May 7	Oct. 3	149	11	2.68	2.25	2.63	3.67	4.36	2.76	3.70	3.38	2.82	2.21	2.36	1.87	34.69
Warrick	Boonville						8	Apr. 19	Oct. 22	186	11	5.10	2.62	3.88	3.70	4.57	4.49	3.01	3.42	3.71	3.41	2.88	3.19	43.98
Washington	Salem	40	32.6	76.3	112	−27	40	Apr. 26	Oct. 15	172	40	4.46	2.69	4.48	3.80	4.25	3.88	3.24	3.62	3.42	3.26	3.24	3.80	44.14
Wayne	Cambridge City	40	28.4	73.9	108	−29	39	May 5	Oct. 8	156	40	3.29	2.18	4.16	3.80	3.82	4.14	3.57	3.48	3.73	3.05	2.65	3.02	40.89
	Richmond	40	28.5	73.0	103	−27	40	May 4	Oct. 9	158	40	3.10	1.91	3.71	3.18	3.67	4.02	3.58	3.48	3.42	3.10	2.46	2.58	38.21
Wells	Bluffton	40	27.1	75.0	111	−23	40	May 6	Oct. 8	155	39	2.70	1.93	3.67	3.31	3.68	3.98	3.87	3.28	3.28	2.66	2.44	2.72	37.52
White	Monticello						13	May 9	do.	152	26	2.57	1.66	2.92	3.38	3.76	3.30	3.20	3.46	3.68	2.87	2.42	2.25	35.47
Whitley	Columbia City						19	May 3	Oct. 15	165	17	2.48	1.93	3.58	3.51	3.64	3.41	3.18	3.41	4.07	2.76	2.58	2.44	36.99

[1] The following counties, for which no records are available, are best represented by the stations indicated: Blackford—Salamonia; Clay—Worthington; Floyd—Jeffersonville; Hendricks—Greencastle; Henry—Cambridge City; Miami—Wabash; Newton—Wheatfield; Ohio—Vevay; Owen—Bloomington; Pike—Washington; Ripley—Moores Hill; Spencer—Rome; Tipton—Frankfort; Union—Richmond; Vermillion—Rockville.

[2] Length of growing season between average dates of last killing frost in spring and first in fall.

298737°—41——55 +

INDIANA—Continued

Precipitation and temperature—State unit values

[This tabulation gives the mean annual, mean monthly, and average seasonal precipitation, 1886–1938, and the mean annual temperatures, 1902–38, for Indiana]

Precipitation		Precipitation		Precipitation		Precipitation		Temperature		Temperature	
Year	Mean	Year	Mean	Year	Mean	Month	Mean	Year	Mean	Year	Mean
	In.		*In.*		*In.*		*In.*		°*F.*		°*F.*
1886	39.96	1907	44.84	1928	36.76	May	4.04	1902	52.2	1921	56.3
1887	36.12	1908	34.33	1929	47.04	June	3.84	1903	51.5	1922	54.4
1888	39.77	1909	47.36	1930	29.71	July	3.34	1904	50.1	1923	52.9
1889	36.28	1910	37.55	1931	38.36	August	3.42	1905	51.7	1924	50.5
1890	49.58	1911	40.05	1932	42.83	September	3.41	1906	53.0	1925	53.0
1891	40.20	1912	40.78	1933	40.74	October	2.73	1907	51.4	1926	51.5
1892	41.79	1913	44.10	1934	29.72	November	3.07	1908	53.8	1927	53.4
1893	41.46	1914	31.52	1935	39.32	December	2.84	1909	52.3	1928	52.0
1894	32.13	1915	41.60	1936	33.74			1910	51.9	1929	51.3
1895	30.99	1916	40.34	1937	46.03	Annual	39.45	1911	53.9	1930	53.5
1896	40.55	1917	36.71	1938	41.11			1912	50.6	1931	55.6
1897	40.74	1918	40.60					1913	54.1	1932	53.4
1898	45.71	1919	38.91			Season	Average	1914	52.8	1933	54.8
1899	35.05	1920	36.96	Month	Mean			1915	52.2	1934	53.9
1900	37.48	1921	45.80					1916	52.4	1935	52.6
1901	30.65	1922	38.73					1917	49.3	1936	53.0
1902	40.08	1923	42.86		*In.*		*In.*	1918	52.4	1937	52.0
1903	36.73	1924	37.73	January	3.15	Winter	8.38	1919	53.6	1938	55.0
1904	38.25	1925	34.59	February	2.39	Spring	11.26	1920	51.7		
1905	43.15	1926	43.73	March	3.73	Summer	10.60				
1906	39.61	1927	49.19	April	3.49	Fall	9.21				

Dates of last killing frost in spring and first in fall, with length of growing season

Year	Bluffton			Farmersburg			La Fayette			Mauzy			Paoli			South Bend		
	Last in spring	First in fall	Growing season[1]	Last in spring	First in fall	Growing season[1]	Last in spring	First in fall	Growing season[1]	Last in spring	First in fall	Growing season[1]	Last in spring	First in fall	Growing season[1]	Last in spring	First in fall	Growing season[1]
			Days			*Days*			*Days*			*Days*			*Days*			*Days*
1899	Apr. 16	Sept. 27	164	Apr. 5	Sept. 27	175	Apr. 16	Sept. 27	164	Apr. 16	Sept. 27	164	Apr. 9	Sept. 30	174	Apr. 16	Sept. 30	167
1900	May 10	Oct. 17	160	Apr. 10	Oct. 18	191	May 10	Oct. 17	160	May 10	Oct. 17	160	Apr. 5	Nov. 9	218	May 3	Oct. 17	167
1901	May 13	Sept. 19	129	Apr. 21	Sept. 19	151	Apr. 21	Oct. 5	167	Apr. 24	Oct. 3	162	Apr. 22	Sept. 19	150	May 15	Oct. 5	143
1902	May 28	Sept. 14	109	Apr. 8	Oct. 29	204	Apr. 5	Sept. 14	162	Apr. 15	Sept. 14	152	Apr. 8	Oct. 29	204	May 28	Oct. 31	156
1903	May 4	Oct. 21	170	May 2	Oct. 18	169	May 1	Sept. 18	140	May 4	Sept. 18	137	May 1	Oct. 18	170	May 4	Oct. 10	159
1904	May 11	Sept. 22	134	Apr. 20	Oct. 23	186	Apr. 21	Oct. 23	185	May 16	Oct. 7	144	Apr. 21	Oct. 23	185	May 16	Oct. 3	140
1905	May 1	Oct. 12	164	Apr. 23	Oct. 12	172	Apr. 22	Oct. 12	173	Apr. 22	Oct. 12	173	Apr. 17	Oct. 12	178	Apr. 22	Oct. 25	186
1906	May 29	Oct. 10	134	do	Oct 11	171	May 7	Oct. 10	156	May 10	Oct. 10	153	Apr. 24	Oct. 11	170	Apr. 24	Oct. 10	169
1907	May 21	Sept. 26	128	Apr. 26	Oct. 13	170	May 21	Oct. 14	146	May 28	Oct. 12	137	Apr. 21	Oct. 9	171	May 21	Oct. 14	146
1908	May 3	Oct. 2	152	Apr. 12	do	184	May 2	Oct. 2	153	May 2	Oct. 2	153	May 1	Oct. 2	154	May 3	Oct. 2	152
1909	May 2	Sept. 28	149	Apr. 11	Oct. 12	184	May 11	Oct. 12	154	May 11	Sept. 28	140	May 11	Sept. 28	140	May 11	Sept. 27	139
1910	Apr. 24	Oct. 10	169	Apr. 25	Oct. 28	186	May 14	Oct. 23	162	May 14	Oct. 23	162	May 14	Oct. 23	162	May 14	Oct. 28	167
1911	May 5	Oct. 24	172	Apr. 15	Oct. 24	192	May 5	Oct. 24	172	May 5	Oct. 24	172	May 5	Oct. 25	173	May 5	Oct. 24	172
1912	Apr. 23	Sept. 30	160	Apr. 19	do	188	Apr. 23	Sept. 30	160	Apr. 19	Sept. 30	164	Apr. 19	Oct. 1	165	Apr. 23	do	184
1913	May 11	Sept. 23	135		Oct. 21		Apr. 6	Oct. 21	198	May 11	Sept. 23	135	May 12	Oct. 22	163	May 11	Oct. 19	161
1914	May 2	Oct. 27	178	Apr. 21	Oct. 27	189	Apr. 21	Oct. 27	189	Apr. 21	Oct. 27	189	May 15	Oct. 27	165	Apr. 21	Oct. 25	187
1915	May 20	Oct. 8	172	Apr. 13	Oct. 10	180	Apr. 13	Oct. 8	178	Apr. 15	Oct. 10	178	Apr. 13	Oct. 8	178	May 19	Oct. 8	142
1916	Apr. 28	Sept. 18	143	Apr. 10	Sept. 16	159	Apr. 9	Sept. 16	160	May 19	Sept. 16	120	Apr. 9	Sept. 30	174	Apr. 28	Sept. 30	155
1917	May 12	Sept. 11	122	Apr. 14	Oct. 6	175	Apr. 15	Oct. 9	177	May 12	Sept. 11	122	Apr. 15	Oct. 1	169	May 29	Sept. 11	105
1918	May 11	Sept. 22	134	Apr. 13	Nov. 2	203	May 1	Nov. 2	185	Apr. 14	Oct. 14	183	May 2	Sept. 22	143	May 1	Nov. 1	184
1919	Apr. 27	Oct. 17	173	Apr. 26	do	190	Apr. 26	Oct. 29	186	Apr. 27	Nov. 2	189	Apr. 26	Oct. 18	175	Apr. 27	Oct. 12	168
1920	May 16	Oct. 30	167	Apr. 14	Oct. 2	171	May 15	Oct. 2	140	May 15	Oct. 2	140	Apr. 14	Oct. 28	197	May 15	Oct. 29	167
1921	May 17	Oct. 12	148	Apr. 19	Oct. 13	177	Apr. 18	Oct. 13	178	May 1	Oct. 5	157	Apr. 18	Oct. 13	178	Apr. 18	Nov. 3	198
1922	Apr. 29	Nov. 9	194	Apr. 1	Oct. 12	194	Apr. 1	Oct. 18	200	Apr. 29	Oct. 13	167	Apr. 23	do	173	Apr. 22	Oct. 19	180
1923	May 13	Sept. 15	125	Apr. 18	Oct. 21	186	May 10	Sept. 14	127	May 13	Sept. 14	124	May 10	Oct. 20	163	May 10	Oct. 5	148
1924	May 22	Oct. 21	152	Apr. 23	Oct. 1	161	May 22	Oct. 1	132	May 22	Oct. 1	132	Apr. 23	Oct. 23	183	Apr. 11	Oct. 21	193
1925	May 25	Oct. 10	138	May 25	Oct. 10	138	May 25	Oct. 10	138	May 26	Oct. 10	137	May 25	Oct. 10	138	May 25	Oct. 10	138
1926	May 4	Oct. 7	156	May 4	Oct. 21	170	May 4	Oct. 7	156	May 23	Oct. 21	151	Apr. 20	Oct. 21	184	May 4	Oct. 25	174
1927	Apr. 24	Oct. 15	174	Apr. 24	Nov. 6	196	Apr. 24	Nov. 4	194	Apr. 24	Oct. 17	176	Apr. 25	Nov. 6	195	May 1	Oct. 17	169
1928	Apr. 28	Sept. 24	149	Apr. 28	Sept. 24	149	Apr. 28	Sept. 24	149	May 12	Sept. 22	133	Apr. 28	Sept. 26	151	May 13	Sept. 30	140
1929	Apr. 19	Oct. 18	182	Apr. 2	Oct. 24	205	Apr. 2	Oct. 25	206	May 7	Sept. 19	135	Apr. 2	Oct. 18	199	May 21	Oct. 4	136
1930	Apr. 26	Oct. 20	177	Apr. 28	Oct. 18	173	Apr. 25	Oct. 18	176	Apr. 27	Oct. 20	176	Apr. 26	Oct. 20	177	May 30	Sept. 30	123
1931	May 24	Oct. 18	147	Apr. 7	Nov. 5	212	Apr. 7	do	194	Apr. 7	Oct. 18	194	Apr. 28	Oct. 18	173	May 24	Nov. 6	166
1932	Apr. 27	Oct. 28	184	Apr. 27	Oct. 11	167	Apr. 27	Oct. 6	162	May 29	Oct. 28	152	Apr. 27	Oct. 30	186	Apr. 27	Oct. 28	184
1933	do	Oct. 13	169	do	Oct. 25	181	do	Nov. 4	191	Apr. 26	Oct. 13	170	Apr. 26	Nov. 8	196	do	Oct. 23	179
1934	May 12	Oct. 14	155	Apr. 28	Oct. 28	183	Apr. 28	Oct. 28	183	Apr. 28	Oct. 14	169	Apr. 28	Oct. 28	183	May 26	Oct. 14	141

[1] Number of days between last killing frost in spring and first in fall.

INDIANA—Continued

Dates of last killing frost in spring and first in fall, with length of growing season

Year	Bluffton			Farmersburg			La Fayette		
	Last in spring	First in fall	Growing season [1]	Last in spring	First in fall	Growing season [1]	Last in spring	First in fall	Growing season [1]
			Days			*Days*			*Days*
1935	Apr. 18	Oct. 2	167	Apr. 17	Oct. 6	172	Apr. 17	Oct. 4	170
1936	Apr. 23	Oct. 3	163	Apr. 23	Oct. 24	184	Apr. 23	Oct. 24	184
1937	Apr. 11	Oct. 24	196	Apr. 16	Oct. 14	181	May 10	Oct. 8	151
1938	May 13	Oct. 7	147	Apr. 10	Oct. 24	197	May 13	Oct. 24	164
Mean	May 6	Oct. 8	155	Apr. 19	Oct. 16	180	Apr. 27	Oct. 12	168
Extremes	Apr. 11 [2]	Sept. 11 [4]	[6] 109	Apr. 1 [2]	Sept. 16 [4]	[6] 138	Apr. 1 [2]	Sept. 14 [4]	[6] 127
	May 29 [3]	Nov. 9 [5]	[7] 196	May 25 [3]	Nov. 6 [5]	[7] 212	May 25 [3]	Nov. 4 [5]	[7] 206

Year	Mauzy			Paoli			South Bend		
	Last in spring	First in fall	Growing season [1]	Last in spring	First in fall	Growing season [1]	Last in spring	First in fall	Growing season [1]
			Days			*Days*			*Days*
1935	Apr. 17	Oct. 2	168	Apr. 17	Oct. 7	173	May 4	Oct. 6	155
1936	Apr. 23	Oct. 24	184	Apr. 23	Oct. 27	187	May 14	Oct. 24	162
1937	Apr. 12	Oct. 14	185	Apr. 12	Oct. 15	186	May 15	Sept. 20	127
1938	May 13	Oct. 7	147	May 13	Oct. 24	164	Apr. 21	Oct. 28	190
Mean	May 3	do	157	Apr. 25	Oct. 16	174	May 7	Oct. 15	161
Extremes	Apr. 7 [2]	Sept. 11 [4]	[6] 120	Apr. 2 [2]	Sept. 19 [4]	[6] 138	Apr. 11 [2]	Sept. 11 [4]	[6] 105
	May 29 [3]	Nov. 2 [5]	[7] 194	May 25 [3]	Nov. 9 [5]	[7] 218	May 30 [3]	Nov. 6 [5]	[7] 198

[2] Earliest date in spring.
[3] Latest date in spring.
[4] Earliest date in fall.
[5] Latest date in fall.
[6] Shortest growing season.
[7] Longest growing season.

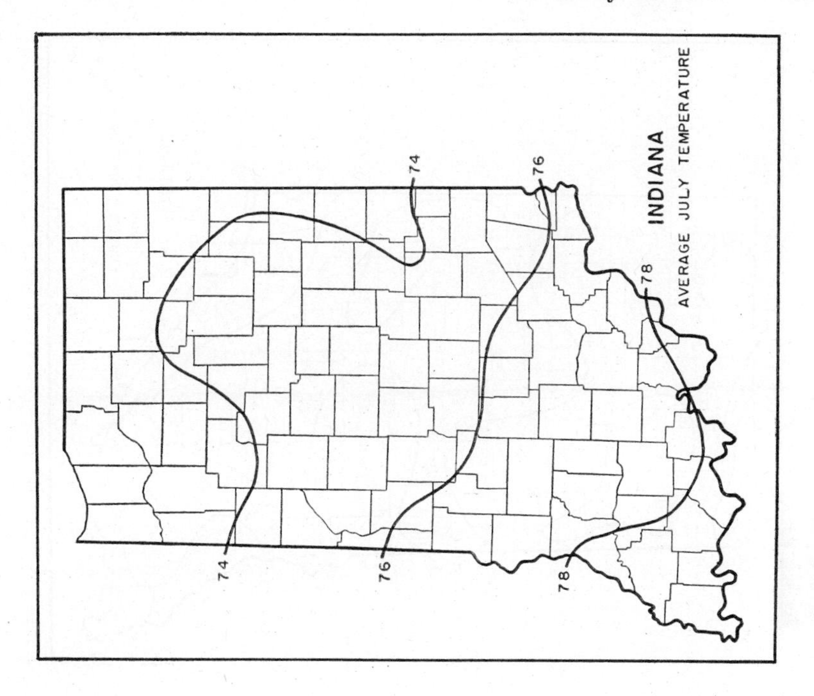
INDIANA
AVERAGE JULY TEMPERATURE
74
76
78

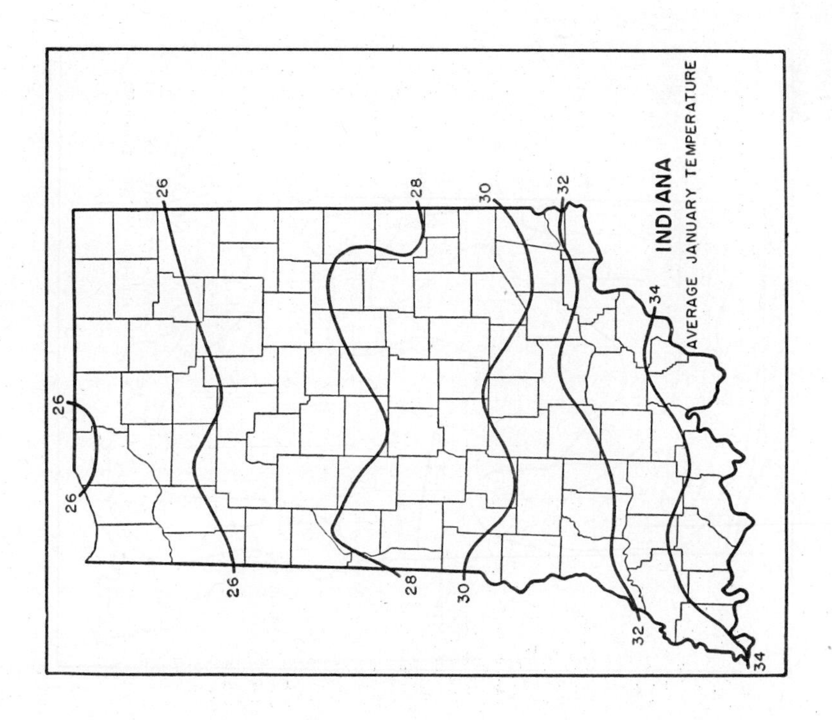
INDIANA
AVERAGE JANUARY TEMPERATURE
26
28
30
32
34

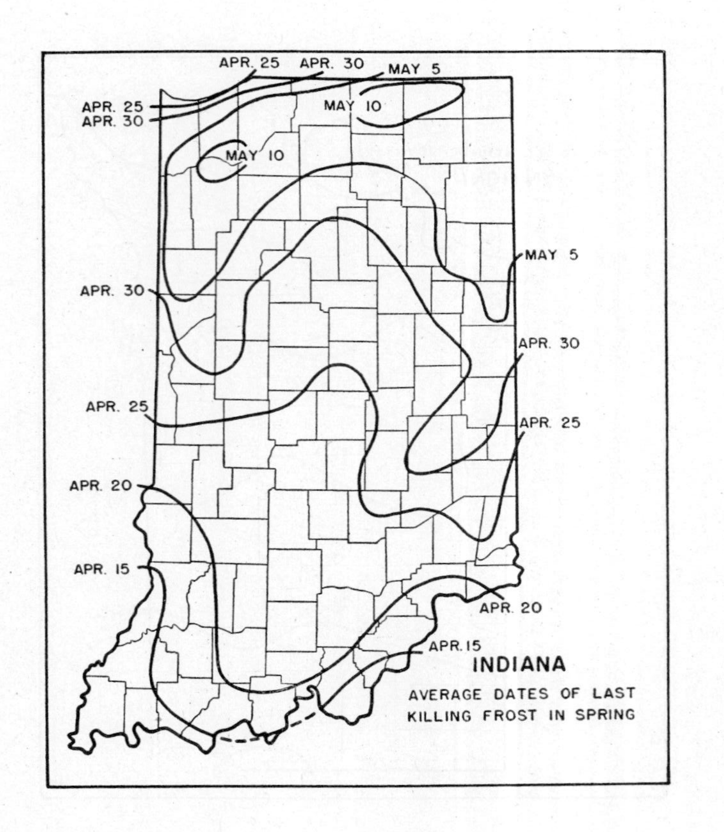
APR. 25
APR. 30
MAY 5
MAY 10
APR. 20
APR. 15
INDIANA
AVERAGE DATES OF LAST
KILLING FROST IN SPRING

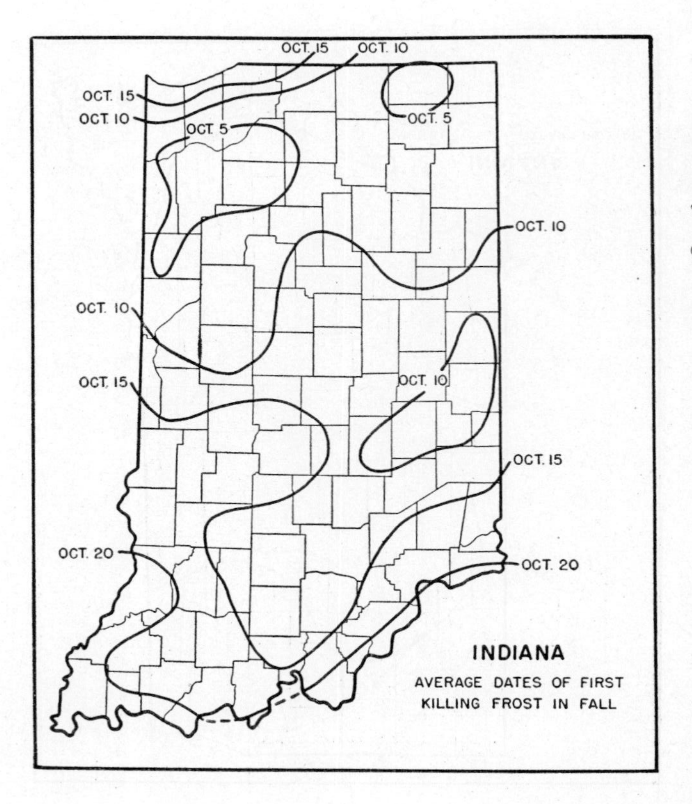
OCT. 15
OCT. 10
OCT. 5
OCT. 20
INDIANA
AVERAGE DATES OF FIRST
KILLING FROST IN FALL

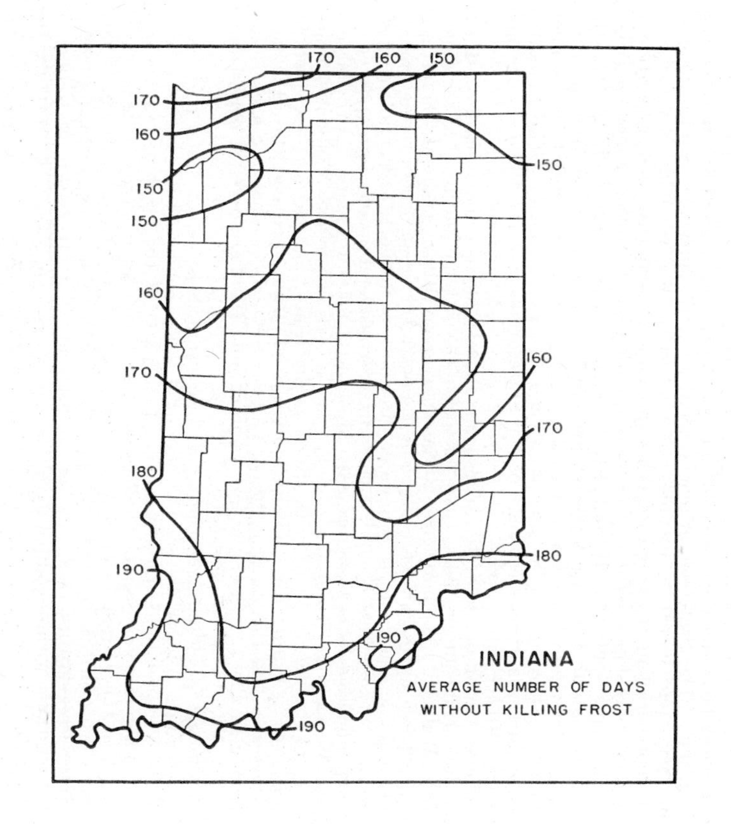
INDIANA
AVERAGE NUMBER OF DAYS
WITHOUT KILLING FROST
150
160
170
180
190

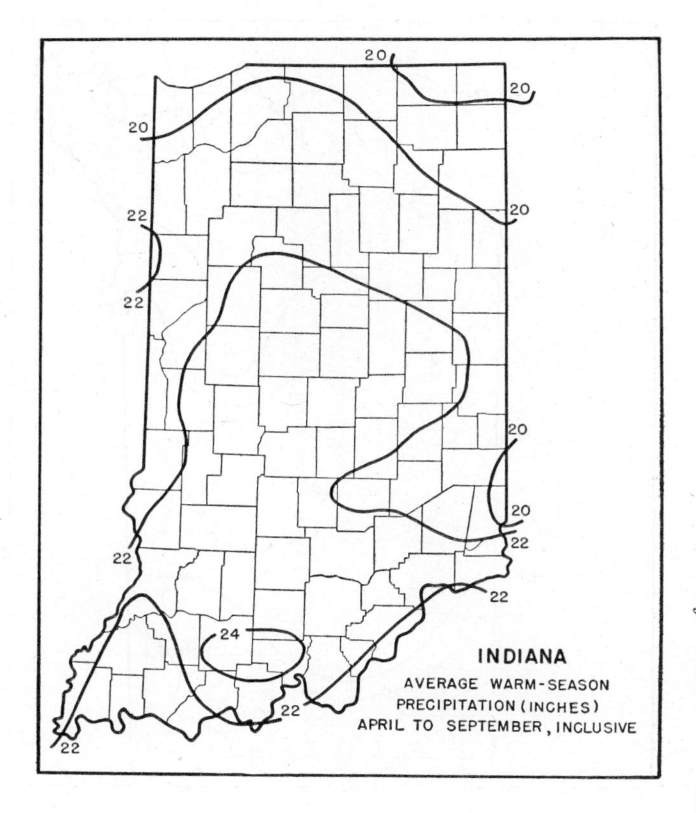
INDIANA
AVERAGE WARM-SEASON
PRECIPITATION (INCHES)
APRIL TO SEPTEMBER, INCLUSIVE
20
22
24

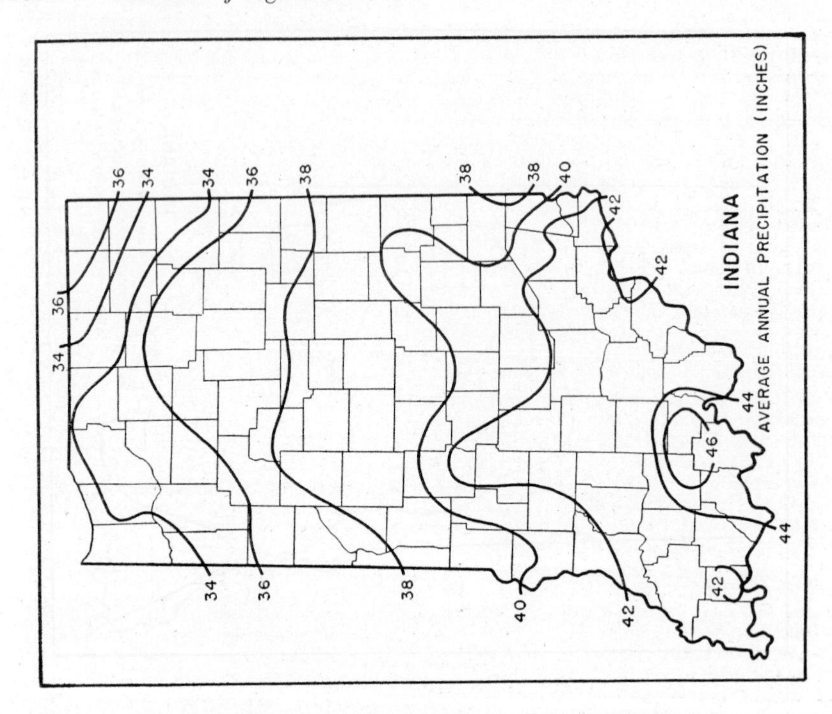

SUPPLEMENTARY CLIMATIC NOTES FOR INDIANA

Indiana lies mainly between 36° and 42° north latitude and 85° and 88° west longitude. The State has a general southwesterly slope, and two-thirds of its approximately 36,000 square miles is drained by the Wabash-White River system. The northern half of the State has a slope more westerly than southwesterly; the southern part slopes to the southwest except for a section in the extreme southeast which slopes southeasterly and is drained by the Whitewater River. In the northeast an area of over 1,000 square miles is drained by the Maumee River northeasterly into Lake Erie, while along the extreme northern border the main drainage is through the St. Joseph River into Lake Michigan. The Kankakee Valley in the northwestern part of the State drains into the Illinois River and thence into the Mississippi.

The elevation of the State ranges from about 1,200 feet above sea level in the north-central counties to less than 400 feet in the extreme southwest at the mouth of the Wabash. The northern half has an average altitude of about 700 feet and the south of about 600 feet. Much of the north is level prairie or former marshland, but there are numerous moraines and hills, particularly in the northeastern sections. These hills break up the surface considerably and form pockets in which numerous lakes have formed. Most of the lakes are small, but the largest, Lake Wawasee in Kosciusko County, has an extreme length of about 6 miles. Much of the southern half of the State is unglaciated and has been considerably weathered into miniature mountain areas with steep precipices, through which the streams find their way in rather narrow, tortuous channels. Some are lost through sinkholes in the limestone bedrock, and there are caves of considerable size.

Indiana, especially the northern half, lies within the sweep of winter cold waves on the west and northwest, and in summer it is occasionally visited by hot periods which overspread the middle and northern parts of the great central valleys. Its climate, therefore, is largely continental, and there are no large bodies of water, except in the extreme northwest, to influence climatic conditions, which vary largely with latitude. In the southern half of the State, however, considerable surface irregularities result in many variations in temperature, and some in precipitation, within comparatively small areas. On calm, clear nights the numerous ravines and valley bottoms often experience considerably lower temperatures than the slopes and tops of the surrounding hills, the difference in spring and fall being such as to result in frost, and even damage from freezing, on the lower areas, while the higher ground escapes harm.

Mean annual temperature and precipitation both decrease over the State from south to north. Severe cold is occasionally experienced in the winter season, although on the whole the 3 winter months are characterized in the majority of years by mean temperatures only slightly below the freezing point.

Precipitation is fairly evenly distributed throughout the year, but a somewhat greater amount occurs in the growing season than during the other months. Droughts are occasionally of considerable severity for rather prolonged periods, but the diversity possible in crops is such that there is seldom or never a complete failure of all products grown in the State.

In the extreme southern and southwestern counties the last killing frost in the spring occurs, on an average, about April 15. The date gradually becomes later to the northward; it is as late as about May 10 in parts of the Kankakee Valley, with its large areas of dark peat soil, and the extreme northeastern counties, with their relatively high altitudes. There is a considerable area in the south where the last killing spring frost occurs between April 20 and 25, and owing to the protective influence of Lake Michigan, the date of occurrence in close proximity to its shores is April 25 to 30.

In the fall, the first killing frost occurs about October 5 in the Kankakee Valley and the extreme northeast, but southward the date becomes later rather steadily until it is about October 20 along the Ohio and lower Wabash Rivers. The influence of Lake Michigan delays killing frosts until about October 15 or slightly later around the Indiana shore. The average growing season is thus more than 190 days in the extreme southern section, decreasing rather steadily northward to about 150 days in the Kankakee Valley and the northeast, but lengthening again to nearly 170 days near Lake Michigan. Thus the extreme range between different parts of the State is about 40 days.

On the whole, except in seasons of drought, the entire State is well watered as far as the requirements of vegetation are concerned. The percentage of annual precipitation received during the growing season increases from 51 in the extreme south to 57 in the extreme north. This is the reverse of the south-to-north decrease in precipitation for the entire year, and it is probably due largely to the greater frequency of storm movement to the north of the State during the season when the sun is north of the Equator.

Much more snowfall occurs, as a rule, in the northern than in the southern third of the State, and large amounts of snow brought by winds from Lake Michigan cause an average annual fall of more than 50 inches in parts of the St. Joseph Valley and areas immediately adjoining. Annual snowfalls of more than 30 inches occur in most northeastern counties from the Grant-Adams border to the Michigan line, and the amount decreases to about 15 to 16 inches in the area along the Ohio River. The annual average for the State is about 23 inches. However, marked winter depressions occasionally pass eastward to the south of Indiana and result in much heavier snowfall in individual storms over the southern counties than to the northward.

On the whole, precipitation occurs throughout Indiana on an average of slightly less than 1 day in every 3, and there are 147 clear days to 118 cloudy days.

JOHN H. ARMINGTON, *Senior Meteorologist and Climatic Section Director for Indiana, Weather Bureau, Indianapolis.*

IOWA

Climatic summary

County[1]	Station	Temperature: Length of record	Temperature: January average	Temperature: July average	Temperature: Maximum	Temperature: Minimum	Killing frost average dates: Length of record	Killing frost: Last in spring	Killing frost: First in fall	Growing season[2]	Average precipitation: Length of record	January	February	March	April	May	June	July	August	September	October	November	December	Annual
		Yr.	° F.	° F.	° F.	° F.	Yr.			Days	Yr.	In.	In.	In.	In.	In.	In.	In.	In.	In.	In.	In.	In.	In.
Adair	Greenfield	24	21.6	74.9	107	-34	25	Apr. 29	Oct. 10	164	30	0.83	0.94	1.67	2.90	4.35	4.87	3.42	4.24	3.79	2.43	1.44	0.99	31.87
Adams	Corning	38	22.7	75.9	115	-32	40	May 1	Oct. 9	161	40	.95	1.07	1.65	2.72	4.27	4.37	3.60	3.97	4.44	2.69	1.68	1.00	32.41
Allamakee	Lansing	6	21.1	72.8	101	-30					33	.99	1.15	1.89	2.49	4.44	4.20	3.97	3.73	4.35	2.35	2.06	1.02	32.64
Appanoose	Centerville	28	25.1	77.5	110	-28	30	Apr. 25	Oct. 9	167	34	.98	1.18	1.92	2.99	4.11	4.59	3.05	3.56	4.56	2.61	2.07	1.19	32.81
Audubon	Audubon	35	19.3	74.6	113	-35	38	May 4	Oct. 6	155	40	.98	1.08	1.43	2.47	3.62	4.47	3.31	3.82	4.36	2.15	1.66	.90	30.25
Benton	Belle Plaine	40	19.9	74.6	111	-32	40	May 3	Oct. 5	155	40	1.39	1.43	2.29	2.97	4.34	4.50	4.03	3.64	4.41	2.43	2.20	1.41	35.04
Black Hawk	Waterloo	40	18.2	74.6	112	-33	40	May 4	Oct. 4	153	40	1.03	1.12	1.93	2.36	3.92	4.24	3.74	3.77	4.28	2.34	1.82	1.14	31.69
Boone	Boone	33	18.7	74.9	111	-35	33	May 6	do	151	40	.95	.99	1.54	2.46	4.24	4.42	3.63	3.74	4.68	2.43	1.67	.92	31.67
Bremer	Waverly	40	17.1	73.4	109	-34	39	do	do	151	40	1.16	1.02	1.87	2.52	4.00	4.24	3.85	3.71	4.01	2.33	1.84	1.14	31.69
Buchanan	Independence	40	18.4	73.5	108	-32	40	May 4	do	153	40	.96	.94	1.55	2.38	3.99	4.38	3.64	3.63	4.17	2.35	1.77	1.16	30.92
Buena Vista	Alta	40	16.6	72.1	110	-36	40	do	Oct. 8	157	40	.81	1.02	1.47	2.67	4.54	4.55	3.75	3.51	3.99	1.92	1.55	.95	30.73
	Storm Lake	40	17.3	74.2	109	-36	39	May 3	Oct. 6	156	40	.71	.92	1.27	2.60	4.05	4.37	3.49	3.39	3.88	1.82	1.39	.78	28.67
Butler	Allison	24	16.7	74.2	109	-31	25	May 6	Oct. 5	152	25	1.06	1.08	1.66	2.37	3.95	3.85	3.57	3.43	4.66	2.09	1.86	1.02	30.60
Calhoun	Rockwell City	40	18.8	74.5	110	-35	38	May 5	Oct 9	157	40	1.12	1.26	1.59	2.58	4.36	4.56	3.72	3.98	4.25	2.09	1.73	.98	32.22
Carroll	Carroll	40	18.9	74.6	112	-40	40	May 6	Oct. 7	154	40	.77	.96	1.38	2.38	3.94	4.56	3.36	4.24	4.25	2.23	1.49	.98	30.54
Cass	Atlantic	40	21.4	75.8	117	-38	40	May 5	Oct. 6	154	40	.94	1.08	1.46	2.51	3.59	4.61	3.24	4.05	4.11	2.48	1.72	1.00	30.79
	Cumberland						17	Apr. 28	Oct. 8	163	40	.85	.89	1.39	2.31	3.56	4.36	3.13	3.66	3.73	2.36	1.42	.81	28.47
Cedar	Tipton (near)	37	21.4	75.6	108	-28	38	Apr. 30	Oct. 11	164	38	1.35	1.27	2.24	2.82	3.88	4.28	3.58	3.92	4.28	2.57	2.14	1.42	33.75
Cerro Gordo	Clear Lake	15	16.8	73.7	106	-36	14	May 2	Oct. 15	166	15	.59	.67	1.36	1.67	5.09	4.29	3.91	4.07	2.83	2.13	1.29	.76	28.66
	Mason City	36	15.2	72.8	107	-35	38	May 8	Oct. 3	148	38	.92	.98	1.48	2.33	4.19	4.66	3.25	4.05	3.86	2.08	1.62	.96	30.38
Cherokee	Cherokee	17	16.7	74.6	109	-32	17	May 7	Oct. 5	151	17	.63	.59	1.09	2.26	3.48	3.60	3.38	3.27	4.35	1.50	1.22	.69	26.06
	Washta	28	18.7	72.9	107	-47	28	May 15	Oct. 4	142	35	.65	.80	1.14	2.69	4.13	4.61	3.75	3.29	3.75	1.80	1.36	.81	28.78
Chickasaw	New Hampton	40	15.7	72.7	110	-34	38	May 7	Oct. 3	149	40	1.00	1.02	1.88	2.52	4.46	4.20	3.53	4.07	4.27	2.32	1.92	1.08	32.27
Clarke	Murray	14	22.0	76.1	109	-31	21	Apr. 26	Oct. 9	166	23	.79	1.09	1.63	3.15	4.72	4.07	3.80	3.58	4.38	2.53	1.47	.98	32.19
	Woodburn										11	1.21	1.59	1.86	2.81	4.39	4.24	4.08	4.81	4.07	2.09	1.47	1.33	36.89
Clay	Spencer	26	15.3	74.8	113	-38	26	May 9	Oct. 3	147	26	.83	1.00	1.42	2.79	3.74	3.69	2.70	3.78	4.21	1.62	1.38	1.03	28.19
Clayton	Postville (near)	40	16.2	71.1	108	-35	40	May 6	Oct. 4	151	40	1.08	1.16	1.79	2.67	4.46	4.17	3.98	3.98	4.33	2.53	1.97	1.16	33.28
	Elkader	26	15.9	74.0	111	-36	26	May 7	Oct. 3	149	24	1.09	1.23	2.01	2.66	4.60	4.19	4.14	3.44	3.93	2.54	1.72	1.23	32.78
Clinton	Clinton	40	21.7	75.5	109	-31	40	Apr. 28	Oct. 10	165	40	1.49	1.44	2.45	2.88	4.13	4.27	3.63	3.93	4.26	2.60	2.19	1.52	34.79
Crawford	Denison	40	19.5	75.0	112	-40	39	May 7	Oct. 4	150	40	.75	.82	1.15	2.23	3.81	3.94	3.32	3.72	3.63	2.06	1.45	.73	27.61
Dallas	Perry	39	21.0	75.5	111	-34	39	May 1	Oct. 8	160	39	1.01	1.10	1.55	2.38	3.85	4.23	3.57	3.98	4.04	2.23	1.63	.96	30.53
	Waukee	35	20.7	75.7	112	-36	34	do	Oct. 7	159	37	1.15	1.10	1.68	2.79	4.03	4.45	3.78	3.74	4.33	2.18	1.68	1.01	31.92
Davis	Bloomfield	19	21.8	77.5	113	-26	18	Apr. 22	Oct. 6	167	26	1.48	1.42	2.27	3.16	5.09	4.28	3.73	3.27	4.19	2.35	1.82	1.37	34.43
Decatur	Lamoni	32	23.4	76.4	113	-29	31	Apr. 29	Oct. 9	163	33	.93	1.21	1.63	2.97	4.06	4.64	3.83	3.72	4.46	2.85	1.90	.98	33.18
	Leon	14	22.5	75.1	109	-30	14	Apr. 28	Oct. 12	167	15	1.36	1.51	1.84	3.00	5.18	4.21	4.66	3.57	4.32	2.63	1.60	1.23	35.11
Delaware	Delaware (near)	30	18.1	73.3	108	-31	31	May 4	Oct. 9	158	31	.92	.90	1.74	2.61	4.38	4.23	3.54	3.60	4.05	2.40	1.69	1.18	31.24

Des Moines	Burlington	40	24.5	77.1	111	−27	40	Apr. 20	Oct. 16	179	40	1.79	1.67	2.58	3.11	4.17	4.66	3.47	3.46	4.48	2.52	2.18	1.62	35.71
Dickinson	Lake Park	25	14.5	73.4	107	−33	24	May 8	Oct. 4	149	27	.65	.81	1.36	2.16	3.55	3.83	2.89	3.73	3.89	1.45	1.11	.71	26.14
Dubuque	Dubuque	40	19.9	74.6	110	−32	40	Apr. 19	Oct. 18	182	40	1.19	1.23	2.06	2.51	4.00	4.02	3.34	3.56	3.98	2.31	1.87	1.25	31.32
Emmet	Estherville	40	14.2	72.9	108	−38	40	May 8	Oct. 4	149	40	.67	.87	1.33	2.45	4.12	4.36	3.51	3.58	3.89	1.78	1.40	.76	28.72
Fayette	Oelwein	16	17.8	74.6	109	−28	16	May 5	Oct. 7	155	16	1.00	.89	1.90	2.58	3.40	5.13	3.77	4.11	4.65	2.16	2.27	.97	32.83
	Fayette	40	16.6	72.8	110	−35	39	May 9	Oct. 1	145	40	1.15	1.30	2.17	2.76	4.39	4.26	4.01	4.04	4.44	2.33	2.06	1.30	34.21
Floyd	Charles City	40	15.6	73.2	108	−34	35	Apr. 27	Oct. 6	162	40	1.08	1.09	1.87	2.53	4.47	4.22	3.48	4.11	4.12	2.13	1.80	1.20	32.10
Franklin	Hampton	35	16.9	73.9	109	−34	28	May 3	Oct. 7	157	32	1.08	1.09	1.82	2.49	4.55	4.40	3.97	3.80	4.35	2.36	1.84	1.14	32.89
Fremont	Thurman	40	23.5	77.2	114	−37	40	Apr. 30	Oct. 9	162	40	.76	1.11	1.46	2.72	4.31	4.85	3.68	4.22	4.27	2.47	1.83	1.02	32.70
Greene	Jefferson	31	19.9	74.6	111	−37	34	May 3	Oct. 5	155	38	1.00	1.09	1.51	2.42	3.98	4.27	3.43	3.60	4.49	2.23	1.56	1.08	30.66
Grundy	Grundy Center	40	19.2	74.6	108	−34	39	Apr. 29	Oct. 4	158	40	1.10	.96	1.93	2.75	4.44	4.72	3.56	3.85	4.49	2.47	1.94	1.11	33.32
Guthrie	Guthrie Center	36	21.0	75.5	113	−35	40	May 3	Oct. 6	156	40	.94	1.10	1.48	2.56	3.87	4.63	3.40	3.92	4.08	2.37	1.69	1.07	31.11
Hamilton	Webster City	32	19.2	74.5	109	−34	34	May 11	Oct. 3	145	36	.90	.98	1.41	2.33	4.08	4.09	3.24	3.31	4.62	2.14	1.65	.91	29.66
Hancock	Britt	40	16.0	73.2	109	−36	40	May 8	do	148	40	.74	.74	1.31	2.26	4.37	4.35	3.44	3.98	4.26	2.06	1.60	.80	29.91
Hardin	Iowa Falls	40	17.0	73.1	111	−34	40	May 5	Oct. 2	150	40	1.18	1.31	1.91	2.59	4.14	4.56	3.41	3.70	4.31	2.27	1.81	1.20	32.39
	Whitten	18	17.9	73.5	106	−33	12	May 7	Oct. 7	153	22	1.05	1.02	1.50	2.78	4.70	4.92	3.61	3.15	4.05	2.71	1.35	1.03	31.87
Harrison	Little Sioux	34	20.6	76.4	114	−39	34	May 5	Oct. 9	157	35	.79	1.03	1.32	2.44	3.75	4.21	3.47	3.53	3.43	1.88	1.49	.86	28.20
	Logan	40	21.5	76.0	117	−35	40	May 2	Oct. 7	158	40	.75	.88	1.28	2.39	3.54	4.49	3.51	3.55	3.37	1.98	1.59	.81	28.14
Henry	Mount Pleasant	40	24.2	76.7	114	−27	40	Apr. 26	Oct. 11	168	40	1.36	1.25	2.21	3.11	3.94	4.99	3.82	3.46	4.58	2.33	2.14	1.40	34.59
Howard	Cresco	8	13.4	71.6	106	−43					8	.75	.99	1.92	2.23	5.08	4.19	3.86	3.15	4.24	2.52	1.62	1.11	31.66
Humboldt	Humboldt	40	17.9	74.2	111	−42	39	May 7	Oct. 4	150	40	.88	.90	1.42	2.30	4.18	4.89	3.47	3.52	3.94	2.08	1.78	.81	30.17
Iowa	Williamsburg	23	20.6	75.7	111	−28	23	May 4	Oct. 7	156	23	1.00	.95	1.90	2.63	3.37	4.72	3.58	3.15	4.51	2.35	2.28	1.25	31.69
Jackson	Maquoketa	28	20.0	73.5	108	−32	28	May 3	Oct. 2	152	28	1.27	1.05	2.08	2.52	4.16	4.26	3.57	3.32	4.40	2.98	2.22	1.26	33.09
Jasper	Baxter	39	20.8	74.7	110	−33	40	Apr. 30	Oct. 7	160	40	.92	.68	1.75	2.75	4.56	4.44	3.71	3.25	4.40	2.28	1.75	.95	31.44
	Monroe	27	21.8	77.0	110	−32	27	Apr. 28	Oct. 10	165	28	1.01	1.18	1.78	3.02	3.98	4.42	3.30	3.94	5.16	2.61	2.00	1.09	33.49
Jefferson	Fairfield	34	23.5	75.8	114	−29	33	Apr. 27	Oct. 7	163	34	1.23	1.49	2.06	3.28	4.42	4.93	3.79	3.50	4.36	2.98	2.15	1.35	35.54
Johnson	Iowa City	40	20.8	75.1	109	−32	40	Apr. 28	Oct. 10	165	40	1.24	1.32	2.19	2.89	4.39	4.69	3.80	3.93	4.23	2.54	2.02	1.40	34.64
Jones	Olin	37	20.1	74.3	111	−35	40	May 4	Oct. 3	152	40	1.35	1.24	2.08	2.66	4.07	4.45	3.77	3.87	4.00	2.52	2.03	1.34	33.38
Keokuk	Sigourney	40	22.6	76.1	113	−30	40	Apr. 30	Oct. 9	162	40	1.18	1.27	2.13	2.86	4.00	4.76	3.67	3.45	4.04	2.36	1.93	1.26	32.91
Kossuth	Algona	40	16.7	73.7	110	−36	40	May 4	Oct. 7	156	40	.86	.96	1.41	2.58	4.24	4.23	3.04	4.01	4.39	2.02	1.60	.94	30.28
Lee	Keokuk	40	26.7	77.9	113	−27	40	Apr. 15	Oct. 19	187	40	1.54	1.32	2.33	2.81	3.84	4.23	3.08	3.11	4.29	2.21	2.07	1.43	32.26
	Fort Madison						16	Apr. 25	Oct. 9	167	20	1.85	1.64	2.32	3.14	5.26	4.73	3.68	3.47	4.12	1.93	2.00	1.42	35.56
Linn	Cedar Rapids	40	20.2	75.6	110	−36	39	Apr. 28	Oct. 10	165	40	1.08	1.07	1.71	2.47	3.81	4.07	3.65	3.67	4.06	2.25	1.72	1.09	30.65
Louisa	Columbus Junction	38	23.5	75.6	110	−28	38	Apr. 25	Oct. 14	172	39	1.28	1.33	2.11	3.00	3.89	4.66	3.66	4.00	4.15	2.50	2.07	1.32	33.97
	Wapello	14	24.6	74.7	111	−22	14	Apr. 22	Oct. 11	172	19	1.30	1.39	2.06	2.66	4.09	3.79	3.41	3.77	3.75	1.89	1.79	1.28	31.18
Lucas	Chariton	40	23.2	75.3	114	−31	40	Apr. 30	Oct. 9	162	40	.90	1.04	1.66	2.81	3.89	4.46	3.60	3.63	4.37	2.34	1.76	1.02	31.48
Lyon	Inwood (near)	35	14.7	73.9	115	−46	35	May 9	Oct. 1	145	36	.62	.77	1.18	2.20	3.61	4.34	3.03	2.99	3.09	1.53	1.12	.75	25.23
	Rock Rapids	35	14.6	73.8	111	−40	34	May 8	Oct. 2	147	36	.66	.74	1.19	2.41	3.81	4.17	3.16	3.11	3.08	1.59	1.17	.71	25.80
Madison	Earlham (near)	29	20.3	73.4	112	−36	29	May 9	Oct. 4	148	29	1.12	1.23	1.61	2.97	3.76	4.42	3.34	4.05	3.67	2.33	1.58	.99	31.07
	Winterset	40	22.7	76.5	113	−34	40	Apr. 28	Oct. 10	165	40	.88	1.07	1.71	2.86	3.96	4.24	3.33	3.55	4.10	2.43	1.74	1.01	30.88
Mahaska	Oskaloosa	40	22.3	75.5	112	−31	40	Apr. 29	Oct. 9	163	40	1.22	1.23	2.06	2.82	3.87	4.60	3.65	3.68	4.20	2.38	2.09	1.28	33.08
Marion	Knoxville	40	23.0	76.3	114	−30	36	Apr. 26	Oct. 8	165	40	1.17	1.24	1.91	2.82	3.84	4.57	3.48	4.08	4.52	2.35	1.90	1.26	33.14
	Pella	23	22.2	75.2	112	−33	23	do	Oct. 6	163	28	.89	1.20	1.71	2.96	4.09	4.62	3.64	3.72	4.52	2.47	1.57	1.06	32.45
Marshall	Marshalltown	40	19.7	75.2	112	−32	40	Apr. 29	Oct. 9	163	40	1.18	1.14	1.98	2.76	4.18	4.34	3.75	3.35	4.79	2.47	1.86	1.13	32.93
Mills	Glenwood	28	24.2	77.4	115	−33	37	Apr. 27	Oct. 10	166	30	.64	.86	1.35	2.58	3.65	4.52	3.75	4.03	3.77	2.13	1.74	.73	29.75
Mitchell	Osage	31	15.4	73.0	107	−35	30	May 7	Oct. 5	151	32	1.02	1.06	1.54	2.29	4.74	4.74	3.25	3.53	3.99	2.26	1.89	1.16	31.47
Monona	Onawa	38	20.8	76.1	110	−32	38	May 2	Oct. 8	159	40	.77	1.02	1.37	2.52	3.91	4.42	3.72	3.80	3.81	1.92	1.48	.93	29.67
Monroe	Albia	40	24.9	76.0	113	−29	40	Apr. 25	Oct. 10	168	40	1.11	1.25	1.93	2.89	4.25	4.65	3.48	3.51	4.39	2.30	1.86	1.09	32.71
Montgomery	Red Oak (near)	8	26.0	76.0			12	May 1	Oct. 14	166	22	.89	.97	1.54	2.39	4.05	4.25	3.66	4.06	4.57	2.42	1.65	.88	31.33
Muscatine	Muscatine										39	1.56	1.51	2.24	2.97	3.92	4.13	3.40	3.96	4.03	2.36	2.11	1.51	33.70

[1] Ida county, for which no records are available, is best represented by Sac City, Sac County.
Length of growing season between average dates of last killing frost in spring and first in fall.

IOWA—Continued

Climatic summary—Continued

County	Station	Temperature					Killing frost average dates				Average precipitation													
		Length of record	January average	July average	Maximum	Minimum	Length of record	Last in spring	First in fall	Growing season	Length of record	January	February	March	April	May	June	July	August	September	October	November	December	Annual
		Yr.	°*F.*	°*F.*	°*F.*	*F.*	*Yr.*			*Days*	*Yr.*	*In.*	*In.*	*In.*	*In.*	*In.*	*In.*	*In.*	*In.*	*In.*	*In.*	*In.*	*In.*	*In.*
O'Brien	Sanborn	24	15.3	73.9	110	−35	25	May 8	Oct. 4	149	25	0.81	0.99	1.43	2.73	3.65	3.98	3.33	3.46	4.07	1.41	1.38	0.97	28.21
	Sheldon	26	16.7	73.8	110	−42	27	May 9	Sept. 29	143	29	.86	.86	1.41	2.34	3.94	3.76	3.91	3.55	3.68	1.87	1.20	.89	28.27
Osceola	Sibley	23	13.3	71.3	108	−40	24	May 17	Sept. 26	132	25	.66	.84	1.34	2.28	4.59	4.71	3.95	3.71	3.62	1.76	1.12	.77	29.35
Page	Clarinda	40	23.0	76.5	114	−31	40	Apr. 30	Oct. 10	163	40	.90	1.06	1.60	2.66	4.13	4.66	3.92	3.87	4.49	2.69	1.78	1.02	32.78
Palo Alto	West Bend	40	16.4	73.7	109	−36	39	May 7	Oct. 4	150	40	.81	.82	1.30	2.36	3.91	4.18	3.31	3.72	3.84	1.82	1.49	.96	28.52
Plymouth	Le Mars	40	18.3	74.2	111	−37	39	do	Oct. 3	149	40	.63	.83	1.19	2.50	4.08	3.98	3.68	2.87	3.64	1.64	1.22	.76	27.02
Pocahontas	Pocahontas	35	16.8	73.8	111	−36	35	do	Oct. 5	151	35	.84	.93	1.44	2.64	4.02	4.49	3.15	3.67	3.95	2.07	1.59	.92	29.71
Polk	Des Moines	40	22.1	76.3	110	−30	40	Apr. 19	Oct. 11	175	40	1.03	1.08	1.79	2.62	4.17	4.23	3.20	3.66	4.01	2.19	1.62	1.09	30.69
Pottawattamie	Oakland	20	23.0	77.4	109	−28	20	May 5	Oct. 10	158	26	.84	.81	1.18	2.15	2.88	4.46	3.29	3.98	4.20	2.02	2.08	.67	28.56
	Council Bluffs	14	19.9	73.8	108	−32					11	.52	1.21	1.58	2.22	3.97	3.96	3.47	4.79	3.64	2.39	.70	1.32	29.77
Poweshiek	Grinnell	39	21.0	75.5	110	−31	40	Apr. 28	Oct. 10	165	40	1.14	1.10	1.83	3.06	4.32	4.60	3.80	3.65	4.47	2.40	1.99	1.16	33.52
Ringgold	Tingley	15	22.8	77.2	112	−23	15	Apr. 27	Oct. 12	168	15	1.23	.97	1.57	2.52	3.18	5.39	2.42	3.94	4.98	2.63	2.57	1.22	32.62
	Mt. Ayr	40	23.6	76.2	112	−30	40	Apr. 29	do	166	40	1.03	1.17	1.81	3.06	4.32	4.93	4.08	3.84	4.61	2.65	2.03	1.09	34.62
Sac	Sac City	39	18.6	74.3	114	−35	35	May 4	Oct. 5	154	40	.89	1.04	1.29	2.26	3.74	4.17	3.46	3.65	3.87	1.99	1.48	.89	28.73
	Odebolt	15	19.4	74.9	109	−37	16	do	Oct. 2	151	16	.49	.84	1.14	2.39	4.44	4.30	4.13	3.53	4.33	2.20	1.34	.91	30.04
Scott	Davenport	40	22.7	76.6	111	−27	40	Apr. 18	Oct. 17	182	40	1.37	1.42	2.37	2.79	3.61	4.25	3.23	3.59	3.96	2.28	1.99	1.43	32.29
	Le Claire										16	1.64	1.69	2.20	2.76	4.54	4.60	3.47	3.37	4.39	2.81	2.04	1.53	35.04
Shelby	Harlan	39	20.3	74.9	114	−37	40	May 5	Oct. 5	153	40	.80	.92	1.24	2.41	3.64	4.40	3.49	3.86	3.99	2.21	1.52	.83	29.31
Sioux	Alton	34	16.9	74.1	110	−42	34	May 8	Oct. 3	148	34	.79	.87	1.22	2.22	3.78	3.60	3.05	3.27	3.18	1.44	1.22	.80	25.44
	Sioux Center	39	16.4	73.4	109	−37	39	May 5	Oct. 1	149	40	.74	.89	1.26	2.57	4.08	3.86	3.40	3.15	3.75	1.64	1.21	.79	27.34
Story	Ames	40	20.0	74.8	109	−37	40	Apr. 30	Oct. 6	159	40	.86	.93	1.44	2.64	4.34	4.08	3.18	3.59	4.44	2.39	1.55	1.02	30.46
Tama	Toledo	39	19.9	74.6	109	−31	40	May 4	Oct. 4	153	40	1.12	1.10	1.91	2.76	4.40	4.76	3.93	3.49	4.75	2.42	2.01	1.16	33.81
	Dysart										15	.87	1.00	1.74	2.24	4.55	3.97	3.38	4.08	3.13	2.30	1.38	.96	29.60
Taylor	Lenox	40	23.0	76.7	115	−37	40	Apr. 28	Oct. 8	163	40	.73	.95	1.45	2.83	3.95	4.50	3.51	4.03	4.58	2.60	1.75	.92	31.80
	Bedford	22	22.8	74.7	110	−32	23	May 3	Oct. 6	156	34	.97	1.20	1.60	2.73	4.21	4.12	3.77	3.78	4.12	2.71	1.97	.95	32.13
Union	Creston	33	21.3	75.2	111	−31	34	May 2	Oct. 10	161	34	.93	1.01	1.46	2.88	3.71	4.82	2.96	3.80	4.62	2.41	1.87	.89	31.36
	Afton	40	24.5	76.6	112	−30	40	Apr. 27	do	166	40	.94	1.10	1.77	3.19	4.40	4.74	3.20	4.02	4.48	2.67	1.85	1.02	33.38
Van Buren	Keosauqua	40	24.3	76.4	115	−36	40	Apr. 28	Oct. 9	164	40	1.38	1.34	2.28	3.01	4.07	5.24	3.89	3.36	4.32	2.59	2.06	1.37	34.91
	Bonaparte	40	23.8	75.5	114	−31	40	Apr. 25	Oct. 10	168	40	1.28	1.19	1.91	2.91	3.94	5.04	3.68	3.34	4.43	2.38	2.01	1.13	33.24
Wapello	Ottumwa	36	24.0	77.3	115	−36	38	do	Oct. 11	169	40	1.13	1.42	2.10	2.93	4.16	4.80	3.30	3.66	4.36	2.64	1.87	1.20	33.57
Warren	Indianola	40	22.6	76.2	113	−32	40	Apr. 27	Oct. 10	166	40	1.09	1.21	1.64	2.76	4.08	4.55	3.21	3.86	4.08	2.36	1.83	1.09	31.76
	Lacona										39	1.54	1.55	2.10	2.89	4.14	5.26	3.17	3.78	4.62	2.56	1.96	1.46	35.03
Washington	Washington	40	22.7	75.5	113	−26	40	Apr. 26	Oct. 9	166	40	1.35	1.44	2.38	3.08	3.78	4.64	3.61	3.80	4.34	2.51	1.98	1.38	34.29
Wayne	Millerton	40	23.7	74.7	113	−31	36	Apr. 29	Oct. 11	165	40	1.06	1.24	1.90	3.18	4.28	4.61	3.60	3.48	4.54	2.55	1.91	1.16	33.51
	Allerton	17	22.6	75.1	108	−33	16	Apr. 26	Oct. 9	166	18	1.33	1.46	2.00	3.17	5.03	4.50	4.08	3.65	4.17	2.35	1.58	1.12	34.44

Webster	Fort Dodge	37	17.3	74.4	110	−35	39	May 4	Oct. 3	152	39	.93	.86	1.58	2.50	4.09	4.28	3.79	4.02	4.74	2.29	1.62	.94	31.64
Winnebago	Forest City	40	15.1	73.1	108	−36	40	May 3	do	153	40	1.05	1.03	1.49	2.21	4.22	4.40	3.29	3.64	4.04	2.19	1.68	.97	30.21
Winneshiek	Decorah	40	15.9	73.4	111	−37	39	May 11	Sept. 30	142	40	1.20	1.07	1.92	2.55	4.36	3.96	3.88	3.91	4.21	2.44	2.03	1.20	32.73
Woodbury	Sioux City	40	19.5	75.9	111	−35	40	Apr. 25	Oct. 7	165	40	.67	.86	1.16	2.28	3.76	3.83	3.19	2.91	3.44	1.61	1.12	.82	25.65
Worth	Northwood	37	14.9	72.3	107	−37	40	May 3	Oct. 4	154	40	1.09	1.19	1.87	2.65	4.78	4.58	3.37	3.95	4.37	2.30	1.99	1.26	33.40
Wright	Belmond	27	15.7	74.5	111	−37	29	May 8	Oct. 3	148	30	1.14	1.07	1.51	2.72	4.18	4.47	3.34	3.84	4.57	1.99	1.92	1.11	31.86

Precipitation and temperature—State unit values

[This tabulation gives the mean annual, mean monthly, and average seasonal precipitation, 1886–1938, and the mean annual temperatures, 1896–1938, for Iowa]

Precipitation		Precipitation		Precipitation		Precipitation		Temperature		Temperature	
Year	Mean	Year	Mean	Year	Mean	Month	Mean	Year	Mean	Year	Mean
	In.		*In.*		*In.*		*In.*		°*F.*		°*F.*
1886	24.71	1908	35.09	1930	26.10	July	3.51	1896	48.6	1918	49.2
1887	26.31	1909	40.01	1931	35.37	August	3.51	1897	47.8	1919	48.6
1888	31.44	1910	19.89	1932	32.27	September	3.86	1898	47.7	1920	48.2
1889	24.95	1911	31.37	1933	24.91	October	2.19	1899	47.3	1921	52.2
1890	29.48	1912	28.65	1934	26.85	November	1.64	1900	49.3	1922	50.2
1891	32.90	1913	29.95	1935	33.16	December	1.14	1901	49.0	1923	49.0
1892	36.58	1914	31.93	1936	26.00			1902	47.7	1924	46.4
1893	27.59	1915	39.53	1937	27.60	Annual	30.89	1903	47.2	1925	48.8
1894	21.94	1916	28.90	1938	36.29			1904	46.3	1926	48.3
1895	26.77	1917	27.81					1905	47.2	1927	48.8
1896	37.23	1918	32.78					1906	48.4	1928	49.4
1897	26.98	1919	36.76	Month	Mean	Season	Average	1907	47.4	1929	46.4
1898	31.34	1920	31.75					1908	49.4	1930	50.2
1899	28.68	1921	32.03					1909	47.4	1931	53.2
1900	35.05	1922	29.98					1910	48.6	1932	48.2
1901	24.41	1923	29.50		*In.*		*In.*	1911	49.5	1933	50.8
1902	43.82	1924	31.39	January	1.09	Winter	3.29	1912	46.3	1934	51.5
1903	35.39	1925	28.24	February	1.06	Spring	8.57	1913	49.7	1935	48.6
1904	28.51	1926	33.07	March	1.72	Summer	11.34	1914	49.1	1936	48.6
1905	36.56	1927	29.35	April	2.76	Fall	7.69	1915	47.8	1937	47.5
1906	31.60	1928	35.96	May	4.09			1916	47.2	1938	51.2
1907	31.61	1929	30.20	June	4.32			1917	44.8		

IOWA—Continued

Dates of last killing frost in spring and first in fall, with length of growing season

Year	Alta			Clarinda			Fayette			Harlan			Iowa Falls			Oskaloosa		
	Last in spring	First in fall	Growing season [1]	Last in spring	First in fall	Growing season [1]	Last in spring	First in fall	Growing season [1]	Last in spring	First in fall	Growing season [1]	Last in spring	First in fall	Growing season [1]	Last in spring	First in fall	Growing season [1]
			Days			Days			Days			Days			Days			Days
1899	May 13	Sept. 29	139	Apr. 16	Sept. 26	163	Apr. 22	Sept. 26	157	Apr. 16	Sept. 26	163	May 18	Sept. 26	131	Apr. 16	Sept. 29	166
1900	May 3	Oct. 8	158	Apr. 13	Oct. 17	187	May 5	Oct. 8	156	May 3	Sept. 17	137	May 5	Oct. 8	156	Apr. 13	Sept. 17	157
1901	Apr. 20	Oct. 4	167	Apr. 20	Sept. 18	151	Apr. 21	Oct. 4	166	May 13	Sept. 18	128	Apr. 20	Oct. 4	167	Apr. 20	Oct. 4	167
1902	Apr. 23	Sept. 12	142	Apr. 23	Oct. 14	174	Apr. 27	Sept. 12	138	Apr. 23	Sept. 12	142	Apr. 24	Sept. 12	141	Apr. 23	Sept. 13	143
1903	May 3	Oct. 16	166	May 3	Oct. 18	168	June 12	Oct. 5	115	May 3	Oct. 17	167	May 3	Sept. 24	144	May 3	Oct. 18	168
1904	Apr. 26	Oct. 23	180	Apr. 27	Oct. 22	178	May 15	Sept. 15	123	Apr. 27	Oct. 23	179	May 15	Sept. 15	123	Apr. 21	Oct. 23	185
1905	Apr. 30	Oct. 10	163	Apr. 22	Oct. 11	172	May 26	Oct. 11	138	Apr. 22	Oct. 12	173	Apr. 30	Oct. 12	165	Apr. 18	Oct. 12	177
1906	May 6	Oct. 6	153	May 9	Oct. 10	154	May 28			May 9	Oct. 1	145	May 7	Oct. 1	147	May 9	Oct. 6	150
1907	May 20	Oct. 11	144	May 16	Oct. 8	145	May 27	Sept. 25	121	May 16	Sept. 25	132	May 20	Sept. 25	128	May 4	Oct. 12	161
1908	May 3	Sept. 28	148	May 3	Sept. 29	149	May 3			May 2	Sept. 28	149	May 3	Sept. 29	149	May 2	Sept. 28	149
1909	May 10	Oct. 12	155	May 10	Oct. 12	155	May 11	Sept. 27	139	May 10	Oct. 12	155	May 10	Oct. 12	155	May 3	Oct. 12	162
1910	May 3	Oct. 21	171	Apr. 26	Oct. 22	179	May 14	Oct. 6	145	May 13	Oct. 22	162	May 14	Oct. 6	145	Apr. 24	Oct. 22	181
1911	do	do	171	May 2	Oct. 21	172	May 5	Oct. 20	168	May 2	Oct. 20	171	May 4	Oct. 8	157	May 2	Oct. 21	172
1912	May 14	Sept. 26	135	Apr. 23	Sept. 26	156	May 14	Sept. 26	135	May 17	Sept. 26	132	Apr. 27	Sept. 26	152	Apr. 20	Sept. 26	159
1913	Apr. 27	Sept. 22	148	Apr. 28	Sept. 22	147	Apr. 29	Sept. 22	146	Apr. 27	Sept. 22	148	Apr. 29	Sept. 22	146	Apr. 28	Sept. 22	147
1914	May 12	Oct. 25	166	Apr. 20	Oct. 27	190	Apr. 20	Oct. 27	190	May 13	Oct. 25	165	Apr. 20	Oct. 25	188	Apr. 20	Oct. 27	190
1915	Apr. 12	Oct. 5	176	May 9	Oct. 9	153	May 17	Aug. 30	105	May 9	Oct. 5	149	May 9	Oct. 8	152	May 17	Oct 9	145
1916	May 2	Sept. 15	136	Apr. 11	Sept. 29	171	May 2	Sept. 17	138	May 18	Sept. 15	120	May 2	Sept. 17	138	Apr. 9	Sept. 14	158
1917	May 4	Oct. 8	157	May 7	Oct. 6	152	May 23	Sept. 11	111	May 7	Sept. 27	143	May 23	Sept. 11	111	May 7	Oct. 1	147
1918	May 10	Sept. 20	133	May 1	Sept. 20	142	May 13	Sept. 20	130	May 13	Sept. 20	130	May 14	Sept. 21	130	May 1	Sept. 21	143
1919	Apr. 25	Oct. 10	168	Apr. 25	Oct. 11	169	May 2	Oct. 11	162	Apr. 26	Oct. 10	167	May 2	Oct. 11	162	Apr. 26	Oct. 11	168
1920	Apr. 28	Sept. 30	155	Apr. 28	Sept. 30	155	May 14	Oct. 1	140	Apr. 28	Sept. 30	155	Apr. 28	Sept. 30	155	Apr. 28	Sept. 30	155
1921	May 14	Oct. 8	147	May 4[2]	Oct. 8[2]	157	May 16	Oct. 4	141	May 4[2]	Oct. 4[2]	153	May 16[2]	Oct. 4[2]	141	Apr. 18	Oct. 4	169
1922	Apr. 19[2]	Oct. 12	176	Apr. 20	Oct. 9[2]	172	Apr. 30[2]	Oct. 9	162	Apr. 20[2]	Oct. 9	172	Apr. 29[2]	Oct. 9	163	Apr. 20[2]	Oct. 12	175
1923	May 12	Oct. 19	160	May 9	Oct. 20	164	May 9	Sept. 14[2]	128	May 9[2]	Oct. 27	171	May 9[2]	Sept. 14	128	May 9	Oct. 20	164
1924	May 24	Nov. 2	162	May 11[2]	Sept. 29	141	May 20[2]	Sept. 30	133	May 24	Sept. 28[2]	127	Apr. 22[2]	Sept. 30[2]	161	May 24	Sept. 30	129
1925	May 25	Oct. 9	137	May 25	Oct. 7[2]	135	May 25	Oct. 10	138	May 16	Oct. 6	143	May 11	Oct. 10	152	May 25	Oct. 10	138
1926	May 14	Sept. 25	134	Apr. 28[2]	Sept. 25	150	May 3[2]	Sept. 25	145	May 14	Sept. 25	134	May 3[2]	Sept. 25[2]	145	Apr. 28	Sept. 26	151
1927	Apr. 24[2]	Nov. 2	192	Apr. 24[2]	Oct. 31[2]	190	Apr. 23	Oct. 14	174	Apr. 24[2]	Oct. 14[2]	173	Apr. 23	Oct. 14	174	Apr. 24	Oct. 14	173
1928	Apr. 27[2]	Sept. 25	151	Apr. 28[2]	Sept. 26[2]	151	May 12[2]	Sept. 24	135	Apr. 27[2]	Sept. 25[2]	151	May 12[2]	Sept. 25	136	Apr. 28	Sept. 26	151
1929	May 16	Sept. 18	125	May 16[2]	Oct. 21[2]	158	May 19	Sept. 18	122	May 16[2]	Oct. 21[2]	158	May 19	Sept. 18	122	May 5	Oct. 23	171
1930	May 17	Oct. 16	152	Apr. 22[2]	Oct. 17[2]	178	May 17	Sept. 28	134	Apr. 24[2]	Oct. 17	176	May 17[2]	do	134	Apr. 25	Oct. 17	175
1931	May 21	Nov. 2	165	May 7[2]	Nov. 1[2]	178	May 23	Oct. 17[2]	147	May 22[2]	Nov. 1	163	May 22	Nov. 2	164	May 21	Nov. 4	167
1932	Apr. 27	Oct. 5	161	Apr. 27	Oct. 6[2]	162	May 2[2]	Sept. 29[2]	150	Apr. 27[2]	Sept. 29[2]	155	Apr. 27	Sept. 29	155	Apr. 27	Oct. 6	162
1933	do	Oct. 8	164	Apr. 15[2]	Oct. 22[2]	190	Apr. 27	Oct. 13	169	do[2]	Sept. 27	153	do	Oct. 5[2]	161	do	Oct. 18	174
1934	do[2]	Sept. 27	153	Apr. 27[2]	Sept. 27[2]	153	do[2]	Oct. 28	184	do[2]	do[2]	153	do[2]	Sept. 27[2]	153	do[2]	Oct. 28	184

1935	Apr. 30	...do...	150	May 4[2]	Oct. 4[2]	153	May 4[2]	Sept. 28[2]	147	May 5[2]	Oct. 4[2]	152	May 4	Oct. 4	153	May 4	Oct. 4	153
1936	Apr. 22[2]	Oct. 21	182	Apr. 22[2]	Oct. 22[2]	183	Apr. 26[2]	Oct. 2[2]	159	May 3[2]	Oct. 21[2]	171	Apr. 26[2]	Oct. 21	178	Apr. 22[2]	Oct. 22	183
1937	May 14[2]	Oct. 13	152	May 14[2]	Oct. 14	153	Apr. 22[2]	Sept. 16[2]	147	May 14[2]	Sept. 16[2]	125	Apr. 11[2]	Sept. 26	168	Apr. 26[2]	Sept. 26	153
1938	Apr. 9[2]	Oct. 23	197	Apr. 22[2]	Oct. 20	181	...do[2]...	Oct. 21[2]	182	Apr. 22[2]	Oct. 20[2]	181	Apr. 22[2]	Oct. 23	184	Apr. 22[2]	Oct. 24	185
Mean	May 4[2]	Oct. 8	157	Apr. 30	Oct. 10	163	May 9	Oct. 1	145	May 5	Oct. 5	153	May 5	Oct. 2	150	Apr. 29	Oct. 9	163
Extremes	Apr. 9[3]	Sept. 12[5]	[7] 125	Apr. 11[3]	Sept. 18[5]	[7] 135	Apr. 20[3]	Aug. 30[5]	[7] 105	Apr. 16[3]	Sept. 12[5]	[7] 120	Apr. 11[3]	Sept. 11[5]	[7] 111	Apr. 9[3]	Sept. 13[5]	[7] 129
	May 25[4]	Nov. 2[6]	[8] 197	May 25[4]	Nov. 1[6]	[8] 190	June 12[4]	Oct. 28[6]	[8] 190	May 24[4]	Nov. 1[6][8]	[8] 181	May 23[4]	Nov. 2[6]	[8] 188	May 25[4]	Nov. 4[6]	[8] 19

[1] Number of days between last killing frost in spring and first in fall.
[2] Date of last temperature of 32° or lower in the spring, or first temperature of 32° or lower in the autumn when frost was not reported.
[3] Earliest date in spring.
[4] Latest date in spring.
[5] Earliest date in fall.
[6] Latest date in fall.
[7] Shortest growing season.
[8] Longest growing season.

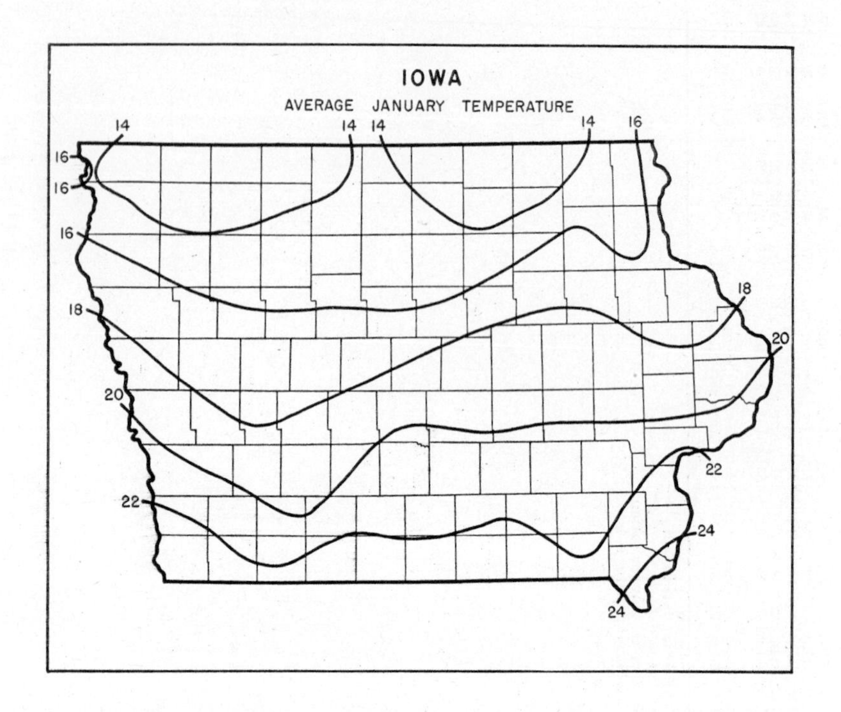
IOWA
AVERAGE JANUARY TEMPERATURE
14
14
14
14
16
16
16
16
18
18
20
20
22
22
24
24

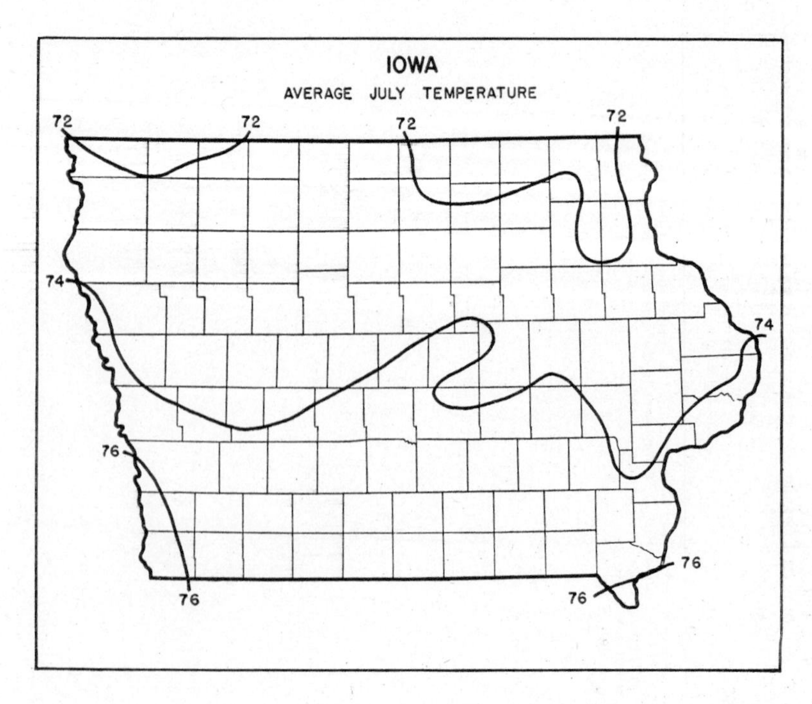
IOWA
AVERAGE JULY TEMPERATURE
72
72
72
72
74
74
76
76
76
76

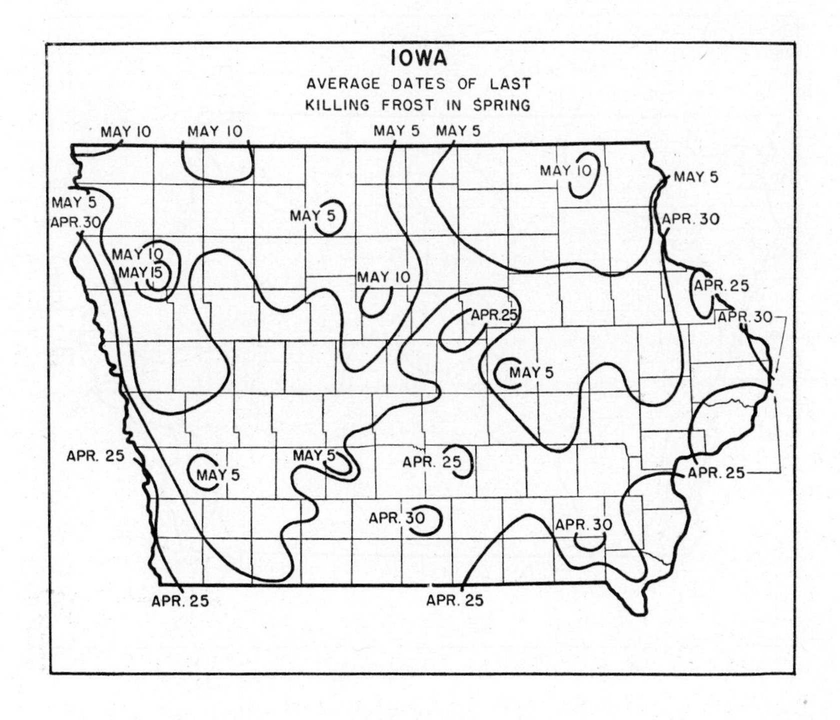
IOWA
AVERAGE DATES OF LAST
KILLING FROST IN SPRING
MAY 10
MAY 10
MAY 5
MAY 5
MAY 10
MAY 5
MAY 5
APR. 30
MAY 5
APR. 30
MAY 10
MAY 15
MAY 10
APR. 25
APR. 25
APR. 30
MAY 5
APR. 25
MAY 5
MAY 5
APR. 25
APR. 25
APR. 30
APR. 30
APR. 25
APR. 25

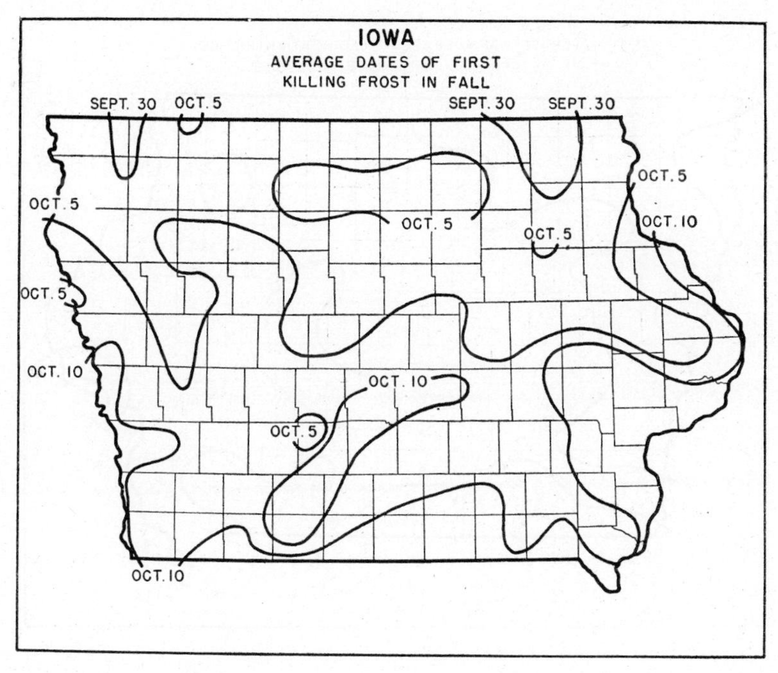
IOWA
AVERAGE DATES OF FIRST
KILLING FROST IN FALL
SEPT. 30
OCT. 5
SEPT. 30
SEPT. 30
OCT. 5
OCT. 5
OCT. 10
OCT. 5
OCT. 5
OCT. 5
OCT. 10
OCT. 10
OCT. 5
OCT. 10

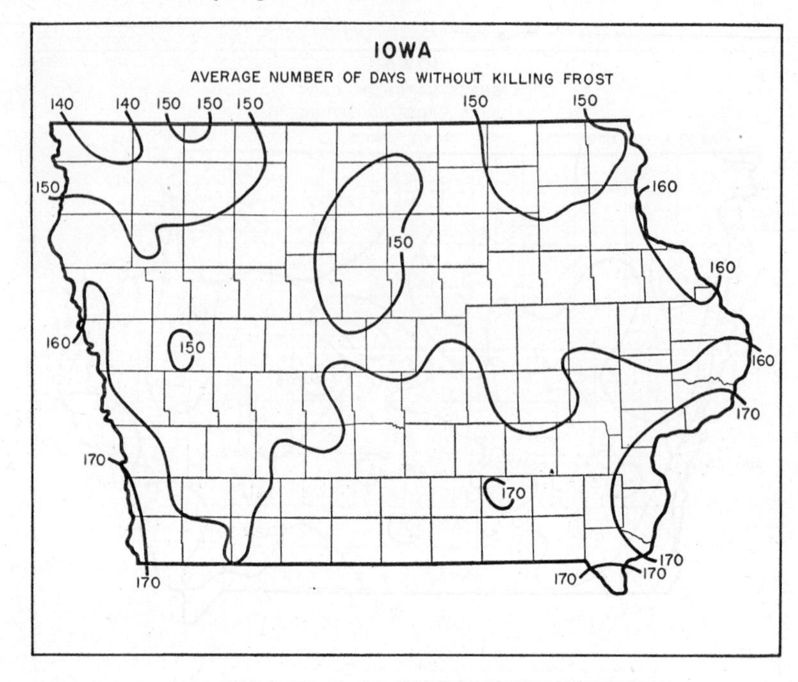
IOWA
AVERAGE NUMBER OF DAYS WITHOUT KILLING FROST
140
140
150
150
150
150
150
150
160
160
160
150
150
160
170
170
170
170
170
170
170

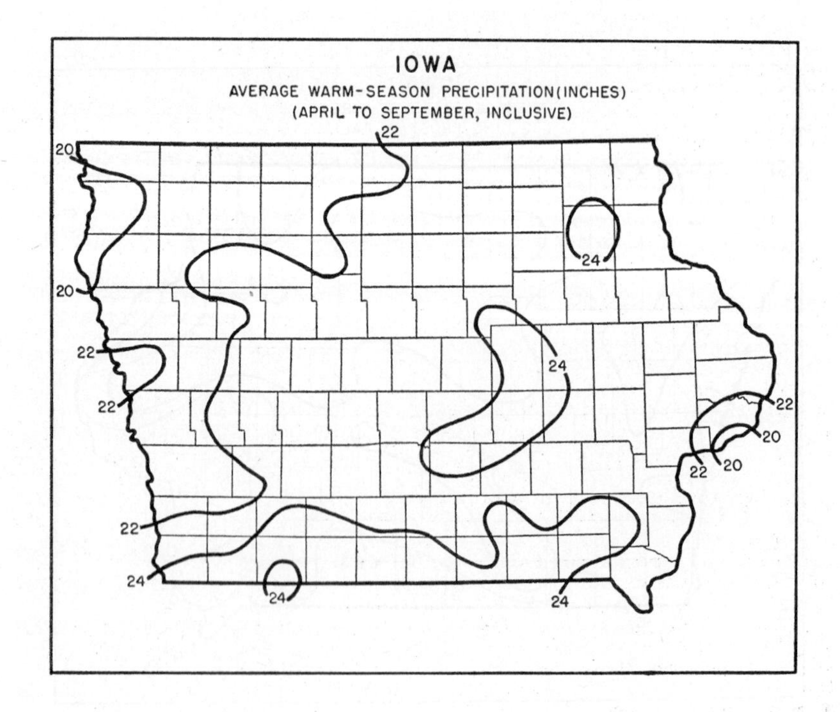
IOWA
AVERAGE WARM-SEASON PRECIPITATION (INCHES)
(APRIL TO SEPTEMBER, INCLUSIVE)
22
20
24
20
22
24
22
22
20
22
20
22
24
24
24

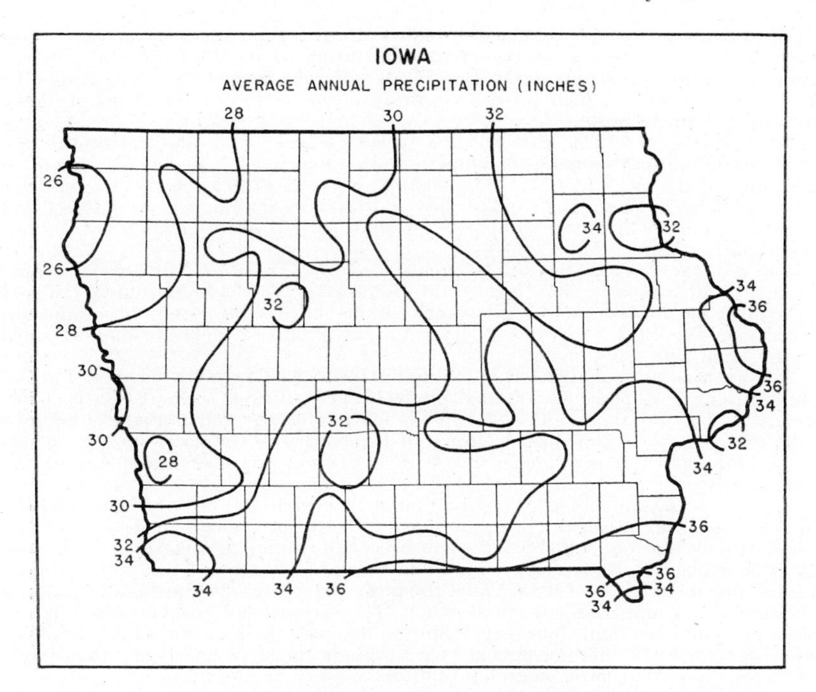

SUPPLEMENTARY CLIMATIC NOTES FOR IOWA

The Iowa climate is mainly of the extreme midcontinental type. The general topography is a minor factor, though locally the influence on climate of the direction and angle of the slope of hills is related to the selection, management, yield, and quality of certain crops. The range of altitude in Iowa is only about 1,200 feet, with the extreme northeastern counties the most rugged. Noticeably higher temperatures prevail along the Missouri and Mississippi Rivers than elsewhere in the State, while the divide between the Missouri and the Raccoon, extending south to the southern boundary of the State, produces lower temperatures than the latitude warrants and shortens drought periods along the ridge.

Hot winds and periods of prolonged high temperature occur occasionally from May to September, more frequently in the southern and western counties than elsewhere because they have less of the cooling influence of the Great Lakes. The intensity and duration of these periods, rather than deficiency of rainfall, in recent years have been the major cause of crop damage.

Cold waves are usually of the boreal type, rushing southward over the State from the continental arctic regions, but they may also be local. In the latter case a rapid net loss of heat by radiation follows a deep, porous snowfall, in the midst of a weak high-pressure area, with clear sky and light wind. The winters average about 4° F. milder now than when climatic records began, yet the most prolonged severe cold in 119 years was during a period of 20 to 36 days from about January 18 to February 22, 1936.

For the State the average growing season is 158 days, from May 2 to October 7. Light frosts have been observed in all summer months. It is the earliness or lateness of the corn crop and not the earliness or lateness of the frost that determines the amount of corn damaged by frost. A warm June indicates that very little corn will be frosted. All of the important frost damage to immature corn has followed a June temperature 2° F. or more below normal.

Precipitation in Iowa (1886–1938) ranges from slightly less than 26 inches along the Big Sioux River in the extreme northwest to somewhat more than 36 inches at places along the Mississippi River. About 71 percent of the annual precipitation occurs in the warm season, April to September, and 51 percent in the months of greatest crop growth, May to August.

Droughts are particularly important to the major, spring-planted crops, from

April to September, but prolonged droughts at any season affect the general water supply. The cold season is the dry season, during which all of the State, except along the Mississippi and lower Des Moines Rivers, has had at some time 100 days or more with 1 inch or less of precipitation. Only a few droughts have covered the entire State.

For the 16 years 1923–38, according to the assessors' annual farm census, the average annual hail damage to crops in Iowa was $3,266,773, or 1.05 percent of the value of the crops at risk. The greatest loss was $7,975,686 in 1925, and the least was $961,147 in 1935. The heaviest and most frequent hail losses are usually in the northwestern counties. A good many south-central counties have been nearly immune.

The average annual snowfall is greatest—46.7 inches—at Northwood, Worth County, and smallest—19.6 inches—at Bonaparte, Van Buren County. There have often been blizzards of great severity in one part of Iowa and not in another. Sometimes the line is very sharp between an area with 12 inches or more of snow and an area with little or none.

The average annual relative humidity in Iowa, based on 7 a. m. and 7 p. m. observations, is 72 percent, ranging from 69 in the southwest to 78 at Charles City. April and May are the months of lowest relative humidity and January of highest.

Northwest winds prevail in winter, but from April to October southerly winds predominate with great regularity. April is the windiest month and August the least windy.

Crops in Iowa, under exceptionally intelligent husbandry, have become adapted to the prevailing weather. Any important departure above or below normal weather is deleterious, but recent scientific corn breeding and methods of culture have developed in that plant remarkable resistance to adverse weather. Heavy winter precipitation is of little value to spring-planted crops and may be a cause of late planting and the ills that follow it. The exceptionally heavy accumulation of snow in January and February 1936 was followed by calamitous destruction of corn by heat in the summer of that year. Where the snow had been the deepest, the corn was the most complete failure.

Charles D. Reed, *Senior Meteorologist and Climatic Section Director for Iowa, Weather Bureau Des Moines.*

KANSAS

Climatic summary

County	Station	Temperature					Killing frost average dates				Average precipitation													
		Length of record	January average	July average	Maximum	Minimum	Length of record	Last in spring	First in fall	Growing season [1]	Length of record	January	February	March	April	May	June	July	August	September	October	November	December	Annual
		Yr.	°F.	°F.	°F.	°F.	Yr.			Days	Yr.	In.	In.	In.	In.	In.	In.	In.	In.	In.	In.	In.	In.	In.
Allen	Moran	19	32.4	78.6	110	-30	20	Apr. 16	Oct. 17	184	21	1.40	1.76	2.34	3.34	5.09	4.83	4.62	3.73	4.18	2.61	1.73	1.24	36.87
	Iola	33	32.1	79.9	114	-18	34	Apr. 7	Oct. 20	196	33	1.38	1.37	2.52	3.78	4.97	5.02	3.15	3.38	4.72	3.19	2.47	1.26	37.21
Anderson	Garnett	6	32.7	78.3	108	-19	16	Apr. 19	Oct. 21	185	30	1.24	1.50	2.62	3.48	5.18	5.16	3.63	3.27	3.86	3.01	2.46	1.42	36.83
Atchison	Atchison	38	28.2	78.5	111	-28	39	Apr. 14	Oct. 18	187	40	.94	1.26	2.06	3.14	4.61	4.53	3.64	4.04	4.84	2.48	2.01	1.03	34.58
Barber	Medicine Lodge	39	33.5	81.2	118	-22	37	do	Oct. 22	191	39	.45	.80	1.26	2.28	4.43	3.52	2.91	2.71	2.99	2.02	1.41	.63	25.41
Barton	Beaver										11	.29	.68	1.49	2.22	2.80	4.85	3.41	3.77	2.08	1.98	1.56	.60	25.73
	Great Bend						26	Apr. 24	Oct. 15	174	20	.36	.89	1.03	1.69	3.70	3.61	2.68	3.02	2.37	1.48	1.41	.48	22.72
Bourbon	Fort Scott	38	33.1	80.0	118	-24	37	Apr. 14	Oct. 20	189	40	1.64	1.72	2.68	3.91	5.04	5.26	3.90	3.33	4.77	3.62	2.47	1.50	39.84
Brown	Horton	40	27.1	77.9	112	-25	40	Apr. 20	Oct. 16	179	40	.69	1.13	1.57	2.98	4.47	4.89	3.54	3.51	4.51	2.36	1.74	.90	32.29
Butler	El Dorado	34	32.2	80.3	117	-28	35	Apr. 19	Oct. 20	184	36	.78	1.24	1.87	2.85	4.79	3.91	3.34	3.45	3.55	2.69	2.28	1.00	31.75
Chase	Cottonwood Falls	34	30.7	79.8	118	-30	34	Apr. 22	Oct. 16	177	16	.85	1.62	1.69	2.22	5.49	3.95	3.98	3.58	3.34	2.24	1.81	1.14	31.91
Chautauqua	Sedan	39	34.3	80.7	118	-24	40	Apr. 14	Oct. 22	191	40	1.30	1.48	2.38	3.62	5.19	5.46	3.79	3.47	4.29	3.47	2.37	1.42	38.24
Cherokee	Columbus	40	34.2	78.9	115	-28	40	Apr. 9	Oct. 24	198	40	1.88	1.85	3.17	4.44	5.21	5.93	3.76	3.67	3.94	3.33	2.51	1.88	41.57
Cheyenne	Bird City (near)										22	.20	.49	.79	1.69	2.54	2.48	2.50	2.85	1.61	.98	.52	.38	17.03
	St. Francis	30	29.1	76.7	111	-28	30	May 3	Oct. 8	158	31	.18	.51	.74	1.91	3.04	3.06	3.10	2.95	1.85	1.32	.60	.58	19.84
Clark	Ashland	40	33.6	81.0	114	-24	31	Apr. 21	Oct. 22	184	40	.38	.85	1.09	2.10	3.55	3.42	2.82	2.72	2.55	1.59	1.42	.61	23.10
	Mineola						12	Apr. 14	do	191	27	.29	.62	1.10	1.84	3.11	3.04	2.25	2.55	2.20	1.28	.88	.55	19.71
Clay	Clay Center	35	28.4	80.3	117	-35	36	Apr. 26	Oct. 15	172	37	.58	1.06	1.30	2.46	4.12	4.43	3.13	3.49	2.98	1.92	1.44	.66	27.57
Cloud	Concordia	40	27.4	79.3	116	-25	40	Apr. 12	Oct. 20	191	40	.46	.88	1.06	2.20	3.99	4.18	3.30	3.20	2.65	1.86	1.09	.60	25.47
Coffey	Burlington	40	31.6	79.6	117	-27	38	Apr. 18	Oct. 19	184	40	.98	1.30	2.43	3.24	5.36	5.19	3.43	3.74	4.50	2.89	2.16	1.22	36.44
	Lebo	36	30.2	78.5	112	-26	36	Apr. 17	Oct. 18	184	40	.82	1.24	2.11	2.82	4.95	4.92	3.45	3.56	4.27	2.68	2.07	1.20	34.09
Comanche	Coldwater	32	33.3	81.4	115	-18	32	Apr. 18	Oct. 27	192	33	.31	.68	1.04	1.95	3.22	3.60	2.53	2.77	2.74	1.66	1.26	.59	22.35
Cowley	Winfield	40	33.3	80.8	118	-27	39	Apr. 14	Oct. 22	191	40	.92	1.31	1.76	3.03	4.87	4.93	3.57	3.12	3.60	2.74	2.02	1.21	33.08
Crawford	Walnut	16	32.1	78.7	111	-27	18	Apr. 12	Oct. 17	188	36	1.65	1.78	2.97	4.21	5.30	5.48	3.82	3.87	4.55	3.49	2.44	1.46	41.02
Decatur	Dresden	39	28.6	77.7	118	-29	40	Apr. 29	Oct. 7	161	40	.32	.76	1.00	2.11	3.02	2.78	2.91	2.65	1.91	1.28	.73	.64	20.11
	Oberlin	26	27.5	78.4	114	-32	30	May 3	Oct. 8	158	40	.27	.66	.93	2.15	2.81	2.79	2.81	2.95	1.80	1.20	.76	.60	19.73
Dickinson	Abilene	16	31.4	86.1	112	-29	17	Apr. 20	Oct. 13	176	30	.54	1.03	1.41	2.66	3.81	4.48	3.72	3.44	2.99	2.13	1.49	.75	28.45
	Chapman	32	28.5	79.9	116	-29	33	Apr. 25	Oct. 14	172	35	.67	1.00	1.62	2.54	4.24	4.44	3.27	3.40	3.21	1.96	1.72	.77	28.84
Doniphan	St. Joseph, Mo	29	27.3	80.0	110	-24	29	Apr. 10	Oct. 19	192	29	1.00	1.26	2.08	3.15	4.15	4.87	3.02	3.59	4.83	2.56	2.00	1.07	33.58
Douglas	Lawrence	40	29.8	78.8	114	-24	35	do	Oct. 22	195	40	.96	1.34	2.20	2.94	4.94	4.52	4.04	4.00	4.47	2.72	2.20	1.10	35.43
	Vinland						9	Apr. 19	do	186	28	.97	1.26	1.96	3.31	4.92	4.68	3.44	3.85	4.81	2.92	2.26	1.22	35.60
Edwards	Trousdale										23	.38	.62	1.20	2.36	3.32	2.78	2.21	2.78	2.57	1.38	1.05	.48	21.13
Elk	Howard	7	34.7	79.6	111	-17	14	Apr. 18	Oct. 19	184	27	1.22	1.37	1.98	3.41	4.97	5.16	3.79	3.02	3.44	2.90	2.70	1.25	35.21
	Grenola	28	33.0	78.6	111	-23	28	Apr. 17	Oct. 17	183	29	1.00	1.33	2.15	3.57	5.45	4.73	3.66	3.36	4.43	3.23	2.08	1.01	36.00
Ellis	Hays	38	29.6	79.1	117	-24	37	Apr. 29	Oct. 14	168	40	.29	.78	.88	2.11	3.41	4.04	2.95	3.09	2.18	1.48	.96	.57	22.74
Ellsworth	Ellsworth	34	29.2	80.7	117	-30	34	Apr. 25	Oct. 16	174	35	.59	1.15	1.41	2.27	3.63	4.32	2.76	3.50	2.54	1.62	1.33	.77	25.89
Finney	Garden City	40	30.9	79.0	113	-32	40	do	do	174	40	.29	.90	1.02	2.08	2.50	2.80	2.56	2.18	1.92	1.26	.75	.62	18.88

[1] Length of growing season between average dates of last killing frost in spring and first in fall.

KANSAS—Continued

Climatic summary—Continued

County	Station	Temperature					Killing frost average dates				Average precipitation													
		Length of record	January average	July average	Maximum	Minimum	Length of record	Last in spring	First in fall	Growing season[1]	Length of record	January	February	March	April	May	June	July	August	September	October	November	December	Annual
		Yr.	*°F.*	*°F.*	*°F.*	*°F.*	*Yr.*			*Day*	*Yr.*	*In.*	*In.*	*In.*	*In.*	*In.*	*In.*	*In.*	*In.*	*In.*	*In.*	*In.*	*In.*	*In.*
Ford	Bucklin										19	0.42	0.68	1.30	2.06	3.06	3.07	2.63	1.92	2.41	1.44	1.19	0.45	20.63
	Dodge City	40	31.2	78.7	109	−26	40	Apr. 15	Oct. 25	193	40	.31	.75	.94	1.93	2.65	2.99	2.71	2.37	2.14	1.27	.93	.53	19.52
Franklin	Ottawa	40	30.1	78.8	114	−28	40	Apr. 19	Oct. 17	181	40	1.10	1.35	2.24	3.02	4.87	4.83	3.71	3.77	4.42	2.76	2.08	1.18	35.33
Geary	Junction City						10	Apr. 18	Oct. 21	186	21	.70	.87	1.70	3.06	4.33	4.51	3.32	4.06	4.02	2.30	2.18	.79	31.84
Gove	Gove	36	30.1	77.9	113	−29	36	Apr. 29	Oct. 11	165	32	.22	.63	.80	2.00	2.67	3.04	2.70	2.56	1.99	1.23	.70	.71	19.25
Graham	Hill City	28	28.7	80.0	117	−24	27	Apr. 30	do	164	32	.23	.68	.89	1.88	2.59	3.56	2.50	2.55	1.84	1.22	.88	.58	19.40
Grant	Ulysses	36	31.5	78.7	111	−28	39	Apr. 28	Oct. 17	172	40	.24	.57	.60	1.46	2.24	2.82	2.34	2.17	1.84	1.11	.59	.42	16.40
Gray	Cimarron	28	30.5	79.8	111	−22	31	Apr. 24	Oct. 16	175	33	.27	.76	.81	1.83	2.63	3.11	2.69	2.52	2.09	1.42	.90	.52	19.55
Greeley	Tribune	27	28.6	76.5	108	−24	28	Apr. 29	Oct. 10	164	31	.21	.42	.84	1.56	2.54	2.65	2.43	2.02	1.43	.92	.49	.45	15.96
Greenwood	Eureka (near)	28	31.4	80.0	120	−20	34	Apr. 15	Oct. 19	187	40	.83	1.20	1.98	3.11	5.07	4.33	3.59	3.27	3.88	2.84	2.03	1.17	33.30
Hamilton	Irene	8	28.7	77.9	110	−21	20	Apr. 30	Oct. 12	165	24	.26	.62	.81	1.47	2.06	2.43	2.35	2.25	1.38	.95	.53	.53	15.64
	Syracuse	19	29.0	77.6	114	−26	28	Apr. 27	Oct. 13	169	38	.24	.58	.83	1.68	2.37	2.45	2.66	2.40	1.66	1.10	.63	.45	17.05
Harper	Anthony	31	33.6	81.3	115	−15	34	Apr. 13	Oct. 25	195	40	.65	.94	1.52	2.60	4.44	3.76	3.00	2.76	2.97	2.21	1.82	.87	27.54
Harvey	Newton	39	30.8	79.9	117	−28	34	Apr. 20	Oct. 20	183	40	.60	1.03	1.60	2.99	4.78	4.55	3.39	3.43	3.32	2.47	1.77	.88	30.81
Haskell	Sublette	23	31.7	79.5	111	−21	20	Apr. 24	do	179	25	.29	.60	.93	1.61	2.62	2.89	2.25	2.05	2.31	1.42	.63	.52	18.12
Hodgeman	Jetmore	36	31.1	79.7	114	−24	36	Apr. 26	Oct. 16	173	38	.26	.76	.96	2.01	3.04	2.95	2.70	2.28	1.77	1.40	.97	.58	19.68
Jackson	Holton	6	28.5	78.7	110	−22	16	Apr. 22	do	177	29	.87	1.03	1.81	3.64	4.72	4.61	3.44	3.75	4.95	2.56	2.10	.98	34.46
Jefferson	Valley Falls	38	28.6	78.3	114	−31	40	Apr. 23	Oct. 17	177	40	.82	1.14	1.74	2.72	4.57	4.37	3.54	4.03	4.35	2.27	1.87	.99	32.41
Jewell	Burr Oak (near)	38	25.7	78.8	117	−30	38	Apr. 28	Oct. 10	165	38	.50	.95	1.12	2.34	3.65	3.78	2.94	3.01	2.69	1.59	1.03	.61	24.21
Johnson	Olathe	36	30.6	79.0	111	−29	36	Apr. 18	Oct. 16	181	38	1.15	1.33	2.30	2.88	4.96	4.37	3.54	3.92	4.57	2.41	2.11	1.30	34.84
Kearny	Deerfield (near)						8	Apr. 26	Oct. 20	177	23	.24	.70	.92	1.67	2.50	2.28	2.58	2.07	1.66	1.20	.62	.52	16.96
	Lakin	39	30.4	78.3	115	−23	38	Apr. 27	Oct. 15	171	40	.21	.60	.61	1.75	2.15	2.22	2.31	1.88	1.53	1.02	.66	.36	15.30
Kingman	Norwich	38	33.3	81.4	117	−21	39	Apr. 14	Oct. 25	194	40	.65	.95	1.54	2.78	4.69	4.22	2.77	3.25	3.23	2.43	1.79	.87	29.17
Kiowa	Greensburg	31	32.2	79.8	113	−20	32	Apr. 20	Oct. 20	183	32	.41	.94	1.02	2.08	3.46	3.23	2.29	2.62	2.61	1.43	1.35	.66	22.10
Labette	Oswego	25	36.0	79.1	110	−30	28	Apr. 11	Oct. 26	198	40	1.68	1.60	2.83	4.30	4.73	5.68	3.77	3.40	4.09	3.27	2.44	1.65	39.44
Lane	Healy	36	29.5	77.8	116	−31	38	Apr. 30	Oct. 14	167	38	.16	.61	.70	1.76	2.71	2.94	2.43	2.57	1.84	1.24	.65	.56	18.17
Leavenworth	Leavenworth	26	29.4	80.1	114	−22	32	Apr. 10	Oct. 20	193	28	1.00	1.18	1.98	3.30	4.79	4.21	2.91	3.89	4.91	2.68	2.28	1.05	34.18
Lincoln	Lincoln (near)	27	28.7	81.8	119	−25	26	Apr. 27	Oct. 15	171	27	.49	.98	1.12	2.41	3.48	3.44	2.72	2.65	2.09	1.57	1.31	.57	22.83
Linn	Pleasanton	14	31.9	77.8	107	−23	26	Apr. 16	Oct. 18	185	36	1.56	1.55	2.79	3.81	4.94	4.94	3.60	3.72	4.52	3.47	2.57	1.50	38.97
Logan	Oakley	18	29.8	78.1	111	−24	26	May 2	Oct. 11	162	19	.31	.56	.92	1.72	3.18	2.72	2.62	2.88	1.75	1.49	.68	.46	19.29
Lyon	Emporia	38	30.8	79.5	116	−23	39	Apr. 16	Oct. 18	185	40	.70	1.14	2.04	2.83	5.39	4.65	3.61	3.70	3.98	2.65	1.87	.98	33.54
	Neosho Rapids										33	.78	1.03	1.83	2.71	4.79	4.65	3.11	3.01	3.78	2.66	2.35	1.02	31.72
McPherson	McPherson	40	30.1	80.6	117	−27	40	Apr. 22	Oct. 16	177	40	.73	1.22	1.44	2.51	4.47	4.24	2.82	3.29	3.23	2.21	1.51	.87	28.54
Marion	Marion	18	31.2	79.9	111	−29	30	Apr. 18	Oct. 17	182	31	.66	1.29	1.78	2.82	4.53	4.02	3.06	3.53	2.90	2.25	1.94	.96	29.74
Marshall	Blue Rapids										34	.55	.96	1.28	2.55	3.59	4.34	3.20	3.27	3.79	2.02	1.38	.69	27.62
	Oketo	30	25.1	79.6	118	−26	30	Apr. 24	Oct. 12	171	31	.51	.79	1.26	2.47	4.18	4.06	3.01	3.50	3.48	2.15	1.44	.74	27.59
Meade	Plains	16	32.5	79.0	110	−20	16	do	Oct. 17	176	29	.30	.69	.92	1.54	2.77	3.03	2.39	2.22	2.02	1.61	.71	.52	18.72
Miami	Paola						14	Apr. 18	Oct. 19	184	30	1.28	1.32	2.47	3.45	4.93	5.04	3.59	3.99	4.17	2.96	2.50	1.30	37.00

Mitchell	Cawker City	16	26.0	79.2	114	−23	18	Apr. 29	Oct. 10	164	19	.47	.75	1.04	2.75	3.44	3.76	3.35	3.11	2.66	1.83	1.20	.59	24.95
	Beloit	19	27.7	80.2	113	−27	20	Apr. 25	Oct. 13	171	40	.39	.72	.92	2.22	3.58	4.15	2.91	3.07	2.38	1.71	.97	.51	23.53
Montgomery	Independence	40	34.8	80.3	116	−23	40	Apr. 15	Oct. 22	190	40	1.37	1.60	2.55	3.83	4.80	5.19	3.68	3.00	4.21	3.29	2.38	1.41	37.31
Morris	Council Grove	29	29.5	79.6	115	−20	29	Apr. 22	Oct. 18	179	30	.68	1.06	1.68	2.70	4.51	4.05	3.56	3.80	3.70	2.44	1.99	.89	31.06
Morton	Elkhart	12	35.3	79.7	110	−17	11	Apr. 16	Oct. 22	189	21	.24	.58	1.06	1.10	2.11	2.11	2.51	1.70	2.22	1.40	.71	.54	16.28
	Richfield	34	31.7	78.6	111	−19	32	Apr. 23	Oct. 20	180	34	.31	.79	.89	1.64	2.02	1.96	2.33	2.03	1.60	1.32	.62	.72	16.23
Nemaha	Centralia	28	26.4	78.8	114	−27	28	Apr. 27	Oct. 15	171	30	.77	1.11	1.57	2.77	4.10	4.81	3.29	3.49	4.06	2.17	1.87	1.04	31.05
Neosho	Chanute	31	33.7	80.3	116	−23	30	Apr. 10	Oct. 21	194	36	1.24	1.65	2.61	4.21	5.60	5.14	3.79	3.61	4.47	2.80	2.23	1.36	38.71
Ness	Ness City	10	30.1	79.3	110	−24	13	May 1	Oct. 18	170	40	.33	.78	.80	2.02	3.33	3.26	2.63	2.69	2.03	1.20	.82	.54	20.43
Norton	Norton (near)	35	27.5	78.2	116	−27	35	Apr. 30	Oct. 13	166	36	.25	.69	1.02	2.20	2.99	3.10	3.08	2.52	1.80	1.46	.87	.59	20.57
Osage	Osage City	34	30.1	78.3	118	−26	34	Apr. 21	Oct. 16	178	39	.84	1.15	1.95	3.01	5.22	5.29	4.08	3.67	4.04	2.69	2.13	1.05	35.12
	Quenemo	9	32.5	78.2	106	−18	10	Apr. 24	Oct. 13	172	27	1.07	1.17	2.26	3.04	4.80	5.01	3.08	3.03	4.15	2.75	2.35	1.18	33.89
Osborne	Alton (near)	35	28.0	80.0	121	−25	33	Apr. 28	Oct. 14	169	39	.40	.85	.95	1.96	2.87	3.52	2.80	2.80	2.35	1.37	.94	.59	21.40
Ottawa	Minneapolis	40	29.0	80.0	119	−29	39	Apr. 22	Oct. 15	176	40	.45	.91	1.07	2.39	3.88	4.10	2.91	3.43	2.74	1.84	1.20	.59	25.51
Pawnee	Larned	34	30.3	79.9	114	−24	35	Apr. 25	Oct. 16	174	35	.41	.81	1.04	2.09	3.53	3.86	3.02	2.87	2.34	1.43	1.24	.61	23.25
Phillips	Phillipsburg	36	27.9	79.8	120	−32	36	Apr. 26	Oct. 13	170	40	.35	.69	.92	2.24	3.13	3.58	2.97	2.83	2.55	1.49	.92	.69	22.36
Pottawatomie	Emmett						14	Apr. 20	Oct. 20	183	27	.72	.88	1.65	3.00	4.26	4.06	3.00	3.51	3.99	2.28	1.89	.88	30.12
	Wamego	34	29.5	79.1	114	−30	34	Apr. 18	Oct. 18	183	40	.75	1.18	1.56	2.86	4.66	4.52	4.08	3.97	4.07	2.32	1.89	.87	32.73
Pratt	Pratt	40	32.7	80.8	115	−24	38	Apr. 17	Oct. 23	189	40	.53	.81	1.19	2.20	3.43	3.32	2.82	2.55	2.73	2.00	1.37	.60	23.55
Rawlins	Atwood	34	27.6	77.3	118	−33	36	May 4	Oct. 4	153	38	.23	.50	.80	1.98	2.69	2.69	2.49	2.70	1.76	1.02	.68	.56	18.10
Reno	Hutchinson	38	31.0	80.1	116	−27	40	Apr. 20	Oct. 19	182	40	.68	1.10	1.51	2.41	4.63	3.87	2.95	3.04	3.00	2.01	1.61	.79	27.60
Republic	Belleville	34	26.2	78.9	115	−31	34	Apr. 28	Oct. 11	166	37	.49	.93	1.07	2.27	4.28	4.04	3.35	3.15	2.78	1.69	1.18	.68	25.91
Rice	Alden	25	31.5	80.5	116	−19	25	Apr. 19	Oct. 18	182	29	.49	.90	1.28	2.39	4.29	3.80	2.44	3.09	2.52	1.64	1.21	.54	24.59
Riley	Manhattan	40	29.1	80.0	116	−32	40	Apr. 24	Oct. 12	171	40	.68	1.25	1.64	2.64	4.40	4.40	3.99	4.28	3.94	2.08	1.81	.81	31.92
Rooks	Plainville	28	28.5	79.4	116	−21	28	Apr. 26	Oct. 14	171	34	.46	.84	1.03	2.16	2.94	3.84	2.65	2.70	2.36	1.41	1.08	.72	22.19
Rush	Bison (near)	34	29.3	79.6	116	−25	34	Apr. 25	do	172	37	.30	.80	.96	1.82	3.15	3.33	2.72	3.13	1.90	1.32	1.08	.53	21.04
Russell	Russell	36	29.6	80.2	118	−28	34	do	Oct. 15	173	39	.37	.90	1.07	2.31	3.47	4.21	2.97	3.38	2.26	1.61	1.14	.55	24.24
Saline	Salina	40	34.2	80.7	118	−31	39	Apr. 22	Oct. 16	177	40	.57	1.08	1.35	2.31	3.96	4.50	2.86	3.27	2.70	1.90	1.38	.67	26.55
Scott	Scott City	36	29.8	78.0	114	−26	34	Apr. 27	Oct. 14	170	37	.30	.81	1.01	1.81	2.79	2.99	2.49	2.63	1.66	1.38	.74	.72	19.33
Sedgwick	Mount Hope						10	Apr. 20	Oct. 25	188	40	.65	1.05	1.53	2.56	4.16	3.85	2.81	3.07	2.87	1.99	1.62	.80	26.96
	Wichita	40	32.2	80.4	114	−22	40	Apr. 10	Oct. 27	200	40	.64	1.16	1.71	2.72	4.69	4.28	2.96	3.04	3.26	2.43	1.81	.94	29.64
Seward	Kismet (near)										30	.24	.59	.63	1.28	2.85	2.51	2.51	2.38	1.92	1.28	.66	.46	17.31
	Liberal	30	33.9	80.6	113	−19	31	Apr. 19	Oct. 25	189	32	.25	.76	.83	1.42	2.70	2.78	2.76	2.40	1.93	1.43	.77	.62	18.65
Shawnee	Topeka	40	29.5	79.5	114	−25	40	Apr. 8	Oct. 20	195	40	.82	1.30	1.99	2.77	4.46	3.96	3.65	4.01	4.18	2.40	1.78	.95	32.27
Sheridan	Hoxie	35	28.9	78.4	113	−30	37	May 2	Oct. 10	161	40	.23	.68	1.04	1.94	2.83	2.93	2.63	2.52	1.84	1.30	.71	.60	19.25
Sherman	Goodland	28	28.9	75.4	110	−23	28	May 4	Oct. 11	160	32	.20	.53	.92	1.74	2.59	2.71	2.44	2.57	1.53	1.22	.65	.57	17.67
Smith	Smith Center	12	26.7	78.3	112	−24	26	Apr. 29	Oct. 8	162	29	.28	.61	.80	2.21	2.96	3.10	2.57	3.15	2.26	1.27	.85	.56	20.62
Stafford	Hudson										17	.49	.64	1.16	2.02	4.09	3.26	2.32	2.59	2.39	1.51	1.39	.44	22.30
	Macksville	32	30.8	78.5	112	−22	30	Apr. 25	Oct. 14	172	32	.40	.85	1.09	2.24	3.38	3.78	2.96	3.26	2.76	1.84	1.32	.64	24.52
Stanton	Johnson	22	31.2	79.5	113	−19	22	Apr. 28	Oct. 20	175	22	.22	.40	1.01	1.12	2.46	2.11	2.12	2.32	1.67	1.16	.59	.29	15.47
Stevens	Hugoton	12	32.5	77.2	116	−22	20	Apr. 24	do	179	35	.24	.58	.74	1.41	2.58	2.80	2.50	2.11	1.74	1.40	.82	.52	17.44
Sumner	Wellington	24	33.2	82.7	120	−19	24	Apr. 18	Oct. 22	187	29	.81	1.13	1.73	2.95	5.11	4.83	3.36	3.14	3.71	2.86	2.25	1.26	33.14
Thomas	Colby	38	29.0	77.1	111	−31	40	May 2	Oct. 9	160	40	.24	.61	.87	2.05	2.48	2.82	2.54	2.34	1.62	1.04	.68	.57	17.86
Trego	Wakeeney	39	30.0	78.5	115	−25	40	Apr. 28	Oct. 10	165	40	.21	.67	.84	2.12	3.11	3.73	3.11	2.64	2.30	1.33	.80	.57	21.43
Wabaunsee	Eskridge	32	28.9	78.9	115	−21	31	Apr. 15	Oct. 17	185	32	.87	1.42	1.96	2.85	4.91	4.81	3.59	3.74	4.00	2.73	2.24	1.11	34.23
	McFarland										20	.74	.97	1.86	3.05	4.42	4.16	3.68	3.86	4.12	2.35	2.39	.68	32.28
Wallace	Sharon Springs	22	28.8	75.7	109	−25	24	May 3	Oct. 7	157	16	.12	.46	.95	1.52	2.96	2.56	2.15	2.34	1.09	1.02	.62	.37	16.16
Washington	Hanover	38	27.5	79.8	116	−24	40	Apr. 25	Oct. 14	172	39	.51	.94	1.33	2.42	4.32	4.13	3.69	3.64	3.20	2.37	1.39	.71	28.65
Wichita	Leoti	30	28.9	77.7	111	−26	30	May 2	Oct. 9	160	31	.22	.67	.79	1.79	2.55	2.58	2.16	2.38	1.42	1.13	.57	.54	16.80
Wilson	Fredonia	32	33.7	80.1	121	−26	34	Apr. 13	Oct. 20	190	36	1.28	1.40	2.19	3.61	5.19	5.29	3.48	3.60	3.95	3.09	2.44	1.33	36.85
Woodson	Toronto	40	31.9	79.7	115	−28	38	Apr. 18	Oct. 19	184	40	1.29	1.49	2.10	3.67	5.39	4.67	3.80	3.33	4.30	2.98	2.32	1.38	36.72
Wyandotte	Kansas City, Mo.	40	30.2	79.7	113	−22	40	Apr. 6	Oct. 28	205	40	1.22	1.56	2.46	3.05	4.86	4.34	3.53	3.90	4.63	2.76	2.12	1.30	35.73

KANSAS—Continued

Precipitation and temperature—State unit values

[This tabulation gives the mean annual, mean monthly, and average seasonal precipitation, 1886–1938, and the mean annual temperatures, 1896–1938, for Kansas]

Precipitation		Precipitation		Precipitation		Precipitation		Temperature		Temperature	
Year	Mean	Year	Mean	Year	Mean	Month	Mean	Year	Mean	Year	Mean
	In.		*In.*		*In.*		*In.*		° *F.*		° *F.*
1886	25.70	1908	32.30	1930	26.87	August	3.09	1896	55.8	1918	55.2
1887	23.37	1909	31.20	1931	25.90	September	2.81	1897	55.1	1919	53.9
1888	23.43	1910	19.67	1932	23.76	October	1.92	1898	54.2	1920	54.5
1889	29.44	1911	24.53	1933	22.18	November	1.27	1899	54.1	1921	57.6
1890	21.16	1912	26.69	1934	20.02	December	.85	1900	55.8	1922	55.8
1891	31.14	1913	23.02	1935	28.47			1901	55.4	1923	54.9
1892	29.02	1914	23.58	1936	18.31	Annual	26.57	1902	54.1	1924	53.0
1893	20.25	1915	40.77	1937	20.88			1903	53.4	1925	55.6
1894	20.72	1916	23.84	1938	27.27			1904	54.2	1926	55.2
1895	28.08	1917	19.60					1905	53.5	1927	55.0
1896	28.72	1918	27.60			Season	Average	1906	54.4	1928	55.2
1897	24.45	1919	25.65	Month	Mean			1907	54.9	1929	53.2
1898	31.79	1920	26.65					1908	55.8	1930	55.5
1899	26.26	1921	24.19				*In.*	1909	54.4	1931	57.4
1900	27.96	1922	29.01		*In.*	Winter	2.53	1910	55.7	1932	54.7
1901	21.35	1923	31.88	January	0.69	Spring	7.81	1911	56.1	1933	57.8
1902	34.42	1924	24.23	February	.99	Summer	10.23	1912	52.9	1934	58.5
1903	31.35	1925	25.08	March	1.44	Fall	6.00	1913	55.5	1935	55.9
1904	31.01	1926	24.80	April	2.53			1914	55.8	1936	56.3
1905	30.77	1927	32.40	May	3.84			1915	53.7	1937	54.6
1906	28.58	1928	33.40	June	3.93			1916	54.1	1938	57.9
1907	26.46	1929	27.96	July	3.21			1917	53.2		

Dates of last killing frost in spring and first in fall, with length of growing season

Year	Columbus			Horton			Hutchinson			Colby			Hays			Garden City		
	Last in spring	First in fall	Growing season[1]	Last in spring	First in fall	Growing season[1]	Last in spring	First in fall	Growing season[1]	Last in spring	First in fall	Growing season[1]	Last in spring	First in fall	Growing season[1]	Last in spring	First in fall	Growing season[1]
			Days			*Days*			*Days*			*Days*			*Days*			*Days*
1899	Apr. 9	Nov. 2	207	Apr. 9	Sept. 29	173	Apr. 4	Nov. 2	212	Mar. 4	Oct. 3	152		Oct. 16		Apr. 22	Oct. 5	166
1900	Apr. 13	Nov. 8	209	Apr. 13	Oct. 8	178	Apr. 13	Oct. 8	178	Apr. 13	Oct. 7	177				Apr. 11	Oct. 8	180
1901	Apr. 3	Oct. 14	194	Apr. 18	Sept. 17	152	Apr. 26	Oct. 14	171	May 26	Oct. 14	141	May 26	Sept. 17	114	May 26	Oct. 16	143
1902	Apr. 1	Nov. 18	231	Apr. 23	Oct. 14	174	Apr. 16	Oct. 5	172	Apr. 26	Sept. 12	139	Apr. 17	Oct. 28	194	Apr. 26	Sept. 30	157
1903	Apr. 4	Oct. 18	197	May 1	Oct. 18	170	May 3	Oct. 23	173	Apr. 30	Sept. 16	139	May 1	Sept. 17	139	Apr. 30	Sept. 17	140
1904	Apr. 17	Oct. 23	189	Apr. 17	Oct. 23	189	Apr. 17	Oct. 25	191	Apr. 17	Oct. 25	191	May 14			Apr. 26	Oct. 25	182
1905	Mar. 9	Oct. 21	226	Apr. 16	Oct. 21	188	Apr. 5	Oct. 11	189	Apr. 21	Oct. 10	172				Apr. 15	Oct. 11	179
1906	Mar. 31	Oct. 10	193	Apr. 1	Oct. 10	192	Mar. 31	Oct. 10	193	Apr. 14	do	179	Apr. 14	Oct. 10	179	Apr. 14	Oct. 23	192
1907	May 4	Oct. 13	162	May 15	Oct. 12	150	May 15	Nov. 10	179	May 27	Nov. 2	159	May 27	Nov. 2	159	May 27	Nov. 10	167
1908	Apr. 3	Oct. 12	192	May 2	Sept. 29	150	May 8	Oct. 24	169	May 8	Sept. 27	142	May 8	Oct. 23	168	Apr. 30	Oct. 24	177
1909	May 1	do	164	May 1	Oct. 12	164	May 1	Oct. 12	164	May 9	Oct. 12	156	May 1	Oct. 12	164	May 1	Oct. 11	163
1910	Mar. 15	Oct. 28	227	Apr. 17	Oct. 22	188	Apr. 6	Oct. 21	198	May 3	Oct. 20	170	Apr. 26	Oct. 21	178	Apr. 26	Oct. 6	163
1911	Apr. 9	Oct. 22	196	May 2	do	173	May 2	Oct. 22	173	May 2	Oct. 8	159	May 2	Oct. 9	160	May 2	Oct. 8	159
1912	Mar. 25	Oct. 23	212	Apr. 7	do	198	Apr. 18	Sept. 26	161	May 14	Sept. 25	134	May 16	Sept. 26	133	Apr. 22	Sept. 25	156
1913	Mar. 28	Oct. 29	215	Apr. 13	Oct. 20	190	Apr. 12	Oct. 18	189	Apr. 13	Sept. 21	161	Apr. 12	Oct. 17	188	Apr. 26	Oct. 11	168
1914	Apr. 12	Oct. 27	198	Apr. 20	Oct. 27	190	Apr. 13	Oct. 27	197	May 13	Oct. 15	155	May 13	Oct. 25	165	Apr. 13	Oct. 15	185
1915	Apr. 3	Oct. 9	189	Apr. 3	Oct. 9	189	Apr. 3	Nov. 12	223	May 21	Oct. 5	137	Apr. 3	Oct. 5	185	Apr. 3	Oct. 5	185
1916	Apr. 9	Sept. 29	173	Apr. 9	Sept. 29	173	Apr. 9	Sept. 29	173	May 16	Sept. 28	135	May 3	Sept. 29	149	May 3	Oct. 19	169
1917	May 1	Oct. 9	161	May 5	Oct. 8	156	May 1	Oct. 8	160	May 8	Oct. 8	153	May 8	Oct. 8	153	May 7	Oct. 8	154
1918	Apr. 21	Nov. 1	194	Apr. 21	Oct. 28	190	Apr. 28	Sept. 20	145	May 10	Oct. 25	168	May 1	Sept. 20	142	Apr. 30	Oct. 26	179
1919	Apr. 17	Oct. 28	194	Apr. 17	Oct. 11	177	Apr. 17	Oct. 17	183	Apr. 25	Oct. 10	168	Apr. 17	Oct. 10	176	Apr. 17	Oct. 10	176
1920	Apr. 27	Nov. 2	189	Apr. 28	Sept. 30	155	Apr. 27	Sept. 30	156	Apr. 27	Sept. 29	155	Apr. 27	Sept. 29	155	Apr. 27	Sept. 30	156
1921	Apr. 17	Oct. 12	178	Apr. 17	Oct. 12	178	May 3	Oct. 26	176	May 3	Oct. 3	153	May 3	Oct. 8	158	Apr. 28	Oct. 31	186
1922	Apr. 1	Oct. 18	200	Apr. 18	do	177	Apr. 18	Oct. 18	183	Apr. 19	Oct. 17	181	Apr. 18	Oct. 9	174	Apr. 19	Oct. 8	172
1923	May 9	Oct. 21	165	May 9	Oct. 21	165	May 9	Oct. 21	165	May 16	Oct. 13	150	May 16	Oct. 21	158	Apr. 24	Oct. 19	178
1924	Apr. 1	Oct. 23	205	May 11	Oct. 22	164	Apr. 1	Oct. 23	205	May 15	Sept. 29	137	May 15	Sept. 29	137	May 11	Sept. 29	141
1925	Mar. 19	Oct. 10	205	Mar. 30	Oct. 10	194	May 1	Oct. 10	162	May 1	Oct. 10	162	May 1	Oct. 9	161	May 1	Oct. 19	171
1926	Apr. 15	Oct. 25	193	Apr. 19	Oct. 24	188	Apr. 15	Oct. 24	192	Apr. 28	Sept. 25	150	Apr. 28	Oct. 24	179	Apr. 28	Oct. 24	179
1927	Apr. 22	Nov. 6	198	Apr. 22	Nov. 2	194	Apr. 22	Nov. 2	194	Apr. 22	Nov. 2	194	Apr. 22	Nov. 2	194	Apr. 21	Nov. 2	195
1928	Apr. 15	Nov. 3	202	Apr. 19	do	197	Apr. 16	do	200	do	Sept. 25	156	Apr. 16	Oct. 22	189	Apr. 16	Oct. 22	189
1929	Apr. 1	Oct. 25	207	Apr. 12	Oct. 25	196	Apr. 12	Oct. 25	196	May 2	Oct. 22	173	May 2	Oct. 25	176	May 2	Oct. 21	172
1930	Mar. 20	Oct. 24	218	Apr. 2	Oct. 17	198	Apr. 1	Oct. 21	203	May 19	Oct. 18	152	Apr. 8	Oct. 18	193	Apr. 3	Oct. 19	199
1931	Apr. 22	Oct. 31	192	Apr. 27	Nov. 1	188	Apr. 22	Oct. 30	191	May 22	Oct. 28	159	May 22	Oct. 30	161	May 22	Oct. 30	161
1932	Mar. 23	Oct. 6	197	do	Oct. 6	162	Apr. 11	Oct. 11	183	Apr. 27	Oct. 5	161	Apr. 11	Oct. 11	183	Apr. 11	Oct. 5	177
1933		Nov. 8		Apr. 16	Oct. 5	172	Apr. 16	Oct. 9	176	Apr. 15	Oct. 8	176	Apr. 16	Oct. 8	175	Apr. 16	Oct. 22	189
1934	Mar. 31	Nov. 1	215	Apr. 25	Oct. 29	187	do	Oct. 28	195	Apr. 20	Sept. 26	159	Apr. 13	Oct. 28	198	Apr. 12	Oct. 28	199

[1] Number of days between last killing frost in spring and first in fall.

KANSAS—Continued

Dates of last killing frost in spring and first in fall, with length of growing season—Continued

Year	Columbus			Horton			Hutchinson			Colby			Hays			Garden City		
	Last in spring	First in fall	Growing season	Last in spring	First in fall	Growing season	Last in spring	First in fall	Growing season	Last in spring	First in fall	Growing season	Last in spring	First in fall	Growing season	Last in spring	First in fall	Growing season
			Days			*Days*			*Days*			*Days*			*Days*			*Days*
1935	Apr. 15	Nov. 5	204	Apr. 30	Oct. 6	159	Apr. 15	Oct. 24	192	Apr. 19	Oct. 10	174	Apr. 19	Oct. 23	187	Apr. 29	Oct. 10	164
1936	Apr. 7	Nov. 3	210	Apr. 22	Oct. 22	183	Apr. 22	Oct. 22	183	Apr. 22	Oct. 21	182	Apr. 17	Oct. 22	188	Apr. 22	Oct. 22	183
1937	Apr. 6	Oct. 23	200	Apr. 11	Oct. 14	186	Apr. 27	do	178	Apr. 27	Oct. 22	178	Apr. 27	do	178	Apr. 27	Nov. 2	189
1938	Apr. 10	do	196	Apr. 22	Oct. 24	185	May 8	Oct. 20	165	May 8	Oct. 20	165	May 8	Oct. 20	165	Apr. 9	Oct. 20	194
Mean	Apr. 9	Oct. 24	198	Apr. 20	Oct. 16	179	Apr. 20	Oct. 19	182	May 2	Oct. 9	160	Apr. 29	Oct. 14	168	Apr. 25	Oct. 16	174
Extremes	Mar. 9[2]	Sept. 29[4]	[6] 161	Mar. 30[2]	Sept. 17[4]	[6] 150	Mar. 31[2]	Sept. 20[4]	[6] 145	Apr. 13[2]	Sept. 12[4]	[6] 134	Apr. 3[2]	Sept. 17[4]	[6] 114	Apr. 3[2]	Sept. 17[4]	[6] 140
	May 9[3]	Nov. 18[5]	[7] 231	May 15[3]	Nov. 2[5]	[7] 198	May 15[3]	Nov. 12[5]	[7] 223	May 27[3]	Nov. 2[5]	[7] 194	May 27[3]	Nov. 2[5]	[7] 198	May 27[3]	Nov. 10[5]	[7] 199

[2] Earliest date in spring.
[3] Latest date in spring.
[4] Earliest date in fall.
[5] Latest date in fall.
[6] Shortest growing season.
[7] Longest growing season.

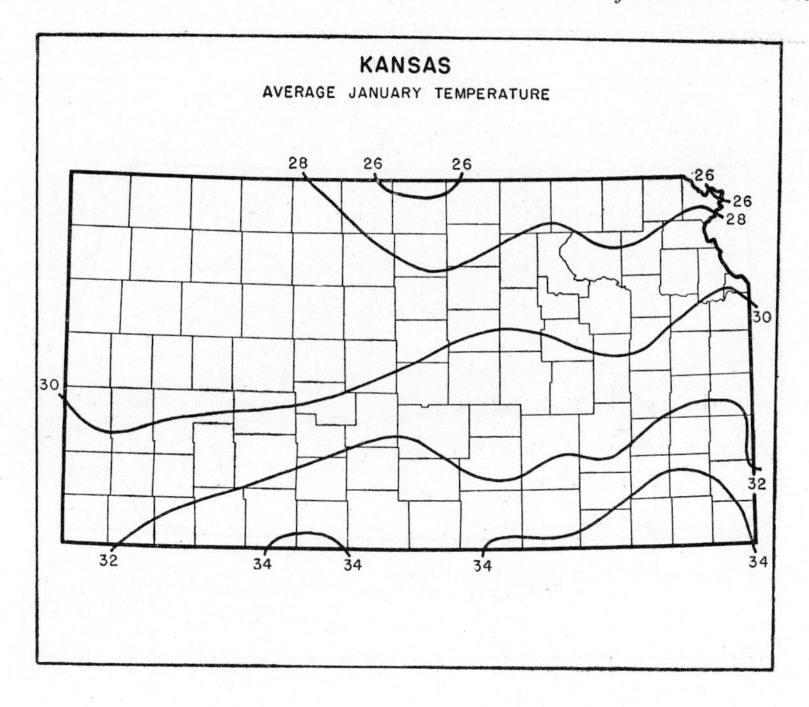
KANSAS
AVERAGE JANUARY TEMPERATURE
28
26
26
26
26
28
30
30
32
32
32
34
34
34
34

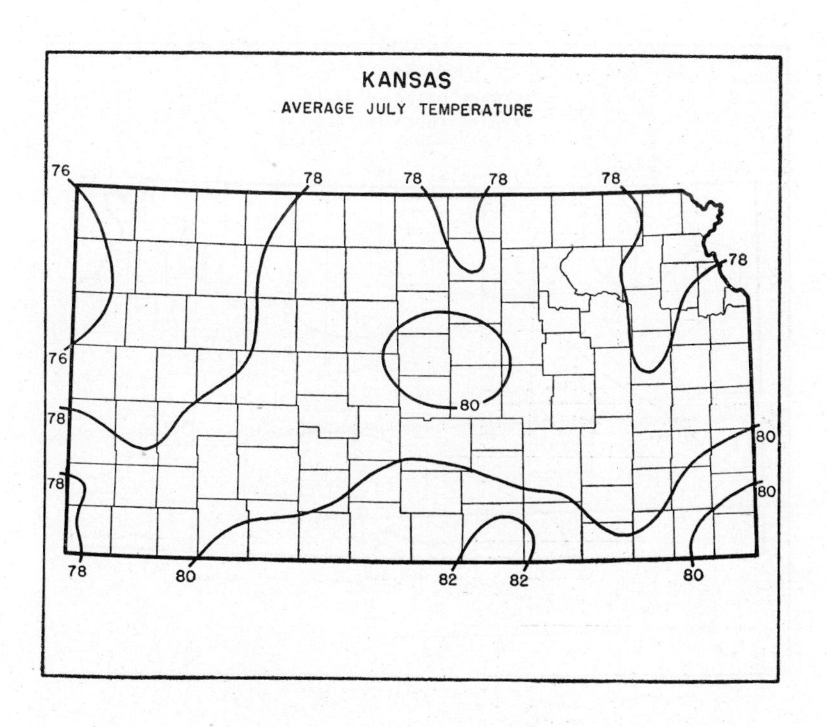
KANSAS
AVERAGE JULY TEMPERATURE
76
78
78
78
78
78
76
80
78
78
80
80
78
80
82
82
80

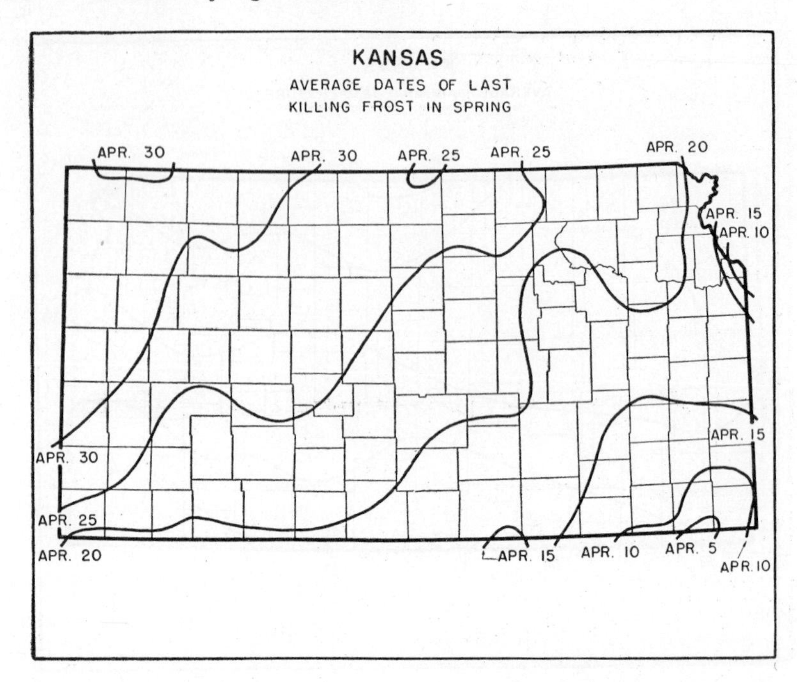
KANSAS
AVERAGE DATES OF LAST
KILLING FROST IN SPRING
APR. 30
APR. 30
APR. 25
APR. 25
APR. 20
APR. 15
APR. 10
APR. 15
APR. 30
APR. 25
APR. 20
APR. 15
APR. 10
APR. 5
APR. 10

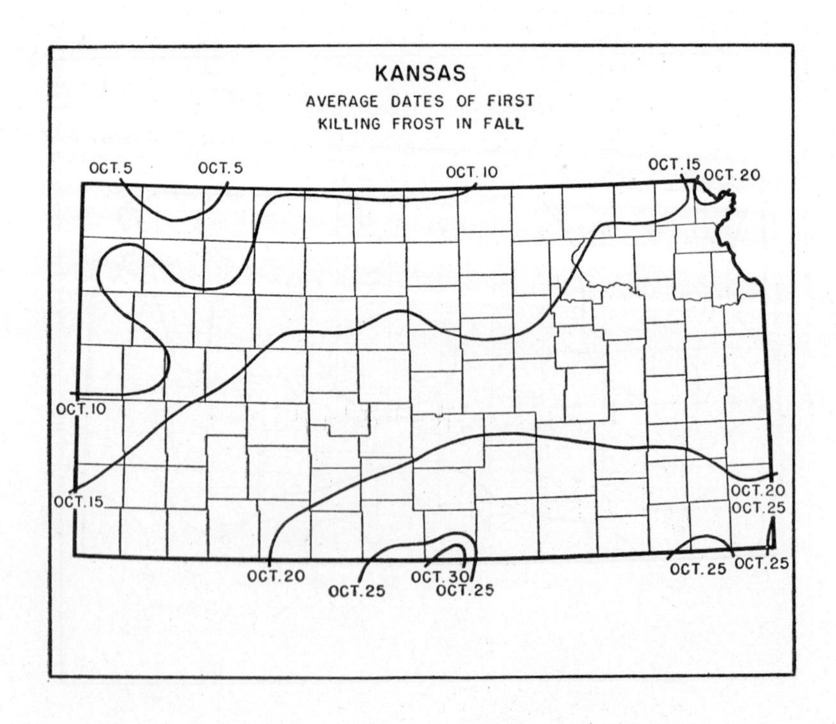
KANSAS
AVERAGE DATES OF FIRST
KILLING FROST IN FALL
OCT. 5
OCT. 5
OCT. 10
OCT. 15
OCT. 20
OCT. 10
OCT. 15
OCT. 20
OCT. 25
OCT. 20
OCT. 25
OCT. 30
OCT. 25
OCT. 25
OCT. 25

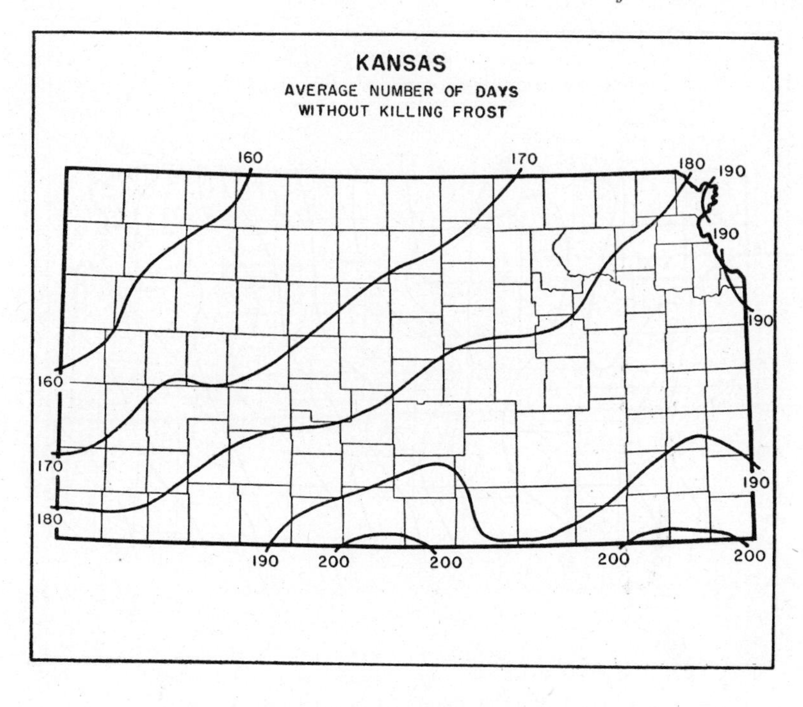
KANSAS
AVERAGE NUMBER OF DAYS
WITHOUT KILLING FROST
160
170
180
190
190
190
160
170
180
190
190
200
200
200
200

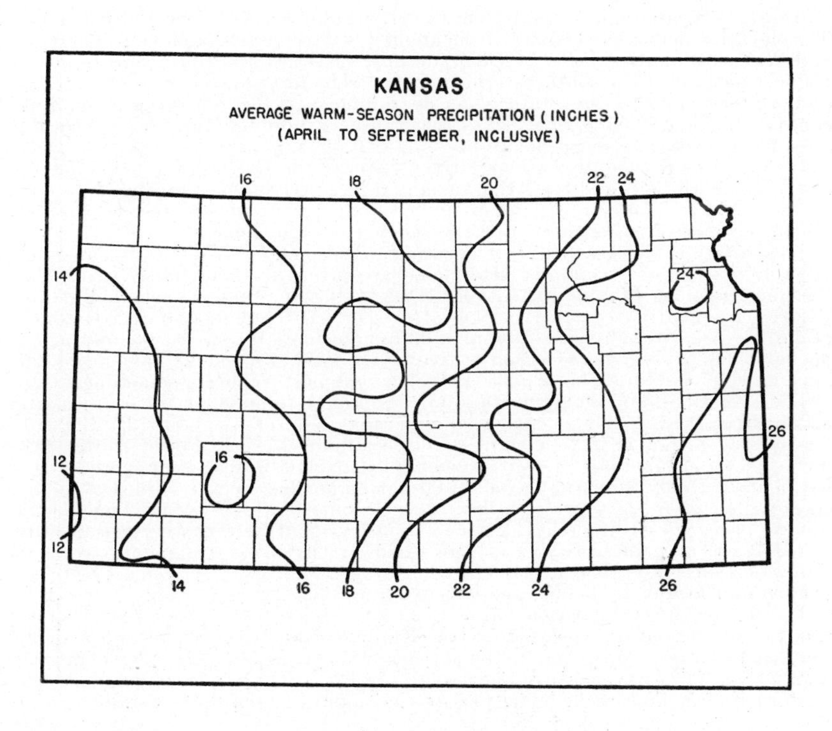
KANSAS
AVERAGE WARM-SEASON PRECIPITATION (INCHES)
(APRIL TO SEPTEMBER, INCLUSIVE)
16
18
20
22
24
14
24
16
12
12
26
14
16
18
20
22
24
26

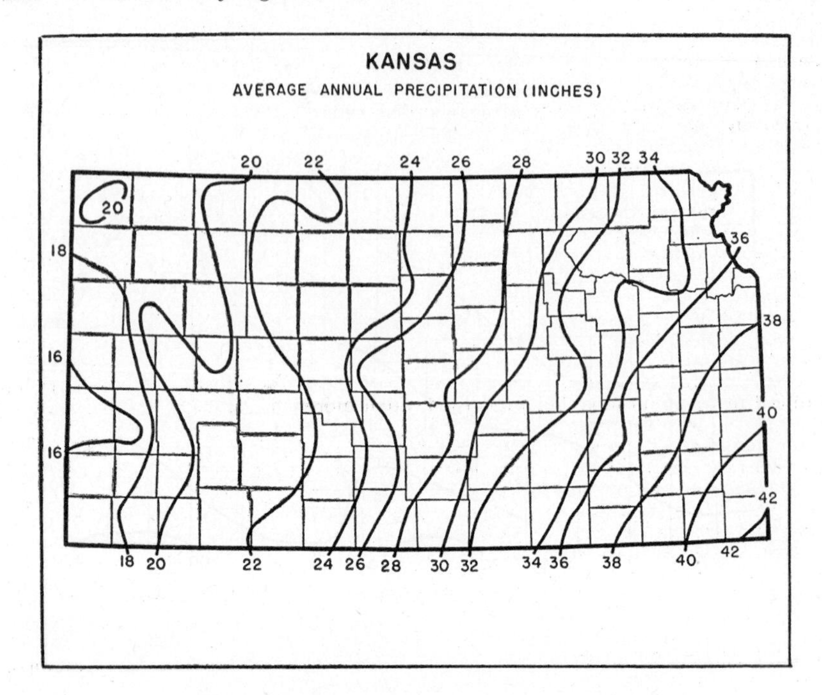

SUPPLEMENTARY CLIMATIC NOTES FOR KANSAS

Kansas is located approximately in the geographic center of the United States. The elevation decreases gradually from about 4,000 feet above sea level in Sherman and Wallace Counties, near the Colorado line, eastward and southward to about 750 feet in the extreme southeastern counties. The terrain over the north-central and western parts of the State is gently rolling. In the central and southern counties the land is quite level. Eastern Kansas is more hilly, but only along the streams are there any sharp elevations.

Drainage is provided by two main river systems, the Kansas and its tributaries in the northern half, and the Arkansas and a large tributary, the Neosho, in the southern half. There are fringes of timber along the streams in eastern Kansas, but in the short-grass country of the west few trees are seen.

The variety in the weather is invigorating and also makes possible a great range of crop production. Summer afternoons are often uncomfortably warm, but the long evenings provide relaxation. During Indian summer, a period of fine weather frequently occurring in the latter part of September and in October, rainfall is usually light, sunshine abundant, mornings rather frosty, and afternoons warm. The winter season is frequently mild, with stock ranging in the open much of the time, though extremely low temperatures occur sometimes.

The average annual temperature is 55° F., ranging from 58° in the southeast to 52° in the northwest. The extreme annual range is normally about 125°. Readings of 100° or higher have been observed in all months from March to October, inclusive. Long periods of heat accompanied by hot winds occur more or less frequently in July and August, and 100° or higher has been recorded at many stations for 20 to 25 successive days during some of the more prolonged heat waves. Freezing weather has occurred in every month of the year except July and August, and temperatures of zero or lower have been commonly recorded somewhere in the State from December through February, occasionally in November and March, and once each in October and April.

The normal growing season varies from nearly 200 days in the southeastern counties to 160 days in the northwest. Killing frosts have been recorded in the southeast as late as May 9 and in the northwest as late as May 27. Temperatures of 32° F. or lower have occurred in the fall as early as the middle of September in western Kansas and in the latter part of that month in the southeast. Farming operations generally begin in south-central counties first, then gradually get started in the eastern and north-central counties, and finally begin in the extreme northwest about 3 weeks later.

The counties in the southeast normally receive a little over 40 inches of precipitation and there is a gradual decrease in amount across the State to the middle counties of the western third, where the average is only 15 inches a year. The average precipitation for the eastern third is 34.76, the middle, 26.05, and the western third, 18.81 inches.

After January, the month of least precipitation, there is a gradual increase until June, the wettest month. In the eastern half of the State there is usually a noticeable decline in precipitation in the latter part of July, with an increase again in early August.

In winter most of the precipitation is rather light, but in summer 24-hour falls of 5 to 10 inches have been recorded in all sections. Although there are many more light than heavy rains, the greatest amount of rain comes in amounts of half an inch or more. About 70 percent of the total precipitation falls in the warm season and thus supplies the demands of growing crops. Two inches or more of rainfall in 24 hours have been recorded much more frequently in eastern Kansas than in the western part.

The average annual number of days with 0.01 inch or more of precipitation is 68. The average number of clear days is 186, partly cloudy 100, and cloudy 79.

The average annual snowfall ranges from approximately 12 inches in the southeastern counties to 25 inches in the northwestern part of the State. January and February are the months of heaviest snow in eastern Kansas and February and March in the western half. While a snow cover does not usually remain very long, there have been winters when the ground was blanketed for several weeks consecutively.

Droughts have occurred at all times of the year, but those of July and August are the most damaging. The long days with intense sunshine and hot winds that usually attend such prolonged dry periods cause serious damage to growing crops, especially corn. Beginning with 1930 there has been a series of years unparalleled for heat and dryness. The accumulated deficiency in precipitation for the last 9 years is more than the normal annual amount. Floods are limited for the most part to the spring and early summer months.

The prevailing wind movement is from the south except in the winter, when northerly winds are more frequent. Wind movement is higher in the western part of the State than in the east and is of greater velocity in the afternoon than at other times of the day.

Tornadoes have occurred in all months of the year except January and December. Normally May and June each have a much greater number than any other month, while about twice as many occur in eastern as in western counties.

Andrew D. Robb, *Junior Meteorologist and Temporary Climatic Section Director for Kansas, Weather Bureau, Topeka.*

KENTUCKY

Climatic summary

County [1]	Station	Temperature					Killing frost average dates				Average precipitation													
		Length of record	January average	July average	Maximum	Minimum	Length of record	Last in spring	First in fall	Growing season [2]	Length of record	January	February	March	April	May	June	July	August	September	October	November	December	Annual
		Yr.	°F.	°F.	°F.	°F.	Yr.			Days	Yr.	In.	In.	In.	In.	In.	In.	In.	In.	In.	In.	In.	In.	In.
Anderson	Tyrone										21	4.91	2.89	3.87	4.14	3.37	4.36	4.01	3.95	3.34	2.93	3.00	3.91	44.68
Ballard	Blandville	30	36.0	77.9	108	−18	32	Apr. 9	Oct. 22	196	29	4.81	3.60	4.68	4.63	4.13	3.55	3.82	3.46	3.39	3.46	3.92	4.52	47.97
Barren	Glasgow	10	38.1	78.8	108	−12	6	Apr. 13	Oct. 25	195	11	6.36	3.53	5.38	4.31	4.00	3.78	5.00	4.31	3.15	2.79	3.98	5.10	51.69
Bell	Middlesboro	36	39.1	75.4	112	−20	37	Apr. 20	Oct. 18	181	39	4.70	4.02	5.40	4.47	3.99	4.49	4.84	4.43	2.93	2.79	3.49	4.86	50.41
Boone	Grant										14	3.74	2.11	3.21	3.15	3.16	3.25	3.68	3.20	3.42	2.43	2.76	2.37	36.48
Boyd	Catlettsburg	10	35.2	76.4	104	−22	9	Apr. 22	Oct. 17	178	21	3.93	3.09	4.45	3.60	4.37	4.58	4.11	3.54	2.46	2.70	2.63	3.71	43.17
Boyle	Shelby City	17	34.8	75.5	105	−28	16	Apr. 25	Oct. 10	168	17	4.40	3.77	4.89	3.76	3.82	3.92	4.19	3.94	3.20	2.29	3.19	4.68	46.05
Breathitt	Quicksand	16	38.5	76.6	107	−10	12	Apr. 24	Oct. 16	175	13	4.49	3.40	5.62	4.44	4.77	3.92	6.29	4.97	3.70	2.94	3.89	4.14	52.57
Breckinridge	Irvington	40	36.0	77.0	107	−25	40	Apr. 13	Oct. 21	191	40	4.45	3.05	4.47	3.90	3.78	3.74	3.22	3.30	2.94	2.85	3.13	3.87	42.70
Butler	Woodbury										22	5.59	3.18	5.12	4.46	3.87	4.33	3.76	4.07	3.22	3.29	3.64	3.84	48.37
Caldwell	Princeton	26	37.2	78.7	108	−30	30	Apr. 10	Oct. 23	196	21	5.34	3.27	5.22	4.53	4.48	4.36	3.77	3.97	3.67	3.61	3.64	3.93	49.79
Calloway	Murray	12	38.4	78.8	110	−20	13	Apr. 15	Oct. 19	187	12	6.53	3.19	6.32	4.41	4.33	4.50	3.72	3.13	3.97	3.43	3.19	4.54	51.26
Campbell	Oneonta										17	4.03	2.50	3.80	3.69	3.45	3.89	4.20	3.99	3.28	2.44	2.83	3.13	41.23
Carroll	Carrollton										29	4.14	2.26	3.85	3.99	4.01	3.79	3.54	4.31	3.31	3.10	2.88	3.10	42.28
Carter	Grayson										9	3.83	2.97	3.56	2.77	3.74	3.31	4.09	3.58	2.21	3.08	2.63	2.74	38.51
Christian	Hopkinsville	40	37.8	79.2	111	−19	40	Apr. 12	Oct. 21	192	40	5.41	3.56	4.79	4.26	4.21	4.44	3.87	3.53	3.17	3.28	3.85	4.69	49.06
Clinton	Alpha	21	39.9	75.6	100	−19	19	Apr. 9	Oct. 19	193	21	5.26	4.49	5.85	5.27	4.27	4.90	5.16	5.02	3.50	3.20	3.34	5.09	55.35
Crittenden	Marion	28	36.7	78.7	109	−22	27	Apr. 6	Oct. 25	202	33	4.70	3.08	4.49	4.35	3.94	3.85	3.05	3.52	3.24	3.00	3.83	4.26	45.31
Daviess	Owensboro	40	35.1	77.9	108	−21	40	Apr. 11	Oct. 23	195	40	4.31	2.73	4.38	3.88	4.04	4.03	3.28	3.42	3.25	3.34	3.23	3.58	43.47
Edmonson	Brownsville										22	5.94	3.66	5.62	4.57	4.27	4.37	3.85	4.36	3.34	3.39	4.06	4.32	51.75
Estill	Ravenna, lock 12										18	4.07	2.85	4.50	3.47	3.96	4.35	4.80	4.25	3.48	2.54	3.09	3.20	44.56
Fayette	Lexington	40	34.1	76.4	108	−20	40	Apr. 16	Oct. 22	189	40	4.34	2.77	4.09	3.37	3.52	3.80	3.78	3.37	2.98	2.49	2.90	3.71	41.12
Fleming	Flemingsburg										14	4.95	2.81	4.48	4.29	3.97	4.20	3.96	4.58	3.30	3.08	3.34	3.42	46.38
Franklin	Frankfort	40	36.0	77.6	111	−17	40	Apr. 15	Oct. 20	188	40	4.31	2.99	4.28	3.83	3.47	3.87	4.21	3.75	2.85	2.61	2.91	3.72	42.80
Garrard	Lancaster										13	5.21	2.71	4.80	3.14	4.17	4.65	4.44	3.83	2.99	3.10	3.44	3.21	45.69
Grant	Williamstown	36	33.3	76.6	110	−16	36	Apr. 21	Oct. 20	182	37	4.20	2.72	4.18	3.79	3.76	3.57	3.79	3.86	3.09	2.88	2.86	3.47	42.17
Graves	Mayfield	31	37.0	79.2	110	−17	30	Apr. 7	Oct. 22	198	22	5.20	3.00	4.77	4.39	4.21	3.92	4.23	3.53	3.51	3.12	3.85	4.03	47.76
Grayson	Leitchfield	40	35.7	77.3	108	−26	40	Apr. 12	Oct. 21	192	40	5.16	3.31	4.49	4.33	4.14	4.06	3.80	3.69	3.45	3.30	3.86	4.63	48.22
Green	Greensburg	40	35.9	76.7	114	−29	40	Apr. 21	Oct. 16	178	40	5.41	3.58	5.17	3.84	4.39	4.53	4.02	4.20	3.30	3.16	3.54	4.35	49.49
Greenup	Greenup, dam 30										19	3.45	2.72	3.76	3.49	3.44	3.78	4.56	3.64	2.69	2.34	2.77	3.10	39.74
Hardin	St. John	39	35.0	76.6	113	−26	40	Apr. 18	Oct. 19	184	40	5.08	3.51	4.61	4.25	4.16	4.19	3.53	4.01	3.14	2.11	3.43	4.42	47.44
Harrison	Cynthiana										21	3.92	2.59	4.13	3.99	3.10	3.31	3.49	3.91	3.31	2.65	3.18	3.65	41.23
Hart	Munfordville										11	5.04	3.50	4.38	3.43	3.95	5.04	3.29	4.25	2.04	3.57	3.91	3.34	45.74
Henderson	Henderson										18	4.49	2.59	4.86	3.71	4.12	4.00	2.55	3.21	3.47	3.50	3.63	4.66	44.79
Henry	Lockport, lock 2										29	4.73	2.55	4.19	4.09	3.80	4.29	3.84	4.00	3.28	2.98	2.81	3.67	44.23
Hopkins	Earlington	40	36.4	79.2	111	−28	40	Apr. 16	Oct. 20	187	40	5.17	3.49	4.74	4.20	4.16	3.96	3.72	3.18	2.93	3.19	3.56	4.16	46.46

Jefferson	Anchorage	38	33.5	76.4	111	−21	38	Apr. 18	Oct. 18	183	38	4.29	2.59	4.13	3.86	3.79	3.59	4.19	3.78	2.95	2.90	3.01	3.73	42.81
	Louisville	40	35.2	78.7	107	−20	40	Apr. 9	Oct. 24	198	40	4.23	2.75	4.19	3.65	3.75	3.52	3.44	3.20	2.66	2.64	2.93	3.62	40.58
Jessamine	High Bridge										36	4.71	3.09	4.25	3.72	3.68	4.00	4.32	3.66	3.15	2.76	3.05	3.86	44.25
Kenton	Scott	32	32.2	75.7	107	−20	31	Apr. 20	Oct. 19	182	32	3.60	2.64	4.15	3.65	3.90	3.80	3.65	3.75	2.73	2.92	2.88	3.32	40.99
Lawrence	Louisa										26	4.14	2.64	4.21	3.33	3.89	3.95	3.98	4.34	2.76	2.91	2.89	3.47	42.51
Lee	Beattyville	30	35.3	76.0	107	−19	30	Apr. 23	Oct. 18	178	31	4.60	3.72	4.77	3.88	4.19	4.55	4.76	4.39	3.17	3.21	3.17	4.23	48.64
Letcher	Jenkins										14	4.00	3.74	4.41	3.89	4.95	4.48	5.22	3.78	2.83	3.60	3.47	3.49	47.86
Lewis	Vanceburg, dam 32										19	4.39	3.20	4.24	4.06	3.69	3.62	4.47	4.20	2.92	2.65	2.95	3.59	43.98
Logan	Russellville	20	36.1	77.7	108	−22	22	Apr. 12	Oct. 23	194	21	6.07	2.99	4.44	4.13	3.50	4.03	4.26	3.35	3.39	3.10	3.08	3.88	46.22
McCracken	Paducah	10	37.7	81.3	112	−17	17	Apr. 7	Oct. 24	200	40	4.93	3.30	4.69	4.36	3.79	4.15	3.51	3.66	3.38	3.17	3.88	4.09	46.91
McLean	Calhoun	34	37.1	78.9	109	−18	33	Apr. 6	Oct. 23	200	35	5.19	3.21	4.79	4.35	4.17	3.86	3.85	3.83	3.23	3.49	3.48	4.11	47.56
Madison	Berea	37	37.1	76.4	108	−24	38	Apr. 18	Oct. 19	184	38	5.01	3.14	4.87	3.73	3.99	4.55	4.83	4.16	2.95	2.89	3.19	4.22	47.53
	Richmond	38	36.6	77.0	108	−24	38	Apr. 14	Oct. 22	191	40	4.61	3.10	4.51	3.69	3.87	4.19	4.19	3.83	2.98	2.76	3.25	4.12	45.10
Marion	Loretto	20	36.0	76.3	106	−30	18	Apr. 24	Oct. 11	170	19	4.44	3.06	3.97	3.65	3.97	4.39	3.92	3.65	2.97	2.59	2.89	4.26	43.76
Mason	Maysville	40	33.9	76.9	110	−22	40	Apr. 21	Oct. 19	181	40	4.16	3.04	4.24	3.66	3.77	3.90	4.40	4.08	3.06	2.62	2.94	3.72	43.59
Mercer	Salvisa, lock 6										24	5.33	2.97	3.86	3.79	3.64	4.32	4.29	3.62	3.54	2.89	3.07	4.19	45.51
Metcalfe	Edmonton	17	37.0	76.1	106	−24	19	Apr. 19	Oct. 15	179	18	4.86	4.15	5.56	4.55	4.45	4.31	5.09	3.73	3.31	2.54	3.41	4.62	50.58
Montgomery	Mt. Sterling	40	34.1	76.4	109	−22	40	do	Oct. 18	182	39	4.94	3.49	5.03	4.23	4.33	4.60	4.89	4.16	3.36	2.96	3.42	4.28	49.69
Muhlenberg	Greenville	22	36.8	78.0	111	−15	22	Apr. 13	Oct. 21	191	22	5.08	3.04	5.25	4.74	4.08	4.77	3.77	3.39	3.11	3.68	3.66	3.80	48.37
Nelson	Bardstown	37	36.0	76.1	112	−25	34	Apr. 20	Oct. 19	182	36	4.71	3.53	4.41	3.96	4.06	4.18	3.69	3.97	3.10	3.14	3.30	4.47	46.52
Ohio	Beaver Dam	31	36.4	78.3	110	−20	30	Apr. 14	Oct. 21	190	32	4.44	3.30	4.25	4.03	4.27	3.72	3.68	3.09	2.86	2.98	3.34	3.79	43.75
Owen	Owenton	12	33.3	76.7	106	−19	12	Apr. 19	do	185	13	4.11	4.26	4.58	3.42	3.84	3.93	4.26	2.89	2.55	2.35	3.25	4.25	43.69
Pendleton	Falmouth										39	3.96	2.85	4.06	3.73	3.57	3.99	3.58	3.96	2.72	2.46	2.89	3.63	41.40
Perry	Hazard										14	3.77	3.35	4.38	3.99	5.22	4.52	5.22	4.17	2.82	2.86	3.34	3.69	47.33
Pike	Pikeville										31	3.96	3.22	4.45	3.72	3.78	3.92	4.69	4.29	2.86	2.89	2.62	3.42	43.82
Pulaski	Burnside										40	5.01	3.78	5.40	4.26	4.49	4.21	4.59	4.18	3.63	3.02	3.42	4.61	50.60
	Eubank	39	35.8	75.1	108	−22	40	Apr. 22	Oct. 16	177	40	4.60	3.42	4.73	3.79	4.43	4.17	4.22	4.30	3.32	2.92	3.39	4.07	47.36
Rowan	Farmers	31	35.7	75.3	106	−20	32	do	Oct. 17	178	34	4.60	2.94	4.53	3.94	4.00	4.38	4.48	4.60	2.93	2.97	3.00	3.70	46.07
Shelby	Shelbyville	40	33.9	77.0	112	−23	40	Apr. 17	Oct. 19	185	40	4.82	3.34	4.71	3.91	3.95	3.86	3.89	3.73	2.90	2.79	3.17	4.06	45.13
Simpson	Franklin	32	39.4	78.9	111	−14	30	Apr. 11	Oct. 23	195	31	4.70	4.08	4.70	4.00	4.32	3.94	3.92	3.56	3.27	2.71	3.25	4.38	46.83
Spencer	Taylorsville	33	34.6	76.6	108	−25	34	Apr. 21	Oct. 18	180	35	4.61	3.39	4.52	4.19	3.86	4.12	4.15	3.57	3.24	3.04	3.20	4.28	46.17
Union	Uniontown, dam 49										11	4.88	2.32	4.05	3.31	4.18	3.57	3.39	3.26	4.61	2.75	2.68	2.98	41.98
Warren	Bowling Green	40	37.8	79.5	113	−17	40	Apr. 14	Oct. 22	191	40	5.43	3.52	5.13	4.32	4.21	3.98	4.29	3.73	3.48	3.04	3.57	4.61	49.31
Whitley	Williamsburg	40	39.0	77.3	108	−19	38	Apr. 16	Oct. 21	188	40	4.42	3.53	4.88	4.23	4.32	4.46	4.69	4.52	3.44	2.70	3.28	3.96	48.43
	Ashland	18	36.9	76.5	107	−23	30	Apr. 20	Oct. 17	180	19	4.27	2.85	4.04	3.66	3.77	3.70	4.48	3.94	2.54	2.41	3.05	3.37	42.08

[1] The following counties, for which no records are available, are best represented by the station indicated: Adair and Taylor—Greensburg; Allen and Monroe—Franklin; Bath, Elliot, and Morgan—Farmers; Bourbon, Clark, Scott, and Woodford—Lexington; Bracken—Maysville; Bullitt—Taylorsville; Carlisle—Blandville; Casey and Lincoln—Eubank; Clay, Laurel, McCreary, Russell and Wayne—Burnside; Cumberland—Jenkins; Floyd and Knott—Pikeville; Fulton and Hickman—Mayfield; Gallatin and Trimble—Carrollton; Hancock—Owensboro; Harlan—Middlesboro; Jackson and Rockcastle—Berea; Johnson and Martin—Louisa; Knox—Williamsburg; Larue—Leitchfield; Leslie—Hazard; Livingston and Marshall—Paducah; Lyon—Princeton; Magoffin—Quicksand; Meade—Irvington; Menifee—Mt. Sterling; Nicholas and Robertson—Cynthiana; Oldham—Anchorage; Owsley, Powell and Wolfe—Beattyville; Todd and Trigg—Hopkinsville; Washington—Bardstown; Webster—Calhoun.

[2] Length of growing season between average dates of last killing frosts in spring and first in fall.

298737°—41——57 +

Kentucky—Continued

Precipitation—State unit values

[This tabulation gives the mean annual, mean monthly, and average seasonal precipitation, 1886–1938, for Kentucky]

Precipitation		Precipitation		Precipitation		Precipitation		Precipitation		Precipitation	
Year	Mean	Year	Mean	Year	Mean	Year	Mean	Month	Mean	Season	Average
	In.		In.		In.		In.		In.		In.
1886	44.66	1900	44.40	1914	41.80	1928	45.61	January	4.51	Winter	11.77
1887	37.33	1901	35.65	1915	51.92	1929	48.44	February	3.43	Spring	12.61
1888	44.37	1902	44.35	1916	45.49	1930	27.86	March	4.66	Summer	11.99
1889	35.95	1903	41.16	1917	46.01	1931	41.96	April	3.96	Fall	9.08
1890	58.82	1904	35.10	1918	40.64	1932	49.15	May	3.99		
1891	49.69	1905	47.68	1919	52.13	1933	50.65	June	4.11		
1892	44.25	1906	48.84	1920	46.90	1934	37.12	July	4.11		
1893	44.71	1907	47.76	1921	49.42	1935	57.40	August	3.77		
1894	34.81	1908	41.94	1922	44.43	1936	37.94	September	2.96		
1895	38.47	1909	51.41	1923	33.92	1937	49.86	October	2.64		
1896	44.68	1910	50.67	1924	42.68	1938	46.00	November	3.48		
1897	46.72	1911	46.77	1925	41.11			December	3.83		
1898	52.38	1912	47.93	1926	49.95						
1899	46.38	1913	47.46	1927	53.43			Annual	45.45		

Dates of last killing frost in spring and first in fall, with length of growing season

Year	Bowling Green			Earlington			Eubank			Irvington			Lexington			Maysville		
	Last in spring	First in fall	Growing season [1]	Last in spring	First in fall	Growing season [1]	Last in spring	First in fall	Growing season [1]	Last in spring	First in fall	Growing season [1]	Last in spring	First in fall	Growing season [1]	Last in spring	First in fall	Growing season [1]
			Days			Days			Days			Days			Days			Days
1899	Apr. 9	Sept. 30	174	Apr. 10	Sept. 30	173	Apr. 17	Sept. 27	163	Apr. 9	Sept. 30	174	Apr. 9	Sept. 30	174	Apr. 17	Sept. 30	166
1900	Apr. 12	Nov. 4	206	Apr. 14	Nov. 3	203	May 4	Nov. 4	184	Apr. 14	Oct. 18	187	Apr. 12	Nov. 8	210	Apr. 11	Oct. 17	189
1901	Apr. 21	Oct. 5	167	Apr. 20	Oct. 5	168	Apr. 21	Oct. 5	167	Apr. 21	do	180	Apr. 22	Nov. 4	196	Apr. 10	Oct. 18	191
1902	Apr. 9	Oct. 29	203	Apr. 15	Oct. 29	197	Apr. 13	Sept. 14	154	Apr. 9	Oct. 15	189	Apr. 8	Oct. 15	190	Apr. 15	Oct. 15	183
1903	Apr. 5	Oct. 19	197	Apr. 23	Oct. 18	178	Apr. 24	Oct. 18	177	Apr. 5	Oct. 24	202	Apr. 5	Oct. 24	202	May 2	Oct. 24	175
1904	Apr. 21	Oct. 23	185	Apr. 21	Oct. 26	188	Apr. 21	Oct. 23	185	Apr. 21	Oct. 27	189	Apr. 21	Oct. 27	189	Apr. 21	do	186
1905	Apr. 17	Oct. 22	188	Apr. 19	Oct. 12	176	Apr. 20	Oct. 12	175	Apr. 17	Oct. 12	178	Apr. 17	Oct. 12	178	Apr. 20	Oct. 13	176
1906	Apr. 23	Oct. 11	171	Apr. 17	Oct. 11	177	May 8	Oct. 11	156	Apr. 1	Oct. 11	193	Apr. 23	Oct. 10	170	May 10	Oct. 11	154

1907	Apr. 29	Oct. 13	167	Apr. 21	Oct. 12	174	Apr. 21	Oct. 9	171	Apr. 20	Oct. 14	177	Apr. 20	Oct. 14	177	Apr. 21	Oct. 12	174
1908	May 1	Oct. 25	177	May 1	Oct. 1	153	May 1	Oct. 3	155	May 1	Oct. 31	183	May 1	Oct. 31	183	May 1	Oct. 2	154
1909	May 2	Oct. 13	164	Apr. 24	Oct. 13	172	May 2	Oct. 13	164	Apr. 14	Oct. 13	182	Apr. 11	Oct. 12	184	May 2	Oct. 13	164
1910	Apr. 24	Oct. 28	187	Apr. 25	Oct. 23	181	Apr. 24	Oct. 23	182	Apr. 24	Oct. 28	187	Apr. 24	Oct. 28	187	May 15	Oct. 28	166
1911	Apr. 9	Oct. 23	197	Apr. 2	do	204	May 3	do	173	Apr. 9	Oct. 24	198	Apr. 10	Oct. 23	196	Apr. 25	Oct. 24	182
1912	Apr. 19	Oct. 24	188	Apr. 19	Oct. 24	188	Apr. 19	Oct. 24	188	Mar. 26	do	212	Apr. 19	Oct. 24	188	Apr. 19	Oct. 25	189
1913	Mar. 29	Oct. 20	205	Mar. 29	Oct. 31	216	Apr. 1	Oct. 21	203	Mar. 28	Oct. 21	207	Mar. 29	Oct. 20	205	Apr. 21	Oct. 22	184
1914	Apr. 21	Oct. 27	189	Apr. 13	Oct. 27	197	Apr. 21	Oct. 27	189	Apr. 21	Oct. 27	189	Apr. 10	Oct. 27	200	Apr. 13	Oct. 27	197
1915	Apr. 4	Oct. 9	188	Apr. 4	Oct. 9	188	Apr. 15	Oct. 8	176	Apr. 3	Oct. 10	190	Apr. 4	Oct. 9	188	Apr. 15	Oct. 8	176
1916	Apr. 10	Oct. 22	195	Apr. 10	Oct. 11	184	Apr. 11	Oct. 1	173	Apr. 10	Oct. 22	195	Apr. 10	Oct. 22	195	Apr. 10	Oct. 22	196
1917	Apr. 14	Oct. 7	176	Apr. 14	Oct. 9	178	Apr. 15	Oct. 7	175	Apr. 14	Oct. 9	178	Apr. 14	Oct. 9	178	Apr. 16	Oct. 9	175
1918	Apr. 13	Nov. 2	203	Apr. 13	Nov. 2	203	May 2	Nov. 2	184	Apr. 13	Nov. 2	203	Apr. 13	Nov. 2	203	Apr. 14	Nov. 2	202
1919	Apr. 26	Nov. 5	193	Apr. 26	Nov. 5	193	Apr. 27	Nov. 5	192	Apr. 26	Nov. 5	193	Apr. 26	Nov. 5	193	Apr. 27	Nov. 5	192
1920	Apr. 14	Oct. 29	198	Apr. 14	Oct. 29	198	Apr. 14	Oct. 30	199	Apr. 14	Oct. 29	198	Apr. 14	Oct. 29	198	Apr. 14	Oct. 29	198
1921	Apr. 18	Oct. 13	178	Apr. 18	Oct. 13	178	Apr. 19	Oct. 12	176	Apr. 18	Oct. 13	178	Apr. 18	Oct. 13	178	Apr. 18	Oct. 13	178
1922	Mar. 22	Oct. 18	210	Apr. 23	Oct. 18	178	Apr. 23	Oct. 13	173	Mar. 22	Oct. 18	210	Mar. 23	do	204	Mar. 23	do	204
1923	Apr. 18	Oct. 20	185	Apr. 18	Oct. 22	187	May 10	Oct. 21	164	Apr. 18	Oct. 20	185	May 9	Oct. 20	164	May 10	Oct. 6	149
1924	Apr. 3	Oct. 23	203	Apr. 3	Oct. 23	203	Apr. 23	Oct. 1	161	Apr. 23	Oct. 23	183	Apr. 3	Oct. 23	203	Apr. 3	Oct. 23	203
1925	Apr. 1	Oct. 20	202	Apr. 1	Oct. 20	202	Apr. 1	Oct. 11	193	Apr. 1	Oct. 20	202	Apr. 1	Oct. 10	192	Apr. 6	Oct. 10	187
1926	Apr. 20	Nov. 2	196	Apr. 20	Nov. 2	196	Apr. 27	Oct. 25	181	Apr. 20	Oct. 27	190	Apr. 20	Oct. 25	188	Apr. 27	Oct. 26	182
1927	Apr. 24	Nov. 6	196	Apr. 23	Nov. 3	194	Apr. 25	Oct. 14	172	Apr. 24	Nov. 6	196	Apr. 25	Nov. 5	194	Apr. 25	Oct. 17	175
1928	Apr. 16	Sept. 26	163	Apr. 16	Sept. 26	163	Apr. 28	Sept. 24	149	Apr. 16	Sept. 26	163	Apr. 26	Sept. 26	153	Apr. 26	Oct. 26	183
1929	Mar. 18	Nov. 5	232	Mar. 18	Nov. 5	232	Apr. 19	Oct. 18	182	Mar. 17	Oct. 25	222	Apr. 2	Nov. 5	217	Apr. 23	Oct. 18	178
1930	Mar. 31	Oct. 21	204	Apr. 25	Oct. 20	178	Apr. 26	Oct. 19	176	Apr. 25	Oct. 20	178	Apr. 25	Oct. 19	177	Apr. 27	Oct. 20	176
1931	Apr. 27	Nov. 5	192	Apr. 27	Oct. 18	174	Apr. 28	do	174	Apr. 7	Nov. 5	212	Apr. 28	Nov. 5	191	Apr. 28	Nov. 3	189
1932	Apr. 13	Oct. 28	198	Apr. 15	Oct. 30	198	do	Oct. 6	161	Apr. 15	Oct. 28	196	Apr. 13	Oct. 30	200	do	Oct. 7	162
1933	Apr. 12	Nov. 8	210	Apr. 12	Oct. 26	197	Apr. 12	Oct. 19	190	Mar. 26	Nov. 8	227	Apr. 23	Oct. 26	186	Apr. 27	Oct. 26	182
1934	Mar. 29	Oct. 29	214	Apr. 28	Oct. 28	183	Apr. 28	Oct. 28	183	Apr. 28	Oct. 28	183	Apr. 28	Oct. 28	183	Apr. 28	Oct. 28	183
1935	Apr. 16	Oct. 7	174	Apr. 16	Oct. 7	174	Apr. 17	Oct. 5	171	Apr. 16	Oct. 7	174	Apr. 17	Oct. 4	170	Apr. 17	Oct. 4	170
1936	Apr. 19	Oct. 28	192	Apr. 19	Oct. 28	192	Apr. 23	Oct. 28	188	Apr. 22	Oct. 28	189	Apr. 23	Oct. 28	188	Apr. 23	Oct. 28	188
1937	Apr. 7	Oct. 15	191	Apr. 12	Oct. 14	185	Apr. 12	Oct. 14	185	Apr. 12	Oct. 14	185	Apr. 12	Oct. 14	185	Apr. 12	Oct. 14	185
1938	Apr. 10	Oct. 25	198	Apr. 10	Oct. 24	197	Apr. 10	Oct. 25	198	Apr. 10	Oct. 24	197	Apr. 10	Oct. 25	198	Apr. 10	Oct. 25	198
Mean	Apr. 14	Oct. 22	191	Apr. 16	Oct. 20	187	Apr. 22	Oct. 16	177	Apr. 13	Oct. 21	191	Apr. 16	Oct. 22	189	Apr. 21	Oct. 19	181
Extremes	Mar. 18[2] May 2[3]	Sept. 26[4] Nov. 8[5]	[6] 163 [7] 232	Mar. 18[2] May 1[3]	Sept. 26[4] Nov. 5[5]	[6] 153 [7] 232	Apr. 1[2] May 10[3]	Sept. 14[4] Nov. 5[5]	[6] 149 [7] 203	Mar. 17[2] May 1[3]	Sept. 26[4] Nov. 8[5]	[6] 163 [7] 227	Mar. 23[2] May 9[3]	Sept. 26[4] Nov. 8[5]	[6] 153 [7] 217	Mar. 23[2] May 15[3]	Sept. 30[4] Nov. 5[5]	[6] 149 [7] 204

[1] Number of days between last killing frost in spring and first in fall.
[2] Earliest date in spring.
[3] Latest date in spring.
[4] Earliest date in fall.
[5] Latest date in fall.
[6] Shortest growing season.
[7] Longest growing season.

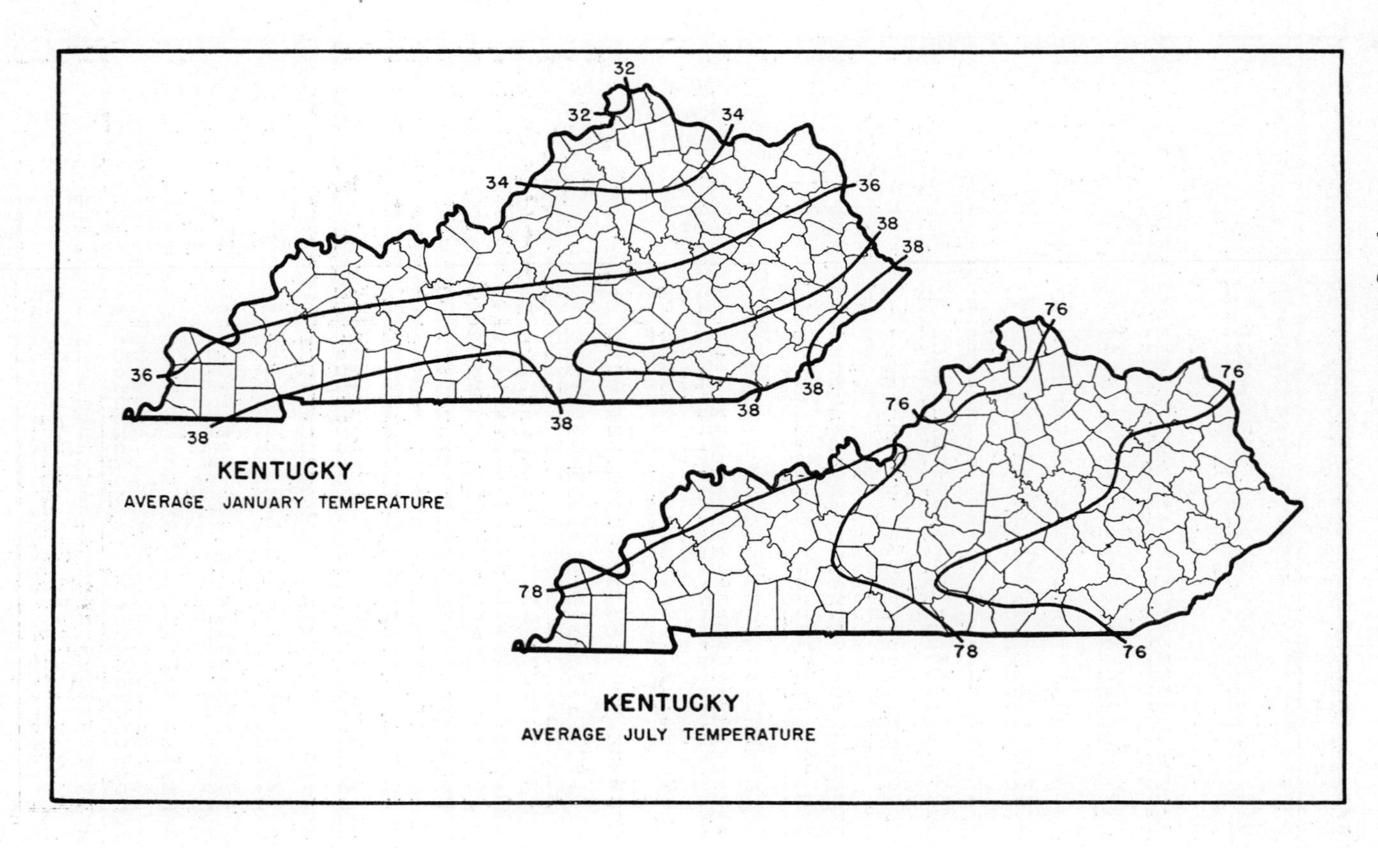
32
32
34
34
36
36
38
38
38
38
38
38
KENTUCKY
AVERAGE JANUARY TEMPERATURE
76
76
76
76
78
78
KENTUCKY
AVERAGE JULY TEMPERATURE

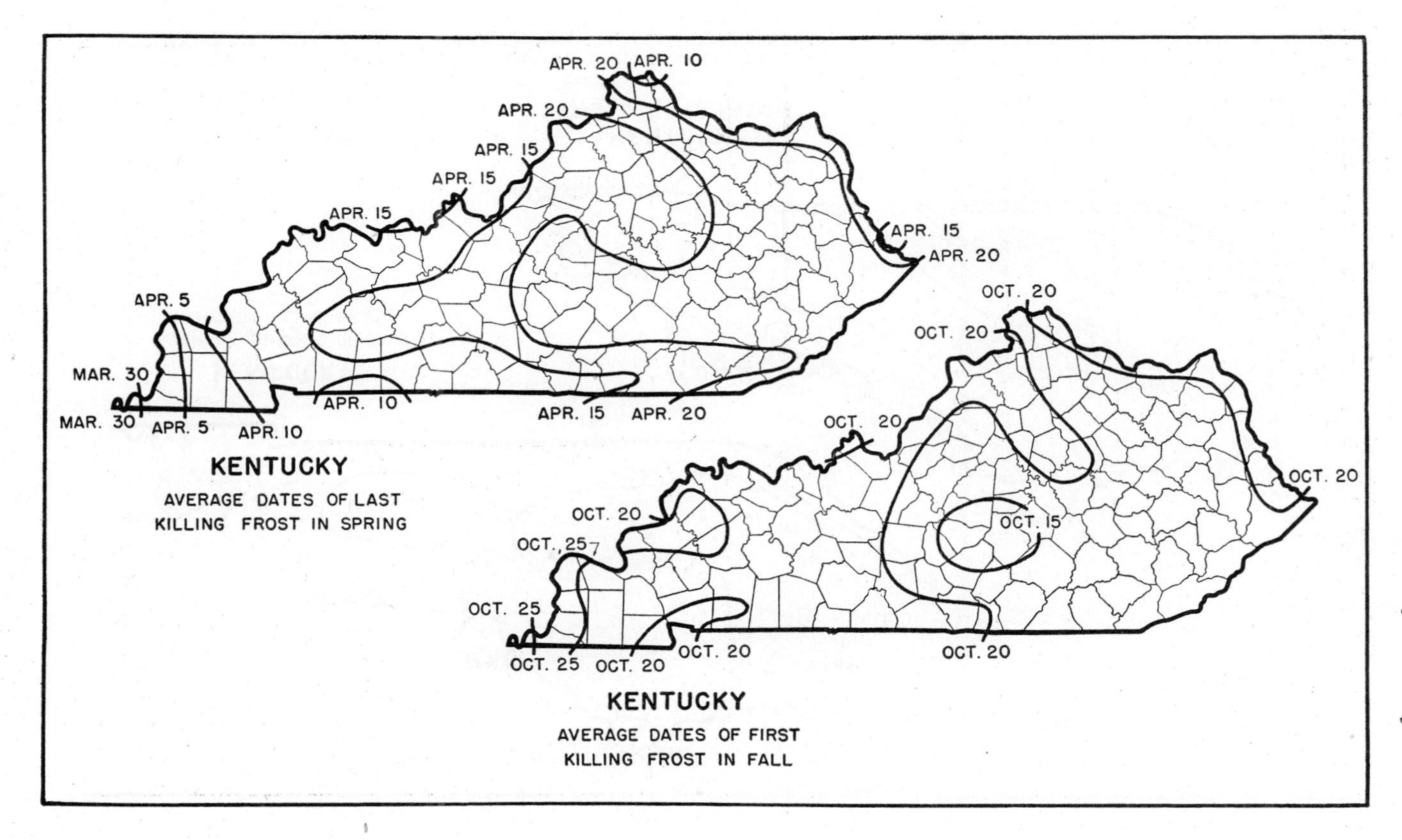
APR. 20
APR. 10
APR. 20
APR. 15
APR. 15
APR. 15
APR. 15
APR. 20
APR. 5
MAR. 30
MAR. 30
APR. 5
APR. 10
APR. 10
APR. 15
APR. 20
KENTUCKY
AVERAGE DATES OF LAST
KILLING FROST IN SPRING
OCT. 20
OCT. 20
OCT. 20
OCT. 20
OCT. 20
OCT. 15
OCT., 25
OCT. 25
OCT. 25
OCT. 20
OCT. 20
OCT. 20
KENTUCKY
AVERAGE DATES OF FIRST
KILLING FROST IN FALL

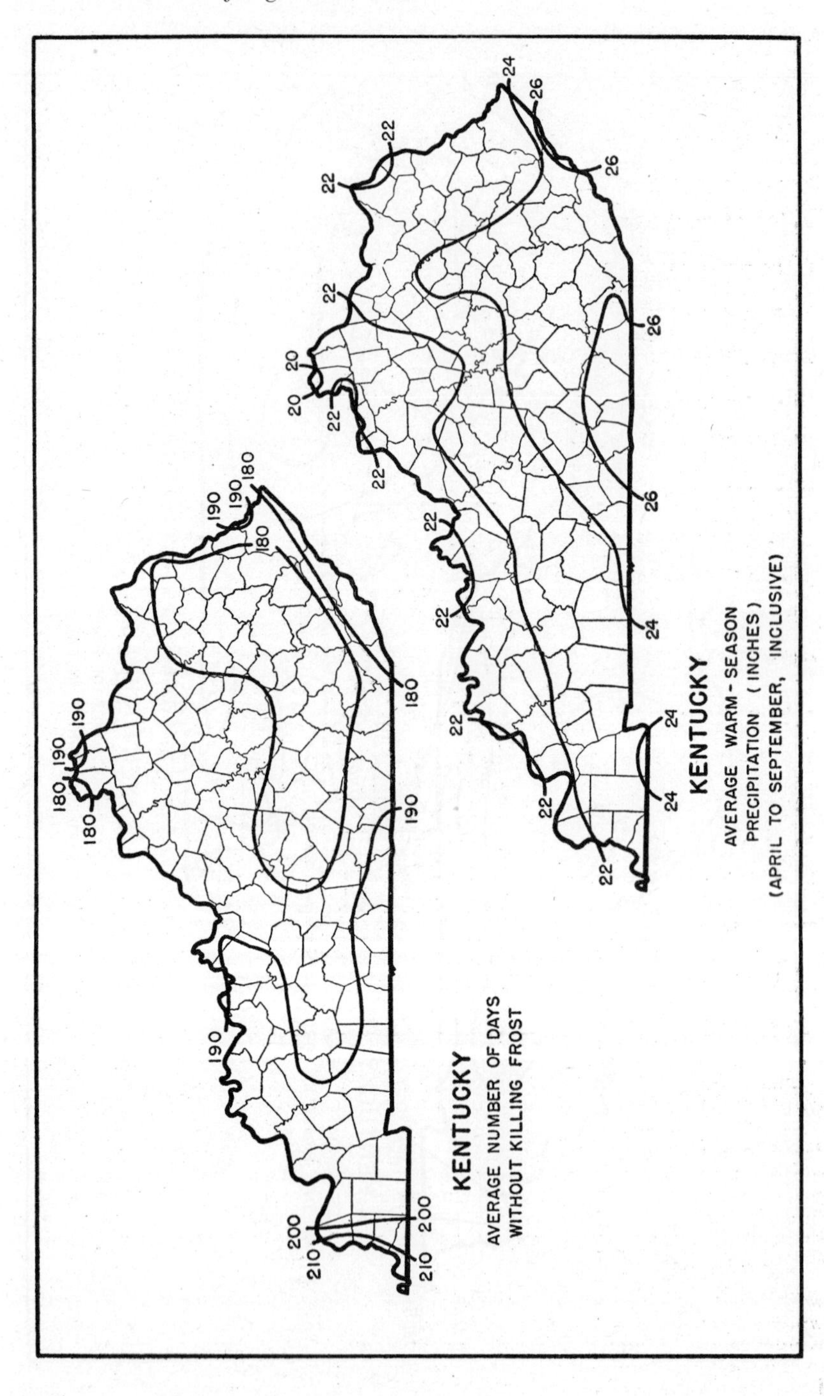
KENTUCKY
AVERAGE NUMBER OF DAYS
WITHOUT KILLING FROST
KENTUCKY
AVERAGE WARM - SEASON
PRECIPITATION (INCHES)
(APRIL TO SEPTEMBER, INCLUSIVE)

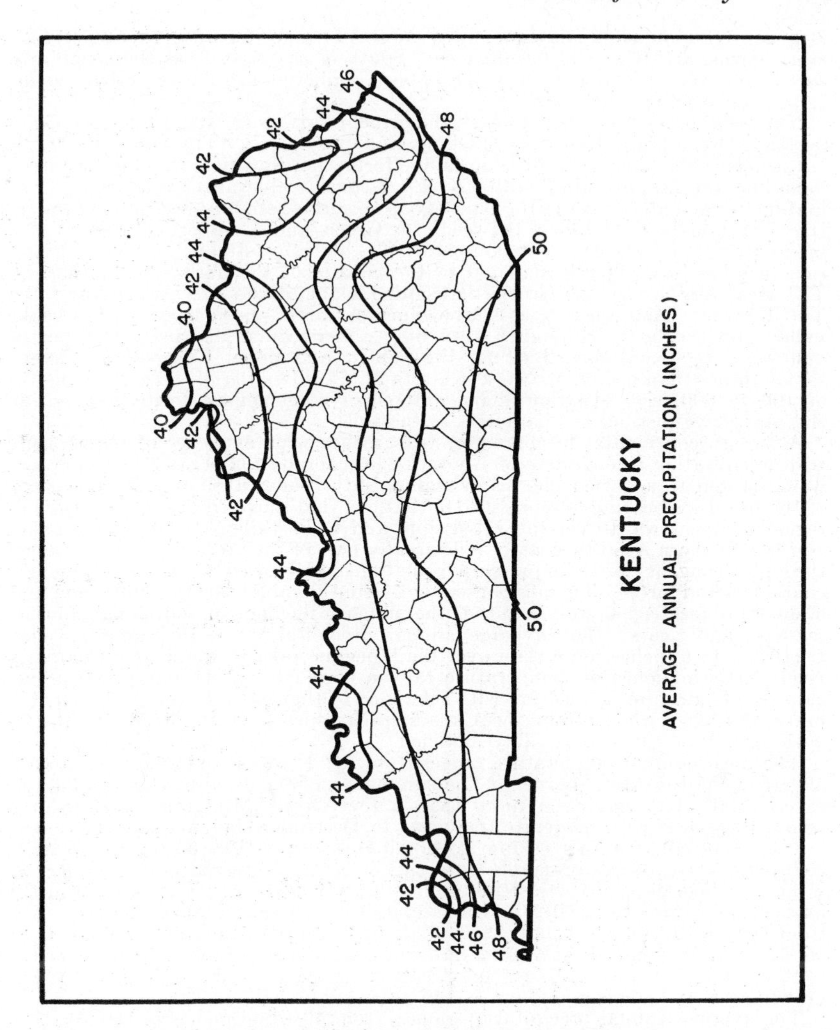

SUPPLEMENTARY CLIMATIC NOTES FOR KENTUCKY

The State of Kentucky, with an area of slightly over 40,000 square miles, lies within 36°30′ to 39°15′ north latitude and 82° to 89°30′ west longitude. Its surface rises unevenly eastward, as a diversified tableland, from bluffs near the Mississippi and lower Ohio Rivers to the mountains that form the eastern and southeastern part of the State. With the exception of a few southeastern counties, the general slope of this tableland is toward the northwest, with elevations ranging from about 400 feet above sea level at the western edge to 1,000 feet in the central districts and 2,800 feet at the summit of Pine Mountain ridge near the southeastern border.

The mountains are long, sharp-crested ranges, extending in a northeast-southwest direction, separated by narrow valleys. Some ranges are almost unbroken while others are deeply cut by streams. A belt of peculiar country called the Knobs, made up largely of conical sandstone hills, parallels the mountains nearly to the southern border of the State and thence turns northwestward to the Ohio River, forming a semicircle that encloses the famous bluegrass area. The latter is a gently undulating plateau, noted for its beauty, fertility, excellent grass, stock farms, and white burley tobacco. South of the Knobs lies the deeply dissected and very irregular area of the upper Cumberland drainage system, which slopes toward the southwest.

Named in order from west to east, the principal rivers are the Tennessee, Cumberland, Green, Salt, Kentucky, Licking, and Big Sandy. The Green River has cut a deep valley across a thick limestone formation in which are many caverns, including the famous Mammoth Cave. A considerable area overlying this formation, immediately west of the Knobs, has no surface streams but drains through the cavernous rock. Lying between the Green and Cumberland Rivers is a moderately high plateau, cut comparatively little by streams, which contains rich farming lands largely devoted to the culture of the dark type of tobacco. The areas drained by the Green, Salt, and Licking Rivers are broken and hilly. The Kentucky and Licking cross the bluegrass area, the former in a gorgelike valley and the latter through a very hilly and irregular district. The narrow valleys of the Kentucky, Licking, Big Sandy, and upper Cumberland Rivers, seldom more than a mile or two in width and often less than a mile, have depths of 100 to 600 feet. Extraordinary differences of geological formations within the State give distinctive characters to the soils.

Although continental in character, with rather wide extremes of temperature and precipitation, the climate of Kentucky is generally temperate, healthful, and well adapted to a varied plant and animal life. The State lies within the path of the moisture-bearing low-pressure formations that move from the western Gulf region northeastward over the Mississippi and Ohio Valleys to the Great Lakes and the northern Atlantic coast. The greater part of the precipitation is obtained through the agency of these pressure formations, which vary greatly in frequency, character, and force. There is consequently considerable variation in the amount of moisture received as well as in the other climatic elements in individual months, seasons, and years. The average annual precipitation in the mountain districts is 3 to 6 inches more than over the bluegrass area to the west. Comparatively little influence on temperature can be traced to the topography, but because of its geographic location with reference to the center of the continent, the midwinter cold waves from the Canadian Northwest usually reach Kentucky with their intensity considerably modified.

The mean annual temperature ranges from 54° F. in the extreme north to 59° along the southwestern border. The summer maxima usually reach or slightly exceed 100°, but rarely on more than a few days. Minimum temperatures below zero occur with moderate frequency in December, January, and February, but severely cold weather seldom predominates longer than 60 days, and long, cold periods are always broken by intervals of moderate temperature.

The average date of the last killing frost in spring ranges from April 9 in the extreme southwest to April 23 in the mountain region, and that of the first in fall from October 15 on the Cumberland Plateau to October 24 near the lower Ohio River. The average length of the growing season varies from 176 days on the southeastern plateau to 197 in the extreme southwestern part of the State. The growing season has been as short as 149 days and as long as 232.

The average annual precipitation ranges from 40 to 46 inches in the northern half of the State and from 46 to 50 in the southern half, approximately half of it occurring in the warm season, April to September.

Twenty-four-hour precipitation in heavy rains is frequently 3 or 4, occasionally 6, inches, and as much as 10 inches in some extremely heavy falls.

During the growing season there is usually sufficient rain for staple crops, and occasionally there is too much, especially in the spring months, delaying planting and cultivation. Droughty conditions sometimes prevail, but even in such periods local rains prevent complete crop failures.

Snowfall varies considerably from year to year, the average annual amount ranging from 10 inches in the extreme southwest to 20 inches in northeastern districts. The ground seldom remains covered with snow for more than a few days.

Southerly to westerly winds prevail over the State in most months. During the colder months north or northwest winds predominate at times. The average velocity of the wind ranges from 6 to 13 miles an hour, maximum velocities from 40 to 60 miles. Storm winds, generally squalls attending thunderstorms, occasionally exceed 60 miles an hour. A number of years may pass without a tornado, or several may visit the State in a single year. The average is about 1 a year.

Thunderstorms may occur in any month but are most frequent from March to September, inclusive. They are occasionally attended by damaging hail, but the area thus affected is nearly always small.

The percentage of possible sunshine averages 35 to 45 for the winter months, 50 to 60 for March and April, and 60 to 70 from May to October, inclusive.

James L. Kendall, *Meteorologist and Climatic Section Director for Kentucky, Weather Bureau, Louisville.*

LOUISIANA

Climatic summary

Parish [1]	Station	Temperature: Length of record	Temperature: January average	Temperature: July average	Temperature: Maximum	Temperature: Minimum	Killing frost average dates: Length of record	Killing frost: Last in spring	Killing frost: First in fall	Growing season [2]	Average precipitation: Length of record	January	February	March	April	May	June	July	August	September	October	November	December	Annual
		Yr.	°F.	°F.	°F.	°F.	Yr.			Days	Yr.	In.	In.	In.	In.	In.	In.	In.	In.	In.	In.	In.	In.	In.
Acadia	Crowley	29	54.2	82.0	103	9	29	Feb. 17	Nov. 24	280	29	5.29	4.03	3.81	3.63	4.93	4.19	6.06	5.27	4.07	3.55	4.31	5.79	54.93
	Rayne	23	53.2	82.3	107	3	23	Mar. 1	Nov. 18	262	23	5.19	4.28	3.59	4.18	4.75	4.35	7.15	5.91	4.09	4.00	3.14	5.96	56.59
Allen	Elizabeth	38	51.8	82.1	106	5	39	Mar. 3	Nov. 22	264	38	5.45	4.79	5.02	5.01	5.09	3.83	5.67	4.76	3.76	3.75	4.35	5.78	57.26
Ascension	Burnside	14	54.0	80.9	102	15	14				14	4.22	4.25	5.10	5.02	5.62	5.45	7.64	5.86	5.78	3.26	2.52	5.99	60.71
	Donaldsonville	40	54.0	82.1	109	3	40	Feb. 26	Nov. 29	276	40	5.16	4.79	4.57	4.68	4.69	4.86	6.70	6.13	4.15	3.86	3.68	5.22	58.49
	Dutchtown										9	6.32	4.37	4.16	4.59	5.02	3.91	7.39	5.76	4.74	4.56	2.60	6.75	60.17
Assumption	Napoleonville										7	6.45	3.82	3.52	3.01	4.60	4.40	6.13	5.30	5.11	4.11	2.24	3.90	52.59
Avoyelles	Simmesport										28	5.76	4.57	4.59	5.49	6.26	3.80	6.12	4.40	2.86	2.51	4.55	6.23	57.14
Beauregard	DeRidder	18	52.5	82.8	106	9	18	Mar. 7	Nov. 20	258	21	5.73	4.14	4.77	5.10	4.79	3.91	4.71	3.96	3.38	3.09	4.20	6.37	54.15
	Merryville										10	5.16	4.74	5.85	7.74	5.91	4.39	5.11	6.47	2.90	3.71	3.93	5.68	61.59
	Sugartown										12	4.29	5.60	4.32	4.41	5.46	4.32	6.54	5.02	3.19	2.78	3.85	4.33	54.11
Bienville	Arcadia										10	7.09	3.87	4.78	4.26	3.70	1.78	5.00	2.59	1.86	2.89	4.44	7.35	49.61
	Liberty Hill	29	48.9	82.7	112	−6	29	Apr. 15	Oct. 31	199	19	3.82	4.67	4.98	4.67	4.66	3.33	5.42	4.01	3.60	1.91	3.55	5.48	50.10
Bossier	Plain Dealing	40	46.3	82.1	114	−14	40	Mar. 28	Nov. 5	222	40	4.34	3.48	4.60	5.16	4.72	3.52	4.91	2.72	2.49	2.64	3.83	5.48	47.89
Caddo	Shreveport	40	47.0	83.2	110	−5	40	Mar. 8	Nov. 15	252	40	3.67	3.10	4.18	4.38	4.23	2.80	3.80	2.71	2.32	2.66	3.19	4.60	41.64
Calcasieu	Lake Charles	39	52.0	82.5	106	3	39	Mar. 3	Nov. 23	265	40	4.71	4.26	3.84	4.36	4.82	4.47	6.27	5.84	4.41	4.14	3.97	5.63	56.72
Cameron	Cameron	13	51.8	81.1	104	13	13	Feb. 24	Dec. 2	281	14	2.76	3.14	2.92	4.30	5.15	4.00	7.93	4.64	6.69	3.79	2.69	4.90	52.91
	Lake Arthur (near)	34	53.9	82.5	103	13	34	Feb. 7	do	298	11	6.73	4.25	3.82	3.26	5.46	3.17	5.32	6.53	4.38	2.98	5.65	4.79	56.34
	Lakeside										25	4.85	3.40	3.18	4.36	5.20	5.68	7.60	5.57	4.52	4.53	4.76	5.85	59.50
De Soto	Grand Cane	40	47.4	81.7	110	−6	32	Mar. 12	Nov. 8	241	40	4.13	3.92	4.57	4.70	3.99	2.84	4.15	2.89	2.86	2.67	3.72	5.18	45.62
	Logansport										34	4.61	4.25	4.81	4.80	5.09	2.78	4.27	2.39	2.74	2.61	4.00	5.75	48.10
East Baton Rouge	Baton Rouge	40	53.1	81.7	110	2	40	Feb. 24	Nov. 20	269	40	5.51	4.75	4.77	4.53	5.25	4.58	6.77	5.56	4.23	3.27	3.51	5.46	58.19
East Carroll	Lake Providence	16	47.7	82.5	109	−4	16	Mar. 20	Nov. 10	235	16	5.09	5.47	6.16	4.79	4.25	2.80	4.35	3.39	2.54	2.24	3.71	5.59	50.38
East Feliciana	Clinton	33	51.0	80.4	103	0	34	Mar. 11	Nov. 12	246	33	5.91	5.31	5.25	4.90	5.25	4.09	6.26	5.49	3.88	2.94	3.25	5.77	58.30
Evangeline	Ville Platte	13	53.5	82.8	107	15	13				13	5.97	4.91	4.53	4.11	5.12	4.16	4.86	4.68	3.74	3.15	5.60	6.58	57.41
Franklin	Winnsboro	13	50.2	82.6	106	8	13	Mar. 4	Nov. 7	248	12	5.56	4.22	5.80	4.60	4.57	3.74	4.36	2.59	2.16	2.64	4.20	6.85	51.29
Iberia	Jeanerette	24	54.3	81.9	104	3	24	Mar. 4	Nov. 20	261	25	4.95	3.78	3.75	3.97	4.46	4.90	8.16	5.98	4.52	3.63	3.40	4.85	56.35
	New Iberia	30	54.2	81.7	101	6	30	Feb. 21	Nov. 26	278	30	4.56	4.28	3.94	4.39	4.76	6.31	8.13	6.37	4.63	3.48	3.43	5.36	59.64
Jefferson	Southern University Farm.										16	3.12	4.54	5.01	5.86	4.85	4.03	5.28	5.53	5.56	2.45	2.53	5.59	54.35
Jefferson Davis	Jennings	40	53.0	82.1	105	3	40	Feb. 27	Nov. 20	266	40	5.23	4.05	3.63	3.85	5.45	4.40	6.13	5.74	3.88	3.54	4.00	5.74	55.64
Lafayette	Lafayette	40	53.1	81.6	107	6	40	Mar. 3	Nov. 14	256	40	5.35	4.42	3.99	4.13	4.84	5.41	6.83	5.16	4.03	3.64	3.69	5.88	57.37
Lafourche	Delta Farms	23	55.1	80.5	101	16	22	Mar. 1	Nov. 27	271	22	4.42	3.81	4.56	4.31	5.07	5.40	6.74	7.25	4.57	4.72	3.79	4.84	59.48
La Salle	Kelly (near)	12	48.0	81.0	110	3	12				12	5.90	4.10	5.44	5.28	4.62	2.65	4.88	3.73	1.97	4.05	3.76	5.49	51.87
	Urania	10	50.9	83.1	107	3	10				9	7.00	4.78	5.81	5.13	5.43	2.06	5.25	3.86	2.49	3.02	5.10	7.10	57.03
Lincoln	Ruston	38	48.0	82.3	108	−15	38	Mar. 16	Nov. 14	243	40	4.72	4.17	5.34	5.02	4.47	3.42	5.00	3.18	2.58	2.64	3.81	5.19	49.54

Madison	Tallulah	25	48.8	81.6	105	2	24	Mar. 20	Oct. 27	221	23	5.29	4.81	5.40	4.62	3.73	3.26	4.15	3.17	2.12	2.53	3.71	6.11	48.90
Morehouse	Bastrop				107	−12					10	5.72	4.16	6.05	5.48	3.66	3.60	3.71	1.98	2.05	2.85	3.95	4.73	47.94
	Collinston	17	48.3	82.0	107	9	17	Mar. 26	Oct. 31	219	16	4.41	4.88	5.53	4.62	4.92	4.08	5.68	3.78	3.42	2.26	3.51	6.21	53.30
Natchitoches	Natchitoches	16	49.6	82.5	108	3	16	Mar. 21	Nov. 8	232	15	5.99	4.47	5.44	4.01	4.29	3.02	3.81	2.63	2.54	3.40	4.56	5.74	49.90
	Robeline	40	48.6	81.7	110	−6	40	Mar. 24	Oct. 31	221	39	4.19	3.78	4.97	5.02	4.57	3.22	4.61	3.48	3.03	2.63	3.64	5.21	48.35
Orleans	New Orleans	40	53.5	80.1	102	7	40	Feb. 20	Dec. 9	292	40	4.50	4.13	5.04	5.48	5.19	5.01	6.84	6.08	5.33	4.07	3.10	4.95	59.72
Ouachita	Calhoun	40	47.2	81.5	110	−13	39	Mar. 23	Nov. 6	228	40	4.70	4.21	5.18	4.88	4.80	3.25	4.62	3.61	2.86	3.00	3.91	5.86	50.88
	Monroe	40	48.0	82.4	109	−3	40	Mar. 11	Nov. 13	247	40	5.29	4.61	5.55	5.17	4.81	3.10	5.06	3.74	2.55	3.26	4.00	6.11	53.25
Plaquemines	Burrwood	30	57.1	82.6	99	10	30	Jan. 11	Dec. 30	353	31	4.29	4.14	3.35	4.08	4.02	3.77	6.81	7.81	6.13	5.39	2.96	4.56	57.31
	Lawrence	21	53.9	82.7	105	6	20	Feb. 15	Dec. 14	302	21	3.27	4.17	3.23	4.11	3.78	5.17	7.58	7.21	6.10	3.75	2.97	5.45	56.79
	Port Eads	27	55.3	82.7	99	10	27	Feb. 8	Dec. 13	308	18	4.10	4.56	4.09	3.77	3.13	3.18	6.13	7.23	6.10	5.13	3.44	4.73	55.59
Rapides	Alexandria	39	50.3	82.9	109	3	39	Mar. 8	Nov. 17	254	40	5.08	5.14	5.53	5.80	5.02	3.83	5.53	3.94	3.03	3.44	4.28	6.44	57.06
	Cheneyville	40	51.1	81.9	108	3	38	Mar. 9	Nov. 11	247	40	5.15	4.77	5.17	5.46	5.09	3.82	5.65	4.64	3.40	3.26	4.28	6.26	56.95
	Richland Plantation	12	51.6	83.0	103	9	12				11	5.35	5.06	5.76	6.83	4.14	3.45	4.25	4.48	3.75	3.95	3.65	6.18	56.85
	Woodworth										10	7.06	3.88	4.80	4.99	5.80	1.59	5.46	4.86	2.71	3.77	5.25	6.52	56.69
St. Charles	Paradis (near)										26	5.45	4.02	4.48	4.25	5.13	5.64	7.08	6.04	4.12	4.60	3.68	5.63	60.12
St. John the Baptist	Reserve	38	53.7	82.5	107	16	38	Feb. 22	Nov. 28	279	38	4.96	4.40	4.90	4.57	4.93	4.59	6.59	5.90	4.44	4.06	3.37	5.22	57.93
St. Landry	Grand Coteau	40	53.4	81.7	107	2	40	Feb. 27	Nov. 27	273	39	5.37	4.62	4.14	4.39	5.70	4.76	6.40	5.06	3.92	2.91	3.86	6.03	57.16
	Melville	40	52.1	81.5	105	5	40	Mar. 8	Nov. 9	246	40	5.69	4.80	5.02	5.17	5.38	3.55	5.52	4.76	3.41	2.64	3.95	6.20	56.09
	Opelousas	20	51.3	81.5	104	2	20	Mar. 9	Nov. 12	248	20	4.51	4.44	4.04	5.16	5.98	4.54	6.65	5.50	3.94	2.96	2.92	6.58	57.22
St. Martin	Cade				101	7					10	4.55	3.87	2.52	3.98	4.44	3.48	8.52	5.76	4.44	4.35	2.90	5.48	54.29
St. Mary	Avoca Island										16	4.44	3.62	3.72	4.65	4.78	5.76	8.77	8.70	5.50	4.12	3.42	5.09	62.57
	Franklin	40	53.7	82.0	104	8	40	Feb. 20	Dec. 2	285	40	4.21	4.15	4.11	4.46	4.61	6.04	9.34	7.59	5.81	4.24	3.50	5.23	63.29
	Morgan City	17	55.1	82.0	100	16	17	Feb. 25	Nov. 25	273	34	4.63	3.64	3.93	3.65	3.87	4.82	8.32	7.30	5.24	3.99	3.50	4.72	57.61
St. Tammany	Covington	38	52.2	81.5	105	9	38	Mar. 4	Nov. 24	265	40	5.14	5.12	5.31	5.33	5.21	4.81	7.95	6.23	4.31	3.95	3.42	5.29	62.07
	Pear River										32	5.00	4.68	4.71	5.30	5.86	5.29	7.39	6.88	4.42	4.17	3.71	5.19	62.60
Tangipahoa	Amite	40	51.3	80.9	105	1	40	Mar. 18	Nov. 6	233	40	5.87	5.48	5.54	5.52	5.70	5.31	7.74	6.03	4.42	3.48	3.41	5.87	64.37
	Hammond (near)	36	52.5	81.4	106	1	38	Mar. 8	Nov. 18	255	36	5.40	5.02	5.29	4.87	4.30	4.68	7.07	5.77	4.17	3.32	3.48	5.01	58.38
Tensas	Newellton										19	4.91	5.35	5.83	5.95	4.41	3.78	4.67	3.51	2.26	2.40	3.67	6.09	52.83
Terrebonne	Houma	40	54.8	81.6	104	5	39	Mar. 1	Nov. 12	256	39	4.13	3.83	3.70	3.83	4.01	5.41	8.20	7.30	5.70	4.46	3.69	5.05	59.31
	Schriever	40	54.6	81.9	105	6	40	Mar. 4	Nov. 15	256	40	4.62	4.15	4.50	4.43	4.53	6.11	8.40	6.96	5.18	4.20	3.67	5.42	62.17
Union	Farmerville	24	46.5	81.1	108	−15	24	Mar. 28	Nov. 1	218	18	3.49	4.47	6.22	5.10	5.19	3.53	4.89	4.01	3.38	2.47	3.39	5.79	51.93
Vermilion	Abbeville	37	53.5	81.6	105	5	38	Mar. 1	Nov. 21	265	38	4.53	4.05	3.49	3.91	4.95	5.26	7.26	5.10	4.96	4.01	3.73	5.23	56.48
Vernon	Leesville	18	49.9	80.9	106	9	18	Mar. 12	Nov. 8	241	15	4.75	3.49	5.07	5.02	4.57	3.61	4.35	3.94	3.37	3.15	4.28	5.76	51.36
Washington	Franklinton	26	51.0	81.3	104	10	25	Mar. 11	Nov. 14	248	27	6.05	4.84	5.33	5.52	4.86	4.50	5.96	5.99	3.97	3.28	4.02	6.09	60.41
Webster	Minden	40	47.2	82.1	112	−16	39	Mar. 24	Nov. 9	230	40	4.67	3.77	4.78	5.00	4.79	3.10	4.69	3.53	2.41	2.70	3.92	5.59	48.95
West Baton Rouge	Cinclare	28	52.8	81.6	103	11	28	Mar. 4	Nov. 19	260	28	6.32	4.67	4.44	4.96	4.70	4.87	6.61	5.85	4.16	3.88	4.10	5.77	60.33
West Feliciana	Angola	23	51.2	82.6	104	8	23	Mar. 6	Nov. 22	261	24	5.63	4.67	5.50	5.32	5.50	3.36	4.86	4.86	2.89	3.03	4.09	5.20	54.91
	St. Francisville	19	50.9	81.1	105	11	19	Mar. 2	Nov. 13	256	19	5.68	4.74	5.97	6.01	5.55	4.00	6.63	5.49	4.74	3.42	3.15	6.24	61.62
Winn	Dodson	30	50.1	83.3	110	3	30	Mar. 21	Nov. 12	236	30	5.34	4.59	5.23	4.94	4.80	3.13	5.06	3.01	2.56	3.08	3.88	5.82	51.44

[1] The following parishes, for which no records are available, are best represented by the stations indicated: Caldwell, Jackson, and Richland—Monroe; Catahoula—Kelly (near); Claiborne—Plain Dealing; Concordia—Simmesport; Grant—Cheneyville; Iberville—Cinclare; Livingston—Hammond; Pointe Coupee—Melville; Red River—Grand Cane; Sabine—Robeline; St. Bernard—Lawrence; St. Helena—Amite; St. James—Reserve; West Carroll—Bastrop.

[2] Length of growing season between average dates of last killing frost in spring and first in fall.

LOUISIANA—Continued

Precipitation—State unit values

[This tabulation gives the mean annual, mean monthly, and average seasonal precipitation, 1886–1938, for Louisiana]

Precipitation		Precipitation		Precipitation		Precipitation		Precipitation		Precipitation	
Year	Mean	Year	Mean	Year	Mean	Year	Mean	Month	Mean	Season	Average
	In.		*In.*		*In.*		*In.*		*In.*		*In.*
1886	55.69	1900	66.45	1913	65.57	1926	65.98	January	4.89	Winter	14.60
1887	49.15	1901	49.86	1914	53.49	1927	59.56	February	4.54	Spring	13.79
1888	53.98	1902	52.89	1915	53.05	1928	56.00	March	4.70	Summer	15.93
1889	41.21	1903	48.95	1916	50.62	1929	63.65	April	4.63	Fall	10.90
1890	55.78	1904	43.60	1917	40.21	1930	53.06	May	4.46		
1891	52.59	1905	75.57	1918	54.72	1931	52.90	June	4.81		
1892	61.61	1906	48.44	1919	69.23	1932	62.68	July	6.05		
1893	49.27	1907	58.18	1920	62.66	1933	54.96	August	5.07		
1894	50.84	1908	58.54	1921	47.54	1934	59.23	September	3.83		
1895	54.52	1909	53.25	1922	65.57	1935	56.90	October	3.29		
1896	46.74	1910	49.65	1923	72.22	1936	45.82	November	3.78		
1897	52.13	1911	61.68	1924	38.34	1937	58.87	December	5.17		
1898	63.64	1912	65.46	1925	52.13	1938	50.25				
1899	42.19							Annual	55.22		

Dates of last killing frost in spring and first in fall, with length of growing season

Year	Amite			Calhoun			Cheneyville			Grand Cane			Houma			Jennings		
	Last in spring	First in fall	Growing season[1]	Last in spring	First in fall	Growing season[1]	Last in spring	First in fall	Growing season[1]	Last in spring	First in fall	Growing season[1]	Last in spring	First in fall	Growing season[1]	Last in spring	First in fall	Growing season[1]
			Days			*Days*			*Days*			*Days*			*Days*			*Days*
1899	Mar. 29	Nov. 3	219	Mar. 29	Nov. 3	219							Mar. 7	Nov. 3	241	Mar. 6	Nov. 3	242
1900	Apr. 1	Nov. 10	223	Mar. 31	Nov. 10	224		Nov. 10					Mar. 2	Nov. 13	256	Mar. 1	Nov. 12	256
1901	Mar. 22	Nov. 5	228	Apr. 3	Nov. 5	216	Apr. 20	Nov. 5	199				Mar. 6	Nov. 16	255	Mar. 15	Nov. 15	245
1902	Apr. 1	Nov. 27	240	Mar. 19	Nov. 28	254	Mar. 17	Dec. 4	262				do	Dec. 5	274	Mar. 5	Dec. 4	274
1903	Feb. 24	Oct. 20	238	Feb. 20	Nov. 18	271	Feb. 18	Oct. 25	249				Feb. 18	Oct. 25	249	Feb. 22	Nov. 18	269
1904	Feb. 14	Oct. 21	250	Mar. 28			Feb. 13	Nov. 23	283				Feb. 13	Nov. 13	274	Feb. 11	Nov. 12	275
1905	Feb. 26	Nov. 11	258	Feb. 26	Nov. 11	258	Feb. 22						Feb. 17	Dec. 4	290	Feb. 16	Dec. 12	299
1906	Mar. 20	Nov. 13	238	Mar. 21	Nov. 13	237	Mar. 21	Nov. 13	237				Mar. 21	Nov. 13	237	Feb. 9	Nov. 13	277
1907	Apr. 2	do	225	Feb. 15			Feb. 9	Nov. 12	276		Nov. 13		Feb. 9	do	277	Feb. 8	Nov. 12	277
1908	Feb. 27	Oct. 25	241		Oct. 29		Feb. 22	Oct. 28	249	Jan. 19	Oct. 24	279	Feb. 21	Nov. 16	269	Feb. 21	Nov. 15	268
1909	Mar. 16	Nov. 18	247	Feb. 17	Nov. 18	274	Feb. 25	Oct. 25	242	Mar. 9	Nov. 19	255	Feb. 3			Feb. 17	Dec. 9	295
1910	do	Oct. 29	227	Apr. 25	Oct. 29	187	Feb. 19	Oct. 29	252	Apr. 25	Oct. 29	187		Oct. 29		Feb. 20	Oct. 29	251
1911	Feb. 25	Nov. 13	261	Mar. 3	Nov. 12	254	Feb. 25	Nov. 13	261	Feb. 25	Nov. 13	261	Feb. 26	Nov. 13	260	Feb. 25	Nov. 13	261
1912	Feb. 28	Nov. 2	248	Mar. 25	Nov. 3	223	Feb. 28	Nov. 3	249	Feb. 7	Nov. 2	269	Feb. 23	Nov. 2	253	Feb. 28	Nov. 2	248
1913	Mar. 28	Oct. 21	207	Mar. 28	Oct. 28	214	Mar. 17	Oct. 28	225	Mar. 28	Oct. 28	214	Feb. 14	Nov. 9	268	Mar. 16	Oct. 28	226
1914	Apr. 10	Oct. 28	201	Apr. 10	do	201	Mar. 23	do	219	Mar. 23	do	219	Mar. 23	Oct. 29	220	Mar. 23	do	219
1915	Apr. 5	Nov. 16	225	Apr. 4	Nov. 15	225	Apr. 3	Nov. 16	227	Apr. 3	Nov. 15	226	Apr. 5			Apr. 3	Nov. 15	226
1916	Mar. 17	Oct. 21	218	Mar. 16	Oct. 21	219	Mar. 16	Nov. 15	244	Mar. 5	Nov. 14	254	Mar. 12	Nov. 15	248	Feb. 16	do	273
1917	Mar. 19	Oct. 11	206	Apr. 10	Oct. 9	182	Mar. 6	Oct. 13	221	Mar. 8	Oct. 9	215	Mar. 6	Oct. 31	239	Mar. 6	Oct. 20	228
1918	Apr. 11	Nov. 19	222	Apr. 11	Nov. 1	204	Feb. 5	Nov. 24	292	Feb. 21	Dec. 24	306	Feb. 5	Nov. 19	287	Feb. 5	Dec. 2	300
1919	Feb. 27	Nov. 14	260	Apr. 2	Nov. 13	225		Nov. 14		Feb. 27	Nov. 14	260	Feb. 27	Dec. 15	291	Feb. 26	Dec. 10	287
1920	Mar. 9	Nov. 4	240	Apr. 5	Oct. 28	206	Mar. 8	Nov. 12	249	Apr. 5	Nov. 13	222	Mar. 7	Nov. 13	251	Apr. 5	Nov. 13	222
1921	Apr. 11	Nov. 28	231	Apr. 19	Nov. 4	199	Feb. 19	Dec. 5	289	Feb. 21	Nov. 10	262	Jan. 28	None	338	Feb. 20	Dec. 5	288
1922	Mar. 5	Nov. 26	266	Mar. 11	Nov. 26	260	Mar. 4	Nov. 26	267	Mar. 8	Nov. 26	263	Mar. 4			Mar. 4	Dec. 19	290
1923	Mar. 20	Oct. 22	216	Mar. 20	Oct. 22	216	Mar. 20	Oct. 23	217	Mar. 20	Oct. 22	216	Mar. 20	Nov. 18	243	Mar. 20	Nov. 7	232
1924	Mar. 16	Nov. 17	246	Mar. 15	Oct. 25	224	Mar. 14	Oct. 25	225	Mar. 21	Oct. 26	219	Mar. 15	Nov. 25	255	Mar. 11	Nov. 25	259
1925	Mar. 4	Nov. 9	250	Mar. 3	Nov. 9	251	Mar. 3	Nov. 16	258	Mar. 3	Oct. 30	241	Feb. 12	Nov. 23	284	Feb. 12	Nov. 23	284
1926	Mar. 16	Nov. 5	234	Apr. 1	Nov. 3	216	Mar. 16	Nov. 5	234	Mar. 16	Nov. 3	232	Feb. 20	Nov. 6	259	Jan. 27	Nov. 10	287
1927	Feb. 21	Nov. 18	270	Apr. 23	do	194	Mar. 4	Dec. 3	274	Mar. 22	Nov. 6	229	Jan. 16	Dec. 3	321	Mar. 3	Dec. 3	275
1928	Mar. 18	Nov. 4	231	Apr. 16	Nov. 20	218	Feb. 28	Nov. 20	266	Feb. 28	Nov. 4	250	Feb. 28	Nov. 21	267	Feb. 19	Nov. 20	275
1929	Mar. 2	Nov. 5	248	Mar. 2	Oct. 25	237	Mar. 2	Nov. 18	261	Mar. 2	Oct. 24	236	Feb. 12	Nov. 30	291	Mar. 2	Nov. 30	273
1930	Mar. 29	Nov. 1	217	Mar. 26	Oct. 31	219	Mar. 29	Nov. 1	217	Mar. 29	Oct. 31	216	Mar. 4	Nov. 25	266	Mar. 4	Nov. 25	266
1931	Mar. 17	do	229	Mar. 29	do	216	Mar. 17	Oct. 31	228	Mar. 28	Dec. 4	251	Mar. 10	None	297	Mar. 10	None	297
1932	Mar. 15	Oct. 6	205	Mar. 14	Nov. 12	243	Mar. 13	Nov. 9	241	Mar. 14	Nov. 9	240	Mar. 13	Nov. 12	244	Mar. 14	Nov. 12	243
1933	Mar. 21	Nov. 9	233	Mar. 21	Nov. 8	232	Mar. 21	Dec. 7	261	Mar. 21	Nov. 25	249	Feb. 12	None	323	Feb. 12	Dec. 7	298

[1] Number of days between last killing frost in spring and first in fall.

LOUISIANA—Continued

Dates of last killing frost in spring and first in fall, with length of growing season—Continued

Year	Amite			Calhoun			Cheneyville			Grand Cane			Houma			Jennings		
	Last in spring	First in fall	Growing season	Last in spring	First in fall	Growing season	Last in spring	First in fall	Growing season	Last in spring	First in fall	Growing season	Last in spring	First in fall	Growing season	Last in spring	First in fall	Growing season
			Days			*Days*			*Days*			*Days*			*Days*			*Days*
1934	Mar. 29	Nov. 12	228	Mar. 19	Nov. 24	250	Mar. 19	Nov. 13	239	Mar. 19	Dec. 1	257	Mar. 11	Dec. 8	272	Mar. 19	Dec. 1	257
1935	Mar. 13	Nov. 18	250	Feb. 28	Nov. 23	268	Mar. 1	Nov. 17	261	Feb. 28	Nov. 17	262	Mar. 1	Nov. 17	261	Feb. 28	Dec. 3	278
1936	Mar. 18	Nov. 5	232	Apr. 3	Nov. 5	216	Apr. 3	Nov. 5	216	Apr. 3	Nov. 4	215	Feb. 19	Nov. 5	260	Feb. 19	Nov. 5	260
1937	Mar. 29	Oct. 23	208	Mar. 31	Oct. 23	206	Mar. 31	Nov. 18	232	Mar. 31	Oct. 23	206	Mar. 16	Nov. 20	249	Mar. 1	Nov. 20	264
1938	Apr. 10	Oct. 25	198	Mar. 7	Oct. 24	231	Feb. 20	Nov. 9	262	Feb. 20	Oct. 24	246	Apr. 10	Nov. 9	213	Feb. 1	Nov. 9	281
Mean	Mar. 18	Nov. 6	233	Mar. 23	Nov. 6	228	Mar. 9	Nov. 11	247	Mar. 12	Nov. 8	241	Mar. 1	Nov. 12	256	Feb. 27	Nov. 20	266
Extremes	Feb. 14[2]	Oct. 6[4]	[6] 198	Feb. 15[2]	Oct. 9[4]	[6] 182	Feb. 5[2]	Oct. 13[4]	[6] 199	Jan. 19[2]	Oct. 9[4]	[6] 187	Jan. 16[2]	Oct. 25[4]	[6] 213	Jan. 27[2]	Oct. 20[4]	[6] 219
	Apr. 11[3]	Nov. 28[5]	[7] 270	Apr. 25[3]	Nov. 28[5]	[7] 274	Apr. 20[3]	Dec. 7[5]	[7] 292	Apr. 25[3]	Dec. 24[5]	[7] 306	Apr. 10[3]	None[5]	[7] 338	Apr. 5[3]	None[5]	[7] 300

[2] Earliest date in spring.
[3] Latest date in spring.
[4] Earliest date in fall.
[5] Latest date in fall.
[6] Shortest growing season.
[7] Longest growing season.

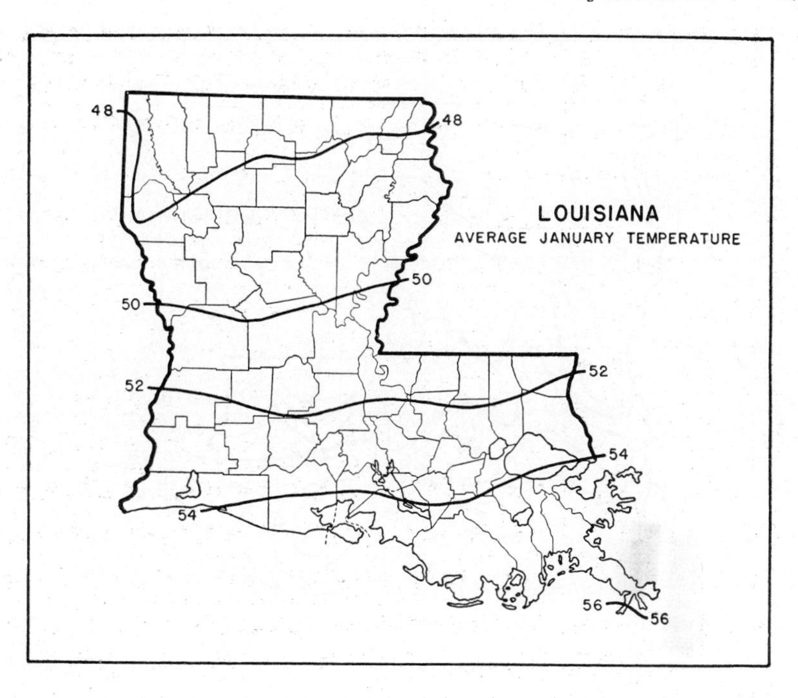
LOUISIANA
AVERAGE JANUARY TEMPERATURE
48
48
50
50
52
52
54
54
56
56

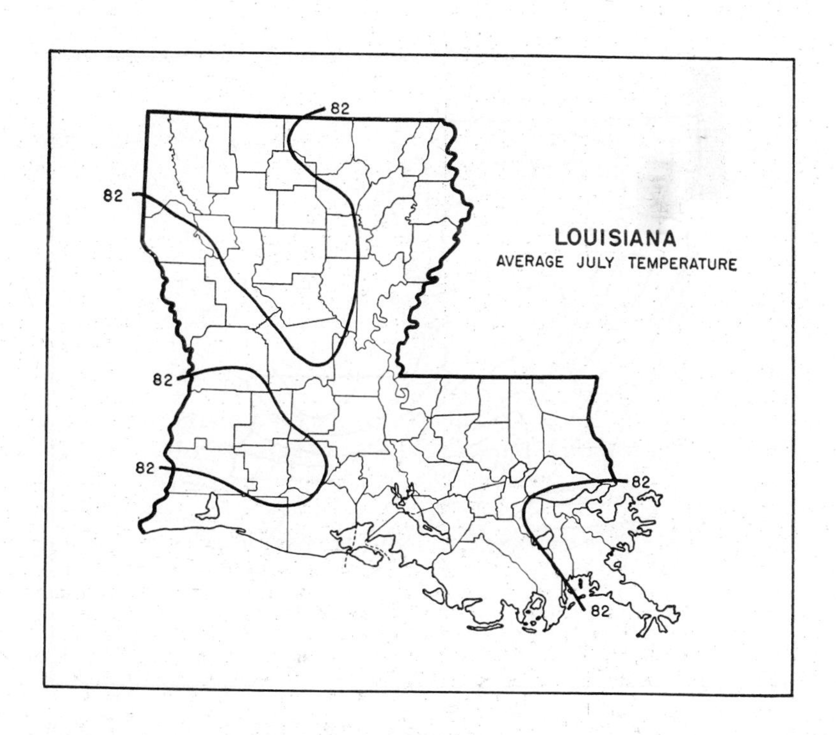
LOUISIANA
AVERAGE JULY TEMPERATURE
82
82
82
82
82
82

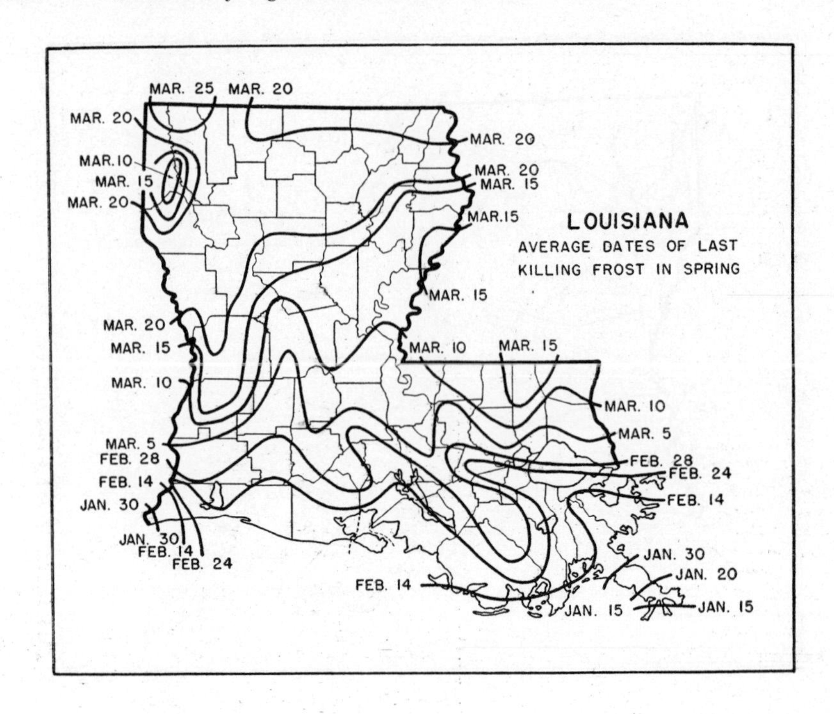
LOUISIANA
AVERAGE DATES OF LAST
KILLING FROST IN SPRING
MAR. 25
MAR. 20
MAR. 10
MAR. 15
MAR. 5
FEB. 28
FEB. 24
FEB. 14
JAN. 30
JAN. 20
JAN. 15

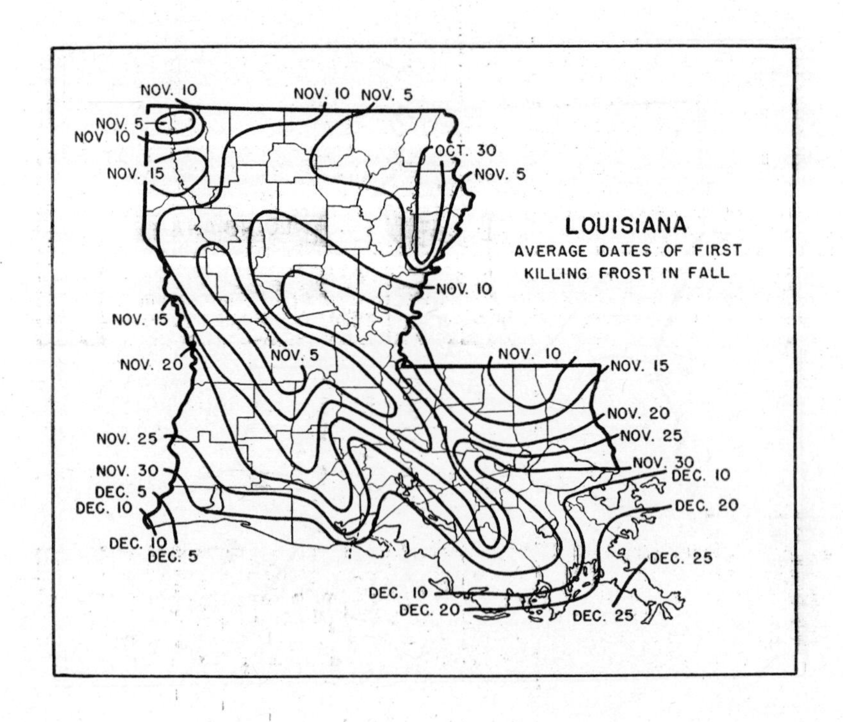
LOUISIANA
AVERAGE DATES OF FIRST
KILLING FROST IN FALL
OCT. 30
NOV. 5
NOV. 10
NOV. 15
NOV. 20
NOV. 25
NOV. 30
DEC. 5
DEC. 10
DEC. 20
DEC. 25

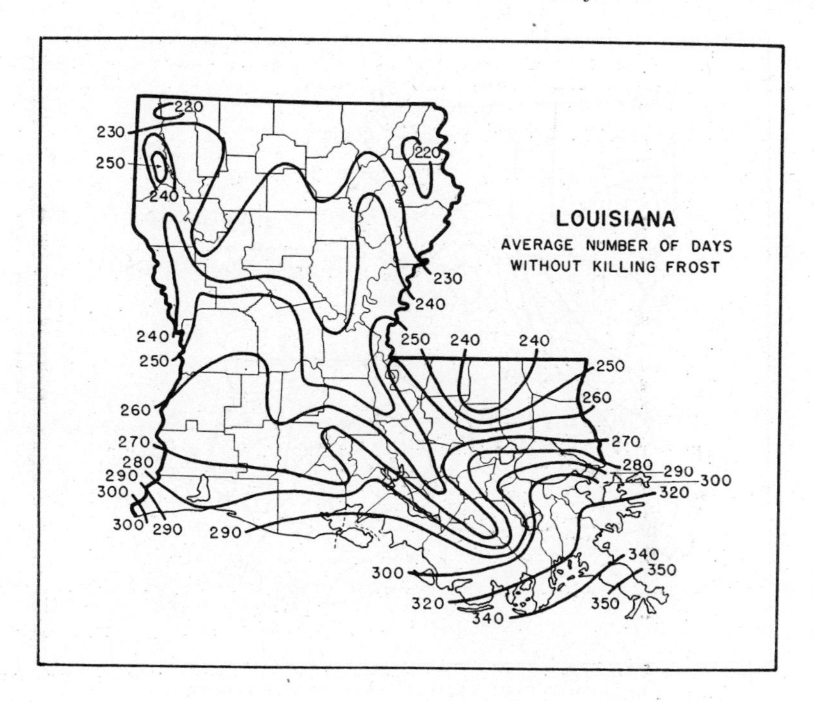
LOUISIANA
AVERAGE NUMBER OF DAYS
WITHOUT KILLING FROST
220
230
250
240
220
230
240
240
250
260
270
280
290
300
300
290
290
250
240
240
250
260
270
280
290
300
320
300
340
350
320
340
350

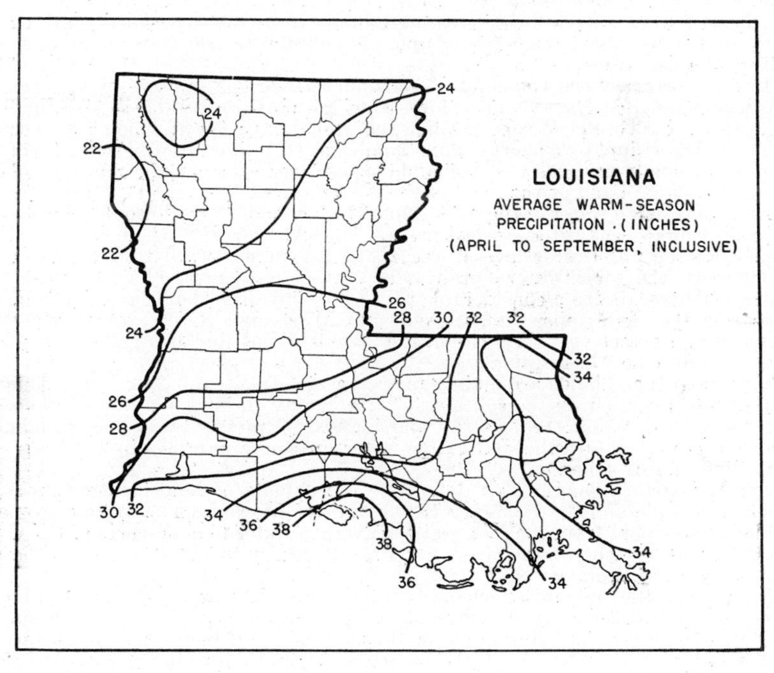
LOUISIANA
AVERAGE WARM-SEASON
PRECIPITATION . (INCHES)
(APRIL TO SEPTEMBER, INCLUSIVE)
24
24
22
22
24
26
28
26
28
30
32
32
32
34
30
32
34
36
38
38
36
34
34

298737°—41——58

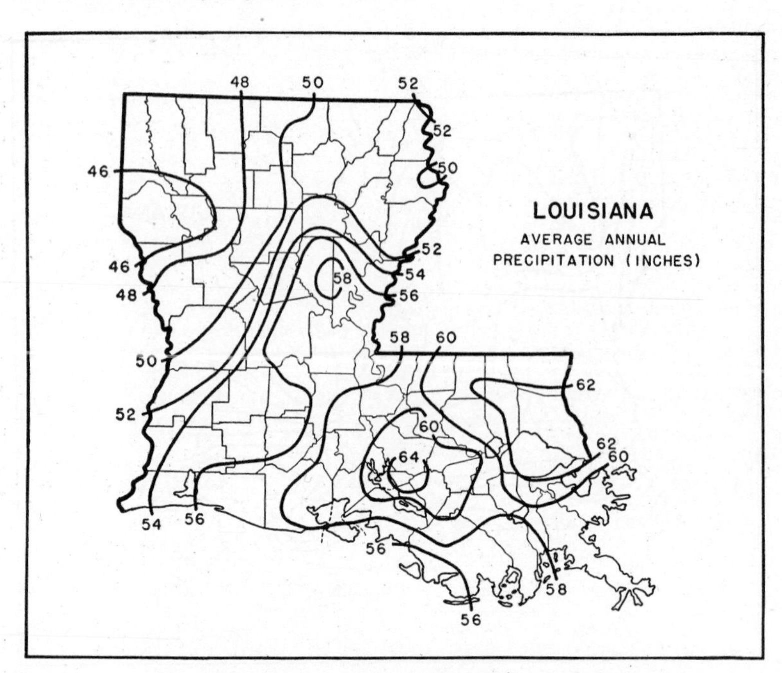

SUPPLEMENTARY CLIMATIC NOTES FOR LOUISIANA

Louisiana extends, roughly, between latitudes 29.5° and 33° and from the ninety-fourth meridian eastward to the Mississippi River, and, in the south, to the Pearl River. Elevations increase gradually from the coast northward, rising to over 100 feet above sea level on uplands and 400 to 500 feet on some of the hills in the northwest.

In the northeast the Ouachita River and the various streams of the Tensas Basin join the Red River, which flows from the northwest. These streams find an outlet to the Gulf of Mexico through the Atchafalaya River, which is connected with the Mississippi by a short channel known as Old River, in which the direction of flow is usually towards the Atchafalaya but depends upon the relative height in the Mississippi and at the head of the Atchafalaya.

At times of high water in the Mississippi the lowlands of the lower Tensas Basin become a large backwater storage basin. The Atchafalaya Basin embraces the area from the lower west levees of the Mississippi westward to Bayou Teche, which skirts the southwestern prairies in part of its course. Farther west the Calcasieu River drains a considerable part of southwestern Louisiana. Lowlands bordering the Red, upper Atchafalaya, and Mississippi Rivers are mostly protected by an extensive levee system, the levees of the Red being less complete than those of the Mississippi.

The larger marshlands are mainly in the coastal area, extending farther inland in the southeast than in the southwest. Higher, tilled land lies along bayous or other streams passing through the marshlands. Drainage work has reclaimed some swamp areas. In the south large water surfaces are formed by the irregular coast line and by lakes.

The principal influences that determine the climate of Louisiana are its subtropical latitude and its proximity to the Gulf of Mexico. The marine tropical influence is evident from the fact that the average water temperatures of the Gulf along its northern shore range from 64° F. in February to 84° in August. Elevation is a minor factor.

In summer the prevailing southerly winds provide a moist, tropical climate when the atmospheric pressure decreases westward from the Atlantic Ocean, a condition favorable for afternoon thundershowers when the ocean high-pressure area is not too far west. When the pressure distribution is altered so as to bring westerly to northerly winds, periods of hotter and drier weather interrupt the prevailing moist condition. In the colder season the State is alternately subjected to tropical air and cold continental air, in periods of varying length. Though warmed by its southward journey, the cold air occasionally brings large and rather sudden drops in temperature, though more gradual in onset here than farther west.

From December to May the water of the Mississippi River averages colder than the air temperature in this latitude, favoring river fogs during this season, particularly when southerly winds prevail with slight barometric gradients. However, the river water is not too cold to ameliorate conditions near its banks during unusual cold spells, as the average water temperature at New Orleans is 47.5° F. in January and 47.1° in February. In the more southern sections lakes also serve to modify the extremes of temperature and to increase fogginess over limited contiguous areas.

Although Louisiana is south of the average track of storms of large cyclonic character, it is occasionally visited by winter storms requiring warnings, while its position on the Gulf coast brings it within the path of an occasional tropical storm.

The average annual temperatures range from 64.1° F. at Farmerville in the extreme north to 70.8° at Burrwood at the mouth of the Mississippi River. The highest monthly average is 83° at Burrwood in August, and the lowest is 46.3° at Plain Dealing, in the extreme northwest, in January. The highest monthly State averages in the warmest summer months have not exceeded 84.3°.

There is a narrow strip along the coast where the temperature on the hottest days rarely reaches 100° F. However, 108° has been recorded in the central part of the State, 110° in the extreme northeast, and 114° in the extreme northwest.

In a 44-year record, temperatures of 32° F. or lower have occurred every winter in the sugar and trucking region of southern Louisiana, with 23° or lower in about half the winters. In the northern parishes of the State, 29° or lower (26° or lower at some stations) has occurred every winter, with 17° or lower in more than half the winters in most northern localities.

The average dates of the last killing frost in spring range from February 1 at the mouth of the Mississippi River to March 28 on the northern border. The risk of killing frost, even in the northern part, is exceedingly slight after March 31, and after March 20 in the south.

The average dates of the first killing frost in fall range from near November 1 in the extreme north to December 14 in the extreme southeast. The earliest dates of the first killing frost have been about mid-October in the north and central parts and about December 1 in the extreme southeast. In the sugar and trucking area temperatures of 32° F. or lower seldom occur before November 11.

The average growing season ranges from 220 days in the extreme north to 320 days in the extreme southeast. Hardy vegetables that can withstand temperatures down to nearly 20° F. live through a normal winter in the southern third of the State. There are occasional winters in the extreme southeast without any freezing temperatures or killing frost.

The average annual precipitation ranges from slightly below 46 inches in the extreme northwest to over 60 just north of Lake Pontchartrain. Droughts occur at times in the growing season, but long periods without rain are seldom experienced, especially in the southeast.

A monthly rainfall of over 20 inches at a station is quite rare, and 24-hour falls of more than 10 inches are exceptional, but not unknown. In the southeast, thunderstorms have in a few instances brought rainfalls exceeding 14 inches in 24 hours.

Snow is infrequent and of slight depth, as a rule. Glaze and sleet are rarer than snow.

The average sunshine as recorded at New Orleans varies from 45 percent of the possible amount in December to 67 in October, with 58 to 62 percent in the summer months. May, June, and July have more actual sunshine because of the longer days.

Local storms, including hailstorms, tornadoes, and other windstorms of small area, have occurred in all seasons but show somewhat more frequency in spring. Compared with their occurrence in the Plains States they are relatively infrequent. Aside from tornadoes, the highest wind velocities in the coastal area have occurred in connection with tropical hurricanes. As these storms diminish in passing inland, the highest winds in the northern part of the State occur with well-defined wind shifts, or squall lines.

RAY A. DYKE, *Senior Meteorologist and Climatic Section Director for Louisiana, Weather Bureau, New Orleans.*

MARYLAND AND DELAWARE

Climatic summary

County [1]	Station	Temperature: Length of record	Temperature: January average	Temperature: July average	Temperature: Maximum	Temperature: Minimum	Killing frost average dates: Length of record	Killing frost average dates: Last in spring	Killing frost average dates: First in fall	Growing season [2]	Average precipitation: Length of record	January	February	March	April	May	June	July	August	September	October	November	December	Annual
MARYLAND		Yr.	°F.	°F.	°F.	°F.	Yr.			Days	Yr.	In.	In.	In.	In.	In.	In.	In.	In.	In.	In.	In.	In.	In.
Allegany	Cumberland	30	32.9	75.9	109	−12	30	Apr. 27	Oct. 14	170	40	2.76	2.28	3.02	3.14	3.29	4.01	3.17	3.72	2.72	2.47	1.95	2.69	35.22
	Frostburg	31	30.5	71.8	104	−22	31	May 1	Oct. 8	160	36	3.43	2.62	3.68	3.81	3.98	4.85	3.80	4.01	3.18	3.03	2.41	2.92	41.72
	Picardy	12	34.7	75.1	105	−11	12	May 3	Oct. 12	162	12	2.45	1.86	3.24	3.68	3.36	3.56	2.73	3.66	2.84	3.37	1.93	2.35	35.03
	Western Port	40	32.3	73.6	107	−17	10	May 7	Oct. 9	155	40	2.76	2.29	3.02	3.13	3.63	4.06	3.62	3.63	2.72	2.59	1.97	2.49	35.91
Anne Arundel	Annapolis	40	35.3	77.5	106	−6	35	Apr. 10	Nov. 1	205	40	3.70	3.26	3.81	3.76	3.58	4.28	4.62	5.11	3.76	2.90	2.52	3.42	44.72
	Jewell	10	34.1	75.7	100	−14	6	Apr. 20	Oct. 24	187	10	2.99	3.23	3.50	3.16	2.71	5.03	5.21	4.80	3.88	3.59	2.37	3.89	44.36
Baltimore	Baltimore	40	35.5	77.9	107	−7	40	Apr. 8	Nov. 2	208	40	3.57	2.96	3.53	3.66	3.37	3.56	4.14	4.98	3.54	2.94	2.46	3.23	41.94
	Freeland										10	3.60	2.75	3.89	3.40	3.73	4.02	5.32	3.73	3.27	2.55	2.45	3.14	41.85
	Lake Montebello	14	34.5	76.1	101	−10	12	Apr. 13	Nov. 2	203	15	3.35	2.66	3.23	3.35	3.40	4.14	5.04	5.39	2.95	2.56	2.59	3.53	42.19
	Lutherville	12	34.4	75.6	108	−18	12	Apr. 26	Oct. 17	174	13	3.66	3.13	3.70	4.36	3.42	3.99	3.91	5.24	3.76	3.87	3.20	2.91	45.15
	Maryland Line	14	32.9	74.6	105	−14	14	Apr. 21	Oct. 23	185	14	3.84	2.80	3.46	4.04	3.37	4.24	4.33	4.61	3.96	3.86	3.10	2.88	44.49
	Pleasant Hill						14	Apr. 26	Oct. 18	175	14	3.56	2.94	3.44	3.95	3.35	3.95	3.72	4.56	3.88	3.62	2.92	2.77	42.66
	Towson	10	32.7	74.9	104	−14	25	Apr. 17	Oct. 22	188	27	3.79	2.91	3.56	4.05	3.49	3.73	3.80	4.95	3.31	3.12	2.70	3.15	42.56
	Woodstock College	40	33.5	75.6	105	−18	40	Apr. 22	Oct. 15	176	40	3.38	2.79	3.34	3.45	3.35	3.91	4.04	4.51	3.58	2.88	2.43	3.14	40.80
Calvert	Ferry Landing	22	35.9	76.0	106	−13	22	Apr. 16	Oct. 23	190	22	3.83	2.77	3.41	4.03	3.89	3.53	5.10	5.25	3.95	2.75	2.78	2.70	43.99
	Solomons	40	36.9	78.1	104	−5	40	Apr. 8	Nov. 7	213	40	3.09	2.69	3.24	3.04	2.98	3.36	4.46	4.27	3.15	2.40	1.97	2.70	37.35
Caroline	Ridgely	16	36.8	76.6	108	−10	17	Apr. 18	Oct. 23	188	40	3.37	2.90	3.45	3.35	3.48	3.93	4.45	5.02	3.70	2.89	2.66	3.17	42.37
	Denton	23	35.1	76.4	108	−17	40	Apr. 15	Oct. 20	188	20	3.04	2.74	3.36	3.16	3.60	3.84	3.98	4.99	3.14	3.21	2.48	3.39	40.93
Carroll	Taneytown	11	31.3	75.6	105	−22	10	Apr. 24	Oct. 16	175	11	2.75	3.19	3.41	3.06	2.89	3.92	3.53	4.77	3.54	2.68	2.21	3.52	39.47
	Westminster	24	32.9	75.2	104	−16	22	Apr. 22	Oct. 19	180	24	3.35	2.88	3.89	3.53	3.61	4.15	3.76	4.87	4.14	3.19	2.60	3.20	43.17
Cecil	Cecilton	17	34.0	76.4	105	−15	8	Apr. 18	Oct. 27	192	16	3.46	3.10	3.66	3.77	3.73	3.40	5.09	5.68	3.53	2.60	2.72	2.87	43.61
	Elkton	12	35.2	76.4	106	−16	12	Apr. 19	Oct. 15	179	13	3.58	3.15	3.55	3.26	3.50	4.25	4.53	6.16	3.64	3.27	2.89	2.90	44.68
Charles	La Plata	16	36.9	76.3	108	−12	16	Apr. 18	Oct. 22	187	17	4.41	2.88	3.63	3.93	4.03	4.12	5.19	5.03	4.28	2.96	3.05	2.93	46.44
Dorchester	Cambridge	40	36.7	77.9	106	−6	38	Apr. 14	Oct. 31	200	40	3.72	3.29	3.91	3.67	3.48	4.00	4.51	5.03	3.57	3.21	2.63	3.33	44.35
Frederick	Emmitsburg	36	32.2	75.2	104	−23	38	Apr. 17	Oct. 27	193	40	3.42	3.00	4.01	3.77	3.82	4.62	4.15	4.42	3.82	3.55	2.74	3.32	44.64
	Frederick	40	33.1	77.0	109	−21	34	Apr. 21	Oct. 17	179	40	3.27	2.93	3.51	3.52	3.37	4.34	4.06	4.44	3.30	3.07	2.35	3.21	41.37
	Monrovia	12	34.0	75.0	105	−14	12	Apr. 22	Oct. 19	180	19	3.33	2.92	3.40	3.04	3.35	4.85	4.54	4.79	3.19	2.97	2.09	3.47	41.94
	State Senator	30	31.3	74.1	104	−14	30	Apr. 20	Oct. 25	188	30	3.44	2.81	3.59	3.90	3.81	4.59	4.07	4.41	4.01	3.57	2.76	3.11	44.07
Garrett	Deer Park	20	26.1	67.0	98	−33	20	May 27	Sept. 20	116	20	4.20	3.50	4.12	3.80	4.39	5.25	4.54	3.82	2.95	2.88	2.31	3.88	45.64
	Friendsville	20	30.7	69.2	97	−19	20	May 21	Oct. 1	133	19	3.92	3.08	4.35	3.79	3.83	4.60	4.82	4.33	3.12	3.15	2.89	3.67	45.55
	Grantsville	40	27.9	68.0	100	−26	40	May 20	Sept. 29	132	40	3.83	3.12	4.12	3.84	4.14	4.46	3.98	4.34	2.95	3.01	2.68	3.57	44.04
	Oakland	36	28.9	67.4	101	−40	36	May 26	Sept. 27	124	35	4.06	3.21	4.05	3.99	4.44	4.57	4.79	4.36	3.30	3.39	2.78	3.76	46.70
	Sines (Deep Creek)	11	29.4	67.9	96	−23	11	May 25	Oct. 2	130	10	4.25	2.91	4.47	3.98	4.70	4.12	4.44	3.98	2.89	3.13	2.58	3.50	44.95
Harford	Aberdeen	20	33.0	75.7	105	−13	20	Apr. 16	Oct. 27	194	20	3.36	2.81	3.20	3.41	3.35	3.55	4.53	5.14	3.47	2.48	2.54	2.53	40.37
	Darlington	40	31.6	74.8	105	−17	40	Apr. 21	Oct. 21	183	40	3.63	3.13	3.55	3.45	3.26	4.16	4.51	5.07	3.82	3.23	2.64	3.66	44.11

	Fallston	40	32.3	74.4	104	−14	40	Apr. 20	Oct. 22	185	40	3.60	3.09	3.55	3.78	3.26	4.01	4.38	5.19	3.86	3.36	2.72	3.50	44.30
	Van Bibber	18	32.3	75.4	101	−18	14	Apr. 19	do	186	19	3.49	3.41	4.01	3.70	3.35	4.51	4.14	5.21	3.94	3.43	2.46	4.07	45.72
Kent	Chestertown	17	33.8	76.4	100	−9	18	Apr. 17	Oct. 27	193	18	3.83	3.40	3.81	3.35	3.27	4.26	4.58	4.74	3.69	3.26	2.65	3.68	44.52
	Coleman	37	34.2	76.7	106	−11	40	Apr. 13	Oct. 29	199	40	3.54	3.07	3.54	3.46	3.41	3.67	4.49	4.84	3.57	2.83	2.52	3.43	42.37
	Millington	16	35.8	76.1	105	−13	16	Apr. 17	Oct. 19	185	40	3.65	3.28	3.82	3.52	3.23	3.72	4.73	4.96	3.77	2.96	2.68	3.54	43.86
	Rock Hall	22	35.0	77.2	104	−12	22	Apr. 16	Oct. 26	193	24	3.62	3.21	3.49	3.57	3.25	3.51	4.85	5.12	3.97	2.74	2.75	3.01	43.09
Montgomery	Boyds	19	33.6	75.2	106	−17	19	Apr. 27	Oct. 17	173	18	3.11	2.69	3.08	3.25	3.17	3.57	3.16	4.23	3.51	2.70	2.30	2.48	37.25
	Great Falls	40	33.2	75.7	106	−21	33	Apr. 24	Oct. 18	177	40	3.31	2.69	3.21	3.29	3.39	3.89	4.03	4.45	3.63	2.97	2.16	3.13	40.15
	Rockville	13	33.0	74.2	104	−14					13	3.35	2.49	3.43	3.35	3.72	4.54	4.15	4.54	3.03	2.44	2.03	3.10	40.17
	Takoma	40	33.3	75.5	108	−10	36	Apr. 15	Oct. 27	195	39	3.61	2.98	3.44	3.55	3.36	3.82	4.16	4.22	3.60	2.76	2.32	3.33	41.15
Prince Georges	Bell	18	34.3	75.8	106	−23	18	Apr. 27	Oct. 16	172	18	3.76	2.88	3.34	4.01	3.78	3.40	3.74	4.70	4.12	2.96	2.90	2.57	42.16
	College Park	40	34.1	75.9	107	−26	37	Apr. 28	Oct. 15	170	40	3.41	2.91	3.54	3.54	3.68	3.93	3.98	4.61	3.58	2.74	2.39	3.10	41.41
	Cheltenham	38	35.1	75.8	106	−16	38	Apr. 18	Oct. 20	185	38	3.79	2.85	3.69	4.06	3.59	4.16	4.53	4.81	3.52	2.90	2.59	3.23	43.72
	Laurel	40	33.5	75.5	106	−19	40	Apr. 22	Oct. 17	178	40	3.49	2.82	3.65	3.72	3.48	3.99	4.26	4.93	3.56	2.95	2.47	3.27	42.59
Queen Annes	Stevensville	12	37.0	77.5	101	−9	12	Apr. 15	Oct. 29	197	13	3.84	3.37	3.93	4.05	3.84	3.64	4.36	5.32	3.86	3.14	2.87	2.90	45.12
	Sudlersville	24	33.7	76.2	105	−12	24	Apr. 14	Oct. 23	192	22	3.46	3.20	4.00	3.56	3.18	3.80	4.75	4.39	3.59	2.97	2.67	3.89	43.46
St. Marys	Charlotte Hall	7	33.0	77.0	102	−19	18	Apr. 16	Oct. 22	189	19	3.43	3.21	3.09	3.94	3.96	4.20	4.72	5.37	3.95	2.95	2.23	3.18	44.23
Somerset	Crisfield	19	38.8	77.6	100	−5	19	Apr. 9	Nov. 7	212	20	3.72	3.70	4.25	3.96	3.57	3.55	5.29	4.97	3.48	2.65	2.68	3.35	45.17
	Princess Anne	40	36.7	75.4	105	−10	40	Apr. 21	Oct. 19	181	40	3.48	3.41	3.88	3.53	3.32	4.02	4.56	5.34	3.43	2.99	2.45	3.31	43.72
Talbot	Easton	40	35.6	76.2	104	−15	40	Apr. 14	Oct. 26	195	40	3.34	3.07	3.68	3.38	3.26	4.07	4.45	4.66	3.66	3.21	2.60	3.09	42.47
Washington	Chewsville	40	31.2	74.1	104	−27	40	May 3	Oct. 9	159	40	2.81	2.30	3.00	2.98	3.39	4.06	3.88	3.77	3.19	2.88	2.04	2.62	36.92
	Clear Spring	34	31.2	74.2	106	−16	40	Apr. 24	Oct. 16	175	33	3.14	2.77	3.42	3.70	3.72	4.20	4.08	4.05	3.01	2.98	2.21	3.12	40.40
	Green Spring Furnace.	18	31.3	75.3	106	−14	18	Apr. 22	Oct. 14	175	18	2.99	2.73	3.20	2.95	3.46	4.59	3.66	4.35	2.64	2.33	1.86	3.08	37.84
	Hancock	19	31.1	74.7	106	−21	23	May 5	Oct. 8	156	25	2.53	2.21	3.13	3.42	3.26	4.09	3.41	3.20	2.81	3.17	2.14	2.68	36.05
	Keedysville	35	32.7	75.9	109	−26	34	May 1	Oct. 14	166	34	2.93	2.42	2.94	3.25	3.32	3.96	3.64	4.09	3.21	3.23	2.16	2.75	37.90
	Tonoloway	15	32.8	74.1	107	−21	15	May 10	Oct. 8	151	10	2.67	1.91	3.51	3.76	3.45	3.88	2.93	3.18	2.90	3.55	2.10	2.51	36.35
Wicomico	Salisbury	33	37.8	76.8	106	−9	33	Apr. 20	Oct. 21	184	33	3.68	3.22	3.84	3.39	3.48	3.88	4.18	5.67	3.95	3.07	2.76	3.22	44.34
Worcester	Pocomoke City	17	38.8	77.7	101	−4	24	Apr. 21	Oct. 23	185	25	2.99	3.31	3.38	3.17	2.71	3.89	3.74	4.81	3.23	3.04	2.19	3.51	39.97
	Public Landing	15	36.0	75.1	106	−1	15	Apr. 16	Oct. 29	196	15	3.16	3.43	3.57	3.62	2.72	3.03	4.14	4.08	2.86	2.68	2.49	3.72	39.50
DELAWARE																								
Kent	Dover	32	36.4	76.7	104	−11	33	Apr. 19	Oct. 24	188	31	3.67	3.21	3.84	3.62	3.67	3.85	4.95	5.15	3.80	2.70	2.89	3.35	44.70
New Castle	Delaware City	40	33.8	76.2	104	−11	36	Apr. 16	do	191	37	3.19	2.83	3.23	3.26	3.16	3.89	4.23	4.58	3.48	2.79	2.41	3.02	40.07
	Newark	20	30.8	74.8	103	−12	12	Apr. 18	Oct. 15	180	20	3.29	3.15	3.64	3.65	3.51	3.79	5.02	4.83	3.59	3.06	2.30	3.87	43.70
	Wilmington	40	33.3	76.0	107	−15	27	Apr. 17	Oct. 28	194	40	3.64	3.11	3.57	3.52	3.24	4.19	4.93	5.09	3.80	3.06	2.84	3.59	44.58
Sussex	Bridgeville	14	37.6	76.4	105	−11	15	Apr. 21	Oct. 22	184	40	3.68	3.22	3.68	3.34	3.56	3.85	5.05	5.06	3.56	3.05	2.48	3.26	43.79
	Milford	40	36.7	76.6	105	−12	40	Apr. 19	Oct. 25	189	40	4.01	3.40	4.23	3.71	3.60	4.00	4.67	5.28	3.39	3.25	2.80	3.86	46.20
	Millsboro	40	36.6	76.4	110	−17	40	Apr. 21	Oct. 21	183	40	3.85	3.48	4.10	3.64	3.41	3.91	4.75	5.64	3.58	3.18	2.74	3.77	46.05

[1] Howard County, Md., for which no records are available, is best represented by Woodstock College, Baltimore County, or Laurel, Prince Georges County.

[2] Length of growing season between average dates of last killing frost in spring and first in fall.

MARYLAND AND DELAWARE—Continued

Precipitation—Unit values

[This tabulation gives the mean annual, mean monthly, and average seasonal precipitation, 1886–1938, for Maryland and Delaware, treated as one section]

Precipitation		Precipitation		Precipitation		Precipitation		Precipitation		Precipitation	
Year	Mean	Year	Mean	Year	Mean	Year	Mean	Month	Mean	Season	Average
	In.		*In.*		*In.*		*In.*		*In.*		*In.*
1886	48.05	1900	36.66	1914	35.97	1928	45.09	January	3.38		
1887	37.52	1901	45.08	1915	43.89	1929	42.46	February	3.13	Winter	9.63
1888	43.21	1902	49.20	1916	40.47	1930	23.78	March	3.70	Spring	11.01
1889	58.30	1903	46.94	1917	40.67	1931	38.68	April	3.49	Summer	12.73
1890	46.39	1904	36.49	1918	37.96	1932	47.15	May	3.82	Fall	9.07
1891	51.44	1905	43.84	1919	47.62	1933	49.30	June	3.88		
1892	41.54	1906	48.00	1920	44.95	1934	46.03	July	4.48		
1893	38.57	1907	48.90	1921	37.72	1935	47.57	August	4.37		
1894	37.76	1908	40.01	1922	40.07	1936	44.44	September	3.45		
1895	34.14	1909	36.90	1923	40.27	1937	51.92	October	2.99		
1896	36.28	1910	37.23	1924	46.44	1938	41.57	November	2.63		
1897	44.97	1911	43.45	1925	34.91			December	3.12		
1898	42.18	1912	44.16	1926	43.90						
1899	40.84	1913	38.80	1927	40.37			Annual	42.44		

Dates of last killing frost in spring and first in fall, with length of growing season

Year	Grantsville, Md.			Frederick, Md.			Fallston, Md.			Cheltenham, Md.			Princess Anne, Md.			Milford, Del.		
	Last in spring	First in fall	Growing season[1]	Last in spring	First in fall	Growing season[1]	Last in spring	First in fall	Growing season[1]	Last in spring	First in fall	Growing season[1]	Last in spring	First in fall	Growing season[1]	Last in spring	First in fall	Growing season[1]
			Days			*Days*			*Days*			*Days*			*Days*			*Days*
1899	May 22	Sept. 15	116				Apr. 17	Oct. 3	169				Apr. 11	Sept. 28	170	Apr. 10	Oct. 2	175
1900	May 10	Sept. 19	132				May 10	Oct. 20	163				Apr. 15	Oct. 18	186	Apr. 15	Nov. 14	213
1901	May 4	Sept. 20	139	Mar. 18			Apr. 1	Oct. 25	207		Oct. 25		Apr. 29	Oct. 4	158	Mar. 31	Oct. 26	209
1902	May 29	Sept. 15	109				Apr. 16	Oct. 22	189	Apr. 4	Oct. 22	201	Apr. 16	Oct. 22	189	Apr. 16	Oct. 30	197
1903	May 9	Oct. 25	169				May 2	Oct. 27	178	Apr. 6	Oct. 28	205	May 2	Oct. 19	170	Apr. 6	Oct. 27	204
1904	May 16	Sept. 22	129		Sept. 23		Apr. 23	Oct. 7	167	Apr. 20	Oct. 16	179	Apr. 23	Oct. 4	164	Apr. 23	Oct. 24	184
1905	Apr. 24	Sept. 26	155				Apr. 19	Oct. 22	186	Apr. 19	Oct. 22	186	Apr. 24	Oct. 13	172	Apr. 19	Oct. 22	186
1906	May 11	Oct. 12	154	May 11	Oct. 12	154	May 11	Oct. 12	154	May 11	Oct. 11	153	May 11	Oct. 12	154	May 11	Oct. 12	154
1907	May 28	Oct. 9	134	May 12	Oct. 20	161	May 12	Oct. 15	156	Apr. 21	Oct. 9	171	Apr. 22	Oct. 9	170	Apr. 22	Oct. 22	183
1908	May 3	Sept. 31	150	Apr. 17	Oct. 12	178	Apr. 17	Oct. 13	179	Apr. 5	Nov. 1	210	do	Oct. 13	174	Apr. 17	Oct. 13	179
1909	May 12	Oct. 2	143	Apr. 12	Oct. 20	191	Apr. 12	Oct. 13	184	Apr. 12	Oct. 14	185	May 3	Oct. 17	167	Apr. 12	Oct. 14	185
1910	May 16	Oct. 24	161	May 16	Oct. 29	166	Mar. 19	Oct. 29	224	Mar. 22	Oct. 29	221	Apr. 29	Oct. 29	183	Apr. 14	Oct. 29	198
1911	May 7	Oct. 25	171	Apr. 11	Nov. 3	206	May 3	Nov. 3	184	Apr. 12	Nov. 3	205	May 6	Nov. 2	180	Apr. 18	Nov. 3	199
1912	Apr. 28	Sept. 28	153	Apr. 9	Oct. 28	202	Apr. 9	Oct. 16	190	Apr. 10	Oct. 16	189	Apr. 9	Oct. 17	191	Apr. 9	Nov. 4	209
1913	June 10	Sept. 11	93	May 12	Oct. 22	163	May 12	Oct. 22	163	May 12	Oct. 22	163	May 12	Oct. 22	163	May 12	Oct. 22	163
1914	June 17	Sept. 28	103	Apr. 10	Oct. 28	201	Apr. 10	Oct. 27	200	Apr. 14	Oct. 28	197	Apr. 14	Oct. 28	197	Apr. 14	Oct. 28	197
1915	May 27	Sept. 23	119	Apr. 15	Oct. 11	179	Apr. 5	Oct. 11	189	Apr. 15	Oct. 11	179	Apr. 16	Oct. 11	178	Apr. 5	Oct. 24	202
1916	Apr. 30	Sept. 19	142	Apr. 11	Oct. 2	174	Apr. 10	Oct. 18	191	Apr. 11	do	183	Apr. 11	do	183	Apr. 11	Nov. 4	207
1917	May 26	Sept. 11	108	Apr. 15	Oct. 7	175	Apr. 15	Oct. 7	175	Apr. 15	Oct. 7	175	Apr. 15	Oct. 13	181	Apr. 15	Oct. 13	181
1918	June 24	Sept. 30	98	Apr. 16	Oct. 23	190	Apr. 13	Nov. 2	203	Apr. 6	Oct. 23	200	Apr. 7	Oct. 23	199	Apr. 6	Oct. 23	200
1919	Apr. 26	Sept. 27	154	Apr. 26	Oct. 13	170	Apr. 27	Nov. 3	190	Apr. 27	Nov. 7	194	Apr. 3	Nov. 7	218	Apr. 26	Nov. 10	198
1920	May 16	Oct. 3	140	Apr. 15	Nov. 4	203	Apr. 15	Oct. 30	198	May 6	Oct. 30	177	May 6	Oct. 31	178	May 6	Nov. 13	191
1921	May 17	Oct. 9	145	Apr. 12	Oct. 13	184	Apr. 12	Oct. 13	184	Apr. 12	Oct. 14	185	Apr. 12	Oct. 14	185	Apr. 12	Oct. 14	185
1922	May 1	Aug. 21	112	Apr. 29	Oct. 19	173	Apr. 29	Oct. 19	173	Apr. 29	Oct. 19	173	May 1	Oct. 21	173	Apr. 29	Oct. 21	175
1923	May 25	Sept. 15	113	Apr. 24	Oct. 7	166	Apr. 19	Nov. 1	196	Apr. 17	Oct. 8	174	Apr. 10	Oct. 8	181	Apr. 10	Nov. 1	205
1924	May 31	Sept. 7	99	Apr. 4	Oct. 22	201	Apr. 21	Oct. 22	184	Apr. 21	Oct. 22	184	Apr. 4	Oct. 23	202	Apr. 4	Oct. 22	201
1925	May 27	Oct. 8	134	Apr. 21	Oct. 11	173	do	Oct. 11	173	do	Oct. 11	173	Apr. 22	Oct. 21	182	Apr. 22	Oct. 11	172
1926	May 12	do	149	Apr. 27	Oct. 22	178	Apr. 20	Oct. 26	189	Apr. 20	Oct. 22	185	Apr. 27	Oct. 22	178	Apr. 27	Oct. 22	178
1927	May 28	Sept. 22	117	Apr. 25	Nov. 7	196	Apr. 25	Nov. 7	196	Apr. 25	Nov. 7	196	Apr. 15	Nov. 14	213	Apr. 25	Nov. 7	196
1928	May 14	Sept. 25	134	Apr. 26	Oct. 27	184	Apr. 18	Oct. 27	192	Apr. 18	Oct. 27	192	Apr. 18	Oct. 27	192	Apr. 18	Oct. 27	192
1929	May 23	Sept. 19	119	Mar. 29	Oct. 11	196	Apr. 2	Oct. 11	192	Mar. 29	Oct. 11	196	Apr. 23	Oct. 11	171	Apr. 23	Oct. 11	171
1930	June 1	Oct. 1	122	Apr. 24	Oct. 19	178	Apr. 25	Oct. 19	177	Apr. 26	Oct. 19	176	Apr. 26	Oct. 19	176	Apr. 25	Oct. 19	177
1931	May 4	Sept. 29	148	Apr. 30	Oct. 13	166	Apr. 30	Nov. 7	191	Apr. 30	Nov. 5	189	May 4	do	168	Apr. 30	Nov. 5	189
1932	June 9	Sept. 25	108	Apr. 17	Oct. 14	180	Apr. 18	Oct. 31	196	Apr. 17	Oct. 15	181	Apr. 20	Oct. 31	194	Apr. 17	Oct. 31	197
1933	June 15	Oct. 14	121	Apr. 27	Oct. 26	182	Apr. 27	Oct. 26	182	Apr. 27	Oct. 26	182	Apr. 27	Oct. 26	182	Apr. 27	Oct. 26	182
1934	May 27	Oct. 13	139	Apr. 29	Oct. 13	167	Apr. 28	Oct. 13	168	Apr. 29	Oct. 13	167	Apr. 29	Oct. 15	169	Apr. 29	Oct. 14	168

[1] Number of days between last killing frost in spring and first in fall.

MARYLAND AND DELAWARE—Continued

Dates of last killing frost in spring and first in fall, with length of growing season—Continued

Year	Grantsville, Md.			Frederick, Md.			Fallston, Md.			Cheltenham, Md.			Princess Anne, Md.			Milford, Del.		
	Last in spring	First in fall	Growing season	Last in spring	First in fall	Growing season	Last in spring	First in fall	Growing season	Last in spring	First in fall	Growing season	Last in spring	First in fall	Growing season	Last in spring	First in fall	Growing season
			Days			*Days*			*Days*			*Days*			*Days*			*Days*
1935	May 26	Sept. 30	127	Apr. 16	Oct. 5	172	Apr. 16	Oct. 5	172	Apr. 16	Oct. 5	172	Mar. 27	Oct. 8	195	Apr. 17	Oct. 8	174
1936	May 29	Oct. 25	149	Apr. 25	Oct. 27	185	Apr. 25	Oct. 27	185	Apr. 23	Oct. 27	187	May 15	Oct. 27	165	Apr. 25	Oct. 27	185
1937	May 11	Sept. 18	130	Apr. 17	Oct. 15	181	Apr. 13	Oct. 15	185	Apr. 12	Oct. 15	186	Apr. 13	Oct. 9	179	Apr. 11	Oct. 15	187
1938	May 25	Oct. 2	130	Apr. 24	Oct. 8	167	Apr. 11	Nov. 16	219	Apr. 24	Oct. 8	167	Apr. 11	Nov. 1	204	Apr. 24	Nov. 1	191
Mean	May 20	Sept. 29	132	Apr. 21	Oct. 17	179	Apr. 20	Oct. 22	185	Apr. 18	Oct. 20	185	Apr. 21	Oct. 19	181	Apr. 19	Oct. 25	189
Extremes	Apr. 24[2]	Aug. 21[4]	[6] 93	Mar. 18[2]	Sept. 23[4]	[6] 154	Mar. 19[2]	Oct. 3[4]	[6] 154	Mar. 22[2]	Oct. 5[4]	[6] 153	Mar. 27[2]	Sept. 28[4]	[6] 154	Mar. 31[2]	Oct. 2[4]	[6] 154
	June 24[3]	Oct. 25[5]	[7] 171	May 16[3]	Nov. 7[5]	[7] 208	May 12[3]	Nov. 7[5]	[7] 224	May 12[3]	Nov. 7[5]	[7] 221	May 15[3]	Nov. 14[5]	[7] 218	May 12[3]	Nov. 14[5]	[7] 213

[2] Earliest date in spring.
[3] Latest date in spring.
[3] Earliest date in fall.
[5] Latest date in fall.
[6] Shortest growing season.
[7] Longest growing season.

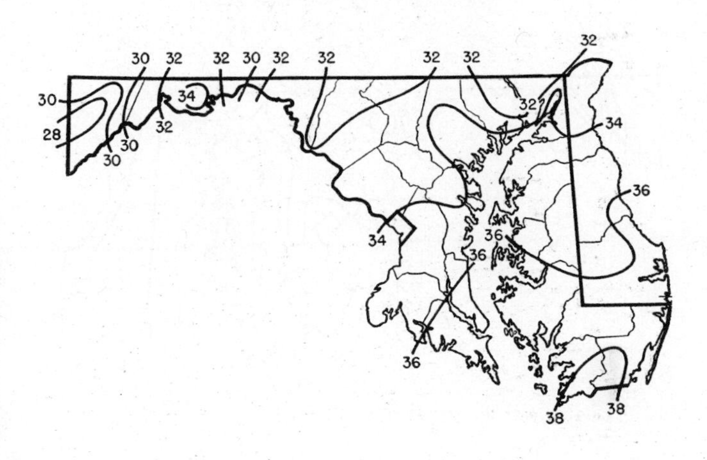
MARYLAND AND DELAWARE
AVERAGE JANUARY TEMPERATURE
28
30
32
34
36
38

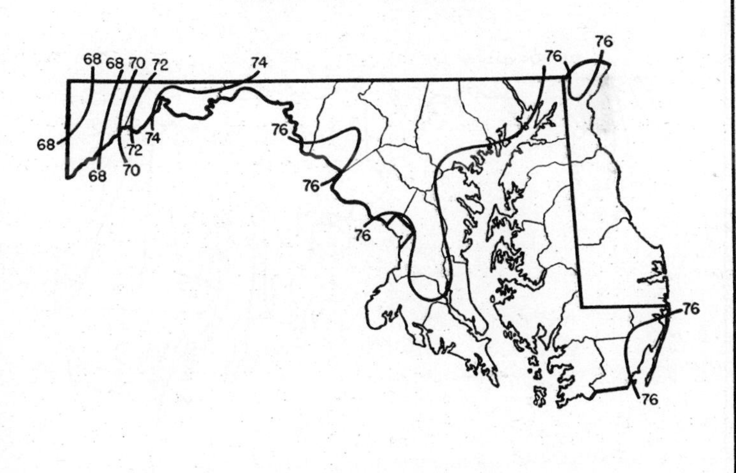
MARYLAND AND DELAWARE
AVERAGE JULY TEMPERATURE
68
70
72
74
76

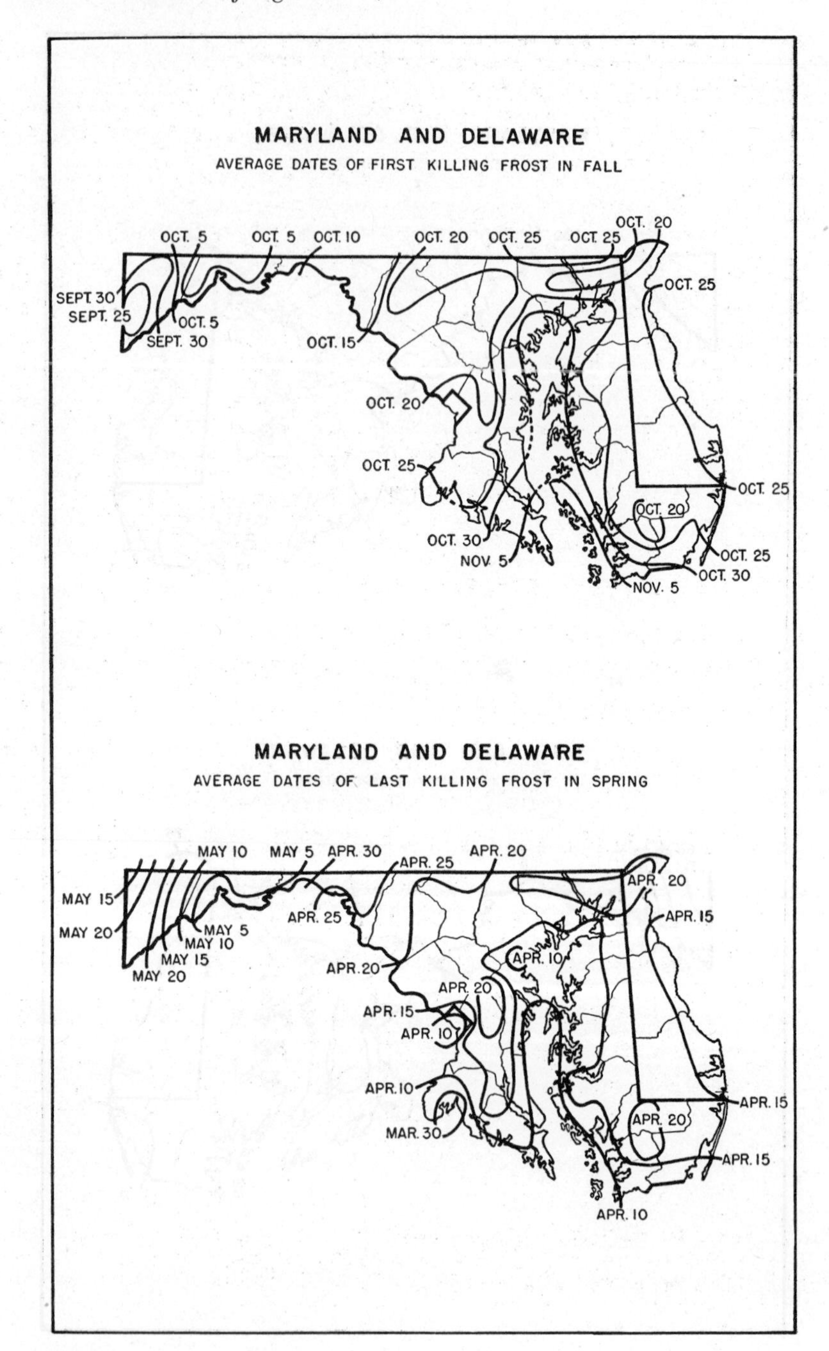
MARYLAND AND DELAWARE
AVERAGE DATES OF FIRST KILLING FROST IN FALL
OCT. 5
OCT. 5
OCT. 10
OCT. 20
OCT. 25
OCT. 25
OCT. 20
OCT. 25
SEPT. 30
SEPT. 25
OCT. 5
SEPT. 30
OCT. 15
OCT. 20
OCT. 25
OCT. 25
OCT. 20
OCT. 30
NOV. 5
OCT. 25
OCT. 30
NOV. 5
MARYLAND AND DELAWARE
AVERAGE DATES OF LAST KILLING FROST IN SPRING
MAY 10
MAY 5
APR. 30
APR. 25
APR. 20
APR. 20
APR. 15
MAY 15
MAY 20
APR. 25
MAY 5
MAY 10
MAY 15
MAY 20
APR. 10
APR. 20
APR. 20
APR. 15
APR. 10
APR. 10
MAR. 30
APR. 15
APR. 20
APR. 15
APR. 10

MARYLAND AND DELAWARE

AVERAGE NUMBER OF DAYS WITHOUT KILLING FROST

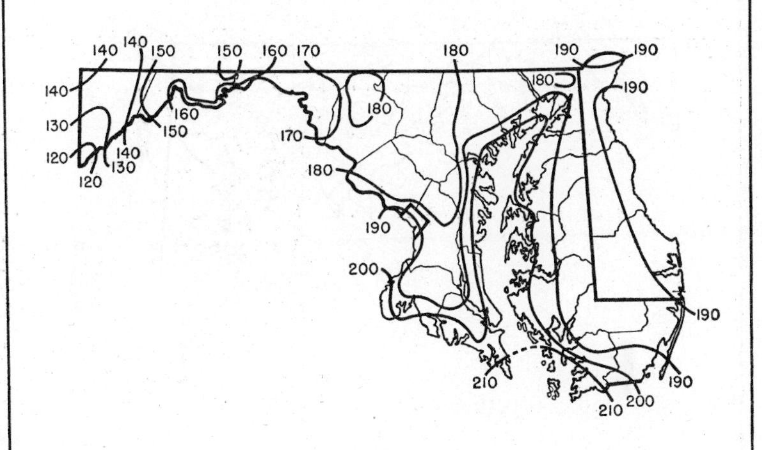

MARYLAND AND DELAWARE

AVERAGE WARM-SEASON PRECIPITATION (INCHES
(APRIL TO SEPTEMBER, INCLUSIVE)

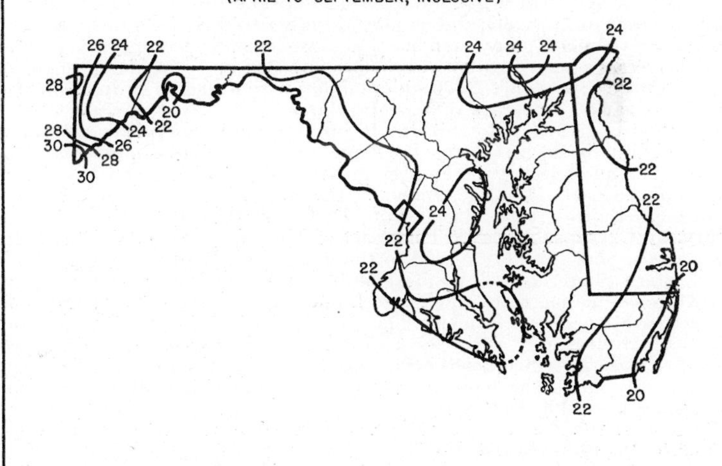

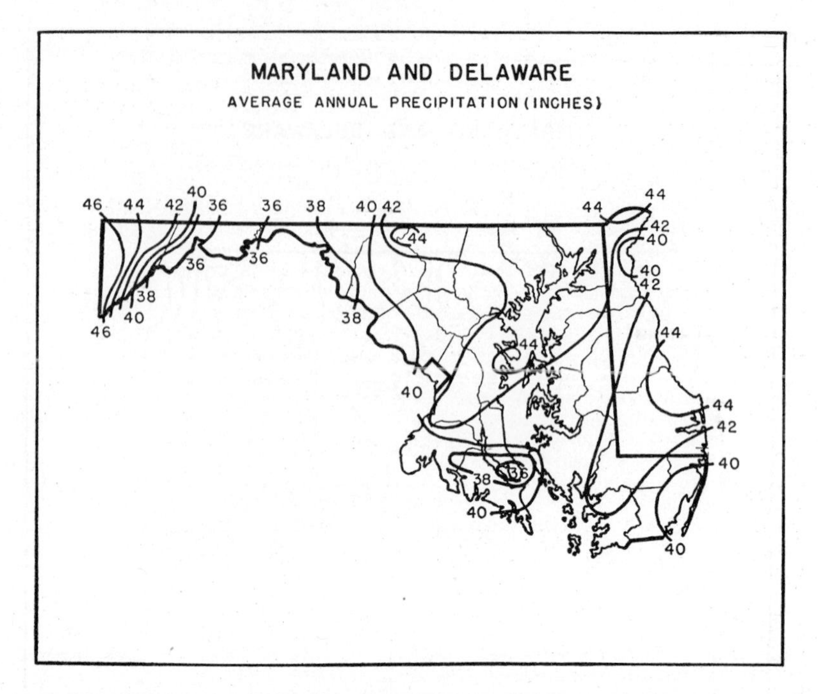

SUPPLEMENTARY CLIMATIC NOTES FOR MARYLAND AND DELAWARE

The Maryland-Delaware section contains within its borders a varied assortment of land and water areas of quite unusual nature. Maryland has a gross area of 12,327 square miles, of which approximately 9,891 are land and the remainder water, a good deal of which is tidewater. Chesapeake Bay comprises 1,203 square miles, Chincoteague Bay, 93, and smaller estuaries and rivers, 1,054. In the tidewater reaches there are many marshes that afford a haven for migrating wild fowl, while the rivers, bays, and estuaries abound with fish and contain excellent oyster beds. Delaware covers only 2,370 square miles, with a smaller proportion of water area and less varied topography than Maryland.

The section is divided into three main physiographic provinces, each of which has several subdivisions. The Coastal Plain province includes more than half the land, including all of Delaware, and the greater part of the water. It lies between the ocean on the east and a line, known as the fall line, running from Wilmington, Del., through Baltimore to Washington, D. C., on the west. It is divided into two parts by Chesapeake Bay. That part of Maryland east of the bay is known as the Eastern Shore while the land to the west is the Western Shore.

The Eastern Shore, as well as most of Delaware, consists of flat, low, and almost featureless plains, while the Western Shore is a rolling upland, reaching four times the elevation of the former. There is a wide variety of soil types, and the differences in topography affect local characteristics of climate. To the west of the Coastal Plain province lies the Piedmont Plateau, a hill country between the fall line already mentioned and the foot of the Appalachian Mountains. Its elevation ranges from 400 feet or less at the fall line to around 1,100 feet at Parrs Ridge. West of the Piedmont Plateau is the Appalachian province, which is subdivided into the Blue Ridge, the Great Valley, the Allegheny Ridges, and the Allegheny Plateau. This mountain region of Maryland contains Backbone Mountain with an elevation of 3,340 feet. The mountain ridges trend from northeast to southwest.

On the Eastern Shore and in southwest Delaware the drainage is southwestward into Chesapeake Bay. In northern and eastern Delaware it is eastward into Delaware Bay and the Atlantic Ocean. From Chesapeake Bay to Parrs Ridge it is southeastward or southward into Chesapeake Bay and the Potomac River. West of Parrs Ridge the drainage is south or southwest to the Potomac River, except in the extreme west, where the Youghiogheny River flows northward toward the Monongahela. West of the fall line the streams are mostly turbulent, while to the east they are quiet, with their courses largely dominated by the tides.

The varied physiographic features have a marked effect on the weather and climate of the different parts of these States. In the Coastal Plain province, including Delaware, the winters tend to mildness and the summers are characterized by high humidity coupled with heat, which is, however, not excessive. In the mountain sections the winters are more severe, though not unduly so, and zero temperatures are not a rarity. Precipitation is well distributed in all seasons and prolonged droughts are unusual. Sunshine is abundant and severe storms are infrequent. Chesapeake Bay is free from ice except in severe winters and is therefore navigable, as a rule, throughout the year. There is almost complete freedom from tornadoes, and summer thunderstorms are not usually attended by gales.

In Maryland the average annual temperature ranges from 58° F. in the extreme southern part, on Chesapeake Bay, to 47° in southwest Garrett County, near the West Virginia border. In Delaware it ranges from 56° near the southern part of Delaware Bay to 53° in the higher land of the extreme northwest.

The extremes of temperature are affected by local characteristics of soil and topography, including adjacent water areas and mountains, and by latitude. The extremes of cold occur with quiet air, clear sky, and the ground covered with snow, while those of heat are related to dry weather. In Maryland temperatures of 100° F. or a little higher occur in some part of the State every year, the record high being 109° in 1898. In Delaware such days are not quite so frequent, but the record is 110° in 1930. Temperatures below zero occur in some parts of Maryland every year, being rather common in the mountain sections but unusual in tidewater districts.

The average date of the last killing frost in spring ranges in Maryland from the first week in May, west of Parrs Ridge, to the last 10 days of April, east of the Ridge. The average time of first killing frost in fall varies from September 27 at Oakland, in the extreme southwestern corner of the State, to November 7 at Solomons, and the same date at Crisfield, on the extreme southern tidewater. Similarly, the growing season varies from 124 days at Oakland to 213 at Solomons and 212 at Crisfield. In Delaware the last killing frost in spring occurs, on an average, between April 17 and 20 and the first in fall from October 17 to 25. The average length of the growing season is between 180 and 194 days.

Precipitation is well distributed throughout the year, with a somewhat greater amount falling in the warm, or growing, season than in the cold season. While different years show much variation, especially locally, droughts and excessively wet periods are uncommon. Excessive rain is most common in the Coastal Plain province.

The proportion of snow to rain in the cold season is, of course, greatest in the mountains of Maryland and least in Delaware and the southern parts of the Eastern Shore. At rare intervals, as in 1939–40, there may be heavy falls of snow in Delaware and the Eastern Shore as well as in other parts of the section. Snow is uncommon in the extreme southern tidewater districts.

Small tornadoes and waterspouts, doing little damage, occur at rare intervals in the section between Parrs Ridge and Delaware and in the southern part of the Eastern Shore. Thundersqualls bring the most frequent high winds and are local in character. Tropical hurricanes or their remnants sometimes cross Chesapeake Bay or sweep the Atlantic coast and are attended by heavy rain, but they do not have winds of hurricane velocity except at or off the Atlantic coast. There are also northeasters and sweeps of northwest winds occasionally in winter.

The prevailing direction of the wind at Baltimore is from the southwest, with an average annual velocity of 7.7 miles an hour. At Washington, D. C., the prevailing direction is from the northwest in winter and from the south in summer, and the average annual hourly velocity is 7.3 miles. The highest recorded velocity at both Baltimore and Washington for a 5-minute period is 54 miles an hour from the west in July 1902.

A feature of the coastal area is the ocean breeze of summer; in lands bordering Chesapeake Bay it is the "bay breeze."

John R. Weeks, *Meteorologist and Climatic Section Director for Maryland and Delaware, Weather Bureau, Baltimore.*

MICHIGAN

Climatic summary

County[1]	Station	Temperature					Killing frost average dates				Average precipitation													
		Length of record	January average	July average	Maximum	Minimum	Length of record	Last in spring	First in fall	Growing season[2]	Length of record	January	February	March	April	May	June	July	August	September	October	November	December	Annual
		Yr.	*°F.*	*°F.*	*°F.*	*°F.*	*Yr.*			*Days*	*Yr.*	*In.*	*In.*	*In.*	*In.*	*In.*	*In.*	*In.*	*In.*	*In.*	*In.*	*In.*	*In.*	*In.*
Alcona	Harrisville	40	21.2	67.0	107	−28	40	May 19	Oct. 4	138	39	1.81	1.87	2.38	2.44	3.30	2.66	2.76	2.66	2.76	2.63	2.34	2.11	29.72
Alger	Chatham	36	15.1	64.2	103	−46	37	June 10	Sept. 11	93	37	2.18	1.71	1.59	1.98	2.80	3.25	3.56	3.01	4.14	3.29	2.99	2.22	32.72
	Grand Marais	38	18.0	61.9	99	−32	36	May 17	Oct. 18	154	38	2.64	1.79	1.79	1.87	2.33	2.56	2.58	2.17	3.14	2.65	2.55	2.53	28.60
	Munising	28	16.3	63.7	103	−40	28	June 13	Sept. 16	95	40	2.48	1.79	1.87	2.21	2.72	2.73	3.35	2.67	3.86	3.11	3.25	2.57	32.61
Allegan	Allegan	38	24.8	72.7	106	−35	38	May 8	Oct. 9	154	40	2.11	1.86	2.43	2.83	3.78	3.44	2.75	2.84	3.68	3.03	2.70	2.58	34.03
	Ganges	34	24.6	71.0	104	−20	34	May 7	Oct. 19	165	35	1.93	1.58	2.20	3.01	3.66	3.07	2.42	2.83	3.97	3.68	2.81	2.39	33.55
	Plainwell Dam										23	2.17	1.76	2.57	2.94	3.47	3.72	2.36	3.00	4.24	3.13	2.76	2.57	34.69
Alpena	Alpena	40	20.1	66.7	104	−28	40	May 10	Oct. 7	150	40	1.48	1.38	1.97	2.17	2.69	2.86	2.56	2.53	2.77	2.38	2.27	1.69	26.75
Antrim	Mancelona	25	18.0	67.7	104	−43	25	June 1	Sept. 17	108	26	1.96	1.61	1.50	1.81	2.41	2.41	2.59	2.23	3.09	2.91	2.84	2.47	27.83
Arenac	Omer	23	19.2	68.0	103	−40	24	May 23	do	117	26	1.35	1.56	2.16	2.02	2.74	2.28	2.78	2.31	2.17	2.30	1.95	1.65	25.27
Baraga	Baraga	10	13.6	66.3	103	−36	12	May 31	Sept. 4	96	10	1.19	1.07	1.20	1.33	2.45	2.69	1.98	2.45	2.50	2.23	1.32	1.42	21.83
Barry	Hastings	30	23.6	72.0	109	−31	31	May 12	Sept. 30	141	32	1.68	1.86	2.39	2.54	3.59	3.18	3.27	2.72	3.47	2.74	2.47	2.16	32.07
Bay	Bay City	38	22.7	71.9	110	−31	40	May 10	Oct. 8	151	40	1.50	1.74	2.10	2.42	3.48	2.87	2.89	3.31	2.90	2.63	2.24	1.92	30.00
Benzie	Benzonia	31	20.7	67.8	101	−29	30	May 16	Oct. 7	144	32	2.46	2.19	2.62	2.49	3.27	2.77	2.75	2.67	3.54	3.48	3.15	2.72	34.11
	Frankfort	36	22.6	66.1	99	−32	37	May 19	Oct. 13	147	37	2.09	1.78	1.66	2.03	2.89	2.72	2.52	2.55	3.36	2.99	2.58	2.18	29.35
Berrien	St. Joseph	38	26.4	72.5	104	−21	38	Apr. 24	Oct. 25	184	40	2.66	2.01	2.23	2.68	3.60	2.89	2.47	2.77	3.67	2.71	2.41	2.66	32.76
Branch	Coldwater	40	25.0	73.3	108	−22	40	May 8	Oct. 8	153	40	1.84	1.57	2.31	2.85	3.87	3.80	3.14	3.23	3.50	2.59	2.39	2.11	33.20
Calhoun	Albion										24	1.69	1.40	2.25	2.79	3.60	3.43	2.34	2.77	3.91	2.39	2.41	2.05	31.03
	Battle Creek	40	24.0	72.8	104	−24	40	May 5	Oct. 10	158	40	1.94	1.70	2.44	2.94	3.75	3.59	2.75	3.03	3.60	2.72	2.55	2.13	33.14
	Ceresco										23	1.66	1.29	2.04	2.99	3.32	3.71	2.04	2.59	3.72	2.71	2.37	1.97	30.41
Cass	Cassopolis	36	24.2	73.6	107	−23	36	May 6	Oct. 15	162	37	2.30	1.52	2.85	3.34	3.90	3.58	3.03	2.79	3.60	2.85	2.72	2.29	34.77
Charlevoix	Charlevoix	22	21.7	68.2	99	−33	26	May 13	Oct. 17	157	39	1.92	1.59	1.98	2.05	2.74	2.46	2.65	2.46	3.11	2.76	2.70	2.05	28.47
	St. James	21	19.0	66.9	97	−28	22	May 14	Oct. 15	154	22	1.62	1.51	1.56	1.79	2.22	2.55	2.24	2.09	2.55	2.66	2.23	1.70	24.72
Cheboygan	Cheboygan	37	19.1	68.0	103	−38	39	May 18	Oct. 3	138	39	1.61	1.40	1.77	1.98	2.81	2.66	2.56	2.87	3.25	2.88	2.38	1.68	27.85
	Mackinaw City	38	19.1	66.8	104	−31	40	May 16	Oct. 11	148	40	1.78	1.40	1.59	1.81	2.70	2.65	2.69	2.76	3.36	2.86	2.22	1.76	27.58
	Wolverine	10	19.2	65.1	104	−43	10	June 11	Sept. 18	99	11	2.24	1.26	1.79	2.03	3.06	2.89	2.29	2.67	4.99	3.41	2.75	1.92	31.30
Chippewa	Sault Ste. Marie	40	14.2	64.1	98	−37	40	May 14	Oct. 3	142	40	1.78	1.30	1.72	2.07	2.44	2.68	2.73	2.62	3.52	3.03	2.84	2.12	28.85
	Whitefish Point	35	17.6	59.4	100	−30	39	May 20	Oct. 15	148	38	2.81	1.92	2.18	2.11	2.81	2.70	2.63	2.41	3.61	3.30	3.32	3.08	32.88
Clare	Harrison	23	19.8	69.1	103	−36	24	May 13	Oct. 3	143	21	1.15	1.40	1.96	2.26	2.84	2.49	2.78	2.90	2.44	2.27	2.29	1.67	26.45
Crawford	Grayling (near)	37	17.5	67.9	106	−41	40	May 27	Sept. 19	115	39	1.56	1.52	1.70	2.36	3.37	2.89	3.41	2.90	3.43	3.16	2.73	1.70	30.73
	Roscommon	36	17.1	66.6	106	−39	35	June 10	Sept. 14	96	36	1.46	1.47	1.82	2.44	2.79	2.59	2.68	2.90	3.21	2.65	2.29	1.62	27.92
Delta	Escanaba	40	16.3	66.1	100	−32	40	May 12	Oct. 5	146	40	1.41	1.43	1.89	2.26	2.54	2.71	3.55	2.89	3.04	2.26	2.04	1.53	27.55
	Maple Ridge	20	14.1	65.4	100	−33	20	June 2	Sept. 14	104	23	1.36	1.44	1.97	2.66	2.80	3.68	4.00	3.51	3.48	2.95	2.70	1.91	32.46
	Sack Bay	18	18.4	65.7	96	−28	18	May 18	Oct. 8	143	18	2.03	2.15	2.41	2.73	2.59	3.00	3.22	2.83	4.03	2.61	2.64	2.06	32.30
Dickinson	Iron Mountain	37	14.8	68.2	104	−39	39	May 22	Sept. 24	125	38	1.01	1.14	1.44	2.33	2.91	3.45	3.83	3.27	3.13	2.25	1.79	1.29	27.84

Eaton	Charlotte	36	23.1	71.5	106	−31	36	May 14	Oct. 4	143	33	1.67	1.30	1.89	2.59	3.34	3.36	2.31	2.59	3.24	2.29	2.08	1.79	28.45
	Grand Ledge										9		1.92	2.08	2.73	3.84								
	Olivet	20	22.9	71.0	102	−23	20	May 5	Oct. 5	153	20	2.05	1.69	2.62	2.87	4.27	3.95	3.62	3.38	3.42	2.87	2.38	1.90	35.02
Emmett	Petoskey	37	20.7	67.2	101	−35	38	May 16	Oct. 8	145	40	1.86	1.40	1.77	1.80	2.62	2.72	2.55	2.49	3.48	2.91	2.67	2.07	28.34
Genessee	Flint	39	22.9	71.8	108	−28	40	May 8	do	153	40	1.48	1.49	2.03	2.58	3.54	2.81	3.13	2.72	3.13	2.48	2.17	1.69	29.25
Gladwin	Gladwin (near)	24	20.1	69.7	105	−39	20	May 13	Sept. 23	133	22	1.44	1.37	1.88	2.32	3.59	2.21	2.78	2.61	3.47	2.90	1.99	1.68	28.24
Gogebic	Ironwood	36	12.2	67.2	104	−37	37	May 22	Sept. 24	125	37	1.93	1.78	2.37	2.44	2.89	3.70	4.10	3.23	3.61	2.78	2.72	2.37	33.92
Grand Traverse	Fife Lake (near)	20	19.0	68.2	107	−45	20	June 8	Sept. 13	97	20	1.71	1.32	2.04	2.37	2.85	2.80	2.71	2.88	3.66	3.17	2.88	1.84	30.23
	Old Mission	32	20.6	68.7	103	−23	32	May 13	Oct. 19	159	32	1.72	1.41	1.99	2.30	3.10	2.77	2.87	2.93	3.24	2.92	2.71	1.76	29.72
	Traverse City	39	22.3	70.1	105	−33	36	May 15	Oct. 11	149	40	1.78	1.59	1.74	1.99	2.71	2.10	2.81	2.59	2.88	2.85	2.65	1.78	27.47
Gratiot	Alma	40	22.1	71.0	108	−29	40	May 11	Oct. 3	145	40	1.78	1.93	2.29	2.61	3.57	2.92	2.97	2.85	3.15	2.74	2.22	1.96	30.99
Hillsdale	Hillsdale	40	23.7	72.2	107	−21	40	May 10	Oct. 6	149	40	2.12	1.91	2.70	3.08	3.72	3.63	2.91	3.04	3.38	2.77	2.75	2.33	34.34
Houghton	Calumet	40	14.4	64.7	101	−26	40	May 18	Oct. 5	140	40	2.95	1.70	1.64	2.01	3.00	3.18	3.16	3.07	3.99	3.00	2.74	3.13	33.57
	Houghton	38	15.2	65.5	104	−31	38	May 12	Oct. 10	151	23	1.34	1.21	1.99	2.53	2.74	2.77	2.38	2.73	2.92	2.97	2.37	1.45	27.40
	Sidnaw	26	12.9	65.9	104	−46	26	June 13	Sept. 1	80	27	1.26	1.30	1.46	1.68	2.56	3.64	3.61	3.26	4.26	2.60	2.01	1.33	28.97
Huron	Harbor Beach (near)	38	22.6	68.5	105	−24	40	May 10	Oct. 10	153	40	1.67	1.56	1.58	2.17	2.96	2.67	2.53	2.47	2.59	2.42	1.95	1.55	26.12
	Port Austin	27	21.5	69.0	109	−25	23	May 14	Oct. 7	146	21	1.44	1.60	1.65	1.89	3.09	3.13	2.36	2.16	2.55	2.34	2.15	1.49	25.85
Ingham	Lansing	40	22.9	71.1	102	−26	40	May 5	Oct. 10	158	40	1.78	1.77	2.43	2.77	3.44	3.28	2.67	2.65	3.03	2.39	2.28	2.03	30.52
Ionia	Saranac	32	23.3	71.8	110	−30	32	May 18	Oct. 1	136	36	1.72	1.74	2.03	2.72	3.62	2.90	2.59	3.05	3.57	2.80	2.41	1.97	31.12
	Webber Dam	26	23.1	72.4	105	−35	25	May 7	Oct. 11	157	25	1.40	1.35	1.88	2.48	3.36	2.93	2.07	2.39	3.07	2.25	1.91	1.66	26.75
Iosco	East Tawas	40	20.8	68.3	106	−29	39	May 21	Sept. 30	132	40	1.52	1.64	2.14	2.42	3.00	2.75	3.00	2.64	2.68	2.52	2.15	1.72	28.18
	Five Channels Dam	26	19.7	68.1	107	−38	26	May 25	Sept. 29	127	26	1.55	1.57	2.06	2.53	2.74	2.88	2.32	2.56	2.77	2.63	2.18	1.78	27.57
Iron	Stambaugh	37	11.2	65.8	103	−47	39	June 7	Sept. 9	94	40	1.28	1.42	1.87	2.75	3.37	4.03	4.03	3.67	4.00	2.69	3.03	1.46	33.60
Isabella	Mt. Pleasant	32	21.3	71.0	106	−30	33	May 19	Oct. 2	136	36	1.58	1.55	2.09	2.12	3.06	2.34	2.70	2.29	2.71	2.29	1.89	1.70	26.32
Jackson	Jackson	40	24.7	73.4	105	−24	39	May 6	Oct. 8	155	40	1.81	1.65	2.16	2.71	3.66	3.52	2.85	2.61	3.27	2.50	2.25	1.98	30.97
Kalamazoo	Kalamazoo	38	24.2	73.0	109	−25	39	May 9	Oct. 9	153	40	2.04	1.96	2.39	2.81	3.87	3.43	2.85	2.85	3.52	2.92	2.85	2.72	34.21
Kalkaska	Ivan	22	17.6	67.8	106	−35	24	May 23	Sept. 25	125	23	1.49	1.23	1.94	2.20	2.94	2.60	3.07	3.19	3.30	2.87	2.40	1.95	29.18
Kent	Grand Rapids	40	24.7	73.0	108	−24	40	May 1	Oct. 17	169	40	1.91	1.82	2.38	2.84	3.59	3.18	2.86	2.62	3.67	2.86	2.44	2.17	32.34
	Kent City										16	2.04	2.02	1.52	2.43	3.16	2.84	2.35	2.32	3.42	2.99	3.18	2.12	30.39
	Lowell										23	1.72	1.73	2.34	2.72	3.63	3.05	2.49	2.57	3.85	2.96	2.34	2.28	31.68
Keweenaw	Eagle Harbor	24	16.8	61.7	100	−26	29	May 20	Oct. 14	147	29	1.73	1.67	1.86	2.03	2.66	2.92	2.99	2.79	3.23	2.35	2.56	2.32	29.11
Lake	Luther	27	20.3	68.9	111	−36	26	May 29	Sept. 21	115	27	1.57	1.67	2.20	2.58	3.23	2.97	2.88	3.22	3.92	3.44	2.87	1.86	32.41
Lapeer	Lapeer	36	22.9	72.2	105	−26	36	May 10	Oct. 11	154	36	1.66	1.55	2.02	2.52	3.39	3.11	2.79	2.75	2.93	2.35	2.31	1.92	29.30
	Thornville	15	23.3	70.4	97	−22	15	May 6	Oct. 5	152	16	2.28	2.11	2.08	2.54	4.10	3.54	3.61	3.99	3.14	3.14	2.46	2.32	35.31
Lenawee	Adrian	39	25.3	73.8	108	−26	38	do	Oct. 12	159	40	1.86	1.63	2.39	2.78	3.46	3.38	2.85	2.94	3.18	2.18	2.23	2.20	31.08
	Morenci	30	25.5	73.5	109	−28	32	May 9	Oct. 5	149	32	2.12	1.78	2.77	3.05	3.54	3.53	2.86	2.89	3.46	2.44	2.22	2.30	32.96
Livingston	Howell	25	21.8	71.4	106	−24	27	do	Oct. 7	151	29	1.57	1.48	2.15	2.69	3.14	2.87	2.75	2.64	2.79	2.61	2.13	1.76	28.58
Luce	Deer Park (near)	36	17.6	63.1	104	−38	37	June 3	Sept. 21	110	39	2.66	2.06	2.01	1.83	2.84	2.81	2.71	2.28	3.55	2.89	2.98	3.17	31.79
	Newberry	35	15.6	65.6	103	−32	36	May 31	Sept. 22	114	35	1.80	1.46	1.91	1.73	2.43	2.80	2.89	2.64	3.32	2.66	2.48	1.70	27.82
Macomb	Armada	24	21.7	70.0	105	−23	24	May 14	Oct. 5	144	24	1.84	1.73	2.33	2.71	3.19	3.06	3.20	3.71	2.99	2.54	2.05	1.91	31.26
	Mt. Clemens	36	24.4	71.6	106	−24	36	May 7	Oct. 12	158	37	1.73	1.70	1.96	2.34	2.96	2.84	2.99	2.48	2.87	2.11	2.04	1.95	27.97
Mackinac	Mackinac Island	36	18.3	65.4	99	−27	37	May 18	Oct. 9	144	36	1.90	1.43	2.17	2.32	2.88	3.11	2.81	2.83	3.76	3.17	2.35	1.86	30.59
	St. Ignace	34	18.8	66.5	99	−35	34	May 16	Oct. 4	141	34	1.42	1.12	1.60	1.80	2.33	2.38	2.64	2.54	2.99	2.62	1.95	1.59	24.98
Manistee	Manistee	36	23.4	68.9	99	−29	34	May 12	Oct. 14	155	33	1.75	1.87	1.97	2.16	2.96	2.93	3.03	2.77	3.14	2.91	2.50	2.06	30.05
	Wellston (near)										17	2.10	2.01	2.12	2.51	3.14	2.98	2.62	2.94	3.85	3.37	2.86	2.29	32.79
Marquette	Humboldt	30	10.1	63.2	102	−49	31	June 19	Aug. 18	60	30	1.29	1.00	1.53	1.93	2.49	2.95	3.63	2.92	3.69	2.52	1.89	1.33	27.17
	Ishpeming	38	13.7	65.4	102	−32	39	June 1	Sept. 16	107	40	1.62	1.50	1.87	2.30	2.80	3.10	3.92	3.05	3.88	2.89	2.45	1.52	30.90
	Marquette	40	17.4	65.3	108	−27	40	May 9	Oct. 14	158	40	2.33	1.70	2.18	2.50	2.80	3.19	3.23	2.61	3.36	2.57	2.88	2.38	31.73

[1] The following counties, for which no records are available, are best represented by the stations indicated: Clinton—Lansing; Leelanau—Old Mission.

[2] Length of growing season between average dates of last killing frost in spring and first in fall.

MICHIGAN—Continued

Climatic summary—Continued

County	Station	Temperature: Length of record	Temperature: January average	Temperature: July average	Temperature: Maximum	Temperature: Minimum	Killing frost average dates: Length of record	Killing frost: Last in spring	Killing frost: First in fall	Growing season	Average precipitation: Length of record	January	February	March	April	May	June	July	August	September	October	November	December	Annual
		Yr.	*°F.*	*°F.*	*°F.*	*°F.*	*Yr.*			*Days*	*Yr.*	*In.*	*In.*	*In.*	*In.*	*In.*	*In.*	*In.*	*In.*	*In.*	*In.*	*In.*	*In.*	*In.*
Mason	Ludington	38	24.1	67.5	97	−21	39	May 10	Oct. 18	161	38	1.81	1.79	2.12	2.37	2.88	2.74	2.50	2.55	3.11	2.80	2.30	1.97	28.94
	Scottville										14	2.53	1.91	1.95	2.78	3.19	2.50	1.68	2.61	3.36	3.19	2.78	2.05	30.53
Mecosta	Big Rapids	40	21.3	69.2	103	−36	40	May 15	Oct. 1	139	40	1.84	1.86	2.36	2.73	3.27	3.08	3.05	2.56	3.18	3.16	2.47	2.00	31.56
	Stanwood										12	2.10	1.76	1.82	2.77	3.25	3.14	1.68	2.65	3.43	3.33	2.97	1.86	30.76
Menominee	Menominee	28	17.2	68.8	102	−27	26	May 11	Oct. 8	150	27	1.13	1.28	1.71	2.48	2.89	3.18	3.56	2.82	2.93	2.16	1.64	1.17	26.95
	Powers	20	12.4	65.9	101	−39	20	June 5	Sept. 14	101	5	1.58	1.52	1.66	2.00	1.93	1.69	3.83	3.13	2.89	1.70	1.92	1.50	25.35
Midland	Midland	33	23.3	71.9	106	−30	32	May 10	Oct. 2	145	36	1.33	1.44	1.76	2.10	3.17	2.44	2.36	2.74	2.65	2.28	1.92	1.48	25.67
Missaukee	Lake City	16	19.4	69.7	106	−41	17	May 26	Sept. 26	123	17	1.47	1.65	1.50	1.96	2.52	2.65	2.30	2.25	2.94	2.33	1.79	1.29	24.65
Monroe	Grape	17	25.1	72.6	100	−22	17	May 6	Oct. 11	158	18	2.06	1.69	2.26	2.45	3.62	3.14	3.31	3.08	2.71	2.15	1.98	2.01	30.46
	Monroe	22	26.4	73.9	106	−21	22	May 7	Oct. 13	159	22	1.88	1.43	2.46	3.17	2.72	3.24	2.68	2.76	3.44	2.10	2.15	2.06	30.09
Montcalm	Greenville	25	23.9	72.4	108	−26	23	May 9	Oct. 9	153	25	1.47	1.51	1.93	2.47	3.36	3.30	2.54	3.00	3.44	2.71	2.19	1.83	29.75
	Howard City	18	21.9	69.3	103	−35	19	May 26	Sept. 24	121	19	1.40	1.40	2.50	2.70	3.25	3.23	2.15	2.24	3.21	3.27	2.21	1.78	29.34
Montmorency	Atlanta	12	19.4	67.1	104	−46	12	May 29	Sept. 21	115	13	1.44	1.16	1.66	2.06	2.87	3.14	2.21	2.24	3.80	2.92	2.04	1.24	26.78
Muskegon	Muskegon (near)	39	24.8	69.5	99	−30	40	May 2	Oct. 19	170	40	2.03	1.87	2.20	2.15	2.93	2.77	2.39	2.32	3.26	2.72	2.44	2.00	29.08
Newaygo	Croton Dam	31	22.2	70.7	111	−37	31	May 15	Oct. 4	142	31	1.80	1.66	2.10	3.00	3.26	2.96	2.79	2.46	3.29	3.14	2.59	1.99	31.04
Oakland	Pontiac	32	23.1	72.1	104	−22	32	May 11	Oct. 9	151	32	1.77	1.87	1.91	2.84	3.09	2.71	2.73	2.67	2.87	2.28	2.06	1.93	28.73
Oceana	Hart	36	22.9	70.7	104	−35	35	May 16	Oct. 6	143	36	1.96	1.73	1.81	2.25	3.40	2.68	2.62	2.46	3.33	2.97	2.57	1.96	29.74
Ogemaw	West Branch (near)	30	18.3	67.7	107	−36	33	June 1	Sept. 19	110	33	1.34	1.43	1.90	2.11	2.48	2.87	2.64	2.80	2.93	2.84	2.08	1.61	27.03
Ontonagon	Bergland	14	11.0	65.6	101	−48	15	June 14	Sept. 6	84	14	1.72	1.57	1.98	2.09	3.02	3.71	3.74	3.42	3.42	2.75	2.04	2.22	31.68
	Ewen	24	10.3	64.2	101	−49	26	June 9	Aug. 30	82	20	2.01	1.93	2.46	2.19	2.73	3.24	3.20	2.75	3.23	2.06	2.84	2.64	31.28
Osceola	Reed City	19	18.7	69.2	102	−42	18	May 21	Sept. 23	125	20	1.70	1.23	2.07	2.14	3.20	2.84	3.81	2.80	2.84	3.11	2.48	1.51	29.73
Oscoda	Mio	28	17.9	66.8	112	−47	28	June 6	Sept. 11	97	27	1.31	1.47	1.90	2.13	2.78	2.77	3.06	2.79	2.91	2.56	1.99	1.56	27.23
Otsego	Gaylord	23	16.3	66.2	101	−39	22	May 28	Sept. 19	114	19	1.50	1.78	1.55	1.81	3.02	2.31	3.04	3.15	3.29	2.68	2.93	1.87	28.93
	Vanderbilt (near)	16	18.1	66.0	108	−51	16	June 14	Aug. 30	77	26	1.36	1.22	1.74	2.22	2.70	3.05	2.84	2.73	3.47	2.96	2.25	1.61	28.15
Ottawa	Grand Haven	40	24.7	69.2	101	−25	40	May 1	Oct. 19	171	40	2.15	1.90	2.28	2.67	3.26	2.70	2.30	2.84	3.51	2.86	2.75	2.20	31.42
	Holland	34	25.6	71.6	105	−24	33	May 8	Oct. 11	156	34	2.07	1.84	2.15	2.97	3.39	2.74	2.34	2.67	3.93	3.25	2.70	2.27	32.32
Presque Isle	Onaway (near)	34	17.7	67.1	107	−46	35	June 5	Sept. 14	101	34	1.68	1.63	1.99	2.24	2.82	2.88	2.63	2.56	3.06	2.85	2.32	1.67	28.33
Roscommon	Houghton Lake (near)	23	19.7	67.6	107	−48	22	June 11	Sept. 3	84	24	1.34	1.21	1.99	2.53	2.74	2.77	2.38	2.73	2.92	2.97	2.37	1.45	27.40
Saginaw	Saginaw	40	22.8	72.0	111	−23	34	May 5	Oct. 10	158	40	1.61	1.74	2.17	2.37	3.52	2.71	2.88	2.85	2.84	2.52	2.13	1.79	29.13
Sanilac	Sandusky	20	20.5	68.8	103	−23	20	May 22	Sept. 30	131	20	1.75	1.62	1.85	2.46	3.45	3.08	3.21	2.74	2.61	2.42	2.03	1.65	28.87
Schoolcraft	Seney (near)	10	14.9	64.8	103	−47	10	June 15	Aug. 27	73	17	1.56	.84	1.30	1.79	2.89	3.18	2.90	2.39	3.33	2.80	2.24	1.53	26.75
Shiawassee	Durand	18	23.8	73.2	105	−28	18	May 12	Oct. 7	148	17	1.47	1.48	2.16	2.59	3.19	2.90	2.14	2.67	2.39	2.18	1.60	1.57	26.34
	Owosso	36	23.4	72.8	105	−26	38	May 13	Oct. 4	144	39	1.55	1.48	2.06	2.55	3.35	2.82	3.05	2.63	2.97	2.59	2.32	1.62	28.99
St. Clair	Jeddo	22	21.5	69.9	104	−25	21	May 6	Oct. 13	160	21	1.92	1.71	2.15	2.43	3.34	2.67	3.14	3.21	2.70	2.51	2.01	1.97	29.76
	Port Huron	40	23.6	70.1	104	−25	40	May 3	Oct. 15	165	39	1.66	1.49	1.95	2.33	2.68	2.46	2.85	2.71	2.77	2.34	2.01	1.73	26.98
St. Joseph	Three Rivers (near)	40	24.6	72.3	107	−22	40	May 6	Oct. 11	158	40	2.15	1.83	2.94	3.18	4.30	3.96	3.21	2.93	3.42	2.90	2.62	2.35	35.79

Tuscola	Arbela	29	21.2	70.1	104	−30	28	May 15	Sept. 27	135	28	1.79	1.83	2.51	2.78	4.12	3.15	3.30	3.09	3.22	2.67	2.38	2.05	32.89
Van Buren	Bloomingdale	34	24.5	71.9	105	−22	34	May 12	Oct. 9	150	34	2.05	1.73	2.20	2.77	3.40	3.02	2.23	2.84	3.92	2.86	2.96	2.54	32.52
	South Haven	37	25.5	70.2	99	−22	38	May 6	Oct. 15	162	40	1.83	1.65	2.48	2.72	3.63	2.87	2.56	2.87	3.54	3.08	2.75	2.47	32.45
Washtenaw	Ann Arbor	40	23.9	72.3	105	−21	40	May 4	Oct. 17	166	40	1.82	1.73	2.35	2.76	3.42	3.07	2.86	2.73	3.08	2.34	2.22	1.97	30.35
	Ypsilanti	40	24.0	71.9	107	−25	40	May 7	Oct. 10	156	40	2.08	1.81	2.38	2.73	3.33	3.06	2.95	2.70	3.37	2.37	2.20	2.20	31.18
Wayne	Detroit	40	25.5	73.1	105	−24	40	Apr. 24	Oct. 18	177	40	2.27	2.01	2.50	2.73	3.10	3.21	3.19	2.62	2.94	2.23	2.04	2.20	31.04
	Eloise	39	24.6	72.7	107	−24	39	May 7	Oct. 9	155	40	1.82	1.70	2.10	2.51	3.02	2.93	2.64	2.50	2.70	2.17	1.88	1.87	27.84
Wexford	Cadillac	30	18.9	69.1	104	−36	26	May 17	Oct. 6	142	30	1.50	1.54	1.73	2.38	2.77	2.73	2.61	2.90	3.61	2.83	2.48	1.45	28.53

Precipitation and temperature—State unit values

[This tabulation gives the mean annual, mean monthly, and average seasonal precipitation, 1886–1938, and the mean annual temperatures, 1896–1938, for Michigan]

Precipitation		Precipitation		Precipitation		Precipitation		Temperature		Temperature	
Year	Mean	Year	Mean	Year	Mean	Month	Mean	Year	Mean	Year	Mean
	In.		*In.*		*In.*		*In.*		°*F.*		°*F.*
1886	31.70	1908	29.64	1930	22.62	July	2.73	1896	45.8	1918	44.2
1887	30.60	1909	32.43	1931	29.80	August	2.71	1897	44.8	1919	45.8
1888	28.68	1910	25.69	1932	33.13	September	3.18	1898	46.0	1920	43.0
1889	26.86	1911	33.31	1933	30.30	October	2.67	1899	44.9	1921	48.3
1890	34.23	1912	31.24	1934	25.57	November	2.53	1900	46.0	1922	45.9
1891	30.65	1913	28.70	1935	28.60	December	2.09	1901	44.6	1923	44.2
1892	33.69	1914	30.05	1936	27.12			1902	45.2	1924	42.7
1893	34.55	1915	30.75	1937	31.18	Annual	30.37	1903	44.2	1925	44.8
1894	28.00	1916	33.97	1938	31.56			1904	41.9	1926	43.0
1895	26.90	1917	27.21					1905	44.2	1927	45.6
1896	31.74	1918	29.47			Season	Average	1906	45.9	1928	44.8
1897	31.23	1919	30.23	Month	Means			1907	42.8	1929	43.6
1898	32.29	1920	29.10					1908	45.9	1930	46.0
1899	28.35	1921	31.85					1909	44.4	1931	48.8
1900	32.31	1922	32.10				*In.*	1910	45.2	1932	45.9
1901	28.06	1923	28.80		*In.*	Winter	5.87	1911	46.0	1933	46.2
1902	32.53	1924	29.79	January	2.02	Spring	7.65	1912	42.9	1934	45.2
1903	32.72	1925	25.51	February	1.76	Summer	8.47	1913	46.1	1935	44.5
1904	29.73	1926	33.06	March	2.07	Fall	8.38	1914	44.7	1936	44.3
1905	33.32	1927	31.52	April	2.38			1915	44.7	1937	45.1
1906	31.41	1928	33.33	May	3.20			1916	44.1	1938	46.8
1907	30.67	1929	31.24	June	3.03			1917	40.9		

298737°—41——59 +

MICHIGAN—Continued

Dates of last killing frost in spring and first in fall, with length of growing season

Year	Grayling			Harbor Beach			Lansing			Newberry			South Haven			Stambaugh		
	Last in spring	First in fall	Growing season [1]	Last in spring	First in fall	Growing season [1]	Last in spring	First in fall	Growing season [1]	Last in spring	First in fall	Growing season [1]	Last in spring	First in fall	Growing season [1]	Last in spring	First in fall	Growing season [1]
			Days			*Days*			*Days*			*Days*			*Days*			*Days*
1899	May 21	Sept. 14	116	May 14	Sept. 27	136	Apr. 15	Sept. 13	151	June 5	Aug. 23	79	May 20	Oct. 1	134		Sept. 13	
1900	May 10	Sept. 28	141	May 10	Oct. 10	153	May 9	Sept. 17	131	June 11	Sept. 8	89	Apr. 10	Oct. 17	190	June 30	Sept. 16	78
1901	May 4	Oct. 3	152	Apr. 21	Sept. 17	149	Apr. 21	Sept. 18	150	do	Oct. 17	128	Apr. 21	Oct. 6	168	May 29		
1902	May 28	Oct. 2	127	May 15	Oct. 17	155	May 28	Sept. 13	108	June 5	Aug. 29	85	May 10	Oct. 21	164	June 24	Aug. 12	49
1903	May 7	Sept. 26	142	May 8	Sept. 28	143	May 4	Oct. 18	167	June 13	Sept. 27	106	May 1	Oct. 23	175	June 12	Sept. 5	85
1904	May 11	Aug. 30	111	May 15	Sept. 22	130	May 16	Sept. 21	128	June 15	Aug. 30	76	May 15	Sept. 21	129	June 16	Aug. 8	53
1905	May 26	Sept. 14	111	May 9	Oct. 23	167	May 9	Oct. 22	166				May 9	Sept. 26	140	May 30	Sept. 13	106
1906	May 28	Oct. 1	126	May 20	Oct. 11	144	May 10	Oct. 10	153				May 20	Oct. 1	134	June 13	Sept. 27	106
1907	May 31			May 28	Oct. 14	139	May 21	Oct. 1	133				May 27	Oct. 13	139	July 2	Sept. 22	82
1908	May 5	Sept. 3	121	May 4	Sept. 30	149	May 5	Oct. 2	150	May 3			May 4	Oct. 2	151	June 15	Aug. 20	66
1909	May 11	Aug. 21	102	do	Oct. 12	161	May 4	Oct. 12	161	May 27	Aug. 16	81	do	Oct. 11	160	June 18	Sept. 1	75
1910				June 4	Oct. 28	146	May 14	Oct. 7	146	May 30	Aug. 30	92	Apr. 25			June 7	Sept. 10	95
1911		Sept. 28		May 13	Sept. 14	124	May 4	Oct. 8	157	May 13	Sept. 26	136	May 5	Oct. 8	156	May 13	Sept. 26	136
1912	May 15	do	136	May 4	Oct. 16	165	Apr. 30	Oct. 16	169	May 29	Sept. 28	122	May 12	Nov. 2	174	June 7	July 19	42
1913	June 8			May 11	Oct. 24	166	May 11	Oct. 13	155	May 26	Sept. 14	111				May 25	Sept. 9	107
1914	May 16	Sept. 28	135	May 2	Oct. 26	177	May 1	Oct. 25	177	June 20	Oct. 13	115	Apr. 21	Oct. 27	189	June 16	Sept. 7	83
1915	May 27	Aug. 26	91	May 18	Oct. 2	137	Apr. 17	Oct. 10	176	May 27	Aug. 27	92		Oct. 10		June 23	Aug. 26	64
1916	May 30	Sept. 2	95	Apr. 30	Sept. 30	153	Apr. 15	Sept. 19	157	May 19	Sept. 30	134		Oct. 22		June 20	Sept. 2	74
1917				Apr. 28	Sept. 11	136	May 3	Oct. 6	156	June 2	Aug. 30	89	May 10	Oct. 12	155	June 22	Aug. 29	68
1918	June 23	Sept. 26	95	May 1	Oct. 1	153	Apr. 25	Oct. 1	159	June 23	Sept. 24	94	Apr. 25	Nov. 3	192	June 23	Sept. 4	73
1919	May 19	Sept. 13	117	Apr. 30	Oct. 12	165	Apr. 29	Oct. 12	166	June 28 [2]	Oct. 7	101	Apr. 27	Oct. 12	168	May 19	Sept. 26	130
1920	May 16	Sept. 16	123	May 15	Oct. 30	168	May 15	Oct. 29	167	May 15	Sept. 19	127	May 5	Oct. 29	177	May 16	Aug. 22	98
1921	June 5	Oct. 8	125	Apr. 18	Oct. 13	178	May 16	Oct. 13	150	May 16	Oct. 8	145	May 17	Oct. 13	149	June 4	Oct. 1	119
1922	July 4	Sept. 17	75	Apr. 30	do	166	Apr. 29	do	167	June 26	Sept. 25	91	Apr. 29	Oct. 20	174	Apr. 30	Sept. 15	138
1923	May 24	Sept. 10	109	May 13	Oct. 7	147	May 13	Oct. 6	146	May 17	Sept. 10	116	May 10	Oct. 6	149	May 21	Sept. 13	115
1924	May 31	Sept. 11	103	May 30	Oct. 23	156	May 22	Oct. 21	152	May 29	Sept. 8	102	May 4	Oct. 22	171	July 18	Sept. 6	50
1925	June 29	Sept. 30	93	May 18	Oct. 10	145	May 18	Oct. 10	145	June 10	Sept. 25	107	May 18	Oct. 10	145	June 29	Aug. 27	59
1926	June 5	Sept. 26	113	May 4	Sept. 26	145	May 4	Oct. 26	175	May 20	Sept. 26	129	May 23	Oct. 27	157	June 19	Sept. 13	86
1927	June 15	Aug. 24	70	Apr. 28	Nov. 3	189	Apr. 24	Nov. 3	193	June 1	Oct. 10	131	May 1	Oct. 17	169	June 15	Aug. 15	61
1928	do	Aug. 25	71	May 13	Sept. 26	136	May 13	Sept. 28	138	June 15	Sept. 25	102	May 13	Oct. 30	170	do	Sept. 5	82
1929	June 8	Sept. 18	102	May 22	Sept. 20	121	May 20	Sept. 19	122	June 5	Sept. 18	105	Apr. 23	Oct. 4	164	June 8	Sept. 18	102
1930	May 31	Oct. 1	123	Apr. 27	Oct. 18	174	Apr. 25	Oct. 18	176	May 30	Oct. 17	140	Apr. 26	Oct. 25	182	May 30	Sept. 4	97
1931	May 22	Oct. 9	140	May 1	Nov. 6	189	Apr. 7	Nov. 6	213	May 22	Oct. 12	143	May 3	Oct. 18	168	June 8	Oct. 9	123
1932	May 23	Sept. 18	118	May 3	Oct. 13	163	Apr. 17	Oct. 28	194	May 2	Oct. 10	161	May 2	Nov. 2	184	do	Sept. 7	91
1933	June 14	Sept. 12	90	Apr. 27	Oct. 25	181	Apr. 27	Oct. 20	176	June 1			May 4	Oct. 20	169	June 14	Sept. 29	107
1934	May 26	Oct. 1	128	May 12	Oct. 14	155	May 12	Oct. 14	155	May 25	Sept. 29	127	May 12	Oct. 19	160	May 15	Sept. 30	138
1935	May 24	Sept. 23	122	May 23	Oct. 5	135	do	do	155	May 23	Sept. 27	127	May 4	Oct. 6	155	May 22	Sept. 9	110

1936	May 20	Sept. 25	128	May 25	Oct. 12	140	May 23	Oct. 23	153	June 3	Sept. 25	114	May 23	Oct. 26	156	May 19	Sept. 28	132
1937	May 15	Sept. 17	125	May 10	Oct. 8	151	Apr. 16	Oct. 13	180	May 15	----------	------	Apr. 16	Oct. 14	181	May 14	Sept. 15	124
1938	May 13	Sept. 16	126	May 12	Oct. 2	143	May 12	Oct. 7	148	May 13	Oct. 6	146	May 13	Oct. 7	147	May 12	Oct. 1	142
Mean	May 27	Sept. 19	115	May 10	Oct. 10	153	May 5	Oct. 10	158	May 31	Sept. 22	114	May 6	Oct. 15	162	June 7	Sept. 9	94
Extremes	May 4[2]	Aug. 21[4]	[6] 70	Apr. 18[2]	Sept. 11[4]	[6] 121	Apr. 7[2]	Sept. 13[4]	[6] 108	May 2[2]	Aug. 16[4]	[6] 76	Apr. 10[2]	Sept. 21[4]	[6] 129	Apr. 30[2]	July 19[4]	[6] 42
	July 4[3]	Oct. 9[5]	[7] 152	June 4[3]	Nov. 6[5]	[7] 189	May 28[3]	Nov. 6[5]	[7] 213	June 28[3]	Oct. 17[5]	[7] 161	May 27[3]	Nov. 3[5]	[7] 192	July 18[3]	Oct. 9[5]	[7] 142

[1] Number of days between last killing frost in spring and first in fall.
[2] Earliest date in spring.
[3] Latest date in spring.
[4] Earliest date in fall.
[5] Latest date in fall.
[6] Shortest growing season.
[7] Longest growing season.

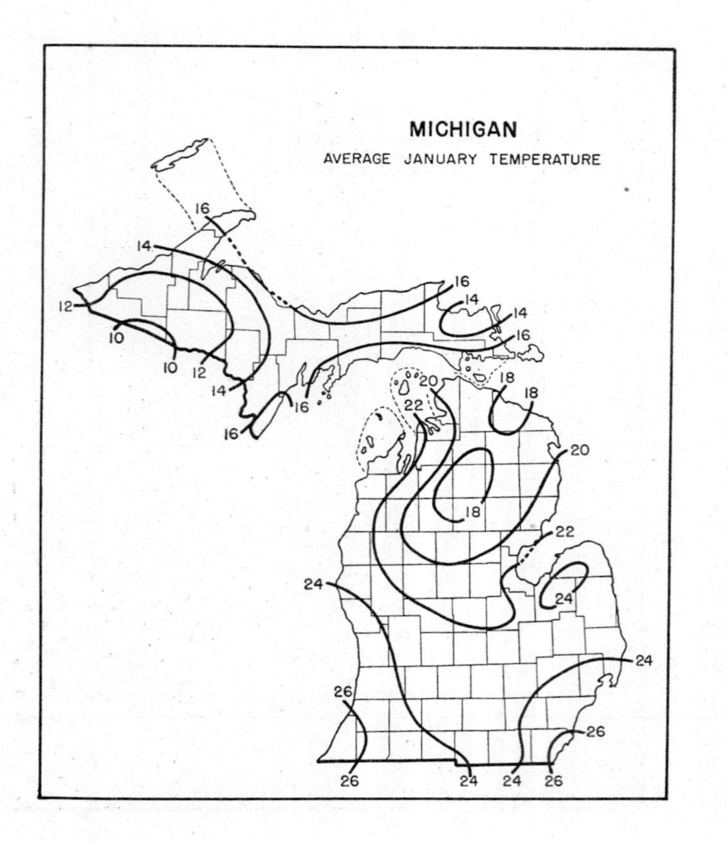
MICHIGAN
AVERAGE JANUARY TEMPERATURE
16
14
16
14
14
16
12
10
10
12
14
16
16
20
22
18
18
20
18
22
24
24
24
26
26
26
24
24
26

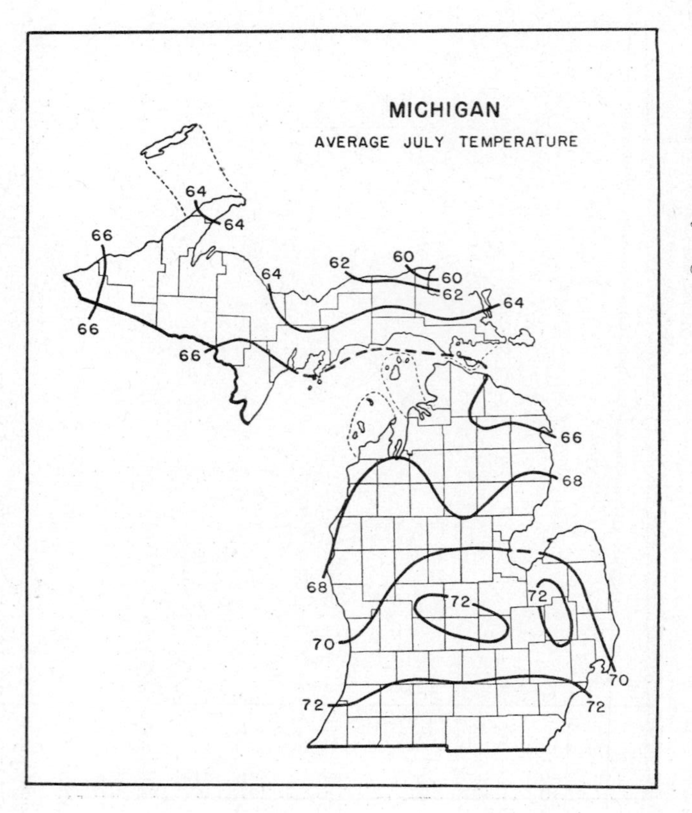
MICHIGAN
AVERAGE JULY TEMPERATURE
64
64
66
66
66
64
62
60
60
62
64
66
68
68
70
72
72
70
72
72

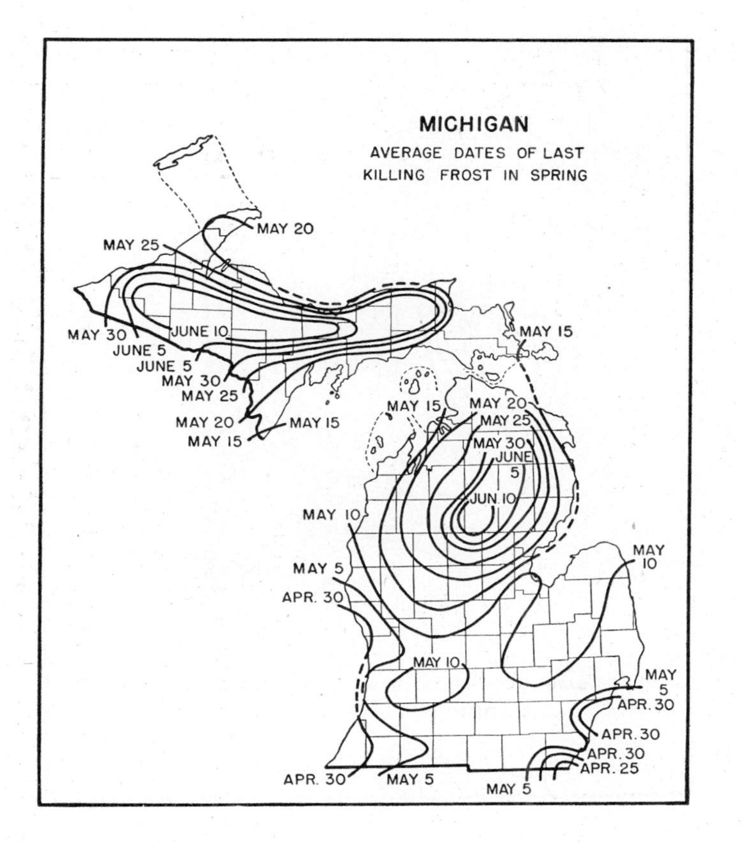
MICHIGAN
AVERAGE DATES OF LAST
KILLING FROST IN SPRING

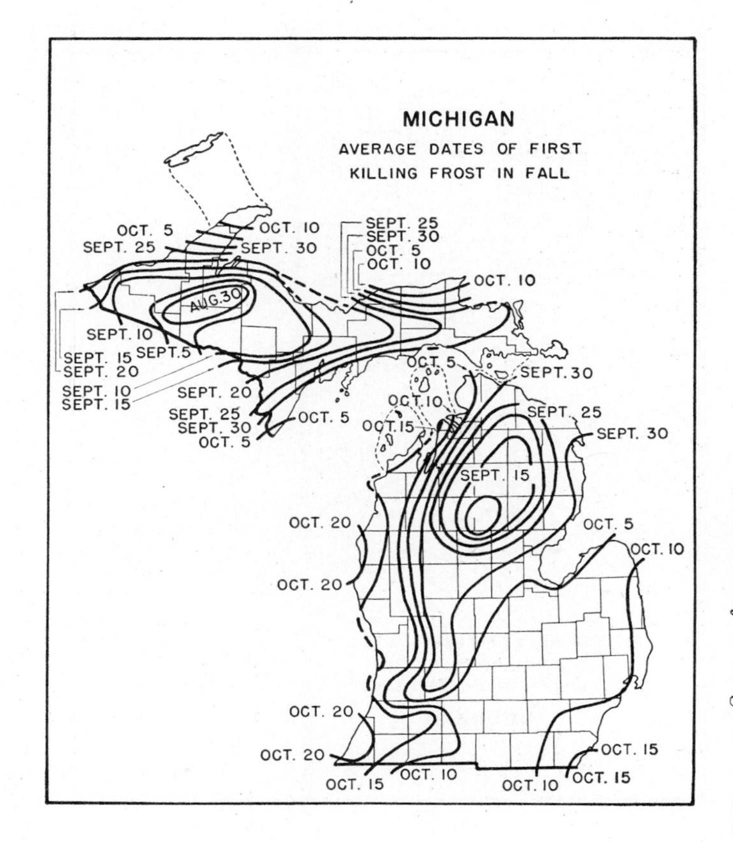
MICHIGAN
AVERAGE DATES OF FIRST
KILLING FROST IN FALL

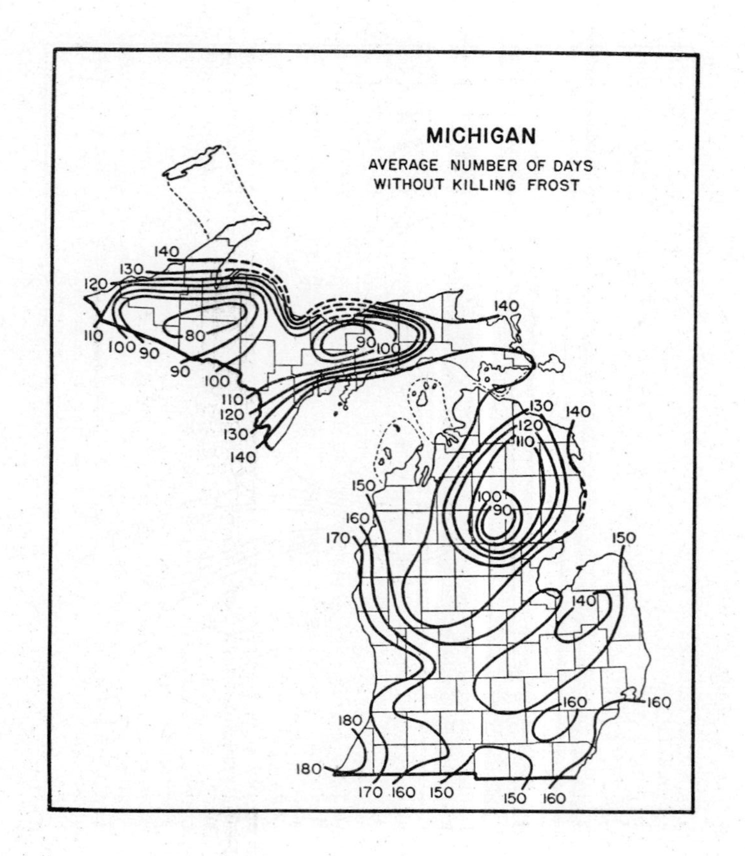
MICHIGAN
AVERAGE NUMBER OF DAYS WITHOUT KILLING FROST

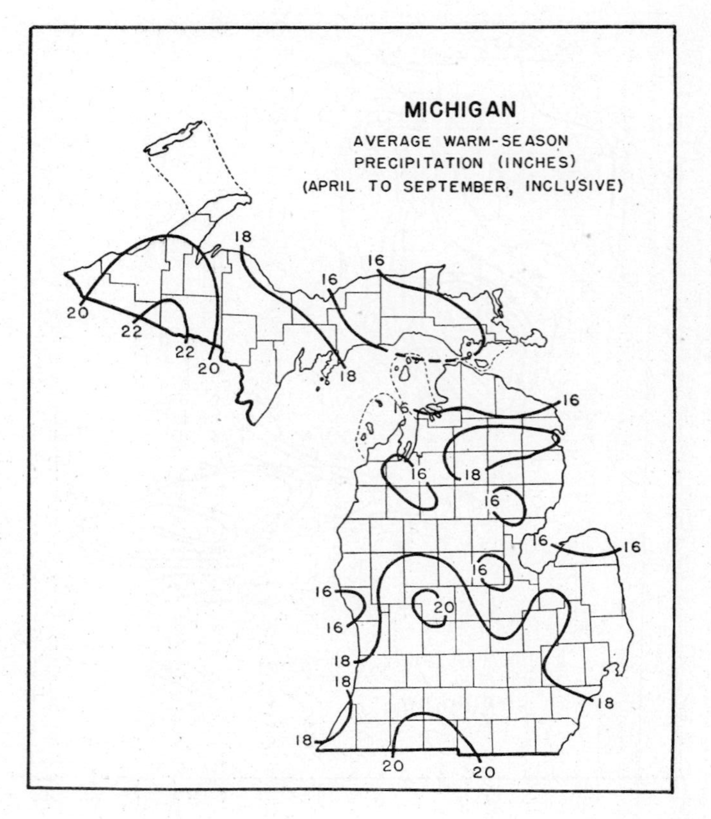
MICHIGAN
AVERAGE WARM-SEASON PRECIPITATION (INCHES)
(APRIL TO SEPTEMBER, INCLUSIVE)

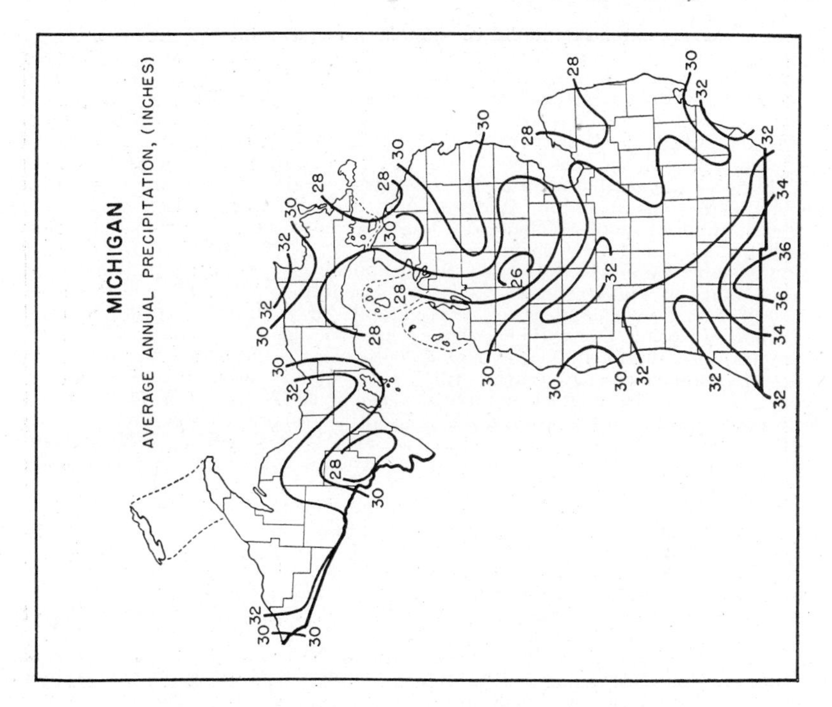

SUPPLEMENTARY CLIMATIC NOTES FOR MICHIGAN

The major part of the eastern half of the Upper Peninsula of Michigan has a terrain nearly level, the highest elevations not exceeding 400 feet above the level of Lakes Superior and Michigan, or 1,000 feet above sea level. In the western half the land rises progressively much higher, especially in parts of Marquette, Baraga, Houghton, Iron, Gogebic, and Ontonagon Counties. The Porcupine Mountains, in Ontonagon County, attain an elevation 1,400 feet above Lake Superior—over 2,000 feet above sea level. The largest rivers flowing into Lake Superior are the Tahquamenon in the east and the Ontonagon in the west. The principal rivers tributary to Lake Michigan are the Manistique, Escanaba, and Menominee, the latter forming the boundary between the Upper Peninsula of Michigan and Wisconsin.

Much of the southern half of the Lower Peninsula is level or gently rolling, though parts of Oakland, Livingston, Washtenaw, Lenawee, Jackson, Hillsdale, and Branch Counties reach elevations of 1,000 to 1,200 feet above sea level. The north-central part of the Lower Peninsula is capped by a tableland ranging in height from 1,200 to 1,400 feet and embracing parts of Antrim, Otsego, Montmorency, Oscoda, Crawford, Kalkaska, Wexford, Missaukee, Roscommon, Clare, and Osceola Counties. From this divide, the rivers flow generally westward to Lake Michigan or eastward to Lakes Huron, St. Clair, and Erie. The main rivers are the Manistee, Muskegon, Grand, Kalamazoo, and St. Joseph in the west, and the Au Sable, Saginaw system, and Clinton in the east.

Located in the heart of the Great Lakes region, Michigan has the longest lake shore line of any State in the Union and is naturally under the climatic influence of these large bodies of water. Two distinct types of climate are observed in the State. The interior counties of both peninsulas have a climate that alternates between continental and semimarine with changing meteorological conditions. The marine type is due to the influence of the Lakes, which, in turn, is governed by the force and direction of the wind. When there is little or no wind, the weather becomes continental in character, which means pronounced fluctuation in temperature—hot weather in summer and severe cold in winter. On the other hand, a strong wind from the Lakes may immediately transform the weather into a semimarine type.

Narrow belts extending along the shores of Lakes Superior and Michigan and to a lesser degree along Lake Huron have a modified marine climate most of the year. The Lakes seldom freeze over entirely, their temperature remaining above the freezing point in the coldest weather. The typical North American cold wave which frequently sweeps down from the northwest attended by strong north or northwest winds, is considerably tempered in severity as it passes over wide stretches of the relatively warm waters of Lakes Superior and Michigan. In this way the temperature of the moving cold air may be raised as much as 20° F., so that the areas immediately along the south shore of Lake Superior and the east shore of Lake Michigan do not experienee the severe cold that prevails farther inland.

Since large bodies of water are less responsive to temperature changes, the Lakes hold the winter cold longer in the spring and the summer heat longer in the fall than do the land areas. This stabilizing influence tends to retard the advance of spring along their shores, thus holding back the development of vegetation till the likelihood of frost is over. In the fall a reverse process slows up the approach of cold weather till vegetation has matured and is safe from frost. The equalizing effect of Lake Superior is also shown in a doubling of the length of the growing season along its southern shore as compared with that farther inland. Moreover, as long as the wind is on shore in the coastal areas, the effect is to temper the extremes of heat and cold, thus producing a more equable climate.

The equalizing influence of Lake Michigan, together with well-adapted soils, sufficient rainfall during the growing season, and abundant sunshine in summer, has produced a flourishing fruit industry on the eastern shore of the lake.

In the Upper Peninsula, the average date of the last killing frost in spring ranges from about May 20 along the shores of Lakes Superior and Michigan to about June 10 in the interior; and in the Lower Peninsula, from May 1–10 in the extreme southern counties to June 10 in the north-central region.

In the Upper Peninsula, the average date of the first killing frost in fall ranges from about September 1 in the interior to October 1–10 along the shores; and in the Lower Peninsula, from September 10 in the northern interior to October 10 in the extreme southeast and October 20 in the extreme west and southwest.

In the Upper Peninsula, the average growing season ranges from 80–90 days in the interior to 140 along the lake shores, and in the Lower Peninsula, from 90–100 days in the northern interior to 150–160 in the extreme southeast, 150–170 along the middle shore of Lake Michigan, and 180 days in the extreme southwestern county. Thus the extreme range in the length of the growing season is more than 3 months.

Precipitation is fairly well distributed through the year, and no conspicuous variation is noted in the seasonal march generally, although the curve shows about 1 inch less a month in winter than in summer, the heavier amounts in summer being due to thundershowers. The variation in annual amounts over the State is not large. Droughts occur occasionally, but are never so severe and prolonged as in the States to the south and west.

The variation in snowfall over the State is wide, ranging from 115–130 inches along the north side of the Upper Peninsula to 30 inches over the extreme southeast border of the Lower Peninsula. This decrease from north to southeast, however, is not uniform since there is another area of moderately heavy snowfall in the highlands of three or four counties to the eastward and southward of Grand Traverse Bay.

The average number of days with appreciable rain in Michigan is 107 a year, or slightly less than 1 day in 3. The total number of cloudy days just about balances the number of clear days. Much cloudiness prevails during the winter season, but sunshine is abundant during the summer months. Similarly, relative humidity remains rather high during the winter but is only moderate in summer.

The prevailing wind is from the southwest over southern Michigan and westerly over northern sections. The State is seldom visited by violent windstorms, although such storms are not unknown, especially in the southern counties. Comparatively few glaze storms of destructive character have occurred. Extensive floods are practically unknown, the only instances of flooding being of a freshet character in connection with the break-up of ice in the spring.

H. Merrill Wills, *Meteorologist and Climatic Section Director for Michigan, Weather Bureau, East Lansing.*

MINNESOTA

Climatic summary

County [1]	Station	Temperature: Length of record	Temperature: January average	Temperature: July average	Temperature: Maximum	Temperature: Minimum	Killing frost average dates: Length of record	Killing frost: Last in spring	Killing frost: First in fall	Killing frost: Growing season [2]	Average precipitation: Length of record	January	February	March	April	May	June	July	August	September	October	November	December	Annual
		Yr.	°F.	°F.	°F.	°F.	Yr.			Days	Yr.	In.	In.	In.	In.	In.	In.	In.	In.	In.	In.	In.	In.	In.
Aitkin	Sandy Lake Dam	40	6.4	67.4	101	−52	40	May 24	Sept. 19	118	40	0.63	.053	0.95	1.68	3.18	3.78	3.60	3.44	2.96	1.87	1.20	0.69	24.51
Becker	Detroit Lakes	40	3.7	68.8	107	−53	40	May 25	Sept. 20	118	40	.61	.66	.83	1.88	3.33	3.90	3.45	3.57	2.55	1.70	.91	.67	24.06
Beltrami	Bemidji	18	4.7	68.9	107	−48	21	do	Sept. 16	114	34	.70	.58	1.01	1.74	2.77	3.79	3.28	3.25	2.60	1.93	1.08	.73	23.46
	Redby	29	3.7	68.3	109	−50	30	May 22	do	117	30	.74	.65	.70	1.30	2.43	3.89	3.48	3.06	2.59	1.38	1.01	.74	21.97
Big Stone	Artichoke Lake	21	11.0	72.4	109	−39	22	May 13	Sept. 26	136	22	.30	.28	.73	1.88	2.48	3.10	2.82	2.53	2.07	.96	1.03	.34	18.52
	Beardsley	36	11.7	72.1	114	−41	34	May 21	Sept. 21	123	37	.66	.58	1.07	2.21	2.93	3.89	3.00	3.16	1.99	1.21	.65	.48	21.83
	Ortonville										10	.61	.75	1.48	1.82	3.86	4.54	3.17	3.53	2.54	1.92	.92	.83	25.97
Blue Earth	Lake Crystal	10	12.3	71.4	99	−37	11	May 4	Oct. 4	153	12	.84	.81	1.40	2.12	4.48	5.18	4.69	3.62	2.85	2.23	1.25	.99	30.46
	Mankato										34	.83	.77	1.22	2.26	3.62	4.87	3.25	3.60	3.46	1.84	1.45	.79	27.96
Brown	New Ulm	40	13.3	73.6	111	−37	40	May 10	Oct. 1	144	40	1.22	1.12	1.77	2.38	3.76	5.09	3.53	3.72	4.09	2.22	1.39	1.13	31.42
Carlton	Cloquet	27	6.9	66.3	105	−45	28	June 6	Sept. 8	94	27	1.18	.87	1.47	1.97	3.31	3.81	3.37	3.03	2.94	2.06	1.63	1.14	26.78
	Moose Lake	14	8.1	66.6	101	−52	12	June 4	Sept. 12	100	14	.90	.80	1.27	1.44	3.38	4.69	3.28	4.11	3.34	2.47	1.12	.66	27.46
Carver	Chaska	14	12.6	74.3	109	−40	14	May 11	Sept. 27	139	13	.78	.65	1.42	1.82	3.63	4.08	2.99	2.88	3.60	1.84	1.27	.87	25.83
Cass	Ah-gwah-ching	30	7.5	69.3	105	−43	30	May 16	Sept. 29	136	30	.72	.69	.97	1.58	2.60	3.71	3.09	3.00	2.51	1.51	1.08	.70	22.16
	Cass Lake	18	7.4	69.2	106	−46	20	May 23	Sept. 20	120	32	.64	.61	.79	1.62	2.93	3.52	2.85	3.11	2.54	1.57	1.06	.61	21.85
	Gull Lake Dam	27	6.8	69.6	107	−47	10	May 17	Sept. 21	127	28	.55	.55	.97	2.04	3.44	3.94	3.38	2.98	2.60	1.79	1.21	.60	24.05
	Leech Lake Dam	40	4.9	67.4	104	−59	40	May 24	Sept. 15	114	40	.69	.61	1.04	1.73	3.02	3.75	3.41	3.68	2.77	1.90	1.17	.81	24.58
Chippewa	Milan	40	10.5	71.5	113	−42	40	May 15	Sept. 26	134	40	.90	.79	1.05	2.05	2.94	3.61	2.88	3.20	2.41	1.41	.97	.86	23.07
	Montevideo	40	12.1	72.6	107	−39	40	May 8	Sept. 30	145	40	.74	.68	1.16	2.09	3.13	3.94	2.73	3.07	2.64	1.49	1.11	.70	23.48
Chisago	Taylors Falls	32	11.7	72.1	106	−47	32	May 15	do	138	31	.69	.66	1.02	1.94	3.39	4.20	3.44	3.19	3.65	2.31	1.38	.78	26.65
Clay	Moorhead	40	6.4	70.2	114	−48	40	May 8	Oct. 1	146	40	.67	.64	.89	1.97	2.62	3.34	2.90	2.90	2.08	1.44	.90	.72	21.07
Clearwater	Bagley	12	1.1	66.5	106	−52	12	May 29	Sept. 6	100	13	.60	.50	.92	1.52	3.15	3.69	3.93	2.93	2.54	1.37	.89	.75	22.79
	Gonvick (near)										17	.83	.82	.79	1.70	2.31	2.95	2.98	2.46	1.95	1.28	1.11	.94	20.12
	Itaska State Park	26	3.3	66.8	105	−51	28	June 4	Sept. 11	99	28	.69	.62	.91	1.91	2.86	3.95	2.93	3.11	2.22	1.64	1.00	.84	22.68
Cook	Grand Marais	18	14.1	59.2	100	−34	24	May 21	Oct. 4	136	27	1.27	1.08	1.66	1.50	2.01	3.00	2.91	2.83	3.43	2.25	1.49	1.28	24.71
	Pigeon River Bridge										14	1.29	1.16	1.64	2.35	2.41	3.86	3.03	3.33	4.55	3.39	3.01	1.51	31.53
Cottonwood	Windom	11	12.1	71.9	100	−32	13	May 16	Sept. 30	137	13	1.02	.88	1.22	2.18	4.46	4.80	3.63	3.40	3.01	1.45	1.24	.53	27.82
Crow Wing	Brainerd	30	7.8	69.2	106	−42	30	May 18	Sept. 24	129	33	.56	.72	1.00	1.77	3.07	3.89	3.22	3.12	2.39	1.86	1.13	.70	23.43
	Fort Ripley	16	5.9	68.6	104	−51	27	May 17	Oct. 3	139	32	.53	.52	.60	1.68	2.92	3.76	2.73	2.89	2.46	1.40	1.18	.49	21.16
	Pine River Dam	40	5.6	68.4	104	−53	40	May 15	Sept. 27	135	40	.56	.56	.99	1.96	3.43	4.19	3.51	3.55	2.90	2.17	1.14	.61	25.57
Dakota	Farmington	40	12.4	71.7	110	−40	38	May 10	Oct. 1	144	40	1.07	.86	1.39	2.10	3.46	3.69	3.25	3.24	3.45	2.22	1.44	.93	27.10

[1] The following counties, for which no records are available, are best represented by the stations indicated: Anoka—Minneapolis; Benton and Wright—St. Cloud (near); Dodge—Rochester; Grant—Morris; Isanti—Milaca; Jackson—Windom; Lac qui Parle and Swift—Milan; Le Sueur and Sibley—St. Peter; Lincoln—Pipestone; Meeker—Bird Island; Murray—Tracy; Pope—Alexandria; Steele—Faribault; Watonwah—Fairmont.

[2] Length of growing season between average dates of last killing frost in spring and first in fall.

MINNESOTA—Continued

Climatic summary—Continued

County	Station	Temperature					Killing frost average dates				Average precipitation													
		Length of record	January average	July average	Maximum	Minimum	Length of record	Last in spring	First in fall	Growing season	Length of record	January	February	March	April	May	June	July	August	September	October	November	December	Annual
		Yr.	*°F.*	*°F.*	*°F.*	*°F.*	*Yr.*			*Days*	*Yr.*	*In.*	*In.*	*In.*	*In.*	*In.*	*In.*	*In.*	*In.*	*In.*	*In.*	*In.*	*In.*	*In.*
Douglas	Alexandria	38	7.5	69.7	105	−44	39	May 12	Sept. 29	140	40	.49	.44	.79	1.75	3.20	3.63	3.27	3.37	2.33	1.51	.86	.48	22.12
Faribault	Winnebago	39	13.5	72.9	107	−35	40	May 6	Oct. 3	150	40	.81	.85	1.28	2.31	3.95	4.50	3.44	3.31	3.73	1.83	1.34	.85	28.20
Fillmore	Chatfield										15	.88	1.05	1.34	2.63	3.87	4.85	3.59	3.35	4.22	1.66	1.39	.98	29.81
Freeborn	Albert Lea	38	14.0	73.3	106	−41	38	May 3	Oct. 5	155	40	.87	.91	1.25	2.32	4.11	4.42	3.39	3.57	4.08	2.00	1.48	.96	29.36
Goodhue	Red Wing	9	12.4	72.7	106	−39	8	May 2	Oct. 11	162	40	1.09	1.08	1.40	2.19	3.64	4.50	3.28	3.42	3.94	2.30	1.64	1.04	29.52
	Zumbrota	38	14.0	71.9	109	−41	38	May 15	Sept. 27	135	34	1.04	.79	1.35	2.16	3.64	4.74	3.12	3.27	3.93	2.23	1.50	.88	28.65
Hennepin	Maple Plain	36	11.4	73.0	112	−37	34	May 8	Sept. 29	144	36	1.15	1.10	1.70	2.19	3.53	4.29	3.28	3.62	3.45	2.28	1.60	1.15	29.34
	Minneapolis	40	13.1	73.2	108	−34	40	Apr. 25	Oct. 13	171	38	.88	.85	1.35	1.95	3.40	4.27	3.44	3.26	3.40	2.19	1.40	.92	27.31
	Tonka										10	.62	.62	1.27	1.94	4.42	4.84	3.74	4.57	4.79	3.10	.98	.66	31.55
Houston	Caledonia	21	14.6	71.2	104	−35	21	May 1	Oct. 3	155	21	1.01	.98	1.76	2.52	4.54	4.46	4.53	3.97	4.33	2.65	1.52	1.29	33.56
Hubbard	Park Rapids	40	4.4	68.6	107	−51	39	May 19	Sept. 22	126	40	.75	.69	1.09	1.95	3.21	3.84	3.30	3.57	2.55	1.78	1.17	.82	24.72
Itasca	Grand Rapids	24	5.0	67.8	104	−51	24	May 26	Sept. 14	111	23	.67	.76	.89	1.76	2.51	3.49	2.92	2.89	2.59	1.85	1.54	.88	22.75
	Pokegame Falls	40	4.3	66.2	103	−59	40	June 1	Sept. 13	104	40	.55	.51	.95	1.58	2.88	3.60	3.30	3.35	3.00	1.93	1.24	.68	23.57
	Winnibigoshish	39	4.9	68.7	103	−49	40	May 18	Sept. 24	129	40	.64	.56	.95	1.73	2.94	3.64	3.36	3.75	2.82	1.76	1.16	.73	24.04
Kanabec	Mora	34	9.2	69.8	108	−48	34	May 17	Sept. 22	128	34	.90	.84	1.17	1.91	3.51	3.91	3.47	3.09	3.23	2.09	1.58	.78	26.48
Kandiyohi	New London	40	9.5	71.7	110	−42	40	May 8	Oct. 2	147	40	.51	.46	.88	1.63	2.82	3.73	3.42	3.28	2.81	1.53	.96	.51	22.54
	Willmar	22	10.3	72.1	107	−38	23	do	Sept. 30	145	27	.43	.76	1.16	1.97	2.66	3.47	2.71	3.22	3.01	1.37	1.13	.59	22.48
Kittson	Hallock	40	.8	67.5	109	−51	40	May 29	Sept. 17	111	39	.58	.58	.85	1.40	2.23	3.30	2.91	2.61	2.41	1.38	.79	.57	19.61
Koochiching	International Falls	18	3.0	67.5	103	−49	18	May 30	Sept. 14	107	18	.89	.93	.85	1.50	2.33	3.22	3.12	3.25	2.67	2.03	1.11	.92	22.82
Lake	Two Harbors	40	12.6	64.1	99	−36	40	May 18	Oct. 1	136	40	.72	.74	1.06	1.73	2.91	3.69	3.45	3.28	3.82	2.17	1.61	.84	26.02
Lake of the Woods	Baudette	28	1.6	67.4	103	−49	29	May 25	Sept. 17	115	29	.60	.52	.75	1.36	2.26	2.98	3.48	2.83	2.30	1.82	1.12	.69	20.71
Lyon	Lynd	28	14.5	70.4	104	−43	28	May 14	Sept. 29	138	30	.66	.80	1.15	2.50	3.33	4.15	2.88	3.47	2.77	1.78	1.02	.70	25.21
	Tracy	26	14.0	74.0	108	−33	26	May 8	Oct. 5	150	26	.58	.65	1.19	1.93	2.85	4.23	2.84	2.50	2.80	1.34	1.15	.59	22.65
McLeod	Glencoe	21	12.5	70.3	103	−38	20	May 13	Sept. 29	139	22	.81	.74	.99	1.84	3.35	4.72	2.86	3.31	3.21	2.50	1.14	.85	26.32
Mahnomen	Mahnomen	10	5.1	67.2	103	−49	13	May 29	Sept. 17	111	23	.43	.34	.69	1.57	2.80	2.88	3.14	3.00	2.03	1.39	.81	.52	19.60
Marshall	Argyle	22	2.4	68.9	107	−43	22	May 25	Sept. 19	117	23	.49	.53	.64	1.50	2.21	2.99	3.40	2.06	1.95	1.31	.81	.62	18.51
	Warren	10	.9	68.6	107	−45	11	May 23	Sept. 18	118	10	.71	.35	.42	1.12	2.32	2.72	3.31	2.26	2.39	1.00	.70	.61	17.91
Martin	Fairmont	39	14.7	73.3	109	−35	40	May 5	Oct. 5	153	40	.85	.96	1.50	2.29	4.00	4.33	3.44	3.65	3.78	1.78	1.50	.92	29.00
Mille Lacs	Milaca	34	9.0	69.7	108	−44	33	May 16	Sept. 24	131	35	.65	.69	.94	1.74	3.22	3.93	3.45	3.43	3.23	2.12	1.27	.66	25.33
Morrison	Little Falls	29	9.0	70.8	106	−46	29	May 13	Sept. 26	136	29	.92	.89	1.01	1.95	2.89	3.83	2.74	3.17	2.81	1.65	1.33	.77	23.96
Mower	Grand Meadow	40	12.9	71.5	107	−39	40	May 11	Sept. 30	142	40	1.07	1.03	1.84	2.47	4.61	4.68	3.63	3.89	4.35	2.41	1.73	1.13	32.84
Nicollet	St. Peter	38	14.4	73.0	109	−40	40	do	Oct. 1	143	39	.93	.71	1.19	2.02	3.49	4.66	3.22	3.37	3.61	2.03	1.30	.75	27.28
Nobles	Worthington	40	14.5	72.1	110	−37	39	May 9	Oct. 3	147	39	.65	.80	1.36	2.13	3.85	4.31	3.38	3.85	3.68	1.61	1.41	.68	27.71
Norman	Ada	26	4.9	69.8	111	−53	38	May 24	Sept. 20	119	38	.51	.50	.66	1.74	2.91	3.50	2.86	2.83	2.04	1.32	.78	.59	20.24
Olmsted	Rochester	22	12.1	72.1	108	−42	22	May 15	Sept. 29	137	22	1.04	.74	1.30	2.41	3.88	4.63	3.32	3.34	3.35	2.05	1.71	.73	28.50
Otter Tail	Fergus Falls	40	7.9	71.5	110	−42	40	May 10	Sept. 24	137	40	.87	.81	1.05	2.03	3.10	3.94	3.25	3.04	2.55	1.55	1.05	.83	24.07

Pennington	Thief River Falls	22	2.4	68.0	108	−47	22	May 25	Sept. 17	115	26	.53	.53	.77	1.66	2.56	3.02	3.36	2.85	2.43	1.49	1.19	.62	21.01
Pine	Hinckley	18	8.8	68.6	104	−41	18	May 22	Sept. 22	123	18	.66	.55	.84	2.08	3.84	3.72	3.63	3.46	3.09	1.80	1.71	.93	26.31
Pipestone	Pipestone	36	13.5	72.7	108	−40	38	May 13	Sept. 25	135	38	.51	.61	.89	1.93	3.18	4.04	2.74	3.51	3.05	1.51	.89	.54	23.40
Polk	Angus	36	1.6	67.3	108	−49	37	May 28	Sept. 14	109	36	.41	.43	.53	1.46	2.33	3.18	2.92	2.54	1.86	1.28	.75	.51	18.20
	Crookston	40	3.9	69.6	106	−51	40	May 18	Sept. 24	129	40	.55	.53	.77	1.66	2.81	3.17	3.00	2.62	2.04	1.42	.71	.69	19.97
	Fosston	28	2.2	68.3	110	−48	28	May 23	Sept. 17	117	30	.56	.59	.88	1.53	2.53	3.62	3.10	2.47	2.14	1.35	.92	.66	20.35
Ramsey	St. Paul	36	13.1	72.2	104	−41	38	Apr. 23	Oct. 10	170	38	.89	.91	1.43	2.10	3.46	4.09	3.23	3.19	3.15	2.16	1.32	.91	26.84
Red Lake	Red Lake Falls	22	2.5	69.6	110	−50	24	May 22	Sept. 18	119	22	.76	.72	.73	1.58	2.56	3.55	3.20	2.44	1.66	1.36	.96	.80	20.32
Redwood	Redwood Falls	24	12.7	74.9	110	−36	24	May 4	Oct. 5	154	30	1.06	.98	1.17	2.22	3.29	4.09	2.69	2.83	2.55	1.67	1.39	.97	24.91
Renville	Bird Island	40	12.0	71.9	106	−38	40	May 9	Sept. 30	144	40	.67	.63	1.08	1.88	3.27	4.31	2.88	3.34	2.92	1.69	1.08	.65	24.40
Rice	Faribault	38	14.2	72.4	108	−36	36	do	Oct. 3	147	38	.67	.65	1.08	1.87	3.33	4.16	3.22	3.36	3.45	1.90	1.16	.70	25.55
Rock	Luverne	14	16.1	70.8	103	−35	14	May 12	Sept. 26	137	16	.41	.56	1.40	2.03	4.26	5.07	4.13	3.64	3.17	2.13	1.00	.70	28.50
Roseau	Roseau	30	.6	67.4	107	−52	31	May 30	Sept. 12	105	30	.63	.54	.77	1.35	2.20	2.93	3.10	2.40	2.21	1.42	.86	.65	19.06
	Warroad	31	1.1	67.3	103	−55	26	May 24	Sept. 19	118	31	0.64	0.55	0.84	1.47	2.20	3.46	3.36	2.35	2.43	1.63	1.05	0.69	20.67
Saint Louis	Babbitt	18	4.8	66.6	103	−41	19	May 18	Sept. 23	128														
	Duluth	40	9.1	64.9	106	−41	40	May 10	Oct. 5	148	40	1.00	.92	1.45	1.89	2.92	3.69	3.63	3.01	3.32	2.16	1.49	1.03	26.51
	Mahoning	18	6.6	68.2	102	−40	29	May 16	Sept. 23	130														
	Meadowlands	22	6.1	66.6	103	−51	29	June 3	Sept. 10	99	27	.67	.73	1.01	1.76	2.82	3.42	3.34	3.13	3.25	1.75	1.03	.84	23.75
	Orr						12	June 1	Sept. 8	99	13	.78	.66	1.11	1.98	2.55	3.57	4.04	3.54	2.58	1.95	1.57	.88	25.21
	Tower						14	May 30	Sept. 10	103	19	.85	.71	1.24	1.60	3.00	4.03	3.50	3.80	3.88	2.37	1.46	.94	27.38
	Virginia	40	6.8	66.8	103	−45	40	May 28	Sept. 16	111	40	.77	.70	1.14	1.60	2.81	3.70	3.64	3.57	3.58	2.11	1.37	1.05	26.04
	Winton						8	May 27	Sept. 22	118	8	1.02	.84	1.22	1.92	2.04	3.66	2.82	3.64	3.60	2.23	1.52	1.07	25.58
Scott	Shakopee	10	14.2	71.0	102	−36	10	May 15	Oct. 2	140	10	.93	.99	1.25	1.94	4.03	4.65	3.77	4.51	4.23	3.24	1.23	.84	31.61
Sherburne	St. Cloud (near)	40	10.1	71.8	107	−40	40	May 8	Sept. 30	145	40	.74	.61	1.08	1.94	3.48	4.13	3.55	3.39	3.31	2.03	1.16	.59	26.01
Stearns	Collegeville	40	11.3	71.1	106	−39	40	do	do	145	40	.69	1.06	1.60	2.64	3.05	3.27	3.65	3.07	1.76	1.03	.63	.70	23.15
Stevens	Morris	39	9.2	71.1	108	−41	39	May 14	Sept. 27	136	40	.81	.70	1.03	1.94	3.17	3.98	3.37	3.05	2.39	1.43	1.02	.66	23.55
Todd	Long Prairie	18	7.4	68.8	105	−45	19	May 16	Sept. 23	130	19	.55	.46	1.06	1.99	3.58	3.80	3.60	3.79	2.60	1.94	.84	.53	24.74
Traverse	Wheaton	24	9.1	72.7	113	−38	24	May 14	Sept. 25	134	24	.58	.57	.94	2.26	2.79	3.89	2.77	2.57	2.10	1.17	.90	.47	21.01
Wabasha	Reads										40	.88	.77	1.26	2.17	3.78	4.56	3.34	3.73	4.37	2.31	1.54	.90	29.61
Wadena	Wadena	18	5.2	69.3	104	−43	19	May 21	Sept. 23	125	19	.62	.68	1.01	1.78	2.75	4.16	3.49	3.06	2.62	1.46	1.23	.55	23.41
Waseca	New Richland	20	13.4	72.2	104	−37	21	May 4	Sept. 30	149	17	.80	.71	.90	2.41	4.19	4.63	3.98	4.41	2.94	2.35	1.38	.91	29.61
	Waseca	24	12.9	72.9	106	−37	24	May 8	do	145	24	.97	1.00	1.47	2.35	3.53	4.17	3.22	3.67	3.47	1.59	1.31	.69	27.44
Washington	Stillwater										13	.93	1.08	1.23	2.08	4.06	4.99	3.86	3.60	3.22	2.37	1.33	.98	29.73
Wilkin	Campbell	33	5.8	70.1	111	−40	34	May 15	Sept. 19	127	40	.76	.83	.90	2.06	3.07	3.63	3.03	2.92	2.54	1.40	.88	.67	22.69
Winona	St. Charles	23	14.0	70.8	104	−40	22	May 12	Oct. 7	148	23	1.01	.96	1.49	2.29	4.29	4.69	3.97	3.50	3.78	2.77	1.34	.98	31.07
	Winona	36	15.9	73.8	108	−40	36	May 3	Oct. 8	158	38	1.04	1.02	1.63	2.26	4.21	4.57	3.86	3.74	4.04	2.10	1.79	1.03	31.29
Yellow Medicine	Canby	18	13.9	74.0	111	−33	16	May 11	Oct. 1	143	19	.75	.87	1.28	2.19	2.95	4.36	2.58	2.51	2.84	1.00	1.19	.70	23.22

MINNESOTA—Continued

Precipitation and temperature—State unit values

[This tabulation gives the mean annual, mean monthly, and average seasonal precipitation, 1886–1938, and the mean annual temperatures, 1902–38, for Minnesota]

Precipitation		Precipitation		Precipitation		Precipitation		Temperature		Temperature	
Year	Mean	Year	Mean	Year	Mean	Month	Mean	Year	Mean	Year	Mean
	In.		*In.*		*In.*		*In.*		*°F.*		*°F.*
1886	27.19	1907	23.00	1928	25.47	May	3.19	1902	42.4	1921	44.4
1887	24.63	1908	29.32	1929	21.27	June	3.97	1903	40.2	1922	42.7
1888	24.94	1909	28.50	1930	22.79	July	3.29	1904	39.8	1923	42.3
1889	18.78	1910	14.77	1931	22.34	August	3.14	1905	41.8	1924	39.5
1890	23.80	1911	28.92	1932	21.60	September	2.81	1906	42.4	1925	41.5
1891	24.51	1912	22.54	1933	20.57	October	1.80	1907	40.0	1926	40.8
1892	27.46	1913	25.48	1934	20.34	November	1.13	1908	43.3	1927	40.5
1893	24.50	1914	28.41	1935	25.71	December		1909	41.0	1928	42.4
1894	22.05	1915	28.43	1936	18.31			1910	42.8	1929	39.4
1895	22.06	1916	28.13	1937	25.83	Annual	24.99	1911	41.6	1930	43.0
1896	31.36	1917	21.47	1938	28.50			1912	39.9	1931	46.9
1897	27.19	1918	24.55					1913	42.0	1932	41.3
1898	24.00	1919	27.40			Season	Average	1914	41.9	1933	42.3
1899	28.96	1920	25.67	Month	Mean			1915	42.0	1934	43.1
1900	28.39	1921	22.66					1916	39.1	1935	41.2
1901	24.27	1922	22.53					1917	37.7	1936	39.7
1902	27.91	1923	19.92		*In.*		*In.*	1918	42.2	1937	40.4
1903	31.91	1924	25.08	January	0.80	Winter	2.36	1919	41.3	1938	43.5
1904	25.19	1925	23.57	February	.75	Spring	6.49	1920	41.6		
1905	32.67	1926	24.71	March	1.15	Summer	10.40				
1906	30.34	1927	24.67	April	2.15	Fall	5.74				

Dates of last killing frost in spring and first in fall, with length of growing season

Year	Duluth			Minneapolis			Moorhead			Morris			New Ulm			Winnibigoshish Dam		
	Last in spring	First in fall	Growing season[1]	Last in spring	First in fall	Growing season[1]	Last in spring	First in fall	Growing season[1]	Last in spring	First in fall	Growing season[1]	Last in spring	First in fall	Growing season[1]	Last in spring	First in fall	Growing season[1]
			Days			*Days*			*Days*			*Days*			*Days*			*Days*
1899	May 4	Sept. 29	148	Apr. 8	Sept. 30	175	May 13	Sept. 29	139	May 18	Sept. 28	133	May 13	Sept. 29	139	May 2	Sept. 22	143
1900	do	Nov. 6	186	May 4	Nov. 7	187	Apr. 18	Oct. 16	181	May 4	Sept. 17	136	May 3	Sept. 27	147	May 8	Sept. 16	131

1901	Apr. 19	Oct. 16	180	Apr. 22	Oct. 14	175	Apr. 20	do	179	June 7	Oct. 2	117	June 7	Sept. 20	105	do	Sept. 20	135
1902	Apr. 30	Oct. 14	167	Apr. 3	Sept. 13	163	Apr. 23	Sept. 12	142	Apr. 29	Sept. 12	136	Apr. 24	Sept. 11	140	May 10	Sept. 13	126
1903	Apr. 16	Sept. 27	164	May 1	Oct. 26	178	May 3	Sept. 16	136	May 6	Sept. 16	133	Apr. 29	Oct. 9	163	June 11	Sept. 28	109
1904	May 16	Oct. 6	143	May 15	Oct. 6	144	Apr. 19	Sept. 20	154	May 10	Sept. 21	134	Apr. 26	Oct. 6	163	May 16	Sept. 22	129
1905	Apr. 29	Oct. 11	165	Apr. 30	Oct. 20	173	Apr. 30	Oct. 11	164	May 12	Oct. 10	151	May 3	Oct. 12	162	May 28	Oct. 12	137
1906	May 7	Oct. 6	152	May 7	Oct. 10	156	May 7	Oct. 10	156	May 10	Oct. 9	152	May 7	Oct. 6	152	May 27	Oct. 9	135
1907	May 8	Sept. 25	140	May 10	Sept. 30	143	May 27	Sept. 27	123	May 27	Sept. 25	121	May 20	Sept. 25	128	May 20	Sept. 27	130
1908	May 3	Sept. 28	148	May 2	Sept. 29	150	May 4	Sept. 29	148	May 7	Sept. 28	144	May 3	Sept. 28	148	May 5	Sept. 28	146
1909	May 10	Oct. 12	155	May 3	Oct. 12	162	May 10	Oct. 12	155	May 10	Oct. 11	154	May 10	Oct. 12	155	May 10	Sept. 24	137
1910	May 14	Oct. 6	145	do	Oct. 22	172	May 12	Sept. 12	123	June 2	Sept. 9	99	May 3	Oct. 22	172	May 13	Sept. 12	122
1911	May 3	Oct. 22	172	May 2	do	173	May 4	Oct. 20	169	May 12	Oct. 20	161	May 2	do	173	May 12	Oct. 19	160
1912	Apr. 30	Sept. 26	149	Apr. 27	Sept. 27	153	Apr. 29	Sept. 26	150	Apr. 27	Sept. 26	152	Apr. 28	Sept. 26	151	May 16	Sept. 27	134
1913	May 25	Sept. 22	120	do	Sept. 22	148	May 18	Sept. 21	126	May 6	Sept. 22	139	May 10	Sept. 22	135	May 26	Sept. 22	119
1914	May 12	Oct. 26	167	Apr. 20	Oct. 26	189	May 12	Oct. 14	155	May 12	Oct. 14	155	Apr. 30	Oct. 26	179	May 15	Sept. 25	133
1915	May 19	Oct. 7	141	Apr. 12	Oct. 9	180	May 18	Oct. 5	140	May 18	Oct. 5	140	May 18	Oct. 5	140	May 19	Aug. 17	90
1916	May 17	Sept. 17	123	Apr. 9	Oct. 10	184	May 17	Sept. 29	135	May 17	Sept. 30	136	May 3	Sept. 17	137	May 16	Sept. 16	123
1917	May 23	Sept. 10	110	Apr. 27	Oct. 6	162	May 27	Sept. 10	106	June 2	Oct. 6	126	Apr. 29	Oct. 6	160	May 27	Sept. 10	106
1918	May 15	Sept. 30	138	Apr. 30	Oct. 3	156	May 12	Sept. 17	128	May 13	Sept. 18	128	May 13	Sept. 18	128	May 13	Sept. 4	114
1919	May 6	Oct. 7	154	Apr. 25	Oct. 11	169	May 5	Oct. 10	158				Apr. 26	Oct. 11	168	May 8	Oct. 7	152
1920	May 3	Sept. 30	150	Apr. 28	Oct. 28	183	May 1	Oct. 28	180	Apr. 30	Sept. 30	153	Apr. 28	Oct. 1	156	May 14	Oct. 5	144
1921	May 15	Oct. 4	142	Apr. 17	Nov. 1	198	May 3	Nov. 1	182	May 15	Oct. 3	141	May 16	Oct. 3	140	May 16	Oct. 4	141
1922	Apr. 27	Oct. 12	168	Apr. 20	Oct. 12	175	Apr. 19	Oct. 12	176	May 12	Oct. 9	150	Apr. 28	Oct. 9	164	Apr. 29	Sept. 16	140
1923	May 16	Sept. 13	120	Apr. 17	Oct. 19	185	May 12	Sept. 13	124	May 16	Sept. 13	120	May 17	Sept. 13	119	May 17	Oct. 4	140
1924	May 29	Sept. 29	123	Apr. 22	Oct. 22	183	May 19	Oct. 10	144	May 24	Nov. 2	162	May 25	Sept. 30	128	May 29	Sept. 9	103
1925	May 25	Sept. 21	119	May 6	Oct. 10	157	May 17	Sept. 21	127	May 17	Sept. 21	127	do	Oct. 5	133	May 24	Oct. 3	132
1926	May 22	Sept. 24	125	Apr. 28	Sept. 25	150	May 22	Sept. 24	125	June 6	Sept. 24	110	May 22	Sept. 26	127	May 22	Sept. 25	126
1927	Apr. 30	Sept. 26	149	Apr. 23	Oct. 9	169	May 14	Sept. 23	132	May 3	Sept. 23	143	May 26	Sept. 20	117	May 18	Sept. 26	131
1928	Apr. 27	Sept. 23	149	Apr. 25	Oct. 29	187	May 5	do	141	May 27	do	119	June 10	Sept. 23	105	June 3	Sept. 25	114
1929	May 19	Sept. 18	122	May 16	Sept. 18	125	May 20	Sept. 18	121	June 1	Sept. 18	109	May 21	Sept. 18	120	do	Sept. 16	105
1930	May 27	Sept. 29	125	Apr. 25	Oct. 17	175	May 24	Sept. 28	127	May 17	Sept. 28	134	May 24	Sept. 28	127	May 18	Sept. 29	134
1931	May 7	Nov. 2	179	Apr. 27	Nov. 6	193	May 22	Sept. 24	125	May 8	Aug. 30	114	May 22	Oct. 12	143	May 21	Sept. 24	126
1932	May 1	Oct. 9	161	Apr. 26	Oct. 13	170	May 1	Oct. 5	157	May 17	Sept. 27	133	May 1	Sept. 29	151	May 17	Sept. 23	129
1933	May 10	Oct. 17	160	do	do	170	May 10	Oct. 8	151	May 2	Oct. 4	155	Apr. 27	Oct. 11	167	May 10	Sept. 29	142
1934	May 15	Oct. 26	164	Apr. 27	Oct. 28	184	May 11	Sept. 21	133	May 23	Sept. 21	121	May 15	Sept. 21	129	May 15	Aug. 20	97
1935	May 4	Sept. 27	146	Apr. 16	Oct. 4	171	May 10	Sept. 27	140	May 4	Sept. 27	146	May 3	Sept. 27	147	May 17	Sept. 21	127
1936	May 5	Oct. 12	160	Apr. 22	Oct. 21	182	Apr. 29	Sept. 29	153	May 3	do	147	Apr. 22	Sept. 30	161	May 3	Sept. 29	149
1937	May 14	Oct. 8	147	Apr. 10	Oct. 8	181	Apr. 27	Oct. 7	163	May 9	Sept. 16	130	May 14	Sept. 16	125	May 19	Sept. 19	123
1938	May 7	Oct. 22	168	Apr. 9	Oct. 24	198	May 6	Oct. 19	166	May 8	Sept. 19	134	Apr. 22	Oct. 20	181	May 24	Oct. 24	153
Mean	May 10	Oct. 5	148	Apr. 25	Oct. 13	171	May 8	Oct. 1	146	May 14	Sept. 27	136	May 10	Oct. 1	144	May 18	Sept. 24	129
Extremes	Apr. 16[2] May 29[3]	Sept. 10[4] Nov. 6[5]	[6] 110 [7] 186	Apr. 3[2] May 16[3]	Sept. 13[4] Nov. 7[5]	[6] 125 [7] 198	Apr. 18[2] May 27[3]	Sept. 10[4] Nov. 1[5]	[6] 106 [7] 182	Apr. 27[2] June 7[3]	Aug. 30[4] Nov. 2[5]	[6] 99 [7] 162	Apr. 22[2] June 10[3]	Sept. 11[4] Oct. 26[5]	[6] 105 [7] 181	Apr. 29[2] June 11[3]	Aug. 17[4] Oct. 24[5]	[6] 90 [7] 160

[1] Number of days between last killing frost in spring and first in fall.
[2] Earliest date in spring.
[3] Latest date in spring.
[4] Earliest date in fall.
[5] Latest date in fall.
[6] Shortest growing season.
[7] Longest growing season.

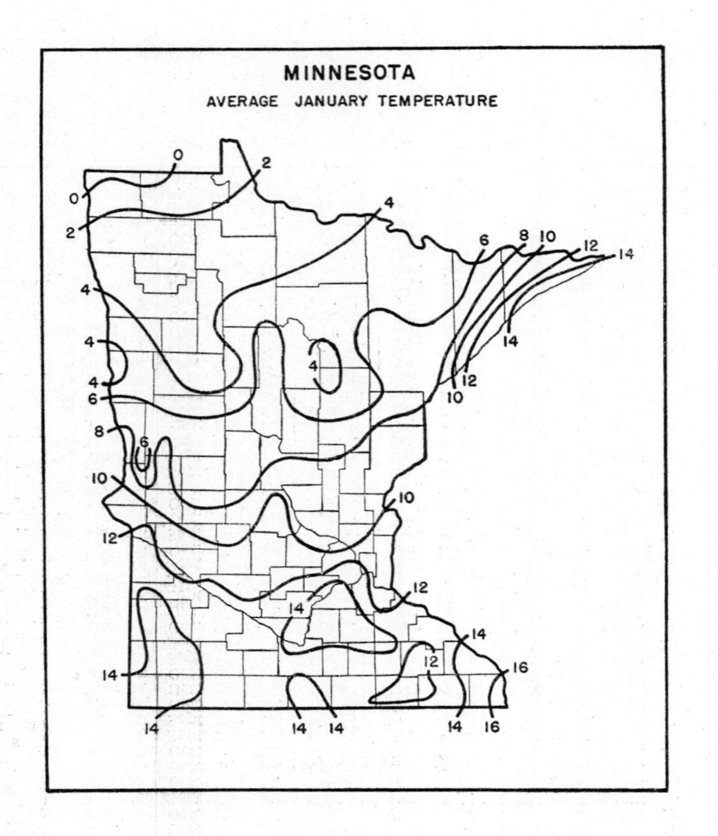
MINNESOTA
AVERAGE JANUARY TEMPERATURE

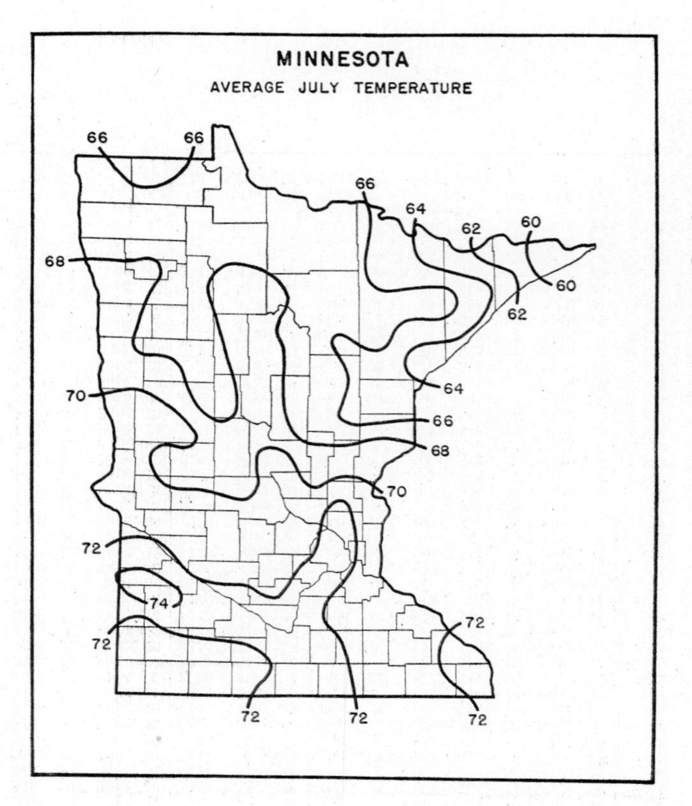
MINNESOTA
AVERAGE JULY TEMPERATURE

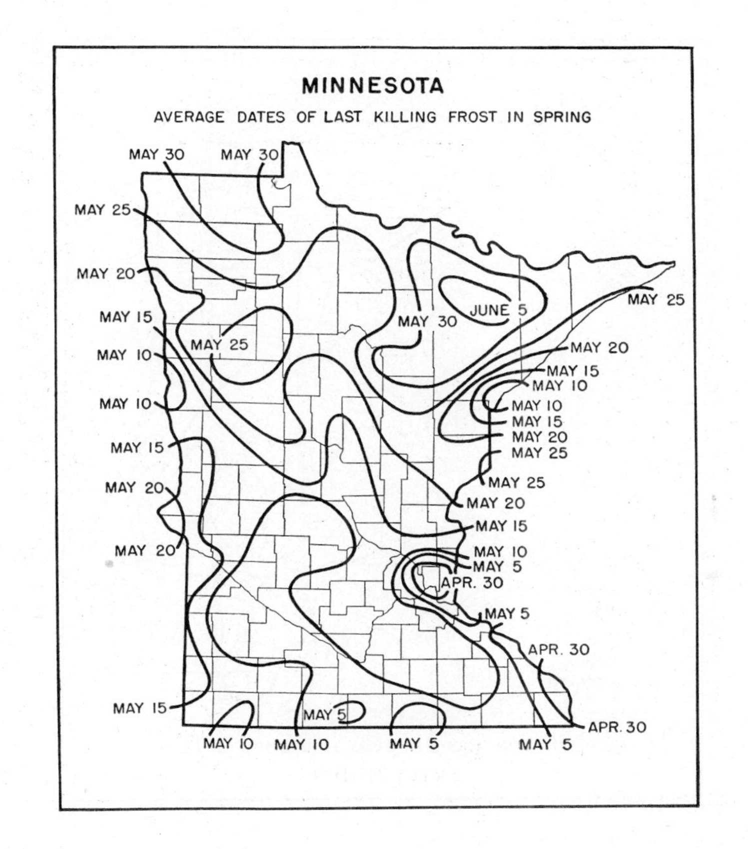
MINNESOTA
AVERAGE DATES OF LAST KILLING FROST IN SPRING
MAY 30
MAY 30
MAY 25
MAY 20
MAY 15
MAY 10
MAY 10
MAY 15
MAY 20
MAY 20
MAY 25
MAY 30
JUNE 5
MAY 25
MAY 20
MAY 15
MAY 10
MAY 10
MAY 15
MAY 20
MAY 25
MAY 25
MAY 20
MAY 15
MAY 10
MAY 5
APR. 30
MAY 5
APR. 30
MAY 15
MAY 5
APR. 30
MAY 10
MAY 10
MAY 5
MAY 5

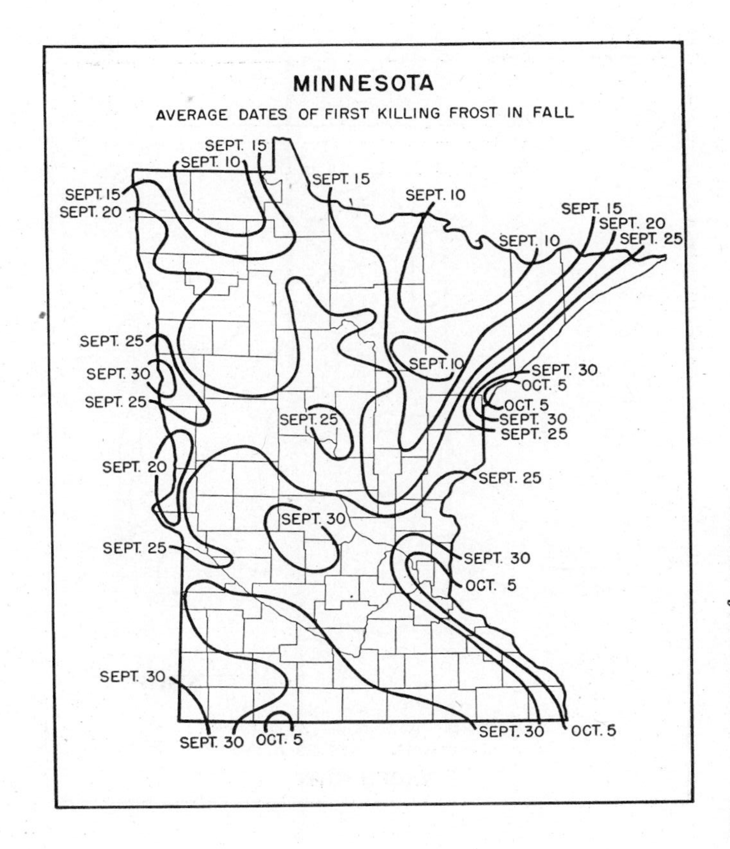
MINNESOTA
AVERAGE DATES OF FIRST KILLING FROST IN FALL
SEPT. 15
SEPT. 10
SEPT. 15
SEPT. 20
SEPT. 15
SEPT. 10
SEPT. 15
SEPT. 20
SEPT. 25
SEPT. 10
SEPT. 25
SEPT. 30
SEPT. 25
SEPT. 10
SEPT. 30
OCT. 5
OCT. 5
SEPT. 30
SEPT. 25
SEPT. 25
SEPT. 20
SEPT. 25
SEPT. 30
SEPT. 25
SEPT. 30
OCT. 5
SEPT. 30
SEPT. 30
OCT. 5
SEPT. 30
OCT. 5

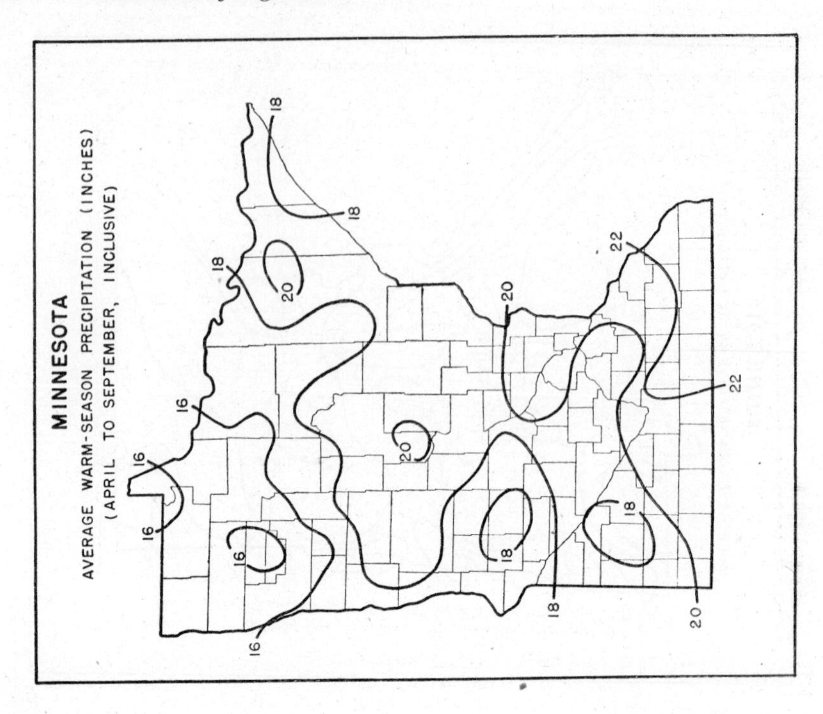
MINNESOTA
AVERAGE WARM-SEASON PRECIPITATION (INCHES)
(APRIL TO SEPTEMBER, INCLUSIVE)

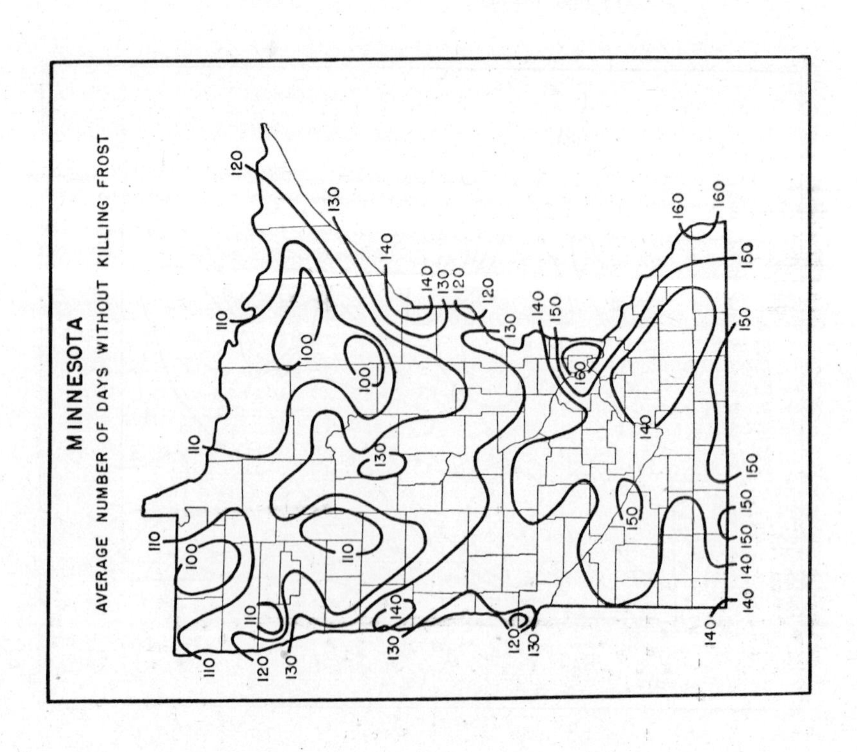
MINNESOTA
AVERAGE NUMBER OF DAYS WITHOUT KILLING FROST

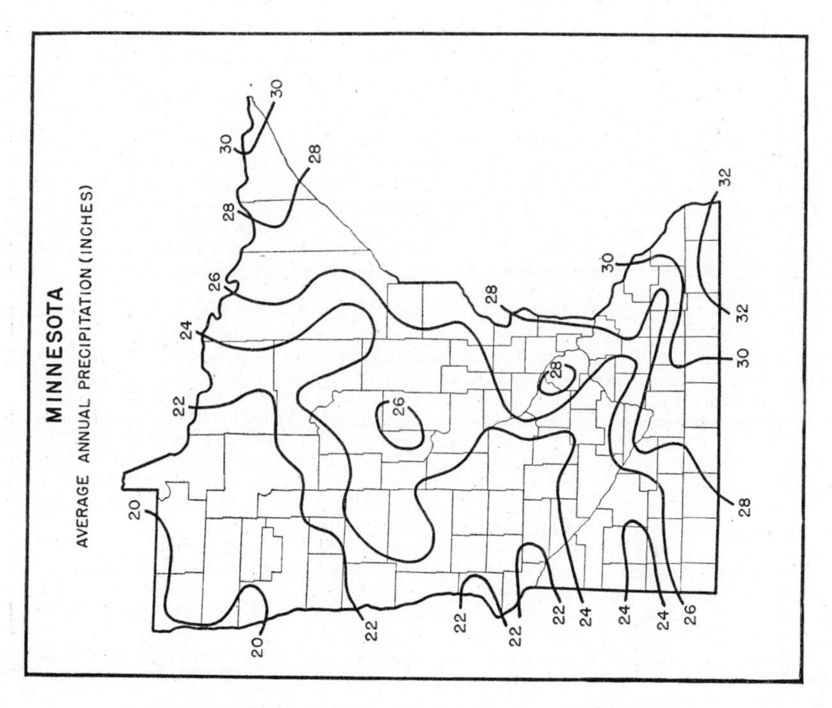

SUPPLEMENTARY CLIMATIC NOTES FOR MINNESOTA

Minnesota occupies a central position on the Continent of North America. The area of the State is 84,682 square miles, of which approximately 5,000 is the water surface of numerous lakes. The greatest distance across the State from north to south is 400 miles, and its greatest width, north of Lake Superior, 357.

The headwaters of 3 extensive drainage systems, flowing in opposite directions, lie within Minnesota. The drainage basins are the Mississippi (southward), the St. Lawrence (eastward), and Hudson Bay (northward). Thus delineated, its domain constitutes a plateau at the head of the Mississippi Valley that has an average elevation of 1,200 feet. This plateau is not high, but it has, in places, considerable relief. The highest point is 2,230 feet in the highlands north of Lake Superior, and the lowest is 602 feet at the surface of that lake. Other relatively low elevations are the Mississippi-Minnesota bottoms and the valley of the Red River of the North. The long, low slopes of prairie lands and forests do not gather water quickly into great volumes or roll it off readily; so the State is not particularly subject to floods.

Owing to its midcontinental location, Minnesota has a marked continental climate, characterized by wide variations in temperature, scanty winter precipitation, normally ample summer rainfall, and a general tendency to extremes in all climatic features. The most important influence on the climate is the succession of highs and lows (anticyclones and cyclones) that continually sweep across the Northern States from west to east. The disturbances of western Canada and the northern Rocky Mountain region, which are carried eastward across the upper Mississippi Valley, are succeeded by the cooler polar air masses of the anticyclones, resulting in alternating periods of heat and cold and of rainy weather and clear skies. The cyclonic control of climate gives Minnesota changeable weather that is stimulating and invigorating.

The average mean temperatures for the four seasons—winter, 12.4° F., spring, 41.6°, summer, 67.5°, and fall, 45°—show the considerable range between winter and summer. In the latitude of Minnesota, where crops are planted late in spring and mature early in fall, less importance is attached to severe winter temperatures than to the warmth and length of the growing season.

298737°—41——60

Because of a favorable growing season, Minnesota maintains a high rank in agricultural production. Wide variations in the length of the growing season are to be expected in a midcontinental area that covers 400 miles of latitude in the Temperate Zone. A short season of 90 to 110 days prevails in the Iron Ranges and along the Canadian boundary, but the season ranges from 130 to 160 days in other sections of the State.

The average date of the last killing frost in spring varies from May 5 in the extreme southeast to May 30 in the extreme north. Owing to the moderating effect of Lake Superior, killing frosts do not occur later in the spring at Duluth than at stations in extreme southern Minnesota. The average date of the first fall frost is September 9 in the Iron Ranges and October 5 in the southeastern lowlands. For the State as a whole, the average growing season for the period 1891–1939 was 133 days.

In recent years there has been a decrease in annual rainfall over vast areas in the Great Plains and the Mississippi Valley. This is not to be interpreted, however, as a definite climatic change to drier weather but rather as a long-period fluctuation to less than normal moisture, with a probable return to more than average rainfall in the generation to come.

The annual amount of precipitation, as of temperature, is less important than its distribution through the year. Vegetation is dormant during 7 months of the year; the major crops of grain and hay are produced during 4 months, May to August, during which 13.59 inches, or 55 percent of the annual rainfall, is normally received. Evaporation is less rapid in this State than in regions farther south, and consequently the demands of vegetation are not so great. These conditions tend to make the Minnesota annual rainfall of 25 inches more effective in crop-producing power than equal or even greater amounts in warmer climates. The average annual precipitation is greatest—32 inches—in the extreme southeastern counties and gradually diminishes in a northwesterly direction across the State to 19 inches in the lower valley of the Red River of the North.

Minnesota's high rank in agriculture indicates that sunshine is ample during the crop season. The average number of hours of sunshine is 2,604, or 57 percent of the possible amount.

Thunderstorms are the principal source of rain during the active vegetative period. The northern districts of the State have an average of 27 thunderstorms a year, and the southern sections 37. An average of 1 damaging or excessive rainstorm is experienced in each county during the summer season. Crop failures due to droughts can be expected on an average once in every 10 years in the western part of the State and about once in 20 years in the eastern districts.

Snowfall varies from 20 inches a year in the extreme southwestern corner of Minnesota to over 70 inches in the extreme northeast. It is light in the lower Red River of the North Valley and in south-central counties and moderately heavy in the Lake Superior district, the northern ranges, and the immediate vicinity of the Mississippi River.

Severe storms, such as tornadoes and ice storms, are not numerous, but they do occur occasionally. Its latitude places the State at the northern edge of the region of maximum tornado frequency, and the average number of active, well-defined, and destructive tornadic storms is three a year. Ice storms usually involve a large area and may do extensive damage to trees and overhead wires; fortunately, such storms are few.

MARTIN R. HOVDE, *Meteorologist and Climatic Section Director for Minnesota, Weather Bureau, Minneapolis.*

MISSISSIPPI

Climatic summary

County[1]	Station	Temperature: Length of record	January average	July average	Maximum	Minimum	Killing frost average dates: Length of record	Last in spring	First in fall	Growing season[2]	Average precipitation: Length of record	January	February	March	April	May	June	July	August	September	October	November	December	Annual
		Yr.	°*F*	°*F.*	°*F.*	°*F.*	*Yr.*			*Days*	*Yr.*	*In.*	*In.*	*In.*	*In.*	*In.*	*In.*	*In.*	*In.*	*In.*	*In.*	*In*	*In.*	*In.*
Adams	Natchez	40	51.0	81.5	105	2	39	Mar. 13	Nov. 13	245	40	5.30	5.09	5.35	5.38	5.03	3.68	5.15	3.88	2.83	2.50	4.12	6.35	54.66
Alcorn	Corinth	40	42.0	81.0	111	−8	38	Mar. 28	Oct. 31	217	40	4.96	4.19	5.60	4.86	4.63	3.78	4.29	4.08	3.31	3.42	3.82	5.57	52.51
Attala	Kosciusko	40	46.6	80.8	109	−8	38	Mar. 29	Nov. 2	218	40	4.98	5.20	6.17	5.04	4.39	3.73	4.45	3.55	2.77	2.86	3.58	5.34	52.06
Bolivar	Cleveland										25	5.18	3.77	5.33	4.83	4.42	3.60	3.67	3.07	2.59	3.03	4.48	5.75	49.72
	Rosedale	38	44.4	82.0	110	−5	29	Mar. 23	Nov. 1	223	29	4.80	4.47	5.44	5.29	4.26	3.01	3.23	3.34	2.62	2.90	4.20	6.02	49.58
	Scott	20	45.8	81.7	108	−4	19	Mar. 25	Nov. 5	225	21	5.02	3.95	5.34	5.33	4.86	3.06	3.45	2.70	2.57	3.20	4.94	5.94	50.36
Chickasaw	Okolona	28	43.2	81.5	110	−6	27	Mar. 29	Nov. 1	217	28	4.39	4.54	5.31	4.63	4.20	3.74	4.69	3.90	2.31	2.39	3.32	5.17	48.59
Claiborne	Port Gibson	40	48.8	80.7	107	−3	39	Mar. 23	Nov. 2	224	40	5.12	4.94	5.58	5.59	4.70	4.47	4.72	3.83	2.68	2.67	3.85	6.16	54.31
Clarke	Enterprise										34	5.65	5.42	5.65	5.42	5.24	4.36	6.02	4.07	3.11	2.63	3.83	5.74	57.14
	Shubuta	24	49.4	81.4	109	10	18	Mar. 22	Nov. 4	227	34	6.05	5.17	5.75	5.48	4.84	4.14	6.12	4.48	3.44	2.67	3.64	5.95	57.73
Clay	West Point	10	47.1	81.3	109	−1	10	Mar. 24	Nov. 5	226	10	4.22	4.20	5.60	3.72	4.56	2.52	3.90	3.02	3.16	3.27	4.36	4.80	47.33
Coahoma	Clarksdale	28	44.5	81.9	108	−8	31	Mar. 29	Nov. 1	217	32	5.06	4.23	5.59	4.84	4.55	3.57	3.40	3.33	2.25	2.99	4.18	5.20	49.19
Copiah	Crystal Springs	40	48.2	81.2	108	−7	40	Mar. 21	Nov. 10	234	40	5.03	5.09	5.32	5.54	5.08	4.27	5.23	4.38	2.57	2.92	3.47	5.72	54.62
	Hazelhurst	23	48.0	80.8	106	5	19	Mar. 10	do	245	21	4.50	5.66	4.90	6.35	5.00	4.77	5.61	4.69	3.20	3.39	3.25	5.92	57.24
Covington	Collins										20	5.76	5.03	5.64	5.39	4.28	3.60	6.60	4.54	3.24	2.78	3.70	5.42	55.98
De Soto	Hernando	38	42.4	80.9	110	−12	38	Mar. 26	Nov. 5	224	33	4.43	3.74	5.46	5.40	4.58	3.36	3.45	3.33	2.85	3.02	3.93	4.95	48.50
Forrest	Fruitland Park	20	51.6	81.7	105	11	15	Mar. 12	Nov. 18	251	22	5.45	5.13	5.89	5.00	5.01	4.84	6.71	5.36	3.09	3.92	4.34	4.89	59.63
	Hattiesburg	40	50.2	82.1	106	−1	34	Mar. 13	Nov. 1	233	37	5.55	5.47	5.60	5.23	4.97	4.72	6.50	5.02	3.53	2.81	3.62	5.50	58.52
Franklin	Meadville	18	50.8	80.8	105	8					22	5.12	5.17	5.36	5.60	5.14	4.23	6.54	5.20	3.06	3.08	3.03	6.30	57.83
George	Merrill										34	5.38	5.54	6.82	5.73	5.55	5.50	7.71	5.49	4.50	3.14	3.60	5.53	64.49
Greene	Leakesville	40	50.7	81.3	109	−5	33	Mar. 17	Nov. 10	238	39	5.25	5.59	5.98	5.36	5.29	5.06	7.37	5.21	4.12	2.95	3.32	5.85	61.35
Grenada	Grenada										28	4.62	4.16	5.40	5.28	3.88	3.40	3.74	3.55	2.55	2.47	3.56	5.59	48.20
Hancock	Bay St. Louis	40	53.3	81.6	104	2	38	Mar. 2	Nov. 28	271	39	5.00	5.22	5.40	5.58	5.51	4.35	6.98	6.73	5.14	3.60	3.41	5.29	62.21
	Pearlington	40	53.0	80.7	105	5	36	Mar. 6	Nov. 20	259	40	4.74	4.52	5.22	5.23	5.07	5.05	7.68	6.70	4.60	3.91	3.30	5.12	61.14
Harrison	Biloxi	40	53.7	81.9	104	1	39	Feb. 26	Nov. 29	276	39	4.20	4.68	5.35	5.15	5.04	4.67	7.00	5.98	5.02	3.68	2.98	4.92	58.67
Hinds	Edwards	21	48.9	81.3	104	−5	21	Mar. 15	Nov. 7	237	21	5.38	5.44	5.46	6.06	4.58	4.21	4.94	3.93	3.05	2.93	3.01	5.57	54.56
	Jackson	40	49.0	81.5	107	3	37	Mar. 19	Nov. 8	234	40	4.91	4.86	5.41	5.43	4.48	4.18	4.43	3.77	2.66	2.42	3.30	5.44	51.29
	Utica	35	50.1	80.9	105	0	32	Mar. 18	Nov. 7	234	35	5.10	4.68	5.43	5.45	4.76	4.33	5.06	3.64	2.64	2.76	3.67	5.54	53.06
Holmes	Ichula	16	47.9	80.4	103	−1	17	Mar. 21	Oct. 31	224	18	5.16	5.14	6.08	6.68	5.05	3.72	4.77	4.72	2.75	2.58	3.42	5.63	55.70
Itawamba	Fulton										30	4.75	4.60	5.93	5.06	4.90	3.87	4.70	3.63	2.81	2.99	3.73	5.48	52.45

[1] The following counties, for which no records are available, are best represented by the stations indicated: Amite—Woodville; Benton—Holly Springs; Calhoun—Water Valley; Carroll—Greenwood; Choctaw-State College; Humphreys—Tohula; Issaquena—Vicksburg; Jefferson Davis—Monticello; Lamar—Columbia; Neshoba—Edinburg; Perry—Hattiesburg; Quitman—Clarksdale; Rankin—Jackson; Simpson—Crystal Springs; Smith—Forrest; Stone—Fruitland Park; Tate—Hernando; Tishomingo—Corinth; Union—Pontotoc; Walthall—Magnolia.

[2] Length of growing season between average dates of last killing frost in spring and first in fall.

MISSISSIPPI—Continued

Climatic summary—Continued

County	Station	Temperature: Length of record	Temperature: January average	Temperature: July average	Temperature: Maximum	Temperature: Minimum	Killing frost average dates: Length of record	Killing frost: Last in spring	Killing frost: First in fall	Growing season	Average precipitation: Length of record	January	February	March	April	May	June	July	August	September	October	November	December	Annual
		Yr.	°F.	°F.	°F.	°F.	Yr.			Days	Yr.	In.	In.	In.	In.	In.	In.	In.	In.	In.	In.	In.	In.	In.
Jackson	Pascagoula	12	53.2	81.0	101	16	11	Feb. 25	Dec. 1	279	11	3.85	3.78	4.15	4.88	3.44	4.11	6.02	7.13	6.36	4.09	3.13	4.66	55.60
Jasper	Lake Como	9	49.3	80.2	105	11	9	Mar. 26	Oct. 31	219	12	4.05	5.44	4.68	4.57	5.65	4.10	5.24	4.01	3.69	1.92	2.89	4.64	50.88
Jefferson	Fayette	34	49.0	80.2	104	−3	33	Mar. 22	Nov. 3	226	33	5.38	5.07	5.49	4.93	4.66	4.41	5.50	4.53	3.32	2.49	3.67	5.89	55.34
Jones	Laurel	35	50.2	81.1	106	9	32	Mar. 21	Nov. 8	232	34	5.50	5.43	5.79	5.50	4.36	4.23	6.47	4.38	3.07	2.52	3.60	5.84	56.69
Kemper	Porterville	11	48.8	80.3	106	11	11	Mar. 31	Oct. 25	208	11	4.37	4.91	5.32	4.83	6.08	5.50	4.91	4.07	3.64	2.12	3.23	5.58	54.56
Lafayette	University	39	43.4	80.2	110	−10	35	Mar. 29	Nov. 2	218	36	5.00	4.22	5.81	4.97	4.42	4.17	4.24	3.36	3.06	2.68	4.21	5.71	51.85
Lauderdale	Merdian	40	48.2	80.3	105	−6	40	Mar. 17	Nov. 11	239	40	5.22	5.16	5.19	5.16	4.37	4.55	5.29	4.37	2.92	2.40	3.45	5.28	53.36
Lawrence	Monticello	31	51.1	81.1	108	7	31	Mar. 25	Nov. 4	224	31	6.31	4.83	5.63	5.94	5.05	4.22	5.63	4.61	2.52	2.83	4.19	5.85	57.61
Leake	Edinburg	28	47.7	80.9	108	0	26	Mar. 28	Nov. 2	219	31	5.03	4.89	6.24	5.55	4.76	3.92	4.34	3.96	2.96	2.55	3.58	5.93	53.71
	Walnut Grove	7	47.2	80.0	104	−7	7	Mar. 21	Nov. 5	229	7	5.64	5.18	5.13	3.78	3.72	3.73	4.05	4.09	2.67	2.90	1.83	4.00	46.72
Lee	Tupelo	32	44.1	80.7	109	−10	31	Mar. 30	Nov. 1	216	37	4.62	4.45	6.14	4.41	4.71	3.87	4.24	3.70	3.15	2.82	3.92	5.46	51.49
Leflore	Greenwood	39	46.5	82.1	111	−6	38	Mar. 24	Oct. 31	221	38	4.99	4.77	5.83	5.45	4.54	3.68	4.25	3.26	2.46	2.83	4.24	6.27	52.57
	Shellmound										9	4.55	3.97	5.74	4.32	4.44	3.15	3.37	2.96	2.37	2.73	4.74	7.83	50.17
Lincoln	Brookhaven	40	50.3	81.9	107	−10	39	Mar. 16	Nov. 13	242	39	5.41	5.16	4.89	5.19	4.88	4.26	5.42	4.38	2.88	2.79	3.72	5.75	54.73
Lowndes	Columbus	40	46.0	82.0	113	−5	40	Mar. 25	Nov. 2	222	40	4.74	4.78	6.01	4.74	4.59	3.77	4.38	4.00	2.74	3.04	3.79	5.17	51.75
Madison	Canton	40	49.0	81.5	108	−3	36	Mar. 21	Nov. 7	231	39	5.14	4.67	5.87	5.24	4.26	3.36	3.91	3.34	2.18	2.47	3.18	5.45	49.07
	Shocco	15	48.6	80.6	105	7	11	Mar. 27	Nov. 3	221	15	4.30	4.86	5.36	4.82	5.43	3.77	4.34	4.80	3.33	2.22	2.35	4.83	50.41
Marion	Columbia	23	51.6	82.1	108	9	22	Mar. 16	Nov. 7	236	35	6.08	5.38	5.51	5.34	5.52	4.57	5.98	4.70	4.03	3.03	3.74	5.89	59.77
Marshall	Holly Springs	40	41.7	80.8	115	−9	38	Mar. 27	Nov. 4	222	40	5.10	4.25	5.82	5.09	4.61	4.12	3.66	3.71	3.39	3.04	3.98	5.70	52.47
Monroe	Aberdeen	40	45.0	81.5	114	−15	38	Mar. 26	Oct. 31	219	40	4.60	4.83	5.83	5.00	4.42	3.94	4.75	3.98	2.53	2.95	3.59	5.16	51.58
Montgomery	Duck Hill	38	45.8	80.6	109	−4	36	Mar. 31	Oct. 21	204	36	5.19	4.68	5.84	5.46	4.23	3.72	4.21	3.55	2.83	2.53	3.96	5.94	52.14
Newton	Hickory										27	6.55	5.05	6.28	5.67	4.23	3.79	6.52	4.08	3.12	2.99	4.50	6.34	59.12
Noxubee	Macon	40	46.3	81.6	109	−5	37	Mar. 27	Nov. 2	220	33	4.97	4.58	5.77	5.32	5.01	3.49	4.47	3.43	3.08	2.93	3.64	5.64	52.33
Oktibbeha	State College	40	46.0	81.5	111	−8	36	Mar. 25	Nov. 6	226	40	4.81	4.58	6.30	4.93	4.50	4.09	4.34	3.67	2.56	2.82	3.49	5.16	51.25
Panola	Batesville	40	43.6	80.8	108	−8	40	Mar. 30	Oct. 28	212	40	5.06	4.24	5.71	4.88	4.48	3.88	3.67	3.57	2.99	2.61	4.24	5.60	50.93
Pearl River	Poplarville	35	53.9	81.3	104	12	18	Mar. 9	Nov. 20	256	35	5.34	5.33	5.46	5.13	5.37	5.16	7.31	5.76	4.48	3.29	3.53	5.35	61.51
Pike	Magnolia	40	52.0	81.4	107	−1	40	Mar. 15	Nov. 10	240	40	6.19	5.74	5.76	5.65	5.18	4.57	6.47	4.92	3.21	2.92	3.58	5.94	60.13
Pontotoc	Pontotoc	40	43.9	79.9	111	−11	37	Mar. 29	Oct. 30	215	39	4.68	3.92	5.24	4.51	3.96	4.00	4.31	3.34	2.78	2.52	3.31	5.09	47.66
Prentiss	Booneville	40	42.5	79.8	108	−10	39	do	Nov. 2	218	40	5.14	4.38	5.76	4.89	4.63	4.02	4.10	3.61	2.95	3.23	3.93	5.90	52.54
Scott	Forest	40	47.7	79.9	107	−10	37	Mar. 23	Nov. 6	228	34	4.89	5.13	5.29	4.86	4.70	4.38	5.38	4.80	2.87	2.46	3.36	5.21	53.33
Sharkey	Anguilla	30	48.0	81.9	107	1	26	Mar. 25	Nov. 5	225	28	5.50	5.01	6.04	5.60	5.29	3.63	4.00	3.50	2.31	3.18	3.97	6.55	54.58
Sunflower	Moorhead	25	46.5	81.8	110	−7	22	Mar. 26	Nov. 2	221	25	5.10	3.80	5.60	5.35	4.27	3.50	3.72	2.84	2.44	2.86	4.15	5.63	49.26
Tallahatchie	Charleston	8	44.3	81.5	104	−3	10	Apr. 1	Oct. 28	210	12	5.60	3.97	5.94	6.20	3.42	4.34	4.02	3.90	3.01	3.26	3.35	6.29	53.30
	Swan Lake										31	4.86	4.38	5.56	5.22	5.39	3.88	3.87	2.95	2.73	2.73	4.39	6.02	51.98
Tippah	Ripley	10	41.8	78.3	105	0	10	Apr. 10	Oct. 24	197	10	4.78	5.38	6.72	4.96	5.67	3.71	4.41	3.69	4.16	3.01	3.70	6.49	56.68
Tunica	Tunica	39	43.7	80.8	108	−9	36	Mar. 25	Nov. 2	222	39	5.73	4.23	5.68	5.15	4.35	3.73	3.85	3.18	3.09	3.06	4.25	5.84	52.14

Warren	Vicksburg	40	49.6	81.0	104	−1	40	Mar. 8	Nov. 15	252	40	4.89	4.71	5.57	5.24	4.21	3.44	4.25	3.20	2.31	2.61	3.46	5.51	49.40
Washington	Greenville	40	46.2	82.2	110	−5	40	Mar. 21	Nov. 5	229	40	4.97	4.49	5.67	5.14	4.68	3.43	3.39	3.66	2.98	2.62	4.16	6.46	51.65
	Stoneville	8	47.5	82.3	109	5	9	Mar. 28	do	222	24	5.10	4.00	5.00	4.78	4.35	3.12	3.12	3.02	2.25	3.10	4.16	6.18	48.18
Wayne	Waynesboro	40	49.8	81.0	109	−2	39	Mar. 23	do	227	40	5.44	5.39	5.87	5.54	4.85	4.38	6.46	4.82	3.58	2.98	3.37	5.86	58.54
Webster	Eupora	8	47.5	81.8	108	0	12	Mar. 27	Nov. 2	220	12	4.78	4.03	6.03	4.37	4.52	3.49	4.64	3.33	2.57	3.14	4.14	5.42	50.46
Wilkinson	Woodville	40	51.8	81.2	104	−3	40	Mar. 15	Nov. 14	244	40	6.09	5.07	5.83	5.79	5.33	4.22	6.69	5.41	3.07	3.26	4.10	6.65	61.51
Winston	Louisville	40	46.9	80.4	107	−13	40	Mar. 28	Nov. 3	220	40	5.00	5.15	6.14	4.97	4.50	3.93	4.56	4.31	2.98	2.64	3.34	5.47	52.99
Yalobusha	Water Valley	39	44.6	80.8	110	−9	40	Mar. 31	Nov. 1	215	40	5.13	4.78	6.25	5.58	5.17	4.47	4.52	3.63	3.00	3.05	4.11	6.38	56.07
Yazoo	Holly Bluff										25	5.16	4.67	6.40	5.38	3.68	3.57	4.03	2.73	2.31	3.05	4.04	5.96	50.98
	Yazoo City	40	47.7	81.8	110	−2	40	Mar. 22	Nov. 2	225	40	4.88	4.65	5.83	5.27	4.43	3.61	4.31	3.69	2.32	2.58	3.65	5.61	50.83

Precipitation—State unit values

[This tabulation gives the mean annual, mean monthly, and average seasonal precipitation, 1886–1938, for Mississippi]

Precipitation		Precipitation		Precipitation		Precipitation		Precipitation		Precipitation	
Year	Mean	Year	Mean	Year	Mean	Year	Mean	Month	Mean	Season	Average
	In.		*In.*		*In.*		*In.*		*In.*		*In.*
1886	56.28	1900	65.16	1914	46.58	1928	51.27	January	5.16	Winter	15.26
1887	43.88	1901	49.85	1915	53.94	1929	60.03	February	4.84	Spring	14.86
1888	50.82	1902	48.07	1916	51.50	1930	47.32	March	5.68	Summer	13.44
1889	38.31	1903	46.59	1917	45.16	1931	52.39	April	4.90	Fall	9.30
1890	56.23	1904	41.47	1918	50.64	1932	67.71	May	4.28		
1891	56.24	1905	63.38	1919	69.24	1933	50.33	June	4.25		
1892	57.47	1906	54.37	1920	62.85	1934	53.43	July	4.98		
1893	51.54	1907	54.12	1921	48.25	1935	51.53	August	4.21		
1894	47.60	1908	54.78	1922	59.44	1936	44.47	September	3.06		
1895	47.69	1909	57.97	1923	71.03	1937	55.21	October	2.62		
1896	43.53	1910	47.12	1924	40.06	1938	48.85	November	3.62		
1897	47.78	1911	59.52	1925	49.23			December	5.26		
1898	54.22	1912	64.87	1926	56.18						
1899	44.79	1913	57.29	1927	55.29			Annual	52.86		

MISSISSIPPI—Continued

Dates of last killing frost in spring and first in fall, with length of growing season

Year	Batesville			Corinth			Kosciusko			Vicksburg			Meridian			Biloxi		
	Last in spring	First in fall	Growing season[1]	Last in spring	First in fall	Growing season[1]	Last in spring	First in fall	Growing season[1]	Last in spring	First in fall	Growing season[1]	Last in spring	First in fall	Growing season[1]	Last in spring	First in fall	Growing season[1]
			Days			*Days*			*Days*			*Days*			*Days*			*Days*
1899	Apr. 1	Nov. 3	216	Apr. 4	Nov. 4	214	Mar. 29	Nov. 3	219	Mar. 7	Nov. 3	241	Apr. 10	Nov. 3	207	Feb. 13	Nov. 3	263
1900	do.	Nov. 9	222	Apr. 1	Nov. 9	222	Apr. 1	Nov. 9	222	Mar. 16	Nov. 12	241	Apr. 1	Nov. 9	222	Feb. 18	None	317
1901	Mar. 21	Nov. 6	230				Mar. 21			Mar. 7	Nov. 16	254	Mar. 21	Nov. 6	230	Mar. 7	Nov. 17	255
1902	Mar. 19			Mar. 19	Oct. 29	224		Oct. 29		Mar. 6	Dec. 6	275	Mar. 19	Nov. 28	254	Mar. 6	Dec. 26	295
1903	Mar. 25	Oct. 19	208		Oct. 24		Mar. 25	Oct. 25	214	Feb. 19	Oct. 25	248	Mar. 26	Oct. 25	213	Feb. 18	Nov. 19	274
1904	Mar. 28	Oct. 23	209	Mar. 28	Oct. 23	209		Oct. 24		Mar. 4	Nov. 12	253	Mar. 4	Nov. 11	252	Jan. 27	Dec. 18	326
1905	Apr. 17	Oct. 22	188	Apr. 17	Nov. 2	199	Apr. 17	Nov. 11	208	Feb. 16	Nov. 30	287	Feb. 16	do.	268	Feb. 16	Dec. 14	291
1906	Apr. 1	Oct. 11	193	Mar. 21	Oct. 11	204	Mar. 21	Oct. 29	222	Mar. 21	Nov. 13	237	Mar. 21	Oct. 29	222	Mar. 21	Nov. 13	237
1907	Apr. 14	Oct. 14	183	Apr. 14	Nov. 12	212	Apr. 14	do.	198	Feb. 6	do.	280	Feb. 16	Nov. 13	270	None	do.	317
1908	Mar. 21	Oct. 29	222	Mar. 21	Nov. 6	230	Mar. 21	Oct. 25	218	Feb. 21	Nov. 12	265	Feb. 28	Oct. 25	240	Feb. 21	Nov. 16	269
1909	Apr. 9	Oct. 13	187	Mar. 16	Oct. 13	211	Mar. 16	Oct. 13	211	Feb. 17	Nov. 18	274	Mar. 16	Nov. 19	248	Feb. 17	Dec. 8	294
1910	Apr. 25	Oct. 28	186	do.	Oct. 29	227	Apr. 26	Oct. 29	186	Feb. 25	Oct. 29	246	Apr. 25	Oct. 29	187	Feb. 19	Oct. 30	253
1911	Mar. 24	Nov. 2	223	do.	Nov. 2	231	Mar. 28	Oct. 23	209	Feb. 23	Nov. 13	263	Mar. 3	Nov. 13	255	Feb. 23	Nov. 13	263
1912	Mar. 25	Nov. 3	223	Mar. 25	Nov. 3	223	Mar. 25	Nov. 3	223	Feb. 27	Nov. 3	250	Mar. 16	Nov. 3	232	Feb. 22	Nov. 28	280
1913	Mar. 28	Oct. 21	207	Mar. 28	Oct. 21	207	Mar. 28	Oct. 21	207	Mar. 16	Oct. 30	228	Mar. 28	Oct. 28	214	Feb. 14	Dec. 9	298
1914	Apr. 10	Oct. 28	201	Apr. 10	Oct. 28	201	Apr. 10	Oct. 28	201	Mar. 23	Oct. 28	219	Apr. 10	do.	201	Mar. 23	Nov. 20	242
1915	Apr. 4	Oct. 10	189	Apr. 4	Nov. 15	225	Apr. 4	Nov. 16	226	Feb. 7	Nov. 16	282	Apr. 4	Nov. 16	226	Mar. 22	Dec. 21	274
1916	Apr. 9	Oct. 21	195	Mar. 16	Oct. 22	220	Mar. 16	Oct. 22	220	Mar. 16	Nov. 15	244	Mar. 16	Oct. 22	220	Feb. 16	Nov. 15	273
1917	Mar. 6	Oct. 13	221	Mar. 28	Oct. 11	197	Mar. 19	Oct. 13	208	Mar. 5	Oct. 20	229	Mar. 6	Oct. 13	221	Mar. 5	Nov. 24	264
1918	Apr. 13	Nov. 1	202	Apr. 12	Nov. 1	203	Apr. 12	Nov. 1	203	Feb. 4	Nov. 24	293	Apr. 12	Dec. 2	234	Jan. 23	Dec. 26	337
1919	Apr. 1	Nov. 13	226	Apr. 26	Nov. 14	202	Apr. 2	Nov. 14	226	Mar. 1	Nov. 14	258	Mar. 1	Nov. 14	258		Dec. 15	
1920	Apr. 5	Nov. 12	221	Apr. 4	Oct. 29	208	Apr. 5	Nov. 4	213	Mar. 8	Nov. 13	250	Mar. 9	Nov. 13	249	Mar. 8	Nov. 13	250
1921	Apr. 18	do.	208	Apr. 11	Oct. 14	186	Apr. 18	Nov. 11	207	Feb. 20	Dec. 18	301	Feb. 24	Dec. 5	284	None	None	366
1922	Mar. 8	Oct. 19	225	Mar. 22	Nov. 10	233	Mar. 8	Nov. 26	263	Mar. 4	Dec. 19	290	Mar. 8	Dec. 13	280	Mar. 4		
1923	Apr. 1	Oct. 22	204	Apr. 1	Nov. 1	214	Apr. 1	Nov. 18	231	Mar. 20	Nov. 30	255	Apr. 1	Nov. 10	223	Mar. 20	None	287
1924	Apr. 2	Oct. 23	204	Apr. 2	Oct. 24	205	Apr. 2	Oct. 25	206	Mar. 15	Nov. 25	255	Mar. 15	Nov. 19	249	Mar. 15	Nov. 25	255
1925	Mar. 15	Oct. 20	219		Oct. 20		Mar. 3	Oct. 20	231	Mar. 3	Nov. 23	265	Mar. 3	Nov. 9	251	Mar. 3	Nov. 23	265
1926	Apr. 1	Oct. 25	207	Apr. 1	Oct. 25	207	Apr. 1	Oct. 25	207	Apr. 1	Nov. 10	223	Apr. 1	Nov. 3	216	Mar. 14	Nov. 19	250
1927	Mar. 25	Oct. 19	208	Mar. 4	Nov. 6	247	Mar. 4	Nov. 18	259	Mar. 3	Nov. 18	260	Mar. 4	Nov. 20	261	Mar. 3	Nov. 18	260
1928	Apr. 16	Nov. 4	202	Apr. 16	Nov. 11	209	Apr. 16	Nov. 5	203	Mar. 18	Nov. 21	248	Mar. 18	Nov. 21	248	Mar. 18	Nov. 21	248
1929	Mar. 17	Oct. 25	222	Mar. 10	Nov. 5	240	Mar. 10	do.	240	Mar. 10	Nov. 23	258	Feb. 23	Nov. 30	280	Feb. 12	Nov. 30	291
1930	Mar. 31	do.	208	Mar. 31	Oct. 31	214	Mar. 31	Oct. 31	214	Mar. 29	Nov. 1	217	Mar. 29	Nov. 1	217	Mar. 29	Nov. 1	217
1931	Mar. 29	Nov. 1	217	Mar. 17	Nov. 7	235	Mar. 29	Nov. 1	217	Mar. 10	Dec. 15	280	Mar. 10	Nov. 7	242	Mar. 10	None	297
1932	Mar. 15	Nov. 12	242	Mar. 15	Nov. 12	242	Mar. 15	Nov. 12	242	Mar. 13	Nov. 12	244	Mar. 15	Nov. 12	242	Mar. 13	Nov. 12	244
1933	Mar. 21	Nov. 8	232	Mar. 21	Nov. 8	232	Mar. 21	Nov. 8	232	Mar. 21	Nov. 10	234	Mar. 21	Nov. 9	233	Mar. 21	Dec. 27	281
1934	Mar. 29	Nov. 12	228	Mar. 28	Nov. 12	229	Mar. 28	Nov. 12	229	Mar. 28	Nov. 12	229	Mar. 20	Nov. 12	237	Mar. 11	Dec. 8	272
1935	Mar. 8	Nov. 18	255	Mar. 8	Nov. 21	258	Mar. 12	Nov. 18	251	Mar. 1	Nov. 23	267	Mar. 1	Nov. 21	265	Mar. 1	Nov. 23	267

1936	Apr. 3	Nov. 5	216	Apr. 3	Nov. 5	216	Apr. 3	Nov. 5	216	Apr. 3	Nov. 5	216	Feb. 22	Nov. 5	257	Feb. 19	Nov. 5	260
1937	Mar. 29	Oct. 24	209	Mar. 29	Oct. 24	209	----------	Oct. 24	------	Mar. 28	Oct. 23	209	Mar. 29	Oct. 24	209	Mar. 16	Nov. 20	249
1938	Apr. 10	Oct. 25	198	Apr. 10	Oct. 25	198	Apr. 10	Oct. 25	198	Apr. 10	Nov. 9	213	Apr. 10	Nov. 25	229	Feb. 1	Nov. 25	297
Mean	Mar. 30	Oct. 28	212	Mar. 28	Oct. 31	217	Mar. 29	Nov. 2	218	Mar. 8	Nov. 15	252	Mar. 17	Nov. 11	239	Feb. 26	Nov. 29	276
Extremes	Mar. 6[2]	Oct. 10[4]	[6] 183	Mar. 4[2]	Oct. 11[4]	[6] 186	Mar. 3[2]	Oct. 13[4]	[6] 186	Feb. 4[2]	Oct. 20[4]	[6] 209	Feb. 16[2]	Oct. 13[4]	[6] 186	None[2]	Oct. 30[4]	[6] 217
	Apr. 25[3]	Nov. 18[5]	[7] 255	Apr. 26[3]	Nov. 21[5]	[7] 258	Apr. 26[3]	Nov. 26[5]	[7] 263	Apr. 10[3]	Dec. 19[5]	[7] 301	Apr. 25[3]	Dec. 13[5]	[7] 284	Mar. 29[3]	None[5]	[7] 365

[1] Number of days between last killing frost in spring and first in fall.
[2] Earliest date in spring.
[3] Latest date in spring.
[4] Earliest date in fall.
[5] Latest date in fall.
[6] Shortest growing season.
[7] Longest growing season.

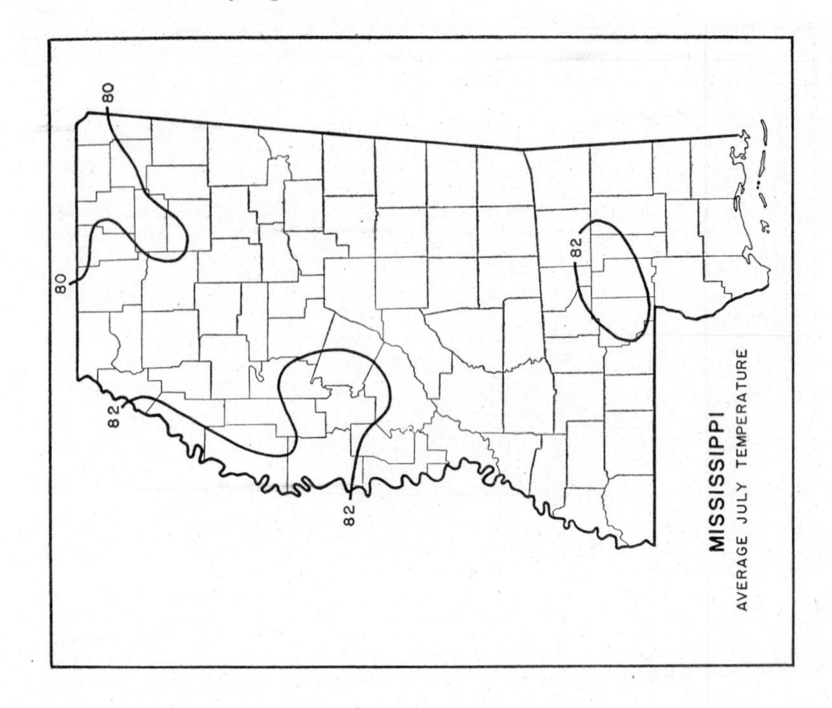
MISSISSIPPI
AVERAGE JULY TEMPERATURE
80
80
82
82
82

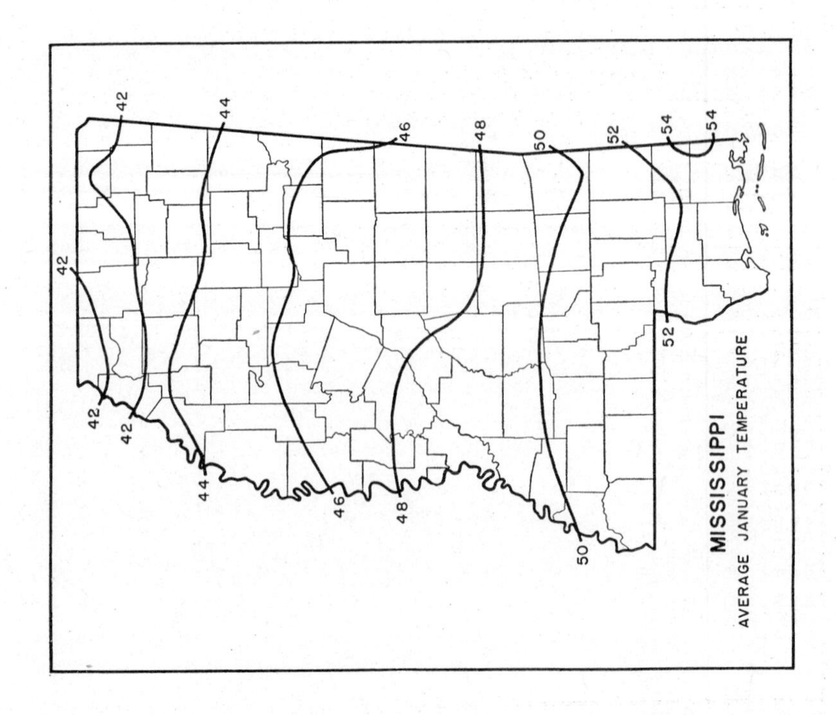
MISSISSIPPI
AVERAGE JANUARY TEMPERATURE
42
42
42
42
44
44
46
46
48
48
50
50
52
52
54
54

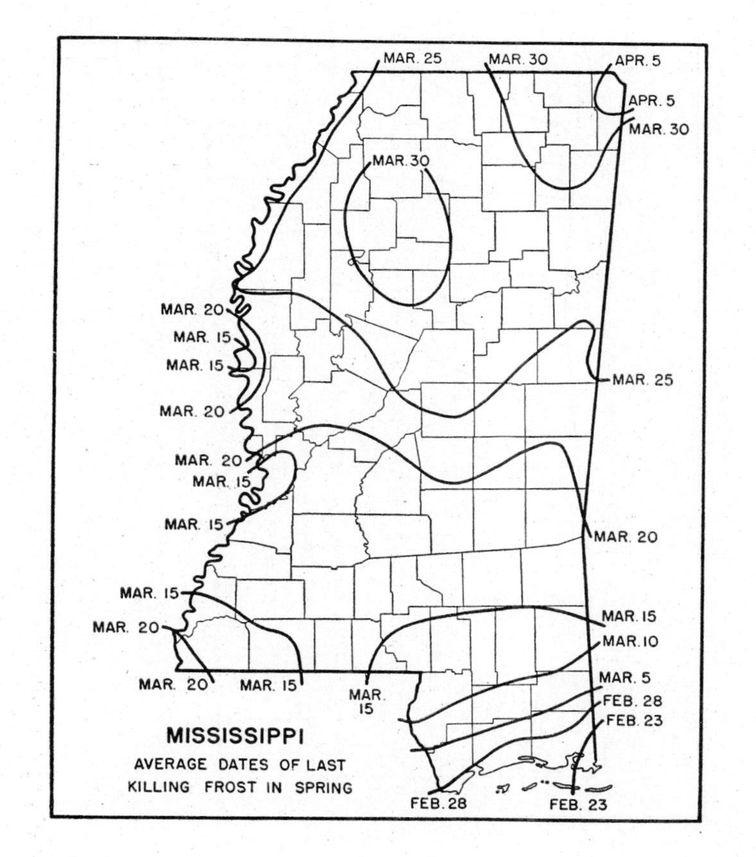
MAR. 25
MAR. 30
APR. 5
APR. 5
MAR. 30
MAR. 30
MAR. 20
MAR. 15
MAR. 15
MAR. 20
MAR. 25
MAR. 20
MAR. 15
MAR. 15
MAR. 20
MAR. 15
MAR. 20
MAR. 15
MAR. 10
MAR. 20
MAR. 15
MAR. 15
MAR. 5
FEB. 28
FEB. 23
MISSISSIPPI
AVERAGE DATES OF LAST
KILLING FROST IN SPRING
FEB. 28
FEB. 23

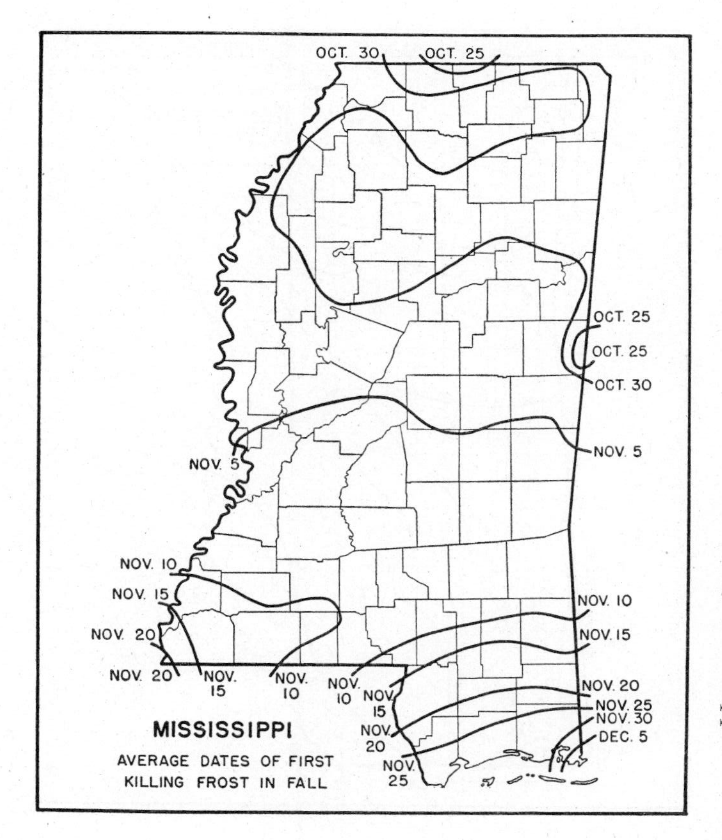
OCT. 30
OCT. 25
OCT. 25
OCT. 25
OCT. 30
NOV. 5
NOV. 5
NOV. 10
NOV. 15
NOV. 10
NOV. 20
NOV. 15
NOV. 20
NOV. 15
NOV. 10
NOV. 10
NOV. 15
NOV. 20
NOV. 20
NOV. 25
NOV. 30
DEC. 5
NOV. 25
MISSISSIPPI
AVERAGE DATES OF FIRST
KILLING FROST IN FALL

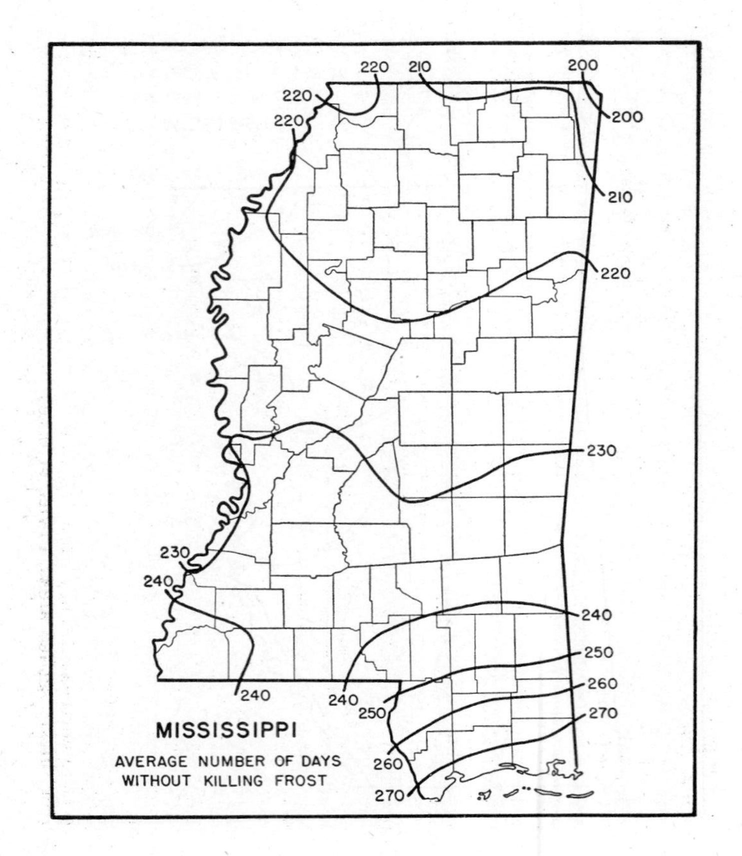
MISSISSIPPI
AVERAGE NUMBER OF DAYS
WITHOUT KILLING FROST
200
210
220
230
240
250
260
270

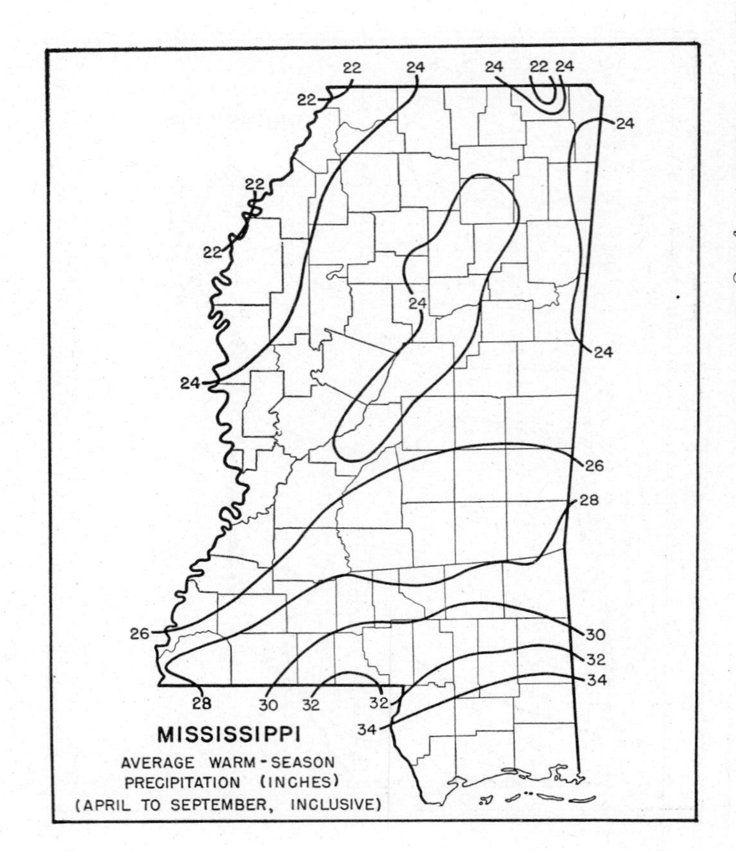
MISSISSIPPI
AVERAGE WARM-SEASON
PRECIPITATION (INCHES)
(APRIL TO SEPTEMBER, INCLUSIVE)
22
24
26
28
30
32
34

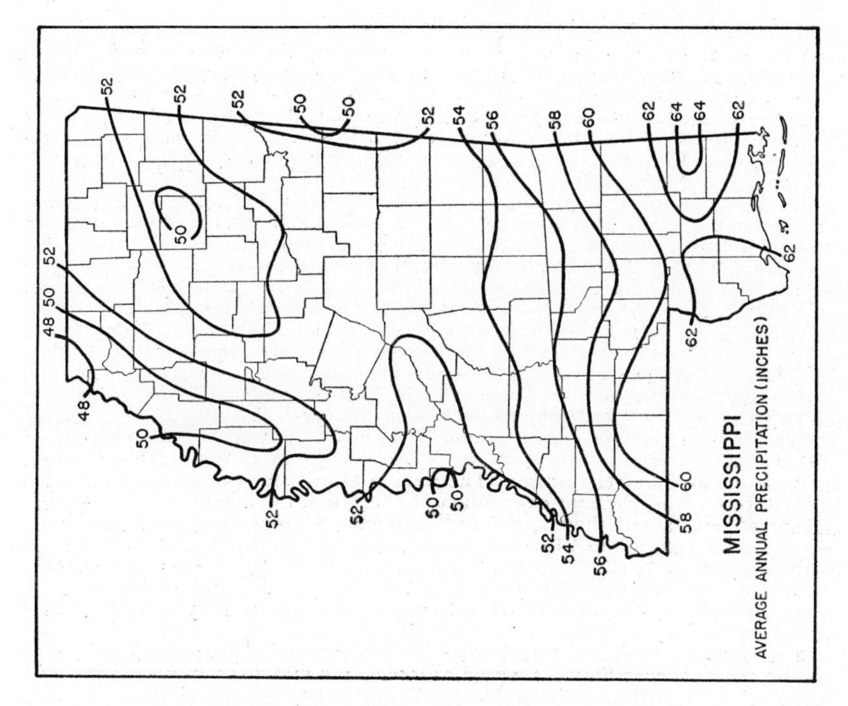

SUPPLEMENTARY CLIMATIC NOTES FOR MISSISSIPPI

The climate of Mississippi is determined more by the extensive land mass of North America to the north and west and the tempering waters of the Gulf of Mexico to the south than by topography. The highest lands within the State, located near the northern border, are less than 800 feet in altitude. About 4½° of latitude intervene between the northern and southern boundaries.

Aside from the alluvial deposits along the numerous streams, much of the median section to the north of latitude 32° is gently rolling to decidedly hilly with a considerable area subject to erosion and requiring the application of fertilizer to grow satisfactory crops. The northeastern prairie belt and the Delta section, the latter located between the Tallahatchie-Yazoo Basin and the Mississippi River, are level and very fertile.

A triangular area with its apex in Rankin County and its base on the coast, comprising nearly a third of the total area of the State, is generally level but lacks natural fertility, except for alluvial deposits along the streams.

The State is well supplied with both surface and underground water. At many places overflowing artesian wells can be obtained at depths ranging from 400 to 1,000 feet.

Except for a limited area in the extreme northeast where drainage is northward into the Tennessee River, drainage in Mississippi is in a southerly direction—into the Tombigbee along the eastern border, directly into the Gulf of Mexico, or into the Mississippi River on the west. Parts of the Tombigbee, the Pearl, and the Yazoo are navigable during at least a part of the year, and the bordering Mississippi at all seasons.

Dense fog occurs occasionally near daybreak, but it is generally dissipated early in the forenoon and rarely lasts throughout the day. However, high humidity is prevalent, and this, combined with hot nights from early in May to about the middle of September, produces discomfort at times during the summer in the interior, relieved occasionally by thunderstorms. These storms are sometimes accompanied by locally violent and destructive winds.

Tornadoes occur occasionally, generally following a narrow path from southwest to northeast. They cause much damage to life and property when they pass over thickly settled areas, towns, or cities. They occur mostly from the middle of March to late in June. Hurricanes of tropical origin sometimes occasion considerable alarm and do much damage on the immediate coast, occurring mostly from early in June to late in October. However, the accompanying violent winds seldom penetrate far inland.

The most agreeable weather in Mississippi usually occurs about the middle of September to the latter part of November, but in many years comfortable, pleasant conditions extend to late December, with flowers blooming in profusion in central and southern parts of the State almost to the New Year. Cold periods in winter are generally of short duration but are acutely felt when they do occur. The prevailing winds are from the north in winter and mostly from a southerly direction in the other seasons of the year. On the coast the hot weather of summer is somewhat relieved by the prevalence of a Gulf breeze.

Since the beginning of state-wide records, in 1888, extreme temperatures of over 100° F. have occurred each summer at one or more stations. Temperatures of zero or lower are recorded during the winter about 1 year in 4. Temperatures of 32° or lower are experienced on the Gulf coast almost every winter.

In Mississippi the nights, as well as the days, are generally warm during much of the year, and the annual average percentage of consecutive days free from killing frost ranges from about 60 percent in the north to about 75 on the coast. The last killing frost in spring varies on an average from the first 10 days in March in the extreme south to as late as April 1 locally in the north-central and northeastern parts of the State. The first in fall occurs, on an average, during the last 10 days in October over much of the State, but in the extreme south it is deferred until about the middle of November. Thus the length of the growing season varies from about 210 days in north-central counties to 250 or 260 in the extreme southern part of the State. However, frost may be expected about 1 year in 10 later than the first 10 days in April in the north and as late as April 1 in the extreme south. Also in fall it occurs on an average of 1 year in 10 as early as November 1 in the more southern sections.

In an average growing season with favorable rainfall, corn and forage crops may be grown successfully if planted as late as the middle of July.

The southern part of Mississippi comes within the area of maximum precipitation east of the Rocky Mountains. The average annual amounts range from more than 60 inches in the extreme south to less than 50 in some northern sections. The relative dryness of the fall favors the harvesting of matured crops.

Thunderstorms occur most frequently in summer, or during the period of highest temperatures, but they form occasionally in the winter season. The average number of days with a measurable amount of precipitation is 93, or about 1 day in 4.

Snowfall is rare. The annual average for the State is only 2.1 inches, but snow may occasionally reach a depth of 10 inches or more. When snow does fall it seldom remains on the ground for any considerable length of time, and occasionally no measurable amount is reported within the State during an entire year.

The cloudiest weather occurs in winter and the sunniest in late summer and fall. For the State as a whole the average number of clear days annually is 171, partly cloudy, 93, and cloudy, 101.

ROBERT T. LINDLEY, *Associate Meteorologist and Climatic Section Director for Mississippi, Weather Bureau, Vicksburg.*

MISSOURI

Climatic summary

County [1]	Station	Temperature					Killing frost average dates				Average precipitation													
		Length of record	January average	July average	Maximum	Minimum	Length of record	Last in spring	First in fall	Growing season [2]	Length of record	January	February	March	April	May	June	July	August	September	October	November	December	Annual
		Yr.	°F.	°F.	°F.	°F.	Yr.			Days	Yr.	In.	In.	In.	In.	In.	In.	In.	In.	In.	In.	In.	In.	In.
Adair	Kirksville	36	27.0	76.9	113	−31	37	Apr. 24	Oct. 13	172	37	1.43	1.49	2.58	3.88	4.73	4.91	3.96	3.97	4.99	2.90	2.22	1.67	38.73
Atchison	Tarkio	26	24.4	77.8	113	−22	30	Apr. 23	Oct. 11	171	32	.86	1.02	1.65	3.24	4.41	4.86	4.06	4.08	4.50	2.70	1.79	.87	34.04
Audrain	Mexico	40	28.4	78.4	116	−25	40	Apr. 20	Oct. 17	180	40	2.05	1.80	2.85	3.62	4.66	4.64	3.11	3.84	4.77	2.90	2.42	1.96	38.62
Barry	Hailey										14	3.18	2.12	3.42	4.14	5.35	5.40	3.48	4.32	4.53	3.90	3.06	2.35	45.25
	Seligman	32	35.8	77.3	110	−29	30	Apr. 14	Oct. 19	188	31	2.90	1.98	3.32	3.99	4.97	4.60	3.53	3.49	4.38	3.74	3.37	2.33	42.60
Barton	Lamar	40	33.4	79.3	118	−28	40	do	Oct. 22	191	40	1.88	1.73	3.00	4.34	5.15	5.37	3.90	4.01	4.52	3.58	2.65	1.83	41.96
Bates	Amoret	18	31.9	78.4	112	−23	18	Apr. 20	Oct. 18	181	18	1.34	1.51	3.24	4.17	4.12	4.24	4.27	4.12	5.04	3.34	1.84	1.66	38.89
Benton	Warsaw	38	33.5	79.4	115	−40	40	Apr. 21	Oct. 15	177	39	2.19	2.15	3.38	4.28	4.98	5.19	3.66	4.37	5.11	3.71	2.79	2.11	43.92
Bollinger	Marble Hill	38	35.6	78.9	116	−31	38	Apr. 18	Oct. 16	181	38	4.06	3.06	4.04	4.50	4.46	4.40	3.92	3.79	3.96	3.21	3.53	3.54	46.47
	Patton (near)										19	2.88	2.15	4.51	3.97	4.41	4.16	3.36	4.22	3.34	3.26	3.03	2.95	42.24
Boone	Columbia	40	30.3	78.0	111	−26	40	Apr. 13	Oct. 19	189	40	1.88	1.67	2.94	3.62	4.40	4.64	2.88	3.95	4.81	2.96	2.27	1.80	37.82
Buchanan	St. Joseph	30	29.7	80.0	110	−24	36	Apr. 12	Oct. 15	186	40	.98	1.24	2.05	3.12	4.25	5.04	3.34	3.76	4.69	2.51	1.95	1.01	33.94
Butler	Poplar Bluff	26	36.5	80.0	112	−25	29	Apr. 11	Oct. 19	191	28	4.45	2.70	4.25	4.37	4.61	4.35	3.50	4.40	4.07	3.35	3.63	4.11	47.79
Caldwell	Kidder	40	26.6	77.5	112	−28	40	Apr. 20	Oct. 18	181	40	1.18	1.43	2.00	3.19	4.59	4.64	3.67	3.72	5.01	2.77	2.22	1.21	35.63
Callaway	Fulton	36	30.4	78.0	113	−26	38	do	do	181	39	2.09	1.66	2.88	3.81	4.57	4.21	3.13	3.46	4.54	3.30	2.48	1.99	38.12
Cape Girardeau	Cape Girard										33	4.16	2.29	3.88	4.04	4.23	4.19	2.89	3.65	4.13	3.42	3.94	3.59	44.41
	Jackson	40	34.8	79.0	112	−26	40	Apr. 17	Oct. 16	182	40	4.05	2.86	4.09	4.30	4.37	4.63	3.38	3.82	3.99	3.41	3.43	3.38	45.71
Cass	Harrisonville	40	28.4	78.6	112	−28	40	do	Oct. 20	186	40	1.53	1.74	2.71	3.23	4.66	4.63	3.27	3.78	4.86	2.84	2.25	1.40	36.90
Cedar	Caplinger Mills										12	2.12	1.31	2.60	3.42	4.88	5.72	2.30	3.66	3.48	3.34	2.64	1.72	37.19
Chariton	Brunswick	40	28.1	78.8	114	−29	40	Apr. 17	Oct. 20	186	40	1.64	1.79	2.57	3.72	4.52	4.87	3.92	3.67	4.88	2.72	2.32	1.65	38.27
Clark	Keokuk, Iowa	40	26.7	77.9	113	−27	40	Apr. 15	Oct. 19	187	40	1.54	1.32	2.33	2.81	3.84	4.22	3.08	3.11	4.29	2.21	2.07	1.43	32.25
Clay	Liberty	26	29.9	78.0	109	−29	26	Apr. 18	Oct. 14	179	29	1.05	1.83	2.66	3.34	4.85	4.55	4.25	3.75	4.98	2.80	1.84	1.18	37.08
Cole	Jefferson City	40	30.1	78.6	114	−25	40	Apr. 15	Oct. 20	188	40	2.06	1.77	2.92	3.86	4.45	4.15	2.94	3.77	4.29	3.26	2.58	1.97	38.02
Cooper	Booneville										40	1.71	1.72	2.90	3.69	4.67	4.74	2.98	4.35	4.91	3.04	2.35	1.70	38.76
	New Palestine	11	33.5	77.2	110	−26	11	Apr. 23	Oct. 17	177	11	1.84	1.97	2.59	3.55	4.40	4.49	3.81	4.66	4.65	3.16	1.90	1.17	38.19
Crawford	Steelville										23	1.89	1.91	2.94	4.47	4.55	3.71	3.25	3.57	3.37	4.04	2.72	2.41	38.83
Dade	Lockwood	33	34.0	78.5	114	−30	34	Apr. 14	Oct. 23	192	34	2.08	1.66	3.22	4.65	5.11	5.56	4.37	4.55	4.77	3.84	2.97	2.12	44.90
Daviess	Gallatin										29	1.12	1.39	1.98	3.72	4.66	5.23	3.46	3.68	4.74	2.84	2.41	1.28	36.51
Dent	Salem (near)	35	32.3	77.4	112	−28	36	Apr. 20	Oct. 19	182	35	2.83	2.18	3.70	4.50	4.69	4.63	3.21	4.24	4.24	3.57	2.70	2.46	42.95
Dunklin	Campbell	13	37.4	80.8	114	−24	13	Apr. 7	Oct. 24	200	13	5.51	3.18	5.53	4.31	4.34	4.08	4.26	4.80	4.53	3.11	3.53	3.95	51.13
Franklin	Pacific	22	32.4	78.2	112	−21	22	Apr. 13	Oct. 22	192	36	2.25	2.01	3.36	4.06	4.88	4.45	3.26	3.97	3.92	3.33	2.73	2.14	40.36

[1] The following counties, for which no records are available, are best represented by the stations indicated: Andrew—Oregon; Camden and Pulaski—Lebanon: Carroll—Brunswick; Carter—Doniphan; Christian—Springfield; Clinton and De Kalb—Kidder; Dallas—Bolivar; Douglas—Mountain Grove; Knox—Steffenville; Lincoln—St. Charles; Moniteau—Columbia; Montgomery—Warrenton; Osage—Jefferson City; Ozark—Hollister; Perry and Ste. Genevieve—Fredericktown; Ralls—Hannibal; Ray—Lexington, Reynolds and Washington—Goodland.

[2] Length of growing season between average dates of last killing frost in spring and first; in fall.

MISSOURI—Continued

Climatic summary—Continued

County	Station	Temperature: Length of record	Temperature: January average	Temperature: July average	Temperature: Maximum	Temperature: Minimum	Killing frost average dates: Length of record	Killing frost average dates: Last in spring	Killing frost average dates: First in fall	Killing frost average dates: Growing season	Average precipitation: Length of record	January	February	March	April	May	June	July	August	September	October	November	December	Annual
		Yr.	*°F.*	*°F.*	*°F.*	*°F.*	*Yr.*			*Days*	*Yr.*	*In.*	*In.*	*In.*	*In.*	*In.*	*In.*	*In.*	*In.*	*In.*	*In.*	*In.*	*In.*	*In.*
Franklin—Cont'd	Union										22	2.01	1.51	3.52	4.20	4.76	4.48	2.99	3.96	4.02	3.53	2.84	2.33	40.15
Gasconade	Herman										40	1.96	1.62	2.82	3.90	4.30	4.16	3.30	3.52	4.43	3.45	2.66	1.84	37.96
	Owensville										15	2.07	1.70	3.34	3.16	4.80	4.54	2.78	3.09	3.66	3.14	2.81	2.20	37.29
Gentry	Albany										12	.76	1.62	1.69	2.79	2.68	5.24	4.63	3.60	5.55	2.79	1.71	.87	33.93
	King City										25	1.30	1.16	1.71	3.23	4.27	4.59	3.13	3.56	4.89	2.86	2.28	.98	33.96
Greene	Springfield	40	33.9	77.6	106	−29	40	Apr. 8	Oct. 28	203	40	2.45	1.77	3.29	3.81	4.75	5.14	3.47	4.24	3.44	3.20	2.64	1.99	40.19
Grundy	Trenton	39	26.7	78.0	114	−26	40	Apr. 18	Oct. 16	181	40	1.33	1.50	2.28	3.42	4.69	4.68	3.74	3.89	4.66	2.82	2.22	1.36	36.59
Harrison	Bethany	37	25.7	77.4	112	−32	38	Apr. 25	Oct. 9	167	37	1.18	1.27	1.99	3.23	4.20	4.44	3.81	3.92	4.63	2.50	2.18	1.10	34.45
Henry	Clinton	38	31.9	79.7	118	−30	36	Apr. 17	Oct. 20	186	38	2.04	1.88	3.20	4.10	4.98	5.02	3.25	3.38	4.51	3.33	2.51	1.88	40.08
Hickory	Wheatland						10	Apr. 23	Oct. 18	178	16	1.97	2.65	3.14	4.37	4.82	4.87	3.66	3.64	4.03	3.00	2.28	1.88	40.31
Holt	Oregon	40	26.5	78.0	112	−26	40	Apr. 19	Oct. 19	183	40	.92	1.26	1.86	3.25	4.59	5.13	3.91	3.74	5.00	2.54	2.02	1.02	35.24
Howard	Fayette	40	28.1	77.8	116	−26	40	Apr. 20	Oct. 15	178	40	1.78	1.66	2.77	3.43	4.45	4.32	3.14	3.49	4.73	2.79	2.24	1.68	36.48
	Glasgow	7	28.2	77.3	109	−26	7	Apr. 18	Oct. 16	181	16	1.43	2.16	2.65	3.77	4.24	3.96	3.65	3.41	4.62	2.71	1.73	1.73	36.06
Howell	Olden	14	35.6	76.3	106	−29	14	Apr. 17	Oct. 17	183	14	2.82	3.37	4.06	5.13	4.76	4.07	4.40	3.59	3.79	2.56	2.82	2.55	43.92
	Willow Springs	10	34.3	75.3	107	−28	11	Apr. 23	Oct. 11	171	26	3.52	2.79	4.05	4.44	4.95	4.74	3.58	3.64	4.26	3.33	3.41	3.86	46.57
Iron	Arcadia	40	32.6	76.4	113	−33	40	Apr. 26	Oct. 13	170	40	3.02	2.42	3.87	4.74	4.27	4.09	3.93	4.09	4.15	3.53	3.19	2.84	44.14
	Goodland	39	33.3	76.2	111	−31	40	do	Oct. 12	169	39	2.74	2.27	3.66	4.83	4.51	4.05	3.33	3.97	4.00	3.63	2.89	2.51	42.39
Jackson	Kansas City Airport	40	30.2	80.0	113	−22	40	Apr. 7	Oct. 28	204	40	1.22	1.56	2.46	3.05	4.86	4.34	3.53	3.90	4.63	2.76	2.12	1.30	35.73
Jasper	Joplin	12	36.9	77.8	104	−21	12	Apr. 16	Oct. 21	188	37	2.11	1.64	2.94	4.06	4.85	4.79	3.17	3.61	4.35	3.54	2.56	1.85	39.47
Jefferson	De Soto						7	Apr. 14	Oct. 12	181	8	2.29	2.20	3.83	3.20	4.56	4.25	3.76	4.27	3.79	2.28	2.47	2.80	39.70
Johnson	Warrensburg	36	31.0	79.7	114	−26	38	do	Oct. 20	189	36	1.85	1.87	2.70	3.36	4.77	4.87	3.57	3.52	4.60	3.04	2.36	1.54	38.05
Laclede	Lebanon	40	32.7	77.6	112	−28	40	Apr. 21	do	182	40	2.59	2.17	3.43	4.32	5.31	5.10	3.69	4.26	4.49	3.68	2.71	2.22	43.97
Lafayette	Concordia										15	1.48	1.66	2.33	3.05	4.57	4.71	2.46	2.85	4.04	3.34	2.94	1.67	35.10
	Lexington	40	29.6	79.2	113	−26	40	Apr. 12	Oct. 21	192	40	1.49	1.79	2.65	3.74	4.99	4.48	3.82	3.27	4.76	2.86	2.24	1.56	37.65
	Waverly										24	1.62	1.48	2.61	3.68	4.92	4.89	3.43	3.44	4.99	3.08	2.68	1.56	38.38
Lawrence	Mt. Vernon	24	34.4	78.0	111	−26	18	Apr. 20	Oct. 16	179	17	2.56	2.46	4.05	4.76	5.65	5.56	5.36	4.67	3.90	2.88	2.87	2.19	46.91
Lewis	Steffenville	40	27.8	78.5	115	−28	40	Apr. 23	Oct. 13	173	40	2.00	1.75	2.83	3.50	4.62	4.48	3.84	4.09	4.56	2.59	2.55	1.66	38.47
Linn	St. Catharine (near)	12	27.3	76.1	106	−28	14	Apr. 17	Oct. 10	176	13	1.24	1.15	2.79	3.44	3.54	5.07	4.24	4.25	4.65	2.22	1.50	1.29	35.38
Livingston	Avalon	26	28.2	77.9	111	−27	27	Apr. 19	Oct. 18	182	27	1.56	1.96	2.94	3.41	4.66	4.69	4.14	3.94	5.14	2.87	1.92	1.60	38.83
	Chillicothe	21	25.8	78.8	116	−29	21	Apr. 24	Oct. 11	170	22	1.32	1.24	2.21	3.50	3.75	5.09	3.00	4.10	5.07	2.99	2.73	1.22	36.22
McDonald	Dean	35	36.2	78.4	115	−29	38	Apr. 19	Oct. 19	183	40	2.54	1.86	3.54	4.57	5.74	5.80	3.93	3.85	4.24	4.02	3.36	2.33	45.78
Macon	Macon	38	27.9	78.3	116	−27	40	Apr. 22	Oct. 17	178	39	1.71	1.64	2.58	3.45	4.38	4.44	3.21	3.59	4.38	2.61	2.34	1.59	35.92
Madison	Fredericktown										15	3.66	2.27	3.81	4.18	3.84	4.33	3.70	3.44	4.32	4.17	3.17	2.97	43.86
Maries	Belle	10	33.2	77.1	109	−24	9	Apr. 21	Oct. 17	179	8	2.03	3.14	2.50	3.70	3.56	4.00	3.58	3.32	3.30	2.72	2.46	1.66	35.97
Marion	Hannibal	40	28.5	77.6	112	−25	40	Apr. 13	Oct. 19	189	40	1.78	1.66	2.60	3.19	4.15	4.06	2.97	3.94	4.39	2.37	2.17	1.56	34.84
	Palmyra	17	26.7	78.6	110	−24	16	Apr. 14	Oct. 14	183	24	1.85	1.45	2.52	3.24	4.51	4.26	2.95	3.82	4.03	2.05	2.36	1.57	34.61
Mercer	Princeton	9	25.7	78.1	111	−28	7	Apr. 23	Oct. 12	172	9	.94	1.74	2.74	3.04	5.41	4.22	4.32	4.38	4.32	1.78	1.67	1.35	35.91
Miller	Eldon	35	31.6	78.3	113	−28	32	Apr. 19	Oct. 18	182	31	1.80	1.57	2.94	3.93	4.30	4.37	2.93	3.68	4.71	3.66	2.82	1.85	38.56

	Tuscumbia										15	1.44	1.29	3.66	4.56	4.59	3.75	2.51	3.63	4.90	4.20	2.73	1.97	39.23
Mississippi	Cairo, Ill	40	36.8	79.7	106	−16	40	Mar. 29	Nov. 1	217	40	4.25	2.66	4.12	3.60	3.42	3.59	2.97	3.14	3.12	2.86	3.24	3.49	40.46
Monroe	Monroe City										17	2.06	1.38	2.51	3.14	3.94	4.69	3.41	4.18	3.71	2.27	2.69	1.94	35.92
Morgan	Stover										15	1.95	1.36	2.44	3.23	5.22	4.79	2.53	3.22	4.62	3.58	3.04	2.00	37.98
	Versailles	10	32.9	79.8	114	−28	12	Apr. 22	Oct. 14	175	12	3.18	1.82	2.38	3.23	4.77	5.21	2.74	3.12	5.62	3.46	2.83	2.02	40.38
New Madrid	Morehouse										14	5.34	2.87	5.28	4.51	4.34	4.69	3.18	3.28	5.44	4.07	4.21	3.56	50.77
	New Madrid										40	5.39	3.62	4.96	4.58	4.32	4.26	4.03	3.76	4.04	3.38	4.00	4.41	50.75
	Parma										15	4.74	2.93	5.86	4.03	4.04	3.54	4.05	4.02	5.22	3.16	4.07	4.29	49.95
Newton	Neosho	40	36.2	77.9	110	−31	40	Apr. 19	Oct. 19	183	40	2.47	1.99	3.42	4.46	5.41	5.80	4.14	4.08	4.47	3.66	3.28	2.24	45.42
Nodaway	Conception	39	25.4	77.9	110	−30	40	do	do	183	40	.80	1.12	1.61	2.72	4.14	4.59	4.20	3.64	4.55	2.72	1.85	.87	32.81
	Maryville	40	24.0	77.2	113	−28	40	Apr. 22	Oct. 13	174	40	1.00	1.31	1.79	2.91	4.65	4.84	4.75	4.01	4.57	2.80	1.97	1.04	35.64
Oregon	Koshkonong	38	37.0	79.3	112	−17	39	Apr. 7	Oct. 29	205	38	3.73	2.79	4.00	4.87	4.56	4.44	3.56	4.21	3.74	3.19	3.27	3.50	45.86
Pemiscot	Caruthersville	39	39.8	82.0	111	−22	38	Mar. 28	Nov. 1	218	40	5.19	3.25	4.78	4.45	4.44	3.68	3.41	3.65	3.29	3.36	3.75	4.34	47.59
Pettis	Lamonte	28	30.2	79.4	114	−27	33	Apr. 22	Oct. 17	178	38	1.86	1.86	2.98	3.57	4.82	4.62	3.32	4.08	5.18	3.13	2.37	1.76	39.55
	Sedalia	9	29.7	76.9	97	−27	8	Apr. 20	Oct. 16	179	10	2.42	2.11	2.71	3.89	4.44	4.61	4.00	5.22	4.87	2.39	1.95	1.36	39.97
Phelps	Jerome										6	1.94	2.02	4.09	3.86	4.88	4.96	3.80	3.39	4.11	2.32	2.84	3.23	41.44
	Rolla	32	33.5	78.3	108	−24	36	Apr. 16	Oct. 24	191	40	2.44	2.02	3.45	4.11	4.78	4.48	3.22	4.25	4.23	3.40	2.74	2.23	41.35
Pike	Louisiana	40	29.3	77.4	117	−27	40	Apr. 24	Oct. 12	171	40	2.14	1.96	3.35	3.64	4.72	3.96	3.31	3.42	4.49	3.19	2.55	1.93	39.66
Platte	Edgerton	19	27.9	78.2	113	−29	19	Apr. 23	Oct. 13	173	19	.88	.95	1.68	3.05	3.73	4.52	2.83	2.93	4.42	2.42	2.13	1.03	30.57
Polk	Bolivar	30	34.7	77.3	109	−29	29	Apr. 17	Oct. 18	184	31	2.00	2.07	3.62	4.46	5.13	5.35	3.75	4.25	4.67	3.40	2.52	2.01	43.23
Putnam	Lucerne										15	1.15	1.02	1.62	3.08	3.02	5.01	2.99	3.83	5.07	2.87	2.30	1.49	33.45
	Unionville	40	24.2	77.1	114	−28	40	Apr. 25	Oct. 13	171	40	1.65	1.67	2.30	3.50	5.13	4.96	3.95	4.12	5.03	2.91	2.33	1.61	39.16
Randolph	Clifton Hill	32	28.6	77.8	116	−26	26	Apr. 22	Oct. 17	178	30	1.65	1.53	2.54	3.53	4.58	4.37	3.23	3.94	4.25	2.37	2.33	1.75	36.07
	Darksville	11	28.8	76.0	112	−28	11	Apr. 25	Oct. 18	176	11	1.77	1.94	2.25	3.37	4.54	5.12	4.05	3.44	4.06	2.19	1.60	1.51	35.84
Ripley	Doniphan	34	35.6	79.3	114	−18	35	Apr. 12	Oct. 20	191	35	4.23	3.03	4.41	4.98	4.27	4.57	4.08	4.20	3.87	3.23	3.41	3.66	47.94
St. Charles	St. Charles	40	31.8	79.4	114	−24	40	Apr. 14	Oct. 23	192	40	2.11	1.94	3.16	3.63	4.17	3.88	2.71	3.93	3.86	3.08	2.18	1.89	36.54
St. Clair	Appleton City	38	32.0	79.4	115	−29	38	Apr. 16	Oct. 21	188	38	1.65	1.63	2.99	4.01	4.86	4.55	3.77	3.53	4.24	2.85	2.41	1.51	38.00
	Osceola										25	2.00	1.84	3.01	4.17	4.81	5.21	3.52	4.31	4.84	3.48	3.04	1.92	42.15
St. Francois	Farmington	24	34.3	78.4	114	−22	23	Apr. 21	Oct. 20	182	23	2.70	2.23	3.56	4.42	5.60	4.04	3.70	3.55	4.02	3.28	3.14	2.69	42.93
St. Louis	Valley Park										22	1.89	1.49	3.42	4.17	4.55	3.41	2.29	3.47	3.59	3.38	2.67	2.37	36.70
	St. Louis City	40	32.9	80.2	110	−22	40	Apr. 2	Oct. 29	210	40	2.35	2.04	3.48	3.73	4.20	3.56	2.87	3.37	3.61	2.92	2.39	2.15	36.67
	St. Louis Univ	27	32.1	80.6	110	−18	26	Apr. 3	do	209	27	2.37	1.87	3.46	3.83	4.06	3.40	2.52	3.77	3.89	3.05	2.57	2.36	37.15
Saline	Marshall	38	29.6	78.7	112	−26	40	Apr. 19	Oct. 17	181	40	1.72	1.78	2.70	3.84	4.81	4.37	3.49	3.84	5.38	2.89	2.47	1.70	38.99
Schuyler	Downing	17	27.3	78.0	115	−23	23	Apr. 23	Oct. 13	173	24	1.24	1.27	2.02	3.62	3.94	5.39	3.54	3.78	5.83	3.00	2.14	1.46	37.23
Scotland	Gorin										40	1.40	1.38	2.12	3.37	4.59	4.83	3.32	3.37	4.68	2.75	2.21	1.37	35.39
Scott	Sikeston	27	37.6	79.8	111	−23	28	Apr. 9	Oct. 22	196	33	4.88	3.26	4.65	4.39	4.33	4.21	4.03	3.64	3.95	3.06	3.75	4.00	48.15
Shannon	Birch Tree (near)	40	35.0	77.5	111	−32	40	Apr. 13	Oct. 20	190	40	3.24	2.51	3.72	4.65	4.35	4.57	3.47	4.43	3.75	3.26	3.14	2.83	43.92
Shelby	Shelbina										27	1.45	1.66	2.78	3.54	4.39	4.36	2.97	3.43	4.42	2.64	2.40	1.58	35.62
Stoddard	Dexter										15	5.01	2.85	4.47	3.98	4.35	4.40	3.52	3.74	4.90	4.01	3.58	3.64	48.45
Stone	Galena										20	2.27	1.83	2.75	3.81	4.74	5.07	3.16	3.33	3.99	3.56	3.58	2.34	40.43
Sullivan	Milan										16	1.61	1.43	2.13	3.65	3.81	5.36	2.80	4.00	5.21	3.24	2.88	1.72	37.84
Taney	Hollister	18	36.6	78.0	110	−17	19	Apr. 19	Oct. 21	185	20	2.72	2.09	3.75	5.17	4.76	4.05	3.90	4.50	4.16	2.98	3.20	2.68	43.96
	Ozark Beach										13	3.15	2.11	2.97	4.15	5.24	4.40	3.31	3.81	3.41	3.57	2.96	2.70	41.78
Texas	Houston	24	34.4	76.4	111	−34	25	Apr. 22	Oct. 13	174	25	2.72	2.37	3.77	4.24	3.84	4.44	4.19	3.66	4.34	3.02	2.49	2.25	41.33
Vernon	Arthur	15	33.1	77.6	110	−35	15	Apr. 18	Oct. 15	180	15	1.47	2.39	2.90	3.78	5.47	5.34	4.27	4.29	3.89	2.90	1.88	1.60	40.18
	Nevada	24	33.6	79.4	117	−27	38	Apr. 15	Oct. 18	186	40	1.85	1.76	2.76	4.09	5.09	5.20	3.44	3.55	4.35	3.08	2.34	1.67	39.18
Warren	Warrenton	40	30.2	78.8	113	−22	40	Apr. 16	Oct. 21	188	40	2.25	1.91	3.21	3.86	4.32	3.83	3.01	3.48	4.40	3.33	2.76	2.17	38.53
Wayne	Greenville	28	35.2	77.5	113	−32	28	Apr. 21	Oct. 11	173	28	3.50	2.66	4.32	4.69	3.95	4.56	3.98	3.82	3.52	3.37	3.34	3.27	44.98
	Leeper										14	4.18	2.42	3.82	4.62	4.43	4.54	3.52	3.62	3.74	3.73	3.14	3.41	45.17
	Williamsville										15	4.39	2.54	3.86	4.54	4.00	5.18	4.19	4.84	3.79	4.13	3.30	3.82	48.58
Webster	Seymour (near)	31	34.4	76.2	108	−26	30	Apr. 24	Oct. 16	175	31	2.48	2.20	3.51	4.03	4.90	5.44	3.92	3.83	4.25	3.56	2.87	2.37	43.36
Worth	Grant City	36	25.3	77.1	112	−29	36	Apr. 21	do	178	39	.96	1.06	1.88	2.83	4.19	4.86	4.41	3.94	4.52	2.88	2.00	1.02	34.55
Wright	Mountain Grove	38	33.3	77.1	110	−21	38	Apr. 19	Oct. 19	183	38	2.90	2.19	3.75	4.45	4.59	4.64	3.65	4.08	4.09	3.34	2.96	2.50	43.14

MISSOURI—Continued

Precipitation and temperature—State unit values

[This tabulation gives the mean annual, mean monthly, and average seasonal precipitation, 1886–1938, and the mean annual temperatures, 1902–38, for Missouri]

Precipitation		Precipitation		Precipitation		Precipitation		Temperature		Temperature	
Year	Mean	Year	Mean	Year	Mean	Month	Mean	Year	Mean	Year	Mean
	In.		*In.*		*In.*		*In.*		°*F.*		°*F.*
1886	36.51	1907	40.92	1928	45.87	May	4.75	1902	54.1	1921	58.2
1887	35.11	1908	43.82	1929	46.73	June	4.62	1903	53.6	1922	56.8
1888	40.40	1909	45.28	1930	31.40	July	3.62	1904	53.2	1923	55.3
1889	38.19	1910	37.80	1931	40.31	August	3.75	1905	53.6	1924	53.0
1890	39.52	1911	37.41	1932	38.23	September	4.11	1906	55.0	1925	55.6
1891	37.18	1912	39.00	1933	37.61	October	2.84	1907	55.4	1926	54.5
1892	44.76	1913	38.19	1934	35.07	November	2.68	1908	56.8	1927	55.6
1893	39.19	1914	34.67	1935	48.02	December	2.14	1909	55.8	1928	55.2
1894	34.60	1915	49.84	1936	29.42			1910	54.6	1929	53.5
1895	40.04	1916	40.62	1937	37.30	Annual	40.15	1911	56.7	1930	55.9
1896	40.36	1917	32.21	1938	41.00			1912	53.5	1931	58.0
1897	40.56	1918	37.68					1913	56.5	1932	55.6
1898	54.27	1919	40.28			Season	Average	1914	56.1	1933	57.3
1899	37.93	1920	37.55	Month	Mean			1915	55.0	1934	57.4
1900	39.01	1921	44.70					1916	55.3	1935	55.0
1901	25.87	1922	39.67					1917	52.6	1936	56.3
1902	45.00	1923	42.17		*In.*		*In.*	1918	55.4	1937	54.5
1903	40.65	1924	40.03	January	2.48	Winter	6.70	1919	55.3	1938	58.4
1904	42.06	1925	39.14	February	2.08	Spring	11.83	1920	54.3		
1905	47.01	1926	42.93	March	3.21	Summer	11.99				
1906	39.44	1927	55.52	April	3.87	Fall	9.63				

Dates of last killing frost in spring and first in fall, with length of growing season

Year	Maryville			Steffenville			Columbia			Springfield			Koshkonong			Arcadia		
	Last in spring	First in fall	Growing season[1]	Last in spring	First in fall	Growing season[1]	Last in spring	First in fall	Growing season[1]	Last in spring	First in fall	Growing season[1]	Last in spring	First in fall	Growing season[1]	Last in spring	First in fall	Growing season[1]
			Days			*Days*			*Days*			*Days*			*Days*			*Days*
1899	Apr. 9	Sept. 29	173	Apr. 16	Sept. 29	166	Apr. 16	Sept. 29	166	Apr. 9	Oct. 29	203				Apr. 16	Sept. 27	164
1900	Apr. 13	No.v 1	202	Apr. 13	Nov. 8	209	Apr. 12	Oct. 18	189	Apr. 13	Nov. 1	202		Nov. 9		May 10	Oct. 9	152
1901	Apr. 18	Sept. 18	153	Apr. 20	Oct. 4	167	Apr. 18	Sept. 18	153	Apr. 18	Oct. 14	179	Apr. 1	Oct. 14	196	Apr. 21	Sept. 19	151

1902	Apr. 23	Oct. 14	174	Apr. 15	Oct. 14	182	Apr. 8	Oct. 14	189	Apr. 8	Nov. 26	232	Apr. 8	Nov. 27	233	Apr. 15	Sept. 13	151
1903	May 3	Oct. 18	168	May 1	Oct. 18	170	May 1	Oct. 18	170	May 1	Nov. 6	189	May 1	Oct. 27	179	May 4	Sept. 18	137
1904	Apr. 21	Oct. 23	185	Apr. 21	Oct. 23	185	Apr. 21	Oct. 23	185	Apr. 10	Oct. 23	196	Apr. 17	Oct. 26	192	May 15	Oct. 23	161
1905	Apr. 18	Oct. 12	177	Apr. 22	Oct. 12	173	Apr. 18	Oct. 21	186	Apr. 16	Oct. 21	188	do	Nov. 1	198	Apr. 22	Oct. 11	172
1906	Apr. 15	Oct. 10	178	May 9	Oct. 3	147	May 9	Oct. 10	154	Mar. 30	Oct. 10	194	Apr. 1	Oct. 10	192	May 7	Oct. 10	156
1907	May 5	Oct. 12	160	May 4	Oct. 13	162	May 4	Oct. 12	161	Apr. 17	Oct. 13	179	Apr. 17	Oct. 13	179	May 28	Oct. 12	137
1908	May 7	Sept. 28	144	May 2	Sept. 29	150	Apr. 30	Oct. 9	162	Apr. 3	Oct. 12	192	Apr. 30	Mar. 5	189	May 1	Sept. 29	151
1909	May 10	Oct. 12	155	May 2	Oct. 12	163	May 1	Oct. 12	164	May 1	do	164	Apr. 10	Oct. 12	185	May 11	Sept. 28	140
1910	Apr. 25	Oct. 28	186	Apr. 25	Oct. 22	180	Apr. 25	Oct. 29	187	Apr. 25	Oct. 28	186	Apr. 25	Oct. 28	186	May 14	Oct. 22	161
1911	May 2	Oct. 22	173	Apr. 9	do	196	Apr. 9	Oct. 22	196	May 2	Oct. 22	173	Mar. 16	Nov. 2	231	May 6	Oct. 18	165
1912	Apr. 7	Sept. 26	172	Apr. 19	Sept. 26	160	Mar. 25	Sept. 30	189	Apr. 2	Oct. 23	204	Mar. 25	Oct. 23	212	Apr. 23	Sept. 27	157
1913	Apr. 26	Sept. 22	149	Apr. 13	Sept. 22	162	Mar. 28	Oct. 30	216	Mar. 28	Oct. 20	206	Mar. 28	Oct. 21	207	Apr. 16	Oct. 20	187
1914	Apr. 20	Oct. 27	190	Apr. 20	Oct. 27	190	Apr. 20	Oct. 27	190	Apr. 9	Oct. 27	201	Apr. 12	Oct. 27	198	Apr. 13	Oct. 27	167
1915	Apr. 12	Oct. 5	176	Apr. 13	Oct. 9	179	Apr. 3	Oct. 9	189	Apr. 3	Nov. 12	223	Apr. 3	Nov. 15	226	do	Oct. 6	176
1916	Apr. 10	Sept. 29	172	Apr. 22	Sept. 29	160	Apr. 9	Oct. 21	195	Apr. 9	Oct. 20	194	Apr. 9	Oct. 20	194	Apr. 9	Sept. 16	160
1917	Apr. 26	Oct. 6	163	May 5	Oct. 6	154	do	Oct. 6	180	do	Oct. 9	183	do	Oct. 9	183	Apr. 15	Oct. 1	169
1918	Apr. 28	Sept. 20	145	Apr. 21	Nov. 1	194	Apr. 11	Nov. 1	204	Apr. 10	Nov. 1	205	Apr. 10	Nov. 1	205	May 1	Nov. 1	184
1919	Apr. 24	Oct. 11	170	Apr. 26	Oct. 17	174	Apr. 1	Oct. 28	210	Apr. 26	Nov. 2	190	Apr. 26	Nov. 5	193	Apr. 26	Oct. 18	175
1920	Apr. 29	Oct. 1	155	Apr. 14	Oct. 1	170	Apr. 13	Oct. 29	199	Apr. 13	Oct. 29	199	Apr. 14	Oct. 29	198	Apr. 14	Oct. 29	198
1921	May 3	Oct. 8	158	Apr. 18	Oct. 8	173	Apr. 18	Nov. 2	198	Apr. 17	Nov. 2	199	Apr. 18	Nov. 10	206	Apr. 19	Oct. 8	172
1922	Apr. 18	Oct. 12	177	do	Oct. 12	177	Mar. 22	Oct. 17	209	Apr. 1	Oct. 18	200	Mar. 22	Nov. 16	239	Apr. 20	Oct. 13	176
1923	May 9	Oct. 20	164	May 11	Oct. 20	162	Apr. 16	Oct. 21	188	Apr. 8	Oct. 21	196	Apr. 9	Oct. 22	196	May 10	Oct. 20	163
1924	Apr. 22	Nov. 7	199	Apr. 2	Sept. 30	181	Apr. 1	Oct. 23	205	Apr. 1	Nov. 19	232	Apr. 2	Nov. 9	221	Apr. 18	Oct. 22	187
1925	Mar. 31	Oct. 9	192	May 25	Oct. 10	138	Mar. 28	Oct. 10	196	Mar. 15	Oct. 10	209	Mar. 16	Oct. 10	208	Apr. 6	Oct. 10	187
1926	Apr. 19	Sept. 26	160	Apr. 19	Sept. 26	160	Apr. 19	Oct. 25	189	Apr. 3	Oct. 25	205	Apr. 19	Oct. 25	189	Apr. 29	Oct. 25	179
1927	Apr. 22	Nov. 2	194	Apr. 23	Oct. 14	174	Apr. 22	Nov. 6	198	Apr. 22	Nov. 6	198	Apr. 22	Nov. 6	198	Apr. 23	Oct. 14	174
1928	Apr. 20	Oct. 28	191	Apr. 28	Sept. 26	151	Apr. 15	Nov. 4	203	Apr. 15	Nov. 3	202	Apr. 16	Oct. 31	198	May 8	Sept. 24	139
1929	May 2	Oct. 23	174	Apr. 12	Oct. 23	194	Mar. 10	Oct. 25	229	Mar. 17	Oct. 25	222	Mar. 10	Nov. 5	240	May 5	Oct. 25	173
1930	Apr. 2	Oct. 17	198	Apr. 25	Oct. 17	175	Mar. 30	Oct. 17	201	Mar. 30	Oct. 31	215	Mar. 30	Oct. 31	215	Apr. 25	Oct. 20	178
1931	May 21	Oct. 28	160	May 7	Nov. 4	181	Apr. 5	Nov. 6	215	Mar. 29	Nov. 25	241	Apr. 5	Nov. 25	234	Apr. 29	Oct. 18	172
1932	Apr. 27	Oct. 6	162	Apr. 28	Oct. 11	166	Mar. 31	Oct. 6	189	Mar. 14	Nov. 1	232	Mar. 22	Nov. 1	224	May 2	Nov. 1	183
1933	Apr. 7	Oct. 22	198	Apr. 27	Oct. 13	169	Apr. 7	Oct. 25	201	Mar. 21	Nov. 8	232	do	Nov. 8	231	Apr. 12	Nov. 8	210
1934	Apr. 25	Oct. 28	186	Apr. 25	Oct. 28	186	Apr. 25	Oct. 28	186	Mar. 31	Oct. 28	211	Mar. 28	Nov. 1	218	Apr. 28	Oct. 28	183
1935	Apr. 16	Oct. 4	171	Apr. 16	Oct. 4	171	Apr. 16	Oct. 4	171	Mar. 17	Nov. 5	233	Mar. 17	Oct. 7	204	Apr. 16	Oct. 6	173
1936	Apr. 18	Oct. 22	187	Apr. 22	Oct. 23	184	Apr. 22	Oct. 24	185	Apr. 3	Nov. 3	214	Apr. 8	Oct. 23	198	Apr. 24	Oct. 24	183
1937	Apr. 10	Oct. 14	187	Apr. 11	Oct. 8	180	Apr. 10	Oct. 14	187	Apr. 6	Oct. 23	200	Mar. 31	Oct. 15	198	Apr. 11	Oct. 14	186
1938	do	Oct. 20	193	Apr. 10	Oct. 24	197	do	Oct. 24	197	Apr. 10	Oct. 24	197	Apr. 10	Oct. 24	197	Apr. 10	Oct. 24	197
Mean	Apr. 22	Oct. 13	174	Apr. 23	Oct. 13	173	Apr. 13	Oct. 19	189	Apr. 8	Oct. 28	203	Apr. 7	Oct. 29	205	Apr. 26	Oct. 13	170
Extremes	Mar. 31[2] May 21[3]	Sept. 18[4] Nov. 7[5]	[6] 144 [7] 202	Apr. 2[2] May 25[3]	Sept. 22[4] Nov. 8[5]	[6] 138 [7] 209	Mar. 10[2] May 9[3]	Sept. 18[4] Nov. 6[5]	[6] 153 [7] 229	Mar. 14[2] May 2[3]	Oct. 9[4] Nov. 26[5]	[6] 164 [7] 241	Mar. 10[2] May 1[3]	Oct. 7[4] Nov. 27[5]	[6] 179 [7] 240	Apr. 6[2] May 28[3]	Sept. 13[4] Nov. 8[5]	[6] 137 [7] 210

[1] Number of days between last killing frost in spring and first in fall.
[2] Earliest date in spring.
[3] Latest date in spring.
[4] Earliest date in fall.
[5] Latest date in fall.
[6] Shortest growing season.
[7] Longest growing season.

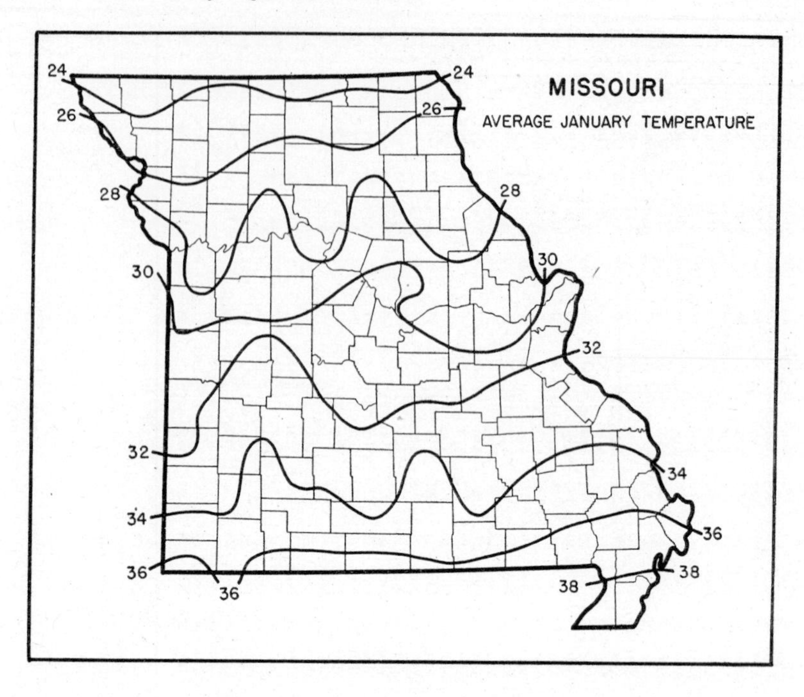
MISSOURI
AVERAGE JANUARY TEMPERATURE
24
24
26
26
28
28
30
30
32
32
34
34
36
36
36
38
38

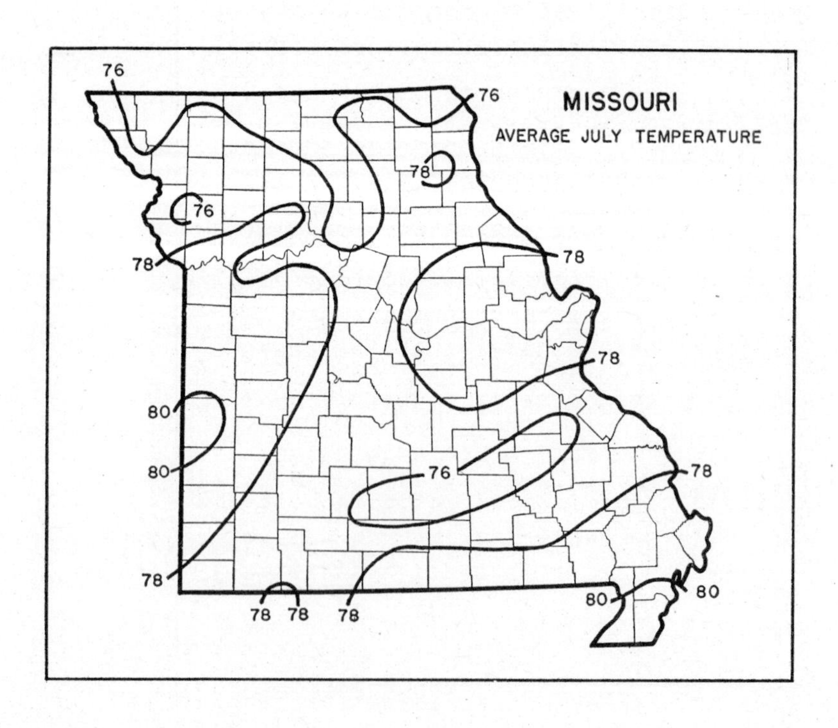
MISSOURI
AVERAGE JULY TEMPERATURE
76
76
78
76
78
78
80
80
76
78
78
78
78
78
80
80

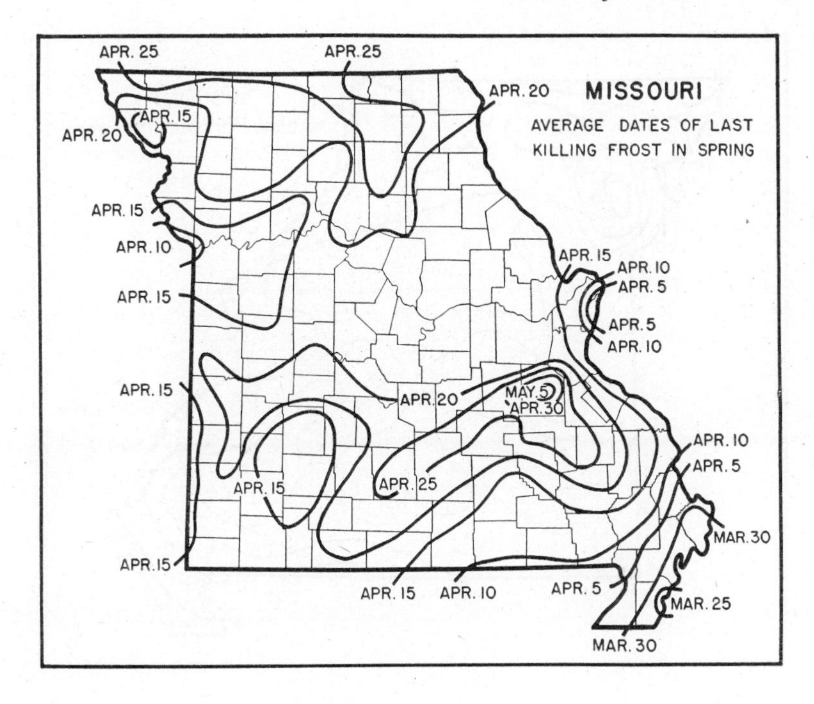
MISSOURI
AVERAGE DATES OF LAST KILLING FROST IN SPRING
APR. 25
APR. 25
APR. 20
APR. 15
APR. 20
APR. 15
APR. 10
APR. 15
APR. 15
APR. 15
APR. 10
APR. 5
APR. 5
APR. 10
APR. 20
MAY 5
APR. 30
APR. 15
APR. 25
APR. 10
APR. 5
MAR. 30
APR. 15
APR. 15
APR. 10
APR. 5
MAR. 25
MAR. 30

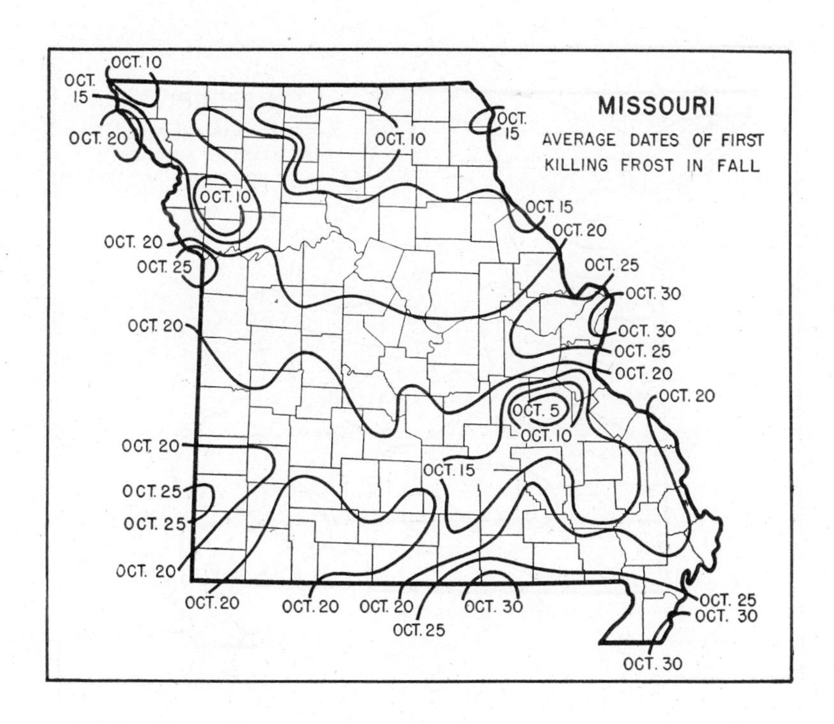
MISSOURI
AVERAGE DATES OF FIRST KILLING FROST IN FALL
OCT. 10
OCT. 15
OCT. 20
OCT. 10
OCT. 15
OCT. 10
OCT. 15
OCT. 20
OCT. 20
OCT. 25
OCT. 25
OCT. 30
OCT. 20
OCT. 30
OCT. 25
OCT. 20
OCT. 20
OCT. 5
OCT. 10
OCT. 20
OCT. 15
OCT. 25
OCT. 25
OCT. 20
OCT. 20
OCT. 20
OCT. 20
OCT. 30
OCT. 25
OCT. 25
OCT. 30
OCT. 30

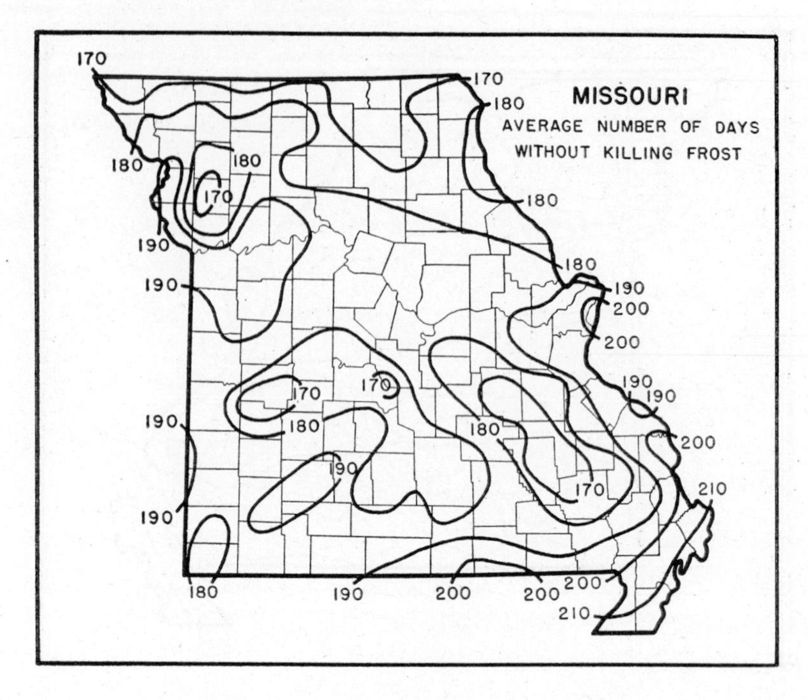
MISSOURI
AVERAGE NUMBER OF DAYS WITHOUT KILLING FROST
170
180
190
200
210

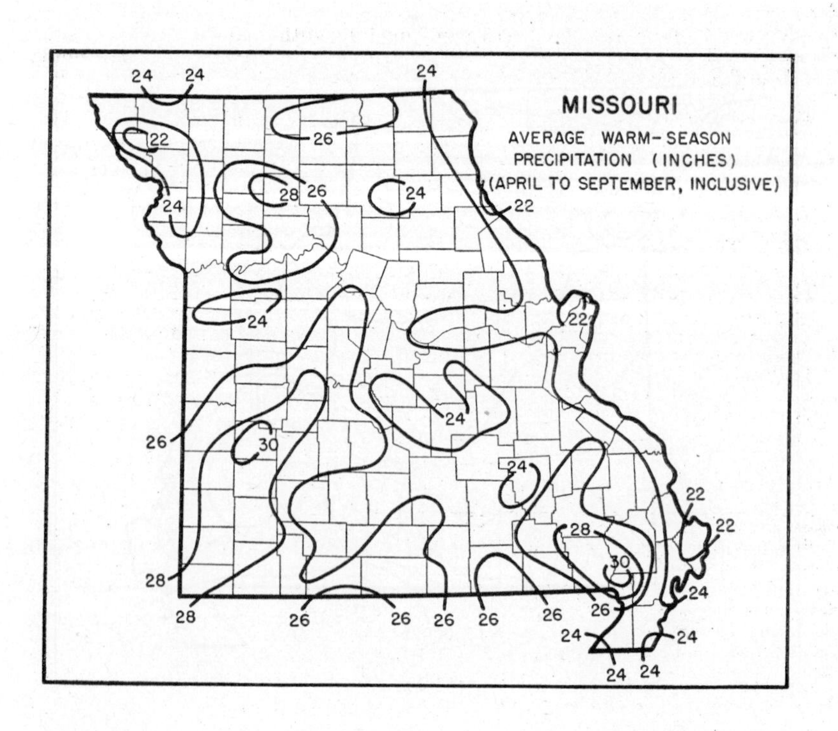
MISSOURI
AVERAGE WARM-SEASON PRECIPITATION (INCHES)
(APRIL TO SEPTEMBER, INCLUSIVE)
22
24
26
28
30

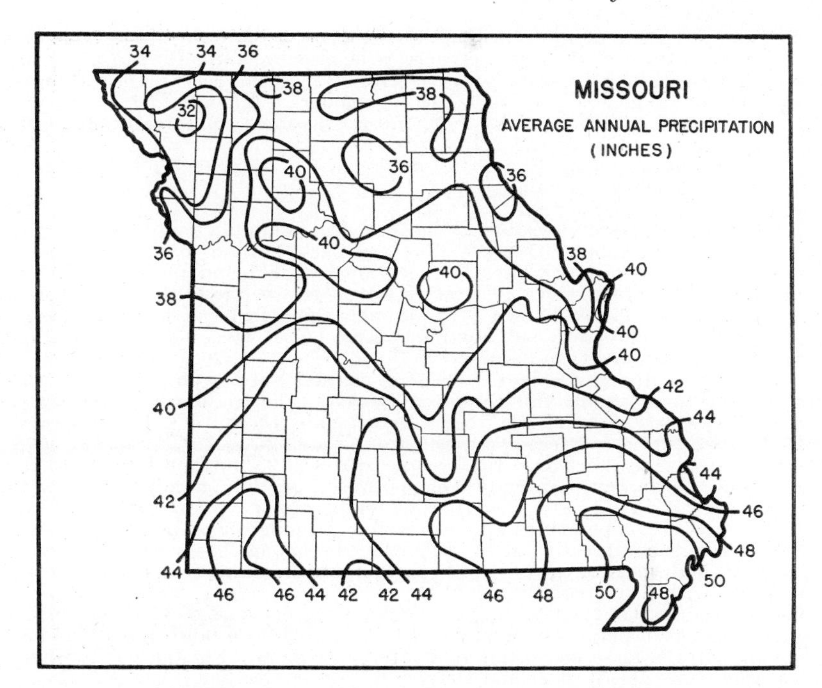

SUPPLEMENTARY CLIMATIC NOTES FOR MISSOURI

Missouri has three distinct topographic divisions—in the north an upland plain, or prairie; in the extreme southeast, a lowland; and between these, the Missouri part of the Ozark uplift. The boundary between the prairie and the Ozark section follows the Missouri River from its mouth to about Glasgow, thence running southwestward, with irregular limits but a direct trend, to Jasper County. The boundary between the Ozark and lowland sections runs due southwest from Cape Girardeau.

The prairie section embraces nearly half of Missouri, including all of the area north of the Missouri River and an appreciable part south of the river in the western part of the State. It is a rolling country with an abundance of streams, more hilly and broken in its western than in its eastern part. Elevations range from nearly 1,200 feet above sea level in the extreme northwest to about 500 feet in the extreme northeast, and to about 900 feet along the border of the Ozark section. The larger streams have valleys 250 to 300 feet deep, which in places are 8 to 10 miles wide, the country bordering on the streams being the most broken.

The Ozark section comprises about half of the State and is substantially a low dome or belt of highland that extends from near the Mississippi River, about Ste. Genevieve County, to Barry County near the southwest corner of the State. Elevations of the crest in Missouri vary from 1,000 to slightly more than 1,600 feet.

The southeast lowland is undulating country with an area of some 3,000 square miles. It is well drained for the most part but swampy in its lowest parts.

The drainage of the State is entirely into the Mississippi River either directly or indirectly, and almost entirely into either that river or the Missouri within the borders of the State. The latter stream forms the northwest border and flows eastward from Kansas City across the State, entering the Mississippi about 12 miles above St. Louis. The area drained into the Mississippi outside the State through the White, St. Francis, and other minor streams is relatively small.

Because of its inland location the entire State has a climate that is essentially of the continental type. While extremes of heat and cold, drought and moisture are marked in some years, they are not so pronounced as in the more northerly States. The weather in general is changeable, but in the course of a year there are many periods when it is settled and moderate. The winters are fairly brisk and stimulating as a rule, seldom severe, but with occasional short spells of extreme cold. Almost every winter has considerable periods of mild weather.

The summers are generally warm, as would be expected from the latitude and the interior-continental situation. There is a large range in the average temperature for the summer season, but excessively warm summers are the exception. Spring and fall are generally characterized by moderate temperatures.

It is worthy of note that winter temperatures average considerably milder in the Ozarks than in the upland plain or prairie section, especially the northern parts of the latter, owing largely to differences in latitude; but in summer the Ozarks average appreciably cooler, the effects of latitude being more than overcome by the higher altitude.

The average number of days during the year with minimum temperatures below 32° F. ranges from about 105 in the northern part to about 65 in the extreme southeast. Occasionally a winter is exceptionally mild and pleasant. On an average, however, about three cold waves a season sweep over the State. As a rule, they are not of the blizzard type, though they do bring marked changes in temperature and occasionally extreme cold. Cold waves have an average duration of slightly less than 3 days.

In a relatively dry atmosphere, such as is characteristic of Missouri, the temperature may occasionally fall considerably below the freezing point of water without the occurrence of visible frost. Occasionally there is a killing frost with an air temperature a few feet above the ground as high as 36° F., and at other times only light frost may form with temperatures of 25° or even lower. In the former case the deposit is usually copious, owing to the humidity. Injury to plants is nearly always greater from freezing temperatures without frost than from heavy frost with temperatures above freezing, although the absence of visible frost may give the impression at the time that no damage has occurred. Owing to the relative dryness of the air in Missouri, however, killing frosts usually coincide closely with a temperature of 32°.

The average date of the last killing frost, or a temperature of 32° F., in spring in the northeastern plain is about April 19, and the first in fall is about October 14, giving a frostless season of approximately 178 days. For the northwestern plateau the dates are April 21 and October 11, respectively, a frostless season of about 173 days. Sometimes during a late, cold spring, temperatures low enough for killing frost occur as late as May 25 in both sections, and locally in the northwestern plateau as late as May 28. In the fall, killing frost has occurred locally as early as September 13 to 18 once or twice in about 30 years, but oftener and more generally during the last 10 days of September, especially the last week.

The average annual precipitation ranges from slightly above 50 inches in the southeast lowlands to 32 in the extreme northwest. About 42 percent of the annual precipitation occurs during the active crop-growing months, May to August, inclusive. Long rainy spells are unusual; they are longer during the spring months than in any other period, 13 consecutive days with rain in May being about the extreme record. Summer rains are frequently in the form of thundershowers, which are occasionally severe, with hail and high winds. Local rains, especially in late spring and summer, are at times excessive; more than 10 inches has been recorded within 24 consecutive hours.

Under average conditions rainfall is sufficient for crop growth and domestic purposes in all parts of the State. Droughts are occasionally experienced, however. Serious droughts during the principal crop-growing season have occurred nearly a dozen times in the 70-year period 1870–1939. In a State of such extent and such variable topography, a drought seldom covers the entire area.

The total seasonal snowfall for the State from year to year ranges from 5 to nearly 40 inches, with an average of nearly 18.

Floods occur in the smaller streams once or twice in most years, principally in the spring or early summer. Severe floods with heavy losses do not often occur in the Missouri and Mississippi Rivers in Missouri.

The average annual number of thunderstorms ranges from about 48 in the northern section to 57 in the southeast. They are of decidedly greater frequency than in the more northern States, but less frequent than in the Southeastern States. Tornadoes occur in some part of Missouri on an average of once or twice a year, with some years none and others several. This is a moderate frequency compared with some other States of the interior valleys. These storms have very narrow paths and often disintegrate within a few miles.

WALTER J. MOXOM, *Senior Meteorologist and Climatic Section Director for Missouri, Weather Bureau, St. Louis.*

MONTANA

Climatic summary

County	Station	Temperature					Killing frost average dates				Average precipitation													
		Length of record	January average	July average	Maximum	Minimum	Length of record	Last in spring	First in fall	Growing season [1]	Length of record	January	February	March	April	May	June	July	August	September	October	November	December	Annual
		Yr.	°F.	°F.	°F.	°F.	Yr.			Days	Yr.	In.	In.	In.	In.	In.	In.	In.	In.	In.	In.	In.	In.	In.
Beaverhead	Bowen	15	9.4	55.4	93	-55	15	(2)	(2)	----	15	0.90	0.77	0.78	0.73	1.41	1.93	1.04	0.78	1.11	0.86	0.88	0.95	12.14
	Dillon	39	24.4	65.1	98	-40	39	May 22	Sept. 12	113	40	.90	.80	1.27	1.80	2.71	2.43	1.49	1.30	1.37	.98	.82	.80	16.67
	Grant	17	16.2	60.1	102	-52	17	June 13	Sept. 9	88	17	.54	.45	.69	1.07	1.63	1.35	1.00	.86	1.08	.82	.65	.65	10.79
	Lima	19	16.3	62.9	100	-43	16	June 11	Sept. 6	87	19	.26	.27	.49	1.20	1.21	1.67	.99	.76	.86	.96	.36	.24	9.27
Big Horn	Busby	36	17.6	69.8	109	-53	36	May 24	Sept. 16	115	35	.65	.42	.66	1.07	2.07	2.17	1.45	.96	1.36	1.07	.57	.53	12.98
	Crow Agency	37	19.7	72.6	110	-50	38	May 13	Sept. 25	135	38	.80	.77	1.25	1.41	2.42	2.01	1.35	.86	1.36	1.38	.90	.82	15.33
	Foster (near)	21	18.3	71.0	108	-49	22	May 18	Sept. 18	123	22	.49	.37	.43	.89	1.88	2.16	1.48	.71	1.10	.95	.67	.46	11.59
	Wyola	----	----	----	----	----	10	May 22	Sept. 25	126	9	.66	.56	1.16	1.61	1.90	1.42	1.00	.66	1.73	1.34	.71	.68	13.43
Blaine	Chinook	38	14.6	69.9	110	-51	39	May 13	Sept. 19	129	37	.54	.37	.48	.80	2.02	2.93	1.60	1.36	1.40	.65	.48	.59	13.22
	Clear Creek	12	15.2	67.0	103	-38	14	May 26	Sept. 23	120	14	1.06	.57	.54	.86	2.34	3.20	1.73	1.51	2.14	1.04	.66	.76	16.41
	Harlem	10	12.2	68.0	107	-50	10	May 16	Sept. 21	128	10	.54	.34	.79	.87	1.36	2.99	1.72	1.41	1.02	.75	.48	.51	12.78
Broadwater	Townsend (near)	----	----	----	----	----	----	----	----	----	9	.37	.29	.78	.56	1.81	2.01	1.23	.80	1.00	.60	.38	.27	10.10
Carbon	Bridger	27	21.5	70.0	110	-35	28	May 18	Sept. 18	123	29	.26	.30	.59	1.01	1.80	1.62	.88	.66	1.31	1.16	.47	.36	10.42
	Red Lodge (near)	37	20.6	62.3	110	-40	37	June 4	Sept. 12	100	38	.70	.71	1.31	2.37	3.26	2.32	1.45	1.23	1.84	1.72	.83	.64	18.38
Carter	Ekalaka	37	19.0	71.2	108	-43	37	May 19	Sept. 23	127	37	.38	.32	.62	1.04	2.29	2.81	1.78	1.32	1.18	.78	.34	.31	13.17
Cascade	Adel (near)	40	21.2	61.0	106	-51	40	June 8	Sept. 5	89	40	1.25	1.22	1.66	2.25	3.51	3.97	1.88	1.83	2.34	1.99	1.05	1.25	24.20
	Cascade (near)	34	23.7	67.2	104	-57	35	May 20	Sept. 17	120	35	.60	.55	.82	1.35	2.59	3.23	1.25	1.17	1.59	1.33	.65	.70	15.83
	Great Falls	40	23.6	69.0	107	-49	40	May 9	Sept. 25	139	40	.60	.58	.89	1.13	2.31	3.14	1.52	1.36	1.44	.94	.62	.68	15.21
Chouteau	Big Sandy	16	13.1	68.5	109	-52	17	May 15	Sept. 20	128	17	.27	.43	.65	.88	1.77	2.71	1.19	1.35	1.20	.46	.56	.64	12.11
	Carter (near)	----	----	----	----	----	10	May 20	Sept. 15	118	11	.24	.33	.55	.90	1.88	2.57	1.30	1.36	1.19	.62	.45	.71	12.10
	Fort Benton	15	18.4	69.4	108	-58	16	May 11	Sept. 25	137	15	.74	.51	.56	.91	2.46	2.49	1.38	1.22	1.29	.60	.46	.49	13.11
	Geraldine (near)	28	23.0	69.8	107	-39	29	May 8	Sept. 28	143	28	.66	.55	.99	1.32	2.14	2.98	1.50	1.24	1.48	1.00	.68	.76	15.30
	Highwood	----	----	----	----	----	28	May 23	Sept. 18	118	33	.75	.71	1.06	1.35	2.60	3.78	1.96	1.49	2.05	1.44	.77	.94	18.90
	Kenilworth (near)	11	11.4	66.9	110	-52	13	May 25	do	116	12	.21	.21	.45	.96	1.88	2.71	1.09	1.60	1.54	.53	.42	.40	12.00
	Lytle	27	19.5	68.6	110	-43	27	May 12	Sept. 25	136	27	.55	.51	.82	1.24	1.64	2.47	1.20	1.29	1.30	.86	.56	.69	13.13
Custer	Garland	15	17.1	70.6	112	-51	17	May 18	Sept. 23	128	17	.44	.34	.65	1.06	1.87	2.06	1.55	.90	1.04	.82	.51	.57	11.81
	Knowlton (near)	14	16.4	71.6	108	-46	15	May 15	Sept. 22	130	15	.63	.58	.69	1.42	2.18	2.96	2.39	1.09	1.09	.98	.71	1.04	15.76
	Miles City	40	14.5	72.9	111	-49	40	Apr. 30	Oct. 5	158	40	.64	.46	.83	.97	1.89	2.42	1.67	1.20	1.07	.83	.55	.63	13.16
Daniels	Scobey	----	----	----	----	----	10	May 24	Sept. 22	121	10	.23	.38	.49	.85	1.18	2.51	2.12	1.11	1.17	.79	.30	.32	11.45
Dawson	Glendive	39	14.1	73.2	117	-50	39	May 13	Sept. 24	134	40	.45	.42	.77	.98	2.01	3.12	1.90	1.44	1.23	.75	.41	.55	14.03
	Paxton (near)	----	----	----	----	----	15	May 7	Sept. 28	144	16	.28	.20	.44	.67	1.35	2.95	1.64	1.11	.99	.73	.41	.32	11.09
Deer Lodge	Anaconda	25	24.2	63.4	102	-35	26	June 8	Sept. 14	98	25	.87	.71	.87	.96	2.12	2.15	1.41	1.02	1.34	1.06	.92	.81	14.24
	East Anaconda	33	22.1	65.5	99	-35	34	May 27	Sept. 21	117	33	.83	.67	.75	1.03	1.78	2.14	1.33	1.14	1.15	.94	.76	.75	13.27

[1] Length of growing season between average dates of last killing frost in spring and first in fall.

[2] Killing frost usually occurs every month.

MONTANA—Continued

Climatic summary—Continued

County	Station	Temperature: Length of record	Temperature: January average	Temperature: July average	Temperature: Maximum	Temperature: Minimum	Killing frost average dates: Length of record	Killing frost: Last in spring	Killing frost: First in fall	Killing frost: Growing season	Average precipitation: Length of record	January	February	March	April	May	June	July	August	September	October	November	December	Annual
		Yr.	°F.	°F.	°F.	°F.	Yr.			Days	Yr.	In.	In.	In.	In.	In.	In.	In.	In.	In.	In.	In.	In.	In.
Fallon	Baker						11	May 9	Sept. 25	139	15	0.75	0.30	0.83	1.07	2.28	2.90	1.61	1.13	1.23	1.07	0.48	0.56	14.21
	Plevna (near)	27	15.2	71.2	111	−52	27	May 18	Sept. 27	132	27	.55	.40	.62	1.18	2.06	2.84	1.79	1.03	1.09	.90	.48	.52	13.46
Fergus	Denton	17	20.0	67.0	106	−46	18	May 15	Sept. 24	132	18	.65	.37	.56	.89	1.86	3.45	1.84	1.04	1.72	.86	.40	.49	14.13
	Lewistown	38	21.7	65.4	105	−46	38	May 28	Sept.;13	108	39	.74	.73	1.01	1.24	2.79	3.53	2.18	1.42	1.50	1.23	.64	.86	17.87
	Pinegrove	13	22.4	61.6	100	−42	14	June 3	do	102	13	1.14	.68	1.31	1.33	3.19	3.67	2.84	1.15	1.79	1.10	.61	.97	19.78
	Valentine	31	16.2	70.8	110	−50	31	May 17	Sept. 19	125	30	.30	.27	.43	.74	1.84	2.33	1.45	1.09	.96	.75	.33	.41	10.90
	Winifred	16	19.1	69.1	108	−48	17	May 15	Sept. 23	131	17	.44	.40	.68	.74	1.61	2.35	1.34	.85	.99	.99	.59	.66	11.64
Flathead	Belton	24	21.0	65.2	101	−42	24	May 28	Sept. 17	112	24	3.13	2.10	1.75	1.52	2.04	2.43	1.16	1.38	2.02	2.59	2.69	3.44	26.25
	Columbia Falls	39	22.3	65.8	103	−40	40	June 1	Sept. 8	99	39	1.93	1.35	1.09	1.26	2.40	2.72	1.37	1.42	1.76	1.52	1.73	2.10	20.65
	Kalispell	40	20.4	64.1	101	−34	40	May 5	Oct. 1	149	40	1.31	.93	.96	.87	1.56	1.89	.98	.97	1.31	1.02	1.35	1.35	14.50
	Pleasant Valley (near)	24	19.0	60.0	99	−51	24	(2)	(2)		23	1.78	1.33	1.54	1.03	1.59	1.90	.79	.98	1.38	1.56	2.19	1.98	18.05
Gallatin	Agricultural College	39	20.8	64.6	112	−53	39	May 24	Sept. 16	115	40	.85	.81	1.28	1.66	2.81	2.40	1.37	1.13	1.65	1.54	1.00	.89	17.39
	Flathead Creek	14	21.4	58.8	96	−43	14	June 4	Sept. 1	89	12	1.21	1.16	1.23	1.87	2.62	3.19	2.23	1.52	2.26	1.30	1.95	1.28	21.82
	Hebgen Dam	35	11.7	59.5	99	−60	35	June 15	Sept. 11	88	34	2.65	1.93	1.97	1.57	2.09	2.16	1.83	1.40	1.53	1.78	1.81	2.12	22.84
	Three Forks	14	21.3	66.9	101	−49	16	May 30	Sept. 19	112	19	.40	.39	.42	1.03	1.73	2.09	1.40	.96	1.34	.92	.63	.55	11.86
Garfield	Jordan	19	14.8	72.4	112	−58	23	May 19	Sept. 21	125	20	.59	.51	.63	.81	1.80	2.41	1.71	.98	.72	.62	.26	.58	11.62
	Sentinel Butte Pass	17	17.9	71.1	110	−39	17	May 7	Oct. 2	148	17	.50	.38	.89	1.09	2.24	3.28	1.51	1.19	1.32	.94	.54	.65	14.53
	Snowbelt	19	16.8	69.4	105	−42	20	May 17	Sept. 28	134	19	.42	.35	.76	1.08	1.98	2.99	1.86	1.22	1.08	.92	.55	.66	13.87
Glacier	Babb (near)	31	17.7	60.1	96	−53	32	May 29	Sept. 8	102	32	.99	.79	1.14	1.62	2.40	3.28	1.95	1.86	2.14	1.25	1.00	1.01	19.43
	Browning	32	19.0	61.0	99	−56	34	June 6	Sept. 7	93	36	.62	.51	.67	.88	1.86	2.64	1.46	1.42	1.68	.85	.64	.69	13.92
	Cut Bank	29	16.8	65.1	102	−47	31	May 23	Sept. 17	117	30	.40	.27	.38	.70	1.67	2.66	1.58	1.24	1.14	.53	.29	.38	11.24
Golden Valley	Emory	17	19.9	68.4	104	−55	19	May 22	Sept. 14	115	19	.56	.55	.90	1.02	2.29	2.85	2.18	1.39	1.35	.69	.52	.60	14.90
	Ryegate										7	.34	.33	.49	1.16	2.27	2.68	1.59	1.28	2.58	1.29	.54	.27	14.82
Granite	Drummond (near)										9	.59	.67	.92	.83	1.23	1.54	.88	.86	.90	1.17	.48	.48	10.55
	Philipsburg	35	22.3	62.5	99	−40	34	June 9	Sept. 4	87	35	.74	.72	.95	1.19	2.24	2.61	1.33	1.08	1.31	1.09	.83	.66	14.75
Hill	Havre	40	12.9	68.3	108	−57	40	May 11	Sept. 22	134	40	.64	.46	.58	.89	1.92	2.71	1.61	1.24	1.23	.64	.51	.64	13.07
Jefferson	Boulder	22	21.0	62.2	105	−39	21	June 11	Sept. 6	87	17	.58	.57	.66	.89	2.04	2.11	1.46	1.06	1.48	.77	.40	.58	12.60
	Dry Land Experiment Station.	11	20.5	65.4	101	−42	14	May 25	Sept. 20	118	14	.65	.53	.85	1.02	1.73	2.02	1.20	1.03	.98	1.21	.82	.63	12.67
	Pipestone Dam						10	June 15	Sept. 6	83	10	.79	.54	.86	1.19	1.36	1.66	1.43	1.11	1.09	.78	.58	.58	11.97
	Renova (near)	32	23.6	65.6	103	−42	34	May 26	Sept. 11	108	34	.37	.31	.50	1.24	1.91	1.92	1.24	.97	1.29	.85	.42	.32	11.34
Judith Basin	Hobson										10	.46	.43	.74	1.14	2.21	3.81	1.97	1.28	1.28	.81	.70	.62	15.45
	Stanford	12	23.8	65.5	102	−44	12	May 23	Sept. 28	128	12	.55	.51	.75	.97	2.06	2.89	1.99	1.56	1.11	.99	.58	.61	14.57
	Utica	29	22.8	64.6	108	−57	29	May 25	Sept. 18	116	29	.61	.42	.79	1.34	2.87	3.36	2.11	1.29	1.45	1.10	.53	.58	16.45
Lake	Dayton	22	24.1	66.3	105	−27	23	May 18	Sept. 25	130	22	1.06	.77	.83	.92	1.64	2.13	1.40	1.14	1.15	.92	.94	1.19	14.09
	Polson	28	24.0	67.7	104	−27	30	May 12	Sept. 27	138	28	1.17	.84	1.06	1.11	1.44	2.06	.90	.91	1.34	1.19	1.24	1.30	14.56

	St. Ignatius	30	24.0	66.7	103	−36	31	May 21	Sept. 23	125	30	.90	.76	1.03	1.41	2.04	2.13	1.04	1.05	1.51	1.31	1.03	.92	15.13
Lewis & Clark	Augusta	38	21.6	63.5	102	−51	38	May 29	Sept. 10	104	38	.66	.44	.91	1.00	2.34	2.73	1.55	1.18	1.47	.84	.56	.67	14.35
	Big Ox	19	21.1	63.7	100	−37	26	June 3	Sept. 8	97	24	1.46	1.23	1.40	1.25	2.81	2.56	1.56	1.21	1.48	1.22	1.53	1.37	19.08
	Canyon Ferry	40	19.9	68.6	104	−41	40	May 13	Sept. 22	132	40	.37	.40	.49	.76	1.95	2.05	1.26	.96	1.09	.75	.44	.47	10.99
	Chessman Reservoir										9	1.27	1.05	1.45	1.82	2.78	3.56	1.64	1.42	2.21	2.04	1.17	.90	21.31
	East Helena	14	18.3	67.9	104	−45	11	May 14	Sept. 22	131	12	.41	.30	.70	.58	1.43	1.60	.99	.92	.90	.64	.37	.55	9.39
	Helena	40	20.2	65.7	103	−42	40	May 2	Oct. 2	153	40	.66	.55	.77	.98	2.10	2.10	1.08	.88	1.18	.91	.59	.74	12.54
	Helena Valley										16	.24	.26	.33	.62	1.22	1.75	.98	.94	.88	.59	.26	.40	8.47
	Holter	35	25.3	68.7	108	−44	36	May 13	Sept. 23	133	36	.53	.52	.60	1.13	2.17	2.57	1.31	.93	1.38	1.05	.50	.55	13.24
	Sun River Canyon	24	21.4	65.8	106	−49	25	May 27	Sept. 21	117	27	.68	.53	1.00	1.09	2.26	2.83	1.63	1.24	1.50	1.07	.79	.90	15.52
Liberty	Chester	14	9.8	66.7	104	−55	17	May 25	Sept. 7	105	15	.60	.26	.34	.50	1.60	2.77	1.02	1.18	1.30	.30	.32	.34	10.53
	Kinread	12	13.8	69.0	106	−53	11	do	Sept. 15	113	13	.24	.11	.33	.96	1.74	2.14	1.34	1.49	1.03	.47	.47	.50	10.82
	Lothair						20	May 15	Sept. 19	127	19	.36	.26	.49	.86	1.29	2.30	1.61	1.32	1.20	.48	.38	.51	11.06
Lincoln	Fortine	32	18.8	62.8	107	−49	33	May 29	Sept. 8	102	33	1.57	1.16	1.20	1.03	1.69	2.28	1.22	1.37	1.47	1.30	1.54	1.60	17.43
	Libby	39	22.8	65.8	109	−46	40	June 1	Sept. 9	100	39	2.34	1.43	1.52	.97	1.33	1.48	.94	.86	1.26	1.68	2.68	2.32	18.81
	Upper Yaak River	22	19.2	61.0	102	−49	22	(2)	(2)		22	2.01	1.40	1.64	1.30	1.54	1.57	.89	1.08	1.61	1.96	2.20	2.58	19.78
Madison	Conway's Ranch	12	14.2	55.2	88	−48	12	(2)	(2)		12	1.14	1.19	1.50	1.50	1.54	1.78	1.62	1.27	1.20	1.27	1.06	1.31	16.38
	Ennis	21	21.7	64.5	100	−43	21	June 2	Sept. 11	101	20	.53	.49	.67	.96	1.43	1.71	1.17	1.04	.95	.89	.44	.41	10.69
	Norris (near)	32	24.7	68.8	101	−36	32	May 15	Sept. 29	137	32	.63	.61	1.13	1.62	3.13	2.53	1.32	1.18	1.68	1.69	.87	.66	17.05
	Virginia City	29	20.8	66.1	103	−43	29	May 30	Sept. 18	111	28	.64	.46	.86	1.18	1.90	1.78	1.28	1.20	1.27	.99	.80	.62	12.98
McCone	Circle (near)	37	14.4	69.3	112	−57	37	May 23	Sept. 16	116	37	.74	.68	1.10	1.09	2.08	3.78	1.76	1.38	1.11	.91	.61	.85	16.09
	Vida (near)						11	May 13	Sept. 25	135	12	.77	.71	1.09	1.22	1.97	2.72	2.10	.94	.90	.87	.75	1.01	15.05
Meagher	Copper						26	June 6	Aug. 29	84	34	.90	.73	.93	1.03	2.22	2.67	1.79	1.16	1.52	1.23	.95	.82	15.95
	Findon	14	22.4	62.4	96	−37	15	May 22	Sept. 22	123	18	.90	.64	.82	1.44	2.48	3.23	2.30	1.48	1.73	.99	.81	.73	17.55
	Fort Logan										9	.58	.76	1.01	.70	2.27	2.25	.67	.64	1.00	.80	.51	.51	11.70
	Loweth	12	17.8	60.4	97	−48	13	June 8	Sept. 9	93	13	.48	.34	.64	.72	1.50	2.20	1.42	1.31	1.16	1.10	.70	.58	12.15
	White Sulphur Springs.	22	20.7	65.0	100	−42	26	May 29	Sept. 14	108	24	.52	.50	1.00	1.02	1.80	2.62	1.58	1.09	1.28	1.21	.66	.91	14.19
Mineral	Haugan	31	22.0	62.6	104	−49	31	June 11	Aug. 30	80	30	4.07	2.56	2.85	1.64	1.65	1.91	.64	.75	1.62	2.32	3.65	3.97	27.63
	Saltese										9	5.59	3.71	2.95	1.31	2.33	1.97	1.21	1.11	1.90	2.44	5.64	4.08	34.24
	Superior	24	23.8	66.6	108	−39	23	June 2	Sept. 11	101	23	1.38	1.09	1.37	1.05	1.47	1.69	.79	.79	1.24	1.33	1.48	1.86	15.54
Missoula	Missoula	40	22.3	67.6	105	−42	40	May 18	Sept. 23	128	40	.96	.81	.98	.98	1.95	1.91	.89	.90	1.31	1.13	1.11	1.08	14.01
Musselshell	Melstone	19	21.1	72.0	108	−51	21	May 10	Sept. 25	138	21	.49	.34	.59	.82	1.80	2.75	1.43	.86	.87	.91	.39	.48	11.73
	Roundup	17	24.0	71.2	107	−52	18	May 9	Sept. 27	141	17	.53	.35	.68	1.05	1.72	2.50	1.45	.87	.91	1.08	.54	.58	12.26
Park	Livingston	33	26.0	68.5	106	−45	34	May 17	Sept. 21	127	32	.55	.59	.86	1.40	2.82	1.85	1.35	1.23	1.43	1.24	.72	.63	14.67
Petroleum	Flatwillow (near)	24	21.1	70.2	107	−48	26	May 18	Sept. 25	130	25	.30	.32	.56	.75	1.89	2.68	1.51	1.04	1.03	.94	.41	.45	11.88
Phillips	Malta	32	11.9	70.4	109	−56	32	May 14	Sept. 24	133	32	.48	.36	.49	.74	2.03	3.34	1.87	1.20	1.36	.71	.41	.48	13.47
	Forks (near)	24	9.7	67.3	108	−51	23	May 24	Sept. 13	112	22	.34	.30	.47	.87	1.76	3.06	1.82	1.73	1.29	.55	.38	.40	12.97
	Zortman										8	.53	.64	.88	.90	4.49	3.12	2.22	1.47	1.36	.91	.51	.48	17.51
Pondera	Conrad	24	17.1	66.8	103	−45	24	May 21	Sept. 19	121	23	.37	.26	.67	1.11	1.62	2.59	1.32	1.12	1.15	.68	.30	.44	11.63
	Valier	27	19.6	65.4	101	−49	28	May 17	Sept. 23	129	27	.35	.20	.48	.88	1.74	2.83	1.52	1.43	1.28	.75	.33	.47	12.26
Powder River	Biddle	19	19.4	70.4	110	−41	22	May 23	Sept. 21	121	20	.46	.35	.50	1.23	2.46	2.98	2.10	1.59	1.50	1.03	.56	.35	15.11
Powell	Deer Lodge	29	21.6	64.6	108	−42	24	June 5	Sept. 9	96	21	.42	.42	.52	.65	1.53	2.14	1.17	.77	1.07	.62	.48	.48	10.27
	Elliston										11	1.46	1.00	1.17	1.76	2.64	3.11	1.72	1.13	2.86	1.99	1.23	1.16	21.23
	Ovando	38	17.2	61.8	101	−52	40	June 8	Aug. 25	78	38	1.71	1.39	1.34	.97	1.86	2.15	1.00	1.03	1.36	1.24	1.50	1.85	17.40
Prairie	Fallon	12	9.6	70.4	108	−54	12	May 19	Sept. 18	122	12	.33	.21	.28	.43	2.54	3.36	1.97	1.56	1.22	.95	.30	.21	13.36
	Mildred	21	14.3	70.9	112	−50	30	May 14	Sept. 25	134	30	.31	.23	.41	.98	1.90	2.89	1.64	1.14	1.17	.68	.34	.34	12.03
Ravalli	Como	14	25.7	65.8	103	−27	14	May 22	Sept. 26	127	14	1.46	1.03	.85	1.15	1.65	1.75	.88	.97	1.56	1.16	1.76	.86	15.08
	Darby (near)	14	26.4	65.7	104	−36	15	May 20	Sept. 16	119	15	1.51	1.43	1.51	1.03	1.44	1.61	.91	.67	1.42	1.26	1.98	1.48	16.25
	Hamilton	31	25.9	67.8	103	−39	34	May 16	Sept. 23	130	33	.82	.72	.71	.85	1.42	1.66	.79	.70	1.13	.99	.80	.72	11.31
	Stevensville	27	23.0	66.3	102	−37	28	May 25	Sept. 15	113	27	.79	.72	.82	.79	1.41	1.54	.87	.95	1.31	1.12	.99	.91	12.22
	Sula										5	1.37	1.44	1.22	2.14	1.79	1.62	1.21	1.12	1.40	1.12	.95	1.19	16.57

MONTANA—Continued

Climatic summary—Continued

County	Station	Temperature					Killing frost average dates				Average precipitation													
		Length of record	January average	July average	Maximum	Minimum	Length of record	Last in spring	First in fall	Growing season	Length of record	January	February	March	April	May	June	July	August	September	October	November	December	Annual
		Yr.	*°F.*	*°F.*	*°F.*	*°F.*	*Yr.*			*Days*	*Yr.*	*In.*	*In.*	*In.*	*In.*	*In.*	*In.*	*In.*	*In.*	*In.*	*In.*	*In.*	*In.*	*In.*
Ravalli—Cont'd	Sunset Orchards	16	21.9	65.6	98	−32	15	May 20	Sept. 21	124	14	0.63	0.84	1.06	0.96	1.84	1.62	0.92	1.08	1.46	0.72	1.18	0.55	12.86
	Victor (near)	24	22.8	65.6	99	−39	24	May 23	Sept. 22	122	22	1.08	.72	1.05	.92	1.18	1.35	.78	.85	1.14	1.18	1.40	1.41	13.06
Richland	Culbertson (near)	27	9.6	68.8	113	−57	34	May 19	Sept. 18	122	33	.31	.25	.42	.76	1.85	2.57	2.00	1.37	1.31	.79	.36	.29	12.28
	Savage	33	12.8	71.9	111	−53	33	May 18	Sept. 22	127	33	.43	.35	.57	.87	1.90	2.91	1.82	1.49	1.17	.71	.41	.45	13.08
	Sidney	17	9.2	68.8	110	−47	17	do	Sept. 21	126	17	.48	.44	.56	.92	2.22	3.31	1.99	1.60	1.69	.83	.39	.50	14.93
Roosevelt	Poplar	38	7.1	71.2	110	−63	40	May 16	Sept. 18	125	39	.38	.32	.62	.75	1.78	3.01	1.90	1.33	1.14	.65	.43	.36	12.67
Rosebud	Ashland (near)	11	21.1	70.5	108	−43	12	May 9	Sept. 28	142	11	.68	.53	1.19	1.65	2.09	2.18	1.57	1.05	1.10	1.20	.73	.54	14.51
	Colstrip	12	19.8	71.0	110	−50	12	May 15	Sept. 24	132	12	.82	.60	1.38	1.51	1.80	1.68	1.52	.98	1.05	1.15	.69	.63	13.81
	Forsyth	12	14.9	71.4	111	−46	12	May 16	Sept. 27	134	12	.70	.47	.65	.58	2.50	2.47	1.64	.59	1.46	.90	.52	.38	12.86
	Ingomar (near)	22	20.7	72.9	109	−55	23	May 20	Sept. 26	129	22	.40	.31	.51	.89	1.46	2.04	1.37	.77	.81	.75	.42	.51	10.24
	Rock Springs (near)	23	14.6	71.7	109	−43	24	May 17	Sept. 24	130	23	.94	.52	.81	1.01	1.44	2.57	1.52	1.12	.89	.74	.59	.93	13.08
Sanders	Heron	27	24.0	64.6	105	−39	27	May 30	Sept. 6	99	27	4.22	3.43	3.56	1.98	1.93	1.96	.93	1.00	1.77	2.61	3.90	5.16	32.45
	Lonepine	17	23.2	69.6	105	−40	18	May 22	Sept. 19	120	17	.96	.68	.66	.61	.90	1.17	.55	.51	.96	.92	1.05	1.13	10.10
	Plains	28	25.2	66.8	106	−34	28	May 30	Sept. 20	113	28	1.23	.83	.78	.83	1.72	1.63	1.15	.91	1.34	.91	1.52	1.23	14.08
	Thompson Falls	27	24.6	67.4	108	−32	28	May 18	Sept. 21	126	27	2.15	1.39	2.04	1.47	1.76	1.70	.94	.84	1.25	1.70	2.19	2.55	19.98
	Trout Creek (near)	24	23.3	63.9	106	−40	26	June 4	Sept. 4	92	26	3.96	2.85	3.24	1.74	1.80	1.75	.85	.77	1.41	2.29	3.69	4.48	28.83
Sheridan	Medicine Lake (near)	21	7.4	67.6	117	−58	26	May 26	Sept. 17	114	21	.33	.29	.40	.82	1.68	3.05	2.08	1.32	1.42	.72	.30	.30	12.71
	Outlook	20	5.8	66.5	115	−53	21	May 23	Sept. 21	121	19	.25	.29	.35	.65	1.86	2.78	1.99	1.36	1.64	.69	.29	.30	12.45
Silver Bow	Butte	40	22.7	64.8	100	−52	40	May 29	Sept. 16	110	40	.76	.73	.94	1.15	1.96	2.17	1.32	1.05	1.05	.96	.67	.75	13.51
Stillwater	Busteed	28	23.8	68.0	108	−45	28	May 22	Sept. 21	122	28	.63	.44	.85	1.10	2.52	2.17	1.50	1.32	1.54	1.30	.65	.49	14.51
	Mystic Lake	14	22.8	63.4	94	−37	15	May 26	Sept. 20	117	14	1.02	1.08	1.94	2.48	2.91	2.87	2.25	1.91	1.62	2.01	1.53	1.06	22.68
	Nye										9	.90	.75	1.31	2.66	5.15	2.17	2.29	1.40	2.09	1.67	.78	.38	21.55
Sweet Grass	Big Timber	30	26.2	70.0	110	−47	30	May 20	Sept. 20	123	30	.63	.55	1.06	1.28	2.39	1.94	1.37	1.15	1.40	1.56	.76	.52	14.61
Teton	Blackleaf	12	20.5	60.4	96	−46	15	June 4	Aug. 30	87	14	.68	.56	.56	1.07	3.09	3.72	1.55	1.55	1.94	1.08	.65	.47	16.92
	Choteau	23	20.2	65.3	106	−50	26	May 26	Sept. 15	112	23	.30	.25	.49	.80	1.76	2.91	1.74	1.08	1.06	.61	.40	.39	11.79
	Fairfield	32	21.6	65.0	112	−49	32	May 19	Sept. 20	124	31	.33	.32	.49	.77	1.66	2.64	1.49	1.24	1.17	.76	.31	.35	11.53
Toole	Dunkirk (near)	17	11.5	65.0	104	−42	27	May 22	Sept. 19	120	27	.40	.31	.50	.93	1.63	2.58	1.72	1.69	1.25	.54	.31	.50	12.36
	Goldbutte	31	15.4	65.5	104	−41	32	May 24	do	118	33	.51	.44	.58	.87	1.97	2.93	1.52	1.35	1.34	.59	.41	.49	13.00
	Knoble's Ranch						12	May 23	Sept. 25	125	12	.51	.46	.40	.70	1.74	2.80	2.24	1.70	2.33	.92	.32	.39	14.51
	Shelby						10	May 27	Sept. 14	110	9	.46	.37	.48	.68	1.79	2.07	1.28	1.43	1.57	.79	.21	.37	11.50
Treasure	Sarpy Creek	13	22.0	71.3	111	−53	14	May 22	Sept. 24	125	14	.50	.38	.87	.95	1.45	1.61	1.09	.97	.76	1.00	.71	.59	10.88
Valley	Frazer	15	9.5	69.3	110	−59	16	May 16	Sept. 20	127	15	.39	.35	.72	.72	1.48	2.68	1.77	1.07	1.09	.90	.47	.43	12.07
	Glasgow	37	9.0	70.7	113	−59	37	May 19	Sept. 19	123	37	.52	.38	.71	.83	2.14	2.86	1.52	1.33	1.24	.69	.43	.56	13.21
	Lustre (near)										17	.34	.31	.42	.83	1.42	2.54	1.73	1.18	1.27	.73	.35	.31	11.43
	Opheim	10	7.5	64.5	102	−41	10	May 24	Sept. 19	118	10	.30	.23	.31	.54	1.22	1.96	1.70	1.20	.96	.59	.23	.32	9.56
Wheatland	Harlowton (near)	33	19.3	63.8	102	−54	32	June 2	Sept. 6	96	19	.39	.51	.55	.69	2.21	2.17	1.62	.72	1.11	.85	.50	.42	11.74
Wibaux	Wibaux	13	15.7	68.8	110	−55	15	May 25	Sept. 13	111	15	.39	.33	.47	1.29	1.86	4.02	2.23	1.67	1.37	.96	.65	.47	15.71

Yellowstone	Ballantine	20	22. 7	71. 8	110−50	20	May 10	Sept. 23	136	20	. 44	. 36	. 71	1. 06	1. 72	1. 93	1. 09	. 86	1. 10	. 93	. 59	. 46	11. 25
	Billings No. 2	36	23. 2	71. 2	112−49	38	May 15	Sept. 25	133	34	. 60	. 43	. 80	1. 11	2. 33	2. 20	1. 34	. 97	1. 22	1. 24	. 65	. 52	13. 41
	Broadview	----	----	----	--------	10	May 14	Sept. 11	120	10	. 67	. 43	. 81	1. 27	2. 65	2. 65	1. 84	1. 14	1. 66	. 87	. 37	. 42	14. 78
	Huntley	13	19. 0	70. 6	108−40	13	May 11	Sept. 25	137	13	. 55	. 39	. 65	. 96	2. 85	2. 20	1. 27	. 93	1. 51	1. 22	. 49	. 37	13. 39

Precipitation and temperature—State unit values

[This tabulation gives the mean annual, mean monthly, and average seasonal precipitation and percentage of normal precipitation for each year, 1886–1938, and the mean annual temperatures, 1902–38, for Montana]

Precipitation		Precipitation	
Year	Mean	Year	Mean
	In.		*In.*
1886	12. 45	1913	15. 41
1887	15. 95	1914	15. 15
1888	13. 50	1915	18. 92
1889	8. 94	1916	18. 58
1890	9. 86	1917	14. 43
1891	17. 17	1918	13. 83
1892	15. 52	1919	10. 88
1893	15. 65	1920	14. 59
1894	15. 18	1921	14. 64
1895	11. 82	1922	15. 12
1896	16. 21	1923	18. 12
1897	15. 80	1924	13. 71
1898	16. 44	1925	16. 34
1899	14. 92	1926	13. 79
1900	13. 81	1927	20. 63
1901	15. 23	1928	13. 06
1902	15. 37	1929	13. 08
1903	15. 58	1930	12. 38
1904	11. 09	1931	10. 09
1905	13. 62	1932	16. 17
1906	18. 64	1933	15. 69
1907	17. 65	1934	11. 22
1908	19. 25	1935	10. 89
1909	19. 92	1936	11. 32
1910	16. 12	1937	12. 93
1911	18. 53	1938	16. 60
1912	17. 35		

Precipitation	
Month	Mean
	In.
January	0. 87
February	. 70
March	. 94
April	1. 13
May	2. 09
June	2. 56
July	1. 42
August	1. 08
September	1. 30
October	1. 02
November	. 91
December	. 86
Annual	14. 88
Season	**Average**
	In.
Winter	2. 43
Spring	4. 16
Summer	5. 06
Fall	3. 23

Annual precipitation (in percent of normal)		Annual precipitation (in percent of normal)	
Year	Percent	Year	Percent
	In.		*In.*
1902	103	1929	88
1903	105	1930	83
1904	85	1931	68
1905	92	1932	109
1906	125	1933	105
1907	119	1934	75
1908	129	1935	73
1909	134	1936	76
1910	108	1937	87
1911	125	1938	112
1912	117		
1913	104		
1914	102		
1915	127		
1916	125		
1917	97		
1918	93		
1919	73		
1920	98		
1921	98		
1922	102		
1923	122		
1924	92		
1925	110		
1926	93		
1927	139		
1928	88		

Temperature		Temperature	
Year	Mean	Year	Mean
	° F.		*° F.*
1902	42. 0	1912	41. 7
1903	42. 3	1913	41. 8
1904	43. 5	1914	43. 5
1905	42. 6	1915	43. 2
1906	43. 5	1916	39. 1
1907	41. 4	1917	41. 3
1908	43. 5	1918	43. 3
1909	41. 2	1919	42. 6
1910	44. 6	1920	42. 6
1911	40. 9	1921	44. 2
		1922	41. 5
		1923	43. 4
		1924	41. 8
		1925	44. 6
		1926	44. 7
		1927	40. 8
		1928	43. 3
		1929	40. 9
		1930	43. 4
		1931	45. 6
		1932	42. 6
		1933	44. 0
		1934	46. 9
		1935	42. 4
		1936	42. 7
		1937	41. 9
		1938	44. 1

MONTANA—Continued

Dates of last killing frost in spring and first in fall, with length of growing season

Year	Billings			Havre			Helena			Kalispell			Miles City			Poplar		
	Last in spring	First in fall	Growing season [1]	Last in spring	First in fall	Growing season [1]	Last in spring	First in fall	Growing season [1]	Last in spring	First in fall	Growing season [1]	Last in spring	First in fall	Growing season [1]	Last in spring	First in fall	Growing season [1]
			Days			Days			Days			Days			Days			Days
1899	May 5 [2]			May 23	Sept. 16	116	May 16	Oct. 10 [2]	147	May 15	Oct. 4	142	May 4	Oct. 13	162	May 17 [2]	Sept. 16	122
1900		Sept. 24 [2]		Apr. 29	Sept. 25	149	Apr. 12	Sept. 25	166	May 23	Sept. 26	126	Apr. 17	Sept. 26	162	May 3 [2]	do. [2]	136
1901	Apr. 28 [2]	Sept. 16 [2]	141	June 6	Sept. 19	105	May 10	Oct. 15	158	May 10	Nov. 2	176	Apr. 19	Oct. 13	177	May 11	Sept. 17	129
1902	May 3 [2]			May 5	Sept. 3	121	May 5	Sept. 17	135	May 5	Oct. 17	165	Apr. 26	Sept. 12	139	May 9 [2]	Sept. 3	117
1903	June 23 [2]	Aug. 28 [2]	66	May 21	Sept. 16	118	May 24	Sept. 14	113	May 2	Oct. 4	155	May 20	Sept. 13	116	May 20 [2]	Sept. 13 [2]	116
1904		Sept. 13 [2]		May 13	Sept. 13	123	Apr. 16 [2]	Oct. 18 [2]	185	May 8	Oct. 5	150	Apr. 18	Sept. 14	149	May 17 [2]	Sept. 10 [2]	116
1905	May 5	Oct. 10 [2]	158	May 16	Sept. 30	137	May 5 [2]	Oct. 14	162	May 22	Oct. 10	141	May 5	Oct. 11	159	May 12 [2]	Sept. 19 [2]	130
1906	May 6 [2]	Sept. 26 [2]	143	May 5	Sept. 26	144	do. [2]	Oct. 15	163	May 5	Sept. 12	130	May 6	Oct. 9	156	May 18 [2]	Sept. 26 [2]	131
1907	May 14 [2]	Sept. 9	118	do.	Sept. 18	136	May 4	Oct. 17	166	May 12	Oct. 3	144	May 7	Sept. 29	145	May 26 [2]	Sept. 14 [2]	111
1908	May 1 [2]	Sept. 25	147	May 1	Sept. 27	149	Apr. 30 [2]	Sept. 26	149	Apr. 29	Sept. 25	149	May 22	Sept. 27	128	May 22	Aug. 22	92
1909	May 19 [2]	Sept. 19 [2]	123	May 19	Sept. 23	127	May 8	Oct. 12	157	May 8	Oct. 7	152	May 9	Oct. 9	153	June 6 [2]	Sept. 22 [2]	108
1910	June 4 [2]	Aug. 25 [2]	82	June 3	Aug. 25	83	June 3	Aug. 25	83	May 1	Sept. 25	147	Apr. 18	Sept. 26	161	May 12 [2]	Aug. 25	105
1911	May 28 [2]	Sept. 15	110	Apr. 30	Aug. 27	119	Apr. 30	Sept. 23	146	Apr. 16	do.	162	May 2	Oct. 20	171	May 28	Aug. 28	92
1912	May 24 [2]	Sept. 16 [2]	115	May 13	Sept. 15	125	Apr. 21	Sept. 21	153	Apr. 22	Sept. 15	146	Apr. 26	Sept. 17	144	May 18 [2]	Sept. 10	115
1913	May 21 [2]	Sept. 25	127	May 20	Sept. 11	114	May 1	Sept. 25	147	May 4	Sept. 24	143	Apr. 25	Sept. 25	153	May 7 [2]	Sept. 11	127
1914	May 7	Oct. 8	154	May 13	Oct. 12	152	Apr. 29	Oct. 11	165	May 6	Oct. 6	153	May 12	Oct. 7	148	May 12	Oct. 12	153
1915	May 6	Oct. 7	154	May 20	Sept. 14	117	Apr. 5 [2]	Sept. 12	160	Apr. 24	Sept. 13	142	Apr. 11	do.	179	June 16	Sept. 20	96
1916	May 8	Sept. 14	129	May 14	do.	123	May 15	Sept. 14	122	May 12	Sept. 28	139	May 17 [2]	Oct. 4 [2]	140	May 8	Sept. 14	129
1917	May 31	Oct. 18	140	June 3	Oct. 11	130	May 31	Oct. 17	139	May 2	Oct. 17	168	May 31	Oct. 11	133	May 5	Sept. 25	143
1918	May 22	Oct. 26	157	May 29	Sept. 9	103	May 27	Oct. 25	151	May 27	Sept. 22	118	Apr. 29 [2]	Oct. 24	178	May 17	Sept. 9	115
1919	June 2 [2]	Sept. 22 [2]	112	May 14	Sept. 29	138	May 6	Sept. 29	146	May 13	Sept. 29	139	May 1 [2]	Oct. 4	156	June 2	Oct. 4	124
1920	May 26 [2]	Oct. 14 [2]	141	May 4	do.	148	May 2	Oct. 16	167	Apr. 25	Oct. 16	174	Apr. 26	Oct. 16 [2]	173	Apr. 26 [2]	Oct. 10 [2]	167
1921	May 1 [2]	Sept. 10 [2]	132	May 3	Sept. 11	131	May 1	Sept. 11	133	May 12	Sept. 10	121	Apr. 30	Oct. 11	164	May 15	Oct. 2	140
1922	Apr. 21 [2]	Sept. 29 [2]	161	May 15	Oct. 7	145	Apr. 29 [2]	Oct. 14	168	May 23	Oct. 14	144	Apr. 20	do.	174	Apr. 19 [2]	Oct. 8	172
1923	May 16 [2]	Oct. 12 [2]	149	do.	Sept. 28	136	May 15	Oct. 12	150	May 15	Sept. 17	125	May 8	Oct. 20	165	May 15	Oct. 12	150
1924	May 27 [2]	Sept. 1 [2]	97	May 9	Sept. 27	141	Apr. 25	Oct. 5	163	June 7	Sept. 18	103	May 7	Sept. 27	143		Sept. 1	
1925	May 10 [2]	Oct. 22 [2]	165	May 16	Sept. 21	128	May 9	Sept. 20	134	May 10	Sept. 20	133	May 16	Oct. 6	143	May 17	Sept. 21	127
1926	Apr. 27 [2]	Sept. 19 [2]	145	Apr. 27	Sept. 24	150	Apr. 24 [2]	Sept. 23	152	May 25	Sept. 19	117	Apr. 9	Sept. 23	167	May 13	Sept. 19 [2]	129
1927	May 10 [2]	Sept. 20 [2]	133	May 3	Sept. 20	140	May 10	Oct. 30	173	May 9	Oct. 11	155	May 10	Sept. 20	133	May 10	Sept. 20	133
1928	June 1 [2]	Sept. 21 [2]	112	Apr. 23	Sept. 24	154	Apr. 13	Oct. 4	174	May 3	Oct. 4	154	Apr. 21	Sept. 25	157	June 9 [2]	do.	103
1929	May 18 [2]	Sept. 4 [2]	109	May 18	Sept. 6	111	May 15	Oct. 11	149	May 15	Sept. 6	114	May 6	Oct. 23	170	May 16 [2]	Sept. 4 [2]	111
1930	June 4 [2]	Sept. 1 [2]	89	May 16	Oct. 13	150	Apr. 1	Oct. 14	196	May 26	Oct. 13	140	Apr. 5	Sept. 26	174	May 23 [2]	Sept. 1 [2]	101
1931	May 22 [2]	Oct. 10 [2]	141	May 10	Sept. 23	136	May 19	Sept. 23	127	Apr. 24	Oct. 8	167	May 20	Sept. 23	126	May 21	Sept. 23 [2]	125
1932	May 27	Sept. 21 [2]	117	May 1	Sept. 26	148	Apr. 30 [2]	Sept. 22	145	Mar. 29	do.	193	Apr. 26	Oct. 7	164	May 27	Sept. 16	112
1933	May 22 [2]	Sept. 20	121	May 10	do.	139	Apr. 18	Sept. 25	160	Apr. 13	Sept. 26	166	Apr. 13	Oct. 16	186	May 10 [2]	Sept. 26	139
1934	May 13	Sept. 23	133	Apr. 16	Sept. 20	157	May 13	Sept. 19	129	Apr. 3	Sept. 20	170	Apr. 16	Sept. 21	158	May 13	Sept. 15	125

1935	Apr. 29	Sept. 22	146	May 9	Sept. 26	140	May 8	Sept. 27	142	Apr. 28	Oct. 23	178	Apr. 29	Oct. 22	176	May 8	Sept. 4	119
1936	do	Oct. 22	176	Apr. 29	Sept. 16	140	Apr. 5	Sept. 26	174	Apr. 5	Sept. 16	164	Apr. 7	Oct. 1	177	Apr. 29	Sept. 16	140
1937	do.[2]	Oct. 16	170	Apr. 24	Sept. 24	153	Apr. 8	Sept. 30	175	May 6	Oct. 5	152	Apr. 25	Oct. 13	171	June 8[2]	Sept. 25	109
1938	May 8	Oct. 19	164	May 8	Oct. 18	163	Apr. 21	Oct. 18	180	Apr. 21	Oct. 14	176	May 7	Oct. 19	165	Apr. 28	Oct. 14	169
Mean	May 15	Sept. 25	133	May 11	Sept. 22	134	May 2	Oct. 2	158	May 5	Oct. 1	149	Apr. 30	Oct. 5	158	May 16	Sept. 18	125
Extremes	Apr. 21[3]	Aug. 25[5]	[7] 66	Apr. 16[3]	Aug. 25[5]	[7] 83	Apr. 1[3]	Aug. 25[5]	[7] 83	Mar. 29[3]	Sept. 6[5]	[7] 103	Apr. 5[3]	Sept. 12[5]	[7] 116	Apr. 19[3]	Aug. 22[5]	[7] 92
	June 23[4]	Oct. 26[6]	[8] 176	June 6[4]	Oct. 18[6]	[8] 163	June 3[4]	Oct. 30[6]	[8] 196	June 7[4]	Nov. 2[6]	[8] 193	May 31[4]	Oct. 24[6]	[8] 186	June 16[4]	Oct. 14[6]	[8] 172

[1] Number of days between last killing frost in spring and first in fall.
[2] No frost reported but a temperature of 32° or lower with conditions favorable for killing frost.
[3] Earliest date in spring.
[4] Latest date in spring.
[5] Earliest date in fall.
[6] Latest date in fall.
[7] Shortest growing season.
[8] Longest growing season.

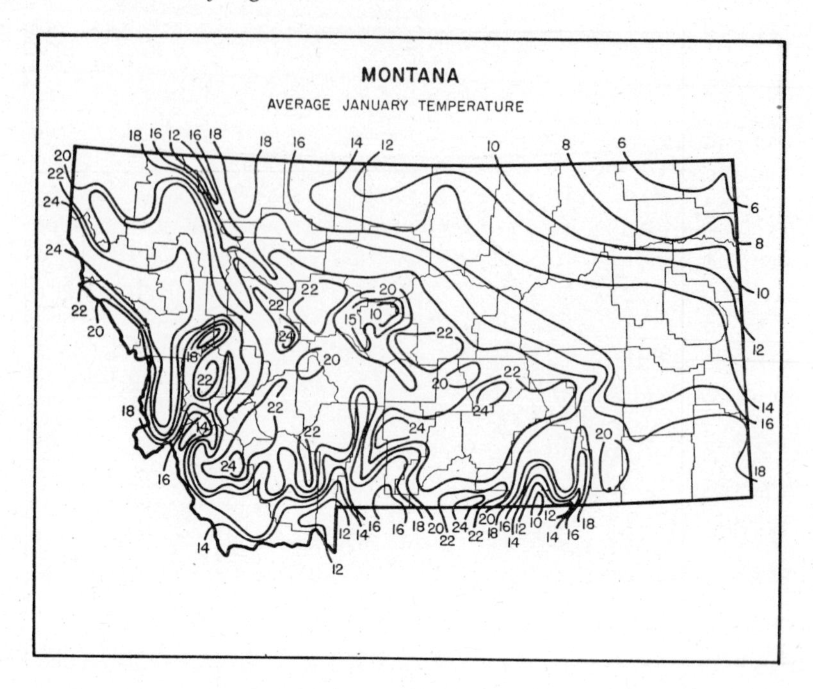
MONTANA
AVERAGE JANUARY TEMPERATURE

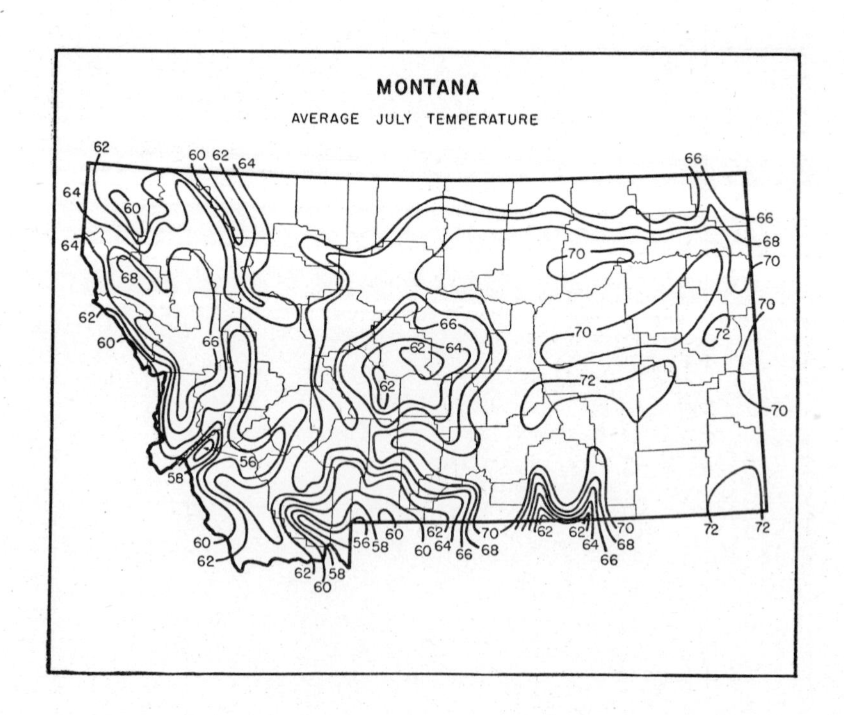
MONTANA
AVERAGE JULY TEMPERATURE

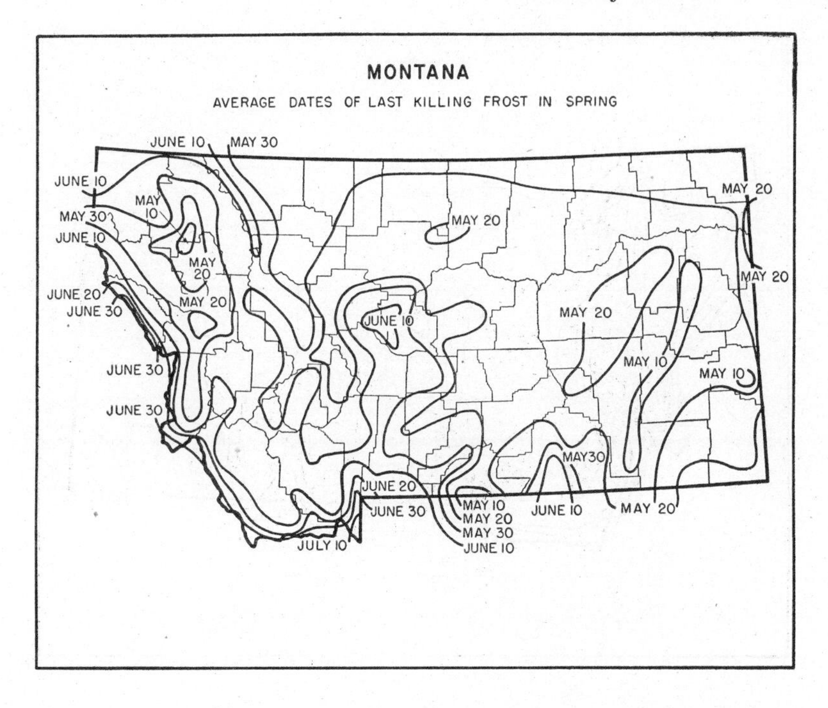
MONTANA
AVERAGE DATES OF LAST KILLING FROST IN SPRING
JUNE 10
MAY 30
JUNE 10
MAY 10
MAY 30
JUNE 10
MAY 20
JUNE 20
JUNE 30
MAY 20
MAY 20
JUNE 10
MAY 20
MAY 20
JUNE 30
MAY 10
MAY 10
JUNE 30
MAY 30
JUNE 20
JUNE 30
MAY 10
MAY 20
MAY 30
JUNE 10
JUNE 10
MAY 20
JULY 10

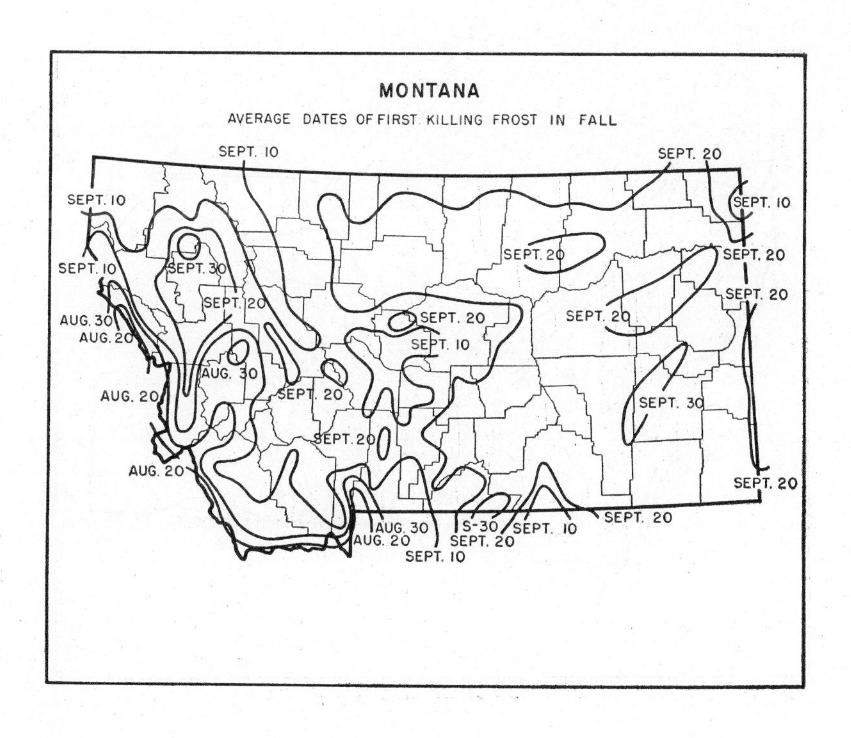
MONTANA
AVERAGE DATES OF FIRST KILLING FROST IN FALL
SEPT. 10
SEPT. 20
SEPT. 10
SEPT. 10
SEPT. 10
SEPT. 20
SEPT. 30
SEPT. 20
SEPT. 20
SEPT. 20
AUG. 30
AUG. 20
SEPT. 20
SEPT. 20
SEPT. 10
AUG. 30
SEPT. 20
SEPT. 30
AUG. 20
SEPT. 20
AUG. 20
SEPT. 20
AUG. 30
S-30
SEPT. 10
SEPT. 20
AUG. 20
SEPT. 20
SEPT. 10

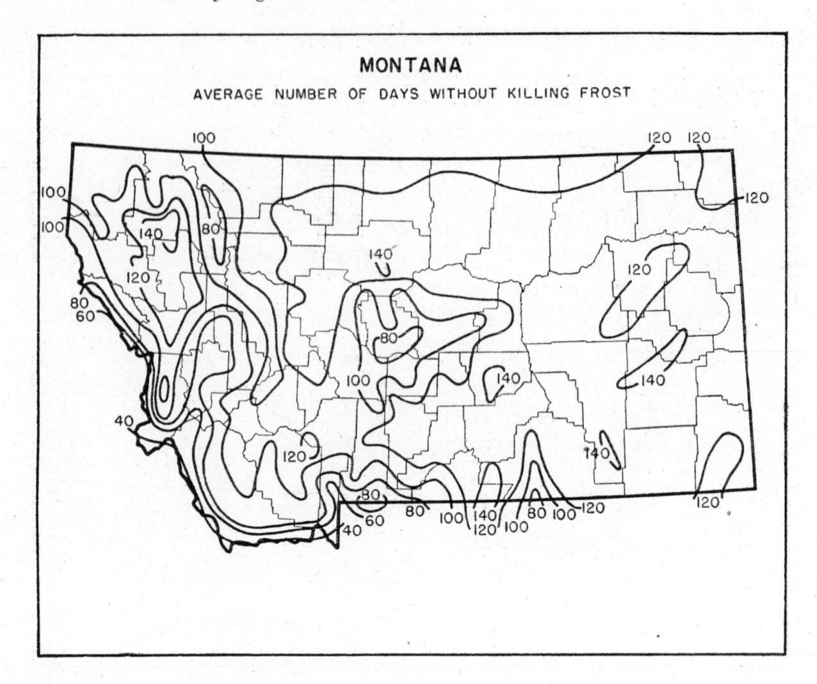
MONTANA
AVERAGE NUMBER OF DAYS WITHOUT KILLING FROST

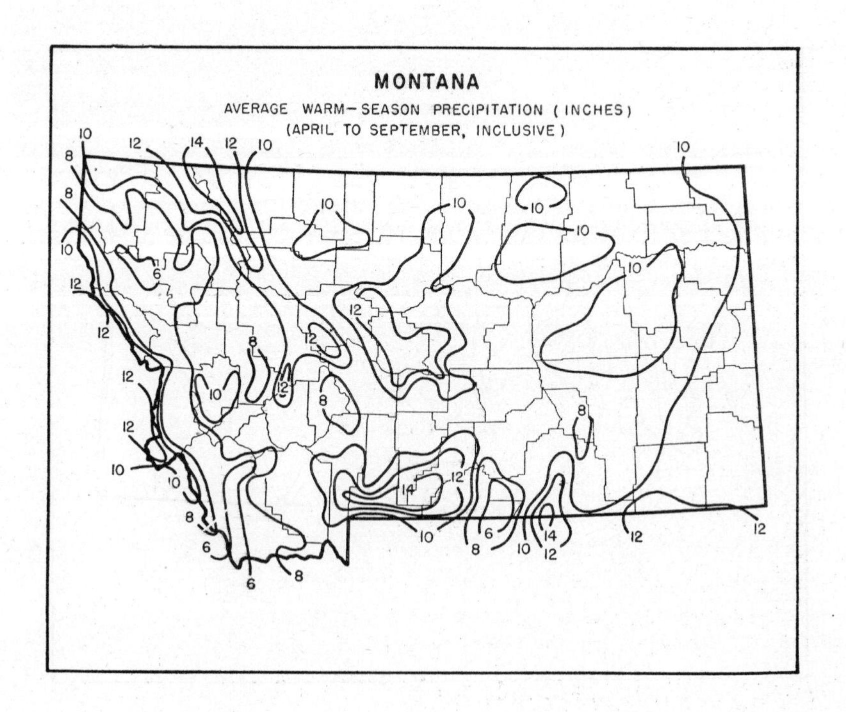
MONTANA
AVERAGE WARM-SEASON PRECIPITATION (INCHES)
(APRIL TO SEPTEMBER, INCLUSIVE)

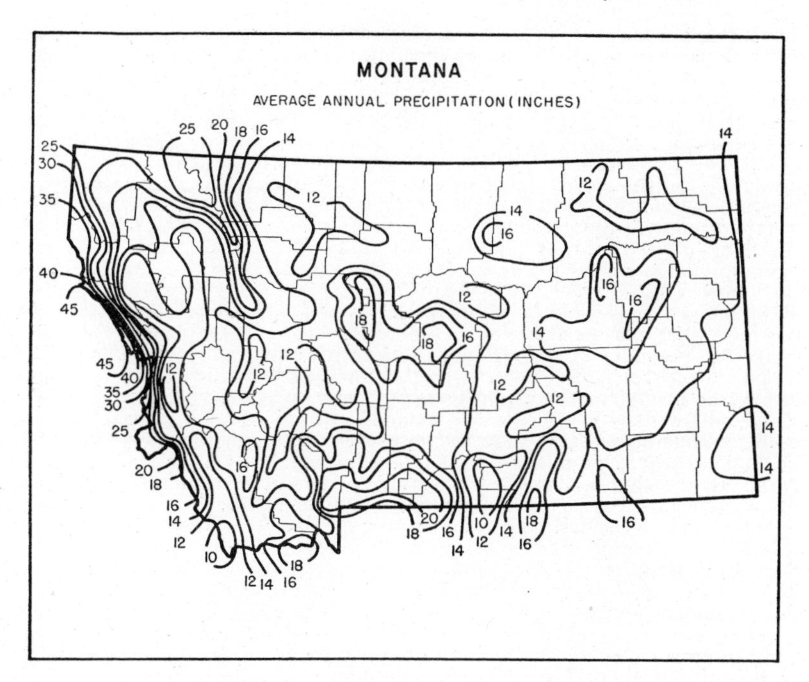

SUPPLEMENTARY CLIMATIC NOTES FOR MONTANA

The main range of the Rocky Mountains crosses the western part of Montana in a northwest-southeast direction, dividing the State into two sections of unequal size. The western part is characterized by rugged mountains and mostly narrow valleys, while the east conforms largely to the Great Plains type of country, broken occasionally by wide valleys and isolated groups of mountains. The approximate mean altitude of 3,400 feet is the lowest for the Rocky Mountain States. The lowest elevation, 1,800 feet, occurs where the Kootenai River leaves the State in the northwest, while the highest, 12,850 feet, is the summit of Granite Peak, near the south-central boundary. Half of the State has an elevation in excess of 5,000 feet. Watersheds divert drainage to the Pacific, Atlantic, and Arctic Oceans. The principal rivers are the Clark Fork of the Columbia in the west and the Missouri and Yellowstone in the east.

The Continental Divide of the Rocky Mountains exerts a marked influence on the State's climate. Conditions west of the Divide are modified to a considerable extent by the influence of the Pacific Ocean, while the east is under continental influences. In consequence, the western area has milder winters, cooler summers, more frequent, abundant, and evenly distributed precipitation, less wind movement, a greater degree of cloudiness, and a shorter growing season than the eastern part.

The mountain ranges afford western districts some protection from the cold waves which during the winter sweep suddenly southward along their eastern slopes from the interior of Canada and the arctic region. At other times in winter, when certain types of air masses are in favorable positions, the presence of the mountains is of peculiar local benefit to areas east of the Divide, through the promotion of rapid descent of relatively warm air from aloft and the occurrence of the well-known chinook wind.

Montana is traversed by, or is in close proximity to, the principal storm paths of the Northwest. Mass air movements of contrasting characteristics generally follow one another from September to June in relatively rapid succession, resulting in marked instability of weather conditions with marked temperature fluctuations. At times there are prolonged periods of winter cold, but long hot spells in summer are more the exception than the rule.

298737°—41——62

The principal moisture-laden air masses approach the State from the Pacific coast, but they are usually forced to precipitate the greater part of their moisture in crossing the more western mountain ranges. The final lift across the main range of the Rockies is attended by further cooling of the air and consequent precipitation over the western part of the State. The air in its descent over the eastern slope is warmed and dried, which largely accounts for the scanty precipitation in the more eastern districts. In winter, snowfall usually accumulates to considerable depths in the higher mountains and furnishes a fairly sustained and dependable run-off for irrigation, power, and other purposes.

Temperatures of 100° or higher may occur in any month from May to September, and of zero or lower in any month from September to May. The highest average annual temperatures occur in the upper half of the Yellowstone Valley, and the lowest over the elevated regions of the extreme southwest.

Winters are usually cold, with an occasional one that is open and mild. Cold waves and blizzards are features of the winter season. Cold waves of varying severity cause sudden, sharp drops in temperature and are often followed by a protracted cold spell, especially over the more eastern districts. The intense cold may be terminated as abruptly as it began by the occurrence of the warm chinook, followed by a more or less extended period of mild, pleasant weather. Freezing temperatures and snowfall may occur late in May, or even early in June, and as early as September in the fall. Autumn is usually mild and pleasant.

Although the summer season is short, crop growth is stimulated by the long hours of daylight peculiar to high latitudes and the greater intensity of suhshine incident to high altitudes. Any discomfort of excessively warm days is usually relieved by cool nights, particularly in the mountain regions.

Successful production of farm crops is ordinarily not possible where the length of the frost-free season is less than 90 days. The growing season in Montana is highly variable in length, elevation being a limiting factor. In some elevated regions freezing temperatures occur every month in the year. In the southwest, where the growing season is about 105 days, the average date of the last killing frost in spring is about May 30 and of the first in fall about September 12. In the southeast, where the season is 20 days longer, the average dates of killing-frost limits are May 18 and September 20.

Approximately half the State has an annual precipitation ranging between 13 and 16 inches. In the driest areas, which are almost exclusively east of the Divide, the totals range from 10 to 13 inches. The wettest sections comprise the higher mountain ranges of the northwest where the annual average is in excess of 25 inches. The average annual number of days with 0.01 inch or more of precipitation is 79, decreasing from 94 in the west to 64 in the east.

Snowfall is lightest over the eastern plains region and heaviest over western mountain districts, where its occurrence over the higher ranges may be expected in any month of the year. The average seasonal amount is 51.9 inches, but it decreases to a minimum of about 15 inches in a few eastern localities. Snow cover over the plains area and lower valleys is seldom continuous through the winter because of the drifting action of wind and melting by the chinook. A snow cover is favorable for overwintering of plants and the prevention of soil erosion, but it limits the use of ranges for winter grazing.

The possible total hours of sunshine a day during the year varies in northern Montana from a minimum of 8¼ on December 22 to a maximum of 16¼ on June 21. Percentages of the possible amount of sunshine that are actually received vary from a maximum of 76 in July to a minimum of 42 in December.

The average annual number of clear days is 158, partly cloudy 106, and cloudy 101. The prevailing winds are westerly. Severe, damaging hail may occur from May to September, most frequently in June and July. Tornadoes are rare.

WILLIAM E. MAUGHAN, *Associate Meteorologist and Climatic Section Director for Montana, Weather Bureau, Helena.*

NEBRASKA

Climatic summary

County[1]	Station	Temperature: Length of record	Temperature: January average	Temperature: July average	Temperature: Maximum	Temperature: Minimum	Killing frost average dates: Length of record	Killing frost: Last in spring	Killing frost: First in fall	Growing season[2]	Average precipitation: Length of record	January	February	March	April	May	June	July	August	September	October	November	December	Annual
		Yr.	*°F.*	*°F.*	*°F.*	*°F.*	*Yr.*			*Days*	*Yr.*	*In.*	*In.*	*In.*	*In.*	*In.*	*In.*	*In.*	*In.*	*In.*	*In.*	*In.*	*In.*	*In.*
Adams	Hastings	39	24.7	77.4	116	−30	40	Apr. 26	Oct. 9	166	40	0.49	0.85	1.03	2.49	3.53	3.83	3.20	3.05	2.76	1.48	1.09	0.71	24.51
Antelope	Arden (near)						22	May 3	Oct. 8	158	28	.75	.96	1.68	2.56	3.42	3.47	2.70	2.93	2.50	1.32	1.09	.96	24.34
	Oakdale	40	19.1	74.2	115	−38	40	May 5	Oct. 5	153	40	.52	.80	1.17	2.35	3.74	3.88	3.23	2.95	2.90	1.57	.85	.70	24.66
Arthur	Arthur	9	22.9	76.4	113	−24	9	do	Oct. 10	158	10	.31	.38	.71	2.76	3.29	2.61	1.58	2.39	1.59	.61	.52	.45	17.20
	Hillside	9	21.9	72.3	104	−35	14	May 18	Sept. 23	128	14	.30	.42	.91	2.16	3.30	2.65	3.45	2.86	1.59	1.30	.58	.74	20.26
Banner	Hull (near)						6	May 13	Sept. 27	137	25	.36	.51	.95	2.08	2.68	1.98	1.71	1.60	1.75	1.16	.55	.73	16.06
Blaine	Brewster						21	May 11	Sept. 29	141	26	.45	.57	1.05	2.56	3.93	3.40	3.05	3.23	2.29	1.28	.70	.69	23.20
	Purdum	36	22.4	74.6	112	−34	37	May 7	Sept. 30	146	37	.59	.74	1.41	2.93	3.47	3.06	2.93	2.98	1.66	1.30	.66	.79	22.52
Boone	Albion	38	20.6	75.5	115	−37	38	May 6	Oct. 2	149	38	.77	.79	1.13	2.30	3.46	3.91	3.01	3.26	2.56	1.50	.92	.84	24.45
Box Butte	Alliance	33	23.2	73.7	106	−40	32	May 12	Sept. 27	138	37	.36	.52	.82	2.16	2.70	2.51	2.45	1.80	1.20	1.03	.46	.50	16.51
Boyd	Butte	31	19.9	75.9	115	−36	30	May 6	Oct. 3	150	32	.51	.72	1.14	2.34	3.41	3.73	2.83	2.43	2.08	1.42	.66	.59	21.86
	Lynch	11	22.1	73.6	110	−42	14	May 14	Sept. 27	136	26	.57	.72	1.29	2.24	3.46	3.61	2.89	3.07	2.33	1.48	.70	.59	22.95
Brown	Ainsworth	30	21.2	75.5	112	−33	32	May 8	Oct. 4	149	39	.58	.81	1.37	2.32	3.77	3.40	2.84	2.89	2.01	1.40	.62	.85	22.86
	Mary						14	May 16	Sept. 29	136	28	.46	.72	1.19	2.44	3.57	3.07	2.64	2.79	1.59	1.42	.56	.66	21.11
Buffalo	Elm Creek										17	.36	.69	1.00	2.58	3.80	3.65	3.41	2.84	2.21	1.65	.75	1.05	23.99
	Kearney	38	24.5	76.8	114	−34	39	May 1	Oct. 6	158	40	.38	.65	.98	2.44	3.67	3.74	3.16	2.97	2.31	1.55	.83	.66	23.34
	Ravenna	40	24.3	76.3	116	−36	40	May 7	Oct. 3	149	40	.50	.76	1.00	2.35	3.46	3.88	3.55	3.08	2.25	1.68	.89	.70	24.10
	Watertown						10	May 15	Oct. 3	141	33	.35	.68	.78	2.49	3.28	3.22	2.65	2.65	2.19	1.69	.76	.70	21.44
Burt	Tekamah	40	21.3	76.8	113	−37	40	Apr. 30	Oct. 11	164	40	.74	.99	1.36	2.53	3.86	4.63	3.81	3.73	3.52	1.78	1.40	.99	29.34
Butler	David City	38	23.0	76.5	114	−30	39	May 1	Oct. 9	161	39	.74	.96	1.36	2.52	4.27	4.18	3.40	3.47	3.12	1.79	1.34	.76	27.91
Cass	Plattsmouth										25	.66	.78	1.31	2.62	3.77	4.89	3.88	4.41	3.45	1.87	1.50	.61	29.75
	Weeping Water	34	22.8	77.2	113	−34	34	May 4	Oct. 8	157	40	.84	1.09	1.38	2.33	3.48	4.42	3.28	3.78	3.61	1.95	1.58	.97	28.71
Cedar	Hartington	40	19.8	75.3	118	−38	40	May 2	Oct. 7	158	40	.76	1.13	1.33	2.48	4.21	4.10	3.16	3.39	3.20	1.64	1.10	.80	27.30
Chase	Imperial	40	26.3	75.3	113	−35	40	May 6	Oct. 4	151	40	.40	.68	1.17	2.32	3.32	3.57	2.91	2.69	1.61	1.33	.67	.73	21.40
	Wauneta										40	.30	.73	.99	2.04	3.06	3.06	2.69	2.74	1.49	1.27	.61	.63	19.61
Cherry	Merriman	22	23.3	74.2	112	−40	23	May 16	Sept. 23	130	25	.44	.41	.92	2.29	3.10	2.97	2.91	1.86	1.22	1.14	.69	.45	18.40
	Nenzel (near)	22	21.7	74.0	111	−43	22	May 17	Sept. 23	129	22	.56	.55	1.25	2.18	2.95	3.32	2.65	2.06	1.13	1.08	.73	.58	19.04
	Valentine	40	21.2	74.2	110	−38	40	May 4	Oct. 3	152	40	.49	.46	1.16	2.02	2.85	2.78	2.78	2.43	1.34	1.17	.54	.57	18.59
Cheyenne	Dalton										18	.30	.44	.82	2.60	2.63	2.47	2.32	1.98	1.38	1.02	.70	.54	17.20
	Lodgepole	38	26.2	73.3	108	−36	36	May 14	Sept. 26	135	39	.35	.54	.85	2.41	2.70	2.55	2.34	2.18	1.40	.95	.41	.56	17.24
	Potter										18	.40	.59	1.29	2.55	2.36	2.43	1.87	1.80	1.25	.91	.92	.79	16.16
	Sidney	10	25.7	75.7	110	−33	10	May 7	Oct. 2	148	12	.18	.38	.84	2.45	2.66	2.40	2.12	2.19	1.23	.87	.44	.47	16.23
	Sidney (near)										26	.42	.64	1.06	2.53	2.78	2.69	2.19	2.48	1.40	1.06	.58	.71	18.54

[1] The following counties, for which no records are available, are best represented by the stations indicated: Dakota—Sioux City; Deuel—Lodgepole; Hooker—Hyannis; McPherson—Stapleton; Wayne—Wakefield; Wheeler—Dumas.

[2] Length of growing season between average dates of last killing frost in spring and first in fall.

NEBRASKA—Continued

Climatic summary—Continued

County	Station	Temperature					Killing frost average dates				Average precipitation													
		Length of record	January average	July average	Maximum	Minimum	Length of record	Last in spring	First in fall	Growing season	Length of record	January	February	March	April	May	June	July	August	September	October	November	December	Annual
		Yr.	*°F.*	*°F.*	*°F.*	*°F.*	*Yr.*			*Days*	*Yr.*	*In.*	*In.*	*In.*	*In.*	*In.*	*In.*	*In.*	*In.*	*In.*	*In.*	*In.*	*In.*	*In.*
Clay	Clay Center	36	24.1	76.7	113	−25	34	May 1	Oct. 7	159	37	0.43	0.83	0.96	2.32	3.72	3.56	3.38	2.97	3.13	1.76	0.96	0.50	24.52
	Edgar										11	.40	1.02	.86	2.65	4.75	4.64	5.31	2.94	3.20	2.26	1.07	.55	29.65
Colfax	Schuyler	7	21.7	78.4	110	−28	26	May 6	Oct. 8	155	39	.57	.91	1.14	2.47	3.84	4.35	3.21	3.72	3.16	1.59	1.06	.82	26.84
Cuming	Westpoint	39	21.6	76.9	113	−38	40	May 1	Oct. 6	158	40	.71	.88	1.24	2.77	4.08	4.80	3.95	4.13	3.59	1.91	1.27	.89	30.22
	Wisner										21	.60	.94	1.21	2.95	4.59	4.94	4.08	3.75	3.89	2.14	1.25	.96	31.30
Custer	Broken Bow	40	23.7	74.5	113	−42	40	May 8	Sept. 30	145	40	.41	.61	.91	2.49	3.59	3.65	3.61	3.03	2.10	1.26	.73	.65	23.04
	Callaway	20	24.7	73.7	108	−36	18	do	Sept. 28	143	22	.42	.66	.86	2.45	3.41	3.55	3.43	2.78	2.22	1.51	.76	.75	22.80
	Mason City										37	.49	.79	1.08	2.66	3.40	3.58	3.12	2.99	2.13	1.58	.69	.91	23.42
Dawes	Chadron	23	24.4	75.6	111	−31	23	May 10	Oct. 3	146	24	.58	.61	1.21	2.43	2.73	2.67	2.24	1.56	1.32	1.21	.80	.61	17.97
	Fort Robinson	37	23.3	71.7	107	−37	32	May 17	Sept. 22	128	40	.47	.63	1.00	2.19	2.79	2.49	2.07	1.64	1.51	1.29	.48	.63	17.19
Dawson	Gothenburg	40	25.1	75.5	111	−33	40	May 6	Oct. 3	150	40	.41	.76	.92	2.25	3.31	3.76	2.49	2.98	1.91	1.38	.73	.67	21.57
	Lexington	39	25.6	75.9	113	−39	38	do	do	150	40	.42	.75	1.10	2.30	3.35	3.50	3.08	3.01	1.97	1.58	.74	.69	22.49
Dixon	Wakefield	39	20.4	75.7	115	−41	40	May 8	Oct. 2	148	40	.59	.90	1.21	2.52	3.82	4.01	3.21	3.80	3.33	1.66	1.07	.78	26.90
Dodge	Fremont	40	22.5	76.9	116	−31	40	May 1	Oct. 9	161	40	.70	.98	1.37	2.49	3.83	4.44	3.46	4.15	3.12	1.79	1.47	.89	28.69
	Hooper	15	21.8	74.7	105	−38	15	May 3	Oct. 2	155	16	.40	.90	1.22	2.37	4.10	5.70	4.38	4.07	3.76	2.31	1.15	.89	31.25
Douglas	Drexel	10	21.1	75.1	110	−25	10	Apr. 29	Oct. 10	164	11	.73	1.05	1.65	2.77	3.81	4.85	3.46	3.55	2.67	1.85	1.42	.76	28.57
	Omaha	40	23.7	78.1	114	−32	40	Apr. 14	Oct. 20	189	40	.75	.90	1.21	1.98	3.04	3.95	3.09	3.17	3.36	1.89	1.29	.86	25.49
Dundy	Benkelman	16	28.3	78.3	113	−26	20	May 2	Oct. 2	153	31	.24	.62	.91	1.67	2.89	2.93	2.67	2.76	1.72	1.05	.55	.58	18.59
	Haigler	10	27.0	80.2	112	−25	23	May 3	Oct. 4	154	38	.20	.46	.70	1.75	2.86	2.78	2.55	2.50	1.42	1.01	.42	.48	17.13
Fillmore	Fairmont	40	22.7	76.9	112	−34	40	May 5	Oct. 7	155	40	.58	.89	1.08	2.33	3.69	3.80	3.61	3.68	2.96	1.84	1.20	.74	26.40
	Geneva	40	25.0	77.8	118	−32	40	Apr. 29	Oct. 9	163	40	.63	1.05	1.11	2.40	4.04	4.05	3.42	3.36	3.13	2.05	1.15	.86	27.25
Franklin	Franklin	38	25.0	77.9	116	−39	38	May 3	Oct. 5	155	40	.38	.73	1.00	2.17	3.38	3.54	3.01	2.94	2.57	1.38	.94	.65	22.69
	Upland										25	.53	.68	.93	2.14	3.58	3.06	2.76	2.98	2.32	1.22	1.08	.60	21.88
Frontier	Curtis	36	26.2	76.3	111	−36	37	May 8	Sept. 30	146	36	.42	.65	1.20	2.37	3.36	3.58	3.05	3.01	1.80	1.31	.64	.63	22.02
Furnas	Beaver City	40	27.7	78.6	116	−35	39	May 3	Oct. 7	157	39	.30	.62	.94	2.20	3.22	3.16	3.24	2.83	1.94	1.36	.90	.63	21.34
	Cambridge	10	25.7	76.5	110	−24	14	May 6	Oct. 3	159	31	.30	.66	.93	2.08	3.28	3.15	2.78	2.82	1.88	1.17	.80	.54	20.39
	Hendley										12	.40	.62	1.23	1.83	2.46	3.95	3.13	3.29	1.19	1.37	.78	1.01	21.26
	Sappa Valley										11	.18	.69	.87	1.93	3.46	3.34	2.22	2.08	1.89	1.24	1.27	.31	19.48
	Wilsonville										10	.26	.68	1.03	2.61	3.75	3.18	3.66	2.29	1.42	1.34	.66	.38	21.26
Gage	Beatrice	39	24.7	78.2	117	−33	38	Apr. 26	Oct. 11	168	40	.63	.92	1.31	2.41	4.04	3.91	3.76	3.36	3.32	1.91	1.41	.82	27.80
	Odell										12	.51	.87	.98	2.14	5.65	5.24	4.92	4.41	3.31	2.19	1.59	.81	32.62
	Virginia										13	.65	.74	1.30	2.68	4.23	3.02	2.41	3.40	4.12	2.02	2.13	.63	27.33
	Wymore										10	.48	.98	1.00	2.46	5.63	4.79	4.76	3.43	2.95	2.67	1.03	.42	30.60
Garden	Kowanda										30	.28	.47	.84	2.17	2.99	2.36	1.95	2.37	1.39	.88	.55	.54	16.79
	Oshkosh	25	24.5	75.1	107	−32	26	May 4	Oct. 4	153	26	.31	.50	.85	2.33	2.79	2.58	2.36	2.34	1.47	1.01	.58	.58	17.70
Garfield	Burwell										37	.43	.65	.93	2.42	3.43	3.83	3.09	2.68	2.24	1.26	.64	.59	22.19
	Dumas	26	21.1	74.3	112	−32	26	May 7	Oct. 5	151	30	.46	.58	.90	2.02	3.48	3.31	2.57	2.73	2.03	1.28	.78	.55	20.69

	Ericson (near)						11	May 4	Sept. 27	146	38	.44	.62	.80	2.34	3.30	3.25	2.64	2.44	2.13	1.38	.74	.65	20.73
Gosper	Gosper										40	.25	.52	.81	2.54	3.57	3.57	3.00	3.06	1.94	1.59	.75	.56	22.16
Grant	Hyannis	10	23.1	75.6	106	−34	11	May 8	Sept. 25	141	11	.26	.55	1.22	2.53	2.55	2.15	2.12	2.16	1.27	.68	.45	.34	16.28
Greeley	Greeley	11	21.1	75.0	108	−38	16	Apr. 29	Sept. 30	157	36	.43	.67	1.09	2.19	3.34	3.62	3.20	2.81	2.15	1.48	.79	.81	22.58
Hall	Cairo										30	.53	.74	1.17	2.43	3.75	3.83	2.79	2.72	2.23	1.60	.99	.85	23.63
	Grand Island	40	24.2	78.0	117	−34	40	Apr. 29	Oct. 6	160	40	.54	.79	1.27	2.34	3.99	3.83	3.35	3.40	2.79	1.95	1.01	.74	26.00
Hamilton	Aurora	14	24.7	76.7	107	−32	23	May 1	do	158	33	.47	.88	1.12	2.22	4.07	3.87	3.21	3.84	3.12	1.89	1.00	.75	26.44
	Marquette						12	Apr. 30	Oct. 8	161	20	.41	.78	1.08	2.24	3.96	4.13	4.47	3.62	2.98	2.65	.85	.84	28.01
Harlan	Alma	40	25.7	77.7	116	−38	40	May 4	Oct. 3	152	40	.29	.62	.89	2.11	3.10	3.22	2.74	3.09	2.10	1.38	.84	.54	20.92
	Orleans										31	.38	.73	1.05	2.37	3.62	3.44	2.95	3.56	2.09	1.48	.95	.62	23.24
Hayes	Hayes Center	32	26.9	76.4	112	−30	35	May 5	Oct. 6	154	40	.51	.93	1.40	2.64	3.84	3.36	2.96	3.06	1.80	1.58	.87	.90	23.85
Hitchcock	Culbertson	34	26.3	77.4	113	−30	40	May 4	Oct. 5	154	40	.33	.57	1.04	1.91	3.15	3.24	2.84	2.62	1.58	1.14	.70	.64	19.76
	Palisade										16	.24	.65	.85	2.28	2.71	2.93	2.50	2.92	1.14	1.33	.63	.88	19.06
	Stratton										40	.26	.61	.98	2.10	3.07	3.22	2.70	2.63	1.56	1.22	.72	.58	19.65
Holt	Atkinson	29	18.8	74.1	111	−35	34	May 10	Oct. 2	145	31	.56	.79	1.18	2.24	3.37	2.70	2.36	2.41	1.79	1.27	.77	.71	20.15
	Ewing	30	20.0	75.5	114	−38	34	do	Oct. 1	144	39	.37	.62	1.02	2.26	3.61	3.63	3.02	2.97	2.37	1.38	.69	.54	22.48
	O'Neill	28	22.9	76.7	112	−33	26	May 7	Sept. 29	145	29	.46	.67	1.23	2.45	3.25	3.65	2.60	2.68	2.09	1.24	.95	.62	21.89
Howard	St. Libory						16	Apr. 29	Oct. 5	157	19	.52	.92	1.17	2.43	4.04	4.53	4.58	3.53	3.02	1.84	.80	.99	28.37
	St. Paul	40	23.9	77.0	115	−32	40	May 6	Oct. 4	151	40	.38	.66	.82	2.23	3.71	4.16	3.69	2.98	2.34	1.55	.82	.59	23.93
Jefferson	Fairbury	40	26.8	79.2	114	−38	40	Apr. 28	Oct. 10	165	40	.64	1.12	1.24	2.61	4.51	4.38	3.56	3.66	3.12	1.90	1.28	.82	28.84
	Plymouth	7	23.2	75.5	109	−32	8	May 3	Oct. 14	161	10	.42	1.12	.91	1.92	4.18	4.40	3.76	2.79	3.64	1.58	1.31	1.15	27.18
Johnson	Tecumseh	36	25.3	77.5	112	−30	38	Apr. 25	Oct. 7	155	40	.71	1.06	1.32	2.62	4.22	4.52	3.61	3.45	4.04	2.26	1.60	.98	30.39
Kearney	Minden	40	25.0	76.9	118	−33	40	May 3	Oct. 5	155	40	.34	.80	1.00	2.43	3.58	3.50	2.99	3.04	2.39	1.52	.96	.69	23.24
Keith	Ogallala	15	24.6	77.0	111	−29	16	May 7	Oct. 4	150	21	.34	.40	.81	2.71	3.48	2.87	2.65	2.82	1.52	.95	.44	.50	19.49
	Paxton										30	.38	.56	.92	2.39	3.03	2.88	2.31	2.90	1.51	1.07	.51	.65	19.11
Keya paha	Springview	13	21.4	72.9	107	−34	16	May 8	Sept. 28	143	28	.41	.61	1.13	2.18	3.04	3.32	2.86	2.86	1.56	1.33	.42	.59	20.31
Kimball	Kimball	38	26.6	71.7	110	−36	40	May 14	do	137	40	.32	.62	1.00	2.21	2.60	2.37	2.16	1.93	1.32	.92	.46	.60	16.51
Knox	Bloomfield	12	18.0	74.4	105	−42	18	May 9	Oct. 1	145	24	.54	1.02	1.31	2.33	3.58	2.75	2.51	2.89	2.65	1.20	.68	.78	22.24
	Creighton	12	16.7	73.5							4	.41	1.02	.56	2.27	3.34	3.62	2.50	3.78	1.71	2.42	.81	1.44	23.88
	Santee	38	21.3	76.9	115	−38	38	May 2	Oct. 3	154	38	.55	.62	1.15	1.90	3.71	4.05	3.17	3.04	2.30	1.65	.84	.65	23.63
Lancaster	Lincoln	40	24.6	78.0	115	−29	40	Apr. 18	Oct. 15	180	40	.61	.93	1.20	2.24	3.56	4.01	3.62	3.70	3.42	1.86	1.37	.79	27.31
	Lincoln University Farm.	39	25.4	78.2	114	−26	40	Apr. 29	Oct. 10	164	40	.58	.96	1.14	2.32	3.46	4.18	3.67	3.54	3.52	1.87	1.48	.79	27.51
Lincoln	North Platte	40	25.2	75.4	108	−35	40	do	Oct. 6	160	40	.32	.54	.86	2.08	2.88	2.94	2.61	2.32	1.53	1.06	.53	.53	18.20
	Sutherland										26	.29	.44	.82	2.13	2.85	3.32	2.65	2.64	1.35	1.20	.51	.65	18.85
Logan	Stapleton	17	24.1	75.8	110	−30	16	May 4	Oct. 5	154	17	.24	.37	.96	2.44	3.08	3.10	2.17	3.08	1.71	1.16	.65	.41	19.37
Loup	Taylor										17	.31	.48	.95	2.11	3.66	3.07	2.33	2.95	1.75	1.10	.64	.48	19.83
Madison	Madison	38	21.0	75.4	117	−34	40	May 3	Oct. 4	155	40	.76	.93	1.34	2.56	3.81	4.18	3.27	3.22	3.20	1.69	1.10	.91	26.97
	Norfolk	40	20.3	75.8	116	−39	40	do	do	155	40	.62	.87	1.32	2.59	4.10	4.43	3.53	3.25	3.11	1.61	1.12	.84	27.39
Merrick	Central City	24	24.1	78.5	116	−26	24	May 1	Oct. 9	161	38	.41	.61	1.03	2.10	3.84	4.16	3.65	3.20	3.02	1.87	1.00	.65	25.54
Morrill	Bridgeport	38	24.9	73.2	111	−36	40	May 12	Sept. 28	139	40	.33	.46	.79	2.07	2.75	2.43	1.85	1.65	1.37	.98	.42	.58	15.68
Nance	Fullerton	20	22.4	75.4	109	−31	23	May 8	Oct. 6	151	37	.63	.81	1.40	2.42	3.93	4.48	3.45	3.54	3.39	1.66	1.00	.85	27.56
	Genoa	40	22.9	76.8	116	−32	34	May 2	Oct. 8	159	40	.53	.75	1.14	2.32	3.88	4.31	3.44	3.16	3.16	1.67	.97	.85	26.18
Nemaha	Auburn	40	26.1	77.9	113	−35	40	Apr. 26	Oct. 11	168	40	.92	1.32	1.72	3.04	4.71	4.75	4.08	3.82	4.18	2.63	1.82	1.11	34.10
	Nemaha										10	.48	1.00	1.35	2.76	5.36	5.42	5.36	5.71	3.16	3.44	1.12	.90	36.06
Nuckolls	Nelson	10	23.5	80.0	114	−28	17	May 4	Oct. 11	160	21	.50	.82	1.15	1.97	3.42	3.45	2.45	3.47	2.14	1.47	.93	.82	22.59
	Superior	14	25.0	76.9	107	−36	15	Apr. 30	Oct. 7	160	27	.47	.91	.92	2.12	3.49	3.98	3.62	2.73	2.22	1.69	.78	.63	23.56
Otoe	Nebraska City	38	25.3	78.2	115	−28	39	Apr. 26	Oct. 13	170	40	.78	1.11	1.39	2.54	4.15	4.42	3.81	3.70	4.40	2.21	1.61	.96	31.08
	Palmyra	13	24.3	75.7	110	−29	12	Apr. 22	Oct. 10	171	14	.48	1.07	1.32	2.29	4.65	4.92	4.57	4.81	4.53	2.23	1.32	.90	33.09
	Syracuse	40	24.4	77.8	116	−33	40	Apr. 29	Oct. 8	162	40	.81	1.16	1.34	2.37	3.92	4.13	3.54	3.56	3.89	2.19	1.55	1.00	29.46
Pawnee	Burchard										11	.36	.92	1.15	2.17	5.21	4.78	5.40	4.21	3.83	2.90	1.70	.75	33.38
	Dubois										10	.82	2.08	1.52	2.14	4.08	4.59	4.08	3.23	5.02	3.24	1.82	1.58	34.20
	Pawnee City	34	25.1	77.8	117	−29	36	Apr. 28	Oct. 11	166	36	.69	1.06	1.46	2.84	4.54	3.97	3.56	3.99	4.17	2.21	1.65	.92	31.06
	Table Rock						39	May 1	Oct. 7	159	40	.75	1.17	1.54	2.84	4.19	4.37	3.97	3.68	3.92	2.37	1.57	.92	31.29

NEBRASKA—Continued

Climatic summary—Continued

County	Station	Temperature: Length of record	Temperature: January average	Temperature: July average	Temperature: Maximum	Temperature: Minimum	Killing frost average dates: Length of record	Killing frost average dates: Last in spring	Killing frost average dates: First in fall	Killing frost average dates: Growing season	Average precipitation: Length of record	January	February	March	April	May	June	July	August	September	October	November	December	Annual
		Yr.	°F.	°F.	°F.	°F.	Yr.			Days	Yr.	In.	In.	In.	In.	In.	In.	In.	In.	In.	In.	In.	In.	In.
Perkins	Elsie										30	0.26	0.39	0.76	2.39	3.28	3.14	2.38	2.63	1.75	1.23	0.57	0.61	19.39
	Madrid	38	25.4	75.6	114	−37	38	May 8	Sept. 30	145	40	.30	.56	1.09	2.04	3.05	3.25	2.45	2.53	1.45	1.07	.65	.58	19.02
Phelps	Bertrand										37	.36	.60	.85	2.42	3.39	3.19	3.25	3.26	2.05	1.50	.71	.59	22.17
	Holdrege	38	26.2	77.5	113	−43	37	May 2	Oct. 9	160	40	.38	.75	1.03	2.48	3.82	3.65	3.03	2.91	2.05	1.54	.88	.68	23.20
Pierce	Osmond										10	.84	.72	1.36	2.00	3.63	3.50	2.50	2.35	2.75	1.14	1.17	.62	22.58
Platte	Columbus	38	22.3	76.4	115	−29	39	May 1	Oct. 8	160	40	.53	.87	1.20	2.28	3.99	4.29	3.53	3.45	3.14	1.69	1.11	.71	26.79
Polk	Osceola	24	22.2	79.2	116	−30	26	May 3	Oct. 7	157	35	.59	.91	1.21	1.93	3.64	3.98	3.58	3.54	2.97	1.67	1.03	.61	25.66
	Lebanon										12	.34	.80	1.19	2.34	3.77	2.98	2.38	2.36	1.84	1.41	1.14	.44	20.99
Red willow	McCook	32	27.4	78.1	114	−38	34	May 3	Oct. 6	156	39	.32	.64	.95	1.88	3.03	3.09	2.93	2.63	1.65	1.10	.74	.54	19.50
Richardson	Falls City	38	27.3	78.3	115	−30	37	Apr. 26	Oct. 9	166	39	.83	1.06	1.59	3.05	4.60	4.31	4.24	3.99	4.62	2.53	1.94	.92	33.68
Rock	Duff										11	.36	.75	.93	2.69	3.92	4.23	3.96	3.19	2.62	1.41	.69	.66	25.41
	Newport	40	20.7	75.1	115	−36	40	May 7	Oct. 1	147	40	.54	.67	1.09	2.33	3.64	3.77	3.33	2.94	2.01	1.46	.60	.63	23.01
Saline	Crete	40	24.6	78.0	114	−27	40	Apr. 28	Oct. 11	165	40	.51	.88	1.10	2.32	4.09	4.18	3.84	3.52	3.28	2.01	1.29	.82	27.84
	Friend										14	.59	.72	1.01	1.89	3.57	3.21	3.31	3.85	2.97	1.86	1.34	.52	24.84
	Western						10	May 4	Oct. 17	166	17	.51	.80	.97	1.95	3.24	3.08	3.07	4.25	3.02	1.43	1.11	.74	24.17
	Wilber										11	.44	.88	.90	2.62	5.14	5.99	5.88	4.19	2.87	2.15	1.50	.76	33.32
Sarpy	Bellevue	12	23.9	75.9	108	−31	16	Apr. 26	Oct. 13	170	19	.83	1.10	1.37	2.21	4.56	4.58	3.75	3.38	3.71	2.12	1.37	1.04	30.02
	Springfield						12	Apr. 29	Oct. 4	158	16	.75	1.11	1.68	2.52	3.04	4.71	3.15	3.72	4.45	1.88	1.28	.82	29.11
Saunders	Ashland	40	23.7	77.8	116	−33	40	Apr. 26	Oct. 10	167	40	.61	.80	.92	2.05	3.49	4.33	3.68	3.38	3.37	1.77	1.31	.79	26.50
	Wahoo										36	.71	1.05	1.36	2.56	3.91	4.20	3.43	4.01	3.29	1.94	1.44	.82	28.72
Scotts Bluff	Lake Minatar	17	24.5	74.0	108	−33	20	May 10	Oct. 2	145	21	.30	.35	.69	1.97	2.57	2.18	1.74	1.57	1.58	1.03	.55	.48	15.01
	Lyman						11	do	Sept. 25	138	14	.29	.43	.97	2.22	2.24	2.24	1.07	1.34	1.48	1.10	.60	.48	14.46
	Mitchell (near)	29	23.5	72.7	106	−37	28	May 12	Sept. 27	138	26	.15	.26	.62	1.61	2.39	2.50	1.64	1.77	1.48	.92	.38	.32	14.04
	Scottsbluff	39	26.3	73.4	108	−45	39	May 11	Sept. 26	138	40	.32	.54	.90	2.10	2.95	2.43	1.85	1.55	1.51	1.06	.47	.56	16.24
Seward	Seward	32	23.8	77.9	114	−30	34	Apr. 30	Oct. 8	161	40	.60	1.06	1.21	2.53	4.28	4.16	4.07	4.02	3.67	2.08	1.29	.86	29.83
	Utica										22	.50	.74	1.13	2.42	3.57	3.54	3.24	3.74	3.06	1.56	1.39	.56	25.45
Sheridan	Gordon	29	20.0	72.1	108	−40	31	May 21	Sept. 21	123	37	.54	.46	1.05	2.05	2.63	2.85	2.49	1.82	1.13	1.09	.62	.63	17.36
	Hay Springs	40	22.0	71.4	108	−41	40	May 15	Sept. 24	132	40	.66	.75	1.48	2.65	3.15	2.94	2.74	1.87	1.38	1.41	.75	.75	20.53
Sherman	Ashton										16	.19	.36	.75	2.47	3.19	4.16	4.74	3.55	2.55	1.95	.54	.61	25.06
	Loup City	38	23.0	75.1	111	−39	38	May 7	Oct. 1	147	39	.32	.49	.93	2.10	3.52	4.07	3.80	3.00	2.51	1.51	.79	.65	23.69
Sioux	Harrison	24	20.8	70.9	107	−35	25	May 20	Sept. 25	128	24	.64	.54	1.32	2.65	3.55	2.77	2.06	1.60	1.21	1.23	.76	.62	18.95
	Sheep Creek Camp										21	.25	.37	.59	1.90	2.59	2.27	1.50	1.10	1.52	1.05	.45	.45	14.04
Stanton	Stanton	39	20.6	75.2	113	−41	40	May 6	Oct. 5	152	40	.71	.88	1.26	2.36	3.53	4.21	3.50	3.23	3.19	1.59	1.03	.82	26.31
Thayer	Bruning						22	Apr. 26	Oct. 10	167	37	.43	.89	1.07	2.60	4.09	4.10	3.45	3.31	3.07	1.97	1.13	.65	26.76
	Hebron	40	25.0	77.8	113	−34	40	Apr. 27	do	166	40	.53	.91	1.11	2.48	4.32	4.36	3.29	3.13	2.91	1.75	1.18	.71	26.68
Thomas	Halsey	34	22.2	74.3	109	−34	36	May 10	Sept. 30	143	36	.39	.51	.99	2.48	3.37	3.02	2.94	3.03	1.67	1.27	.54	.65	20.86
Thurston	Walthill	34	19.3	74.7	113	−45	28	May 5	Oct. 4	152	38	.62	.88	1.18	2.43	3.82	4.14	3.23	3.27	3.39	1.64	1.18	.81	26.59

Valley	Arcadia						18	May 3	Oct. 2	152	39	.39	.62	.98	2.28	3.37	3.76	3.69	3.04	2.18	1.31	.68	.59	22.89
	North Loup	40	22.0	75.5	114	−39	40	May 5	Oct. 4	152	40	.50	.72	1.07	2.55	3.78	4.36	3.53	3.00	2.26	1.43	.91	.69	24.80
	Ord						17	May 3	Oct. 2	152	40	.45	.67	1.06	2.57	3.53	3.90	3.37	2.97	2.32	1.47	.84	.69	23.84
Washington	Blair	40	22.1	76.6	116	−36	40	Apr. 29	Oct. 11	165	40	.64	.95	1.32	2.33	3.93	4.47	3.52	3.40	3.27	2.00	1.56	.93	28.32
Webster	Blue Hill										11	.25	.72	.98	2.41	3.95	5.24	4.67	2.89	3.27	1.83	.89	.49	27.59
	Guide Rock						29	Apr. 30	Oct. 6	159	38	.46	.86	1.19	2.27	3.42	3.84	3.48	2.90	2.87	1.57	1.01	1.14	25.01
	Red Cloud	38	25.8	78.5	117	−28	38	May 2	Oct. 4	155	40	.44	.81	1.02	2.34	3.35	3.68	3.20	2.73	2.54	1.41	.90	.61	23.03
York	Bradshaw										40	.52	.81	1.13	2.84	4.30	4.88	3.65	3.98	3.43	2.27	1.29	.76	29.86
	McCool Junction						20	May 8	Oct. 9	154	40	.59	.86	1.19	2.40	3.98	3.86	3.86	3.53	3.11	1.92	1.06	.77	27.13
	York	40	24.8	77.9	114	−31	40	Apr. 30	Oct. 8	161	40	.62	.92	1.17	2.55	3.88	3.82	3.57	3.44	3.22	1.98	1.11	.80	27.08

Precipitation and temperature—State unit values

[This tabulation gives the mean annual, mean monthly, average seasonal precipitation and percentage of normal precipitation for each year, 1886–1938, and the mean annual temperatures, 1913–38, for Nebraska]

Precipitation		Precipitation		Precipitation		Annual precipitation (in percent of normal)		Annual precipitation (in percent of normal)		Temperature	
Year	Mean	Year	Mean	Month	Mean	Year	Percent	Year	Percent	Year	Mean
	In.		In.		In.	1886	104	1913	98		°F.
1886	23.12	1913	21.89	January	0.51	1887	98	1914	93	1913	49.5
1887	21.79	1914	20.70	February	.71	1888	100	1915	160	1914	50.2
1888	22.37	1915	35.58	March	1.09	1889	100	1916	84	1915	47.8
1889	22.29	1916	18.82	April	2.40	1890	77	1917	92	1916	48.0
1890	17.14	1917	20.52	May	3.36	1891	137	1918	100	1917	47.2
1891	30.61	1918	22.36	June	3.53	1892	109	1919	112	1918	49.7
1892	24.30	1919	25.07	July	2.99	1893	71	1920	110	1919	48.5
1893	15.87	1920	24.45	August	2.80	1894	62	1921	92	1920	48.9
1894	13.93	1921	20.49	September	2.08	1895	85	1922	90	1921	52.3
1895	19.03	1922	20.15	October	1.39	1896	116	1923	126	1922	50.0
1896	25.85	1923	28.20	November	.77	1897	105	1924	94	1923	49.6
1897	23.47	1924	20.91	December	.67	1898	92	1925	93	1924	47.1
1898	20.61	1925	20.78			1899	88	1926	93	1925	50.1
1899	19.54	1926	20.83	Annual	22.30	1900	107	1927	106	1926	50.4
1900	23.92	1927	23.63			1901	103	1928	102	1927	49.1
1901	23.00	1928	22.80			1902	132	1929	102	1928	50.1
1902	29.48	1929	22.76			1903	120	1930	116	1929	47.8
1903	26.66	1930	25.93	Season	Average	1904	106	1931	86	1930	50.4
1904	23.54	1931	19.28			1905	141	1932	92	1931	52.9
1905	31.52	1932	20.54			1906	117	1933	91	1932	49.2
1906	26.03	1933	20.24		In.	1907	90	1934	64	1933	52.1
1907	20.13	1934	14.27	Winter	1.89	1908	119	1935	102	1934	53.4
1908	26.48	1935	22.64	Spring	6.85	1909	110	1936	65	1935	50.2
1909	24.63	1936	14.42	Summer	9.32	1910	75	1937	79	1936	49.9
1910	16.66	1937	17.66	Fall	4.24	1911	95	1938	95	1937	49.1
1911	21.20	1938	21.23			1912	96			1938	52.3
1912	21.43										

NEBRASKA—Continued

Dates of last killing frost in spring and first in fall, with length of growing season

Year	Geneva			Hartington			Imperial			North Loup			Scottsbluff			Valentine		
	Last in spring	First in fall	Growing season [1]	Last in spring	First in fall	Growing season [1]	Last in spring	First in fall	Growing season [1]	Last in spring	First in fall	Growing season [1]	Last in spring	First in fall	Growing season [1]	Last in spring	First in fall	Growing season [1]
			Days			*Days*			*Days*			*Days*			*Days*			*Days*
1899	Apr. 21	Sept. 28	160	May 14	Sept. 26	135	May 4	Sept. 17	136	Apr. 22	Sept. 19	150	May 3	Sept. 27	147	May 9	Oct. 10	154
1900	Apr. 12	Oct. 16	187	May 3	Nov. 1	182	Apr. 18	Sept. 28	163	Apr. 13	Oct. 7	177	Apr. 17	Sept. 20	156	May 3	Sept. 26	146
1901	Apr. 17	Sept. 17	153	Apr. 19	Sept. 18	152	do	Oct. 13	178	May 25	Sept. 17	115	May 7	Sept. 17	133	Apr. 14	Sept. 17	156
1902	Apr. 22	Sept. 11	142	Apr. 23	Sept. 12	142	Apr. 26	Sept. 12	139	Apr. 23	Sept. 12	142	May 1	Sept. 12	134	June 21	Sept. 12	83
1903	Apr. 30	Sept. 15	138	May 3	Sept. 16	136	Apr. 30	Sept. 15	138	May 4	Sept. 16	135	May 3			Apr. 30	Sept. 14	137
1904	Apr. 17	Oct. 22	188		Oct. 19		May 14	Sept. 14	123	May 14	Oct. 25	164	May 9	Sept. 14	128	Apr. 23	do	144
1905	Apr. 18	Oct. 11	176	May 8	Oct. 11	156	May 17	Oct. 9	145	May 5	Oct. 11	159	May 17	Oct. 10	146	Apr. 21	Oct. 10	172
1906	May 6	Oct. 9	156	May 6	Oct. 9	156	May 29	Oct. 5	129	May 6	Sept. 30	147	May 6			May 8	Oct. 5	150
1907	May 27	Oct. 12	138	May 15	Sept. 28	136	May 28	Oct. 12	137	May 27	Oct. 8	134	May 27	Sept. 10	106	May 27	Oct. 12	138
1908	May 2	Oct. 11	162	May 8	do	143	May 7	Sept. 27	143	May 2	Sept. 29	150	May 21	Sept. 27	129	May 6	Sept. 27	144
1909	May 10	Oct. 12	155	May 10	Oct. 11	154	May 17	Sept. 23	129	May 10	Oct. 11	154	May 9	Sept. 23	137	May 9	Oct. 10	154
1910	May 3	Oct. 21	171	May 13	Sept. 27	137	May 3	Oct. 6	156	May 3	Oct. 21	171	May 17	Aug. 25	100	May 3	Oct. 20	170
1911	May 2	do	172	May 2	Oct. 21	172	May 1	Oct. 4	156	May 2	Oct. 20	171	May 27	Sept. 21	117	May 2	Oct. 19	170
1912	Apr. 18	Sept. 30	165	Apr. 22	Sept. 27	158	May 16	Sept. 25	132	May 16	Sept. 25	132	May 14	Sept. 22	131	Apr. 21	Sept. 18	150
1913	Apr. 25	Oct. 11	169	Apr. 27	Sept. 22	148	May 3	Sept. 21	141	Apr. 13	Sept. 21	161	May 15	Sept. 21	129	May 3	Sept. 26	146
1914	May 14	Oct. 27	166	May 13	Oct. 27	167	Apr. 19	Oct. 5	169	May 14	Oct. 15	154	May 7	Sept. 14	130	May 8	Oct. 14	159
1915	May 7	Oct. 5	151	May 18	Oct. 8	143	May 21	do	137	May 17	Sept. 21	127	May 22	Oct. 5	136	do	Oct. 8	153
1916	May 1			May 19	Sept. 15	119	May 15	Sept. 28	136	May 11	Sept. 15	127	May 17	Sept. 15	121	May 11	Sept. 28	140
1917	May 7	Oct. 8	154	May 6	Oct. 8	155	May 8	Oct. 8	153	May 8	Oct. 8	153	May 12	Oct. 8	149	May 6	Oct. 8	155
1918	Apr. 30	Sept. 20	143	Apr. 30	Sept. 18	141	May 11	Sept. 20	132	May 10	Sept. 18	131	May 10	Sept. 20	133	May 10	Sept. 16	129
1919	Apr. 14	Oct. 10	179	Apr. 10	Oct. 10	183	Apr. 16	Oct. 10	177	Apr. 24	Oct. 10	169	June 2	Oct. 5	125	May 7	Oct. 10	156
1920	Apr. 28	Sept. 29	154	Apr. 28	Sept. 30	155	Apr. 30	Sept. 26	149	Apr. 28	Sept. 29	154	Apr. 27	Sept. 27	153	Apr. 26	Sept. 30	157
1921	Apr. 17	Oct. 12	178	May 4	Oct. 12	161	May 2	Oct. 3	154	May 4	Sept. 30	149	May 13	Sept. 30	140	Apr. 17	Oct. 2	168
1922	Apr. 19	do	176	Apr. 19	do	176	Apr. 28	Oct. 8	163	Apr. 29	Oct. 9	163	do	Oct. 8	148	Apr. 14	Sept. 19	158
1923	May 9	Oct. 20	164	May 9	Oct. 20	164	May 16	Oct. 13	150	May 16	Oct. 13	150	May 16	Oct. 13	150	May 8	Oct. 13	158
1924	May 1	Sept. 29	151	May 24	Sept. 29	128	May 24	Oct. 31	160	May 24	Sept. 28	127	May 22	Oct. 5	136	May 13	Nov. 2	173
1925	May 25	Oct. 9	137	May 25	Oct. 9	137	May 1	Oct. 8	160	May 25	Oct. 9	137	May 6	Oct. 6	153	May 1	Oct. 5	157
1926	Apr. 28	Sept. 25	150	Apr. 29	Sept. 25	149	Apr. 28	Sept. 24	149	Apr. 29	Sept. 25	149	Apr. 28	Sept. 24	149	Apr. 28	Sept. 23	148
1927	Apr. 23	Oct. 13	173	May 6	Oct. 31	178	May 10	Sept. 26	139	May 11	Sept. 20	132	May 11	Sept. 19	131	May 14	Sept. 24	133
1928	Apr. 27	Sept. 25	151	Apr. 27	Sept. 25	151	Apr. 27	Sept. 21	147	Apr. 27	Sept. 25	151	May 4	Sept. 21	140	Apr. 27	Sept. 25	151
1929	May 16	Oct. 21	158	May 16	Oct. 22	159	May 20	Oct. 21	154	May 16	Oct. 23	160	May 16	Sept. 9	116	May 16	Oct. 12	149
1930	Apr. 22	Oct. 17	178	Apr. 22	Oct. 14	175	May 19	Oct. 17	151	May 18	Oct. 16	151	May 18	Oct. 16	151	May 17	Oct. 16	152
1931	May 20	Nov. 1	165	May 22	Nov. 1	163	May 22	Oct. 14	145	May 22	Oct. 17	148	May 21	do	148	May 21	Oct. 15	147
1932	Apr. 27	Oct. 20	176	Apr. 27	Oct. 5	161	Apr. 28	Oct. 5	160	May 1	Oct. 5	157	May 1	Oct. 5	157	May 1	Sept. 27	149
1933	Apr. 15	Oct. 8	176	Apr. 15	Oct. 8	176	Apr. 16	Oct. 1	168	Apr. 15	Oct. 8	176	May 14	Oct. 1	140	Apr. 26	Oct. 1	158
1934	Apr. 27	Oct. 28	184	Apr. 27	Sept. 21	147	Apr. 21	Sept. 26	158	Apr. 27	Sept. 26	152	May 13	Sept. 15	125	Apr. 24	Sept. 25	154
1935	May 5	Oct. 6	154	Apr. 16	Sept. 27	164	May 6	Oct. 6	153	Apr. 19	Oct. 4	168	May 9	Sept. 28	142	May 4	Sept. 26	145

1936	Apr. 22	Oct. 22	183	Apr. 22	Oct. 21	182	Apr. 22	Oct. 20	181	Apr. 22	Oct. 7	168	Apr. 11	Sept. 27	169	Apr. 29	Oct. 7	161
1937	Apr. 9	Oct. 14	188	Apr. 10	Oct. 14	187	Apr. 26	Oct. 22	179	Apr. 27	do	163	Apr. 29	Sept. 25	149	Apr. 27	Sept. 25	151
1938	do	Sept. 19	163	Apr. 9	Oct. 22	196	May 8	Oct. 23	168	Apr. 10	Oct. 23	196	May 8	Oct. 19	164	Apr. 9	Oct. 22	196
Mean	Apr. 28	Oct. 9	164	May 2	Oct. 7	158	May 6	Oct. 4	151	May 5	Oct. 4	152	May 11	Sept. 26	138	May 4	Oct. 3	152
Extremes	Apr. 9[2]	Sept. 11[4]	[6] 137	Apr. 9[2]	Sept. 12[4]	[6] 128	Apr. 16[2]	Sept. 12[4]	[6] 123	Apr. 10[2]	Sept. 12[4]	[6] 115	Apr. 11[2]	Aug. 25[4]	[6] 100	Apr. 9[2]	Sept. 12[4]	[6] 83
	May 27[3]	Nov. 1[5]	[7] 188	May 25[3]	Nov. 1[5]	[7] 196	May 29[3]	Oct. 31[5]	[7] 179	May 27[3]	Oct. 25[5]	[7] 196	June 2[3]	Oct. 19[5]	[7] 169	June 21[3]	Nov. 2[5]	[7] 196

[1] Number of days between last killing frost in spring and first in fall.
[2] Earliest date in spring.
[3] Latest date in spring.
[4] Earliest date in fall.
[5] Latest date in fall.
[6] Shortest growing season.
[7] Longest growing season.

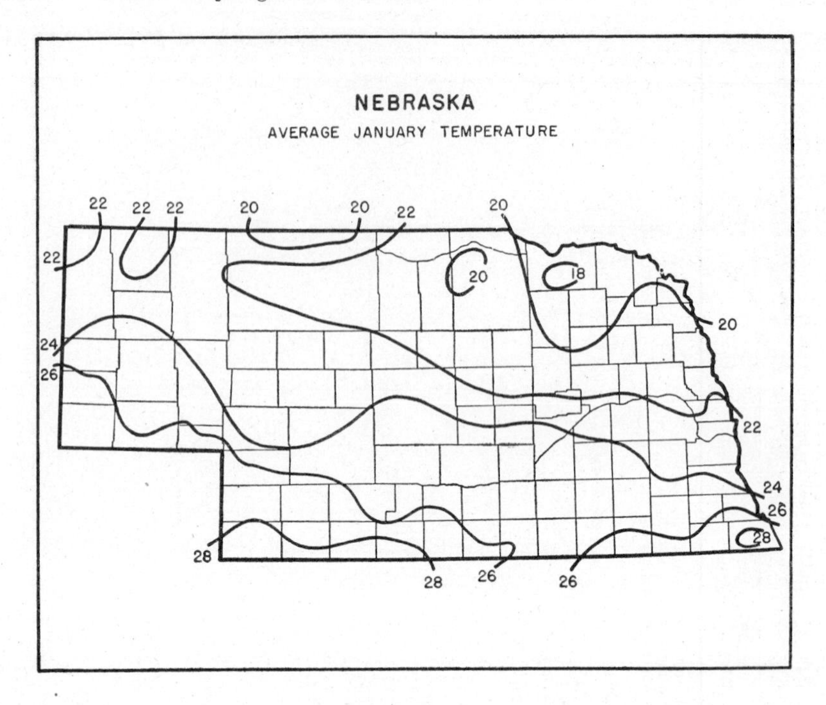
NEBRASKA
AVERAGE JANUARY TEMPERATURE
22
22
22
20
20
22
20
22
20
18
20
24
26
22
24
26
28
28
28
26
26

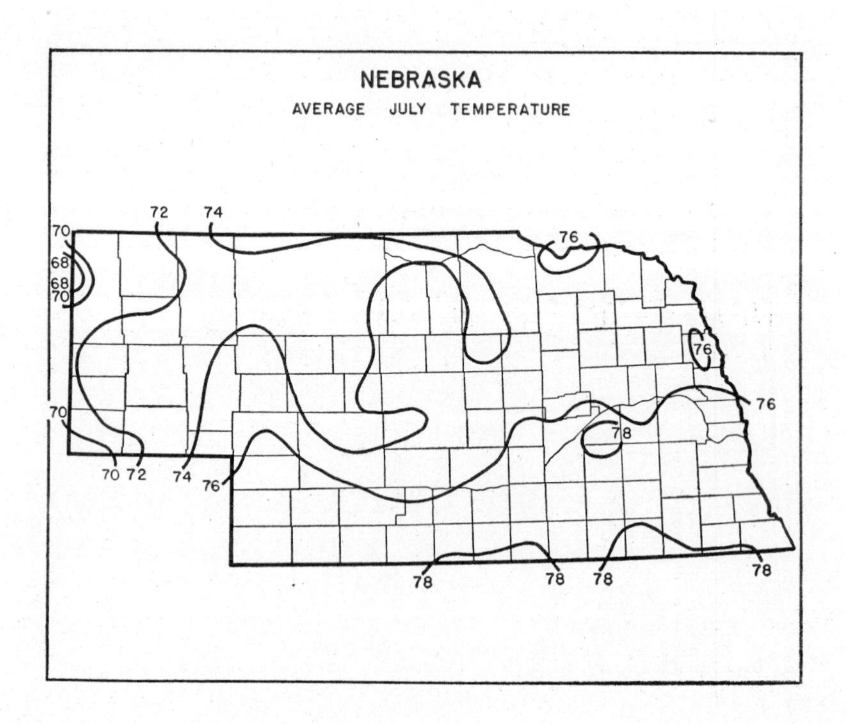
NEBRASKA
AVERAGE JULY TEMPERATURE
72
74
70
68
68
70
76
76
76
70
78
70
72
74
76
78
78
78
78

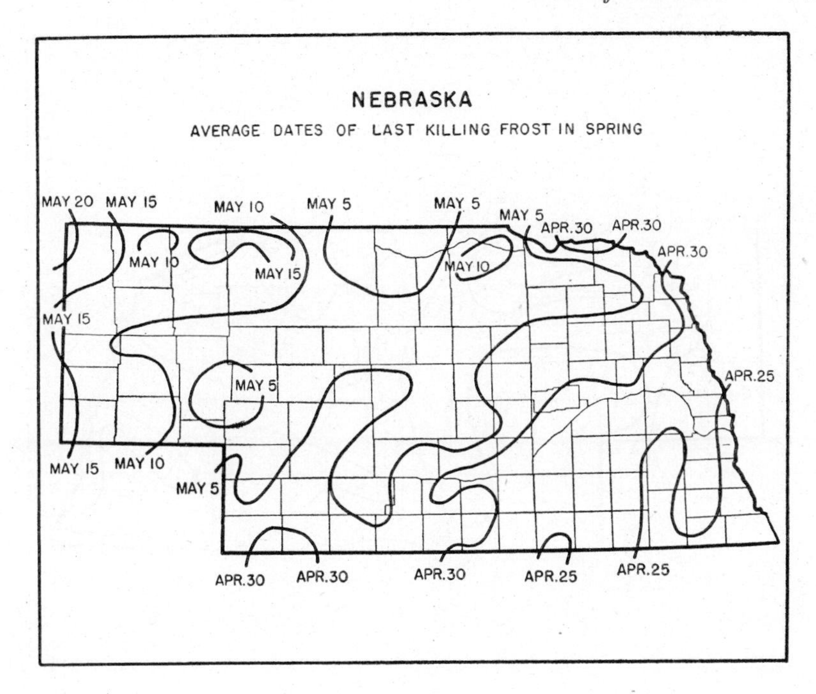
NEBRASKA
AVERAGE DATES OF LAST KILLING FROST IN SPRING
MAY 20
MAY 15
MAY 10
MAY 5
MAY 5
MAY 5
APR.30
APR.30
APR.30
MAY 10
MAY 15
MAY 10
MAY 15
MAY 5
APR.25
MAY 15
MAY 10
MAY 5
APR.30
APR.30
APR.30
APR.25
APR.25

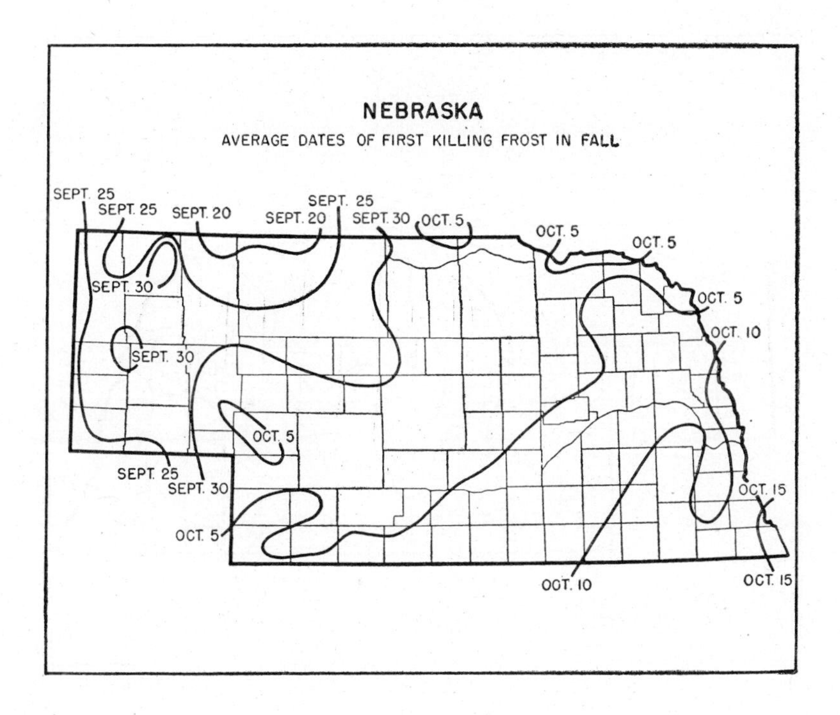
NEBRASKA
AVERAGE DATES OF FIRST KILLING FROST IN FALL
SEPT. 25
SEPT. 25
SEPT. 20
SEPT. 25
SEPT. 20
SEPT. 30
OCT. 5
OCT. 5
OCT. 5
SEPT. 30
OCT. 5
SEPT. 30
OCT. 10
OCT. 5
SEPT. 25
SEPT. 30
OCT. 15
OCT. 5
OCT. 10
OCT. 15

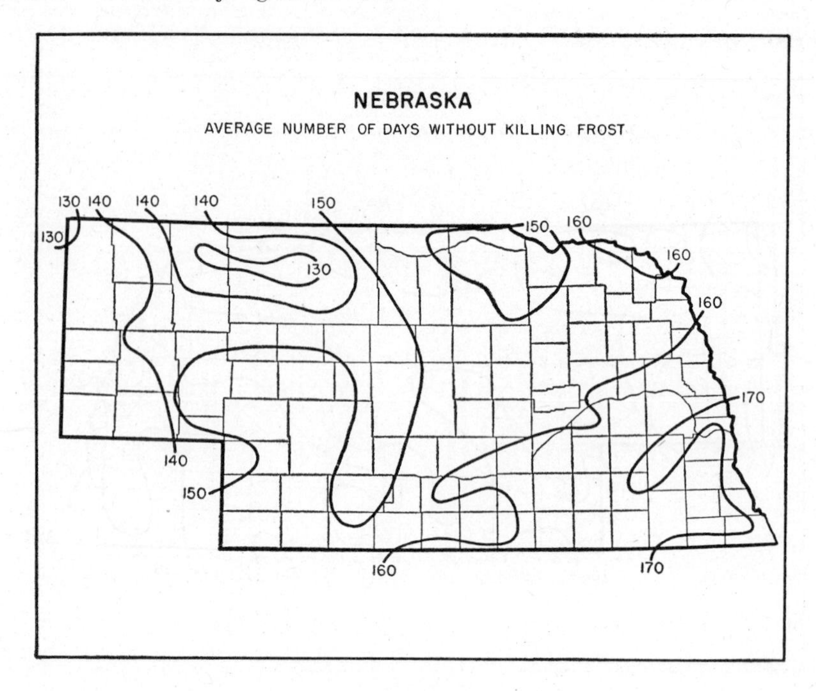
NEBRASKA
AVERAGE NUMBER OF DAYS WITHOUT KILLING FROST
130
140
150
160
170

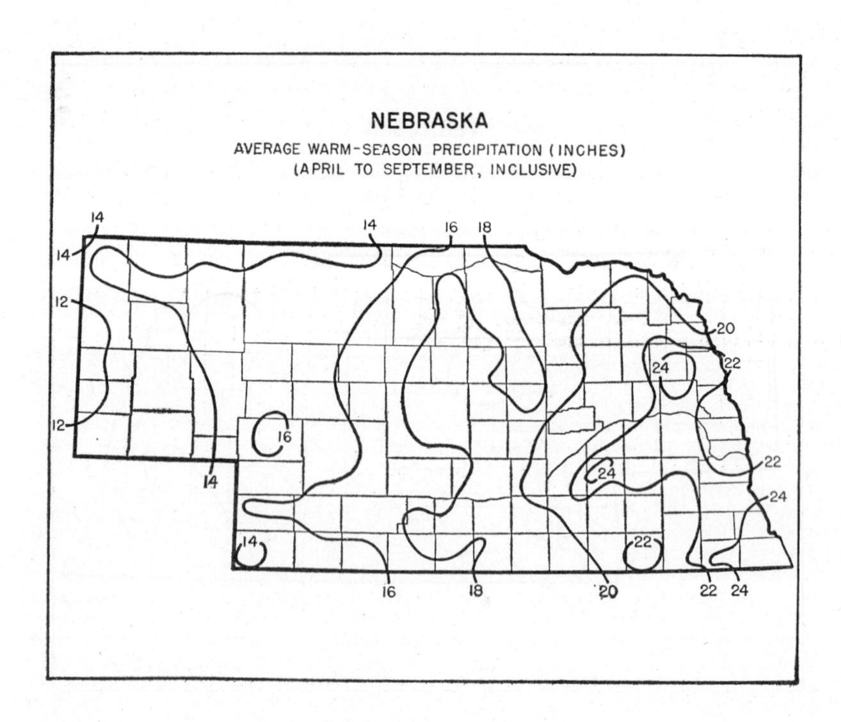
NEBRASKA
AVERAGE WARM-SEASON PRECIPITATION (INCHES)
(APRIL TO SEPTEMBER, INCLUSIVE)
12
14
16
18
20
22
24

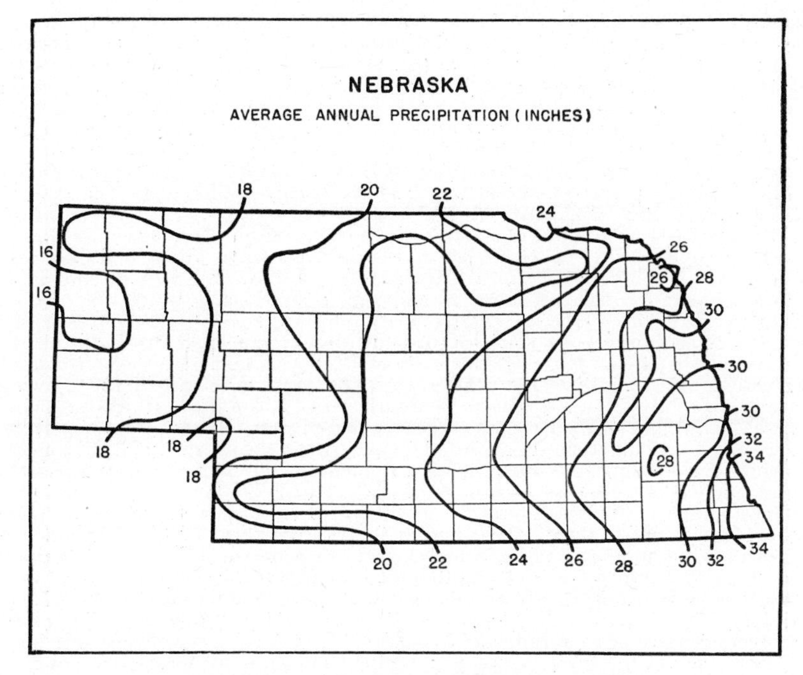

SUPPLEMENTARY CLIMATIC NOTES FOR NEBRASKA

Nebraska is near the geographic center of the United States. On its eastern boundary, along the Missouri River, the elevation above sea level rises from 900 feet in the southeast to 1,200 feet in the northeast. The elevation also increases westward to about 3,000 feet in the southwest and 5,000 feet in the northwest. The landscape changes from level or gently rolling prairie in the east, to rounded sand hills in the north-central part, and thence westward to high plains. The Platte River with its tributaries drains the greater part of the State.

The soils of the State are typical of the three main divisions: (1) The loess section of deep rich silt loams and sandy loams comprises about 42,000 square miles in the eastern third and southwestern quarter of the State, in which corn and winter wheat are the leading commercial crops. (2) The sand-hill section, made up of rounded hills interspersed with thousands of small basins and valleys and numerous shallow lakes, has an area of about 20,000 square miles. The sandy or sandy loam soils are not cultivated but produce abundant pasturage and crops of prairie hay, making this an important cattle-raising district. (3) The high plains section with broad tablelands and considerable areas of bottom land is confined mostly to the western panhandle area and occupies about 15,000 square miles. In this section there are many varieties of loams and sandy soils, having a wide range in texture and structure. Spring wheat, potatoes, and sugar beets are leading products, the latter in the Platte Valley under irrigation.

Nebraska has the typical climate of the interior of large continents in middle latitudes, that is, rather light rainfall, low humidity, hot summers, severe winters, great variations in temperature and rainfall from year to year, and frequent changes in weather from day to day or week to week. The short-period weather changes are brought about by the invasion of large masses of air of different characteristics, such as warm, moist air from the Gulf of Mexico; hot, dry air from the southwest; cool, rather dry air from the north Pacific Ocean; and cold, dry air from the interior of Canada.

The mass movements of air are associated with the eastward travel of areas of low and high pressure (cyclones and anticyclones). The Rocky Mountains influence the tracks of the cyclonic storms, many of which pass either to the north or to the south of Nebraska, often attended by rain farther east but little or none in this State. Air crossing the mountains from the west loses much of its moisture on the windward side and becomes warmer and drier as it descends the eastern slopes. The main factors that control the climate of Nebraska are, therefore, (1) its latitude; (2) its position, far from extensive bodies of warm water, in the middle of a large continent, with large land masses to the north of it; (3) its position to the east of a high mountain system extending north and south; and (4) its altitude.

The mean annual temperature varies from about 52° F. in the southern tier of counties from Redwillow eastward, with a maximum of 53.7° at Falls City, to about 45° in the northwestern counties, the lowest being 44.4° at Harrison.

Maximum temperatures above 100° F. have occurred throughout the State in the months of June, July, August, and September, and temperatures of 110° or higher have been recorded over most of the State except in parts of the northwest. Minimum temperatures of zero or below occur on an average about 10 days a year in the southeast and 25 days in the northwest. Minima of −40° to −45° have been recorded a few times at northern and western stations.

The average date of the last killing frost in spring ranges from about April 25 in the extreme southeastern counties to about May 21 in a small area in the northwest, while the first in fall varies from about October 6 in the southeast to about September 20 in the extreme northwest. The average length of the growing season thus ranges from 164 days in the southeast to 122 in the northwest. There is much variability in the length of the season from year to year. Stations in the southeast show a difference of about 50 days between the shortest and the longest growing season, while the difference is as much as 100 days at places in north-central Nebraska.

The average annual precipitation in the eastern third of the State is 27.69 inches; in the central third, 22.32; and in the western third 17.93. The amount decreases rather uniformly from 34 inches in the extreme southeast to 16 in a small area on the western border. On an average, 77 percent of the yearly total falls in the 6 months from April to September, and 45 in the 3 months of May, June, and July. The seasonal distribution is, therefore, agriculturally very favorable. The average seasonal snowfall is 28.7 inches.

A large part of the summer rainfall results from thunderstorms occurring in warm moist air of the southern sectors of cyclones. The falls are frequently at excessive rates for short periods and are agriculturally unfavorable. In some seasons these storms are numerous and well distributed, but sometimes they are scattered and infrequent. The result is great variability in the monthly amounts of rainfall in different years and also in the annual amounts from year to year. In dry years, periods of 15 to 20 days without appreciable rain may occur in June, July, and August; and under such conditions hot, dry winds often cause serious and extensive damage to crops.

The precipitation records show successions of wet and dry epochs as follows:

1876–92. Wet period with one very dry year.
1893–1901. Dry period with one rather wet year.
1902–09. Wet period with one rather dry year.
1910–20. Tendency irregular; most years dry, but 1915 wettest year of record.
1921–39. Long dry period with only one wet year; especially dry after 1930.

From April to October the mean relative humidity is about 60 percent; for the rest of the year, about 70. During periods of high temperatures, the relative humidity is usually very low.

Sunshine for the year averages 63 percent of the possible amount, ranging from about 55 in December and January to over 70 in July and August.

There are frequent changes in the direction of the wind at all seasons of the year, but the prevailing direction is from the south or southeast from May to September and from the northwest during the rest of the year. The average velocity is about 10 miles an hour.

High winds strong enough to damage trees but not buildings occur occasionally in connection with summer thunderstorms but rarely with winter storms. Several tornadoes occur within the State nearly every year, most frequently in spring, but the area covered by such storms is extremely small. Hail sufficiently heavy to damage crops also occurs over limited areas, averaging about 20 storms a year, 90 percent of which occur from June to August. The total damage from hail is considerably greater than that from tornadoes.

THOMAS A. BLAIR, *Senior Meteorologist and Climatic Section Director for Nebraska, Weather Bureau, Lincoln.*

NEVADA

Climatic summary

County [1]	Station	Temperature: Length of record	Temperature: January average	Temperature: July average	Temperature: Maximum	Temperature: Minimum	Killing frost average dates: Length of record	Killing frost: Last in spring	Killing frost: First in fall	Killing frost: Growing season [2]	Average precipitation: Length of record	January	February	March	April	May	June	July	August	September	October	November	December	Annual
		Yr.	°F.	°F.	°F.	°F.	Yr.			Days	Yr.	In.	In.	In.	In.	In.	In.	In.	In.	In.	In.	In.	In.	In.
Churchill	Fallon	36	29.8	73.1	106	−25	37	May 20	Sept. 24	127	36	0.58	0.56	0.43	0.54	0.49	0.38	0.14	0.21	0.28	0.39	0.34	0.64	4.98
	Lahontan	30	31.7	78.2	110	−17	27	May 4	Oct. 9	158	32	.56	.52	.29	.47	.46	.39	.17	.28	.28	.33	.26	.53	4.54
Clark	Las Vegas	28	44.6	86.1	118	8	32	Mar. 16	Nov. 10	239	31	.56	.60	.37	.26	.20	.20	.60	.61	.39	.31	.24	.50	4.84
	Logandale	33	44.6	87.3	120	6	33	Mar. 19	Nov. 11	237	33	.79	.69	.49	.29	.14	.14	.46	.58	.30	.48	.37	.58	5.31
	Searchlight	25	44.0	83.9	110	6	25	Mar. 18	Nov. 28	255	25	.97	1.10	.64	.49	.26	.19	.93	1.48	.38	.47	.20	.80	7.91
Douglas	Minden	38	32.2	69.3	109	−24	32	May 29	Sept. 20	114	39	1.67	1.69	.73	.58	.41	.37	.30	.22	.23	.41	.82	1.30	8.73
Elko	Arthur										29	1.94	2.00	1.47	1.68	1.48	.92	.72	.59	.81	1.20	1.12	1.72	15.65
	Carlin	15	26.0	71.5	112	−30	14	May 24	Sept. 2	101	14	.77	.66	.62	.45	.56	.54	.24	.13	.16	.32	.59	.59	5.63
	Clover Valley	29	24.0	67.3	98	−32	29	June 5	Sept. 18	105	33	1.91	1.78	1.25	1.04	1.22	.67	.54	.62	.56	.85	1.13	1.24	12.81
	Elko	40	24.4	69.8	107	−43	39	June 1	Sept. 12	103	40	1.33	1.20	.93	.78	.84	.73	.43	.29	.39	.74	.81	.99	9.46
	Gold Creek (near)										17	1.66	1.57	.92	1.31	1.07	1.03	.36	.54	.80	1.25	1.17	1.45	13.13
	Halleck	13	25.2	68.8	109	−32	7	May 30	Sept. 12	105	16	1.01	.60	.97	.82	.94	.85	.47	.19	.44	.59	.35	.77	8.00
	Hylton						19	June 5	Sept. 13	100	29	1.18	1.14	1.29	1.49	1.48	.91	.63	.52	.63	1.17	.97	1.31	12.72
	Lamoille (near)	26	25.7	68.2	100	−32	26	May 29	Sept. 23	117	34	1.47	1.72	1.82	2.08	2.05	1.05	.75	.66	.66	1.39	1.15	1.36	16.16
	Mahoney (Ranger Station.)										12	1.72	1.49	1.69	2.24	1.85	1.22	.62	.71	1.03	1.40	1.28	1.51	16.76
	Montello	40	23.4	71.6	111	−38	18	May 24	Sept. 18	117	40	.53	.53	.27	.49	.73	.50	.43	.40	.37	.49	.39	.43	5.56
	North Fork						20	June 6	Sept. 7	93	29	1.07	1.05	.87	.90	1.05	.66	.45	.47	.46	.70	1.06	1.01	9.75
	Owyhee	16	25.9	68.6	108	−35	10	June 4	Sept. 2	90	17	1.34	1.32	1.20	1.43	1.53	.72	.53	.33	.78	1.17	1.03	1.18	12.56
	San Jacinto	34	24.0	66.2	104	−50	23	June 10	Aug. 30	81	35	.63	.54	.61	.80	1.21	.95	.57	.47	.53	.58	.56	.55	8.00
	Tuscarora (near)						10	June 6	Sept. 10	96	22	1.37	1.36	1.44	1.42	1.51	.93	.41	.52	.59	1.09	1.13	1.50	13.27
	Wells	15	24.8	69.9	104	−37	15	June 11	Sept. 13	94	21	1.06	1.45	1.30	.70	.98	.66	.48	.22	.21	.62	.71	.97	9.36
Esmeralda	Goldfield	33	31.5	73.7	108	−23	33	May 19	Oct. 5	139	33	.64	.57	.65	.41	.48	.32	.42	.56	.36	.43	.25	.44	5.53
	Oasis Ranch	15	29.4	69.6	111	−21	14	May 31	Sept. 19	111	14	.66	.57	.35	.41	.47	.26	.40	.41	.28	.27	.27	.42	4.77
	Palmetto	10	30.7	66.2	99	−17	10	June 13	Sept. 17	96	10	1.86	2.00	2.79	1.61	1.76	.81	1.38	2.32	.81	1.52	1.60	1.17	19.63
Eureka	Beowawe	31	27.9	72.1	107	−42	31	May 26	Sept. 20	117	40	.68	.61	.52	.61	.75	.54	.28	.24	.28	.50	.52	.73	6.26
	Eureka	26	27.2	70.0	110	−26	26	June 8	Sept. 18	102	26	1.14	1.05	1.50	1.33	1.46	.94	.88	.72	.71	.91	.71	.82	12.17
Humboldt	Golconda	39	27.9	74.8	110	−35	33	May 20	Sept. 19	122	40	.70	.57	.55	.57	.69	.53	.23	.16	.33	.48	.48	.69	5.98
	Jungo										11	.40	.41	.17	.30	.35	.24	.06	.22	.40	.40	.32	.53	3.80
	Orovada	27	27.1	71.2	108	−35	26	June 3	Sept. 16	105	27	1.01	1.18	.89	1.24	1.24	1.01	.30	.27	.40	.94	.79	.83	10.10
	Paradise Valley										29	1.19	1.14	.69	.76	.78	.61	.23	.15	.43	.74	.68	1.03	8.43
	Quinn River Ranch	18	25.6	69.7	105	−34	19	June 20	Sept. 5	77	21	1.03	.64	.64	.39	.49	.45	.20	.19	.36	.43	.42	.66	5.90
	Sulphur	24	26.1	74.4	110	−35	24	May 23	Oct. 1	131	24	.48	.46	.34	.43	.60	.30	.10	.12	.29	.54	.29	.58	4.53
	Winnemucca	40	28.0	71.9	108	−36	40	May 11	Sept. 29	141	40	1.02	.93	.88	.85	.73	.66	.26	.23	.41	.63	.69	.91	8.20
Lander	Austin	36	28.5	70.2	105	−25	31	May 29	Sept. 23	117	37	1.15	1.29	1.42	1.74	1.58	.64	.60	.62	.56	.79	.80	1.03	12.22
	Battle Mountain	39	28.4	74.7	112	−40	36	May 26	do	120	40	.77	.68	.57	.73	.68	.45	.18	.19	.27	.41	.53	.71	6.17

NEVADA—Continued

Climatic summary—Continued

County	Station	Temperature					Killing frost average dates				Average precipitation													
		Length of record	January average	July average	Maximum	Minimum	Length of record	Last in spring	First in fall	Growing season [1]	Length of record	January	February	March	April	May	June	July	August	September	October	November	December	Annual
		Yr.	*°F.*	*°F.*	*°F.*	*°F.*	*Yr.*			*Days*	*Yr.*	*In.*	*In.*	*In.*	*In.*	*In.*	*In.*	*In.*	*In.*	*In.*	*In.*	*In.*	*In.*	*In.*
Lincoln	Alamo	18	35.7	78.7	113	−9	19	Apr. 29	Oct. 13	167	17	0.66	0.75	0.74	0.61	0.51	0.23	0.69	0.97	0.18	0.51	0.38	0.65	6.88
	Caliente	14	30.4	74.7	110	−31	14	May 2	Oct. 6	157	16	.98	1.14	.73	.35	.45	.22	.76	.57	.37	.26	.45	.59	6.87
	Geyser										12	.94	.75	1.21	.80	.66	.38	.34	.94	.48	.43	.71	.73	8.37
	Pioche										6	2.25	1.44	1.71	.83	1.18	.06	1.34	1.64	1.36	.75	.81	.85	14.22
Lyon	Fernley	17	34.1	73.7	106	−16	9	May 25	Sept. 25	123	16	1.05	.52	.53	.43	.63	.24	.28	.30	.18	.25	.42	.46	5.29
	Smith						13	May 29	Sept. 21	115	30	1.15	0.98	0.53	0.53	0.56	0.47	0.51	0.30	0.18	0.38	0.51	0.89	6.99
	Yerington	34	30.3	70.5	105	−26	25	May 23	Sept. 18	118	35	.62	.55	.37	.47	.43	.39	.12	.26	.30	.27	.35	.48	4.61
Mineral	Mina	40	32.4	78.0	110	−22	31	May 9	Oct. 4	148	39	.42	.33	.28	.36	.48	.26	.22	.30	.19	.21	.15	.25	3.45
	Schurz	19	31.3	73.4	109	−24	19	May 15	Sept. 28	136	19	.43	.56	.43	.65	.51	.51	.32	.46	.43	.42	.41	.55	5.68
	Thorne	29	34.3	77.3	109	−16	31	May 1	Oct. 16	168	32	.25	.38	.23	.44	.35	.26	.11	.21	.24	.23	.15	.23	3.08
Nye	Beatty	20	40.1	80.0	113	1	20	Apr. 26	Oct. 27	184	22	.79	.71	.47	.46	.41	.19	.18	.21	.14	.33	.23	.51	4.63
	Clay City	15	41.5	86.4	118	3					9	.46	.57	.20	.12	.15	.10	.06	.33	.10	.35	.18	.45	3.07
	Millett	25	26.1	68.9	104	−36	32	June 3	Sept. 12	101	28	.60	.49	.48	.50	.44	.50	.55	.53	.44	.50	.30	.50	5.83
	Potts	21	24.3	65.9	110	−32	21	June 16	Sept. 7	83	21	.50	.56	.72	.68	.70	.44	.42	.40	.31	.38	.35	.36	5.82
	Sharp	25	28.7	70.6	105	−22	24	June 1	Sept. 29	120	23	1.40	1.52	1.35	.98	.98	.37	1.02	1.51	.31	.98	.58	1.29	12.29
	Tonopah	32	30.1	74.0	98	−15	34	May 16	Oct. 12	149	32	.46	.43	.46	.51	.38	.20	.36	.51	.38	.41	.26	.36	4.72
Ormsby	Carson City	23	32.4	68.6	107	−27	24	May 25	Sept. 19	117	23	1.39	1.92	1.19	.65	.47	.30	.16	.17	.21	.53	.98	1.32	9.29
Pershing	Imlay	25	27.0	74.3	110	−35	23	May 21	Sept. 23	125	38	.54	.54	.45	.44	.56	.40	.13	.19	.36	.46	.40	.63	5.10
	Lovelock	40	29.2	73.0	110	−34	36	May 18	do	128	37	.68	.51	.44	.42	.38	.34	.17	.16	.29	.40	.33	.40	4.52
Washoe	Gerlach	26	27.7	75.1	108	−38	26	May 22	Sept. 30	131	26	.56	.64	.38	.35	.51	.43	.20	.11	.26	.38	.35	.62	4.79
	Lewers Ranch	18	33.9	67.8	102	−14	18	June 2	Sept. 26	116	26	5.42	4.09	3.37	1.61	1.20	.57	.28	.42	.55	1.38	2.59	3.76	25.24
	Marlette Lake	14	23.5	60.9	88	−18					17	5.29	6.15	3.26	1.84	1.28	.71	.12	.21	.57	1.39	1.85	4.61	27.28
	Nixon	11	30.7	72.2	107	−24	11	May 13	Sept. 27	137	11	.56	.74	.29	.51	.44	.65	.18	.19	.36	.49	.52	.62	5.55
	Reno	40	32.5	71.0	106	−19	40	May 8	Oct. 10	155	40	1.39	1.24	.81	.53	.50	.39	.29	.33	.27	.44	.53	1.01	7.73
	Sand Pass	24	31.4	74.6	107	−27	24	May 11	Oct. 2	144	24	.73	.92	.59	44	.43	.45	.16	.16	.39	.47	.53	.95	6.22
	Zorra Vista Ranch	14	27.1	65.8	103	−35	13	June 14	Aug. 28	75	19	.59	.69	.49	.51	.64	.39	.15	.22	.37	.52	.51	.67	5.75
White Pine	Cherry Creek	7	26.2	68.4	100	−27	10	June 5	Sept. 14	101	9	1.34	.75	.90	.91	1.12	.95	.78	.68	.67	.91	.59	.70	10.30
	Kimberly	11	23.1	70.7	105	−26	11	May 24	Oct. 2	131	11	1.76	2.08	1.25	1.09	1.01	.49	.84	1.07	.71	.85	.62	1.69	13.46
	McGill	40	25.7	67.6	104	−27	37	May 26	Sept. 22	119	39	.96	.87	.84	.97	1.14	.62	.72	1.03	.62	.80	.59	.23	9.39

[1] The county of Storey, for which no records are available, is best represented by the station at Carson City, Ormsby County.

[2] Length of growing season between average dates of last killing frost in spring and first in fall.

Precipitation—State unit values

[This tabulation gives the mean annual, mean monthly, and average seasonal precipitation, 1886–1938, for Nevada]

Precipitation		Precipitation		Precipitation		Precipitation		Precipitation		Precipitation	
Year	Mean	Year	Mean	Year	Mean	Year	Mean	Month	Mean	Season	Average
	In.		*In.*		*In.*		*In.*		*In.*		*In.*
1886	7.53	1900	7.55	1914	9.43	1928	4.87	January	1.20	Winter	3.25
1887	5.21	1901	11.39	1915	7.97	1929	5.83	February	1.05	Spring	2.58
1888	7.67	1902	7.29	1916	9.76	1930	9.77	March	.97	Summer	1.36
1889	12.41	1903	6.79	1917	6.72	1931	7.98	April	.76	Fall	1.62
1890	13.34	1904	11.26	1918	9.28	1932	8.24	May	.85		
1891	14.06	1905	7.97	1919	7.08	1933	6.67	June	.50		
1892	10.54	1906	13.01	1920	8.89	1934	7.12	July	.38		
1893	9.32	1907	11.77	1921	8.30	1935	8.61	August	.48		
1894	11.33	1908	6.58	1922	9.56	1936	10.26	September	.39		
1895	7.39	1909	10.00	1923	8.70	1937	8.89	October	.58		
1896	9.92	1910	5.81	1924	5.49	1938	11.79	November	.65		
1897	9.94	1911	8.58	1925	10.16			December	1.00		
1898	6.93	1912	7.83	1926	6.39						
1899	8.61	1913	10.99	1927	7.84			Annual	8.81		

NEVADA—Continued

Dates of last killing frost in spring and first in fall, with length of growing season

Year	Reno			Winnemucca			Elko			McGill			Tonopah			Logandale		
	Last in spring	First in fall	Growing season[1]	Last in spring	First in fall	Growing season[1]	Last in spring	First in fall	Growing season[1]	Last in spring	First in fall	Growing season[1]	Last in spring	First in fall	Growing season[1]	Last in spring	First in fall	Growing season[1]
			Days			*Days*			*Days*			*Days*			*Days*			*Days*
1899	May 29	Oct. 4	128	May 19	Aug. 22	95	May 30	Sept. 6	99	May 30	Sept. 9	102						
1900	May 14	Sept. 6	115	Apr. 27	Sept. 18	144	May 17	Sept. 9	115	May 17	do	115						
1901	May 22	Sept. 24	125	June 11	Sept. 27	108	May 31	Sept. 1	93	May 27	Sept. 23	119						
1902	May 3	Sept. 29	149	May 3	Sept. 26	146	May 20	Sept. 16	119	May 13	Sept. 25	136	June 5	Sept. 19	106			
1903	May 28	Sept. 14	109	May 23	Sept. 14	114	July 8	Sept. 8	62	May 28	Sept. 9	104						
1904	May 2	Oct. 12	163	May 5	Oct. 17	165	Apr. 26	Sept. 27	154	May 25	Sept. 26	124						
1905	May 22	Sept. 29	130	May 23	Sept. 29	129		do										
1906	June 7	Oct. 5	120	May 17	Oct. 20	156	May 17	Oct. 5	141		Sept. 16			Oct. 19			Nov. 20	
1907	May 20	Oct. 3	136	May 2	Sept. 19	140	June 13			June 16			June 15	Oct. 2	109	Mar. 28	Nov. 14	231
1908	May 30	Sept. 25	118	June 22	Sept. 24	94		Sept. 25		June 23	Sept. 25	94	June 3	do	121	Mar. 29	Oct. 20	205
1909	May 11	Oct. 29	171	May 24	Sept. 12	111	June 10	Sept. 1	83	June 10	Sept. 12	94	May 23	Oct. 29	159	May 17	Oct. 31	167
1910	May 5	Oct. 14	162	Apr. 16	Oct. 2	169	June 9	Aug. 18	70	May 23	Sept. 7	107	May 4	Oct. 12	161	Mar. 29	Nov. 28	244
1911	May 6	Sept. 18	135	May 27	Sept. 17	113	June 9	Sept. 7	90				May 25	Oct. 10	138	Mar. 5	Nov. 12	252
1912	Apr. 22	Oct. 10	171	May 22	Sept. 16	117	May 22	Sept. 5	106	June 16	Aug. 30	75	May 22	Oct. 4	135	Feb. 29	Nov. 14	259
1913	Mar. 27	Oct. 5	192	May 3	Sept. 23	143	July 14	Sept. 24	72	May 14	Sept. 21	130	May 2	Sept. 30	151	Mar. 28	Nov. 29	246
1914	Apr. 25	Oct. 4	162	June 6	Sept. 13	99	June 22	Sept. 5	75	June 6	Sept. 13	99	June 5	Oct. 22	139	Feb. 28	Nov. 12	257
1915	May 2	Oct. 11	162	May 3	Sept. 14	134	June 15	Sept. 3	80	May 5	Sept. 14	132	May 3	Nov. 9	190	Feb 6	Nov. 11	278
1916	May 24	Oct. 5	134	June 22	Sept. 11	81	June 22	Aug. 19	58	June 22	Sept. 10	80	May 24	Oct. 4	133	Mar. 25	Nov. 6	226
1917	May 16	Oct. 19	156	May 16	Oct. 17	154	June 11	Sept. 14	95	June 1	Sept. 25	116	May 18	Oct. 18	153	Apr. 18	Nov. 13	209
1918	May 10	Oct. 26	169	May 10	Oct. 26	169	May 31	Sept. 24	116	May 31	Sept. 24	116	May 29	Oct. 19	143	Apr. 5	Nov. 7	216
1919	Apr. 20	Oct. 3	166	Apr. 16	Oct. 3	170	June 12	Aug. 11	60	do	Sept. 22	114	Apr. 26	Oct. 3	160	Mar. 15	Nov. 1	231
1920	May 2	Oct. 7	158	May 31	Oct. 16	138	June 2	Sept. 21	111	June 1	Sept. 24	115	May 2	Sept 24	145	Mar. 16	Oct. 20	218
1921	May 17	Oct. 24	160	Apr. 25	Sept. 30	158	May 9	Sept. 13	127	July 3	Oct. 25	115	June 16	Oct. 24	130	Apr. 6	Nov. 18	226
1922	May 26	Oct. 21	148	May 11	Oct. 16	158	May 27	Sept. 9	105	May 26	Oct. 5	132	May 26	Oct. 28	155	Apr. 16	Nov. 27	225
1923	June 13	Oct. 23	132	Apr. 30	Oct. 14	167	June 1	Sept. 18	109	June 1	Oct. 8	129	do	Oct. 7	134	Mar. 7	Nov. 28	266
1924	May 5	Oct. 18	166	May 5	Sept. 20	138	June 20	Sept. 11	83	Apr. 26	Sept. 20	147	May 5	Sept. 20	138	Mar. 14	Oct. 11	211
1925	Apr. 24	Sept. 30	159	Apr. 24	Sept. 22	151	May 8	Sept. 22	137	Apr. 25	Sept. 19	147	Apr. 24	do	149	Mar. 11	Nov. 16	250
1926	May 10	Oct. 8	151	May 10	Sept. 24	137	May 25	Aug. 31	98	May 10	Sept. 24	137	May 8	Oct. 29	174	Mar. 7	Nov. 20	258
1927	May 29	Oct. 6	130	Apr. 20	Sept. 14	147	May 30	Sept. 14	107	May 29	Sept. 30	124	May 29	Sept. 30	124	Mar. 17	Nov. 23	251
1928	May 3	Oct. 14	164	Apr. 21	Sept. 13	145	May 5	Sept. 9	127	June 11	Sept. 14	95	Apr. 21	Oct. 11	173	Apr. 7	Nov. 17	224
1929	May 1	Oct. 3	155	May 28	Oct. 24	149	May 1	Sept. 8	130	May 27	Sept. 8	104	June 10	Oct. 28	140	do	Oct. 30	206
1930	May 22	Oct. 10	141	Mar. 22	Oct. 10	141	May 22	Sept. 25	126	May 22	Sept. 25	126	May 9	Sept. 30	144	Mar. 2	Nov. 15	258
1931	Apr. 25	Oct. 26	184	May 10	Sept. 24	137	June 17	Sept. 11	86	May 19	Sept. 11	115	Apr. 25	Oct. 26	184	Mar. 9	Nov. 13	249
1932	Apr. 22	Oct. 18	179	Apr. 22	Oct. 10	171	May 25	Aug. 30	97	June 5	Oct. 9	126	June 6	Oct. 18	134	Apr. 28	Nov. 10	196
1933	Apr. 18	Nov. 1	197	May 10	Oct. 13	156	May 28	Sept. 8	103	May 13	Oct. 20	160	May 22	Oct. 31	162	Mar. 25	Nov. 6	226
1934	Apr. 4	Sept. 26	175	Apr. 4	Sept. 26	175	May 31	Sept. 25	117	May 1	Sept. 24	146	Apr. 4	Sept. 25	174	Jan. 31	Nov. 21	294
1935	Apr. 18	Oct. 17	182	May 18	Oct. 13	148	May 19	Sept. 28	132	May 12	Sept. 27	138	May 3	Oct. 16	166	Mar. 11	Oct. 24	227

1936	Apr. 7	Oct. 24	200	May 7	Oct. 24	170	May 24	Sept. 15	114	May 6	do	144	May 7	Oct. 23	169	Feb. 10	Nov. 3	266
1937	Apr. 29	Nov. 2	187	Apr. 30	Oct. 6	159	June 18	Sept. 1	75	May 30	Oct. 3	126	Apr. 29	Oct. 4	158	Mar. 23	Nov. 9	231
1938	May 7	Oct. 17	163	May 7	Oct. 3	149	May 22	Sept. 13	114	May 6	Oct. 6	153	May 6	Oct. 16	163	Feb. 18		
Mean	May 8	Oct. 10	155	May 11	Sept. 29	141	June 1	Sept. 12	103	May 26	Sept. 22	119	May 16	Oct. 12	149	Mar. 19	Nov. 11	237
Extremes	Mar. 27[2] June 13[3]	Sept. 6[4] Nov. 2[5]	[6] 109 [7] 200	Apr. 14[2] June 22[3]	Aug. 22[4] Oct. 26[5]	[6] 81 [7] 175	Apr. 26[2] July 14[3]	Aug. 11[4] Oct. 5[5]	[6] 58 [7] 154	Apr. 25[2] July 23[3]	Aug. 30[4] Oct. 25[5]	[6] 75 [7] 160	Mar. 2[2] June 16[3]	Sept. 19[4] Nov. 9[5]	[6] 106 [7] 190	Jan. 31[2] May 17[3]	Oct. 11[4] Nov. 26[5]	[6] 167 [7] 294

[1] Number of days between last killing frost in spring and first in fall.
[2] Earliest date in spring.
[3] Latest date in spring.
[4] Earliest date in fall.
[5] Latest date in fall.
[6] Shortest growing season.
[7] Longest growing season.

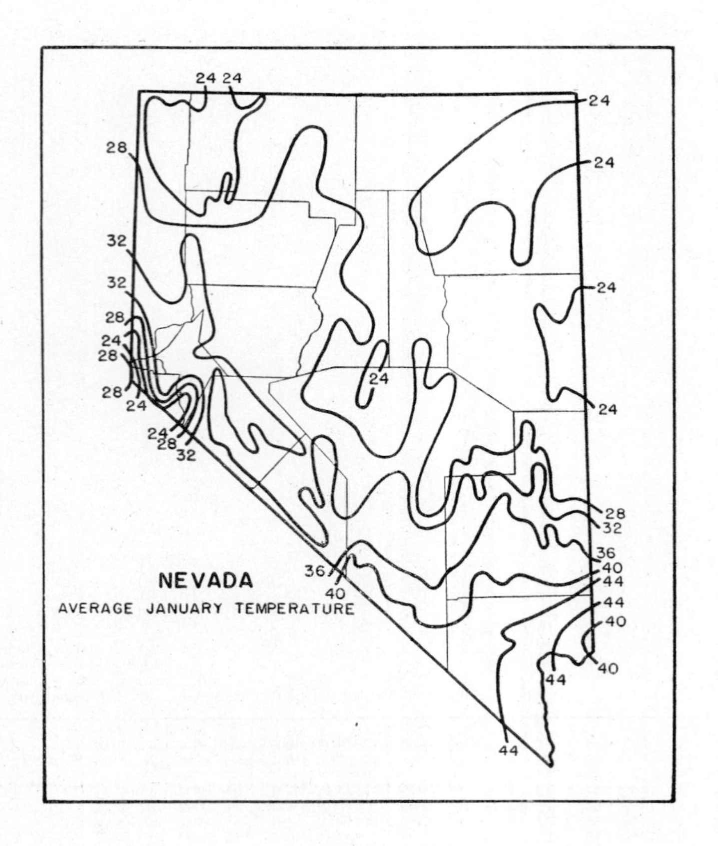
NEVADA
AVERAGE JANUARY TEMPERATURE

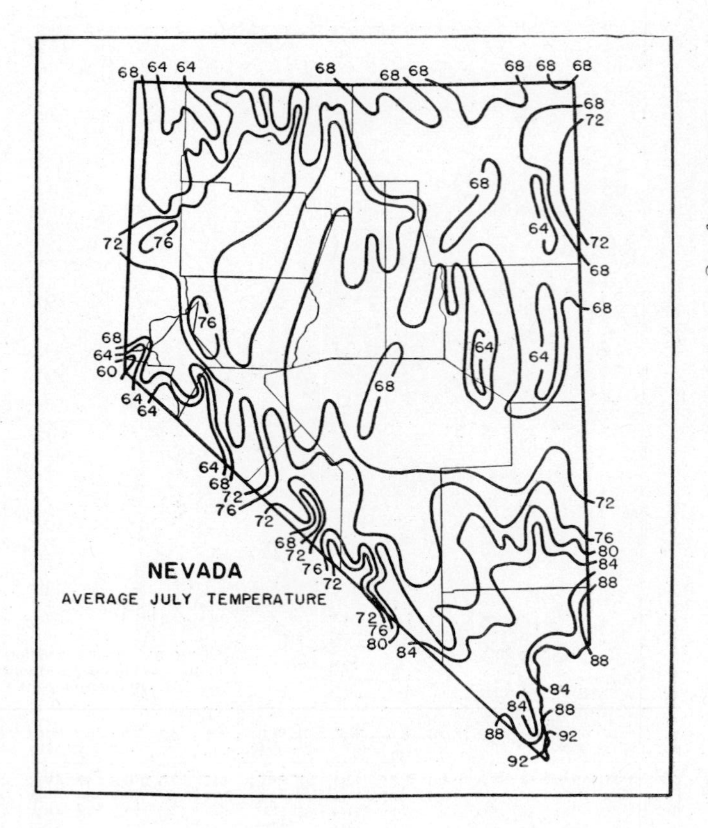
NEVADA
AVERAGE JULY TEMPERATURE

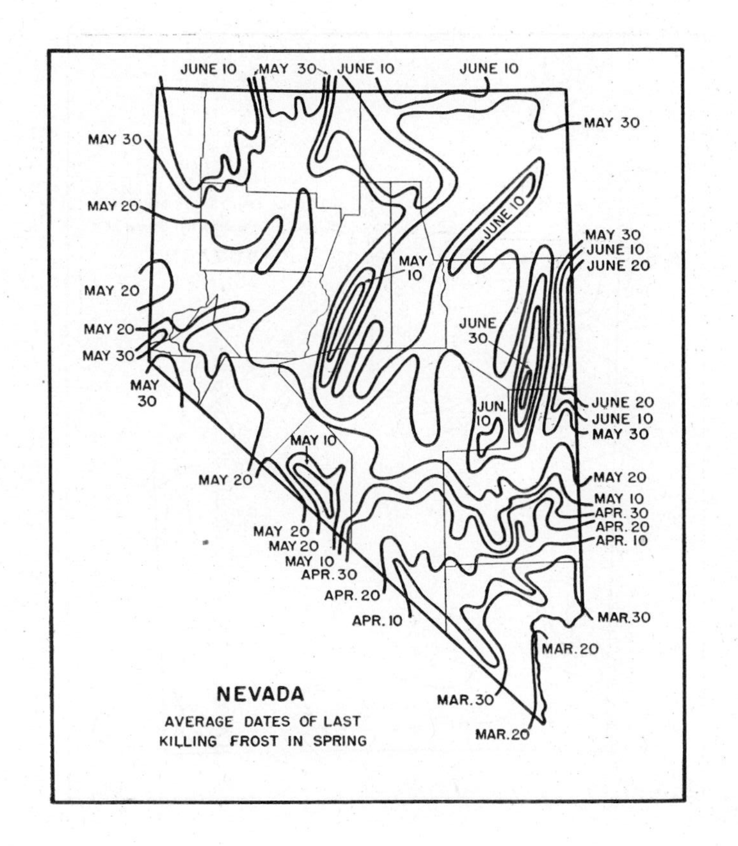

NEVADA
AVERAGE DATES OF LAST KILLING FROST IN SPRING

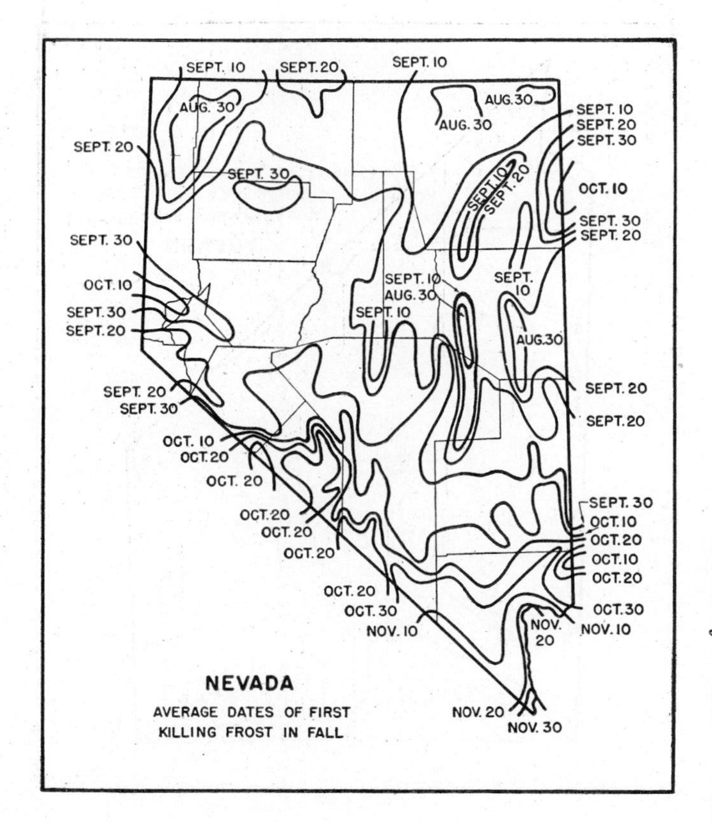

NEVADA
AVERAGE DATES OF FIRST KILLING FROST IN FALL

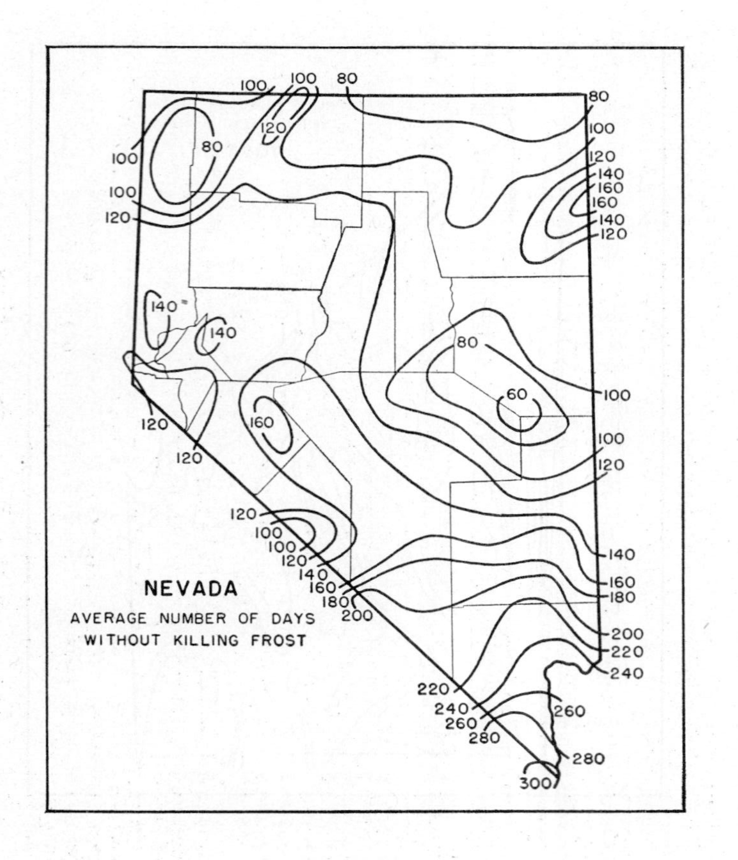
NEVADA
AVERAGE NUMBER OF DAYS
WITHOUT KILLING FROST

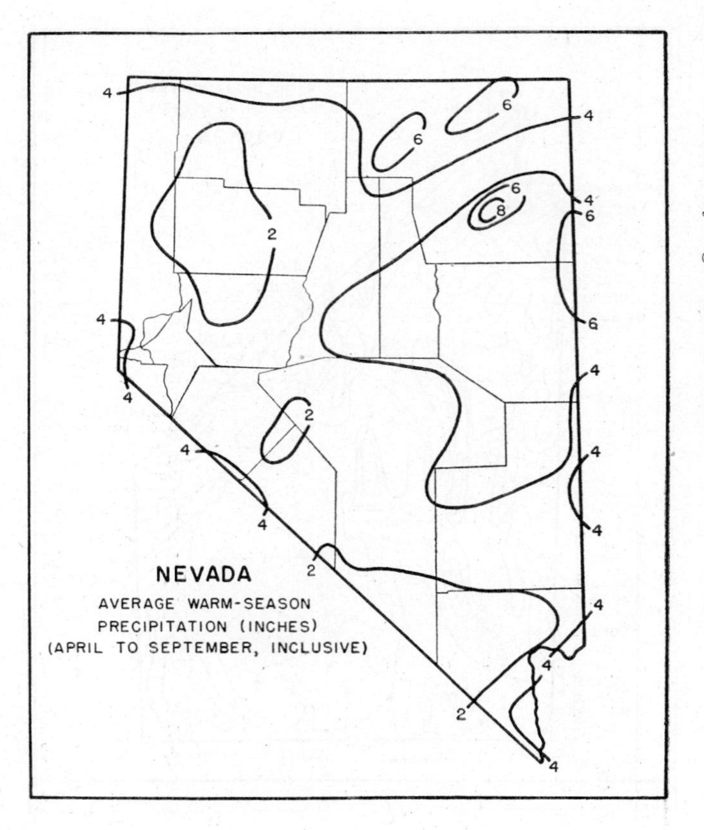
NEVADA
AVERAGE WARM-SEASON
PRECIPITATION (INCHES)
(APRIL TO SEPTEMBER, INCLUSIVE)

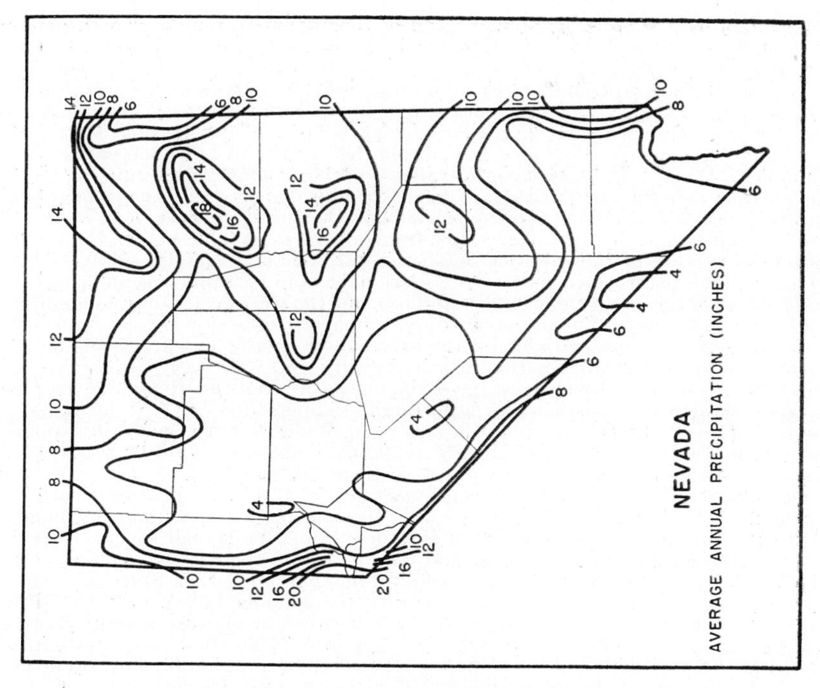

SUPPLEMENTARY CLIMATIC NOTES FOR NEVADA

The surface of Nevada is primarily a plateau. The eastern part has an elevation of between 5,000 and 6,000 feet; the western between 3,800 and 5,000 feet, the lower limit being in the vicinity of Pyramid Lake and Carson Sink; and the southern part between 2,000 and 3,000 feet. From the lower elevations in the west there is a fairly rapid rise to the summits of the eastern ranges of the Sierra Nevada. The southwestern part falls off toward Death Valley, Calif., and the southern toward the channel of the Colorado River, the elevation of which is less than 1,000 feet. The extreme northeastern part drains northerly into the Snake River and thence into the Columbia.

On this plateau there are many mountain ranges, most of them 50 to 100 miles long and running north and south. There is one east-west range in the northeast within the southern limit of the Columbia River drainage. With the exception of this small part and another limited area in the southeast, which drains into the Colorado River, Nevada lies within the confines of the Great Basin, and the waters of its streams disappear into sinks, from which they evaporate, or flow into lakes without outlets.

Nevada lies just east and to the leeward of the Sierra Nevada range, an effective barrier to precipitation from the generally eastward-drifting air, which loses most of its moisture in ascending the western slopes of the mountains. One of the greatest contrasts in precipitation within a short distance found in the United States occurs between the western, or California, slopes of the Sierras and their eastern slopes and the contiguous lowlands of western Nevada. In ascending the west slope, the air loses most of its moisture through condensation and precipitation, and descending the eastern slope it is warmed by compression, so that very little precipitation occurs. This rain barrier is felt not only in the extreme western part but generally throughout the State, with the result that the lowlands of Nevada are largely desert or semidesert.

With its varied and rugged topography—its mountain ranges, narrow valleys, and low, sage-covered deserts, ranging in elevation from about 1,500 to more than 10,000 feet—Nevada presents wide local variations of temperature and rainfall. The most striking climatic features are bright sunshine, small annual rainfall in the valleys and deserts, heavy snowfall in the higher mountains, dryness and purity of air, and phenomenally large daily ranges of temperature.

As in all desert or semiarid regions, heavy downpours of rain occur occasionally in small areas. These storms, locally termed cloudbursts, may bring to a locality as much rain in a few hours as would normally fall in several months.

Because of the arid climate, only about 6 percent of the land in Nevada is under cultivation. The cultivated area lies mostly in the valleys of the Walker, Carson, and Truckee Rivers, where irrigation is maintained by impounding the waters from melting snows in the Sierra Nevada; in the vicinity of Lovelock in the lower Humboldt River Valley; and in the valleys of the Muddy and Virgin Rivers in the southeastern part of the State. A small additional area in pastures and wild hay is watered by flooding when snows melt in the spring.

The mean annual temperatures vary from 44° F. at San Jacinto, in the northeastern part, through 50° at Reno in the west, to 65° at Logandale in the south. In the northeastern part summers are short and hot and winters long and cold. In the west, also, the summers are short and hot, but the winters are only moderately cold, while in the south the summers are long and hot and the winters short and mild.

Because of the high altitude and the extreme dryness and clearness of the air, there is rapid nocturnal radiation of heat, resulting in wide daily ranges in temperature. Even after the hottest days, the nights are cool; at Reno the average range between the highest and the lowest daily temperatures is 22° F. in January, increasing month by month to 35° in July. At Winnemucca it is 25° in January and 38° in July; and at Logandale 25° in January and 37° in July. In extreme instances the daily range may become as great as 50° to 60°.

Over most of the State, frosts continue till late in spring and begin early in autumn. The shortest growing season is in the extreme northeast and the longest in the extreme south, the range being from less than 100 days at several stations in the northeast to 140 in the west and to over 225 in the extreme south.

Nevada has, on an average, less precipitation than any other State and most of that occurs during the winter season, with the summer falls very light. Precipitation is lightest over the lower parts of the western plateau, a series of long valleys extending from the State border opposite Death Valley in California northward to the Idaho line. Over these valleys the average annual precipitation is less than 5 inches, the lowest being 3.07 inches at Clay City, Nye County, on the southwestern border. From this low average it ranges through 15 inches in Lamoille Canyon in the northeastern part on the westerly side of the Ruby Mountains and 25 at Lewers Ranch in the foothills of the Sierra Nevada up to 27 inches at Marlette Lake, high up in the most easterly range of the Sierras. Variations in precipitation are due mainly to differences in elevation and exposure to rain-bearing winds.

The average annual number of days with 0.01 inch or more of precipitation varies from 14 at Clay City to 68 at Winnemucca.

Snowfall is usually heavy in the mountains, but when it is light, as sometimes happens, the result is a shortage of water for irrigation. Long dry spells in summer are injurious to ranges and pastures but of little moment to irrigated crops, which depend almost entirely on stored waters.

Humidity is normally low, and the dryness of the air makes both the heat of summer and the cold of winter less disagreeable.

Nevada has a generous supply of sunshine, the average percentage of the possible amount at Reno and Winnemucca being 74. On an average there are only 7 days a year at Reno with less than 1 percent of sunshine. For the State the average annual number of clear days is 193, partly cloudy 87, and cloudy 85.

The low humidity and ample sunshine produce rapid evaporation. At Clay City, on the southwestern border, the average annual evaporation from a free water surface is 141 inches. A short record, for about 15 years, shows an annual average precipitation at Clay City of only 3.07 inches. Near Lamoille, in the northeastern part, for the 6 warm months during which measurement is possible the average evaporation is 40 inches.

Winds are generally light. Storms with high winds rarely occur and more rarely still cause appreciable damage. The prevailing wind direction is west, though at a few stations, because of local topography, it is south or southwest.

Thunderstorms are infrequent, the average annual number being 14 at Reno and 10 at Winnemucca. Over the southern and eastern sections thunderstorms develop occasionally into heavy local downpours of rain. These storms usually occur over sparsely settled mountain canyons and therefore are seldom destructive.

GEORGE V. SAGER, *Associate Meteorologist and Climatic Section Director for Nevada, Weather Bureau, Reno.*

NEW ENGLAND

Climatic summary

State and county[1]	Station	Temperature: Length of record	Temperature: January average	Temperature: July average	Temperature: Maximum	Temperature: Minimum	Killing frost average dates: Length of record	Killing frost: Last in spring	Killing frost: First in fall	Growing season[2]	Average precipitation: Length of record	January	February	March	April	May	June	July	August	September	October	November	December	Annual
MAINE		*Yr.*	*°F.*	*°F.*	*°F.*	*°F.*	*Yr.*			*Days*	*Yr.*	*In.*	*In.*	*In.*	*In.*	*In.*	*In.*	*In.*	*In.*	*In.*	*In.*	*In.*	*In.*	*In.*
Androscoggin	Lewiston	40	18.7	69.5	102	−28	39	May 2	Oct. 8	159	40	3.84	3.28	4.17	3.69	3.20	3.30	3.59	2.93	3.72	3.38	3.28	3.73	42.11
Aroostook	Ashland						10	June 7	Sept. 22	107	7	1.79	2.43	1.58	2.27	2.81	4.24	3.92	2.86	3.53	4.39	2.44	2.44	34.70
	Fort Fairfield										15	2.99	2.20	2.31	2.30	2.69	3.92	4.43	3.23	3.36	3.61	2.56	2.67	36.27
	Fort Kent										8	2.96	1.88	2.06	2.86	3.30	3.99	4.21	3.56	3.56	3.34	2.34	2.48	36.54
	Houlton	34	13.1	67.3	102	−43	16	May 25	Sept. 19	117	37	2.80	2.03	2.39	2.40	2.39	3.21	2.92	2.81	3.14	3.61	2.53	2.55	32.78
	Squa Pan Lake										11	3.14	2.10	2.51	2.88	3.19	3.77	4.02	2.86	4.27	3.42	2.56	2.34	37.06
	Van Buren	28	8.5	65.0	103	−48	30	June 1	Sept. 16	107	29	2.61	2.22	2.37	2.35	2.81	3.84	3.89	3.92	3.63	3.74	2.47	2.77	36.62
	Presque Isle	27	11.0	65.7	99	−41	22	May 28	Sept. 14	109	26	2.36	1.86	2.19	2.52	2.92	3.61	3.62	3.15	3.35	3.38	2.47	2.34	33.77
Cumberland	Hiram										13	3.97	3.09	3.36	3.85	2.99	3.64	3.57	3.08	3.85	3.38	4.05	3.26	42.09
	N. Bridgton	38	19.2	69.2	105	−34	38	May 18	Sept. 30	135	40	3.74	3.14	3.99	3.64	3.41	3.58	3.87	3.60	3.92	3.33	3.45	3.52	43.19
	Portland	40	23.4	67.8	103	−21	40	Apr. 27	Oct. 17	173	40	4.38	4.05	4.27	3.75	3.13	3.23	3.04	2.93	3.24	2.89	3.10	4.04	42.05
Franklin	Eustis										25	2.73	2.02	2.58	2.92	2.99	3.71	3.42	3.34	3.26	3.37	2.90	2.72	35.96
	Farmington	40	16.7	68.4	104	−36	40	May 24	Sept. 20	119	40	3.37	2.77	3.86	3.57	3.63	3.70	3.69	3.69	4.02	3.63	3.50	3.50	42.93
Hancock	Bar Harbor	30	23.0	66.3	98	−21	30	May 13	Oct. 5	145	34	4.85	3.85	5.18	4.13	3.33	3.20	3.26	2.89	4.48	4.24	4.05	4.38	47.84
	Ellsworth										30	3.90	2.93	3.68	3.84	2.76	3.20	3.18	3.25	4.04	4.32	3.55	3.58	42.23
Kennebec	Gardiner	40	19.7	68.8	102	−41	36	May 21	Sept. 18	120	40	3.76	3.18	4.02	3.67	3.17	3.15	3.65	3.22	3.79	3.72	3.30	3.53	42.16
	Winslow	39	18.4	69.1	101	−39	34	May 20	Sept. 25	128	40	2.97	2.29	3.28	3.08	3.14	3.05	3.64	3.30	3.80	3.59	2.96	2.86	37.96
Oxford	Middle-Dam										34	2.32	1.91	2.53	2.72	3.46	3.64	3.96	3.84	3.82	3.16	2.92	2.30	36.58
	Rumford	40	17.2	68.3	101	−33	40	May 14	Sept. 26	135	40	3.02	2.59	3.45	3.30	3.24	3.47	3.71	3.42	3.78	3.32	3.15	2.97	39.42
	Upper Dam										40	2.34	1.97	2.54	2.42	2.94	3.12	3.36	3.10	3.26	2.66	2.62	2.39	32.72
Penobscot	Bangor	11	22.9	70.8	104	−28	13	May 9	Oct. 6	150	13	3.53	2.31	3.09	3.22	3.42	2.90	2.99	3.30	3.76	4.83	3.26	2.91	39.52
	Millinocket	36	13.9	67.7	106	−41	36	May 27	Sept. 18	114	40	3.56	2.74	3.46	3.17	3.11	3.67	3.66	3.61	3.70	3.84	3.64	3.44	41.60
	Oldtown	21	18.2	68.3	96	−32	22	May 12	Oct. 1	142	26	3.31	2.63	3.03	3.45	3.07	3.44	3.76	3.15	3.53	4.20	3.21	3.23	40.01
	Orono	38	18.4	68.0	104	−40	40	May 18	Sept. 25	130	40	3.89	3.04	3.38	3.04	3.11	3.33	3.58	2.93	3.53	3.96	3.00	3.32	40.11
	Patten	16	11.1	66.2	100	−35	17	May 25	Sept. 11	109	17	2.72	2.59	2.37	2.42	3.29	4.04	4.47	3.60	3.96	4.33	2.83	2.57	39.19
Piscataquis	Greenville	32	12.9	65.0	96	−36	33	May 25	Sept. 20	118	37	3.20	2.68	3.29	3.30	3.54	4.12	4.63	3.42	3.96	3.81	3.27	3.27	42.49
	Milo										17	2.91	1.82	2.04	2.76	3.48	4.21	3.43	3.66	3.86	4.26	3.58	2.59	38.60
Somerset	Fairfield	18	17.4	68.5	98	−37	18	May 12	Sept. 30	141	18	3.04	2.77	3.31	2.57	2.68	2.30	3.25	3.12	2.75	2.61	2.21	2.97	33.58
	Jackman										18	2.81	2.02	2.63	2.88	3.54	3.92	3.55	2.98	3.42	3.21	3.16	2.65	36.77
	Madison	35	14.8	67.8	102	−40	35	May 18	Sept. 22	127	37	3.47	2.78	3.63	3.73	3.54	3.52	3.61	3.79	4.01	3.62	3.35	3.24	42.29
	The Forks										32	2.71	2.27	2.91	3.02	3.36	3.80	3.85	3.24	3.40	3.37	3.22	2.58	37.73

[1] The following counties for which no records are available are best represented by the stations indicated: Maine, Knox—Bar Harbor; Lincoln—Gardner; Sagadahoc—Lewiston; Waldo—Bangor; New Hampshire, Carroll—Waterville; Sullivan—Alstead; Vermont, Grand Isle—Burlington; Massachusetts, Dukes—Falmouth; Connecticut, Middlesex—Colchester.

[2] Length of growing season between average dates of last killing frost in spring and first in fall.

NEW ENGLAND—Continued

Climatic summary—Continued

State and county	Station	Temperature: Length of record	Temperature: January average	Temperature: July average	Temperature: Maximum	Temperature: Minimum	Killing frost average dates: Length of record	Killing frost: Last in spring	Killing frost: First in fall	Killing frost: Growing season	Average precipitation: Length of record	January	February	March	April	May	June	July	August	September	October	November	December	Annual
		Yr.	°*F*	°*F.*	°*F.*	°*F.*	*Yr.*			*Days*	*Yr.*	*In.*	*In.*	*In.*	*In.*	*In.*	*In.*	*In.*	*In.*	*In.*	*In.*	*In.*	*In.*	*In.*
MAINE—continued																								
Washington	Danforth										28	3.17	2.61	2.66	2.90	2.58	3.42	3.18	3.12	3.60	3.81	2.99	2.83	36.87
	Eastport	40	21.5	60.5	93	−23	40	Apr. 29	Oct. 22	176	40	3.68	2.88	3.36	2.69	2.39	2.75	2.72	2.86	2.96	3.27	2.74	3.26	35.56
	Machias (East)										12	4.82	2.85	3.70	4.26	2.71	3.74	2.99	2.79	4.70	5.07	3.88	3.91	45.42
	Woodland	18	15.6	67.3	102	−41	20	May 23	Sept. 21	121	20	3.56	2.30	3.33	3.68	2.77	3.13	2.57	3.27	3.77	4.69	3.63	3.30	40.00
York	Cornish	26	20.0	69.5	103	−36	26	May 14	Sept. 24	133	26	3.61	3.45	4.38	4.21	3.48	3.99	3.88	3.91	3.95	3.40	3.50	3.84	45.60
NEW HAMPSHIRE																								
Belknap	Lakeport										40	3.88	3.67	4.27	3.72	3.02	3.38	3.79	3.31	3.87	2.87	3.46	3.71	42.95
Cheshire	Alstead	24	19.7	69.0	97	−26	22	May 14	Sept. 26	135	24	2.59	2.65	3.55	3.12	3.42	3.51	4.06	4.30	3.94	2.97	2.74	3.10	39.95
	Keene B	40	21.5	68.9	104	−32	40	May 26	Sept. 20	117	40	2.98	2.62	3.31	3.12	3.02	3.19	3.85	3.75	3.73	2.73	2.93	3.03	38.26
Coos	Berlin	28	14.7	66.2	100	−44	28	May 30	Sept. 16	109	26	3.01	2.45	3.53	2.02	2.87	3.52	3.55	3.53	3.76	3.20	3.18	2.96	38.58
	First Conn. Lake	21	11.8	63.3	93	−46	21	June 12	Sept. 15	95	4	4.31	2.63	3.41	3.44	4.61	4.63	5.73	4.05	5.00	4.09	3.77	3.40	49.07
	Lancaster										14	2.56	1.78	2.17	2.72	2.95	3.55	4.12	3.29	3.74	2.87	3.14	2.22	35.11
	Milan						13	May 12	Sept. 28	139	12	3.52	2.17	3.25	2.92	3.27	3.68	3.97	2.97	3.60	3.26	3.20	2.97	38.78
	West Stewardstown										23	2.45	1.75	1.96	2.39	2.60	3.90	4.10	3.92	4.20	3.58	2.72	2.17	35.74
Grafton	Bethlehem	38	16.2	66.5	96	−35	38	May 23	Sept. 23	123	40	2.20	2.13	2.78	2.63	2.84	3.53	4.03	3.40	3.78	2.99	2.64	2.33	35.28
	Glencliff	28	17.3	65.7	97	−32	24	May 18	Sept. 26	131	30	2.74	2.38	3.30	3.69	3.28	3.87	4.19	4.09	4.10	3.56	3.61	2.81	41.62
	Grafton	16	18.3	66.8	99	−33	20	June 3	Sept. 10	99	18	2.65	2.68	3.29	2.75	3.31	3.10	4.17	3.13	3.42	2.58	2.48	2.84	36.40
	Hanover	40	18.1	68.8	101	−37	40	May 22	Sept. 28	129	40	2.45	2.19	2.78	3.02	3.06	3.34	3.78	3.31	3.58	2.82	2.71	2.48	35.52
	Lincoln										18	3.93	2.75	3.73	3.68	3.54	4.41	4.52	4.09	4.67	3.95	4.26	3.63	47.16
	Littleton										6	2.11	1.64	2.22	3.24	3.01	3.91	4.03	3.03	3.50	2.49	2.77	2.37	34.32
	Plymouth	40	18.1	68.1	102	−38	35	May 26	Sept. 18	115	40	3.07	2.49	3.40	3.20	2.88	3.42	3.92	3.28	3.92	3.01	3.08	3.00	38.67
	Woodsville										16	2.25	1.95	2.38	3.05	2.63	3.36	3.68	3.20	3.78	3.24	3.36	2.47	35.35
Hillsboro	Brookline	20	24.4	71.3	105	−36	20	May 17	Sept. 19	125	20	2.95	3.28	4.09	3.76	3.18	3.66	3.52	3.83	3.50	3.25	2.63	3.19	40.84
	Nashua	32	23.9	71.3	106	−25	28	May 18	Sept. 26	131	40	3.20	3.08	3.76	3.49	2.77	3.31	3.33	3.41	3.56	2.75	2.99	3.26	38.91
Merrimack	Concord	40	22.0	69.7	102	−32	40	May 3	Oct. 3	153	40	2.75	2.45	3.19	3.02	2.78	3.25	3.47	3.34	3.66	2.57	2.85	2.91	36.24
	Franklin	38	20.0	69.1	103	−36	32	May 22	Sept. 28	129	37	3.09	2.72	3.37	3.49	3.19	3.75	3.80	3.52	4.03	2.95	3.24	3.05	40.20
Rockingham	Newton	20	23.0	69.0	102	−22	20	May 29	Sept. 20	114	20	3.07	3.16	3.71	3.75	2.89	3.19	3.48	3.23	3.31	2.98	2.75	3.28	38.80
Strafford	Durham	40	23.7	69.4	103	−35	40	May 17	Sept. 28	134	40	3.46	2.81	3.17	3.58	2.81	3.45	3.34	3.19	3.73	3.03	2.97	3.50	39.04
VERMONT																								
Addison	Cornwall	37	20.2	70.2	104	−32	36	May 8	Oct. 5	150	40	2.02	1.88	2.14	2.35	2.69	3.28	3.52	3.07	3.27	2.98	2.58	1.99	31.77
Bennington	Bennington	22	23.7	69.2	96	−32	16	May 16	Sept. 29	136	21	2.52	1.96	2.96	2.90	2.96	3.82	4.76	3.51	3.78	2.54	3.27	2.22	37.20
	Manchester	14	21.1	67.5	95	−30	14	May 13	do	139	14	2.19	2.07	2.45	2.53	3.57	3.08	3.58	3.63	3.75	3.17	2.36	2.43	34.81

Caledonia	St. Johnsbury	40	16.4	68.5	101	−43	40	May 22	Sept. 26	127	40	2.34	2.05	2.57	2.58	2.80	3.28	3.68	3.70	3.58	3.03	2.68	2.40	34.69
Chittendon	Burlington	40	19.0	69.4	100	−29	40	May 4	Oct. 10	159	40	1.75	1.61	2.31	2.49	2.77	3.53	3.54	2.89	3.44	3.13	2.45	1.96	31.87
Essex	Bloomfield	32	15.4	66.5	99	−50	30	May 27	Sept. 17	113	32	2.41	1.90	2.38	3.03	3.09	3.84	4.43	3.87	4.29	3.70	2.96	2.43	38.33
Franklin	Enosburg Falls	38	16.3	67.5	99	−44	39	May 26	Sept. 18	115	39	2.55	2.16	2.91	2.95	3.41	4.16	4.59	3.50	4.19	3.91	3.28	2.60	40.21
Lamoille	Morrisville	12	12.9	63.5	97	−39	13	June 7	Sept. 5	90														
Orange	Chelsea	39	15.8	66.7	100	−40	37	May 30	Sept. 18	111	40	2.55	2.20	2.89	2.96	2.74	3.26	3.30	3.20	3.56	2.98	2.80	2.42	34.86
Orleans	Newport	9	18.1	67.5	93	−40	10	May 14	Sept. 26	135	9	2.71	1.83	2.49	2.72	3.02	4.05	4.76	2.99	3.33	2.99	2.42	2.30	35.61
Rutland	Rutland	22	19.8	69.0	98	−30	17	May 16	Oct. 4	141	22	2.51	1.80	2.56	3.04	3.12	3.85	4.10	3.75	3.92	3.31	3.34	2.13	37.43
	Wells	21	18.4	68.6	95	−33	20	May 12	Sept. 29	140	21	2.51	2.60	3.29	2.59	3.10	3.14	3.72	3.32	3.95	3.29	2.20	2.77	36.48
Washington	Northfield	40	16.1	64.1	98	−41	40	May 21	Sept. 25	127	40	2.12	1.98	2.57	2.55	2.59	3.18	3.42	3.17	3.12	2.79	2.65	2.24	32.38
Windham	Bellows Falls										28	2.80	2.48	3.00	3.13	2.76	3.58	3.85	3.26	3.40	2.61	2.85	2.74	36.46
	Brattleboro	14	21.8	70.3	102	−23	12	May 18	Oct. 2	137	29	3.46	2.93	3.62	3.50	3.11	3.49	3.46	3.50	3.71	3.11	3.66	3.27	40.82
	Somerset	26	17.1	63.6	98	−36	27	June 2	Sept. 16	106	27	4.69	3.68	4.58	4.51	4.16	4.40	4.65	4.43	4.33	4.34	4.85	4.14	52.76
	Vernon	23	21.4	71.5	107	−30	27	May 3	Oct. 16	166	29	3.14	2.68	3.49	3.60	3.03	3.58	3.79	3.98	3.88	2.84	3.47	3.16	40.64
Windsor	Cavendish	34	18.6	68.0	102	−42	27	May 28	Sept. 17	112	36	3.00	2.52	3.11	3.27	3.19	3.85	4.29	3.37	3.79	3.13	3.32	2.87	39.71
	Norwich	26	15.9	67.3	100	−37	26	May 22	do	118	4	2.98	3.29	2.39	2.46	4.44	3.09	3.25	2.98	3.17	3.59	2.13	3.07	36.84
	White River Junction.										25	2.74	2.20	2.82	3.28	2.65	3.22	3.81	3.14	3.28	2.69	2.93	2.53	35.29
	Woodstock	40	18.7	67.6	104	−38	40	May 28	Sept. 21	116	40	2.79	2.56	3.36	3.24	3.16	3.51	3.95	3.29	3.76	2.95	3.15	2.85	38.57
MASSACHUSETTS																								
Barnstable	Falmouth										20	3.78	3.21	4.30	4.04	3.60	4.01	3.36	4.40	4.74	4.16	3.97	3.85	47.42
	Hyannis	24	31.1	70.0	98	−12	22	Apr. 19	Oct. 25	189	40	4.08	3.58	4.28	3.59	3.17	3.37	2.97	3.48	3.54	3.56	3.26	3.92	42.80
	Provincetown	38	31.6	67.0	104	−8	39	Apr. 17	Nov. 3	200	39	3.82	3.24	3.58	3.46	2.85	3.04	2.83	3.07	3.30	3.34	3.07	3.63	39.23
Berkshire	Adams	10	24.8	69.4	98	−23	9	Apr. 28	Oct. 1	156	9	4.35	2.85	3.43	4.00	3.58	4.13	4.39	3.72	4.72	2.81	3.54	3.05	44.57
	Egremont						10	May 28	Sept. 24	119	34	4.13	2.82	2.79	3.35	3.38	4.29	4.39	4.64	4.12	3.31	3.27	2.93	43.42
	Pittsfield	17	23.9	70.8	101	−23	16	May 10	Oct. 1	144	40	3.03	2.71	3.52	3.08	3.05	3.83	4.14	4.16	4.04	3.04	3.13	3.10	40.83
	Williamstown	40	23.2	69.2	97	−26	40	May 6	Oct. 5	152	40	2.65	2.32	3.12	2.96	3.04	3.82	4.05	3.90	3.75	2.90	2.86	2.62	37.99
Bristol	Fall River	40	29.8	71.3	99	−18	40	Apr. 25	Oct. 21	179	40	4.18	3.64	4.24	4.05	3.15	3.36	3.13	3.99	3.56	3.41	3.39	4.27	44.37
	New Bedford	38	30.7	70.7	102	−12	38	Apr. 15	Nov. 4	203	40	3.92	3.43	3.94	3.79	3.10	3.26	2.91	3.73	3.53	3.49	3.26	3.89	42.25
	Somerset	24	28.9	75.0	106	−19	24	Apr. 25	Oct. 15	173	12	3.65	3.66	3.58	3.48	3.50	3.22	4.12	4.03	3.06	3.07	3.23	3.48	42.08
	Taunton	40	27.2	69.7	98	−24	40	May 17	Sept. 28	134	40	4.28	3.59	4.24	4.27	3.27	3.62	3.63	3.87	4.02	3.62	3.53	4.21	46.15
Essex	Haverhill	38	27.3	73.2	104	−19	38	Apr. 28	Oct. 11	166	31	2.89	2.94	3.47	3.57	2.92	3.38	3.62	3.02	3.01	2.84	3.04	3.34	38.04
	Ipswich										28	4.06	3.69	3.92	3.97	2.99	3.72	3.65	3.32	3.92	3.20	3.53	3.75	43.72
	Lawrence	40	25.1	71.4	106	−25	40	May 1	Oct. 11	163	40	3.54	3.30	3.86	3.70	2.77	3.41	3.93	3.18	3.57	2.87	3.11	3.59	40.83
	Middleton										13	3.88	2.98	3.81	3.76	2.54	3.63	2.87	3.46	4.45	3.57	3.17	3.62	41.74
	Rockport	34	29.4	67.9	98	−13	36	Apr. 18	Oct. 30	195	35	3.79	3.28	3.58	3.98	2.79	3.39	3.59	3.01	3.65	3.09	3.42	3.62	41.19
	Swampscott	25	25.9	67.2	96	−19	13	Apr. 26	Oct. 18	175	9	4.71	3.01	4.12	4.02	2.76	4.42	3.46	3.64	4.33	3.39	3.03	3.47	44.36
Franklin	Heath										19	3.63	3.00	3.88	4.01	3.64	4.62	4.10	3.99	4.89	3.58	4.61	3.10	47.05
	Turners Fall	34	24.1	72.1	104	−26	38	May 1	Oct. 8	160	36	3.40	2.70	3.38	3.20	3.34	3.60	3.41	3.80	3.93	2.75	3.30	3.01	39.82
Hampshire	Amherst	40	24.4	71.0	104	−26	38	May 7	Oct. 2	148	40	3.52	3.20	3.81	3.51	3.45	3.76	3.69	4.09	4.36	3.11	3.24	3.35	43.09
	Chesterfield										19	3.49	2.89	3.85	3.97	4.00	4.93	4.20	4.30	5.25	3.67	4.50	3.04	48.09
Hampden	Springfield	30	27.3	73.2	104	−18	30	Apr. 27	Oct. 15	171	40	3.27	3.35	3.57	3.40	3.18	3.75	3.76	4.03	3.76	3.13	3.02	3.05	41.27
	Westfield	12	27.8	72.2	98	−20	80	Apr. 30	Oct. 13	166	33	3.91	3.70	3.83	4.08	3.83	4.30	4.04	4.24	4.27	3.72	4.04	3.73	47.69
	Chester										26	3.63	3.10	3.61	3.71	3.60	4.02	3.90	4.07	4.20	3.44	3.99	3.23	44.50
Middlesex	Ashland										40	3.76	3.59	4.16	3.79	3.05	3.58	3.41	3.64	4.09	3.09	3.39	3.71	43.26
	Bedford	25	25.6	69.6	98	−17					9	2.65	3.43	2.91	3.11	3.23	3.89	4.30	3.34	3.07	2.04	3.22	3.05	38.24
	Concord	40	24.9	69.9	103	−27	34	May 12	Oct. 1	142	40	3.37	3.17	3.61	3.64	3.01	3.61	3.51	3.36	4.07	2.88	3.11	3.48	40.82
	Framingham	40	27.2	71.8	104	−24	39	Apr. 30	Oct. 9	162	40	3.86	3.71	4.24	3.85	3.07	3.61	3.46	3.51	3.92	2.91	3.36	3.85	43.35
	Groton	10	22.5	69.7	97	−17	10	May 9	Sept. 29	143	36	3.45	3.47	4.00	3.85	3.21	3.85	3.50	3.58	4.01	3.10	3.32	3.57	42.91
	Lake Cochituate	39	26.3	71.2	105	−28	40	May 20	Sept. 27	130	32	3.60	3.84	3.98	3.82	2.99	3.42	3.48	3.31	3.39	2.95	3.51	3.81	42.10
	Lowell	40	26.0	72.3	103	−26	39	Apr. 28	Oct. 14	169	40	3.42	3.31	3.81	3.72	2.78	3.35	3.55	3.37	3.79	2.91	3.18	3.49	40.68
	Spot Pond										40	3.98	3.87	4.17	4.07	3.06	3.92	3.41	3.60	3.88	3.06	3.26	3.86	44.14

NEW ENGLAND—Continued

Climatic summary—Continued

County	Station	Temperature: Length of record	Temperature: January average	Temperature: July average	Temperature: Maximum	Temperature: Minimum	Killing frost average dates: Length of record	Killing frost average dates: Last in spring	Killing frost average dates: First in fall	Killing frost average dates: Growing season	Average precipitation: Length of record	January	February	March	April	May	June	July	August	September	October	November	December	Annual
MASSACHUSETTS—Continued		Yr.	°F.	°F.	°F.	°F.	Yr.			Days	Yr.	In.	In.	In.	In.	In.	In.	In.	In.	In.	In.	In.	In.	In.
Middlesex—Cont'd	Waltham										22	3.74	3.54	4.00	4.01	3.13	3.34	3.41	3.27	3.99	2.89	3.03	3.74	42.09
	Weston	18	27.0	70.5	98	−21	16	May 9	Oct. 4	148	11	3.63	2.46	3.79	3.96	3.11	4.16	3.31	3.78	5.04	2.98	3.21	3.35	42.78
Nantucket	Nantucket	40	32.6	68.0	92	−6	40	Apr. 23	Oct. 31	191	40	3.97	3.42	3.90	3.18	2.77	3.22	2.76	3.25	3.02	3.48	3.18	4.05	40.20
Norfolk	Blue Hill	40	26.0	70.0	99	−21	40	Apr. 26	Oct. 19	176	40	4.18	3.82	4.23	4.19	3.46	3.89	4.00	4.12	4.13	3.46	3.46	4.07	47.01
	Franklin										17	3.97	2.84	3.64	3.64	2.82	3.70	3.32	4.35	3.98	3.24	2.94	3.49	41.93
Plymouth	Brockton	25	31.0	72.2	103	−19	24	Apr. 23	Oct. 16	176	32	3.29	3.19	3.45	3.44	3.06	3.00	3.63	3.46	3.43	3.07	2.94	3.49	39.45
	East Wareham	16	29.8	70.0	99	−22	10	May 4	Oct. 13	162	13	4.20	3.19	3.99	3.92	2.70	4.06	2.96	3.93	4.88	3.88	3.82	4.32	45.85
	Hingham										35	3.85	3.81	4.09	3.75	3.22	3.58	3.92	3.63	3.63	3.58	3.39	3.98	44.43
	Middleboro	17	27.6	69.6	99	−26	16	May 14	Sept. 26	135	40	4.03	3.64	4.08	3.83	2.80	3.29	3.39	3.44	3.60	3.33	3.20	3.87	42.50
	Plymouth	37	29.4	69.3	98	−12	38	Apr. 26	Oct. 19	176	40	4 42	4.06	4.52	4.26	3.12	3.60	3.45	3.70	3.91	3.73	3.76	4.34	46.87
Suffolk	Boston	40	29.8	72.4	104	−18	40	Apr. 13	Oct. 29	199	40	3.39	3.13	3.60	3.67	2.87	3.22	3.27	3.28	3.45	2.78	2.87	3.41	38.94
	Chestnut Hill	40	28.2	72.1	106	−19	40	Apr. 27	Oct. 18	174	40	4.05	3.96	4.13	4.10	3.08	3.77	3.46	3.66	3.93	3.18	3.32	3.88	44.52
	Thompsons Island	16	28.2	70.6	101	−13	18	Apr. 18	Oct. 28	193														
Worcester	Ashburnham										2	2.40	1.47	2.25	2.32	1.91	3.87	5.27	2.04	1.46	4.10	3.88	3.38	34.35
	Boylston										40	3.89	3.78	4.20	3.91	3.25	3.95	3.89	3.79	4.24	3.15	3.64	3.88	45.57
	Clinton	37	25.6	70.3	100	−22	36	May 2	Oct. 10	161	37	4.01	3.71	4.20	3.92	3.25	4.17	3.83	3.81	4.19	3.27	3.69	3.95	46.00
	Fitchburg	40	25.1	71.4	103	−17	37	Apr. 30	Oct. 13	166	40	4.51	3.08	3.84	3.57	3.19	3.87	3.78	3.64	4.06	3.02	3.26	3.50	43.32
	Hardwick										19	3.60	2.72	3.49	4.07	3.31	4.77	4.35	4.05	5.13	3.24	3.64	3.14	45.51
	Hubbardston										19	3.23	2.56	3.77	3.89	3.29	4.54	4.38	3.77	5.25	3.48	4.09	2.97	45.22
	Jefferson										39	4.11	4.06	4.42	4.12	3.40	4.13	4.00	4.22	4.40	3.42	3.69	4.04	48.01
	Milford										24	3.51	2.94	3.47	3.58	2.78	3.81	3.91	3.95	4.20	2.92	3.47	3.25	41.79
	Mount Wachusett										11				4.49	3.62	4.35	3.74	4.74	5.52	4.03			30.49
	Northbridge										40	3.75	3.30	4.12	3.85	3.20	3.71	3.80	3.95	3.96	3.24	3.65	3.71	44.24
	Petersham										23	3.82	3.21	3.52	3.63	3.19	4.34	3.92	3.96	4.78	3.12	3.93	3.26	44.68
	Princeton										40	3.76	3.56	3.88	3.86	3.30	3.77	3.95	3.92	4.16	3.29	3.46	3.66	44.57
	Rutland	22	22.0	68.6	100	−23	24	May 6	Oct. 6	153	22	3.39	3.33	3.59	3.67	3.21	3.89	4.26	4.18	3.78	3.21	3.06	3.31	42.88
	Sterling										40	3.61	3.61	4.07	3.82	3.19	3.80	3.66	3.59	3.98	3.15	3.44	3.80	43.72
	Webster										40	3.47	3.32	3.85	3.58	3.04	3.90	3.45	3.84	3.95	3.01	3.09	3.68	42.18
	Westboro	26	27.2	72.4	105	−22	26	Apr. 28	Oct. 9	164	26	3.49	3.73	4.32	3.95	3.56	3.81	3.90	3.54	3.66	3.10	3.60	3.58	44.24
	Worcester	40	25.8	71.1	102	−20	40	do	Oct. 14	169	40	3.19	2.67	3.67	3.38	3.07	3.54	3.58	3.61	3.89	2.87	3.03	3.24	39.74
	Worcester (Clark University).	12	27.0	71.3	99	−18					6	4.60	2.81	4.38	3.79	3.34	4.32	2.46	3.81	3.04	2.64	2.73	3.56	41.48

RHODE ISLAND																								
Bristol	Bristol	26	28.8	69.7	92	-12	26	Apr. 16	Nov. 4	202	28	3.71	3.73	3.98	3.81	2.94	3.09	2.94	3.30	2.67	2.75	2.79	3.89	39.60
Kent	Greene	15	26.8	68.9	102	-16	16	May 28	Sept. 18	113	12	3.79	3.28	3.44	3.65	3.48	4.09	4.57	4.40	3.62	2.63	3.56	3.59	44.10
Newport	Block Island	40	32.2	68.7	92	-10	40	Apr. 10	Nov. 14	218	40	3.56	3.17	3.77	3.50	3.00	2.91	2.61	3.42	3.02	3.07	2.99	3.79	38.81
Providence	Pawtucket	38	30.2	73.5	101	-18	40	Apr. 13	Oct. 28	198	39	4.18	4.01	4.33	3.95	3.18	3.41	3.74	4.00	3.84	3.11	3.38	4.21	45.34
	Providence	40	29.5	72.5	100	-17	40	Apr. 17	Oct. 26	192	40	3.67	3.24	3.78	3.56	2.94	3.16	3.25	3.40	3.62	2.81	2.84	3.57	39.84
Washington	Kingston	40	28.1	69.2	99	-22	40	May 8	Oct. 8	153	40	4.76	4.13	4.65	4.65	3.64	3.61	3.22	4.32	4.02	3.58	3.96	4.88	49.42
	Narragansett Pier	20	28.7	69.0	97	-13	20	Apr. 21	Oct. 14	176	20	3.93	3.82	4.40	4.19	3.36	2.93	3.14	3.56	3.33	3.29	3.14	4.28	43.37
CONNECTICUT																								
Fairfield	Bridgeport	40	29.4	72.9	102	-20	39	Apr. 26	Oct. 16	173	40	3.99	3.73	4.20	4.07	3.38	3.55	3.92	4.54	4.08	3.63	3.29	3.98	46.36
	Norwalk	40	27.8	72.8	101	-22	40	May 2	Oct. 12	163	40	3.65	3.56	4.10	3.81	3.44	3.54	3.85	4.62	4.21	3.55	3.13	3.76	45.22
Hartford	Canton	24	24.7	69.8	100	-26	24	May 24	Oct. 6	165	24	3.61	3.56	4.06	3.99	3.83	3.98	4.11	4.03	4.41	4.00	3.27	4.06	46.91
	East Hartland										22	3.96	3.40	3.88	3.95	4.17	4.70	4.03	4.54	4.69	3.83	4.12	3.27	48.54
	Hartford	40	27.9	72.5	101	-24	40	Apr. 19	Oct. 18	182	40	3.54	3.33	3.87	3.66	3.43	3.49	3.93	4.00	3.86	3.09	3.08	3.58	42.86
	Southington	23	27.0	70.9	100	-27	22	May 7	Oct. 5	151	23	3.33	3.64	4.23	3.49	3.28	3.26	3.71	3.77	4.00	3.50	2.94	4.24	43.39
Litchfield	Falls Village	23	25.3	71.0	103	-26	24	May 19	Sept. 27	131	34	2.93	3.17	3.31	3.32	3.52	4.24	4.67	4.21	4.57	3.12	3.07	3.12	43.25
	Cream Hill	40	24.1	69.4	98	-26	40	May 6	Oct. 8	155	40	3.72	3.37	3.76	3.54	3.89	4.29	4.58	4.36	4.56	3.62	3.46	3.60	46.75
	Torrington	20	23.6	70.2	103	-22	20	May 11	Sept. 30	142	21	3.44	3.18	3.69	4.05	3.60	4.48	4.29	4.34	4.42	4.99	3.11	3.44	47.03
New Haven	New Haven	40	29.7	72.6	101	-15	40	Apr. 11	Oct. 23	195	40	3.86	3.68	4.22	3.96	3.50	3.81	3.59	3.86	3.81	3.37	3.26	4.04	44.96
	Waterbury	40	28.6	73.3	105	-20	40	May 1	Oct. 11	163	40	3.75	3.60	4.12	3.92	3.62	3.72	4.11	4.18	4.03	3.72	3.22	3.73	45.72
New London	Colchester	40	26.9	71.0	100	-18	40	May 4	Oct. 7	156	39	4.22	3.91	4.62	4.54	3.64	3.83	3.95	4.44	4.03	3.65	3.77	4.34	48.94
	Lake Konomoc										38	4.35	3.88	4.48	4.31	3.29	3.72	3.54	4.44	4.06	3.61	3.57	4.58	47.83
	New London	40	30.1	72.3	99	-17	40	Apr. 14	Oct. 26	195	40	4.13	3.68	3.99	3.86	3.31	3.54	3.46	4.21	3.59	3.24	3.37	3.93	44.31
	Voluntown	26	26.8	69.8	102	-29	26	May 23	Sept. 25	125	26	3.89	3.85	4.36	3.92	3.18	3.17	3.73	3.55	3.64	3.11	3.19	4.18	43.77
Tolland	Storrs	38	26.6	69.8	101	-20	31	May 5	Oct. 7	155	39	3.57	3.28	4.29	3.65	3.31	3.34	4.11	4.11	4.13	3.23	3.14	3.63	43.79
Windham	Danielson	20	26.7	71.2	99	-27	19	May 4	Oct. 5	154	15	4.01	3.32	3.68	3.21	3.07	3.12	3.59	3.99	4.03	3.04	3.16	3.78	42.00
	North Grosvenordale	34	25.4	70.0	103	-25	35	May 10	Sept. 30	143	35	3.53	3.66	4.21	3.80	3.10	3.45	3.63	3.90	3.60	3.15	3.31	3.72	43.06

NEW ENGLAND—Continued

Precipitation and temperature—State unit values

[This tabulation gives the mean annual, mean monthly, and average seasonal precipitation and the percentage of normal precipitation for each year, 1886–1938, and the mean annual temperatures, 1903–38, for the 6 New England States: Maine, New Hampshire, Vermont, Massachusetts, Rhode Island, and Connecticut]

Precipitation		Precipitation	
Year	Mean	Year	Mean
	In.		*In.*
1886	45.50	1913	40.62
1887	47.54	1914	34.78
1888	55.76	1915	40.73
1889	49.37	1916	40.50
1890	50.33	1917	39.80
1891	44.95	1918	39.14
1892	38.79	1919	43.03
1893	40.14	1920	48.63
1894	35.85	1921	37.37
1895	41.27	1922	42.37
1896	40.97	1923	40.05
1897	46.79	1924	35.62
1898	50.66	1925	41.23
1899	40.39	1926	39.19
1900	45.69	1927	45.63
1901	47.92	1928	40.70
1902	46.94	1929	39.55
1903	41.78	1930	34.11
1904	40.05	1931	41.28
1905	36.96	1932	43.61
1906	40.55	1933	44.70
1907	43.24	1934	43.01
1908	35.62	1935	38.54
1909	40.56	1936	50.20
1910	35.52	1937	47.33
1911	38.76	1938	50.65
1912	41.88		

Precipitation	
Month	Mean
	In.
January	3.60
February	3.21
March	3.65
April	3.32
May	3.34
June	3.44
July	3.78
August	3.87
September	3.80
October	3.50
November	3.48
December	3.37
Annual	42.36

Season	Average
	In.
Winter	10.18
Spring	10.31
Summer	11.09
Fall	10.78

Annual precipitation (in percent of normal)		Annual precipitation (in percent of normal)	
Year	Percent	Year	Percent
1886	107	1918	92
1887	112	1919	102
1888	132	1920	115
1889	117	1921	88
1890	119	1922	100
1891	106	1923	95
1892	92	1924	84
1893	95	1925	97
1894	85	1926	93
1895	97	1927	108
1896	97	1928	96
1897	110	1929	93
1898	120	1930	81
1899	95	1931	97
1900	108	1932	103
1901	113	1933	106
1902	111	1934	102
1903	99	1935	91
1904	95	1936	119
1905	87	1937	112
1906	96	1938	120
1907	102		
1908	84		
1909	96		
1910	84		
1911	92		
1912	99		
1913	96		
1914	82		
1915	96		
1916	96		
1917	94		

Temperature		Temperature	
Year	Mean	Year	Mean
	°*F.*		°*F.*
1903	45.8	1908	46.7
1904	42.8	1909	46.0
1905	44.6	1910	46.5
1906	46.4	1911	46.5
1907	44.1	1912	45.4
		1913	48.0
		1914	44.8
		1915	47.0
		1916	45.2
		1917	43.2
		1918	45.0
		1919	46.3
		1920	45.0
		1921	47.3
		1922	46.0
		1923	44.6
		1924	44.6
		1925	45.6
		1926	43.4
		1927	46.4
		1928	45.9
		1929	45.8
		1930	46.9
		1931	47.9
		1932	47.1
		1933	46.3
		1934	45.2
		1935	45.4
		1936	45.8
		1937	47.4
		1938	47.2

Dates of last killing frost in spring and first in fall, with length of growing season

Year	Orono, Maine			Concord, N. H.			Northfield, Vt.			Boston, Mass.			Providence, R. I.			Hartford, Conn.		
	Last in spring	First in fall	Growing season[1]	Last in spring	First in fall	Growing season[1]	Last in spring	First in fall	Growing season[1]	Last in spring	First in fall	Growing season[1]	Last in spring	First in fall	Growing season[1]	Last in spring	First in fall	Growing season[1]
			Days			*Days*			*Days*			*Days*			*Days*			*Days*
1899	May 17	Sept. 16	122	May 16	Sept. 14	121	May 17	Sept. 16	122	Apr. 6	Oct. 3	180	Apr. 13	Oct. 2	172	Apr. 22	Oct. 2	163
1900	do	Sept. 19	125	May 29	Sept. 19	113	May 11	Sept. 19	131	Apr. 11	Oct. 20	192	May 10	Oct. 20	163	May 11	Oct. 18	160
1901	Apr. 27	Sept. 26	152	May 2	Sept. 26	147	May 6	Sept. 20	137	Mar. 31	Oct. 26	209	Apr. 14	Oct. 29	198	Apr. 1	Oct. 21	203
1902	May 21	Sept. 25	127	May 21	Sept. 6	108	May 21	Sept. 6	108	Mar. 26	Oct. 22	210	Apr. 19	Oct. 22	186	Apr. 5	Oct. 22	200
1903	May 26	Sept. 30	127	Apr. 6	Sept. 30	177	May 25	Sept. 8	106	Apr. 6	do	199	Apr. 18	Oct. 25	190	May 2	Oct. 25	176
1904	May 6	Sept. 22	139	Apr. 23	Sept. 22	152	May 2	Sept. 7	128	Apr. 20	Oct. 28	191	Apr. 20	Sept. 23	156	Apr. 22	Sept. 23	154
1905	June 7	Sept. 15	100	Apr. 24	Oct. 7	166	May 31	Sept. 14	106	Apr. 19	Oct. 26	190	Apr. 19	Sept. 27	161	Apr. 19	Oct. 26	190
1906	May 22	Sept. 25	126	May 21	Sept. 25	127	June 12	Sept. 24	104	Apr. 3	Oct. 12	192	Apr. 9	Oct. 14	188	Apr. 7	Oct. 13	189
1907	May 26	Oct. 3	130	May 23	Oct. 2	132	May 26	Oct. 2	129	Apr. 21	Oct. 22	184	Apr. 20	Oct. 22	185	May 12	Oct. 19	160
1908	May 16	Sept. 15	122	Apr. 22	Oct. 5	166	June 3	Sept. 15	104	do	Nov. 2	195	Apr. 21	Oct. 13	175	Apr. 21	Oct. 13	175
1909	June 2	Oct. 17	137	May 1	Oct. 16	168	May 26	Aug. 31	97	Apr. 29	Oct. 20	174	Apr. 29	Oct. 20	174	Apr. 29	Oct. 14	168
1910	June 5	Sept. 23	110	June 5	Oct. 8	125	June 5	Sept. 30	117	Mar. 19	Oct. 31	226	Apr. 13	Oct. 29	199	Apr. 13	Oct. 29	199
1911	May 17	Sept. 14	120	May 6	Sept. 14	131	May 17	Sept. 14	120	Apr. 18	Oct. 8	173	Apr. 21	do	191	May 4	Oct 8	157
1912	June 11	Sept. 29	110	May 5	Oct. 3	151	June 10	Oct. 9	121	Apr. 9	Oct. 16	190	Apr. 11	Nov. 3	206	Apr. 9	Oct. 21	195
1913	May 18	Sept. 15	120	May 12	Sept. 15	126	do	Sept. 10	92	Apr. 10	Nov. 1	205	Apr. 10	Oct. 23	196	Apr. 20	Oct. 23	186
1914	May 17	Sept. 28	134	May 16	Sept. 29	136	May 7	Sept. 29	145	Apr. 14	Oct. 28	197	Apr. 17	Oct. 28	194	Apr. 14	Sept. 29	168
1915	June 3	Sept. 26	115	May 15	Oct. 4	142	May 30	Oct. 11	134	Apr. 4	Nov. 18	228	Apr. 5	Nov. 4	213	Apr. 5	Oct. 25	203
1916	May 1	Oct. 2	154	Apr. 25	Oct. 2	160	May 10	Oct. 1	144	Apr. 9	Nov. 6	211	Apr. 10	Nov. 7	211	Apr. 9	Oct. 18	190
1917	May 31	Sept. 23	115	May 4	Sept. 11	130	May 16	Sept. 23	130	Apr. 11	Nov. 5	208	Apr. 14	Oct. 31	200	May 4	Sept. 11	132
1918	May 5	Sept. 11	129	Apr. 20	Oct. 8	171	June 20	Sept. 11	83	Apr. 12	Nov. 12	214	Apr. 20	Nov. 12	206	Apr. 20	Oct. 19	182
1919	May 10	Sept. 27	140	May 1	do	160	May 1	Sept. 27	149	Apr. 26	Oct. 30	187	Apr. 26	Nov. 3	191	Apr. 26	Oct. 8	165
1920	May 17	Sept. 21	127	May 6	Nov. 6	18	May 17	Oct. 13	149	Apr. 11	Nov. 11	214	Apr. 11	Nov. 13	216	Apr. 11	Nov. 11	214
1921	May 24	Sept. 21	120	Apr. 2	Oct. 26	207	May 19	Oct. 9	143	Apr. 2	Nov. 26	238	Apr. 2	Oct. 26	207	do	Oct. 26	198
1922	May 5	Sept. 19	137	Mar. 30	Sept. 26	180	May 1	Sept. 26	148	Apr. 21	Oct. 19	181	Apr. 22	Oct. 19	180	Apr. 24	Oct. 14	173
1923	Apr. 30	Sept. 15	138	Apr. 15	Oct. 7	175	May 24	Sept. 15	114	Apr. 19	Nov. 1	196	Apr. 19	Nov. 1	196	May 11	Oct. 7	149
1924	May 3	Sept. 26	146	Apr. 17	Sept. 25	161	May 23	Sept. 25	125	Apr. 2	Oct. 23	204	Apr. 3	Oct. 23	203	Apr. 3	Oct. 14	194
1925	May 19	Oct. 20	154	Apr. 21	Sept. 23	155	May 19	Sept. 26	130	Apr. 21	Oct. 31	193	Apr. 21	Oct. 11	173	Apr. 6	do	191
1926	May 5	Oct. 16	164	May 5	Oct. 16	164	May 21	Oct. 16	148	Apr. 20	Nov. 5	199	Apr. 20	Oct. 22	185	Apr. 14	Oct. 22	191
1927	June 28			Apr. 25	Oct. 11	169	May 8	Oct. 11	156	Apr. 9	Nov. 8	213	Apr. 24	Oct. 31	190	Apr. 5	Oct. 31	209
1928	Apr. 25	Sept. 25	153	Apr. 16	Sept. 27	164	May 15	Sept. 10	118	Apr. 17	Oct. 27	193	Apr. 17	Oct. 27	193	Apr. 21	Oct. 27	189
1929	May 23	Sept. 20	120	Apr. 14	Sept. 20	159	May 23	Sept. 20	120	Apr. 14	Nov. 22	222	Apr. 11	Oct. 9	181	Apr. 14	Oct. 10	179
1930	May 15	Oct. 2	140	Apr. 24	Oct. 21	180	May 12	Oct. 4	145	Apr. 24	Oct. 21	180	Apr. 10	Oct. 21	194	Apr. 24	Oct. 21	180
1931	May 13	Sept. 30	140	May 2	Oct. 10	161	May 2	Oct. 19	170	Apr. 12	Nov. 7	209	Mar. 28	Nov. 7	224	Apr. 12	Nov. 7	209
1932	May 24	Oct. 1	130	May 24	Oct. 14	143	June 8	Oct. 1	115	Apr. 17	Nov. 4	201	Apr. 28	Nov. 4	190	Apr. 17	Nov. 4	201
1933	May 9	Sept. 16	130	May 6	do	161	May 18	Oct. 3	138	Apr. 23	Oct. 26	186	Apr. 23	Oct. 26	186	Apr. 28	Oct. 15	170
1934	June 8	Oct. 2	116	May 9	Oct. 10	154	June 8	Oct. 2	116	Apr. 5	Oct. 13	191	Apr. 29	Nov. 2	187	Apr. 29	Nov. 15	200
1935	May 5	Sept. 17	135	May 24	Oct. 3	132	May 24	Sept. 17	116	Apr. 18	Oct. 25	190	Apr. 18	Nov. 19	215	May 24	Oct. 8	137
1936	May 22	Sept. 26	127	May 22	Sept. 30	131	May 22	Sept. 26	127	May 16	Oct. 13	150	Apr. 25	Oct. 27	185	Apr. 23	Oct. 25	185
1937	Apr. 27	Sept. 9	135	Apr. 30	Oct. 3	156	May 16	Oct. 3	140	Apr. 3	Oct. 15	195	Apr. 4	Oct. 17	196	Apr. 1	Oct. 9	191
1938	May 5	Oct. 2	150	Apr. 24	do	162	May 9	Sept. 9	123	Apr. 11	Nov. 16	219	Apr. 11	Nov. 15	218	Apr. 6	Oct. 8	185
Mean	May 18	Sept. 25	130	May 3	do	153	May 21	Sept. 25	127	Apr. 13	Oct. 29	199	Apr. 17	Oct. 26	192	Apr. 19	Oct. 18	182
Extremes	Apr. 25[2]	Sept. 9[4]	[6] 100	Mar. 30[2]	Sept. 6[4]	[6] 113	May 1[2]	Sept. 6[4]	[6] 83	Mar. 19[2]	Oct. 3[4]	[6] 150	Mar. 28[2]	Sept. 23[4]	[6] 156	Apr. 1[2]	Sept. 11[4]	[6] 130
	June 28[3]	Oct. 20[5]	[7] 164	June 5[3]	Nov. 6[5]	[7] 207	June 20[3]	Oct. 19[5]	[7] 170	May 16[3]	Nov. 26[5]	[7] 228	May 10[3]	Nov. 19[5]	[7] 224	May 24[3]	Nov. 15[5]	[7] 214

[1] Number of days between last killing frost in spring and first in fall.
[2] Earliest date in spring.
[3] Latest date in spring.
[4] Earliest date in fall.
[5] Latest date in fall.
[6] Shortest growing season.
[7] Longest growing season.

NEW ENGLAND
AVERAGE JULY TEMPERATURE

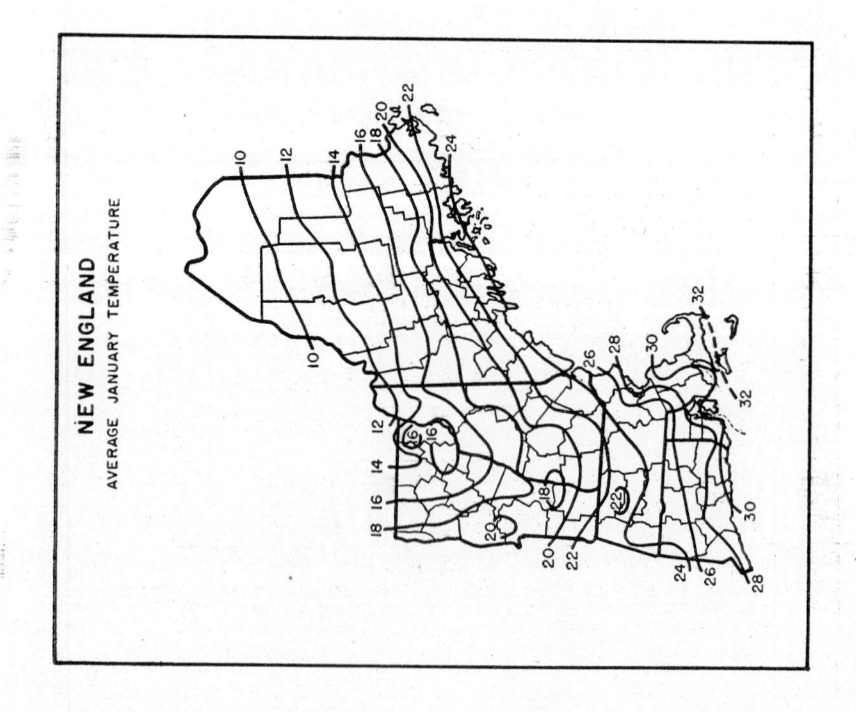

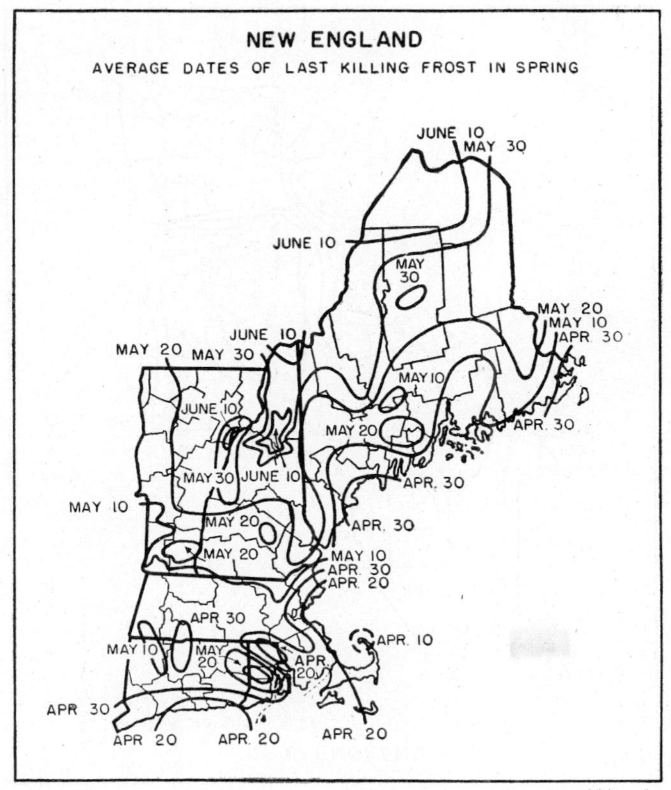
NEW ENGLAND
AVERAGE DATES OF LAST KILLING FROST IN SPRING
JUNE 10
MAY 30
JUNE 10
MAY 30
MAY 20
MAY 10
APR. 30
MAY 20
JUNE 10
MAY 30
MAY 10
JUNE 10
MAY 20
APR. 30
MAY 30
JUNE 10
APR. 30
MAY 10
MAY 20
APR. 30
MAY 20
MAY 10
APR. 30
APR. 20
APR 30
APR. 10
MAY 10
MAY 20
APR. 20
APR 30
APR 20
APR. 20
APR 20

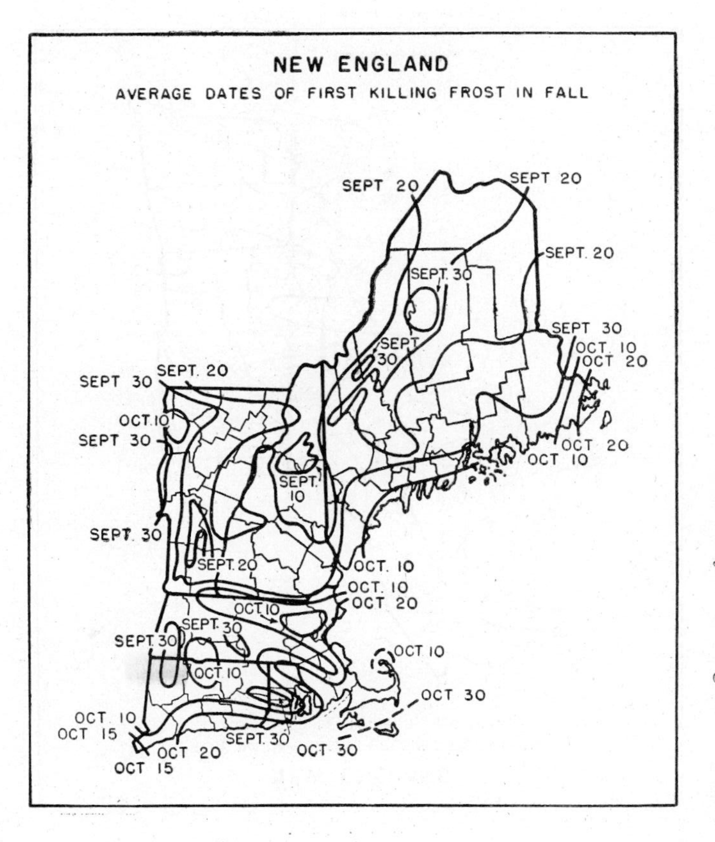
NEW ENGLAND
AVERAGE DATES OF FIRST KILLING FROST IN FALL
SEPT 20
SEPT 20
SEPT. 20
SEPT. 30
SEPT 30
SEPT 30
OCT. 10
OCT 20
SEPT. 20
OCT. 10
SEPT 30
OCT 20
OCT 10
SEPT. 10
SEPT. 30
SEPT. 20
OCT. 10
OCT. 10
OCT 20
OCT. 10
SEPT. 30
SEPT. 30
OCT 10
OCT 10
OCT 30
OCT. 10
OCT 15
SEPT. 30
OCT 20
OCT 30
OCT 15

298737°—41——64

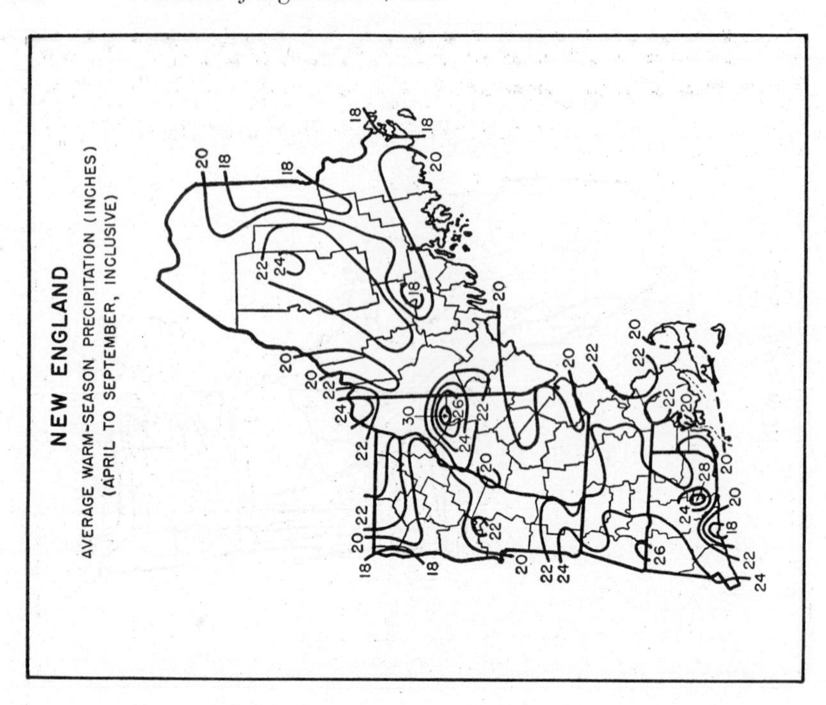
NEW ENGLAND
AVERAGE WARM-SEASON PRECIPITATION (INCHES)
(APRIL TO SEPTEMBER, INCLUSIVE)

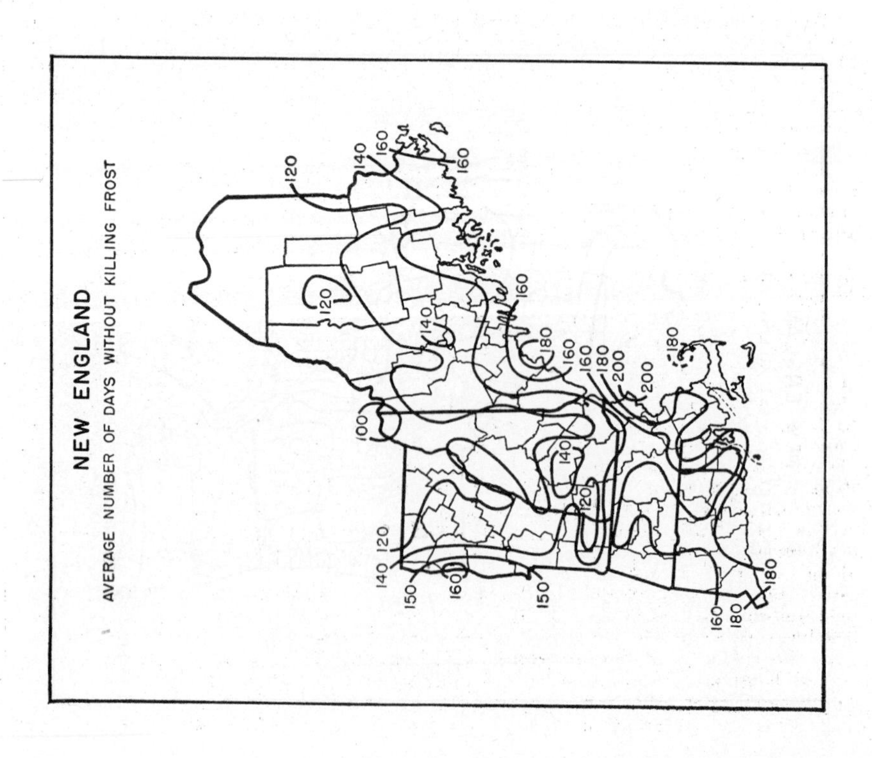
NEW ENGLAND
AVERAGE NUMBER OF DAYS WITHOUT KILLING FROST

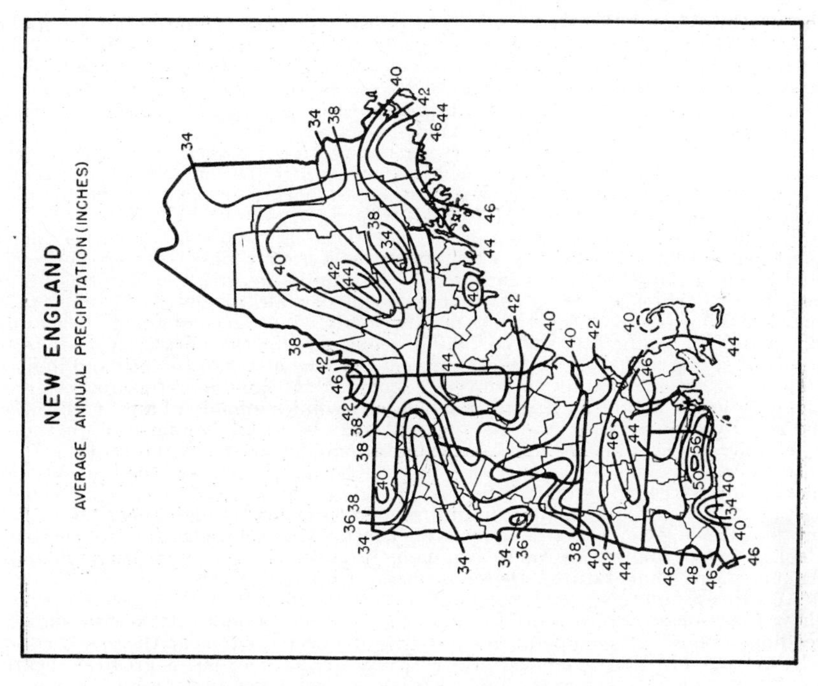

SUPPLEMENTARY CLIMATIC NOTES FOR NEW ENGLAND

The drainage systems of New England are dominated by the moderately high elevations of the northern parts, notably the White Mountains, where rise the Merrimac River and the rivers of western Maine. To the eastward and northeastward of this mountain group a vast forested and lake-studded upland extends for 200 miles. Here rise the Kennebec and the Penobscot. Still farther east are the high plains of Aroostook, where the favorable climate and loose, open, easily cultivated soil are peculiarly well suited to potato production.

West of the White Mountains is the valley of the Connecticut River, which rises in extreme northern New Hampshire and drains parts of four States—New Hampshire, Vermont, Massachusetts, and Connecticut. The valley embraces approximately 11,000 square miles. The Connecticut, like most New England rivers, in their upper valleys at least, is divided into long, smooth reaches and short rapids, or falls, favorable for power development. The best grass and tillage lands lie along the terraced slopes of the Connecticut River.

From the White Mountains southward to the Monadnock section of southwestern New Hampshire are scores of wooded peaks of lesser heights covering a smaller area. Farther west, the Green Mountains form a rugged, forested highland 10 to 20 miles wide, extending southward to the ranges of western Massachusetts and Connecticut. The uplands of western Connecticut descend gently to Long Island Sound, which separates the region from the moraines of Long Island. Sands and clays from melting glaciers fill the heads of many bays, forming plains and tidal estuaries. The moraine reappears farther east in the hills from Woods Hole to Plymouth; and still farther east, the terminal moraine and glacial wash form Cape Cod.

The glacial depressions west of Plymouth are unsurpassed for production of cranberries, which thrive in the rich, black, peaty soil. In the Boston basin, along the lower Merrimac Valley, and from the vicinity of Worcester northward into New Hampshire and southward into Connecticut, the terrain is diversified by numerous drumlins; in Boston Bay these appear as islands, and the barrier beaches formed by their dissolution are used as shore resorts.

In this region of abundant rainfall the rivers flow freely at all seasons.

New England, lying in middle latitudes, comes within the influence of constant conflicts between cold, dry air masses flowing out of the great subpolar region to the northwest and the warmer, moisture-bearing, tropical marine air from the south. The tendency of most of the general cyclonic disturbances to skirt the polar front brings their paths of movement through this region and results in a more or less regular succession of biweekly storms of snow or rain, with intervening 2- or 3-day periods of fair weather, typically with warm west to southwest winds in summer and cold northwesterly winds in winter.

Topography and configuration of the coast present varied influences within the moving air masses. Thus in winter there is little permanent snow cover in the lowlands near the southern coast, whereas the mountains and the forested uplands to the north are buried deep all winter long.

The most active precipitation-producing storms are those in which the moist southeast or east winds flow over the uplands and the air mass is forced aloft over cold resident air to condensation levels. In winter the great snowstorms occur usually with northeasters; as a wedge of cold dry air displaces the moist air, they are followed by the prevailing northwesterly winds, accompanied by clearing sky and with temperature often falling below zero in the north. The easterly winds of spring and early summer, however, may be of shallow depth and limited trajectory, serving mainly to convert a hot day into one of refreshing coolness along the coast and often penetrating only a few miles inland. Land-sea breezes, induced by an unbalanced thermal gradient, may be strictly confined to the shore.

Winter becomes increasingly and rapidly more severe from the southern and eastern coastal areas to the northern interior, but in midsummer the heat may be more oppressive and temperature readings higher in some of these same inland sections. In fact, average maximum temperatures are as high (near 80° F.) in interior Maine, even far to the north, as in central Massachusetts and Connecticut. Cool, pleasant nights are more common, however, in the northern highlands. Annual mean temperatures, therefore, have little significance.

An expression of the interior winter severity is afforded by the records, which show that some extreme northern stations have 60 or more days with subzero readings, while such temperatures are rare or never occur near the south coast. The average annual number of days with maxima of over 90° is greatest (nearly 14) in interior Massachusetts, but there have been a few instances of maximum readings of near or slightly over 100° as far north as Berlin, N. H. The coolest weather in summer is found on the extreme eastern Maine coast.

The last killing frosts in spring occur usually between May 3 and 15 in eastern Maine and a few days later in central New Hampshire and Vermont. In the cultivated parts of extreme northern Maine, New Hampshire, and Vermont, killing frosts may occur as late as the first 10 days in June. In interior Massachusetts and Connecticut, destructive frosts may come as late as May 10, a little earlier in the Connecticut Valley, and 15 to 20 days earlier along the South Shore; on the immediate coast, frosts are seldom recorded later than the end of April.

The first killing frosts in the fall normally range from sometime during the first half of September in the north to 1 or 2 weeks later in the central part and late October near the southern coast. In individual years the first occurrence of frost may vary 3 to 4 weeks from the average dates.

Thus the average length of the growing season ranges from 100 to 125 days on northern upland farms, through about 150 in central areas, to as many as 175 to 200 days near the coastal borders of Massachusetts, Connecticut, and Rhode Island. However, in special exposures, such as the cranberry bogs and lowland flat valleys with excessive nocturnal radiation, they occur later in spring and earlier in fall than the latitude and geographic position would indicate.

New England may be considered fortunate in that precipitation is rather evenly distributed throughout the 12 months in all six States. The lowest annual averages are less than 32 inches in the Champlain Valley and in northern Maine, while they exceed 45 in the area from the southern Connecticut-New York line eastward beyond New Haven and in some of the higher regions where mountain slopes receive the rain-bearing winds. The seasonal variation is not marked, except in the north and in mountain sections, where the winter average is generally less than half that of summer. The variations from month to month, however, may be extreme; there have been instances in all States of months with no measurable rainfall, while other months, in contrast, have had more than 15 inches.

Precipitation occurs on an average about 1 day in 3, but it is somewhat more frequent than this on the high terrain, and in extreme northern New Hampshire nearly half the days of the year have a measurable amount. Within a single 24-hour period on rare occasions there have been amounts exceeding 6 inches and in a few instances over 8 inches in southern Connecticut and southern Vermont.

Severe droughts over large areas are uncommon, but local shortages of rainfall sometimes occasion inconvenience by lowering ground-water supplies.

The average seasonal snowfall decreases rapidly from north to south and from west to east. In the south normally 26 to 40 inches may be expected, but there may be four times that much near the northern boundary. This winter storage is a factor of prime importance when rapid spring thaws occur, especially if accompanied by heavy rains.

Severe coastal disturbances occur when deep low-pressure areas pass over or near the southern part of New England. Occasionally in early fall a storm of tropical origin, perhaps a hurricane, may reach the coast with its intensity maintained because it has passed over water and not been diminished by land friction. Such was the historic meteorological catastrophe of September 21, 1938. In summer, local damage to crops, pleasure craft, and summer tent colonies by thunderstorms, line squalls, and hailstorms is rather frequent. Hail is the dread of the tobacco growers of the lower Connecticut Valley. Tornadoes of the western type are not unknown, but they are of very rare occurrence and none have been recorded near the coast. Waterspouts, however, occasionally develop offshore.

The average percentage of the possible amount of sunshine ranges in southern and eastern sections from 50 to 58, but the highlands of New Hampshire and Vermont and, to a less extent, the Berkshires, rise within a cloudy belt that extends eastward from the Great Lakes. The percentage in these areas is 44 to 50.

The prevalence of dense fog on the northeastern coast, especially in summer, is well known, but its frequency diminishes considerably toward Massachusetts Bay. At Eastport, Maine, the average annual number of days with fog exceeds 60, but in interior northern parts there may be less than one-fifth as many fogs, and these are mostly the ground fogs of early morning.

MARK T. NESMITH, *Associate Meteorologist and Acting Climatic Section Director for New England, Weather Bureau, Boston.*

NEW JERSEY

Climatic summary

County	Station	Temperature					Killing frost average dates				Average precipitation													
		Length of record	January average	July average	Maximum	Minimum	Length of record	Last in spring	First in fall	Growing season [1]	Length of record	January	February	March	April	May	June	July	August	September	October	November	December	Annual
		Yr.	*°F.*	*°F.*	*°F.*	*°F.*	*Yr.*			*Days*	*Yr.*	*In.*	*In.*	*In.*	*In.*	*In.*	*In.*	*In.*	*In.*	*In.*	*In.*	*In.*	*In.*	*In.*
Atlantic	Atlantic City	40	34.8	72.9	104	−9	40	Apr. 6	Nov. 7	215	40	3.48	3.21	3.55	3.15	2.91	3.19	3.67	4.69	3.40	3.05	2.67	3.94	40.91
	Hammonton	7	36.0	76.3	103	−5	10	Apr. 23	Oct. 22	182	25	4.08	3.22	4.03	3.66	3.38	4.13	4.57	4.50	3.97	3.59	2.89	3.60	45.62
	Northfield										31	3.50	2.90	3.32	3.38	3.21	3.36	3.98	4.49	3.46	2.93	2.65	3.60	40.78
	Pleasantville	15	34.4	73.4	106	−11	16	Apr. 22	Oct. 15	176	40	3.42	3.10	3.36	3.45	3.15	3.55	4.00	4.99	3.57	3.29	2.73	3.95	42.56
Bergen	Highwood	26	28.8	72.1	103	−28	27	Apr. 26	Oct. 11	168	28	3.74	3.95	3.93	3.62	3.44	4.04	4.63	4.92	3.88	4.05	2.91	3.87	46.98
	Mahwah										11	3.74	3.58	4.69	4.35	3.59	4.29	3.70	4.77	4.60	4.46	2.96	3.27	48.00
	New Milford										20	3.48	2.97	3.54	3.59	3.42	4.05	4.81	4.78	4.56	3.07	3.14	3.02	44.43
	Ridgefield	21	28.5	72.9	103	−17	20	Apr. 21	Oct. 15	177	21	3.34	3.27	3.74	3.35	3.58	4.28	4.82	4.27	4.25	3.36	3.00	3.23	44.49
	Rivervale	12	28.1	71.8	103	−34	11	May 7	Oct. 4	150	13	4.14	4.29	4.36	3.93	3.47	4.01	3.83	4.83	4.17	4.29	2.61	4.18	48.11
	Woodcliff Lake										20	3.56	3.02	3.33	3.66	3.46	3.88	4.14	4.17	4.39	3.02	3.11	3.06	42.80
Burlington	Burlington	26	33.0	76.8	106	−14	26	Apr. 19	Oct. 22	186	40	3.61	3.26	3.80	3.72	3.42	3.98	4.71	5.74	4.00	3.44	2.99	3.80	46.47
	Indian Mills	40	33.2	74.4	107	−25	37	Apr. 27	Oct. 18	174	38	3.98	3.44	3.93	3.81	3.29	4.40	4.61	5.79	3.89	3.59	2.87	3.96	47.56
	Moorestown	40	32.8	74.9	106	−16	40	Apr. 24	Oct. 19	178	40	3.41	3.17	3.60	3.63	3.46	3.97	4.56	5.51	3.99	3.39	2.77	3.62	45.08
	Rancocas						10	Apr. 25	Oct. 14	172	12	3.35	3.67	3.96	3.53	3.44	4.17	4.39	6.20	4.44	4.12	2.64	4.12	48.03
Camden	Haddonfield						7	Apr. 16	Oct. 27	194	13	3.75	3.87	3.93	3.99	3.36	3.47	4.34	5.82	3.23	3.49	2.67	4.65	46.57
Cape May	Belleplain	40	33.0	73.4	106	−15	40	Apr. 29	Oct. 13	167	38	3.64	3.17	3.72	3.58	3.26	3.22	4.27	4.51	3.75	3.16	2.40	3.85	42.53
	Cape May	33	34.9	74.2	100	−3	32	Apr. 8	Nov. 12	218	34	3.23	2.97	3.51	3.07	2.82	3.12	3.51	4.49	2.74	2.65	2.22	3.56	37.89
Cumberland	Bridgeton	40	33.9	76.3	104	−12	38	Apr. 20	Oct. 23	186	38	3.60	3.17	3.89	3.35	3.17	3.83	4.60	4.91	3.66	3.03	2.58	3.59	43.38
	Vineland	29	33.3	75.5	105	−13	29	Apr. 21	Oct. 21	183	29	3.46	3.32	3.52	3.51	3.22	3.51	4.70	4.64	3.40	3.00	2.54	3.84	42.66
Essex	Newark	30	31.7	74.8	105	−13	26	Apr. 14	Oct. 28	197	30	3.88	3.35	3.77	3.86	3.69	4.56	4.77	4.70	3.82	4.14	2.68	4.06	47.28
	South Orange	32	29.2	73.3	102	−14	31	Apr. 21	Oct. 23	185	31	3.51	3.78	3.81	3.89	3.76	3.80	4.66	4.94	3.77	3.85	2.71	3.98	46.46
Gloucester	Clayton	32	32.1	75.2	105	−13	27	Apr. 24	Oct. 16	175	25	3.49	3.28	3.60	3.58	3.17	3.75	4.69	5.25	3.77	3.14	2.52	3.83	44.07
Hudson	Bayonne	18	31.4	74.8	102	−14	16	Apr. 16	Oct. 24	191	18	3.67	3.72	3.93	3.80	3.29	3.46	4.00	4.72	3.50	4.50	2.57	3.86	45.02
	Bergen Point	33	30.8	74.0	104	−14	33	Apr. 14	Oct. 31	200	32	3.66	3.75	3.70	4.06	3.73	3.84	4.67	4.85	3.63	4.18	3.10	4.03	47.20
	Jersey City	33	32.8	75.8	106	−12	32	do	Nov. 2	202	33	3.68	3.56	3.69	3.74	3.55	3.78	4.15	4.10	3.77	3.57	2.86	3.51	43.96
Hunterdon	Flemington	38	30.8	74.8	108	−18	39	Apr. 24	Oct. 21	180	40	3.56	3.18	3.67	3.63	3.38	3.78	4.90	4.58	3.92	3.46	2.82	3.57	44.45
	Lambertville	38	30.8	74.1	105	−19	38	do	Oct. 20	179	39	3.51	3.21	3.63	3.84	3.65	4.02	4.76	4.84	3.63	3.47	2.89	3.66	45.11
Mercer	Hightstown	40	30.1	74.1	105	−16	40	Apr. 26	Oct. 16	173	37	3.47	3.33	3.72	3.83	3.51	4.10	4.85	4.94	3.84	3.60	2.78	3.46	45.43
	Trenton	40	32.7	75.0	106	−14	40	Apr. 13	Oct. 27	197	40	3.28	3.04	3.49	3.35	3.33	3.74	4.24	5.34	3.82	3.04	2.59	3.24	42.50
Middlesex	New Brunswick	40	31.5	74.5	106	−16	40	Apr. 22	Oct. 20	181	40	3.46	3.22	3.52	3.58	3.59	3.81	5.07	5.24	3.85	3.71	2.70	3.44	45.19
	Runyon	14	31.5	73.5	110	−31	13	May 15	Oct. 2	140	15	3.65	3.16	3.15	3.71	3.52	4.36	4.28	4.81	4.37	3.90	3.07	2.95	44.93
Monmouth	Asbury Park	34	33.4	72.6	104	−12	35	Apr. 13	Oct. 30	200	36	3.45	3.41	3.69	3.53	3.25	3.63	4.06	4.84	2.85	3.14	2.55	3.82	42.22
	Freehold	13	33.2	74.6	102	−20	12	Apr. 22	Oct. 20	181	11	4.18	3.67	4.34	3.65	3.56	4.06	4.40	4.36	4.69	3.95	3.23	3.96	48.05
	Imlaytown	29	31.1	74.5	104	−14	31	Apr. 24	Oct. 17	176	28	3.48	3.36	3.62	3.43	3.11	3.64	4.30	5.14	3.25	3.62	2.57	3.67	43.19
	Long Branch	30	31.5	72.1	106	−12	28	Apr. 13	Oct. 29	199	29	4.17	3.58	3.83	4.28	3.40	3.87	4.68	4.79	3.73	3.40	3.17	3.76	46.66
	Oceanic	11	31.5	74.9	99	−11	10	Apr. 10	Oct. 25	198	11	3.65	3.74	4.39	3.54	3.29	3.97	5.08	5.93	3.53	3.55	2.17	4.42	47.26

	Sandy Hook	33	31.3	73.5	101	−11	27	Apr. 5	Nov. 13	222	27	3.20	2.95	2.93	3.02	2.93	3.80	4.46	4.12	3.56	2.85	2.42	3.06	39.30
Morris	Boonton	30	27.1	71.9	103	−21	30	May 1	Oct. 8	160	34	3.38	3.20	3.41	3.76	3.59	3.96	4.40	4.34	4.25	3.54	3.24	3.32	44.39
	Chatham										35	4.09	3.56	3.92	4.18	3.74	4.38	4.74	4.65	4.57	3.89	3.32	3.95	48.99
	Dover	40	27.6	71.9	102	−21	39	May 6	Oct. 8	155	40	4.01	3.66	4.08	4.02	3.56	4.64	5.23	4.53	4.48	3.97	3.48	4.10	49.76
	Pompton Plains										17	3.72	3.76	3.96	4.11	3.60	4.21	4.78	4.40	4.29	4.43	2.98	4.02	48.26
Ocean	Lakewood	34	31.5	73.0	106	−16	34	Apr. 25	Oct. 21	179	34	3.85	3.50	3.83	3.73	3.29	4.27	4.60	5.25	3.48	3.79	2.81	3.85	46.25
	Tuckerton	40	32.9	74.0	105	−13	40	Apr. 26	Oct. 18	175	40	3.76	3.41	3.85	3.69	3.32	3.74	3.97	5.49	3.68	3.49	2.95	4.16	45.51
Passaic	Charlottsburg	40	27.7	70.9	105	−26	40	May 13	Sept. 27	137	40	3.74	3.56	4.04	4.30	3.71	4.64	4.52	4.60	4.57	4.25	3.58	3.95	49.46
	Little Falls	24	28.5	73.8	105	−18	24	Apr. 22	Oct. 21	182	35	3.74	3.42	3.60	4.25	3.86	4.28	4.48	4.66	4.29	3.98	3.38	3.71	47.65
	Paterson	40	31.3	75.0	105	−16	40	Apr. 18	Oct. 19	184	39	3.69	3.73	3.94	3.86	3.62	3.98	4.42	4.66	4.03	3.90	2.96	3.78	46.57
Salem	Canton										13	3.05	3.58	3.45	3.40	3.19	4.35	4.94	5.55	3.44	3.11	2.59	3.99	44.64
	Friesburg	11	32.8	75.3	105	−11	11	Apr. 28	Oct. 15	170	11	3.01	3.69	3.79	3.42	2.90	4.14	4.66	5.17	4.21	3.46	2.41	3.95	44.81
Somerset	Somerville	40	30.4	74.0	109	−20	40	May 2	Oct. 14	165	39	3.61	3.32	3.69	3.63	3.42	3.70	5.21	4.99	3.91	3.54	2.80	3.62	45.44
Sussex	Culvers Lake						31	May 7	Oct. 3	149	37	3.16	2.83	3.22	3.55	3.45	4.84	4.58	4.50	4.32	3.69	3.08	3.19	44.41
	Layton	37	25.0	70.9	103	−32	37	May 15	Sept. 30	138	38	3.08	2.82	3.39	3.59	3.34	4.26	4.41	4.12	4.06	3.64	3.08	3.25	43.04
	Newton	40	27.1	72.5	105	−20	40	Apr. 27	Oct. 12	168	39	3.37	3.03	3.44	3.52	3.43	4.71	4.78	4.31	4.18	3.62	2.98	3.34	44.71
	Sussex	40	26.8	72.0	106	−24	40	May 3	Oct. 6	156	35	3.27	3.03	3.33	3.65	3.45	4.45	4.40	4.45	4.38	3.33	2.86	3.24	43.84
Union	Elizabeth	40	31.6	75.3	105	−16	40	Apr. 20	Oct. 23	186	40	3.81	3.68	3.87	3.82	3.52	3.74	4.74	4.34	3.96	3.73	2.76	3.80	45.77
	Plainfield	40	30.5	73.9	106	−17	40	Apr. 27	Oct. 17	173	39	3.84	3.56	3.94	3.78	3.56	4.08	5.47	5.13	4.45	3.91	2.88	3.78	48.38
Warren	Belvidere	40	25.7	73.8	106	−15	40	Apr. 29	Oct. 14	168	40	3.85	3.46	3.81	3.78	3.41	4.31	4.71	4.73	4.00	3.72	3.13	3.85	46.76
	Phillipsburg	40	28.4	73.9	105	−12	35	Apr. 26	Oct. 16	173	39	3.47	3.26	3.47	3.43	3.18	4.08	4.61	4.66	3.89	3.49	2.78	3.42	43.74

[1] Length of growing season between average dates of last killing frost in spring and first in fall.

NEW JERSEY—Continued

Precipitation—State unit values

[This tabulation gives the mean annual, mean monthly, and average seasonal precipitation, 1886–1938, for New Jersey]

Year	Mean	Year	Mean	Year	Mean	Year	Mean	Month	Mean	Season	Average
	In.		In.		In.		In.		In.		In.
1886	46.51	1900	42.74	1914	39.63	1928	46.22	January	3.67	Winter	10.81
1887	48.21	1901	51.87	1915	47.36	1929	42.96	February	3.52	Spring	11.07
1888	53.91	1902	56.25	1916	37.86	1930	35.28	March	3.78	Summer	13.32
1889	62.68	1903	56.20	1917	40.86	1931	37.07	April	3.60	Fall	10.66
1890	49.33	1904	43.55	1918	37.36	1932	46.06	May	3.69		
1891	47.98	1905	41.89	1919	52.11	1933	49.70	June	3.88		
1892	42.04	1906	46.63	1920	51.32	1934	45.43	July	4.79		
1893	48.26	1907	51.62	1921	38.33	1935	42.35	August	4.65		
1894	46.69	1908	42.61	1922	41.11	1936	47.44	September	3.88		
1895	37.31	1909	41.15	1923	40.18	1937	47.63	October	3.61		
1896	42.26	1910	39.65	1924	44.46	1938	52.52	November	3.17		
1897	51.42	1911	50.30	1925	41.71			December	3.62		
1898	52.22	1912	45.72	1926	44.41						
1899	45.87	1913	46.23	1927	49.68			Annual	45.86		

Dates of last killing frost in spring and first in fall, with length of growing season

Year	Atlantic City			Bridgeton			Dover			Indian Mills			New Brunswick			Trenton		
	Last in spring	First in fall	Growing season [1]	Last in spring	First in fall	Growing season [1]	Last in spring	First in fall	Growing season [1]	Last in spring	First in fall	Growing season [1]	Last in spring	First in fall	Growing season [1]	Last in spring	First in fall	Growing season [1]
			Days			Days			Days			Days			Days			Days
1899	Apr. 10	Oct. 1	174	Apr. 1	Oct. 1	183	Apr. 29	Oct. 1	155				Apr. 17	Oct. 2	168	Apr. 17	Oct. 2	168
1900	Apr. 11	Nov. 16	219	May 10	Oct. 20	163	May 11	Oct. 17	159				Apr. 11	Oct. 20	192	May 10	Oct. 18	161
1901	Mar. 30	Nov. 7	222	Mar. 30	Oct. 26	210	May 6	Oct. 4	151		Oct. 5		Apr. 2	Oct. 25	206	Mar. 30	Oct. 26	210
1902	Mar. 20	Oct. 30	224	May 29	Oct. 22	146	May 29	Oct. 10	134	May 29	Oct. 22	146	Apr. 16	Oct. 22	189	Mar 27	Oct. 10	197
1903	Apr. 5	Nov. 7	216	May 2	Oct. 27	178	May 11	Sept. 30	142	May 22	Oct. 27	158	May 2	Oct. 25	176	May 2	Oct. 25	176
1904	Apr. 20	Oct. 28	191	Apr. 23	Sept. 22	152	May 3	Sept. 22	142	Apr. 23	Sept. 22	152	Apr. 23	Sept. 22	152	Apr. 23	Sept. 22	152
1905	Apr. 19	Nov. 2	197	Apr. 19	Oct. 22	186	May 2	Oct. 7	158	May 2	Oct. 22	173	May 2	Oct. 22	173	Apr. 19	Oct. 13	177

1906	Apr. 3	Nov. 9	220	May 11	Oct. 12	154	May 11	Oct. 12	154	Apr. 7	Oct. 12	188	May 11	Oct. 12	154	Apr. 24	Oct. 12	171
1907	Apr. 21	Nov. 14	207	May 12	Oct. 22	163	May 12	Oct. 9	150	May 22	Oct. 10	141	May 12	Oct. 10	151	May 12	Oct. 22	163
1908	Apr. 5	Nov. 2	211	Apr. 17	Oct. 21	187	Apr. 21	Oct. 13	175	Apr. 22	Oct. 3	164	Apr. 21	Oct. 13	175	Apr. 21	Oct. 13	175
1909	Apr. 11	Oct. 29	201	Apr. 12	Oct. 14	185	Apr. 25	do	171	Apr. 12	Oct. 13	184	Apr. 29	Oct. 14	168	Apr. 12	do	184
1910	Mar. 18	Oct. 30	226	Apr. 14	Oct. 29	198	May 5	do	161	May 6	Oct. 29	176	May 6	Oct. 13	160	Apr. 13	Oct. 29	199
1911	Apr. 10	Nov 3	207	May 3	do	179	do	Sept. 14	132	do	Oct. 9	156	Apr. 18	Oct. 29	194	Apr. 17	do	195
1912	Apr. 4	do	213	Apr. 11	Nov. 3	206	May 1	Oct. 17	169	Apr. 20	Oct. 17	180	Apr. 11	Nov. 3	206	Apr. 20	Nov. 3	197
1913	Apr. 21	Nov. 1	194	May 12	Oct. 22	163	May 11	Sept. 16	128	May 11	Oct. 22	164	May 11	Oct. 22	164	May 12	Nov. 1	173
1914	Apr. 6	Nov. 10	218	Apr. 14	Oct. 28	197	May 1	Sept. 29	151	Apr. 24	Oct. 28	187	May 1	Oct. 28	180	Apr. 6	Oct. 28	205
1915	Apr. 4	Nov. 18	228	Apr. 5	Oct. 24	202	Apr. 22	Oct. 11	172	Apr. 15	Oct. 11	179	Apr. 5	Oct. 10	188	Apr. 5	Nov. 4	213
1916	Mar. 24	Nov. 16	237	Apr. 10	Oct. 15	188	Apr. 11	Oct. 1	173	Apr. 16	do	178	Apr. 10	Oct. 15	188	Apr. 10	Nov. 11	215
1917	Apr. 15	Oct. 31	199	Apr. 15	Oct. 13	181	May 24	Sept. 11	110	May 4	Oct. 7	156	May 4	Oct. 7	156	Apr. 15	Nov. 13	212
1918	Mar. 29	Nov. 24	240	Apr. 7	Nov. 25	232	May 17	Oct. 4	140	Apr. 6	Oct. 15	192	Apr. 6	Oct. 20	197	Apr. 13	Nov. 7	208
1919	Apr. 3	Nov. 14	225	Apr. 25	Nov. 7	196	Apr. 23	Sept. 27	157	Apr. 26	Nov. 7	195	Apr. 26	Nov. 9	197	Apr. 16	Nov. 9	207
1920	Apr. 9	Nov. 13	218	Apr. 10	Nov. 13	217	May 5	Nov. 4	183	May 3	Oct. 30	180	Apr. 11	Nov. 12	215	Apr. 11	Nov. 12	215
1921	Apr. 11	do	216	Apr. 2	Oct. 26	207	Apr. 20	Oct. 27	190	Apr. 12	Oct. 14	185	do	Oct. 16	188	Apr. 2	Oct. 26	207
1922	Apr. 3	Nov. 22	233	Apr. 24	Oct. 19	178	May 1	Sept. 26	148	Apr. 23	Oct. 19	179	Apr. 23	Oct. 21	181	Mar. 23	Oct. 21	212
1923	Apr. 2	Nov. 9	221	Apr. 19	Oct. 27	191	May 11	Oct. 25	167	Apr. 18	Oct. 7	172	May 11	Oct. 7	149	Apr. 10	Nov. 1	205
1924	Apr. 3	Nov. 17	228	Apr. 3	Oct. 21	201	May 5	Oct. 2	150	Apr. 12	Oct. 21	192	Apr. 4	Oct. 23	202	Apr. 4	Oct. 23	202
1925	Mar. 4	Oct. 29	239		Oct. 11		May 9			May 8	Oct. 20	165	May 9	Oct. 24	168	Apr. 21	Oct. 11	173
1926	Apr. 20	Nov. 4	198	Apr. 20	Oct. 22	185	May 5	Oct. 16	164	Apr. 27	Oct. 22	178	Apr. 27	Oct. 22	178	Apr. 20	Oct. 22	185
1927	Apr. 11	Nov. 8	211	Apr. 25	Oct. 31	189	Apr. 28	Oct. 31	186	Apr. 26	Oct. 31	188	Apr. 26	Oct. 31	188	Apr. 11	Nov. 7	210
1928	Apr. 18	Oct. 30	195	Apr. 21			May 25	Oct. 1	129	Apr. 27	Oct. 27	183	Apr. 27	Oct. 27	183	Apr. 18	Oct. 27	192
1929	Mar. 18	Nov. 25	252				May 23	Oct. 10	140	Apr. 23	Oct. 11	171	Mar. 21	Oct. 10	203	Mar. 18	Oct. 11	207
1930	Apr. 24	Nov. 7	197	Apr. 23	Oct. 18	178	Apr. 29	Oct. 19	173	Apr. 27	Oct. 19	175	Apr. 24	Oct. 19	178	Apr. 24	Oct. 21	180
1931	Mar. 21	do	231	Apr. 30	Nov. 7	191	May 1	Nov. 5	188	May 5	Oct. 13	161	May 4	Oct. 13	162	Mar. 22	Nov. 7	230
1932	Apr. 17	Nov. 14	211	Apr. 17	Oct. 31	197	Apr. 24	Oct. 14	173	Apr. 24	Oct. 14	173	Apr. 16	Oct. 24	191	Apr. 15	Nov. 4	203
1933	Mar. 29	Oct. 26	211	Apr. 27	Oct. 26	182	Apr. 28	Oct. 15	170	Apr. 28	Oct. 26	181	Apr. 27	Oct. 26	182	Apr. 23	Oct. 26	186
1934	Apr. 28	Nov. 3	189	Apr. 25	Oct. 12	170	Apr. 30	Oct. 2	155	Apr. 30	Oct. 14	167	Apr. 28	Oct. 14	169	Apr. 5	Nov. 3	212
1935	Apr. 16	Nov. 19	217	Apr. 16	Oct. 16	183	Apr. 26	Oct. 3	160	Apr. 17	Oct. 5	171	Apr. 17	Oct. 8	174	do	Nov. 25	234
1936	Apr. 8	Oct. 27	202	Apr. 24	Oct. 27	186	May 29	Oct. 4	128	Apr. 25	Oct. 27	185	Apr. 25	Oct. 27	185	Apr. 8	Oct. 27	202
1937	Mar. 29	Oct. 15	200	Apr. 12	Oct. 16	187	May 12	Sept. 18	129	Apr. 13	Oct. 15	185	Apr. 13	Oct. 15	185	Apr. 11	Nov. 4	207
1938	Mar. 28	Nov. 15	232	Apr. 11	Nov. 1	204	May 14	Oct. 4	143	Apr. 24	Nov. 1	191	Apr. 11	Nov. 21	224	Apr. 6	Nov. 24	232
Mean	Apr. 6	Nov. 7	215	Apr. 20	Oct. 23	186	May 6	Oct. 8	155	Apr. 27	Oct. 18	174	Apr. 22	Oct. 20	181	Apr. 13	Oct. 27	196
Extremes	Mar. 4[2]	Oct. 1[4]	[6] 174	Mar. 30[2]	Sept. 22[4]	[6] 146	Apr. 11[2]	Sept. 11[4]	[6] 110	Apr. 6[2]	Sept. 22[4]	[6] 141	Apr. 2[2]	Sept. 22[4]	[6] 149	Mar. 18[2]	Oct. 2[4]	[6] 152
	Apr. 28[3]	Nov. 25[5]	[7] 252	May 29[3]	Nov. 25[5]	[7] 232	May 29[3]	Nov. 5[5]	[7] 190	May 29[3]	Nov. 7[5]	[7] 195	May 12[3]	Nov. 21[5]	[7] 224	May 12[3]	Nov. 25[5]	[7] 234

1 Number of days between last killing frost in spring and first in fall.
2 Earliest date in spring.
3 Latest date in spring.
4 Earliest date in fall.
5 Latest date in fall.
6 Shortest growing season.
7 Longest growing season.

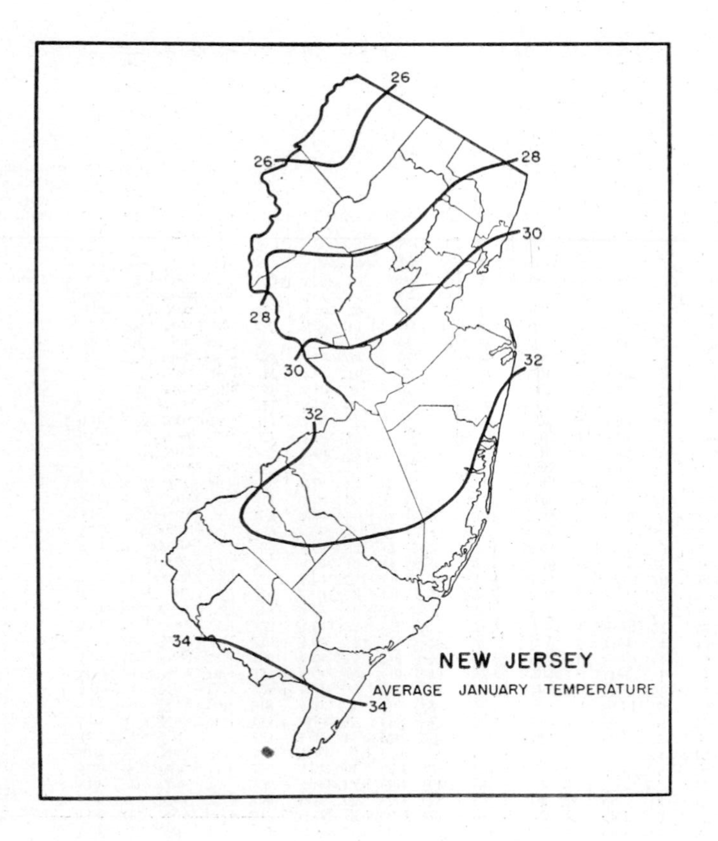
NEW JERSEY
AVERAGE JANUARY TEMPERATURE
26
28
30
32
34

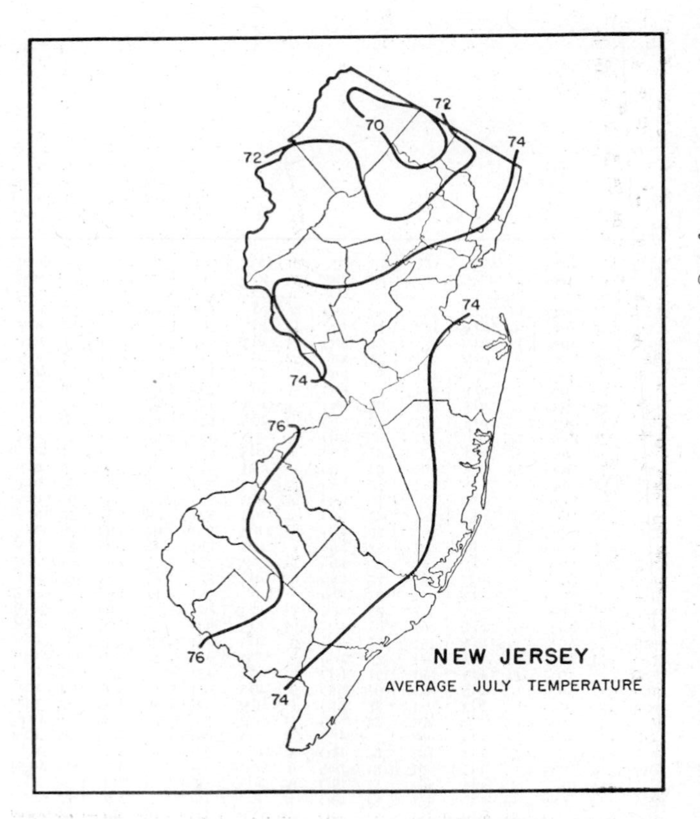
NEW JERSEY
AVERAGE JULY TEMPERATURE
70
72
74
76

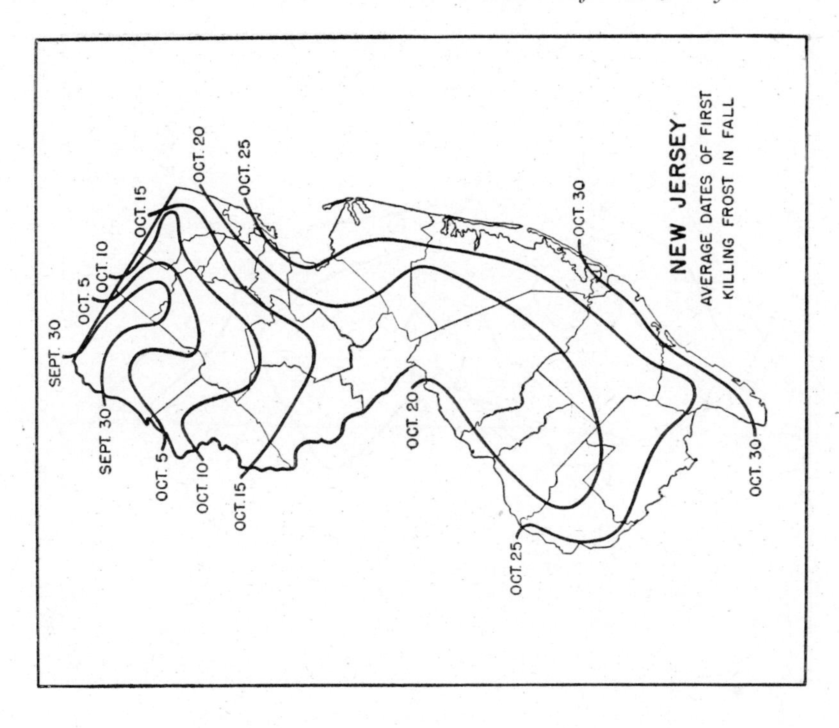
NEW JERSEY
AVERAGE DATES OF FIRST KILLING FROST IN FALL
SEPT. 30
OCT. 5
OCT. 10
OCT. 15
OCT. 20
OCT. 25
OCT. 30
SEPT. 30
OCT. 5
OCT. 10
OCT. 15
OCT. 20
OCT. 25
OCT. 30

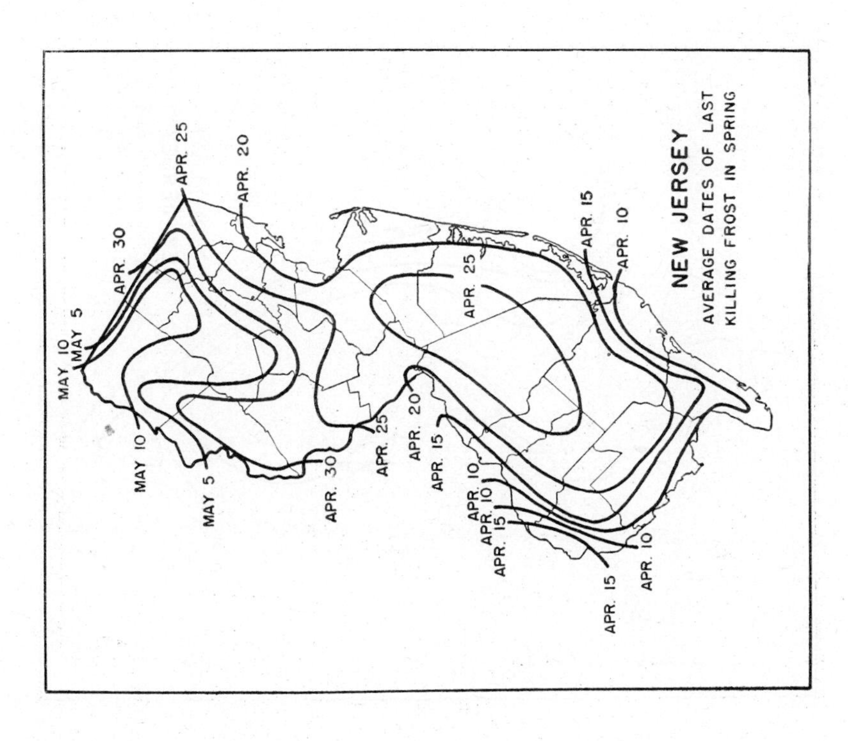
NEW JERSEY
AVERAGE DATES OF LAST KILLING FROST IN SPRING
MAY 10
MAY 5
APR. 30
APR. 25
APR. 20
APR. 15
APR. 10
APR. 25
MAY 10
MAY 5
APR. 30
APR. 25
APR. 20
APR. 15
APR. 10
APR. 10
APR. 15
APR. 15
APR. 10

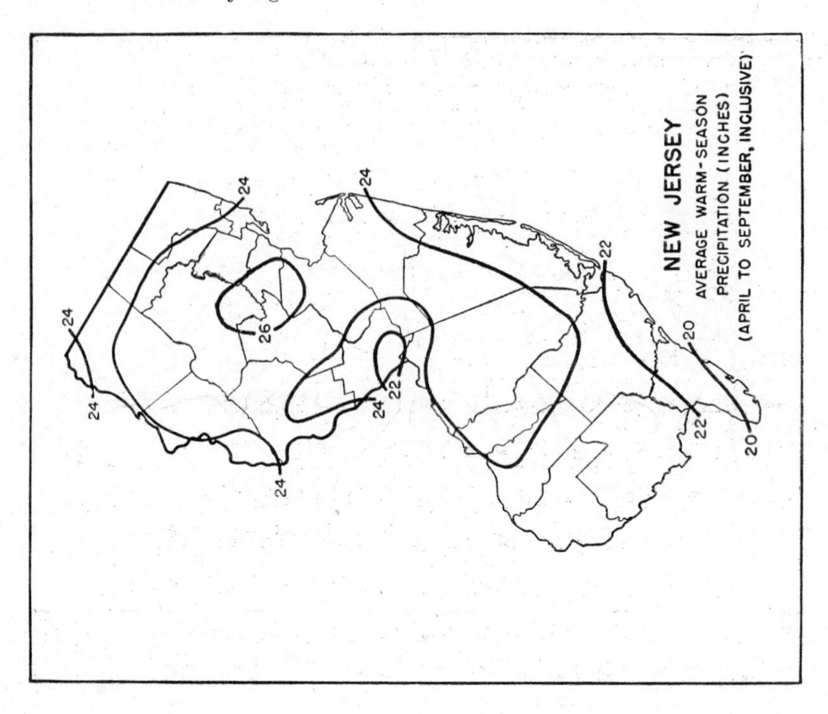
NEW JERSEY
AVERAGE WARM-SEASON
PRECIPITATION (INCHES)
(APRIL TO SEPTEMBER, INCLUSIVE)
24
26
22
20

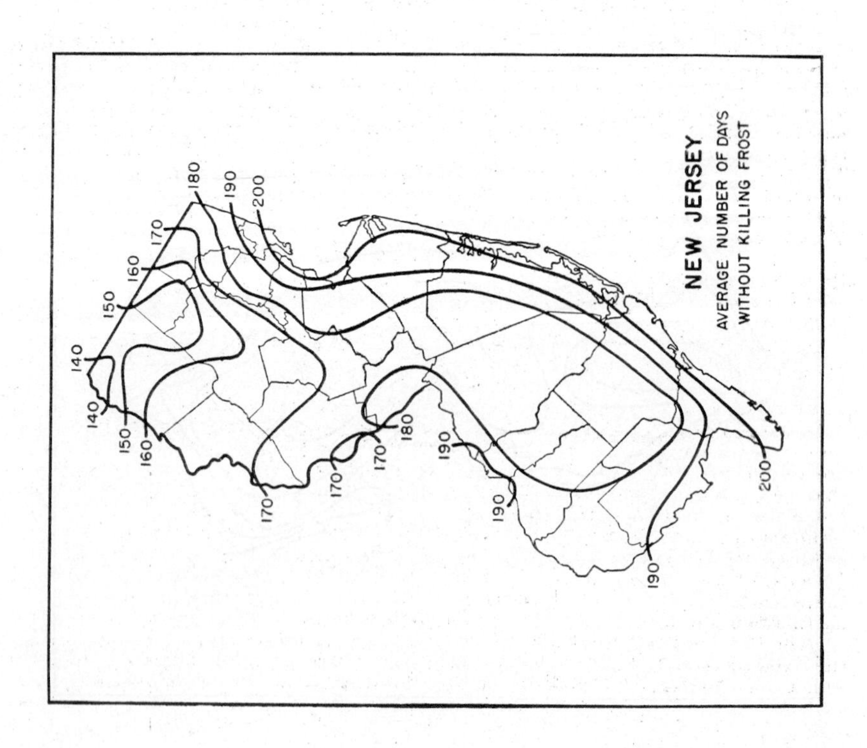
NEW JERSEY
AVERAGE NUMBER OF DAYS
WITHOUT KILLING FROST
140
150
160
170
180
190
200

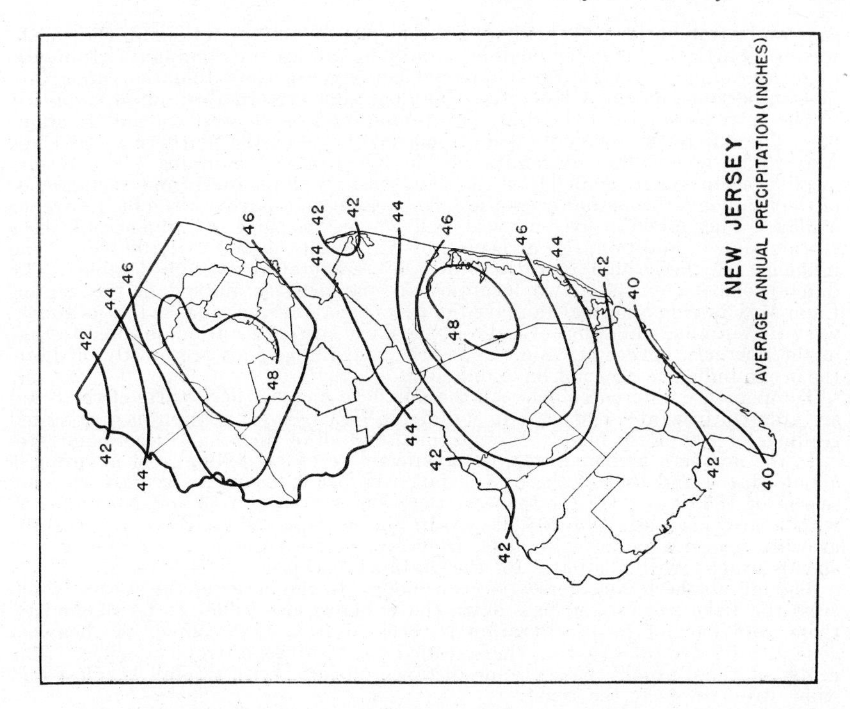

SUPPLEMENTARY CLIMATIC NOTES FOR NEW JERSEY

New Jersey, though one of the smaller States, has a varied topography. In the northwestern part a section comprising about one-fifth of the area of the State is known as the Highlands and Kittatinny Valley. This region is traversed by several low mountain ridges extending northeasterly across the State with valleys and rolling hills between. The highest of these ranges is the Kittatinny, which rises from the banks of the Delaware River at the famous Delaware Water Gap. To the eastward this region is studded with numerous lakes, some of the largest of which are Lakes Hopatcong, Mohawk, and Greenwood. Elevations up to 1,800 feet above sea level are found in the Kittatinny Mountains near the New York State line.

South and east of the Highlands is a region of about equal area known as the Red Sandstone Plain, or the Piedmont of New Jersey. It is generally hilly in its northwestern part, becoming rolling and then flat toward the south and southeast. At its northeastern corner are the Palisades, cliffs which rise abruptly from the Hudson River to heights of 200 to 500 feet. The seacoast section extends from Sandy Hook to Cape May, or about 125 miles. This area is characterized by long stretches of sandy beaches, now occupied largely by summer resorts. Tidewater marshes become numerous toward the south.

In the southern interior is a region, known as the Pines, covered with scrubby forests of pine and some oak. The land is low and some of it is swampy. Here are found the large cranberry bogs of New Jersey. In fact, most of the State that lies south of a line connecting Jersey City and Trenton is low and flat with few elevations higher than 100 feet above mean sea level, these being mainly in Monmouth County.

About 30 percent of the area of the State drains into the Delaware River and Delaware Bay, which form the western boundary. The remainder drains into the Atlantic Ocean through the Passaic, Hackensack, and Raritan Rivers in the north and a number of small rivers and streams in the south.

Over the southern interior the soil changes from the predominant sand near the coast to clay and marl in the western part. However, there is no steady transformation, the change being effected mostly by alternating stretches of the different soils and combinations of them. In the most productive sections in the southwestern part, the light to medium sandy loams are predominant. Immense quantities of garden truck for commercial canning, especially tomatoes, are grown in Cumberland, Salem, Gloucester, Camden, and western Burlington Counties.

The extreme length of the State is 166 miles and its greatest width only about 65. The difference in climate is quite marked between the southern tip at Cape May and the northern extremity in the Kittatinny Mountains. The former locality is almost surrounded by water and is fairly well removed from the influence of the frequent storms that cross the Lakes region and move out the St. Lawrence Valley. The northern extremity is well within the zone of influence of these storms and, in addition, lies at elevations varying from 800 to 1,800 feet. The influence of these high elevations on the temperature is considerable. The differences between these two localities are particularly marked in the winter, Cape May having a normal January temperature about the same as that of southwestern Virginia, while that of Layton, the most northern station, is equal to that of the northern border of Ohio. Since the prevailing winds are mostly offshore, the ocean influence does not have full effect.

Temperature differences between the northern and southern parts of the State are greatest in winter and least in summer. Nearly every station has registered readings of 100° F. or higher at some time, and all of them have records of zero.

In the northern highland area, the average date of last killing frost in spring is about May 4 and that of the first in fall, October 6, giving an average growing season of 155 days. On the seacoast these dates are April 13 and November 2, with a growing season of 203 days. In the central and southern interior the growing season averages 178 days, from April 23 to October 18, which corresponds exactly with the dates for the State as a whole.

Though northern New Jersey is near enough to the paths of the storms which cross the Lakes region and pass down the St. Lawrence Valley to be affected by them, and part of its precipitation is received from that source, the heaviest general rains are produced by the so-called coast storms of tropical origin. The center of these usually passes some distance offshore, with rainfall heaviest and wind strongest near the coast.

The average annual precipitation ranges from about 40 inches along the southeast coast to 49 in north-central parts of the State. In other sections the annual averages are mostly between 43 and 47 inches. Rainfall is normally well distributed during the warm months. Heavy 24-hour falls of 7 or 8 inches are occasionally recorded.

The season during which measurable quantities of snow are likely to fall extends from about the middle of October to April 20 in the Highlands, and from about the middle of November to March 15 in the vicinity of Cape May. Normal seasonal amounts range from about 14 inches at Cape May to nearly 50 in the Highlands. Falls of 10 or 12 inches of snow in a single storm rarely occur.

The number of days a month with 0.01 inch or more of precipitation averages 8 for each of the fall months, September, October, and November, and 9 to 11 for the other months of the year; the average yearly number is 113.

Normally, sunshine varies from slightly over half the possible amount in the northern counties to about 60 percent in the south. The prevailing wind is from the northwest from October to April, inclusive, and from the southwest for the other months of the year.

ARKAS E. WHITE, *Associate Meteorologist and Climatic Section Director for New Jersey, Weather Bureau, Trenton.*

NEW MEXICO

Climatic summary

County	Station	Temperature					Killing frost average dates				Average precipitation													
		Length of record	January average	July average	Maximum	Minimum	Length of record	Last in spring	First in fall	Growing season[1]	Length of record	January	February	March	April	May	June	July	August	September	October	November	December	Annual
		Yr.	*°F.*	*°F.*	*°F.*	*°F.*	*Yr.*			*Days*	*Yr.*	*In.*	*In.*	*In.*	*In.*	*In.*	*In.*	*In.*	*In.*	*In.*	*In.*	*In.*	*In.*	*In.*
Bernalillo	Albuquerque	40	34.1	76.7	104	−10	37	Apr. 13	Oct. 28	198	40	0.34	0.31	0.38	0.68	0.68	0.68	1.46	1.25	0.94	0.73	0.50	0.45	8.40
	Barton	12	30.8	70.7	104	−10	12	May 7	Oct. 10	156	12	1.08	1.00	1.49	1.35	.76	.80	2.56	2.49	1.06	1.50	.59	1.22	15.90
	Tijeras Ranger Station.	22	28.5	70.3	101	−29	27	May 19	Oct. 2	136	27	.75	.79	.95	1.02	1.44	.93	2.42	2.00	1.52	1.20	.68	.87	14.57
Catron	Alma	27	37.8	74.0	106	−13	24	Apr. 29	Oct. 17	171	25	.86	.92	1.13	.61	.47	.71	2.62	2.45	1.57	1.26	1.12	1.07	14.79
	Datil	16	27.6	65.0	98	−18	20	May 28	Sept. 24	119	27	.71	.71	.60	.74	.72	.81	2.56	2.65	1.61	.78	.67	.82	13.38
	Hood Ranger Station										22	.82	1.00	1.20	.93	.55	.69	2.41	2.41	1.65	.84	.90	.92	14.32
	Horse Springs	26	27.6	66.8	105	−21	33	May 24	Oct. 1	130	36	.79	.85	.80	.66	.48	.52	2.56	2.44	1.44	1.02	.83	.93	13.32
	Jewett Ranger Station.										16	.94	.97	.99	.90	.70	.57	2.55	3.26	2.23	.85	.55	.90	15.41
	Luna Ranger Station	30	28.2	64.4	97	−32	32	June 12	Sept. 20	100	39	1.04	1.08	1.04	.62	.56	.71	3.00	2.93	1.83	1.25	.97	1.23	16.26
	Quemado	13	27.9	66.3	97	−29	13	May 31	Oct. 2	124	17	.84	.74	.70	.71	.71	.67	2.71	2.65	1.73	.71	.71	.90	13.78
Chaves	Boaz	30	37.4	77.5	109	−26	30	Apr. 15	Oct. 26	194	30	.27	.34	.60	.92	1.40	1.56	1.80	2.14	1.98	1.22	.45	.40	13.08
	Elk (near)	28	38.9	70.5	106	−11	30	Apr. 21	Oct. 24	186	28	.42	.47	.59	.64	1.32	1.46	3.78	3.03	2.73	1.50	.75	.52	17.21
	Hagerman										8	.37	.30	.76	.64	2.21	1.81	1.53	2.00	1.42	.68	.30	.31	12.33
	Roswell	40	39.8	78.1	110	−29	40	Apr. 7	Oct. 31	207	40	.37	.51	.65	.90	1.09	1.41	1.79	1.68	2.29	1.06	.81	.50	13.06
Colfax	Aurora										30	.53	.83	1.22	1.42	1.90	2.42	3.92	3.52	2.13	1.39	.71	.59	20.58
	Black Lake										30	.45	.60	.85	.91	1.38	1.88	3.39	3.20	1.63	1.12	.50	.43	16.34
	Cimarron	35	32.4	68.7	100	−35	35	May 6	Oct. 11	158	35	.28	.62	.97	1.44	1.85	1.74	2.66	2.40	1.58	1.32	.49	.39	15.74
	Dawson	27	30.7	69.8	102	−36	27	May 5	do	159	30	.31	.56	.64	1.15	1.97	1.99	2.87	2.60	1.40	1.45	.40	.37	15.71
	Elizabethtown	34	19.4	57.6	92	−37	34	June 22	Sept. 9	79	34	.80	1.08	1.55	1.47	1.37	1.21	3.03	3.01	1.29	1.13	.72	.71	17.37
	Johnsons Park						8	May 9	Oct. 3	147	13	.18	.41	.67	1.52	2.53	2.45	3.33	2.77	1.39	1.32	.33	.53	17.43
	Lake Alice (near)						12	May 15	do	141	30	.53	.70	1.23	1.86	2.67	2.24	2.97	3.16	1.90	1.54	.68	.70	20.18
	Maxwell										26	.17	.33	.68	1.20	1.75	1.82	2.74	2.78	1.46	.94	.40	.31	14.58
	Miami	29	31.7	68.8	100	−30	29	May 9	Oct. 6	150	31	.25	.56	.86	1.05	2.10	2.12	2.65	2.52	1.49	1.44	.55	.35	15.94
	Raton (near)	40	30.3	69.1	104	−26	40	do	Oct. 2	146	38	.34	.54	.70	1.29	1.96	1.90	2.89	2.36	1.96	1.12	.60	.46	16.12
	Springer	37	30.0	70.9	104	−29	37	May 7	Oct. 8	154	38	.26	.42	.54	1.01	1.82	1.80	2.77	2.46	1.61	.82	.50	.32	14.33
	Taylor	18	29.0	71.8	104	−29	20	May 6	do	155	23	.25	.49	.80	1.04	2.08	1.74	2.79	2.76	1.43	1.33	.47	.46	15.64
	Vermejo Park	19	28.3	63.1	95	−30	18	May 25	Sept. 23	121	21	.47	.60	.95	1.64	1.29	1.52	3.73	3.07	1.39	1.14	.52	.56	16.88
Curry	Bellview						12	Apr. 24	Oct. 18	177	18	.31	.30	.58	.86	2.70	2.38	2.74	2.81	1.95	1.61	.58	.41	17.23
	Clovis	27	36.9	78.7	109	−11	26	Apr. 15	Oct. 29	197	28	.33	.44	.70	1.37	2.25	2.76	2.56	2.90	2.46	1.64	.50	.52	18.43
	Field (near)										14	.25	.39	.69	96	2.09	2.11	2.48	3.09	1.81	2.10	.58	.46	17.01
	Melrose										29	.34	.39	.77	1.25	1.81	2.12	2.26	2.58	2.13	1.33	.64	.57	16.19
	St. Vrain (near)										27	.39	.43	.79	1.34	2.10	2.28	2.40	2.42	1.99	1.49	.54	.60	16.77

[1] Length of growing season between average dates of last killing frost in spring and first in fall.

NEW MEXICO—Continued

Climatic summary—Continued

County	Station	Temperature: Length of record	Temperature: January average	Temperature: July average	Temperature: Maximum	Temperature: Minimum	Killing frost average dates: Length of record	Killing frost average dates: Last in spring	Killing frost average dates: First in fall	Killing frost average dates: Growing season	Average precipitation: Length of record	January	February	March	April	May	June	July	August	September	October	November	December	Annual
		Yr.	*°F.*	*°F.*	*°F.*	*°F.*	*Yr.*			*Days*	*Yr.*	*In.*	*In.*	*In.*	*In.*	*In.*	*In.*	*In.*	*In.*	*In.*	*In.*	*In.*	*In.*	*In.*
De Baca	Fort Sumner	28	37.9	78.7	109	−23	29	Apr. 11	Oct. 25	197	31	0.41	0.58	0.79	1.10	1.78	1.74	2.29	2.75	1.58	1.29	0.70	0.69	15.70
	Lagunita	17	38.4	76.0	109	−16	18	Apr. 20	Oct. 21	184	22	.39	.50	.68	1.16	1.13	1.66	2.15	2.17	1.73	1.31	.74	.72	14.34
Dona Ana	Agr. College	40	41.8	80.2	106	−8	40	Apr. 6	Oct. 31	208	40	.30	.39	.43	.25	.34	.58	1.58	1.79	1.21	.70	.57	.54	8.68
	Garfield	20	41.3	78.8	114	−10	24	Apr. 11	Oct. 22	194	23	.33	.44	.39	.34	.15	.72	1.47	2.31	1.25	.71	.44	.67	9.22
	Jornada Experiment Range.	22	38.3	78.8	109	−7	22	Apr. 17	Oct. 30	196	25	.35	.38	.38	.20	.57	.56	1.75	1.77	1.41	.89	.45	.62	9.33
	Lanark										25	.26	.32	.43	.22	.13	.70	1.45	1.77	1.17	.70	.54	.51	8.20
	Noria						10	Mar. 29	Nov. 2	218	12	.59	.36	.47	.23	.30	.98	1.78	1.56	.79	.46	.37	1.12	9.01
Eddy	Artesia	31	41.5	79.6	116	−35	31	Apr. 6	do	210	32	.31	.53	.62	1.00	1.28	1.21	2.00	1.44	1.63	1.26	.58	.52	12.38
	Carlsbad	36	44.3	80.5	112	−17	40	Mar. 29	Nov. 4	220	40	.33	.43	.54	.86	.92	1.49	2.23	1.70	2.03	1.44	.60	.56	13.13
	Carson Seep (near)										25	.81	.70	.82	1.04	1.54	1.65	3.37	3.42	3.06	1.45	.83	.83	19.52
	Hope	18	42.2	77.2	106	−22	24	Apr. 5	Nov. 4	213	20	.51	.66	.96	.51	1.48	1.66	1.75	1.54	2.65	1.02	.45	.64	13.83
	Lake Avalon										25	.30	.39	.51	.81	1.30	1.26	1.46	1.54	2.00	1.24	.42	.56	11.79
	Lakewood (near)	15	42.2	80.2	110	−11	16	Apr. 15	Nov. 3	202	17	.21	.34	.57	.80	.73	.90	1.36	2.08	1.95	1.18	.36	.47	10.95
	Loving										21	.32	.38	.39	.73	1.18	1.05	1.27	1.63	1.96	1.31	.47	.48	11.17
Grant	Cliff	18	40.8	76.9	111	−7	18	Apr. 28	Oct. 16	171	26	.93	1.06	.74	.57	.32	.45	2.86	2.61	1.74	.92	.94	1.21	14.35
	Fort Bayard	39	38.7	72.6	103	−12	40	Apr. 19	Oct. 30	194	40	.80	1.05	.92	.53	.49	.80	3.01	3.44	2.22	1.24	.82	1.06	16.38
	Hachita	11	40.8	78.2	108	9	24	Apr. 2	Nov. 11	223	30	.33	.65	.62	.22	.18	.40	2.22	2.54	1.22	.87	.60	.92	10.77
	Mimbres (near)						11	May 4	Oct. 13	162	25	1.15	1.32	.93	.61	.50	.93	4.03	3.31	2.31	1.21	.97	1.16	18.43
	Pinos Altos						18	May 30	Oct. 4	127	28	1.25	1.84	1.37	.79	.80	1.34	4.91	4.29	2.53	1.51	.91	1.54	23.08
	Redrock						11	Apr. 27	Oct. 13	169	34	.78	1.03	.72	.46	.33	.40	2.50	2.29	1.12	.98	.73	.98	12.32
	Silver City	14	35.3	71.9	100	−12	14	Apr. 26	Oct. 23	180	30	.78	1.37	1.05	.60	.46	.82	3.30	3.19	1.86	1.21	.86	1.33	16.83
	Tyrone						10	Apr. 18	Oct. 25	190	17	.88	.77	.83	.43	.57	.53	2.91	2.84	1.64	1.41	.83	1.34	14.98
Guadalupe	Cuervo	19	39.1	78.6	108	−8	19	Apr. 12	Nov. 2	204	30	.29	.46	.58	.86	1.66	1.48	1.98	1.98	1.56	1.13	.51	.54	13.03
	Isidore										13	.39	.60	.58	.73	1.96	2.18	2.17	2.28	1.50	1.15	.48	.49	14.51
	Pastura	15	36.0	75.3	105	−19	25	Apr. 23	Oct. 21	181	30	.30	.45	.49	.79	1.40	1.35	1.95	2.34	1.59	1.08	.36	.50	12.60
	Santa Rosa	26	38.9	77.2	108	−18	33	Apr. 10	Oct. 27	200	32	.30	.45	.54	.90	1.84	1.54	2.27	2.26	1.45	1.28	.46	.55	13.84
	Vaughn						12	Apr. 24	Oct. 21	180	30	.34	.43	.52	.81	1.58	1.41	2.15	1.81	1.79	1.09	.38	.56	12.87
Harding	Abbott						22	Apr. 28	Oct. 13	168	30	.24	.42	.60	.96	1.74	1.99	2.51	2.87	1.81	1.19	.40	.33	15.06
	Albert	20	38.7	77.0	108	−10	10	Apr. 17	Oct. 20	186	16	.22	.53	.40	1.73	2.24	2.02	2.42	2.36	1.90	.85	.86	.54	16.07
	Hoosier Ranch						26	May 12	Oct. 14	155	28	.22	.44	.62	1.07	2.09	1.91	2.29	2.55	1.84	1.61	.43	.50	15.57
	Mills	9	31.8	72.4	102	−25	21	Apr. 29	Oct. 16	170	19	.24	.42	.93	.97	1.79	2.01	2.57	3.12	1.44	1.56	.43	.35	15.83
	Mosquero	12	33.4	74.1	100	−14	22	Apr. 26	Oct. 24	181		.24	.45	.59	1.00	2.14	2.10	2.88	2.93	1.52	1.36	.46	.44	16.11
	Mosquero (near)	12	34.9	72.1	104	−19	11	Apr. 28	Oct. 20	175	13	.21	.46	.76	.88	3.09	2.24	3.25	2.82	1.78	1.34	.46	.43	17.72
	Paloverde						10	Apr. 27	Oct. 15	171	28	.25	.48	.65	1.19	2.11	1.96	2.47	2.60	1.74	1.67	.44	.55	16.11
	Roy	14	31.8	72.7	102	−19	15	Apr. 28	do	170	30	.25	.43	.52	.98	2.22	1.87	2.16	2.38	1.88	1.59	.41	.54	15.23
	Solano	10	33.9	73.0	105	−20	18	Apr. 30	Oct. 20	173	30	.23	.48	.61	1.11	2.07	2.06	2.81	2.92	2.03	1.40	.57	.45	16.74

Hidalgo	Animas	12	39.6	79.0	110	2	12	Apr. 9	Nov. 5	210	16	.31	.73	.62	.21	.36	.46	2.33	2.10	1.35	.83	.62	.90	10.82
	Cloverdale Ranger Station										14	1.25	.83	1.69	.78	.39	.54	3.80	3.69	1.89	1.44	1.45	1.33	19.08
	Dunagan Ranch										10	.60	1.20	1.12	.50	.54	.39	3.26	2.92	1.55	1.05	.66	1.11	14.90
	Lordsburg	10	43.8	79.5	108	−9	21	Mar. 21	Nov. 5	229	40	.69	.72	.70	.24	.24	.38	1.78	1.69	1.13	.78	.60	.88	9.83
	Rodeo						16	Apr. 4	Nov. 8	218	30	.63	.58	.62	.24	.26	.36	2.54	2.07	1.44	.73	.68	1.00	11.15
Lea	Hobbs	19	41.0	79.3	109	−7	20	Apr. 10	Nov. 3	207	21	.26	.31	.61	1.03	1.13	2.60	1.65	3.01	2.30	1.79	.43	.56	15.68
	Lovington	27	42.1	78.1	107	−10	28	Apr. 5	Oct. 31	209	31	.29	.48	.56	.72	1.34	1.65	2.06	2.31	2.37	1.59	.51	.46	14.34
	Pearl (near)	14	39.5	78.4	107	−30	21	Apr. 12	Nov. 2	204	23	.43	.45	.61	.94	1.28	1.37	1.54	2.11	2.25	1.45	.43	.47	13.33
	Plainview						23	do	Oct. 29	200	27	.40	.55	.63	.99	1.55	1.82	1.83	2.27	2.42	1.45	.51	.65	15.07
	Tatum	16	38.7	77.1	108	−32	12	Apr. 17	Oct. 28	194	20	.36	.51	.67	.75	1.79	1.88	2.35	2.73	2.42	1.19	.49	.54	15.68
Lincoln	Ancho	8	35.5	71.8	100	−7	15	Apr. 25	Oct. 22	180	30	.58	.55	.63	.59	.73	1.14	2.33	2.10	1.28	.92	.50	.88	12.23
	Arabela (near)						10	Apr. 27	do	178	16	.79	.57	.93	.87	1.96	2.00	2.58	3.46	3.68	1.48	.78	.51	19.61
	Baca Ranch Ranger Station.										14	.53	.45	.66	.56	1.76	1.43	3.27	3.39	2.10	.99	.46	.50	16.10
	Capitan						24	May 7	Oct. 11	157	30	.68	.78	.90	.86	1.26	1.62	3.22	3.08	2.45	.91	.51	.82	17.09
	Carrizozo	29	38.2	75.3	110	−9	30	Apr. 12	Oct. 31	202	31	.62	.80	.79	.69	.82	1.01	2.46	2.46	1.39	.96	.58	.80	13.38
	Corona	26	33.6	69.4	105	−14	27	Apr. 29	Oct. 21	175	30	.71	.82	.90	.91	1.18	1.29	2.62	2.37	1.52	1.00	.54	.81	14.67
	Fort Stanton	38	34.9	69.2	105	−21	40	Apr. 30	Oct. 11	164	39	.46	.62	.68	.78	1.04	1.51	3.07	2.90	2.15	1.06	.59	.54	15.40
	Gallinas Ranger Station.										29	.61	.68	.81	.90	1.18	1.13	2.59	2.15	1.67	1.02	.52	.81	14.07
	Nogal						12	May 18	Oct. 5	140	13	1.85	1.11	1.35	1.45	1.20	1.86	4.66	4.12	2.20	1.42	.98	1.61	23.81
	Oscura						10	Apr. 3	Nov. 1	212	19	.49	.47	.78	.64	.32	.62	1.89	1.60	1.16	.82	.48	.68	9.95
Luna	Cambray						26	Mar. 29	Nov. 2	218	35	.38	.52	.38	.31	.21	.58	1.74	1.84	1.14	.77	.48	.65	9.00
	Columbus	16	42.5	82.5	111	−6	28	Mar. 22	Nov. 8	231	30	.43	.52	.47	.24	.25	.58	1.99	2.19	.96	.69	.54	.73	9.59
	Deming	33	41.6	78.8	110	−7	39	Apr. 2	Nov. 1	213	40	.35	.58	.48	.25	.28	.52	1.85	1.71	1.36	.80	.43	.59	9.20
	Gage	31	41.2	79.6	111	−9	32	Apr. 8	Nov. 3	209	40	.41	.72	.62	.21	.22	.52	2.05	1.61	1.41	.77	.57	.82	9.93
	Hermanas										24	.45	.68	.40	.20	.22	.59	2.02	1.83	1.13	.82	.58	.81	9.73
McKinley	Blackrock	29	28.6	70.8	103	−31	28	May 7	Oct. 18	164	31	.81	.88	.87	.73	.62	.45	2.46	1.99	1.29	.88	.63	.82	12.43
	Crownpoint	23	28.6	71.4	97	−17	22	May 3	Oct. 17	167	25	.61	.64	.57	.60	.61	.65	2.33	2.02	1.42	.78	.49	.56	11.28
	Fort Wingate	12	32.1	69.6	99	−14	14	May 8	Oct. 2	147	13	.81	1.01	1.16	1.51	.70	.70	2.06	2.79	1.43	.76	.74	.81	14.48
	Gamerco	17	26.7	70.0	98	−20	17	May 5	Oct. 9	157	21	.61	.80	.85	.75	.76	.48	1.88	2.29	1.32	.85	.77	.72	12.08
	McGaffey Ranger Station.	20	22.2	64.8	97	−32	22	June 2	Sept. 26	116	26	1.35	1.71	1.71	1.16	.81	.70	2.74	2.53	1.76	1.12	.94	1.26	17.79
	Ramah										14	.65	1.48	1.01	1.06	.79	.51	2.09	2.61	1.38	.92	.80	.78	14.08
	Tohatchi	16	30.4	73.2	101	−10	15	May 1	Oct. 19	171	23	.70	.60	.70	.65	.70	.55	2.19	1.69	1.43	.75	.56	.66	11.18
Mora	Chacon										30	.75	.99	1.51	1.39	1.95	1.86	3.47	3.75	1.93	1.28	.74	.76	20.38
	Fort Union	21	32.2	65.8	99	−29	23	May 17	Oct. 5	141	20	.26	.53	.52	1.16	1.73	2.75	3.53	3.29	2.16	1.36	.62	.43	18.34
	Levy	27	30.1	68.6	98	−29	26	May 8	Oct. 3	148	29	.35	.63	.81	1.17	2.05	2.11	3.12	3.30	1.60	1.07	.58	.48	17.27
	Valmora	19	31.3	69.0	97	−30	20	May 9	Oct. 11	155	21	.36	.55	.80	.97	2.28	2.01	2.86	3.04	1.83	1.02	.49	.35	16.56
Otero	Alamogordo No. 1	36	42.5	79.4	109	−8	37	Apr. 6	Nov. 5	213	38	.57	.56	.51	.48	.55	.73	1.75	2.09	1.52	1.07	.79	.64	11.26
	Cloudcroft	35	30.1	59.7	87	−11	35	May 16	Oct. 8	145	37	1.59	1.69	1.44	.80	1.11	1.61	4.56	4.77	2.78	1.48	1.30	1.45	24.58
	Mayhill Ranger Station.										22	.60	.70	.74	.60	1.50	1.84	3.59	4.14	3.21	1.61	.63	.67	19.83
	Mescalero	26	33.5	66.5	100	−10	26	May 2	Oct. 17	168	27	.92	1.03	.93	.70	1.07	1.47	4.01	3.71	2.11	1.41	.97	1.11	19.44
	Mountain Park	19	35.7	68.5	99	−10	19	do	Oct. 30	181	24	1.10	1.03	.93	.73	.89	1.52	3.09	3.52	2.21	1.44	.93	1.01	18.40
	Newman						18	Mar. 25	Nov. 7	227	24	.27	.35	.44	.39	.43	.71	1.85	1.53	1.33	.77	.47	.51	9.05
	Orogrande	17	42.7	82.8	116	−11	25	do	Nov. 9	229	32	.39	.45	.52	.32	.47	.85	1.59	1.79	1.23	.77	.50	.57	9.45
	Three Rivers						21	Apr. 4	Nov. 6	216	24	.42	.55	.61	.52	.58	.57	1.61	1.68	1.09	.84	.48	.61	9.56
	Tularosa	28	42.7	79.3	107	−4	30	do	do	216	30	.48	.46	.54	.46	.56	.73	1.38	1.57	1.37	.64	.46	.57	9.22
	Weed Ranger Station						8	May 14	Oct. 5	144	15	.91	.74	1.03	.60	1.54	1.88	4.61	4.34	2.19	1.78	.82	.83	21.27
	Whitetail						16	May 26	Sept. 22	119	25	.99	1.03	1.32	.77	1.77	1.88	4.35	4.47	2.99	1.45	.81	1.02	22.85

NEW MEXICO—Continued

Climatic summary—Continued

County	Station	Temperature: Length of record	Temperature: January average	Temperature: July average	Temperature: Maximum	Temperature: Minimum	Killing frost average dates: Length of record	Killing frost average dates: Last in spring	Killing frost average dates: First in fall	Killing frost average dates: Growing season	Average precipitation: Length of record	January	February	March	April	May	June	July	August	September	October	November	December	Annual
		Yr.	*°F.*	*°F.*	*°F.*	*°F.*	*Yr.*			*Days*	*Yr.*	*In.*	*In.*	*In.*	*In.*	*In.*	*In.*	*In.*	*In.*	*In.*	*In.*	*In.*	*In.*	*In.*
Quay	Glen Rio						12	Apr. 10	Oct. 26	199	15	0.31	0.47	0.70	1.05	1.92	1.87	1.53	3.16	1.17	1.63	0.63	0.52	14.96
	Hassell										10	.40	.40	.30	.76	2.07	1.33	2.14	2.36	2.00	.67	.61	.41	13.45
	Logan	30	36.7	78.5	109	−23	30	Apr. 20	Oct. 18	181	33	.25	.50	.64	1.43	2.14	2.17	2.59	2.60	1.57	1.33	.62	.53	16.37
	Obar	29	36.8	76.6	112	−17	30	do	Oct. 24	187	33	.31	.47	.71	1.60	2.16	2.36	2.24	2.55	1.45	1.43	.60	.50	16.38
	Montoya						20	Apr. 3	Nov. 2	213	24	.28	.52	.63	1.16	1.52	1.68	2.00	2.36	1.25	1.36	.59	.68	14.03
	Porter (near)										16	.28	.48	.74	1.06	2.24	2.23	2.13	2.94	1.54	2.15	.70	.62	17.11
	Quay										16	.25	.38	.62	.83	2.16	1.76	1.81	2.62	1.39	1.54	.83	.63	14.82
	San Jon	31	37.6	78.5	107	−19	31	Apr. 23	Oct. 26	186	32	.25	.34	.51	1.18	2.05	2.24	2.44	2.82	1.35	1.47	.57	.51	15.73
	Tucumcari No. 1	34	38.2	78.9	108	−18	33	Apr. 16	Oct. 27	194	34	.28	.49	.68	1.37	2.34	1.97	2.38	2.86	1.44	1.32	.74	.59	16.46
	Tucumcari No. 2	23	38.7	80.2	108	−10	27	Apr. 15	do	195	29	.39	.44	.71	1.32	2.28	2.05	2.33	3.00	1.34	1.30	.59	.70	16.45
Rio Arriba	Aspen Grove Ranch						8	May 29	Sept. 10	104	30	1.65	2.20	2.29	1.65	1.57	1.27	3.75	2.85	1.80	1.76	1.13	1.69	23.61
	Bateman's Ranch						19	June 4	Sept. 19	107	30	1.75	1.94	2.24	1.31	1.71	1.46	2.86	3.25	2.44	1.98	1.26	1.78	23.98
	Capulin Range Station.										15	.79	1.04	1.14	.94	.98	.91	3.04	2.25	1.43	1.00	.63	.80	14.95
	Chama	40	21.5	63.0	99	−28	36	June 4	Sept. 24	112	34	1.87	2.14	1.91	1.50	1.46	.96	2.85	2.78	1.99	1.50	1.08	1.89	21.93
	Dulce	38	17.6	66.2	99	−48	32	June 10	Sept. 19	101	33	1.17	1.57	1.59	1.32	1.09	.90	2.73	2.33	1.65	1.31	1.30	1.37	18.33
	Espanola	29	29.1	72.1	106	−23	38	Apr. 29	Oct. 10	164	29	.40	.42	.47	.89	.96	.77	1.48	1.77	1.08	.89	.62	.36	10.11
	Gavilan	10	17.6	64.3	97	−44	10	June 21	Sept. 10	81	14	.92	1.55	1.27	.93	1.18	1.16	2.63	3.07	2.34	1.15	1.10	1.09	18.39
	Governador							May 22	Oct. 8	139	8	.50	1.81	.75	.67	.88	.79	1.29	1.53	2.12	.70	.53	.80	12.37
	Haynes	13	22.3	68.8	99	−36	13	May 18	Sept. 23	128	16	.69	.74	.78	.80	.56	.72	2.25	1.68	1.10	1.27	.39	.82	11.80
	San Antone Ranger Station.										12	.76	1.18	1.86	.92	.88	.88	2.15	1.76	.97	.89	.76	1.53	14.54
	Truchas	29	26.6	62.9	95	−32	31	May 17	Oct. 4	140	30	.63	.84	.83	1.14	1.33	1.23	2.56	2.47	1.78	1.31	.71	.78	15.61
Roosevelt	Elida										26	.27	.30	.62	1.10	1.69	2.08	2.19	2.44	2.20	1.17	.50	.46	15.02
	Portales	31	37.0	77.0	109	−28	28	Apr. 15	Oct. 22	190	32	.25	.39	.84	1.32	2.27	2.33	2.52	2.80	2.28	1.29	.66	.63	17.58
	Richland (near)	24	38.7	76.4	109	−29	24	Apr. 18	Oct. 27	192	26	.28	.29	.62	.96	1.61	2.04	2.20	2.14	2.16	1.24	.55	.48	14.57
	Texico (near)										18	.28	.45	.76	1.96	1.76	2.93	2.23	2.52	2.54	1.81	.50	.80	18.54
	Valley View										16	.30	.31	.55	.75	1.65	1.52	2.20	2.16	1.79	1.60	.41	.46	13.70
Sandoval	Alamos Ranch	18	27.2	66.7	95	−14	23	May 8	Oct. 18	163	28	.96	.70	.98	1.10	1.48	1.46	3.30	3.34	2.05	1.51	.68	.71	18.27
	Frijoles Canyon										14	.42	.90	.81	.75	1.59	1.17	2.53	2.55	2.00	1.15	.59	.80	15.26
	Jemez Springs	29	31.9	69.4	95	−13	29	May 1	Oct. 24	176	29	.78	1.09	1.03	1.13	1.45	1.52	3.11	2.77	2.09	1.61	.78	.83	18.19
	Lee Ranch	15	20.5	58.6	90	−24	15	June 11	Sept. 17	98	15	.68	1.81	1.27	.98	1.73	1.74	4.09	3.75	3.14	1.39	.87	1.00	22.45
	Regina	22	23.0	64.8	106	−30	22	May 30	Sept. 26	119	24	.75	1.36	1.10	1.22	1.23	.90	2.68	2.30	2.11	1.38	.92	.92	16.87
	Selsor Ranch	24	19.5	61.3	96	−40	24	June 22	Sept. 6	76	27	1.29	1.81	1.69	1.44	1.73	1.32	3.81	2.88	2.39	1.44	1.06	1.44	22.30
San Juan	Aztec	27	26.8	73.7	104	−27	29	May 5	Oct. 7	155	33	.57	.65	.77	.55	.50	.50	1.20	1.21	1.08	.85	.66	.63	9.17
	Bloomfield	34	26.8	74.7	106	−35	34	May 12	Oct. 6	147	35	.45	.73	.66	.69	.54	.55	1.23	1.32	1.05	.77	.57	.58	9.14
	Chaco Canyon										8	.30	.93	.37	.21	.67	.29	1.23	1.44	1.17	.59	.63	.46	8.29

	Fruitland	28	29.6	74.0	110	−21	28	May 4	Oct. 12	161	26	.49	.51	.48	.54	.28	.23	1.03	.84	.62	.73	.51	.50	6.76
	Farmington										24	.50	.72	.67	.57	.52	.37	1.19	1.05	1.05	.80	.50	.50	8.44
	Rosa (near)										13	.61	.77	1.02	1.39	.85	.73	1.97	1.89	1.38	.70	1.20	.66	13.17
	Shiprock	12	28.1	76.6	106	−18	12	May 8	Oct. 18	163	13	.31	.52	.68	.62	.56	.33	.92	.98	1.36	.32	.50	.49	7.59
San Miguel	Bell Ranch	34	36.3	77.7	107	−26	34	Apr. 19	Oct. 23	187	40	.24	.42	.59	1.35	1.90	2.00	2.56	2.19	1.65	1.28	.60	.47	15.25
	Cabeza										13	.31	.46	.55	1.40	1.66	1.40	3.02	2.53	1.53	1.39	.40	.50	15.15
	Campana	15	35.8	79.0	108	−16	15	Apr. 20	Oct. 24	187	20	.25	.39	.62	1.36	2.06	1.88	2.18	2.49	1.48	1.50	.52	.62	15.35
	Doretta										21	.60	.63	1.09	.97	1.90	1.43	2.86	2.35	2.07	1.01	.42	.45	15.78
	Harvey's Upper Ranch.	11	26.4	58.2	85	−18	15	May 25	Sept. 21	119	15	1.51	1.84	2.37	2.52	2.41	3.43	5.96	6.10	2.16	2.49	1.10	1.54	33.43
	Gallinas Plant Station.	20	30.1	63.2	93	−24	20	May 20	Oct. 2	135	31	.64	1.20	1.42	1.72	2.12	2.27	4.85	3.81	2.11	1.42	.79	.83	23.18
	Las Vegas	40	32.4	70.3	99	−31	40	May 6	Oct. 8	155	40	.42	.64	.74	1.17	1.86	2.09	3.37	3.16	2.07	1.03	.60	.52	17.67
	Mineral Hill										20	.70	.99	.98	2.03	1.33	2.42	4.21	3.52	1.72	1.53	.88	.75	21.06
	Onava										31	.39	.65	.68	.97	1.70	1.86	2.73	3.19	1.55	1.13	.44	.47	15.76
	Pecos Ranger Station										21	.67	.79	.99	1.02	1.71	1.18	2.63	2.72	2.09	1.15	.51	.53	15.99
	Rencona (near)										14	.57	.82	.80	.55	1.96	1.33	2.60	3.01	1.82	.97	.51	.63	15.57
	Rociado	20	31.0	62.0	93	−32	22	May 28	Sept. 23	118	23	.68	.98	1.42	2.26	1.72	2.04	4.61	3.76	1.76	1.51	.96	1.05	22.75
	Trementina										22	.29	.49	.67	1.38	2.09	1.92	2.12	2.41	1.51	1.50	.66	.64	15.68
	Trujillo										16	.41	.52	1.25	1.23	2.23	2.07	2.83	2.52	1.66	1.91	.84	.61	18.08
	Winsor's	38	26.7	59.4	90	−27	40	June 11	Sept. 19	100	40	1.12	1.69	1.76	1.67	1.91	2.04	4.33	3.74	2.45	1.72	1.07	1.06	24.56
Sante Fe	Cundiyo										15	.46	.46	.60	.76	.70	.88	1.26	1.20	.81	1.01	.47	.58	9.19
	Sante Fe	40	29.2	68.9	97	−13	40	Apr. 24	Oct. 19	178	40	.66	.74	.81	1.07	1.46	1.19	2.28	1.90	1.68	1.11	.71	.58	14.19
	Sante Fe Canyon										13	.79	.87	1.22	1.38	1.45	1.29	3.36	2.22	1.49	1.85	.76	1.01	17 69
	Stanley (near)	25	28.1	70.2	99	−27	24	May 14	Oct. 6	145	28	.62	.48	.56	.60	1.07	1.09	2.37	1.90	1.42	1.11	.38	.53	12.13
Sierra	Chloride Ranger Station.										22	.36	.80	.50	.64	.76	.74	3.07	3.33	2.28	.87	.74	.84	14.93
	Elephant Butte Dam	37	40.6	79.0	109	−5	40	Apr. 2	Nov. 11	223	40	.31	.49	.46	.44	.35	.55	1.69	1.96	1.30	.79	.47	.60	9.41
	Hermosa	12	30.8	66.4	100	−23	14	May 13	Oct. 8	148	15	.66	.60	.86	.67	.57	.93	3.76	3.62	2.06	1.66	.92	1.48	17.79
	Hillsboro	12	41.4	76.3	107	1	15	Apr. 12	Oct. 30	201	25	.44	.88	.54	.38	.44	.59	2.43	2.24	2.05	.91	.55	.84	12.29
	Kingston						12	Apr. 26	Oct. 26	183	24	.89	1.20	1.08	.53	.69	.84	3.25	3.90	2.61	1.32	.93	1.05	18.29
	Lake Valley						16	Apr. 11	Oct. 30	202	32	.60	.93	.63	.43	.41	.87	2.72	2.84	1.46	.96	.75	.85	13.45
Socorro	Augustine	11	30.5	69.5	100	−25	11	May 24	Sept. 24	123	10	.39	.69	.83	.55	1.31	.63	2.49	2.35	2.18	1.04	.19	.66	13.31
	Glorieta Ranch	14	39.4	76.2	103	1	17	Apr. 10	Nov. 6	210	19	.41	.49	.59	.50	.66	.78	2.24	2.03	1.50	1.24	.51	.93	11.88
	Magdalena	28	32.9	70.8	102	−21	30	Apr. 29	Oct. 19	173	32	.61	.51	.68	.97	.64	.73	2.63	2.68	1.48	.86	.53	.67	12.99
	Rosedale (near)	26	35.5	70.2	102	−10	26	Apr. 28	Oct. 18	173	28	.53	.62	.76	.90	.68	1.07	3.19	3.47	1.46	1.16	.75	.97	15.56
	San Marcial	37	38.2	78.0	113	−9	40	Apr. 9	Oct. 25	199	40	.33	.41	.38	.36	.41	.67	1.61	1.43	1.21	.63	.43	.44	8.31
	Socorro	40	37.4	79.7	108	−16	40	do	Oct. 22	196	39	.44	.48	.59	.71	.64	.62	1.75	1.56	1.50	.97	.47	.61	10.34
Taos	Cerro	23	20.7	64.4	100	−34	24	May 12	Sept. 30	141	7	.54	.84	.49	.68	2.15	.90	1.60	2.52	2.37	.95	.34	.49	13.87
	Eagle Rock Ranger Station.										17	.68	.61	.94	1.23	1.87	1.17	2.73	2.15	1.68	1.42	.58	.65	15.71
	Red River Canyon	29	18.8	59.4	94	−34	32	June 13	Sept. 9	88	33	1.24	1.48	2.09	1.99	1.89	1.47	3.69	3.02	1.76	1.36	.94	1.11	22.04
	Taos	37	26.3	68.5	101	−27	37	May 12	Oct. 5	146	38	.68	.76	.87	1.05	1.40	.96	1.85	1.83	1.26	.96	.60	.49	12.71
	Taos Canyon										30	1.13	1.31	1.58	1.60	1.83	1.53	3.12	2.71	1.70	1.38	.83	.99	19.71
	Tres Piedras	22	20.4	62.9	93	−35	32	June 1	Sept. 22	113	34	.88	1.17	1.04	1.02	1.23	1.03	2.96	2.17	1.42	1.38	.70	.84	15.84
Torrance	Duran	21	35.2	72.0	102	−11	21	Apr. 24	Oct. 19	178	25	.43	.65	.81	.95	1.33	1.45	2.53	2.53	1.44	.97	.45	.69	14.23
	Estancia	29	29.6	69.4	102	−33	29	May 13	Oct. 8	148	34	.54	.54	.65	.93	.99	1.01	2.31	2.43	1.38	1.07	.68	.69	13.22
	McIntosh (near)	11	29.0	66.3	98	−22	11	May 9	Oct. 17	161	12	.14	.32	.62	.23	1.60	1.64	1.35	1.20	3.72	.54	.14	.34	11.84
	Mountainair	27	31.7	70.5	99	−21	30	do	Oct. 8	152	32	.68	.91	.89	1.22	1.15	1.07	2.71	2.70	1.63	1.05	.82	1.11	15.94
	Palma						8	May 12	Oct. 13	154	25	.49	.63	.90	.81	.98	.97	1.79	1.59	1.18	.92	.60	.71	11.57
	Progresso										9	.54	.70	.72	.80	1.15	1.46	3.21	2.51	1.73	.74	.84	.86	15.26
	Tajique (near)	19	28.0	65.0	92	−17	19	May 17	Oct. 3	139	19	.93	1.25	1.33	1.41	2.02	1.51	2.93	2.97	1.95	1.24	.90	1.08	19.52
	Torrance						13	Apr. 29	Oct. 16	170	19	.46	.59	.59	.67	.67	1.25	2.77	2.43	1.52	.86	.29	.79	12.89

NEW MEXICO—Continued

Climatic summary—Continued

County	Station	Temperature					Killing frost average dates				Average precipitation													
		Length of record	January average	July average	Maximum	Minimum	Length of record	Last in spring	First in fall	Growing season	Length of record	January	February	March	April	May	June	July	August	September	October	November	December	Annual
		Yr.	*°F.*	*°F.*	*°F.*	*°F.*	*Yr.*			*Days*	*Yr.*	*In.*	*In.*	*In.*	*In.*	*In.*	*In.*	*In.*	*In.*	*In.*	*In.*	*In.*	*In.*	*In.*
Union	Amistad						8	Apr. 26	Oct. 24	181	14	0.20	0.27	0.57	0.81	2.66	1.94	1.64	2.59	1.49	1.20	0.34	0.44	14.15
	Capulin	12	27.0	66.9	97	−25	12	May 13	Oct. 3	143	19	.68	.86	.95	.83	1.21	1.14	2.83	2.16	1.56	.91	.56	.66	14.35
	Clayton	32	34.3	74.2	105	−18	34	Apr. 23	Oct. 17	177	31	.22	.39	.72	1.40	2.40	1.77	2.74	2.06	1.76	1.34	.55	.44	15.79
	Clayton (near)	13	33.3	75.9	105	−13	12	Apr. 25	Oct. 21	179	13	.14	.22	.58	.69	2.29	1.79	1.74	1.76	1.77	1.35	.38	.26	12.97
	Des Moines	24	31.0	68.3	102	−18	23	May 13	Oct. 7	147	23	.39	.48	1.02	1.39	2.11	1.70	2.72	3.12	1.97	1.23	.70	.40	17.23
	Folsom	16	30.8	68.4	97	−21	15	May 10	Oct. 2	145	15	.32	.74	.70	2.61	2.53	2.00	2.83	2.75	2.09	1.12	.86	.64	19.19
	Hayden (near)	18	34.3	74.4	108	−19	24	Apr. 27	Oct. 19	175	29	.22	.33	.56	1.23	2.14	1.92	2.29	2.52	1.61	1.33	.35	.50	15.00
	Ione						14	Apr. 28	Oct. 24	179	29	.27	.30	.67	1.36	2.26	2.28	2.41	3.09	1.48	1.54	.37	.56	16.59
	Pasamonte	13	31.3	71.1	101	−20	18	Apr. 30	Oct. 15	168	29	.18	.35	.62	1.31	1.97	2.35	2.60	2.66	1.46	1.16	.29	.40	15.35
	Pennington (near)						10	May 3	Oct. 14	164	14	.22	.32	.47	.88	2.26	2.19	2.36	2.34	1.84	1.90	.31	.25	15.34
	Vance (near)					−5	24	Apr. 26	Oct. 18	175	28	.20	.37	.62	1.22	2.21	2.22	2.34	2.47	1.48	1.49	.35	.44	15.41
Valencia	Bluewater	30	27.5	69.1	105	−25	30	do	Sept. 25	122	30	.43	.53	.54	.50	.63	.51	2.15	2.21	1.46	.61	.38	.40	10.35
	Laguna	24	33.0	74.0	103	−20	21	Apr. 25	Oct. 17	175	26	.38	.52	.55	.86	.58	.91	2.39	1.78	1.45	.55	.46	.62	11.05
	Los Lunas (near)	40	31.6	77.4	106	−25	39	Apr. 20	Oct. 20	183	40	.39	.31	.48	.60	.56	.65	1.23	1.31	1.20	.76	.41	.41	8.31
	San Fidel	19	30.0	72.0	100	−11	12	May 2	do	171	19	.30	.46	.40	.55	.86	.79	1.84	2.13	1.61	.53	.39	.41	10.27

Precipitation and temperature—State unit values

[This tabulation gives the mean annual, mean monthly, and average seasonal precipitation, 1886–1938, the percentage of normal precipitation for spring and for summer for each year, 1902–38, and the mean annual temperatures, 1892–1938, for New Mexico]

Precipitation

Year	Mean
	In.
1886	15.97
1887	15.32
1888	14.63
1889	10.97
1890	12.83
1891	14.69
1892	9.51
1893	12.40
1894	10.47
1895	15.56
1896	13.23
1897	16.52
1898	14.03
1899	10.98
1900	13.52
1901	14.50
1902	9.97
1903	11.25
1904	14.41
1905	20.95
1906	15.89
1907	16.13
1908	12.68
1909	12.83
1910	9.46
1911	17.92
1912	13.92
1913	15.36
1914	19.45
1915	17.64
1916	15.95
1917	9.49
1918	15.08
1919	20.95
1920	14.87
1921	16.46

Precipitation

Year	Mean
	In.
1922	10.86
1923	19.46
1924	10.65
1925	13.86
1926	17.44
1927	13.94
1928	15.09
1929	16.48
1930	14.64
1931	18.32
1932	16.20
1933	12.83
1934	10.08
1935	14.85
1936	13.50
1937	15.00
1938	14.62

Month	Mean
	In.
January	0.58
February	.72
March	.75
April	.87
May	1.15
June	1.26
July	2.48
August	2.41
September	1.73
October	1.12
November	.64
December	.70

Precipitation

Season	Average
	In.
Winter	2.00
Spring	2.77
Summer	6.15
Fall	3.49

Spring precipation (in percent of normal)

Year	Percent
1902	56
1903	49
1904	39
1905	206
1906	100
1907	112
1908	91
1909	76
1910	46
1911	103
1912	112
1913	75
1914	164
1915	205
1916	105
1917	73
1918	64
1919	234
1920	100
1921	105
1922	107
1923	93
1924	97
1925	62
1926	224
1927	43

Spring precipitation (in percent of normal)

Year	Percent
1928	135
1929	135
1930	93
1931	157
1932	108
1933	45
1934	77
1935	119
1936	87
1937	166
1938	73

Summer precipitation (in percent of normal)

Year	Percent
1902	75
1903	110
1904	94
1905	91
1906	102
1907	123
1908	107
1909	100
1910	87
1911	123
1912	116
1913	97
1914	148
1915	104
1916	108
1917	71
1918	95
1919	113

Summer precipitation (in percent of normal)

Year	Percent
1920	113
1921	175
1922	70
1923	118
1924	80
1925	121
1926	83
1927	131
1928	93
1929	122
1930	110
1931	104
1932	111
1933	122
1934	72
1935	93
1936	83
1937	82
1938	92

Temperature

Year	Mean
	°F.
1892	52.4
1893	52.4
1894	52.8
1895	52.6
1896	54.0
1897	52.4
1898	52.4
1899	52.8
1900	54.2
1901	54.2

Temperature

Year	Mean
	°F.
1902	53.6
1903	52.0
1904	53.7
1905	52.8
1906	53.0
1907	53.8
1908	52.8
1909	53.0
1910	54.6
1911	52.8
1912	50.5
1913	50.9
1914	52.9
1915	51.6
1916	53.0
1917	52.2
1918	52.1
1919	51.2
1920	51.9
1921	53.8
1922	53.0
1923	52.0
1924	52.4
1925	53.0
1926	52.2
1927	53.9
1928	52.4
1929	51.2
1930	51.7
1931	52.2
1932	51.7
1933	53.0
1934	55.1
1935	52.7
1936	52.7
1937	52.5
1938	52.6

NEW MEXICO—Continued

Dates of last killing frost in spring and first in fall, with length of growing season

Year	Agricultural College			Albuquerque			Bloomfield			Deming			Roswell			Taos		
	Last in spring	First in fall	Growing season [1]	Last in spring	First in fall	Growing season [1]	Last in spring	First in fall	Growing season [1]	Last in spring	First in fall	Growing season [1]	Last in spring	First in fall	Growing season [1]	Last in spring	First in fall	Growing season [1]
			Days			*Days*			*Days*			*Days*			*Days*			*Days*
1899	May 4	Oct. 14	163		Oct. 16					Mar. 16	Nov. 3	232	Apr. 9	Oct. 17	191			
1900	Apr. 11	Oct. 22	194	Apr. 12	Oct. 31	202				Mar. 1			Apr. 13	Nov. 1	202			
1901	Apr. 18	Nov. 4	200	Apr. 18	Nov. 4	200				Apr. 1			Apr. 18	Nov. 4	200			
1902	Apr. 10	Oct. 26	199	Apr. 23	Oct. 27	187				Mar. 26	Nov. 2	221	Mar. 31	Nov. 3	217	May 20	Oct. 4	137
1903	Mar. 24	Oct. 22	212	Apr. 13	Sept. 17	157				Mar. 19			Apr. 30	Oct. 16	169	May 19	Oct. 3	137
1904	May 3	Oct. 20	170	Apr. 30	Oct. 19	172		Sept. 28		Mar. 14	Oct. 25	225	Apr. 10	Oct. 19	192	May 8	Oct. 17	162
1905	Mar. 29	Oct. 25	210	Apr. 20	Oct. 18	181	May 11	Oct. 10	152	Apr. 4	do	204	Apr. 5	Oct. 26	204	May 11	Sept. 19	131
1906	Mar. 20	Oct. 23	217	Apr. 27	Oct. 14	170	May 30	Oct. 5	128	Mar. 20	Oct. 23	217	Mar. 20	Oct. 22	216	May 31	Oct. 5	127
1907	Apr. 23	Nov. 14	205	Apr. 20	Nov. 11	205	May 24	Sept. 23	122	Apr. 22	Nov. 12	204	Apr. 22	Nov. 11	203	May 24	Sept. 30	129
1908	Mar. 13	Oct. 20	221	Apr. 9	Oct. 26	200	June 4	Sept. 27	115	Mar. 19	Oct. 21	216	Mar. 23	Oct. 20	211	May 28	Sept. 27	122
1909	Apr. 8	Oct. 10	185	May 1	Nov. 16	199	May 31	Sept. 23	115	Apr. 23	Oct. 9	169	May 2	Oct. 10	161	Apr. 26	Oct. 9	166
1910	Apr. 17	Oct. 21	187	Apr. 4	Oct. 21	200	May 22	Oct. 3	134	Mar. 30	Oct. 20	204	Apr. 16	Oct. 21	188	Apr. 22	Oct. 20	181
1911	Mar. 12	Oct. 22	224	Apr. 19	Oct. 17	181	May 21	do	135	Mar. 13	Oct. 22	223	Mar. 15	Oct. 17	216	May 21	Oct. 16	148
1912	May 4	Oct. 29	178	Apr. 14	Oct. 29	198	May 17	Sept. 17	123	Apr. 13	Oct. 13	183	Apr. 3	Oct. 30	210	May 15	Sept. 22	130
1913	Apr. 12	Oct. 27	198	Apr. 12	Oct. 27	198	May 20	Oct. 7	140	Mar. 26	Oct. 25	213	Apr. 12	Oct. 27	198	Apr. 25	Oct. 7	165
1914	Mar. 23	Oct. 28	219	Mar. 22	Nov. 12	235	May 3	Sept. 23	143	Mar. 21	Nov. 20	244	Mar. 23	Nov. 9	231	Apr. 27	Oct. 5	161
1915	Mar. 22	Nov. 8	231	Apr. 28			May 4	Sept. 14	133	Mar. 22	Nov. 11	234	Apr. 2	Nov. 12	224	May 4	Sept. 27	146
1916	Mar. 25	do	228		Oct. 20		May 27	Oct. 20	146	Apr. 8	Nov. 10	216	Apr. 8	Oct. 20	195	May 16	Oct. 19	156
1917	Apr. 6	Oct. 19	196				May 7	Sept. 25	141	Apr. 5	Oct. 19	197	May 7	Oct. 19	165	May 27	Oct. 18	144
1918	Mar. 18	Oct. 27	223				May 31	Oct. 26	148	Apr. 6	Oct. 27	204	Apr. 21	Nov. 8	201	Apr. 28	Oct. 26	181
1919	Mar. 17	Nov. 1	229	Apr. 9	Oct. 28	202	June 1	Oct. 19	140	Mar. 24	Nov. 10	231	Mar. 11	Nov. 2	236	June 2	Oct. 17	137
1920	Apr. 5	Oct. 14	192	Apr. 27	Oct. 22	178	Apr. 27	Sept. 27	153	Apr. 27	Oct. 12	168	Apr. 12	Oct. 29	200	Apr. 27	Sept. 26	152
1921	Apr. 26	Oct. 26	183	Apr. 26	Oct. 29	186	May 7	Oct. 26	172	Apr. 25	Oct. 28	186	Apr. 18	Oct. 27	192	May 7	Oct. 26	172
1922	Apr. 19	Nov. 1	196	Apr. 11	do	201	May 12	Oct. 7	148	Apr. 19	Oct. 31	195	Apr. 19	Oct. 31	195	May 12	Oct. 16	157
1923	Mar. 21	Oct. 27	220	Mar. 24	Oct. 26	216	May 2	Oct. 11	162	Mar. 22	Oct. 28	220	Mar. 24	Nov. 6	227	Apr. 24	Sept. 29	158
1924	Apr. 17	Oct. 28	194	Apr. 27	Oct. 31	187	May 7	Sept. 21	137	Apr. 26	Nov. 24	212	Apr. 1	Oct. 31	213	May 29	Sept. 19	113
1925	Apr. 3	Nov. 7	218	Mar. 20	Oct. 30	224	Apr. 25	Oct. 15	173	Mar. 19	Nov. 4	230	Mar. 19	Oct. 28	223	Apr. 25	Sept. 24	152
1926	Mar. 30	Nov. 5	220	Mar. 30	Oct. 31	215	Mar. 31	Oct. 31	214	Mar. 31	Nov. 9	223	Mar. 30	Nov. 9	224	May 16	Oct. 4	141
1927	Apr. 14	Oct. 31	200	Mar. 21	Nov. 15	239	May 23	Oct. 1	131	Apr. 13	Oct. 30	200	Apr. 22	Nov. 12	204	May 24	Sept. 28	127
1928	Apr. 15	Nov. 17	216	Apr. 10	Nov. 17	221	May 4	Oct. 15	164	Apr. 21	Nov. 14	207	Apr. 10	Nov. 3	207	May 4	Sept. 14	133
1929	Mar. 21	Oct. 31	224	Apr. 11	Oct. 24	196	May 29	Oct. 24	148	Mar. 17	Oct. 25	222	May 2	Oct. 24	175	May 3	Sept. 9	129
1930	Mar. 30	Nov. 20	235	Mar. 30	Oct. 29	213		Sept. 26		Mar. 29	Oct. 29	214	Mar. 27	Nov. 16	234	May 23	Sept. 26	126
1931	Mar. 31	Nov. 14	228	Mar. 28	Nov. 15	232	Apr. 21	Oct. 13	175	Mar. 28	Nov. 15	232	Mar. 31	Nov. 20	234	May 12	Oct. 14	155
1932	Apr. 28	Oct. 26	181	Apr. 28	Oct. 26	181	May 6	Oct. 5	152	Mar. 23	Nov. 12	234	Mar. 22	Oct. 26	218	May 31	Oct. 5	127
1933	May 13	Nov. 3	174	Apr. 14	Nov. 3	203	May 15	Oct. 16	154	Apr. 15	Nov. 3	202	Apr. 14	Nov. 4	204	May 16	Oct. 15	152

1934	Mar. 20	Nov. 21	246	Apr. 4	Oct. 24	203	Apr. 25	Sept. 26	154	Mar. 18	Nov. 21	248	Mar. 19	Nov. 22	248	Apr. 18	Oct. 20	185
1935	Mar. 12	Nov. 12	245	Apr. 10	Oct. 25	198	May 4	Oct. 17	166	May 2	Oct. 26	177	Mar. 12	Nov. 5	238	May 15	Sept. 28	136
1936	Apr. 8	Nov. 4	210	do	Nov. 3	207	May 9	Oct. 7	151	Apr. 8	Nov. 3	209	Apr. 7	Nov. 3	210	May 11	Sept. 26	138
1937	Apr. 6	Nov. 9	217	Apr. 25	Nov. 9	198		Sept. 26		Apr. 1	Nov. 12	225	Apr. 5	Nov. 11	220	May 8	Oct. 19	164
1938	Apr. 11	Nov. 3	206	Apr. 9	Oct. 21	195	May 8	Oct. 17	162	Apr. 9	Nov. 3	208	Apr. 7	Oct. 24	200	May 23	Oct. 5	135
Mean	Apr. 6	Oct. 31	208	Apr. 13	Oct. 28	198	May 12	Oct. 6	147	Apr. 2	Nov. 1	213	do	Oct. 31	207	May 12	do	146
Extremes	Mar. 12[2]	Oct. 10[4]	[6] 163	Mar. 20[2]	Sept. 17[4]	[6] 157	Mar. 31[2]	Sept. 14[4]	[6] 115	Mar. 1[2]	Oct. 9[4]	[6] 168	Mar. 12[2]	Oct. 10[4]	[6] 161	Apr. 18[2]	Sept. 9[4]	[6] 113
	May 13[3]	Nov. 21[5]	[7] 246	May 1[3]	Nov. 17[5]	[7] 239	June 4[3]	Oct. 31[5]	[7] 214	May 2[3]	Nov. 24[5]	[7] 248	May 7[3]	Nov. 22[5]	[7] 248	June 2[3]	Oct. 26[5]	[7] 185

[1] Number of days between last killing frost in spring and first in fall.
[2] Earliest date in spring.
[3] Latest date in spring.
[4] Earliest date in fall.
[5] Latest date in fall.
[6] Shortest growing season.
[7] Longest growing season.

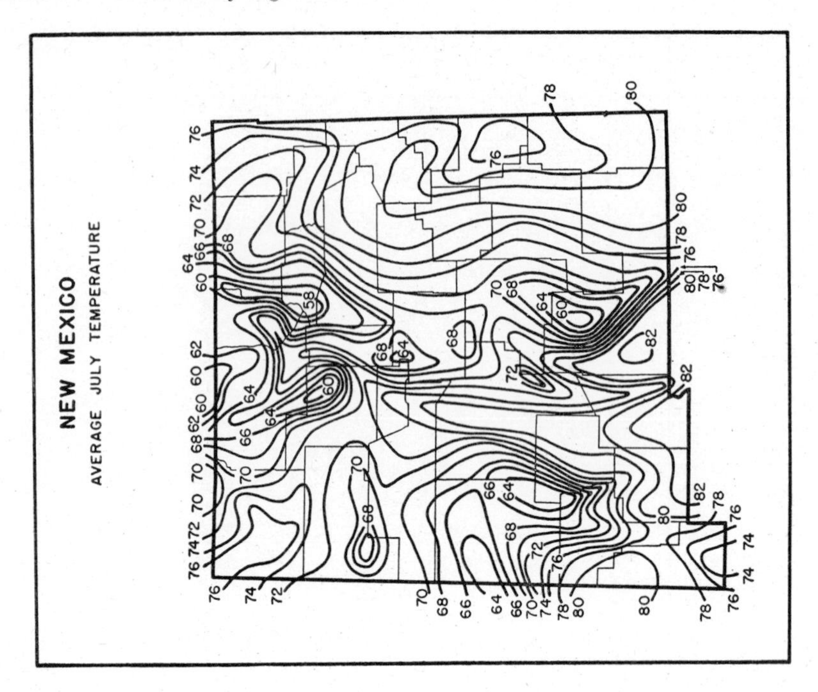
NEW MEXICO
AVERAGE JULY TEMPERATURE

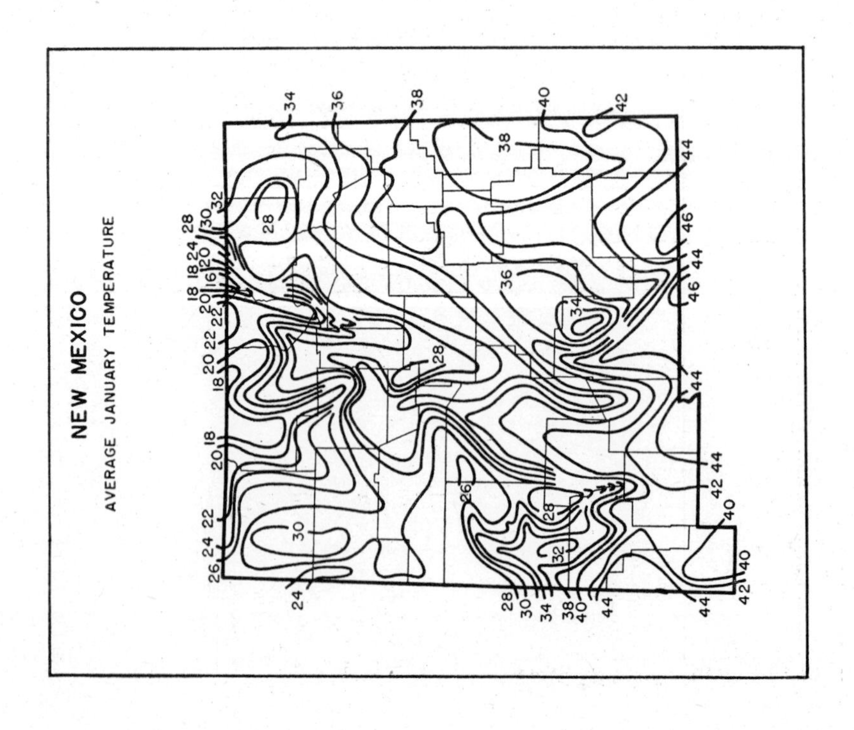
NEW MEXICO
AVERAGE JANUARY TEMPERATURE

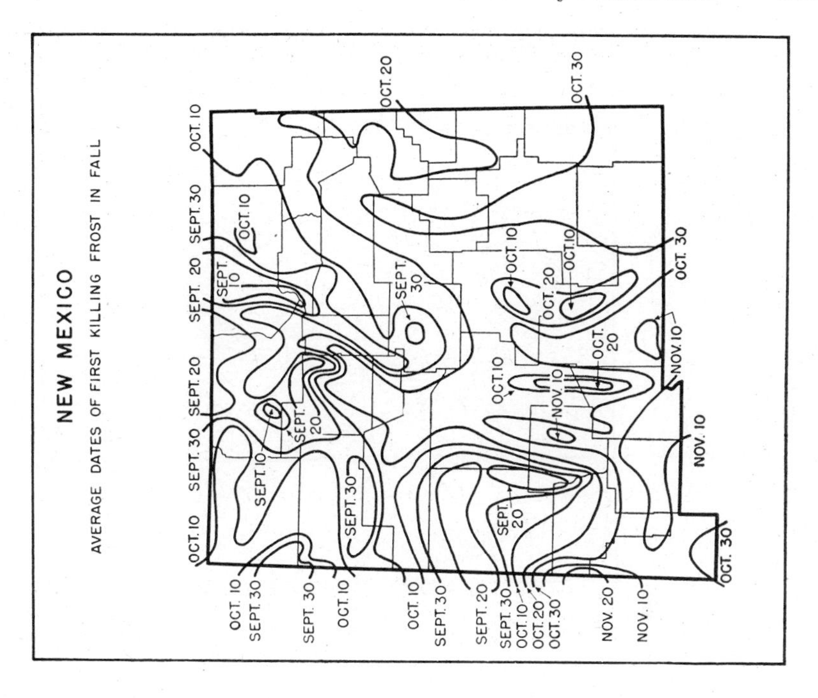
NEW MEXICO
AVERAGE DATES OF FIRST KILLING FROST IN FALL

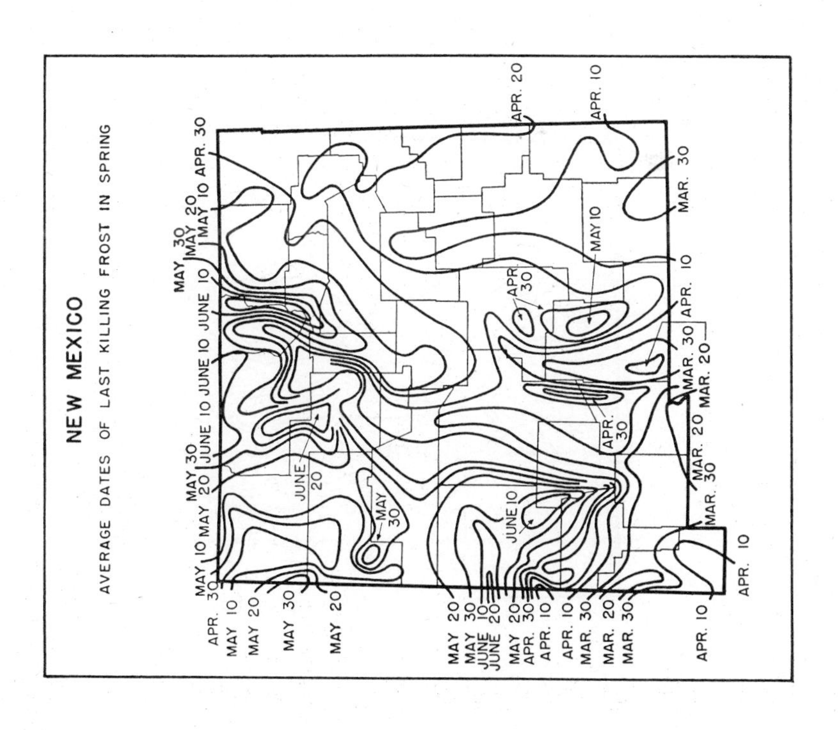
NEW MEXICO
AVERAGE DATES OF LAST KILLING FROST IN SPRING

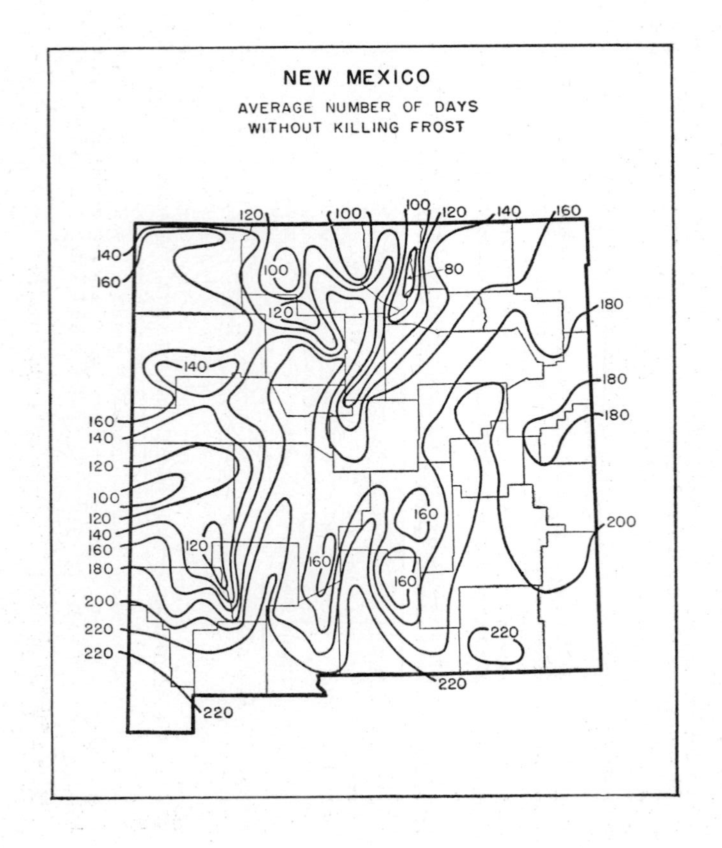
NEW MEXICO
AVERAGE NUMBER OF DAYS
WITHOUT KILLING FROST

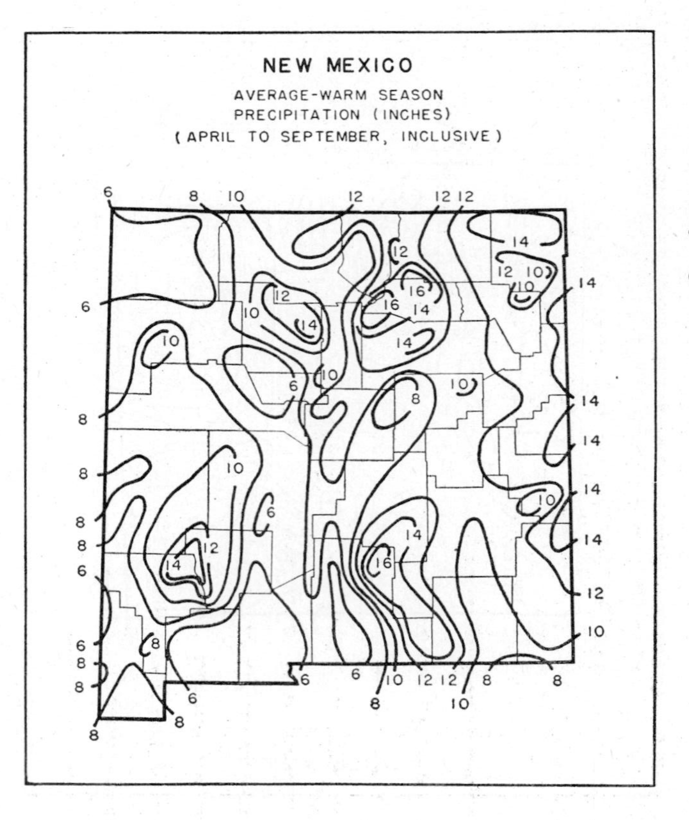
NEW MEXICO
AVERAGE-WARM SEASON
PRECIPITATION (INCHES)
(APRIL TO SEPTEMBER, INCLUSIVE)

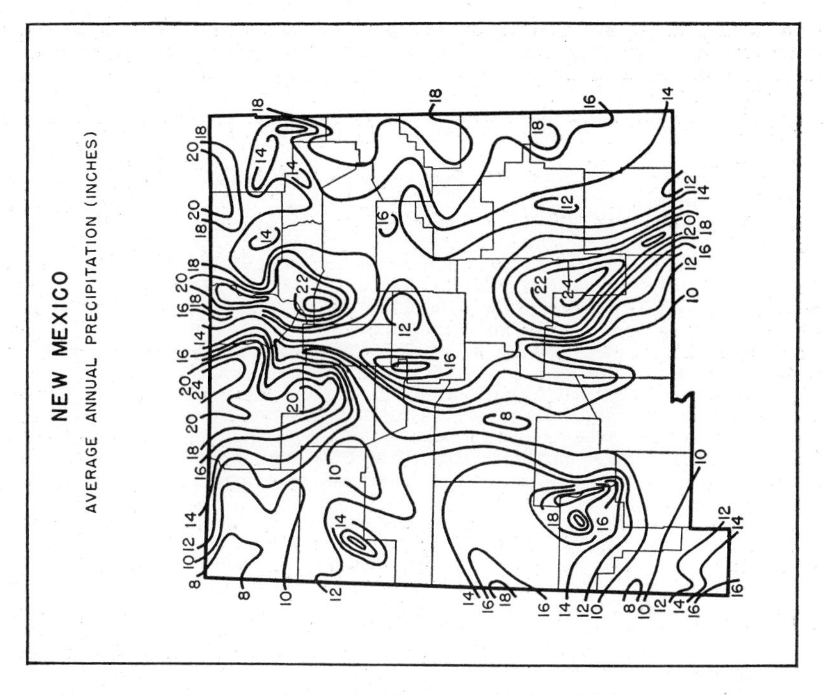

SUPPLEMENTARY CLIMATIC NOTES FOR NEW MEXICO

New Mexico contains 122,634 square miles, extending about 350 miles from north to south and slightly less from east to west. Its topography is extremely varied, with elevations ranging from 3,000 feet along the southeastern border to about 14,000 feet at the top of the highest mountains. Some 28 percent of the area of the State, mostly in the higher sections, is covered with timber, consisting principally of pine, cedar, piñon, and juniper. Only about 5 percent of the area is suitable for agriculture; the land is used largely for grazing purposes.

The State is drained by the Canadian, Pecos, Rio Grande, San Juan, and Gila Rivers. The first two have their headwaters in the northeast and drain all of the region east of the Sangre de Cristo, Jicarilla, and Sacramento Mountains. Between these mountains and the Continental Divide, the Rio Grande flows in a southwesterly direction until near the southern border, thence southeasterly, serving approximately two-fifths of the State, an area nearly as large as the Pecos and Canadian watersheds combined. The San Juan in the northwest and the Gila in the southwest drain the area west of the Continental Divde, with the exception of the San Augustine Plains, which is a large closed basin lying between these two watersheds.

On the whole, the State consists of high plateaus or mesas, with numerous mountain ranges, canyons, valleys, and normally dry arroyos. Some of the valleys are large enough to make agricultural operations possible under irrigation, with several extensive projects operating in the Rio Grande and Pecos Valleys, and others now under way in the Canadian River watershed.

New Mexico is semiarid, with an average annual precipitation of about 15 inches. However, it is not unusual during the summer months for heavy downpours to occur in connection with local thunderstorms. Some farming is done in east-central counties without the aid of irrigation; but for the most part, all agricultural areas are dependent upon irrigation for the successful raising of crops. The months of greatest rainfall are July and August, during which nearly one-third of the annual amount is received.

While the mean annual temperature is 53° F., variations in the mean of as much as 26° occur within the State, the temperature for any given locality depending largely upon latitude and altitude. The eastern section has some of the characteristics of the Great Plains, with large daily, monthly, and annual variations in temperature. The daily range is wide, 40° or more being common. Over the mountain ranges these differences are not so pronounced, and the temperature is lower and more equable. The number of hours of sunshine during the year is large, and the number of days with precipitation small. The average humidity is low, and this is an important factor in mitigating the effect of extremes of temperature.

The normal temperatures for the State vary greatly with elevation, latitude, and local topography, the annual mean decreasing from 63° F. in the lower Pecos and Rio Grande Valleys to 37° at the higher stations in the Sangre de Cristo Mountains and probably to even lower at the crest.

The probability of frost follows rather closely the minimum temperatures of a district. During periods of low wind velocity, vast differences in elevation permit drainage of cold, dry air from higher to lower levels, and in sheltered valleys and the more exposed mesas this becomes an important factor in causing variation from the average conditions for the region. Frost may be expected in the lowlands of the south until the latter part of April, and over the mountains until May. The first fall frost usually occurs during the latter part of September in the higher regions, and by October 10 to 20 it extends quite generally over all districts except the extreme southern lower valleys, where it is delayed till about November 10. In the northern part of the State, where the growing season is shortest, it is not unusual for frost to occur during every month of the year in some mountain sections.

Over the lower Pecos and Rio Grande Valleys the average growing season exceeds 220 days, but the length decreases with altitude, reaching a minimum of 79 days a year in the higher regions on the western slope of the Sangre de Cristo.

Precipitation varies from less than 10 inches in the Rio Grande and San Juan Valleys to over 30 in the high regions along the north-central border. More than half the State receives less than 15 inches annually, the areas having more than this being the northeast, the east-southeastern border, and the mountain areas with elevations of 6,000 feet or more. From May to September precipitation is mostly in the form of local showers, with an occasional heavy rain in an area where the normal is comparatively low; a 24-hour fall of 9.91 inches is of record near the east-central border. The average number of days with precipitation ranges from nearly 30 in the southern Rio Grande Valley to over 100 at the headwaters of the Pecos, with the maximum in July and August. In general, altitude is an important factor in the increase of precipitation in all except the northwestern part of the State.

Snow falls in every part of the State, increasing in amount with altitude and latitude from 2 to 5 inches in the lower Rio Grande Valley to nearly 300 inches over the crest of the main ridge of the Sangre de Cristo Mountains.

The prevailing direction of the wind in New Mexico is from the west or southwest for nearly all localities, the few variations from these directions being caused by local influences. The wind movement in all except the sheltered districts is fairly strong, with the extreme velocities occasionally reaching 50 miles or more an hour during the early summer and the spring months. During recent years of scanty precipitation these high winds have resulted in considerable blowing of the topsoil, especially in eastern counties.

Because of the low humidity and frequent high winds evaporation is rapid, the loss from a free water surface amounting to more than 100 inches annually in the lower valleys. This loss, however, decreases with altitude, and at higher stations it is 40 to 45 inches for the 6 warmer months of the year.

ERLE L. HARDY, *Associate Meteorologist and Climatic Section Director for New Mexico, Weather Bureau, Albuquerque.*

NEW YORK

Climatic summary

County [1]	Station	Temperature: Length of record	Temperature: January average	Temperature: July average	Temperature: Maximum	Temperature: Minimum	Killing frost average dates: Length of record	Killing frost average dates: Last in spring	Killing frost average dates: First in fall	Killing frost average dates: Growing season [2]	Average precipitation: Length of record	January	February	March	April	May	June	July	August	September	October	November	December	Annual
		Yr.	°F.	°F.	°F.	°F.	Yr.			Days	Yr.	In.	In.	In.	In.	In.	In.	In.	In.	In.	In.	In.	In.	In.
Albany	Albany	40	24.6	73.2	104	−24	40	Apr. 23	Oct. 14	174	40	2.24	2.20	2.71	2.68	2.75	3.43	3.30	3.34	3.22	2.50	2.47	2.27	33.11
	Voorheesville	21	20.7	70.6	103	−25	13	May 3	Oct. 7	157	23	2.43	2.30	2.66	3.01	2.74	3.62	3.32	3.50	3.38	2.85	2.96	2.16	34.93
	West Berne	33	22.3	68.6	100	−33	33	May 18	Sept. 27	132	34	1.96	2.37	2.59	3.10	3.15	3.80	3.74	3.60	3.07	3.13	2.36	2.03	34.90
Allegany	Alfred	29	23.5	67.3	101	−35	31	May 19	Oct. 1	135	31	2.22	1.74	2.62	2.95	3.51	3.49	3.71	3.55	3.14	2.93	2.72	2.14	34.72
	Andover	16	25.2	67.4	100	−34	17	May 21	Sept. 27	129	17	2.23	1.72	2.48	2.98	3.26	4.00	3.81	3.01	3.13	2.59	2.33	1.87	33.41
	Angelica	38	24.4	67.8	104	−40	38	May 26	Sept. 24	121	38	2.40	1.88	2.62	3.11	3.43	3.49	3.81	3.56	2.96	2.83	2.52	2.17	34.78
	Bolivar	26	22.9	67.1	101	−37	24	May 30	Sept. 16	109	26	3.21	2.35	2.92	3.08	3.50	4.09	4.41	4.02	3.76	3.28	2.51	3.01	40.14
Broome	Binghamton	40	25.4	70.5	103	−28	40	May 2	Oct. 10	161	40	2.26	2.04	2.69	2.82	3.09	3.57	3.60	3.43	3.22	2.88	2.26	2.15	34.01
Cattaraugus	Allegheny State Pk	19	25.9	67.1	101	−35	20	May 28	Sept. 23	118	14	2.95	2.44	3.40	3.60	3.69	4.13	4.33	3.59	4.09	3.70	4.14	2.99	43.05
	Franklinville	19	23.5	67.3	99	−45	19	May 22	Sept. 24	125	19	3.06	2.68	2.99	3.17	3.49	3.88	4.13	3.51	3.20	3.44	2.73	2.71	38.99
Cayuga	Auburn	39	25.7	71.5	101	−32	40	May 2	Oct. 17	168	40	2.38	2.06	2.89	2.87	3.30	3.65	3.71	3.18	3.12	3.05	2.65	2.40	35.26
Chautauqua	Fredonia	25	27.0	71.6	98	−24	25	May 1	Oct. 19	171	25	2.79	2.11	2.55	3.14	3.19	3.50	2.99	2.78	3.32	3.92	3.34	2.98	36.61
	Jamestown	28	26.0	70.1	100	−31	27	May 15	Oct. 6	144	27	3.65	2.80	3.51	3.41	3.45	4.07	4.45	3.22	3.79	3.27	3.93	3.92	43.47
	Volusia	22	23.4	68.4	98	−18	20	May 10	Oct. 8	151	22	2.90	2.37	2.59	2.88	3.41	3.22	3.62	3.44	3.60	4.10	3.35	3.00	38.48
	Westfield	21	25.0	69.9	100	−19	22	May 3	Oct. 23	173	21	3.00	2.55	2 92	2 99	4 09	3 45	4 10	3 50	3 60	4 18	3 16	3 12	40 66
Cheming	Elmira	38	26 7	72.1	104	−24	39	May 6	Oct. 6	153	39	1 90	1.70	2 60	2.85	3.26	3.74	3.42	3.67	3.02	2.63	2.00	1.83	32.62
Chenango	Norwich	29	22.7	68.6	101	−31	29	May 17	Oct. 1	137	32	3.02	2.79	3.14	3.35	3.40	3.72	4.26	3.91	3.82	3.55	3.13	2.76	40.85
	Oxford	15	22.5	68.9	99	−31	15	May 14	Sept. 26	135	15	3.45	3.18	3.89	2.82	3.74	3.71	3.95	3.69	3.70	3.65	2.76	3.93	42.47
	Sherburne										31	2.47	2.19	2.94	3.06	3.39	3.62	3.99	3.68	3.65	3.30	2.77	2.48	37.54
Clinton	Chazy	35	16.8	69.6	104	−37	32	May 13	Sept. 30	140	34	1.37	1.24	1.47	1.64	2.29	3.08	3.62	2.84	3.04	2.54	1.78	1.22	26.13
	Dannemora	32	16.8	67.7	96	−37	32	do	Oct. 3	143	33	2.79	2.48	2.91	2.83	3.26	3.61	3.83	2.96	3.49	3.10	2.79	2.88	36.93
	Harkness	30	18.4	68.8	102	−32	30	May 10	Oct. 6	149	31	1.40	1.45	1.70	1.95	2.39	3.12	3.15	2.50	2.92	2.65	1.96	1.50	26.69
Columbia	Chatham	20	23.4	71.3	103	−24	17	May 11	Oct. 6	148	20	2.30	2.49	3.06	3.21	3.04	3.99	3.77	3.93	3.57	3.37	2.21	2.77	37.71
Cortland	Cortland	38	24.4	70.2	102	−30	38	May 13	Oct. 3	143	40	2.55	2.15	2.73	2.77	3.24	3.82	4.45	3.80	3.38	3.42	2.81	2.59	37.71
Delaware	Roxbury	21	23.0	67.6	101	−30	23	May 27	Sept. 25	121	23	3.09	2.55	3.23	3.46	3.54	4.23	4.32	4.52	3.97	3.54	3.47	2.81	42.73
Dutchess	Wappingers Falls	40	26.3	72.5	106	−34	40	May 4	Oct. 11	160	40	3.42	3.48	3.52	3.65	3.87	4.27	4.50	4.64	4.09	3.66	3.02	3.38	45.50
Erie	Buffalo	40	25.8	70.1	97	−20	40	Apr. 26	Oct. 23	180	40	3.30	2.64	2.70	2.58	2.51	2.54	2.68	2.59	2.65	2.91	2.55	3.12	32.77
Essex	Keene Valley	17	18.8	67.5	105	−36	16	May 27	Sept. 17	113	18	2.71	2.26	3.12	2.59	3.31	3.90	3.50	3.10	3.51	3.57	2.57	2.87	37.01
	Lake Placid	30	15.1	63.7	94	−39	29	June 5	Sept. 11	98	30	3.42	2.87	3.64	2.94	3.11	3.49	4.02	3.42	3.37	3.03	3.02	2.93	39.26
Franklin	Gabriels	33	15.6	64.7	96	−46	33	June 2	Sept. 9	99	34	2.77	2.35	2.75	2.36	3.14	3.53	3.88	3.42	3.64	3.36	2.92	2.51	36.63
	Moira	29	15.4	68.5	99	−36	31	May 16	Sept. 28	135	29	3.11	2.96	3.03	2.37	3.08	3.72	3.55	3.31	3.10	3.16	2.87	2.76	37.02
	Tupper Lake	25	16.6	64.8	98	−38	19	May 26	Sept. 19	116	27	2.88	2.19	2.85	2.36	3.21	3.84	4.42	3.84	3.72	3.75	2.72	2.44	38.22
Fulton	Gloversville	40	19.6	69.1	100	−34	39	May 11	Sept. 29	141	40	3.56	3.06	3.64	3.20	3.33	4.06	4.27	3.88	4.10	3.49	3.30	3.33	43.22

[1] The following counties, for which no records are available, are best represented by the station indicated: Bronx—Mount Vernon; Kings and Richmond—New York City; Rockland—Warwick.

[2] Length of growing season between average dates of last killing frost in spring and first in fall.

NEW YORK—Continued

Climatic summary—Continued

County	Station	Temperature: Length of record	Temperature: January average	Temperature: July average	Temperature: Maximum	Temperature: Minimum	Killing frost average dates: Length of record	Killing frost: Last in spring	Killing frost: First in fall	Growing season	Average precipitation: Length of record	January	February	March	April	May	June	July	August	September	October	November	December	Annual
		Yr.	°F.	°F.	°F.	°F.	Yr.			Days	Yr.	In.	In.	In.	In.	In.	In.	In.	In.	In.	In.	In.	In.	In.
Genesee	Elba	17	23.4	69.7	100	−21	18	May 8	Oct. 6	151	18	3.70	3.35	3.21	3.25	3.23	2.89	3.78	2.92	2.49	2.80	2.12	3.11	36.85
	Linden										15	2.47	2.10	2.56	2.83	2.57	3.59	3.79	3.35	2.79	3.31	2.95	2.40	34.71
Greene	Cairo	14	26.8	72.8	104	−26	14	May 5	Oct. 6	154	15	2.62	2.37	2.84	3.75	3.40	4.11	3.34	3.49	4.01	3.18	3.59	2.19	38.89
Hamilton	Hoffmeister										33	4.60	3.74	4.14	4.21	4.36	4.49	5.15	4.57	4.82	4.96	4.39	3.97	53.40
	Indian Lake	38	16.9	64.7	105	−42	38	June 12	Sept. 5	85	38	3.21	2.53	3.02	3.04	3.40	3.75	3.94	3.51	3.78	3.68	3.21	2.99	40.06
	Raquette Lake	23	15.8	65.4	95	−42	24	May 22	Sept. 29	130	35	3.76	3.17	3.70	3.30	3.77	4.10	4.35	3.49	3.88	4.01	3.91	3.88	45.32
Herkimer	Frankfort										8	2.48	2.16	1.88	3.45	3.88	3.91	4.20	3.33	4.11	2.91	3.55	2.34	38.20
	Little Falls No. 1	39	20.7	69.4	99	−28	40	May 9	Oct. 6	150	40	2.73	2.36	2.85	2.76	3.28	4.12	4.19	3.74	3.84	3.28	2.87	2.51	38.53
	McKeever										16	4.38	2.68	3.52	4.04	3.86	3.99	4.75	4.34	4.71	4.94	4.03	3.42	48.66
	North Lake	34	16.3	65.1	98	−47	34	May 28	Sept. 22	117	36	4.68	3.94	4.39	3.71	4.18	4.59	4.84	3.91	4.48	4.48	4.19	3.96	51.35
	Salisbury	38	18.1	67.3	98	−36	40	May 22	Sept. 23	124	40	3.38	2.77	3.39	3.43	4.22	4.69	4.97	4.68	4.42	4.54	3.81	3.38	47.68
	Stillwater Reservoir	12	16.6	65.4	97	−52	12	May 26	Sept. 20	117	16	4.67	3.04	4.18	4.43	4.03	4.30	4.79	4.40	4.17	4.97	4.40	4.02	51.40
Jefferson	Adams Center	16	20.4	70.8	97	−36	19	May 13	Oct. 5	145	23	4.63	4.17	3.65	3.23	3.99	4.27	4.00	3.24	3.98	4.92	3.99	5.59	49.66
	Philadelphia	26	19.1	68.9	98	−47	28	do	Sept. 30	140	27	2.83	2.48	2.65	3.15	3.44	3.30	3.09	3.11	3.04	3.89	3.35	3.13	37.46
	Watertown	40	21.3	70.5	99	−39	40	May 6	Oct. 9	156	40	3.23	2.62	3.01	2.93	3.33	3.33	3.30	2.95	3.56	4.03	3.65	3.40	39.34
Lewis	Copenhagen										12	3.77	2.81	2.79	2.97	2.91	3.42	2.97	3.54	3.88	4.25	4.08	3.15	40.54
	Lowville	39	18.2	67.9	100	−37	39	May 19	Sept. 23	127	40	3.29	2.67	2.69	2.74	3.04	3.44	3.08	2.98	2.91	3.82	3.26	3.28	37.20
Livingston	Avon	39	25.2	70.9	103	−30	38	May 9	Oct. 6	150	40	1.71	1.47	1.82	2.37	2.83	3.14	3.27	2.81	2.66	2.56	1.95	1.70	28.29
	Dansville	19	28.7	72.2	103	−12	19	May 5	Oct. 10	158	21	1.60	1.19	2.02	2.33	2.61	2.92	3.13	2.73	2.64	2.15	2.04	1.50	26.86
	Hemlock	40	24.7	70.9	100	−27	40	May 6	Oct. 15	162	40	1.81	1.46	2.16	2.55	3.00	3.33	3.42	2.86	2.66	2.61	1.98	1.76	29.60
	Hunt	19	24.6	69.4	100	−25	18	May 12	Oct. 3	144	20	2.30	2.08	2.71	3.09	3.72	3.01	3.85	2.78	2.57	3.08	1.57	2.36	33.12
Madison	Bouckville	18	20.2	68.2	95	−27	18	May 14	Sept. 27	136	18	3.32	3.33	3.45	2.75	3.36	3.97	4.26	3.67	3.36	3.47	2.81	3.47	41.22
	De Ruyter	22	20.9	66.9	98	−40	22	May 21	Sept. 29	131	23	3.26	2.96	3.09	3.04	3.40	4.54	4.20	3.64	4.20	3.75	3.07	2.91	42.06
	Morrisville	22	22.0	68.1	100	−37	27	May 22	Sept. 24	125	26	2.57	2.23	2.70	3.22	3.18	3.93	3.80	3.87	3.73	3.44	2.94	2.63	38.24
Monroe	Brockport	38	24.9	71.1	104	−25	39	May 4	Oct. 13	162	39	2.60	2.21	2.74	2.65	2.70	2.94	3.13	2.75	2.52	2.83	2.44	2.41	31.92
	Rochester	40	25.9	71.6	102	−22	40	Apr. 26	Oct. 21	178	40	2.63	2.34	2.94	2.51	2.50	2.84	2.84	2.71	2.54	2.65	2.30	2.49	31.29
Montgomery	Amsterdam	20	19.8	69.8	100	−30	20	May 5	Oct. 2	150	21	2.67	2.60	3.12	2.87	3.12	4.24	3.84	3.80	3.55	3.31	2.68	2.70	38.50
	Canajoharie										19	1.79	1.70	2.83	2.93	2.74	3.76	3.64	3.57	2.89	2.93	2.69	2.21	33.68
	Tribes Hill										35	2.85	2.41	2.82	3.32	3.20	4.05	3.56	3.78	3.73	3.34	3.06	2.76	38.88
Nassau	Roslyn	18	30.4	72.7	103	−9	19	Apr. 22	Oct. 28	189	19	3.69	3.78	3.63	3.73	3.70	3.97	3.80	4.95	3.65	3.40	3.45	3.71	45.46
New York	New York	40	32.1	74.4	102	−14	40	Apr. 9	Nov. 6	211	40	3.32	3.39	3.56	3.36	3.09	3.56	4.16	4.22	3.68	3.50	2.48	3.31	41.63
Niagara	Appleton	25	25.4	70.6	106	−13	24	May 2	Oct. 18	169	24	2.04	1.61	1.92	2.50	2.50	2.31	2.90	2.34	2.19	2.98	1.91	1.84	27.04
	Lockport	39	25.2	70.1	103	−24	40	May 7	Oct. 14	160	40	2.28	1.87	2.18	2.48	2.76	3.02	3.10	2.62	2.69	2.92	2.39	2.14	30.45
Oneida	Delta										12	3.14	2.75	3.22	3.71	3.57	3.94	4.46	3.27	3.99	3.84	4.31	3.40	43.60
	Hinckley										17	4.45	2.74	3.61	4.08	3.48	4.14	4.40	4.17	4.19	4.31	4.40	3.24	47.21
	New London										12	2.23	1.79	2.45	3.50	3.23	4.01	4.70	3.08	3.77	3.38	3.77	2.10	38.01
	Utica	11	23.1	70.7	100	−34	14	May 13	Oct. 7	147	29	3.09	2.61	2.79	3.39	3.47	3.84	4.17	3.99	3.94	3.63	3.36	2.92	41.20

	Trenton Falls										30	3.60	2.78	3.27	3.64	3.98	4.34	4.44	4.00	4.32	4.42	3.94	3.40	46.13
Onondaga	Baldwinsville	10	23.4	71.4	99	−28	10	May 2	Oct. 13	164	22	2.85	2.49	2.97	3.15	3.10	4.13	4.30	3.30	3.25	3.58	3.23	2.94	39.29
	Fayetteville	19	23.8	71.5	103	−29	18	May 11	Oct. 10	152	19	2.17	2.08	2.52	2.63	3.46	4.36	3.76	3.46	2.96	3.35	2.15	2.46	35.36
	Skaneateles										40	2.72	2.44	3.25	3.23	3.64	3.87	4.10	3.58	3.65	3.67	3.20	2.92	40.27
	Syracuse	36	25.1	71.1	102	−24	36	Apr. 23	Oct. 22	182	36	2.82	2.36	3.09	2.90	2.78	3.66	3.42	3.13	2.89	2.93	2.44	2.64	35.06
Ontario	Geneva	40	25.6	72.0	106	−31	26	May 3	Oct. 12	162	24	2.44	2.24	2.70	2.89	3.15	3.49	3.19	3.14	2.67	2.82	2.83	2.41	33.97
	Shortsville	37	24.3	69.7	103	−25	37	May 8	Oct. 15	160	37	1.71	1.54	2.30	2.68	2.77	3.48	3.56	2.77	2.69	2.65	2.07	1.76	29.98
Orange	Port Jervis	40	26.4	72.4	105	−26	40	May 6	Oct. 8	155	40	3.02	2.90	3.55	3.64	3.51	4.51	4.80	4.25	4.05	3.59	2.96	3.19	43.97
	Walden	14	28.2	72.1	102	−24	14	Apr. 28	Oct. 9	164	17	3.23	2.49	3.21	3.95	3.97	4.63	4.65	4.63	4.99	3.30	3.65	2.88	45.58
	Warwick										39	2.86	2.79	2.98	3.13	3.40	3.90	4.13	4.62	3.94	3.45	3.93	3.02	42.15
	West Point	30	28.3	74.6	106	−17	32	Apr. 19	Oct. 30	194	35	3.18	2.96	3.57	3.62	3.14	3.56	3.79	3.78	4.09	3.16	3.16	3.17	41.18
Orleans	Lyndonville										11	1.71	1.74	1.59	2.17	2.42	2.07	3.59	2.29	2.21	2.46	2.21	2.13	26.59
Oswego	Oswego	40	24.2	69.3	100	−23	40	Apr. 23	Oct. 24	184	40	2.72	2.46	2.74	2.63	2.88	3.03	2.79	2.57	2.85	3.34	3.02	3.04	34.07
	Palermo										27	3.32	3.23	2.74	2.67	2.75	3.27	3.04	2.87	3.06	3.30	3.26	3.83	37.34
Otsego	Cooperstown	34	21.6	67.2	99	−34	38	May 14	Oct. 2	141	38	3.19	2.76	3.20	3.14	3.52	4.45	4.80	4.43	4.05	3.67	3.07	2.92	43.20
	New Lisbon	25	19.8	65.9	96	−37	25	May 25	Sept. 23	121	25	2.55	2.69	3.24	2.72	3.56	4.24	5.31	3.95	3.57	3.35	2.57	2.90	40.65
	Oneonta	40	24.5	70.3	104	−28	40	May 14	Sept. 27	136	40	2.60	2.41	2.97	2.76	2.89	3.99	4.24	4.35	3.54	3.29	2.56	2.45	38.05
Putnam	Boyds Corners										40	3.80	3.59	4.24	4.04	4.02	4.25	4.61	4.71	4.55	3.98	3.46	3.90	49.15
	Carmel	40	25.4	71.5	103	−24	40	Apr. 29	Oct. 14	168	40	3.60	3.39	4.01	3.86	3.85	4.18	4.56	4.91	4.49	3.86	3.28	3.62	47.61
Queens	Flushing	23	31.7	73.5	104	−14	23	Apr. 12	Nov. 2	204	23	3.60	3.44	3.56	3.47	3.49	4.11	4.12	4.10	4.49	3.07	3.07	3.40	43.92
Rensselaer	Troy	17	24.3	73.8	108	−18	17	Apr. 24	Oct. 15	174	22	2.00	2.19	2.49	2.85	2.98	3.24	3.15	3.31	3.64	2.74	2.83	2.04	33.46
Saratoga	Ballston Lake	26	20.6	70.0	101	−34	27	May 8	Oct. 3	148	27	2.47	2.44	2.84	3.05	3.11	3.85	3.73	3.37	3.46	2.82	2.84	2.48	36.46
	Greenfield Center	40	20.7	70.0	100	−35	39	May 10	Oct. 2	145	40	3.42	2.78	3.28	3.18	3.12	3.60	4.02	3.46	3.86	3.08	3.03	3.06	39.89
	Mechanicsville										15	2.35	1.71	2.36	3.14	2.84	4.04	3.87	3.36	3.56	2.76	2.86	2.05	34.90
	Mount McGregor	23	21.0	70.3	99	−30	23	May 2	Oct. 11	162	25	3.60	3.02	3.21	3.10	3.02	4.09	4.74	3.79	3.47	3.19	3.58	3.14	41.95
	Spier Falls	35	21.2	71.1	104	−39	35	May 7	Oct. 2	148	37	3.05	2.76	3.25	3.12	3.05	3.72	3.95	3.14	3.44	3.17	2.92	3.14	38.71
Schenectady	Scotia										11	1.87	2.02	2.27	3.55	2.85	3.94	3.04	3.54	3.14	2.82	3.59	1.91	34.54
Schoharie	Sharon Springs	25	22.9	70.2	102	−30	25	May 5	Oct. 5	153	25	3.11	2.70	3.11	3.51	3.34	4.02	4.03	3.80	3.74	3.07	3.23	2.70	40.36
Schuyler	Wedgewood	23	22.7	69.9	103	−19	22	May 9	Oct. 9	153	22	2.35	2.12	2.83	3.12	3.50	3.82	3.79	3.98	3.09	3.09	2.25	2.31	36.25
Seneca	Mays Point										12	1.55	1.90	2.59	2.95	3.04	3.81	3.58	3.01	3.09	2.86	3.03	2.10	33.51
	Romulus	23	24.9	71.1	98	−19	20	May 5	Oct. 11	159	21	2.01	1.76	2.38	2.40	2.82	3.41	3.06	2.77	2.19	2.65	2.06	1.93	29.44
Steuben	Addison	36	25.6	70.5	106	−35	34	May 16	Oct. 4	141	33	1.92	1.67	2.42	2.91	3.65	3.89	3.54	3.56	3.05	2.72	1.98	1.90	33.21
	Haskinville										40	1.89	1.58	2.46	2.75	3.43	3.59	3.77	3.35	3.06	2.64	2.33	1.98	32.83
St. Lawrence	Canton	35	17.5	68.7	99	−43	35	May 3	Sept. 30	150	40	2.48	2.20	2.73	2.68	2.92	3.53	3.40	3.07	3.35	3.25	2.92	2.50	35.03
	Ogdensburg	38	17.9	70.2	100	−43	39	May 6	Oct. 5	152	40	2.06	1.94	2.25	2.29	2.66	3.24	3.19	2.87	2.73	3.17	2.46	2.02	30.88
	Wanakena	28	16.1	64.8	100	−45	26	May 27	Sept. 15	111	28	3.24	3.54	3.39	3.09	3.30	3.51	4.08	3.78	3.79	4.23	3.51	2.80	42.26
Suffolk	Cutchogue	40	30.9	71.5	96	−10	39	Apr. 18	Oct. 31	196	40	4.11	3.65	4.30	3.98	3.32	3.49	3.43	4.01	3.77	3.51	3.35	4.34	45.26
	Medford	20	29.6	71.7	100	−14	20	May 1	Oct. 20	172	21	4.13	3.52	3.89	4.13	3.77	3.45	3.93	4.44	2.92	3.69	3.59	4.48	45.94
	Setauket	40	31.8	72.3	98	−11	40	Apr. 11	Nov. 8	211	40	3.90	3.60	4.05	3.92	3.37	3.21	3.48	4.03	3.87	3.54	3.27	3.93	44.17
	Southampton	18	31.0	70.4	96	−8	17	Apr. 21	Oct. 25	187	18	4.04	3.62	4.29	4.39	3.26	2.85	3.09	3.85	2.92	3.28	2.87	4.89	43.35
Sullivan	Jeffersonville	35	23.4	67.9	99	−34	35	May 20	Sept. 29	132	36	3.04	2.74	3.01	3.30	3.17	3.73	4.57	4.77	3.71	3.45	2.97	2.86	41.32
Tioga	Newark Valley						11	May 25	Sept. 22	120	21	2.40	2.16	2.97	3.03	3.66	4.03	4.08	4.11	3.32	3.37	2.28	2.73	38.14
	Waverly	16	24.7	71.2	102	−31	16	May 15	Sept. 28	136	16	2.49	2.17	3.01	3.31	3.07	3.72	3.60	3.43	2.94	2.76	2.06	3.62	36.18
Tompkins	Ithaca	40	25.4	70.6	103	−24	40	May 5	Oct. 10	158	40	2.09	1.82	2.58	2.75	3.07	3.53	3.58	3.47	3.01	2.85	2.11	2.22	33.08
Ulster	Mohonk Lake	39	25.1	69.9	96	−24	39	Apr. 28	Oct. 18	173	40	3.42	3.36	3.76	4.12	3.59	4.17	4.50	4.87	4.51	3.59	3.25	3.69	46.83
	Rifton	14	25.5	72.0	104	−24	14	May 2	Oct. 9	160	17	3.81	2.79	3.29	4.12	3.55	4.66	4.34	5.25	4.50	3.40	4.15	3.01	46.87
Warren	Glens Falls	33	20.6	70.6	101	−36	33	May 5	Oct. 4	152	34	3.01	2.95	3.35	3.07	3.03	3.55	3.72	3.53	3.41	3.22	2.92	3.08	38.84
	Lake George	19	19.6	69.6	102	−34	15	May 13	Sept. 29	139	20	3.04	3.54	3.74	2.78	3.14	4.02	3.94	3.87	3.64	3.64	2.47	3.62	41.44
Washington	Carvers Falls	13	18.3	68.8	99	−37	13	May 12	Sept. 30	141	13	2.37	2.78	2.96	2.23	2.83	3.86	3.30	3.37	3.58	2.66	2.05	2.62	34.56
	Whitehall										12	2.85	2.10	2.67	3.50	2.79	3.66	3.79	2.83	2.81	3.34	3.61	2.59	36.54
Wayne	Clyde										12	1.88	1.64	2.60	3.51	3.27	4.11	3.97	3.30	3.10	3.16	3.41	2.20	36.15
	Macedon										12	2.02	2.17	2.30	2.76	2.31	3.78	3.47	2.44	3.21	2.82	2.63	2.39	32.30
Westchester	Bedford Hills	36	28.8	72.8	105	−19	38	Apr. 27	Oct. 14	170	40	3.46	3.13	3.60	3.61	3.64	4.17	4.56	4.67	4.31	3.58	2.95	3.51	45.19

NEW YORK—Continued

Climatic summary—Continued

County	Station	Temperature: Length of record	Temperature: January average	Temperature: July average	Temperature: Maximum	Temperature: Minimum	Killing frost average dates: Length of record	Killing frost average dates: Last in spring	Killing frost average dates: First in fall	Killing frost average dates: Growing season	Average precipitation: Length of record	January	February	March	April	May	June	July	August	September	October	November	December	Annual
		Yr.	*°F.*	*°F.*	*°F.*	*°F.*	*Yr.*			*Days*	*Yr.*	*In.*	*In.*	*In.*	*In.*	*In.*	*In.*	*In.*	*In.*	*In.*	*In.*	*In.*	*In.*	*In.*
Westchester—Con.	Mount Vernon	24	31.8	74.1	103	−14	24	Apr. 12	Nov. 6	208	24	3.89	3.74	3.66	3.58	3.85	4.14	4.67	4.78	4.62	3.11	3.12	3.64	46.80
	Scarsdale	35	29.6	73.0	105	−18	35	Apr. 21	Oct. 21	183	30	3.65	3.12	3.60	3.92	3.61	4.12	4.72	4.85	4.34	3.54	3.38	3.53	46.38
Wyoming	Letchwork Park	24	25.2	69.1	101	−33	25	May 14	Oct. 2	141	25	1.87	1.29	1.72	2.12	3.25	3.16	2.88	2.76	2.73	2.48	2.16	1.54	27.96
Yates	Penn Yan	25	24.9	71.2	106	−25	26	May 12	Oct. 8	149	25	1.90	1.46	2.58	2.61	2.95	3.12	3.58	2.89	2.41	2.50	2.32	1.91	30.23

Precipitation and temperature—State unit values

[This tabulation gives the mean annual, mean monthly, and average seasonal precipitation, 1886–1938, and the mean annual temperatures, 1896–1938, for New York]

Precipitation: Year	Mean	Precipitation: Year	Mean	Precipitation: Year	Mean
	In.		*In.*		*In.*
1886	37.56	1907	38.45	1928	39.03
1887	39.67	1908	33.54	1929	43.02
1888	43.11	1909	36.03	1930	32.18
1889	48.19	1910	37.26	1931	38.08
1890	49.74	1911	36.61	1932	42.19
1891	38.45	1912	38.34	1933	37.53
1892	42.60	1913	39.66	1934	35.11
1893	42.11	1914	36.39	1935	37.96
1894	38.54	1915	40.91	1936	40.16
1895	33.89	1916	38.03	1937	43.72
1896	39.07	1917	38.73	1938	41.59
1897	40.15	1918	38.23		
1898	43.68	1919	39.69		
1899	34.18	1920	40.57		
1900	38.03	1921	35.41		
1901	43.30	1922	39.53		
1902	42.95	1923	35.46		
1903	43.27	1924	36.98		
1904	38.63	1925	41.41		
1905	39.02	1926	40.11		
1906	37.48	1927	45.50		

Precipitation: Month	Mean
	In.
January	3.03
February	2.72
March	3.04
April	3.00
May	3.44
June	3.67
July	3.94
August	3.80
September	3.50
October	3.28
November	3.11
December	2.92
Annual	39.45

Season	Average
	In.
Winter	8.67
Spring	9.48
Summer	11.41
Fall	9.89

Temperature: Year	Mean	Temperature: Year	Mean
	°F.		*°F.*
1896	46.1	1918	46.2
1897	46.4	1919	47.3
1898	48.1	1920	45.7
1899	46.9	1921	49.4
1900	47.4	1922	47.3
1901	45.8	1923	45.8
1902	45.9	1924	44.9
1903	45.9	1925	46.5
1904	43.2	1926	44.4
1905	45.0	1927	47.0
1906	46.7	1928	46.9
1907	44.6	1929	46.8
1908	46.7	1930	47.6
1909	45.8	1931	48.9
1910	45.8	1932	47.7
1911	46.7	1933	47.7
1912	45.1	1934	46.0
1913	48.0	1935	45.8
1914	44.8	1936	46.6
1915	46.7	1937	47.5
1916	45.8	1938	48.0
1917	43.4		

Dates of last killing frost in spring and first in fall, with length of growing season

Year	Albany			Angelica			Indian Lake			Oneonta			Oswego			Setauket		
	Last in spring	First in fall	Growing season [1]	Last in spring	First in fall	Growing season [1]	Last in spring	First in fall	Growing season [1]	Last in spring	First in fall	Growing season [1]	Last in spring	First in fall	Growing season [1]	Last in spring	First in fall	Growing season [1]
			Days			*Days*			*Days*			*Days*			*Days*			*Days*
1899	Apr. 11	Oct. 3	175	May 14	Sept. 14	123				May 16	Sept. 16	123	Apr. 17	Oct. 3	169	Apr. 11	Nov. 12	215
1900	May 11	Oct. 20	162	May 10	Sept. 19	132	May 30	Sept. 15	108	May 11	Oct. 17	159	May 7	Oct. 20	166	do	Nov. 17	220
1901	Apr. 13	do	190	May 16	do	126	May 16			Apr. 17	Sept. 20	156	Apr. 13	Oct. 26	196	Mar. 31	Nov. 20	234
1902	May 11	Oct. 10	152	June 9	Oct. 9	122	June 11	Aug. 13	63	May 21	Sept. 15	117	May 10	Oct. 17	160	Mar. 27	Nov. 29	247
1903	May 2	Oct. 25	176	May 31	Sept. 29	121	June 3	Aug. 8	66	May 6	Sept. 30	147	Apr. 6	Oct. 27	204	Apr. 5	Nov. 7	216
1904	Apr. 23	Sept. 23	153	May 12			June 28	Aug. 27	60	Apr. 23	Sept. 22	152	Apr. 22	Oct. 7	168	Apr. 23	Oct. 29	189
1905	May 2	Oct. 25	176		Sept. 26		June 9	Sept. 14	97	May 24	Sept. 15	114	do	Oct. 26	187	Apr. 19	Nov. 3	198
1906	Apr. 17	Oct. 12	178	June 13	Oct. 8	117	June 15	Aug. 15	61	May 21	Oct. 1	133	May 11	Oct. 31	173	Apr. 4	Nov. 15	225
1907	May 12	Oct. 9	150	May 31	Aug. 19	80	July 4	Aug. 22	49	May 25	Oct. 2	130	Apr. 27	Oct. 26	182	Apr. 21	Oct. 25	187
1908	Apr. 21	Oct. 13	175	May 5	Oct. 14	162	June 17	Sept. 15	90	May 5	Sept. 15	133	Apr. 21	Oct. 13	175	do	Nov. 5	198
1909	Apr. 29	do	167	May 12	Sept. 6	117	June 8	Aug. 31	84	May 12	Sept. 29	140	Apr. 29	Oct. 29	183	Apr. 25	Nov. 18	207
1910	Apr. 13	do	183	May 16	Sept. 15	122	June 5	Aug. 30	86	May 16	Oct. 13	150	do	Oct. 13	167	Mar. 27	Nov. 12	230
1911	May 4	Oct. 8	157	May 8	Oct. 3	148	June 24	Sept. 13	81	May 6	Sept. 14	131	May 4	Oct. 28	177	Apr. 13	Nov. 2	203
1912	Apr. 24	Oct. 16	175	May 4	Sept. 28	147	July 25	Aug. 31	37	May 1	Sept. 30	152	Apr. 20	Nov. 3	197	Apr. 9	Nov. 4	209
1913	Apr. 21	Sept. 15	147	June 13	Sept. 10	89	June 18	Aug. 20	63	June 11	Sept. 10	91	do	Oct. 31	194	Apr. 10	Nov. 11	215
1914	May 2	Sept. 29	150	June 17	Sept. 28	103	June 17	Aug. 25	69	May 17	Sept. 26	132	Apr. 24	Oct. 27	186	Apr. 14	Oct. 28	197
1915	Apr. 22	Oct. 11	172	May 30	Sept. 23	116	June 21	Aug. 27	67	May 27	Sept. 23	119	Apr. 14	Nov. 18	218	Apr. 5	Nov. 18	227
1916	Apr. 11	Oct. 1	173	June 1	Sept. 3	94	June 3	Sept. 3	92	Apr. 20	Sept. 17	150	Apr. 9	Oct. 18	192	Apr. 11	Nov. 15	218
1917	Apr. 25	Sept. 23	151	June 4	Sept. 11	99	May 31	Sept. 10	102	May 18	Sept. 11	116	Apr. 17	Oct. 30	196	Apr. 15	Oct. 31	199
1918	Apr. 26	Oct. 8	165		do		June 21	Aug. 18	58	Apr. 28	Sept. 30	155	Apr. 26	Nov. 6	194	Apr. 13	Nov. 7	208
1919	Apr. 27	Oct. 13	169	May 13	Sept. 27	137	June 22	Sept. 5	75	Apr. 30	Oct. 8	161	do	Nov. 3	191	Apr. 26	Nov. 14	202
1920	May 5	Oct. 24	172	May 30	Sept. 20	113	June 8	Sept. 20	104	May 16	Sept. 20	127	Apr. 16	Nov. 11	209	Apr. 11	Nov. 12	215
1921	Apr. 12	Oct. 26	197	May 17	Oct. 26	162	June 5	Sept. 27	114	May 17	Oct. 14	150	Apr. 18	Oct. 26	191	do	Oct. 27	199
1922	Apr. 24	Oct. 14	173	May 2	Sept. 27	148	May 28	Sept. 18	113	May 1	Sept. 18	140	Apr. 21	Oct. 19	181	Mar. 23	Oct. 21	212
1923	May 11	Oct. 22	164	May 30	Sept. 17	110	July 7	Aug. 16	40	May 24	Sept. 15	114	May 11	Oct. 31	173	Apr. 2	Nov. 9	221
1924	May 2	Oct. 13	164	June 1	Oct. 9	130	June 19	Sept. 25	98	May 21	Oct. 13	145	Apr. 20	Oct. 18	181	do	Nov. 17	229
1925	Apr. 22	Oct. 1	162	May 27	Aug. 28	93	June 23	Aug. 22	60	May 27	Sept. 23	119	Apr. 21	Oct. 31	193	Apr. 21	Oct. 29	191
1926	Apr. 27	Oct. 22	178	June 4	Oct. 16	134		Sept. 14		June 20	Oct. 10	112	May 4	Oct. 28	177	Apr. 20	Nov. 11	205
1927	Apr. 15	Oct. 31	199	June 16	Sept. 24	100	June 17	Sept. 5	80	May 8	Oct. 11	156	Apr. 9	Nov. 6	211	Mar. 30	Nov. 8	223
1928	Apr. 11	Oct. 15	187	June 11	Sept. 26	107	do	Sept. 19	94	May 15	Sept. 25	133	Apr. 29	Oct. 27	181	Apr. 17	Nov. 24	221
1929	Apr. 11	Oct. 10	182	June 9	Sept. 19	102	June 8	Sept. 12	96	June 3	Sept. 19	108	Apr. 11	Oct. 10	182	Apr. 2	Oct. 30	211
1930	Apr. 24	Oct. 21	180	May 30	Oct. 2	125	June 2	Sept. 8	98	Apr. 29	Oct. 4	158	Apr. 24	Oct. 19	178	Apr. 24	Oct. 21	180
1931	Mar. 24	Nov. 7	228	May 4	Sept. 29	148	do	Sept. 29	119	May 4	Oct. 10	159	Mar. 21	Oct. 10	203	Mar. 15	Nov. 7	237
1932	Apr. 17	Oct. 14	180	May 23	Sept. 11	111	June 8	Sept. 10	94	May 19	Sept. 26	130	Apr. 25	Nov. 4	193	Apr. 17	Nov. 4	201
1933	Apr. 29	Oct. 25	179	May 5	Oct. 14	162	June 2	Sept. 12	102	May 5	Oct. 15	163	Apr. 27	Oct. 29	185	Apr. 23	Oct. 26	186
1934	Apr. 29	Oct. 14	168	May 27	Oct. 2	128	June 8	Aug. 21	74	May 13	Oct. 2	142	Apr. 29	Oct. 2	156	Apr. 5	Nov. 3	212
1935	Apr. 11	Oct. 8	180	May 26	Sept. 30	127	June 2	Sept. 8	98	May 24	Sept. 24	123	Apr. 17	Oct. 8	174	Apr. 17	Nov. 19	216
1936	Apr. 25	Oct. 27	185	June 22	Sept. 26	96	July 1	Sept. 5	66	May 22	Sept. 26	127	May 16	Oct. 27	164	Apr. 8	Oct. 27	202
1937	Apr. 13	Oct. 14	184	May 21	Sept. 18	120	May 29	Sept. 15	109	May 16	Sept. 18	125	Apr. 17	Oct. 14	180	Apr. 3	Nov. 12	223
1938	Apr. 11	Oct. 8	180	May 25	Oct. 2	130	June 10	Sept. 2	84	May 14	Oct. 3	142	Apr. 11	Oct. 8	180	Apr. 11	Nov. 16	219
Mean	Apr. 23	Oct. 14	174	May 26	Sept. 24	121	June 13	Sept. 5	84	do	Sept. 27	136	Apr. 23	Oct. 24	184	do	Nov. 8	211
Extremes	Mar. 24[2] May 12[3]	Sept. 15[4] Nov. 7[5]	[6] 147 [7] 228	May 2[2] June 22[3]	Aug. 19[4] Oct. 26[5]	[6] 80 [7] 162	May 16[2] July 25[3]	Aug. 8[4] Sept. 29[5]	[6] 37 [7] 119	Apr. 17[2] June 20[3]	Sept. 10[4] Oct. 17[5]	[6] 91 [7] 163	Mar. 21[2] May 16[3]	Oct. 2[4] Nov. 18[5]	[6] 156 [7] 218	Mar. 15[2] Apr. 26[3]	Oct. 21[4] Nov. 29[5]	[6] 180 [7] 247

[1] Number of days between last killing frost in spring and first in fall.
[2] Earliest date in spring.
[3] Latest date in spring.
[4] Earliest date in fall.
[5] Latest date in fall.
[6] Shortest growing season.
[7] Longest growing season.

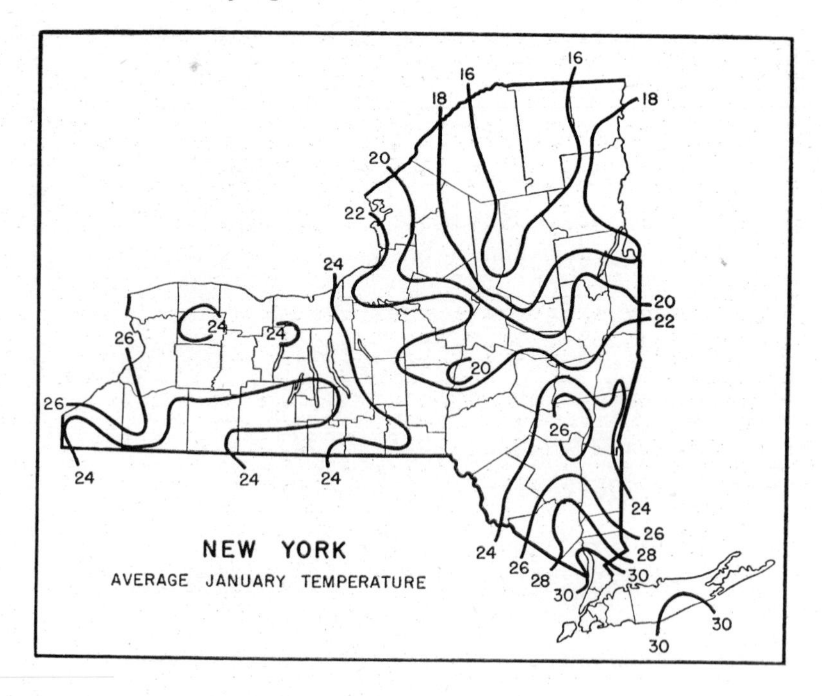
NEW YORK
AVERAGE JANUARY TEMPERATURE
16
16
18
18
20
22
24
24
24
26
26
24
24
24
20
22
20
26
24
26
28
30
24
26
28
30
30
30

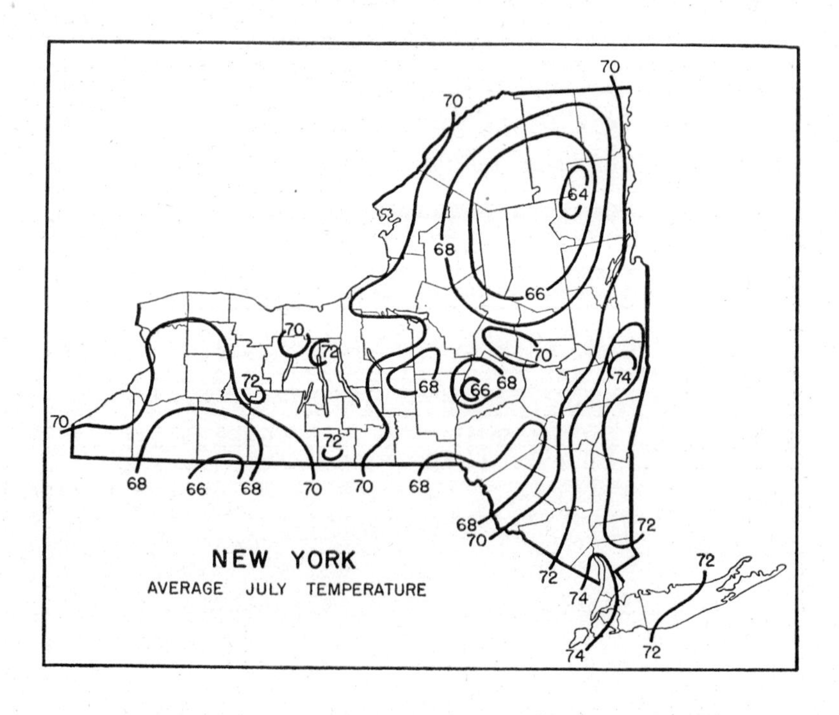
NEW YORK
AVERAGE JULY TEMPERATURE
70
70
64
68
66
70
72
72
70
68
66
68
74
72
70
68
66
68
70
70
68
68
70
72
72
72
74
74
72

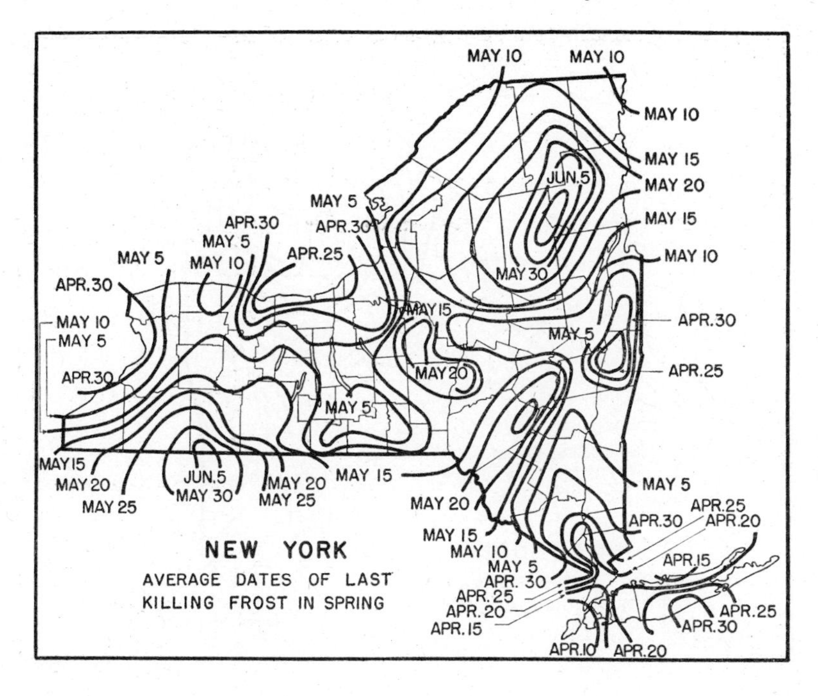

NEW YORK
AVERAGE DATES OF LAST KILLING FROST IN SPRING

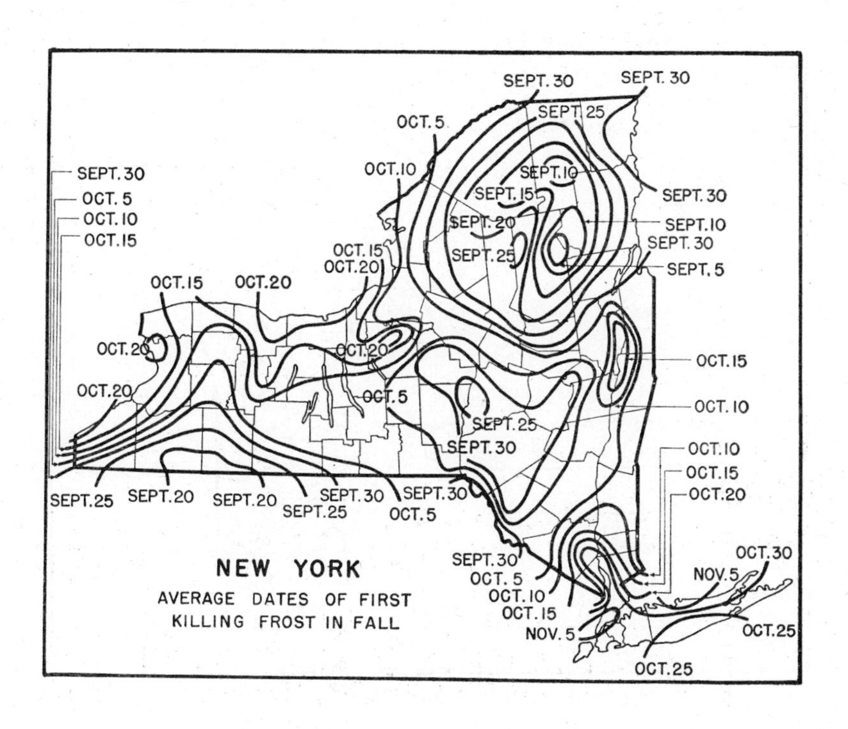

NEW YORK
AVERAGE DATES OF FIRST KILLING FROST IN FALL

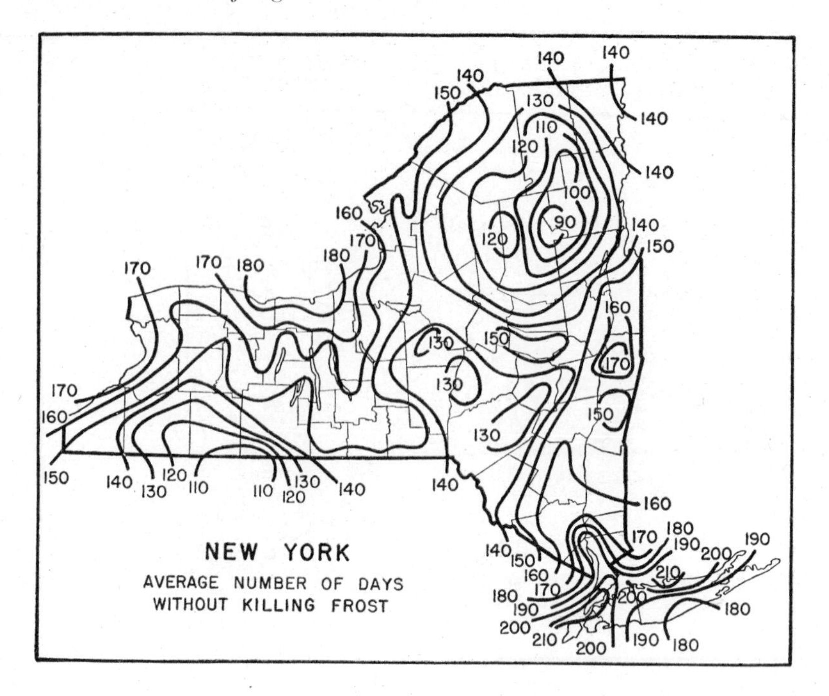

NEW YORK

AVERAGE NUMBER OF DAYS WITHOUT KILLING FROST

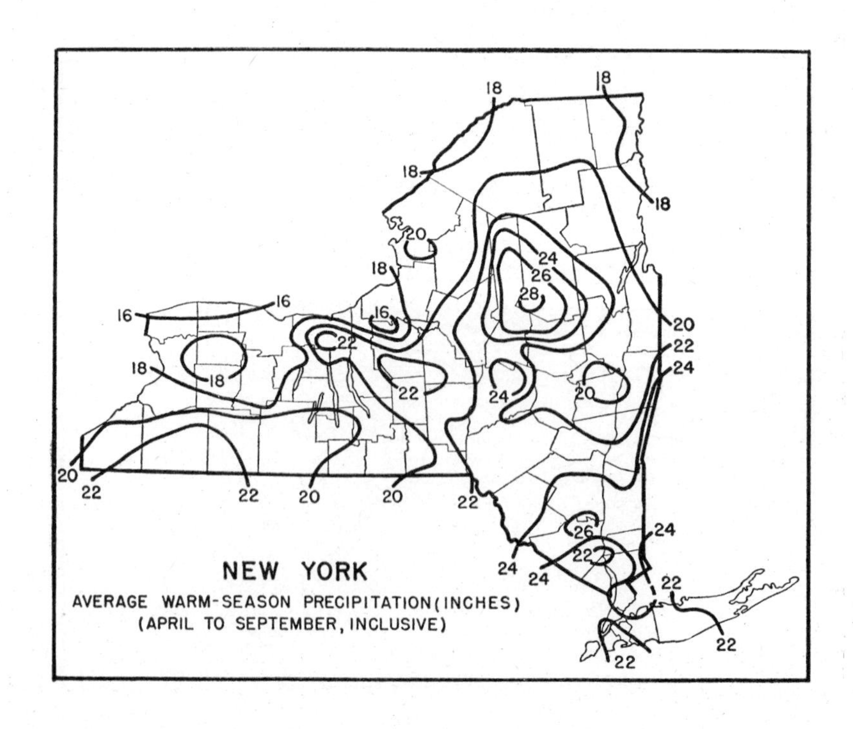

NEW YORK

AVERAGE WARM-SEASON PRECIPITATION (INCHES) (APRIL TO SEPTEMBER, INCLUSIVE)

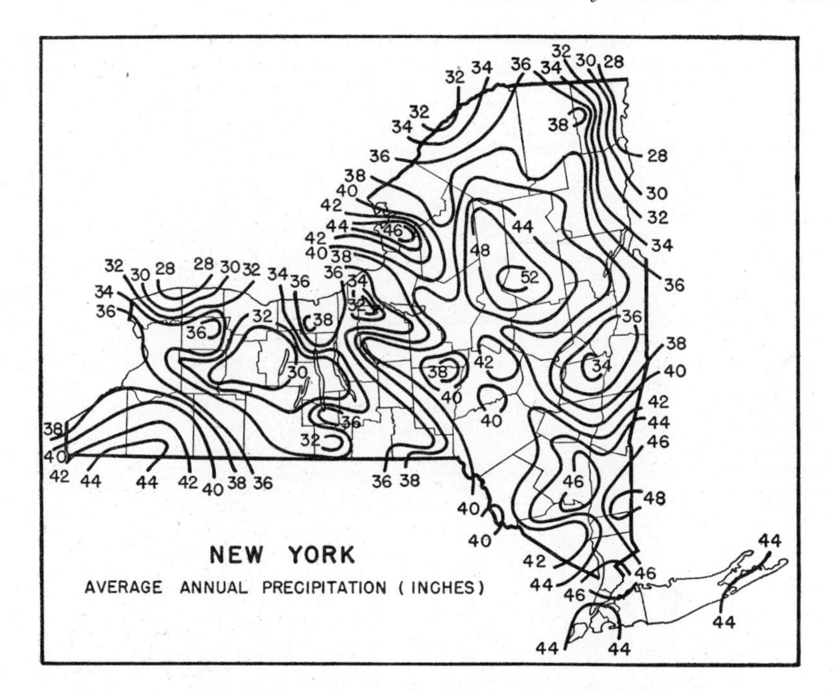

SUPPLEMENTARY CLIMATIC NOTES FOR NEW YORK

The topography of New York is mostly hilly and mountainous, the main exception being the plateau district that parallels the southern shore of Lake Ontario and extends back from the Lake a distance of about 30 miles. At the southern edge of this plateau, the average elevation of which is about 1,000 feet, are the northern shores of the Finger Lakes, so called from their resemblance in shape to the outstretched fingers of the human hand. The northeastern part of the State, in the Lake Champlain country, is the most mountainous, and the highest elevations are found there in the Adirondacks. Numerous small lakes abound, most of which are less than 10 miles long. The northern extensions of the Allegheny and Appalachian Mountains in the southern two-thirds of the State are not as high as the Adirondacks.

The most important of the Finger Lakes are Canandaigua, Cayuga, Keuka, Oneida, and Seneca. Lakes Erie and Ontario, as well as the various mountain ranges, have a marked influence on the climate, especially during the frost season, in the fruit belts in this section.

There is a rather wide variation in the elevations of the different stations from which climatic records have been obtained; they range from sea level on Long Island to about 2,000 feet at about 10 percent of the stations. The average for all stations is 870 feet, with approximately one-third below the 500-foot level and another third above 1,300 feet.

Many rivers serve to carry off the surplus waters to the Atlantic and the Gulf of Mexico, chiefly the St. Lawrence, Hudson, Mohawk, Chemung, Genesee, Susquehanna, and Allegheny. The drainage of the northern and northwestern parts of the State is into Lakes Erie and Ontario and the St. Lawrence River; of the southeastern and southern into the Atlantic Ocean; and of parts of the southwest into the Gulf of Mexico, through the Ohio and Mississippi Rivers.

Nearly all of the atmospheric disturbances which move easterly across the Great Lakes either cross New York or their centers pass closely enough to the north to affect the weather of the State. The influence of coastal storms is felt on Long Island and in the lower Hudson Valley section, while the cold air masses from the Hudson Bay country have a relatively short distance to go to reach the northern part of the State. The general results of these conditions, combined with the varied climatic controls before mentioned, are a rigorous winter climate with abundant snowfall and a moderately warm summer, usually with reliable amounts of rainfall for agricultural purposes. The winters are generally long and cloudy, sunshine being especially deficient in November, December, and January.

The State cannot well be treated as a climatic whole. It may be said, however, that the climate of the western and extreme southern sections is relatively mild, owing to the tempering influence of the lower Lakes and the Atlantic Ocean and to the lower latitude, and that that of the northern part is more severe, with short summers and long winters, owing to its continental character and the more northern location. Chazy, the most northern station, is 300 miles north of New York City, which is the extreme southern point. Geographically there is a wide range in annual mean normal temperatures, from 39.6° F. at Lake Placid to 52.3° at New York City.

As would be expected from the varied topography, the ranges in latitude and altitude, and the influence of the various bodies of water, the dates of frost occurrence show wide divergence. The shortest growing season is naturally found in the more extreme north-central parts of the State, particularly in Hamilton, Essex, and Franklin Counties, where its duration ranges mostly between 85 and 105 days. All stations on whose records these data are based were located at elevations of 1,500 feet or more. However, small lakes abound in Hamilton and southern Franklin Counties, and locally there are exceptions to these general figures. As would be expected, Long Island has the longest growing season; the average length there is close to 200 days, with all stations, of course, near sea level. The next longest season is found in the fruit-growing sections along the southern shores of Lakes Erie and Ontario, where the average is about 180 days.

The areas of greatest average annual rainfall are east of Lakes Ontario and Erie and in the Long Island and lower Hudson Valley sections, especially during the first half of the growing season; after that the distribution of rain over the State tends to be more even, and the average amounts of precipitation from season to season for the State are remarkably uniform.

Geographically there is a wide variation in snowfall; between two and three times as much falls in the Adirondacks as at New York City.

The prevailing winds come from the west, but there are considerable differences due to topography. The average annual number of clear days is 133, partly cloudy 105, and cloudy 127.

Floods occur occasionally during the spring break-up and more rarely in the summer when certain meteorological conditions cause excessive downpours. On account of rugged contours, many streams are of a flash character on such occasions, rising and subsiding quickly.

Although the State is outside of what is known as the tornado belt, such storms have occurred at rare intervals.

HARRY O. GEREN, *Meteorologist and Climatic Section Director for New York, Weather Bureau, Ithaca.*

NORTH CAROLINA

Climatic summary

County [1]	Station	Temperature: Length of record	Temperature: January average	Temperature: July average	Temperature: Maximum	Temperature: Minimum	Killing frost average dates: Length of record	Killing frost average dates: Last in spring	Killing frost average dates: First in fall	Killing frost average dates: Growing season [2]	Average precipitation: Length of record	January	February	March	April	May	June	July	August	September	October	November	December	Annual
		Yr.	*°F.*	*°F.*	*°F.*	*°F.*	*Yr.*			*Days*	*Yr.*	*In.*	*In.*	*In.*	*In.*	*In.*	*In.*	*In.*	*In.*	*In.*	*In.*	*In.*	*In.*	*In.*
Alamance	Graham										37	3.92	3.56	4.00	3.74	3.51	4.27	5.44	4.92	3.46	2.87	2.51	3.78	45.98
Ashe	Jefferson	25	36.1	69.8	97	−20	30	Apr. 29	Oct. 10	164	33	3.68	3.26	4.17	3.93	4.44	4.36	5.27	5.04	3.90	3.77	2.93	3.69	48.44
	Parker	20	34.0	67.9	92	−17	21	May 5	Oct. 8	156	21	4.31	3.40	4.53	4.23	5.31	5.66	5.71	5.23	3.35	3.22	2.54	3.47	50.96
Avery	Banners Elk	31	34.4	66.4	95	−21	32	May 11	Oct. 6	148	31	4.12	3.45	5.10	4.40	4.80	4.77	6.58	5.46	3.85	4.42	2.98	4.02	53.95
Beaufort	Belhaven	25	46.0	79.9	106	0	20	Mar. 29	Nov. 7	223	31	3.87	3.49	3.52	3.48	3.68	4.83	6.72	6.02	5.68	2.71	2.73	3.90	50.63
Bladen	Elizabethtown										28	3.32	3.17	3.47	3.35	3.48	4.71	6.08	5.25	4.79	2.92	2.33	3.33	46.20
Brunswick	Southport	40	47.9	80.3	103	1	40	Mar. 16	Nov. 16	245	40	3.64	4.30	3.40	3.00	3.25	4.42	6.34	5.55	5.14	3.58	2.63	3.78	49.03
Buncombe	Asheville	38	35.4	71.7	97	−6	36	Apr. 11	Oct. 22	194	40	2.73	2.83	3.79	3.07	3.18	3.89	4.17	3.86	3.04	2.79	1.96	3.16	38.47
Burke	Linville Falls										22	4.28	3.07	4.50	4.38	4.76	4.58	8.23	5.99	4.44	5.53	3.50	4.38	57.64
	Morganton	39	40.2	76.3	105	−10	38	Apr. 14	Oct. 21	190	39	3.99	4.07	4.80	3.77	3.82	4.60	5.66	5.60	3.69	4.11	2.43	4.58	51.12
Caldwell	Lenoir	36	38.4	75.4	106	−18	36	Apr. 16	Oct. 19	186	40	3.83	3.54	4.58	3.77	3.95	4.98	5.54	5.66	3.54	3.93	2.52	4.30	50.14
Carteret	Beaufort	33	48.4	79.9	97	8	32	Mar. 8	Dec. 2	269	34	4.18	4.21	3.89	3.63	3.55	4.57	6.74	5.65	5.39	3.91	2.94	4.60	53.26
Catawba	Hickory	26	41.4	77.1	99	−9	26	Apr. 4	Oct. 28	207	26	4.59	3.73	4.47	3.64	3.32	3.86	5.57	5.38	3.43	4.19	2.87	4.59	49.64
Chatham	Moncure	40	42.3	78.5	106	−9	40	Apr. 16	Oct. 24	191	40	3.38	3.78	3.66	3.50	3.62	4.43	5.14	5.00	3.45	2.59	2.26	3.54	44.35
Cherokee	Andrews	22	41.2	73.8	99	−6	20	Apr. 25	Oct. 19	177	30	5.76	5.48	6.32	5.02	5.15	4.83	6.21	4.88	3.58	3.44	3.58	6.49	60.74
	Murphy										40	5.22	5.04	6.05	4.56	4.36	4.96	5.20	5.14	3.18	3.08	3.36	5.44	55.59
Chowan	Edenton	40	43.3	79.5	102	0	39	Apr. 1	Nov. 4	217	40	3.63	4.06	3.91	3.83	3.96	5.14	7.09	5.44	4.21	2.82	2.76	3.92	50.77
Cleveland	Shelby										15	4.46	3.66	4.40	3.67	3.37	3.35	5.48	3.90	3.41	4.07	3.20	4.71	47.68
Columbus	Chadbourn										8	3.90	3.96	3.01	2.76	3.43	4.26	7.35	4.84	6.52	2.37	2.34	3.53	48.27
Craven	New Bern	40	46.4	79.5	105	2	40	Mar. 28	Nov. 10	227	40	3.95	4.15	4.09	3.73	4.00	6.26	7.95	6.36	5.40	3.30	2.74	4.22	56.15
Cumberland	Fayetteville	40	44.9	79.4	108	1	40	do	Nov. 5	222	40	3.20	3.92	3.61	3.58	3.89	5.02	5.94	5.58	4.18	2.55	2.30	3.38	47.15
Currituck	Wash Woods										10	3.10	4.12	3.31	2.51	2.96	3.26	5.22	5.28	3.82	2.88	2.29	3.73	42.48
Dare	Hatteras	40	47.1	78.2	93	8	40	Feb. 27	Dec. 13	289	40	3.54	3.84	3.56	3.30	3.47	4.30	5.40	5.22	5.40	3.55	2.83	4.18	48.59
Davie	Mocksville										12	4.03	4.05	5.14	3.94	3.34	4.02	4.00	4.74	3.51	3.17	3.32	3.67	46.93
Duplin	Sloan	40	46.4	78.5	104	1	40	Apr. 7	Nov. 1	208	40	3.54	3.88	3.72	2.93	4.15	5.24	7.36	5.93	4.98	2.88	2.40	3.38	50.39
Durham	Durham	17	41.6	78.7	105	6	18	Apr. 9	Oct. 27	201	33	3.33	2.92	3.56	3.44	3.16	4.08	4.42	4.85	3.08	2.76	2.20	3.17	40.97
Edgecombe	Tarboro	40	42.6	79.8	106	−2	40	Apr. 6	Oct. 31	208	40	3.57	4.07	3.74	3.67	3.68	4.61	6.12	5.14	3.72	2.79	2.43	3.67	47.21
Forsyth	Winston-Salem	40	38.5	77.5	104	−4	40	Apr. 11	Oct. 25	197	40	3.64	3.68	4.15	3.54	3.83	4.28	4.81	4.71	3.12	3.11	2.43	3.60	44.90
Franklin	Louisburg	40	41.0	78.5	106	−10	39	Apr. 12	Oct. 27	198	40	3.52	3.81	3.82	3.73	3.55	4.65	5.45	4.80	3.52	2.75	2.31	3.39	45.30
Gaston	Mount Holly										29	4.10	4.16	4.36	3.41	4.26	4.51	5.29	5.88	3.88	3.39	2.67	4.78	50.69
Granville	Oxford	19	40.8	77.6	106	2	18	Apr. 7	Oct. 26	202	19	3.87	3.31	3.80	4.01	3.72	4.31	5.28	4.42	3.43	2.68	2.52	3.20	44.55

[1] The following counties, for which no records are available, are best represented by the stations indicated: Alexander—Hickory; Alleghany—Brewers; Anson and Scotland—Rockingham; Bertie and Martin—Scotland Neck; Cabarrus—Albemarle; Camden and Gates—Elizabeth City; Caswell—Reidsville; Clay and Graham—Andrews; Davidson—Salisbury; Greene—Goldsboro; Hertford—Eagletown; Jones—New Berne; Lee—Moncure; Montgomery—Pinehurst; Perquimans—Edenton; Sampson—Fayetteville; Tyrrell—Wenona; Warren—Henderson; Wilson—Rocky Mount; Yadkin—Winston-Salem.

[2] Length of growing season between average dates of last killing frost in spring and first in fall.

NORTH CAROLINA—Continued

Climatic summary—Continued

County	Station	Temperature: Length of record	Temperature: January average	Temperature: July average	Temperature: Maximum	Temperature: Minimum	Killing frost average dates: Length of record	Killing frost average dates: Last in spring	Killing frost average dates: First in fall	Killing frost average dates: Growing season	Average precipitation: Length of record	January	February	March	April	May	June	July	August	September	October	November	December	Annual
		Yr.	*°F.*	*°F.*	*°F.*	*°F.*	*Yr.*			*Days*	*Yr.*	*In.*	*In.*	*In.*	*In.*	*In.*	*In.*	*In.*	*In.*	*In.*	*In.*	*In.*	*In.*	*In.*
Guilford	Greensboro	40	40.6	78.0	105	-3	36	Apr. 7	Oct. 30	206	40	3.80	3.76	4.31	3.69	3.85	4.80	5.28	5.06	3.36	2.96	2.56	3.74	47.17
Halifax	Scotland Neck	33	43.6	77.9	105	-4	34	Apr. 5	Oct. 29	207	35	3.48	3.61	3.65	3.55	3.53	5.05	5.74	4.02	3.76	2.58	2.34	3.55	44.86
	Weldon	40	40.2	79.3	107	-9	40	Apr. 11	Oct. 27	199	40	3.36	3.40	3.79	3.45	3.52	4.50	5.58	4.63	3.55	2.62	2.29	3.36	44.05
Harnett	Chalybeate Springs	13	42.8	78.2	102	0	10	Apr. 19	Oct. 28	192	10	2.92	3.88	3.66	3.13	3.75	4.96	5.87	6.23	3.85	2.56	2.15	4.38	47.34
Haywood	Waynesville	35	38.6	70.9	97	-12	36	Apr. 25	Oct. 13	171	40	4.02	4.12	5.06	3.68	3.93	4.01	4.72	4.18	2.90	2.94	2.34	4.41	46.31
Henderson	Hendersonville	40	39.2	72.9	99	-9	40	Apr. 21	Oct. 18	180	40	4.77	4.58	5.32	4.35	4.77	5.41	6.20	6.04	4.68	4.35	3.21	5.57	59.25
Hoke	Sanatorium	14	43.9	78.4	105	2	15	Mar. 29	Nov. 14	230	16	3.40	3.65	3.35	2.95	3.52	5.18	5.83	4.68	4.24	2.45	2.13	3.19	44.57
Hyde	New Holland	26	46.1	78.6	102	6	22	Mar. 21	Nov. 12	236	23	4.01	3.87	3.38	3.73	3.26	4.84	7.30	5.60	5.43	2.42	2.75	4.52	51.11
Iredell	Settle	14	40.2	75.7	101	-5					40	3.79	3.69	4.34	3.62	3.81	4.45	4.96	5.17	3.47	3.61	2.56	4.20	47.67
	Statesville	33	41.0	77.5	103	-3	34	Apr. 13	Oct. 27	197	39	4.01	4.02	4.38	3.54	3.70	4.29	5.63	5.89	3.49	3.55	2.67	4.31	49.48
Jackson	Cullowhee	29	40.4	73.5	99	-11	29	Apr. 24	Oct. 18	177	29	4.29	3.85	4.79	3.50	3.68	3.81	4.38	3.77	3.26	2.85	2.52	4.47	45.17
Johnston	Smithfield	38	42.7	79.2	105	-6	27	Apr. 5	Oct. 29	207	40	3.74	4.05	3.75	3.81	3.81	5.22	6.03	5.20	4.34	2.85	2.44	3.45	48.69
Lenoir	Kinston	33	46.1	80.3	106	0	28	Apr. 3	Nov. 2	213	34	3.42	3.72	3.59	3.33	3.58	5.27	6.93	5.46	4.83	2.47	2.36	3.16	48.12
Lincoln	Lincolnton	16	40.0	77.0	103	-2	15	Apr. 12	Oct. 23	194	16	3.80	4.18	3.95	3.47	4.15	4.65	6.20	4.44	3.49	3.21	2.08	3.76	47.38
McDowell	Marion	37	40.0	75.4	105	-10	38	Apr. 15	Oct. 24	192	40	4.25	4.16	5.21	4.22	4.69	5.43	6.02	6.31	4.25	4.39	2.88	5.12	56.93
Macon	Highlands	16	39.7	70.5	98	-10	16	Apr. 26	Oct. 21	178	36	6.99	6.86	8.20	6.53	5.71	7.44	8.37	7.15	6.25	5.79	5.10	8.24	82.63
	Rock House No. 1	40	38.9	70.6	95	-13	40	Apr. 16	Oct. 24	191	40	6.77	6.55	7.67	6.09	6.10	7.34	8.67	8.24	6.38	5.80	4.98	8.37	82.96
Madison	Hot Springs	37	41.8	75.7	105	-12	36	do	Oct. 23	190	33	3.26	2.85	4.25	3.79	3.78	4.15	5.39	4.75	3.12	2.95	2.32	3.21	43.82
	Marshall	37	38.8	74.6	102	-10	36	Apr. 18	Oct. 21	186	40	2.73	2.81	3.93	3.40	3.32	4.06	4.40	4.08	2.96	2.54	1.95	2.95	39.13
Mecklenburg	Charlotte	40	41.2	78.4	103	-5	40	Mar. 18	Nov. 11	238	40	3.53	3.83	3.91	3.39	3.40	4.12	4.83	4.99	3.17	2.84	2.30	3.91	44.22
Mitchell	Altapass	19	36.8	68.8	95	-19	18	May 9	Oct. 10	154	25	3.82	3.06	4.72	3.99	4.33	3.84	6.92	4.75	4.06	4.09	3.30	4.37	51.25
Moore	Pinehurst	34	44.2	79.2	106	2	34	Apr. 2	Nov. 2	214	36	3.54	3.68	3.69	3.52	3.51	4.59	5.84	5.38	3.88	2.89	2.08	3.56	46.16
	Southern Pines	38	44.1	79.0	107	-4	38	Apr. 3	do	213	40	3.42	3.95	3.92	3.74	4.03	5.22	6.59	5.87	4.27	3.07	2.42	3.80	50.30
Nash	Nashville	34	43.0	78.7	107	-8	34	Apr. 8	Oct. 30	205	40	3.62	4.04	3.71	3.91	3.76	4.97	6.23	4.94	4.10	2.94	2.46	3.53	48.21
	Rocky Mount No. 1										33	3.53	3.71	3.49	3.50	3.61	4.47	5.58	4.45	3.95	2.79	2.24	3.49	44.81
New Hanover	Wilmington	40	46.5	79.1	103	5	40	Mar. 16	Nov. 17	246	40	2.90	3.31	3.11	2.73	3.22	4.49	6.95	5.96	4.89	2.66	2.10	3.08	45.40
Northampton	Eagletown	17	42.1	77.5	100	-4	18	Apr. 13	Oct. 26	196	19	3.55	4.08	4.20	3.61	3.89	5.75	6.83	5.34	3.21	2.41	2.26	4.11	49.24
Onslow	Swansboro	14	47.6	79.2	101	5	15	Mar. 15	Nov. 18	248	16	4.89	4.05	3.97	3.41	4.04	5.68	7.10	6.29	7.10	2.60	3.79	4.61	57.53
Orange	Chapel Hill	36	41.2	78.8	107	-6	38	Apr. 5	Nov. 1	210	40	3.61	3.92	4.11	4.03	3.66	4.71	5.22	5.17	3.47	2.93	2.57	3.79	47.19
Pamlico	Stonewall										16	4.40	3.71	3.58	3.02	3.43	5.18	7.37	4.96	6.07	2.46	3.12	3.68	50.98
Pasquotank	Elizabeth City	25	45.0	78.9	104	2	26	Apr. 4	Nov. 4	214	27	4.16	3.75	3.71	3.59	3.79	4.87	6.35	4.78	4.64	2.26	2.72	3.88	48.50
Pender	Willard	29	47.9	79.4	105	-4	31	Apr. 9	Oct. 30	204	32	3.33	3.66	3.39	3.18	4.05	5.37	6.91	5.60	4.75	2.82	2.33	3.40	48.79
Person	Rotsboro										20	3.71	3.58	4.15	4.45	3.83	4.13	4.57	5.08	3.67	3.13	2.43	3.36	46.09
Pitt	Greenville	26	44.2	79.4	104	0	26	Apr. 2	Nov. 3	215	35	3.60	3.90	3.53	3.68	3.87	5.86	6.96	4.74	4.75	2.87	2.39	3.58	49.73
Polk	Tryon	21	42.9	77.0	105	-3	21	Apr. 15	Oct. 29	197	27	5.27	4.64	5.30	4.54	4.86	4.28	6.45	5.47	4.62	4.65	3.48	5.55	59.11
Randolph	Randleman										34	3.91	3.68	4.09	3.53	3.98	4.28	5.95	4.95	3.34	2.92	2.31	3.87	46.81
	Ramseur	16	39.1	77.0	104	-16	11	Apr. 18	Oct. 22	187	17	3.02	3.89	3.96	3.52	3.87	4.51	4.58	5.54	3.24	2.64	2.39	4.13	45.29

Richmond	Rockingham	36	43.0	79.9	108	−15	38	Apr. 3	Oct. 30	210	40	3.37	4.13	3.62	3.60	3.60	5.42	5.36	5.63	4.02	2.94	2.15	3.65	47.49
Robeson	Lumberton	40	45.3	80.2	108	−1	40	Mar. 27	Nov. 7	225	40	3.21	4.15	3.68	3.64	3.82	5.21	5.62	5.02	4.53	2.93	2.25	3.44	47.50
Rockingham	Reidsville	37	40.1	77.5	105	−2	36	Apr. 9	Oct. 29	203	37	3.64	3.20	3.80	3.51	3.58	4.37	4.69	4.77	3.34	3.03	2.37	3.56	43.86
Rowan	Salisbury	40	41.6	78.9	105	−1	39	do	Oct. 26	200	40	4.09	4.01	4.68	3.94	4.03	4.37	5.30	5.20	3.44	3.05	2.49	4.27	48.87
Rutherford	Caroleen	38	41.9	78.9	106	−7	38	do	Oct. 28	202	39	4.40	4.28	4.68	4.00	3.69	4.91	5.14	5.53	4.02	3.53	2.94	4.91	52.03
Stanly	Albemarle	27	43.1	79.1	105	−2	27	Apr. 13	Oct. 19	189	28	3.97	3.60	4.24	3.98	3.48	4.50	5.29	4.87	3.89	2.85	2.58	4.04	47.29
Stokes	Saxon	15	37.4	76.2	102	−8	24	Apr. 18	Oct. 17	182	16	3.20	3.80	4.28	3.42	3.46	5.44	4.34	5.14	2.74	3.23	2.31	4.22	45.58
Surry	Elkin										18	3.78	3.28	4.03	3.26	3.71	3.60	4.84	4.97	3.57	3.84	2.52	3.98	45.38
	Mount Airy	39	38.0	75.3	104	−15	38	Apr. 23	Oct. 16	176	40	3.63	3.30	4.06	3.49	3.79	4.52	5.16	4.86	3.40	3.65	2.59	3.87	46.32
Swain	Bryson City										40	4.93	5.01	6.01	4.55	4.36	4.68	5.31	4.68	3.21	2.97	3.06	5.40	54.17
Transylvania	Brevard	31	38.5	72.4	99	−12	28	Apr. 28	Oct. 15	170	37	4.97	4.30	5.43	4.49	5.21	5.47	6.81	6.18	4.78	4.65	3.48	5.46	61.23
Union	Monroe	40	43.3	78.7	107	−10	40	Apr. 13	Oct. 23	193	40	3.50	4.13	3.86	3.58	3.35	4.69	4.71	5.49	3.39	3.08	2.43	3.80	46.01
Vance	Henderson	39	40.9	78.1	106	0	39	Apr. 8	Nov. 3	209	40	3.52	3.58	4.11	3.95	3.63	4.49	5.39	5.21	3.51	3.06	2.50	3.62	46.57
Wake	Raleigh	40	41.1	78.8	103	−2	40	Mar. 23	Nov. 9	231	40	3.30	3.79	3.70	3.53	3.61	4.65	5.36	5.15	3.88	2.61	2.35	3.55	45.48
Washington	Wenona	23	43.7	77.0	101	−4	24	Apr. 22	Oct. 23	184	24	4.01	3.54	3.51	3.84	3.58	5.07	7.30	5.77	5.27	2.64	2.94	3.68	51.15
Watauga	Boone	10	37.1	69.9	96	−7	10	Apr. 30	Oct. 5	158	10	4.59	3.19	5.49	4.63	4.65	3.98	6.05	5.02	4.35	4.78	3.49	4.20	54.42
Wayne	Goldsboro	40	43.6	79.8	108	2	36	Apr. 1	Nov. 4	217	40	3.40	4.12	3.64	3.80	4.28	4.96	7.08	4.99	4.55	2.72	2.42	3.47	49.43
Wilkes	Brewers	29	38.5	74.8	104	−10	29	Apr. 24	Oct. 14	173	31	3.73	3.79	4.55	4.03	4.42	5.62	5.55	5.96	4.26	4.29	2.57	4.24	53.01
Yancey	Mount Mitchell	13	27.6	59.3	87	−21	10	June 1	Oct. 7	128	13	5.77	4.29	6.52	5.77	6.23	4.86	6.91	7.14	6.51	5.12	5.26	4.32	68.70

NORTH CAROLINA—Continued

Precipitation and temperature—State unit values

[This tabulation gives the mean annual, mean monthly, and average seasonal precipitation, 1886–1938, and the mean annual temperatures, 1902–38, for North Carolina]

Precipitation		Precipitation		Precipitation		Precipitation		Temperature		Temperature	
Year	Mean	Year	Mean	Year	Mean	Month	Mean	Year	Mean	Year	Mean
	In.		*In.*		*In.*		*In.*		*In.*		*In.*
1886	52.38	1907	48.04	1928	56.21	May	4.11	1902	58.8	1923	59.3
1887	52.44	1908	58.31	1929	62.06	June	4.74	1903	58.5	1924	57.6
1888	55.24	1909	47.10	1930	38.04	July	5.93	1904	57.1	1925	60.0
1889	50.63	1910	47.90	1931	43.57	August	5.52	1905	58.3	1926	58.9
1890	46.49	1911	42.25	1932	52.38	September	4.00	1906	59.5	1927	60.1
1891	54.08	1912	47.92	1933	39.28	October	3.33	1907	58.8	1928	58.8
1892	47.34	1913	51.82	1934	53.74	November	2.66	1908	59.6	1929	59.2
1893	53.84	1914	46.74	1935	48.08	December	3.85	1909	59.5	1930	58.8
1894	46.57	1915	50.34	1936	60.27			1910	58.6	1931	60.1
1895	50.23	1916	48.49	1937	52.66	Annual	49.76	1911	60.5	1932	60.3
1896	47.54	1917	50.33	1938	48.18			1912	58.2	1933	60.9
1897	46.19	1918	49.31					1913	59.9	1934	59.4
1898	50.04	1919	47.56	Month	Mean	Season	Average	1914	58.5	1935	59.2
1899	52.08	1920	55.57					1915	58.9	1936	59.3
1900	48.40	1921	42.56					1916	59.3	1937	59.2
1901	62.66	1922	56.40					1917	56.9	1938	60.2
1902	44.46	1923	45.25		*In.*		*In.*	1918	58.8		
1903	50.13	1924	55.04	January	3.80	Winter	11.64	1919	59.7		
1904	43.27	1925	37.23	February	3.99	Spring	11.94	1920	57.8		
1905	51.73	1926	43.33	March	4.21	Summer	16.19	1921	61.0		
1906	59.38	1927	44.95	April	3.62	Fall	9.99	1922	60.1		

Dates of last killing frost in spring and first in fall, with length of growing season

Year	Asheville			Charlotte			Edenton			Raleigh			Wilmington			Winston-Salem		
	Last in spring	First in fall	Growing season[1]	Last in spring	First in fall	Growing season[1]	Last in spring	First in fall	Growing season[1]	Last in spring	First in fall	Growing season[1]	Last in spring	First in fall	Growing season[1]	Last in spring	First in fall	Growing season[1]
			Days			*Days*			*Days*			*Days*			*Days*			*Days*
1899				Apr. 5	Nov. 4	213	Apr. 6	Nov. 13	221	Apr. 5	Nov. 5	214	Apr. 5	Nov. 13	222	Apr. 17	Oct. 2	168
1900				Apr. 1	Nov. 9	222	Apr. 5	Nov. 17	226	do	Nov. 9	218	Mar. 17	Dec. 12	270	Apr. 5	Nov. 9	218
1901				Mar. 22	Nov. 15	238	Mar. 17	Nov. 7	235	Mar. 22	Nov. 7	230	do	Nov. 16	244	Mar. 29	Oct. 26	211
1902				Mar. 19	Nov. 28	254	Mar. 7	Oct. 23	230	Mar. 19	Nov. 28	254	Mar. 19	Dec. 9	265	Apr. 5	Oct. 15	193

1903	Apr. 24	Oct. 19	178	Mar. 2	Nov. 7	250	Apr. 5	Oct. 29	207	Apr. 5	Oct. 28	206	Feb. 23	Nov. 8	258	do	Oct. 27	205
1904	Apr. 17	Oct. 16	182	Apr. 4	Nov. 15	225	do	Nov. 7	216	Apr. 17	Nov. 15	212	Mar. 5	Nov. 15	255	Apr. 22	Oct. 16	177
1905	Apr. 18	Oct. 13	178	Feb. 24	Nov. 11	260	Mar. 17	Nov. 14	242	do	do	212	Feb. 24	do	264	Apr. 19	Oct. 13	177
1906	May 10	Oct. 11	154	Mar. 21	Oct. 12	205	Mar. 21	Oct. 12	205	Mar. 25	Oct. 12	201	Mar. 21	Nov. 12	236	May 10	Oct. 11	154
1907	Apr. 20	Oct. 13	176	Apr. 15	Nov. 14	213	Apr. 15	Oct. 22	190	Apr. 2	Oct. 22	203	Apr. 15	Nov. 14	213	Apr. 21	Oct. 15	177
1908	Apr. 4	Oct. 3	182	Mar. 22	Nov. 15	238	Apr. 4	Nov. 2	212	Mar. 21	Nov. 5	229	Mar. 21	Nov. 6	230	Apr. 4	Nov. 1	211
1909	May 3	Oct. 13	163	Feb. 26	Oct. 25	241	Apr. 11	Oct. 14	186	Mar. 5	Oct. 30	239	Mar. 23	Nov. 19	241	Apr. 11	Oct. 13	185
1910	Apr. 22	Oct. 24	185	do	Oct. 29	245	Mar. 16	Oct. 30	228	Mar. 15	Oct. 29	228	Mar. 16	Oct. 30	228	May 15	Oct. 29	167
1911	Apr. 2	Nov. 3	215	Mar. 31	Nov. 3	217	Mar. 25	Nov. 3	223	Mar. 25	Nov. 3	223	Mar. 25	Nov. 2	222	Apr. 25	Nov. 3	192
1912	Apr. 9	Oct. 27	201	Mar. 10	do	238	Mar. 17	Nov. 16	244	Mar. 11	do	237	Mar. 10	Nov. 16	251	Apr. 9	Oct. 28	202
1913	Mar. 29	Oct. 22	207	Mar. 28	Oct. 23	209	Mar. 18	Oct. 22	218	Mar. 18	Oct. 22	218	Mar. 7	Nov. 10	248		Oct. 22	
1914	Apr. 4	Oct. 28	207	Mar. 23	Oct. 28	219	Apr. 11	Oct. 28	200	Apr. 10	Oct. 28	201	Mar. 23	Nov. 18	240	Apr. 10	Oct. 28	201
1915	Apr. 5	Oct. 10	188	Apr. 4	Nov. 16	226	Apr. 5	Oct. 25	203	Apr. 5	Nov. 16	225	Apr. 4	Nov. 30	240	Apr. 4	Oct. 10	189
1916	Apr. 10	Oct. 22	195	Apr. 10	Nov. 15	219	Mar. 20	Nov. 4	229	Mar. 20	do	241	Mar. 18	Nov. 16	243	Apr. 10	Nov. 2	206
1917	do	Oct. 13	186	Mar. 19	Oct. 24	219	Apr. 10			Mar. 19	Oct. 31	226	Mar. 19	Nov. 25	251	Mar. 20	Oct. 13	207
1918	Apr. 14	Nov. 2	202	Mar. 11	Nov. 13	247	Apr. 6	Nov. 8	216	Mar. 16	Nov. 24	253	Mar. 11	Dec. 5	269	Apr. 14	Nov. 2	202
1919	Apr. 27	Nov. 6	193	Apr. 1	Nov. 14	227	Apr. 26	Nov. 6	194	Apr. 2	Nov. 14	226	Feb. 20	Nov. 15	268	Apr. 27	Nov. 6	193
1920	Apr. 15	Oct. 30	198	Apr. 14	Oct. 30	199	Apr. 11	Nov. 13	216	Mar. 10	Nov. 13	248	Mar. 9	Nov. 14	250	Apr. 14	Oct. 29	198
1921	Apr. 12	Oct. 9	180	Feb. 24	Nov. 13	262	Apr. 12			Feb. 26	do	260	Apr. 12	Nov. 13	215	Apr. 19	Oct. 9	173
1922	Apr. 2	Oct. 19	200	Mar. 5	Nov. 23	263	Mar. 23	Oct. 19	210	Mar. 23	Nov. 22	244	Feb. 18	Nov. 26	281	Mar. 23	Nov. 11	233
1923	Apr. 10	Nov. 1	205	Apr. 2	Nov. 9	220	Apr. 10	Nov. 10	214	Apr. 2	Nov. 2	214	Apr. 2	Nov. 10	222	Apr. 10	Nov. 2	206
1924	Apr. 3	Oct. 23	203	do	Nov. 19	231	Apr. 5	Nov. 17	226	Apr. 3	Nov. 18	229	Mar. 17	Nov. 19	247	Apr. 3	Oct. 23	203
1925	Apr. 1	Oct. 11	193	Mar. 3	Oct. 29	240	Mar. 24	Oct. 11	201	Mar. 4	Oct. 29	239	Mar. 4	Nov. 17	258	do	Oct. 11	191
1926	Mar. 18	Nov. 4	231	Mar. 16	Nov. 11	240	Apr. 20	Oct. 28	191	Apr. 20	Nov. 4	198	Apr. 20	Oct. 28	191	Apr. 20	Oct. 28	191
1927	Apr. 25	Nov. 7	196	Mar. 25	Nov. 7	227	Apr. 12	Nov. 7	209	Mar. 5	Nov. 7	247	Mar. 5	Nov. 7	247	Apr. 23	Nov. 7	198
1928	Apr. 17	Nov. 5	202	Mar. 20	Nov. 21	246	Apr. 17	Nov. 12	209	Mar. 20	Nov. 21	246	Mar. 19	Nov. 24	250	Apr. 16	Nov. 12	210
1929	Mar. 18	do	232	Mar. 11	Nov. 30	264	Mar. 11	do	246	Mar. 10	Nov. 22	257	Mar. 11	Nov. 30	264	Mar. 18	Nov. 6	233
1930	Apr. 1	Oct. 21	203	Mar. 5	Nov. 1	241	Apr. 25	Oct. 22	180	Mar. 23	Nov. 1	223	Mar. 5	Nov. 2	242	Mar. 23	Oct. 22	213
1931	Mar. 22	Oct. 19	211	Mar. 17	Dec. 8	266	Mar. 21	Nov. 7	231	Mar. 17	Dec. 3	261	Mar. 17	Dec. 16	274	Mar. 30	Oct. 19	203
1932	Mar. 16	Oct. 7	205	Mar. 15	Nov. 13	243	Mar. 24	Nov. 13	234	Mar. 16	Nov. 13	242	Mar. 11	Nov. 14	248	Mar. 25	Nov. 12	232
1933	Apr. 13	Oct. 26	196	Mar. 11	Nov. 9	243	Mar. 30	Nov. 9	224	Mar. 11	Nov. 9	243	do	Nov. 9	243	Mar. 30	Oct. 26	210
1934	Apr. 14	Oct. 29	198	Mar. 15	Nov. 13	243	Mar. 24	Oct. 29	219	Mar. 25	Oct. 29	218	Mar. 21	Oct. 29	222	Apr. 22	Oct. 14	175
1935	Apr. 17	Oct. 7	173	Mar. 1	Nov. 24	268	Mar. 15	Nov. 24	254	Mar. 1	Nov. 24	268	Mar. 1	Nov. 24	268	Apr. 17	Oct. 8	174
1936	Apr. 20	Oct. 31	194	Feb. 12	Nov. 17	279	Apr. 4	Oct. 31	210	Apr. 4	Nov. 16	226	Feb. 23	Nov. 16	266	Apr. 20	Oct. 31	194
1937	Apr. 17	Oct. 15	181	Mar. 17	Nov. 5	233	Apr. 11	Nov. 4	207	Mar. 28	Oct. 15	201	Mar. 17	Nov. 18	246	Apr. 17	Oct. 15	181
1938	Apr. 4	Oct. 26	205	Feb. 26	Nov. 25	272	Mar. 7	Nov. 25	263	Mar. 1	Nov. 25	269	Mar. 1	Nov. 25	269	Apr. 11	Nov. 15	218
Mean	Apr. 11	Oct. 22	194	Mar. 18	Nov. 11	238	Apr. 1	Nov. 4	217	Mar. 23	Nov. 9	231	Mar. 16	Nov. 17	246	do	Oct. 25	197
Extremes	Mar. 16[2] May 10[3]	Oct. 3[4] Nov. 7[5]	[6] 154 [7] 232	Feb. 12[2] Apr. 15[3]	Oct. 12[4] Dec. 8[5]	[6] 199 [7] 279	Mar. 7[2] Apr. 26[3]	Oct. 11[4] Nov. 25[5]	[6] 180 [7] 262	Feb. 26[2] Apr. 20[3]	Oct. 12[4] Dec. 3[5]	[6] 198 [7] 268	Feb. 18[2] Apr. 20[3]	Oct. 28[4] Dec. 16[5]	[6] 191 [7] 281	Mar. 18[2] May 15[3]	Oct. 2[4] Nov. 15[5]	[6] 154 [7] 233

[1] Number of days between last killing frost in spring and first in fall.
[2] Earliest date in spring.
[3] Latest date in spring.
[4] Earliest date in fall.
[5] Latest date in fall.
[6] Shortest growing season.
[7] Longest growing season.

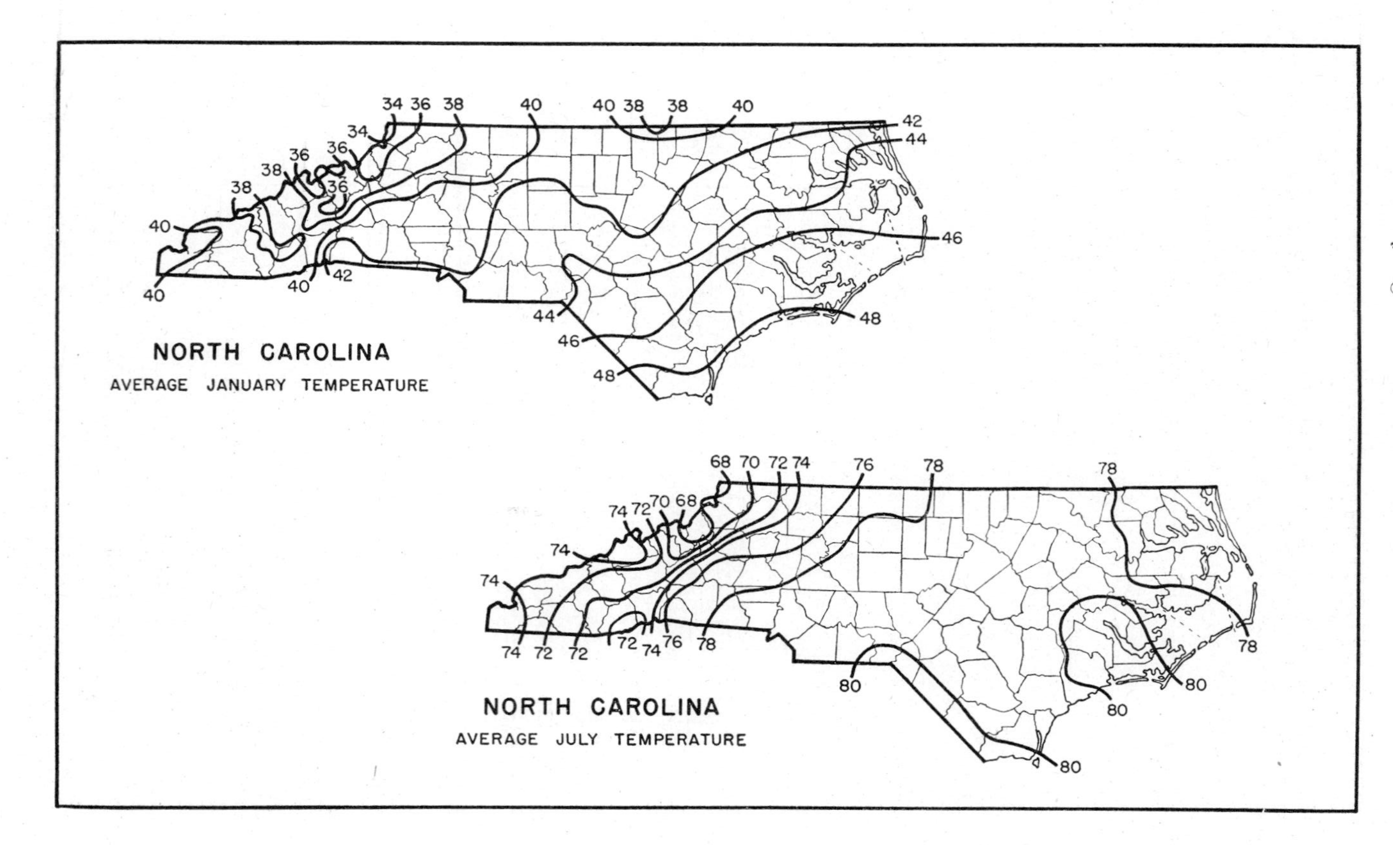
NORTH CAROLINA
AVERAGE JANUARY TEMPERATURE
NORTH CAROLINA
AVERAGE JULY TEMPERATURE

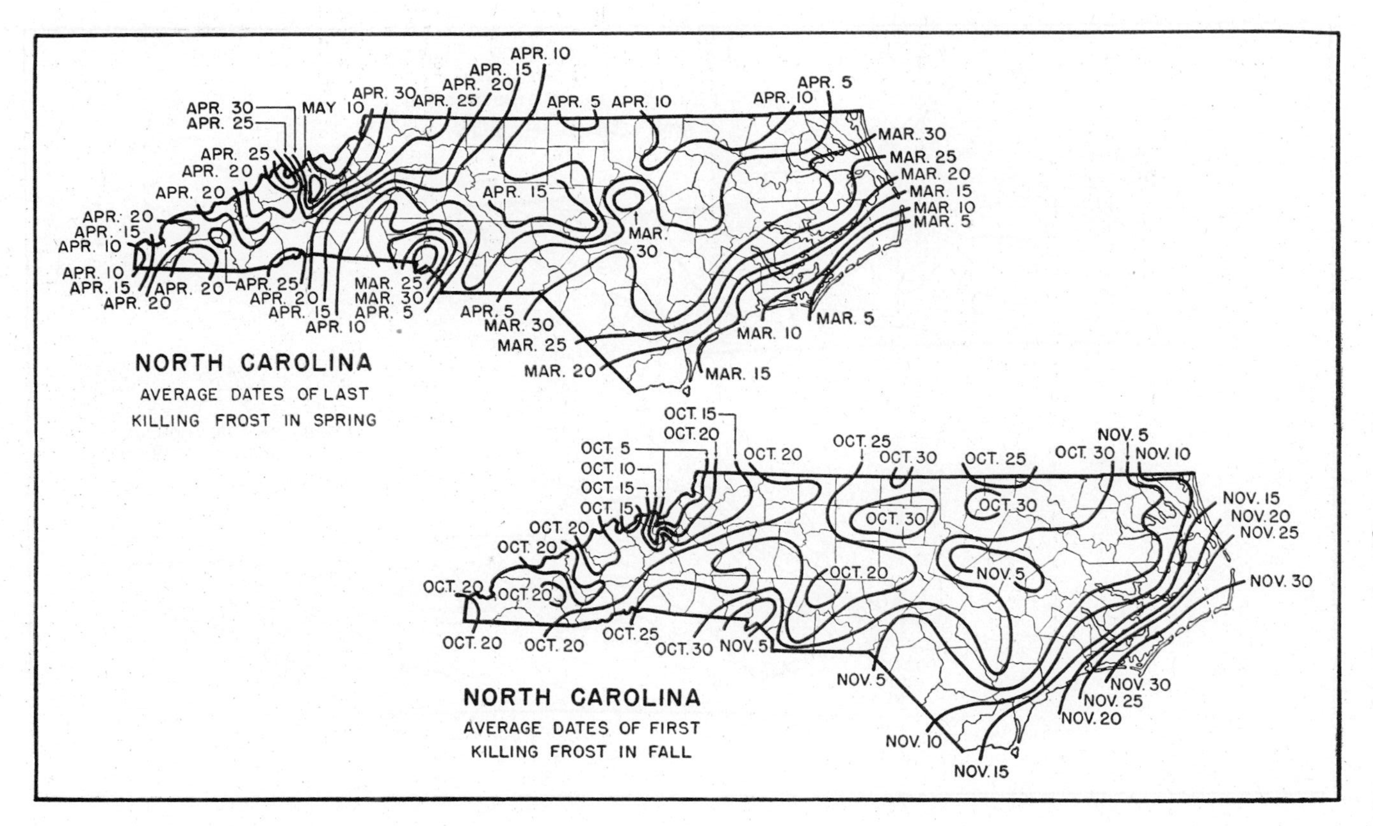
NORTH CAROLINA
AVERAGE DATES OF LAST
KILLING FROST IN SPRING
NORTH CAROLINA
AVERAGE DATES OF FIRST
KILLING FROST IN FALL

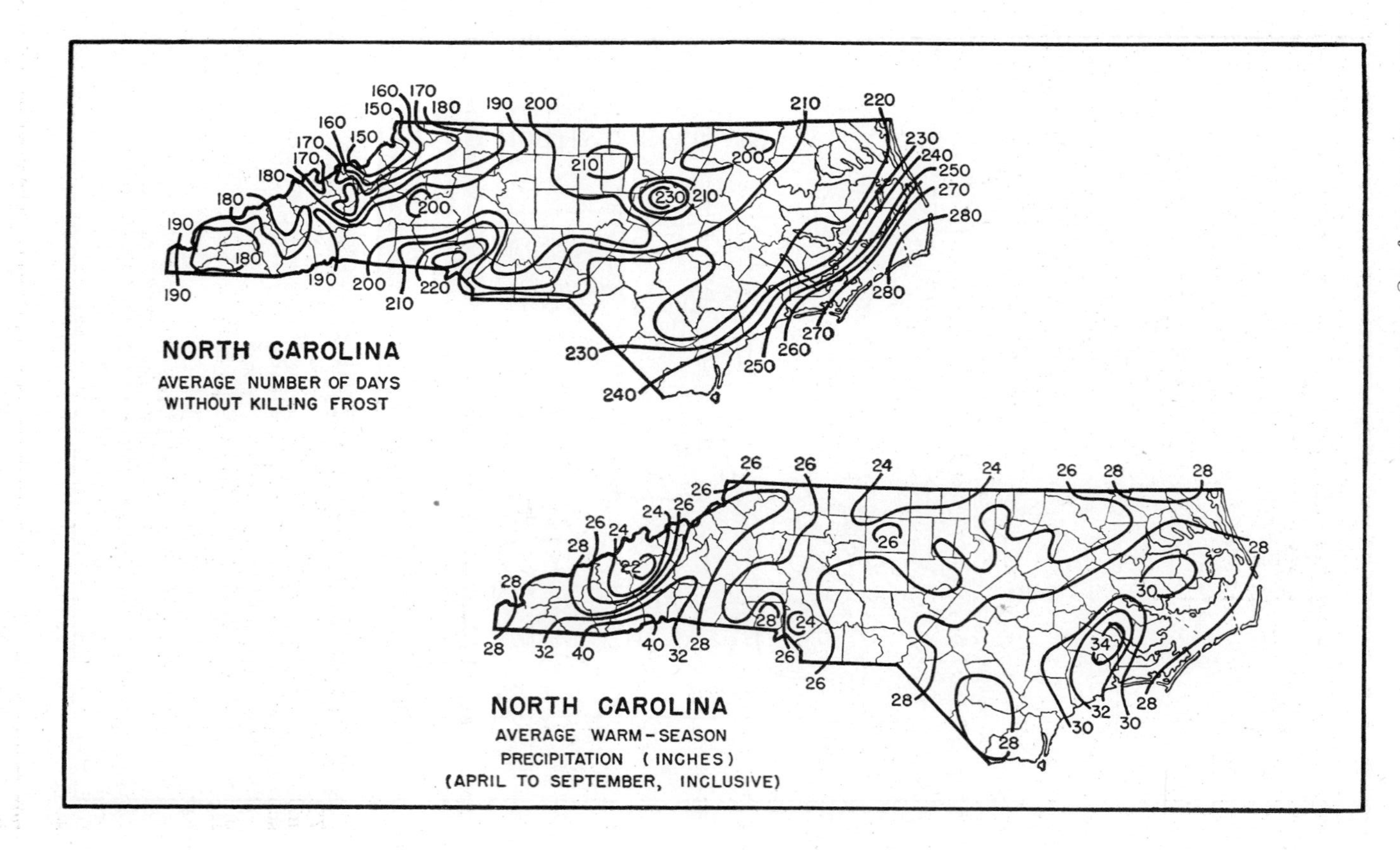
NORTH CAROLINA
AVERAGE NUMBER OF DAYS
WITHOUT KILLING FROST
NORTH CAROLINA
AVERAGE WARM-SEASON
PRECIPITATION (INCHES)
(APRIL TO SEPTEMBER, INCLUSIVE)

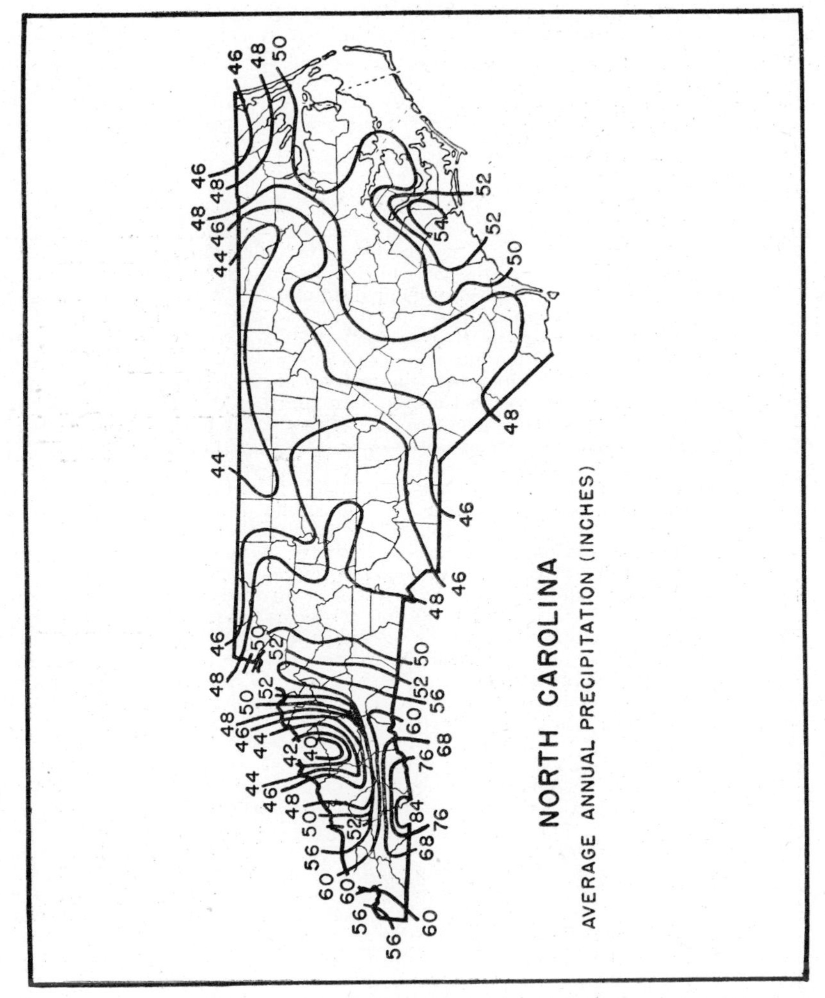

SUPPLEMENTARY CLIMATIC NOTFS FOR NORTH CAROLINA

North Carolina lies approximately between 34° and 36½° north latitude and 75½° and 84½° west longitude. Its extreme length from east to west is 503 miles, average breadth 100, and extreme breadth 187. It has an area of 52,426 square miles, 48,740 of which are land and 3,686 water.

The topography of the State may best be conceived as a vast declivity, sloping down from the summits of the Smoky Mountains, at an altitude of nearly 7,000 feet, to sea level at the Atlantic Coast. The Smoky Mountains are the highest part of the great Appalachian chain.

The slope of the State is made up of three wide, extended "terraces": (1) A high mountain plateau, distinguished as the western or mountain section; (2) a submontane plateau, designated the middle section, or Piedmont; and (3) the Atlantic plain, comprising the low country or Coastal Plain area, including that part from the head of the tides downward as a tidewater subdivision. From the first section to the second there is a sharp descent, through a few miles only, of not less than 1,500 feet. From the middle to the low country there is a rather constant downward grade, with a difference of only about 200 feet. The drainage, except in the extreme west, is into the ocean.

The climate of North Carolina varies greatly from the southeast corner, where it approaches the subtropical, to the mountain region in the west, where it is a modified continental type, except that the summers are cooler and the rainfall is greater than is usual in the interior States. Some of the mountain districts have more rainfall than is found anywhere else in the eastern half of the United States.

The mountain ranges form a partial barrier to the cold waves that move southeastward from the interior of the country, and these cold waves usually reach the Piedmont in modified form. The average growing season in the Piedmont may be 2 months or more longer than in some of the higher mountain districts.

The climate in the more eastern and southeastern sections is affected by the modifying influence of the Atlantic Ocean and to some extent by the sounds and smaller bodies of water, so that near the coast the changes in temperature, both daily and seasonal, are reduced and there is an increase in the amount of precipitation.

The average annual temperature may vary as much as 20° F. in different parts of the State. Valleys, cross chains, and sharp differences in elevation are largely responsible for significant temperature variations An outstanding characteristic in western North Carolina is the thermal belts, which are probably more pronounced here than at any other place in the eastern United States. Frequent observations have shown temperature inversions of 20° or more along some mountainsides. In eastern North Carolina temperature changes, both diurnal and seasonal, are relatively small because of the modifying effect of the Atlantic Ocean; parts of this section extend somewhat into the Atlantic. Perhaps the most interesting temperature feature of the extreme southeast is the relatively high mean in the vicinity of Southport—about 64°. In this section vegetation of semitropical origin, such as palmetto and magnolia, is found.

Temperatures rarely go as low as zero, except during rather unusual cold periods. All stations in the western part of the State, however, have records of below zero. During a normal winter in central districts the temperature drops to about 10° or 12° F., but such low readings are of infrequent occurrence, and the cold periods are usually of short duration. During an average summer, maximum temperatures reach 100° or higher on only 2 or 3 days.

Contrary to the more or less prevailing impression, the nearness of the Gulf Stream has comparatively little effect on the climate of eastern North Carolina because the stream is separated from the coast by 50 miles of comparatively cold water and the prevailing wind is from the southwest.

Precipitation received in different sections of the State varies widely in amount. For instance, the extreme southwestern part is one of the wettest sections east of the Rocky Mountains; 80 inches, or slightly more, normally falls annually in Madison County, along the Georgia-South Carolina border. The driest part of the State is likewise in the mountain districts, in parts of Buncombe and Madison Counties. Many mountain areas with comparatively low elevations have relatively little precipitation. The moisture-laden winds from the south Atlantic and Gulf coasts are cooled and have their moisture condensed and largely exhausted in passing over the mountain heights; they descend to less elevated or somewhat enclosed areas, such as the French Broad Valley, as relatively dry winds. Precipitation is comparatively heavy along and near the coast. A considerable part of the summer precipitation results from afternoon thunderstorms.

Widespread droughts are almost rarities, even though there are occasional local shortages of moisture, particularly in the summer and fall.

Snowfall is heaviest in the west and diminishes toward the coast. Most of the snow in the central and eastern parts of the State occurs during the passage of storms up the coast accompanied by north or northeast winds.

The average relative humidity is about 71 percent for the State, generally highest in winter and lowest in spring. Averages in the west are somewhat lower than in the east.

North Carolina is rather sunny. The percentage of the possible amount of sunshine varies from about 53 in the winter to about 68 in the fall. The average for the year is about 61 percent. The variation in sunshine is related very closely to the average daily cloudiness, which is highest in winter and lowest in fall.

The prevailing wind is from the southwest, but occasionally in winter the wind is from the northeast. North Carolina is out of the path of cyclonic storms but does lie in the path of the occasional tropical storms that move up the coast from the vicinity of Florida and sometimes are accompanied by heavy rains and dangerous winds. Records show few destructive tornadoes within the borders of the State.

HERBERT E. KICHLINE, *Associate Meteorologist and Climatic Section Director for North Carolina, Weather Bureau, Raleigh.*

NORTH DAKOTA

Climatic summary

County	Station	Temperature: Length of record	Temperature: January average	Temperature: July average	Temperature: Maximum	Temperature: Minimum	Killing frost average dates: Length of record	Killing frost average dates: Last in spring	Killing frost average dates: First in fall	Killing frost average dates: Growing season [1]	Average precipitation: Length of record	January	February	March	April	May	June	July	August	September	October	November	December	Annual
		Yr.	*°F.*	*°F.*	*°F.*	*°F.*	*Yr.*			*Days*	*Yr.*	*In.*	*In.*	*In.*	*In.*	*In.*	*In.*	*In.*	*In.*	*In.*	*In.*	*In.*	*In.*	*In.*
Adams	Hettinger	32	13.3	70.7	113	−47	31	May 21	Sept. 19	121	32	0.32	0.28	0.63	0.96	2.24	3.32	2.35	1.27	1.32	0.72	0.40	0.35	14.16
	Stowers										20	.33	.46	.74	1.06	2.33	3.33	1.70	1.28	1.22	1.04	.32	.45	14.26
Barnes	Valley City	31	6.4	70.5	116	−41	19	May 18	Sept. 18	123	34	.52	.48	.57	1.56	2.78	3.23	2.75	2.01	1.72	1.06	.73	.44	17.85
Benson	Maddock	24	4.5	68.7	110	−50	24	May 27	Sept. 13	109	24	.33	.36	.38	1.21	2.09	3.29	2.73	2.09	1.71	.89	.45	.26	15.79
Billings	Fryburg						16	May 13	Sept. 24	134	21	.52	.45	.86	1.26	2.12	3.38	2.03	1.28	1.35	1.03	.62	.52	15.42
	Medora	14	14.8	68.5	114	−52	14	May 21	Sept. 9	111	18	.56	.51	.84	.86	2.59	3.38	2.38	1.95	1.28	.71	.51	.45	16.02
Bottineau	Bottineau	39	1.5	67.7	111	−49	38	May 24	Sept. 13	112	40	.43	.35	.64	.82	2.07	3.22	2.42	2.39	1.58	.92	.48	.49	15.81
	Eckman	33	2.6	67.8	111	−53	32	May 28	Sept. 9	104	34	.41	.33	.46	.99	2.00	2.79	2.35	1.87	1.36	.87	.57	.48	14.48
	Westhope	33	2.2	68.0	111	−53	30	May 25	Sept. 16	114	33	.37	.25	.47	.93	1.85	2.95	2.27	1.96	1.31	.84	.58	.31	14.09
	Willow City	40	1.1	66.5	110	−54	38	May 28	Sept. 12	107	40	.56	.55	.73	.90	1.81	3.11	2.30	2.10	1.66	.79	.57	.60	15.68
Bowman	Bowman	19	14.2	70.9	112	−43	20	May 16	Sept. 22	129	24	.51	.31	.65	1.27	2.36	3.25	2.17	1.38	1.10	1.00	.41	.32	14.73
Burke	Portal	20	4.8	67.3	109	−50	18	May 22	Sept. 15	116	29	.44	.39	.58	.87	2.03	2.97	1.89	1.97	1.36	.72	.50	.52	14.24
	Powers Lake	13	8.2	70.7	108	−55	14	do	Sept. 14	115	25	.53	.50	.65	1.39	2.06	3.52	2.65	1.61	1.42	1.30	.56	.58	16.77
Burleigh	Bismarck	40	9.4	70.9	114	−45	40	May 10	Sept. 27	140	40	.40	.39	.88	1.12	2.28	3.22	2.22	1.64	1.41	.86	.51	.50	15.43
Cass	Amenia	40	5.0	66.6	115	−43	40	May 17	Sept. 22	128	40	.47	.51	.53	1.70	2.82	3.58	2.55	2.39	1.87	1.31	.62	.53	18.88
Cavalier	Hannah	24	−.5	66.4	108	−54	26	May 30	Sept. 9	102	38	.70	.62	.66	1.04	2.07	3.24	2.26	2.00	2.14	1.05	.76	.62	17.16
	Langdon	35	−.7	65.8	112	−51	36	May 28	Sept. 15	110	40	.63	.64	.76	1.16	1.98	3.22	2.45	2.42	2.21	1.02	.77	.64	17.90
Dickey	Ellendale	28	10.4	70.3	112	−39	30	May 13	Sept. 27	137	32	.38	.38	.87	1.83	2.66	3.21	2.70	2.74	1.57	.94	.67	.38	18.33
	Fullerton	40	8.9	70.1	113	−44	40	May 16	Sept. 24	131	40	.84	.94	1.24	2.21	3.06	3.68	2.98	2.50	1.99	1.28	.88	.89	22.49
Divide	Crosby	31	3.6	67.7	111	−47	30	May 19	Sept. 18	122	32	.41	.28	.57	.97	1.86	2.92	2.15	1.78	1.22	.88	.58	.47	14.09
Dunn	Dunn Center	27	12.1	69.0	111	−52	29	May 21	Sept. 19	121	34	.39	.46	.78	1.20	2.27	3.82	2.43	1.48	1.29	.72	.48	.47	15.79
Eddy	McHenry	16	1.2	67.8	108	−45	15	May 23	Sept. 13	113	6	.60	.67	.56	1.83	2.74	3.34	3.35	2.65	1.71	.98	.63	.78	19.84
Emmons	Linton	22	9.2	72.6	116	−52	19	May 18	Sept. 19	124	22	.35	.41	.54	1.32	2.06	2.75	2.06	1.68	1.37	.95	.52	.33	14.34
Foster	Carrington	40	7.0	69.5	116	−43	39	May 20	Sept. 21	124	40	.33	.38	.66	1.26	2.49	3.49	2.58	2.02	1.41	.98	.58	.42	16.60
Golden Valley	Alpha										13	.34	.22	.68	1.00	2.43	3.04	1.44	1.41	1.11	.67	.32	.35	13.01
	Beach	36	11.2	69.5	110	−43	36	May 19	Sept. 20	124	33	.50	.37	.67	1.14	2.35	3.71	1.76	1.51	1.17	.92	.50	.46	15.06
	Trotters										13	.52	.36	.67	.81	2.18	3.02	1.75	1.31	.83	.82	.46	.49	13.22
Grand Forks	Grand Forks	40	3.7	68.5	109	−43	40	May 16	Sept. 25	132	40	.54	.54	.73	1.59	2.58	3.16	2.75	2.57	1.88	1.36	.86	.62	19.18
	Larimore	38	3.4	68.2	111	−42	40	May 21	Sept. 20	122	40	.65	.55	.74	1.62	2.81	3.63	3.15	2.67	2.08	1.47	.88	.59	20.84
Grant	Carson	25	10.7	70.5	116	−43	26	May 20	Sept. 16	119	27	.41	.35	.71	1.36	2.25	3.80	1.99	1.30	1.51	.91	.61	.48	15.68
Griggs	Cooperstown	10	2.4	68.4	118	−47	12	do	Sept. 17	120	33	.50	.54	.62	1.32	2.34	3.33	2.43	2.53	1.74	1.07	.71	.54	17.67
Hettinger	Mott	32	10.2	71.4	114	−47	31	May 18	Sept. 16	121	32	.76	.53	.89	1.26	2.22	3.48	2.19	1.63	1.35	.92	.51	.58	16.32
	New England	33	13.2	70.6	114	−46	36	May 21	Sept. 15	117	40	.53	.47	.79	.97	1.98	3.09	2.04	1.58	1.28	.74	.47	.42	14.36
Kidder	Lamoine	25	5.0	66.9	108	−45	24	May 26	Sept. 14	111	30	.51	.43	.70	1.02	2.35	3.28	2.68	1.83	1.34	.70	.48	.42	15.74
	Pettibone	26	3.6	69.6	118	−54	26	May 27	Sept. 13	109	30	.43	.46	.59	1.26	2.37	2.93	2.70	2.16	1.39	.98	.61	.51	16.39

[1] Length of growing season between average dates of last killing frost in spring and first in fall.

NORTH DAKOTA—Continued

Climatic summary—Continued

County	Station	Temperature: Length of record	Temperature: January average	Temperature: July average	Temperature: Maximum	Temperature: Minimum	Killing frost average dates: Length of record	Killing frost average dates: Last in spring	Killing frost average dates: First in fall	Killing frost average dates: Growing season	Average precipitation: Length of record	January	February	March	April	May	June	July	August	September	October	November	December	Annual
		Yr.	°*F.*	°*F.*	°*F.*	°*F.*	*Yr.*			*Days*	*Yr.*	*In.*	*In.*	*In.*	*In.*	*In.*	*In.*	*In.*	*In.*	*In.*	*In.*	*In.*	*In.*	*In.*
Kidder—Continued	Steele	36	6.9	70.5	121	−50	36	May 24	Sept. 17	114	40	0.43	0.40	0.76	1.11	2.56	3.47	2.99	2.20	1.45	1.10	0.51	0.53	17.51
La Moure	Edgeley	38	8.7	69.8	116	−41	38	May 20	Sept. 19	122	38	.34	.33	.64	2.58	1.77	3.66	2.53	2.16	1.60	.97	.44	.38	17.40
Logan	Napoleon	40	6.6	69.4	118	−48	40	May 26	Sept. 11	108	40	.36	.40	.85	1.47	2.33	3.32	2.56	2.19	1.41	1.00	.60	.46	16.95
McHenry	Granville	32	5.4	68.5	114	−52	30	May 19	Sept. 17	121	32	.42	.45	.49	1.06	1.88	2.95	2.28	1.69	1.42	.91	.56	.50	14.61
	Tower	34	3.9	69.1	111	−49	32	May 22	Sept. 15	116	34	.47	.44	.62	1.03	2.08	2.75	2.39	1.87	1.71	.95	.56	.45	15.32
McIntosh	Ashley	37	9.0	69.5	114	−46	34	May 23	Sept. 16	116	36	.46	.46	.87	1.69	2.33	3.39	2.73	2.45	1.43	1.11	.64	.52	18.08
	Wishek	18	9.4	70.3	120	−43	18	May 21	do	118	18	.50	.47	.66	1.39	2.41	3.03	2.47	1.72	1.28	.84	.45	.52	15.74
McKenzie	Watford City	23	9.0	70.7	112	−45	22	May 17	Sept. 21	127	26	.54	.42	.68	1.28	1.97	2.89	2.04	1.26	1.21	.94	.44	.56	14.23
McLean	Berthold Agency	36	8.9	69.6	112	−56	36	May 21	Sept. 15	117	40	.28	.39	.51	.99	2.14	3.73	2.38	1.82	1.43	.78	.40	.36	15.21
	Energy	16	9.3	71.3	114	−54	20	May 18	Sept. 16	120	27	.32	.34	.55	1.05	2.04	3.36	2.40	1.77	1.30	.77	.42	.41	14.73
	Garrison	32	8.5	69.4	116	−47	40	May 16	Sept. 21	128	40	.39	.51	.79	1.06	2.29	3.45	2.51	1.91	1.45	.83	.51	.50	16.20
	Turtle Lake	20	6.4	69.4	115	−50	17	do	Sept. 23	130	26	.37	.36	.67	1.04	2.20	3.46	2.72	1.94	1.21	.63	.42	.46	15.48
	Washburn	20	7.2	71.1	115	−45	19	May 14	Sept. 22	133	30	.34	.38	.48	.94	2.11	3.63	2.60	1.64	1.11	.85	.46	.37	14.91
Mercer	Zep	12	8.0	68.4	108	−50	13	May 28	Sept. 14	109	24	.30	.25	.55	.96	2.14	3.42	2.08	1.51	1.17	.87	.32	.26	13.83
Morton	Mandan	24	8.5	71.7	115	−46	24	May 11	Sept. 26	138	25	.35	.39	.78	1.35	2.20	3.18	2.55	1.27	1.33	.80	.54	.43	15.17
	New Salem	33	9.7	70.7	119	−45	32	May 20	Sept. 21	124	33	.49	.45	.81	1.11	2.22	3.31	2.11	1.51	1.23	.84	.52	.54	15.14
Montrail	Parshall	7	3.9	70.5	112	−60	12	May 26	Sept. 16	113	24	.21	.31	.26	1.07	1.95	2.99	2.32	1.57	1.25	.74	.35	.34	13.36
Nelson	Lakota	13	−.6	65.7	105	−45	14	May 25	Sept. 19	117	14	.72	.57	.47	1.59	2.08	3.00	2.45	2.42	1.30	.91	.88	.96	17.35
Oliver	Center	30	10.0	70.7	119	−45	31	May 20	Sept. 18	121	33	.49	.45	.78	1.15	2.19	3.33	2.12	1.50	1.23	.85	.50	.55	15.14
Pembina	Pambina	38	3.7	67.6	109	−46	38	May 27	do	114	40	.66	.78	.77	1.22	2.22	3.12	2.44	2.19	2.10	1.17	.77	.64	18.08
	Walhalla	15	2.4	69.2	104	−43	14	May 23	Sept. 19	119	16	.84	.56	.67	1.14	2.65	2.49	2.59	2.37	2.19	.95	.87	1.05	18.37
Pierce	Rugby										10	.31	.37	.36	.83	1.42	2.31	2.53	1.22	.92	.87	.38	.43	11.95
Ramsey	Devils Lake	40	3.7	68.0	112	−46	40	May 15	Sept. 23	131	40	.46	.44	.68	1.28	2.03	3.18	2.58	2.45	1.80	1.07	.61	.47	17.05
Ransom	Lisbon	34	7.4	70.3	113	−40	36	May 18	Sept. 19	124	35	.62	.64	.59	1.96	2.84	3.87	2.95	2.46	1.97	1.11	.73	.52	20.26
	McLeod	26	8.2	71.3	114	−41	26	May 15	Sept. 21	129	27	.58	.59	.65	2.12	2.94	3.84	2.76	2.37	2.05	1.24	.71	.43	20.28
Renville	Mohall	38	5.8	67.2	112	−48	40	May 25	Sept. 11	109	39	.34	.30	.60	.92	1.98	2.93	2.43	1.88	1.59	1.04	.54	.43	14.98
Richland	Power	18	5.7	68.5	102	−43	23	do	Sept. 22	120	33	.70	.64	.67	1.74	2.83	3.93	2.99	2.48	2.23	1.49	.80	.66	21.16
	Wahpeton	38	8.8	71.0	111	−42	37	May 17	Sept. 23	129	40	.47	.48	.65	2.08	2.64	3.60	3.02	2.78	2.25	1.39	.74	.51	20.61
Rolette	Dunseith	39	2.0	66.6	110	−49	39	May 23	Sept. 16	116	40	.42	.40	.60	.81	1.88	3.00	2.64	2.39	1.61	.86	.52	.44	15.57
Sargent	Forman	20	7.1	71.4	110	−45	24	May 18	Sept. 23	128	39	.48	.63	.72	1.99	2.84	3.43	2.89	2.73	2.03	1.30	.59	.57	20.20
Sheridan	McClusky	16	6.2	69.9	115	−53	17	May 27	Sept. 12	109	21	.52	.61	.68	1.29	2.51	3.20	2.41	1.75	1.23	1.00	.68	.59	16.47
Sioux	Fort Yates	17	9.7	73.5	119	−50	16	May 10	Sept. 19	132	22	.39	.44	.80	.99	2.13	3.28	2.12	2.03	1.24	.91	.44	.38	15.15
Slope	Amidon	13	14.1	69.7	103	−38	11	May 15	Sept. 14	122	17	.42	.49	.70	1.20	2.55	3.35	2.36	1.09	1.52	1.05	.46	.47	15.66
	Marmarth	24	13.7	71.1	108	−52	26	May 17	Sept. 20	126	30	.44	.34	.64	.99	2.36	3.18	1.82	1.50	1.25	.81	.40	.41	14.14
Stark	Dickinson	40	10.9	69.2	114	−47	40	May 20	Sept. 17	120	40	.45	.42	.73	1.06	2.26	3.39	2.17	1.87	1.20	.85	.50	.48	15.38
	Richardton	23	10.7	70.9	113	−48	23	May 14	Sept. 26	135	23	.45	.37	.62	1.36	2.20	3.52	2.30	1.52	1.16	.69	.58	.36	15.13
Steele	Sharon	12	3.2	70.6	114	−48	14	May 17	Sept. 20	126	15	.40	.41	.61	1.51	2.79	3.42	2.34	2.17	1.71	1.71	.81	.39	18.27

Stutsman	Jamestown	40	6.8	69.1	118	−42	39	May 20	Sept. 21	124	40	.58	.60	.88	1.65	2.80	3.44	2.74	2.57	1.66	1.21	.71	.69	19.53
Tower	Cando	30	−.0	68.1	115	−48	30	May 27	Sept. 19	115	35	.46	.35	.67	1.08	2.22	3.43	2.59	2.11	1.58	.90	.52	.44	16.35
	Hansboro	30	.5	65.5	109	−44	31	May 28	Sept. 11	106	31	.65	.52	.73	1.43	2.21	3.15	2.52	2.29	1.79	1.16	.63	.59	17.67
Traill	Hillsboro	33	4.7	70.6	115	−40	32	May 15	Sept. 27	135	33	.53	.60	.67	1.77	3.14	3.22	2.49	2.40	1.99	1.29	.89	.67	19.66
	Mayville	36	5.3	70.2	114	−41	35	May 21	Sept. 20	122	40	.41	.43	.66	1.54	2.79	3.31	2.78	2.48	2.05	1.25	.66	.55	18.91
Walsh	Grafton	38	3.3	68.9	108	−47	34	May 22	Sept. 17	118	40	.52	.54	.63	1.28	2.12	3.27	2.65	2.41	2.14	1.09	.73	.54	17.92
	Park River	34	2.8	68.5	108	−45	32	May 20	Sept. 19	122	35	.38	.38	.55	1.33	2.17	3.28	2.60	2.09	1.90	1.15	.73	.46	17.02
Ward	Donnybrook	16	4.9	66.4	106	−45	18	May 25	Sept. 14	112	22	.39	.51	.77	1.05	2.24	2.86	2.63	2.14	1.66	.98	.59	.48	16.30
	Foxholm	18	7.0	68.8	110	−44	18	May 19	Sept. 21	125	18	.41	.50	.69	1.28	1.78	2.74	2.30	1.46	1.34	.94	.70	.48	14.62
	Minot	37	6.9	68.6	109	−49	38	May 23	Sept. 16	116	40	.38	.42	.59	1.18	2.17	3.07	2.03	1.94	1.60	.92	.69	.48	15.47
Wells	Fessenden	27	4.6	69.2	116	−47	27	do	Sept. 17	117	27	.52	.53	.71	1.40	2.15	3.25	2.45	1.94	1.60	1.00	.71	.58	16.84
	Manfred	26	6.6	67.1	106	−42	24	May 18	Sept. 18	123	36	.55	.49	.74	1.29	2.18	3.35	2.36	2.19	1.45	.97	.66	.60	16.83
Williams	Epping	14	8.0	69.7	111	−38	17	May 19	Sept. 15	119	29	.47	.42	.53	1.11	2.16	3.24	2.08	1.57	1.40	.92	.44	.40	14.74
	Howard	32	4.4	67.2	111	−52	31	May 22	Sept. 11	112	32	.62	.57	.94	1.13	2.26	2.60	1.86	1.45	1.32	.87	.57	.71	14.90
	Williston	40	7.9	69.4	110	−50	40	May 15	Sept. 25	133	40	.47	.40	.70	.98	1.84	3.20	1.93	1.60	1.13	.74	.53	.56	14.08

NORTH DAKOTA—Continued

Precipitation and temperature—State unit values

[This tabulation gives the mean annual, mean monthly, and average seasonal precipitation, 1886–1938, and the mean annual temperatures, 1902–38, for North Dakota]

Precipitation		Precipitation		Precipitation		Precipitation		Temperature		Temperature	
Year	Mean	Year	Mean	Year	Mean	Month	Mean	Year	Mean	Year	Mean
	In.		*In.*		*In.*		*In.*		°*F.*		°*F.*
1886	17.06	1907	14.30	1928	17.88	June	3.45	1902	39.4	1921	42.0
1887	18.02	1908	18.56	1929	14.31	July	2.48	1903	38.3	1922	39.7
1888	15.92	1909	18.10	1930	14.90	August	1.96	1904	37.6	1923	40.7
1889	11.54	1910	12.53	1931	14.99	September	1.48	1905	39.3	1924	38.2
1890	17.45	1911	18.42	1932	17.18	October	1.03	1906	39.4	1925	40.6
1891	19.81	1912	20.35	1933	13.43	November	.59	1907	36.9	1926	40.7
1892	18.33	1913	14.65	1934	9.47	December	.51	1908	40.7	1927	38.0
1893	15.84	1914	18.98	1935	18.03			1909	38.2	1928	41.1
1894	15.61	1915	19.29	1936	8.83	Annual	16.89	1910	41.1	1929	38.0
1895	17.35	1916	19.88	1937	17.03			1911	38.0	1930	41.4
1896	22.60	1917	10.75	1938	15.33			1912	38.2	1931	44.9
1897	15.99	1918	16.00			Season	Average	1913	40.0	1932	40.0
1898	16.15	1919	15.57	Month	Mean			1914	40.1	1933	41.1
1899	17.62	1920	15.29					1915	39.7	1934	43.4
1900	19.06	1921	19.45				*In.*	1916	36.2	1935	39.4
1901	19.42	1922	19.88		*In.*	Winter	1.50	1917	36.3	1936	38.8
1902	19.35	1923	17.78	January	0.50	Spring	4.40	1918	40.0	1937	39.1
1903	19.25	1924	17.11	February	.49	Summer	7.89	1919	38.6	1938	41.9
1904	17.85	1925	16.64	March	.75	Fall	3.10	1920	39.5		
1905	18.89	1926	15.37	April	1.42						
1906	20.02	1927	21.52	May	2.23						

Dates of last killing frost in spring and first in fall, with length of growing season

Year	Bismarck			Devils Lake			Dickinson			Fullerton			Grand Forks			Williston		
	Last in spring	First in fall	Growing season [1]	Last in spring	First in fall	Growing season [1]	Last in spring	First in fall	Growing season [1]	Last in spring	First in fall	Growing season [1]	Last in spring	First in fall	Growing season [1]	Last in spring	First in fall	Growing season [1]
			Days			*Days*			*Days*			*Days*			*Days*			*Days*
1899	May 13	Sept. 19	129	May 14	Sept. 19	128	May 13	Sept. 18	128	May 18	Sept. 17	122		Sept. 13		May 24	Sept. 28	127
1900	May 4	Sept. 26	145	May 9	Sept. 16	130	May 17	Sept. 16	122	June 8	do	101	May 9	Sept. 16	130	May 16	Sept. 16	123
1901	June 7	Sept. 18	103	June 7	Sept. 18	103	May 25	Sept. 17	115	June 7	Sept. 18	103	June 6	do	102	May 12	Sept. 17	128

1902	Apr. 29	Sept. 12	136	May 10	Sept. 11	124	June 21	----------	------	June 21	Sept. 4	75	May 10	Sept. 11	124	May 26	Sept. 3	100
1903	May 5	Sept. 14	132	do	Sept. 13	126	May 8	Sept. 13	128	June 11	Sept. 14	95	May 5	Sept. 15	133	June 10	Sept. 12	94
1904	May 14	Sept. 11	120	May 14	Aug. 8	86	May 14	Sept. 11	120	May 14	Sept. 11	120	May 10	Sept. 20	133	May 26	Sept. 11	108
1905	May 12	Oct. 11	152	May 25	Sept. 12	110	May 13	Sept. 3	113	May 25	Oct. 10	138	May 28	Oct. 11	136	May 8	Oct. 11	156
1906	May 27	Oct. 9	135	May 27	Sept. 29	125	May 26	Sept. 26	123	May 27	Sept. 30	126	May 19	Sept. 27	131	do	Sept. 29	144
1907	May 14	Sept. 27	136	May 26	Sept. 21	118	June 5	Sept. 14	101	do	Aug. 20	85	June 5	Aug. 20	76	May 26	Sept. 20	117
1908	May 2	do	148	May 5	Aug. 22	109	May 22	Aug. 22	92	May 8	Sept. 28	143	June 14	Sept. 28	106	May 21	Sept. 28	130
1909	May 13	Sept. 24	134	May 9	Oct. 9	153	May 15	Oct. 9	147	May 16	Sept. 24	131	May 16	Oct. 11	148	May 15	Oct. 9	147
1910	May 17	Sept. 9	115	May 12	Oct. 20	161	June 6	Sept. 9	95	June 2	Sept. 9	99	June 3	Sept. 12	101	May 17	Sept. 9	115
1911	May 3	Oct. 20	170	May 1	Oct. 21	173	May 28	Aug. 28	92	May 3	Oct. 20	170	May 4	Sept. 26	145	May 2	Oct. 20	171
1912	May 13	Sept. 25	135	May 13	Sept. 25	135	June 16	Sept. 25	101	May 13	Sept. 16	126	Apr. 27	do	152	Apr. 28	Oct. 17	172
1913	May 6	Sept. 21	138	May 18	Sept. 21	126	May 22	Sept. 11	112	May 9	Sept. 22	136	May 18	Sept. 21	126	May 18	Sept. 20	125
1914	May 13	Oct. 14	154	May 14	Oct. 13	152	May 14	Oct. 5	144	May 14	Oct. 14	153	May 12	Oct. 13	154	May 13	Oct. 5	145
1915	May 19	Oct. 7	141	May 18	Aug. 26	100	June 16	Aug. 24	69	May 18	Oct. 7	142	May 18	Oct. 5	140	June 16	Sept. 13	89
1916	May 16	Sept. 15	122	May 19	Sept. 15	119	June 8	Sept. 14	98	May 2	Sept. 15	136	May 3	Sept. 17	137	May 17	Sept. 14	120
1917	May 5	Oct. 5	153	June 4	Sept. 9	97	June 1	Aug. 9	69	do	Oct. 5	156	May 27	Sept. 10	106	May 3	Sept. 26	146
1918	May 20	Sept. 18	121	May 20	Sept. 3	106	May 22	Sept. 15	116	May 20	Sept. 18	121	May 14	Sept. 20	129	May 22	Sept. 9	110
1919	May 7	Oct. 4	150	May 5	Sept. 25	143	June 2	Oct. 4	124	Apr. 28	Sept. 25	150	May 5	Sept. 25	143	May 8	Oct. 4	149
1920	Apr. 27	Sept. 30	156	May 1	Oct. 20	172	Apr. 27	Sept. 29	155	Apr. 30	Sept. 30	153	May 1	Sept. 30	152	Apr. 27	Sept. 29	155
1921	May 3	Oct. 1	151	May 15	Oct. 3	141	May 17	Oct. 1	137	May 14	Oct. 7	146	May 14	Oct. 3	142	May 15	Oct. 1	139
1922	Apr. 25	Oct. 8	166	Apr. 26	Oct. 8	165	Apr. 26	Oct. 7	164	Apr. 21	Sept. 10	142	Apr. 27	Oct. 8	164	Apr. 26	Oct. 8	165
1923	May 8	Oct. 13	158	May 15	Sept. 12	120	May 16	Sept. 13	120	May 12	Oct. 5	146	May 16	Sept. 13	120	May 15	Sept. 12	120
1924	May 25	Sept. 27	125	May 27	Oct. 7	133	May 31	Sept. 27	119	May 25	Sept. 29	127	May 24	Oct. 7	136	May 25	Sept. 27	125
1925	May 17	Sept. 21	127	May 17	Sept. 21	127	May 17	Sept. 12	118	May 17	Sept. 21	127	May 17	Oct. 8	144	May 16	Sept. 21	128
1926	May 3	Sept. 24	144	May 19	Sept. 22	126	Apr. 28	Sept. 19	144	May 19	Sept. 25	129	May 22	Sept. 22	123	May 13	Sept. 23	133
1927	May 11	Sept. 21	133	May 11	Sept. 19	131	May 10	Sept. 20	133	May 5	Sept. 27	145	Apr. 24	Sept. 25	154	May 10	Sept. 20	133
1928	Apr. 27	Sept. 23	149	May 27	Sept. 23	119	May 3	Sept. 23	143	May 12	Sept. 23	134	Apr. 27	Sept. 26	152	May 11	Sept. 17	129
1929	May 20	Sept. 18	121	May 23	Sept. 17	117	May 20	Sept. 8	111	May 20	Sept. 18	121	May 23	Sept. 17	117	May 15	Sept. 8	116
1930	May 17	Sept. 27	133	May 24	Sept. 28	127	May 18	Sept. 26	131	May 17	Sept. 26	132	May 24	Sept. 28	127	May 16	Sept. 25	132
1931	May 20	Oct. 8	141	May 22	Oct. 11	142	May 21	Oct. 8	140	May 22	Oct. 11	142	May 22	Oct. 11	142	May 21	Oct. 8	140
1932	Apr. 27	Sept. 22	148	May 1	Oct. 5	157	May 28	Sept. 16	111	May 27	Oct. 5	131	May 16	Oct. 5	142	May 16	Sept. 28	135
1933	Apr. 26	Sept. 26	153	Apr. 26	Oct. 4	161	May 1	Sept. 26	148	Apr. 26	Sept. 26	153	May 10	Oct. 4	147	May 10	Sept. 26	139
1934	Apr. 27	Sept. 15	141	May 13	Sept. 15	125	May 14	Aug. 24	102	May 24	Sept. 15	114	May 22	Sept. 21	122	May 13	Sept. 15	125
1935	Apr. 30	Sept. 26	149	May 10	Sept. 26	139	May 4	Aug. 30	118	May 4	Sept. 27	146	June 6	Sept. 26	112	May 4	Sept. 26	145
1936	Apr. 29	Sept. 27	151	Apr. 29	Sept. 24	148	Apr. 30	Sept. 16	139	Apr. 29	do	151	Apr. 29	Sept. 29	153	Apr. 29	Sept. 16	140
1937	May 13	Sept. 25	135	May 13	Oct. 7	147	May 13	Sept. 25	135	Apr. 26	Sept. 25	152	May 13	Sept. 19	129	May 13	Sept. 28	138
1938	May 9	Oct. 19	163	May 23	Sept. 18	118	May 9	Sept. 18	132	May 8	Sept. 19	134	May 6	do	136	May 9	Oct. 18	162
Means	May 10	Sept. 27	140	May 15	Sept. 23	131	May 20	Sept. 17	120	May 16	Sept. 24	131	May 16	Sept. 25	132	May 15	Sept. 25	133
Extremes	Apr. 23[2] June 7[3]	Sept. 9[4] Oct. 20[5]	[6] 102 [7] 169	Apr. 26[2] June 7[3]	Aug. 8[4] Oct. 21[5]	[6] 96 [7] 172	Apr. 26[2] June 21[3]	Aug. 9[4] Oct. 9[5]	[6] 62 [7] 164	Apr. 21[2] June 21[3]	Aug. 20[4] Oct. 20[5]	[6] 75 [7] 170	Apr. 24[2] June 6[3]	Aug. 20[4] Oct. 13[5]	[6] 164 [7] 76	Apr. 26[2] June 16[3]	Sept. 3[4] Oct. 20[5]	[6] 89 [7] 165

[1] Number of days between last killing frost in spring and first in fall.
[2] Earliest date in spring.
[3] Latest date in spring.
[4] Earliest date in fall.
[5] Latest date in fall.
[6] Shortest growing season.
[7] Longest growing season.

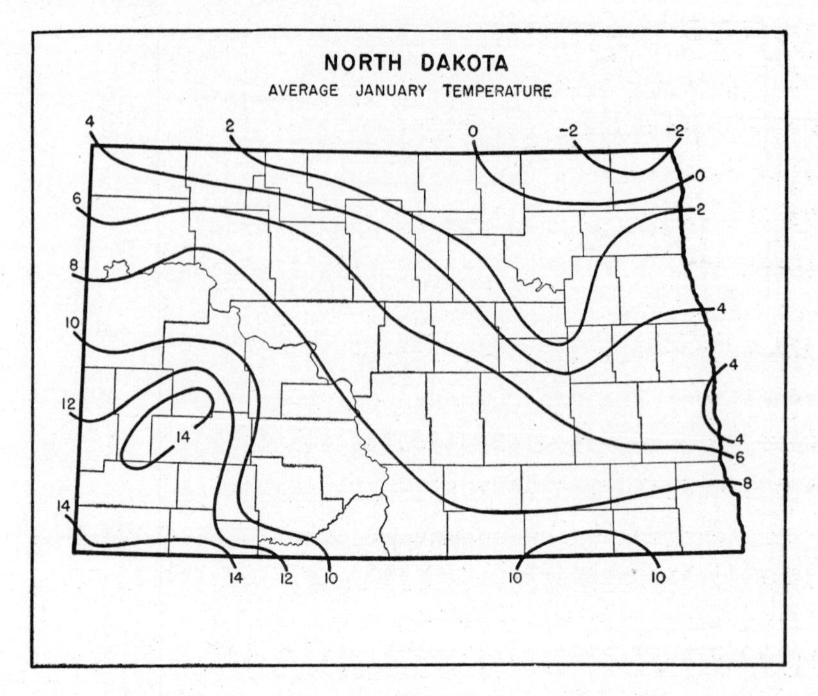

NORTH DAKOTA
AVERAGE JANUARY TEMPERATURE
4
2
0
-2
-2
0
2
6
8
10
12
14
14
4
4
4
6
8
14
12
10
10
10

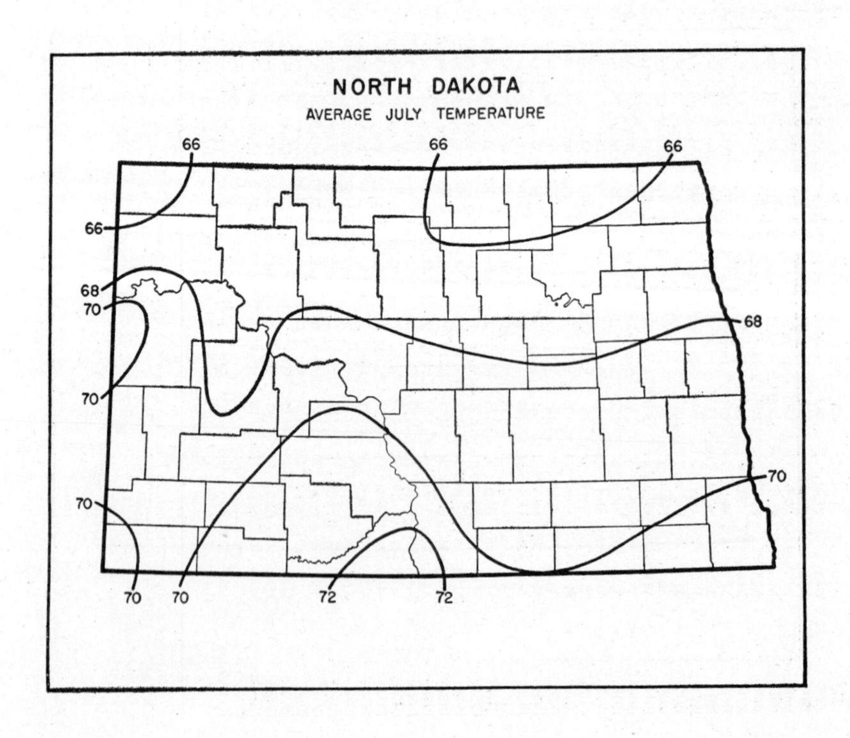

NORTH DAKOTA
AVERAGE JULY TEMPERATURE
66
66
66
66
68
70
68
70
70
70
70
70
72
72

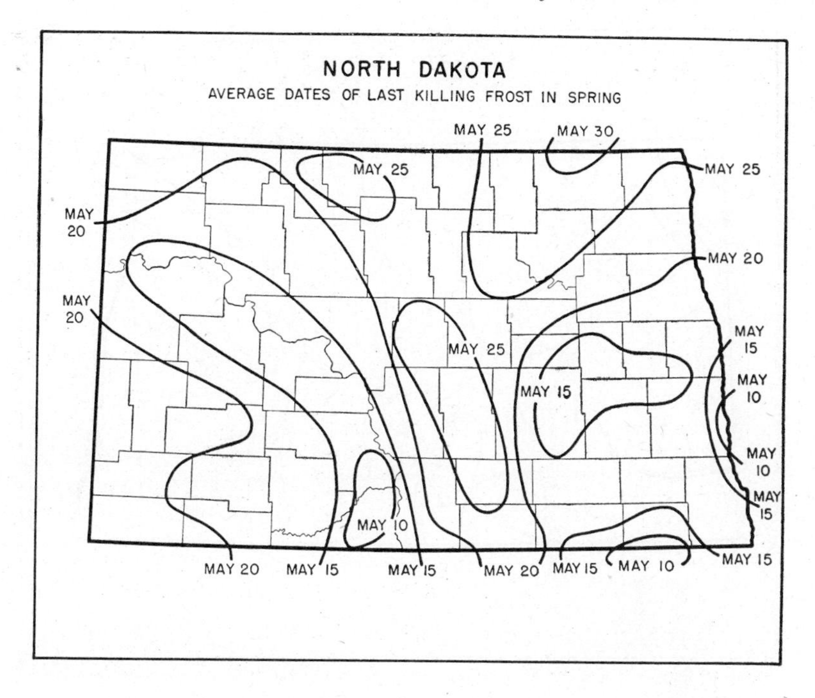
NORTH DAKOTA
AVERAGE DATES OF LAST KILLING FROST IN SPRING
MAY 25
MAY 30
MAY 25
MAY 25
MAY 20
MAY 20
MAY 20
MAY 25
MAY 15
MAY 15
MAY 10
MAY 10
MAY 15
MAY 10
MAY 20
MAY 15
MAY 15
MAY 20
MAY 15
MAY 10
MAY 15

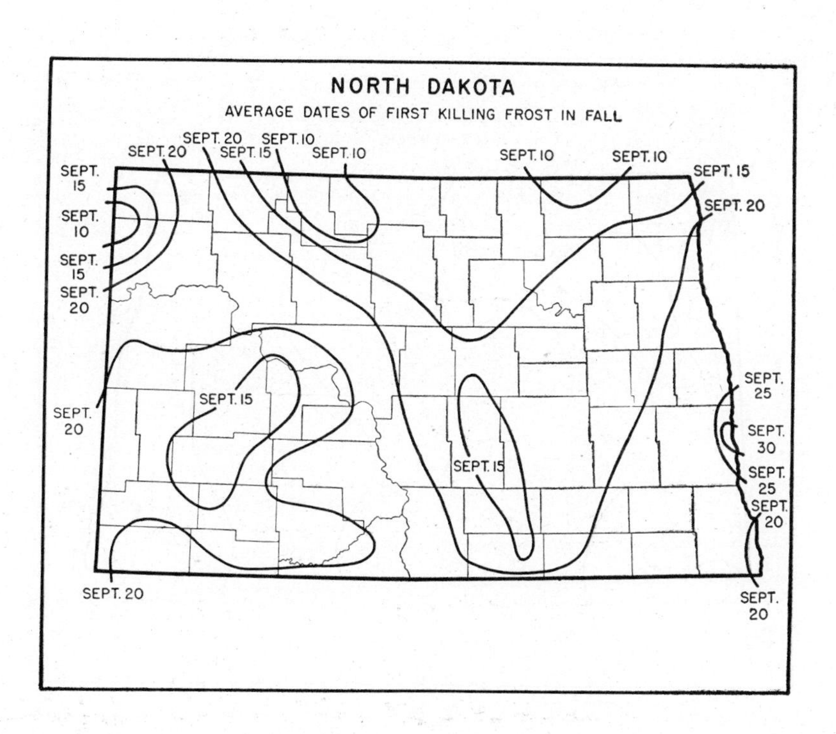
NORTH DAKOTA
AVERAGE DATES OF FIRST KILLING FROST IN FALL
SEPT. 20
SEPT. 10
SEPT. 20
SEPT. 15
SEPT. 10
SEPT. 10
SEPT. 10
SEPT. 15
SEPT. 15
SEPT. 10
SEPT. 15
SEPT. 20
SEPT. 20
SEPT. 15
SEPT. 20
SEPT. 15
SEPT. 25
SEPT. 30
SEPT. 25
SEPT. 20
SEPT. 20
SEPT. 20

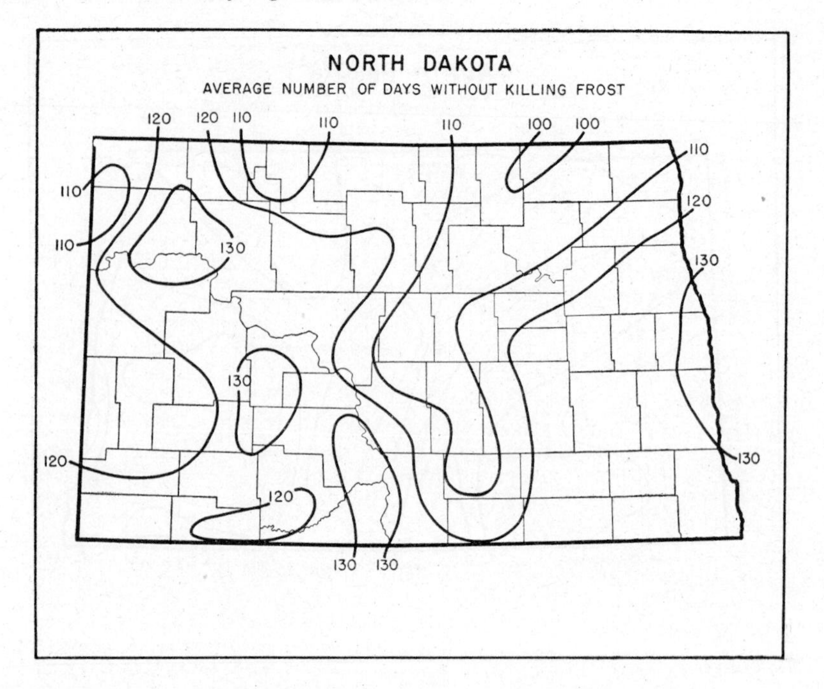
NORTH DAKOTA
AVERAGE NUMBER OF DAYS WITHOUT KILLING FROST
120
120
110
110
110
100
100
110
110
120
110
130
130
130
120
130
120
130
130

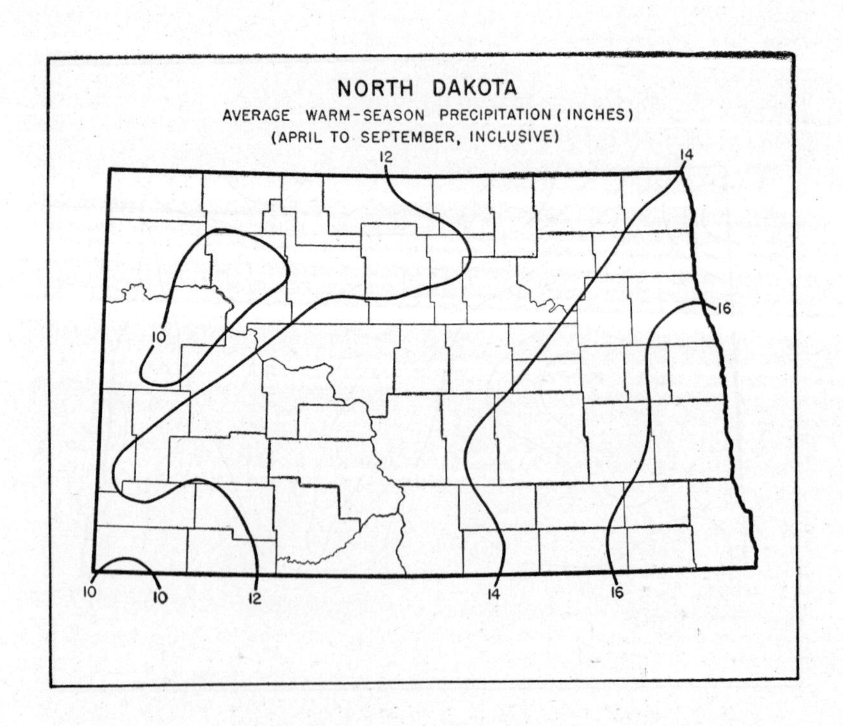
NORTH DAKOTA
AVERAGE WARM-SEASON PRECIPITATION (INCHES)
(APRIL TO SEPTEMBER, INCLUSIVE)
12
14
16
10
10
10
12
14
16

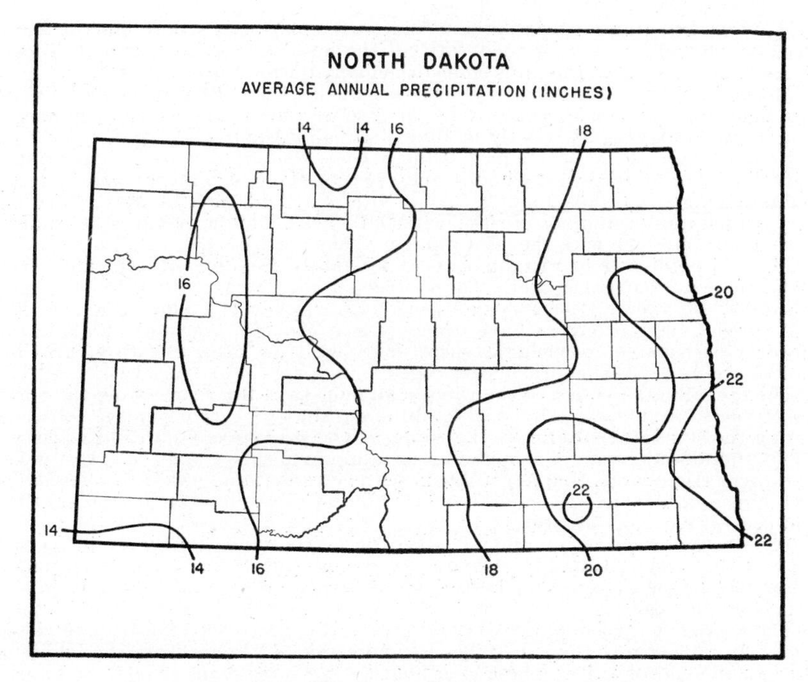

SUPPLEMENTARY CLIMATIC NOTES FOR NORTH DAKOTA

Eastern North Dakota is drained by the James, Souris, Pembina, and Sheyenne Rivers, while the west is drained, with the single exception of the Souris, by the Missouri and its tributaries—the Cannonball, Grand, Heart, Knife, and Little Missouri.

The eastern part of the State is very flat, with an elevation in the valley of the Red River of the North of 789 feet at Pembina. To the westward there is a gradual rise of terrain until an elevation of 3,468 feet is reached at Black Butte in the Badlands of the southwestern part of the State.

Most of the eastern part has fine agricultural lands, the soil consisting of a black loam of varying depth, underlaid with a subsoil of clay. The west is gently rolling, with soil ranging from poor in the Badlands to excellent in some other sections. Cereals are grown in large quantities, and diversified farming is universal. Much has been done in recent years to improve the dairy herds and the feed crops, especially corn. Poultry has become important in all sections, with North Dakota turkeys at a premium.

The annual mean temperature for North Dakota ranges from about 36° to 44° F., with the lowest along the northern border. Temperatures above 100° are occasionally recorded, and zero readings are common in winter. The average number of days a year when the temperature reaches 90° or higher is 14, and the average number with zero or lower is 53.

The average growing season has about 121 days without severe frosts—more in the southern part and fewer in the northern. For the State the average date of the last killing frost in spring is May 19, and the first in fall September 18. Killing frosts have occurred, however, as late as the first part of June and as early in the fall as the first few days of September.

Precipitation in the eastern third of the State averages 19.53 inches, in the middle third 16.32, and in the western third 15.38. On an average, about 77 percent of the annual precipitation occurs during the crop-growing season, April to September, inclusive, and almost 50 percent falls during May, June, and July. The normal precipitation for the driest months—November to February, inclusive—is about half an inch a month.

In North Dakota precipitation is considered the most important climatic factor. Because the soil is well supplied with all the necessary plant nutrients, it is of prime importance that the rains come principally during the crop season.

Most of the rain in the summer months occurs in storms accompanied by thunder and lightning, often with heavy falls for a short time. The average number of thunderstorm days is 28, mostly in June, July, and August.

In most years at least some part of the State is visited by a storm that brings a rainfall of 2 or 3 inches in 24 hours, and occasionally 5 or 6 inches falls in 1 day. On an average, rain falls about 1 day in 4 during the 3 months May, June, and July. The annual number of days with 0.01 inch or more averages 66, ranging from about 50 to 90, with the least number in the northwest.

The first light snow in autumn occasionally falls in September, but usually very little occurs until after October. The average number of days with 0.1 inch or more of snow is 23.

In recent years droughts have been severe. Much of the North Dakota soil, however, is capable of yielding surprisingly well on little moisture, provided moisture is present when it is most needed.

The prevailing direction of the wind in all months of the year is from the northwest, unless it is influenced by local conditions. More southerly winds are observed during the summer than during the winter. The average annual wind velocity is about 10 miles an hour. The highest velocities are in spring and the lowest in late summer. High winds frequently accompany severe thunderstorms. Tornadoes are of rare occurrence, although they are not entirely unknown in the southern and central parts of the State.

The average relative humidity is about 68 percent, slightly higher in the east than in the west. Humidity is frequently low during the afternoon in summer, sometimes below 20 percent. Dense fogs are experienced, on an average, on only 8 days of the year.

The average annual number of clear days is 161, partly cloudy 101, and cloudy 103. On a clear day the sun shines for more than 15 hours from the middle of May to the end of July. These long hours of sunshine make it possible to grow many crops in what appears to be a comparatively short growing season. The yearly average amount of sunshine is 59 percent of the possible amount, with 74 percent in July and 72 percent in August.

FRANK J. BAVENDICK, *Assistant Meteorologist and Climatic Section Director for North Dakota, Weather Bureau, Bismarck.*

OHIO

Climatic summary

County[1]	Station	Temperature: Length of record	Temperature: January average	Temperature: July average	Temperature: Maximum	Temperature: Minimum	Killing frost average dates: Length of record	Killing frost average dates: Last in spring	Killing frost average dates: First in fall	Growing season[2]	Average precipitation: Length of record	January	February	March	April	May	June	July	August	September	October	November	December	Annual
		Yr.	°*F.*	°*F.*	°*F.*	°*F.*	*Yr.*			*Days*	*Yr.*	*In.*	*In.*	*In.*	*In.*	*In.*	*In.*	*In.*	*In.*	*In.*	*In.*	*In.*	*In.*	*In.*
Adams	Green	27	34.2	75.9	106	-24	27	Apr. 23	Oct. 20	180	27	4.29	3.26	4.47	3.45	3.96	4.25	4.51	3.61	2.76	2.76	3.02	3.52	43.86
	Peebles (near)	29	32.5	74.2	109	-31	28	May 7	Oct. 12	158	28	4.22	2.77	4.15	4.02	3.81	3.75	4.66	4.77	3.37	2.81	2.82	3.70	44.85
Allen	Lima	38	27.7	73.7	109	-20	38	May 4	Oct. 14	163	38	2.98	2.05	3.54	3.32	3.23	3.65	3.64	3.36	3.37	2.63	2.30	2.59	36.66
Ashland	Ashland	28	28.2	73.2	106	-21	28	May 7	Oct. 11	157	28	2.79	1.92	3.56	2.96	3.47	3.73	3.55	3.58	2.95	2.47	2.58	2.44	36.00
Athens	Amesville	26	31.4	74.7	110	-32	26	May 6	do	158	27	3.59	2.69	3.55	3.10	3.70	4.06	4.19	4.34	2.75	2.94	2.59	3.19	40.69
Auglaize	New Bremen	34	27.7	73.7	108	-25	26	May 1	do	163	37	2.47	1.69	3.11	2.95	3.03	3.20	3.29	3.03	3.28	2.51	2.09	2.42	33.07
	Wapakoneta	19	26.7	74.4	102	-22	19	Apr. 29	Oct. 10	164	19	2.77	1.52	3.28	3.05	3.62	3.88	3.25	3.06	3.37	2.65	2.21	2.38	35.04
Belmont	Demos	40	29.6	73.2	106	-26	40	Apr. 30	Oct. 19	172	40	3.39	2.46	3.76	3.44	3.61	3.91	4.40	3.95	3.49	2.79	2.74	3.35	41.29
Butler	Hamilton	25	31.8	76.8	111	-20	25	Apr. 26	Oct. 18	175	27	3.80	2.21	4.08	3.49	3.76	3.55	3.30	3.87	3.89	2.86	2.93	3.09	40.83
	Oxford										18	3.11	2.09	4.01	3.92	3.94	3.71	3.11	3.61	3.58	2.88	3.18	3.30	40.44
Champaign	Saint Paris										15	3.48	1.85	3.90	3.61	3.78	4.55	3.77	3.80	2.75	3.07	3.02	3.28	40.86
	Urbana	40	28.4	74.1	110	-24	40	May 2	Oct. 12	163	40	3.20	2.17	3.66	3.49	3.80	4.08	4.08	3.64	3.36	2.94	2.53	2.67	39.62
Clark	New Carlisle										12	3.29	1.78	3.70	3.43	3.83	4.03	3.79	4.01	2.87	2.52	2.66	2.92	38.83
	Plattsburg	18	29.1	73.8	103	-23	18	May 2	Oct. 9	160	18	3.36	2.48	3.66	2.97	3.65	4.08	3.79	2.93	2.71	2.84	2.18	3.08	37.73
	Springfield										40	3.13	2.19	3.58	3.22	3.65	4.23	3.77	3.06	2.98	2.69	2.59	2.68	37.77
Clermont	Batavia (near)	24	32.4	75.9	110	-19	24	Apr. 24	Oct. 19	178	24	3.54	1.85	3.13	3.43	3.94	3.79	3.76	4.46	3.39	2.81	2.75	2.92	39.77
	Chilo										18	3.71	2.43	3.74	3.95	3.43	3.58	3.81	3.99	2.78	2.31	3.01	3.41	40.15
Clinton	Wilmington	22	30.7	75.1	111	-22	22	May 4	Oct 13	162	24	4.18	2.62	4.61	4.10	4.35	3.75	4.84	4.64	3.66	3.14	3.02	3.64	46.55
Columbiana	Green Hill	27	26.0	69.5	104	-29	24	May 15	Oct. 2	140	27	2.69	2.00	3.21	2.90	3.15	4.01	4.36	3.16	2.82	2.42	1.97	2.51	35.20
	Millport	40	27.0	70.4	103	-28	40	May 18	Oct. 4	139	40	2.96	2.15	3.20	3.05	3.29	4.04	4.32	3.44	3.10	2.51	2.39	2.57	37.02
Coshocton	Coshocton	23	29.3	74.9	106	-26	24	May 3	Oct. 12	162	31	3.43	2.51	3.38	3.57	3.51	4.28	3.97	4.31	3.43	2.69	2.90	3.18	41.16
	Walhonding										23	3.27	1.92	3.24	3.09	3.57	3.75	3.09	3.61	3.01	2.35	2.64	2.79	36.33
Crawford	Bucyrus	40	27.7	73.6	106	-28	39	May 7	Oct. 8	154	40	3.16	2.26	3.36	3.28	3.59	4.04	4.12	3.16	3.29	2.94	2.55	2.64	38.39
Cuyahoga	Cleveland	40	28.3	72.4	100	-17	40	Apr. 16	Nov. 5	203	40	2.60	2.05	2.73	2.62	2.60	2.79	3.44	2.74	3.12	2.57	2.36	2.27	31.89
	North Royalton	24	26.1	72.0	102	-22	24	May 6	Oct. 15	162	24	3.15	2.23	3.11	3.23	3.65	3.33	4.44	3.52	3.38	3.17	2.52	2.71	38.44
Darke	Greenville	40	28.4	74.0	105	-20	40	Apr. 25	Oct. 17	175	40	3.26	2.11	3.96	3.40	3.67	4.33	3.30	3.25	3.37	2.74	2.59	2.77	38.75
	Versailles										25	3.01	1.80	3.63	3.72	3.84	4.14	3.53	3.61	3.71	2.76	2.58	2.75	39.08
Defiance	Defiance	20	27.0	74.0	111	-26	18	May 5	Oct. 12	160	28	2.10	1.83	2.69	2.90	3.11	3.81	3.51	2.51	3.40	2.37	2.34	2.46	33.03
Delaware	Bellpoint										23	2.65	1.68	2.86	2.92	3.24	3.42	3.52	3.49	2.90	2.37	2.32	2.67	34.04
	Delaware	40	28.5	74.0	110	-25	40	May 4	Oct. 8	157	40	3.08	2.18	3.53	3.16	3.55	3.54	4.06	3.46	2.98	2.55	2.28	2.69	37.06
Erie	Sandusky	40	27.9	74.0	105	-16	40	Apr. 17	Oct. 28	194	40	2.45	1.81	2.80	2.73	2.94	3.42	3.32	3.05	3.08	2.37	1.95	2.13	32.05
Fairfield	Lancaster	40	31.2	73.9	106	-23	40	Apr. 29	Oct. 15	169	40	3.67	2.52	4.07	3.28	3.81	4.14	4.07	3.73	2.96	2.57	2.58	3.17	40.57
Fayette	Washington C. H.	18	30.4	75.1	107	-18	18	Apr. 26	Oct. 14	171	26	3.18	2.01	3.45	3.05	3.73	3.81	3.86	3.03	2.76	2.41	2.46	2.72	36.47

[1] The following counties, for which no records are available, are best represented by the station indicated: Ashtabula—Kinsman; Brown—Peebles; Carroll—Millport; Geauga—Hiram; Mercer—New Bremen.

[2] Length of growing season between average dates of last killing frost in spring and first in fall.

OHIO—Continued

Climatic summary—Continued

County	Station	Temperature: Length of record	Temperature: January average	Temperature: July average	Temperature: Maximum	Temperature: Minimum	Killing frost average dates: Length of record	Killing frost average dates: Last in spring	Killing frost average dates: First in fall	Killing frost average dates: Growing season	Average precipitation: Length of record	January	February	March	April	May	June	July	August	September	October	November	December	Annual
		Yr.	*°F.*	*°F.*	*°F.*	*°F.*	*Yr.*			*Days*	*Yr.*	*In.*	*In.*	*In.*	*In.*	*In.*	*In.*	*In.*	*In.*	*In.*	*In.*	*In.*	*In.*	*In.*
Franklin	Columbus	40	30.5	75.4	106	−20	40	Apr. 19	Oct. 23	187	40	2.93	2.09	3.40	2.72	3.13	3.30	3.50	3.22	2.60	2.36	2.25	2.60	34.10
	Dublin										21	2.63	2.02	3.52	3.19	3.31	3.30	3.47	3.27	2.39	2.50	2.27	2.62	34.49
	Valley Crossing	23	30.0	74.4	108	−19	24	Apr. 29	Oct. 17	171	23	3.19	2.04	3.43	3.28	3.56	3.43	3.94	3.52	2.80	2.21	2.72	2.85	36.97
Fulton	Wauseon	40	25.0	73.3	109	−32	37	May 8	Oct. 10	155	40	2.38	1.87	2.94	3.18	3.44	3.79	3.16	2.93	3.20	2.33	2.23	2.45	33.90
Gallia	Gallipolis (near)										28	3.72	2.94	3.95	3.18	3.76	3.56	3.90	3.62	2.75	2.70	2.63	3.33	40.04
	Thurman	19	34.4	75.2	113	−32	19	Apr. 23	Oct. 13	173	19	3.68	2.82	3.54	2.64	3.57	4.79	3.78	2.70	1.99	1.97	2.41	3.40	37.29
Greene	Xenia	18	30.0	75.0	108	−23	18	Apr. 29	Oct. 17	171	20	3.06	2.00	3.20	3.37	3.55	3.41	3.65	4.07	3.35	2.56	2.58	2.76	37.56
Guernsey	Cambridge	40	31.0	73.2	104	−33	40	May 7	Oct. 10	156	40	3.34	2.25	3.72	3.12	3.67	4.06	4.46	3.87	3.04	2.66	2.46	3.07	39.72
Hamilton	Cincinnati	40	32.6	76.8	108	−17	40	Apr. 12	Oct. 25	196	40	3.41	2.21	3.86	3.05	3.62	3.55	3.56	3.42	2.81	2.47	2.42	2.83	37.21
	Fernbank										25	3.49	1.92	3.67	3.12	3.45	3.51	3.54	3.77	3.36	2.55	2.84	3.00	38.22
	Mt. Healthy (near)	25	31.5	75.6	109	−17	25	Apr. 23	Oct. 20	180	25	3.26	2.08	3.83	3.47	3.94	3.57	3.75	4.01	3.71	3.04	2.97	2.98	40.61
Hancock	Benton Ridge	28	27.4	73.7	105	−20	27	May 10	Oct. 9	152	28	2.76	2.09	3.27	3.31	3.54	3.94	3.62	3.04	3.49	2.81	2.14	2.62	36.63
	Findlay	40	27.1	74.2	108	−21	40	May 4	Oct. 10	159	39	2.68	2.01	3.28	3.18	3.60	3.78	3.78	3.18	3.40	2.64	2.01	2.42	35.96
Hardin	Kenton (near)	37	27.3	73.3	106	−24	37	May 8	do	155	37	2.62	1.99	3.33	3.08	3.25	3.90	3.61	2.98	3.03	2.69	2.32	2.29	35.09
Harrison	Cadiz	35	29.6	73.8	106	−18	34	Apr. 30	Oct. 16	169	35	3.58	2.54	3.68	3.37	3.26	3.98	4.96	3.77	3.20	2.83	2.81	3.13	41.11
Henry	Napoleon	40	26.5	73.6	110	−22	37	May 4	Oct. 13	162	40	2.45	1.90	3.15	3.31	3.71	3.86	3.19	3.10	3.46	2.52	2.23	2.50	35.38
Highland	Hillsboro	33	31.3	74.1	105	−30	32	Apr. 29	Oct. 15	169	33	3.68	2.76	3.93	3.77	3.93	4.24	4.25	4.61	3.17	2.60	2.85	3.51	43.30
Hocking	Logan						12	do	Oct. 9	163	12	3.70	2.39	3.88	2.99	3.67	3.89	3.22	4.08	2.80	3.02	3.28	3.38	40.30
Holmes	Killbuck	20	28.1	72.3	105	−23	20	May 5	Oct. 5	153	20	3.21	2.47	4.14	3.05	3.91	3.81	4.65	3.46	2.72	2.78	2.27	3.03	39.50
	Millersburg	20	29.9	73.6	104	−17	20	May 11	Oct. 11	153	22	2.92	2.00	3.26	3.30	3.69	3.76	3.96	3.64	3.12	2.54	2.81	2.59	37.59
Huron	Norwalk	40	27.7	73.2	108	−25	40	May 7	do	157	40	2.69	2.12	3.20	3.00	3.37	3.70	3.88	3.26	3.27	2.75	2.24	2.43	35.91
Jackson	Jackson	24	33.0	74.1	104	−22	24	Apr. 26	Oct. 12	169	33	3.64	2.49	4.02	3.11	3.74	4.17	3.81	3.71	2.38	2.62	2.66	3.30	39.65
Jefferson	Brilliant	9	30.9	73.1	107	−20	10	May 1	Oct. 20	172	24	3.18	2.52	3.55	3.92	3.53	4.25	4.41	4.01	3.00	2.84	2.12	3.24	40.57
Knox	Mt. Vernon (near)	40	27.5	72.6	105	−28	40	May 8	Oct. 6	151	40	3.00	2.12	3.34	2.98	3.60	3.83	4.14	3.50	2.86	2.45	2.43	3.00	37.25
Lake	Hillhouse	22	25.4	70.4	100	−25	22	May 16	Oct. 11	148	22	2.88	2.15	2.89	3.08	4.12	3.70	3.80	3.01	3.77	4.36	2.99	2.82	39.57
	Willoughby										29	2.62	1.98	2.51	2.66	2.66	3.01	3.01	2.51	3.71	3.05	2.66	2.49	32.87
Lawrence	Dam No. 28										23	4.10	2.72	3.97	3.38	4.00	3.93	4.32	3.86	2.69	2.85	2.92	3.25	41.99
	Ironton	39	35.4	76.4	107	−27	40	Apr. 25	Oct. 18	176	40	4.03	2.89	4.26	3.49	3.69	4.15	4.67	3.72	2.68	2.58	2.71	3.41	42.28
Licking	Pataskala	32	28.2	72.9	104	−24	32	May 4	Oct. 8	157	32	3.55	2.54	4.04	3.36	3.82	4.24	4.23	3.43	3.12	2.84	2.84	3.31	41.32
Logan	Bellefontaine	39	27.3	73.0	106	−21	40	May 6	Oct. 12	159	40	2.98	1.92	3.54	3.26	3.46	3.96	4.00	3.22	3.06	2.67	2.53	2.63	37.23
	Lakeview										23	2.82	1.64	3.46	3.02	3.35	4.16	3.51	2.75	3.57	2.50	2.42	2.44	35.64
Lorain	Oberlin	40	27.7	72.9	105	−23	40	May 7	Oct. 12	158	40	2.65	2.04	2.98	3.06	3.24	3.37	3.88	3.03	3.33	2.68	2.32	2.38	34.96
Lucas	Toledo	40	26.9	74.0	105	−16	40	Apr. 20	Oct. 22	185	40	2.39	1.89	2.86	3.04	3.11	3.30	2.82	2.89	3.08	2.32	2.02	2.39	32.11
Madison	London (near)	20	29.3	74.2	109	−18	21	May 1	Oct. 17	169	21	3.00	2.02	3.42	3.64	3.93	3.23	3.79	3.70	3.27	2.54	3.04	2.85	38.43
Mahoning	Canfield	22	27.0	70.9	104	−20	22	May 13	Oct. 4	144	23	2.23	1.55	2.70	3.08	3.62	3.85	3.77	3.15	3.06	2.53	2.69	2.33	34.56
	Lake Milton										24	2.30	1.50	2.57	2.95	3.47	3.47	3.83	3.33	3.25	2.45	2.51	2.12	33.75
	Youngstown	8	32.6	75.4	103	−16	9	Apr. 25	Oct. 17	175	33	2.61	1.98	2.63	3.05	3.00	3.39	3.45	3.17	2.89	2.48	2.15	2.37	33.17

Marion	Marion	40	29.0	74.5	106	−22	40	May 1	Oct. 15	167	40	3.23	2.30	3.78	3.45	3.65	4.33	3.96	3.19	3.19	2.93	2.48	2.80	39.29
	Prospect										26	2.90	1.90	3.14	3.07	3.66	3.92	3.49	3.13	2.73	2.65	2.40	2.58	35.57
Medina	Medina (near)	40	27.0	72.0	103	−24	40	May 13	Oct. 10	150	40	2.84	2.09	3.14	3.26	3.35	3.68	3.82	3.23	3.52	2.65	2.45	2.45	36.48
Meigs	Middleport	13	35.3	76.9	106	−6	13	Apr. 13	Oct. 22	192	33	3.64	2.90	3.97	3.36	3.66	4.28	4.15	4.08	2.56	2.66	2.67	3.25	41.18
Miami	Piqua										29	3.24	1.98	3.71	3.58	3.59	4.06	3.96	3.11	3.73	3.21	2.70	2.88	39.75
	Pleasant Hill										17	2.80	1.80	3.25	3.19	3.54	4.13	3.32	3.19	3.31	2.49	2.38	2.61	36.01
Monroe	Clarington	24	32.2	73.8	107	−20	23	Apr. 29	Oct. 20	174	24	4.30	3.28	4.11	3.72	4.15	4.39	4.81	4.20	3.37	3.42	2.74	3.76	46.25
Montgomery	Dayton (W. B. O.)	28	30.5	75.9	108	−28	28	Apr. 19	Oct. 25	189	40	3.26	2.20	3.65	3.19	3.65	3.65	3.40	3.12	3.08	2.77	2.48	2.68	37.13
	Germantown	24	30.7	75.4	109	−22	24	Apr. 27	Oct. 15	171	25	3.35	2.03	3.50	3.27	3.67	3.44	3.24	3.81	3.44	2.96	2.82	2.91	38.44
Morgan	McConnelsville	40	31.6	73.5	105	−29	40	May 1	Oct. 14	166	40	3.45	2.49	3.87	3.52	4.09	4.29	4.49	3.67	2.74	2.69	2.54	3.11	40.95
Morrow	Cardington	18	27.8	72.7	101	−21	17	May 7	Oct. 10	156	40	2.83	2.06	3.31	2.75	3.61	4.01	4.10	3.67	2.89	2.41	2.19	2.66	36.49
Muskingum	Philo	40	31.2	74.4	106	−20	37	Apr. 28	Oct. 14	169	18	3.00	2.51	3.40	3.14	3.43	4.00	4.40	3.19	2.74	2.71	1.86	2.56	36.94
	Zanesville										40	3.06	2.20	3.54	3.02	3.54	3.80	4.27	3.97	2.62	2.44	2.30	2.87	37.63
Noble	Caldwell (near)	32	31.6	72.5	107	−28	32	May 10	Oct. 10	153	33	3.75	2.47	3.86	3.36	4.03	4.24	4.74	4.80	3.21	3.04	2.81	3.26	43.57
Ottawa	Catawba Island	23	27.7	75.0	104	−20	22	Apr. 19	Oct. 29	193	23	2.15	1.46	2.55	2.81	2.58	2.79	2.28	2.22	3.00	2.24	2.11	2.00	28.19
	Danbury	22	25.2	75.1	108	−18	21	Apr. 22	Oct. 26	187	21	2.01	1.39	2.65	2.84	2.62	2.87	2.24	2.56	3.30	2.45	2.13	2.16	29.22
	Put-in-Bay	22	26.8	74.7	104	−19	22	Apr. 17	Nov. 4	201	22	1.98	1.41	2.35	2.93	2.61	2.89	2.32	2.63	3.08	2.34	2.02	1.98	28.54
Paulding	Paulding	38	26.5	73.7	111	−24	24	May 9	Oct. 6	150	40	2.50	1.78	3.25	3.22	3.54	3.78	3.20	2.63	3.15	2.57	2.37	2.70	34.69
Perry	Somerset	20	29.9	74.7	107	−26	20	Apr. 24	Oct. 15	174	21	3.30	2.04	3.14	3.27	3.67	4.72	3.93	3.52	2.45	2.79	2.14	2.81	37.78
Pickaway	Circleville	38	31.4	75.7	109	−23	39	Apr. 30	Oct. 14	167	40	3.39	2.47	3.86	3.44	3.73	4.14	4.39	3.84	2.91	2.66	2.65	2.99	40.47
Pike	Waverly	40	33.0	75.4	107	−29	39	do	Oct. 10	163	40	3.66	3.64	3.89	3.36	3.96	4.24	4.12	3.86	2.79	2.40	2.54	3.16	41.62
Portage	Hiram	40	26.9	71.4	102	−22	40	May 2	Oct. 17	168	40	2.99	2.14	3.17	3.28	3.51	3.59	3.82	3.51	3.32	3.02	2.92	2.65	37.92
Preble	Eaton										24	3.41	1.97	3.72	3.68	3.71	3.91	3.71	3.71	3.66	2.93	2.91	3.08	40.40
	West Manchester										21	3.21	1.85	4.16	3.40	3.77	3.90	3.45	4.00	3.07	2.79	2.65	2.98	39.23
Putnam	Ottawa	40	27.1	73.8	107	−22	40	May 4	Oct. 9	158	40	2.54	1.82	3.29	3.12	3.35	3.46	3.62	3.00	3.30	2.55	2.21	2.53	34.79
Richland	Bangorville	40	27.4	72.7	103	−26	39	May 5	Oct. 16	164	39	3.61	2.57	3.97	3.48	3.97	4.37	4.50	3.62	3.30	2.74	2.72	3.17	42.02
	Mansfield	21	27.6	72.7	105	−17	20	May 3	Oct. 12	162	29	3.00	2.23	3.82	3.35	3.96	4.14	4.38	3.43	3.45	2.64	2.75	2.78	39.93
Ross	Chillicothe	18	32.7	76.4	109	−16	16	Apr. 26	Oct. 16	173	36	3.52	2.40	3.81	3.45	3.57	4.07	4.04	3.70	2.84	2.39	2.46	3.06	39.31
	Frankfort	22	31.2	75.1	105	−31	22	Apr. 27	Oct. 15	171	24	3.11	2.42	3.81	3.05	3.59	3.21	3.37	3.43	2.56	2.39	2.23	3.02	36.19
Sandusky	Fremont	38	27.1	74.1	110	−17	38	May 1	Oct. 16	168	38	2.67	2.07	3.11	3.46	3.52	3.98	3.54	3.38	3.32	2.03	2.21	2.58	35.87
	Vickery	40	27.1	73.7	108	−24	40	May 6	Oct. 13	160	40	2.40	1.81	2.88	2.95	3.11	3.76	3.48	2.97	3.13	2.57	2.05	2.18	33.29
Scioto	Portsmouth [1]	40	34.6	77.0	107	−18	40	Apr. 20	Oct. 20	183	40	4.12	2.96	4.23	3.44	3.53	3.92	4.50	3.80	2.58	2.56	2.74	3.36	41.74
Seneca	Tiffin	40	27.9	73.8	106	−20	40	May 3	Oct. 12	162	40	3.00	2.25	3.44	3.35	3.62	3.69	3.74	2.99	3.30	2.70	2.30	2.61	36.99
Shelby	Sidney	40	28.7	74.7	109	−34	40	Apr. 29	do	166	40	3.19	2.05	3.72	3.23	3.64	3.85	3.75	3.42	3.39	2.79	2.43	2.70	38.16
Stark	Canton	40	28.5	72.6	104	−20	40	May 2	Oct. 16	167	40	3.03	2.31	3.52	3.33	3.40	4.09	4.33	3.49	3.21	2.49	2.50	2.73	38.43
Summit	Akron	40	27.2	72.9	104	−20	40	Apr. 29	do	170	40	2.56	1.93	2.94	2.99	3.60	3.56	3.76	3.45	3.49	2.58	2.17	2.41	35.44
	Hudson	23	26.5	72.4	104	−22	24	May 8	Oct. 13	158	24	2.80	2.43	3.39	3.64	3.81	3.23	4.67	4.16	3.63	3.24	2.51	2.49	40.00
Trumbull	Kinsman										25	2.59	1.74	2.73	3.03	3.50	3.58	3.86	3.26	3.62	2.99	2.96	2.54	36.40
	Warren	39	28.1	72.5	105	−25	39	May 13	Oct. 6	146	40	3.08	2.39	3.35	3.34	3.42	3.38	4.05	3.37	3.30	2.58	2.82	2.77	37.85
Tuscarawas	Dennison	29	30.3	73.3	105	−25	29	do	Oct. 10	150	30	3.54	2.30	3.32	3.07	3.52	3.85	3.94	3.82	3.37	2.81	2.68	2.94	39.16
	Dover	36	27.9	72.8	105	−25	36	May 8	do	155	38	2.99	2.34	3.47	3.19	3.46	3.69	4.24	3.63	3.18	2.45	2.39	2.81	37.84
Union	Marysville	22	28.4	73.5	109	−22	22	May 5	Oct. 11	159	22	2.96	1.78	3.37	3.59	3.69	4.14	3.63	3.93	3.26	2.66	2.85	2.81	38.67
Van Wert	Van Wert	17	28.0	75.6	110	−24	17	May 6	Oct. 7	154	17	2.17	1.63	3.35	2.88	3.50	3.42	3.45	2.80	3.52	2.18	2.40	2.53	33.83
Vinton	McArthur	23	32.3	74.0	109	−38	22	May 10	Oct. 6	149	23	3.70	2.60	3.84	3.16	3.50	3.88	3.78	4.40	2.85	2.40	2.85	3.16	40.12
Warren	Kings Mills										26	3.98	2.50	4.44	3.81	4.05	3.69	4.06	4.53	3.41	2.90	3.03	3.26	43.66
	Waynesville	30	29.4	73.7	105	−23	29	Apr. 28	Oct. 16	171	29	3.07	2.29	3.99	3.42	4.14	3.89	3.24	3.90	2.81	3.01	2.41	2.98	39.15
Washington	Beverly										25	3.17	2.24	3.40	3.30	3.80	4.06	3.97	4.15	2.85	2.52	2.68	2.92	39.06
	Marietta	40	33.5	75.4	106	−22	40	Apr. 23	Oct. 21	181	40	3.70	2.73	3.78	3.46	3.84	4.31	4.41	4.07	2.61	2.67	2.69	3.28	41.55
Wayne	Wooster	40	27.9	72.1	105	−24	40	May 10	Oct. 9	152	40	3.17	2.19	3.53	3.19	3.57	3.87	4.04	3.85	3.34	2.50	2.43	2.68	38.36
Williams	Montpelier	28	25.8	73.7	108	−25	30	May 6	do	156	40	2.52	2.15	2.92	3.17	3.79	3.90	3.29	3.15	3.19	2.69	2.49	2.60	35.86
Wood	Bowling Green	40	26.6	73.4	110	−22	39	May 7	Oct. 12	158	40	2.24	1.71	2.94	3.00	3.35	3.52	3.41	2.65	3.17	2.57	2.06	2.38	33.00
Wyandot	Upper Sandusky	40	27.9	74.0	106	−22	40	May 5	Oct. 9	157	40	2.92	2.27	3.64	3.44	3.74	4.19	3.93	3.37	3.36	2.85	2.40	2.70	38.81

OHIO—Continued

Precipitation and temperature—State unit values

[This tabulation gives the mean annual, mean monthly, and average seasonal precipitation, 1886–1938, and the mean annual temperatures, 1902–38, for Ohio]

Precipitation		Precipitation		Precipitation		Precipitation		Temperature		Temperature	
Year	Mean	Year	Mean	Year	Mean	Month	Mean	Year	Mean	Year	Mean
	In.		*In.*		*In.*		*In.*		*°F.*		*°F.*
1886	37.84	1907	43.54	1928	35.21	May	3.66	1902	50.7	1921	54.6
1887	34.78	1908	34.61	1929	46.11	June	3.81	1903	50.5	1922	52.8
1888	38.52	1909	42.82	1930	26.74	July	3.83	1904	48.6	1923	51.4
1889	33.45	1910	36.11	1931	38.33	August	3.42	1905	50.0	1924	49.3
1890	50.37	1911	42.98	1932	37.13	September	3.00	1906	51.6	1925	51.4
1891	38.87	1912	38.03	1933	38.69	October	2.49	1907	49.6	1926	50.0
1892	37.15	1913	45.32	1934	26.61	November	2.74	1908	52.1	1927	52.1
1893	39.60	1914	35.39	1935	40.67	December	2.74	1909	50.9	1928	51.1
1894	29.72	1915	41.04	1936	33.52			1910	50.4	1929	50.4
1895	28.46	1916	37.34	1937	44.62	Annual	37.93	1911	52.6	1930	52.5
1896	39.58	1917	36.55	1938	39.63			1912	49.6	1931	54.2
1897	38.59	1918	36.48					1913	52.3	1932	52.6
1898	43.78	1919	40.49			Season	Average	1914	50.9	1933	53.2
1899	34.19	1920	37.49	Month	Mean			1915	50.8	1934	52.2
1900	32.92	1921	43.00					1916	51.0	1935	51.3
1901	31.43	1922	37.03					1917	47.9	1936	51.6
1902	37.33	1923	39.18		*In.*		*In.*	1918	51.5	1937	51.1
1903	36.39	1924	37.38	January	3.12	Winter	8.34	1919	52.3	1938	53.6
1904	35.80	1925	34.26	February	2.48	Spring	10.30	1920	50.3		
1905	40.45	1926	43.81	March	3.48	Summer	11.06				
1906	37.25	1927	43.42	April	3.16	Fall	8.23				

Dates of last killing frost in spring and first in fall, with length of growing season

Year	Cleveland			Findlay			Columbus			Cambridge			Cincinnati			Portsmouth		
	Last in spring	First in fall	Growing season [1]	Last in spring	First in fall	Growing season [1]	Last in spring	First in fall	Growing season [1]	Last in spring	First in fall	Growing season [1]	Last in spring	First in fall	Growing season [1]	Last in spring	First in fall	Growing season [1]
			Days			*Days*			*Days*			*Days*			*Days*			*Days*
1899	Apr. 5	Oct. 2	180	Apr. 10	Sept. 30	173	Apr. 9	Sept. 30	174	Apr. 17	Sept. 14	150	Apr. 5	Sept. 30	178	Apr. 5	Oct. 1	179
1900	Apr. 11	Nov. 9	212	May 5	Nov. 6	185	Apr. 14	Nov. 6	206	May 10			Apr. 3	Nov. 9	220	Apr. 10	Oct. 17	190
1901	Apr. 20	Oct. 26	189	Apr. 21	Oct. 4	166	Apr. 21	Oct. 18	180	Apr. 23	Oct. 4	164	Apr. 1	Oct. 18	200	Apr. 21	Oct. 26	188

1902	Apr. 8	Nov. 28	234	Apr. 24	Sept. 14	143	Apr. 15	Oct. 15	183	May 10	Sept. 14	127	Apr. 15	Nov. 28	227	Apr. 8	Nov. 9	215
1903	May 2	Nov. 8	190	May 2	Oct. 24	175	Apr. 5	Oct. 24	202	May 5	Sept. 19	137	Apr. 5	Oct. 24	202	Apr. 5	Oct. 25	203
1904	Apr. 20	Oct. 24	187	May 15	Oct. 7	145	Apr. 21	Oct. 16	178	May 16	Oct. 4	141	Apr. 20	Oct. 28	191	Apr. 21	Oct. 24	186
1905	Apr. 8	Oct. 26	201	May 1	Oct. 22	174	Apr. 17	Oct. 30	196	May 1	Oct. 13	165	Apr. 8	Oct. 22	197	Apr. 18	Oct. 22	187
1906	Apr. 1	Nov. 2	215	May 10	Oct. 11	154	Apr. 1	Oct. 11	193	May 10	Oct. 10	153	Apr. 1	Oct. 11	193	Apr. 24	Oct. 11	170
1907	Apr. 21	Oct. 19	181	May 11	Oct. 13	155	Apr. 27	Oct. 14	170	May 28	Oct. 9	134	Apr. 15	Oct. 19	187	Apr. 20	Oct. 19	182
1908	Apr. 4	Nov. 2	212	May 3	Oct. 2	152	Apr. 16	Oct. 31	198	May 3	Sept. 30	150	Apr. 3	Oct. 31	211	Apr. 3	Oct. 2	182
1909	Apr. 23	Nov. 24	215	May 4	do	151	Apr. 26	Oct. 13	170	May 12	Sept. 28	139	Apr. 11	Oct. 13	185	Apr. 11	Oct. 13	185
1910	Apr. 19	Nov. 7	202	May 15	Oct. 29	167	Apr. 24	Oct. 28	187	May 15	Oct. 24	162	Apr. 24	Oct. 28	187	May 15	Oct. 30	168
1911	Apr. 9	Nov. 2	207	May 6	Oct. 24	171	Apr. 9	do	202	May 6	do	171	Apr. 9	Oct. 24	198	May 5	Nov. 2	181
1912	Apr. 3	Nov. 3	214	Apr. 25	Sept. 27	155	Apr. 8	Oct. 25	200	June 7	Sept. 30	115	Apr. 3	Nov. 3	214	Apr. 8	Oct. 27	202
1913	Apr. 21	Oct. 22	184	May 12	Sept. 23	134	May 11	Oct. 21	163	May 12	Sept. 23	134	Apr. 8	Oct. 21	196	May 11	Oct. 14	156
1914	Apr. 13	Oct. 28	198	May 2	Oct. 27	178	Apr. 12	Oct. 27	198	May 16	Oct. 27	164	Apr. 9	Oct. 27	201	Apr. 10	Oct. 27	200
1915	Apr. 8	Oct. 24	199	May 19	Oct. 8	142	Apr. 15	Oct. 10	178	Apr. 18	Oct. 10	175	Apr. 4	Oct. 10	189	Apr. 17	Oct. 10	176
1916	Apr. 10	Oct. 14	218	Apr. 15	Sept. 19	157	Apr. 10	Oct. 11	184	Apr. 15	Sept. 30	168	Apr. 10	Oct. 22	195	Apr. 10	Sept. 30	173
1917	Apr. 15	do	182	May 14	Sept. 11	120	Apr. 14	Oct. 9	178	May 10	Sept. 11	124	Apr. 14	Oct. 9	178	Apr. 14	Oct. 9	178
1918	Apr. 24	Nov. 12	202	Apr. 25	Sept. 22	150	Apr. 10	Nov. 2	206	May 2	Sept. 22	143	Apr. 10	Nov. 2	206	May 1	Oct. 15	167
1919	Apr. 26	Nov. 13	201	Apr. 27	Oct. 13	169	Apr. 26	Nov. 5	193	Apr. 27	Nov. 6	193	Apr. 26	Nov. 5	193	Apr. 26	Nov. 6	194
1920	Apr. 13	Nov. 11	212	May 16	Oct. 7	144	May 3	Oct. 30	180	May 16	Oct. 7	144	Apr. 13	Oct. 30	200	Apr. 14	Oct. 30	199
1921	Apr. 18	Nov. 6	202	do	Oct. 13	150	Apr. 18	Oct. 13	178	Apr. 19	Oct. 13	177	Apr. 18	Oct. 13	178	Apr. 12	Oct. 13	184
1922	Apr. 22	Nov. 10	202	Apr. 29	do	167	Apr. 29	Oct. 18	172	Apr. 29	do	167	Mar. 23	Oct. 19	210	Apr. 23	do	173
1923	Apr. 14	Oct. 31	200	May 13	Sept. 14	124	May 9	Oct. 6	150	May 10	Oct. 6	149	Apr. 9	Oct. 6	180	Apr. 17	Oct. 6	172
1924	Apr. 8	Nov. 9	215	May 22	Oct. 22	153	Apr. 8	Oct. 23	198	May 5	Oct. 21	169	Apr. 3	Oct. 23	203	Apr. 23	Oct. 23	183
1925	Apr. 6	Oct. 29	206	May 25	Oct. 10	138	Apr. 6	Oct. 10	187	May 25	Oct. 10	138	Apr. 6	Oct. 10	187	Apr. 6	Oct. 10	187
1926	Apr. 27	Nov. 10	197	May 11	Oct. 17	159	Apr. 27	Nov. 2	189	May 4	Oct. 26	175	Apr. 20	Oct. 27	190	Apr. 27	Nov. 3	190
1927	Apr. 24	Nov. 13	203	May 1	Oct. 15	167	Apr. 24	Nov. 6	196	May 1	Oct. 17	169	Apr. 24	Nov. 6	196	Apr. 25	Nov. 6	195
1928	Apr. 20	Nov. 21	215	May 13	Sept. 28	138	Apr. 26	Oct. 30	187	May 13	Oct. 29	169	Apr. 16	Oct. 29	196	Apr. 16	Oct. 29	196
1929	Apr. 2	Nov. 20	232	May 8	Sept. 19	134	Apr. 19	Nov. 5	200	May 17	Oct. 15	151	Mar. 17	Nov. 5	233	Apr. 19	Oct. 18	182
1930	Apr. 24	Oct. 18	177	Apr. 26	Oct. 18	175	Apr. 24	Oct. 20	179	May 30	Oct. 2	125	Apr. 25	Oct. 20	178	Apr. 25	Oct. 20	178
1931	Apr. 27	Nov. 7	194	Apr. 30	do	171	Mar. 30	Nov. 6	221	May 24	Oct. 18	147	Apr. 7	Nov. 5	212	May 4	Oct. 19	168
1932	do	Nov. 11	198	Apr. 27	Nov. 11	198	Apr. 27	Nov. 11	198	May 2	Nov. 2	184	Apr. 27	Nov. 2	189	Apr. 15	Oct. 30	198
1933	Apr. 26	Nov. 5	193	do	Oct. 25	181	Apr. 23	Oct. 26	186	Apr. 28	Oct. 14	169	Apr. 23	Oct. 26	186	Apr. 12	Oct. 14	185
1934	Apr. 28	Nov. 2	188	------	Oct. 14	------	Apr. 28	Oct. 14	169	do	Oct. 13	168	Apr. 28	Nov. 2	188	Apr. 28	do	169
1935	Apr. 17	Nov. 21	218	Apr. 18	Oct. 2	167	Apr. 17	Oct. 7	173	Apr. 23	Oct. 4	164	Apr. 17	Oct. 7	173	Apr. 17	Oct. 7	173
1936	Apr. 23	Nov. 15	206	Apr. 23	Oct. 24	184	Apr. 23	Oct. 28	188	do	Oct. 28	188	Apr. 23	Oct. 27	187	Apr. 23	Oct. 28	188
1937	Apr. 11	Oct. 24	196	Apr. 16	Oct. 8	175	Apr. 12	Oct. 14	185	Apr. 12	Oct. 8	179	Apr. 12	Oct. 15	186	Apr. 12	Oct. 14	185
1938	Apr. 10	Nov. 9	213	May 12	Oct. 7	148	do	Oct. 31	172	May 13	Oct. 7	147	Apr. 10	Nov. 9	213	May 12	Oct. 31	172
Mean	Apr. 16	Nov. 5	203	May 4	Oct. 10	159	Apr. 19	Oct. 23	187	May 7	Oct. 10	156	Apr. 12	Oct. 25	196	Apr. 20	Oct. 20	183
Extremes	Apr. 1[2] May 2[3]	Oct. 2[4] Nov. 28[5]	[6] 177 [7] 234	Apr. 10[2] May 25[3]	Sept. 11[4] Nov. 11[5]	[6] 120 [7] 198	Mar. 20[2] May 12[3]	Sept. 30[4] Nov. 11[5]	[6] 150 [7] 221	Apr. 12[2] June 7[3]	Sept. 11[4] Nov. 6[5]	[6] 115 [7] 193	Mar. 17[2] Apr. 28[3]	Sept. 30[4] Nov. 28[5]	[6] 173 [7] 233	Apr. 3[2] May 15[3]	Sept. 30[4] Nov. 9[5]	[6] 156 [7] 215

[1] Number of days between last killing frost in spring and first in fall.
[2] Earliest date in spring.
[3] Latest date in spring.
[4] Earliest date in fall.
[5] Latest date in fall.
[6] Shortest growing season.
[7] Longest growing season.

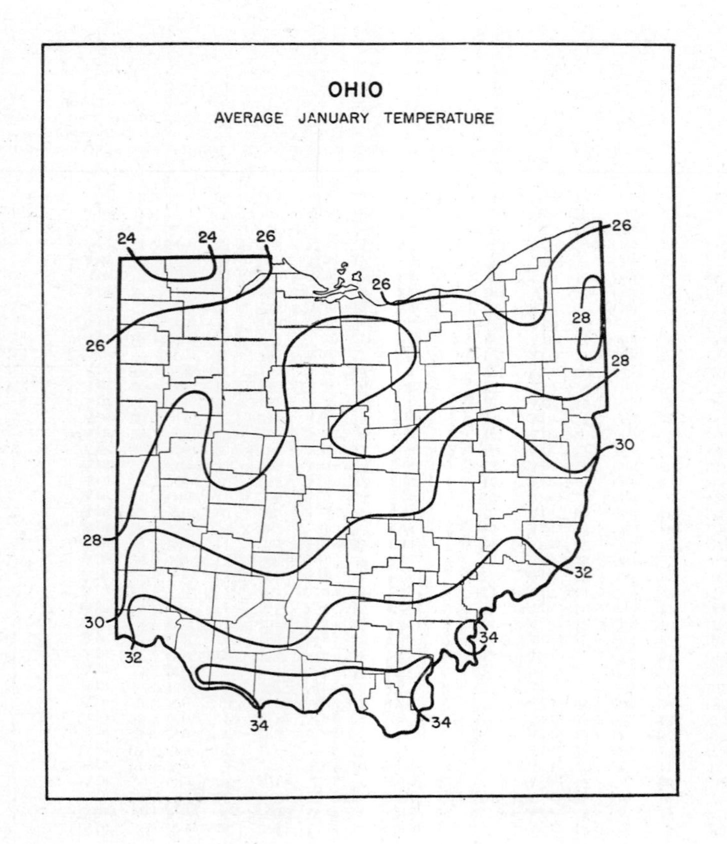
OHIO
AVERAGE JANUARY TEMPERATURE
24
24
26
26
26
26
28
28
28
30
30
32
32
34
34
34

OHIO
AVERAGE JULY TEMPERATURE
72
72
72
74
74
76
76
76

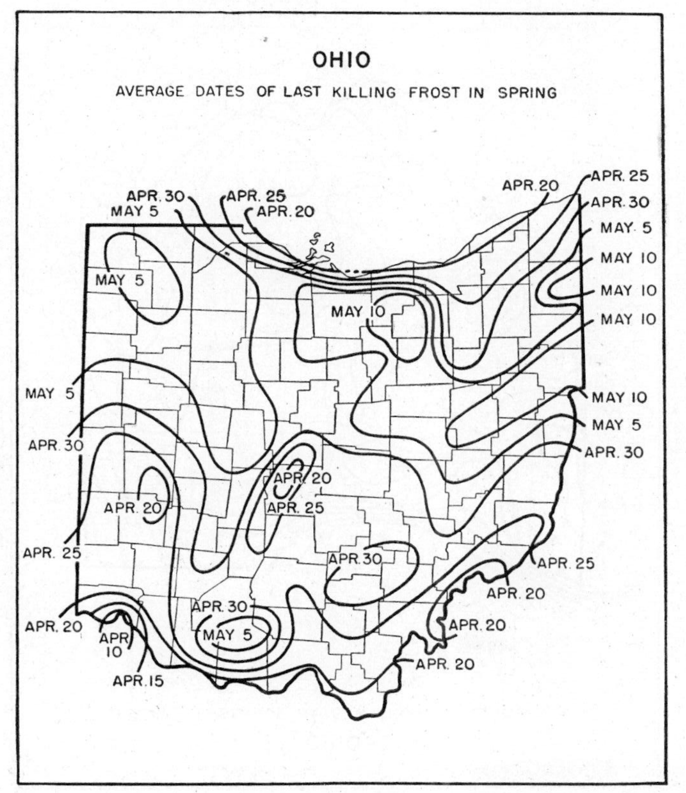
OHIO
AVERAGE DATES OF LAST KILLING FROST IN SPRING
APR. 20
APR. 25
APR. 30
MAY 5
MAY 10
MAY 10
MAY 10
APR. 30
MAY 5
APR. 25
APR. 20
MAY 5
MAY 10
MAY 5
APR. 30
APR. 20
APR. 25
APR. 30
MAY 10
MAY 5
APR. 30
APR. 25
APR. 20
APR. 20
APR. 30
APR. 25
APR. 20
APR. 20
APR. 30
MAY 5
APR. 20
APR 10
APR. 15
APR. 20

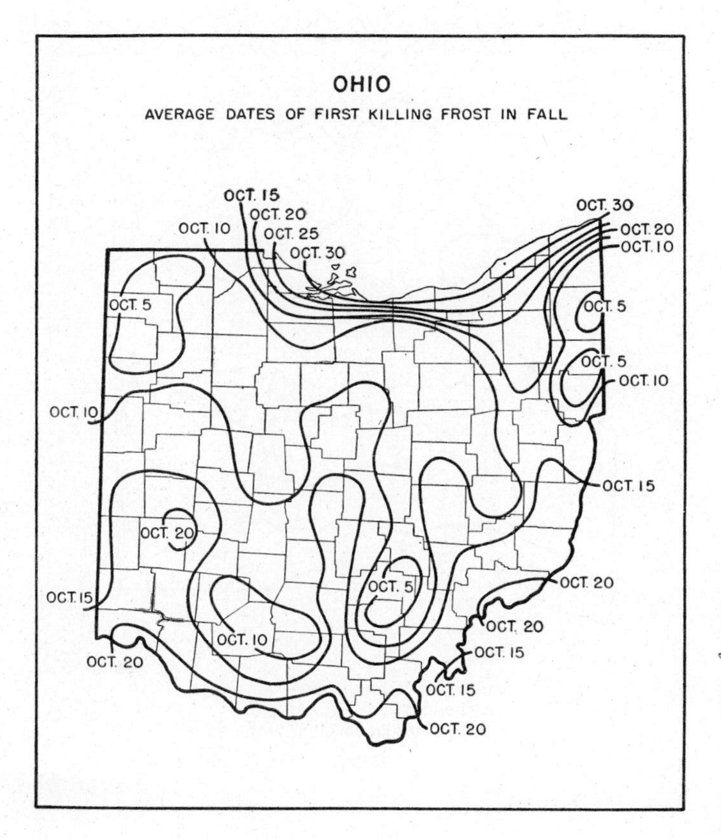
OHIO
AVERAGE DATES OF FIRST KILLING FROST IN FALL
OCT. 15
OCT. 20
OCT. 10
OCT. 25
OCT. 30
OCT. 30
OCT. 20
OCT. 10
OCT. 5
OCT. 5
OCT. 5
OCT. 10
OCT. 10
OCT. 15
OCT. 20
OCT. 15
OCT. 5
OCT. 20
OCT. 10
OCT. 20
OCT. 20
OCT. 15
OCT. 15
OCT. 20

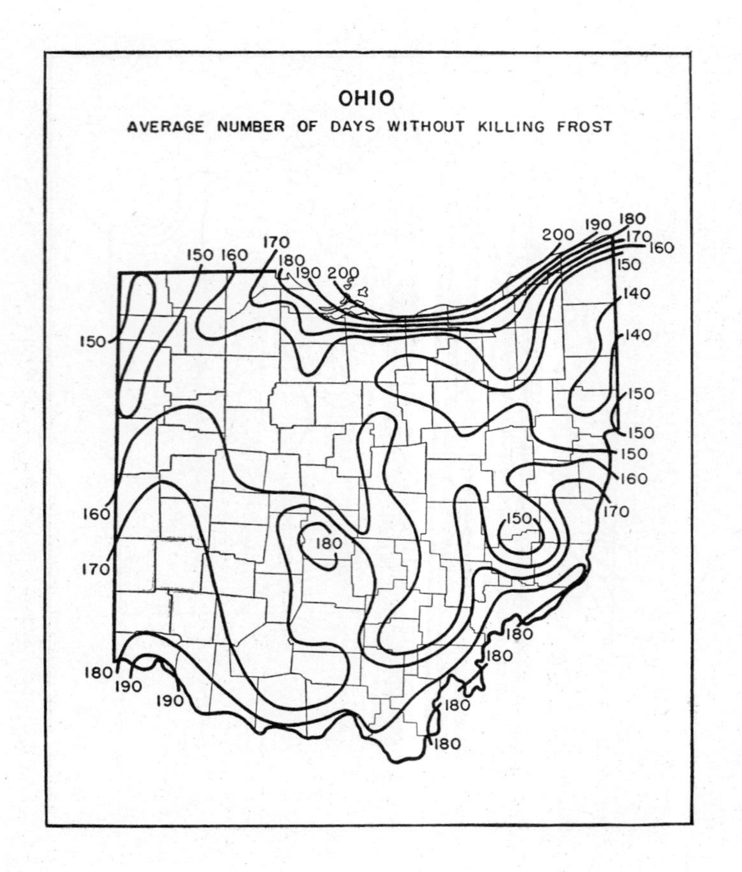
OHIO
AVERAGE NUMBER OF DAYS WITHOUT KILLING FROST

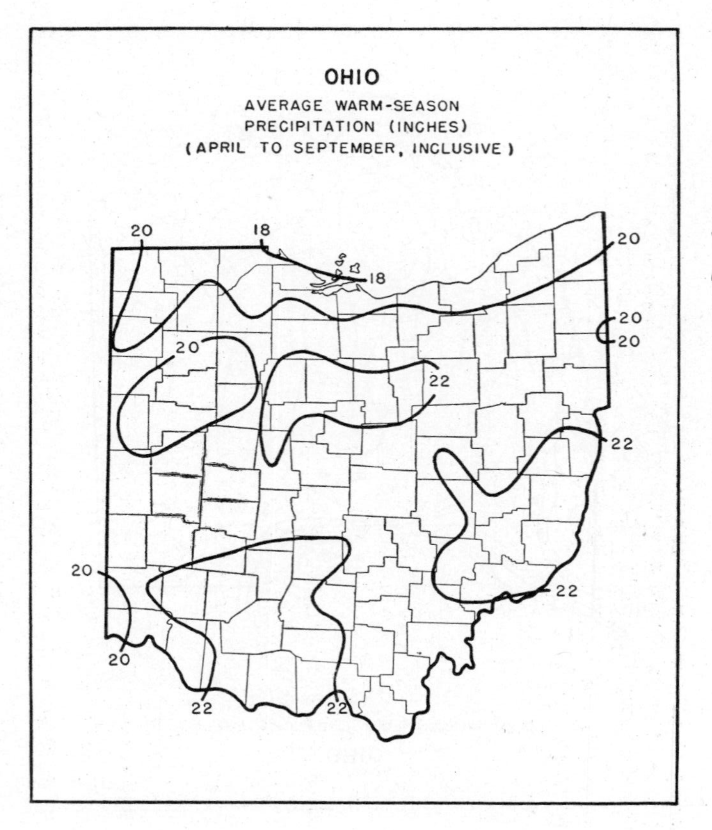
OHIO
AVERAGE WARM-SEASON
PRECIPITATION (INCHES)
(APRIL TO SEPTEMBER, INCLUSIVE)

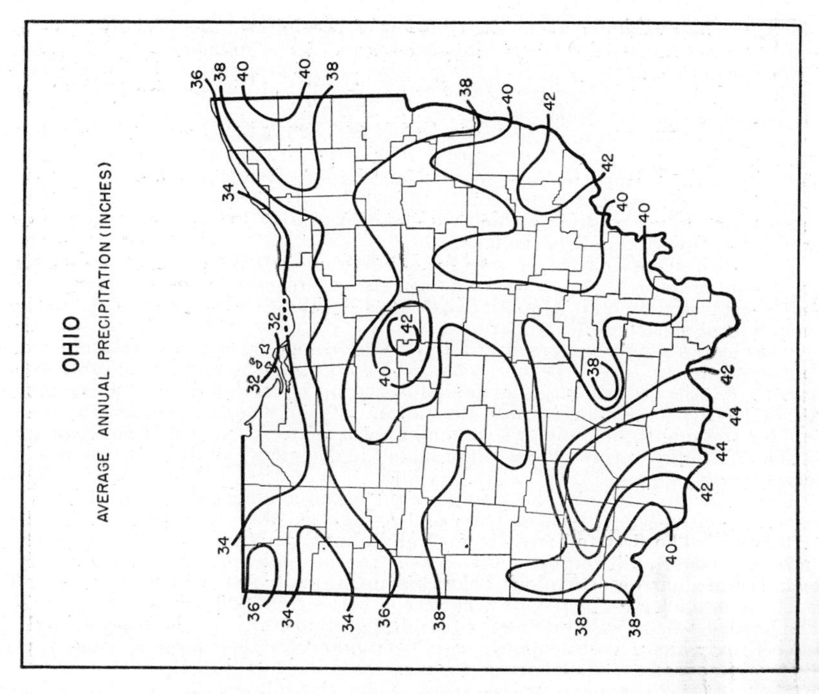

SUPPLEMENTARY CLIMATIC NOTES FOR OHIO

Ohio has no great range of elevation. The highest point in the State is an isolated summit, 1,550 feet above sea level, in the northwest-central part, while the lowest elevation, some 430 feet, is in the southwest corner, where the Ohio River meets the Indiana-Ohio line.

The drainage is either northerly to Lake Erie or southerly to the Ohio River. The divide between these two drainage areas lies well to the north of the center of the State, and in the northeastern part it is only 20 to 30 miles from Lake Erie.

The northwestern part of the State is extremely flat, while the southeast is rough and hilly. This difference is due to the fact that the southeast was not glaciated, while the northwest during the glacial age was submerged by the waters of a lake with a higher level than the present Lake Erie. Much of the best agricultural land in Ohio is found in this old lake bed in the northwestern counties, while in the unglaciated counties of the southeastern section thousands of acres are unsuited for agriculture.

The streams of southwestern Ohio furnish much valuable water power, as evidenced by the large number of important manufacturing centers located there. This abundant water power is due primarily to the fact that the Miami River and its tributaries connect the most elevated parts of the State (Logan County) with the lowest parts; in other words, the range in elevation is greater in this section than in any other part of the State. The Miami rises at an elevation of more than 1,200 feet in Logan County and descends rather uniformly to about 500 feet at the Ohio River, a fall of 700 feet or more in a distance of about 160 miles.

Ohio enjoys a climate characterized normally by abundant precipitation, well distributed throughout the year; serious droughts are of infrequent occurrence. Summer temperatures are rather high but not unduly oppressive, and they are a factor in the success of agriculture in the State. Winter temperatures usually are not severe, and snowfall is moderate in most sections. Destructive storms seldom occur.

The average number of days with a measurable amount of precipitation is 120. During the year there are on an average 134 clear days, 107 days with partly cloudy skies, and 124 cloudy days.

Probably the greatest variations in climate are those incident to latitude. However, although there is no great altitude range in the State, differences in elevation clearly influence the distribution of precipitation (especially snowfall), temperature, and length of the growing season. The influence of Lake Erie is strikingly shown in the length of the growing season at stations near its shore and is also apparent in the comparatively great amounts of rainfall and snowfall over the northeastern highlands.

Ohio has no geographic divisions that exhibit, as a whole, marked contrasts in climate, though the part of the State that drains into Lake Erie—about one-third of the total area—may be considered a fairly distinctive climatic province. The remainder of the State, which drains into the Ohio River, has appreciably different characteristics. The dividing line runs approximately in an east-west direction and rather closely parallels the lake shore.

The southern drainage area may be subdivided into three great watersheds—the Muskingum in the east, the Scioto in the central part, and the Miami in the southwest. In general, climatic variations in these valleys are not marked, though local aspects differ materially.

The mean annual temperatures for the State range from 55° F. in the extreme southern part to 48° in the northeast. This variation is mainly due to the difference in latitude, although the annual isotherms clearly show an altitude factor. About 1 year in 8, on an average, no station in Ohio records a temperature below zero for the month of January, while in approximately 1 year in 3 no locality experiences a temperature of 100° F. or higher in the month of July. The absolute temperature range is 152°.

The last killing frost in the spring occurs, on an average, about April 10 in the extreme southwestern part of Ohio and as late as May 10 in the northeastern highlands. The first fall frost is generally about October 5 in the northeastern and southeastern hill counties, as well as in the extreme northwest, while the Bass Islands and a narrow strip along Lake Erie are normally frost-free until October 30.

The average length of the growing season varies from 200 days to less than 150. The longest season without frost is found, quite naturally, on the Bass Islands in Lake Erie, which have for many years been noted for their large acreage of productive vineyards. The shortest growing season is found in the elevated region in the northeastern part of the State, while the hill sections in the southern counties have a season of less than 160 days, as does also a considerable northwestern area.

The average annual precipitation of the northern area is about 36 inches, but the distribution varies materially. The individual station averages range from about 30 to 40 inches, with the greatest amount in the more elevated districts along or near the divide. Precipitation is quite evenly distributed throughout the year, with the warm months having slightly greater amounts than the winter months. Serious droughts are of infrequent occurrence.

The greatest average annual snowfall, over 50 inches, is in the northeastern hill counties, and the least, less than 20 inches, along the southern border.

Ohio is so situated as to come under the influence of many general storm areas, and the development of local disturbances, such as thunderstorms, hailstorms, windstorms, and heavy rainstorms, is favored. Now and then such a storm develops the true characteristics of the tornado. The heaviest rains and highest winds are usually incident to the passage of thunderstorms, and any given locality may expect, on an average, some 40 to 50 thunderstorms a year.

Flooding of the lowlands along the streams of the State occurs practically every year, but general floods of a serious character are much less frequent.

The climate of Ohio is favorable for a diversified agriculture, and few States have a greater income from farm crops and livestock. The principal crops are winter wheat, corn, oats, potatoes, hay, tobacco, and grapes.

JOHN C. FISHER, *Senior Meteorologist and Climatic Section Director for Ohio, Weather Bureau, Columbus.*

OKLAHOMA

Climatic summary

County[1]	Station	Temperature: Length of record	Temperature: January average	Temperature: July average	Temperature: Maximum	Temperature: Minimum	Killing frost average dates: Length of record	Killing frost average dates: Last in spring	Killing frost average dates: First in fall	Growing season[2]	Average precipitation: Length of record	January	February	March	April	May	June	July	August	September	October	November	December	Annual
		Yr.	°F.	°F.	°F.	°F.	Yr.			Days	Yr.	In.	In.	In.	In.	In.	In.	In.	In.	In.	In.	In.	In.	In.
Adair	Watts	17	38.7	79.8	114	−27	16	Apr. 10	Oct. 27	200	16	3.33	2.61	3.35	4.79	4.98	5.31	3.40	3.33	4.99	4.24	3.52	2.99	46.84
Alfalfa	Cherokee	24	36.0	83.1	117	−14	22	Apr. 8	Nov. 2	208	24	.76	.69	1.66	2.60	3.48	3.64	1.96	3.11	3.06	2.24	1.54	.84	25.58
Atoka	Atoka	13	40.4	82.7	110	−2	6	Mar. 26	Nov. 6	225	9	3.58	3.05	2.86	3.89	5.72	3.79	3.47	2.93	2.53	4.91	1.76	3.22	41.71
Beaver	Beaver	40	33.4	81.5	115	−25	39	Apr. 15	Oct. 23	191	39	.38	.79	.98	1.75	2.59	2.80	2.02	2.45	2.21	1.37	.95	.66	18.95
Beckham	Elk City	15	37.5	82.5	113	−12	14	Mar. 31	Nov. 1	215	16	.54	.73	1.60	2.16	3.98	3.00	1.46	2.00	2.19	1.94	1.10	1.16	21.86
	Erick	34	37.8	82.1	113	−17	33	Apr. 5	Oct. 31	209	34	.65	.75	1.42	2.44	3.80	3.18	2.19	2.24	2.73	2.51	1.36	1.00	24.27
Blaine	Canton										25	.87	.86	1.75	2.97	3.73	3.48	1.63	2.79	2.64	2.46	1.55	1.07	25.80
	Geary	27	37.6	83.4	116	−10	27	Apr. 1	Nov. 3	216	27	.92	1.09	1.81	3.02	3.76	3.88	2.19	2.73	3.25	2.54	1.71	1.42	28.32
	Okeene	36	36.5	82.7	115	−18	32	Apr. 4	Oct. 31	210	35	.97	1.04	1.65	3.06	3.75	3.73	2.26	2.91	2.90	2.54	1.77	1.17	27.75
	Watonga										11	1.07	.91	1.97	2.10	4.18	3.40	2.25	2.32	2.46	2.18	2.14	1.71	26.69
Bryan	Durant	37	42.4	82.8	118	−6	37	Mar. 22	Nov. 11	234	37	2.48	2.28	3.01	4.22	5.18	3.72	3.23	2.83	2.87	3.97	2.45	2.68	38.92
Caddo	Apache	29	39.2	83.2	116	−12	29	Apr. 4	Oct. 31	210	29	1.23	1.27	2.39	3.62	4.27	3.79	2.35	2.62	3.50	3.41	1.83	1.72	32.00
	Carnegie	25	37.6	82.9	117	−15	24	Apr. 6	Oct. 30	207	25	.96	.93	1.90	3.46	3.92	3.62	2.03	2.53	3.56	3.16	1.38	1.25	28.70
	Neola	10	41.1	81.3	112	−11	10	Apr. 13	Oct. 24	194	10	.74	1.14	1.37	3.15	4.55	3.40	3.40	3.10	2.22	2.57	2.13	1.71	29.48
Canadian	El Reno										22	1.12	1.22	1.84	3.24	3.75	3.76	1.84	3.07	3.23	2.27	1.84	1.41	28.59
	Fort Reno	35	37.5	81.8	114	−15	33	Apr. 5	Nov. 4	213	36	.87	1.10	2.12	3.44	4.47	3.59	2.35	2.81	3.37	2.64	2.15	1.31	30.22
	Union City										23	1.22	1.17	2.05	3.38	4.14	4.09	2.03	2.76	3.77	3.29	2.00	1.35	31.25
Carter	Ardmore	37	42.7	83.6	114	−8	37	Mar. 21	Nov. 10	234	38	1.97	1.95	2.62	4.01	4.89	3.59	2.82	2.73	3.29	3.50	2.39	2.26	36.02
	Healdton	23	41.2	81.5	115	−14	23	Apr. 10	Oct. 28	201	23	1.61	1.46	2.28	4.44	5.78	4.04	3.17	3.80	3.08	3.42	2.90	2.04	38.02
Cherokee	Tahlequah	26	38.5	81.4	118	−23	30	Apr. 6	Oct. 30	207	30	2.53	1.97	3.21	4.26	4.46	4.84	3.26	3.42	4.04	4.11	2.86	2.21	41.17
Choctaw	Hugo	26	43.8	82.8	118	−3	26	Mar. 23	Nov. 8	230	26	3.68	2.59	3.60	4.35	5.95	4.16	3.43	3.15	3.25	3.97	3.13	3.28	44.54
Cimarron	Boise City	31	33.5	77.3	108	−20	31	Apr. 20	Oct. 21	184	31	.44	.66	.95	1.55	2.73	2.90	2.82	2.57	1.92	1.81	.86	.58	19.79
	Kenton	38	34.8	78.9	108	−20	38	Apr. 22	Oct. 19	180	38	.32	.66	.83	1.60	2.40	2.06	2.37	2.37	1.75	1.27	.55	.55	16.73
Cleveland	Norman	36	38.8	82.0	116	−17	36	Apr. 3	Nov. 2	213	39	1.31	1.26	2.44	3.45	5.02	3.79	2.40	2.74	3.45	3.35	2.25	1.56	33.02
Comanche	Chattanooga	33	41.2	82.9	114	−7	32	Apr. 5	Nov. 7	216	33	.99	1.04	1.67	2.59	4.11	3.66	2.47	2.37	2.99	3.15	1.56	1.40	28.00
	Lawton	36	40.3	82.5	115	−11	26	Mar. 31	Nov. 6	220	36	1.19	1.26	1.76	3.30	5.27	3.50	2.58	2.40	3.72	3.41	2.01	1.58	31.98
	Lawtonka Lake										8	1.32	1.36	1.69	3.91	4.19	3.35	2.28	3.48	2.94	4.00	1.88	1.71	32.11
	Wichita Mountains, W. L. R.	20	38.3	81.3	112	−16	32	Apr. 10	Oct. 30	203	30	.93	1.09	1.83	3.30	4.22	3.49	2.54	3.20	3.29	3.32	2.09	1.44	30.74
Cotton	Walters	18	40.9	84.0	114	−10	20	Mar. 30	Nov. 7	222	19	1.40	1.28	1.69	2.74	3.45	3.47	2.06	2.21	3.28	2.93	1.50	1.53	27.54
Craig	Vinita	35	36.3	80.8	117	−27	34	Apr. 7	Oct. 26	202	34	2.19	1.74	3.33	4.22	5.23	5.36	3.77	3.72	3.82	3.77	2.93	2.19	42.27
Creek	Bristow	18	39.1	82.9	115	−18	20	Mar. 30	Nov. 2	217	20	2.09	1.37	2.81	3.51	3.78	4.59	3.18	2.68	3.65	3.72	2.54	1.61	35.53

[1] The following counties for which no records are available are best represented by the stations indicated: Coal—Ada; Delaware—Spavinaw, Haskell—Poteau; Latimer—McAlester; Love—Ardmore; Major—Okeene; Marshall—Tishomingo; Nowata—Vinita; Seminole—Shawnee.

[2] Length of growing season between average dates of last killing frost in spring and first in fall.

OKLAHOMA—Continued

Climatic summary—Continued

County	Station	Temperature: Length of record	January average	July average	Maximum	Minimum	Killing frost average dates: Length of record	Last in spring	First in fall	Growing season	Average precipitation: Length of record	January	February	March	April	May	June	July	August	September	October	November	December	Annual
		Yr.	*°F.*	*°F.*	*°F.*	*°F.*	*Yr.*			*Days*	*Yr.*	*In.*	*In.*	*In.*	*In.*	*In.*	*In.*	*In.*	*In.*	*In.*	*In.*	*In.*	*In.*	*In.*
Custer	Arapaho	32	37.1	81.3	112	−16	29	Apr. 8	Oct. 29	204	31	0.82	0.86	1.49	3.27	4.44	3.60	3.08	2.43	2.93	2.95	1.67	0.98	28.52
	Weatherford	37	37.5	82.3	115	−14	37	Apr. 1	Nov. 3	216	38	.80	.98	1.71	2.96	4.60	3.75	2.54	2.45	3.08	2.66	1.78	1.14	28.45
Dewey	Camargo										24	.52	.77	1.46	2.58	3.46	3.67	2.12	2.49	2.95	2.27	1.45	.72	24.46
	Oakwood	25	36.1	81.0	118	−14	28	Apr. 8	Oct. 25	200	27	.92	.95	1.42	3.30	3.68	3.63	1.84	2.39	2.84	2.29	1.56	1.11	25.93
Ellis	Arnett	19	34.0	79.9	110	−20	10	Apr. 5	Oct. 27	205	26	.55	.69	1.36	2.25	3.57	3.30	2.40	2.65	2.36	1.85	1.71	.78	23.47
Garfield	Enid	34	36.5	82.7	118	−20	33	Mar. 30	Oct. 24	208	37	1.07	1.15	1.59	3.10	4.21	3.95	2.45	3.50	3.24	2.71	1.65	1.24	29.86
	Waukomis	40	36.6	82.3	115	−18	39	Apr. 6	Nov. 3	211	40	.97	1.14	1.57	3.35	4.11	4.03	2.70	3.01	3.13	2.95	1.76	1.25	29.97
Garvin	Pauls Valley	38	40.3	82.2	114	−14	36	do	Oct. 30	207	39	1.51	1.61	2.29	3.67	5.36	4.17	2.72	2.94	3.40	3.27	2.32	1.60	34.86
Grady	Chickasha	37	39.3	82.9	116	−11	36	Mar. 31	Nov. 2	216	36	1.12	1.08	2.14	3.35	5.12	3.48	2.04	2.48	3.53	3.02	1.81	1.41	30.58
Grant	Jefferson	36	34.5	82.3	118	−23	38	Apr. 9	Oct. 26	200	40	.90	1.06	1.63	2.74	4.17	3.99	2.64	2.99	3.44	2.58	1.69	1.18	29.01
Greer	Mangum	38	39.3	83.6	117	−17	38	Mar. 26	Nov. 6	225	40	.68	.98	1.54	2.88	4.64	3.29	2.18	2.48	3.00	2.70	1.44	1.00	26.81
Harmon	Hollis	16	39.9	84.9	117	−12	16	Mar. 29	Nov. 8	224	16	.61	.67	1.57	2.65	3.52	2.59	1.79	2.16	3.17	3.08	.86	1.10	23.77
Harper	Buffalo	24	35.6	82.8	115	−13	24	Apr. 10	Nov. 17	221	27	.55	.77	1.43	1.98	3.12	3.06	2.12	2.26	2.46	1.46	1.24	.81	21.26
Hughes	Calvin										34	2.16	2.04	2.74	4.09	5.45	4.29	2.64	3.56	3.63	3.51	2.49	2.10	38.70
	Holdenville	38	40.0	82.1	118	−12	38	Mar. 26	Nov. 6	225	38	2.26	1.82	2.99	3.74	5.35	3.91	2.70	3.15	4.02	3.35	2.47	2.07	37.83
Jackson	Altus	26	40.9	84.6	120	−9	26	Mar. 28	Nov. 9	226	26	.69	.84	1.67	2.66	3.36	3.02	2.10	2.39	2.82	3.11	1.29	1.29	25.24
	Eldorado	11	42.4	83.3	112	−8	12	Mar. 25	Oct. 29	218	14	.49	1.11	1.38	1.63	2.56	3.69	1.56	2.25	1.62	2.43	1.22	1.13	21.07
Jefferson	Waurika	29	41.7	83.8	115	−6	29	Mar. 26	Nov. 9	228	29	1.34	1.46	1.94	2.84	4.03	3.36	2.51	2.76	2.79	2.90	1.81	1.80	29.54
Johnston	Tishomingo	36	42.1	83.4	114	−12	36	Mar. 25	Nov. 5	225	36	2.17	2.09	2.67	3.93	5.06	4.42	3.16	2.46	3.25	3.76	2.21	2.23	37.41
Kay	Blackwell	15	34.7	81.3	109	−20	16	Apr. 6	Nov. 1	209	22	.99	.82	1.96	3.21	3.46	5.08	2.67	2.96	3.58	2.74	2.16	1.26	30.89
	Newkirk	38	35.0	82.2	115	−22	40	Apr. 3	Oct. 31	211	40	1.07	1.26	1.79	3.26	4.99	5.25	2.98	3.42	3.78	2.75	2.15	1.23	33.93
	White Eagle	14	36.8	81.2	111	−25	14	Apr. 7	Oct. 21	197	14	1.13	1.51	1.51	3.27	5.10	4.57	3.18	3.90	3.66	2.54	1.87	1.17	33.41
Kingfisher	Hennessey	37	36.9	82.8	116	−18	38	Apr. 5	Oct. 31	209	39	1.03	1.15	1.78	3.06	4.05	3.71	2.59	2.53	2.59	2.65	1.66	1.15	27.95
	Kingfisher	40	37.9	83.1	118	−20	40	do	Oct. 30	208	40	.97	1.19	2.04	3.10	4.41	3.85	2.67	2.79	2.97	2.92	1.92	1.22	30.05
Kiowa	Hobart	36	39.2	83.1	117	−11	36	Apr. 8	Nov. 2	208	36	.80	.96	1.59	2.90	4.28	3.45	2.09	2.40	2.84	3.17	1.58	1.19	27.25
	Snyder	13	40.5	82.7	111	−9	12	Apr. 6	Nov. 3	211	14	.58	.93	1.30	2.70	4.21	3.54	2.25	2.10	3.14	3.07	2.39	1.51	27.72
Le Flore	Poteau	21	41.7	83.2	120	−16	21	Mar. 27	Nov. 1	219	25	3.11	2.50	3.20	4.29	5.57	4.26	2.82	2.92	3.67	3.57	3.07	3.13	42.11
Lincoln	Chandler	37	38.6	82.8	118	−20	37	Mar. 28	Oct. 31	217	37	1.44	1.24	2.47	3.63	4.95	3.90	2.56	3.04	3.30	3.04	2.20	1.54	33.31
	Meeker	40	38.2	82.2	119	−21	39	Mar. 31	Oct. 29	212	40	1.62	1.30	2.53	3.59	5.17	4.05	2.38	3.23	3.53	3.43	2.46	1.72	35.01
	Sac and Fox Agency	17	38.7	80.8	110	−20	17	Apr. 11	Oct. 26	198	20	1.07	1.33	2.01	3.66	5.44	3.78	2.82	3.40	3.09	2.74	2.00	1.52	32.86
Logan	Guthrie	40	38.8	82.4	116	−24	38	Apr. 2	Oct. 30	211	39	1.10	1.22	2.25	3.54	4.80	3.65	2.50	2.98	3.55	3.02	2.26	1.47	32.34
McClain	Purcell	12	38.8	83.4	114	−11	12	Mar. 30	Nov. 7	222	12	1.93	2.23	2.67	2.92	4.57	3.73	2.47	3.12	4.05	3.35	1.83	2.23	35.10
McCurtain	Broken Bow										8	3.30	2.86	3.52	6.22	4.69	5.89	3.78	2.70	3.97	3.69	3.45	2.09	46.16
	Idabel	18	44.7	82.4	114	−6	17	Mar. 15	Nov. 10	240	18	4.18	3.57	3.18	4.82	5.17	3.68	3.50	2.79	2.40	2.83	3.18	4.40	43.70
	Smithville	14	41.8	80.4	115	−6	24	Apr. 6	Oct. 30	207	16	4.63	3.18	3.71	5.03	5.50	4.46	3.88	2.76	4.74	4.33	3.79	4.67	50.68

McIntosh	Eufaula	23	40.6	82.1	116	−18	24	Mar. 29	do	215	24	3.20	2.49	3.00	4.46	4.96	3.80	2.75	3.87	3.90	3.68	2.80	2.53	41.44
Mayes	Pensacola										15	2.53	1.58	2.76	4.42	4.31	5.31	3.06	3.02	5.33	4.01	2.79	1.99	41.11
	Pryor	13	37.6	81.9	117	−21	12	Apr. 3	Oct. 31	211	13	2.73	1.90	2.76	4.06	5.06	5.72	3.61	3.32	5.47	3.81	3.03	2.07	43.54
	Spavinaw	14	37.6	82.6	114	−25	15	Mar. 31	do	214	16	2.94	1.76	2.88	4.35	4.81	5.52	3.41	3.11	5.37	4.92	2.97	2.35	44.39
Murray	Sulphur	22	41.2	83.0	114	−15	22	Mar. 29	Nov. 2	218	21	2.27	2.22	2.73	4.08	5.53	3.69	2.81	2.70	3.58	3.53	2.37	2.28	37.79
Muskogee	Fort Gibson										34	2.73	2.04	3.35	4.51	4.97	4.34	2.97	3.59	3.95	3.43	2.66	2.26	40.80
	Muskogee	40	38.3	82.1	118	−14	40	Mar. 26	Nov. 4	223	40	2.42	1.91	3.19	4.33	4.88	4.13	3.11	3.20	3.64	3.75	2.73	2.21	39.50
	Webbers Falls	37	39.8	82.5	115	−16	36	Apr. 1	Oct. 29	211	40	2.72	2.11	3.22	4.25	5.30	4.44	3.63	3.27	3.76	3.66	2.91	2.62	41.89
Noble	Billings										11	1.07	1.10	2.00	4.05	3.73	5.81	2.22	2.83	4.28	4.22	2.00	1.18	34.49
	Perry	38	37.3	82.4	117	−20	37	Apr. 9	Oct. 29	203	37	.99	1.28	1.85	3.68	5.09	4.07	2.57	3.64	3.52	3.05	2.26	1.45	33.45
Okfuskee	Okemah	26	39.2	82.6	115	−10	26	Mar. 30	Nov. 8	223	27	2.22	1.67	3.13	3.95	4.31	3.82	2.35	2.86	4.09	3.89	2.61	1.87	36.77
Oklahoma	Oklahoma City	40	37.6	81.6	113	−17	40	Mar. 28	Nov. 7	224	40	1.17	1.09	2.10	3.23	4.86	3.74	2.40	2.71	3.17	3.02	2.24	1.42	31.15
Okmulgee	Okmulgee	35	39.5	81.9	114	−20	34	Mar. 30	Oct. 28	212	35	2.14	1.60	2.94	4.14	4.66	4.33	2.92	2.93	3.53	3.64	2.22	1.92	36.97
Osage	Pawhuska	36	36.9	81.8	116	−26	38	Apr. 4	Oct. 26	205	38	1.37	1.46	2.54	3.79	4.84	4.97	3.51	3.48	3.77	3.21	2.23	1.41	36.58
Ottawa	Fairland	17	37.9	79.5	110	−23	16	Apr. 13	Oct. 23	193	18	1.94	1.86	3.05	4.08	5.53	5.28	3.80	4.06	3.57	3.19	2.51	1.90	40.77
	Miami	21	36.2	81.2	114	−25	20	Apr. 4	Oct. 28	207	21	2.15	1.56	3.31	4.26	4.36	5.54	3.48	3.36	4.36	4.35	3.08	2.12	41.93
	Wyandotte										27	1.66	1.49	3.05	4.35	5.08	5.38	3.27	3.24	4.36	3.58	2.98	1.92	40.36
Pawnee	Cleveland	36	37.7	82.5	114	−24	34	Apr. 4	Oct. 26	205	37	1.72	1.63	2.72	4.05	5.18	4.48	3.01	3.35	3.99	3.07	2.66	1.64	37.50
	Ralston										17	1.14	.99	1.84	3.48	4.10	4.88	2.60	3.20	3.66	2.63	2.69	1.41	32.62
Payne	Stillwater	40	36.6	80.7	115	−18	40	Mar. 31	Oct. 30	213	40	1.03	1.25	2.34	3.77	4.66	4.02	2.67	3.10	3.79	2.94	2.36	1.38	33.31
Pittsburg	Hartshorne	14	42.6	82.2	110	−6	14	Apr. 3	Oct. 27	207	15	1.81	2.70	3.24	3.56	6.23	4.30	3.47	3.44	3.11	3.67	2.53	2.28	40.34
	McAlester	36	41.4	82.7	116	−10	36	Mar. 27	Nov. 5	223	40	2.84	2.32	3.12	4.35	6.01	4.60	2.87	3.50	3.57	4.03	2.95	2.62	42.78
Pontotoc	Ada	30	40.4	82.9	116	−10	32	do	Nov. 6	224	32	2.19	1.75	2.77	3.81	5.49	4.31	2.49	3.29	3.50	3.61	2.48	2.13	37.82
Pottawatomie	Macomb	12	39.7	80.1	109	−17	8	Apr. 11	Oct. 27	199	12	.80	1.14	1.34	3.63	6.73	3.40	2.88	2.78	3.45	2.91	2.79	1.09	32.94
	Shawnee	37	39.1	82.2	116	−14	36	Apr. 1	Nov. 2	215	38	1.55	1.56	2.71	3.77	4.90	4.17	2.42	2.87	3.57	3.43	2.23	1.63	34.81
Pushmataha	Antlers	18	43.3	82.5	116	−9	21	Mar. 24	Nov. 6	227	20	4.12	3.04	3.80	5.18	6.42	3.49	3.17	2.69	4.23	4.81	3.45	4.02	48.42
	Tuskahoma										21	3.61	2.78	3.46	5.07	5.74	4.75	2.95	3.43	4.14	4.68	3.58	3.61	47.80
Rogers Mills	Cheyenne										16	.48	.69	1.35	3.21	3.63	2.75	1.92	2.52	3.10	2.59	1.37	.77	24.38
	Hammon	24	36.8	82.5	113	−13	25	Apr. 3	Oct. 29	209	25	.67	.70	1.62	2.78	3.65	3.37	1.90	2.11	3.35	2.61	1.34	1.01	25.11
	Rankin	15	36.4	78.0	110	−17	16	Apr. 8	Oct. 26	201	15	.63	1.04	1.06	2.61	3.30	3.31	2.93	2.40	2.79	2.29	1.73	1.02	25.11
Rogers	Claremore	24	36.8	82.0	116	−21	24	Apr. 1	Oct. 28	210	25	2.45	1.27	2.91	3.80	4.83	4.73	3.13	3.48	3.57	3.44	2.79	1.75	38.15
Sequoyah	Sallisaw	16	39.9	83.1	115	−19	18	Mar. 31	Nov. 3	217	18	3.27	2.45	2.93	4.35	5.11	4.31	2.72	3.26	3.81	4.27	2.72	2.59	41.79
Stephens	Marlow	38	40.2	82.3	114	−11	38	Mar. 30	Nov. 5	220	38	1.37	1.41	2.23	3.75	5.05	3.93	2.22	2.46	3.30	3.23	2.08	1.68	32.71
Texas	Goodwell	28	34.4	79.7	109	−19	28	Apr. 17	Oct. 25	191	28	.27	.59	.79	1.33	2.49	2.12	2.29	2.29	1.92	1.21	.65	.54	16.49
	Hooker	33	33.3	79.6	112	−20	32	Apr. 21	Oct. 21	183	33	.24	.72	.71	1.36	2.76	2.43	2.26	2.22	2.02	1.51	.75	.51	17.49
Tillman	Frederick	33	41.3	83.8	114	−8	30	Mar. 30	Nov. 9	224	33	1.03	1.14	1.85	2.76	4.04	3.26	2.29	1.98	3.02	3.06	1.68	1.45	27.56
Tulsa	Broken Arrow	13	36.2	80.2	107	−12	13	Mar. 28	Nov. 4	221	13	2.12	1.31	3.06	4.82	4.07	4.32	3.25	3.21	3.70	4.24	2.73	1.84	38.67
	Tulsa	34	38.1	82.8	115	−16	32	Mar. 25	Nov. 1	221	40	1.86	1.62	2.94	4.05	5.02	4.76	3.04	3.37	3.71	3.55	2.61	1.85	38.38
Wagoner	Okay										27	2.64	1.93	3.19	4.27	4.47	4.28	2.78	3.38	4.00	3.95	3.05	2.17	40.11
	Wagoner	18	37.7	81.5	117	−23	21	Apr. 11	Oct. 25	197	22	2.40	2.01	2.99	4.14	5.91	3.46	3.92	2.52	3.64	2.93	2.11	1.86	37.79
Washington	Bartlesville	29	36.5	82.4	114	−25	29	Mar. 30	Oct. 30	214	31	1.52	1.61	2.63	3.92	4.63	4.51	3.08	2.84	4.02	3.18	2.21	1.71	35.86
Washita	Cloud Chief	35	38.6	83.0	119	−14	36	Apr. 6	Nov. 1	209	37	.65	1.05	1.84	2.98	4.46	3.40	2.51	2.30	3.11	2.48	1.70	1.19	27.67
Woods	Alva	34	35.2	82.2	120	−16	34	Apr. 7	do	208	33	.86	1.14	1.58	2.59	4.27	3.73	2.62	3.36	3.12	2.26	1.84	1.02	28.39
	Dacoma	12	36.1	79.3	109	−19	12	Apr. 18	Oct. 29	194	12	.75	.84	1.42	3.01	4.90	4.09	3.51	2.21	1.93	2.43	1.84	.76	27.69
Woodward	Mutual	31	36.0	82.4	116	−17	30	Apr. 7	Oct. 31	207	31	.53	.85	1.41	2.47	3.22	3.23	1.73	2.55	2.96	2.18	1.52	.84	23.49
	Supply										18	.43	.66	1.04	1.93	3.04	2.71	2.00	2.06	2.02	1.89	1.82	.61	20.21
	Woodward	34	36.0	82.1	115	−18	33	Apr. 12	Oct. 27	198	40	.59	1.05	1.40	2.42	3.64	3.43	2.64	2.60	2.80	2.17	1.61	.79	25.14

OKLAHOMA—Continued

Precipitation and temperature—State unit values

[This tabulation gives the mean annual, mean monthly, and average seasonal precipitation, 1886–1938, and the mean annual temperatures, 1902–38, for Oklahoma]

Precipitation		Precipitation		Precipitation		Precipitation		Temperature		Temperature	
Year	Mean	Year	Mean	Year	Mean	Month	Mean	Year	Mean	Year	Mean
	In.		*In.*		*In.*		*In.*		*°F.*		*°F.*
1886	16.61	1907	33.85	1928	36.48	May	4.56	1902	60.1	1921	62.9
1887	24.14	1908	47.73	1929	35.39	June	3.69	1903	58.6	1922	61.6
1888	27.88	1909	27.01	1930	30.70	July	2.82	1904	60.1	1923	60.9
1889	31.01	1910	18.92	1931	31.59	August	3.00	1905	58.7	1924	59.2
1890	39.57	1911	28.93	1932	33.99	September	3.13	1906	58.9	1925	61.7
1891	29.66	1912	28.40	1933	30.56	October	2.90	1907	60.8	1926	60.1
1892	39.57	1913	33.05	1934	27.46	November	1.98	1908	60.5	1927	61.4
1893	25.49	1914	25.97	1935	36.71	December	1.64	1909	60.7	1928	60.8
1894	25.57	1915	45.42	1936	22.69			1910	61.3	1929	59.4
1895	35.08	1916	29.18	1937	28.21	Annual	31.94	1911	61.9	1930	61.0
1896	23.78	1917	22.39	1938	33.21			1912	58.4	1931	62.1
1897	30.61	1918	33.56					1913	59.8	1932	60.6
1898	39.45	1919	34.41	Month	Mean	Season	Average	1914	60.6	1933	63.0
1899	36.07	1920	36.35					1915	59.2	1934	63.0
1900	32.51	1921	30.02					1916	60.3	1935	60.8
1901	22.78	1922	33.89					1917	58.8	1936	61.8
1902	40.54	1923	44.98		*In.*		*In.*	1918	60.2	1937	60.2
1903	29.41	1924	27.86	January	1.42	Winter	4.41	1919	59.4	1938	62.8
1904	29.80	1925	28.31	February	1.35	Spring	10.01	1920	59.6		
1905	39.76	1926	39.04	March	2.15	Summer	9.51				
1906	36.88	1927	39.55	April	3.30	Fall	8.01				

Dates of last killing frost in spring and first in fall, with length of growing season

Year	Kenton			Alva			Mangum			Oklahoma City			Muskogee			Durant		
	Last in spring	First in fall	Growing season [1]	Last in spring	First in fall	Growing season [1]	Last in spring	First in fall	Growing season [1]	Last in spring	First in fall	Growing season [1]	Last in spring	First in fall	Growing season [1]	Last in spring	First in fall	Growing season [1]
			Days			*Days*			*Days*			*Days*			*Days*			*Days*
1899							Apr. 3	Nov. 2	213	Apr. 9	Nov. 3	208		Nov. 2				
1900							Apr. 12	Nov. 11	213	Mar. 31	Nov. 12	226	Mar. 31	Nov. 9	223			
1901	May 3	Oct. 13	163							Apr. 18	Nov. 4	200	Apr. 18	Oct. 14	179			

1902	Apr. 23	Oct. 28	188	----	----	----	Mar. 5	Nov. 17	257	Mar. 30	Nov. 17	232	Mar. 31	Nov. 26	240	Mar. 18	Nov. 4	231
1903	Apr. 30	Oct. 16	169	----	----	----	Mar. 2	Nov. 16	259	Apr. 30	Nov. 16	200	Apr. 5	Nov. 17	226	May 1	Nov. 17	200
1904	Apr. 24	Oct. 19	178	----	----	----	Mar. 27	Nov. 11	229	Mar. 27	Oct. 28	215	Mar. 28	Nov. 11	228	Mar. 27	Nov. 11	229
1905	Apr. 21	Oct. 11	173	Apr. 5	Nov. 1	210	----	Oct. 20	----	Feb. 21	Oct. 20	241	Feb. 28	Nov. 1	246	Mar. 10	Nov. 30	265
1906	Apr. 14	Oct. 21	190	Mar. 20	Oct. 30	224	Mar. 31	Nov. 14	228	Mar. 20	Oct. 30	224	Mar. 2	Oct. 10	204	Mar. 21	Nov. 13	237
1907	May 3	Oct. 8	158	May 15	Nov. 10	179	Mar. 14	Nov. 12	243	Apr. 30	Nov. 12	196	Feb. 19	Nov. 11	265	Feb. 15	Nov. 12	270
1908	Apr. 29	Oct. 23	177	May 7	Oct. 25	171	Feb. 21	Oct. 24	246	Mar. 10	Oct. 24	228	Feb. 27	Oct. 24	240	Feb. 17	Nov. 14	271
1909	May 2	do	174	May 1	----	----	----	Nov. 16	----	Apr. 23	Nov. 17	208	Mar. 30	Nov. 17	232	Apr. 13	Nov. 17	218
1910	Apr. 6	Oct. 7	184	Mar. 12	Oct. 21	223	Mar. 31	Oct. 21	204	Mar. 11	Oct. 21	224	Mar. 11	Oct. 29	232	Feb. 25	Oct. 29	246
1911	Apr. 15	Oct. 17	185	Mar. 25	Oct. 30	219	Mar. 27	Nov. 2	220	Mar. 27	Nov. 2	220	Mar. 16	Nov. 2	231	Mar. 3	Nov. 12	254
1912	Apr. 22	Sept. 27	158	Mar. 26	Nov. 2	221	Mar. 26	Oct. 22	210	Mar. 25	Nov. 1	221	Mar. 25	do	222	Mar. 25	Nov. 2	222
1913	Apr. 14	Oct. 11	180	Mar. 28	Oct. 27	213	Mar. 29	Oct. 27	212	Mar. 28	Oct. 27	213	Mar. 28	Oct. 29	215	Mar. 28	Oct. 27	213
1914	Apr. 13	Oct. 14	184	Apr. 12	do	198	Apr. 12	do	198	Apr. 12	do	198	Apr. 9	Oct. 27	201	Apr. 9	Oct. 28	202
1915	May 7	Oct. 7	153	Apr. 3	Nov. 14	225	Apr. 1	Nov. 15	228	Apr. 3	Nov. 15	226	Apr. 3	Nov. 15	226	Apr. 3	Nov. 15	226
1916	May 3	Oct. 20	170	Apr. 28	Oct. 20	175	Apr. 8	Oct. 20	195	Apr. 9	Oct. 20	194	Apr. 9	Oct. 20	194	Mar. 4	Oct. 20	230
1917	May 8	Oct. 19	164	May 8	Oct. 12	157	Apr. 5	Oct. 19	197	Mar. 27	Oct. 19	206	Mar. 27	Oct. 12	199	Mar. 8	Oct. 19	225
1918	Apr. 25	Oct. 31	189	Apr. 11	Nov. 22	225	Mar. 16	Nov. 23	252	Mar. 16	Nov. 22	251	Apr. 21	Nov. 24	217	Mar. 10	Nov. 19	254
1919	Apr. 17	Oct. 21	187	Mar. 27	Oct. 28	215	Mar. 6	Nov. 12	251	Mar. 9	Nov. 12	248	Mar. 11	Nov. 12	246	Mar. 9	Nov. 12	248
1920	Apr. 27	Oct. 25	181	Apr. 13	Nov. 2	203	Apr. 5	Nov. 2	211	Apr. 5	Nov. 11	220	Apr. 5	Nov. 3	212	Apr. 5	do	221
1921	May 2	Nov. 1	183	Apr. 17	Nov. 9	206	Apr. 17	Nov. 10	207	Apr. 17	Nov. 10	207	Apr. 17	Nov. 10	207	Apr. 1	Nov. 10	223
1922	Apr. 19	Oct. 18	182	Mar. 11	Oct. 18	221	Mar. 11	Nov. 13	247	Mar. 11	Nov. 14	248	Mar. 7	Oct. 18	225	Mar. 11	Nov. 26	260
1923	Apr. 5	Oct. 19	197	Apr. 5	Oct. 30	208	Apr. 5	Nov. 6	215	Mar. 23	Oct. 31	222	Mar. 23	Oct. 31	222	Mar. 20	Nov. 30	255
1924	May 15	Oct. 31	169	Apr. 1	Oct. 24	206	Apr. 1	Nov. 25	238	Mar. 21	Nov. 24	248	Apr. 1	Nov. 24	237	Apr. 1	Nov. 19	232
1925	Apr. 4	Oct. 18	197	Mar. 19	Oct. 19	214	Mar. 19	Oct. 19	214	Mar. 15	Oct. 25	224	Mar. 15	Oct. 20	219	Mar. 15	Oct. 31	230
1926	Apr. 15	Oct. 24	192	Apr. 15	Nov. 2	201	Apr. 3	Nov. 2	213	Apr. 3	Nov. 9	220	Mar. 31	Nov. 4	218	Mar. 31	Nov. 18	232
1927	Apr. 21	Oct. 12	174	Apr. 21	Nov. 6	199	Mar. 25	Nov. 12	232	Mar. 21	Nov. 12	236	Mar. 21	Nov. 17	241	Mar. 22	Nov. 17	240
1928	Apr. 23	Oct. 22	182	Apr. 15	Nov. 3	202	----	Nov. 2	----	Mar. 17	Nov. 3	231	Apr. 15	Nov. 4	203	Apr. 15	Nov. 3	202
1929	Apr. 28	Oct. 21	176	Mar. 17	Nov. 4	232	Mar. 17	Oct. 24	221	Mar. 1	Nov. 19	263	Mar. 17	Nov. 20	248	Feb. 26	Nov. 5	252
1930	Apr. 4	Oct. 27	206	Mar. 30	Oct. 31	215	Mar. 30	Nov. 6	221	Mar. 28	Nov. 6	223	Mar. 30	Oct. 31	215	Mar. 30	Nov. 25	240
1931	May 22	do	158	Apr. 5	do	209	Mar. 31	Nov. 22	236	Mar. 29	Nov. 25	241	Mar. 28	Nov. 1	218	Mar. 29	Dec. 4	250
1932	Apr. 28	Oct. 5	160	Mar. 23	Oct. 30	221	Mar. 22	Nov. 9	232	Mar. 22	Nov. 11	234	Mar. 22	Nov. 11	234	Mar. 14	Nov. 11	242
1933	Apr. 20	Oct. 22	185	Apr. 15	Nov. 6	205	Mar. 23	----	----	Mar. 21	Nov. 8	232	Mar. 21	Nov. 8	232	Mar. 21	Nov. 8	232
1934	Apr. 5	Oct. 30	208	Mar. 31	Nov. 23	237	Mar. 19	Nov. 30	256	Mar. 19	Dec. 1	257	Mar. 27	Nov. 23	241	Mar. 19	Dec. 1	257
1935	Apr. 12	Oct. 25	196	Mar. 17	Nov. 6	234	Mar. 7	Nov. 5	243	Mar. 7	Nov. 5	243	Mar. 17	Nov. 5	233	Mar. 7	Dec. 2	270
1936	Apr. 10	Oct. 8	181	Apr. 7	Oct. 26	202	Apr. 7	Oct. 27	203	Apr. 6	Oct. 27	204	Apr. 7	Nov. 3	210	Apr. 7	Nov. 4	211
1937	Apr. 25	Nov. 2	191	Apr. 9	Nov. 16	221	Apr. 5	Nov. 16	225	Mar. 31	Nov. 16	230	Mar. 31	Oct. 23	206	Mar. 31	Oct. 23	206
1938	Apr. 10	Oct. 20	193	do	Oct. 23	197	Apr. 9	Nov. 7	212	Apr. 9	Nov. 7	212	Mar. 7	do	230	Apr. 9	Oct. 24	198
Mean	Apr. 22	Oct. 19	180	Apr. 7	Nov. 1	208	Mar. 26	Nov. 6	225	Mar. 28	do	224	Mar. 26	Nov. 4	223	Mar. 22	Nov. 11	234
Extremes	Apr. 4[2]	Sept. 27[4]	[6] 153	Mar. 11[2]	Oct. 12[4]	[6] 157	Feb. 21[2]	Oct. 19[4]	[6] 195	Feb. 21[2]	Oct 19[4]	[6] 194	Feb. 19[2]	Oct 10[4]	[6] 179	Feb. 15[2]	Oct 19[4]	[6] 198
	May 22[3]	Nov. 2[5]	[7] 208	May 15[3]	Nov. 23[5]	[7] 237	Apr. 17[3]	Nov. 30[5]	[7] 259	Apr. 30[3]	Dec. 1[5]	[7] 257	Apr. 21[3]	Nov. 26[5]	[7] 265	May 1[3]	Dec. 4[5]	[7] 271

[1] Number of days between last killing frost in spring and first in fall.
[2] Earliest date in spring.
[3] Latest date in spring.
[4] Earliest date in fall.
[5] Latest date in fall.
[6] Shortest growing season.
[7] Longest growing season.

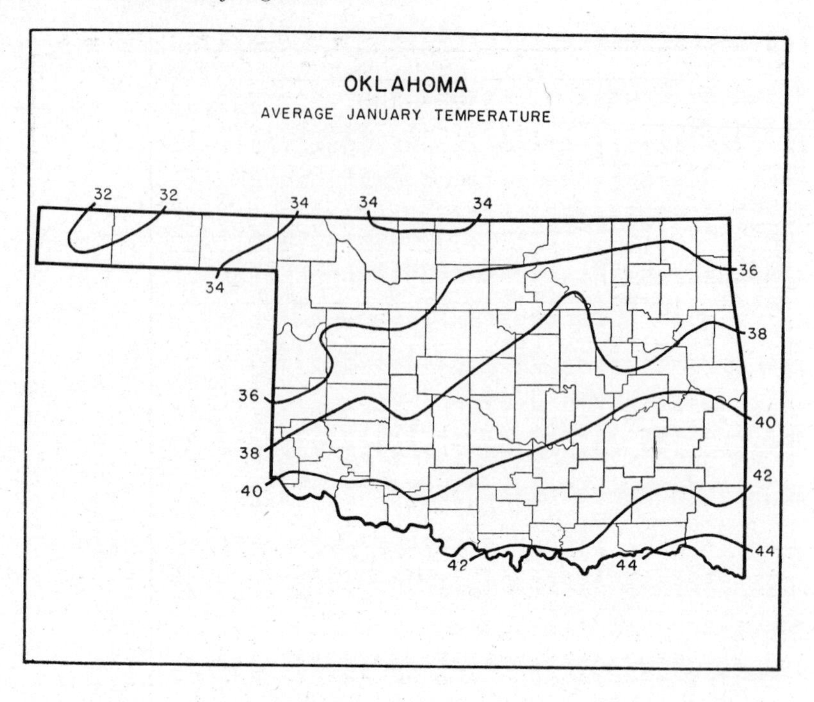
OKLAHOMA
AVERAGE JANUARY TEMPERATURE
32
32
34
34
34
34
36
36
38
38
40
40
42
42
44
44

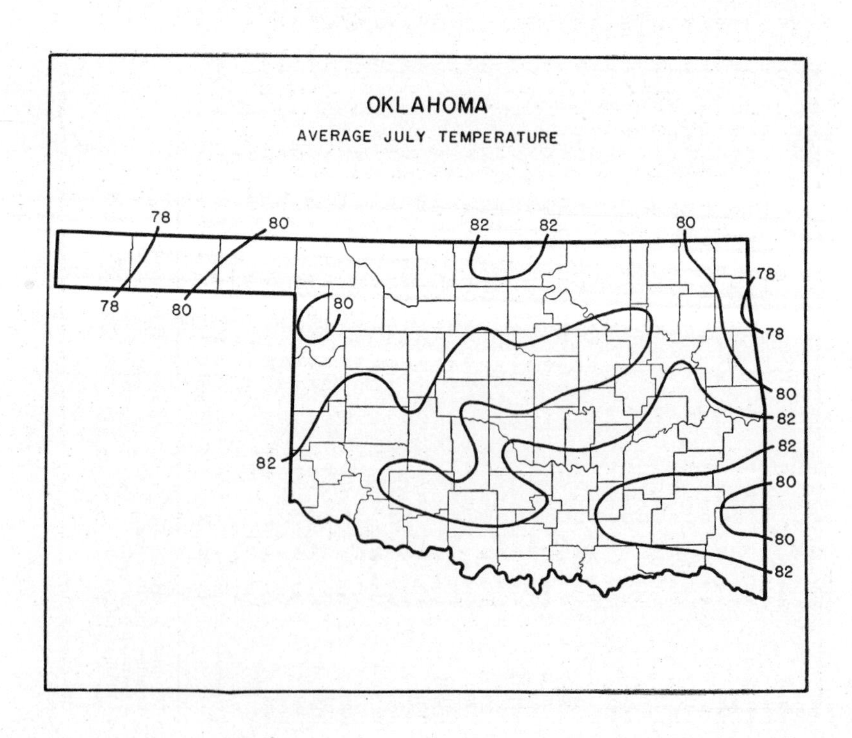
OKLAHOMA
AVERAGE JULY TEMPERATURE
78
78
80
80
80
82
82
80
78
78
80
82
82
82
80
80
82

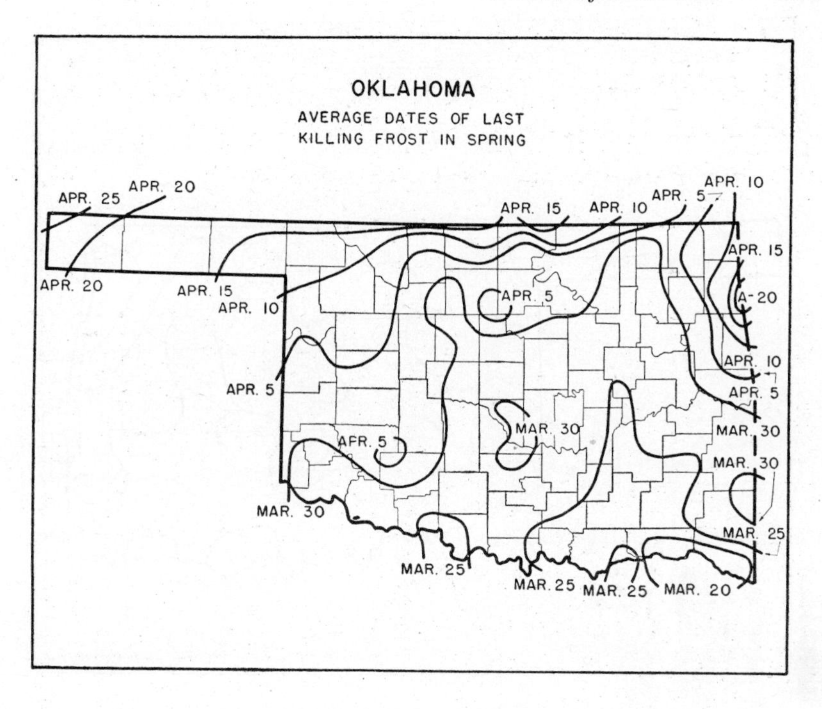
OKLAHOMA
AVERAGE DATES OF LAST
KILLING FROST IN SPRING
APR. 25
APR. 20
APR. 20
APR. 15
APR. 10
APR. 5
APR. 15
APR. 10
APR. 5
APR. 10
APR. 15
A-20
APR. 5
APR. 10
APR. 5
APR. 5
MAR. 30
MAR. 30
MAR. 30
MAR. 30
MAR. 25
MAR. 25
MAR. 25
MAR. 25
MAR. 20

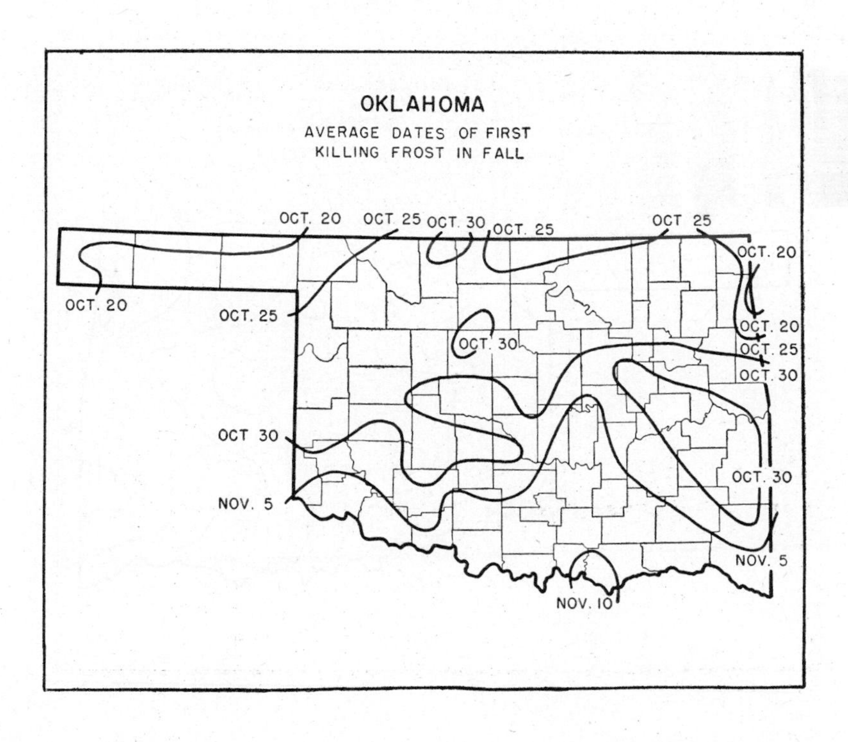
OKLAHOMA
AVERAGE DATES OF FIRST
KILLING FROST IN FALL
OCT. 20
OCT 25
OCT. 30
OCT. 25
OCT 25
OCT. 20
OCT. 20
OCT. 25
OCT. 30
OCT. 20
OCT. 25
OCT. 30
OCT 30
OCT. 30
NOV. 5
NOV. 5
NOV. 10

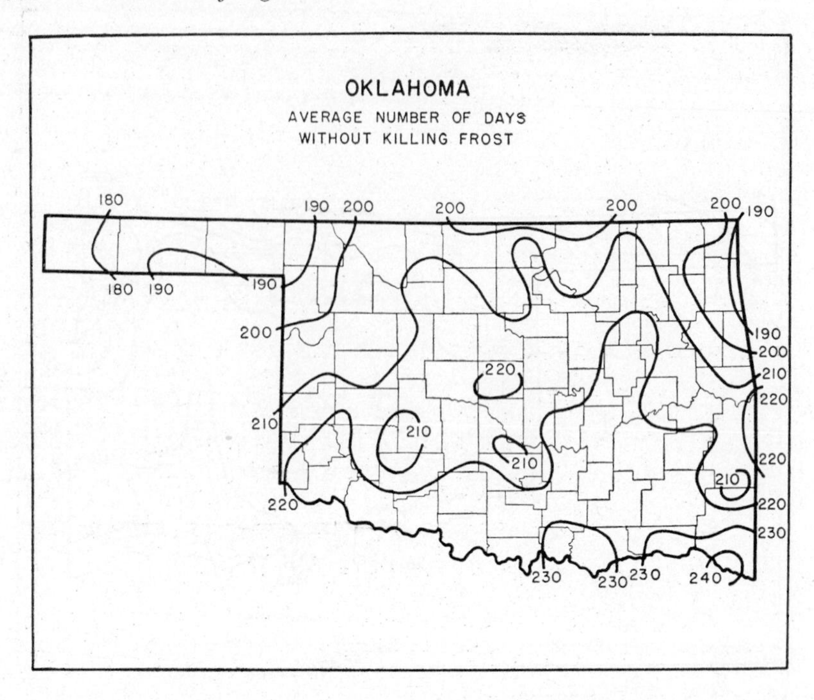
OKLAHOMA
AVERAGE NUMBER OF DAYS
WITHOUT KILLING FROST
180
190
200
210
220
230
240

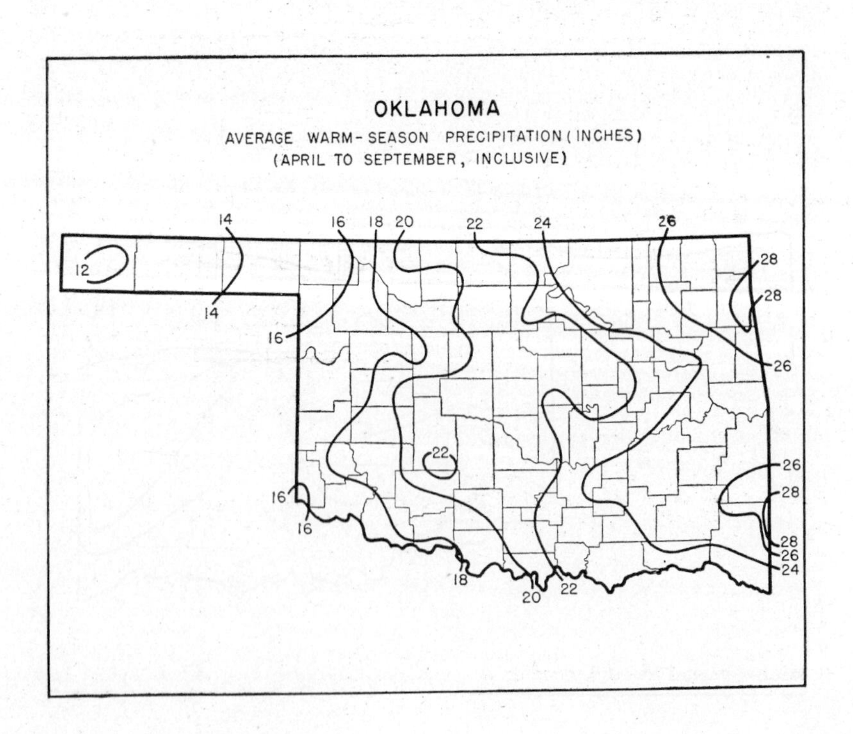
OKLAHOMA
AVERAGE WARM-SEASON PRECIPITATION (INCHES)
(APRIL TO SEPTEMBER, INCLUSIVE)
12
14
16
18
20
22
24
26
28

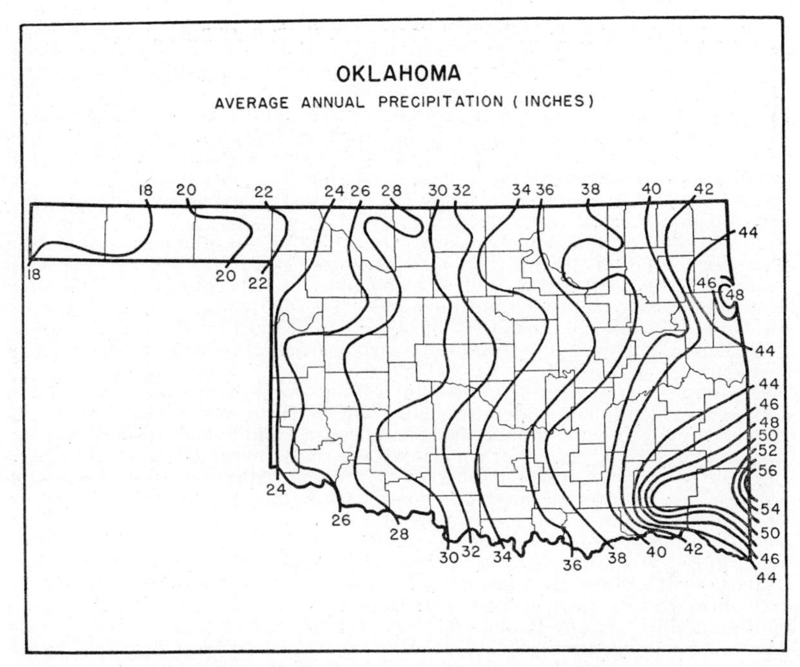

SUPPLEMENTARY CLIMATIC NOTES FOR OKLAHOMA

Oklahoma, situated in the southern part of the Great Plains, comprises an area of approximately 70,000 square miles. The highest point in the State, about 4,500 feet above sea level, is the Black Mesa, in the northwestern corner of Cimarron County. From this point the altitude decreases eastward and southward to a minimum level of somewhat less than 350 feet in the extreme southeastern corner of the State. There are elevated regions, ranging from 200 to 1,200 feet higher than the surrounding plains, in the Wichita, Kiamichi, Ouachita, and Arbuckle Mountains and in the extension of the Ozarks. Considerable timber is found in the mountain districts, especially in the Ouachita Mountains.

Most of the State is well watered. It is drained by the Cimarron, Canadian, North Canadian, Washita, Arkansas, and Red Rivers. The streams in the western and central parts do not generally carry a large volume of water, and most of them have wide sandy beds; during very dry periods, nearly all of the water sinks beneath the surface sands. The streams are, however, subject to sudden rises, occasionally amounting to 10 feet or more in the course of a few hours, though such floods are usually of short duration.

The soil of the bottom lands is very fertile and extremely productive, while that of the uplands compares favorably with other soils similarly located in the Plains; the rougher sections of the eastern mountain areas cannot be successfully cultivated, however.

Agriculture is practically the sole industry of the western half of the State and is practiced extensively in other sections. Corn, cotton, oats, alfalfa, grain sorghums, and winter wheat are grown. Broomcorn of exceptionally fine quality is produced in large quantities in two widely separated areas, one in the northwestern part, where the dwarf variety is grown, and the other, in the Lindsay area, slightly south of the center of the State, where standard broomcorn is produced. Oklahoma normally grows about half the Nation's broomcorn.

The climate of Oklahoma is of the continental type, with pronounced seasonal and geographic ranges in both temperature and precipitation. The central and western parts of the State are, in the main, vast open plains, with considerably greater elevation than the eastern part and somewhat less subjected to the warm moist winds from the Gulf of Mexico. Western sections of the State, therefore, are cooler and drier; in the east showers are more frequent because of the moister atmosphere and the influence of the hilly, wooded terrain. In late spring eastern

Oklahoma and parts of the adjoining States receive, on an average, more rainfall than any other part of the country east of the Rocky Mountains. In general, the annual range in temperature is marked, the mean for midsummer being about 45° F. higher than that for midwinter.

The annual precipitation varies from more than 50 inches in the northeastern part of McCurtain County, in the extreme southeastern part of the State, to only slightly more than 17 in Texas and Cimarron Counties, both in the Panhandle. Snowfall also varies greatly, the averages ranging from less than 3 inches in the extreme southeastern section to more than 20 in the extreme western part of Cimarron County.

The mean annual temperatures range from 63.8° F. at Idabel, in the extreme southeastern corner of the State, to 53.6° at Boise City, in the western part of the Panhandle. Temperatures of 100° or higher may be expected in Oklahoma from June to September, inclusive, and have been recorded as early as March and as late as October, while maxima of 90° or higher are of record in January, February, and November. The summers are long with occasional periods of very high day temperatures.

High summer temperatures almost invariably occur with clear skies and are usually attended by dry, moderate winds from south to west. Occasionally, hot winds accompany the high temperatures and cause rapid evaporation of moisture. When these conditions persist for considerable periods, severe droughts often follow.

Clear skies and dry atmosphere facilitate rapid radiation, and the summer nights are nearly always agreeably cool. Minimum temperatures of zero or lower have been reported at one or more stations in all except 3 of the 48 winters of record. In general the winters are comparatively mild and of short duration.

While killing frosts or freezing temperatures have occurred as late as May 1 in all parts of the State, they are not to be expected in the southern section later than the first week in April, and not later than April 15 to 20 in the north, exclusive of the Panhandle. In the Panhandle frost may be expected during the last week of April and has occurred as late as May 15. The average dates of the first killing frost in fall range from about October 20 in the western part of the Panhandle to as late as the second week in November in the extreme southeast.

The average length of the growing season varies from 180 days in the western part of Cimarron County to 240 days in the extreme southeast.

Oklahoma has wide variations in precipitation, and heavy to almost torrential rains occasionally occur; 24-hour falls of more than 10 inches are of record at a number of stations in scattered localities. On an average, 75 percent of the annual precipitation occurs during the growing season, March to October, inclusive. Rains are most general and abundant during the spring and early summer, while in late summer and early fall they are more local and often uncertain in the western part of the State. However, general rains frequently set in again during September and October, thus conditioning the soil for the seeding and germination of winter grains.

Snowfall varies considerably and is of rather infrequent occurrence in the southeastern part of the State. Snow has been recorded in the Panhandle in all months except July and August, but other sections have been free from snow from May to September, inclusive, and snow has seldom fallen outside the Panhandle during April and September.

Droughts of several weeks' duration, or even longer, sometimes are destructive to crops. Duststorms occur quite frequently in the central and western parts of the State, being most severe in the northwest. In the Panhandle counties, visibility is occasionally reduced almost to zero by blowing dust. Except in the Panhandle and extreme northwestern parts, damage from duststorms is generally slight.

The prevailing wind direction for the State is southerly, although in December, January, and February northerly winds predominate. Winds are generally light in the southeastern part of the State and relatively high in the north and west. The average hourly velocity at Oklahoma City is 11.4 miles an hour, while the monthly averages vary from slightly more than 9 miles an hour in August to nearly 14 miles in March and April. The highest wind velocity for a 5-minute period at Oklahoma City was 57 miles an hour.

The average annual number of clear days is 195, partly cloudy 90, and cloudy 80. Sunshine is abundant, averaging about 66 percent of the possible amount.

HARRY F. WAHLGREN, *Meteorologist and Climatic Section Director for Oklahoma, Weather Bureau, Oklahoma City.*

OREGON

Climatic summary

County	Station	Temperature					Killing frost average dates				Average precipitation													
		Length of record	January average	July average	Maximum	Minimum	Length of record	Last in spring	First in fall	Growing season [1]	Length of record	January	February	March	April	May	June	July	August	September	October	November	December	Annual
		Yr.	*°F.*	*°F.*	*°F.*	*°F.*	*Yr.*			*Days*	*Yr.*	*In.*	*In.*	*In.*	*In.*	*In.*	*In.*	*In.*	*In.*	*In.*	*In.*	*In.*	*In.*	*In.*
Baker	Baker	39	24.9	65.6	104	−24	39	May 12	Oct. 3	144	40	1.09	0.98	0.99	0.97	1.12	1.13	0.44	0.50	0.65	0.72	0.96	1.14	10.69
	Cornucopia										25	7.08	5.65	4.46	3.43	2.72	2.20	.68	.87	1.64	2.74	6.31	6.56	44.34
	Huntington	26	27.5	78.6	110	−17	23	Apr. 16	Oct. 15	182	27	1.89	1.61	1.39	.92	.77	.89	.27	.28	.38	.79	1.40	1.49	12.08
	Richland	17	27.9	71.2	110	−22	18	May 21	Sept. 28	130	19	1.13	.99	.70	.79	1.17	.80	.33	.47	.64	.83	1.03	1.28	10.16
	Rock Creek										19	2.58	1.93	1.90	1.52	1.23	1.70	.44	.63	.70	1.27	1.85	2.53	18.28
	Sparta	23	24.6	67.4	106	−22	21	May 8	Oct. 14	159	25	3.02	2.26	1.71	1.10	1.51	1.32	.60	.65	.84	1.32	2.40	3.25	19.98
Benton	Alpine-Monroe	14	39.8	65.2	102	−1	14	Apr. 21	Nov. 4	197	15	8.53	6.96	5.21	2.59	2.01	1.27	.33	.60	1.76	3.32	8.90	8.01	49.49
	Corvallis	40	39.3	65.9	106	−14	38	Apr. 15	Oct. 23	191	40	6.63	5.24	4.21	2.46	1.73	1.14	.32	.43	1.59	2.90	6.51	6.90	40.06
	Summit										22	10.42	7.89	7.48	4.24	2.96	1.74	.47	.60	2.31	4.47	9.82	10.00	62.40
Clackamas	Cazadero	30	39.4	65.6	109	−6	21	Apr. 11	Oct. 22	194	30	7.81	6.01	6.27	4.51	3.41	2.46	.71	.87	2.67	4.41	8.02	8.00	55.15
	Government Camp	39	30.3	56.0	96	−16					23	12.28	9.67	9.53	5.89	5.05	3.29	1.52	1.93	4.29	6.81	12.49	12.06	84.81
	Headworks	33	36.9	65.0	110	−2	32	Apr. 11	Nov. 1	204	40	10.77	8.10	8.69	6.08	5.12	3.72	1.25	1.50	4.07	6.15	10.95	11.25	77.65
	Intake										18	7.60	6.03	5.86	3.78	2.83	2.17	.46	.62	2.32	4.19	7.43	8.27	51.56
	Miramonte Farm	25	38.4	65.4	101	−11	23	Apr. 23	Nov. 11	202	24	6.51	4.96	4.35	2.98	2.46	1.72	.66	.62	2.41	3.00	6.96	6.10	42.73
	Oregon City										11	7.60	5.50	5.83	3.72	2.22	1.97	.69	.98	2.53	3.43	6.98	7.25	48.70
	Stafford	20	39.1	66.2	106	0	21	Apr. 10	Oct. 31	204	20	7.65	5.93	4.76	3.38	2.77	1.95	.72	.87	2.39	3.59	7.96	6.70	48.67
	Three Links	14	36.0	65.9	107	3	12	Apr. 15	Oct. 30	198	14	8.57	6.52	7.46	4.90	3.76	2.47	.30	.71	2.52	4.81	8.26	10.08	60.36
	Zigzag										26	11.02	7.68	8.51	6.26	4.81	3.46	1.08	1.23	3.77	6.09	11.79	10.47	76.17
Clatsop	Astoria	40	40.3	60.9	97	10	28	Mar. 8	Dec. 6	273	40	12.43	9.15	8.38	4.97	3.72	2.83	1.09	1.24	3.20	6.31	11.20	12.94	77.46
	Jewell	11	37.0	62.2	103	−4					12	10.74	8.69	7.86	4.90	3.27	1.69	.40	1.12	3.42	6.20	9.84	12.14	70.27
Columbia	Doraville	35	36.3	62.1	101	−5	29	Apr. 18	Nov. 1	197	34	7.33	5.29	5.10	3.24	2.48	1.86	.81	.94	2.17	3.82	7.26	8.09	48.39
Coos	Bandon										2	8.09	6.76	6.39	4.82	4.74	1.98	.11	1.22	1.24	8.42	10.62	9.87	64.26
	Coquille River Light										40	8.64	6.72	6.27	3.78	2.46	1.44	.31	.33	1.95	3.67	8.12	7.86	51.55
	McKinley	32	43.3	61.0	107	6	22	Apr. 26	Oct. 30	187	30	11.46	8.88	8.58	4.78	3.28	1.62	.37	.38	2.23	4.51	9.60	10.03	65.72
	Marshfield	37	44.4	59.2	100	16	29	Apr. 17	Oct. 31	197	37	10.86	8.74	7.81	4.73	3.11	1.74	.41	.36	2.21	4.25	9.62	1.00	54.84
Crook	Bear Creek										23	1.29	1.10	.73	.88	1.02	1.11	.49	.24	.70	.76	1.19	1.34	10.85
	Maury										11	1.56	1.57	.79	1.04	1.35	1.38	.63	.30	.93	.92	2.13	1.49	14.09
	Ochoco										14	1.98	1.74	1.17	1.47	1.60	1.38	.80	.37	.99	1.45	2.73	1.51	17.19
	Prineville	40	31.6	65.2	119	−35	28	May 29	Sept. 18	112	36	.94	.85	.62	.78	.93	.85	.32	.26	.61	.73	1.02	.93	8.84
Curry	Brookings	26	46.3	58.2	100	17	14	Mar. 15	Dec. 9	269	26	11.84	8.88	9.07	6.07	3.24	2.73	.52	.45	2.87	5.50	11.15	11.31	73.63
	Gold Beach	22	46.0	57.7	98	20	14	Mar. 31	Nov. 24	238	20	12.39	10.38	10.96	5.08	3.92	2.37	.41	.22	1.82	4.53	11.70	11.65	75.43
	Port Orford	27	46.1	59.1	90	15	24	Feb. 25	Dec. 8	286	30	11.94	8.45	8.24	5.10	3.42	2.31	.43	.30	2.78	4.92	9.38	10.94	68.21
	Willow Creek										16	13.46	9.64	9.66	5.98	3.53	2.62	.30	.46	2.28	5.64	11.45	12.71	77.73

[1] Length of growing season between average dates of last killing frost in spring and first in fall.

OREGON—Continued

Climatic summary—Continued

County	Station	Temperature					Killing frost average dates				Average precipitation													
		Length of record	January average	July average	Maximum	Minimum	Length of record	Last in spring	First in fall	Growing season	Length of record	January	February	March	April	May	June	July	August	September	October	November	December	Annual
		Yr.	*°F.*	*°F.*	*°F.*	*°F.*	*Yr.*			*Days*	*Yr.*	*In.*	*In.*	*In.*	*In.*	*In.*	*In.*	*In.*	*In.*	*In.*	*In.*	*In.*	*In.*	*In.*
Deschutes	Bend	37	30.8	65.1	105	−26	34	June 8	Sept. 7	91	35	1.76	1.42	1.09	0.88	1.05	1.11	0.50	0.28	0.57	0.66	1.61	1.71	12.64
	Lapine	10	26.0	59.9	104	−38					11	1.59	1.75	1.09	.89	1.12	1.63	.96	.28	.59	1.17	1.87	2.31	15.25
	Redmond	15	32.3	65.8	105	−24	10	May 22	Sept. 29	130	11	.92	.69	.65	.80	.80	1.17	.54	.17	.39	.46	.75	.81	8.15
	Sisters										13	2.64	1.94	1.16	.85	1.09	.68	.68	.32	.86	1.05	3.24	2.14	16.65
Douglas	Drain	33	41.0	66.0	107	−1	27	Apr. 20	Oct. 24	187	33	7.26	5.52	4.69	2.94	2.21	1.24	.33	.37	1.73	3.20	6.85	6.72	43.06
	Gardiner	13	44.5	60.7	102	16	11	Mar. 20	Nov. 30	255	16	13.42	10.38	9.07	5.30	4.35	2.67	.55	.75	3.25	5.77	12.50	10.71	78.72
	Glendale	13	39.5	68.1	109	11	13	May 19	Oct. 8	142	13	9.08	5.28	3.91	2.55	2.30	1.01	.35	.19	.82	2.10	4.62	5.58	37.79
	Riddle	26	41.3	68.0	110	3	18	Mar. 31	Oct. 17	200	30	4.80	3.70	2.72	2.36	1.36	.96	.22	.30	.98	2.16	4.41	4.53	28.50
	Roseburg	40	41.2	67.4	107	−6	40	Mar. 30	Nov. 19	234	40	4.86	3.99	3.07	2.19	1.71	1.15	.22	.30	1.23	2.41	4.72	4.64	30.49
	Umpqua	15	44.4	57.4	101	15					20	9.66	8.22	7.30	4.34	3.20	1.39	.62	.62	1.97	3.95	8.78	10.05	60.10
Gilliam	Arlington (near)	22	33.3	75.2	113	−25	12	Apr. 7	Oct. 29	205	22	1.50	1.09	.69	.45	.45	.56	.04	.14	.44	.68	1.40	1.35	8.79
	Blalock	17	33.7	77.8	114	−19	18	Mar. 22	Nov. 3	226	17	1.73	1.16	.78	.52	.60	.49	.09	.11	.49	.64	1.72	1.48	9.81
	Condon	32	29.0	67.1	111	−25	23	May 27	Sept. 24	120	32	1.41	.99	.90	1.01	1.15	1.10	.36	.29	.86	1.02	1.59	1.30	11.98
	Lonerock	8	31.7	62.0	106	−22					10	1.68	1.44	1.99	1.18	1.18	1.35	.50	.54	1.08	1.16	1.81	1.53	15.44
	Mikkalo										29	1.28	.92	.70	.56	.57	.72	.15	.16	.54	.69	1.35	1.32	8.96
Grant	Austin	17	19.8	60.7	108	−52					17	3.05	2.40	1.79	1.46	1.05	1.32	.59	.36	.70	1.26	1.82	2.88	18.68
	Bear Valley										21	2.22	1.40	1.20	1.13	1.05	1.21	.66	.56	.88	.88	1.76	1.94	14.89
	Beech Creek										28	2.12	1.50	1.39	1.62	1.68	1.80	.47	.50	.89	1.24	1.85	1.98	17.04
	Dayville	37	33.9	69.2	111	−33	32	May 19	Sept. 28	132	37	1.16	1.12	.97	1.08	1.11	1.20	.40	.42	.63	.79	1.12	1.26	11.26
	Ibex Mine										14	4.55	4.08	2.73	2.36	2.00	1.54	.57	.62	1.20	1.75	3.27	3.88	28.55
	Olive Lake										19	4.92	3.40	3.96	2.88	1.82	2.35	.52	.79	1.44	2.33	4.31	4.33	33.05
	Prairie City	27	29.1	69.0	112	−31	21	Apr. 28	Oct. 13	168	28	1.79	1.28	1.33	1.58	1.27	1.28	.49	.51	.88	1.17	1.53	1.52	14.63
Harney	Andrews	23	29.2	72.5	107	−33	14	Mar. 6	Sept. 30	208	23	.72	.77	.62	.80	.66	.58	.22	.20	.37	.67	.76	.65	7.02
	Blitzen	18	24.7	66.5	108	−50	16	June 12	Aug. 30	79	18	.81	.83	.95	.85	.91	.78	.25	.34	.56	.82	.76	.76	8.62
	Burns	19	24.8	67.1	102	−32	19	May 24	Sept. 18	117	17	1.77	1.38	1.14	.76	.68	.97	.46	.24	.88	.66	1.30	1.40	11.64
	Diamond	2	29.1	63.9	102	−31					6	1.01	.76	.75	1.26	1.48	1.20	.44	.50	.51	.93	.89	.78	10.51
	Drewsey	14	22.4	67.0	102	−53	13	May 29	Sept. 9	103	15	1.53	1.59	.84	1.20	1.10	.67	.24	.74	.68	1.00	1.45	1.54	12.58
	Harney Experiment Station.	18	21.3	66.8	105	−45	16	June 7	Sept. 3	88	17	1.11	.87	.73	.92	.58	.75	.18	.18	.33	.65	.95	1.02	8.27
Hood River	Cascade Locks	40	35.7	68.0	107	−9	30	Apr. 7	Nov. 10	217	40	11.73	8.67	8.46	5.21	3.51	2.24	.56	1.01	3.05	5.84	12.21	12.70	75.19
	Hood River	40	32.9	67.3	106	−27	31	Apr. 20	Oct. 20	183	40	4.78	3.65	3.11	1.56	.95	.72	1.17	.30	1.04	1.98	5.35	5.45	30.06
	Parkdale	27	30.4	63.2	101	−22	18	May 17	Oct. 7	143	29	7.29	4.55	4.38	2.16	1.48	1.00	.23	.30	1.35	2.65	6.50	7.58	39.47
Jackson	Ashland	40	37.9	69.4	106	−1	32	Apr. 23	Oct. 22	182	40	2.77	2.25	2.02	1.58	1.51	.93	.35	.32	.92	1.49	2.80	2.82	19.76
	Fish Lake	16	28.4	61.7	100	−15					21	5.70	4.28	4.90	4.46	2.83	1.61	.34	.54	2.01	3.26	5.10	5.68	40.71
	Hillcrest Orchard	19	37.6	70.8	107	−9	17	May 7	Oct. 17	163	19	2.37	2.00	1.49	1.41	1.02	.98	.35	.29	.84	1.44	2.80	2.68	17.67
	Jacksonville	40	36.7	70.8	106	−1	32	Apr. 20	Oct. 27	190	40	4.26	3.40	2.20	1.65	1.30	.92	.31	.32	.79	1.76	3.82	3.96	24.69

	Lake Creek	22	36.6	66.0	107	0	13	May 6	Oct. 5	152	21	3.18	2.73	2.99	2.60	2.17	1.20	.17	.26	1.25	2.54	3.47	3.44	26.00
	Medford	28	37.5	72.0	110	−10	20	do	Oct. 14	161	28	2.39	1.92	1.34	1.41	1.04	.88	.27	.17	.71	1.26	2.53	2.56	16.48
	Modoc Orchard	24	37.1	70.7	110	−8	14	May 3	Oct. 13	163	24	3.01	2.76	1.80	1.42	.97	.72	.19	.20	.65	1.56	3.34	3.71	20.33
	Prospect	31	35.0	66.0	105	−12	24	May 31	Sept. 16	108	32	6.13	4.88	3.85	3.12	2.29	1.42	.46	.28	1.59	3.02	6.08	5.50	38.62
	Siskiyou Summit	12	33.1	64.9	100	−5					33	5.62	4.68	3.15	2.49	1.67	1.13	.51	.38	1.15	2.24	4.36	5.12	32.50
	Talent	26	37.2	71.1	107	2	18	Apr. 28	Oct. 15	170	26	2.12	1.80	1.45	1.48	1.23	.87	.37	.18	.84	1.53	2.33	2.44	16.64
Jefferson	Hay Creek	21	31.7	65.3	110	−28	14	May 20	Sept. 26	129	22	1.13	.79	.76	.91	1.19	1.16	.30	.31	.80	.75	1.48	1.24	10.82
	Madras	28	31.1	66.2	112	−45	14	June 7	Sept. 16	101	24	1.09	.65	.58	.56	.92	.74	.20	.21	.65	.59	1.21	1.24	8.64
	Warmspring	24	33.5	70.5	109	−38	25	May 16	Oct. 3	140	25	1.49	.95	.78	.49	.85	.63	.40	.31	.66	.59	1.59	1.35	10.09
Josephine	Buckhorn Farm	12	39.4	68.2	108	7	12	May 9	Oct. 6	150	12	13.26	12.88	8.49	2.94	2.26	1.00	.19	.37	1.20	4.91	11.11	11.90	70.51
	Grants Pass	40	39.0	70.0	114	0	32	May 19	Sept. 28	132	40	5.35	4.51	2.94	1.92	1.22	.72	.16	.20	.82	2.15	4.42	4.80	29.21
	Waldo (near)	18	36.4	67.2	109	−1	17	May 9	Oct. 11	155	22	8.90	6.82	5.07	3.96	1.96	.81	.23	.16	1.65	3.83	8.50	7.50	49.39
	Williams	28	38.7	67.0	107	3	28	do	Oct. 1	145	30	5.89	5.10	2.96	1.74	1.17	.79	.29	.17	.77	2.34	5.44	5.15	31.81
	Wolf Creek	14	38.0	67.4	110	−3	13	Apr. 26	Oct. 7	164	14	6.42	4.83	4.85	3.11	1.35	1.09	.10	.12	.87	2.57	5.37	7.60	38.28
Klamath	Cascade Summit	13	25.7	58.0	107	−16					12	8.37	5.90	6.52	4.46	2.28	1.80	.20	.13	1.56	3.37	5.79	8.68	49.06
	Chiloquin	31	25.5	60.7	102	−28					30	2.56	1.62	1.09	1.14	.89	.93	.41	.24	.73	1.24	2.53	2.25	15.63
	Crater Lake	18	26.0	56.6	100	−20					17	9.66	7.29	6.97	4.97	2.42	2.33	.59	.52	2.37	4.24	7.29	9.64	58.29
	Crescent										13	3.62	3.02	1.67	.99	1.37	1.27	.64	.32	.84	1.03	2.25	2.23	19.25
	Fort Klamath																							
	Gerber Dam										13	2.15	1.97	1.88	1.87	1.17	1.01	.18	.40	.44	1.13	2.31	1.90	16.41
	Keno										9	2.87	1.74	1.66	1.45	1.01	.86	.25	.09	.42	1.13	2.00	2.61	16.09
	Klamath Falls	40	28.7	68.2	104	−25	38	May 18	Sept. 26	131	39	2.00	1.46	1.12	.82	.73	.71	.27	.23	.50	1.00	1.83	1.71	12.38
	Malin	16	27.5	65.5	103	−25	13	May 28	Sept. 15	110	14	1.27	1.05	1.12	1.38	.89	.55	.08	.11	.36	.87	1.44	1.14	10.26
	Merrill	22	27.7	65.2	102	−23	20	May 23	Sept. 17	117	21	1.12	1.08	.70	.80	.76	.68	.38	.34	.45	1.12	1.67	1.49	10.59
	Round Grove	17	26.5	62.9	100	−29					18	1.47	1.57	1.52	1.66	1.18	1.10	.33	.35	.73	1.31	1.84	1.81	14.87
	Yonna	31	26.7	65.2	103	−30	14	June 1	Sept. 17	108	30	1.76	1.33	1.05	1.15	.95	.83	.33	.28	.55	1.04	1.97	1.67	12.91
Lake	Fremont	20	26.6	61.2	109	−40					28	.99	.89	.64	.75	.69	.85	.46	.28	.55	.61	.99	1.08	8.78
	Lake	13	26.4	65.4	109	−41					21	.65	.61	.49	.90	.83	1.03	.56	.21	.44	.52	.61	.60	7.45
	Lakeview	40	23.4	66.5	108	−24	25	May 27	Sept. 25	121	37	1.69	1.64	1.34	1.09	1.04	.74	.34	.23	.55	.95	1.58	1.52	12.71
	Paisley	15	29.7	67.7	103	−29					16	.84	.73	.77	.95	.79	.67	.43	.15	.31	.52	.81	1.00	7.97
	Paisley (near)	14	31.4	67.9	98	−9	12	May 1	Oct. 9	161	13	1.23	1.23	.92	.73	1.08	1.16	.68	.30	.83	.70	1.46	.80	11.12
	Silver Lake	27	28.1	63.7	105	−35	23	June 20	Sept. 7	79	21	1.11	1.14	.84	.72	.92	.81	.55	.34	.66	.79	.77	1.18	9.83
	Valley Falls	25	30.4	66.7	105	−39	17	May 30	Sept. 20	113	29	1.09	1.16	.98	1.20	1.32	.90	.44	.28	.55	.79	1.22	1.17	11.10
Lane	Black Butte	13	37.7	63.7	100	5	13	May 3	Sept. 22	142	13	7.24	6.53	5.17	3.20	3.31	2.02	.74	.25	2.68	3.56	8.21	6.36	49.27
	Cottage Grove	23	39.7	64.5	105	−7	14	May 13	Oct. 26	166	22	6.52	5.27	4.78	3.78	2.11	1.46	.14	.44	1.94	3.23	6.49	6.66	42.82
	Deadwood	21	41.0	63.8	102	11	21	Apr. 21	Oct. 30	192	22	16.21	12.40	10.50	5.82	3.87	2.17	.70	.66	3.58	6.40	15.29	14.18	91.78
	Eugene	40	40.1	65.9	104	−4	32	Apr. 13	Nov. 4	205	40	5.59	4.77	3.99	2.70	2.26	1.53	.36	.46	1.90	2.80	5.76	5.76	37.88
	Eula										15	6.78	6.03	5.40	4.72	2.92	2.16	.32	.38	1.59	3.66	6.27	6.74	46.97
	Florence										14	12.38	8.72	7.30	4.74	3.26	2.13	.78	.60	3.13	5.03	11.30	10.04	69.41
	McKenzie Bridge	20	35.0	65.6	108	−3	12	June 5	Sept. 10	97	15	10.14	8.53	7.18	4.69	3.91	3.03	.91	.95	2.54	5.54	11.49	9.62	68.53
	Oakridge	15	36.9	67.7	110	0	12	Apr. 17	Oct. 21	187	22	5.80	4.90	4.27	3.46	2.35	1.64	.37	.44	1.46	2.79	5.29	4.88	37.65
	Rujada										10	7.12	5.32	5.84	5.09	3.16	2.56	.18	.28	1.65	4.08	5.30	7.70	48.28
	Wicopee										10	8.12	5.06	6.82	5.23	4.09	3.18	.60	.36	2.24	3.74	6.03	7.91	53.38
Lincoln	Newport	40	43.7	56.8	100	1	29	Mar. 23	Nov. 26	248	39	10.15	8.15	7.61	4.52	3.45	2.54	.74	.93	2.86	5.00	10.00	10.24	66.19
	Toledo	26	43.0	60.9	102	8	31	Apr. 20	Nov. 1	195	27	11.89	10.07	8.73	5.43	3.76	2.40	.70	1.03	2.81	5.48	11.75	11.60	75.65
Linn	Albany	40	39.5	66.9	104	−15	25	Apr. 4	Nov. 2	212	40	6.13	5.00	4.15	2.54	2.02	1.30	.41	.54	1.71	2.94	6.40	6.37	39.51
	Cascadia	17	36.7	65.1	103	1	15	Apr. 15	Oct. 17	185	28	8.99	6.98	6.91	5.29	4.54	2.95	.77	.88	2.92	4.99	7.66	8.69	61.57
	Waterloo										14	5.18	4.84	4.65	3.53	2.53	1.90	.10	.42	1.82	3.04	5.87	6.63	40.51
Malheur	Beulah	9	23.7	67.8	112	−23					7	1.62	1.43	1.19	1.02	1.20	.75	.29	.45	.41	.79	1.46	1.53	12.14
	Harper	20	24.1	72.5	107	−41	11	May 13	Sept. 17	127	19	.95	.69	.49	.59	.73	.85	.21	.23	.22	.51	.67	1.06	7.20
	Kingman	22	27.1	76.5	108	−35	14	Apr. 27	Oct. 13	169	29	1.10	.85	.68	.79	.79	.76	.22	.24	.42	.65	.84	.94	8.28

298737°—41——69 +

OREGON—Continued

Climatic summary—Continued

County	Station	Temperature: Length of record	Temperature: January average	Temperature: July average	Temperature: Maximum	Temperature: Minimum	Killing frost average dates: Length of record	Killing frost average dates: Last in spring	Killing frost average dates: First in fall	Killing frost average dates: Growing season	Average precipitation: Length of record	January	February	March	April	May	June	July	August	September	October	November	December	Annual
		Yr.	*°F.*	*°F.*	*°F.*	*°F.*	*Yr.*			*Days*	*Yr.*	*In.*	*In.*	*In.*	*In.*	*In.*	*In.*	*In.*	*In.*	*In.*	*In.*	*In.*	*In.*	*In.*
Malheur—Con.	Riverside	35	25.8	71.3	111	−53	29	June 4	Sept. 14	102	40	1.13	0.98	0.77	0.83	0.89	0.86	0.45	0.25	0.48	0.68	0.92	1.04	9.28
	Sunrise Valley	22	27.3	71.4	108	−38	18	May 31	Sept. 10	102	17	.94	1.04	.71	1.06	.91	.88	.22	.29	.41	.85	1.17	.97	9.45
	Vale	39	26.2	72.6	111	−39	28	May 17	Sept. 18	124	36	1.25	.88	.84	.67	.73	.77	.25	.21	.32	.67	1.00	1.05	8.64
	Warmspring Reservation.	12	25.7	73.3	109	−40	11	May 20	Sept. 20	123	34	1.30	.89	.76	.57	.76	.70	.42	.23	.56	.56	1.27	1.16	9.18
Marion	Detroit										29	11.17	8.16	7.58	5.04	3.55	2.28	.65	.71	2.94	4.92	11.49	10.90	69.39
	Mehama										15	8.99	7.38	7.41	5.38	3.82	2.56	.47	.81	2.82	4.95	8.41	9.81	62.81
	Mount Angel	33	39.6	67.2	106	−15	27	Mar. 30	Nov. 3	218	28	6.95	5.77	4.71	3.16	2.84	1.73	.70	.80	2.33	3.60	7.83	7.05	47.47
	Salem	40	39.7	66.6	108	−6	31	Apr. 1	Oct. 31	213	40	5.61	4.69	3.91	2.39	1.84	1.22	.39	.44	1.70	2.88	5.72	6.45	37.24
Morrow	Ella										15	1.42	.94	.64	.65	.75	.64	.23	.30	.40	.77	1.41	.99	9.14
	Heppner	36	32.8	68.8	110	−21	30	Apr. 29	Oct. 14	168	37	1.38	1.27	1.17	1.30	1.22	1.12	.40	.37	.84	1.11	1.38	1.31	12.87
	Morgan										16	1.27	.84	.72	.60	.43	.65	.15	.09	.45	.64	1.05	1.15	8.04
Multnomah	Irvington										1	5.55	4.13	2.37	2.18	3.50	1.00	.32	2.60	1.25	3.73	8.19	5.58	40.40
	Portland	40	39.4	66.7	105	−2	40	Mar. 6	Nov. 24	263	40	6.02	4.63	4.04	2.68	1.93	1.46	.50	.64	1.85	2.85	6.15	6.68	39.43
Polk	Falls City	27	38.1	64.0	106	−5	18	May 6	Oct. 18	165	28	11.84	9.81	7.79	4.02	2.67	1.38	.24	.41	2.03	4.72	11.86	12.73	69.50
	Willamina (near)										4	8.08	7.37	6.98	3.89	1.82	1.39	.31	.36	.93	2.73	5.28	8.91	48.05
	Wallace Orchard	25	38.7	65.6	101	−14	21	Apr. 28	Oct. 22	177	25	6.04	4.52	3.91	2.61	1.90	1.27	.37	.42	1.97	2.97	5.94	6.49	38.41
Sherman	Grass Valley	13	29.9	65.1	106	−30	12	June 1	Sept. 15	106	12	1.59	.78	.75	.64	1.26	1.04	.13	.30	.60	.86	1.70	1.49	11.14
	Kent	15	29.2	68.6	108	−15	15	May 17	Oct. 8	144	15	1.29	.96	.97	.76	.81	.91	.19	.22	.62	.78	1.25	1.25	10.01
	Moro	29	30.0	69.0	110	−20	14	May 3	Oct. 15	165	29	1.57	1.16	.91	.76	.84	.66	.16	.20	.72	.89	1.64	1.62	11.13
	Wasco	26	30.8	70.4	111	−28	21	Apr. 25	do	173	31	1.90	1.26	.99	.70	.72	.63	.16	.19	.65	.93	1.85	1.88	11.86
Tillamook	Glenora	18	36.6	62.5	106	3	19	May 18	Oct. 5	140	19	21.00	15.60	12.20	7.79	5.68	3.58	1.32	1.52	5.22	9.23	25.09	21.24	129.47
	Nehalem										10	14.80	13.27	10.56	7.39	5.66	4.48	1.94	1.84	5.64	8.16	16.88	16.34	106.96
	Tillamook	25	42.4	58.8	101	0	17	May 5	Nov. 3	182	28	14.21	10.95	11.03	6.57	5.25	3.29	1.22	1.40	4.14	6.95	13.96	15.02	93.99
Umatilla	Echo	34	32.4	76.0	116	−29	26	Apr. 20	Oct. 11	174	35	1.36	1.08	.88	.78	.64	.62	.19	.28	.48	.75	1.28	1.22	9.56
	Hermiston	32	31.0	74.2	110	−37	25	Apr. 29	Oct. 9	163	33	1.13	.89	.66	.62	.54	.49	.13	.27	.42	.64	1.17	1.11	8.07
	Meacham	11	23.5	57.5	100	−52					15	5.09	3.95	4.44	2.82	2.95	2.14	.39	.58	1.49	2.57	3.95	3.90	34.27
	Milton	24	32.4	74.3	107	−21	16	Apr. 17	Oct. 24	190	24	1.58	1.38	1.42	1.29	1.05	1.08	.25	.38	.81	1.03	1.76	1.67	13.70
	Pendleton	40	33.2	72.1	119	−28	32	May 3	Oct. 5	155	40	1.65	1.50	1.34	1.08	1.10	1.05	.32	.49	.83	1.14	1.57	1.61	13.68
	Pilot Rock	30	33.0	72.8	116	−21	21	Apr. 29	Oct. 13	167	30	1.40	1.30	1.23	1.35	1.19	1.36	.26	.42	.72	1.04	1.42	1.47	13.16
	Power House										30	2.35	2.23	2.31	1.99	1.58	1.61	.38	.34	1.09	1.68	2.28	2.23	20.07
	Ukiah	17	23.0	61.9	106	−54					17	1.92	1.31	1.45	1.45	1.18	2.35	.31	.42	.83	1.39	1.82	2.00	16.43
	Umatilla	37	33.1	76.3	115	−23	28	Apr. 9	Oct. 23	197	40	1.03	.80	.61	.55	.51	.45	.12	.29	.43	.64	1.04	.96	7.43
	Weston	39	31.6	69.9	110	−23	30	May 5	Oct. 10	158	38	2.30	2.19	2.41	1.94	1.84	1.39	.40	.55	1.12	1.74	2.54	2.37	20.79
Union	Cove	22	29.3	67.9	103	−24	14	May 4	Oct. 3	152	22	2.43	1.80	2.36	2.38	1.75	1.94	.38	.80	1.40	1.94	2.46	2.43	22.07
	Hilgard										18	2.38	2.25	2.32	1.93	2.35	1.77	.80	.83	.88	1.57	2.07	2.16	21.31

	LaGrande	40	30.0	70.0	108	−34	32	Apr. 26	Oct. 3	160	40	2.16	1.91	2.14	1.71	1.81	1.53	.54	.73	1.12	1.52	2.23	2.12	19.52
	Starkey										18	1.56	1.48	1.30	1.68	1.93	1.72	.92	.91	1.13	1.35	1.82	1.50	17.30
	Union	27	28.8	66.5	103	−24	19	May 22	Sept. 16	117	27	1.16	.95	1.25	1.40	1.28	1.46	.45	.62	.86	1.10	1.12	1.12	12.77
Wallowa	Gumboot										12	4.11	2.69	2.30	2.65	2.70	1.96	.80	.55	1.30	1.80	3.11	2.97	26.94
	Howardville										30	3.65	2.98	2.61	2.00	1.83	1.71	.63	.70	1.34	1.86	3.21	3.15	25.67
	Joseph	40	23.3	63.7	100	−34	32	May 19	Sept. 30	134	40	1.64	1.54	1.78	1.76	2.06	1.87	.76	.83	1.19	1.29	1.65	1.64	18.01
	Wallowa	35	24.4	65.4	108	−38	28	May 22	Sept. 7	108	36	1.78	1.54	1.53	1.39	1.53	1.63	.59	.68	1.09	1.48	1.93	1.64	16.81
Wasco	Antelope	16	30.6	68.1	110	−27	14	May 24	Oct. 1	130	14	1.31	1.06	1.01	.94	1.20	.98	.08	.26	.66	.84	1.33	1.43	11.10
	Big Eddy	24	34.6	73.9	115	−26	10	Apr. 11	Oct. 25	197	23	1.96	1.35	1.10	.47	.35	.45	.12	.17	.57	.82	2.01	2.44	11.81
	Dufur	29	29.7	66.1	110	−25	21	May 11	Oct. 14	156	29	1.97	1.46	.92	.68	.74	.73	.25	.15	.83	.82	1.99	2.16	12.70
	Friend										15	2.22	1.56	1.27	.62	.64	.76	.06	.14	.56	.83	2.21	2.90	13.77
	Ramsey										17	2.54	1.86	1.39	.77	.99	.80	.35	.20	.89	.90	2.25	2.40	15.34
	The Dalles	40	32.7	72.5	115	−30	32	Apr. 11	Oct. 24	196	40	2.55	1.78	1.12	.60	.52	.53	.17	.18	.65	.86	2.39	2.33	13.68
	Wamic	16	32.5	66.2	108	−34	17	May 31	Sept. 18	110	16	2.69	2.19	1.13	.68	.79	.75	.29	.22	.95	.89	2.48	2.28	15.34
Washington	Forest Grove	39	37.4	66.1	108	−15	28	May 4	Oct. 15	164	34	7.42	6.14	4.82	2.68	1.86	1.31	.37	.51	1.69	3.28	7.51	8.29	45.88
Wheeler	Fossil										16	1.70	1.33	1.43	1.14	1.12	1.44	.27	.19	.81	1.04	1.49	1.52	13.48
Yamhill	McMinnville	39	38.9	66.3	110	−24	32	Apr. 26	Oct. 17	174	37	7.00	5.34	4.43	2.52	1.76	1.19	.38	.50	1.86	2.85	7.24	7.08	42.15
	Newberg-Springbrook										4	6.53	6.42	5.28	3.99	3.02	1.37	.62	.74	2.74	3.40	8.90	6.94	49.95

OREGON—Continued

Precipitation and temperature—State unit values

[This tabulation gives the mean annual, mean monthly, and average seasonal precipitation, 1886–1938, the percentage of normal precipitation for each year, 1887–1938, and the mean annual temperatures, 1907–38, for Oregon]

Precipitation		Precipitation		Precipitation		Annual precipitation (in percent of normal)		Annual precipitation (in percent of normal)		Temperature	
Year	Mean	Year	Mean	Month	Mean	Year	Percent	Year	Percent	Year	Mean
	In.		*In.*		*In.*						*°F.*
1886	33.75	1913	27.48	January	4.11	1887	157	1911	85	1907	48.9
1887	42.31	1914	26.40	February	3.10	1888	121	1912	121	1908	48.6
1888	32.65	1915	26.09	March	2.85	1889	111	1913	102	1909	47.8
1889	29.79	1916	28.64	April	2.06	1890	83	1914	98	1910	49.0
1890	22.24	1917	24.33	May	1.75	1891	108	1915	97	1911	46.9
1891	29.16	1918	20.61	June	1.30	1892	85	1916	106	1912	47.6
1892	22.87	1919	26.21	July	.43	1893	110	1917	90	1913	47.0
1893	29.57	1920	26.48	August	.40	1894	121	1918	77	1914	48.4
1894	32.52	1921	27.26	September	1.18	1895	93	1919	97	1915	48.7
1895	25.17	1922	23.85	October	1.97	1896	123	1920	98	1916	46.1
1896	33.13	1923	23.37	November	3.67	1897	106	1921	101	1917	47.8
1897	28.60	1924	21.76	December	4.10	1898	78	1922	89	1918	49.3
1898	21.02	1925	23.71	Annual	26.92	1899	115	1923	87	1919	47.9
1899	31.06	1926	25.49	Season	Average	1900	91	1924	81	1920	48.0
1900	24.57	1927	31.12		*In.*	1901	92	1925	88	1921	49.0
1901	24.75	1928	22.42	Winter	11.31	1902	111	1926	95	1922	47.3
1902	29.88	1929	19.93	Spring	6.66	1903	93	1927	116	1923	48.6
1903	24.96	1930	19.22	Summer	2.13	1904	121	1928	83	1924	48.4
1904	32.46	1931	24.52	Fall	6.82	1905	78	1929	74	1925	50.3
1905	21.05	1932	26.69			1906	110	1930	71	1926	51.0
1906	29.50	1933	28.16			1907	118	1931	91	1927	48.3
1907	31.71	1934	25.87			1908	78	1932	99	1928	48.9
1908	20.90	1935	20.42			1909	122	1933	105	1929	47.2
1909	32.85	1936	23.27			1910	100	1934	96	1930	47.6
1910	26.96	1937	34.70					1935	76	1931	48.9
1911	22.76	1938	26.31					1936	86	1932	47.8
1912	32.50							1937	129	1933	48.2
								1938	98	1934	52.0
										1935	47.7
										1936	48.8
										1937	47.7
										1938	48.8

Dates of last killing frost in spring and first in fall, with length of growing season

Year	Portland			Corvallis			Roseburg			Baker			Bend			Klamath Falls		
	Last in spring	First in fall	Growing season[1]	Last in spring	First in fall	Growing season[1]	Last in spring	First in fall	Growing season[1]	Last in spring	First in fall	Growing season[1]	Last in spring	First in fall	Growing season[1]	Last in spring	First in fall	Growing season[1]
			Days			*Days*			*Days*			*Days*			*Days*			*Days*
1899	Apr. 13	Oct. 14	184	Apr. 21	Oct. 13	175	May 2	Oct. 14	165	June 6	Oct. 2	118				May 2		
1900	Feb. 18	Nov. 19	274	Apr. 22	Nov. 19	211	Apr. 8	Nov. 21	227	Apr. 26	Sept. 26	153				Apr. 28		
1901	Feb. 21	Dec. 12	294	Apr. 7	Nov. 7	214	Apr. 27	Nov. 13	200	June 9	Oct. 30	143	July 14	Sept. 9	57	Apr. 25	Nov. 2	191
1902	Mar. 29	Nov. 23	239	Apr. 12	Sept. 28	169	Mar. 29	Dec. 14	260	May 4	Sept. 28	147	do	do	57	May 30	Oct. 21	144
1903	Mar. 12	Nov. 17	250	May 7	Sept. 30	146	May 7	Dec. 4	211	Apr. 5	Sept. 15	163	June 4	July 2		Apr. 14		
1904	Apr. 23	Dec. 3	224	Apr. 23	Sept. 22	152	Mar. 23	Dec. 6	258	June 23	Oct. 17	116	June 12	Aug. 20	69	June 24		
1905	Mar. 30	Oct. 18	202	Apr. 26	Oct. 18	175	Apr. 11	Nov. 1	204	May 22	Oct. 10	141	June 28	Aug. 14	47	May 24	Sept. 29	128
1906	Mar. 17	Nov. 23	251	do	Oct. 20	177	Apr. 17	Oct. 22	188	May 17	Oct. 19	155	June 22	Aug. 19	58	Apr. 26		
1907	Mar. 12	Dec. 8	271	May 1	Nov. 2	185	May 1	Dec. 5	218	Apr. 25	Sept. 13	141	June 16	Aug. 18	63	June 14	Nov. 16	155
1908	Mar. 9	Nov. 27	263	May 10	Sept. 24	137	May 10	Sept. 24	137	May 17	Sept. 24	130				May 10	Sept. 24	137
1909	Jan. 28	Nov. 14	290	May 6	Nov. 6	184	May 5	Nov. 14	193	May 8	Oct. 8	153				May 12	Oct. 8	149
1910	Feb. 23	Dec. 20	300	Apr. 14	Oct. 28	197	May 6	Nov. 26	265							Apr. 29	Oct. 2	156
1911	Mar. 26	Nov. 10	229	Apr. 29	Oct. 27	181	Apr. 29	Nov. 11	196	Apr. 13	Sept. 28	168		Sept. 16		May 25	Oct. 10	138
1912	Mar. 9	Nov. 28	264	Mar. 22	Oct. 7	199	Apr. 14	Nov. 21	221	Apr. 16	Aug. 30	136	June 16	Aug. 29	74	Apr. 22	do	171
1913	Mar. 25	Dec. 4	254	Apr. 28	Oct. 3	158	Apr. 22	Dec. 23	245	May 1	Sept. 24	146		Aug. 14		May 2	Sept. 22	143
1914	Feb. 9	Dec. 11	305	do	Nov. 14	200	Mar. 25	Nov. 20	240	May 5	Nov. 6	185	July 21	Sept. 12	53	Apr. 27	Sept. 12	138
1915	Feb. 15	Dec. 29	317	May 1	Oct. 11	163	Feb. 21	Dec. 30	312	May 2	Sept. 14	135	June 21	Sept. 1	72	Apr. 8	Oct. 12	187
1916	Mar. 4	Nov. 12	253	May 11	Oct. 4	146	Apr. 12	Oct. 4	175	May 14	Oct. 3	142	June 12	Sept. 11	91	May 10	July 27	78
1917	Mar. 16	Oct. 28	226	Mar. 18	Oct. 18	214	Mar. 31	Oct. 17	200	June 2	Oct. 17	137	July 29	Sept. 24	57	June 12	Sept. 24	104
1918	Apr. 3	Dec. 23	264	Apr. 3	Oct. 22	202	Apr. 4	Nov. 29	239	May 26	Oct. 18	145	June 3	Oct. 24	143	May 24	Sept. 23	122
1919	Jan. 28	Oct. 27	272	May 31	Oct. 10	132	Mar. 25	Nov. 7	227	June 11	Sept. 29	110	June 16	Sept. 22	98	June 11	Oct. 9	120
1920	Mar. 17	Nov. 1	229	May 30	Nov. 1	155	Apr. 18	Oct. 31	196	June 1	Oct. 13	134	June 23	Aug. 18	56	May 31	Sept. 21	113
1921	Feb. 17	Nov. 20	276	Apr. 4	Nov. 17	227	Apr. 4	Dec. 15	255	May 27	Sept. 12	108	July 2	Sept. 1	61	June 16	Sept. 3	79
1922	Mar. 27	Nov. 3	221	Apr. 18	Nov. 3	199	Mar. 25	Dec. 7	257	May 11	Sept. 28	140	May 27	Sept. 4	100	May 26	Sept. 28	125
1923	Mar. 15	Dec. 1	261	Mar. 18	Oct. 24	220	Mar. 15	Nov. 30	260	May 28	Oct. 19	144	June 2	Sept. 26	116	June 18	Oct. 5	109
1924	Apr. 15	Nov. 12	211	Apr. 4			Mar. 26	Dec. 16	265	Apr. 25	Sept. 26	154	May 5	Sept. 10	128	May 5	Sept. 20	138
1925	Mar. 6	Nov. 23	262	Mar. 29	Nov. 22	238	do	Dec. 15	264	June 4	Sept. 30	118	June 3	Aug. 15	73	May 8	Oct. 2	147
1926	Jan. 25	Dec. 13	322				Jan. 26	Sept. 25	242	May 9	Sept. 23	137	June 11	Sept. 19	100	May 25	Sept. 17	115
1927	Feb. 12	Dec. 7	298	Apr. 20	Oct. 31	194	Apr. 20	Nov. 1	195	May 2	Oct. 6	157	May 29	Sept. 15	109	May 29	Sept. 13	107
1928	Mar. 14	Nov. 18	249		Oct. 22		Feb. 16	Oct. 13	240	May 3	Oct. 12	162	June 8	Sept. 19	103	May 30	Oct. 1	124
1929	Feb. 18	Nov. 13	268	Apr. 5	Oct. 29	207	Mar. 29	Oct. 29	214	Apr. 30	Sept. 21	144	June 19	Sept. 7	80	June 2	Sept. 21	111
1930	Mar. 1	Nov. 24	268	Mar. 2	Oct. 13	225	Mar. 17	Dec. 20	278	Apr. 16	Oct. 9	176	Mar. 14			May 23	Sept. 23	123
1931	Feb. 22	Nov. 21	272	Mar. 26	Nov. 22	241	Mar. 7	Nov. 21	259	May 21	Oct. 21	153	May 18	Sept. 7	112	June 29	Sept. 24	87
1932	Mar. 3	Dec. 7	279	Mar. 21	Oct. 28	221	Mar. 3	Dec. 8	280	May 27	Sept. 21	117	June 5	Aug. 29	85	Apr. 29	Aug. 30	123
1933	Mar. 1	None	306	Apr. 9	Oct. 15	189	Mar. 23	None	284	May 8	Sept. 30	145	May 9	Sept. 25	139	May 19	Sept. 21	125
1934	None	None	365	Apr. 3	Sept. 25	175	None	None	366	Apr. 2	Sept. 26	177	May 12	Sept. 24	135	Apr. 29	Sept. 25	149
1935	Feb. 25	Oct. 30	247	Mar. 27	Oct. 23	210	Mar. 10	Nov. 1	236	May 11	Oct. 20	162	June 15	Aug. 15	61	May 18	Oct. 16	151
1936	Apr. 1	Nov. 2	215	Apr. 2	Oct. 29	210	Apr. 1	Oct. 29	211	Apr. 6	Sept. 15	162	May 6	Sept. 15	132	May 7	Sept. 13	129
1937	Feb. 10	Dec. 23	316	Mar. 18	Nov. 30	257	Mar. 18	Dec. 25	282	May 29	Sept. 23	117	do	Sept. 23	140	May 19	Aug. 1	74
1938	Mar. 31	Nov. 12	226	Apr. 6	Oct. 15	192	Apr. 1	Oct. 17	199	May 17	Oct. 13	140	June 10	Oct. 16	128	May 18	Oct. 16	151
Mean	Mar. 6	Nov. 24	263	Apr. 15	Oct. 23	191	Mar. 30	Nov. 19	234	May 12	Oct. 3	144	June 8	Sept. 7	91	do	Sept. 26	131
Extremes	Jan. 28[2] Apr. 23[3]	Oct. 14[4] Dec. 29[5]	[6] 184 [7] 365	Mar. 2[2] May 3[3]	Sept. 22[4] Nov. 30[5]	[6] 132 [7] 257	Jan. 26[2] May 10[3]	Sept. 24[4] Dec. 30[5]	[6] 137 [7] 365	Apr. 2[2] June 23[3]	Sept. 12[4] Nov. 6[5]	[6] 108 [7] 185	Mar. 14[2] July 29[3]	Aug. 14[4] Oct. 24[5]	[6] 0 [7] 143	Apr. 8[2] June 29[3]	July 27[4] Nov. 16[5]	[6] 74 [7] 191

[1] Number of days between last killing frost in spring and first in fall. [2] Earliest date in spring. [3] Latest date in spring. [4] Earliest date in fall. [5] Latest date in fall. [6] Shortest growing season. [7] Longest growing season.

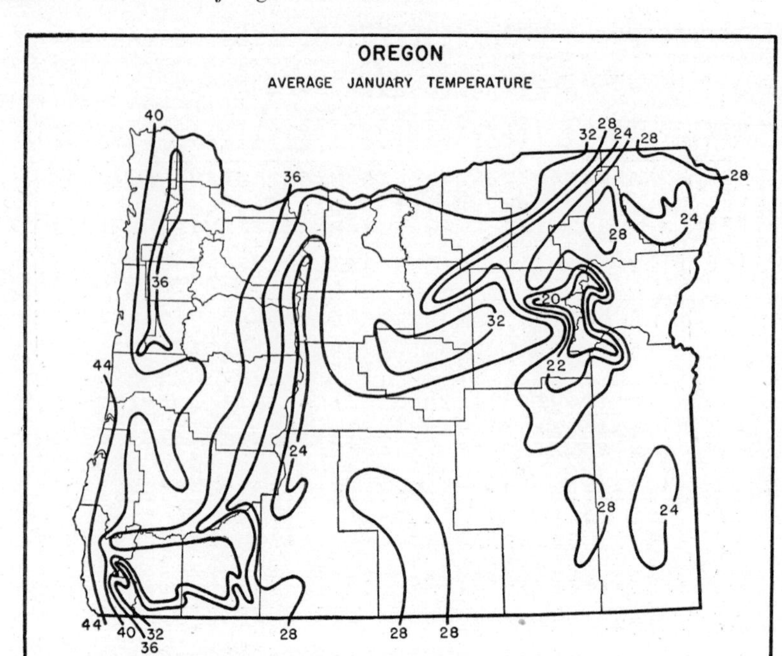
OREGON
AVERAGE JANUARY TEMPERATURE
40
36
44
32
28
24
20
22
40
36

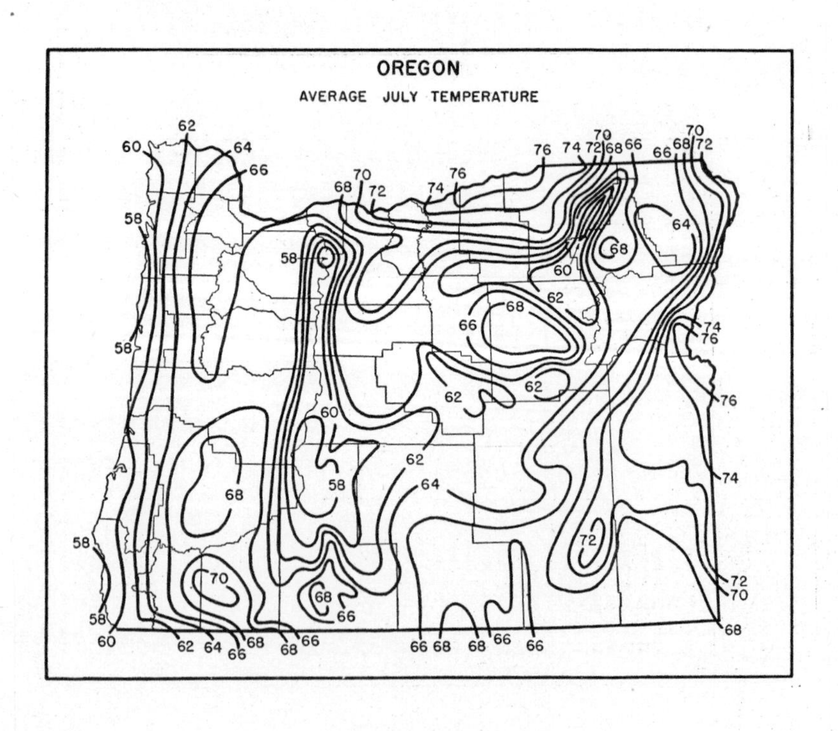
OREGON
AVERAGE JULY TEMPERATURE
62
60
64
66
58
70
68
72
74
76
60
62
64
66

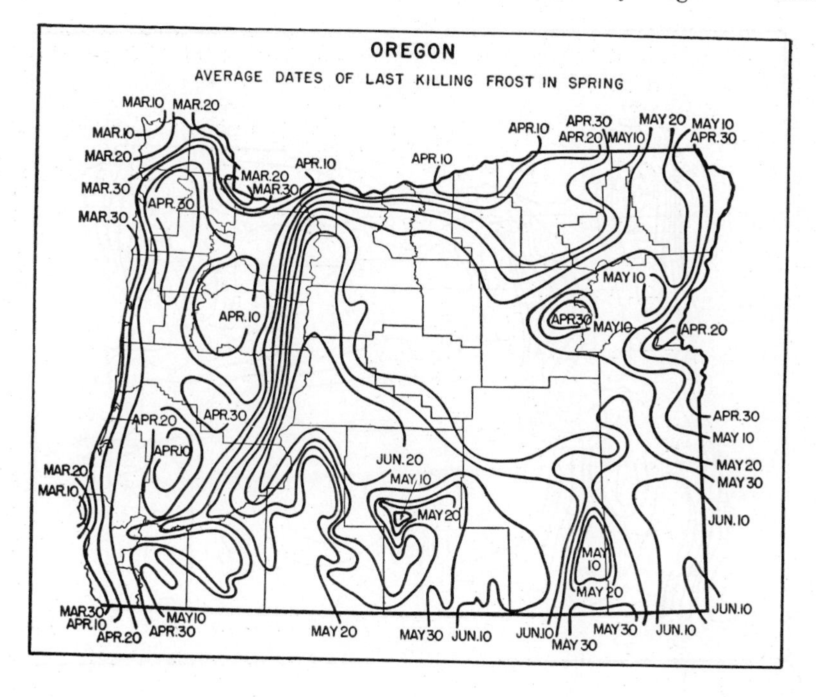
OREGON
AVERAGE DATES OF LAST KILLING FROST IN SPRING
MAR.10
MAR.20
MAR.30
APR.10
APR.20
APR.30
MAY 10
MAY 20
MAY 30
JUN.10
JUN.20

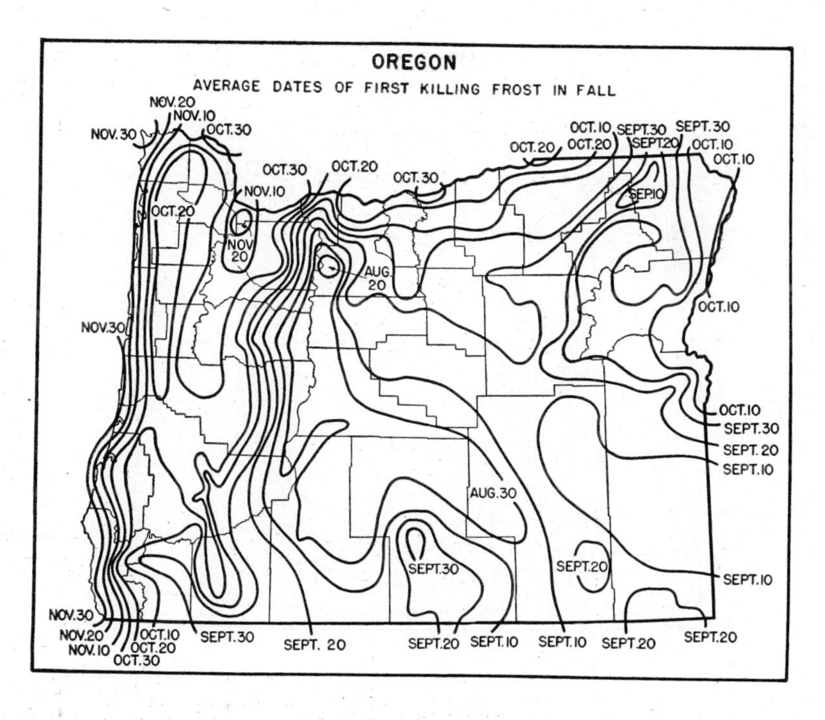
OREGON
AVERAGE DATES OF FIRST KILLING FROST IN FALL
NOV.30
NOV.20
NOV.10
OCT.30
OCT.20
OCT.10
SEPT.30
SEPT.20
SEPT.10
AUG.20
AUG.30

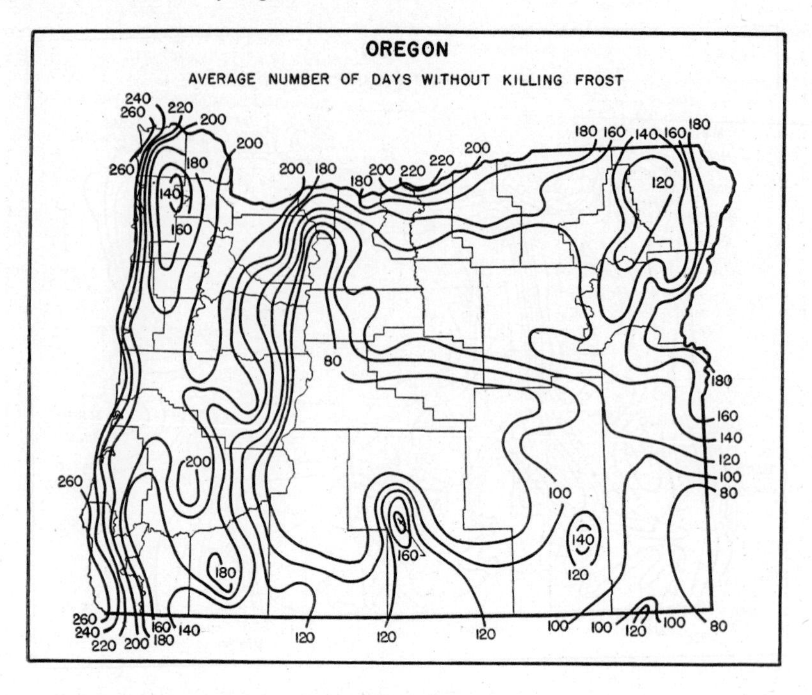
OREGON
AVERAGE NUMBER OF DAYS WITHOUT KILLING FROST

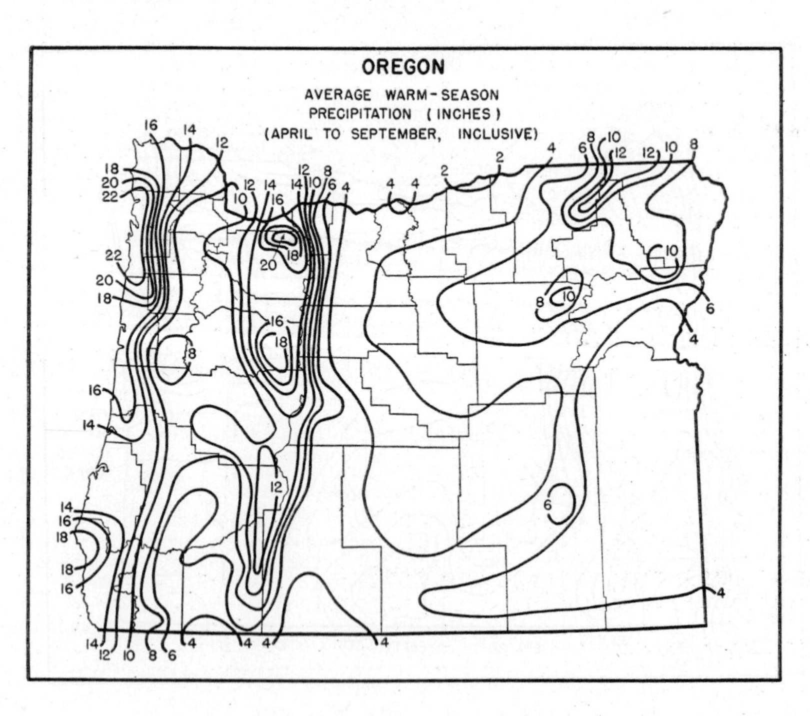
OREGON
AVERAGE WARM-SEASON
PRECIPITATION (INCHES)
(APRIL TO SEPTEMBER, INCLUSIVE)

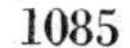

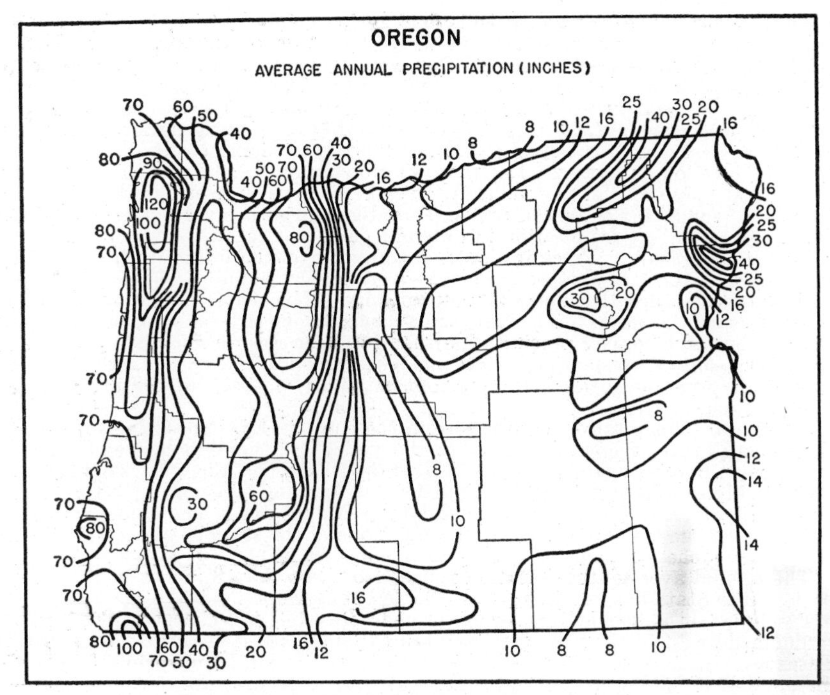

SUPPLEMENTARY CLIMATIC NOTES FOR OREGON

Oregon lies mostly between latitudes 42° and 46° N. and extends from the Pacific Ocean inland for 375 miles. The area is 96,699 square miles, including more than 1,000 square miles of water surface. The outstanding topographic feature is the Cascade Range, which extends north and south with more than two-thirds of the State lying to the eastward of it. The highest point is Mount Hood, elevation 11,253 feet. Near the coast, the Coast Range also extends from north to south; it is quite low in the north but higher toward the south. Several large valleys lie between these ranges, the largest being the Willamette. The Blue Mountains are an irregular group of mountains covering much of the northeastern quarter of the State. There are some deep canyons in this area. The southeastern section—a fourth or more of the State—is largely a great plateau but has sharp relief in places.

Westerly winds predominate, carrying the modifying effect of the ocean over the western part of the State, and to a less extent to the eastern parts.

Disregarding the highest mountain areas, for which no records are available, the mean annual temperature ranges from about 56° F. in the lower Snake River Canyon, in the extreme northeast, to about 38° in the Cascade Mountains. Normal minimum temperatures for January range from about 12° to 40°. The greatest extremes of cold are over the high plateau, while the mildest winter nights occur on the southern coast.

The normal maximum temperatures for July range from about 65°F. on the middle and southern coast to 95° in the Snake River Canyon and along the middle reaches of the Columbia River. It often happens in summer that abnormally warm weather in the interior is accompanied by subnormal temperature on the coast. In the Willamette Valley hot spells are short. In southern Oregon, where the Coast Range is higher, warm spells are more pronounced and last longer, while east of the Cascades they are still more persistent.

The coldest weather in winter and the warmest in summer occur when the ocean winds cease and the State is dominated by a mass of continental air.

The Columbia River gorge, cut through the Cascade Mountains nearly to sea level, permits continental air to flow into western Oregon to a greater extent than it otherwise would. This is particularly true of cold air in winter.

It is difficult to determine the length of the growing season in the colder parts of Oregon, for in these areas agriculture is mostly confined to the growing of the hardier crops. Moreover, in sections where the nights are uniformly cold, even the less hardy crops seem to develop some resistance to frost.

The records show that over most of the area west of the Cascade Mountains the average period between the last killing frost in spring and the first in fall is 150 days or more, reaching 250 days on the coast. In the principal agricultural areas east of the Cascades it is between 100 and 200 days. Some of the high plateau districts have, on an average, less than 50 growing days, and there are districts where frost may occur in any month. Even here, however, considerable areas are devoted to some kind of agriculture, and potatoes and garden vegetables are grown.

The variation in precipitation in different parts of Oregon is as pronounced as that in temperature. Precipitation is largely of cyclonic origin, incident to the eastward movement of low-pressure areas over British Columbia, but the geographic distribution is greatly affected by topography. The heaviest rains occur on the slopes toward the ocean. There are some localities on the west slope of the Coast Range that have heavier precipitation than has been recorded in any other State except in some corresponding areas in Washington, while east of the Cascade Mountains some localities have less than any part of the United States east of the Continental Divide.

In general, precipitation increases from the coast to a belt near the summit of the Coast Range, thence decreases in the valleys of the Willamette, Umpqua, and Rogue Rivers, again increases to certain heights on the west slope of the Cascade Mountains, with another rapid decrease on the east slope of the Cascades, and finally increases once more in the Blue Mountains. The same variation occurs along the Columbia River, although none of the stations along the middle and lower reaches of the Columbia is much above sea level.

The annual average precipitation ranges from less than 8 inches in the driest parts of the State to more than 130 on some Pacific slopes.

Precipitation is decidedly seasonal in character, but this characteristic is more pronounced west of the Cascade Mountains than it is east of them. West of the Cascades 44 percent of the precipitation occurs in winter, 24 in spring, 5 in summer, and 27 in fall. East of the Cascades 37 percent occurs in winter, 27 in spring, 12 in summer, and 24 in fall.

In the coastal areas snow seldom falls, and when it does it melts almost at once. In the interior of the western part of the State there are occasionally considerable falls of snow, but these are quite infrequent, and ordinarily this area is free from snow most of the winter. East of the Cascade Mountains a considerable part of the winter precipitation is in the form of snow, but usually the ground is bare for long periods. Where measurements have been made, the average annual snowfall ranges from less than 1 inch at some coastal stations to more than 40 feet at some mountain stations. Glaciers are found on several of the higher peaks. Mountain snow storage is an important factor in providing summer water for irrigation, power, and domestic use.

Low humidity is the normal condition in eastern Oregon in summer, and east winds occasionally bring very low humidity to western sections; this occurs sometimes even in the winter season. Otherwise, humidity is high west of the Cascade Mountains in winter, and on the coast throughout the year. Humidity is normally moderately low in eastern Oregon in winter and in the interior of western Oregon in summer.

Thunderstorms are rare in the western valleys, somewhat more frequent in summer in eastern valleys and over the plateau, and still more frequent in the Cascade and Blue Mountains, where many forest fires result from lightning. Hail occurs occasionally but seldom does material damage. Glaze storms are experienced at rather long intervals.

Strong southerly winds are an occasional feature of winter weather on the coast, and sometimes they are destructive. Strong easterly winds in the Columbia River gorge are often rather discomforting, but they seldom do material damage. The few tornadoes that have occurred were poorly developed and not serious.

In summer there is abundant sunshine in most of Oregon, but in winter there is much cloudiness, particularly in the area west of the Cascade Mountains. At Baker the average number of hours of sunshine a year is 2,719 and at Portland 2,117. No sunshine record for the Oregon coast is available, but North Head, on the southern Washington coast, has an annual average of 1,981 hours.

EDWARD L. WELLS, *Senior Meteorologist and Climatic Section Director for Oregon, Weather Bureau, Portland.*

PENNSYLVANIA

Climatic summary

County[1]	Station	Temperature: Length of record	Temperature: January average	Temperature: July average	Temperature: Maximum	Temperature: Minimum	Killing frost average dates: Length of record	Killing frost: Last in spring	Killing frost: First in fall	Growing season[2]	Average precipitation: Length of record	January	February	March	April	May	June	July	August	September	October	November	December	Annual
		Yr.	°F.	°F.	°F.	°F.	Yr.			Days	Yr.	In.	In.	In.	In.	In.	In.	In.	In.	In.	In.	In.	In.	In.
Adams	Arendtsville	17	30.6	74.5	106	−10	18	Apr. 30	Oct. 15	168	15	2.89	2.41	3.73	3.82	4.03	4.17	3.99	4.36	3.62	3.69	3.04	3.10	42.85
	Gettysburg	40	31.4	75.2	105	−20	36	Apr. 21	Oct. 18	180	36	3.31	2.66	3.57	3.67	3.66	4.26	4.37	4.43	3.89	3.43	2.48	3.12	42.85
Allegheny	Coraopolis										23	3.29	2.65	3.29	3.10	3.32	4.29	3.67	3.05	3.28	2.94	2.44	2.76	38.08
	Herrs Island Dam										35	3.20	2.40	3.30	3.16	3.19	4.00	3.65	3.52	2.64	2.77	2.20	2.71	36.74
	Pittsburgh	40	31.6	74.2	103	−20	40	Apr. 20	Oct. 20	183	40	2.96	2.23	3.23	3.08	2.93	3.71	3.53	3.31	2.50	2.54	2.09	2.66	34.77
Armstrong	Lock No. 5, Freeport										40	3.61	2.70	3.76	4.10	3.38	4.47	3.98	3.90	3.12	3.02	2.61	3.25	41.90
	Parkers Landing										40	3.61	2.70	3.79	3.54	3.67	4.06	3.94	3.86	3.19	2.94	2.88	3.37	41.55
Beaver	Beaver Dam	22	30.9	73.9	106	−19	22	May 7	Oct. 17	163	37	2.90	2.32	3.30	3.11	3.36	4.56	3.78	3.56	3.03	2.51	2.41	2.86	37.70
	Beaver Falls										30	3.00	2.25	2.87	3.06	3.30	3.92	3.33	3.56	3.02	2.50	2.33	2.55	35.69
	Ellwood Junction										16	3.00	2.44	3.76	3.75	3.36	4.79	4.42	4.01	2.70	2.59	2.15	3.02	39.99
Bedford	Everett	22	28.1	71.6	102	−25	22	May 9	Oct. 4	148	23	2.94	2.29	3.21	3.17	3.67	4.90	3.97	3.86	3.23	2.49	1.88	2.88	38.49
	Hyndman	24	31.4	73.2	107	−28	22	May 11	Oct. 3	145	27	3.03	2.36	3.33	3.57	3.08	4.22	3.16	3.91	2.92	3.10	2.05	2.66	37.39
Berks	Hamburg	34	29.0	73.4	104	−13	36	Apr. 29	Oct. 12	166	39	3.49	3.24	3.90	4.19	3.88	4.45	4.92	5.27	4.09	3.84	2.77	3.58	47.62
	Reading	40	31.1	75.2	105	−14	40	Apr. 16	Oct. 24	191	40	3.22	3.03	3.46	3.36	3.08	3.65	4.42	4.28	3.33	2.86	2.43	3.13	40.25
Blair	Altoona	38	28.0	70.9	102	−20	40	May 6	Oct. 4	151	40	3.07	2.31	3.39	3.62	3.96	3.83	4.07	3.61	3.10	3.02	2.46	2.80	39.24
Bradford	Le Roy	19	24.4	69.8	100	−20	18	May 8	Oct. 3	148	19	2.67	2.28	3.24	3.41	3.14	3.77	3.73	3.96	3.16	2.69	2.11	3.07	37.23
	Towanda	40	26.1	70.5	104	−31	40	May 7	Oct. 5	151	40	2.10	1.93	2.65	3.06	3.30	3.81	3.82	3.50	3.34	2.81	2.16	2.19	34.67
Bucks	Doylestown										38	3.64	3.34	3.68	3.90	3.61	4.10	5.00	5.18	3.89	3.64	2.81	3.71	46.50
	George School	31	31.7	74.2	106	−18	32	Apr. 27	Oct. 16	172	32	3.49	2.80	3.27	3.49	3.55	3.70	4.41	4.73	3.59	3.25	2.80	3.25	42.33
	Neshaminy Falls	24	29.8	73.9	105	−18	24	Apr. 26	Oct. 17	174	24	3.41	2.70	3.19	3.32	3.52	4.16	4.58	5.15	4.10	3.45	2.76	3.13	43.47
	Quakertown	28	28.5	73.3	105	−20	28	May 4	Oct. 5	154	31	3.62	3.02	3.59	3.55	3.35	4.23	5.28	4.81	3.76	3.37	2.81	3.50	44.89
Butler	Butler	14	30.0	72.4	104	−27	16	May 11	Oct. 4	146	24	2.99	2.22	3.40	3.39	3.42	4.49	4.30	4.09	3.16	3.01	2.85	2.72	40.04
Cambria	Cresson										15	3.15	3.08	3.37	4.08	4.02	4.19	4.84	3.52	3.61	2.79	3.34	2.79	42.78
	Ebensburg	20	26.5	68.5	98	−30	21	May 19	Sept. 27	131	21	3.31	2.67	3.18	3.38	4.25	4.37	4.19	4.23	3.63	3.08	3.19	3.01	42.49
	Johnstown	38	30.5	73.7	104	−18	39	May 2	Oct. 11	162	40	4.43	3.39	4.49	3.98	4.06	4.99	4.37	4.62	3.37	3.09	2.78	3.75	47.32
Cameron	Driftwood										16	2.54	2.31	3.01	3.42	3.85	3.81	3.27	3.30	3.14	2.57	3.11	2.90	37.23
	Emporium	40	26.1	69.5	103	−31	40	May 20	Oct. 2	135	40	3.60	2.78	3.69	3.66	4.12	4.34	4.36	3.96	3.42	3.13	2.88	3.20	43.14
Carbon	Lansford										33	3.18	2.62	3.14	3.83	3.60	4.48	4.53	4.91	3.90	3.70	2.95	3.24	44.08
	Mauch Chunk	38	28.0	72.4	104	−20	39	May 3	Oct. 7	157	39	3.70	3.41	4.23	4.00	3.51	4.60	5.08	4.80	4.51	3.71	3.25	3.97	48.77
	Palmerton	20	28.8	73.3	106	−19	22	May 1	Oct. 6	158	22	2.88	2.19	2.92	3.17	3.61	4.36	4.41	4.17	3.75	3.37	3.13	2.56	40.52
Centre	Bellefonte	18	28.5	72.8	108	−31	16	May 6	do	153	30	2.65	2.18	3.36	3.72	3.73	4.41	3.74	4.00	3.04	2.98	2.13	2.57	38.51
	Center Hall	34	26.6	70.9	102	−19	34	May 9	Oct. 3	147	39	2.49	2.35	3.15	3.46	3.93	4.27	4.23	4.12	3.08	2.84	2.40	2.49	38.81
	State College	40	27.1	71.0	102	−20	40	May 2	Oct. 5	156	40	3.09	2.49	3.41	3.65	3.81	4.05	3.91	3.49	3.00	2.92	2.39	2.72	38.93

[1] The following counties, for which no records are available, are best represented by the stations indicated: Forest—Franklin and Ridgway; Fulton—Everett; Mifflin—Mifflintown; Montour—Catawissa; Wyoming—Scranton.

[2] Length of growing season between average dates of last killing frost in spring and first in fall.

PENNSYLVANIA—Continued

Climatic summary—Continued

County	Station	Temperature: Length of record	Temperature: January average	Temperature: July average	Temperature: Maximum	Temperature: Minimum	Killing frost average date: Length of record	Killing frost: Last in spring	Killing frost: First in fall	Killing frost: Growing season	Average precipitation: Length of record	January	February	March	April	May	June	July	August	September	October	November	December	Annual
		Yr.	*°F.*	*°F.*	*°F.*	*°F.*	*Yr.*			*Day*	*Yr.*	*In.*	*In.*	*In.*	*In.*	*In.*	*In.*	*In.*	*In.*	*In.*	*In.*	*In.*	*In.*	*In.*
Chester	Coatesville	40	30.7	75.1	107	−19	40	Apr. 25	Oct. 17	175	40	4.03	3.62	4.08	3.80	3.55	4.53	4.67	4.80	3.54	3.30	2.89	3.88	46.69
	Kennett Square	22	31.1	73.9	101	−13	21	Apr. 19	Oct. 22	186	20	3.69	3.54	4.00	3.71	3.55	4.30	4.68	5.51	3.86	3.03	2.64	4.30	46.81
	Phoenixville	22	32.0	76.2	111	−16	24	Apr. 29	Oct. 15	169	24	3.69	2.95	3.42	3.43	3.69	3.80	5.21	5.20	3.46	3.09	2.90	3.08	43.92
	West Chester	39	31.5	75.0	105	−15	36	Apr. 16	Oct. 22	189	40	3.90	3.43	3.87	3.76	3.75	4.63	4.87	5.19	3.80	3.57	3.00	3.68	47.45
Clarion	Clarion										24	3.53	2.72	3.73	3.43	3.74	4.24	4.38	4.34	3.41	3.58	2.74	3.38	43.22
Clearfield	Clearfield	26	27.6	71.6	106	−34	28	May 16	Oct. 2	139	32	3.61	2.52	3.62	3.65	4.43	4.65	4.27	4.21	3.39	3.21	3.07	2.95	43.58
Clinton	Lock Haven	36	28.4	74.0	106	−22	36	May 4	Oct. 13	162	37	3.07	2.43	3.38	3.58	3.94	4.15	4.02	4.15	3.29	3.09	2.21	2.80	40.11
	Renovo										39	2.77	2.30	2.97	3.36	3.78	4.15	4.03	3.57	2.95	2.98	2.48	2.54	37.88
Columbia	Catawissa	28	28.9	73.2	105	−23	37	May 3	Oct. 8	158	28	2.94	2.41	3.05	3.67	3.43	3.83	3.80	3.84	3.80	3.05	2.57	2.66	39.05
Crawford	Linesville										25	3.00	2.14	3.06	3.18	3.28	3.71	3.45	3.47	3.78	3.34	3.07	3.11	38.59
	Penn Line										19	2.70	2.11	2.90	3.28	3.20	3.64	3.49	3.72	4.42	2.98	3.33	2.91	38.68
	Saegertown	38	26.1	69.8	103	−35	39	May 18	Oct. 3	138	29	3.17	2.65	3.44	3.52	4.11	4.17	4.03	3.62	3.73	3.82	3.33	3.26	42.85
	Westford										22	2.80	2.32	2.75	2.91	3.24	3.75	3.68	3.47	3.98	3.01	3.63	3.09	38.63
Cumberland	Bloserville										26	3.21	2.34	3.23	3.78	4.12	4.88	5.12	5.43	3.87	3.75	2.88	2.84	45.45
	Carlisle	24	29.8	75.3	108	−16	24	Apr. 29	Oct. 7	161	25	3.19	3.00	3.40	3.45	3.60	4.14	4.19	4.38	3.20	3.37	2.78	2.87	41.57
Dauphin	Harrisburg	40	30.6	75.3	104	−14	40	Apr. 9	Oct. 30	204	40	3.00	2.72	3.13	2.99	2.93	3.70	3.48	4.05	3.37	2.96	2.04	2.87	37.24
	Lykens	24	29.1	72.6	106	−18	24	May 11	Oct. 2	144	24	3.10	2.50	3.15	3.53	3.91	4.55	5.08	4.09	4.15	3.68	3.28	2.77	43.79
Delaware	Marcus Hook	12	36.1	79.0	108	−12	12	Apr. 12	Nov. 7	209	12	3.71	2.41	3.57	3.36	3.09	3.80	3.71	5.56	3.69	2.43	3.00	2.83	41.16
Elk	Ridgway	23	25.6	67.8	101	−29	25	May 26	Sept. 25	122	24	3.12	2.18	3.19	3.13	3.72	4.40	3.73	3.26	3.13	3.21	2.97	2.66	38.70
Erie	Corry	20	25.6	69.7	110	−30	20	May 27	Sept. 23	119	20	3.51	2.61	3.77	3.83	3.45	4.53	3.22	3.27	3.77	3.66	4.24	3.51	43.37
	Erie	40	27.8	71.8	98	−16	40	Apr. 20	Oct. 31	194	40	2.54	1.90	2.58	3.04	2.84	2.97	3.07	2.95	3.24	3.37	2.80	2.50	33.80
Fayette	Newell	19	33.1	73.8	102	−20	18	May 4	Oct. 14	163	29	3.02	2.20	3.19	3.06	3.06	3.85	3.71	3.54	2.63	2.49	2.30	2.59	35.64
	Uniontown	39	33.0	73.7	102	−22	39	Apr. 28	Oct. 18	173	40	3.68	2.83	4.07	3.75	3.72	4.53	4.52	4.70	3.24	3.20	2.88	3.32	44.44
Franklin	Chambersburg	21	30.4	75.0	107	−15	21	May 2	Oct. 11	162	25	3.18	2.51	3.34	3.36	3.44	4.07	4.24	3.87	3.45	3.14	2.47	2.72	39.79
Greene	Aleppo	18	30.4	72.0	100	−27	18	May 11	Oct. 1	143	18	3.86	2.63	3.66	3.50	3.80	4.10	4.83	3.49	2.80	2.88	2.07	3.26	40.88
	Greensboro										38	3.38	2.56	3.75	3.36	3.73	4.47	4.45	3.60	3.08	2.83	2.55	3.04	40.80
Huntingdon	Huntingdon	40	29.2	72.7	105	−29	38	May 12	Oct. 6	147	40	3.20	2.60	3.52	3.54	3.72	4.04	4.09	4.07	3.26	2.87	2.25	2.92	40.08
Indiana	Indiana	32	29.4	71.9	106	−22	32	May 15	Oct. 3	141	28	4.02	2.98	3.82	3.93	4.15	4.80	4.73	3.90	3.79	3.55	2.73	3.33	45.73
	Saltsburg										36	3.54	2.71	3.33	3.30	3.45	4.39	4.23	4.17	3.57	3.09	2.35	3.10	41.23
Jefferson	Brookville	28	25.1	68.2	105	−32	27	May 29	Sept. 18	112	35	3.29	2.20	3.31	3.07	3.46	4.35	4.34	3.88	3.11	3.19	2.95	3.13	40.28
Juniata	Mifflintown	34	29.2	73.4	106	−31	32	May 8	Oct. 8	153	33	2.93	2.30	2.92	3.75	3.89	4.14	4.45	3.91	3.65	3.23	2.30	2.65	40.12
Lackawanna	Scranton	39	28.0	72.1	103	−19	40	Apr. 22	Oct. 15	176	40	2.64	2.60	3.04	2.90	2.88	3.86	4.09	3.76	3.29	2.95	2.45	2.70	37.16
Lancaster	Ephrata	36	30.6	74.8	106	−21	38	Apr. 26	Oct. 16	173	38	3.16	2.83	3.38	3.24	3.11	4.33	4.66	4.43	3.50	3.09	2.35	3.05	41.13
	Holtwood	19	32.1	77.1	104	−9	18	Apr. 12	Nov. 3	205	25	3.18	2.52	2.98	2.97	2.90	3.34	4.05	4.17	2.69	2.55	2.49	2.36	36.20
	Lancaster	28	30.6	74.3	107	−27	27	May 3	Oct. 8	158	39	3.22	2.62	3.42	3.36	2.98	4.13	4.67	4.50	3.48	3.04	2.45	3.14	41.01
Lawrence	New Castle	34	27.6	71.7	104	−25	25	May 12	do	149	33	3.15	2.14	3.18	3.40	3.56	4.13	3.78	3.69	3.03	2.73	2.40	2.68	37.87
Lebanon	Colebrook	22	28.4	72.3	102	−14	22	May 3	Oct. 13	163	29	3.39	2.79	3.65	3.87	3.32	4.24	4.60	4.69	3.68	3.43	2.69	3.11	43.46

	Lebanon	38	29.6	74.6	106	−23	40	Apr. 26	Oct. 11	168	40	3.35	3.07	3.54	3.53	3.09	4.42	4.49	4.43	3.61	3.28	2.49	3.32	42.62
Lehigh	Allentown	16	29.8	74.1	103	−12	17	Apr. 20	Oct. 18	181	27	3.49	2.86	3.31	3.60	3.53	3.92	4.99	4.66	3.58	3.30	2.75	3.19	43.18
Luzerne	Freeland	18	24.8	69.7	97	−24	20	May 10	Oct. 6	149	34	3.62	3.22	4.01	4.55	4.01	4.84	4.99	4.51	3.97	4.03	3.58	3.66	48.99
	Wilkes-Barre	12	27.8	73.6	101	−18	11	Apr. 27	Oct. 7	163	40	2.42	2.53	2.88	3.01	3.05	4.03	4.32	3.86	3.56	3.06	2.28	2.74	37.74
Lycoming	Williamsport	40	28.1	73.6	106	−18	40	Apr. 25	Oct. 15	173	40	2.90	2.46	3.27	3.68	3.72	3.75	3.77	3.92	3.22	3.12	2.52	2.84	39.17
McKean	Bradford	14	24.2	68.8	100	−24	18	May 26	Sept. 23	120	21	3.38	2.60	3.22	3.60	3.63	4.47	3.83	3.41	4.08	3.41	3.48	2.96	42.07
Mercer	Greenville	34	27.6	71.6	104	−27	36	May 20	Oct. 2	135	35	3.43	2.49	3.34	3.44	3.61	3.90	4.27	3.54	3.36	3.38	2.95	2.80	40.51
	Grove City	32	27.7	70.6	102	−32	32	May 16	Oct. 3	140	32	3.31	2.27	3.16	3.39	3.96	3.82	4.22	3.41	3.41	3.14	2.99	2.99	40.07
	Sharon	26	28.3	73.1	108	−23	26	May 10	Oct. 8	151	27	2.53	1.69	2.73	3.04	3.10	3.25	3.58	3.71	2.79	2.61	2.34	2.28	33.65
Monroe	Mount Pocono	32	23.6	65.7	103	−35	33	May 21	Sept. 25	127	33	3.16	2.83	3.72	3.86	3.89	5.12	5.18	4.45	5.09	4.79	3.19	3.44	48.72
	Stroudsburg	22	27.3	71.8	102	−35	21	May 8	Sept. 29	144	23	3.25	2.72	3.80	3.86	3.46	4.69	4.98	4.86	3.59	3.90	3.57	3.23	45.91
Montgomery	Ardmore	18	32.1	74.4	105	−14	20	Apr. 19	Oct. 25	189	7	4.58	2.75	4.09	3.52	3.87	4.77	5.39	5.71	4.73	3.56	3.84	2.96	49.77
	Browers Lock										22	3.59	3.63	3.77	3.40	3.27	4.14	4.22	5.00	3.31	3.44	2.61	4.00	44.31
	Graterford										20	3.17	2.79	3.25	3.23	3.43	3.82	4.86	4.15	3.20	2.72	2.82	2.61	40.05
	Pottstown										25	3.26	2.87	3.30	3.11	3.32	3.47	4.61	4.11	2.79	2.69	2.51	3.26	39.30
Northampton	Bethlehem	30	30.8	75.0	105	−16	27	Apr. 18	Oct. 20	185	33	3.47	2.97	3.34	3.52	3.09	4.18	4.80	4.56	3.66	3.30	2.83	3.18	42.90
	Easton	16	29.0	74.4	99	−14	11	Apr. 16	Oct. 15	182	11	3.35	3.52	3.74	3.37	3.14	4.05	4.04	4.80	4.21	3.43	2.08	3.96	43.69
Northumberland	Bear Gap										22	2.66	3.12	3.46	3.45	2.99	4.03	4.87	4.47	3.70	3.56	2.02	3.32	41.65
	Sunbury										26	3.22	2.63	3.03	3.70	3.70	4.02	4.00	3.62	3.23	3.23	2.54	2.76	39.68
Perry	New Germantown	10	29.2	72.4	99	−26	10	May 2	Oct. 10	161	10	3.05	2.16	2.88	3.45	3.86	4.44	3.42	3.90	3.92	3.53	1.75	2.97	39.33
Philadelphia	Philadelphia	40	34.4	76.7	106	−11	40	Apr. 5	Nov. 2	211	40	3.33	3.18	3.50	3.35	3.23	3.74	4.20	4.90	3.61	2.84	2.62	3.36	41.86
	Shawmont	22	32.3	76.6	105	−12	22	Apr. 20	Oct. 25	188	40	3.39	3.05	3.47	3.38	3.23	3.55	4.43	5.08	3.46	3.15	2.72	3.45	42.36
Pike	Matamoras										7	3.60	2.49	3.28	3.29	3.71	3.83	4.00	4.33	4.80	4.12	3.16	2.84	43.45
	Milford	18	24.9	70.1	102	−26	18	May 17	Sept. 29	135	18	2.88	2.94	3.40	3.31	3.03	3.87	4.46	4.13	3.79	3.82	2.60	3.44	41.67
	Paupack										22	2.80	2.54	3.25	3.63	3.49	3.93	4.51	4.64	3.93	3.77	2.94	2.82	42.25
Potter	West Bingham	15	22.3	64.6	98	−31	14	June 17	Sept. 2	77	14	2.42	2.00	2.63	3.03	3.92	3.90	3.68	3.60	3.23	3.04	2.21	2.13	35.79
Schuylkill	Girardville										40	3.92	3.57	4.24	3.98	3.74	4.74	5.09	4.84	4.22	4.15	3.13	3.97	49.59
	Gordon	36	27.2	70.5	101	−26	34	May 20	Sept. 26	129	35	3.72	3.20	3.94	4.17	3.95	4.45	5.02	4.47	4.02	4.19	3.27	3.72	48.12
	Pottsville										39	3.60	3.34	4.04	3.83	3.65	4.29	4.96	4.82	4.21	3.94	2.94	3.78	47.40
Snyder	Selinsgrove	40	29.0	73.4	105	−27	40	May 4	Oct. 9	158	39	3.03	2.72	3.64	3.68	3.56	4.02	3.96	3.83	3.51	3.43	2.58	3.02	40.98
Somerset	Confluence										40	4.01	2.88	3.90	3.71	4.07	4.58	4.64	4.45	3.07	2.94	2.82	3.47	44.54
	Somerset	38	27.1	68.7	103	−29	38	May 19	Sept. 27	131	39	4.70	3.67	4.70	4.63	4.38	5.44	4.94	4.80	3.64	3.04	3.08	3.91	50.93
Sullivan	Muncy Valley	27	25.6	69.8	103	−23	26	May 18	Sept. 28	133	27	3.15	2.29	2.85	3.99	4.31	4.49	4.51	4.66	4.01	3.57	3.18	2.80	43.81
Susquehanna	Forest City										18	2.89	2.39	2.49	3.59	3.88	4.41	4.53	4.29	3.70	3.68	3.26	2.61	41.72
	Montrose	33	23.6	68.0	100	−27	34	May 17	Oct. 1	137	33	2.61	2.05	2.66	3.38	3.94	4.15	4.02	4.18	3.93	3.67	2.62	2.47	39.68
Tioga	Ansonia										30	2.12	1.76	2.27	3.25	3.55	3.77	3.20	3.65	3.14	2.87	2.25	1.90	33.73
	Lawrenceville	39	25.5	70.4	107	−39	40	May 17	Sept. 27	133	39	1.91	1.76	2.38	2.91	3.67	3.95	4.04	3.92	3.13	2.75	2.26	1.80	34.58
	Lloyd										19	2.72	1.90	2.51	2.91	3.57	3.69	3.27	3.50	3.08	2.98	2.03	2.09	34.25
	Wellsboro	40	24.2	69.0	104	−30	40	May 27	Sept. 22	118	40	2.27	1.94	2.65	2.92	3.17	3.68	3.13	3.44	2.92	2.76	2.22	2.10	33.20
Union	Lewisburg	36	28.0	73.8	106	−30	34	May 4	Oct. 12	161	36	3.22	2.81	3.64	3.66	3.69	4.21	4.03	4.10	3.58	3.28	2.28	3.14	41.64
	Weikert										27	3.05	2.43	3.47	3.93	3.85	4.03	3.99	3.62	3.19	3.80	2.99	2.75	41.10
Venango	Franklin	40	26.6	70.9	106	−30	40	May 16	Oct. 3	140	39	3.42	2.50	3.37	3.54	3.79	4.05	4.32	3.67	3.38	3.15	2.95	3.11	41.25
Warren	Warren	40	26.4	69.7	100	−27	40	do.	Oct. 7	144	40	2.99	2.40	3.35	3.58	3.90	4.43	4.35	3.65	3.68	3.44	3.37	3.04	42.18
Washington	Claysville	34	31.5	73.4	108	−23	35	May 15	Oct. 2	140	35	3.33	2.43	3.49	3.44	3.64	4.24	4.17	3.87	3.16	3.08	2.47	2.91	40.23
	Lock No. 4										40	3.06	2.48	3.51	3.45	3.44	3.86	3.68	3.70	2.78	2.77	2.28	2.88	37.89
Wayne	Gouldsboro	14	23.4	65.0	94	−26	14	May 26	Sept. 18	115	24	3.28	2.90	3.26	3.60	4.01	4.78	5.00	4.41	3.73	3.86	3.51	2.83	45.17
	Hawley	20	25.8	70.3	100	−25	18	May 20	Sept. 24	127	27	2.72	2.65	3.05	3.24	3.52	3.87	4.30	4.12	3.56	3.28	2.75	2.77	39.83
Westmoreland	Derry	40	30.8	72.5	105	−29	40	May 11	Oct. 4	146	40	3.83	3.00	3.93	3.81	3.78	4.83	4.66	4.30	3.26	3.17	2.65	3.28	44.50
	Greensburg	31	31.5	72.6	103	−18	30	May 6	Oct. 6	153	31	3.62	2.87	3.44	3.75	3.92	4.30	3.71	4.19	3.21	3.00	2.49	3.13	41.63
	Irwin	38	30.5	72.7	104	−22	37	May 7	Oct. 7	153	40	3.00	2.38	3.33	3.28	3.25	4.41	3.79	3.92	2.88	2.81	2.33	2.92	38.30
	Lycippus	40	30.8	72.6	100	−22	40	May 1	Oct. 18	170	40	4.15	3.11	4.14	3.92	4.02	4.84	4.70	4.42	3.39	3.30	2.71	3.50	46.20
	Unity Reservoir						29	May 9	Oct. 6	150	23	4.08	3.03	3.78	3.87	3.75	4.29	4.14	3.99	3.41	3.14	2.59	3.54	43.61

PENNSYLVANIA—Continued

Climatic summary—Continued

County	Station	Temperature: Length of record	Temperature: January average	Temperature: July average	Temperature: Maximum	Temperature: Minimum	Killing frost average dates: Length of record	Killing frost average dates: Last in spring	Killing frost average dates: First in fall	Killing frost average dates: Growing season	Average precipitation: Length of record	January	February	March	April	May	June	July	August	September	October	November	December	Annual
		Yr.	*°F.*	*°F.*	*°F.*	*°F.*	*Yr.*			*Days*	*Yr.*	*In.*	*In.*	*In.*	*In.*	*In.*	*In.*	*In.*	*In.*	*In.*	*In.*	*In.*	*In.*	*In.*
Westmoreland—Con.	Vandergrift	24	31.3	73.7	106	−17	25	May 6	Oct. 12	159	25	2.94	2.56	3.01	2.82	3.36	4.24	4.11	4.36	3.14	2.97	2.60	2.74	38.85
	West Newton										40	3.26	2.67	3.54	3.32	3.55	4.00	3.91	3.93	2.85	2.78	2.36	3.10	39.27
York	Hanover	34	33.1	75.8	105	−15	35	Apr. 26	Oct. 16	173	35	3.22	2.60	3.30	3.50	3.33	4.03	4.15	4.36	3.26	2.98	2.35	2.99	40.07
	York	29	30.1	74.9	107	−21	28	do	Oct. 9	166	40	3.10	2.72	3.17	3.27	2.98	3.87	4.35	4.36	3.22	3.00	2.25	2.88	39.17
	York Haven										18	2.79	2.30	2.95	3.46	3.45	4.49	4.26	3.93	3.62	3.36	2.41	2.45	39.47

Precipitation and temperature—State unit values

[This tabulation gives the mean annual, mean monthly, and average seasonal precipitation, 1886–1938, and the mean annual temperatures, 1896–1938, for Pennsylvania]

Precipitation		Precipitation		Precipitation		Precipitation		Temperature		Temperature	
Year	Mean	Year	Mean	Year	Mean	Month	Mean	Year	Mean	Year	Mean
	In.		*In.*		*In.*		*In.*		*°F.*		*°F.*
1886	42.93	1907	45.45	1928	42.06	May	3.87	1896	50.5	1918	50.2
1887	41.10	1908	39.58	1929	44.21	June	4.13	1897	50.0	1919	51.1
1888	45.91	1909	37.38	1930	28.82	July	4.33	1898	51.3	1920	49.2
1889	52.67	1910	38.99	1931	37.36	August	4.19	1899	50.0	1921	53.1
1890	51.28	1911	45.52	1932	39.02	September	3.46	1900	51.5	1922	51.4
1891	45.65	1912	44.13	1933	45.43	October	3.18	1901	49.4	1923	50.4
1892	41.30	1913	43.25	1934	39.17	November	2.90	1902	49.6	1924	48.4
1893	44.26	1914	38.24	1935	40.43	December	3.10	1903	49.6	1925	50.3
1894	43.69	1915	44.26	1936	42.57			1904	47.5	1926	48.7
1895	33.51	1916	40.98	1937	46.62	Annual	42.23	1905	49.4	1927	50.9
1896	41.95	1917	41.71	1938	40.31			1906	50.8	1928	50.5
1897	42.73	1918	41.06			Season	Average	1907	48.5	1929	50.5
1898	45.49	1919	46.86	Month	Mean			1908	50.9	1930	51.2
1899	40.93	1920	40.63					1909	50.2	1931	52.8
1900	37.31	1921	41.80					1910	49.9	1932	51.6
1901	45.54	1922	34.88					1911	51.1	1933	51.7
1902	47.29	1923	39.17		*In.*		*In.*	1912	49.0	1934	50.6
1903	46.27	1924	43.13	January	3.27	Winter	9.28	1913	51.7	1935	50.2
1904	40.44	1925	37.86	February	2.91	Spring	10.76	1914	49.3	1936	50.4
1905	43.34	1926	43.11	March	3.48	Summer	12.65	1915	50.1	1937	50.7
1906	42.78	1927	47.30	April	3.41	Fall	9.54	1916	49.6	1938	51.8
								1917	47.3		

PENNSYLVANIA—Continued

Dates of last killing frost in spring and first in fall, with length of growing season

Year	Coatesville			Towanda			Emporium			State College			Uniontown			Franklin		
	Last in spring	First in fall	Growing season [1]	Last in spring	First in fall	Growing season [1]	Last in spring	First in fall	Growing season [1]	Last in spring	First in fall	Growing season [1]	Last in spring	First in fall	Growing season [1]	Last in spring	First in fall	Growing season [1]
			Days			*Days*			*Days*			*Days*			*Days*			*Days*
1899	Apr. 17	Oct. 2	168	Apr. 17	Oct. 2	168	Apr. 18	Oct. 2	167	Apr. 11	Sept. 30	172	Apr. 11	Oct. 1	173	Apr. 17	Sept. 30	166
1900	May 10	Oct. 18	161	May 7	Sept. 19	135	May 10	Oct. 17	160	May 10	Oct. 17	160	May 10	Nov. 9	183	May 22	Oct. 11	142
1901	Apr. 12	Oct. 7	178	Apr. 27	Oct. 7	163	May 7	Oct. 4	150	Apr. 12	Oct. 4	175	Apr. 12	Oct. 25	196	May 16	Oct. 4	141
1902	Apr. 6	Oct. 22	199	May 16	Oct. 10	147	May 29	Oct. 10	134	May 10	Oct. 10	153	Apr. 1	Oct. 30	212	May 29	Oct. 10	134
1903	May 2	Oct. 29	180	May 2	Oct. 25	176	May 5	Sept. 29	147	May 2	Oct. 25	176	Apr. 5	Oct. 25	203	May 5	Sept. 29	147
1904	Apr. 22	Sept. 22	153	Apr. 22	Sept. 22	153	May 12	Sept. 22	133	May 12	Sept. 22	133	Apr. 22	Oct. 7	168	May 12	Sept. 22	133
1905	Apr. 19	Oct. 22	186	May 24	Sept. 27	126	May 24	Oct. 26	155	Apr. 19	Oct. 22	186	Apr. 23	Oct. 22	182	May 21	Oct. 26	158
1906	Apr. 24	Oct. 11	170	May 21	Oct. 8	140	May 21	Oct. 12	144	May 10	Oct. 8	151	May 8	Oct. 11	156	June 12	Oct. 11	121
1907	May 12	Oct. 9	150	May 12	Oct. 9	150	May 22	Oct. 19	150	May 12	Oct. 9	150	May 28	Oct. 19	144	May 29	Oct. 1	125
1908	Apr. 17	Oct. 13	179	Apr. 21	Oct. 13	175	May 4	Sept. 30	149	May 3	Oct. 3	153	May 1	Oct. 3	155	May 4		
1909	May 3	do	163	Apr. 29	do	167	May 12	Oct. 13	154	May 4	Oct. 13	162	May 2	Oct. 13	164	May 12	Sept. 28	139
1910	Apr. 14	Oct. 29	198	May 16	do	150	May 16	do	150	May 16	do	150	May 6	Oct. 30	177	May 13	Oct. 8	148
1911	Apr. 18	do	194	May 6	Oct. 8	155	May 6	Oct. 8	155	May 5	Oct. 8	156	May 5	do	178	May 7	Oct. 3	149
1912	Apr. 9	Nov. 3	208	May 1	Oct. 17	169	May 14	Oct. 15	154	Apr. 28	Oct. 16	171	Apr. 23	Oct. 16	176	June 8	Oct. 16	130
1913	Apr. 21	Oct. 22	184	May 12	Sept. 15	126	June 10	Sept. 10	92	May 12	Oct. 22	163	May 12	Oct. 22	163	May 12	Sept. 10	121
1914	Apr. 14	Oct. 28	197	May 3	Sept. 29	149	May 17	Sept. 26	132	Apr. 16	Sept. 28	165	May 1			May 3	Oct. 27	177
1915	Apr. 15	Oct. 11	179	May 27	Oct. 9	135	May 27	Sept. 22	118	Apr. 15	Sept. 29	167		Oct. 10		May 27	Sept. 29	125
1916	Apr. 9	Oct. 2	176	Apr. 19	Oct. 1	165	May 21	Sept. 19	121	Apr. 11	Sept. 19	161	Apr. 10	Sept. 19	162	Apr. 19	Sept. 19	153
1917	May 4	Oct. 7	156	May 18	Sept. 11	116	May 26	Sept. 11	108	May 4	Sept. 11	130	Apr. 16	Oct. 14	181	May 26	Oct. 2	129
1918	Apr. 13	Oct. 9	179	Apr. 26	Oct. 8	165	May 2	do	132	Apr. 25	Oct. 8	166	May 2	Oct. 15	166	May 2	Oct. 1	152
1919	Apr. 27	Nov. 14	201	Apr. 30	do	161	May 3	Oct. 8	158	Apr. 30	do	161	Apr. 27	Nov. 13	200	Apr. 30	Oct. 8	161
1920	Apr. 15	Nov. 13	212	May 16	Oct. 7	144	May 17	Oct. 7	143	May 5	Oct. 7	155	May 16	Oct. 30	167	May 16	Oct. 30	167
1921	Apr. 12	Oct. 26	197	Apr. 20	Oct. 14	177	do	Oct. 13	149	Apr. 18	Oct. 13	178	Apr. 19	Oct. 14	178	May 17	Oct. 13	149
1922	May 1	Sept. 26	148	Apr. 22	Oct. 19	180	May 13	Sept. 25	135	May 1	Sept. 26	148	Apr. 30	Oct. 19	172	May 1	Sept. 26	148
1923	May 11	Oct. 7	149	May 11	Oct. 5	147	May 30	Sept. 17	110	May 14	Sept. 16	125	May 10	Oct. 6	149	May 14	Sept. 15	124
1924	May 5	Oct. 10	158	Apr. 28	Oct. 14	169	June 11	Oct. 9	130	Apr. 21	Oct. 9	171	Apr. 11	Oct. 21	193	May 5	Oct. 9	157
1925	May 9	Sept. 26	140	May 26	Oct. 10	137	May 26	Sept. 23	120	Apr. 29	Sept. 26	150	Apr. 7	Oct. 10	186	May 25	Oct. 10	138
1926	May 5	Oct. 10	158	May 5	do	158	June 4	Oct. 9	127	May 5	Oct. 16	164	Apr. 27	Oct. 26	182	June 4	Oct. 9	127
1927	May 28	Oct. 16	141	May 1	Oct. 11	163	June 6	do	125	May 28	Sept. 24	119	May 13	Oct. 27	167	May 1	Sept. 24	146
1928	May 15	Sept. 27	135	Apr. 30	Sept. 25	148	May 24	Sept. 25	124	Apr. 26	Oct. 8	165	Apr. 23	Oct. 18	178	May 24	Sept. 26	125
1929	May 10	Oct. 5	148	May 23	Sept. 21	121	June 3	Sept. 19	108	May 20	Sept. 19	122	May 30	Oct. 2	125	June 3	Sept. 22	111
1930	Apr. 27	Oct. 19	175	Apr. 27	Oct. 5	161	June 1	Oct. 5	126	May 27	Oct. 2	128	May 1	Nov. 6	189	June 1	Aug. 13	73
1931	May 4	Nov. 25	205	May 18	Oct. 13	148	May 18	Oct. 12	147	May 4	Oct. 10	159	May 4	Oct. 19	168	May 5	Oct. 11	159
1932	Apr. 17	Oct. 14	180	May 23	Sept. 26	126	June 24	Sept. 26	94	May 3	Sept. 26	146	May 3	Oct. 13	163	May 30	Sept. 26	119
1933	Apr. 28	Oct. 26	181	May 5	Oct. 14	162	May 5	Oct. 14	162	Apr. 28	Oct. 14	169	Apr. 27	Oct. 14	170	Apr. 28	Oct. 14	169
1934	Apr. 29	Oct. 13	167	May 13	Oct. 2	142	May 16	Aug. 31	107	Apr. 29	Oct. 2	156	Apr. 28	Oct. 13	168	May 26	Oct. 2	129
1935	Apr. 17	Oct. 5	171	May 24	Sept. 30	129	May 25	Sept. 30	128	Apr. 17	Sept. 30	166	Apr. 22	Sept. 30	161	May 24	Sept. 30	129

1936	Apr. 25	Oct. 27	185	May 15	Sept. 26	134	May 22	Sept. 26	127	May 15	Sept. 26	134	Apr. 24	Oct. 25	184	May 15	Oct. 4	142
1937	Apr. 17	Oct. 9	175	Apr. 17	Sept. 21	157	May 11	Sept. 27	139	Apr. 17	Sept. 27	163	Apr. 17	Oct. 14	180	Apr. 17	Sept. 18	154
1938	Apr. 11	Nov. 1	204	May 14	Oct. 5	144	May 25	Oct. 2	130	May 25	Oct. 2	130	May 13	Oct. 7	147	May 25	Oct. 7	135
Mean	Apr. 25	Oct. 17	175	May 7	Oct. 5	151	May 20	Oct. 2	135	May 2	Oct. 5	156	Apr. 28	Oct. 18	173	May 16	Oct. 3	140
Extremes	Apr. 6[2] May 28[3]	Sept. 22[4] Nov. 25[5]	[6] 135 [7] 212	Apr. 17[2] May 27[3]	Sept. 11[4] Oct. 25[5]	[6] 116 [7] 180	Apr. 18[2] June 24[3]	Aug. 31[4] Oct. 26[5]	[6] 92 [7] 167	Apr. 11[2] May 28[3]	Sept. 11[4] Oct. 25[5]	[6] 119 [7] 186	Apr. 1[2] May 30[3]	Sept. 19[4] Nov. 13[5]	[6] 125 [7] 212	Apr. 17[2] June 12[3]	Aug. 13[4] Oct. 30[5]	[6] 73 [7] 177

[1] Number of days between last killing frost in spring and first in fall.
[2] Earliest date in spring.
[3] Latest date in spring.
[4] Earliest date in fall.
[5] Latest date in fall.
[6] Shortest growing season.
[7] Longest growing season.

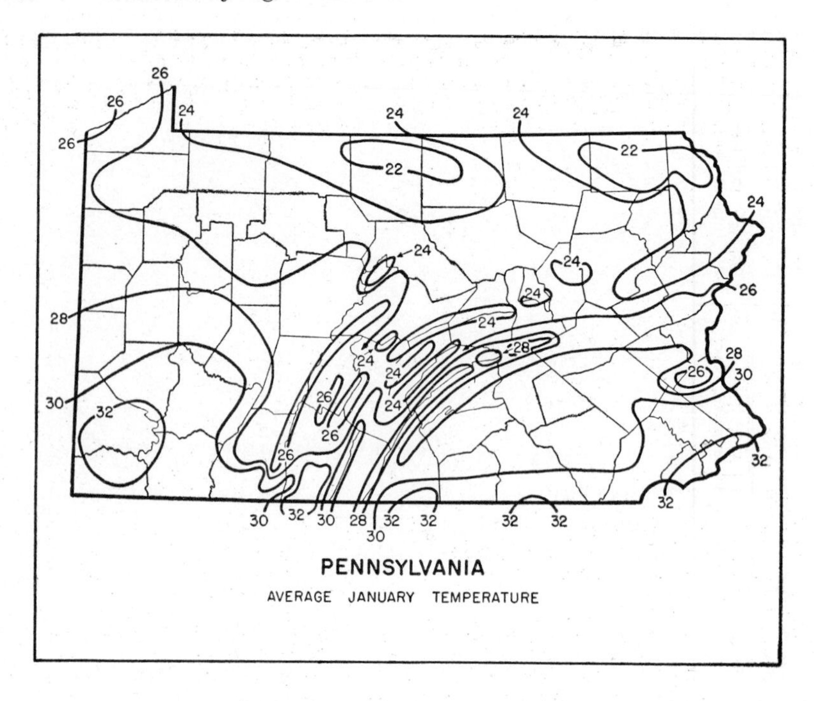

PENNSYLVANIA
AVERAGE JANUARY TEMPERATURE

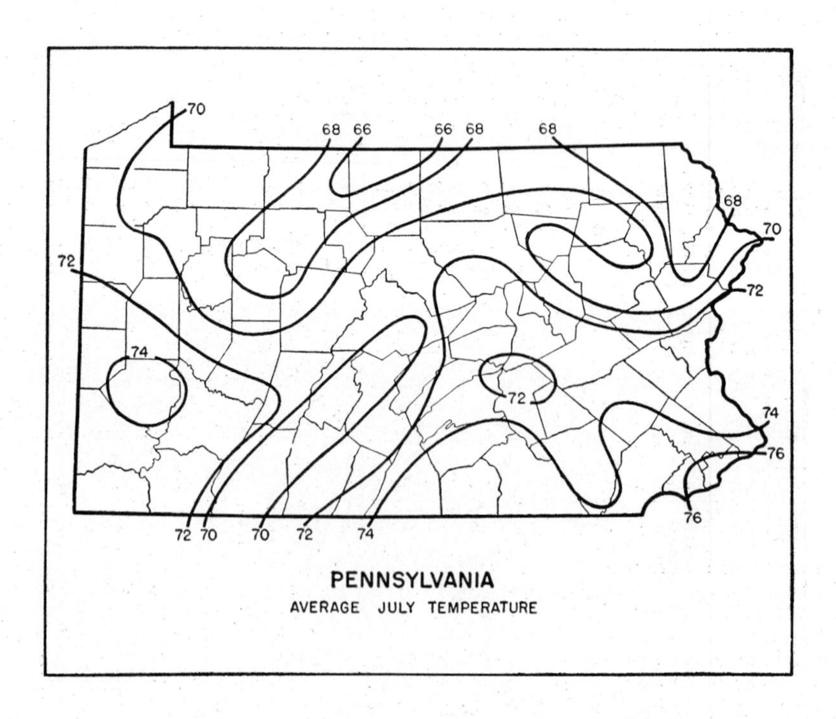

PENNSYLVANIA
AVERAGE JULY TEMPERATURE

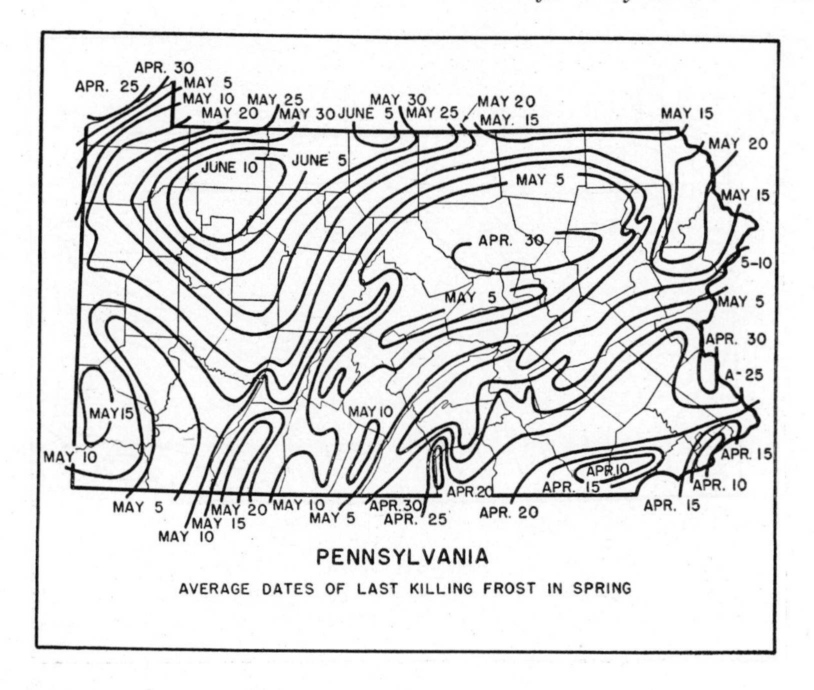

PENNSYLVANIA

AVERAGE DATES OF LAST KILLING FROST IN SPRING

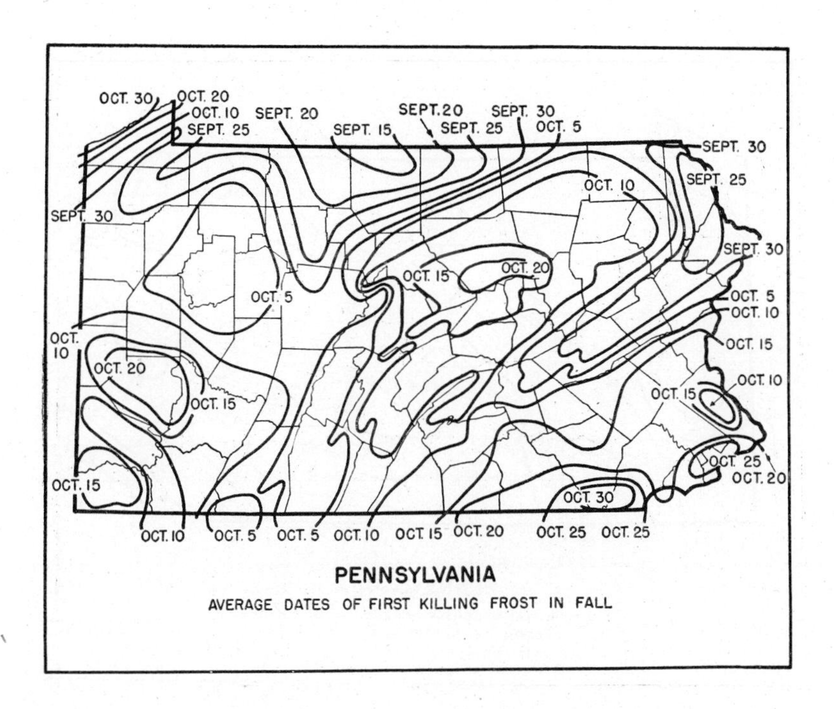

PENNSYLVANIA

AVERAGE DATES OF FIRST KILLING FROST IN FALL

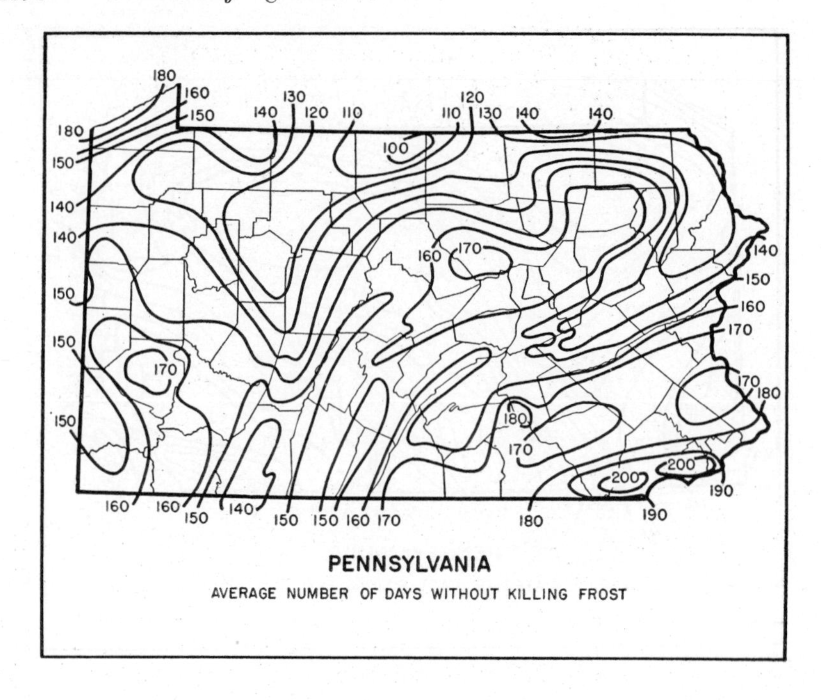

PENNSYLVANIA

AVERAGE NUMBER OF DAYS WITHOUT KILLING FROST

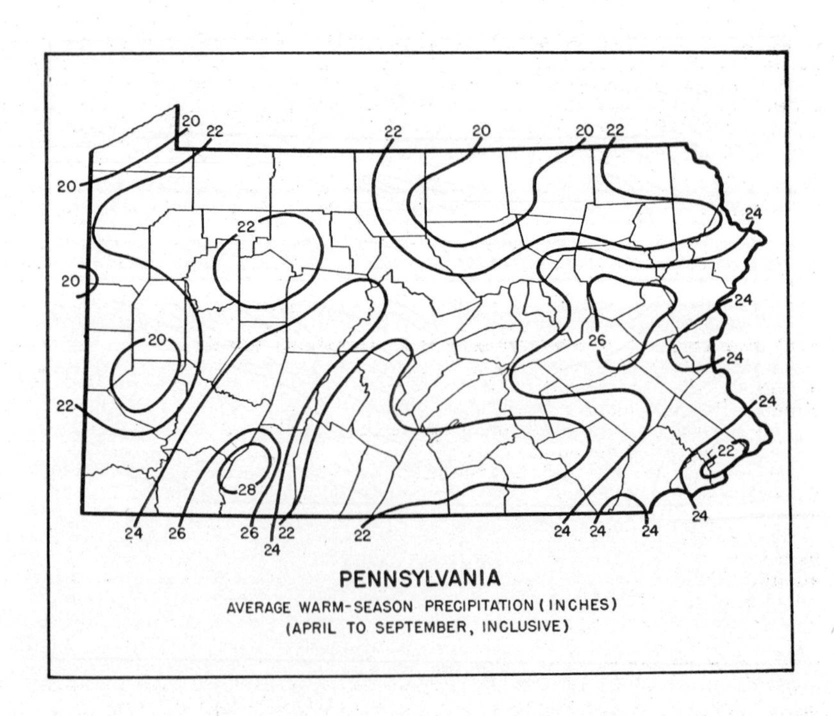

PENNSYLVANIA

AVERAGE WARM-SEASON PRECIPITATION (INCHES)
(APRIL TO SEPTEMBER, INCLUSIVE)

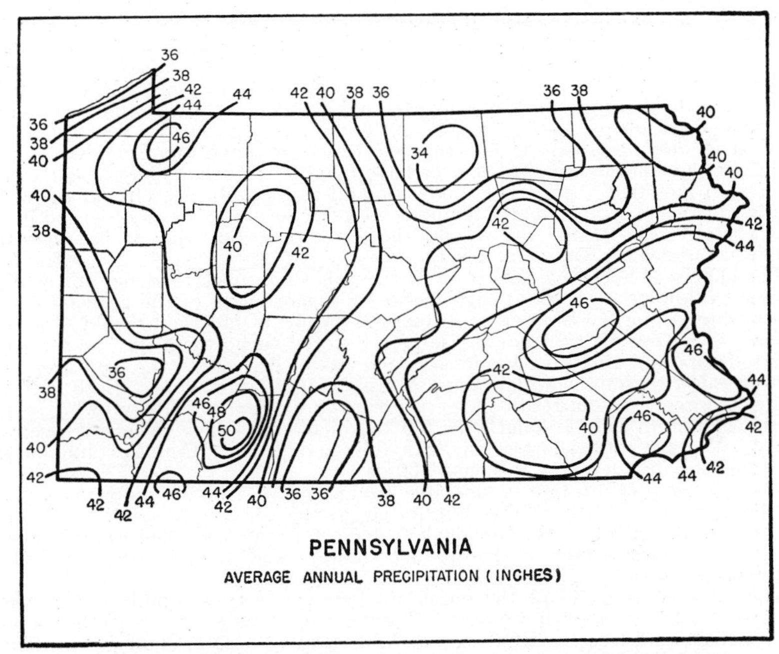

SUPPLEMENTARY CLIMATIC NOTES FOR PENNSYLVANIA

The chief feature of the topography of Pennsylvania is the Appalachian Mountain system, which is composed of several parallel ridges extending across the State in a long sweeping curve in a general northeast-to-southwest direction and having varying elevations, mostly between 1,500 and 2,500 feet. The intervening valleys are generally fertile.

The Blue Ridge marks the southern border of the mountain system, to the south and east of which lie chiefly rolling or undulating agricultural lands with rugged strips along some of the streams. The beds of the streams in this area are mostly below 300 feet in elevation. These lands comprise the chief agricultural area of the State and generally rank high in quality.

The northern tier of counties and the greater part of the second tier consist of high, rolling ground, with elevations mostly between 1,200 and 1,600 feet. There are several rounded mountains that rise 2,500 feet or higher, but there are no ridges or deep valleys. The general character of the area is that of an elevated plateau. A fairly large part of this northern area is adapted to agriculture, although it cannot be classed as among the choice lands of the State.

The western part of the State lies within the Ohio drainage basin and is generally hilly and rugged, or mountainous, with elevations mostly above 1,200 feet. Its arable lands are confined to small, local areas. Owing to the rapid drainage of the area and the rapidity with which flood waters accumulate in the larger streams, this area has an exceedingly important flood aspect.

The general topographic features of Pennsylvania naturally divide the State into four rather distinct climatic areas.

(1) The area south and east of the Blue Ridge has a modified type of climate, in which the temperature extremes are usually moderate and the rainfall is generally ample and fairly dependable.

Temperatures of 100° F. or higher are comparatively rare; in fact, readings as high as 90° occur on an average of only 15 days during the summer season. From about July 1 to the middle of September this area occasionally experiences uncomfortably warm periods, 4 or 5 days to a week in length, during which light wind movement and high relative humidity make conditions oppressive. In general, the winters are comparatively mild, there being an average of less than 100 days with minimum temperature below the freezing point. Temperatures of zero or lower occur at Philadelphia, on an average, one winter in four and at Harrisburg one in three. The growing season averages 170 to 200 days.

Average annual precipitation in the area ranges from about 38 inches in the lower Susquehanna Valley to about 46 in Chester County. Under the influence of an occasional severe coast storm, a normal month's rainfall, or more, may occur within a period of 48 hours. The average seasonal snowfall is about 30 inches, and fields are ordinarily snow-covered about one-third of the time during the winter season.

(2) The mountain belt is not rugged enough to have anything like a true mountain type of climate, but it does have many of the characteristics of such a climate in modified form. The mountain-and-valley influence on the air movements causes somewhat greater temperature extremes than are experienced in the southeastern part of the State, and the daily range of temperature increases somewhat under the valley influences.

The effects of nocturnal radiation in the valleys and the tendency for cool air masses to flow down them at night result in a shortening of the growing season by causing killing frosts later in spring and earlier in fall than would otherwise occur. Since the valley lands are largely devoted to horticulture, the tendency to late frosts in spring greatly increases the risk of damage to the fruit crop, and there are few seasons in which more or less damage is not done. Early autumn frosts, however, seldom result in serious or extensive harm. The growing season in the mountain belt is longest in the Susquehanna Valley, where it averages about 165 days, and shortest in Schuylkill and Carbon Counties and on the Pocono Plateau, averaging less than 130 days.

The annual precipitation in this area averages 3 or 4 inches more than in the southeastern part of the State, but its geographic distribution is less uniform. The mountain ridges are high enough to have a pronounced deflecting influence on general storm winds, while summer showers and thunderstorms are often shunted up the valleys.

The seasonal snowfall of the mountain belt varies considerably within short distances. It is greatest in Somerset County, averaging 88 inches in the vicinity of Somerset, and least in Huntingdon, Mifflin, and Juniata Counties, averaging about 37 inches.

(3) The climate of the northern counties is fairly typical of a true continental plateau. The average elevation is greater than that of the inhabited valleys of the mountain belt. These elevations, together with the influence of latitude and of favorable radiation conditions, serve to make this the coolest area in the State. Occasionally winter minimum temperatures are severe. The daily temperature range is fairly large, averaging about 20° F. in midwinter and 26° in midsummer.

The growing season is comparatively short, being less than 130 days in the greater part of the area. In Erie County, it lengthens rapidly toward the lake, increasing from 120 days in the southeastern corner to about 175 days along the lake shore.

The annual precipitation of this area averages about 41 inches, ranging from less than 35 in the northern parts of Tioga and Bradford Counties to more than 45 in parts of Crawford, Warren, and Wayne Counties. The seasonal snowfall averages about 54 inches, and fields are normally snow-covered about three-fourths of the time during the winter season.

(4) The western part of the State, lying within the Ohio drainage basin and south of the lake drainage, has a continental type of climate, with changeable temperatures and more frequent precipitation than other parts of the State. It is too rugged for a true plateau type, and its climate may be said to partake of both the plateau and the mountain-belt conditions.

The daily temperature range averages a few degrees higher than that for the plateau section, and the same may be said of the normal annual range. Because of the rugged topography the growing season is variable, ranging between 140 and 175 days.

With rapidly flowing streams in the drainage system (except the Monongahela), it is fortunate that this part of the State is not subject to torrential rains such as sometimes occur along the Atlantic slope. The average annual precipitation is about equal to that for the State as a whole, but it usually occurs in smaller amounts at more frequent intervals; 24-hour rains exceeding 2.5 inches are comparatively rare. The average seasonal snowfall is about 50 inches, and fields are normally snow-covered for as much of the winter as they are in the plateau region. Heavy snows sometimes occur in April.

George S. Bliss, *Senior Meteorologist and Climatic Section Director for Pennsylvania, Weather Bureau, Philadelphia.*

SOUTH CAROLINA

Climatic summary

County [1]	Station	Temperature: Length of record	Temperature: January average	Temperature: July average	Temperature: Maximum	Temperature: Minimum	Killing frost average dates: Length of record	Killing frost average dates: Last in spring	Killing frost average dates: First in fall	Killing frost average dates: Growing season [2]	Average precipitation: Length of record	January	February	March	April	May	June	July	August	September	October	November	December	Annual
		Yr.	°F.	°F.	°F.	°F.	Yr.			Days	Yr.	In.	In.	In.	In.	In.	In.	In.	In.	In.	In.	In.	In.	In.
Abbeville	Calhoun Falls	22	43.9	80.4	111	4	22	Mar. 29	Nov. 5	221	40	4.10	4.81	4.58	3.74	3.77	3.88	5.17	4.29	3.62	3.15	2.32	4.74	48.17
	Due West	22	43.5	79.2	105	6	22	Mar. 24	Nov. 16	237	18	3.60	4.64	4.49	3.13	3.50	3.68	5.00	4.04	3.73	2.22	2.29	4.94	45.26
Aiken	Aiken	36	46.8	80.3	107	3	36	Mar. 17	Nov. 19	247	37	3.42	4.18	3.61	3.19	3.05	4.37	4.93	4.32	3.57	2.72	2.18	3.65	43.19
	Monetta	16	47.3	79.6	105	6	16	Mar. 24	Nov. 10	231	16	3.34	4.75	4.34	2.94	2.94	5.34	5.48	4.85	3.00	3.52	2.18	3.28	45.96
Allendale	Allendale	22	48.1	83.3	106	10	22	Mar. 13	Nov. 14	246	24	3.02	3.93	3.78	2.71	3.42	5.36	6.17	5.24	3.35	2.38	1.58	2.87	43.81
Anderson	Anderson	38	44.7	79.6	106	2	38	Mar. 25	Nov. 9	229	38	4.38	4.91	4.58	3.83	3.44	4.09	4.94	4.92	3.37	3.14	2.42	5.09	49.11
	Pelzer										34	4.76	4.54	4.60	4.00	3.87	4.02	5.26	4.41	3.50	3.49	2.78	5.08	50.31
Bamberg	Edisto										18	3.14	4.46	3.94	3.16	3.34	6.20	6.13	6.29	3.68	2.51	1.98	3.52	48.35
Barnwell	Blackville	40	48.0	81.4	111	−3	40	Mar. 20	Nov. 14	239	40	3.27	3.98	3.24	3.67	3.38	5.30	5.39	5.04	4.23	2.60	2.08	3.26	45.44
Beaufort	Beaufort (near)	39	50.9	81.5	104	7	39	Feb. 24	Dec. 5	284	40	2.84	3.74	3.20	2.62	3.27	5.51	6.16	5.67	4.91	3.03	2.11	2.98	46.04
Berkeley	Pinopolis	34	48.2	78.3	98	2	34	Mar. 5	Nov. 25	265	40	2.84	3.69	3.18	3.25	3.70	5.60	7.30	5.88	4.55	3.13	2.20	2.91	48.23
Calhoun	St. Mathews	22	46.4	80.2	106	0	22	Mar. 16	Nov. 11	240	22	3.32	4.40	3.21	3.22	3.36	6.42	5.28	5.46	3.71	2.82	1.98	3.31	46.49
Charleston	Charleston	40	49.9	81.4	104	7	40	Feb. 23	Dec. 5	285	40	2.43	3.04	2.66	2.34	3.04	3.80	6.14	5.62	4.30	2.83	1.78	2.28	40.26
Cherokee	Gaston Shoals										34	4.59	4.40	4.68	3.64	3.79	4.13	4.78	5.15	3.34	3.48	2.74	4.50	49.22
Chester	Chester	14	44.3	80.2	110	0	14	Apr. 6	Nov. 10	218	11	5.12	4.05	4.23	4.13	2.90	4.00	6.22	4.66	5.34	2.51	2.57	3.86	49.59
Chesterfield	Cheraw	40	44.3	80.1	108	−9	40	Mar. 29	Nov. 3	219	40	3.25	4.05	3.66	3.46	3.51	5.14	5.80	5.76	3.91	2.94	2.26	3.59	47.33
Colleton	Walterboro	20	50.9	80.1	106	10	20	Mar. 20	Nov. 8	233	20	3.00	3.83	3.44	3.55	3.59	5.68	7.12	6.30	4.40	3.09	1.86	2.77	48.63
Darlington	Darlington	38	46.0	80.2	109	4	38	Mar. 29	Nov. 4	220	40	3.09	3.51	3.04	3.25	3.61	5.03	5.17	4.65	4.45	3.09	2.13	3.17	44.19
	Society Hill	40	44.6	79.8	110	0	40	Mar. 24	Nov. 8	229	40	3.26	4.09	3.41	3.52	3.61	5.12	6.20	5.18	4.30	3.11	2.31	3.51	47.62
Dillon	Dillon	20	46.4	80.4	105	−8	20	Mar. 29	Nov. 2	218	21	3.04	4.25	3.43	3.89	3.28	5.91	5.91	5.01	4.28	3.12	1.96	3.12	47.20
Dorchester	St. George	27	47.6	80.8	106	0	27	Mar. 12	Nov. 14	247	25	2.97	3.49	3.30	3.40	3.12	5.35	6.38	5.81	3.60	2.48	1.72	3.21	44.83
	Summerville	40	49.6	80.2	106	−1	40	Mar. 16	Nov. 13	242	40	3.04	3.76	3.14	3.46	3.37	5.42	6.78	6.47	5.01	2.87	2.14	3.12	48.58
Edgefield	Edgefield										25	4.06	3.86	4.10	4.11	3.31	3.66	5.75	4.04	3.47	2.55	2.04	3.36	44.31
	Trenton	38	47.0	80.3	109	−4	38	Mar. 20	Nov. 15	240	39	3.43	4.52	4.27	3.49	3.48	4.34	5.32	4.73	3.35	3.01	2.22	4.01	46.17
Fairfield	Blairs										33	3.77	3.91	3.72	3.35	3.16	3.87	5.16	4.96	3.25	2.79	2.19	4.04	44.17
	Winnsboro	37	44.5	80.1	108	−3	37	Mar. 25	Nov. 13	233	36	3.68	4.00	4.05	3.59	3.51	4.50	5.09	5.41	3.38	3.04	2.07	3.86	46.18
Florence	Effingham										40	3.30	4.31	3.69	3.59	3.67	5.54	6.10	5.22	4.72	2.95	1.99	3.21	48.29
	Florence No. 1	39	46.1	81.3	108	−1	39	Mar. 19	Nov. 12	238	40	2.95	3.89	3.29	3.34	3.84	5.47	5.80	4.69	4.32	2.88	1.92	3.09	45.48
	Florence No. 2										24	3.27	3.20	3.17	3.63	4.14	4.61	6.57	4.30	4.83	2.42	1.97	3.26	45.37
	Mars Bluff Bridge										15	3.27	3.29	2.78	3.25	3.61	4.11	5.35	4.74	6.18	2.56	2.06	3.24	44.44
Georgetown	Georgetown	36	48.8	80.7	104	4	36	Mar. 14	Nov. 18	249	35	3.31	3.86	3.32	3.23	3.61	5.73	7.31	6.59	5.04	3.06	2.36	3.44	50.86
	Smith Mills										18	3.08	4.20	3.90	3.12	4.33	5.65	5.66	7.04	4.36	3.88	1.99	3.47	50.68

[1] The following counties, for which no records are available, are best represented by the station indicated: Clarendon—Rimini; Jasper—Yemassee; Lee—Sumter; Marion—Mars Bluff Bridge; Marlboro—Cheraw.

[2] Length of growing season between average dates of last killing frost in spring and first in fall.

SOUTH CAROLINA—Continued

Climatic summary—Continued

County	Station	Temperature: Length of record	Temperature: January average	Temperature: July average	Temperature: Maximum	Temperature: Minimum	Killing frost average dates: Length of record	Killing frost average dates: Last in spring	Killing frost average dates: First in fall	Killing frost average dates: Growing season	Average precipitation: Length of record	January	February	March	April	May	June	July	August	September	October	November	December	Annual
		Yr.	*°F.*	*°F.*	*°F.*	*°F.*	*Yr.*			*Days*	*Yr.*	*In.*	*In.*	*In.*	*In.*	*In.*	*In.*	*In.*	*In.*	*In.*	*In.*	*In.*	*In.*	*In.*
Greenville	Greenville	40	40.3	76.9	106	−5	40	Mar. 27	Nov. 10	228	40	4.56	4.87	4.86	4.01	3.88	4.25	4.96	5.29	3.92	3.48	2.76	5.26	52.10
	Caesars Head	14	39.5	71.7	98	−2	14	Apr. 21	Oct. 25	187	14	6.77	4.76	6.08	5.25	4.42	5.10	5.97	8.44	6.12	6.63	5.97	7.65	73.16
Greenwood	Greenwood	40	43.4	79.6	109	−5	40	Mar. 24	Nov. 9	230	40	4.05	4.75	4.28	3.68	3.31	4.07	5.14	4.75	3.51	3.23	2.48	4.53	47.78
Hampton	Garnett	17	50.9	81.5	110	11	17	Mar. 10	Nov. 13	248	17	2.91	3.54	3.59	3.22	4.27	5.35	6.48	4.99	5.27	2.34	2.33	3.11	47.40
	Yemassee	40	49.4	80.7	107	4	40	Mar. 15	do	243	40	2.99	3.43	3.28	3.02	3.73	6.18	7.00	5.85	4.61	3.02	2.13	3.01	48.25
Horry	Conway	38	48.7	80.1	105	6	38	Mar. 23	Nov. 9	231	40	3.37	4.02	3.35	3.18	3.59	5.58	6.79	6.59	5.15	3.33	2.16	3.32	50.43
Kershaw	Camden	31	46.2	80.5	106	−1	31	Mar. 14	Nov. 13	244	40	3.71	4.06	3.77	3.62	3.05	5.07	5.67	5.27	4.31	3.08	2.23	3.80	47.64
	Kershaw	23	45.4	79.9	107	5	23	Mar. 28	Nov. 7	224	23	3.57	3.45	3.50	4.08	3.09	4.73	5.39	4.78	3.66	2.81	2.07	3.62	44.75
Lancaster	Heath Springs	37	44.2	79.1	106	0	37	Mar. 27	Nov. 6	224	37	3.44	3.73	3.61	3.57	3.04	5.08	4.83	5.49	3.30	2.71	2.17	3.67	44.64
Laurens	Laurens	26	43.6	79.9	107	1	26	Apr. 2	do	218	26	4.32	4.58	4.18	3.83	3.24	4.44	5.38	4.51	3.46	2.94	2.41	4.60	47.89
Lexington	Batesburg	24	45.4	79.7	107	−4	24	Mar. 25	Nov. 13	233	23	3.84	5.47	4.42	3.25	3.01	4.87	4.84	5.42	3.52	2.96	2.54	4.08	48.22
McCormick	Meriwether	18	47.2	80.2	107	8	18	do	Nov. 2	222	17	3.54	4.29	4.14	2.75	2.73	4.56	5.15	4.40	2.78	2.48	2.30	3.57	42.69
Newberry	Chappells										33	3.80	3.97	3.98	3.61	3.40	3.70	5.24	4.47	3.51	2.94	2.18	4.29	45.09
	Little Mountain	40	45.7	80.1	108	−4	40	Mar. 25	Nov. 11	231	40	3.72	4.23	3.85	3.49	3.21	4.14	4.76	5.01	3.50	3.07	2.27	3.73	44.98
	Newberry	35	45.5	80.9	108	−2	35	Mar. 29	Nov. 5	221	35	4.04	4.21	3.85	3.70	3.53	4.20	4.78	5.01	3.28	2.97	2.44	4.42	46.43
Oconee	Clemson College	40	43.4	78.3	104	−7	40	Apr. 1	Nov. 2	215	40	5.16	5.28	5.04	4.27	4.29	4.63	5.26	4.79	3.63	3.61	2.78	5.78	54.52
	Walhalla	33	42.7	77.4	108	−9	33	Apr. 8	Oct. 28	203	33	5.38	5.47	5.81	4.79	4.21	4.91	5.51	5.89	4.73	3.98	3.29	6.27	60.24
Orangeburg	Bowman	21	48.1	79.9	104	6	21	Mar. 25	Nov. 4	224	20	3.26	4.03	4.16	3.38	3.69	4.92	6.52	6.15	3.40	2.43	1.97	3.22	47.13
	Ferguson	39	47.5	79.9	107	−3	39	Mar. 26	Nov. 8	227	40	3.37	3.76	3.19	3.37	3.53	5.18	6.24	6.11	4.40	2.85	2.02	3.07	47.09
	Orangeburg	23	48.8	80.6	106	8	23	Mar. 18	Nov. 15	242	22	3.17	3.55	3.01	3.43	3.20	4.69	5.56	5.04	4.15	2.03	1.74	2.95	42.52
Pickens	Liberty	26	43.0	78.9	105	0	26	Apr. 1	Nov. 2	215	26	4.92	5.40	5.14	4.70	4.71	4.65	5.64	5.94	3.99	3.64	2.25	6.08	57.66
Richland	Columbia	40	46.0	80.9	106	−2	40	Mar. 15	Nov. 18	248	40	3.03	3.73	3.17	3.31	3.05	4.22	5.14	5.24	3.48	2.55	1.83	3.20	41.95
Saluda	Saluda	37	45.3	80.1	109	4	37	Apr. 3	Oct. 31	211	36	3.91	4.30	4.21	3.50	3.25	4.31	4.85	4.94	3.63	2.92	2.25	3.98	46.05
Spartanburg	Landrum	24	43.2	78.2	105	−6	24	Apr. 5	do	209	23	5.59	4.40	5.53	4.82	5.15	4.68	6.62	5.73	4.41	4.68	3.67	5.23	60.51
	Spartanburg	40	42.1	79.1	106	−4	40	Mar. 31	Nov. 3	217	40	4.40	4.53	4.62	3.69	3.82	4.24	4.86	5.31	3.55	3.35	2.78	4.63	49.78
	Cherokee	11	43.8	78.2	102	2	11	Apr. 9	Oct. 27	201	10	4.96	3.81	4.65	3.97	3.90	4.11	4.59	4.22	3.42	4.57	3.54	5.05	50.79
	Crescent										12	4.90	4.59	4.98	4.78	3.92	3.90	5.56	6.28	4.69	5.09	3.56	6.21	58.46
Sumter	Rimini										25	3.43	3.82	3.10	3.69	3.99	4.62	6.30	4.92	4.92	2.20	1.95	3.25	46.19
	Sumter	14	49.5	81.2	105	7	14	Mar. 19	Nov. 14	240	15	2.67	3.25	2.81	3.44	3.31	5.16	5.37	4.46	4.01	2.89	1.85	3.39	42.61
	Wedgefield	28	46.8	79.6	108	3	28	Mar. 21	Nov. 19	243	25	3.35	4.05	3.18	3.77	3.52	5.19	4.69	5.62	4.67	2.48	2.07	3.59	46.18
Union	Santuck	40	43.5	79.7	110	−11	40	Apr. 5	Oct. 30	208	40	3.94	4.52	4.37	3.56	3.49	3.80	5.05	5.87	3.61	3.16	2.60	4.38	48.35
Williamsburg	Kingstree	40	48.6	80.6	107	6	40	Mar. 15	Nov. 12	242	40	3.08	3.65	3.40	3.19	3.09	5.32	6.68	5.78	4.50	2.75	2.02	2.98	46.44
York	Catawba										32	3.84	4.09	3.95	3.47	3.55	3.96	5.62	4.80	3.35	3.29	2.39	4.01	46.32
	Winthrop College	39	43.9	79.6	106	1	39	Mar. 28	Nov. 6	223	39	3.88	3.94	4.09	3.54	3.97	4.40	5.06	5.14	3.32	3.00	2.40	4.29	47.03
	York	10	43.0	80.6	103	−3	10	Mar. 30	Nov. 15	230	9	3.44	5.12	4.87	3.82	4.11	4.81	4.12	7.09	3.74	2.32	2.88	5.11	51.43

Precipitation—State unit values

[This tabulation gives the mean annual, mean monthly, and average seasonal precipitation, 1886–1938, for South Carolina]

Precipitation		Precipitation		Precipitation		Precipitation		Precipitation		Precipitation	
Year	Mean	Year	Mean	Year	Mean	Year	Mean	Month	Mean	Season	Average
	In.		*In.*		*In.*		*In.*		*In.*		*In.*
1886	43.98	1900	51.14	1913	47.45	1926	42.43	January	3.60	Winter	11.30
1887	43.60	1901	56.91	1914	43.48	1927	42.23	February	4.14	Spring	10.69
1888	54.13	1902	46.70	1915	48.81	1928	62.06	March	3.85	Summer	16.30
1889	46.68	1903	50.97	1916	44.25	1929	64.36	April	3.25	Fall	9.40
1890	42.43	1904	40.65	1917	43.28	1930	40.71	May	3.59		
1891	49.08	1905	45.03	1918	46.24	1931	35.48	June	4.82		
1892	47.89	1906	54.83	1919	46.30	1932	53.81	July	5.83		
1893	52.57	1907	47.67	1920	52.01	1933	35.84	August	5.65		
1894	50.22	1908	53.11	1921	42.87	1934	44.58	September	4.10		
1895	49.05	1909	45.26	1922	58.09	1935	42.49	October	2.98		
1896	45.32	1910	45.59	1923	46.17	1936	57.03	November	2.32		
1897	47.32	1911	40.08	1924	56.99	1937	51.69	December	3.56		
1898	49.88	1912	54.16	1925	36.37	1938	40.68				
1899	47.45							Annual	47.69		

SOUTH CAROLINA—Continued

Dates of last killing frost in spring and first in fall, with length of growing season

Year	Charleston			Cheraw			Columbia			Greenville			Greenwood			Kingstree		
	Last in spring	First in fall	Growing season [1]	Last in spring	First in fall	Growing season [1]	Last in spring	First in fall	Growing season [1]	Last in spring	First in fall	Growing season [1]	Last in spring	First in fall	Growing season [1]	Last in spring	First in fall	Growing season [1]
			Days			*Days*			*Days*			*Days*			*Days*			*Days*
1899	Mar. 8	Dec. 6	273	Apr. 5	Nov. 4	213	Apr. 5	Dec. 5	244	Apr. 11	Nov. 26	229	Apr. 5	Nov. 4	213	Mar. 9	Dec. 5	271
1900	Mar. 17	Dec. 16	274	Apr. 5	Nov. 9	218	Apr. 1	Nov. 9	222	Apr. 13	Nov. 9	210	do	Nov. 9	218	Apr. 1	Nov. 10	223
1901	Mar. 7	Nov. 16	254	Mar. 22	Nov. 7	230	Mar. 22	Nov. 16	239	Mar. 23	Nov. 6	228	Mar. 22	Nov. 6	229	Mar. 17	Nov. 16	244
1902	Mar. 19	Nov. 28	254	Apr. 2	Nov. 28	240	Mar. 19	Nov. 28	254	Apr. 10	Nov. 28	232	Apr. 2	Nov. 28	240	Apr. 2	Nov. 28	240
1903	Feb. 18	Nov. 19	274	Apr. 5	Oct. 27	205	Feb. 23	Nov. 8	258	Apr. 24	Oct. 25	184	Mar. 2	Oct. 25	237	Feb. 21	Oct. 28	249
1904	do	Dec. 13	299	do	Nov. 7	216	Mar. 5	Dec. 11	281	Apr. 18	Oct. 23	188	Mar. 17	Nov. 15	243	Mar. 5	Nov. 14	254
1905	Feb. 16	Dec. 11	298	Apr. 17	Nov. 12	209	Apr. 17	Nov. 15	212	Apr. 19	Nov. 4	199	Apr. 17	Nov. 11	208	Apr. 18	Dec. 10	236
1906	Feb. 28	Nov. 16	261	Mar. 26	Oct. 11	199	Mar. 21	Nov. 13	237	Apr. 3	Oct. 11	191	Mar. 26	Oct. 11	199	Feb. 28	Dec. 24	299
1907	Feb. 9	Nov. 14	278	Apr. 15	Nov. 8	207	Apr. 15	Nov. 14	213	Apr. 16	Oct. 15	182	Apr. 15	Nov. 14	213	Feb. 8	Nov. 14	279
1908	Feb. 28	None	308	Mar. 22	Nov. 6	229	Feb. 28	Nov. 15	261	Mar. 22	Nov. 6	229	Feb. 29	Nov. 15	260	Feb. 28	Nov. 16	262
1909	Feb. 2	Dec. 10	311	Mar. 26	Oct. 26	214	Mar. 16	Nov. 19	248	Mar. 27	Oct. 25	212	Apr. 1	Nov. 18	231	Mar. 16	Nov. 19	248
1910	Feb. 14	Dec. 1	290	Mar. 16	Oct. 30	228	do	Oct. 30	228	Mar. 17	Oct. 29	226	Mar. 16	Oct. 29	227	do	Oct. 31	229
1911	Feb. 22	Nov. 25	276	Mar. 31	Nov. 3	217	do	Nov. 13	242	do	Nov. 3	231	Mar. 31	Nov. 3	217	Apr. 1	Nov. 30	243
1912	Feb. 12	Nov. 29	291	Mar. 11	do	237	Mar. 10	Nov. 4	239	Apr. 3	do	214	Mar. 11	do	237	Mar. 11	Nov. 3	237
1913	None	Nov. 11	314	Mar. 28	Oct. 22	208	Mar. 28	Nov. 2	219	Mar. 28	Oct. 21	207	Mar. 28	Oct. 31	217	Mar. 7	Oct. 22	229
1914	Mar. 23	Nov. 21	243	Mar. 24	Oct. 28	218	Mar. 23	Nov. 17	239	Mar. 25	Oct. 28	217	Mar. 24	Oct. 28	218	Mar. 23	Oct. 28	219
1915	Apr. 1	Nov. 30	243	Apr. 4	Nov. 16	226	Apr. 4	Nov. 16	226	Apr. 4	Oct. 10	189	Apr. 4	Nov. 16	226	Apr. 4	Nov. 17	227
1916	Mar. 17	Nov. 17	245	Mar. 17	do	244	Mar. 17	do	244	Apr. 10	Nov. 4	208	Apr. 10	do	220	Apr. 10	Nov. 16	220
1917	Mar. 6	Nov. 25	264	Mar. 19	Oct. 25	220	Mar. 6	Nov. 3	242	Apr. 7	Oct. 24	200	Mar. 19	Oct. 24	219	Mar. 19	Oct. 25	220
1918	Feb. 5	Dec. 29	327	Feb. 22			Feb. 6	Dec. 26	323	Mar. 11	Dec. 2	266	Mar. 12	Nov. 13	246	Feb. 24	Nov. 8	257
1919	Feb. 17	Dec. 15	301	Apr. 4	Nov. 15	225	Feb. 17	Nov. 15	271	Apr. 1	Nov. 14	227	Apr. 2	Nov. 15	227	Apr. 2	Nov. 15	227
1920	Mar. 9	Dec. 29	295	Apr. 6	Oct. 30	207	Apr. 6	Nov. 13	221	Apr. 6	Nov. 13	221	Apr. 15	Nov. 13	212	Mar. 10	Nov. 13	248
1921	Jan. 27	None	339	Apr. 12	Oct. 14	185	Feb. 24	Dec. 30	309	Feb. 25	do	261	Feb. 25	do	261	Feb. 26	Oct. 9	225
1922	Feb. 17	None	318	Mar. 23	Nov. 21	243	Mar. 5	Nov. 22	262	Mar. 5	Nov. 25	265	Mar. 5	Nov. 25	265	Mar. 6	Nov. 22	261
1923	Feb. 9	None	326	Apr. 2	Nov. 9	221	Apr. 1	Nov. 9	222	Apr. 2	Nov. 10	222	Apr. 2	Nov. 9	221	Apr. 2	Nov. 10	222
1924	Mar. 11	Dec. 2	266	Apr. 3	Nov. 19	230	Mar. 17	Nov. 19	247	do	Nov. 19	231	Apr. 3	Nov. 19	230	Mar. 17	Nov. 19	247
1925	Mar. 3	Nov. 24	266	Mar. 4	Oct. 11	221	Mar. 4	Nov. 17	258	Mar. 4	Nov. 24	265	Mar. 4	Nov. 10	251	Mar. 4	Nov. 17	258
1926	Mar. 14	Dec. 19	280	Apr. 20	Oct. 26	189	Mar. 16	Nov. 11	240	Mar. 28	Nov. 11	228	Mar. 28	Nov. 6	223	Mar. 18	Oct. 28	224
1927	Mar. 3	Dec. 9	281	Apr. 11	Nov. 7	210	Mar. 4	Nov. 21	262	Mar. 25	Nov. 19	239	Mar. 25	Nov. 7	227	Mar. 5	Nov. 7	247
1928	Feb. 19	Nov. 26	281	Apr. 1	Nov. 12	225	Mar. 19	do	247	Mar. 20	Nov. 21	246	Mar. 31	Nov. 21	235	Apr. 1	Nov. 21	234
1929	Feb. 2	Nov. 30	301	Mar. 18	Nov. 6	233	Mar. 10	Nov. 6	241	Mar. 11	Nov. 22	256	Mar. 10	Nov. 6	241	Mar. 11	Nov. 30	264
1930	Mar. 3	Nov. 27	269	Mar. 31	Oct. 25	208	Mar. 4	Nov. 1	242	Mar. 26	Nov. 7	226	Mar. 6	Oct. 26	234	Mar. 5	Oct. 26	235
1931	Feb. 15	None	320	Mar. 18	Oct. 19	215	Mar. 5	Dec. 27	297	Mar. 12	None	295	Mar. 19	Nov. 7	233	Mar. 18	Nov. 1	228
1932	Mar. 15	None	293	Mar. 16	Nov. 13	242	Mar. 15	Nov. 13	243	Mar. 15	Nov. 13	243	Mar. 16	Nov. 12	241	Mar. 16	Nov. 13	242
1933	Feb. 12	Nov. 16	277	Mar. 27	Nov. 9	227	Mar. 11	Nov. 9	243	Mar. 11	Nov. 8	242	Mar. 22	Nov. 9	232	Mar. 6	Nov. 9	248
1934	Mar. 12	Nov. 15	248	Mar. 25	Oct. 29	218	Mar. 15	Nov. 12	242	Apr. 14	Nov. 12	212	Mar. 16	Nov. 12	241	Mar. 21	Oct. 29	222
1935	Jan. 29	Nov. 26	301	Mar. 1	Oct. 7	220	Mar. 1	Nov. 24	268	Mar. 13	Nov. 23	255	Mar. 2	Nov. 23	266	Mar. 1	Oct. 26	239

1936	Feb. 22	Nov. 28	280	Apr. 4	Nov. 16	226	Feb. 23	Nov. 16	267	Apr. 4	Nov. 16	226	Apr. 4	Nov. 16	226	Apr. 4	Nov. 16	226
1937	Mar. 1	Nov. 21	265	Apr. 13	Oct. 16	186	Mar. 29	Nov. 5	221	Mar. 28	Oct. 24	210	Mar. 29	Oct. 24	209	Mar. 29	Oct. 25	210
1938	Jan. 28	Nov. 28	304	Apr. 11	Nov. 15	218	Mar. 1	Nov. 25	269	Mar. 1	Nov. 25	269	Apr. 10	Nov. 25	229	Mar. 2	Nov. 25	268
Mean	Feb. 23	Dec. 5	285	Mar. 29	Nov. 3	219	Mar. 15	Nov. 18	248	Mar. 27	Nov. 10	228	Mar. 24	Nov. 9	230	Mar. 15	Nov. 12	242
Extremes	None [2]	Nov. 11 [4]	[6] 243	Feb. 22 [2]	Oct. 7 [4]	[6] 185	Feb. 6 [2]	Oct. 30 [4]	[6] 212	Feb. 25 [2]	Oct. 10 [4]	[6] 182	Feb. 25 [2]	Oct. 11 [4]	[6] 199	Feb. 8 [2]	Oct. 9 [4]	[6] 210
	Apr. 1 [3]	None [5]	[7] 339	Apr. 20 [3]	Nov. 28 [5]	[7] 244	Apr. 17 [3]	Dec. 30 [5]	[7] 323	Apr. 24 [3]	None [5]	[7] 295	Apr. 17 [3]	Nov. 28 [5]	[7] 266	Apr. 18 [3]	Dec. 24 [5]	[7] 299

[1] Number of days between last killing frost in spring and first in fall.
[2] Earliest date in spring.
[3] Latest date in spring.
[4] Earliest date in fall.
[5] Latest date in fall.
[6] Shortest growing season.
[7] Longest growing season.

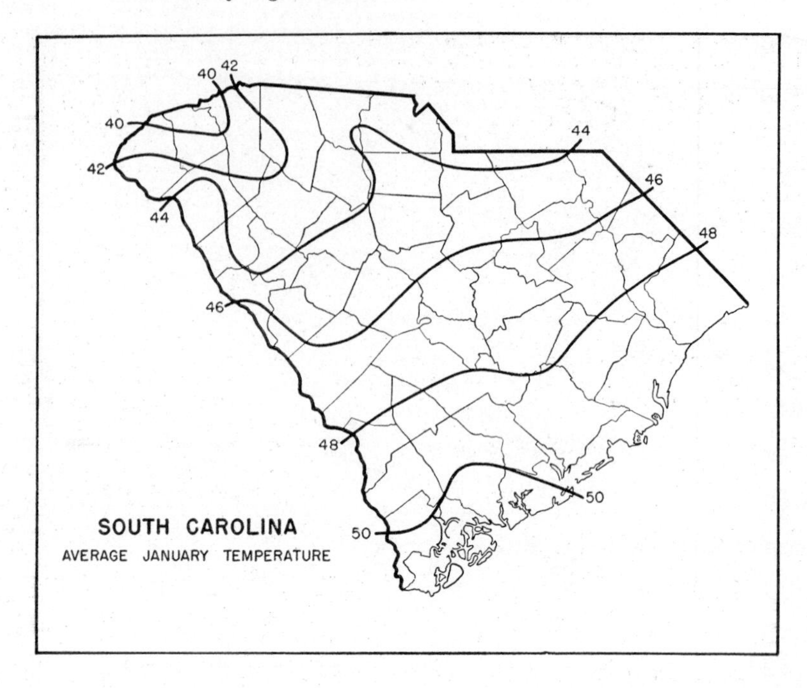
40
42
40
42
44
44
46
48
46
48
50
50
SOUTH CAROLINA
AVERAGE JANUARY TEMPERATURE

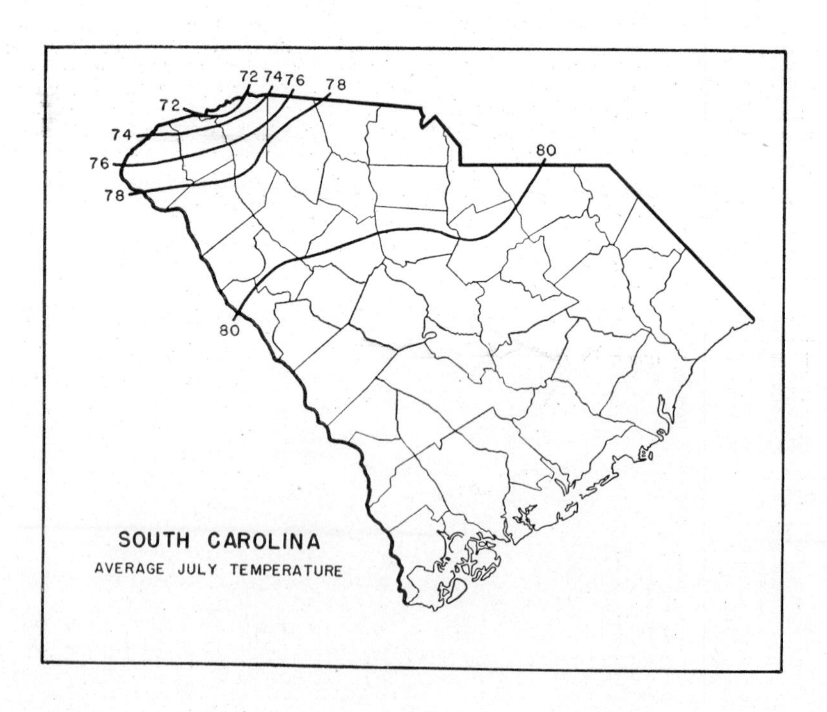
72
74
76
78
72
74
76
78
80
80
SOUTH CAROLINA
AVERAGE JULY TEMPERATURE

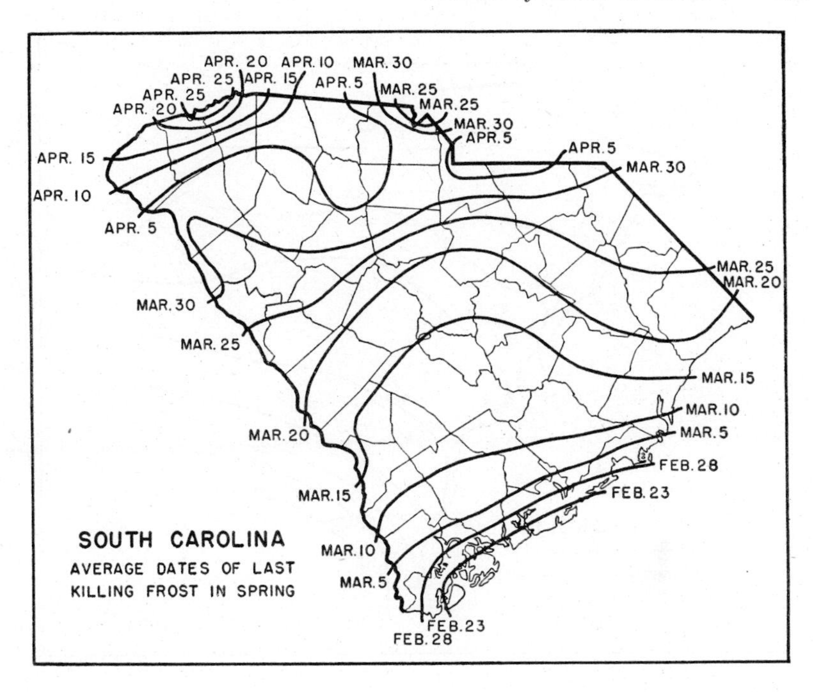

SOUTH CAROLINA
AVERAGE DATES OF LAST KILLING FROST IN SPRING

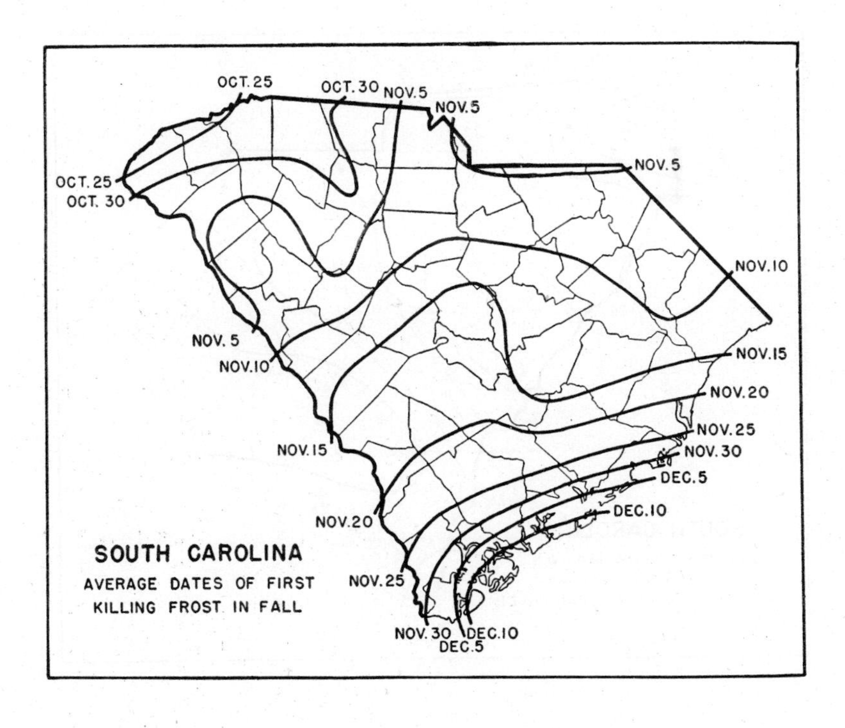

SOUTH CAROLINA
AVERAGE DATES OF FIRST KILLING FROST IN FALL

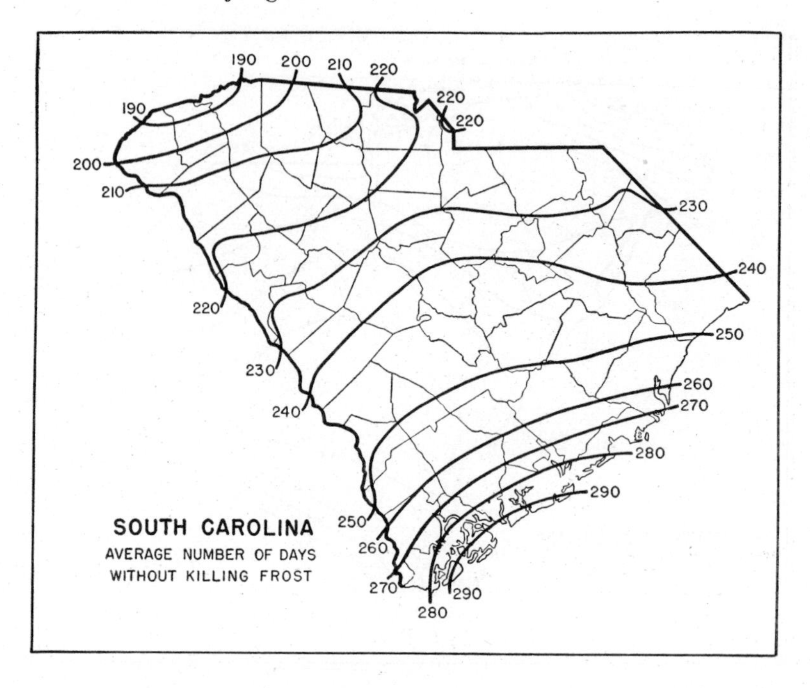

SOUTH CAROLINA
AVERAGE NUMBER OF DAYS WITHOUT KILLING FROST

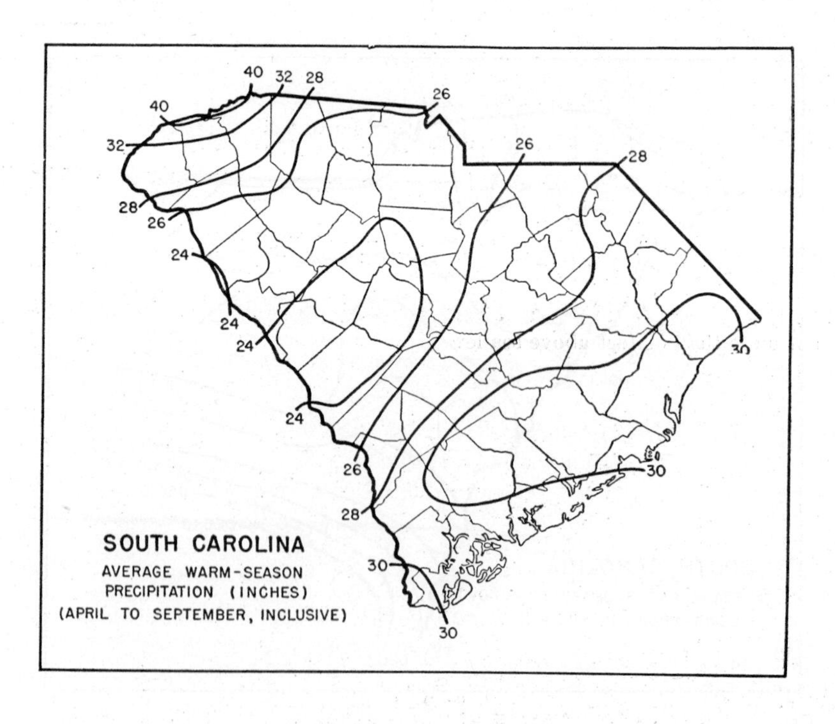

SOUTH CAROLINA
AVERAGE WARM-SEASON PRECIPITATION (INCHES)
(APRIL TO SEPTEMBER, INCLUSIVE)

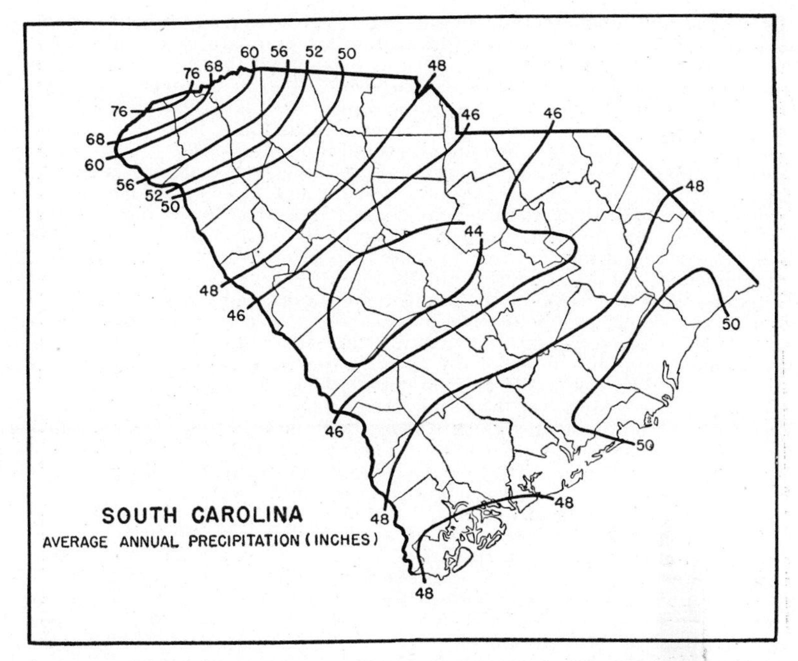

SOUTH CAROLINA
AVERAGE ANNUAL PRECIPITATION (INCHES)

SUPPLEMENTARY CLIMATIC NOTES FOR SOUTH CAROLINA

South Carolina lies practically between latitudes 32° and 35° N. and extends in a triangular shape from the Blue Ridge Mountains in the extreme northwestern part southeastward to the Atlantic Ocean, embracing an area of 30,989 square miles.

The State may be divided into two distinct areas, commonly known as the Piedmont and the Coastal Plain. The line of demarcation runs from the eastern boundary of Aiken County, through central Chesterfield County, to the North Carolina border, where the general elevations begin at about 300 feet above sea level and increase in various steps to over 1,000 feet in northwestern counties, with higher, isolated peaks along the border. The highest peak is Sassafras Mountain in upper Greenville County, with an elevation of 3,548 feet. East of this line are low hills and rather broken country between the Congaree River and the north fork of the Edisto River; also there is a rather hilly and rolling area in the upper Lynches River drainage basin between the Catawba-Wateree and the Pee Dee Rivers. In the upper Coastal Plain, the elevations decrease somewhat abruptly from 300 to 100 feet, and thence to the coast the major part of the land is not more than 60 feet above sea level. In the area of lower levels to the eastward and southward great swamp systems predominate.

The general slope of the land from the mountains toward the sea is southeasterly, and the three primary river systems—the Pee Dee, the Santee, and the Savannah—naturally flow in that general direction. As the Savannah watershed in South Carolina is narrow, the general drainage of the State may be said, on the whole, to be through the other two river systems, which have a total drainage area of nearly 31,000 square miles. Practically all the large power sites are located in the western part of the State, where drainage is rapid and foundations on the various shoals are good.

The principal coast indentations are Winyah Bay, Charleston Harbor, St. Helena Sound, and Port Royal Sound, with Tybee Roads at the mouth of the Savannah River. There are a large number of low sea islands, separated from the mainland by numerous comparatively shallow straits, sounds, and coastal streams.

The climate of South Carolina varies considerably according to elevation, and from late fall to midspring weather changes are frequent. During the winter one to four cold waves usually occur, with night temperatures of 20° F. or lower in the central and upper sections of the State. However, these cold periods are generally brief, and on the whole the winters are comparatively mild. Except along the southern coast, zero temperatures overspread the entire State at irregular intervals, averaging once in about 20 years. During summer, temperatures of 90° or above are more or less frequent except at the higher elevations.

On an average, the most rain occurs in July and the least in November. Throughout the central part the annual rainfall is about 45 inches, while there are greater amounts in two widely separated areas, along the seaboard and over the northwestern counties. In the mountains the annual precipitation ranges from 55 to more than 65 inches, and over the coastal areas it is 50 or more. Distribution is fairly regular throughout the State, and only occasionally is drought or an excess of moisture harmful to crops. The average number of days with measurable precipition is 94 a year. Sunshine is ample.

Thunderstorms are frequent in summer, and occasionally destroy property in limited areas. Hail, accompanying thunderstorms, also is locally destructive to crops. Tornadoes average about three a year, occurring mostly about 50 miles from the mountains but occasionally in other sections. A few tornadoes have caused considerable loss of life and property when they have struck towns and cities. Hurricanes rarely occur in full force.

Mean annual temperatures range from about 66.5° F. in extreme southern parts to about 59.5° in the mountains. The range between the lower coast and the high elevations is about 10°, the decrease in temperature being proportional to the increase in altitude. Seasonal temperature averages for the State as a whole are: Winter, 46.7°; spring, 62.6°; summer, 78.8°; and autumn, 64°.

The average growing season ranges from about February 20 to December 11, 294 days, in the extreme southern part to 186 days in extreme northwestern elevations, where the terminal dates are about April 21 and October 25. Killing frost in spring has occurred as late as May 3 in a few northern localities and April 26 along the coast; in the fall, as early as October 9 over most of the State and November 10 in the extreme south.

The normal seasonal precipitation in winter is 11.30 inches; spring, 10.69; summer, 16.30; and fall, 9.40. Thus the heaviest rainfall is in the summer season and the lightest in the fall.

The average annual snowfall is 2.4 inches. In the central and upper parts of the State snowstorms are not infrequent.

The average annual sunshine is 64 percent of the possible amount, while the average number of clear days is 175, with 95 partly cloudy and 95 cloudy. The average hourly wind velocity is about 9 miles. The highest velocity ever recorded for a 5-minute period was 81 miles an hour from the southeast. The prevailing direction of the wind is from the southwest. Disastrous floods and droughts are of rare occurrence.

GERALD C. MERCHANT, *Associate Meteorologist and Climatic Section Director for South Carolina, Weather Bureau, Columbia.*

SOUTH DAKOTA

Climatic summary

County [1]	Station	Temperature: Length of record	Temperature: January average	Temperature: July average	Temperature: Maximum	Temperature: Minimum	Killing frost average dates: Length of record	Killing frost average dates: Last in spring	Killing frost average dates: First in fall	Killing frost average dates: Growing season [2]	Average precipitation: Length of record	January	February	March	April	May	June	July	August	September	October	November	December	Annual
		Yr.	°F.	°F.	°F.	°F.	Yr.			Days	Yr.	In.	In.	In.	In.	In.	In.	In.	In.	In.	In.	In.	In.	In.
Aurora	Plankington	8	18.2	72.2	108	−40	11	May 20	Sept. 30	133	14	0.38	0.47	0.91	1.94	2.98	4.43	3.30	3.13	1.98	1.93	0.51	0.78	22.74
	White Lake	18	17.4	77.2	116	−31	26	May 3	Oct. 7	157	30	.45	.56	.89	2.08	2.53	3.44	2.25	2.06	1.67	1.13	.65	.49	18.20
Beadle	Huron	40	13.8	73.3	111	−43	40	May 4	Oct. 2	151	40	.52	.50	.90	1.79	2.71	3.41	2.64	2.27	1.69	1.17	.57	.54	18.71
	Wolsey						8	May 20	Sept. 26	129	10	.42	.42	1.41	1.61	3.34	3.88	2.53	3.26	1.85	1.46	.37	.66	21.21
Bon Homme	Tyndall	34	18.6	75.6	115	−41	34	May 3	Oct. 3	153	34	.43	.59	1.26	2.38	3.92	3.26	3.11	3.43	2.27	1.56	.81	.53	23.55
Brookings	Brookings	40	13.1	71.8	107	−41	40	May 15	Sept. 28	136	40	.39	.42	.76	1.88	2.82	3.80	2.51	2.73	2.19	1.29	.69	.47	19.95
Brown	Aberdeen	40	10.8	72.9	115	−46	40	May 11	Sept. 27	139	40	.73	.84	1.36	2.63	3.42	3.80	3.01	2.94	2.03	1.46	.86	.88	23.96
Brule	Chamberlain	16	17.6	74.6	109	−42	16	May 6	Oct. 3	150	16	.52	.59	.83	1.87	2.68	2.98	2.69	2.67	1.34	1.14	.42	.55	18.28
	Kimball	18	16.5	73.1	107	−39	18	May 9	Sept. 30	144	18	.39	.48	.71	1.89	3.10	3.60	3.27	2.86	1.55	1.31	.33	.51	20.00
	Pukwana	16	16.8	77.8	118	−37	16	May 5	Oct. 3	151	16	.34	.37	.90	1.61	2.04	2.86	1.73	1.66	1.40	.94	.46	.33	14.64
Buffalo	Gannvalley	36	16.0	76.1	120	−42	36	May 10	Sept. 26	139	35	.59	.50	.92	1.96	2.83	3.39	2.84	2.53	1.55	1.04	.62	.60	19.37
Butte	Belle Fourche	30	20.6	72.0	112	−42	30	May 15	Sept. 24	132	30	.38	.28	.80	1.58	2.34	2.41	1.85	1.33	1.30	.89	.48	.43	14.07
	Newell	18	17.5	73.2	110	−38	18	May 10	Oct. 1	144	18	.42	.28	.81	1.54	2.94	2.77	2.49	1.45	1.26	1.16	.59	.38	16.09
	Orman	32	19.8	73.4	110	−38	33	May 12	Sept. 30	141	33	.45	.27	.77	1.61	2.64	2.47	2.09	1.32	1.33	.96	.43	.44	14.78
	Vale	30	19.3	72.7	113	−39	30	May 16	Sept. 22	129	31	.40	.28	.89	1.59	3.00	2.92	2.21	1.48	1.46	1.24	.47	.46	16.40
Campbell	Pollock	29	9.2	72.4	118	−51	30	do	Sept. 16	123	30	.49	.42	.66	1.35	2.02	3.10	2.04	1.63	1.52	1.03	.48	.39	15.13
Charles Mix	Academy	40	19.5	75.5	115	−37	40	May 6	Oct. 3	150	40	.42	.60	1.15	2.39	2.98	3.79	2.66	2.58	1.61	1.36	.59	.62	20.75
	Greenwood	17	21.8	74.3	107	−37	16	Apr. 29	Oct. 5	159	17	.57	.77	1.16	2.12	3.28	3.73	4.02	3.62	2.23	2.02	.60	.78	24.90
	Wagner	22	18.5	78.2	115	−39	22	May 1	Oct. 6	158	23	.91	.85	1.53	2.47	3.36	3.34	2.66	2.46	2.17	1.19	.90	.84	22.68
Clark	Clark	38	11.4	71.1	110	−42	38	May 13	Sept. 29	139	40	.73	.61	1.14	2.14	2.86	4.00	2.86	2.94	2.41	1.49	.90	.62	22.70
Clay	Vermillion	35	19.8	76.3	114	−38	38	May 1	Oct. 8	160	38	.57	.80	1.24	2.52	3.69	3.87	3.18	2.97	3.31	1.59	1.13	.70	25.57
Codington	Watertown	40	11.0	70.6	110	−40	39	May 16	Sept. 27	134	40	.52	.47	.83	2.04	2.73	3.69	2.70	2.81	2.18	1.29	.75	.50	20.51
Corson	McIntosh	21	11.2	71.2	114	−58	18	do	Sept. 23	130	16	.42	.56	.92	1.44	2.61	3.51	1.79	1.94	1.55	1.10	.45	.52	16.81
	McLaughlin	16	10.4	74.0	114	−45	16	May 13	Sept. 20	130	17	.45	.48	.82	1.42	2.09	3.08	1.93	1.49	1.50	.95	.62	.39	15.22
Custer	Custer						12	May 18	Sept. 12	117	27	.45	.45	.81	1.83	2.99	2.75	3.08	2.42	1.28	1.16	.52	.36	18.10
	Elk Mountain	9	18.4	69.3	100	−33	14	May 28	Sept. 18	113	16	.62	.46	.62	1.31	1.96	2.72	2.64	1.70	1.53	1.06	.66	.51	15.79
	Hermosa	25	22.0	71.8	106	−44	24	May 15	Sept. 26	134	26	.34	.31	.70	1.65	3.88	3.23	2.65	2.09	1.44	1.07	.39	.46	18.21
Davison	Mitchell	40	16.5	74.5	115	−39	40	May 5	Oct. 6	154	40	.51	.66	1.24	2.33	3.24	4.03	3.13	2.61	2.30	1.39	.67	.55	22.66
Day	Webster (near)	38	9.2	70.1	108	−44	38	May 16	Sept. 25	132	38	.44	.40	.76	1.92	2.62	3.56	3.02	3.35	2.36	1.23	.67	.49	20.82
Deuel	Clear Lake	10	13.5	70.1	102	−35	9	do	Sept. 23	130	10	.30	.68	1.10	1.95	3.88	4.77	3.55	3.99	3.27	1.79	.80	.61	26.69
Dewey	Timber Lake	19	11.6	74.7	115	−46	16	May 12	Sept. 27	138	17	.67	.40	1.12	2.07	3.02	3.59	2.44	2.13	1.34	.97	.39	.43	18.57
Douglas	Armour	40	18.2	75.8	113	−45	40	May 8	Sept. 30	145	40	.50	.64	1.15	2.12	3.18	3.89	2.70	3.18	1.96	1.40	.65	.72	22.09
Edmunds	Bowdle	11	12.1	69.7	114	−39	22	May 19	Sept. 25	129	22	.46	.47	1.00	1.95	2.82	3.63	2.60	2.83	1.67	1.23	.45	.53	19.64
	Ipswich	38	10.7	72.0	115	−45	38	May 16	Sept. 24	131	40	.42	.45	.76	2.01	3.11	3.30	2.43	2.55	1.62	1.07	.52	.39	18.63

[1] The following counties, for which no records are available, are best represented by the station indicated: Armstrong—Hopewell; Bennett and Washington—Pine Ridge; Jerauld—Gann Valley.

[2] Length of growing season between average dates of last killing frost in spring and first in fall.

298737°—41——71 +

SOUTH DAKOTA—Continued

Climatic summary—Continued

County	Station	Temperature: Length of record	Temperature: January average	Temperature: July average	Temperature: Maximum	Temperature: Minimum	Killing frost average dates: Length of record	Killing frost average dates: Last in spring	Killing frost average dates: First in fall	Killing frost average dates: Growing season	Average precipitation: Length of record	January	February	March	April	May	June	July	August	September	October	November	December	Annual
		Yr.	*°F.*	*°F.*	*°F.*	*°F.*	*Yr.*			*Days*	*Yr.*	*In.*	*In.*	*In.*	*In.*	*In.*	*In.*	*In.*	*In.*	*In.*	*In.*	*In.*	*In.*	*In.*
Fall River	Ardmore	25	18.6	73.7	110	-34	26	May 11	Sept. 29	141	28	0.39	0.41	0.84	1.92	2.91	2.58	1.98	1.65	1.05	1.12	0.49	0.44	15.78
	Hot Springs	31	23.4	73.6	112	-41	28	do	Sept. 30	142	33	.71	.53	1.16	1.93	3.16	3.01	2.30	2.00	1.37	1.39	.65	.59	18.80
	Oelrichs	38	21.1	73.2	112	-42	38	May 13	Sept. 24	134	40	.65	.63	1.17	2.15	3.26	3.36	2.31	1.57	1.29	1.38	.64	.64	19.05
Faulk	Faulkton	39	13.1	72.6	114	-41	39	May 9	Sept. 29	143	39	.46	.60	.98	2.21	2.98	3.08	2.16	2.30	1.49	1.10	.64	.47	18.47
	Onaka						18	May 7	Oct. 1	147	27	.52	.56	.95	2.28	3.02	3.33	2.61	2.51	1.62	1.10	.56	.58	19.64
Grant	Milbank	39	11.6	71.8	110	-37	39	May 11	Sept. 29	141	40	.85	.80	1.50	2.17	2.88	3.77	2.72	2.87	2.26	1.50	1.01	.82	23.15
Gregory	Fairfax	34	18.8	74.9	114	-35	35	May 7	Oct. 4	150	34	.48	.64	1.00	2.20	3.37	3.81	2.88	2.65	1.72	1.37	.54	.50	21.16
	Gregory	8	21.2	78.5	114	-32	12	Apr. 30	Oct. 5	158	13	.39	.36	1.05	2.29	3.15	3.22	2.20	2.08	1.64	1.28	.53	.32	18.51
Haakon	Hardingrove	10	16.6	73.9	109	-39	10	May 3	Oct. 1	151	10	.39	.65	1.61	2.66	4.07	2.08	2.61	2.17	1.45	1.07	.45	.45	19.66
	Hilland	30	19.3	75.6	115	-36	27	May 10	Oct. 5	148	30	.46	.39	.76	1.56	2.85	2.96	2.29	2.02	1.20	.99	.58	.43	16.49
	Leslie	8	21.0	74.6	115	-45					10	.18	.18	.70	.86	2.45	3.01	1.91	2.75	1.55	.95	.14	.48	15.16
	Ottumwa	30	17.0	75.0	115	-44	28	May 14	Sept. 25	134	28	.48	.56	.87	1.70	2.75	2.29	1.72	1.94	.99	1.01	.59	.48	15.38
Hamlin	Castlewood	33	11.7	70.7	109	-43	33	May 13	Sept. 26	136	33	.42	.39	.85	2.19	2.64	4.00	2.74	2.86	2.19	1.11	.91	.41	20.71
Hand	Miller	37	13.2	73.1	113	-48	37	May 9	Sept. 29	143	37	.35	.39	.84	1.89	2.76	3.05	2.28	2.21	1.39	1.00	.53	.41	17.10
Hanson	Alexandria	38	16.0	74.9	114	-41	39	May 8	Oct. 2	147	40	.50	.63	1.14	2.20	3.31	4.06	2.84	2.61	2.33	1.31	.74	.54	22.21
Harding	Camp Crook	36	16.7	71.2	114	-57	36	May 20	Sept. 21	124	35	.51	.40	.88	1.01	2.30	2.78	1.98	1.33	1.07	.70	.34	.36	13.66
	Ludlow	15	17.0	71.5	113	-37	15	May 13	Sept. 25	135	15	.26	.14	.56	.90	2.18	3.19	1.83	1.11	.89	.69	.22	.32	12.29
	Redig	24	15.2	71.3	111	-46	24	May 17	Sept. 23	129	24	.60	.39	1.02	1.27	2.11	2.55	1.82	1.25	.99	.76	.55	.46	13.77
	Reva (near)	26	15.5	72.2	113	-48	27	May 15	Sept. 22	130	2	.25	.13	1.08	.82	2.48	3.62	1.75	.28	.64	.23	.30	.01	11.59
Hughes	Pierre	40	17.6	76.3	115	-40	40	Apr. 30	Oct. 8	161	40	.41	.48	.97	1.68	2.56	2.54	2.26	2.12	1.20	1.01	.47	.51	16.21
Hutchinson	Menno	38	17.6	75.0	117	-42	39	May 5	Oct. 2	150	40	.59	.79	1.20	2.20	3.53	3.86	3.08	3.11	2.41	1.44	.90	.69	23.80
	Parkston						16	May 1	Oct. 9	161	23	.61	.80	1.34	2.17	2.87	3.30	2.52	2.84	2.32	1.26	.66	.67	21.36
Hyde	Highmore	36	13.8	73.7	113	-45	40	May 12	Sept. 28	139	40	.38	.38	.94	1.82	2.72	3.04	2.28	2.23	1.43	1.07	.51	.40	17.20
	Stephan	15	11.7	71.3	108	-43	15	May 15	Sept. 24	132	15	.55	.55	.56	1.67	3.19	3.27	3.35	2.30	1.46	.97	.35	.52	18.74
Jackson	Belvidere	14	18.8	78.2	113	-38	14	May 2	Oct. 6	157	14	.54	.44	1.58	2.21	2.92	2.47	1.65	1.90	.93	1.17	.58	.54	16.93
	Cottonwood	30	18.5	75.0	116	-42	30	May 14	Sept. 27	136	30	.40	.33	.71	1.86	2.66	2.50	2.14	1.74	1.08	.89	.45	.37	15.13
	Interior	10	23.3	75.6	111	-38	10	May 6	Oct. 1	148	10	.45	.34	.78	1.75	2.97	2.64	2.62	1.74	1.05	1.20	.52	.47	16.53
	Kadoka	12	19.4	74.5	109	-36	12	May 9	Oct. 3	147	12	.45	.74	.61	2.17	3.25	2.48	2.67	2.15	1.32	.96	.31	.50	17.61
Jones	Murdo	28	19.4	76.5	116	-35	30	May 6	Oct. 8	155	31	.66	.67	1.09	2.24	2.85	2.74	2.26	1.74	1.26	1.37	.57	.59	18.04
Kingsbury	Arlington										8	.53	.45	1.40	2.23	2.41	2.85	1.86	2.56	2.63	1.11	.79	.62	19.44
	De Smet	33	13.4	71.9	110	-44	33	May 9	Sept. 25	139	31	.64	.57	1.08	2.13	2.75	4.00	2.73	2.75	2.04	1.56	.64	.62	21.51
Lake	Wentworth	38	13.0	71.5	113	-40	37	May 12	Oct. 1	142	39	.54	.51	.92	2.07	3.32	4.22	3.06	3.25	2.81	1.53	.80	.55	23.58
Lawrence	Deadwood	14	23.2	66.9	101	-30	15	May 28	Sept. 13	108	14	1.15	1.04	2.29	3.78	4.55	3.69	3.88	2.49	2.34	2.06	1.28	1.44	29.99
	Dumont	---	---	---	---	---	24	June 3	Sept. 4	93	30	1.41	1.07	1.69	2.24	2.66	3.02	2.91	1.89	1.42	1.21	.97	1.12	21.61
	Greenmont	---	---	---	---	---					14	1.40	1.30	1.70	3.45	3.43	3.10	2.85	2.56	1.64	1.69	1.25	1.36	25.73
	Hardy Ranger Station.	---	---	---	---	---	15	May 31	Aug. 31	92	30	1.60	1.11	1.54	2.06	2.41	2.66	2.03	1.70	1.42	1.40	.97	1.18	20.08

	Harvey's Ranch						26	June 9	Sept. 2	85	29	1.52	1.19	1.82	2.72	3.46	4.02	3.37	2.04	1.46	1.28	1.11	1.05	25.04
	Lead	30	22.5	68.5	101	−40	30	May 18	Sept. 24	129	30	1.04	.84	1.67	2.87	3.77	3.45	2.85	2.00	1.73	1.64	1.01	.98	23.85
	Spearfish	38	25.4	71.0	110	−32	38	May 10	Oct. 2	145	40	.61	.62	1.32	2.12	3.37	3.31	2.44	1.68	1.67	1.39	.84	.70	20.07
	Waters Ranch						15	May 20	Sept. 18	121	30	.75	.54	1.22	2.07	2.64	2.81	2.35	1.63	1.83	1.49	.73	.72	18.78
Lincoln	Canton	36	17.0	74.1	115	−47	37	May 8	Oct. 2	147	39	.51	.53	1.15	2.20	3.75	4.17	3.30	3.00	2.69	1.53	1.00	.61	24.44
Lyman	Kennebec	32	17.1	76.0	119	−42	30	May 10	do	145	40	.54	.55	.86	1.90	2.59	3.08	2.10	2.08	1.30	1.09	.48	.58	17.15
	Vivian	23	17.3	76.4	117	−39	24	May 11	Sept. 29	141	24	.48	.45	1.01	2.40	2.93	3.24	2.02	1.76	1.21	1.23	.59	.37	17.69
McCook	Canistota						14	May 5	Oct. 3	151	16	.72	.70	1.22	2.10	2.84	3.63	1.79	3.01	2.63	.88	.97	.68	21.17
McPherson	Eureka	30	9.0	71.9	114	−45	30	May 16	Sept. 25	132	30	.32	.38	.57	1.41	2.24	3.08	2.32	2.18	1.50	.99	.44	.36	15.79
	Leola						14	May 20	Sept. 23	126	18	.39	.42	1.14	2.10	2.95	2.69	1.98	2.82	1.52	1.03	.50	.41	17.95
Marshall	Britton	26	9.5	72.8	114	−44	26	May 7	Sept. 24	140	26	.50	.60	.69	1.78	2.68	3.48	2.42	2.70	1.97	1.12	.73	.46	19.13
Meade	Faith	14	16.4	76.6	114	−33	13	May 9	Sept. 28	142	14	.34	.46	1.16	1.55	2.48	2.50	1.90	1.04	1.00	.96	.47	.25	14.11
	Fort Meade	18	24.5	71.5	109	−31	19	May 8	Sept. 25	140	19	.56	.71	1.54	1.98	4.60	3.58	2.99	1.97	1.31	1.22	.45	.69	21.60
Mellette	Wood	26	20.9	76.1	116	−36	26	May 14	Sept. 29	138	26	.50	.59	1.08	2.29	2.80	2.82	2.34	2.11	1.21	1.18	.73	.48	18.13
Miner	Howard	37	13.7	72.3	113	−46	40	May 13	Sept. 25	135	40	.50	.52	.94	2.05	2.78	3.76	3.13	2.87	2.35	1.39	.73	.54	21.56
Minnehaha	Sioux Falls	40	15.8	73.6	110	−42	40	May 6	Oct. 3	150	40	.65	.72	1.20	2.43	3.83	4.33	3.43	3.40	2.94	1.60	1.16	.74	26.43
Moody	Flandreau (near)	37	13.0	71.3	110	−38	38	May 12	Sept. 27	138	39	.48	.53	.96	2.12	3.10	3.94	2.62	3.00	2.72	1.42	1.00	.58	22.47
Pennington	Deerfield						22	May 28	Sept. 7	102	29	.59	.41	.78	1.76	2.66	3.34	2.94	2.16	1.38	1.10	.57	.40	18.09
	Farmingdale						8	May 23	Sept. 21	121	10	.20	.28	.90	1.27	3.60	3.92	2.51	1.44	1.46	.95	.24	.44	17.21
	Rapid City	40	23.4	71.9	106	−34	40	May 1	Oct. 4	156	40	.41	.40	.98	1.87	3.69	3.20	2.56	1.68	1.33	1.06	.48	.43	18.09
	Rochford						22	June 6	Sept. 12	98	32	.86	.72	1.12	2.17	2.94	3.16	2.86	2.27	1.39	1.28	.81	.69	20.27
Perkins	Bison	16	16.0	72.6	111	−38	17	May 23	Sept. 24	124	17	.44	.47	.78	1.10	2.40	2.44	2.02	1.78	1.12	.70	.46	.32	14.03
	Lemmon	27	14.2	72.4	115	−45	26	May 15	Sept. 26	134	27	.59	.48	.78	1.09	2.21	3.41	1.69	1.34	1.23	.74	.51	.47	14.54
	Meadow	16	14.8	69.4	107	−41	15	May 21	Sept. 27	129	16	.37	.41	1.02	1.28	2.53	3.50	2.11	1.55	1.19	.88	.44	.43	15.71
Potter	Eales						16	May 15	Sept. 25	133	20	.61	.67	.72	1.53	2.67	3.15	2.47	1.93	1.08	1.25	.53	.50	17.11
Roberts	Sisseton	11	10.9	72.3	113	−37	14	May 8	Sept. 29	144	12	.51	.39	1.24	2.53	3.03	3.74	3.10	2.90	2.77	1.10	.41	.60	22.32
	Victor						14	do	Sept. 27	142	16	.47	.45	.98	2.10	2.36	3.63	2.46	2.95	2.12	1.05	.88	.56	20.01
Sanborn	Forestburg	39	14.2	73.7	116	−46	40	May 11	Sept. 28	140	40	.56	.59	1.05	2.24	3.14	3.71	2.72	2.37	1.91	1.30	.68	.62	20.89
Shannon	Pine Ridge	18	22.6	74.1	109	−43	23	May 17	Sept. 22	128	23	.32	.37	.80	1.80	2.57	2.68	2.47	1.95	1.19	1.22	.29	.45	16.11
Spink	Ashton						12	May 10	Sept. 29	142	12	.46	.42	.96	2.16	2.20	3.12	2.04	2.10	1.61	1.33	.64	.65	17.69
	La Delle	38	12.6	73.1	115	−47	38	May 15	Sept. 22	130	40	.49	.50	1.04	2.40	3.28	4.28	3.04	3.15	2.22	1.60	.86	.57	23.43
	Mellette	39	12.4	72.6	112	−45	40	May 14	Sept. 25	134	40	.57	.67	1.03	2.16	2.95	3.13	2.49	2.50	1.95	1.22	.75	.56	19.98
	Redfield	39	11.9	73.3	116	−44	40	May 12	Sept. 29	140	40	.44	.54	.93	2.03	2.57	3.11	2.48	2.50	1.73	1.23	.65	.53	18.74
Stanley	Hopewell	29	16.2	75.3	116	−38	30	May 8	Oct. 4	149	29	.55	.53	.97	1.80	2.61	2.56	2.15	1.72	1.24	1.01	.58	.51	16.23
Sully	Marston	10	11.5	72.1	111	−46	10	May 21	Sept. 20	122	10	.86	1.02	1.02	1.99	2.46	2.82	2.62	2.30	1.31	.68	.39	.56	18.03
	Onida	16	12.8	75.7	115	−37	24	May 13	Sept. 29	139	26	.32	.54	.74	1.85	2.83	2.97	2.27	1.87	.98	.92	.33	.25	15.87
Todd	Rosebud	18	23.1	73.4	109	−38	19	do	Sept. 24	134	20	.74	.74	1.22	1.77	2.76	2.61	2.92	2.10	1.30	1.06	.53	1.05	18.80
Tripp	Winner	18	21.2	76.8	115	−38	18	May 2	Oct. 3	154	18	.40	.60	1.25	2.51	2.60	3.17	2.23	2.16	1.21	1.11	.32	.45	18.01
Turner	Centerville	34	16.7	74.8	113	−44	38	May 7	Oct. 4	150	40	.65	.84	1.22	2.08	3.61	3.94	3.26	3.01	2.83	1.51	.97	.76	24.68
	Marion	38	15.9	74.6	118	−41	38	May 8	Oct. 1	146	38	.64	.96	1.58	2.33	3.64	4.42	3.34	2.91	2.81	1.65	1.04	.71	26.03
Union	Elk Point	12	21.0	74.3	106	−39	11	May 6	Oct. 6	153	11	.56	1.27	1.08	2.23	3.67	3.81	3.82	3.13	4.97	2.30	1.14	.88	28.86
Walworth	Glenham						8	May 9	Sept. 27	141	11	.30	.37	.64	1.14	2.32	2.26	1.86	1.69	1.11	.75	.36	.25	13.05
	Mobridge	20	10.7	75.5	116	−44	20	May 10	Sept. 28	141	22	.54	.58	.94	1.62	2.43	2.77	1.94	2.16	1.10	.98	.38	.37	15.81
Washabaugh	Longvalley	10	22.0	77.5	115	−30	12	May 4	Oct. 3	152	2	.20	.22	1.31	2.09	3.30	2.12	1.90	1.36	.56	.29	.40	.12	13.87
Yankton	Yankton	40	18.9	75.4	116	−36	40	May 1	Oct. 9	161	40	.58	.83	1.27	2.23	3.60	3.59	2.94	3.14	2.85	1.39	.89	.72	24.03
Ziebach	Dupree	16	15.1	75.0	114	−35	17	May 13	Sept. 25	135	17	.77	.56	1.04	1.46	1.87	3.12	1.84	1.67	1.01	.85	.82	.61	15.62

SOUTH DAKOTA—Continued

Precipitation and temperature—State unit values

[This tabulation gives the mean annual, mean monthly, and average seasonal precipitation, 1886–1938, and the mean annual temperatures, 1902–38, for South Dakota]

Precipitation		Precipitation		Precipitation		Precipitation		Temperature		Temperature	
Year	Mean	Year	Mean	Year	Mean	Month	Mean	Year	Mean	Year	Mean
	In.		*In.*		*In.*		*In.*		°*F.*		°*F.*
1886	18.45	1907	18.70	1928	17.42	May	2.85	1902	44.9	1921	48.3
1887	23.22	1908	22.62	1929	20.63	June	3.30	1903	44.4	1922	44.8
1888	17.02	1909	22.74	1930	17.83	July	2.50	1904	44.6	1923	46.1
1889	18.34	1910	15.03	1931	14.28	August	2.20	1905	44.5	1924	43.5
1890	15.37	1911	18.26	1932	19.09	September	1.51	1906	45.3	1925	46.3
1891	18.64	1912	18.02	1933	15.01	October	1.12	1907	44.0	1926	46.4
1892	23.83	1913	17.49	1934	12.58	November	.63	1908	46.6	1927	44.0
1893	16.89	1914	21.36	1935	16.82	December	.57	1909	44.0	1928	46.8
1894	15.62	1915	28.61	1936	10.93			1910	46.7	1929	43.6
1895	16.31	1916	20.66	1937	17.27	Annual	18.97	1911	45.4	1930	47.0
1896	21.03	1917	16.66	1938	17.50			1912	43.8	1931	50.0
1897	18.74	1918	21.52					1913	45.8	1932	45.2
1898	14.52	1919	19.64	Month	Mean	Season	Average	1914	46.0	1933	47.9
1899	18.84	1920	23.41					1915	43.8	1934	49.6
1900	19.97	1921	18.87					1916	42.6	1935	46.4
1901	21.23	1922	21.44					1917	42.1	1936	45.1
1902	19.54	1923	21.98		*In.*		*In.*	1918	45.5	1937	44.6
1903	21.05	1924	17.92	January	0.55	Winter	1.69	1919	44.6	1938	47.9
1904	16.61	1925	15.76	February	.57	Spring	6.02	1920	45.0		
1905	24.66	1926	17.36	March	1.09	Summer	8.00				
1906	24.62	1927	23.13	April	2.08	Fall	3.26				

Dates of last killing frost in spring and first in fall, with length of growing season

Year	Huron			Watertown			Sioux Falls			Pierre			Camp Crook			Rapid City		
	Last in spring	First in fall	Growing season[1]	Last in spring	First in fall	Growing season[1]	Last in spring	First in fall	Growing season[1]	Last in spring	First in fall	Growing season[1]	Last in spring	First in fall	Growing season[1]	Last in spring	First in fall	Growing season[1]
			Days			*Days*			*Days*			*Days*			*Days*			*Days*
1899	May 13	Sept. 28	138	May 13	Sept. 18	128	May 13	Sept. 20	130	Apr. 21	Sept. 29	161	May 17	Sept. 7	113	May 3	Sept. 29	149
1900	Apr. 18	Sept. 17	152	May 21	Sept. 27	129	May 3	Sept. 17	137	Apr. 18	Sept. 27	162	May 3	Sept. 19	139	Apr. 18	Sept. 26	161

1901	May 12	Sept. 18	129				May 25	do	115	May 12	Sept. 18	129	May 24	Sept. 16	115	do	Sept. 17	152
1902	June 21	Sept. 12	83	June 21	Sept. 12	83	Apr. 23	Sept. 12	142	Apr. 23	Sept. 12	142	June 20	Sept. 11	83	Apr. 23	Sept. 13	143
1903	May 13	Sept. 16	126	June 11	Sept. 16	97	May 3	Sept. 16	136	Apr. 30	Nov. 5	189	June 10	Sept. 12	94	May 2	Sept. 14	135
1904	Apr. 27	Sept. 21	147	May 10	Sept. 21	134	May 14	Sept. 21	130	Apr. 26	Oct. 25	182	May 18	Sept. 13	118	May 14	do	123
1905	May 8	Oct. 11	156	May 9	Oct. 11	155	May 9	Oct. 10	154	May 5	Oct. 11	159	May 30			May 6	Oct. 10	157
1906	do	Oct. 6	151	May 27	Oct. 5	131	May 8	Oct. 8	153	May 8	Oct. 9	154		Sept. 26		May 8	Oct. 5	150
1907	May 20	Sept. 28	131	May 21	Sept. 8	110	May 27	Sept. 28	124	May 14	Oct. 11	150	June 4	Sept. 14	102	May 14		
1908	May 2	Sept. 27	148	June 10	Sept. 28	110	May 8	Sept. 27	142	May 2	Sept. 27	148	May 21	Sept. 27	129	May 21	Sept. 27	129
1909	May 10	Sept. 24	137	May 16	Oct. 11	148	May 10	Oct. 10	153	do	Oct. 11	162	May 18	Sept. 19	124	May 9	Oct. 11	155
1910	May 13	Sept. 12	122	June 2	Sept. 9	99	May 3	Oct. 26	176	Apr. 23	Oct. 20	180				May 3	Sept. 26	146
1911	May 4	Oct. 20	169	May 12	Oct. 19	160	do	Oct. 19	169	May 2	Oct. 21	172	May 27	Aug. 28	93	do	Oct. 20	170
1912	Apr. 29	Sept. 25	149	June 7	Sept. 16	101	May 15	Sept. 25	133	Apr. 22	Sept. 25	156	May 11	Sept. 18	130	Apr. 22	Sept. 25	156
1913	Apr. 27	Sept. 22	148	May 18	Sept. 22	127	Apr. 28	Sept. 21	146	May 3	Oct. 18	168	May 22	Sept. 11	112	May 3	do	145
1914	May 12	Oct. 14	155	May 13	Oct. 11	151	Apr. 20	Oct. 14	177	Apr. 29	Oct. 14	168	May 9	Oct. 5	149	May 13	Oct. 10	150
1915	May 18	Oct. 8	143	June 9	Oct. 5	118	May 18	Oct. 5	140	May 6	Oct. 8	155	May 22	Sept. 14	115	May 8	Oct. 7	152
1916	May 3	Sept. 15	135	May 4	Sept. 15	134	May 3	Sept. 15	135	May 14	Sept. 15	124	May 27	Sept. 12	108	Apr. 27	Oct 5	161
1917	May 6	Oct. 8	155	May 24	Sept. 30	129	May 6	Oct. 8	155	Apr. 16	Oct. 8	175	June 14	Sept. 26	104	May 6	Oct. 8	155
1918	Apr. 30	Sept. 18	141	May 14	Sept. 16	125	May 1	Sept. 18	140	Apr. 30	Sept. 19	142				Apr. 30	Sept. 20	143
1919	Apr. 24	Oct. 10	169	Apr. 30	Sept. 25	148	Apr. 25	Oct. 10	168	Apr. 24	Oct. 10	169		Sept. 25		Apr. 16	Oct. 5	172
1920	Apr. 28	Sept. 30	155	Apr. 28	Sept. 30	155	Apr. 27	Sept. 30	156	Apr. 27	Sept. 30	156	May 4	Sept. 29	148	Apr. 30	Sept. 29	152
1921	May 2	do	151	May 15	Oct. 3	141	May 14	Oct. 7	146	Apr. 17	Oct. 11	177	May 15	Oct. 1	139	Apr. 29	Oct. 11	165
1922	Apr. 19	Oct. 9	173	Apr. 21	Oct. 9	171	Apr. 19	Oct. 9	173	Apr. 19	Oct. 8	172	Apr. 29	Sept. 10	134	Apr. 18	Oct. 12	177
1923	Apr. 24	Oct. 13	172	May 12	Oct. 13	154	May 12	Oct. 13	154	Apr. 24	Oct. 13	172	May 16	Oct. 13	150	May 8	Oct. 13	158
1924	May 24	Sept. 29	128	May 25	Oct. 22	150	May 24	Sept. 28	127	May 24	Nov. 2	162	May 28	Sept. 13	108	May 24	Oct. 6	135
1925	May 17	Oct. 1	137	do	Sept. 21	119	May 25	Oct. 9	137	May 1	Oct. 14	166	May 27	Oct. 1	127	May 9	Oct. 14	158
1926	Apr. 25	Sept. 25	153	May 22	Sept. 24	125	May 3	Sept. 25	145	Apr. 28	Sept. 25	150	June 1	Sept. 23	114	Apr. 14	Sept. 25	164
1927	Apr. 22	Oct. 9	170	May 15	Sept. 22	130	Apr. 24	Nov. 2	192	May 5	Sept. 27	145	May 11	Sept. 20	132	May 11	Sept. 20	132
1928	Apr. 27	Sept. 25	151	May 27	Sept. 23	119	Apr. 25	Sept. 25	153	Apr. 27	Sept. 25	151	June 10	Sept. 25	107	Apr. 24	Sept. 27	156
1929	May 16	Oct. 21	158	May 20	Sept. 18	121	May 20	Sept. 18	121	May 16	Oct. 24	161	May 21	Sept. 6	108	Apr. 26	Oct. 24	181
1930	May 17	Sept. 27	133	May 24	Sept. 27	126	May 17	Sept. 27	133	Apr. 7	Oct. 15	191	May 18	Sept. 20	125	Apr. 1	Oct. 16	198
1931	May 22	Nov. 1	163	May 22	Oct. 8	139	May 22	Nov. 1	163	May 21	Oct. 31	163	May 22	Oct. 9	140	May 21	Oct. 30	162
1932	Apr. 14	Sept. 29	168	May 1	Sept. 27	149	Apr. 27	Oct. 10	166	Apr. 27	Oct. 9	165	May 27	Sept. 16	112	Apr. 26	Oct. 5	162
1933	Apr. 26	Oct. 8	165	Apr. 27	Oct. 7	163	do	Oct. 12	168	Apr. 15	Oct. 7	175	Apr. 26	Sept. 22	149	Apr. 14	Oct. 16	185
1934	Apr. 27	Sept. 21	147	do	Sept. 21	147	do	Sept. 21	147	Apr. 24	Sept. 26	155	May 13	Sept. 14	124	Apr. 24	Sept. 15	144
1935	Apr. 16	Sept. 27	164	May 4	Sept. 26	145	Apr. 30	Sept. 27	150	Apr. 15	Sept. 27	165	May 9			May 8	Oct. 5	150
1936	Apr. 29	Oct. 13	167	Apr. 29	Sept. 27	151	Apr. 22	Oct. 20	181	Apr. 29	do	151	Apr. 30	Sept. 16	139	Apr. 17	Oct. 20	186
1937	Apr. 9	do	187	Apr. 26	Sept. 25	152	Apr. 26	Oct. 12	169	Apr. 26	Oct. 13	170	May 1			Apr. 26	Oct. 17	174
1938	do	Oct. 23	197	Apr. 22	Sept. 19	150	Apr. 9	Oct. 23	197	May 9	Oct. 23	167	May 8	Oct. 18	163	May 7	Oct. 19	165
Mean	May 4	Oct. 2	151	May 16	Sept. 27	134	May 6	Oct. 3	150	Apr. 30	Oct. 8	161	May 20	Sept. 21	124	May 1	Oct. 4	156
Extremes	Apr. 9[2]	Sept. 12[4]	[6]83	Apr. 21[2]	Sept. 8[4]	[6]83	Apr. 9[2]	Sept. 12[4]	[6]115	Apr. 7[2]	Sept. 12[4]	[6]124	Apr. 26[2]	Aug. 28[4]	[6]83	Apr. 1[2]	Sept. 13[4]	[6]123
	June 21[3]	Nov. 1[5]	[7]197	June 21[3]	Oct. 22[5]	[7]171	May 27[3]	Nov. 2[5]	[7]197	May 24[3]	Nov. 5[5]	[7]191	June 20[3]	Oct. 18[5]	[7]163	May 24[3]	Oct. 30[5]	[7]198

[1] Number of days between last killing frost in spring and first in fall.
[2] Earliest date in spring.
[3] Latest date in spring.
[4] Earliest date in fall.
[5] Latest date in fall.
[6] Shortest growing season.
[7] Longest growing season.

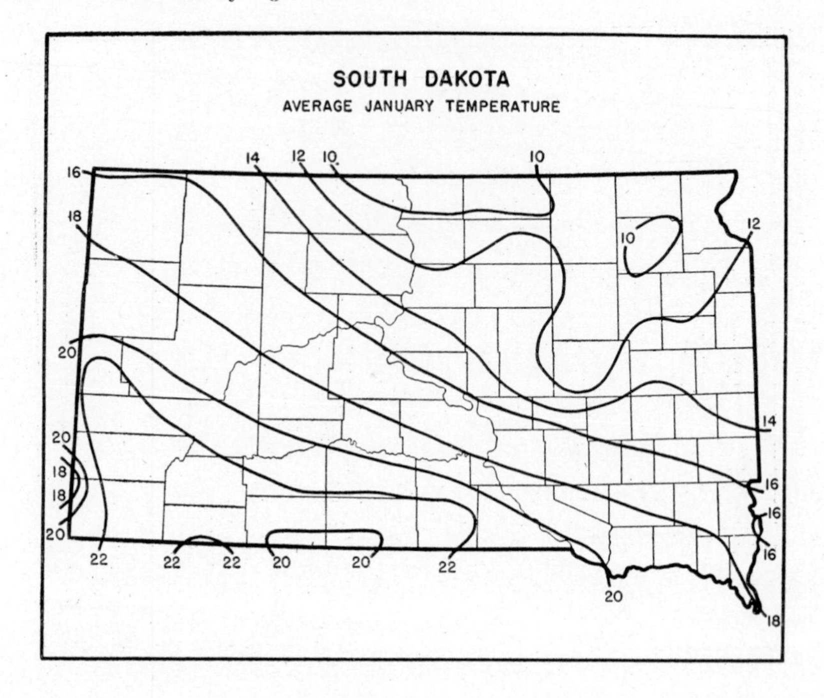
SOUTH DAKOTA
AVERAGE JANUARY TEMPERATURE
16
18
20
20
18
18
20
22
22
22
20
20
22
20
14
12
10
10
10
12
14
16
16
16
18

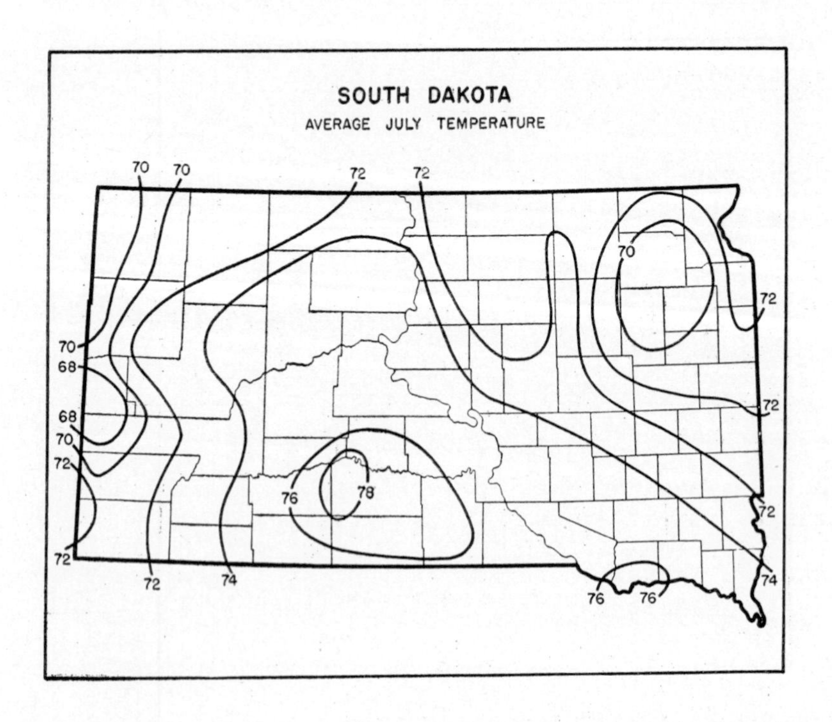
SOUTH DAKOTA
AVERAGE JULY TEMPERATURE
70
70
72
72
70
68
68
70
72
72
72
74
76
78
70
72
72
72
74
76
76

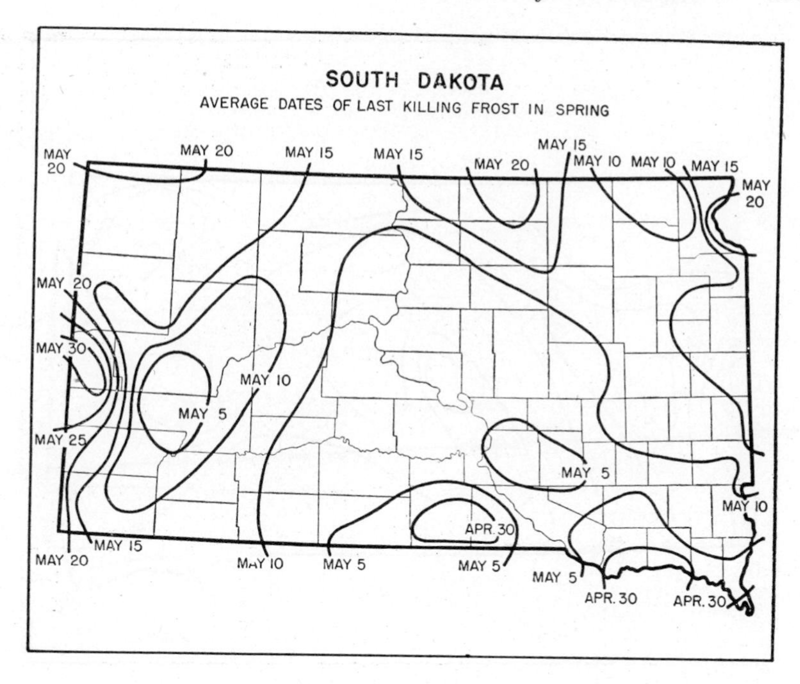
SOUTH DAKOTA
AVERAGE DATES OF LAST KILLING FROST IN SPRING
MAY 20
MAY 20
MAY 15
MAY 15
MAY 15
MAY 20
MAY 10
MAY 10
MAY 15
MAY 20
MAY 20
MAY 30
MAY 10
MAY 5
MAY 25
MAY 5
MAY 10
APR. 30
MAY 15
MAY 20
MAY 10
MAY 5
MAY 5
MAY 5
APR. 30
APR. 30

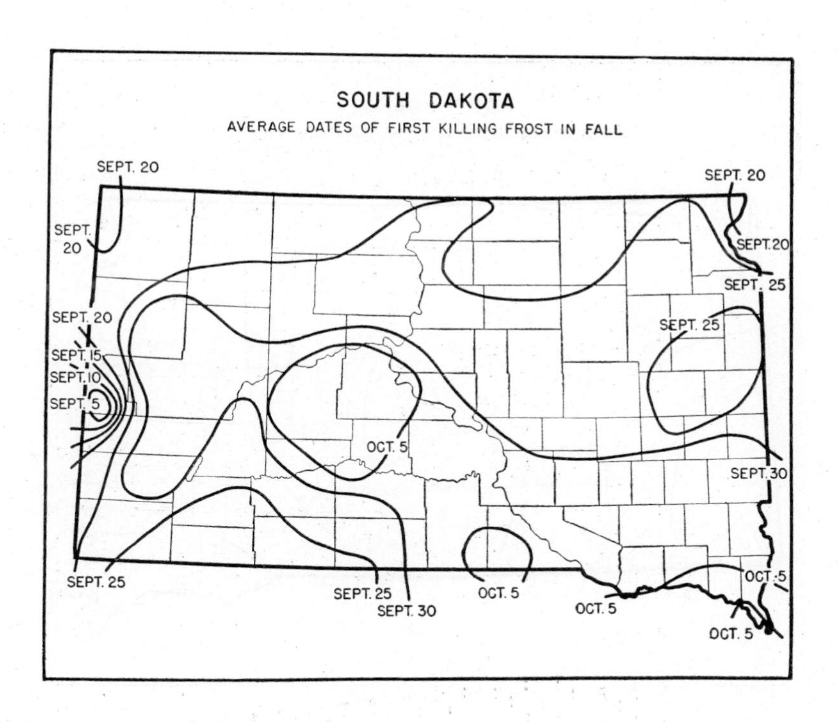
SOUTH DAKOTA
AVERAGE DATES OF FIRST KILLING FROST IN FALL
SEPT. 20
SEPT. 20
SEPT. 20
SEPT. 20
SEPT. 25
SEPT. 20
SEPT. 25
SEPT. 15
SEPT. 10
SEPT. 5
OCT. 5
SEPT. 30
SEPT. 25
SEPT. 25
SEPT. 30
OCT. 5
OCT. 5
OCT. 5
OCT. 5

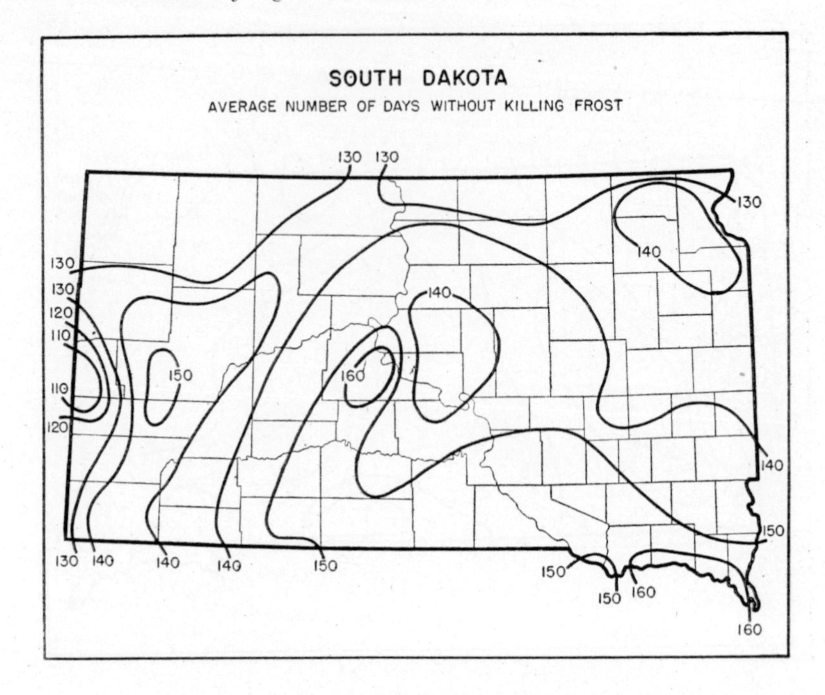
SOUTH DAKOTA
AVERAGE NUMBER OF DAYS WITHOUT KILLING FROST
130
130
130
140
130
130
120
110
140
150
160
110
120
140
150
130
140
140
140
150
150
150
160
160

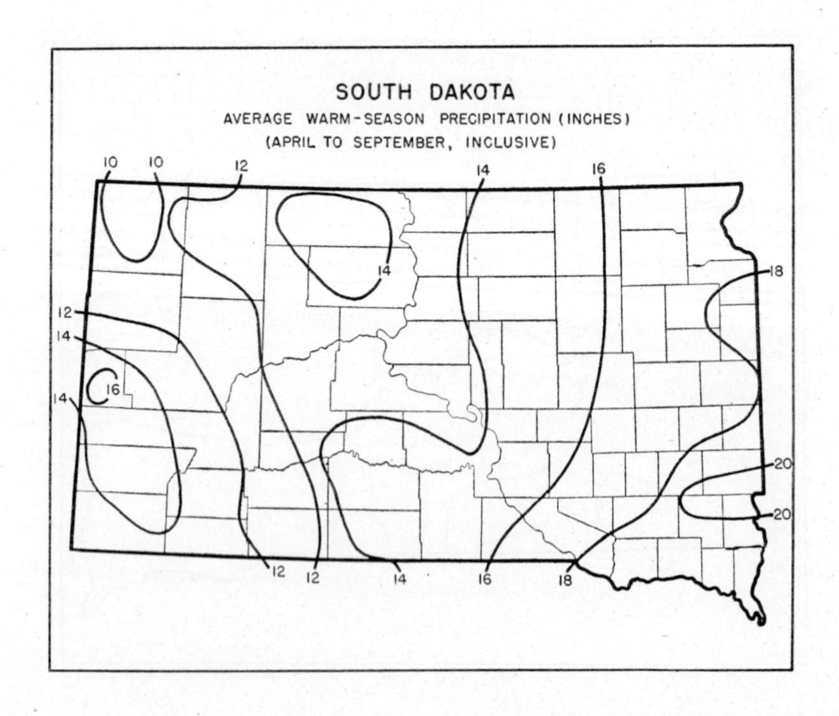
SOUTH DAKOTA
AVERAGE WARM-SEASON PRECIPITATION (INCHES)
(APRIL TO SEPTEMBER, INCLUSIVE)
10
10
12
14
16
14
18
12
14
16
14
20
20
12
12
14
16
18

TENNESSEE

Climatic summary

County [1]	Station	Temperature: Length of record	Temperature: January average	Temperature: July average	Temperature: Maximum	Temperature: Minimum	Killing frost average dates: Length of record	Killing frost: Last in spring	Killing frost: First in fall	Killing frost: Growing season [2]	Average precipitation: Length of record	January	February	March	April	May	June	July	August	September	October	November	December	Annual
		Yr.	°F.	°F.	°F.	°F.	Yr.			Days	Yr.	In.	In.	In.	In.	In.	In.	In.	In.	In.	In.	In.	In.	In.
Anderson	Clinton										40	4.84	4.65	5.62	4.53	3.91	5.05	4.97	4.42	2.91	2.73	3.41	5.24	52.28
Bedford	Palmetto	40	40.9	78.4	108	−18	40	Apr. 14	Oct. 24	193	40	4.66	4.14	5.51	4.24	4.55	4.35	4.65	4.10	2.92	3.39	3.40	4.85	50.76
Blount	Maryville	14	39.7	77.6	104	−14	14	Apr. 10	do	197	14	3.55	4.79	5.74	4.51	3.92	4.68	5.41	4.30	3.01	2.31	3.19	4.99	50.40
Bradley	Charleston										40	4.72	4.80	5.92	4.85	4.01	4.72	4.75	4.28	2.73	3.33	3.34	5.46	52.91
Carroll	McKenzie	13	40.9	81.5	111	−11	14	Apr. 4	Nov. 3	213	13	6.73	3.93	4.25	3.60	3.81	4.66	3.13	2.76	3.71	3.56	3.30	4.73	48.17
Carter	Elizabethton	17	38.9	75.9	104	−17	17	Apr. 20	Oct. 20	183	39	3.54	3.30	4.28	3.38	4.13	4.55	4.97	4.75	3.07	2.72	2.12	3.36	44.17
Chester	Center Point										13	3.55	3.93	3.81	4.50	4.09	4.20	3.11	3.43	2.67	2.55	3.74	5.69	45.27
Claiborne	Springdale	12	35.8	76.4	104	−24	12	Apr. 19	Oct. 17	181	12	3.66	4.64	4.95	4.15	3.64	4.96	4.88	4.59	3.23	2.58	3.54	4.43	49.25
	Tazewell	15	35.2	74.3	106	−29	16	Apr. 25	Oct. 16	174	28	4.70	4.29	5.35	4.41	4.00	4.37	4.55	5.10	3.20	2.88	2.96	4.96	50.77
Clay	Celina										35	5.51	3.87	5.50	4.38	4.62	4.13	4.81	4.53	3.58	3.23	3.76	4.76	52.68
Cocke	Newport	40	38.8	76.7	106	−18	40	Apr. 10	Oct. 25	198	40	3.78	4.02	4.94	3.75	4.18	4.17	4.73	3.95	2.75	2.52	2.48	3.89	45.16
Coffee	Tullahoma	40	40.7	77.1	107	−22	40	Apr. 12	Oct. 21	192	40	4.92	4.63	5.94	5.03	4.37	4.18	4.93	4.44	3.16	3.43	3.66	5.65	54.34
Cumberland	Crossville	25	38.2	73.6	103	−14	26	Apr. 20	Oct. 12	175	27	5.36	4.32	5.75	4.64	4.10	4.44	5.39	5.17	3.01	3.48	3.43	5.08	54.17
	Erasmus	20	37.2	72.1	97	−30	20	Apr. 23	Oct. 11	171	20	5.72	4.80	6.52	5.42	4.48	5.69	5.91	5.13	3.90	3.57	3.20	5.48	59.82
Davidson	Madison College										16	5.53	3.88	5.70	3.86	4.79	3.46	4.12	3.52	3.16	3.39	3.54	4.70	49.65
	Nashville	40	39.9	79.3	106	−13	40	Mar. 30	Oct. 30	214	40	4.59	3.36	5.00	3.91	4.03	3.87	3.68	3.47	2.92	2.66	3.11	4.17	44.77
Decatur	Perryville	27	41.1	80.2	113	−10	27	Apr. 6	Oct. 23	200	40	5.40	4.16	5.74	4.75	4.29	4.34	4.10	3.67	3.18	3.37	3.74	5.23	51.97
De Kalb	Liberty										33	5.38	4.07	5.84	4.35	4.07	4.61	4.68	4.91	3.05	3.34	3.88	4.73	52.91
Dickson	Dickson	38	39.6	78.0	110	−20	39	Apr. 11	Oct. 21	193	40	5.33	3.73	5.39	4.79	4.72	4.22	4.22	3.82	3.00	3.12	3.72	4.79	50.85
Dyer	Dyersburg	22	39.3	80.2	105	−13	21	Apr. 1	Oct. 29	211	25	5.06	3.58	4.80	5.13	4.58	3.92	3.32	3.90	3.04	3.42	4.11	4.99	49.85
	Newbern	15	40.3	81.1	109	−11	15	Mar. 25	Oct. 30	219	40	5.36	3.44	4.80	4.85	4.29	4.02	3.36	3.85	3.26	3.31	3.74	4.70	48.98
Fayette	Moscow	18	42.2	80.0	107	−4	18	Mar. 31	Oct. 23	206	18	5.35	3.98	6.23	4.39	4.24	4.37	4.44	3.45	3.25	3.22	4.35	5.08	52.35
Franklin	Sewanee	40	39.2	75.3	103	−11	37	Apr. 13	Oct. 31	201	40	4.91	4.40	5.89	5.00	4.71	5.08	5.41	4.95	3.12	3.28	3.92	5.09	55.76
Gibson	Milan	40	38.8	79.6	110	−17	38	Apr. 5	Oct. 28	206	40	5.20	3.75	4.69	4.67	4.41	3.53	3.82	3.62	3.00	3.29	4.00	4.92	48.90
	Trenton	20	39.5	79.0	106	−29	22	do	Oct. 22	200	20	5.28	3.60	4.14	4.79	4.23	3.72	2.78	4.08	2.92	3.16	4.21	4.81	47.72
Giles	Lynnville	40	40.0	77.6	109	−15	40	Apr. 8	Oct. 23	198	40	4.88	4.60	5.90	4.79	4.41	4.55	4.94	4.37	2.99	3.45	3.59	5.14	53.61
Greene	Greeneville	14	38.7	75.6	101	−20	14	Apr. 16	Oct. 20	187	17	3.90	3.67	4.58	3.42	3.50	4.15	4.09	4.54	2.38	2.30	2.21	3.58	42.32
Grundy	Tracy City	10	37.4	73.9	104	−18	10	Apr. 20	Oct. 18	181	10	4.28	5.47	6.03	4.83	4.05	4.68	4.27	5.23	3.21	2.81	3.74	6.00	54.60
Hamilton	Chattanooga	40	42.5	78.6	104	−10	40	Mar. 21	Nov. 11	235	40	4.64	4.48	5.96	5.04	4.08	3.95	4.47	4.16	2.59	3.23	3.34	5.41	51.35
Hardeman	Bolivar	35	40.3	79.6	109	−13	34	Apr. 4	Oct. 27	206	35	5.06	4.00	5.43	4.73	4.41	3.88	3.87	3.51	2.99	3.27	3.87	5.03	50.05

[1] The following counties, for which no records are available, are best represented by the stations indicated: Benton and Houston—Johnsonville; Bledsoe—Dunlap; Campbell and Union—Tazewell; Cannon—McMinnville; Cheatham—Nashville; Crockett—Brownsville; Fentress—Rugby; Grainger and Hancock—Rogersville; Hamblen—Newport; Jackson—Carthage; Marion—Chattanooga; Moore—Tullahoma; Overton—Cookeville; Rhea—Decatur; Trousdale—Lebanon; Van Buren—Erasmus.

[2] Length of growing season between average dates of last killing frost in spring and first in fall.

TENNESSEE—Continued

Climatic summary—Continued

County	Station	Temperature: Length of record	Temperature: January average	Temperature: July average	Temperature: Maximum	Temperature: Minimum	Killing frost average dates: Length of record	Killing frost average dates: Last in spring	Killing frost average dates: First in fall	Killing frost average dates: Growing season	Average precipitation: Length of record	January	February	March	April	May	June	July	August	September	October	November	December	Annual
		Yr.	°F.	°F.	°F.	°F.	Yr.			Days	Yr.	In.	In.	In.	In.	In.	In.	In.	In.	In.	In.	In.	In.	In.
Hardin	Savannah	40	41.6	79.5	112	−12	40	Apr. 3	Oct. 26	206	40	5.20	4.00	5.75	4.94	4.65	4.23	4.26	3.93	3.23	3.26	3.79	5.38	52.62
Hawkins	Rogersville	40	38.9	75.7	104	−18	40	Apr. 18	Oct. 21	186	40	3.99	3.77	4.71	3.64	3.64	3.89	4.81	3.90	2.83	2.51	2.63	4.08	44.40
Haywood	Brownsville	40	41.2	80.6	109	−13	38	Mar. 29	Oct. 29	214	33	5.87	3.89	5.41	4.65	4.43	3.23	3.35	3.58	2.95	3.21	3.79	5.04	49.40
Henderson	Wildersville	18	41.2	78.2	110	−18	18	Apr. 8	Oct. 25	200	22	5.96	3.76	4.76	4.44	4.66	4.05	4.22	4.07	2.96	3.14	3.52	4.99	50.53
Henry	Springville	20	39.2	78.0	105	−22	20	Apr. 9	Oct. 21	195	20	5.12	3.72	5.07	4.87	4.86	3.25	4.01	3.71	3.47	2.91	3.95	4.93	49.87
Hickman	Pinewood	17	40.0	77.3	108	−18	17	Apr. 22	Oct. 12	173	19	5.34	3.61	4.92	5.18	4.57	3.67	4.03	4.32	2.72	2.91	3.50	5.33	50.10
Humphreys	Johnsville	40	40.3	79.0	110	−23	40	Apr. 9	Oct. 23	197	40	5.79	3.68	5.22	4.78	4.82	4.36	4.38	4.19	3.65	3.18	3.84	4.95	52.84
Jefferson	Dandridge										34	4.22	3.83	4.75	3.80	4.12	3.82	4.76	4.17	2.83	2.77	2.59	4.28	45.94
	Jefferson City										10	4.23	3.83	4.34	3.93	3.67	4.06	4.85	4.46	2.32	2.99	2.50	4.55	45.73
Johnson	Mountain City	23	36.1	70.2	95	−32	22	Apr. 27	Oct. 11	167	22	3.69	3.60	4.56	3.73	4.05	4.68	5.86	5.23	3.09	2.83	2.23	3.67	47.22
Knox	Knoxville	40	40.3	77.9	104	−16	40	Mar. 30	Nov. 2	217	40	4.13	4.18	5.03	4.04	3.77	4.35	4.39	4.01	2.84	2.52	2.96	4.63	46.85
Lake	Tiptonville	10	39.3	81.7	111	−8	14	Mar. 23	Oct. 29	220	14	6.08	3.10	5.32	4.26	4.02	3.71	4.07	3.53	3.98	3.77	4.02	4.41	50.27
Lauderdale	Halls	13	41.4	81.0	109	−12	13	Mar. 28	Nov. 2	219	13	6.40	3.21	5.07	4.73	4.21	3.53	3.87	4.16	2.71	3.36	3.59	4.49	49.33
Lawrence	Iron City	17	40.9	77.8	107	−17	16	Apr. 17	Oct. 21	187	17	4.88	4.75	5.63	4.80	4.64	4.31	4.61	4.59	3.87	2.46	2.95	5.91	53.40
	Loretto	6	39.2	77.6	107	−17	6	Apr. 18	Oct. 24	189	29	5.28	4.39	6.06	5.13	4.57	4.09	4.29	4.49	3.17	3.23	3.37	5.46	53.53
Lewis	Hohenwald	32	40.0	77.0	108	−23	32	Apr. 14	Oct. 20	189	36	5.40	4.23	5.96	5.27	4.67	4.41	4.26	4.71	2.95	3.30	3.97	5.68	54.81
Lincoln	Coldwater	40	41.3	78.1	110	−16	37	Apr. 7	Oct. 26	202	40	5.04	4.63	6.07	4.91	4.52	4.02	4.32	4.33	3.05	3.43	3.79	5.45	53.56
	Fayetteville										13	4.42	3.78	5.83	4.19	4.35	3.37	4.15	4.73	2.66	3.85	4.40	4.77	50.50
Loudon	Loudon	25	39.3	78.9	108	−5	25	Apr. 11	Oct. 24	196	34	4.97	4.51	5.38	4.59	4.05	4.35	4.70	4.30	3.08	3.08	3.46	5.34	51.81
McMinn	Etowah	14	43.0	79.9	110	−8	14	do	Oct. 23	195	14	4.81	4.40	5.52	4.57	4.39	3.30	5.08	3.98	2.72	3.03	4.06	5.53	51.39
McNairy	Selmer										15	5.54	3.85	5.99	4.17	4.53	4.21	3.33	3.74	3.30	3.63	3.88	4.84	51.01
Macon	LaFayette	10	38.2	77.8	101	−18	10	Apr. 15	Oct. 18	186	9	4.38	3.39	6.31	4.11	3.82	4.23	3.96	3.45	4.39	2.12	3.81	4.18	48.15
Madison	Jackson No. 1	39	40.8	79.5	110	−21	40	Apr. 6	Oct. 25	202	39	5.04	3.50	5.07	4.54	4.51	3.76	3.73	3.79	3.37	3.24	3.43	4.74	48.72
	Jackson No. 2										12	6.77	3.80	6.15	4.89	4.72	4.10	4.03	4.46	3.81	3.47	3.49	5.17	54.86
Marshall	Lewisburg	40	40.7	78.8	110	−15	40	Apr. 10	Oct. 22	195	40	4.91	4.33	5.87	4.50	4.34	4.23	4.37	4.35	3.00	3.26	3.55	5.13	51.84
Maury	Ashwood	40	40.7	78.1	108	−14	40	Apr. 9	Oct. 21	195	40	4.76	3.88	5.42	4.24	4.48	3.88	3.71	3.93	3.17	3.07	3.33	4.56	48.43
Meigs	Decatur	40	40.6	77.9	108	−20	40	Apr. 15	Oct. 23	191	40	4.87	4.88	5.92	4.80	4.35	4.43	4.96	4.81	2.87	3.28	3.71	5.80	54.68
Monroe	McGhee										34	4.60	4.31	5.02	4.27	4.13	4.02	4.90	4.14	3.04	2.98	3.27	5.17	49.85
	Tellico Plains	10	41.5	77.4	101	−22	10	Apr. 14	Oct. 20	189	23	4.48	4.86	6.21	4.52	4.68	4.78	5.01	5.23	3.22	2.61	3.87	4.87	54.34
Montgomery	Clarksville	40	39.3	79.7	112	−14	40	Apr. 3	Oct. 26	206	40	5.62	3.69	4.93	4.46	4.48	4.04	3.79	3.49	3.02	3.08	3.46	4.86	48.92
Morgan	Rugby	40	37.0	74.4	104	−19	39	Apr. 24	Oct. 12	171	40	5.24	4.42	6.06	4.86	4.28	5.10	5.39	4.78	3.49	3.15	4.00	5.19	55.96
Obion	Kenton	32	38.6	79.0	108	−18	32	Apr. 2	Oct. 23	204	33	5.05	3.58	4.83	4.90	4.24	3.74	3.85	3.79	3.12	3.11	3.80	4.94	48.95
	Union City	37	38.7	80.0	111	−16	35	Apr. 4	Oct. 26	205	35	5.47	3.50	4.78	4.55	4.59	3.40	3.91	3.81	3.45	3.16	3.87	4.79	49.28
Perry	Pope	12	39.7	78.9	106	−20	12	Apr. 20	Oct. 19	182	13	4.01	4.45	4.77	4.51	4.00	4.64	3.70	3.37	2.91	2.95	4.11	5.59	49.01
Pickett	Byrdstown	21	39.0	76.5	101	−19	21	Apr. 13	Oct. 22	192	21	5.10	4.06	5.36	4.63	4.26	4.93	5.25	4.55	3.32	3.45	3.76	4.52	53.19

Polk	Benton	16	40.9	77.1	105	−28	16	Apr. 12	Oct. 21	192	15	4.18	5.09	6.12	4.79	4.37	5.64	4.82	4.21	3.04	2.68	2.98	5.34	53.26
	Copper Hill	22	41.3	76.5	103	−3	25	Apr. 8	Oct. 24	199	25	5.82	4.57	5.70	5.14	4.16	4.09	5.55	4.68	2.86	3.18	3.50	5.78	55.03
	Parksville										30	4.45	4.36	5.61	4.78	4.24	5.01	4.68	3.83	2.94	2.86	3.42	5.16	51.34
Putnam	Buffalo Valley										11	5.37	4.25	6.11	4.28	3.80	4.90	4.68	3.53	3.09	2.92	4.09	4.09	51.11
	Cookeville	24	40.4	76.7	105	−10	24	Apr. 11	Oct. 23	195	24	5.65	4.05	5.64	4.38	4.50	4.25	4.97	4.60	2.98	3.57	4.08	4.71	53.38
Roane	Harriman	13	38.3	77.0	104	−12	13	Apr. 17	Oct. 20	186	13	3.95	5.20	5.87	4.92	3.75	4.50	6.00	3.64	3.20	2.82	3.28	5.24	52.37
	Kingston										40	4.57	4.48	5.50	4.51	3.94	4.29	4.91	4.03	2.99	2.91	3.38	5.29	50.80
	Rockwood										11	4.41	5.03	5.35	4.25	4.34	4.07	4.63	4.81	3.58	2.75	4.68	6.24	54.14
Robertson	Cedar Hill	38	38.9	79.7	110	−22	35	Apr. 8	Oct. 26	201	39	5.83	3.92	5.40	4.76	4.69	4.58	4.37	3.85	3.35	3.32	3.69	5.07	52.83
Rutherford	Florence	40	39.5	78.0	108	−16	40	Apr. 5	Oct. 24	202	32	4.66	3.67	5.23	4.48	4.35	4.16	4.23	4.30	3.09	2.99	3.56	4.53	49.25
	Halls Hill										34	4.48	4.02	5.66	4.35	4.07	4.62	4.94	3.95	2.97	3.27	3.58	4.61	50.52
Scott	New River										31	5.37	4.00	5.35	4.82	4.29	4.59	4.25	4.65	2.71	2.68	3.16	4.46	50.33
Sequatchie	Dunlap	9	41.4	77.3	104	−4	8	Apr. 7	Oct. 21	197	13	6.05	3.75	5.13	5.06	3.64	4.03	5.55	4.49	3.05	3.61	3.00	5.19	52.55
Sevier	Elkmont	14	40.5	72.6	98	−10	14	Apr. 24	Oct. 17	176	14	5.82	5.28	6.74	5.18	5.78	5.59	6.33	5.87	3.46	3.94	3.93	5.63	63.55
	Gatlinburg	13	40.7	75.3	106	−10	9	Apr. 17	Oct. 22	188	13	4.82	3.87	5.25	4.47	5.07	4.62	6.08	5.65	2.94	3.15	2.54	4.50	52.96
	Sevierville	25	39.9	76.1	105	−12	25	Apr. 10	Oct. 23	196	25	4.02	3.84	4.98	3.86	4.58	4.74	4.63	4.21	3.07	2.75	2.72	4.54	47.94
Shelby	Arlington						13	Apr. 11	Oct. 22	194	21	6.24	1.96	5.32	4.52	4.79	4.23	3.54	4.07	2.55	2.78	4.60	3.29	47.89
	Memphis	40	42.3	80.9	106	−9	40	Mar. 17	Nov. 10	238	40	4.71	3.58	4.90	4.46	4.00	3.10	3.16	2.98	2.68	3.01	3.89	4.82	45.29
Smith	Carthage	40	41.1	79.3	111	−18	38	Apr. 7	Oct. 26	202	40	4.96	3.88	5.41	4.20	4.13	4.63	4.33	4.27	3.18	3.19	3.74	4.69	50.61
Stewart	Dover	38	39.3	78.6	108	−18	37	Apr. 12	Oct. 20	191	40	5.51	3.66	4.79	4.26	4.24	4.03	3.39	3.53	3.27	3.29	3.69	4.49	48.15
Sullivan	Bluff City										40	3.81	3.63	4.41	3.49	3.83	4.06	5.35	4.54	2.95	2.66	2.48	3.70	44.91
	Bristol	10	34.7	74.4	96	−20	11	Apr. 19	Oct. 17	181	16	2.45	3.27	3.99	3.22	3.37	4.37	4.87	3.49	2.30	2.24	2.86	3.78	40.21
	Kingsport	14	38.9	76.4	104	−13	13	Apr. 18	do	182	16	4.18	3.67	3.80	3.87	4.72	4.01	5.09	4.29	2.66	2.88	2.69	4.21	46.07
Sumner	Worsham										37	5.39	3.66	5.41	4.39	4.45	3.81	4.22	3.90	3.19	3.17	3.60	4.90	50.09
Tipton	Covington	40	40.2	80.1	108	−15	37	Mar. 28	Oct. 29	215	40	5.41	3.45	5.03	4.86	4.70	3.75	3.59	3.99	3.15	3.46	3.89	4.92	50.20
Unicoi	Erwin	7	42.4	74.8	101	−5	8	Apr. 18	Oct. 12	177	11	3.49	3.55	5.27	3.59	5.29	4.14	5.73	4.65	3.04	3.39	2.39	3.10	47.63
Warren	McMinnville	40	40.4	77.2	106	−26	40	Apr. 12	Oct. 24	195	40	4.76	4.06	5.59	4.30	4.10	4.20	5.19	4.21	3.26	3.25	3.25	4.85	51.02
	Rock Island										34	4.86	4.10	5.89	4.38	4.35	4.56	5.28	4.37	3.60	3.29	3.33	4.79	52.80
Washington	Embreeville										13	3.49	3.65	4.67	3.47	4.70	4.05	5.77	4.28	2.73	3.39	2.32	3.11	45.63
	Johnson City	20	38.5	75.6	105	−25	20	Apr. 16	Oct. 23	190	33	3.24	3.38	4.41	3.59	4.01	4.36	4.48	4.59	2.82	2.62	2.44	3.54	43.48
	Jonesboro	11	36.5	74.5	94	−15	12	Apr. 19	Oct. 20	184	11	2.73	3.79	4.71	3.90	4.21	4.46	4.40	4.75	2.56	2.16	2.82	3.96	44.45
Wayne	Waynesboro	39	40.0	77.0	106	−15	36	Apr. 14	do	189	40	5.13	4.16	5.88	5.27	4.87	4.15	4.80	4.52	3.17	3.29	3.77	5.45	54.46
Weakley	Dresden										15	6.28	3.59	5.00	4.48	4.45	4.43	3.37	3.25	3.51	3.48	3.48	4.74	50.06
White	Sparta	12	41.1	76.9	104	−20	15	Apr. 15	Oct. 23	191	21	4.67	3.76	5.49	4.21	4.21	5.61	5.60	4.95	3.44	2.96	3.27	4.73	52.90
	Walling										22	4.97	3.96	5.49	4.59	4.49	5.18	5.47	4.68	4.00	3.40	2.98	4.95	54.16
Williamson	Franklin	40	39.7	77.9	108	−15	40	Apr. 9	Oct. 24	198	40	4.86	3.84	5.30	4.54	4.08	4.02	3.64	3.77	2.92	2.88	3.57	4.63	48.05
Wilson	Lebanon	22	40.1	78.8	111	−17	23	Apr. 6	Oct. 23	200	24	4.83	3.86	5.56	4.66	4.60	4.54	4.48	4.76	2.91	3.71	3.90	5.01	52.82

TENNESSEE—Continued

Precipitation and temperature—State unit values

[This tabulation gives the mean annual, mean monthly, and average seasonal precipitation, 1886–1938, and the mean annual temperatures, 1902–38, for Tennessee]

Precipitation		Precipitation		Precipitation		Precipitation		Temperature		Temperature	
Year	Mean	Year	Mean	Year	Mean	Month	Mean	Year	Mean	Year	Mean
	In.		In.		In.		In.		°F.		°F.
1886	51.75	1907	49.14	1928	53.13	May	4.20	1902	58.5	1921	61.8
1887	44.97	1908	45.59	1929	59.78	June	4.16	1903	57.7	1922	60.4
1888	48.29	1909	50.63	1930	39.80	July	4.48	1904	57.6	1923	59.1
1889	45.50	1910	45.17	1931	43.24	August	4.09	1905	57.9	1924	57.2
1890	57.60	1911	53.11	1932	59.51	September	3.08	1906	58.6	1925	60.4
1891	52.80	1912	54.40	1933	51.08	October	2.82	1907	59.0	1926	58.5
1892	54.17	1913	47.42	1934	47.34	November	3.59	1908	59.8	1927	60.6
1893	45.56	1914	43.97	1935	49.73	December	4.57	1909	59.3	1928	58.3
1894	42.65	1915	54.18	1936	47.14			1910	57.8	1929	58.7
1895	43.10	1916	50.79	1937	56.03	Annual	49.92	1911	60.8	1930	59.5
1896	47.09	1917	51.51	1938	49.69			1912	57.3	1931	60.7
1897	50.89	1918	47.30					1913	59.9	1932	60.1
1898	50.45	1919	57.65					1914	58.8	1933	60.8
1899	47.97	1920	56.46	Month	Mean	Season	Average	1915	58.6	1934	59.7
1900	51.43	1921	49.94					1916	58.6	1935	59.4
1901	46.97	1922	54.35					1917	56.3	1936	59.5
1902	49.42	1923	57.63		In.		In.	1918	59.0	1937	58.8
1903	47.23	1924	46.20	January	4.85	Winter	13.68	1919	59.8	1938	60.6
1904	40.74	1925	40.50	February	4.26	Spring	14.02	1920	58.0		
1905	50.85	1926	54.69	March	5.41	Summer	12.73				
1906	53.86	1927	55.37	April	4.41	Fall	9.49				

Dates of last killing frost in spring and first in fall, with length of growing season

Year	Jackson			Clarksville			Lewisburg			McMinnville			Decatur			Rogersville		
	Last in spring	First in fall	Growing season [1]	Last in spring	First in fall	Growing season [1]	Last in spring	First in fall	Growing season [1]	Last in spring	First in fall	Growing season [1]	Last in spring	First in fall	Growing season [1]	Last in spring	First in fall	Growing season [1]
			Days			Days			Days			Days			Days			Days
1899	Apr. 2	Nov. 4	216	Apr. 9	Nov. 3	208	Apr. 10	Sept. 30	173	Apr. 10	Nov. 4	208	Apr. 10	Nov. 4	208	Apr. 11	Sept. 30	172
1900	Mar. 31	Nov. 9	223	Apr. 1	Nov. 9	222	Apr. 6	Nov. 4	212	Apr. 1	do	217	Apr. 14	Nov. 9	209	Apr. 14	Nov. 8	208
1901	Mar. 21	Nov. 4	228	Mar. 21	Nov. 4	228	Mar. 21	Nov. 5	229	Apr. 3	Oct. 15	195	Apr. 4	Oct. 15	194	Apr. 22	Oct. 18	179

1902	Apr. 8	Oct. 29	204	Apr. 9	Oct. 29	203	Apr. 2	Oct. 29	210	Apr. 9	do	189	Apr. 9	Oct. 29	203	Apr. 3	Oct. 15	195
1903	May 2	Oct. 24	175	Apr. 4	Oct. 25	204	Apr. 5	Oct. 24	202	Apr. 24	Oct. 25	184	Apr. 24	Oct. 25	184	Apr. 24	Oct. 25	184
1904	Apr. 16	Oct. 23	190	Apr. 17	Oct. 27	193	Apr. 13	Oct. 23	193	Apr. 17	Oct. 21	187	Apr. 21	Oct. 21	183	Apr. 22	Oct. 23	184
1905	Apr. 17	Nov. 2	199	do	Nov. 2	199	Apr. 18	Oct. 22	187	Apr. 18	Oct. 12	177	Apr. 17	Oct. 12	178	Apr. 19	Oct. 12	176
1906	Apr. 1	Oct. 11	193	Apr. 1	Oct. 11	193	Apr. 2	Oct. 10	191	May 10	Oct. 10	153	May 10	Oct. 11	154	May 10	Oct. 11	154
1907	Apr. 14	Oct. 13	182	Apr. 14	Oct. 14	183	Apr. 20	Oct. 13	176	Apr. 20	Oct. 13	176	Apr. 15	Oct. 14	182	Apr. 20	Oct. 13	176
1908	Mar. 21	do	206	May 1	Oct. 31	183	Apr. 4	Oct. 25	204	May 1	Oct. 25	177	May 1	Oct. 26	178	Apr. 4	Oct. 4	183
1909	May 2	do	164	Apr. 9	Oct. 13	187	May 2	Oct. 13	164	May 2	Oct. 13	164	May 2	Oct. 13	164	May 2	Oct. 13	164
1910	Mar. 16	Oct. 29	227	Mar. 16	Oct. 29	227	Apr. 25	Oct. 29	187	Apr. 24	Oct. 28	187	Apr. 24	Oct. 29	188	Apr. 28	Oct. 30	185
1911	do	Nov. 3	232	Apr. 1	Oct. 23	205	Apr. 2	Oct. 23	204	Mar. 31	Nov. 3	217	Apr. 2	Oct. 23	204	May 3	Nov. 3	184
1912	Mar. 26	Oct. 24	212	Mar. 26	Nov. 3	222	Mar. 26	Oct. 24	212	Mar. 26	Oct. 25	213	Mar. 26	Oct. 24	212	Apr. 9	Oct. 25	199
1913	Mar. 28	Oct. 21	207	Mar. 28	Oct. 31	217	Mar. 29	Oct. 21	206	Mar. 29	Oct. 21	206	Apr. 6	Oct. 21	198	Mar. 29	Nov. 1	217
1914	Apr. 10	Oct. 28	201	Apr. 10	Oct. 27	200	Apr. 10	Oct. 28	201	Apr. 10	Oct. 28	201	Apr. 10	Oct. 28	201	Apr. 10	Oct. 28	201
1915	Apr. 4	Oct. 9	188	Apr. 4	Oct. 9	188	Apr. 4	Oct. 9	188	Apr. 4	Oct. 9	188	Apr. 4	Oct. 10	189	Apr. 5	Oct. 10	188
1916	Apr. 9	Oct. 22	196	Apr. 10	Oct. 22	195	Apr. 10	Oct. 22	195	Apr. 10	Oct. 22	195	Apr. 10	Oct. 21	194	Apr. 10	Oct. 22	195
1917	Apr. 14	Oct. 9	178	do	Oct. 11	184	do	Oct. 9	182	Apr. 15	Oct. 9	177	May 14	Oct. 11	150	do	Oct. 13	186
1918	Apr. 12	Nov. 2	204	Apr. 12	Nov. 2	204	Apr. 12	Nov. 2	204	Apr. 12	Nov. 2	204	Apr. 12	Nov. 2	204	May 2	Nov. 2	184
1919	Apr. 26	Nov. 13	201	Apr. 26	Nov. 5	193	Apr. 27	Nov. 14	201	Apr. 26	Nov. 13	201	Apr. 27	Nov. 14	201	Apr. 26	Nov. 14	202
1920	Apr. 14	Oct. 29	198	Apr. 14	Oct. 2	171	Apr. 14	Oct. 2	171	Apr. 14	Oct. 29	198	Apr. 15	Oct. 2	170	Apr. 15	Oct. 30	198
1921	Apr. 11	Oct. 13	185	Apr. 11	Oct. 13	185	Apr. 19	Oct. 13	177	Apr. 11	Oct. 13	185	Apr. 12	Oct. 13	184	Apr. 19	Oct. 9	173
1922	Mar. 22	Oct. 19	211	Mar. 22	Oct. 18	210	Apr. 23	do	173	Mar. 23	Oct. 19	210	Mar. 23	Nov. 8	230	Apr. 23	Oct. 19	179
1923	Apr. 9	Oct. 31	205	Apr. 9	Oct. 31	205	Apr. 9	Oct. 25	199	Apr. 9	Oct. 23	197	May 10	Oct. 21	164	May 10	Oct. 21	164
1924	Apr. 3	Oct. 24	204	Apr. 3	Oct. 24	204	Apr. 3	Oct. 23	203	Apr. 2	do	204	Apr. 3	Oct. 23	203	Apr. 3	Oct. 23	203
1925	Mar. 28	Oct. 19	205	Mar. 20	Oct. 20	214	Apr. 2	Oct. 11	192	do	Oct. 20	201	Apr. 2	Oct. 11	192	Apr. 1	Oct. 11	193
1926	Apr. 16	Oct. 25	192	Apr. 4	Nov. 3	213	Apr. 20	Nov. 3	197	Apr. 20	Oct. 25	188	Apr. 20	Nov. 1	195	Apr. 20	Oct. 26	189
1927	Mar. 4	Oct. 19	229	Mar. 4	Nov. 6	247	Apr. 23	Nov. 6	197	Apr. 23	Nov. 6	197	Apr. 23	Oct. 14	174	Apr. 25	Nov. 6	195
1928	Apr. 16	Nov. 11	209	Apr. 16	Nov. 11	209	Apr. 16	Nov. 5	203	Apr. 16	Nov. 11	209	Apr. 17	Oct. 25	191	Apr. 17	Sept. 26	162
1929	Mar. 17	Nov. 5	233	Mar. 17	Nov. 6	234	Mar. 18	do	232	Mar. 18	Nov. 6	233	Mar. 18	Oct. 24	220	Apr. 19	Oct. 26	190
1930	Mar. 31	Oct. 31	214	Mar. 29	Oct. 26	211	Apr. 25	Oct. 25	183	Apr. 24	Oct. 21	180	Apr. 25	Oct. 18	176	Apr. 26	Oct. 18	175
1931	Apr. 22	Oct. 18	179	Mar. 30	Nov. 7	222	Apr. 7	Oct. 18	194	Apr. 7	Oct. 18	194	Apr. 7	Oct. 19	195	Apr. 27	do	174
1932	Mar. 28	Oct. 12	198	Mar. 24	Oct. 28	218	Apr. 15	Oct. 7	175	Apr. 15	Oct. 7	175	Apr. 13	Oct. 7	177	Apr. 16	Oct. 7	174
1933	Mar. 27	Nov. 8	226	do	Oct. 26	216	Mar. 29	Oct. 26	211	Mar. 29	Nov. 8	224	Mar. 27	Oct. 26	213	Mar. 28	Oct. 9	195
1934	Mar. 28	Oct. 29	215	Mar. 29	Oct. 29	214	do	Oct. 28	213	Apr. 21	Oct. 28	190	Apr. 26	Oct. 29	186	Apr. 28	Oct. 28	183
1935	Apr. 16	Oct. 7	174	Mar. 9	Oct. 2	207	Apr. 16	Oct. 7	174	Mar. 14	Oct. 7	207	Apr. 17	Oct. 7	173	Apr. 17	Oct. 7	173
1936	Apr. 19	Oct. 29	193	Apr. 8	Oct. 28	203	Apr. 19	Oct. 29	193	Apr. 8	Nov. 6	212	Apr. 19	Nov. 16	211	Apr. 20	Nov. 16	210
1937	Apr. 10	Oct. 24	197	Apr. 12	Oct. 24	195	Apr. 12	Oct. 15	186	Apr. 12	Oct. 24	195	Apr. 13	Oct. 24	194	Apr. 12	Oct. 15	186
1938	do	Oct. 25	198	Apr. 3	Oct. 25	205	Apr. 10	Oct. 25	198	Apr. 3	Nov. 9	220	Apr. 11	Oct. 25	197	Apr. 3	Oct. 25	205
Mean	Apr. 6	do	202	do	Oct. 26	206	do	Oct. 22	195	Apr. 12	Oct. 24	195	Apr. 15	Oct. 23	191	Apr. 18	Oct. 21	186
Extremes	Mar. 4[2]	Oct. 7[4]	[6] 164	Mar. 4[2]	Oct. 2[4]	[6] 171	Mar. 18[2]	Sept. 30[4]	[6] 164	Mar. 14[2]	Oct. 7[4]	[6] 153	Mar. 18[2]	Oct. 2[4]	[6] 150	Mar. 28[2]	Sept. 26[4]	[6] 154
	May 2[3]	Nov. 13[5]	[7] 233	May 1[3]	Nov. 11[5]	[7] 247	May 2[3]	Nov. 14[5]	[7] 232	May 10[3]	Nov. 13[5]	[7] 233	May 14[3]	Nov. 16[5]	[7] 230	May 10[3]	Nov. 16[5]	[7] 216

[1] Number of days between last killing frost in spring and first in fall.
[2] Earliest date in spring.
[3] Latest date in spring.
[4] Earliest date in fall.
[5] Latest date in fall.
[6] Shortest growing season.
[7] Longest growing season.

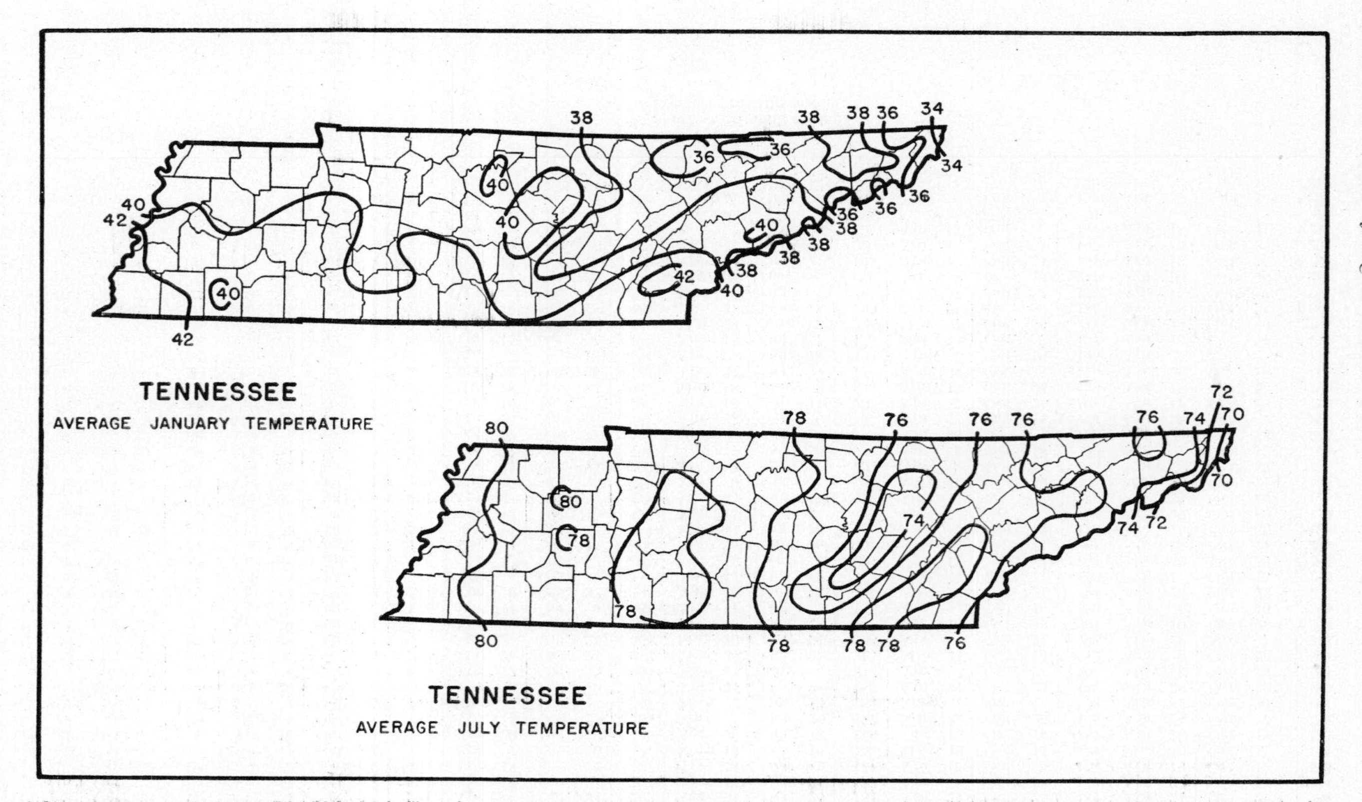

TENNESSEE
AVERAGE JANUARY TEMPERATURE

TENNESSEE
AVERAGE JULY TEMPERATURE

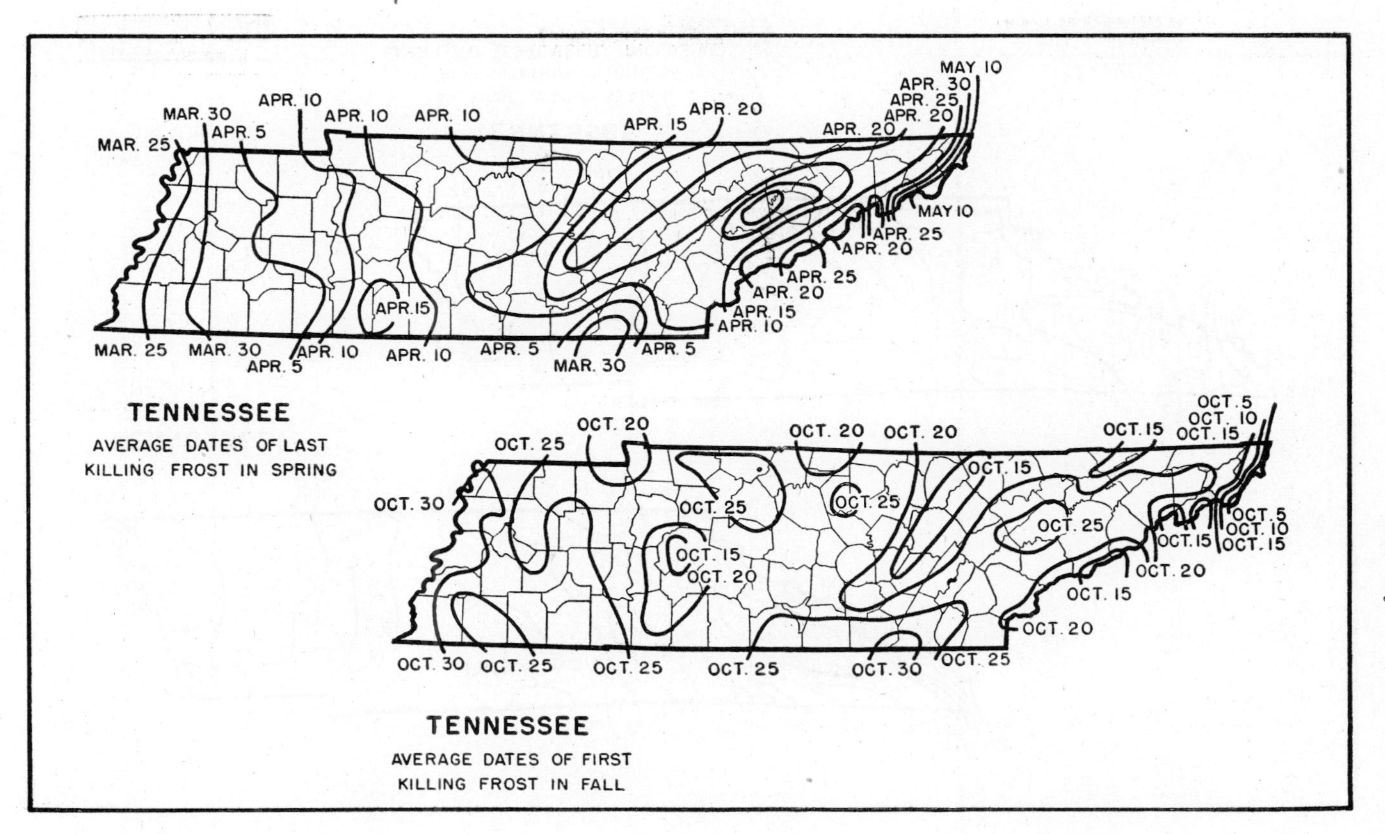

TENNESSEE
AVERAGE DATES OF LAST
KILLING FROST IN SPRING

TENNESSEE
AVERAGE DATES OF FIRST
KILLING FROST IN FALL

298737°—41——72

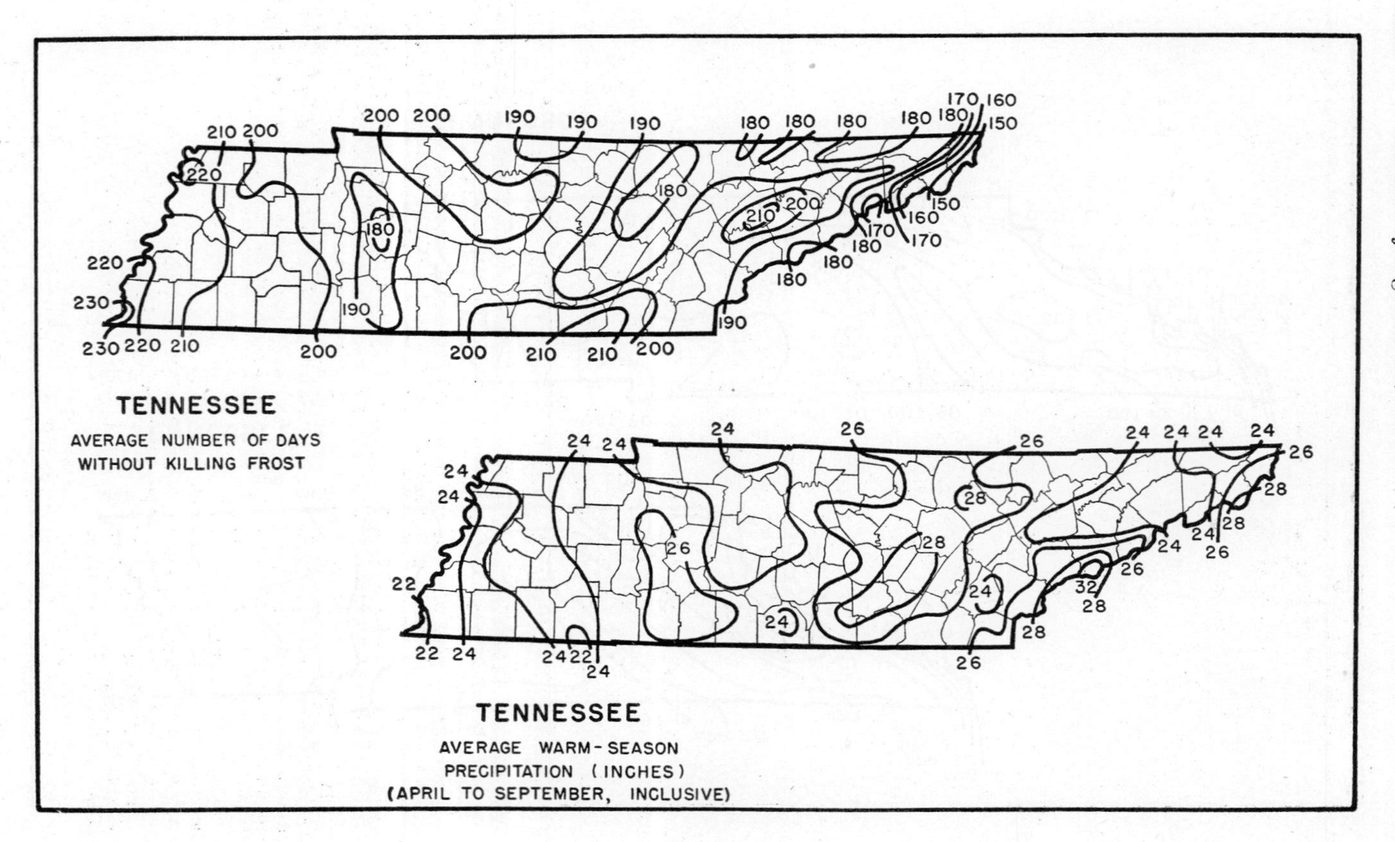

TENNESSEE
AVERAGE NUMBER OF DAYS WITHOUT KILLING FROST

TENNESSEE
AVERAGE WARM-SEASON PRECIPITATION (INCHES) (APRIL TO SEPTEMBER, INCLUSIVE)

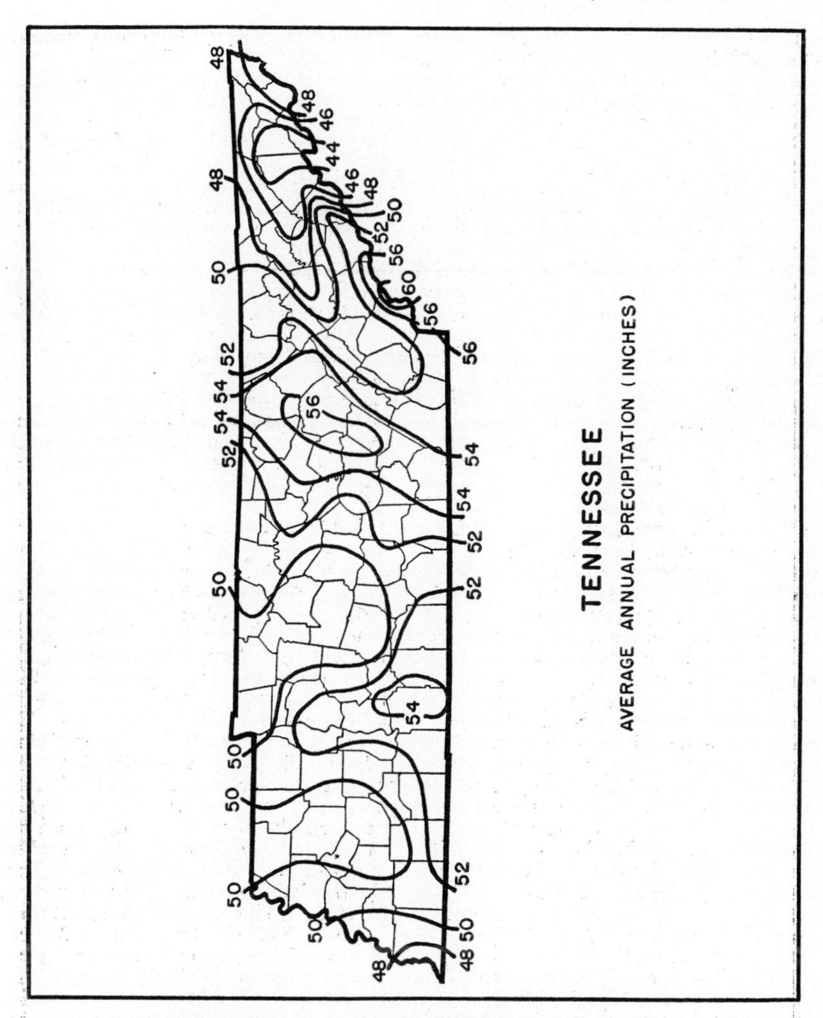

SUPPLEMENTARY CLIMATIC NOTES FOR TENNESSEE

The topography of Tennessee is varied in character, particularly in the eastern part, which is largely mountainous yet has broad, fertile valleys that produce abundant crops. These valleys range in elevation from 700 to 1,500 feet, while numerous ridges that parallel the valleys rise to 2,000 feet or more. Along the Tennessee-North Carolina boundary lie the Great Smoky Mountains, with many peaks rising to 5,000 and some to 6,000 feet or more above sea level. The Cumberland Plateau, which crosses near the center of the State in a southwest-northeast direction, has an average elevation of about 1,800 feet.

The Central Basin, an extensive agricultural section of central Tennessee, ranges from 400 to 800 feet in elevation, while surrounding it is a hilly section several hundred feet higher, commonly called the Highland Rim. The western valley of the Tennessee River falls to about 370 feet, and the plateau of west Tennessee rises from the valley to about 700 feet above sea level and then descends gradually to the west, ending in a line of bluffs near the Mississippi River. The entire State is well watered and well drained, with scarcely a swamp, in the usual sense of the word, outside the Mississippi bottom lands.

Among the natural resources of Tennessee the forests are very important. The mountains are mostly covered with deep soil, and, except where cleared, are well timbered to their tops. Even the tops of the high mountains produce abundant grass.

Agricultural resources are varied and include the production of wheat, corn, peanuts, oats, tobacco, fruits, vegetables, and cotton. Horses, mules, cattle, and hogs are produced, and there has recently been an increase in dairying in the Central Basin.

Tennessee does not lie directly within any of the principal storm tracks that cross the country but comes under the influence of the storm centers that pass along the Gulf coast and thence up the Atlantic coast, and also of those that pass from Oklahoma northeastward to the Great Lakes and thence to the coast of Maine. Weather changes are therefore frequent as compared with the remarkably stable conditions of the far Southwest but not nearly so frequent as in the Lakes region and the Northeastern States.

Zero temperatures occur, on an average, about once a year over the lowlands, but they are comparatively frequent in the mountains. Occasionally the temperature falls to considerably below zero. Maximum temperatures exceeding 100° F. are occasionally recorded. On an average they reach 95° or above at the lower levels on about 15 days during June to September, inclusive, but at elevations of 2,000 feet or more temperatures rarely go above 95°. At the lower elevations there are periods of sultry weather, such as are to be expected where moisture-laden winds from the Gulf are effective. In the highlands the conditions of heat and humidity are somewhat modified, the nights being cooler and the air movement greater; the greatest differences between mountain and lowland temperatures occur in summer.

The period between the last killing frost of spring and the first in fall gives a long crop-growing season. The average date of the last spring frost is about April 7 in the western half of the State and April 15 in the eastern half; that of the first in fall is October 23 in the western half and October 21 in the eastern. Killing frosts have been known to occur as early as September 18 and as late as May 26 at stations above 2,000 feet elevation.

Tennessee is in the region of abundant rainfall and receives an average of about 50 inches a year. This insures many unfailing springs and streams, which are of great value in a stock-raising country. The heaviest rains come in the late winter or early spring, and the driest season is midfall.

The differences in elevation in the western part of the State are not sufficient to produce any marked local peculiarities of rainfall, and the distribution there is rather uniform. However, it is slightly greater over the highlands than at lower elevations. In the eastern part, rainfall varies between the windward side of a mountain and the leeward side, and between the floor of a valley and the mountaintop. Rainfall is considerably heavier, for instance, on the Cumberland Plateau and in the Smoky Mountains than in the valley of East Tennessee, owing to the fact that a large percentage of the winds reaching this valley must first pass over the mountains on either side, thus having their moisture largely condensed and reaching the enclosed area as comparatively dry winds. A large area of the Cumberland Plateau receives an annual average of about 55 inches, while in the upper East Tennessee Valley the average is about 44 inches. Precipitation increases rapidly up the slopes of the Great Smoky Mountains. During the last 4 or 5 years measurements have been made near the tops of several high peaks on the Tennessee-North Carolina line, and annual amounts averaging slightly in excess of 80 inches have been recorded.

The average annual snowfall is only about 9 inches, and the ground is rarely blanketed for more than a few days at a time. The average amounts range from 6 inches at Memphis in the west to 22 at Elkmont and Mountain City in the east.

There are about 115 days a year with measurable precipitation in the western half of the State and 130 such days in the eastern half. Clear skies prevail on about 130 days, partly cloudy 115, cloudy 120. Sunshine averages about 59 percent of the possible amount for the State as a whole, with a winter minimum of 45 and a summer maximum of 66. Relative humidity, based on observations at 8 a. m. and 8 p. m., averages about 72 percent. Thunderstorms occur frequently during the spring and summer months. Tornadoes occur occasionally in the western and central counties, but rarely in the eastern. There are occasional droughts lasting from 20 to 30 days, and coming mostly in the late summer and fall. In all parts of the State there are occasional heavy rains, amounting to 2.5 inches or more in 24 hours.

ROBERT M. WILLIAMSON, *Meteorologist and Climatic Section Director for Tennessee, Weather Bureau, Nashville.*

TEXAS

Climatic summary

County [1]	Station	Temperature: Length of record	Temperature: January average	Temperature: July average	Temperature: Maximum	Temperature: Minimum	Killing frost average dates: Length of record	Killing frost average dates: Last in spring	Killing frost average dates: First in fall	Killing frost average dates: Growing season [2]	Average precipitation: Length of record	January	February	March	April	May	June	July	August	September	October	November	December	Annual
		Yr.	°*F.*	°*F.*	°*F.*	°*F.*	*Yr.*			*Days*	*Yr.*	*In.*	*In.*	*In.*	*In.*	*In.*	*In.*	*In.*	*In.*	*In.*	*In.*	*In.*	*In.*	*In.*
Anderson	Long Lake										32	2.99	2.87	3.76	4.45	4.18	2.80	2.42	1.98	2.86	2.90	3.44	4.43	39.08
	Palestine	40	49.0	82.2	108	−6	40	Mar. 7	Nov. 23	261	40	2.94	2.82	3.47	4.04	4.05	2.93	2.76	1.94	2.87	3.10	3.40	3.99	38.31
Angelina	Lufkin	28	50.9	83.5	110	−2	27	Mar. 15	Nov. 17	247	29	4.13	3.64	3.85	4.35	4.76	3.07	3.80	3.04	2.64	2.55	4.38	5.21	45.42
Aransas	Rockport	12	56.1	82.3	100	10	12	Feb. 2	Dec. 23	324	12	1.04	1.91	2.52	2.39	3.07	4.04	2.04	1.92	4.81	3.11	1.99	2.88	31.72
Archer	Archer City										10	.65	1.05	1.13	3.09	3.64	2.67	1.44	2.55	2.24	2.89	1.91	1.90	25.16
	Dundee (near)										17	1.13	1.38	1.73	1.92	3.12	2.38	2.01	1.49	2.70	3.02	1.38	1.30	23.56
Armstrong	Claude						14	Apr. 21	Oct. 30	192	34	.29	.64	.83	1.64	3.06	2.29	2.22	2.63	2.63	1.96	1.04	.62	19.85
Atascosa	Rossville	18	53.5	85.5	108	13	17	Mar. 9	Nov. 20	256	19	1.26	1.59	1.80	3.13	3.09	1.88	1.93	2.06	2.90	2.92	2.39	1.73	26.68
Austin	Sealy	19	53.9	84.2	108	2	26	Feb. 28	Nov. 29	274	27	3.30	2.52	3.43	3.59	4.13	3.00	3.30	2.45	3.39	3.98	3.50	4.83	41.42
Bailey	Muleshoe	10	37.0	78.2	108	−13	12	Apr. 25	Oct. 19	177	17	.36	.39	.86	1.27	2.44	3.02	2.16	2.02	2.80	1.45	.75	.43	17.95
Bastrop	Smithville	18	51.4	84.0	110	−1	20	Mar. 9	Nov. 27	263	22	3.13	2.52	2.95	3.94	4.88	3.13	2.66	1.44	2.91	3.30	2.50	3.16	36.52
Baylor	Seymour	24	42.4	83.7	120	−6	24	Apr. 1	Nov. 4	217	26	.74	1.11	1.45	2.61	3.70	2.70	2.44	2.08	2.95	2.53	1.16	1.38	24.85
Bee	Beeville	40	55.3	83.8	108	5	39	Feb. 22	Dec. 2	283	40	1.79	1.74	2.26	2.20	3.68	3.09	2.84	2.19	3.75	2.45	2.31	2.51	30.81
Bell	Salado										10	1.52	1.62	1.65	4.62	3.14	2.68	1.23	2.30	1.86	3.54	2.87	3.55	30.58
	Temple	40	48.0	84.3	111	−4	40	Mar. 7	Nov. 20	258	40	1.81	2.16	2.49	4.23	4.84	2.80	2.50	1.87	3.07	3.08	3.12	3.08	35.05
Bexar	San Antonio	40	53.1	83.7	107	4	40	Feb. 24	Dec. 3	282	40	1.45	1.47	1.80	3.25	3.50	2.58	2.30	1.64	2.86	2.33	1.78	1.83	26.79
Blanco	Blanco	37	48.4	82.9	110	−6	38	Mar. 26	Nov. 11	230	40	1.72	1.66	1.85	3.54	3.89	2.33	2.99	1.78	2.90	2.94	2.17	2.25	30.02
Bosque	Clifton						26	Mar. 22	Nov. 18	241	28	2.57	2.15	2.83	3.82	4.34	2.57	2.37	2.75	3.69	2.88	2.62	3.16	35.75
	Kopperl										33	1.81	2.06	2.24	3.63	4.69	2.46	2.51	2.20	2.41	2.83	2.62	2.23	31.69
Brazoria	Alvin						20	Feb. 27	Dec. 1	277	38	3.42	2.71	2.90	3.35	3.99	3.82	5.31	4.20	4.30	4.04	3.44	5.26	46.74
	Angleton	26	54.8	81.7	105	10	25	Mar. 1	Nov. 28	272	26	3.43	2.83	3.14	3.02	4.03	3.97	4.53	4.36	4.69	4.45	3.55	4.74	46.74
	Brazoria	29	55.1	81.7	104	6	28	Mar. 2	Dec. 1	274	31	3.06	2.99	2.74	3.67	3.79	5.03	5.07	3.93	5.55	4.53	3.69	4.54	48.59
	Freeport										18	3.84	2.91	2.81	2.69	2.84	3.23	4.59	2.75	6.49	3.36	3.88	4.53	43.92
Brazos	College Station	36	51.2	84.0	110	0	37	Mar. 8	Nov. 22	259	38	3.03	3.04	2.91	4.01	4.85	2.86	2.82	2.25	2.37	3.30	3.35	3.87	38.66
Brewster	Alpine	9	46.7	77.0	106	−2	11	Apr. 3	Nov. 11	222	17	.27	.49	.47	.46	1.36	1.73	2.48	2.12	2.54	1.04	.51	.82	14.29
Brooks	Falfurrias	31	59.2	85.6	112	10	31	Feb. 20	Dec. 7	290	32	1.13	.85	1.01	1.86	3.00	2.92	2.17	1.98	3.96	1.95	1.43	1.66	23.92
Brown	Brownwood	36	46.8	84.1	113	−3	37	Mar. 25	Nov. 12	232	39	1.38	1.27	1.70	3.07	3.90	2.43	1.93	1.75	3.02	2.43	2.08	1.61	26.57

[1] The following counties, for which no records are available, are best represented by the stations indicated: Andrews—Seminole; Bandera—Kerrville; Borden—Snyder; Bowie—Naples; Briscoe—Tulia (near); Camp—Mt. Pleasant; Cass—Jefferson; Cochran—Plains; Coke—Sterling City; Collingsworth—Memphis; Crane—Buena Vista; Crockett and Schleicher—Sonora; Culberson—Balmorhea; Deaf Smith—Vega; Delta—Honey Grove; Duval—Alice; Ector, Martin, and Upton—Midland; Edwards—Substation No. 14; Floyd—Plainview; Freestone—Mexia; Hardin—Liberty; Hockley—Brownfield; Hudspeth—El Paso; Irion—San Angelo; Jasper and Polk—Rockland; Kent—Aspermont; King and Motley—Spur; Lee—Somerville; Loving and Winkler—Barstow; Lynn—Post; McMullen—Fowlerton; Madison—Huntsville; Mason—Llano; Mills—San Saba; Moore—Amarillo; Nolan—Colorado; Panola—Marshall; Rains and Wood—Wills Point; Reagan—Garden City; Real—Montell; Rockwall—Greenville; San Augustine—Nacogdoches; San Jacinto and Trinity—Riverside; Shelby—Bronson; Somervell—Cleburne; Terrell—Del Rio; Upshur—Longview; Wheeler—Miami; Wilbarger—Chillicothe; Zapata—Hebbronville.

[2] Length of growing season between average dates of last killing frost in spring and first in fall.

TEXAS—Continued

Climatic summary—Continued

County	Station	Temperature					Killing frost average dates				Average precipitation													
		Length of record	January average	July average	Maximum	Minimum	Length of record	Last in spring	First in fall	Growing season	Length of record	January	February	March	April	May	June	July	August	September	October	November	December	Annual
		Yr.	*°F.*	*°F.*	*°F.*	*°F.*	*Yr.*			*Days*	*Yr.*	*In.*	*In.*	*In.*	*In.*	*In.*	*In.*	*In.*	*In.*	*In.*	*In.*	*In.*	*In.*	*In.*
Burleson	Somerville	16	51.4	85.1	111	4	19	Mar. 6	Nov. 22	261	19	2.05	2.50	2.72	3.91	4.18	2.62	1.17	2.23	2.17	3.49	2.93	3.78	33.75
Burnet	Fairland	33	49.5	84.1	114	-3	32	Mar. 16	Nov. 20	249	37	1.52	1.72	2.11	2.96	3.51	2.95	2.13	1.98	2.90	2.65	2.08	2.18	28.69
	Marble Falls										30	1.73	1.62	1.89	3.15	3.76	2.78	1.79	1.93	3.26	2.76	2.10	2.48	29.25
Caldwell	Luling	40	51.7	84.7	110	2	40	Mar. 1	Nov. 26	270	40	2.04	2.37	2.29	3.66	4.31	2.59	2.92	1.76	2.93	3.08	2.61	2.93	33.49
Calhoun	Port Lavaca	14	55.6	83.4	103	13	14	Feb. 19	Dec. 8	292	17	1.02	2.22	1.95	3.04	3.98	2.60	3.19	3.03	4.50	4.68	2.89	3.06	36.16
Callahan	Putnam										28	1.07	1.03	1.45	2.54	3.82	2.22	1.69	2.02	2.63	2.47	1.53	1.41	23.88
Cameron	Brownsville	39	59.8	83.6	104	12	38	Jan. 30	Dec. 26	330	40	1.31	1.10	1.12	1.64	2.58	2.77	2.03	2.06	5.17	2.88	1.81	1.79	26.26
	Harlingen	24	61.0	83.7	108	22	24	Feb. 11	Dec. 21	313	25	1.49	1.18	1.22	1.27	3.24	2.74	2.40	2.28	5.70	2.58	1.75	1.64	27.49
	San Benito	14	62.0	83.7	107	24	14	Feb. 18	Dec. 23	308	19	1.31	1.31	1.08	1.25	3.28	3.03	2.10	2.00	6.68	2.90	1.54	2.07	28.55
Carson	Panhandle										14	.48	.79	1.06	1.86	2.45	2.72	2.32	3.02	3.35	2.34	.84	1.03	22.26
Castro	Dimmitt (near)										16	.27	.37	.80	1.04	3.13	2.45	1.94	2.67	2.78	2.08	.73	.42	18.68
Chambers	Anahuac (near)	8	56.4	82.9	105	15					24	4.06	3.00	3.38	3.77	4.03	4.31	5.91	4.50	5.08	4.24	2.99	5.07	50.34
Cherokee	Dialville	35	48.5	82.7	111	-5	34	Mar. 16	Nov. 16	245	36	3.74	3.47	4.23	4.92	4.36	3.12	3.51	2.65	2.75	3.39	3.78	4.89	44.81
Childress	Childress	17	39.8	82.9	114	-13	18	Mar. 30	Nov. 6	221	33	.47	1.00	1.28	2.37	3.32	2.62	2.25	2.10	3.01	2.16	1.04	1.03	22.65
Clay	Henrietta	39	41.8	84.7	116	-6	38	Mar. 27	Nov. 11	229	40	1.09	1.25	1.71	2.95	3.99	3.12	2.21	2.29	2.56	2.63	1.91	1.42	27.13
Coleman	Coleman	39	47.9	83.1	113	-6	40	Mar. 22	Nov. 15	238	40	1.15	1.22	1.47	3.09	4.31	2.78	2.58	1.99	3.17	2.67	1.81	1.38	27.62
Collin	McKinney	28	45.6	83.7	118	-7	26	Mar. 28	Nov. 11	228	28	2.74	2.34	2.73	4.32	5.41	3.16	2.71	2.60	2.73	3.44	2.28	2.67	37.13
Colorado	Columbus										35	2.76	2.65	2.95	3.68	4.34	2.89	3.14	2.43	3.23	3.54	3.37	3.92	38.90
Comal	New Braunfels	39	51.5	83.6	109	2	40	Feb. 27	Nov. 26	272	40	1.84	1.91	2.29	3.44	3.83	2.69	2.41	1.69	2.82	3.16	2.08	2.54	30.70
Comanche	Comanche	8	46.2	82.3	112	3	18	Mar. 25	Nov. 13	233	22	1.65	1.68	1.79	2.65	4.35	2.40	2.07	1.54	2.73	2.79	1.76	1.64	27.05
Concho	Paint Rock										20	1.08	1.20	1.37	2.11	3.32	2.14	2.35	1.65	3.17	3.27	1.43	1.19	24.28
Cooke	Gainesville	39	43.8	83.4	114	-12	40	Mar. 27	Nov. 8	226	40	1.90	2.02	2.57	3.79	4.80	3.08	3.39	2.42	3.34	3.46	2.17	2.22	35.16
Coryell	Copperas Cove										23	2.28	2.02	2.32	3.77	4.33	2.36	2.31	1.72	3.64	2.98	2.27	2.07	32.07
	Gatesville	21	48.5	83.5	111	0	21	Mar. 23	Nov. 10	232	29	1.64	1.83	2.24	4.11	4.12	3.13	2.30	2.22	3.19	3.03	2.59	2.31	32.71
Cottle	Paducah (near)						22	Apr. 6	Nov. 13	221	26	.66	.70	1.16	2.10	3.17	2.74	1.62	2.54	2.52	2.70	.88	.96	21.75
Crosby	Crosbyton	39	40.2	79.3	110	-14	39	Apr. 9	Nov. 2	207	40	.53	.70	.82	1.75	2.69	2.72	2.58	2.65	2.71	2.34	1.17	.74	21.40
Dallam	Dalhart	31	33.4	77.0	110	-17	32	Apr. 23	Oct. 19	179	33	.23	.38	.75	1.62	2.82	3.00	2.23	2.65	1.52	1.65	.57	.53	17.95
Dallas	Dallas	40	45.8	83.7	110	-3	40	Mar. 18	Nov. 17	244	40	2.23	2.03	2.65	3.88	4.43	3.11	2.49	2.12	2.91	2.82	2.49	2.44	33.60
	Carrolton										15	2.70	2.26	2.52	3.39	4.91	2.89	2.90	1.43	3.20	3.43	2.08	2.77	34.48
Dawson	Lamesa	12	42.7	81.3	111	-6	14	Apr. 3	Nov. 8	219	29	.42	.85	.81	1.51	1.97	2.51	1.87	2.26	2.40	2.13	.76	.83	18.32
Denton	Denton	25	44.6	84.1	113	-3	26	Mar. 27	Nov. 9	227	26	2.36	1.89	2.35	3.63	4.54	2.80	2.11	2.53	2.57	3.30	2.03	2.51	32.62
De Witt	Cuero	39	53.9	84.9	109	4	40	Mar. 1	Nov. 27	271	40	2.29	2.27	2.44	3.06	4.34	3.47	3.32	2.30	3.21	3.16	2.89	2.99	35.74
Dickens	Spur	27	40.9	82.0	114	-17	26	Apr. 5	Nov. 3	212	27	.47	.69	.93	2.03	2.87	2.41	1.98	2.66	2.91	2.51	.94	.90	21.30
Dimmitt	Big Wells										23	1.02	1.20	1.15	1.64	2.27	1.91	1.83	1.52	2.92	1.82	.98	1.55	19.81
	Carrizo Springs	16	54.6	86.1	111	13	14	Feb. 28	Dec. 6	281	17	1.14	.86	.97	1.59	2.44	2.28	2.10	2.01	3.11	1.71	.99	1.37	20.57
Donley	Clarendon	32	38.9	81.1	117	-11	33	Apr. 10	Oct. 29	202	32	.43	.76	1.12	1.91	3.70	3.07	2.21	2.76	3.26	2.30	1.09	.86	23.47

Eastland	Eastland	27	43.7	83.2	115	−5	27	Mar. 30	Nov. 9	224	28	1.40	1.35	1.72	2.68	3.91	2.55	1.84	1.83	2.83	2.67	1.80	1.72	26.30
Ellis	Waxahachie	39	46.0	84.2	115	−9	40	Mar. 27	Nov. 11	229	40	2.24	2.21	2.88	3.88	4.80	2.82	2.48	1.75	2.96	2.65	2.79	2.92	34.38
El Paso	El Paso	40	45.4	81.4	106	−5	40	Mar. 21	Nov. 14	238	40	.37	.42	.31	.31	.30	.68	1.61	1.56	1.27	.72	.52	.49	8.56
	Socorro	21	41.3	78.7	107	−1	21	Apr. 12	Nov. 4	206	21	.40	.29	.31	.26	.31	45	1.50	1.50	1.20	.88	.39	.40	7.89
Erath	Dublin	35	45.7	83.3	114	−9	34	Mar. 21	Nov. 14	238	37	1.55	1.69	1.96	3.62	4.82	2.57	2.26	1.74	2.75	2.60	2.29	2.01	29.86
Falls	Marlin						11	Mar. 18	Nov. 22	249	10	2.10	2.65	2.76	3.98	4.71	3.42	4.40	1.10	2.60	2.62	3.96	3.70	38.00
Fannin	Bonham	33	43.4	83.5	115	−5	34	Mar. 29	Nov. 8	224	35	2.81	2.52	3.30	4.20	4.95	3.78	3.86	2.39	2.65	3.58	2.30	2.97	39.31
	Honey Grove						12	Apr. 4	Nov. 2	212	23	3.65	2.81	3.21	4.68	4.90	3.32	3.34	2.51	3.27	4.07	2.96	3.00	41.72
Fayette	Flatonia	31	53.5	85.0	111	4	31	Mar. 6	Nov. 30	269	31	2.57	2.45	2.67	3.59	4.83	2.74	2.64	2.59	2.72	3.17	2.75	3.24	35.96
	LaGrange						22	Mar. 7	Nov. 25	263	29	2.95	2.58	3.09	3.81	4.87	2.79	2.67	2.22	2.67	3.64	2.72	3.69	37.70
Fisher	Claytonville	17	44.4	82.0	111	−12	17	Mar. 31	Nov. 4	218	21	.60	.75	1.09	2.78	2.73	3.12	2.23	2.42	1.80	2.51	1.68	.91	22.62
	Rotan										13	.80	1.00	1.09	1.57	3.34	1.91	2.12	1.82	3.01	1.93	1.11	1.05	20.75
Foard	Crowell										22	.78	.92	1.60	2.10	3.60	2.83	1.64	2.17	2.89	2.94	1.15	1.06	23.68
Fort Bend	Rosenberg										34	3.02	2.52	2.96	3.52	4.46	3.20	3.81	3.13	3.25	3.59	3.12	4.07	40.65
	Sugarland	33	54.3	83.3	108	8	35	Feb. 23	Nov. 29	279	38	3.12	2.80	3.08	3.45	4.52	3.41	3.84	3.18	3.34	3.63	3.26	4.57	42.20
Franklin	Winfield						18	Mar. 27	Nov. 8	226	27	4.14	3.16	4.24	6.10	5.41	3.28	3.19	3.00	3.04	3.98	3.20	4.36	47.10
Frio	Dilley	22	53.5	85.6	110	14	22	Feb. 23	Dec. 4	284	29	1.02	1.22	1.55	1.79	3.14	2.06	1.78	1.34	2.91	1.62	1.28	1.67	21.38
	Pearsall						13	Feb. 23	Nov. 30	280	34	.99	1.21	1.63	2.02	3.34	2.36	2.16	1.44	2.69	1.78	1.44	1.61	22.67
Gaines	Seminole	15	41.8	79.2	112	−23	14	Apr. 5	Nov. 5	214	16	.33	.79	.62	.95	1.88	1.63	2.03	2.12	2.18	1.96	.59	.62	15.70
Galveston	Galveston	40	54.6	82.8	101	8	40	Jan. 21	Dec. 28	341	40	3.50	2.79	2.54	3.46	3.46	3.45	4.14	3.77	5.35	4.51	3.28	4.11	44.36
Garza	Post						9	Apr. 4	Nov. 6	216	29	.40	1.03	.79	2.07	2.48	2.63	1.83	2.77	2.72	2.30	.74	.91	20.67
Gillespie	Fredericksburg	16	49.2	81.1	104	−1	16	Mar. 13	Nov. 12	244	16	.93	1.36	2.01	3.61	3.33	2.01	2.68	1.78	2.29	2.77	2.83	1.86	27.46
	Morris Ranch						8	Mar. 30	Nov. 22	237	18	1.46	1.77	2.03	2.50	3.95	3.20	2.06	1.71	3.50	3.00	1.63	1.82	28.63
Glasscock	Garden City						12	Apr. 8	Nov. 4	210	26	.55	.71	1.06	1.90	2.27	2.09	1.54	2.92	2.35	1.71	1.08	.76	18.94
Goliad	Goliad										26	2.30	1.71	2.21	2.23	3.49	2.81	2.79	2.14	3.77	2.71	2.56	2.75	31.47
Gonzales	Gonzales										35	1.89	2.08	2.34	3.32	3.92	2.58	2.40	1.94	2.82	2.92	2.46	2.84	31.51
	Nixon										18	2.13	1.77	2.50	3.14	3.62	2.84	2.55	1.51	3.31	2.50	1.80	2.89	30.56
Gray	Pampa										14	.40	.92	1.13	1.37	3.58	2.80	1.94	2.95	1.98	1.45	1.24	.65	20.41
Grayson	Denison	8	42.6	82.1							31	2.15	1.96	2.49	4.09	4.72	2.77	2.67	2.66	2.29	3.28	1.92	2.51	33.51
	Sherman	38	44.0	83.5	113	0	36	Mar. 21	Nov. 14	238	40	2.31	2.23	2.95	3.86	4.93	3.32	3.55	2.84	2.94	3.59	2.19	2.56	37.27
Gregg	Longview	38	47.6	83.8	113	−7	38	Mar. 10	Nov. 17	252	40	3.39	3.27	4.07	4.62	4.17	3.10	3.58	2.65	2.15	3.04	3.69	4.55	42.28
Grimes	Anderson										24	4.15	2.99	3.04	4.32	5.38	3.00	3.10	3.28	2.75	3.41	3.44	3.88	42.74
	Navasota										24	3.98	2.74	2.95	4.06	4.78	3.04	2.89	2.80	2.58	3.28	3.17	3.87	40.14
Guadalupe	Seguin	16	53.1	85.4	109	9	16	Mar. 5	Dec. 1	271	16	2.12	2.09	2.58	2.49	4.64	2.83	1.94	1.69	3.48	2.29	1.68	2.66	30.49
Hale	Plainview	38	40.9	78.2	108	−8	38	Apr. 11	Nov. 1	204	40	.43	.69	.88	1.79	2.80	2.96	3.08	2.69	2.74	1.94	1.10	.68	21.78
Hall	Mamphis	28	39.4	82.4	117	−11	28	Apr. 1	Nov. 5	218	31	.50	.58	1.08	1.78	3.54	2.90	2.17	2.30	2.61	2.44	.91	.77	21.58
Hamilton	Hamilton										23	2.20	1.68	1.90	3.48	4.48	3.17	2.39	1.66	2.84	2.20	2.24	1.83	30.07
	Hico	21	45.9	83.8	113	−2	22	Mar. 29	Nov. 10	226	26	1.88	1.81	2.13	3.30	4.16	2.42	2.14	2.09	3.14	2.56	2.30	1.95	29.88
Hansford	Spearman	29	35.3	80.7	111	−11	14	Apr. 21	Oct. 29	191	18	.45	.78	1.46	1.68	3.30	3.44	1.85	1.93	1.93	1.39	1.01	.51	19.73
Hardeman	Chillicothe										32	.68	.94	1.48	2.43	3.21	3.29	2.07	2.37	2.93	3.00	1.41	1.16	24.97
	Quanah	32	41.3	84.6	119	−9	34	Mar. 28	Nov. 7	224	34	.57	.86	1.46	2.64	2.98	3.32	2.10	2.16	2.61	2.71	1.34	1.18	23.93
Harris	Goose Creek										17	4.27	3.11	3.45	3.40	4.17	3.33	4.08	2.71	3.37	2.95	4.11	5.86	44.81
	Houston	39	54.2	83.1	108	5	38	Feb. 10	Dec. 8	301	40	3.19	2.88	3.10	3.50	4.39	3.77	4.51	3.73	3.71	3.74	3.50	4.82	44.84
Harrison	Marshall	30	48.9	83.3	112	−9	31	Mar. 17	Nov. 12	240	32	4.02	3.53	4.17	5.05	4.13	3.01	3.31	2.91	2.19	2.93	3.82	5.18	44.25
Hartley	Romero	20	35.7	78.1	110	−20	24	Apr. 19	Oct. 17	181	22	.37	.66	1.08	2.07	3.46	3.05	2.20	2.56	1.51	2.01	.71	.91	20.59
Haskell	Haskell	38	43.0	84.1	115	−3	37	Mar. 29	Nov. 10	226	39	.76	1.02	1.15	2.58	3.56	3.17	2.22	1.89	2.61	2.48	1.31	1.08	23.83
Hays	San Marcos	37	50.9	83.6	111	1	38	Mar. 13	Nov. 24	256	40	1.96	2.29	2.60	3.70	4.11	2.55	3.04	1.62	2.66	3.29	2.21	2.79	32.82
Hemphill	Canadian	29	36.4	81.3	112	−14	30	Apr. 12	Oct. 30	201	31	.36	.87	1.10	2.10	3.10	3.25	1.78	2.22	2.48	1.87	1.20	.70	21.03
Henderson	Trinidad										24	3.25	2.32	3.35	4.44	4.03	2.40	2.03	1.56	2.84	2.83	2.80	3.68	35.53
Hidalgo	Mercedes	25	61.0	83.8	110	21	24	Feb. 8	Dec. 19	314	25	1.43	.90	1.04	1.16	3.50	2.40	2.21	1.96	4.19	2.16	1.52	1.51	23.98
	Mission	22	60.3	84.9	110	18	22	Feb. 7	Dec. 22	318	23	1.27	.91	1.09	1.17	2.51	2.22	2.14	1.26	4.10	1.76	1.41	1.44	21.28
Hill	Hillsboro	34	46.4	84.8	113	−1	34	Mar. 21	Nov. 12	236	36	2.39	2.31	3.00	4.40	4.74	3.02	2.09	1.86	3.34	2.83	2.63	3.20	35.81
Hood	Panter										19	1.11	1.36	1.89	3.61	4.61	2.93	2.25	2.72	2.57	2.31	2.48	1.91	29.75

TEXAS—Continued

Climatic summary—Continued

County	Station	Temperature: Length of record	Temperature: January average	Temperature: July average	Temperature: Maximum	Temperature: Minimum	Killing frost average dates: Length of record	Killing frost average dates: Last in spring	Killing frost average dates: First in fall	Killing frost average dates: Growing season	Average precipitation: Length of record	January	February	March	April	May	June	July	August	September	October	November	December	Annual
		Yr.	*°F.*	*°F.*	*°F.*	*°F.*	*Yr.*			*Days*	*Yr.*	*In.*	*In.*	*In.*	*In.*	*In.*	*In.*	*In.*	*In.*	*In.*	*In.*	*In.*	*In.*	*In.*
Hopkins	Ringo Crossing										29	3.53	2.63	3.73	4.70	4.11	3.40	2.88	2.79	2.77	2.97	2.95	3.76	40.22
	Sulphur Springs	11	45.4	82.1	114	−10	14	Mar. 13	Nov. 13	245	28	2.84	2.78	3.57	3.92	4.47	3.14	3.53	2.03	3.17	3.00	2.88	3.38	38.71
Houston	Crockett	13	52.8	84.1	114	−10	16	Mar. 14	Nov. 21	252	28	3.57	3.43	3.77	4.82	5.53	2.93	3.16	2.17	2.55	3.02	4.15	5.20	44.30
Howard	Big Spring	37	44.5	82.9	117	−7	38	Apr. 1	Nov. 8	221	39	.47	.73	.91	1.97	2.59	2.08	1.95	2.03	2.12	2.04	1.07	.71	18.67
Hunt	Greenville	38	44.8	84.5	116	−4	37	Mar. 22	Nov. 12	235	39	2.72	2.42	2.96	4.38	4.64	3.08	3.16	2.56	3.08	3.13	2.74	3.02	37.89
Hutchinson	Lieb (near)	18	35.1	78.1	107	−19	18	Apr. 22	Oct. 22	183	20	.39	.82	.84	1.83	2.86	2.94	2.29	2.42	2.03	1.63	.93	.86	19.84
Jack	Antelope										10	1.23	.96	1.95	3.44	3.31	2.75	1.81	3.60	2.33	2.83	1.88	1.62	27.71
Jackson	Edna										30	2.64	2.15	2.46	2.89	4.20	3.72	3.22	2.51	3.60	3.31	2.64	3.57	36.91
Jeff Davis	Fort Davis	5	43.8	75.1	111	3	6	Apr. 1	Oct. 18	200	31	.38	.47	.32	.60	1.38	1.77	2.74	3.07	2.35	1.27	.65	.57	15.57
Jefferson	Beaumont	35	54.7	83.5	108	4	36	Feb. 23	Dec. 6	286	40	3.97	3.70	3.54	4.03	5.23	4.35	5.40	5.06	4.28	3.56	3.84	5.41	52.37
	Port Arthur	22	53.6	82.7	102	11	22	Jan. 28	Dec. 15	321	28	4.25	3.32	3.29	3.16	4.52	4.19	6.39	5.10	4.57	3.30	3.24	5.33	50.66
Jim Hogg	Hebbronville	6	61.1	85.2	108	20	5	Feb. 28	Dec. 13	288	32	.87	.78	1.19	1.52	2.66	2.42	1.70	1.53	3.65	1.78	1.16	1.24	20.50
Jim Wells	Alice	28	56.7	85.1	109	17	28	Feb. 21	Dec. 6	288	28	1.31	1.19	1.62	1.58	3.26	3.10	2.09	1.89	3.77	2.66	1.50	1.79	25.76
Johnson	Cleburne	26	46.5	85.3	112	−3	26	Mar. 25	Nov. 15	235	28	2.42	1.99	2.63	3.91	5.00	2.68	1.85	1.63	2.74	3.23	2.87	2.49	33.44
Jones	Hamlin										12	.47	.76	1.18	3.26	2.46	2.87	2.08	2.69	1.71	2.20	1.16	1.38	22.22
	Stamford										20	.62	1.41	1.12	2.27	3.89	2.12	1.84	2.46	2.88	2.59	1.11	1.89	24.20
Karnes	Karnes City										19	2.57	1.75	2.48	2.40	4.19	3.16	2.44	1.55	3.25	2.55	2.18	2.92	31.44
	Runge	6	53.8	84.2	106	6	8	Feb. 16	Dec. 1	288	39	1.67	1.86	1.95	2.96	3.53	2.68	2.71	1.55	3.18	2.23	2.06	2.54	28.92
Kaufman	Kaufman	39	46.7	85.0	113	−2	39	Mar. 19	Nov. 15	241	37	2.77	2.81	3.12	4.55	5.17	3.49	2.57	2.48	3.62	3.61	3.17	3.84	41.20
Kendall	Boerne	40	50.1	80.9	112	0	40	Mar. 18	Nov. 16	243	40	1.79	1.99	2.04	3.81	4.52	2.74	3.19	1.83	3.87	3.36	2.47	2.40	34.01
Kenedy	Sarita (near)										8	.52	.88	1.13	1.64	1.90	2.48	1.54	2.32	.93	2.12	.79	1.39	17.64
Kerr	Kerrville	40	48.8	80.8	109	−4	40	Mar. 30	Nov. 6	221	40	1.38	1.48	1.73	3.04	4.00	2.98	2.78	2.04	3.57	2.71	2.30	2.07	30.08
Kimble	Junction	29	47.3	81.4	110	−11	31	Apr. 5	Nov. 5	214	36	1.09	1.26	1.50	2.74	3.82	2.87	2.52	1.72	3.40	2.57	1.68	1.26	26.43
Kinney	Brackettsville	30	51.4	83.9	109	9	30	Feb. 26	Nov. 28	275	4	.70	.15	.96	1.22	3.60	2.95	4.40	.88	2.58	1.40	.90	1.91	21.65
Kleberg	Kingsville										31	1.24	1.41	1.63	1.73	2.74	3.13	2.09	1.79	3.29	2.01	1.94	1.71	24.71
	Ricardo	18	56.2	83.5	108	13	18	Feb. 28	Nov. 27	272	28	1.21	.95	1.47	1.78	3.82	3.26	1.89	1.88	5.02	2.20	1.59	1.80	26.87
Knox	Munday						18	Apr. 4	Nov. 8	218	26	.89	1.06	1.46	2.88	3.73	2.95	1.93	1.82	2.66	2.96	1.15	1.15	24.64
Lamar	Arthur City										40	2.71	2.38	3.59	4.47	5.37	3.48	3.60	2.37	2.84	3.27	2.89	2.79	39.76
	Paris	40	44.3	83.5	115	−13	40	Mar. 20	Nov. 13	238	40	2.94	2.41	3.52	4.86	5.02	3.72	3.42	2.98	3.05	3.09	3.10	3.12	41.23
Lamb	Littlefield										11	.45	.59	.95	.97	3.24	2.38	1.52	2.18	2.45	1.52	.78	.61	17.64
Lampasas	Lampasas	40	47.7	83.3	112	−7	40	Mar. 24	Nov 10	231	40	1.46	1.86	2.05	3.37	3.89	2.48	2.10	1.51	3.20	2.86	2.30	2.17	29.25
La Salle	Cotulla										27	.99	1.36	1.48	2.02	3.20	1.62	1.42	1.95	2.58	1.44	1.18	1.68	20.92
	Encinal	29	55.7	86.6	115	10	29	Feb. 19	Dec. 8	292	29	1.28	1.08	1.52	1.59	2.64	1.97	1.76	1.49	3.20	2.21	1.24	1.33	21.31
	Fowlerton										17	1.11	1.36	1.38	2.17	2.82	2.02	1.63	1.94	2.71	1.28	1.58	1.46	21.46
Lavaca	Hallettsville	40	54.0	84.5	108	5	40	Mar. 3	Nov. 25	267	40	2.38	2.40	2.68	3.30	4.28	2.70	3.35	1.99	2.83	3.36	2.98	3.18	35.43
	Yoakum										20	2.75	2.39	2.27	3.39	5.80	3.51	3.12	2.79	3.09	3.02	2.90	2.84	37.87
Leon	Jewett	12	50.6	83.5	113	8	14	Mar. 23	Nov. 5	227	14	1.60	2.80	2.77	5.01	5.19	2.92	2.21	2.92	2.19	2.83	2.97	4.21	37.62

Liberty	Liberty	34	54.9	83.1	108	8	34	Mar. 5	Nov. 26	266	35	3.75	3.31	3.65	3.87	5.33	4.65	4.15	3.95	3.62	4.23	3.77	5.48	49.76
Limestone	Groesbeck	13	47.1	82.9	105	−2	12	Mar. 9	Nov. 25	261	13	2.68	2.49	2.98	3.72	5.04	3.65	1.53	1.58	2.80	4.48	3.35	2.99	37.29
	Mexia	34	47.3	83.9	112	−2	34	Mar. 14	Nov. 20	251	34	2.55	2.55	3.12	4.44	4.52	2.75	1.89	1.90	2.93	3.22	2.79	3.82	36.48
Lipscomb	Booker										12	.20	.43	1.15	1.84	2.60	3.07	2.33	2.49	1.66	1.93	1.20	.49	19.39
Live Oak	George West										23	1.72	1.32	1.99	1.64	2.66	3.02	2.20	1.75	4.19	2.35	1.85	2.73	27.42
	Whitsett										25	1.48	1.17	1.97	2.26	2.63	2.37	2.12	1.81	3.63	1.92	1.46	2.31	25.13
Llano	Llano	38	48.7	85.1	115	−7	39	Mar. 20	Nov. 14	239	40	1.28	1.53	1.55	2.80	3.57	2.18	2.01	1.57	2.62	2.50	1.93	1.56	25.10
Lubbock	Lubbock	25	39.8	79.0	108	−17	28	Apr. 12	Nov. 3	205	28	.42	.56	.92	1.44	2.37	2.55	2.05	1.92	2.91	2.35	.64	.69	18.82
McCulloch	Rochelle	19	48.0	82.5	109	−2	19	Mar. 26	Nov. 13	232	19	1.41	1.39	1.82	3.01	3.05	2.13	1.53	1.91	3.37	2.26	1.50	1.20	24.58
McLennan	Hewitt						15	Apr. 8	Nov. 23	229	40	1.78	2.01	2.38	3.69	4.39	2.99	2.34	1.49	2.81	2.97	2.50	2.77	32.12
	McGregor						5	Mar. 15	Nov. 24	254	27	2.25	2.03	2.51	3.56	3.92	3.04	1.96	1.74	3.08	2.83	2.46	2.84	32.22
	Waco	40	48.6	85.7	111	−5	40	Mar. 10	Nov. 15	250	40	1.90	2.29	2.96	4.13	4.68	3.39	2.27	1.82	3.06	2.78	2.60	3.02	34.90
Marion	Jefferson						6	Mar. 17	Nov. 13	241	29	4.41	3.50	4.36	5.15	4.46	3.69	4.06	2.68	2.57	3.19	4.13	5.72	47.92
Matagorda	Matagorda	11	56.3	83.2	102	11	18	Feb. 21	Dec. 8	290	29	2.56	2.45	2.49	3.38	4.37	3.47	3.29	2.80	4.63	3.70	3.31	4.43	40.88
Maverick	Eagle Pass	38	53.1	87.5	115	7	39	Feb. 26	Nov. 28	275	40	.73	.69	.82	1.95	3.32	2.93	2.06	1.78	3.04	1.87	1.13	.95	21.27
Medina	Hondo	36	53.2	84.9	110	10	38	Mar. 11	Nov. 22	256	40	1.39	1.49	1.93	3.29	4.64	2.72	2.48	1.62	3.06	2.40	1.74	1.90	28.66
	Rio Medina						9	Mar. 10	Nov. 28	263	16	1.54	1.74	2.11	2.58	3.63	3.47	2.42	1.32	2.45	1.85	.95	2.02	26.08
Menard	Fort McKavett	18	45.4	81.9	114	−6	23	Apr. 7	Nov. 6	213	26	.85	1.24	1.02	1.99	2.88	2.43	2.11	1.83	3.63	2.50	1.63	.94	23.05
	Menard	5	45.3	81.7							18	1.05	1.44	1.21	1.71	3.64	2.92	3.08	1.47	3.89	2.01	2.54	1.21	26.17
Midland	Midland	22	43.5	81.4	116	−10	22	Mar. 31	Nov. 3	217	28	.46	.81	.65	1.69	2.12	1.89	1.66	1.79	2.30	1.76	.82	.80	16.75
Milam	Cameron	27	49.7	85.9	114	−7	28	Mar. 13	Nov. 21	253	30	2.66	2.55	2.64	4.01	4.22	2.27	1.53	1.84	2.97	2.94	2.62	3.52	33.77
Mitchell	Colorado	16	46.1	82.9	115	−4	18	Apr. 4	Nov. 8	218	30	.58	.77	1.12	2.53	3.09	2.41	2.79	2.01	2.77	2.18	1.09	.85	22.19
Montague	Bowie	28	44.0	83.8	112	−3	28	Mar. 24	do	229	29	1.37	1.37	1.89	3.93	4.00	2.93	2.36	2.45	2.49	3.29	2.12	1.68	29.88
Montgomery	Conroe	18	51.1	83.5	109	2	18	Mar. 11	Nov. 26	260	18	5.02	3.51	4.15	3.61	5.47	4.28	3.63	3.16	2.73	2.95	4.40	5.42	48.33
Morris	Naples										7	5.71	2.74	3.84	4.66	3.37	3.17	4.06	2.04	1.72	2.67	2.88	5.75	42.61
Nacogdoches	Nacogdoches	38	48.2	81.7	110	−4	38	Mar. 22	Nov. 13	236	39	3.81	3.72	4.10	4.94	5.22	3.42	3.98	2.39	2.74	2.90	4.13	4.88	46.23
Navarro	Corsicana	40	47.7	84.8	113	−7	39	Mar. 16	Nov. 21	250	40	2.31	2.42	2.97	3.94	4.56	2.73	2.35	2.18	2.87	2.86	2.73	3.51	35.43
Newton	Bon Wier										25	5.08	4.56	5.49	5.64	5.21	3.85	4.61	4.14	3.20	3.27	4.16	5.93	55.14
	Wiergate	12	53.0	81.7	106	4	13	Mar. 22	Nov. 12	235	12	5.32	3.70	4.81	4.34	4.49	2.73	4.86	2.47	2.71	2.90	4.47	5.07	47.87
Nueces	Brighton	20	58.3	83.3	105	7	20	Feb. 5	Dec. 14	312	21	1.09	1.68	1.35	2.51	3.86	2.19	1.75	1.17	4.28	2.78	2.18	1.69	26.53
	Corpus Christi	40	56.9	82.7	105	11	40	Jan. 26	Dec. 27	335	40	1.14	1.20	1.56	1.81	3.12	2.66	1.84	1.49	4.46	2.47	1.81	1.98	25.54
Ochiltree	Perryton										27	.29	.90	.97	1.56	2.75	2.97	2.00	2.63	2.04	1.47	1.11	.62	19.31
Oldham	Vega	16	34.2	77.7	106	−12	16	Apr. 10	Oct. 27	200	16	.46	.41	1.25	1.17	2.89	2.86	2.07	2.98	2.12	1.76	1.08	.71	19.76
Orange	Orange										27	4.65	3.93	3.87	4.06	4.90	3.74	4.96	4.59	4.45	3.23	3.59	5.03	51.00
Palo Pinto	Brazos										27	1.62	1.38	1.45	3.25	4.09	2.29	1.70	2.36	2.14	2.71	1.64	2.03	26.66
Parker	Weatherford	37	44.1	83.8	113	−11	37	Mar. 23	Nov. 11	233	40	1.86	1.73	2.15	3.67	4.83	2.76	2.51	2.04	2.71	2.71	2.01	2.05	31.03
Parmer	Friona (near)						10	Apr. 10	Oct. 28	201	11	.42	.43	.67	.60	2.72	1.58	1.91	2.18	1.74	1.19	.72	.36	14.52
Pecos	Buena Vista						10	Apr. 1	Nov. 8	221	19	.32	.47	.45	1.30	1.36	1.07	.73	1.63	2.27	1.36	.79	.45	12.20
	Fort Stockton	33	47.5	81.6	114	−7	35	do	Nov. 13	226	38	.47	.63	.47	1.04	1.69	1.54	1.87	1.77	2.37	1.36	.76	.69	14.66
Potter	Amarillo	40	35.3	76.8	106	−16	40	Apr. 11	Nov. 2	205	40	.44	.72	.96	1.70	3.09	2.62	2.54	3.09	2.43	1.59	1.13	.65	20.96
Presidio	Presidio	11	48.6	84.2	111	11	11	Mar. 29	Nov. 15	231	11	.35	.29	.19	.46	.51	.64	1.31	.92	1.49	.82	.39	.43	7.80
Randall	Canyon										16	.37	.59	1.14	1.12	2.92	2.54	2.18	2.48	2.72	1.83	1.03	.45	19.37
Red River	Clarksville	33	45.0	83.5	115	−7	33	Mar. 20	Nov. 9	234	34	3.64	2.80	3.79	4.88	5.01	3.91	3.30	3.13	2.73	3.25	2.87	4.41	43.72
Reeves	Balmorhea (near)	15	46.3	80.4	110	−9	16	Mar. 30	Nov. 14	229	15	.34	.72	.47	.80	1.19	1.27	1.65	1.86	2.57	1.41	.49	.80	13.57
Refugio	Austwell						14	Feb. 23	Dec. 7	287	29	2.05	1.62	1.89	2.76	3.52	3.40	2.91	2.04	4.81	3.43	2.28	3.21	33.92
	Woodsboro										22	2.14	1.34	2.26	2.73	3.24	3.04	3.08	1.91	4.97	2.26	1.96	2.94	31.87
Roberts	Miami	32	37.4	84.9	114	−15	33	Apr. 15	Oct. 25	193	34	.49	.77	1.13	1.86	3.10	3.25	2.42	3.07	2.67	2.08	1.36	.75	22.95
Robertson	Valley Junction										36	2.58	2.92	2.69	3.67	4.54	2.58	2.59	2.29	2.61	3.58	3.34	3.76	37.15
Runnels	Ballinger	39	45.6	83.2	116	−2	40	Mar 28	Nov 10	227	40	.84	1.06	1.21	2.57	3.64	2.22	1.81	1.90	3.17	2.57	1.57	1.24	23.80
	Winters						6	Mar 27	Nov 13	231	21	1.02	1.01	1.34	2.43	3.43	2.45	1.36	1.53	2.64	2.59	1.36	1.34	22.50
Rusk	Henderson										30	3.85	3.38	4.30	4.56	4.17	2.73	3.25	2.42	2.57	3.10	3.50	4.96	42.79
Sabine	Bronson	5	50.6	81.5	105	16	7	Mar 12	Nov 14	247	14	5.60	3.23	4.77	3.84	4.91	2.80	4.68	2.69	1.99	2.39	3.99	5.80	46.69
San Patricio	Sinton										16	1.82	1.47	2.12	2.50	3.48	2.46	2.91	2.07	4.22	2.69	1.91	2.97	30.62

TEXAS—Continued

Climatic summary—Continued

County	Station	Temperature: Length of record	Temperature: January average	Temperature: July average	Temperature: Maximum	Temperature: Minimum	Killing frost average dates: Length of record	Killing frost average dates: Last in spring	Killing frost average dates: First in fall	Killing frost average dates: Growing season	Average precipitation: Length of record	January	February	March	April	May	June	July	August	September	October	November	December	Annual
		Yr.	*°F.*	*°F.*	*°F.*	*°F.*	*Yr.*			*Days*	*Yr.*	*In.*	*In.*	*In.*	*In.*	*In.*	*In.*	*In.*	*In.*	*In.*	*In.*	*In.*	*In.*	*In.*
San Saba	San Saba	17	49.0	82.6	109	5	16	Apr 3	Nov 1	212	17	0.65	1.54	1.68	3.34	3.71	2.45	1.93	1.62	2.57	2.60	2.51	1.33	25.93
Scurry	Snyder	26	41.4	81.8	115	−8	26	Apr 5	Nov 5	214	28	.56	.76	1.07	2.27	2.70	2.13	1.82	2.27	2.58	2.36	1.01	.96	20.49
Shackleford	Albany	38	44.1	83.8	114	−8	38	Mar 31	Nov 7	221	38	1.06	1.20	1.61	2.61	3.90	2.83	2.23	2.17	2.50	2.65	1.68	1.44	25.88
Sherman	Stratford	5	32.6	76.0	105	−12	10	Apr 26	Oct 28	185	15	.24	.56	.62	1.16	2.22	2.71	2.28	1.96	1.60	1.44	.45	.54	15.78
Smith	Flint	27	47.9	83.7	108	−3	30	Mar 19	Nov 19	245	29	3.58	3.00	3.88	4.75	4.24	2.51	2.84	2.58	2.29	2.92	3.45	4.41	40.45
Starr	Rio Grande	18	60.3	86.1	112	7	18	Feb 10	Dec 16	309	33	.84	.79	.88	.99	2.60	1.84	1.91	.99	2.84	1.43	1.09	.90	17.10
Stephens	Breckenridge	14	42.7	82.9	114	−2	14	Mar 24	Nov 19	240	16	1.17	1.22	1.74	1.91	3.30	2.24	2.39	1.32	3.13	2.45	1.23	1.81	23.91
Sterling	Sterling City										12	.59	1.27	1.46	1.34	3.62	2.09	2.56	1.62	2.90	1.98	.74	1.30	21.47
Stonewall	Aspermont										26	.72	.87	1.10	2.50	3.08	2.60	1.88	2.54	2.34	2.90	1.03	1.12	22.68
Sutton	Sonora	11	47.7	80.5	108	5	12	Apr 10	Nov 1	205	12	.50	.70	.93	2.86	2.90	2.62	2.37	1.84	3.04	2.25	1.88	.82	22.71
	Substation No 14	17	48.4	80.5	105	0	16	Mar 24	Nov 20	241	17	.88	.96	1.31	1.64	3.41	2.40	2.39	1.89	4.03	2.56	1.18	1.63	24.28
Swisher	Tulia (near)	15	37.5	77.7	109	−23	18	Apr 18	Oct 20	185	33	.44	.79	.88	2.08	2.94	2.17	2.94	3.15	2.59	2.46	1.18	.78	22.40
Tarrant	Fort Worth	40	46.0	83.8	112	−8	40	Mar 11	Nov 17	251	40	1.81	1.78	2.27	3.68	4.52	2.96	2.38	2.27	2.76	2.86	2.30	2.04	31.63
	Grapevine	18	47.4	83.8	115	−12	18	Mar 23	Nov 7	229	19	1.54	1.99	2.58	4.59	4.46	2.69	3.10	2.13	2.82	2.38	2.73	2.16	33.17
Taylor	Abilena	40	45.4	83.1	110	−6	40	Mar 25	Nov 12	232	40	.87	.98	1.27	2.69	4.39	2.40	2.04	1.99	2.81	2.69	1.36	1.29	24.78
Terry	Brownfield	6	41.0	79.0	107	−7	8	Apr 17	Oct 29	195	24	.34	.73	.75	1.32	2.30	2.43	1.60	2.78	2.69	2.42	.55	.60	18.51
Throckmorton	Throckmorton	14	44.1	84.6	114	−6	14	Apr. 12	Nov. 9	211	14	1.06	1.40	1.83	1.76	3.54	2.44	2.09	1.70	3.04	2.17	1.12	1.70	23.85
Titus	Mt. Pleasant	22	46.8	82.8	118	2	22	Mar. 25	do	229	22	4.76	2.84	4.00	4.64	4.53	2.85	3.21	2.30	2.37	3.90	3.42	4.38	43.20
Tom Green	Knickerbocker	27	47.0	83.1	113	−6	26	Apr. 5	Nov. 5	214	27	.69	.82	.85	2.06	2.36	1.73	1.47	2.29	2.21	2.39	1.22	.94	19.03
	San Angelo	30	46.3	83.7	111	1	30	Mar. 25	Nov. 9	229	31	.86	.98	.91	2.20	2.94	1.96	1.71	2.04	3.20	2.18	1.35	1.24	21.57
Travis	Austin	40	50.8	83.9	109	−1	40	Mar. 6	Nov. 25	264	40	2.06	2.31	2.33	4.07	4.80	2.58	2.74	1.73	3.22	3.27	2.38	2.94	34.43
	Duval	18	51.7	84.3	111	−5	18	Mar. 8	Nov. 21	258	18	1.10	2.02	1.97	4.79	4.29	2.12	3.24	1.87	2.28	3.07	2.82	3.23	32.80
Tyler	Rockland										35	4.10	3.58	4.41	4.54	5.61	3.02	3.67	3.39	2.66	2.70	3.84	5.36	46.88
Uvalde	Montell										26	1.05	.98	1.29	2.31	3.74	4.05	2.63	2.51	3.08	2.45	1.19	1.38	26.66
	Sabinal	34	53.9	84.1	110	9	34	Mar. 9	Nov. 19	255	35	.98	1.05	1.42	2.91	3.87	2.62	2.45	1.94	2.98	2.65	1.37	1.50	25.74
	Uvalde	30	53.6	84.9	114	10	29	Mar. 11	Nov. 21	255	31	1.09	1.05	1.48	2.43	3.42	2.79	2.67	1.73	2.63	2.00	1.10	1.42	23.81
Val Verde	Del Rio	33	52.3	86.3	111	12	33	Feb. 22	Nov. 29	280	33	.54	.71	.89	1.48	2.42	2.29	2.17	1.35	2.47	2.18	1.17	.82	18.49
Van Zandt	Wills Point	17	47.2	83.4	115	−1	17	Mar. 22	Nov. 12	235	18	2.46	2.43	2.83	5.05	4.32	3.20	2.53	3.38	2.27	3.79	3.04	3.71	39.01
Victoria	Victoria	36	56.0	84.2	109	9	37	Feb. 24	Dec. 4	283	40	2.40	2.07	2.42	3.05	4.18	3.22	3.57	2.61	3.72	3.24	2.59	2.88	35.95
Walker	Huntsville	38	50.4	83.1	107	−2	38	Mar. 8	Nov. 25	262	40	3.24	3.56	3.82	4.69	5.15	3.49	3.60	2.35	2.45	3.26	4.09	4.39	44.09
	Riverside										35	3.51	3.26	3.80	4.42	5.30	3.02	3.06	3.01	2.70	2.99	3.62	4.58	43.27
Waller	Hempstead										34	2.96	3.20	3.33	3.79	4.92	2.58	2.90	2.73	2.78	3.32	3.29	3.93	39.73
Ward	Barstow	14	46.4	82.2	114	−4	14	Mar. 28	Nov. 4	221	15	.18	.26	.44	.64	.67	.79	1.59	1.27	1.86	1.67	.77	.50	10.64
	Grand Falls						6	Mar. 31	Nov. 13	227	23	.21	.64	.63	1.11	1.27	1.01	.87	1.47	2.18	1.26	.61	.64	11.90
Washington	Brenham	40	51.4	83.8	111	−2	40	Mar. 4	Nov. 28	269	40	2.88	2.91	3.04	3.92	4.70	3.31	3.19	2.32	2.84	3.55	3.63	4.18	40.47
Webb	Ft. McIntosh	32	56.3	87.1	115	5	32	Feb. 18	Dec. 4	289	33	.88	.81	.83	1.52	3.06	2.06	1.71	1.36	2.83	2.03	1.57	.91	19.57
	Laredo	38	55.6	87.1	115	5	6	do	Dec. 2	287	26	1.14	.88	.84	1.14	3.64	1.77	1.60	1.46	3.35	2.04	1.25	1.36	20.47

Wharton	Danevang	39	54.8	83.5	106	3	40	Feb. 26	Nov. 30	277	40	2.61	2.44	2.76	3.33	3.71	3.74	4.21	3.10	3.96	3.74	3.26	4.02	40.88
	Pierce	32	54.2	82.3	106	8	33	Mar. 7	Nov. 24	262	33	2.82	2.63	2.96	3.01	4.27	3.36	3.70	3.02	3.94	3.22	3.35	4.08	40.36
Wichita	Wichita Falls	16	42.6	85.0	113	−3	18	Mar. 22	Nov. 14	237	36	1.05	1.25	1.72	2.61	4.89	3.27	2.50	2.20	2.92	2.71	1.89	1.54	28.55
Willacy	Raymondville	25	59.2	83.9	109	16	26	Feb. 15	Dec. 23	311	28	1.63	.94	1.37	1.27	3.75	3.02	2.69	1.70	4.93	2.75	1.53	1.75	27.33
Williamson	Jarrell	23	47.5	83.7	113	−2	32	Mar. 16	Nov. 15	244	40	1.91	2.06	2.11	3.83	4.72	2.72	2.32	1.77	3.20	3.10	2.88	2.89	33.51
	Taylor	37	49.7	83.2	110	0	37	Mar. 6	Nov. 26	265	37	1.98	2.28	2.14	3.69	4.09	2.26	2.30	1.90	3.36	3.08	2.49	2.76	32.33
Wilson	Floresville										22	1.81	1.80	1.90	2.60	3.35	3.06	2.19	1.39	2.80	2.53	1.50	2.13	27.06
Wise	Bridgeport										30	1.79	1.39	2.11	3.55	4.32	3.11	2.37	1.98	1.98	2.98	1.86	2.02	29.46
Yoakum	Plains										9	.29	.32	.99	.82	1.77	1.82	2.08	3.54	1.85	1.67	.58	.60	16.33
Young	Graham	22	45.1	84.5	117	−2	27	Apr. 4	Nov. 4	214	35	1.34	1.26	1.66	2.61	3.92	3.25	2.28	2.02	2.69	2.50	1.76	1.54	26.83
Zavala	LaPryor	20	52.2	84.6	111	10	20	Feb. 28	Nov. 29	274	21	1.24	1.13	1.03	2.22	3.03	2.74	2.75	1.71	2.50	1.82	.87	1.01	22.05

TEXAS—Continued

Precipitation and temperature—State unit values

[This tabulation gives the mean annual, mean monthly, and average seasonal precipitation, 1886–1938, the percentage of normal precipitation for each year and for each summer, 1886–1938, and the mean annual temperatures, 1889–1938, for Texas]

Precipitation

Year	Mean
	In.
1886	22.75
1887	27.88
1888	42.30
1889	38.06
1890	34.62
1891	30.45
1892	29.40
1893	20.47
1894	27.65
1895	32.92
1896	27.41
1897	27.32
1898	28.43
1899	28.70
1900	42.17
1901	22.23
1902	33.92
1903	33.03
1904	30.02
1905	41.73
1906	31.51
1907	33.86
1908	32.91
1909	23.45
1910	21.46
1911	29.13
1912	26.12
1913	36.05
1914	37.88
1915	32.01
1916	24.59
1917	16.21
1918	28.90
1919	45.64
1920	34.24
1921	28.64
1922	32.91
1923	40.34
1924	23.50
1925	25.79
1926	36.33
1927	27.77
1928	29.03
1929	31.17
1930	29.67
1931	29.26
1932	34.06
1933	25.96
1934	26.78
1935	37.48
1936	30.71
1937	26.78
1938	27.18

Month	Mean
	In.
January	1.89
February	1.80
March	2.07
April	2.96
May	3.67
June	3.07
July	2.62
August	2.40
September	3.04
October	2.57
November	2.20
December	2.25
Annual	30.54

Season	Average
	In.
Winter	5.94
Spring	8.70
Summer	8.09
Fall	7.81

Annual precipitation (in percent of normal)

Year	Percent
1886	74
1887	91
1888	139
1889	125
1890	113
1891	100
1892	96
1893	67
1894	91
1895	108
1896	90
1897	89
1898	93
1899	94
1900	138
1901	73
1902	111
1903	108
1904	98
1905	137
1906	103
1907	111
1908	108
1909	77
1910	70
1911	95
1912	86
1913	118
1914	124
1915	105
1916	81
1917	53
1918	95
1919	149
1920	112
1921	94
1922	108
1923	132
1924	77
1925	84
1926	119
1927	91
1928	95
1929	102
1930	97
1931	96
1932	112
1933	85
1934	88
1935	123
1936	101
1937	88
1938	89

Summer precipitation (in percent of normal)

Year	Percent
1886	86
1887	112
1888	171
1889	143
1890	87
1891	83
1892	112
1893	73
1894	123
1895	133
1896	61
1897	83
1898	125
1899	131
1900	140
1901	65
1902	100
1903	149
1904	114
1905	122
1906	135
1907	79
1908	104
1909	98
1910	56
1911	82
1912	91
1913	76
1914	116
1915	128
1916	95
1917	59
1918	64
1919	172
1920	146
1921	122
1922	80
1923	86
1924	54
1925	68
1926	115
1927	103
1928	108
1929	62
1930	58
1931	88
1932	110
1933	99
1924	50
1935	110
1936	89
1937	84
1938	98

Temperature

Year	Mean
	°F.
1889	65.9
1890	66.9
1891	65.1
1892	65.6
1893	66.6
1894	66.6
1895	64.6
1896	67.2
1897	66.0
1898	65.7
1899	66.0
1900	66.7
1901	66.8
1902	67.4
1903	64.6
1904	66.8
1905	64.9
1906	65.1
1907	67.1
1908	66.6
1909	67.3
1910	67.5
1911	67.8
1912	64.9
1913	65.3
1914	65.4
1915	65.8
1916	67.1
1917	66.1
1918	66.4
1919	64.9
1920	65.6
1921	68.6
1922	67.3
1923	66.5
1924	65.4
1925	67.3
1926	65.8
1927	68.1
1928	66.2
1929	65.7
1930	65.7
1931	66.4
1932	65.7
1933	68.4
1934	68.1
1935	66.6
1936	65.6
1937	65.9
1938	67.4

Dates of last killing frost in spring and first in fall, with length of growing season

Year	Abilene			Amarillo			Brownsville			Corsicana			Crosbyton			Eagle Pass		
	Last in spring	First in fall	Growing season[1]	Last in spring	First in fall	Growing season[1]	Last in spring	First in fall	Growing season[1]	Last in spring	First in fall	Growing season[1]	Last in spring	First in fall	Growing season[1]	Last in spring	First in fall	Growing season[1]
			Days			*Days*			*Days*			*Days*			*Days*			*Days*
1899	Apr. 7	Nov. 2	209	Apr. 21	Nov. 1	194	Feb. 14			Mar. 28	Nov. 3	220	Apr. 9	Nov. 1	206	Mar. 7	Nov. 2	240
1900	Mar. 15	Nov. 12	242	Apr. 19	Nov. 9	204	Feb. 18	Dec. 29	312	Mar. 16	Nov. 12	241	Apr. 12	Nov. 11	213	Feb. 17	Nov. 11	267
1901	Mar. 6	Dec. 4	273	Apr. 17	Nov. 12	209	Mar. 5	Nov. 15	255	Mar. 6	Nov. 4	243	Apr. 18	Nov. 4	200	Mar. 15	Nov. 3	233
1902	Mar. 5	Dec. 1	271	Mar. 30	Nov. 3	218	Feb. 2	None	333	Mar. 5	Dec. 4	274	Mar. 13	Nov. 3	235	Feb. 20	Nov. 26	279
1903	Mar. 2	Nov. 17	260	Apr. 30	Oct. 16	169	Feb. 16	do	319	May 1	Nov. 18	201	Apr. 30	Oct. 24	177	Mar. 22	Oct. 20	212
1904	Mar. 27	Nov. 11	229	Apr. 23	Oct. 19	179	Jan. 28	do	339	Mar. 4	Nov. 12	253	Apr. 17	Oct. 26	192	Mar. 7		
1905	Apr. 16	Dec. 2	230	Apr. 16	Nov. 2	200	Feb. 14	do	321	Feb. 22	Nov. 30	281	Mar. 8	Nov. 10	247	Feb. 14	Dec. 3	292
1906	Mar. 20	Oct. 24	218	Mar. 27	Oct. 26	213	Feb. 8			Mar. 21	Nov. 20	244	Mar. 31	Oct. 23	206	Mar. 20	Nov. 21	246
1907	Apr. 23	Nov. 11	202	Apr. 20	Oct. 24	187				Mar. 1	Nov. 12	256	May 4	Nov. 10	190	Feb. 14	None	321
1908	Mar. 11	Oct. 28	231	Apr. 18	Oct. 27	192	Jan. 13	None	354	Feb. 20	Nov. 14	268	Mar. 21	Oct. 23	216	Feb. 16	Dec. 21	309
1909	Apr. 9	Nov. 17	222	Apr. 19	Nov. 1	196	Feb. 16	do	319	Mar. 15	Dec. 5	265	May 1	Nov. 17	200	Feb. 15	Dec. 16	304
1910	Feb. 27	Nov. 28	274	Apr. 20	Nov. 3	197	Feb. 18	do	317	Feb. 25	Oct. 29	246	Apr. 16	Oct. 21	188	Feb. 18	Dec. 6	291
1911	Mar. 2	Oct. 22	234	Mar. 27	Oct. 22	209	Jan. 4	Nov. 29	329	Mar. 2	Oct. 22	234	Mar. 27	Oct. 22	209		Nov. 29	
1912	Mar. 24	Nov. 2	223	Apr. 22	Oct. 31	192	Feb. 7	None	329	Mar. 25	Nov. 28	248	Apr. 2	Nov. 1	213	Feb. 6	Nov. 2	270
1913	Mar. 27	Oct. 27	214	Apr. 24	Oct. 26	185	Jan. 8	do	358	Mar. 27	Oct. 30	217	Mar. 28	Oct. 26	212	Mar. 27	Oct. 27	214
1914	Apr. 9	Nov. 17	222	Apr. 19	Oct. 27	191	Feb. 25	do	310	Apr. 9	Oct. 28	202	Apr. 9	Oct. 13	187	Mar. 13	Dec. 14	276
1915	Apr. 2	Nov. 15	227	May 7	Nov. 14	191	Jan. 25	do	341	Mar. 22	Nov. 15	238	Apr. 3			Mar. 24	Nov. 15	236
1916	Mar. 3	Oct. 20	231	Apr. 9	Oct. 19	193	Feb. 2	do	334	Mar. 4	Nov. 14	255	Apr. 9			Feb. 3	Nov. 14	285
1917	Mar. 27	Oct. 17	204	May 6	do	166	Mar. 5	Dec. 9	279	Mar. 5	Oct. 30	239	May 7	Oct. 19	165	Mar. 5	Oct. 30	239
1918	Mar. 17	Nov. 18	246	Apr. 20	Oct. 26	189	Feb. 2	None	333	Feb. 22	Nov. 26	277	Apr. 21	Oct. 26	188	Feb. 3	Nov. 28	298
1919	Mar. 5	Nov. 12	252	Apr. 9	Nov. 2	207	Jan. 9	Dec. 10	335	Mar. 6	Nov. 30	269	Apr. 9	Nov. 12	217	Feb. 26	Dec. 10	287
1920	Apr. 5	do	221	Apr. 4	do	212	Mar. 8	Nov. 16	253	Apr. 5			Apr. 27	Nov. 2	189	Apr. 5	Nov. 16	225
1921	Apr. 17	Nov. 10	207	Apr. 17	Nov. 9	206	None	None	365	Apr. 18	Dec. 18	244	Apr. 17	Oct. 8	174	Feb. 21	Dec. 5	287
1922	Mar. 11	Nov. 14	248	Apr. 19	Nov. 6	201	Mar. 4	do	303	Mar. 5	do	288	Apr. 19	Nov. 14	209	Mar. 4	Dec. 19	290
1923	Mar. 19	Nov. 6	232	Apr. 5	Nov. 28	237	Feb. 6	do	329	Mar. 20	Dec. 14	269	Apr. 5	Oct. 30	208	Mar. 20	Dec. 14	269
1924	Mar. 21	Nov. 18	242	Apr. 26	Oct. 31	188	None	Dec. 19	353	Mar. 21	Nov. 24	248	Apr. 26	Nov. 24	212	Mar. 10	Nov. 25	260
1925	Mar. 15	Oct. 28	227	Mar. 15	Oct. 19	218	Jan. 28	Dec. 27	333	Mar. 15	Nov. 9	239	Mar. 27	Oct. 28	215	Jan. 28	Nov. 23	299
1926	Mar. 31	Nov. 9	223	Apr. 3	Nov. 2	213	None	None	365	Mar. 31	Nov. 18	232	Apr. 15	Nov. 9	208	Jan. 26	Dec. 29	337
1927	Apr. 22	Nov. 16	208	Apr. 22	Nov. 6	198	do	do	365	Mar. 22	Nov. 17	240	Apr. 22	Nov. 2	194	Mar. 2	Dec. 3	276
1928	Apr. 15	Nov. 19	218	Apr. 10	Nov. 2	206	Jan. 2	do	365	Apr. 15	Dec. 18	247	Apr. 27	Nov. 3	190	Mar. 16	Dec. 19	278
1929	Feb. 23	Oct. 24	243	Mar. 18	Oct. 24	220	None	Dec. 23	356	Feb. 24	Nov. 22	271	Mar. 19	Oct. 23	218	Feb. 12	Nov. 14	275
1930	Mar. 28	Nov. 21	238	Mar. 29	Nov. 20	236	Jan. 23	None	343	Mar. 19	Dec. 17	273	Mar. 28	Oct. 31	217	Jan. 24	Dec. 16	326
1931	Apr. 5	Nov. 27	236	Mar. 31	Nov. 22	236	None	do	365	Mar. 28	Dec. 15	262	Apr. 10	Nov. 22	226	Mar. 8	Dec. 31	298
1932	Mar. 22	Nov. 12	235	Mar. 27	Oct. 29	216	Mar. 14	Dec. 17	278	Mar. 15	Nov. 16	246	Feb. 23	Oct. 26	246	Mar. 12	Nov. 11	244
1933	Mar. 20	Dec. 6	261	Apr. 14	Nov. 5	205	Feb. 8	None	327	Mar. 21			Apr. 20	Nov. 5	199	Feb. 11	Dec. 18	310
1934	Mar. 27	Nov. 30	248	Mar. 18	Nov. 22	249	None	do	365	Mar. 19	Dec. 12	268	Mar. 26	Oct. 28	216	Feb. 19	Dec. 3	287

[1] Number of days between last killing frost in spring and first in fall.

TEXAS—Continued

Dates of last killing frost in spring and first in fall, with length of growing season—Continued

Year	Abilene			Amarillo			Brownsville			Corsicana			Crosbyton			Eagle Pass		
	Last in spring	First in fall	Growing season	Last in spring	First in fall	Growing season	Last in spring	First in fall	Growing season	Last in spring	First in fall	Growing season	Last in spring	First in fall	Growing season	Last in spring	First in fall	Growing season
			Days			*Days*			*Days*			*Days*			*Days*			*Days*
1935	Mar. 7	Nov. 11	249	Mar. 12	Nov. 4	237	Feb. 27	None	308	Feb. 28	Dec. 2	277	Mar. 13	Nov. 5	237	Feb. 27	None	308
1936	Apr. 7	Nov. 3	210	Apr. 6	Nov. 3	211	Feb. 18	do	318	Feb. 21	Nov. 4	257	Apr. 6	Nov. 10	218	Feb. 17	Nov. 3	260
1937	Apr. 5	Nov. 17	226	Mar. 30	Nov. 16	231	None	do	365	Apr. 1	Nov. 21	234	Apr. 10	Nov. 17	221	Feb. 28	Nov. 20	265
1938	Apr. 9	Nov. 7	212	Apr. 9	Nov. 6	211	do	do	365	Feb. 20	Nov. 8	261	Apr. 8	Nov. 4	210	Jan. 31	Nov. 8	281
Mean	Mar. 25	Nov. 12	232	Apr. 11	Nov. 2	205	Jan. 30	Dec. 26	330	Mar. 16	Nov. 21	250	Apr. 9	Nov. 2	207	Feb. 26	Nov. 28	275
Extremes	Feb. 23 [2] Apr. 23 [3]	Oct. 17 [4] Dec. 6 [5]	[6] 202 [7] 274	Mar. 12 [2] May 7 [3]	Oct. 16 [4] Nov. 28 [5]	[6] 166 [7] 249	None [2] Mar. 14 [3]	Nov. 15 [4] None [5]	[6] 253 [7] 365	Feb. 20 [2] May 1 [3]	Oct. 22 [4] Dec. 18 [5]	[6] 201 [7] 288	Feb. 23 [2] May 7 [3]	Oct. 8 [4] Nov. 24 [5]	[6] 165 [7] 247	Jan. 24 [2] Apr. 5 [3]	Oct. 20 [4] None [5]	[6] 212 [7] 337

[2] Earliest date in spring.
[3] Latest date in spring.
[4] Earliest date in fall.
[5] Latest date in fall.
[6] Shortest growing season.
[7] Longest growing season.

Year	El Paso			Fort Stockton			Gainesville			Galveston			Paris			San Antonio		
	Last in spring	First in fall	Growing season[1]	Last in spring	First in fall	Growing season[1]	Last in spring	First in fall	Growing season[1]	Last in spring	First in fall	Growing season[1]	Last in spring	First in fall	Growing season[1]	Last in spring	First in fall	Growing season[1]
			Days			*Days*			*Days*			*Days*			*Days*			*Days*
1899	Mar. 12	Nov. 2	235	Mar. 31			Apr. 7	Nov. 3	210	Feb. 13	None	322	Apr. 1	Nov. 3	216	Mar. 4	Dec. 4	275
1900	Mar. 1	Nov. 1	245	Apr. 11	Oct. 31	203	Apr. 12	Nov. 12	214	Feb. 18	do	317	Apr. 12	Nov. 12	214	Mar. 1	Nov. 12	256
1901	Mar. 21	Dec. 2	256				Apr. 18	Nov. 4	200	None	Dec. 15	348	Apr. 3	Nov. 16	227	Mar. 6	Dec. 10	279
1902	Mar. 5	Nov. 3	243				Mar. 31	Nov. 27	241	do	None	365	Mar. 19	Nov. 27	253	Feb. 5	Dec. 16	314
1903	Mar. 3	Nov. 18	260				May 1	Nov. 17	200	Feb. 17	do	318	Mar. 24	Nov. 17	238	Feb. 18	Nov. 18	273
1904	Feb. 21	Nov. 11	264		Oct. 25		Mar. 28	Nov. 11	228	Jan. 29	do	338	Mar. 4	Nov. 10	251	Feb. 12	Nov. 12	274
1905	Feb. 18	Dec. 2	287	Apr. 4	Nov. 29	239	Mar. 10	Oct. 21	225	Feb. 14	do	321	Feb. 21	do	282	Feb. 21	Dec. 4	286
1906	Mar. 20	Oct. 23	217	Mar. 19			Mar. 21	Oct. 31	224	None	do	365	Mar. 22	Nov. 21	244	Mar. 20	Nov. 20	245
1907	Apr. 22	Nov. 12	204		Nov. 11			Nov. 12		do	do	365	Feb. 19	Nov. 12	266	Feb. 5	Nov. 13	281
1908	Feb. 19	Oct. 27	251	Mar. 23	Oct. 27	218	Feb. 27	do	259	do	do	366	Feb. 22	Nov. 14	266	Feb. 20	Nov. 14	268
1909	Mar. 14	Nov. 17	248	Apr. 13	Nov. 17	218	Apr. 8	Nov. 17	223	Feb. 16	do	319	Apr. 10	Nov. 17	221	Feb. 17	Dec. 9	295
1910	Feb. 18	Nov. 22	277	Apr. 16	Oct. 21	188	Mar. 11	Oct. 29	232	Feb. 18	do	317	Feb. 5	Oct. 29	266	Feb. 24	Dec. 1	280
1911	Feb. 26	Nov. 20	267	Feb. 28	Oct. 22	236	Mar. 1	Nov. 12	256	Jan. 4	Nov. 29	329	Mar. 2	Nov. 12	255	Feb. 23	Nov. 29	279
1912	Mar. 1	do	264	Mar. 24	Nov. 28	249	Mar. 25	Nov. 2	222	Jan. 13	None	354	Mar. 26	Nov. 2	221	Feb. 7	Nov. 28	295
1913	Mar. 27	Nov. 30	248	Apr. 12	Oct. 27	198	Mar. 27	Oct. 27	214	Jan. 8	do	358	Mar. 28	Oct. 24	210	Mar. 27	Dec. 26	274
1914	Mar. 22	Dec. 3	256	Apr. 9	Nov. 17	222	Apr. 9	Oct. 28	202	Feb. 25	do	310	Apr. 9	Oct. 28	202	Mar. 13	Dec. 10	272
1915	do	Nov. 12	235	Apr. 2	Nov. 14	226	Apr. 3	Nov. 15	226	None	do	365	Mar. 17	Nov. 15	243	Mar. 22	Dec. 29	282
1916	Apr. 1	Nov. 13	226	Apr. 8	do	220	Apr. 9	Oct. 20	194	do	do	366	Apr. 9	Oct. 20	194	Feb. 3	Nov. 14	285
1917	Apr. 5	Dec. 8	247	May 7	Oct. 19	165	Mar. 27	Oct. 9	196	Feb. 5	Dec. 8	306	Mar. 6	Oct. 9	217	Mar. 5	Oct. 30	239
1918	Mar. 18	Nov. 23	250	Mar. 17	Nov. 18	246	Mar. 17	Nov. 24	252	Jan. 22	None	344	Mar. 7	Nov. 24	262	Feb. 2	Nov. 28	299
1919	Mar. 5	Nov. 11	251	Apr. 10	Nov. 13	217	Mar. 9	Nov. 12	248	Jan. 4	do	362	do	Nov. 13	251	Feb. 26	Dec. 10	287
1920	Mar. 29	Nov. 13	229	Apr. 4	Nov. 12	222	Apr. 5	Nov. 1	210	None	do	366	Apr. 5	Nov. 12	221	Apr. 5	Nov. 16	225
1921	Apr. 26	Nov. 19	207	Mar. 29	Nov. 19	235	Apr. 18	Nov. 10	206	do	do	365	Apr. 17	Nov. 10	207	Feb. 21	Dec. 9	291
1922	Apr. 19	Nov. 1	196	Apr. 19	Nov. 14	209	Mar. 11	Nov. 29	263	do	do	365	Mar. 11	Nov. 26	260	Mar. 3	Dec. 19	291
1923	Mar. 20	Nov. 20	245	Mar. 19	Nov. 29	255	Mar. 24	Nov. 6	227	Mar. 19	do	288	Mar. 21	Nov. 18	242	Mar. 20	Dec. 31	286
1924	Apr. 18	Nov. 15	211	Mar. 20	Nov. 24	249	Apr. 1	Oct. 24	206	Jan. 7	Dec. 19	347	Apr. 1	Oct. 24	206	Mar. 10	Dec. 19	284
1925	Mar. 16	Nov. 5	234	Mar. 15	Nov. 8	238	Mar. 15	Oct. 25	224	Jan. 27	Dec. 23	330	Mar. 15	Oct. 29	228	Jan. 28	Nov. 16	292
1926	Mar. 31	Nov. 9	223	Mar. 31	Nov. 9	223	Apr. 3	Nov. 3	214	Jan. 24	None	342	Apr. 1	Nov. 5	218	Jan. 25	Nov. 18	297
1927	Mar. 22	Nov. 17	240	Mar. 21	Nov. 16	240	Mar. 24	Nov. 12	233	None	Dec. 8	341	Mar. 23	Nov. 17	239	Mar. 2	Dec. 8	281
1928	Apr. 15	Nov. 18	217	Apr. 15	Nov. 19	218	Apr. 15	Nov. 3	202	Jan. 4	None	363	Mar. 18	Nov. 20	247	Mar. 17	Dec. 20	278
1929	Mar. 16	Nov. 10	239	Mar. 18	Nov. 4	231	Feb. 23	Nov. 5	255	Feb. 11	Dec. 3	295	Feb. 24	Nov. 23	272	Feb. 12	Nov. 23	284
1930	Mar. 4	Nov. 20	261	Mar. 29	Nov. 21	237	Mar. 30	Nov. 23	238	Jan. 24	None	342	Mar. 5	Nov. 25	265	Jan. 30	Dec. 17	321
1931	Mar. 28	Nov. 15	232	Mar. 31	Dec. 3	247	Mar. 29	Dec. 4	250	None	do	365	Mar. 29	Dec. 3	249	Jan. 14	None	352
1932	Mar. 31	Oct. 26	209	Mar. 22	Nov. 11	234	Mar. 22	Nov. 1	224	Mar. 10	Dec. 17	282	Mar. 13	Nov. 17	249	Mar. 13	Dec. 12	274
1933	Apr. 15	Nov. 3	202	Apr. 20	Dec. 6	230	Mar. 21	Nov. 8	232	Feb. 9	None	326	Mar. 21	Dec. 20	274	Feb. 11	None	324
1934	Mar. 19	Nov. 22	248	Mar. 27	Nov. 30	248	Mar. 19	Nov. 28	254	None	do	365	Mar. 19	Dec. 1	257	Mar. 19	Dec. 8	264

[1] Number of days between last killing frost in spring and first in fall.

TEXAS—Continued

Dates of last killing frost in spring and first in fall, with length of growing season—Continued

Year	El Paso			Fort Stockton			Gainesville			Galveston			Paris			San Antonio		
	Last in spring	First in fall	Growing season	Last in spring	First in fall	Growing season	Last in spring	First in fall	Growing season	Last in spring	First in fall	Growing season	Last in spring	First in fall	Growing season	Last in spring	First in fall	Growing season
			Days			*Days*			*Days*			*Days*			*Days*			*Days*
1935	Mar. 12	Nov. 12	245	Mar. 12	Nov. 12	245	Mar. 12	Nov. 13	246	Jan. 22	None	344	Mar. 8	Nov. 17	254	Feb. 27	None	308
1936	Apr. 7	Nov. 4	211	Apr. 7	Nov. 4	211	Apr. 3	Nov. 3	214	Feb. 18	do	318	Apr. 3	Nov. 4	215	Feb. 19	Nov. 4	259
1937	Apr. 5	Nov. 19	228	Apr. 5	Nov. 19	228	Mar. 31	Oct. 23	206	None	do	365	Mar. 31	Nov. 18	232	Feb. 28	Nov. 20	265
1938	Apr. 9	Nov. 7	212	Apr. 9	Nov. 7	212	Apr. 9	Nov. 28	233	do	do	365	Apr. 9	Nov. 8	213	Jan. 31	Nov. 8	281
Mean	Mar. 21	Nov. 14	238	Apr. 1	Nov. 13	226	Mar. 27	Nov. 8	226	Jan. 21	Dec. 28	341	Mar. 20	Nov. 13	238	Feb. 24	Dec. 3	282
Extremes	Feb. 18[2]	Oct. 23[4]	[6] 196	Feb. 28[2]	Oct. 19[4]	[6] 165	Feb. 23[2]	Oct. 9[4]	[6] 194	None[2]	Nov. 29[4]	[6] 282	Feb. 5[2]	Oct. 9[4]	[6] 194	Jan. 14[2]	Oct. 30[4]	[6] 225
	Apr. 26[3]	Dec. 8[5]	[7] 287	May 7[3]	Dec. 6[5]	[7] 255	May 1[3]	Dec. 4[5]	[7] 263	Mar. 19[3]	None[5]	[7] 366	Apr. 17[3]	Dec. 20[5]	[7] 282	Apr. 5[3]	None[5]	[7] 351

[2] Earliest date in spring.
[3] Latest date in spring.
[4] Earliest date in fall.
[5] Latest date in fall.
[6] Shortest growing season.
[7] Longest growing season.

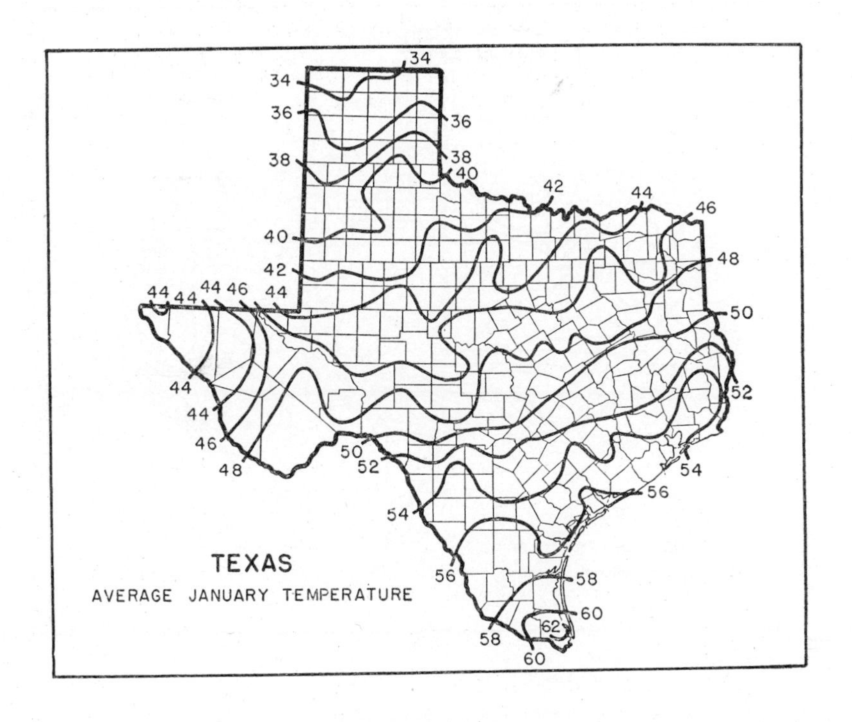
34
34
36
36
38
38
40
40
42
42
44
44
46
48
50
52
54
56
58
60
62
44 44 44 46 44
TEXAS
AVERAGE JANUARY TEMPERATURE

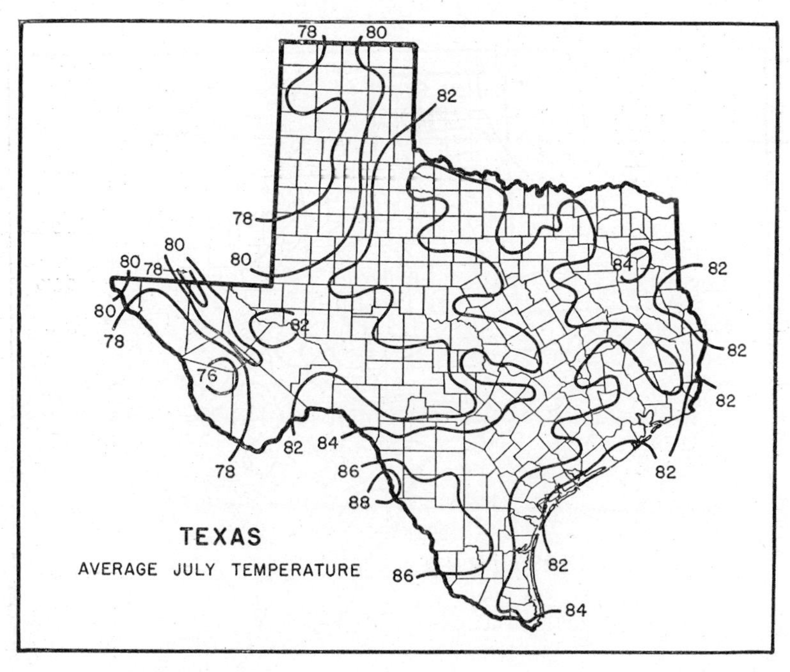
78
80
82
78
80
80
80 78
80
78
82
76
78
82 84
86
88
84
82
82
82
82
82
86
84
TEXAS
AVERAGE JULY TEMPERATURE

298737°—41——73 +

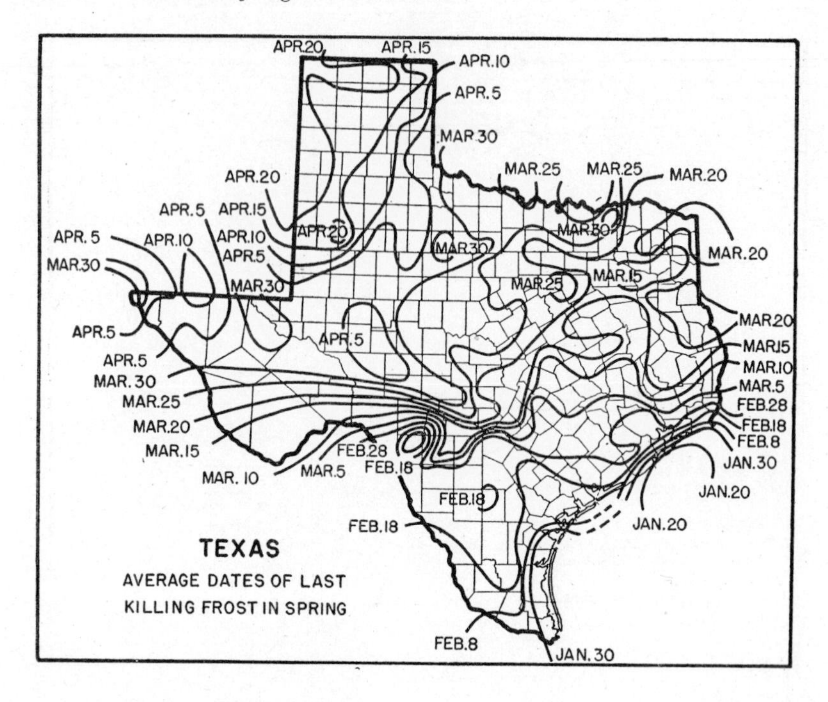
TEXAS
AVERAGE DATES OF LAST
KILLING FROST IN SPRING
APR.20
APR.15
APR.10
APR.5
MAR.30
MAR.25
MAR.20
MAR.15
MAR.10
MAR.5
FEB.28
FEB.18
FEB.8
JAN.30
JAN.20

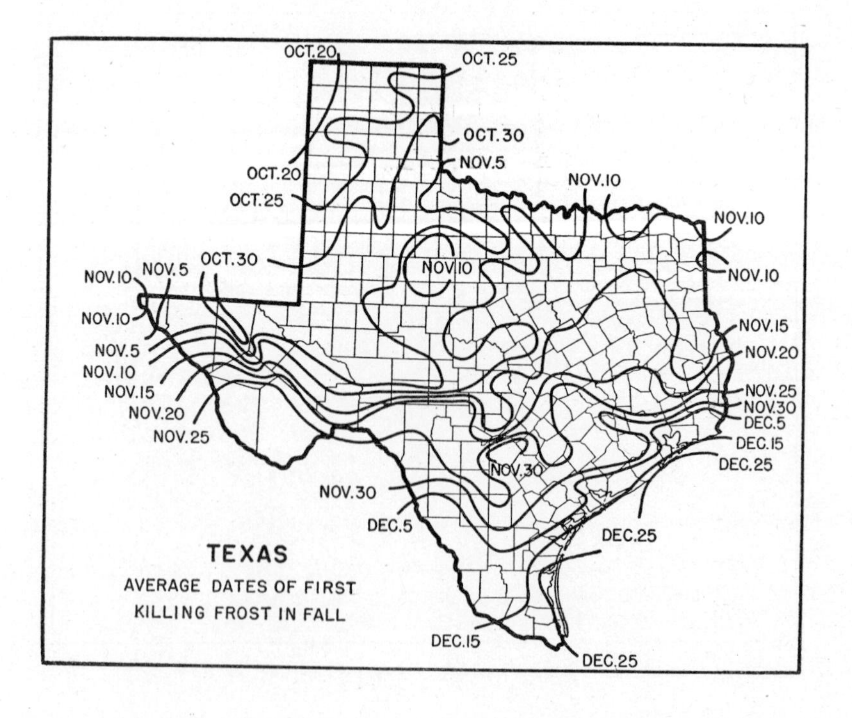
TEXAS
AVERAGE DATES OF FIRST
KILLING FROST IN FALL
OCT.20
OCT.25
OCT.30
NOV.5
NOV.10
NOV.15
NOV.20
NOV.25
NOV.30
DEC.5
DEC.15
DEC.25

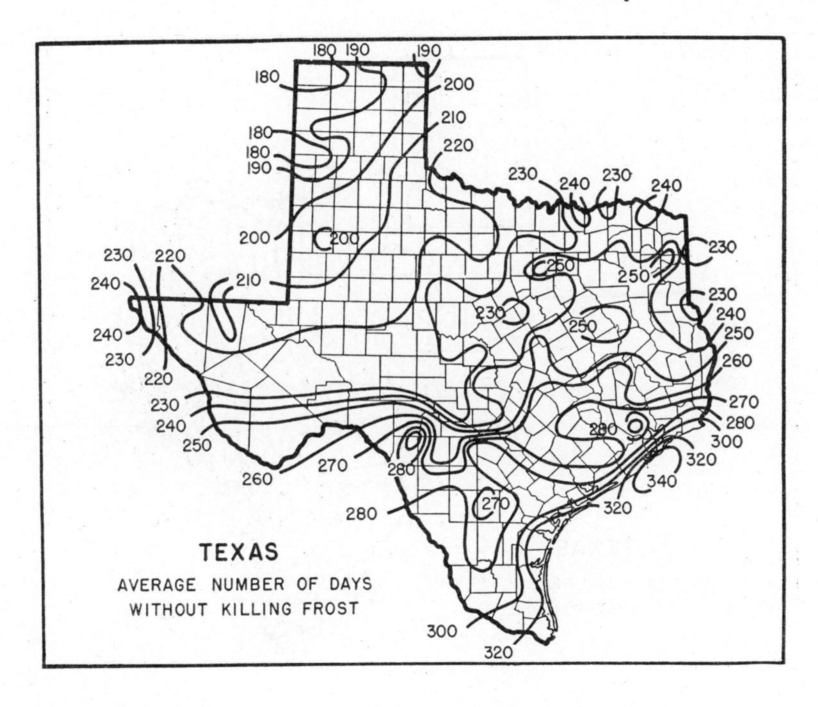

TEXAS
AVERAGE NUMBER OF DAYS
WITHOUT KILLING FROST

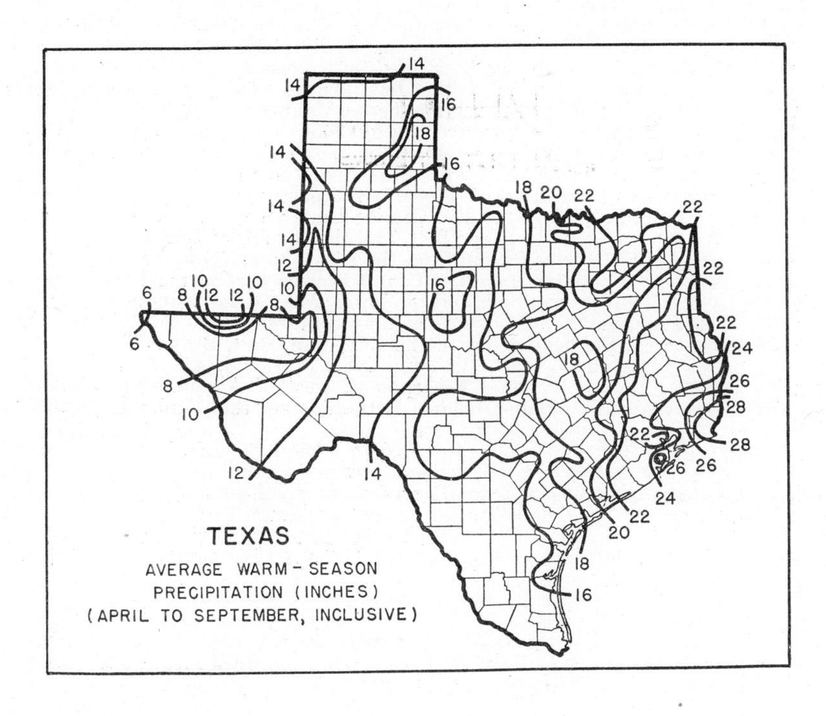

TEXAS
AVERAGE WARM-SEASON
PRECIPITATION (INCHES)
(APRIL TO SEPTEMBER, INCLUSIVE)

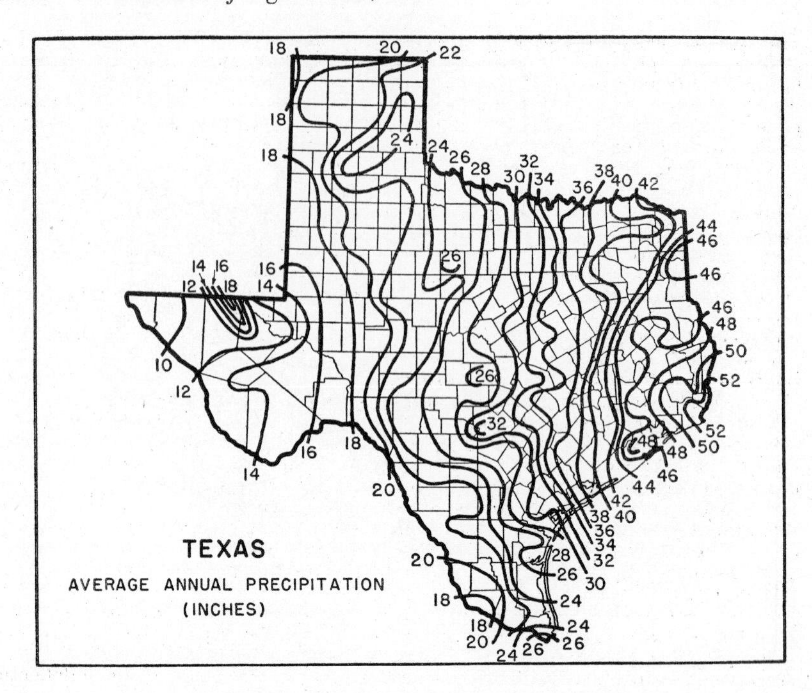

SUPPLEMENTARY CLIMATIC NOTES FOR TEXAS

The distance from the most southern point of Texas near the mouth of the Rio Grande to the northwestern corner of the Panhandle is 801 miles, while the greatest reach from east to west is 773 miles. The State has an area of 265,896 square miles and consequently presents great diversity in topography and climate. Most authorities divide Texas into four physiographical provinces: The Coastal Plains, sometimes called the East Texas Plains; the North-Central Plains; the Great Plains; and the Trans-Pecos Mountain area.

The Coastal Plains is the lowest of the divisions and extends from the coast to the Balcones Escarpment, a geologic fault line extending in a great semicircle from the Rio Grande, near Del Rio, to the Red River just west of Gainesville. This region has five natural subdivisions, based partly on surface characteristics and partly on timber types—the Rio Grande Embayment, the Coastal Prairies, the Pine Woods area, the Post Oak Belt, and the Black Land Prairies.

The North-Central Plains extend from the Black Lands westward to the Great Plains and has four subdivisions—the Grand Prairie, the Burnet-Llano country, the West Cross Timbers country, and the lower West Texas Rolling Prairie.

The Great Plains come down from the north and northwest into Texas on the high ridge between the headwaters of the Canadian, Red, Brazos, and Colorado Rivers on the east and the Pecos Valley in New Mexico on the west. They extend southward to the Balcones Escarpment, west of Austin. There are two subdivisions—the High Plains (Llano Estacado) of the Panhandle and the Edwards Plateau of southwestern Texas.

The Trans-Pecos area is a plateau 3,000 to 5,000 feet high, lying west of the Pecos Valley. It is traversed by several mountain ranges (part of the Rocky Mountain system) having a general trend from northwest to southeast. The principal ranges are the Guadalupe, of which Guadalupe Peak (El Capitan) with an elevation of 9,020 feet is the highest; this is also the highest point in Texas. Other ranges include the Davis Mountains (Mount Livermore, 8,382 feet) and the Chisos (Mount Emory, 7,835 feet).

The northern part of the Panhandle is drained by the Canadian River, which flows eastward into the Arkansas and thence to the Mississippi. The southern part of the Panhandle and a strip along the northern border of the State east of the Panhandle are drained by the Red River southeastward into the Mississippi.

The rest of the State also is drained southeastward, but directly into the Gulf of Mexico. The Rio Grande and its principal tributary, the Pecos, drain narrow basins in the southwest. These two rivers, as well as the Canadian, rise in the Rocky Mountains in Colorado and New Mexico, while the Brazos and Colorado have their sources in the plains of New Mexico. All other rivers by which the State is drained have their sources within its borders.

The Sabine, Neches, Trinity, Brazos, and Colorado Rivers traverse regions where the heavy rains cause great erosion, and as a result the streams are very muddy, carrying hundreds of thousands of tons of soil into the Gulf. The Guadalupe and Nueces have their sources in the Edwards Plateau, and since they flow over rocky terrain there is little erosion and their waters are clear and clean, in marked contrast to the larger streams to the eastward.

The marine, continental, and mountain types of climate are all found in Texas—the continental and mountain types in true form, but the marine type somewhat modified and subdued to a coast climate. The continental type of climate obtains over by far the greater part of the State. The mountain type is confined to a relatively small area of western Texas, the Trans-Pecos area; while the coastal type prevails over a comparatively narrow strip of the Coastal Plains.

Continental climate is characterized by rapid changes in temperature, marked extremes, and large temperature ranges, both diurnal and annual. Mountain climates are cooler throughout the year than those of the adjacent lowlands, the decrease in temperature with increase in altitude averaging about 1° F. for each 300 feet of ascent. However, the rate of change varies with the season, being more rapid in summer than in winter and greatest during the warmer hours of the day. The marine type is characterized by comparatively uniform temperatures in all seasons, with a small diurnal range; also, the progress of the seasons is retarded, winter lingering into spring and summer into fall. This gives a marine climate comparatively pleasant summers, mild winters, cool springs, and warm autumns, conditions rather characteristic of the Coastal Plains of Texas.

Roughly, the annual isotherms in Texas lie east and west, with a fairly regular decrease in temperature with increase in latitude. There is, of course, a deflection of the isotherms to the southward over the Great Plains and the Trans-Pecos section. The warmest part of the State is the lower Rio Grande Valley, with an annual mean temperature of 74° F.; the coldest section is the northwestern Panhandle, with an annual mean of 54°.

No part of the State is free from occasional periods of excessive heat when temperatures of 100° F. or higher are recorded, nor from occasional periods of freezing temperature, although the coastal counties and the lower Rio Grande Valley experience damaging freezes only at infrequent intervals.

A few stations along the Gulf coast and in the lower Rio Grande Valley (Galveston, Rockfort, Corpus Christi, Brownsville, and Raymondville) have occasionally had years with no killing frost, but it is safe to say that no part of Texas is entirely safe from damage by frost or freezing weather.

The average date of the last killing frost in spring ranges from January 21 on the upper Gulf coast (Galveston Island) to April 26 at Stratford, Sherman County. Killing frosts occur later in spring in the Panhandle High Plains than in the lower country of eastern Texas because of the influence of latitude and altitude.

The average date for the first killing frost in fall ranges from October 17 at Hereford, Deaf Smith County (elevation, 3,750 feet) to December 27 at Corpus Christi, Nueces County (elevation, 20 feet). The advance in fall of the average killing-frost date line across the State from the Panhandle to the Gulf coast is quite regular, but it is interesting to note that for practically the entire State it falls in November; only in the High Plains of the Panhandle does it come as early as October, and only in the Coastal Prairies and the lower Rio Grande Valley as late as December.

The average length of the growing season increases slowly from 185 days in the northern Panhandle (Sherman County) to 230 days along the eastern and southern borders of the north-central physiographical divisions, but from there to the coast the increase to over 300 days is rapid, particularly in the coastal counties. Thus one section becomes frost-free in spring an average of more than 3 months before another on the opposite side of the State, and there is a range of more than 2 months between the first fall frost dates. The growing season in upper coast sections is more than 5 months longer than in the northern Panhandle.

The principal sources of moisture for Texas are the Gulf of Mexico and the tropical Atlantic. Warm and very moist tropical maritime air masses, carried by the prevailing southeasterly winds, move inland up the land slope and up the slopes of cold fronts of continental air masses and, becoming cooled by expansion, lose more or less of their moisture supply.

Rainfall is heaviest over eastern Texas, especially in the extreme southeastern part, and diminishes steadily westward, the average amount in the extreme eastern part being over 50 inches, while in parts of the extreme west it is less than 10. Isohyetals—lines of equal precipitation—are roughly parallel and run north and south over most of the State, there being some departure from this regularity in the Trans-Pecos area.

The average precipitation in winter is 5.94 inches, spring 8.70, summer 8.09, and fall 7.81. Much the greater part of the State has an annual average of over 20 inches, and most of it has enough precipitation to supply agricultural needs without irrigation. In some sections where the amount of rain borders on being too scant for crop needs, this unfavorable feature is offset to some extent by its very favorable seasonal distribution, the greater amount, from 60 to 70 percent of the annual total, falling during the crop-growing season. However, there is a considerable area west of the one hundred and first meridian where it is necessary to resort to irrigation, where possible, or to use extraordinary conservation methods to produce crops; and there is also a considerable area that cannot be cropped at all.

Rainfall distribution, even in the best watered sections of Texas, is occasionally erratic, and as a result droughts of several weeks or even months occur. On the other hand, rains are occasionally so heavy and frequent, particularly in the wetter regions, that crops suffer from too much moisture and lack of cultivation.

Snow is of rare occurrence in the coastal counties, a few stations never having had any at all, but there is an increase in amount from the Coastal Plains to the High Plains of the Panhandle where the annual average is 23.7 inches. The heavier snowfall occurs to the westward of the Balcones Escarpment. Sleet storms occur occasionally. Hail has been observed in all sections of the State but is infrequent in coastal districts. It is most frequent and severe in the Panhandle counties.

The absence of sheltering mountains or extensive forests, and the great extent of plains and prairies give the wind free play, and as a result its movement is brisk much of the time. The highest wind of record for the State was 84 miles an hour from the northwest. The prevailing direction of the wind is south.

The coastal areas are subject to the hazard of infrequent hurricanes during the summer and early autumn, while the interior counties have the tornado as a threat. Fortunately tornadoes are small in extent and the probability that any given locality will be visited by one is remote.

CLINTON E. NORQUEST, *Senior Meteorologist, and Climatic Section Director for Texas, Weather Bureau, Houston.*

UTAH

Climatic summary

County	Station	Temperature: Length of record	Temperature: January average	Temperature: July average	Temperature: Maximum	Temperature: Minimum	Killing frost average dates: Length of record	Killing frost: Last in spring	Killing frost: First in fall	Killing frost: Growing season[1]	Average precipitation: Length of record	January	February	March	April	May	June	July	August	September	October	November	December	Annual
		Yr.	°*F.*	°*F.*	°*F.*	°*F.*	*Yr.*			*Days*	*Yr.*	*In.*	*In.*	*In.*	*In.*	*In.*	*In.*	*In.*	*In.*	*In.*	*In.*	*In.*	*In.*	*In.*
Beaver	Beaver	30	27.1	68.3	102	−34	32	June 6	Sept. 18	104	32	0.86	1.00	1.36	1.04	1.02	0.43	1.63	1.83	0.99	1.01	0.83	0.93	13.93
	Milford	30	25.4	73.4	104	−34	30	May 20	Sept. 23	126	30	.64	.89	1.02	.78	.70	.29	1.04	.73	.40	.77	.59	.80	8.65
	Minersville	---	---	---	---	---	---	---	---	---	17	.86	.87	1.36	.94	.99	.39	1.08	.96	.87	.87	.85	.87	10.91
	Nada										22	1.08	.86	1.16	.85	.86	.28	.87	1.07	.44	.81	.70	.81	9.79
Box Elder	Brigham City	25	25.4	75.8	108	−27	25	May 2	Oct. 11	162	27	1.64	1.75	1.80	2.03	1.68	.93	.66	.84	1.22	1.74	1.36	1.68	17.33
	Corinne	40	24.3	74.9	110	−32	38	May 14	Sept. 30	139	40	1.31	1.31	1.39	1.39	1.62	.76	.57	.82	.84	1.52	1.08	1.27	13.88
	Kelton	28	22.2	72.2	114	−30	26	May 26	Sept. 22	119	31	.64	.67	.53	.54	.85	.61	.45	.36	.55	.75	.49	.60	7.04
	Lemay	19	24.5	77.8	110	−26	20	Apr. 28	Oct. 7	162	20	.31	.32	.36	.37	.53	.60	.23	.26	.40	.49	.25	.33	4.45
	Lucin	28	22.6	73.1	106	−28	26	May 27	Sept. 20	116	28	.47	.42	.27	.48	.81	.59	.43	.36	.42	.54	.24	.37	5.40
	Midlake	16	28.8	78.2	98	3	18	Apr. 4	Nov. 14	224	19	.42	.57	.71	.76	.67	.63	.33	.33	.39	.65	.38	.48	6.32
	Park Valley	9	22.7	72.8	101	−26	11	May 25	Oct. 2	130	28	.83	.83	.74	.98	.97	.96	.94	.94	.60	.97	.59	.86	10.21
	Standrod	13	27.1	67.2	95	−18	13	May 29	Sept. 24	118	17	1.08	.92	1.28	1.30	1.75	1.47	1.45	1.05	1.07	1.36	.99	.70	14.42
	Tremonton	24	22.2	75.5	106	−25	24	May 13	Oct. 7	147	25	1.17	1.42	1.41	1.53	1.56	.75	.81	.67	.94	1.30	.91	1.21	13.68
Cache	Clarkston	---	---	---	---	---	---	---	---	---	21	1.32	1.65	1.77	1.84	1.73	1.10	1.02	1.00	1.02	1.73	1.60	1.36	17.14
	Lewiston	14	19.8	70.2	104	−44	14	May 17	Sept. 27	133	14	1.65	1.56	2.05	2.12	1.95	.97	.87	.78	1.00	1.70	1.64	1.63	17.92
	Logan	40	24.3	73.1	102	−25	39	May 7	Oct. 11	157	40	1.60	1.57	1.93	1.90	1.91	.83	.65	.70	1.14	1.74	1.25	1.26	16.48
	Logan Sugar Factory	14	22.1	72.0	107	−38	17	May 14	Sept. 28	137	14	1.62	1.74	1.83	1.95	1.72	.68	.65	.74	1.01	1.46	1.48	1.60	16.48
	Millville	---	---	---	---	---	---	---	---	---	26	1.74	1.57	1.97	1.82	1.95	.89	.49	.78	1.20	1.90	1.60	1.40	17.31
	Richmond	---	---	---	---	---	16	May 29	Sept. 28	122	27	1.81	1.85	2.30	2.28	1.88	1.03	.89	.71	1.24	1.99	1.55	1.75	19.28
Carbon	Clear Creek	16	15.8	58.3	98	−41	15	July 4	Aug. 30	57	3	2.73	5.07	2.90	1.12	1.66	1.25	2.96	1.53	1.52	2.02	1.14	2.21	26.11
	Hiawatha	17	21.7	68.8	95	−18	17	May 17	Oct. 5	141	21	.67	1.20	1.02	.79	1.13	.89	1.45	2.09	1.24	.95	.56	.69	12.68
	Price	24	21.4	72.6	108	−31	24	May 16	Sept. 29	136	27	.77	.75	.75	.72	.69	.70	1.13	1.41	1.18	.79	.53	.85	10.27
	Sunnyside	10	25.7	71.3	96	−10	11	May 18	Oct. 13	148	22	.98	.88	1.01	.98	1.06	.64	1.49	1.70	1.76	1.36	.89	.75	13.50
Daggett	Manila	22	21.4	66.4	99	−33	20	June 17	Sept. 9	84	28	.34	.62	.89	1.50	1.22	.60	1.00	1.02	.97	1.16	.52	.41	10.25
Davis	Farmington	38	28.4	74.5	106	−20	36	May 2	Oct. 6	157	38	2.16	2.22	2.19	2.22	2.19	.92	.74	.93	1.22	1.66	1.74	2.02	20.21
Duchesne	Duchesne	32	15.6	68.5	98	−43	33	May 29	Sept. 18	112	33	.60	.68	.78	.64	.72	.67	1.10	1.33	1.08	.91	.53	.57	9.61
	Fruitland	16	21.0	64.3	96	−27	16	June 11	Sept. 20	101	21	1.01	1.14	1.11	.71	.70	.86	1.25	1.42	1.50	1.41	.66	.84	12.61
	Mount Emmons	14	16.0	68.1	98	−30	14	May 23	Sept. 28	128	16	.31	.48	.49	.75	.84	.46	.80	1.18	.95	.69	.48	.49	7.92
	Myton	20	15.4	72.4	103	−39	21	May 18	Oct. 1	136	23	.29	.30	.40	.63	.63	.39	.86	.99	.96	.71	.38	.36	6.90
Emery	Castle Dale	38	18.4	69.4	104	−35	38	May 28	Sept. 24	119	40	.72	.69	.58	.55	.51	.54	1.03	1.29	.92	.76	.52	.65	8.76
	Emery	36	23.8	67.3	99	−20	37	May 27	Sept. 23	119	37	.46	.60	.44	.38	.60	.41	.95	1.21	.97	.65	.29	.48	7.44
	Green River	37	22.2	79.6	112	−42	34	May 3	Oct. 6	156	37	.35	.44	.40	.49	.47	.36	.57	.74	.79	.66	.45	.41	6.13

[1] Length of growing season between average dates of last killing frost in spring and first in fall.

UTAH—Continued

Climatic summary—Continued

County	Station	Temperature					Killing frost average dates				Average precipitation													
		Length of record	January average	July average	Maximum	Minimum	Length of record	Last in spring	First in fall	Growing season	Length of record	January	February	March	April	May	June	July	August	September	October	November	December	Annual
		Yr.	°F.	°F.	°F.	°F.	Yr.			Days	Yr.	In.	In.	In.	In.	In.	In.	In.	In.	In.	In.	In.	In.	In.
Garfield	Escalante	30	25.4	69.9	102	−22	32	May 18	Sept. 29	134	33	1.06	0.94	0.96	0.53	0.58	0.47	1.64	2.04	1.22	0.94	0.56	0.98	11.92
	Hatch										17	.81	.86	.90	.77	.73	.37	1.57	1.86	1.20	.92	.50	.76	11.25
	Panguitch	24	20.4	63.5	95	−38	28	June 18	Sept. 9	83	31	.73	.55	.93	.64	.63	.33	1.66	1.52	.81	.83	.47	.58	9.68
	Tropic	26	27.4	67.7	101	−32	24	May 31	Sept. 18	110	27	1.12	1.01	1.05	.74	.51	.40	1.39	1.76	1.23	.91	.70	.86	11.68
	Widtsoe	16	23.1	64.8	93	−22	15	June 9	do	101	21	.74	.86	.76	.79	.77	.37	1.63	1.58	1.15	.72	.65	.66	10.68
Grand	Moab	38	28.6	78.4	113	−24	40	Apr. 24	Oct. 10	169	40	.77	.69	.86	.75	.79	.41	.98	.88	.93	.91	.68	.93	9.58
	Thompsons	24	23.7	78.5	110	−25	22	Apr. 26	Oct. 19	176	26	.48	.57	.75	.51	.54	.33	.87	.87	.95	.84	.58	.72	8.01
Iron	Cedar City	32	30.6	73.6	99	−26	32	May 9	Oct. 6	150	33	.90	1.12	1.36	1.19	.95	.41	1.50	1.33	.92	1.28	1.07	.96	12.99
	Modena	38	26.3	71.4	101	−32	38	May 17	Oct. 2	138	38	.87	.96	1.12	.78	.85	.34	1.40	1.51	.86	.88	.55	.66	10.78
	Parowan	38	28.6	71.0	102	−27	39	May 24	Sept. 29	128	40	.92	1.05	1.41	1.14	1.04	.46	1.40	1.45	.89	1.01	.86	.95	12.58
Juab	Levan	40	25.1	71.9	104	−28	40	May 17	Oct. 4	140	39	1.27	1.42	1.74	1.46	1.54	.50	.88	1.02	1.04	1.19	1.04	1.29	14.39
	Nephi (near)	18		72.7	105		26	May 25	Sept. 29	127	33	1.11	1.13	1.37	1.24	1.47	.58	1.00	1.02	.87	1.03	.88	1.00	12.70
Kane	Alton	24	25.7	64.7	94	−20	24	June 3	Sept. 28	117	23	1.57	1.85	1.67	1.19	.87	.56	1.70	1.83	1.43	1.23	.84	1.65	16.39
	Kanab	29	32.7	74.1	106	−20	24	May 9	Oct. 7	151	29	1.35	1.52	1.59	1.03	.71	.28	1.31	1.35	1.10	.83	.89	1.22	13.18
	Orderville										29	1.83	1.85	1.49	1.09	.72	.38	1.46	1.40	1.34	1.07	.82	1.46	14.91
Millard	Black Rock	25	25.2	72.2	106	−33	22	June 1	Sept. 15	106	25	.60	.78	.96	.96	.91	.35	.63	.61	.72	1.01	.64	.51	8.68
	Deseret	39	25.2	73.3	106	−32	39	May 25	Sept. 20	118	39	.57	.69	.79	.89	1.00	.37	.51	.58	.64	.68	.58	.57	7.87
	Fillmore	40	29.5	76.7	115	−23	40	May 14	Oct. 3	142	40	1.18	1.47	1.79	1.62	1.47	.55	.90	.75	.91	1.22	1.08	1.21	14.15
	Kanosh						13	Apr. 15	Oct. 15	183	31	1.17	1.50	1.72	1.53	1.38	.53	1.00	1.10	.80	1.28	1.17	1.25	14.43
	McCormick										18	.89	1.06	1.27	1.35	1.09	.37	.55	.44	.71	1.12	.78	.95	10.58
	Oak City	28	27.4	76.9	108	−25	29	May 14	Oct. 8	147	30	.95	1.17	1.45	1.38	1.56	.52	.87	1.00	.87	1.24	1.04	1.06	13.11
	Scipio	39	26.1	70.6	106	−40	39	June 6	Sept. 14	100	39	1.25	1.52	1.56	1.25	1.30	.55	.80	1.12	.98	1.09	.99	1.08	13.49
Morgan	Morgan	32	22.7	68.5	105	−38	30	June 2	Sept. 13	103	32	2.33	2.28	2.31	1.59	1.74	.77	.79	1.06	1.00	1.62	1.65	1.97	19.11
Piute	Alunite	21	25.5	71.8	106	−27	22	May 23	Oct. 2	132	22	.77	.97	1.13	.67	.93	.52	1.50	1.28	.84	.72	.70	.90	10.93
	Marysvale	16	28.2	67.1	99	−33	15	June 10	Sept. 15	97	15	.82	.83	1.08	.79	.93	.60	.95	1.42	1.25	.85	.78	.76	11.06
	Piute Dam	20	25.6	71.3	101	−32	21	May 23	Oct. 1	131	28	.48	.57	.70	.60	.67	.47	1.16	.93	.70	.71	.53	.56	8.08
Rich	Laketown	38	21.0	65.5	106	−37	38	June 14	Sept. 10	88	39	1.23	1.20	1.22	1.31	1.33	.75	.65	.82	1.14	1.34	.87	.75	12.61
	Randolph										22	.75	.64	.73	.93	1.01	.88	1.05	1.01	1.10	1.11	.52	.62	10.35
	Woodruff	31	15.1	61.9	102	−50	30	June 27	Aug. 22	56	28	.63	.76	.76	.79	1.04	.75	.91	.91	.87	1.07	.48	.49	9.46
San Juan	Blanding	32	26.2	71.7	110	−23	32	May 12	Oct. 6	147	33	1.34	1.47	1.24	.90	.76	.46	1.30	1.44	1.33	1.40	1.23	1.67	14.54
	Bluff	22	27.9	80.2	109	−20	19	Apr. 11	Oct. 16	188	23	.56	.81	.74	.52	.42	.29	.74	.66	.84	.66	.42	.70	7.36
	LaSal	32	24.1	68.4	100	−27	30	May 26	Sept. 29	126	34	.80	.93	.76	.84	.82	.62	1.56	1.43	1.27	1.18	.81	.98	12.00
	Monticello	25	23.7	67.7	98	−21	26	May 21	Oct. 4	136	27	1.41	1.64	1.73	1.00	.84	.60	1.81	1.77	1.71	1.78	1.23	1.25	16.77
Salt Lake	Cottonwood Weir										22	1.59	1.95	2.40	2.48	2.14	.78	1.02	1.21	1.27	1.78	1.70	1.69	20.01
	High line, City Creek										23	2.68	2.88	3.53	3.12	2.59	.83	.87	1.35	1.39	1.96	2.34	2.68	26.22
	Lower Mill Creek	24	29.1	75.9	103	−11	24	Apr. 29	Oct. 18	172	25	2.03	2.22	2.45	2.44	2.24	1.05	.83	1.15	1.39	1.89	1.91	2.01	21.61

	Midvale	27	27.5	75.5	110	−25	27	May 18	Sept. 28	133	27	1.15	1.45	1.68	1.78	1.44	.71	.77	.82	.91	1.40	1.34	1.25	14.70
	Mountain Dell										19	1.89	2.16	2.57	2.47	2.09	.81	1.04	1.29	1.44	1.65	2.21	1.91	21.53
	Saltair	34	28.0	76.5	103	−22	32	Apr. 12	Oct. 23	194	33	1.01	1.10	1.46	1.41	1.52	.82	.66	.75	.91	1.44	1.34	1.00	13.42
	Salt Lake City	40	30.1	77.0	105	−20	40	Apr. 13	Oct. 22	192	40	1.31	1.55	2.00	1.85	1.94	.74	.57	.91	.95	1.43	1.28	1.26	15.79
	Silver Lake										23	4.90	5.67	5.20	4.01	2.52	.99	1.67	2.19	2.39	2.91	3.65	4.72	40.82
Sanpete	Great Basin						16	June 11	Sept. 14	95	24	3.24	3.22	3.84	3.13	2.37	.91	2.01	1.77	1.49	1.87	2.25	2.88	28.98
	Great Basin (Oaks)						10	June 15	do	91	15	1.36	1.29	2.01	1.53	1.64	.63	1.38	1.57	1.19	1.42	1.68	1.38	17.08
	Mammoth Ranger Station.										21					1.10	.79	1.59	1.54	1.53	2.51	3.78	3.32	
	Manti	40	25.0	69.2	110	−27	39	May 25	Sept. 26	124	39	.97	1.16	1.36	1.24	1.30	.56	.91	.86	1.01	1.07	.85	.87	12.16
	Moroni	28	23.5	70.4	107	−30	30	May 26	Sept. 21	118	30	1.22	1.09	1.21	1.08	1.08	.53	.95	1.06	.89	1.05	.85	.99	12.00
Summit	Castle Rock										22	1.44	1.54	1.55	1.49	1.59	1.00	1.19	1.21	1.31	1.42	.88	1.13	15.75
	Henefer	20	22.5	65.1	101	−39	18	June 19	Aug. 31	73	20	2.27	2.15	2.36	1.66	1.69	1.01	.89	.95	1.38	1.31	1.60	1.56	18.83
	Park City	32	22.0	66.1	101	−30	34	June 9	Sept. 14	97	34	2.75	2.66	2.64	1.80	1.21	.65	1.32	1.59	1.10	1.39	1.73	2.12	20.96
Sevier	Gooseberry Range Station.										16		.78	.87		1.29	.68	1.86	1.67	1.47	.97	1.74	2.11	
	Richfield	34	28.2	71.6	104	−28	32	May 23	Sept. 23	123	34	.59	.76	.91	.75	.73	.40	.82	.80	.71	.69	.57	.64	8.37
	Salina										15	.51	.97	1.07	.72	1.03	.50	.58	1.01	.62	.53	.51	.52	8.57
Tooele	Benmore						7	May 26	Oct. 3	130	27	1.07	1.32	1.53	1.20	1.28	.69	1.00	1.00	.75	1.13	.90	1.01	12.88
	Government Creek	38	26.4	73.8	105	−25	38	do	Sept. 29	126	38	1.04	1.21	1.66	1.33	1.52	.64	.87	1.03	.74	1.01	.97	.95	12.97
	Grantsville										28	.84	.78	1.05	1.24	1.24	.67	.70	.89	.83	1.11	.81	.70	10.86
	Ibapah	34	24.0	68.4	106	−39	34	June 16	Sept. 9	85	34	.79	1.15	1.20	1.24	1.76	.88	.96	1.20	.64	1.03	.70	.77	12.32
	International										15	.94	1.36	1.97	2.20	1.78	.52	.70	.74	1.00	2.03	1.39	1.02	15.65
	Orr's Ranch	18	24.1	73.4	108	−35	18	June 7	Sept. 12	97	19	.62	.86	.91	.86	1.08	.41	.51	.85	.38	.84	.61	.75	8.68
	St. John	16	22.2	69.9	110	−36	16	June 6	Sept. 11	97	17	.86	.76	.84	.97	.98	.63	.73	.62	.48	.93	.69	.67	9.16
	Tooele	40	28.7	74.7	104	−16	39	May 5	Oct. 14	162	40	1.36	1.58	2.00	2.14	1.84	.76	.84	.94	.98	1.50	1.47	1.24	16.65
	Wendover	25	27.1	79.7	112	−19	24	Apr. 16	Oct. 20	187	28	.26	.33	.27	.45	.66	.52	.42	.34	.42	.41	.19	.35	4.62
Uintah	Elkhorn										27	.84	1.05	.99	1.04	1.41	.90	1.35	1.25	1.53	1.04	.84	.95	13.19
	Fort Duchesne	38	14.3	70.7	107	−40	37	May 25	Sept. 20	118	39	.43	.40	.58	.62	.64	.46	.51	.67	1.03	.67	.42	.40	6.83
	Jensen						6	May 22	Sept. 23	124	16	.51	.51	.54	.80	.83	.53	.79	.72	.88	.93	.35	.59	7.98
	Trout Creek Ranger Station.										18	4.00	2.90				1.62	2.39	2.60	2.24	2.93	.87	.84	
	Vernal	32	17.1	70.4	106	−38	34	May 26	Sept. 21	118	35	.59	.56	.77	.90	.83	.34	.61	.77	1.00	.90	.68	.58	8.53
	Watson	27	20.3	71.9	99	−24	28	May 22	Oct. 28	159	28	.52	.55	.93	1.01	.90	.72	1.47	1.43	1.23	1.02	.84	.68	11.30
Utah	Alpine										35	1.52	1.74	1.91	1.86	1.84	.71	.71	1.00	1.04	1.48	1.24	1.55	16.60
	Elberta	35	26.4	74.9	109	−28	36	May 19	Sept. 30	134	36	.84	1.01	1.13	1.03	1.21	.51	.82	.86	.76	.98	.78	.73	10.66
	Lower American Fork.	24	28.5	75.8	108	−15	25	Apr. 28	Oct. 19	174	25	1.75	1.54	1.63	1.67	1.69	.63	.92	1.02	1.09	1.35	1.18	1.44	15.91
	Maplewood										20	1.58	1.82	1.93	2.09	1.69	.88	1.06	1.18	1.14	1.92	1.70	1.63	18.62
	Payson										35	1.52	1.52	1.85	1.72	1.79	.71	.88	.95	1.04	1.45	1.15	1.42	16.30
	Provo	38	26.6	72.3	110	−35	39	May 24	Sept. 25	124	40	1.61	1.64	1.65	1.50	1.53	.61	.65	.93	1.02	1.45	1.30	1.44	15.33
	Santaquin	22	27.3	74.4	103	−19	24	May 13	Oct. 6	146	25	1.62	1.72	2.06	2.11	1.91	.76	.84	1.04	.83	1.56	1.61	1.61	17.67
	Spanish Fork	29	28.5	76.3	108	−19	29	Apr. 28	Oct. 13	168	30	1.76	1.63	2.00	1.92	1.72	.66	.91	.92	1.07	1.60	1.62	1.80	17.61
	Thistle	36	24.3	68.3	112	−35	34	June 10	Sept. 8	90	40	2.22	2.00	2.03	1.82	1.44	.62	1.02	1.12	1.20	1.34	1.53	1.82	18.16
	Utah Lake (Lehi)	30	24.9	72.6	106	−28	29	May 13	Sept. 25	135	31	1.18	1.30	1.16	1.24	1.29	.54	.92	1.01	.91	1.08	.86	1.19	12.68
Wasatch	East Portal	18	12.3	60.9	97	−50	19	June 27	Sept. 3	68	17	2.38	2.26	2.34	1.54	1.39	1.03	1.71	1.59	1.78	1.92	1.39	1.74	21.07
	Heber	40	21.5	66.8	105	−38	40	June 14	Sept. 5	83	40	1.99	2.05	1.83	1.45	1.25	.61	.83	1.07	1.04	1.38	1.38	1.57	16.45
	Snake Creek	25	20.6	65.6	97	−30	25	June 11	Sept. 12	93	25	2.89	3.27	2.56	2.14	1.40	.60	1.16	1.30	1.45	1.54	1.89	2.62	22.82
	Soldier Summit	22	17.6	61.9	100	−34	21	June 27	Sept. 2	67	27	1.26	1.73	1.41	.98	1.15	.47	1.33	1.26	1.03	.88	.93	1.47	13.90

UTAH—Continued

Climatic summary—Continued

County	Station	Temperature					Killing frost average dates				Average precipitation													
		Length of record	January average	July average	Maximum	Minimum	Length of record	Last in spring	First in fall	Growing season	Length of record	January	February	March	April	May	June	July	August	September	October	November	December	Annual
		Yr.	*°F.*	*°F.*	*°F.*	*°F.*	*Yr.*			*Days*	*Yr.*	*In.*	*In.*	*In.*	*In.*	*In.*	*In.*	*In.*	*In.*	*In.*	*In.*	*In.*	*In.*	*In.*
Washington	Enterprise						8	May 28	Sept. 23	118	18	2.30	1.95	2.07	1.03	0.89	0.48	1.39	1.59	1.32	1.29	1.02	1.34	16.67
	Hurricane										17	1.15	1.33	1.03	1.04	.67	.38	.78	1.00	.83	1.27	.62	.95	11.05
	Leeds (near)	24	35.7	80.3	115	−15	24	Apr. 10	Nov. 5	209	27	1.73	1.93	1.32	1.05	.65	.31	.73	.92	.59	1.03	.77	1.68	12.71
	Pinto	24	26.9	66.0	102	−27	22	June 20	Sept. 11	83	25	1.49	1.44	1.85	1.23	1.01	.37	1.50	1.80	1.26	1.45	1.11	1.12	15.63
	St. George	39	38.4	82.9	116	−11	38	Apr. 10	Oct. 23	196	40	.93	1.11	.88	.54	.39	.22	.88	.95	.64	.78	.57	.84	8.73
	Springdale	32	39.2	81.4	112	−15	29	Apr. 15	Oct. 28	196	32	1.49	1.75	1.69	1.17	.79	.26	1.12	1.59	1.23	1.07	.99	1.36	14.51
Wayne	Hanksville	26	22.9	78.0	112	−35	28	May 5	Oct. 3	151	29	.39	.33	.32	.24	.38	.36	.77	.77	.58	.55	.27	.38	5.34
	Loa	26	20.9	65.6	110	−37	25	June 14	Sept. 7	85	28	.46	.55	.63	.49	.43	.33	1.14	1.36	.76	.39	.34	.47	7.35
	Teasdale	14	24.4	66.3	107	−20	12	May 26	Sept. 23	120	16	.42	.72	.58	.72	.43	.51	1.22	1.28	.90	.72	.44	.48	8.42
Weber	Huntsville						18	June 7	Sept. 14	99	28	3.09	2.69	2.59	1.98	1.96	.65	.62	.90	1.24	1.83	2.04	2.10	21.69
	Ogden	40	27.4	74.7	105	−23	37	May 6	Oct. 8	155	39	1.80	1.89	2.06	1.87	1.93	.87	.58	.96	1.14	1.63	1.52	1.67	17.92
	Riverdale	24	25.8	75.3	106	−25	23	May 1	do	160	25	1.55	1.84	1.57	1.75	1.56	.74	.58	.53	1.07	1.48	1.38	1.49	15.54

Precipitation and temperature—State unit values

[This tabulation gives the mean annual, mean monthly, and average seasonal precipitation, 1886–1938, and the mean annual temperatures, 1898–1938 for Utah]

Precipitation		Precipitation		Precipitation		Precipitation		Temperature		Temperature	
Year	Mean	Year	Mean	Year	Mean	Month	Mean	Year	Mean	Year	Mean
	In.		*In.*		*In.*		*In.*		°*F.*		°*F.*
1886	9.67	1907	16.07	1928	10.70	May	1.16	1898	47.0	1919	47.7
1887	6.35	1908	14.82	1929	13.60	June	.57	1899	48.0	1920	46.9
1888	8.83	1909	19.31	1930	15.14	July	.88	1900	50.1	1921	49.8
1889	12.67	1910	11.16	1931	10.06	August	.99	1901	49.5	1922	47.2
1890	8.44	1911	13.02	1932	13.36	September	.94	1902	48.2	1923	46.8
1891	13.52	1912	14.15	1933	10.57	October	1.06	1903	46.9	1924	47.1
1892	9.68	1913	13.02	1934	9.52	November	.91	1904	48.5	1925	48.4
1893	11.56	1914	13.60	1935	10.83	December	1.12	1905	48.1	1926	49.5
1894	11.43	1915	13.33	1936	16.97			1906	48.4	1927	48.6
1895	10.66	1916	15.93	1937	14.74	Annual	12.63	1907	49.2	1928	48.7
1896	11.20	1917	11.88	1938	15.19			1908	47.0	1929	47.5
1897	14.55	1918	14.12					1909	47.7	1930	47.1
1898	10.61	1919	11.83	Month	Mean	Season	Average	1910	50.3	1931	48.3
1899	11.83	1920	16.57					1911	47.2	1932	46.6
1900	8.38	1921	15.49					1912	46.6	1933	47.9
1901	10.05	1922	14.83					1913	46.8	1934	52.3
1902	9.17	1923	13.60		*In.*		*In.*	1914	48.6	1935	48.8
1903	10.21	1924	10.57	January	1.19	Winter	3.56	1915	47.9	1936	49.2
1904	11.43	1925	14.50	February	1.25	Spring	3.72	1916	46.4	1937	47.7
1905	13.58	1926	12.43	March	1.40	Summer	2.44	1917	46.2	1938	48.7
1906	18.34	1927	16.58	April	1.16	Fall	2.91	1918	47.8		

UTAH—Continued

Dates of last killing frost in spring and first in fall, with length of growing season

Year	Salt Lake City			Logan			Manti			St. George			Moab			Vernal		
	Last in spring	First in fall	Growing season [1]	Last in spring	First in fall	Growing season [1]	Last in spring	First in fall	Growing season [1]	Last in spring	First in fall	Growing season [1]	Last in spring	First in fall	Growing season [1]	Last in spring	First in fall	Growing season [1]
			Days			*Days*			*Days*			*Days*			*Days*			*Days*
1899	May 3	Oct. 24	174	June 6	Oct. 2	118	May 28	Oct. 1	126	May 20	Oct. 4	137	May 4	Oct. 16	165	May 21	Oct. 3	135
1900	Apr. 14	Oct. 7	176	Apr. 26	Oct. 7	164	June 17			Apr. 15	Sept. 28	166	Apr. 12	Oct. 7	178	Apr. 25	Sept. 18	146
1901	Apr. 4	Nov. 3	213	Apr. 27	Nov. 2	189	June 14	Sept. 9	87	Apr. 19	Sept. 25	159	Apr. 18	Sept. 25	160	Apr. 27	Sept. 25	151
1902	Apr. 10	Nov. 2	206	May 5	Sept. 26	144	June 2	Sept. 26	116	Apr. 14	Nov. 3	203	Apr. 15	Oct. 4	172	May 18	Sept. 26	131
1903	Apr. 13	Oct. 30	200	May 18	Sept. 14	119	May 25	Sept. 12	110	May 19	Oct. 20	154	Apr. 30	Sept. 15	138	May 19	Sept. 12	116
1904	Apr. 8	Oct. 18	193	May 8	Oct. 17	162	May 9	Oct. 16	160	May 1	Oct. 18	170	Apr. 9	Sept. 28	172			
1905	Apr. 1	Oct. 10	192	May 21	Oct. 8	140	May 12	Sept. 18	129	Mar. 30	Oct. 17	201	Apr. 6	Oct. 9	186	May 11	Oct. 8	150
1906	Apr. 5	Oct. 20	198	Apr. 25			May 17	Oct. 4	140	Apr. 5	Oct. 6	184	Apr. 3	Oct. 5	185	May 2	Oct. 4	155
1907	Apr. 30	Nov. 1	185	May 12	Nov. 4	176	May 22			Mar. 31	Nov. 12	226	June 17	Sept. 20	95	May 3		
1908	May 10	Sept. 27	140	May 10	Sept. 25	138		Aug. 31		Mar. 29	Oct. 21	206	Apr. 30	Sept. 27	150		Sept. 26	
1909	May 1	Oct. 31	183		Oct. 8		May 17	Sept. 23	129	May 12			May 2	Sept. 22	143	May 30	Sept. 22	115
1910	Apr. 15	Oct. 28	196	May 16	Oct. 19	156	do	Oct. 3	139	May 5	Oct. 13	161	May 17	Oct. 6	142	May 22	Sept. 26	127
1911	May 10	Oct. 21	164	May 26	Oct. 10	137	May 21	Sept. 6	108	Apr. 21	Oct. 11	173	May 11	Oct. 3	145	May 27	Sept. 6	102
1912	May 3	Sept. 25	145	May 5	Sept. 21	139	June 17	Sept. 15	90	May 4	Oct. 31	180	Apr. 26	Sept. 15	142	June 16	Sept. 14	90
1913	Apr. 23	Oct. 9	169	May 19	Sept. 24	128	May 4	Sept. 20	139	Apr. 24	Oct. 6	165	Apr. 24	Oct. 6	165	May 25		
1914	Mar. 24	Nov. 15	236	June 7	Sept. 13	98	May 13	Sept. 14	124	Mar. 22	Nov. 5	228	Mar. 25	Sept. 14	173			
1915	Mar. 9	Nov. 11	247	May 4	Oct. 12	161	June 14	do	92		Oct. 13		May 3	Oct. 13	163	June 13	Sept. 14	93
1916	May 11	Oct. 19	161	May 15	Oct. 19	157	June 23	Sept. 10	79		Oct. 24		May 16	Oct. 20	157	June 23	Sept. 11	80
1917	Apr. 16	Oct. 18	185	June 13	Oct. 17	126	June 13	Sept. 15	94	Apr. 4	Oct. 18	197	Apr. 30	Oct. 18	171	May 20		
1918	Apr. 5	Oct. 26	204	Apr. 28	Oct. 26	181	May 30	Oct. 19	142	Apr. 5	Oct. 26	204	May 12					
1919	Apr. 8	Oct. 10	185	May 31	Oct. 9	131	June 2	Sept. 22	112	Mar. 16	do	224	Apr. 16	Oct. 19	186	June 1		
1920	Apr. 24	Oct. 21	180	May 3	Oct. 13	163	May 6	Sept. 25	142	Apr. 1	Oct. 22	204	Apr. 25	Oct. 21	179	do	Sept. 9	100
1921	Apr. 25	Oct. 26	184	Apr. 27	Oct. 25	181	July 3	Sept. 21	80	Apr. 24	Nov. 18	208	Apr. 7	Oct. 28	204	July 4	Sept. 4	62
1922	Apr. 19	Nov. 2	197	May 10	Oct. 3	146	May 27	Oct. 7	133	Apr. 19	Oct. 24	188	Apr. 20	Oct. 18	181	June 1	Sept. 9	100
1923	Apr. 22	Oct. 29	190	May 1	Oct. 13	165	June 1	Sept. 27	118	Mar. 24	Oct. 26	216	Apr. 15	Oct. 14	182		Sept. 19	
1924	Apr. 17	Oct. 30	196	May 7	Sept. 22	138	May 8	Sept. 19	134	Apr. 17	Oct. 9	175	Apr. 27	Oct. 12	168	June 20	do	91
1925	Mar. 18	Oct. 24	220	Apr. 20	Oct. 14	177	Apr. 28	Sept. 23	148	Mar. 20	Nov. 4	229	Mar. 31	Oct. 19	202	May 12	Sept. 29	140
1926	Mar. 29	Sept. 25	180	May 9	Sept. 24	138	May 10	Sept. 25	138	Mar. 30	Oct. 30	214	Apr. 2	Oct. 30	211	May 13	Sept. 22	132
1927	Apr. 21	Oct. 7	169	May 29	Oct 6	130	May 30	Oct. 3	126	Apr. 13	Oct. 23	193	May 29	Oct. 8	132	May 29		
1928	Apr. 9	Oct. 22	196	Apr. 22	Oct. 10	171	May 4	Sept. 13	132	Apr. 10	do	196	Apr. 24	Oct. 22	181	June 17	Sept. 12	87
1929	Apr. 11	Oct. 28	200	May 1	Oct. 24	176	May 29	Oct. 11	135	Apr. 8	Oct. 25	200	May 2	Oct. 21	172	June 18	Sept. 9	83
1930	Mar. 27	Oct. 16	203	May 9	Oct. 16	160	May 23	Sept. 26	126	Mar. 19	Oct. 29	224	May 10	Oct. 16	159	May 31	Sept. 25	117
1931	Apr. 4	Oct. 27	206	May 8	Oct. 27	172	May 21	Sept. 25	127	Mar. 27	Nov. 13	231	Apr. 15	Oct. 27	195	May 21	Sept. 20	122
1932	Apr. 6	Oct. 20	197	Apr. 9	Oct. 19	193	June 8	Oct. 4	118	Mar. 22	Oct. 19	211	Apr. 11	Oct. 5	177	June 8	Aug. 31	84
1933	Apr. 14	Nov. 2	202	Apr. 14	Oct. 21	190	May 24	Oct. 16	145	Apr. 14	Nov. 1	201	Apr. 15	Oct. 16	184	May 28	Oct. 6	131
1934	Apr. 2	Sept. 27	178	Apr. 5	Sept. 26	174	Apr. 5	Sept. 25	173	Mar. 18	Oct. 24	220	Apr. 1	Sept. 27	179	May 15	Sept. 24	132
1935	Mar. 28	Oct. 17	203	Apr. 28	Oct. 17	172	May 31	Oct. 17	139	Mar. 29	Oct. 22	207	Apr. 11	Oct. 18	190	May 21	Sept. 28	130

1936	Apr. 6	Oct. 23	200	Apr. 9	Oct. 23	197	May 22	Sept. 28	129	Mar. 28	Nov. 3	220	Apr. 9	Oct. 7	181	May 6	Sept. 15	132
1937	Apr. 24	Nov. 8	198	Apr. 24	Oct. 19	178	June 5	Sept. 25	112	Mar. 19	Nov. 8	234	Apr. 25	Oct. 13	171	June 6	Sept. 24	110
1938	Apr. 6	Oct. 19	196	May 6	do	166	May 9	Oct. 18	162	Apr. 1	Nov. 6	219	May 9	Oct. 19	163	May 8	Oct. 10	155
Means	Apr. 13	Oct. 22	192	May 7	Oct. 11	157	May 25	Sept. 26	124	Apr. 10	Oct. 23	196	Apr. 24	Oct. 10	169	May 26	Sept. 21	118
Extreme	Mar. 9 [2] May 11 [3]	Sept. 25 [4] Nov. 15 [5]	[6] 140 [7] 246	Apr. 5 [2] June 13 [3]	Sept. 13 [4] Nov. 4 [5]	[6] 98 [7] 197	Apr. 5 [2] July 3 [3]	Aug. 31 [4] Oct. 19 [5]	[6] 79 [7] 173	Mar. 16 [2] May 20 [3]	Sept. 25 [4] Nov. 18 [5]	[6] 137 [7] 234	Mar. 25 [2] June 17 [3]	Sept. 14 [4] Oct. 30 [5]	[6] 95 [7] 211	Apr. 25 [2] July 4 [3]	Aug. 31 [4] Oct. 10 [5]	[6] 62 [7] 155

[1] Number of days between last killing frost in spring and first in fall.
[2] Earliest date in spring.
[3] Latest date in spring.
[4] Earliest date in fall.
[5] Latest date in fall.
[6] Shortest growing season.
[7] Longest growing season.

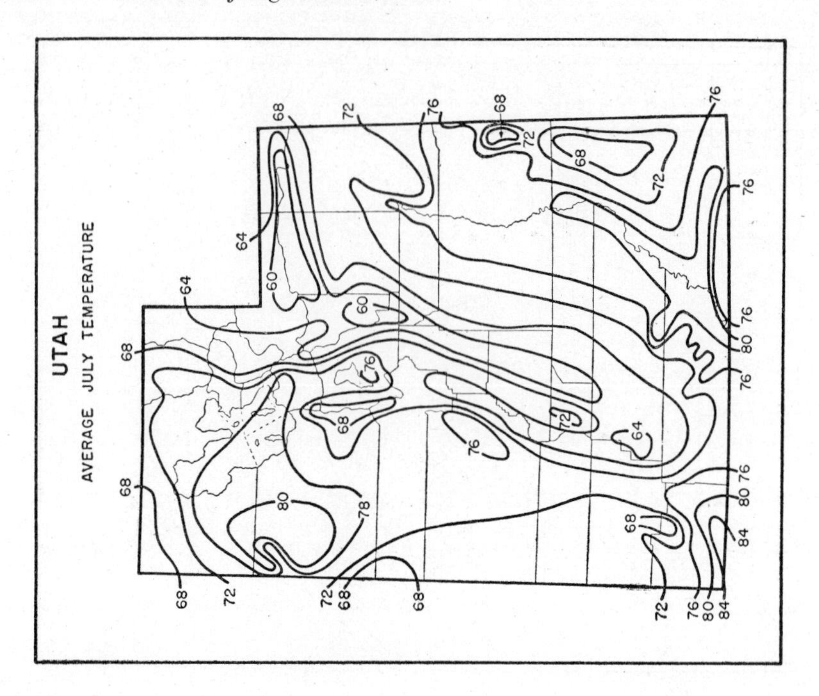
UTAH
AVERAGE JULY TEMPERATURE

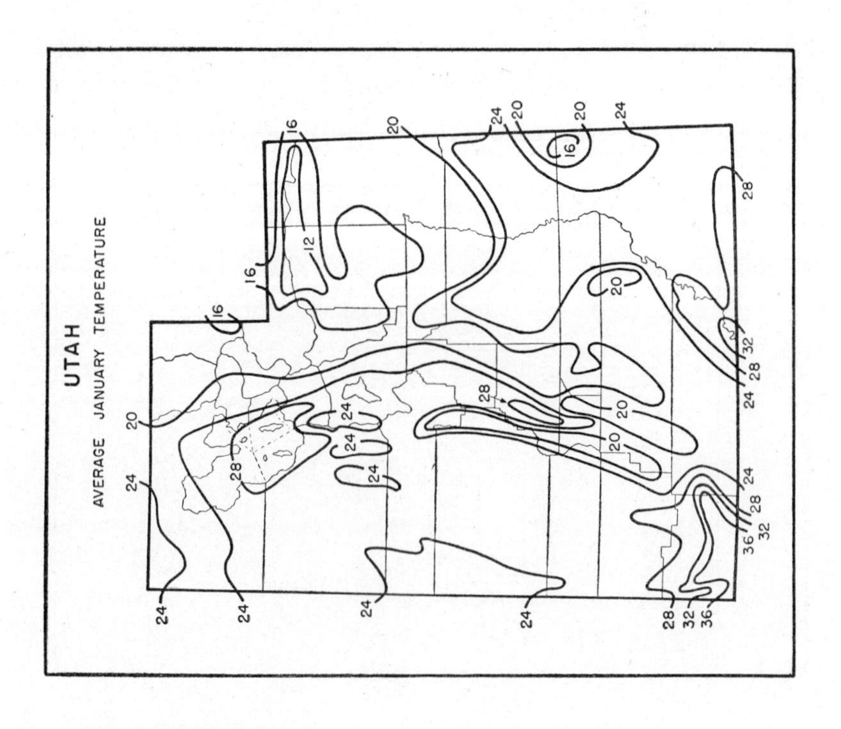
UTAH
AVERAGE JANUARY TEMPERATURE

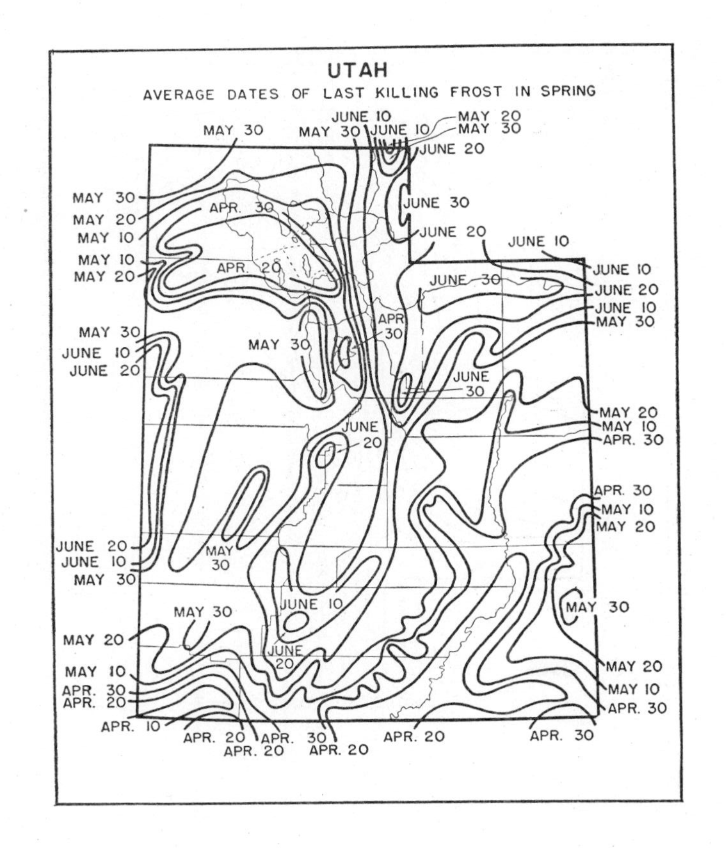
UTAH
AVERAGE DATES OF LAST KILLING FROST IN SPRING
MAY 30
JUNE 10
MAY 30
JUNE 10
MAY 20
MAY 30
JUNE 20
JUNE 30
JUNE 20
JUNE 10
MAY 30
MAY 20
MAY 10
MAY 10
MAY 20
APR. 30
APR. 20
JUNE 30
JUNE 10
JUNE 20
JUNE 10
MAY 30
MAY 30
JUNE 10
JUNE 20
MAY 30
APR 30
JUNE 30
JUNE 20
MAY 20
MAY 10
APR. 30
APR. 30
MAY 10
MAY 20
JUNE 20
JUNE 10
MAY 30
MAY 30
MAY 30
JUNE 10
MAY 30
MAY 20
MAY 10
APR. 30
APR. 20
JUNE 20
MAY 20
MAY 10
APR. 30
APR. 10
APR. 20
APR. 20
APR. 30
APR. 20
APR. 20
APR. 30

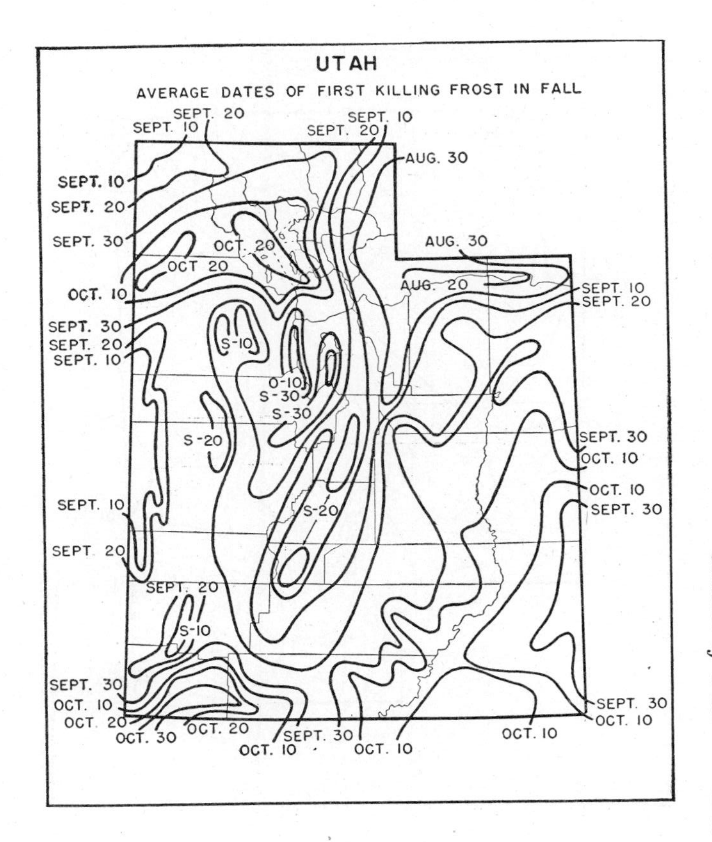
UTAH
AVERAGE DATES OF FIRST KILLING FROST IN FALL
SEPT. 20
SEPT. 10
SEPT. 10
SEPT. 20
AUG. 30
SEPT. 10
SEPT. 20
SEPT. 30
OCT 20
OCT 20
AUG. 30
AUG. 20
OCT. 10
SEPT. 10
SEPT. 20
SEPT. 30
SEPT. 20
SEPT. 10
S-10
O-10
S-30
S-30
S-20
SEPT. 30
OCT. 10
OCT. 10
SEPT. 30
SEPT. 10
S-20
SEPT. 20
SEPT. 20
S-10
SEPT. 30
OCT. 10
OCT. 20
OCT. 30
OCT. 20
SEPT. 30
OCT. 10
OCT. 10
OCT. 10
SEPT. 30
OCT. 10

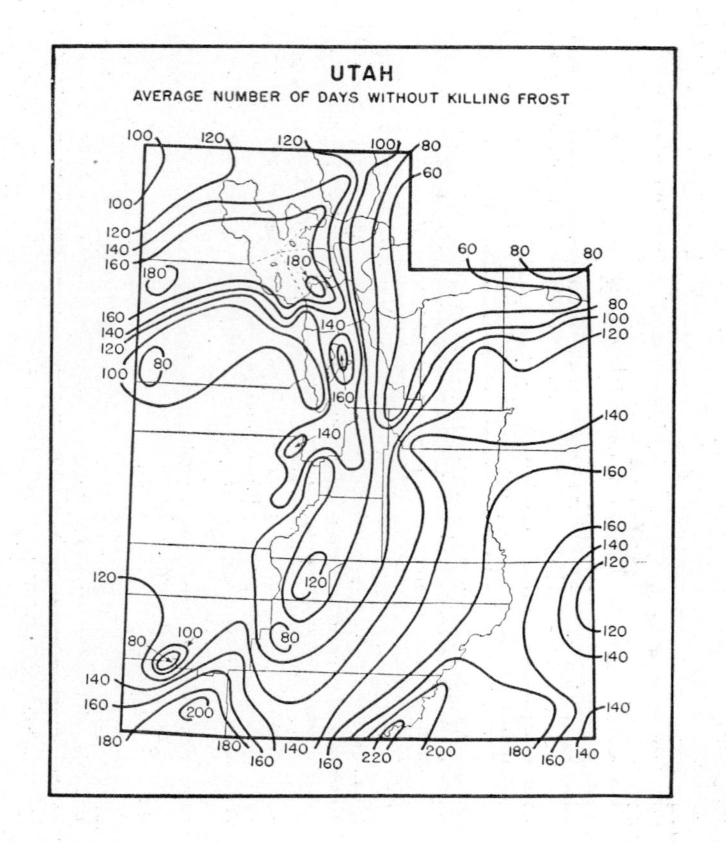
UTAH
AVERAGE NUMBER OF DAYS WITHOUT KILLING FROST

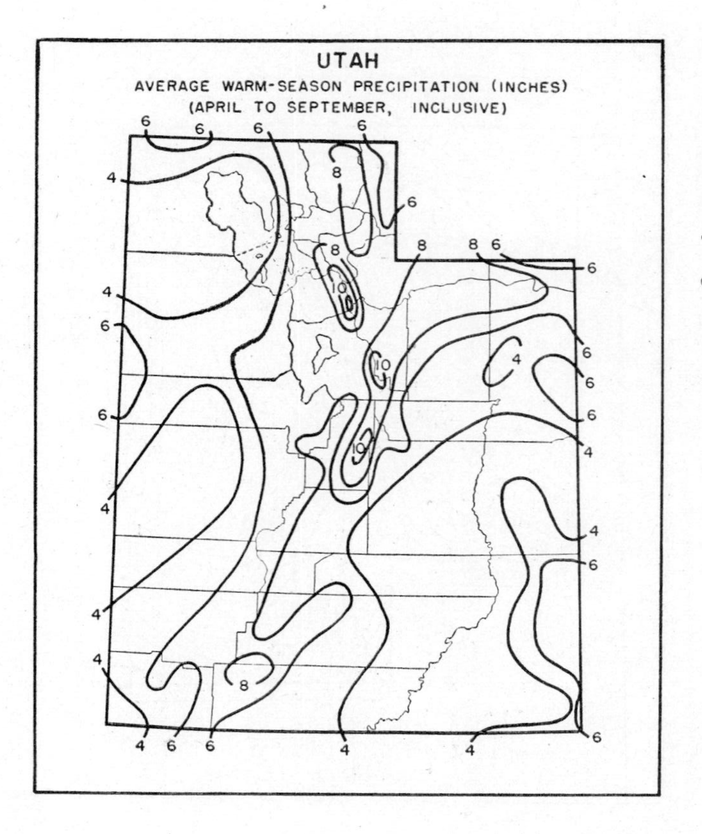
UTAH
AVERAGE WARM-SEASON PRECIPITATION (INCHES)
(APRIL TO SEPTEMBER, INCLUSIVE)

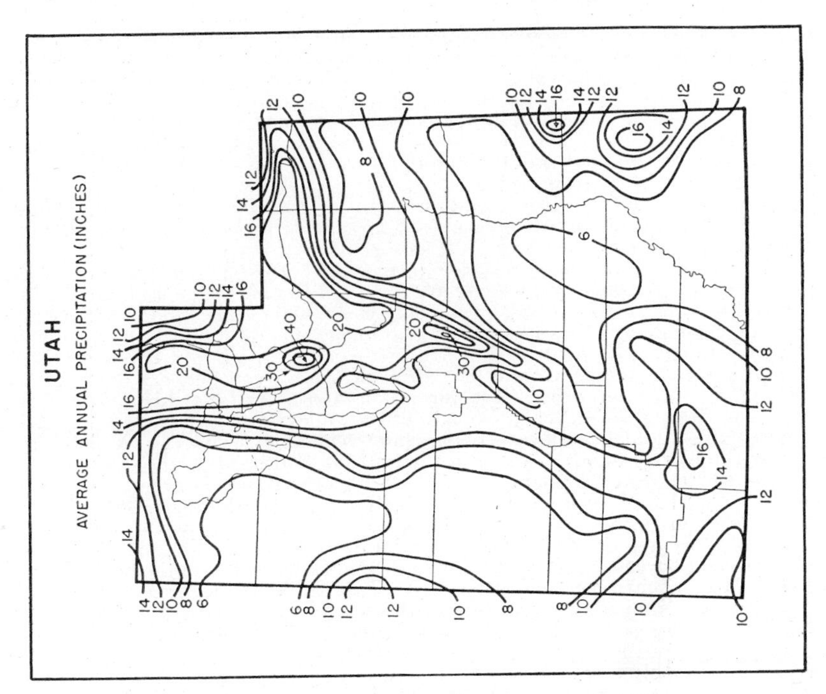

SUPPLEMENTARY CLIMATIC NOTES FOR UTAH

The general elevation of Utah is about 5,500 feet above sea level, though the Wasatch and Uinta Mountains extend diagonally across the State from southwest to northeast, with crest lines mostly above 10,000 feet. Minor mountains are scattered over the rest of the State, though the flatter part of the Great Salt Lake drainage basin is below 4,500 feet in elevation, the lake being about 4,215 feet. The lowest area in the State is the Virgin River Valley in the extreme southwestern part, its elevation being between 2,500 and 3,500 feet.

Practically the entire area east of the Wasatch Mountains is drained by the Green and Colorado Rivers, the State's largest streams, though neither rises within its borders. Western Utah is almost entirely within the Great Basin, without outlet to the sea. The largest rivers are the Bear, Weber (and Ogden), and Provo, all emptying into Great Salt Lake (the Provo through Utah Lake and Jordan River). Sevier River drains the west-central counties and empties into Sevier Lake, a brackish saline basin, when its waters are not wholly withdrawn for irrigation purposes.

Utah has two principal geographical provinces of slightly different climatic features. The western half of the State, about the size of Indiana, has temperature conditions similar in many respects to those of Nebraska. Eastern Utah is about the size of Ohio and has temperatures much like those of that State. Naturally the more elevated valleys have the cooler climates, and the lower sections have much higher temperatures.

The average annual precipitation for the State is about one-third that of the Middle Western or Eastern States generally, necessitating the practice of irrigation for growing farm crops. But the mountains, whose winter snows form the chief reservoirs of moisture, are conveniently adjacent to practically all the farming regions, and there is usually an abundance of water for all lands under irrigation. The bulk of the moisture falls in late winter and spring in the State's leading agricultural areas. The summer and early fall months are almost invariably the driest.

There are also definite variations in temperature with latitude, amounting to about 1.5° or 2° F. increase in mean annual temperatures for each 1° decrease in latitude. Thus the weather stations in the southern tier of counties have average annual temperatures 6° to 8° higher than those at similar altitudes over the ex-

298737°—41——74

treme northern counties. Solely because of variations in altitude, the southern part of the State varies from semitropical to cool temperate conditions.

Temperatures somewhat above 100° F. occur occasionally in nearly all parts of the State. Temperatures below zero occur quite generally in cold winters, though prolonged periods of severely low temperatures are not nearly so common as in the Northern, Middle, and Eastern States. This is because the mountains ward off the intensely cold continental polar and arctic air masses that sometimes move out of Canada into the United States.

Actual frost seldom forms in Utah, owing to the comparatively dry air, though crops may be damaged by temperatures of freezing or lower without frost. Such a condition is known as black frost. It has been customary to record temperatures of 32° F. in lieu of actual deposits of hoar frost. Most of the State's farming lands are near the mountains, which have a very important influence in preventing frost or freezing temperatures. On cold, clear nights the coldest air usually forms, or accumulates by radiation and drainage, on the valley-bottoms, while the gravitational movement of the cooling air on the mountain slopes serves to mix and unify the temperature of the air near the ground over the foothill and bench lands, thus retarding frost formation and freezing temperatures. For this reason the higher lands at the edges of the valleys are usually devoted to the more valuable and delicate fruits, berries, and vegetables, while the hardier grains and vegetables are usually planted in the bottom lands.

Owing to the varied topography of the State, there are no orderly, extensive zones of equal length of growing season between the last killing frost (or 32° F. temperature) in spring and the first in fall. There are, however, from 4½ to 5 months of frost-free growing weather in the State's principal agricultural areas. A difference of 2 weeks is often noted in the same valley between the bottom lands and the adjacent farming lands at the foot of the mountains.

The average annual precipitation at the levels occupied by the bulk of the population, between 4,250 and 5,250 feet above sea level, is about 12.75 inches, though the general state-wide average (1886-1938) is 12.63. Northwestern Utah receives appreciably more moisture in a year than is received at similar elevations over the rest of the State, chiefly because during the wettest months of winter and spring the storms come from the west. In summer this area is comparatively dry, while eastern Utah usually gets more rain from thundershowers.

The areas below 4,000 feet, all in the southern part, receive somewhat less than 10 inches of moisture in a normal year; weather stations situated at elevations between 4,000 and 5,000 feet receive about 12.5 inches on an average, while those located between 5,000 and 6,000 feet receive about 13.5. The least precipitation occurs in the area of the Great Salt Lake Desert of northwestern Utah, west of Great Salt Lake. This area is 75 to 125 miles west of the Wasatch Mountains, where the State's greatest precipitation occurs. In the Great Salt Lake Desert an area of about 5,000 square miles receives an average of less than 5 inches of moisture annually, while parts of the mountains to the east receive more than 40.

Snowfall is moderately heavy in the mountains, particularly over the northern part. While the principal population centers along the base of the mountains receive more snow, as a rule, than many Middle and Eastern States, a deep snow cover seldom remains long on the ground. There are about 52 days a year over eastern Utah with measurable amounts of precipitation, or roughly 1 day a week; over the west the average is about 64, 2 or 3 days a month in summer and 6 or 8 in winter and spring.

Sunny skies predominate most of the year in Utah. In spring, summer, and fall there is an average of about 65 to 75 percent of the possible amount of sunshine at Salt Lake City, and 70 to 80 percent at Modena. In winter Salt Lake City has about 50 and Modena 65 percent of the possible sunshine. The State average is about 180 clear days, 110 partly cloudy days, and 75 cloudy days a year.

Wind velocities are usually light to moderate, ranging normally from about 7 to 12 miles an hour at Modena and Salt Lake City. There has never been a destructive tornado in Utah, though strong winds occur occasionally, some of them attaining damaging proportions in limited areas.

The Utah atmosphere is comparatively dry, the noon and evening relative humidities observed being between 35 and 45 percent for the year. The wind, sunshine, and temperature and the low atmospheric humidity in summer all tend to promote rapid evaporation.

J. Cecil Alter, *Meteorologist and Climatic Section Director for Utah, Weather Bureau, Salt Lake City.*

VIRGINIA

Climatic summary

County[1]	Station	Temperature: Length of record	Temperature: January average	Temperature: July average	Temperature: Maximum	Temperature: Minimum	Killing frost average dates: Length of record	Killing frost: Last in spring	Killing frost: First in fall	Growing season[2]	Average precipitation: Length of record	January	February	March	April	May	June	July	August	September	October	November	December	Annual
		Yr.	*°F.*	*°F.*	*°F.*	*°F.*	*Yr.*			*Days*	*Yr.*	*In.*	*In.*	*In.*	*In.*	*In.*	*In.*	*In.*	*In.*	*In.*	*In.*	*In.*	*In.*	*In.*
Accomac	Onley	20	39.2	77.8	103	−3	21	Apr. 7	Nov. 5	212	21	3.69	3.54	3.84	3.75	3.44	3.52	4.38	4.84	3.64	2.64	2.54	3.52	43.34
Albemarle	Charlottesville	40	37.0	76.9	107	−9	40	Apr. 6	do	213	40	3.56	2.87	3.54	3.75	3.79	5.14	4.69	4.92	3.45	3.51	2.58	3.42	45.22
Alleghany	Clifton Forge										11	3.11	2.89	3.92	2.76	3.23	3.25	3.59	3.83	2.92	3.38	2.39	2.47	37.74
Arlington	Clarendon										14	3.48	2.84	2.90	3.59	3.78	3.54	3.47	5.08	4.00	3.74	2.80	2.52	41.74
Augusta	Deerfield						6	Apr. 10	Oct. 7	180	11	3.04	2.06	3.40	3.48	2.93	2.65	4.69	3.57	2.36	3.29	2.42	2.69	36.58
	Staunton	38	36.1	74.8	106	−13	40	Apr. 22	Oct. 19	180	39	2.90	2.34	3.17	3.08	3.14	4.06	4.31	4.09	2.87	2.88	2.11	2.64	37.59
Bath	Hot Springs	40	32.4	69.5	98	−20	40	May 1	Oct. 12	164	40	3.38	2.63	3.69	3.37	3.49	4.42	4.30	4.19	3.03	3.20	2.60	3.05	41.35
Bedford	Bedford	5	36.1	78.8	103	−6	12	Apr. 10	Oct. 27	200	14	4.17	3.31	4.34	3.48	2.81	5.04	3.93	4.98	2.88	3.38	2.71	3.70	44.73
Botetourt	Buchanan	21	36.4	76.0	107	−13	25	Apr. 16	Oct. 22	189	35	3.64	2.68	3.43	3.15	3.53	4.36	4.57	4.41	3.20	3.73	2.54	3.35	42.59
Brunswick	Callaville	40	39.0	77.1	104	−12	39	Apr. 17	do	188	40	3.81	3.54	4.48	3.89	3.89	4.47	5.38	5.08	3.89	2.93	2.32	3.47	47.15
Buckingham	New Canton	40	37.3	76.1	105	−16	34	do	Oct. 21	187	40	3.86	3.05	3.90	3.53	3.44	3.80	4.04	4.78	3.22	3.07	2.38	3.26	42.33
Campbell	Lynchburg	40	38.5	77.2	106	−7	40	Apr. 4	Oct. 25	204	40	3.36	2.65	3.56	3.09	3.06	4.28	3.83	4.16	2.96	3.07	2.27	3.15	39.44
Charlotte	Randolph						12	Apr. 17	Oct. 20	186	34	3.78	3.15	3.65	3.37	3.67	3.90	4.56	4.30	2.83	2.85	2.34	3.29	41.69
	Saxe	7	38.3	76.7	104	−2	8	Apr. 21	Oct. 19	181	9	2.96	3.38	3.53	3.73	3.33	4.47	4.14	4.84	2.60	2.82	2.40	3.52	41.72
Culpeper	Culpeper	31	34.5	75.3	104	−20	32	Apr. 15	Oct. 23	191	31	3.25	2.43	2.89	3.56	3.89	4.31	3.51	4.45	3.53	2.85	2.56	2.87	40.10
Elizabeth City	Langley Field	40	40.9	78.4	102	4	19	Mar. 18	Nov. 17	244	20	3.31	3.11	3.05	3.09	3.44	4.04	4.69	4.22	3.58	1.91	2.18	2.85	39.47
Fauquier	Leeds Manor	10	32.4	73.7	107	−9	11	Apr. 8	Nov. 2	208	9	3.21	2.25	3.28	3.84	3.70	5.66	4.79	5.33	3.03	2.89	2.49	3.09	43.56
Fluvanna	Columbia	40	37.0	75.9	110	−15	39	Apr. 17	Oct. 20	186	40	3.60	2.80	3.62	3.61	3.66	3.95	4.49	4.50	3.23	2.86	2.36	3.07	41.75
Franklin	Rockymount	39	37.7	75.0	103	−6	40	Apr. 14	Oct. 22	191	40	3.57	3.14	3.96	3.44	3.64	4.73	4.64	4.50	3.54	3.78	2.53	3.58	45.05
Frederick	Winchester	27	34.3	76.6	107	−9	27	Apr. 17	Oct. 27	193	27	2.50	1.94	2.94	3.26	3.72	3.54	3.31	3.62	2.56	3.00	2.27	2.45	35.11
	Stephens City	12	33.4	75.1	106	−17	12	Apr. 25	Oct. 13	171	12	2.51	2.57	3.25	2.97	3.58	5.16	3.71	3.23	3.00	2.84	1.74	2.89	37.45
Giles	Glen Lyn	7	38.4	75.2	100	−9	7	Apr. 22	Oct. 15	176	25	3.52	3.09	3.44	2.85	3.16	3.35	4.28	4.04	2.63	3.12	2.44	3.03	38.95
Goochland	Lassiter										12	3.54	3.14	3.77	3.05	3.40	4.16	5.06	3.77	2.72	2.41	2.48	3.03	40.53
Hanover	Ashland	30	36.5	76.6	105	−16	30	Apr. 20	Oct. 20	183	30	3.07	2.80	3.57	3.48	3.42	4.29	4.58	5.13	3.26	2.96	2.13	3.16	41.85
	Doswell	12	38.1	77.1	107	−15	14	do	Oct. 19	182	13	2.95	2.46	3.15	3.51	3.37	4.64	4.12	4.74	2.64	3.28	1.88	3.20	39.94
Henrico	Richmond	40	39.1	78.0	107	−3	40	Mar. 29	Nov. 2	218	40	3.50	3.05	3.57	3.50	3.51	4.34	4.61	4.81	3.12	2.60	2.09	3.23	41.93
Highland	Monterey										10	3.91	2.90	4.83	3.35	4.04	4.03	5.11	4.98	2.73	3.60	2.50	3.55	45.53
James City	Williamsburg	40	40.4	77.0	102	−3	40	Apr. 9	Oct. 31	205	38	3.65	3.43	4.00	3.77	3.82	4.77	6.15	5.55	3.42	2.81	2.26	3.58	47.21
King George	Dahlgren	19	36.3	76.7	106	−3	19	Mar. 31	Nov. 4	218	19	3.37	2.67	3.23	3.51	3.19	3.55	4.32	4.96	3.57	2.31	2.36	2.58	39.62

[1] The following counties, for which no records are available, are best represented by the station indicated: Amelia, Appomattox, and Nottoway—Farmville; Amherst—Lynchburg; Bland—Burkes Garden; Buchanan and Dickenson—Dante; Caroline and Grayson—Ivanhoe; Charles City—Hopewell; Chesterfield—Richmond; Clarke—Winchester; Craig—Catawba; Cumberland—Powhatan; Dinwiddie, Greensville, and Southampton—Callaville; Essex and Northumberland—Warsaw; Fairfax—Clarendon; Floyd—Stuart; Gloucester—Williamsburg; Greene—Orange; Halifax—Randolph; Henry—Danville; Isle of Wight and Sussex—Runnymede; King and Queen and New Kent—West Point; Lancaster and Mathews—Christchurch; Lunenburg—Saxe; Madison and Rappahannock—Culpeper; Nansemond—Wallaceton; Nelson—Lexington; Northampton—Onley; Page—Woodstock; Pulaski—Radford; Stafford—Fredericksburg; Warren—Stephens City; Westmoreland—Dahlgren; York—Williamsburg; Carroll—Wytheville.

[2] Length of growing season between average dates of last killing frost in spring and first in fall.

VIRGINIA—Continued

Climatic summary—Continued

County	Station	Temperature: Length of record	Temperature: January average	Temperature: July average	Temperature: Maximum	Temperature: Minimum	Killing frost average dates: Length of record	Killing frost average dates: Last in spring	Killing frost average dates: First in fall	Growing season	Average precipitation: Length of record	January	February	March	April	May	June	July	August	September	October	November	December	Annual
		Yr.	*°F.*	*°F.*	*°F.*	*°F.*	*Yr.*			*Days*	*Yr.*	*In.*	*In.*	*In.*	*In.*	*In.*	*In.*	*In.*	*In.*	*In.*	*In.*	*In.*	*In.*	*In.*
King William	West Point	14	37.5	77.0	108	−4	15	Apr. 13	Oct. 27	197	16	3.13	3.13	4.13	3.28	3.46	3.98	5.68	4.10	3.11	3.11	2.24	3.40	42.75
Lee	Elk Knob	18	38.8	73.1	98	−10	17	Apr. 21	Oct. 23	185	17	4.64	3.63	4.95	4.02	3.72	4.52	4.79	4.74	3.04	3.29	2.69	4.43	48.46
Loudoun	Lincoln	38	33.0	76.5	109	−25	38	Apr. 19	Oct. 21	185	38	3.12	2.56	3.13	3.45	3.59	4.60	3.42	4.45	2.83	3.12	2.34	2.80	39.41
	Mt. Weather	35	30.6	71.2	100	−10	32	do	Oct. 25	189	35	2.96	2.32	2.85	3.64	3.80	4.26	3.66	4.44	3.22	3.71	2.46	2.58	39.90
Louisa	Mineral	23	35.2	74.8	108	−18	23	Apr. 23	Oct. 21	181	23	3.59	2.53	3.27	3.58	3.61	3.58	4.24	4.20	3.36	2.69	2.29	2.63	39.57
Mecklenburg	Clarksville	21	37.6	77.0	104	0	25	Apr. 8	Oct. 29	204	40	3.63	3.44	3.83	3.67	3.77	4.30	4.43	4.70	3.21	2.72	2.39	3.46	43.55
Middlesex	Christchurch	15	41.1	77.8	104	2	15	Mar. 31	Nov. 8	222	15	4.27	3.30	3.48	4.13	3.78	4.12	5.57	4.57	4.55	2.95	2.39	3.16	46.27
Montgomery	Blacksburg	40	34.4	71.3	100	−27	40	Apr. 26	Oct. 11	168	40	3.43	3.06	3.72	3.29	3.54	4.39	5.25	4.08	3.13	3.11	2.35	3.31	42.66
	Radford										33	3.16	2.61	3.24	2.77	3.16	3.53	4.24	3.14	2.77	3.06	2.05	2.91	36.64
Norfolk	Norfolk	40	42.4	78.3	105	2	40	Mar. 19	Nov. 16	242	40	2.93	3.03	3.40	2.99	3.29	4.22	5.51	4.49	3.19	2.39	1.96	3.05	40.45
	Wallaceton						8	Apr. 11	Oct. 30	202	12	3.56	3.79	4.14	5.02	3.77	5.11	7.66	5.05	5.62	3.25	3.46	3.96	54.39
Orange	Orange										8	4.36	2.62	3.32	3.92	3.54	3.96	4.39	3.90	4.78	3.34	2.85	2.33	43.31
Patrick	Stuart	17	40.4	76.0	105	0	16	Apr. 16	Oct. 22	189	16	3.91	2.99	4.27	3.68	3.50	4.05	5.47	5.51	4.45	4.03	3.13	3.78	48.77
Pittsylvania	Chatham	16	40.0	78.0	105	0	16	Apr. 14	Oct. 25	194	16	3.96	2.72	3.56	3.60	3.34	3.28	4.23	3.94	3.56	3.09	2.71	3.37	41.36
	Danville	23	40.1	79.5	107	−4	23	Apr. 2	Oct. 30	211	40	3.62	3.24	3.78	3.45	3.64	3.97	4.30	4.33	3.18	2.77	2.32	3.53	42.13
Powhatan	Powhatan						15	Apr. 8	Oct. 23	198	16	3.70	2.47	3.23	3.69	3.20	3.37	4.32	4.57	3.68	2.69	2.41	2.86	40.19
Prince Edward	Farmville	16	38.9	79.5	106	−8	16	Apr. 13	Oct. 21	191	16	4.01	3.04	4.50	3.27	4.13	4.82	4.17	4.77	3.18	3.16	2.36	3.27	44.68
Prince George	Hopewell	40	39.9	78.7	108	−10	40	Apr. 4	Oct. 31	210	39	3.32	3.04	3.70	3.37	3.70	4.93	4.71	4.71	3.61	2.52	2.14	3.34	43.09
Princess Anne	Cape Henry	40	41.8	77.5	103	5	40	Mar. 19	Nov. 17	243	40	2.92	3.11	3.43	2.97	3.02	4.09	4.97	4.30	2.87	2.29	1.93	3.11	39.01
	Diamond Springs	30	43.3	77.6	103	2	30	Mar. 31	Nov. 12	226	30	3.88	3.39	3.80	3.52	4.09	4.81	5.93	4.68	4.15	2.74	2.56	3.79	47.34
Prince William	Manassas						9	Apr. 16	Oct. 18	185	17	3.64	2.78	3.28	3.20	3.74	3.21	3.61	4.16	3.34	3.04	2.71	2.91	39.62
	Quantico	40	35.0	77.0	107	−16	40	Apr. 14	Oct. 31	200	36	3.13	2.36	2.92	3.07	3.16	3.54	3.83	4.34	3.08	2.54	2.08	2.53	36.58
Richmond	Warsaw	29	36.8	76.4	102	−10	29	Apr. 15	Oct. 25	193	30	3.20	3.19	3.91	3.37	3.18	4.49	4.34	4.90	2.82	3.01	2.46	3.27	42.14
Roanoke	Catawba	28	36.4	72.7	102	−10	30	Apr. 19	do	189	28	3.40	2.70	3.65	3.22	3.35	4.13	4.78	4.65	3.32	3.75	2.58	3.20	42.73
	Roanoke	37	37.8	75.7	105	−12	34	Apr. 15	Oct. 22	190	35	3.34	2.73	3.45	2.92	3.05	4.20	4.47	4.01	3.05	3.72	2.67	3.19	40.80
Rockbridge	Lexington	40	34.2	74.5	105	−16	40	Apr. 24	Oct. 19	178	40	3.22	2.73	3.52	3.01	3.22	4.09	3.77	4.09	2.76	3.01	2.26	3.08	38.76
Rockingham	Dale Enterprise	40	33.9	73.4	105	−25	40	Apr. 27	Oct. 17	173	40	2.70	2.21	2.90	2.85	3.42	4.54	4.44	4.14	2.77	2.66	1.96	2.58	37.17
Russell	Dante	21	35.7	71.8	100	−13	22	Apr. 25	Oct. 19	177	22	4.23	3.44	4.64	3.84	4.93	4.58	5.75	4.64	3.46	3.30	2.94	3.69	49.44
Scott	Speers Ferry										34	4.38	4.11	4.69	3.81	4.08	4.47	4.84	4.56	3.34	2.69	2.91	4.69	48.57
Shenandoah	Woodstock	40	33.8	74.9	109	−23	40	Apr. 19	Oct. 18	182	40	2.59	1.96	2.79	2.72	3.33	3.90	3.36	3.83	2.67	2.64	1.81	2.29	33.89
Smyth	Marion	20	34.6	72.3	100	−16	13	Apr. 27	Oct. 12	168	20	3.09	3.36	3.85	3.62	3.56	5.10	4.37	4.52	2.95	2.59	2.46	3.92	43.39
	Saltville	20	35.0	73.5	102	−6	16	Apr. 20	Oct. 15	178	16	3.62	3.54	3.97	3.44	3.87	4.14	4.42	3.76	2.96	3.12	2.63	3.82	43.29
Spotsylvania	Fredericksburg	40	37.1	76.4	105	−21	40	Apr. 15	Oct. 25	193	40	3.50	2.73	3.36	3.44	3.62	4.20	4.42	4.89	3.49	3.04	2.18	2.95	41.82
Surry	Runnymede	17	39.8	77.1	104	−15	33	do	Oct. 22	190	32	3.43	3.77	4.46	3.80	3.90	5.13	5.75	4.94	3.42	3.10	2.39	3.71	47.80
Tazewell	Burkes Garden	40	32.6	67.0	97	−27	40	May 8	Oct. 5	150	40	3.81	3.54	4.67	3.88	4.21	4.69	4.44	4.43	3.43	3.12	2.86	3.62	46.70
Warwick	Newport News	29	40.8	77.4	105	1	28	Mar. 29	Nov. 6	222	27	3.12	3.61	4.19	3.25	3.86	4.79	6.24	5.77	2.82	2.81	2.18	3.62	46.26

Washington	Damascus										10	2.69	3.41	4.62	3.94	4.39	3.50	4.64	4.20	3.71	2.51	2.52	2.84	42.97
	Emory	14	37.4	73.1	100	−11	14	Apr. 25	Oct. 13	171	13	4.10	3.71	4.82	3.93	4.25	3.80	4.33	5.02	2.89	2.85	2.43	3.29	45.42
	Mendota										34	4.41	3.58	4.70	3.90	4.10	4.42	5.10	4.23	3.15	3.11	2.75	3.97	47.42
Wise	Big Stone Cap	12	35.9	73.3	97	−26	14	Apr. 25	Oct. 13	171	13	3.91	4.46	5.42	4.20	3.69	5.19	4.66	4.59	3.48	2.36	3.75	4.63	50.34
Wythe	Ivanhoe						9	Apr. 20	Oct. 19	182	32	3.25	2.49	3.40	2.98	3.52	4.12	4.20	4.25	2.99	3.25	2.38	2.93	39.76
	Max Meadows	15	34.8	71.0	96	−12	15	Apr. 26	Oct. 14	171	15	2.62	2.55	4.02	3.28	3.89	5.23	4.02	3.54	3.48	2.69	1.76	2.70	39.78
	Wytheville	40	34.9	71.5	96	−8	40	Apr. 17	Oct. 16	182	40	2.82	2.56	3.35	3.00	3.46	4.16	3.90	3.89	2.93	2.86	2.05	2.79	37.77

Precipitation—State unit values

[This tabulation gives the mean annual, mean monthly, and average seasonal precipitation, 1886–1938, for Virginia]

Precipitation		Precipitation		Precipitation		Precipitation		Precipitation		Precipitation	
Year	Mean	Year	Mean	Year	Mean	Year	Mean	Month	Mean	Month	Mean
	In.		*In.*		*In.*		*In.*		*In.*		*In.*
1886	48.35	1900	39.52	1913	42.33	1926	41.41	January	3.30	November	2.49
1887	43.44	1901	49.99	1914	36.66	1927	41.64	February	3.12	December	3.07
1888	47.84	1902	40.67	1915	40.03	1928	43.07	March	3.73	Annual	42.63
1889	61.12	1903	44.09	1916	38.94	1929	46.31	April	3.37		
1890	43.34	1904	36.11	1917	40.11	1930	24.99	May	3.94	Season	Average
1891	47.44	1905	43.27	1918	43.48	1931	38.00	June	4.20		
1892	39.45	1906	50.03	1919	41.65	1932	44.68	July	4.61		
1893	46.22	1907	44.41	1920	45.91	1933	39.46	August	4.40		
1894	35.76	1908	46.17	1921	34.94	1934	45.73	September	3.30		
1895	38.23	1909	38.02	1922	45.15	1935	46.68	October	3.09	Winter	9.49
1896	42.64	1910	41.37	1923	40.90	1936	45.33			Spring	11.04
1897	39.19	1911	41.00	1924	47.34	1937	53.22			Summer	13.22
1898	44.71	1912	40.88	1925	32.53	1938	42.23			Fall	8.88
1899	42.20										

VIRGINIA—Continued

Dates of last killing frost in spring and first in fall, with length of growing season

Year	Callaville			Lynchburg			Norfolk			Richmond			Woodstock			Wytheville		
	Last in spring	First in fall	Growing season [1]	Last in spring	First in fall	Growing season [1]	Last in spring	First in fall	Growing season [1]	Last in spring	First in fall	Growing season [1]	Last in spring	First in fall	Growing season [1]	Last in spring	First in fall	Growing season [1]
			Days			*Days*			*Days*			*Days*			*Days*			*Days*
1899	Apr. 17	Oct. 2	168	Apr. 10	Oct. 2	175	Apr. 5	Nov. 25	234	Mar. 28	Nov. 13	230	Apr. 10	Oct. 1	174	Apr. 17	Oct. 1	167
1900	Apr. 5	Oct. 8	186	Mar. 22	Nov. 10	233	Mar. 22	Nov. 10	233	Apr. 5	Nov. 10	219	Apr. 15	Oct. 18	186	Apr. 5	Nov. 6	215
1901	Mar. 29	Oct. 26	211	Mar. 18	Oct. 26	222	Mar. 8	Nov. 11	248	Mar. 17	Nov. 6	234	Apr. 12	Oct. 25	196	Apr. 12	Oct. 5	176
1902	Apr. 14	Oct. 30	199	Mar. 19	Oct. 30	225	Mar. 19	Dec. 6	262	Mar. 7	Oct. 30	237	Apr. 14	Oct. 15	184	Apr. 14	Oct. 15	184
1903	Apr. 5	Oct. 27	205	Apr. 5	Oct. 27	205	Apr. 5	Oct. 28	206	Apr. 5	Nov. 7	216	Apr. 5	Oct. 19	197	Apr. 5	Sept. 19	167
1904	Apr. 22	Oct. 16	177	Apr. 22	Oct. 24	185	Mar. 29	Nov. 7	223	Apr. 20	Oct. 28	191	Apr. 22	Oct. 7	168	Apr. 21	Oct. 15	177
1905	Apr. 19	Oct. 13	177	Apr. 19	Oct. 22	186	Apr. 18	Nov. 15	211	Apr. 19	Nov. 2	197	Apr. 24	Oct. 21	180	Apr. 19	Oct. 13	177
1906	May 10	Oct. 11	154	Apr. 4	Oct. 11	190	Mar. 24	Nov. 13	234	Apr. 1	Oct. 12	194	Apr. 3	Oct. 11	191	Apr. 3	Oct. 10	190
1907	Apr. 20	Oct. 22	185	Apr. 21	Oct. 15	177	Mar. 16	Nov. 14	243	Apr. 15	Oct. 22	190	Apr. 22	Oct. 13	174	Apr. 7	Oct. 9	185
1908	Apr. 4	Nov. 1	211	Mar. 22	Nov. 1	224	Mar. 22	Nov. 2	225	Apr. 4	Oct. 31	210	do	Oct. 3	164	Apr. 4	Oct. 3	182
1909	Apr. 12	Oct. 20	191	Apr. 11	Oct. 17	189	Mar. 5	Nov. 19	259	Apr. 11	Oct. 20	192	May 3	Oct. 13	163	May 3	Oct. 13	163
1910	Apr. 9			Mar. 18	Oct. 30	226	Mar. 16	Nov. 9	238	Mar. 16	Oct. 30	228	Apr. 8	Oct. 30	205	May 15	Oct. 24	162
1911		Nov. 3		Apr. 10	Nov. 3	207	Mar. 25	Nov. 17	237	Apr. 2	Nov. 3	215	Apr. 11	Oct. 25	197	Apr. 25	Oct. 25	183
1912	Apr. 9	Oct. 17	191	Mar. 26	Nov. 4	223	Feb. 28	do	263	Mar. 26	do	222	Apr. 24	Oct. 27	186	Apr. 9	Oct. 27	201
1913	Apr. 22	Oct. 22	183	Mar. 29	Oct. 22	207	Mar. 3	Nov. 3	245	Mar. 29	Oct. 22	207	Apr. 12	Oct. 22	193	Apr. 21	Oct. 21	183
1914	Apr. 11	Oct. 28	200	Apr. 10	Oct. 28	201	Mar. 14	Nov. 21	252	Apr. 10	Oct. 28	201	Apr. 11	Oct. 28	200	Apr. 13	Oct. 27	197
1915	Apr. 16	Oct. 25	192	Apr. 5	Oct. 11	189	Apr. 3	Nov. 23	234	Apr. 1	Oct. 25	207	Apr. 16	Oct. 10	177	Apr. 14	Oct. 10	179
1916	Apr. 11	Oct. 11	183	Apr. 9	Oct. 27	201	Mar. 20	Nov. 16	241	Mar. 23	Nov. 2	224	Apr. 27	Oct. 11	167	Apr. 10	Oct. 1	174
1917	Apr. 15	Oct. 13	181	Apr. 14	Oct. 10	179	Apr. 10	Nov. 25	229	Apr. 14	Oct. 31	200	Apr. 14	Oct. 10	179	Apr. 15	Oct. 2	170
1918	do	Oct. 23	191	Apr. 6	Oct. 23	200	Mar. 16	do	254	Apr. 6	Nov. 3	211	Apr. 30	Oct. 8	161	Apr. 14	Oct. 15	184
1919	Apr. 26	Nov. 6	194	Apr. 3	Nov. 14	225	Apr. 2	Nov. 15	227	Apr. 26	Nov. 9	197	Apr. 25	Oct. 6	164	Apr. 3	Nov. 6	217
1920	Apr. 15	Nov. 4	203	Apr. 11	Nov. 4	207	Mar. 9	Nov. 14	250	Mar. 22	Nov. 13	236	Apr. 24	Oct. 9	168	Apr. 15	Oct. 3	171
1921	Apr. 12	Oct. 13	184	Apr. 2	Oct. 14	195	Mar. 5	Nov. 13	253	Apr. 2	Nov. 6	218	Mar. 30	Oct. 13	197	Apr. 12	Oct. 13	184
1922	Apr. 30	Oct. 27	180	Apr. 24	Nov. 1	191	Mar. 23	Nov. 23	245	Mar. 23	Nov. 10	232	Apr. 29	Oct. 27	181	Apr. 23	Oct. 19	179
1923	Apr. 10	Nov. 1	205	Apr. 10	do	205	Apr. 2	Nov. 18	230	Apr. 1	Nov. 1	214	Apr. 15	Nov. 2	201	Apr. 10	Oct. 10	183
1924	Apr. 3	Oct. 24	204	Apr. 4	Oct. 22	201	do	Nov. 20	232	Apr. 3	Oct. 24	204	Apr. 3	Oct. 23	203	Apr. 12	Oct. 22	193
1925	Apr. 7	Oct. 11	187	Apr. 7	Oct. 11	187	Mar. 4	Oct. 11	221	Apr. 7	Oct. 23	199	Apr. 22	Oct. 11	172	May 27	Oct. 11	137
1926	May 21	Oct. 27	159	Apr. 16	Oct. 28	195	Apr. 20	Nov. 11	205	Apr. 20	Oct. 28	191	May 5	Oct. 27	175	Apr. 27	Oct. 22	178
1927	Apr. 12	Nov. 6	208	Mar. 5	Nov. 7	247	Mar. 5	Nov. 7	247	Mar. 5	Nov. 7	247	Apr. 25	Nov. 7	196	Apr. 25	Oct. 15	173
1928	Apr. 18	Oct. 27	192	Apr. 17	Oct. 27	193	Mar. 20	Nov. 24	249	Mar. 6	Nov. 12	251	May 14	Oct. 26	165	Apr. 17	Oct. 27	193
1929	Apr. 19	Nov. 6	201	Mar. 11	Nov. 6	240	Mar. 11	Nov. 30	264	Mar. 11	Nov. 22	256	Apr. 2	Oct. 9	190	Apr. 23	Nov. 6	197
1930	Apr. 27	Oct. 6	162	Apr. 1	Oct. 21	203	Mar. 5	Oct. 23	232	Mar. 5	Oct. 22	231	Apr. 27	Oct. 18	174	Apr. 27	Oct. 20	176
1931	Apr. 28	Oct. 27	182	Mar. 21	Nov. 3	227	Mar. 13	Dec. 3	265	Mar. 24	Nov. 3	224	May 4	Oct. 19	168	Mar. 21	Oct. 18	211
1932	do	Oct. 12	167	Mar. 16	Nov. 2	231	Mar. 14	Nov. 27	258	Mar. 11	Nov. 13	247	Apr. 19	Oct. 29	193	Apr. 19	Oct. 29	193
1933	Apr. 27	Oct. 26	182	Mar. 30	Oct. 27	211	Mar. 11	Nov. 9	243	Mar. 30	Nov. 9	224	Apr. 27	Oct. 26	182	Apr. 13	Oct. 11	181
1934	Apr. 22	Oct. 14	175	Apr. 28	Oct. 14	169	Mar. 24	Nov. 13	234	do	Oct. 14	198	Apr. 28	Oct. 13	168	Apr. 28	Oct. 14	179

1935	Apr. 18	Oct. 7	172	Apr. 16	Oct. 7	174	Mar. 1	Nov. 24	268	Mar. 15	Nov. 19	249	Apr. 18	Oct. 5	170	Apr. 17	Oct. 5	171
1936	Apr. 25	Oct. 28	186	Apr. 23	Oct. 28	188	Feb. 24	Nov. 19	268	Mar. 8	Oct. 28	234	Apr. 23	Oct. 27	187	Apr. 18	Oct. 28	193
1937	Apr. 11	Oct. 15	187	Mar. 27	Oct. 15	202	Mar. 28	Nov. 21	238	Mar. 28	Oct. 15	201	Apr. 17	Oct. 15	181	Apr. 17	Oct. 15	181
1938	Mar. 29	Nov. 10	226	Mar. 11	Nov. 10	244	Mar. 4	Nov. 25	266	Mar. 11	Nov. 10	244	Apr. 3	Oct. 8	188	Apr. 11	Oct. 8	180
Mean	Apr. 17	Oct. 22	188	Apr. 4	Oct. 25	204	Mar. 19	Nov. 16	242	Mar. 29	Nov. 2	218	Apr. 19	Oct. 18	182	Apr. 17	Oct. 16	182
Extremes	Mar. 29[2] May 21[3]	Oct. 2[4] Nov. 10[5]	[6] 154 [7] 226	Mar. 5[2] Apr. 28[3]	Oct. 2[4] Nov. 14[5]	[6] 169 [7] 247	Feb. 24[2] Apr. 20[3]	Oct. 11[4] Dec. 6[5]	[6] 205 [7] 268	Mar. 5[2] Apr. 20[3]	Oct. 12[4] Nov. 22[5]	[6] 190 [7] 256	Mar. 30[2] May 14[3]	Oct. 1[4] Nov. 7[5]	[6] 161 [7] 205	Mar. 21[2] May 27[3]	Sept. 19[4] Nov. 6[5]	[6] 137 [7] 217

[1] Number of days between last killing frost in spring and first in fall.
[2] Earliest date in spring.
[3] Latest date in spring.
[4] Earliest date in fall.
[5] Latest date in fall.
[6] Shortest growing season.
[7] Longest growing season.

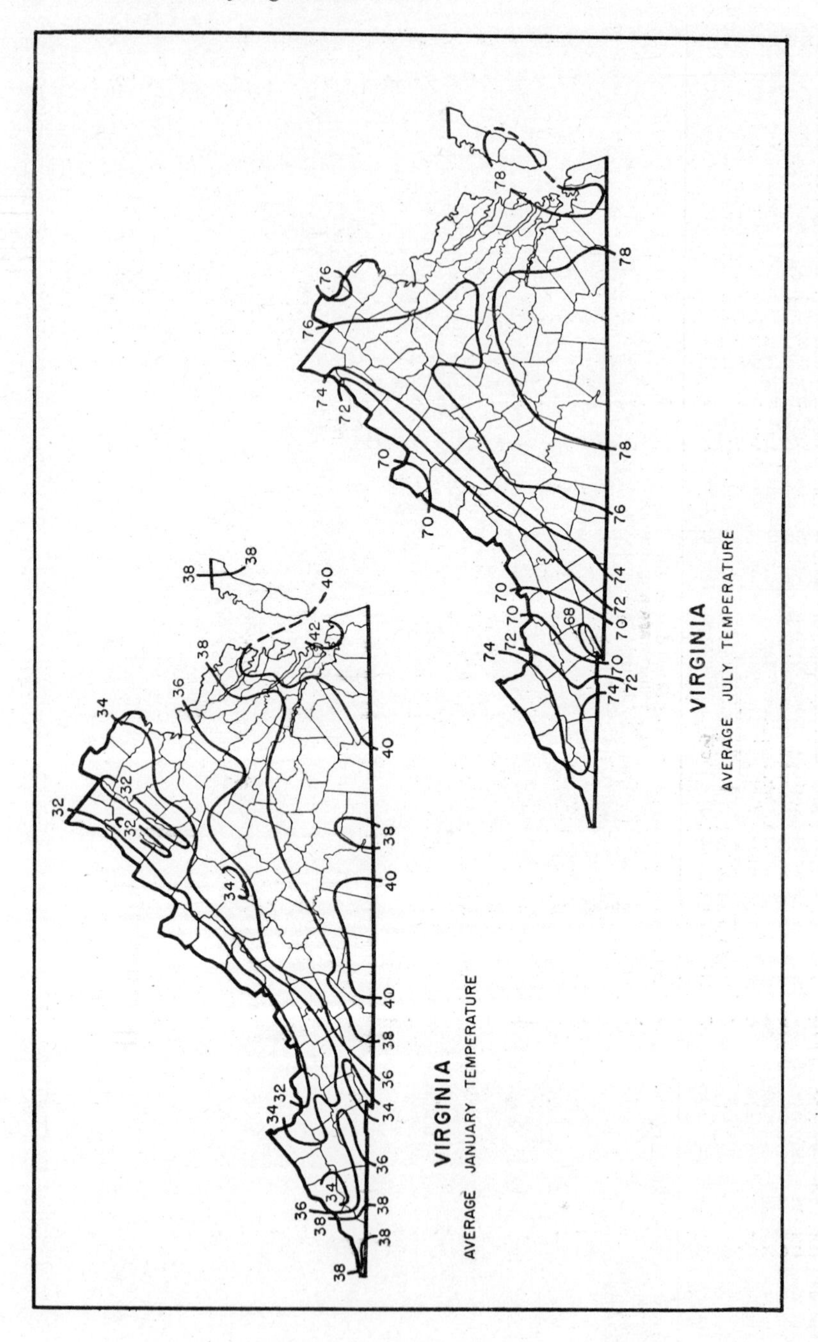
VIRGINIA
AVERAGE JANUARY TEMPERATURE
VIRGINIA
AVERAGE JULY TEMPERATURE

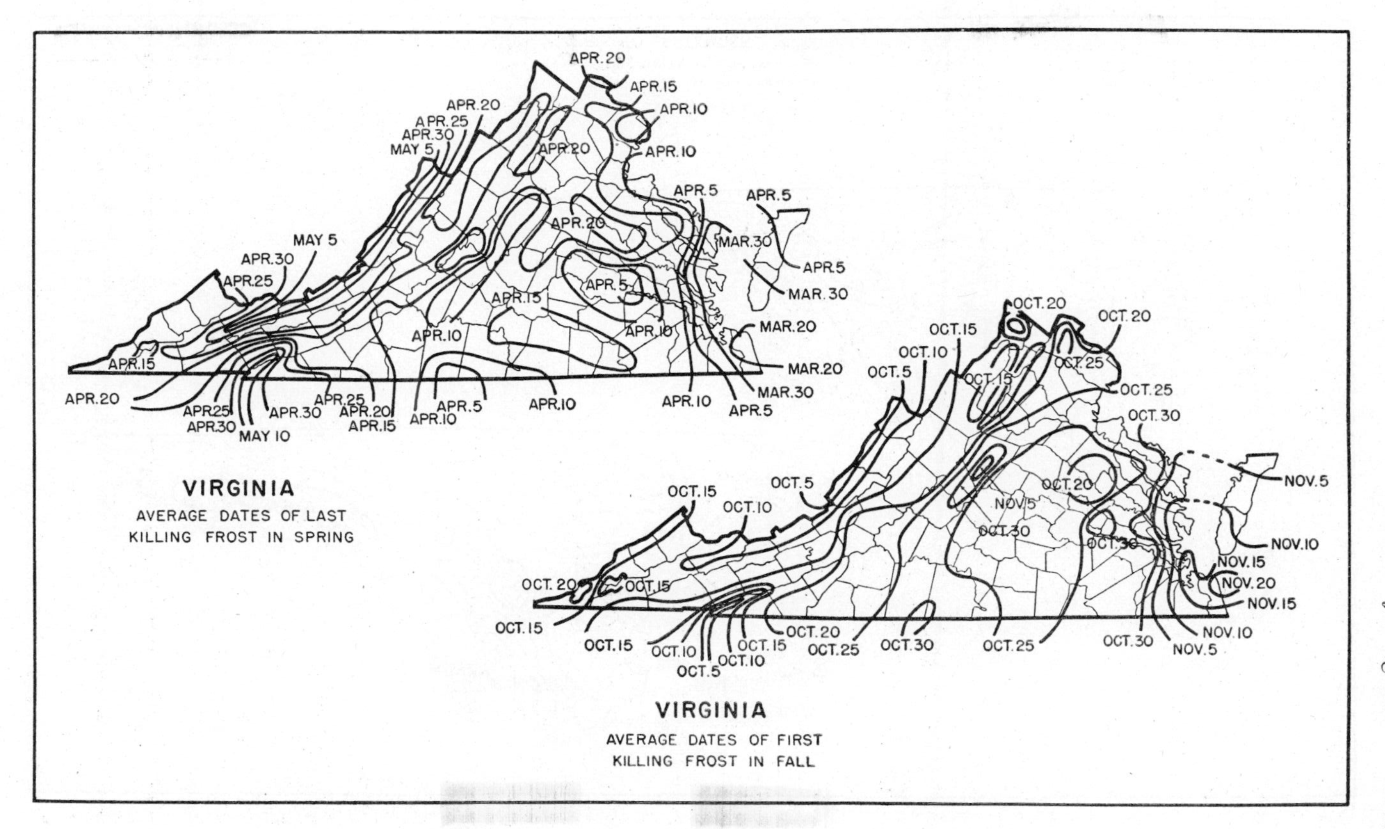

VIRGINIA
AVERAGE DATES OF LAST KILLING FROST IN SPRING

VIRGINIA
AVERAGE DATES OF FIRST KILLING FROST IN FALL

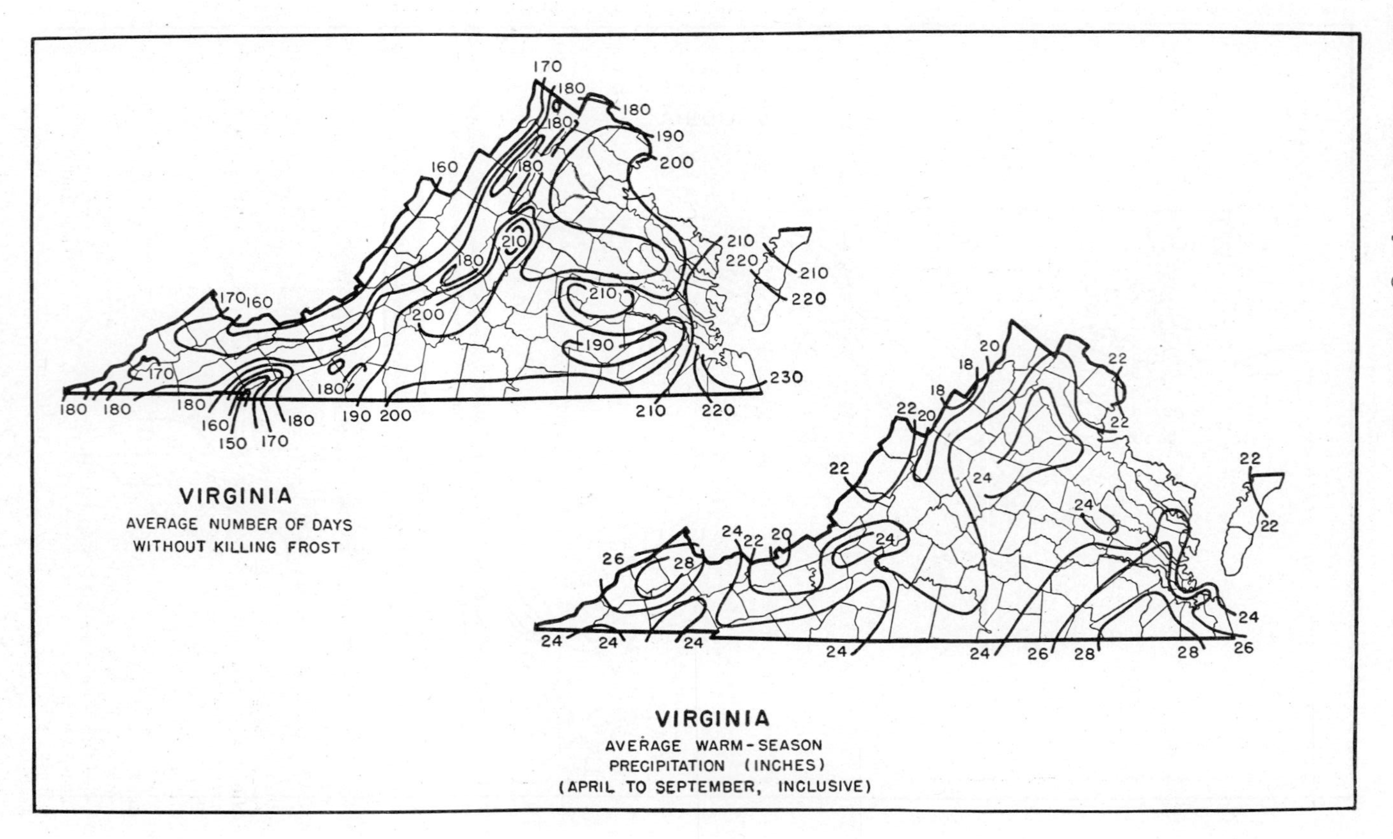
VIRGINIA
AVERAGE NUMBER OF DAYS
WITHOUT KILLING FROST
VIRGINIA
AVERAGE WARM-SEASON
PRECIPITATION (INCHES)
(APRIL TO SEPTEMBER, INCLUSIVE)

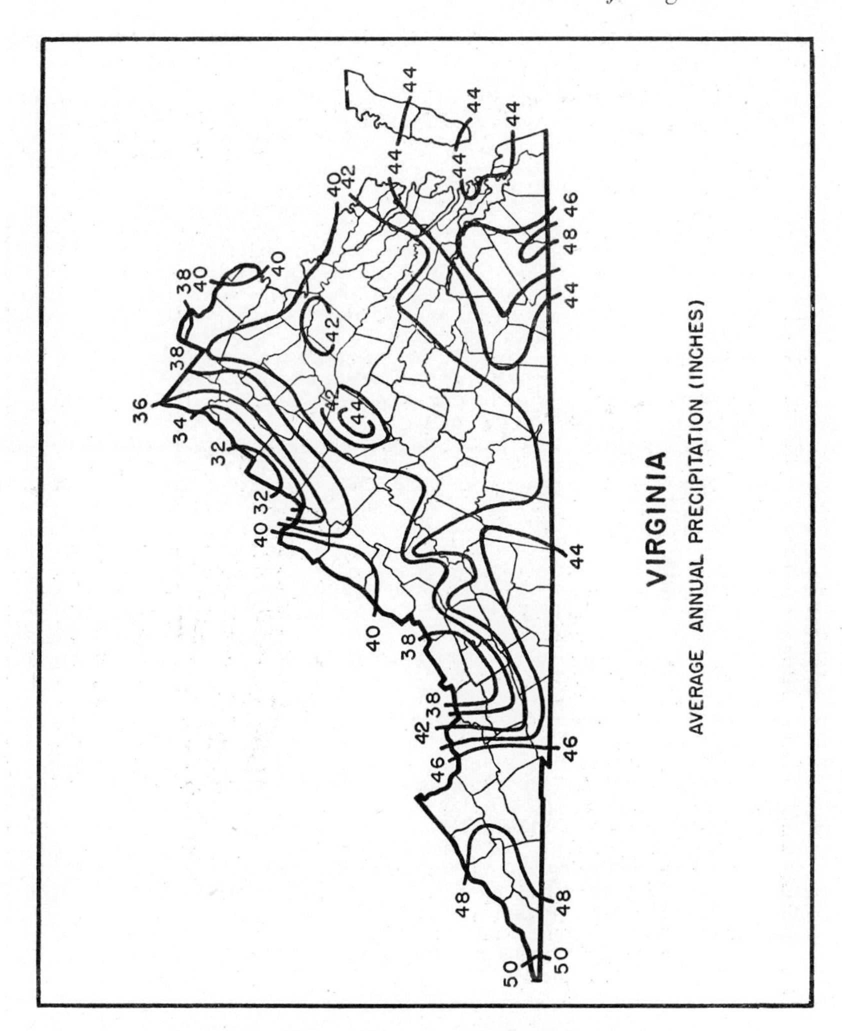

SUPPLEMENTARY CLIMATIC NOTES FOR VIRGINIA

Virginia is a triangular-shaped State, extending 200 miles from north to south and 430 from east to west. The climate is dependent principally on latitude, surroundings, and topography. The latitude is entirely within the milder part of the North Temperate Zone; the surroundings include continental areas to the northwest and west, warm rolling lands to the south, and the Atlantic Ocean to the east; the interior topography varies from indented coastal plains in the east to rugged mountain ranges in the west.

For climatic as well as for commercial purposes, the transition from east to west is divided conveniently into the Tidewater, middle Virginia, and the Great Valley. Tidewater Virginia comprises the flat and near-sea-level sections east of a line from Quantico through Richmond to Emporia. Its chief characteristics are extensive truck fields, numerous peninsulas, wide estuaries, and many swamps.

From the Tidewater line westward the land becomes more rolling and rises gradually in height to the Blue Ridge Mountains, which extend southwesterly from Loudoun County in the north to Carroll County in the southwest, the ridge itself having an elevation of 1,500 to 3,500 feet above sea level. This middle portion of Virginia is suited to general farm crops. Drainage of the area is into the Atlantic, via the Potomac, Rappahannock, James, and Roanoke Rivers.

West of the Blue Ridge is the Great Valley, extending from the northernmost point of the State southwestward to Scott County and embracing the Shenandoah Valley in the north, parts of the James and New River Valleys in the middle, and the Holston Valley in the south. This section is suited for orchards and stock raising in the north and central parts and for mining in the south. Its general elevation runs from 1,000 to 2,000 feet, with its western edge merging with the high ridges of the Appalachians.

Each of the three divisions of the State has a distinctive climate. That of the Tidewater is semimarine. The wide expanse of nearby water tempers both the summer heat and the winter cold, especially the latter, while the comparatively high humidity is mitigated by land and sea breezes. Relatively heavy precipitation and a long growing season favor prolific truck crops and peanuts.

Prevailing westerly winds prevent the extension of the ocean influences far westward; consequently, latitude controls the climate of middle Virginia. Fairly warm summers and mild winters characterize this part of the State, the temperatures of both seasons varying mainly in a north-south direction. As in the Tidewater section, rainfall is plentiful, but the shorter growing season limits agriculture to earlier maturing vegetation, such as cotton and tobacco in the south and general farm crops in central and northern parts.

In the Great Valley elevation is the principal climatic factor. Temperatures here are distinctly lower, with wide variations within short distances. Summers are comparatively cool and winters invigorating. Snow is generally plentiful in winter, but it does not cap the ridges in summer. Precipitation is ample, on an average, but the amounts vary widely with location, depending on the mountains and prevailing winds. The growing season is relatively short and limits commercial crops to those harvested early. The lower ridges and slopes favor the production of apples and peaches, and the valleys generally are adapted to gardens, small farms, dairy herds, and horses.

Temperature variations due to latitude are not great. In July the averages range from 76° F. in the north to 79° in the south; in January from 33° in the north to 39° in the south. A horizontal cross section of the State, however, carries one from ocean influences to mountain extremes and shows a sharper contrast. Freezing weather has been experienced even in July in some agricultural sections of southwestern Virginia.

There are some very interesting temperature relations at nearby points of different elevation. Mountain Lake, in a hollow at an altitude of 4,000 feet, is 7° F. colder both winter and summer than Blacksburg, 13 miles southeast, at an altitude of 2,100 feet; and Big Meadows, on the crest of the Blue Ridge, altitude 3,500 feet, is colder than Culpeper, 25 miles due east and 3,000 feet lower, by an average ranging from 6° on a winter night to 15° on a summer day.

Frost is controlled in Virginia not only by ocean, latitude, and elevation, but by soil characteristics, night radiation of heat, air drainage, and imported cool air masses. The interplay of these factors occasionally gives widely different frost effects in neighboring localities and even in nearby fields, but in general the average date of the last killing frost in spring ranges from the latter part of March at the Virginia Capes to mid-April in northern Virginia and early May in the Alleghenies. The average date of the first fall frost varies from October 10 in the Alleghenies and October 22 in northern Virginia, to mid-November at the Capes. The length of the growing season ranges from 160 days in the extreme western counties to 200 days around Chesapeake Bay, the lower James Basin, and extreme southern Virginia, and 230 days at the Capes. Various hills and slopes along the Blue Ridge also are singularly safe from frosts and have much longer growing seasons than neighboring valleys. As a general rule, frost is most likely in the pockets and flats between ridges.

Precipitation in Virginia is dependent primarily on nearness to the ocean, prevailing winds, topography, and the types and paths of the general storms. The variation from north to south is from 36 to 44 inches, with an average of 50 in the extreme southeast and extreme southwest corners of the State. The heavy amounts in the southeastern counties are due, of course, to the nearness of the ocean, while those in the southwest represent condensation from moist southerly winds rising over the higher ranges of the Alleghenies. Rain during the growing season is normally ample, averaging from 22 inches in the north to 26 or 28 in the south.

Sunshine usually is plentiful and droughts are infrequent. Snowfall is infrequent in the warmer sections, by far the greater part being in the Great Valley. The average amounts range from 7 inches at the Virginia Capes to 25 in the Valley; the State average is 17 inches.

The cloudiest month of record had 21 cloudy and 18 rainy days, both about double the usual number. Tornadoes are negligible and gale winds are limited mostly to tropical storms touching the east coast.

FOY N. HIBBARD, *Associate Meteorologist and Climatic Section Director for Virginia, Weather Bureau, Richmond.*

WASHINGTON

Climatic summary

County	Station	Temperature					Killing frost average dates				Average precipitation														
		Length of record	January average	July average	Maximum	Minimum	Length of record	Last in spring	First in fall	Growing season [1]	Length of record	January	February	March	April	May	June	July	August	September	October	November	December	Annual
		Yr.	*°F.*	*°F.*	*°F.*	*°F.*	*Yr.*			*Days*	*Yr.*	*In.*	*In.*	*In.*	*In.*	*In.*	*In.*	*In.*	*In.*	*In.*	*In.*	*In.*	*In.*	*In.*
Adams	Hatton (near)	33	27.5	72.4	112	−29	34	May 13	Sept. 30	140	34	1.13	0.86	0.75	0.61	0.66	0.72	0.19	0.34	0.47	0.71	1.34	1.26	9.04
	Lind (near)	27	27.7	72.9	116	−33	26	May 10	Oct. 6	149	30	1.09	.90	.79	.68	.66	.84	.20	.31	.57	.73	1.36	1.36	9.49
	Ritzville	23	29.4	71.2	109	−21	23	May 15	Sept. 28	136	37	1.30	1.10	.83	.65	.70	.73	.19	.40	.65	.71	1.47	1.64	10.37
Asotin	Anatone	24	26.0	64.7	104	−30	24	do	do	136	26	3.08	2.21	2.12	1.86	1.67	2.23	.50	.73	1.14	1.76	2.45	2.72	22.47
Benton	Hanford	26	29.6	75.3	114	−27	26	Apr. 17	Oct. 17	183	27	.92	.56	.31	.39	.40	.47	.14	.17	.30	.52	.90	.85	5.93
	Kennewick (near)	38	32.2	75.6	115	−29	37	Apr. 18	Oct. 16	181	40	1.03	.84	.54	.46	.42	.43	.13	.24	.33	.59	1.02	1.02	7.05
	Kiona	33	31.4	74.4	114	−30	32	Apr. 22	Oct. 12	173	33	1.08	.84	.66	.44	.49	.50	.18	.19	.46	.69	1.24	1.22	7.99
	Mottinger	39	33.6	76.4	114	−24	39	Mar. 30	Oct. 29	213	39	1.09	.87	.80	.70	.70	.55	.14	.33	.45	.72	1.19	1.09	8.63
	Prosser	27	31.0	72.2	111	−31	26	Apr. 28	Oct. 14	169	26	.98	.66	.50	.55	.46	.46	.15	.22	.45	.68	1.03	1.15	7.29
Chelan	Blewett Pass	11	21.6	62.4	101	−16	11	May 28	Oct. 3	128	11	3.77	2.48	3.40	.98	.78	1.58	.24	.27	.99	1.88	3.11	5.46	24.94
	Chiwawa River										14	10.02	7.77	6.57	2.59	1.54	1.81	.58	.52	2.28	5.12	8.54	12.43	59.77
	Domke Lake	11	23.0	63.4	100	−13	11	May 15	Oct. 13	151	12	5.00	3.69	2.93	1.20	.75	1.48	.44	.43	.93	1.86	4.11	6.84	29.66
	Dryden										15	3.24	1.77	1.18	.78	.58	.63	.44	.30	.65	1.26	2.87	3.17	16.87
	Lakeside	38	25.4	73.6	106	−15	39	Apr. 9	Oct. 25	199	40	1.39	1.13	.80	.51	.66	.81	.31	.29	.60	.76	1.59	1.63	10.48
	Lake Wenatchee										2	3.85	4.52	2.32	2.96	.28	3.58	.34	.33	.85	2.83	7.46	8.40	37.72
	Leavenworth	20	24.0	68.6	109	−27	24	May 13	Oct. 6	146	24	3.68	2.44	2.00	.82	.55	.63	.31	.33	.71	1.79	3.35	4.86	21.47
	Stehekin (near)	25	26.8	67.6	103	−18	26	May 10	Oct. 3	146	25	6.12	3.61	3.01	1.27	.69	.88	.41	.40	1.07	2.64	5.31	6.97	32.38
	Wenatchee	26	25.6	73.0	110	−29	26	Apr. 24	Oct. 14	173	27	1.27	.87	.54	.29	.59	.72	.26	.23	.43	.71	1.16	1.70	8.77
	Wenatchee (near)	37	25.2	70.6	107	−16	38	Apr. 17	Oct. 22	188	38	1.84	1.34	.99	.52	.89	.91	.39	.28	.74	.90	1.73	2.21	12.74
Clallam	Clallam Bay	11	37.4	56.2	94	8	12	Apr. 30	Oct. 23	176	11	12.20	9.10	8.85	5.36	3.54	3.17	1.62	1.54	3.48	7.48	9.51	12.67	78.52
	Forks	23	38.0	59.4	98	−4	26	Apr. 25	Oct. 16	174	29	18.69	13.49	13.04	8.12	5.13	3.70	1.73	2.06	5.30	11.91	15.29	18.48	116.94
	Lake Sutherland										10	8.56	6.24	4.98	3.02	2.09	2.06	.30	.93	2.27	4.25	5.89	13.59	54.18
	Port Angeles	23	37.3	57.1	92	−1	22	Mar. 23	Nov. 8	230	40	4.01	2.97	2.04	1.16	1.01	.82	.46	.65	1.36	2.16	3.48	4.53	24.65
	Port Crescent	19	36.7	55.6	93	7	19	Apr. 9	Oct. 29	203	18	6.21	4.31	3.40	1.90	1.75	1.36	.59	.83	2.04	3.44	8.27	6.29	40.39
	Sequim	20	37.6	58.8	91	−3	16	Apr. 21	Oct. 22	184	22	2.28	1.38	1.33	1.02	.77	.78	.47	.57	.98	1.57	2.03	3.21	16.39
	Tatoosh Island	40	41.2	55.1	88	7	40	Feb. 8	Dec. 16	311	40	11.16	8.54	7.67	4.97	3.51	3.04	1.37	1.81	4.11	8.11	11.09	11.90	77.28
Clark	La Center	37	37.4	64.2	107	−13	26	Apr. 24	Oct. 23	182	37	6.96	5.54	5.24	3.44	2.76	2.01	.65	1.07	2.42	4.14	7.54	7.78	49.55
	Vancouver	40	38.5	66.6	103	−10	40	Mar. 30	Nov. 11	226	40	5.41	4.30	3.56	2.54	1.96	1.53	.53	.73	1.90	2.71	5.88	6.11	37.16
	Yacolt						12	May 10	Sept. 23	136	24	11.42	8.28	9.26	5.82	3.49	2.91	.84	1.28	3.55	6.24	11.06	13.27	77.42
Columbia	Dayton	37	32.6	70.8	109	−22	38	May 2	Oct. 12	163	38	2.33	2.15	2.40	1.53	1.43	1.13	.41	.54	.94	1.64	2.53	2.31	19.34
	Touchet Ridge						20	May 1	Sept. 25	147	30	5.23	4.35	4.88	3.13	2.80	1.96	.72	.84	1.89	3.47	5.61	5.04	39.92
Cowlitz	Castlerock	21	38.2	63.5	105	−13	20	Apr. 23	Oct. 22	182	21	9.05	6.32	6.45	3.63	2.51	1.96	.55	1.22	2.61	4.42	7.19	10.82	56.73
	Kalama (near)						18	Apr. 4	Oct. 30	209	22	9.73	7.38	8.25	5.36	3.07	2.35	.64	1.30	3.13	5.39	8.39	11.63	66.62
	Kelso										14	5.04	3.90	4.39	2.67	1.92	1.79	.50	1.01	1.88	3.26	5.41	6.77	38.54
	Longview	14	38.3	63.1	103	−20	14	Apr. 30	Oct. 18	171	14	5.56	4.22	4.93	2.80	2.04	1.94	.50	1.20	1.95	3.44	5.52	7.20	41.30
	Yale	12	35.8	64.9	104	3	12	Apr. 29	Oct. 29	183	13	15.18	10.97	9.48	5.61	4.86	3.23	1.19	.83	3.99	7.20	16.97	14.23	93.74

Douglas	Mansfield										16	1.16	.79	.68	.53	.40	1.25	.29	.36	.66	.58	1.19	1.30	9.19
	Rock Island	24	25.4	74.3	110	−26	24	Apr. 22	Oct. 16	177	24	.92	.86	.59	.37	.52	.69	.30	.17	.49	.49	1.07	1.24	7.71
	Waterville	38	21.0	67.3	104	−30	37	May 16	Sept. 29	136	40	1.46	1.13	.76	.59	.65	.85	.45	.39	.57	.76	1.43	1.59	10.63
Ferry	Laurier	29	21.8	69.2	109	−26	29	May 17	Sept. 22	128	29	1.98	1.25	1.10	1.31	1.49	1.82	.89	.89	1.19	1.44	1.99	2.03	17.38
	Republic	33	21.8	64.9	108	−35	34	June 5	Sept. 9	96	34	1.56	1.05	.89	1.14	1.35	1.61	.79	.79	1.04	.97	1.54	1.54	14.27
Franklin	Kahlotus (near)						8	May 9	Oct. 5	149	26	1.27	.97	.93	.76	.66	.80	.12	.22	.49	.74	1.35	1.46	9.77
Garfield	Peola						10	May 25	Sept 11	109	27	2.43	2.13	2.23	1.75	1.76	1.94	.72	.84	1.14	1.68	2.80	2.47	21.89
	Pomeroy	36	32.6	71.3	112	−24	34	May 3	Oct. 6	156	35	2.06	1.86	1.87	1.27	1.44	1.14	.45	.50	.85	1.23	2.09	2.09	16.85
Grant	Ephrata	27	25.8	76.6	112	−23	38	Apr. 15	Oct. 17	185	26	1.01	.63	.54	.39	.50	.85	.21	.36	.49	.60	1.01	1.15	7.74
	Hartline	9	23.1	72.0	106	−20	10	May 4	Sept. 30	149	11	1.13	.49	.70	.52	.57	1.20	.27	.20	.72	.50	1.07	1.31	8.68
	Ruff	19	26.6	72.6	112	−23	20	May 17	Oct. 2	138	20	1.12	.68	.61	.44	.52	.77	.15	.23	.57	.73	1.20	1.22	8.24
	Trinidad	35	27.2	76.8	113	−16	33	Apr. 7	Oct. 25	201	35	1.04	.81	.51	.36	.41	.64	.21	.13	.36	.47	1.10	1.20	7.24
	Wahluke (near)	33	29.9	77.6	118	−23	32	Apr. 11	Oct. 23	195	34	.90	.57	.44	.32	.36	.51	.17	.27	.32	.51	.98	.90	6.25
Grays Harbor	Aberdeen	40	39.2	59.6	105	6	40	Apr. 19	Oct. 27	191	40	12.94	9.63	8.87	5.52	3.88	2.86	1.07	1.43	3.93	7.38	12.64	13.50	83.65
	Canto										11	17.07	11.32	14.82	7.85	4.29	3.97	1.87	2.25	5.77	10.30	15.22	18.60	113.33
	Lone Tree	9	40.9	58.1	86	17	10	Feb. 22	Dec. 14	295	12	13.25	8.01	7.04	4.83	3.00	2.31	1.13	1.07	3.00	6.93	12.71	10.57	73.85
	Oakville	22	38.6	62.7	103	−8	22	May 3	Oct. 13	163	22	7.97	5.76	5.86	3.50	1.98	1.31	.40	1.28	2.37	4.69	6.43	9.80	51.35
	Quinault	27	38.4	63.5	104	11	26	Apr. 13	Nov. 7	208	29	20.25	14.06	13.44	8.30	6.26	4.56	1.65	2.45	6.70	12.21	18.02	20.68	128.58
	Satsop										11	9.14	7.49	8.26	4.51	2.47	2.69	.82	.88	2.94	5.78	7.92	12.36	65.26
	Wishkah Headworks										12	17.79	13.17	15.60	9.40	5.92	4.54	2.06	2.08	5.70	11.37	13.94	20.69	122.26
Island	Coupeville	24	38.6	61.0	96	5	24	Apr. 7	Nov. 1	208	33	2.27	1.69	1.80	1.39	1.33	1.12	.56	.77	1.29	1.65	2.14	2.76	18.77
Jefferson	Chimacum										12	2.67	2.08	1.79	1.91	1.50	1.28	.52	.69	1.26	1.79	2.42	3.84	21.75
	Clearwater	12	38.7	60.6	100	11	12	Apr. 22	Nov. 7	199	21	17.41	14.43	13.48	8.61	5.76	4.95	2.10	2.23	6.05	11.50	17.85	18.76	123.13
	Port Townsend	40	39.4	59.6	90	−3	40	Mar. 9	Nov. 29	265	40	2.28	1.63	1.46	1.20	1.37	1.23	.61	.71	1.13	1.46	2.21	2.59	17.88
	Quilcene	19	37.0	62.2	99	0	16	Apr. 27	Oct. 11	167	19	5.58	4.49	3.07	2.59	2.13	1.68	.66	.98	1.70	3.63	5.32	7.71	39.54
	Spruce										14	18.39	13.99	13.47	8.78	6.10	4.22	1.94	2.21	5.33	11.71	14.50	21.00	121.64
King	Cedar Lake	29	35.2	62.0	98	0	25	Apr. 9	Nov. 5	210	38	14.79	10.47	11.30	7.62	6.83	4.61	1.85	2.70	5.40	10.28	14.26	15.86	105.97
	Kent	25	38.4	63.4	101	−4	25	Apr. 24	Oct. 14	173	27	5.70	3.58	3.50	2.47	1.79	1.62	.68	.82	1.81	3.70	5.09	6.11	36.87
	Landsburg	23	37.1	62.2	101	0	22	May 1	Oct. 12	164	36	7.38	4.96	5.21	4.09	3.40	2.76	1.16	1.48	3.08	5.15	7.27	7.78	53.72
	Lester						10	May 25	Sept. 10	108	18	6.37	5.16	5.11	3.44	3.12	2.25	.62	1.02	2.32	5.35	7.95	8.54	51.25
	Palmer (near)	14	35.2	62.0	102	4	14	Apr. 17	Oct. 28	194	15	11.06	8.08	11.39	6.97	5.78	4.31	1.54	2.62	4.30	9.10	10.42	12.83	88.40
	Scenic										10	12.45	8.70	10.35	4.33	4.07	2.99	.95	1.08	3.19	7.47	10.82	14.45	80.85
	Seattle	40	39.5	63.1	98	3	40	Mar. 14	Nov. 24	255	40	4.87	3.49	2.79	2.04	1.69	1.37	.56	.73	1.58	2.69	4.83	5.16	31.80
	Snoqualmie Falls	38	37.8	65.0	104	3	36	Apr. 29	Oct. 18	172	39	7.96	5.47	5.51	4.14	3.48	2.57	1.08	1.39	2.91	5.28	7.54	8.36	55.69
	Snoqualmie Pass	20	26.2	56.8	101	−15	21	May 27	Sept. 19	115	23	15.21	11.04	11.36	5.37	3.85	3.65	1.01	2.25	4.02	8.66	12.33	17.42	96.17
	Vashon Island	36	39.3	62.6	95	5	38	Apr. 3	Nov. 12	223	38	6.66	4.76	3.79	2.63	2.12	1.55	.62	.79	2.15	3.88	7.03	7.48	43.46
Kitsap	Bremerton						10	Apr. 7	Nov. 4	211	40	6.13	4.40	3.34	2.21	1.62	1.25	.60	.69	1.58	2.97	6.21	6.45	37.45
	Keyport	17	39.7	63.1	98	10	21	Apr. 14	Nov. 10	210	23	5.74	3.88	3.29	2.04	1.42	1.27	.54	.81	1.51	2.75	4.36	6.94	34.55
Kittitas	Cle Elum	39	26.7	64.6	105	−27	40	May 31	Sept. 15	107	39	3.93	2.58	2.38	1.05	.96	.87	.34	.33	.88	1.77	3.62	4.34	23.05
	Ellensburg	39	25.4	68.2	110	−31	26	May 10	Sept. 29	142	38	1.37	.98	.60	.37	.54	.73	.28	.24	.55	.60	1.50	1.46	9.22
	Lake Cle Elum	26	27.2	63.6	105	−19	40	May 29	Sept. 15	109	30	6.25	3.84	3.73	1.57	1.25	.96	.39	.52	1.47	3.33	5.63	6.55	35.49
	Lake Kachess	31	25.7	63.2	102	−17	31	May 16	Oct. 2	139	31	8.95	5.74	5.65	2.51	2.00	1.44	.62	.80	2.10	4.56	7.44	9.61	51.42
	Lake Keechelus	21	26.2	60.9	102	−20	26	May 22	Sept. 29	130	31	10.96	6.97	7.27	3.69	2.58	1.73	.71	1.09	2.73	6.05	9.14	11.79	64.71
Klickitat	Bickleton	11	25.8	67.4	102	−11	10	May 17	Oct. 11	147	11	1.20	.94	1.17	.69	.36	.89	.08	.11	.33	.79	1.21	2.37	10.14
	Goldendale	31	29.8	68.1	109	−29	30	May 17	Oct. 4	140	34	2.92	1.83	1.35	.80	.83	.63	.19	.29	.67	1.17	2.69	2.89	16.26
	Laurel										11	7.31	4.86	3.54	2.08	1.63	.86	.40	.22	1.59	2.42	6.75	6.37	38.03
	Lyle	11	33.2	69.6	105	−11	11	Apr. 26	Oct. 17	174	11	4.27	3.68	1.82	1.10	.60	.87	.20	.32	.90	1.74	5.03	4.43	24.96
	Mount Adams Ranger Station.	14	29.6	65.0	106	−26	15	June 1	Sept. 13	104	1	6.12	6.96	8.92	1.55	.20	.27	.00	.00	.43	3.31	4.18	6.05	37.99
	Sixprong	30	30.2	75.5	113	−24	32	Apr. 11	Oct. 22	194	32	1.44	.88	.53	.47	.48	.54	.18	.16	.38	.54	1.26	1.36	8.22
	White Salmon (near)	28	30.9	66.5	106	−14	28	Apr. 17	Oct. 18	184	28	5.58	3.61	3.19	1.52	1.09	.76	.25	.31	1.19	2.08	5.04	5.87	30.49

[1] Length of growing season between average dates of last killing frost in spring and first in fall.

WASHINGTON—Continued

Climatic summary—Continued

County	Station	Temperature					Killing frost average dates				Average precipitation													
		Length of record	January average	July average	Maximum	Minimum	Length of record	Last in spring	First in fall	Growing season	Length of record	January	February	March	April	May	June	July	August	September	October	November	December	Annual
		Yr.	*°F.*	*°F.*	*°F.*	*°F.*	*Yr.*			*Days*	*Yr.*	*In.*	*In.*	*In.*	*In.*	*In.*	*In.*	*In.*	*In.*	*In.*	*In.*	*In.*	*In.*	*In.*
Lewis	Centralia	38	38.5	64.0	105	−16	37	Apr. 27	Oct. 17	173	37	6.59	5.02	4.81	2.85	2.37	1.92	0.60	0.97	2.16	3.65	7.19	7.51	45.64
	Kosmos	23	36.8	64.6	105	−15	22	May 10	Oct. 4	147	23	8.51	5.36	5.84	4.10	2.98	2.58	.91	1.54	3.01	4.93	8.59	9.47	57.82
	Mayfield										14	7.84	5.55	7.70	4.72	3.93	3.34	.99	1.06	2.84	4.90	8.26	9.33	60.46
	Packwood										13	8.61	5.64	6.38	2.71	2.22	2.28	.39	.70	1.80	4.86	7.96	10.32	53.87
	Randle										12	8.95	6.05	7.50	3.75	2.87	2.63	.56	1.13	2.17	5.48	7.87	10.65	59.61
Lincoln	Davenport	28	2.32	66.8	105	−27	29	May 27	Sept. 23	119	30	1.71	1.31	1.01	.91	1.06	1.21	.35	.48	.76	.96	1.87	1.80	13.43
	Harrington										24	1.41	1.05	.84	.79	.61	1.04	.23	.29	.73	.84	1.59	1.78	11.20
	Odessa	35	26.0	71.0	111	−33	36	May 17	Sept. 23	129	36	1.23	.79	.66	.57	.72	.89	.26	.28	.56	.77	1.41	1.32	9.46
	Reardan	18	25.4	66.6	104	−24	18	May 19	Sept. 20	124	19	1.70	1.84	1.08	.99	1.65	1.03	.67	.62	.79	1.15	2.46	1.98	15.96
	Sprague										24	1.61	1.48	1.19	1.04	.96	1.04	.38	.22	.76	1.17	2.16	1.89	13.90
	Wilbur	39	22.4	66.0	110	−30	39	June 5	Sept. 12	99	39	1.52	1.13	.81	.81	1.06	1.01	.39	.47	.72	1.01	1.74	1.54	12.21
Mason	Cushman Dam	10	36.6	63.4	101	6	12	Apr. 11	Nov. 6	209	17	16.21	12.47	9.39	6.47	4.22	2.56	1.05	.87	4.51	9.34	13.55	17.02	97.66
	Grapeview	31	38.8	64.8	102	10	31	Apr. 14	Nov. 9	209	31	8.87	6.23	5.05	3.07	2.22	1.44	.64	.87	2.21	4.51	8.21	9.18	52.50
Okanogan	Brewster	19	27.6	73.8	110	−23	18	Apr. 17	Oct. 12	178	20	1.33	.98	.53	.58	.84	1.07	.37	.42	.72	.78	1.67	1.37	10.66
	Chesaw	8	20.7	64.5	101	−27	10	June 8	Sept. 10	94	12	1.02	.71	.77	.85	1.04	1.87	.66	.69	1.02	.95	1.07	1.31	11.96
	Conconully	39	20.8	66.6	109	−29	38	May 19	Sept. 26	130	39	1.39	1.21	1.03	.93	1.34	1.63	.79	.64	.94	1.05	1.77	1.64	14.36
	Gunn's Ranch										27	2.32	1.18	.86	.54	.86	.95	.48	.56	.70	1.13	2.49	2.65	14.72
	Hassan										11	1.16	1.00	.95	1.02	.78	2.15	.44	.35	.87	.97	1.78	1.77	13.24
	Irene Mountain						24	June 7	Sept. 5	90	30	.91	.73	.58	1.04	1.51	1.88	1.24	.96	1.11	1.00	1.10	1.03	13.09
	Lemanasky Lake						10	May 8	Sept. 22	137	30	1.72	1.42	1.24	1.29	1.50	1.73	.94	.80	1.34	1.26	2.05	1.95	17.24
	Lost Creek										30	1.28	.91	.81	1.02	1.31	1.52	.82	.88	.97	1.01	1.48	1.31	13.32
	Nespelem	22	22.2	68.0	106	−28	22	May 14	Sept. 25	134	23	1.15	.98	.82	.81	.77	1.18	.38	.39	.83	.94	1.66	1.24	11.15
	Okanogan	13	23.8	74.6	110	−23	13	Apr. 25	Oct. 8	166	13	1.18	.87	.80	.69	.44	1.33	.36	.31	.73	.64	1.31	1.41	10.07
	Omak	29	23.0	73.8	114	−23	28	May 7	Oct. 3	149	30	1.47	.85	.63	.60	.71	1.18	.52	.39	.58	.70	1.40	1.36	10.39
	Oroville	25	25.6	73.0	111	−19	24	May 1	Oct. 5	157	25	1.00	.85	.65	.76	.70	1.29	.62	.57	.81	.84	1.34	1.18	10.61
	Stockdill Ranch	28	17.7	62.8	109	−33	28	June 23	Sept. 6	75	30	2.72	1.55	1.13	.63	.81	1.29	.42	.48	.80	1.29	2.54	3.10	16.76
	Timentwa										13	1.59	.98	.74	.81	.53	.93	.47	.59	.85	.89	1.44	1.63	11.45
	Winthrop	27	17.9	69.4	110	−31	27	May 18	Sept. 26	131	30	1.91	1.16	.74	.59	.87	1.18	.36	.44	.68	.93	2.06	2.33	13.25
Pacific	Brooklyn										11	11.52	8.57	10.55	5.20	3.05	2.74	.92	.94	2.59	6.48	9.21	13.76	75.53
	North Head	40	42.1	57.2	97	11	36	Feb. 14	Dec. 8	297	36	7.91	5.74	5.31	3.21	2.44	2.03	.63	.99	2.56	4.27	7.29	8.47	50.85
	South Bend	37	40.4	61.4	103	4	36	Apr. 14	Nov. 2	202	38	12.83	9.28	9.42	5.98	3.95	2.97	1.03	1.58	3.71	7.17	12.02	13.72	83.66
Pend Oreille	Newport	22	23.5	64.2	106	−36	22	June 5	Sept. 6	93	22	2.62	1.90	2.18	1.54	1.64	1.51	.68	.75	1.41	1.82	3.49	3.05	22.59
	Sullivan Lake	12	20.8	64.8	101	−26	13	May 21	Sept. 12	114	18	2.88	2.09	2.30	2.04	2.17	2.50	1.20	.85	1.84	2.25	2.96	3.11	26.19
Pierce	Buckley	26	37.6	63.2	100	5	26	Apr. 11	Oct. 25	197	26	6.18	4.07	4.88	3.85	3.01	2.74	1.11	1.27	2.60	4.64	5.76	6.90	47.01
	Headworks	21	36.8	60.2	99	−8	22	May 19	Oct. 8	142	22	6.52	4.56	4.83	3.63	2.59	2.10	.59	1.07	2.15	3.96	5.60	8.08	45.68
	Longmire	26	29.8	60.3	105	−9	24	May 26	Oct. 7	134	26	12.07	8.00	8.28	5.29	3.92	2.85	1.06	1.73	3.62	7.81	10.63	13.38	78.64
	Paradise Inn	17	26.1	51.7	92	−20	10	June 27	Sept. 14	79	17	15.69	9.62	10.46	6.46	4.57	3.97	1.34	2.95	6.18	9.77	12.65	15.69	99.35

	Puyallup	25	38.6	63.6	99	−2	25	Apr. 23	Oct. 17	177	25	5.92	3.99	4.07	2.82	2.20	1.65	.76	.80	1.89	3.47	5.00	6.58	39.15
	Sumner	12	37.5	62.5	94	−7	12	May 12	do	158	12	6.12	5.32	3.75	3.17	2.65	1.78	.93	.70	1.91	3.51	7.03	6.09	42.96
	Tacoma	40	38.8	62.8	98	7	40	Mar. 13	Nov. 18	250	40	5.95	3.97	3.62	2.46	1.92	1.45	.57	.78	1.88	3.31	5.91	6.18	38.00
San Juan	Olga	40	39.0	59.6	89	−3	40	Mar. 29	Nov. 13	229	40	4.09	2.76	2.52	1.72	1.46	1.24	.72	.93	1.88	2.86	4.17	4.69	29.04
Skagit	Anacortes	32	38.7	61.6	95	7	33	Mar. 26	Nov. 12	231	40	3.65	2.39	2.43	1.75	1.50	1.27	.64	.95	1.64	2.66	3.66	3.97	26.51
	Concrete	23	34.5	64.5	106	−1	23	Apr. 11	Nov. 1	204	23	8.95	6.34	6.03	3.57	2.95	2.45	1.05	1.34	3.50	6.46	9.76	9.13	61.53
	Sedro Woolley	40	37.4	62.3	99	−1	40	Apr. 22	Oct. 22	183	40	5.87	4.20	4.38	3.32	2.82	2.41	1.21	1.57	3.25	4.73	6.06	6.51	46.33
Skamania	Cougar (near)										11	16.68	12.00	16.29	8.61	4.67	4.14	1.11	1.20	4.48	11.19	14.91	22.48	117.76
	Mt. Pleasant	22	37.6	65.0	101	−3	22	Apr. 3	Nov. 10	221	22	7.91	6.11	5.76	4.37	3.77	2.75	1.12	1.06	3.03	4.48	8.91	7.57	56.84
	Wind River	28	32.3	64.2	107	−13	28	May 19	Sept. 30	134	28	14.82	9.48	10.07	5.83	3.64	2.13	.47	.98	3.57	6.76	13.38	15.71	86.84
Snohomish	Darrington	17	33.5	61.9	105	−11	18	May 11	Oct. 3	145	20	11.44	8.30	8.85	4.96	3.55	2.95	1.11	1.08	3.44	7.33	10.45	13.69	77.15
	Everett	34	38.0	61.2	99	3	24	Apr. 6	Nov. 5	213	24	4.56	3.14	3.47	2.45	1.99	1.63	.78	1.00	1.89	3.01	3.78	5.04	32.74
	Granite Falls										20	7.14	5.16	5.87	4.95	4.28	3.58	1.68	1.75	3.78	5.70	7.66	7.86	59.41
	Monroe	10	36.8	62.7	101	2	10	Apr. 5	Oct. 19	197	10	5.97	3.98	5.00	3.08	2.91	2.50	.91	1.12	2.63	4.27	5.56	6.77	44.70
	Silverton	11	33.0	61.2	103	0					10	13.04	9.58	7.56	5.04	6.09	3.73	1.68	2.70	7.12	11.25	15.16	11.85	94.80
	Snohomish	20	37.8	61.6	97	0	19	Apr. 24	Oct. 20	179	20	5.28	4.63	3.88	3.30	2.90	2.44	1.33	1.34	2.34	3.49	6.20	5.83	42.96
	Startup	15	38.6	64.2	106	5	14	Apr. 2	Nov. 7	219	14	7.66	5.50	6.93	4.32	3.88	3.27	1.05	1.94	3.89	6.66	6.48	8.37	59.95
Spokane	Cheney	8	28.1	70.2	107	−26					13	1.95	1.56	1.15	.90	1.78	.94	.67	.63	.88	1.48	2.49	1.92	16.35
	Deer Park	27	24.6	65.8	107	−42	28	June 4	Sept. 14	102	28	2.79	1.85	1.69	1.47	1.23	1.30	.45	.84	1.15	1.45	2.72	3.02	19.96
	Spokane	40	27.5	69.0	108	−30	40	Apr. 12	Oct. 13	184	40	1.85	1.41	1.16	.96	1.17	1.08	.50	.63	.82	1.06	1.97	2.01	14.62
Stevens	Chewelah	13	23.8	65.2	107	−38	12	May 26	Sept. 6	103	13	2.49	1.62	1.69	1.19	1.12	1.62	.38	.56	1.38	1.48	2.13	2.92	18.58
	Colville	39	23.8	67.3	106	−29	40	May 20	Sept. 22	125	40	2.01	1.30	1.08	1.08	1.41	1.48	.74	.71	1.13	1.20	2.18	2.03	16.35
	Kettle Falls	29	24.6	69.6	113	−32	30	May 10	Oct. 1	144	30	2.14	1.32	1.23	1.18	1.11	1.29	.65	.72	1.13	1.23	2.30	2.21	16.51
	Northport	28	23.5	67.8	110	−32	28	May 16	Sept. 16	123	28	2.05	1.29	1.27	1.27	1.42	1.64	.90	.81	1.29	1.60	2.22	2.17	17.93
	Wellpinit										15	2.29	1.43	1.58	1.03	.87	1.42	.26	.49	1.11	1.42	2.03	2.43	16.36
Thurston	Olympia	37	38.4	63.3	104	−2	38	Apr. 20	Oct. 28	191	40	8.35	6.29	5.22	3.23	2.27	1.56	.64	.68	2.27	4.53	8.37	8.96	52.37
Wahkiakum	Cathlamet (near)										9	12.62	8.87	11.39	5.85	3.32	2.78	1.22	1.56	3.30	6.99	11.01	15.67	84.58
Walla Walla	Lowden	31	31.9	73.2	113	−36	32	Apr. 27	Sept. 29	155	32	1.32	1.11	.88	.74	.77	.75	.12	.35	.51	.71	1.19	1.33	9.78
	Mill Creek						18	Apr. 19	Oct. 13	177	23	4.54	3.31	4.87	3.28	2.45	2.26	.39	.78	1.91	3.28	4.78	5.02	36.87
	Walla Walla	40	32.7	74.0	113	−29	40	Mar. 31	Nov. 5	219	40	1.77	1.65	1.66	1.30	1.40	1.02	.32	.50	.91	1.39	2.00	1.79	15.71
Whatcom	Bellingham	10	36.8	63.0	92	2	32	Apr. 20	Oct. 23	186	25	4.21	3.19	2.95	1.97	2.05	1.71	.91	1.13	2.22	2.94	4.46	4.48	32.22
	Blaine	33	36.0	61.2	95	−9	32	Apr. 22	Oct. 14	175	34	6.06	3.98	3.93	2.17	2.11	1.71	.93	1.24	2.85	4.56	5.79	6.18	41.51
	Clearbrook	36	34.3	61.4	98	−4	36	May 10	Sept. 30	143	36	6.35	4.31	4.47	3.07	2.64	2.36	1.24	1.62	3.54	5.17	6.53	6.94	48.24
	Marietta	25	37.5	62.0	94	0	25	Apr. 18	Oct. 16	181	25	4.64	2.94	3.37	2.23	1.52	1.64	.85	.88	2.12	3.40	4.02	5.25	32.86
	Mt. Baker Lodge										10	13.26	10.55	14.52	9.08	5.92	5.11	2.74	2.12	7.61	10.61	13.58	15.86	110.96
	Skagit Power Plant	19	32.6	66.5	109	−4	14	Apr. 4	Nov. 1	211	19	11.59	7.50	7.47	3.87	2.92	2.31	1.15	1.33	3.80	8.12	11.92	11.89	73.87
Whitman	Colfax	36	29.8	65.9	113	−27	36	May 23	Sept. 17	117	40	2.42	2.00	2.05	1.39	1.38	1.38	1.30	.56	.59	.97	1.55	2.72	18.31
	Lacrosse (near)	31	29.9	69.8	110	−28	31	May 18	Sept. 29	134	33	1.98	1.49	1.38	1.02	.99	.94	.34	.38	.80	1.25	2.15	1.95	14.67
	Pullman	39	28.6	68.0	104	−21	39	Apr. 30	Oct. 10	163	40	2.75	2.07	2.19	1.48	1.40	1.33	.46	.58	1.07	1.53	2.70	2.73	20.29
	Rosalia	40	27.9	67.2	108	−26	40	May 13	Sept. 30	140	40	2.07	1.58	1.64	1.29	1.46	1.22	.60	.58	1.03	1.52	2.51	2.28	17.78
Yakima	Bumping Lake	27	24.4	58.4	96	−32	29	June 17	Sept. 11	86	28	8.34	4.93	4.49	1.99	1.47	1.31	.53	.52	1.52	3.48	6.79	8.75	44.12
	Fort Simcoe	18	28.4	75.2	112	−20	17	Apr. 30	Oct. 10	163	18	2.53	1.75	.74	.47	.52	.40	.35	.16	.65	.60	2.34	1.78	12.29
	Gold Creek										13	2.24	1.74	1.30	.81	1.20	.72	.55	.28	1.08	1.41	2.79	2.16	16.28
	McCumbers Ranch										13	5.78	3.37	2.58	1.43	1.05	.62	.24	.35	1.53	2.46	5.80	4.88	30.09
	Moxee	40	28.0	71.0	109	−28	40	May 14	Sept. 27	136	40	1.10	.78	.49	.38	.56	.60	.26	.23	.50	.55	1.05	.96	7.46
	Naches Heights	28	27.8	70.5	102	−15	28	Apr. 23	Oct. 25	185	28	1.21	.85	.53	.37	.47	.60	.27	.22	.42	.50	1.05	1.45	7.94
	Rimrock	21	26.9	63.4	103	−28	22	May 31	Sept. 24	116	30	4.58	2.78	2.59	1.07	.93	.77	.45	.36	.86	1.83	4.10	4.85	25.17
	Sunnyside	39	30.0	71.6	108	−30	39	May 2	Oct. 10	161	40	.83	.62	.40	.41	.49	.53	.19	.20	.49	.58	.90	.84	6.48
	Tieton Canyon	28	26.0	67.4	107	−17	28	May 13	Sept. 28	138	29	2.58	1.36	1.52	.75	.83	.82	.42	.32	.66	1.03	2.63	2.72	15.64
	Wapato	22	29.4	73.7	110	−27	21	Apr. 22	Oct. 11	172	23	.70	.57	.45	.28	.32	.45	.20	.19	.33	.41	.91	1.14	5.95
	Yakima	29	27.4	71.4	111	−24	30	Apr. 15	Oct. 22	190	30	.98	.69	.41	.36	.47	.51	.20	.16	.48	.49	.96	1.08	6.79

298737°—41——75

WASHINGTON—Continued

Precipitation and temperature—State unit values

[This tabulation gives the mean annual, mean monthly, and average seasonal precipitation and the percentage of normal precipitation for each year, 1886–1938, and the mean annual temperatures, 1908–38, for Washington]

Precipitation		Precipitation		Precipitation		Annual precipitation (in percent of normal)		Annual precipitation (in percent of normal)		Temperature	
Year	Mean	Year	Mean	Month	Mean	Year	Percent	Year	Percent	Year	Mean
	In.		*In.*		*In.*						°*F.*
1886	41.33	1918	30.12	January	5.04	1886	117	1918	86	1911	48.2
1887	43.93	1919	31.00	February	3.67	1887	125	1919	88	1912	48.8
1888	41.43	1920	34.19	March	3.43	1888	118	1920	97	1913	48.0
1889	31.83	1921	36.80	April	2.42	1889	90	1921	105	1914	49.6
1890	33.66	1922	24.67	May	1.97	1890	96	1922	70	1915	50.1
1891	43.32	1923	29.64	June	1.69	1891	123	1923	84	1916	46.3
1892	32.97	1924	27.70	July	.67	1892	94	1924	79	1917	48.7
1893	41.23	1925	28.09	August	.77	1893	117	1925	80	1918	50.0
1894	43.47	1926	32.12	September	1.80	1894	124	1926	91	1919	48.0
1895	35.55	1927	42.02	October	2.98	1895	101	1927	119	1920	48.5
1896	46.20	1928	31.93	November	5.08	1896	131	1928	91	1921	48.6
1897	43.18	1929	23.74	December	5.66	1897	123	1929	67	1922	47.3
1898	33.04	1930	27.28			1898	94	1930	78	1923	49.4
1899	45.07	1931	42.17	Annual	35.18	1899	128	1931	120	1924	48.9
1900	36.67	1932	44.22			1900	104	1932	126	1925	50.7
1901	34.41	1933	47.48			1901	98	1933	135	1926	50.8
1902	40.24	1934	38.27	Season	Average	1902	114	1934	109	1927	47.7
1903	31.53	1935	29.19			1903	90	1935	83	1928	48.9
1904	32.38	1936	32.62			1904	92	1936	93	1929	47.0
1905	28.96	1937	43.32			1905	82	1937	123	1930	47.6
1906	35.64	1938	29.35			1906	101	1938	83	1931	49.0
1907	31.93				*In.*	1907	91			1932	47.9
1908	32.23			Winter	14.37	1908	92			1933	48.0
1909	35.87			Spring	7.82	1909	102	Temperature		1934	51.8
1910	33.43			Summer	3.13	1910	95			1935	48.1
1911	26.68			Fall	9.86	1911	76	Year	Mean	1936	48.7
1912	34.99					1912	99			1937	47.9
1913	31.50					1913	90			1938	49.8
1914	33.05					1914	94		°*F.*		
1915	34.39					1915	98	1908	49.8		
1916	33.93					1916	96	1909	48.1		
1917	33.80					1917	96	1910	49.6		

Dates of last killing frost in spring and first in fall, with length of growing season

Year	Sedro Wolley			Vancouver			Lakeside			Rosalia			Sunnyside			Walla Walla		
	Last in spring	First in fall	Growing season[1]	Last in spring	First in fall	Growing season[1]	Last in spring	First in fall	Growing season[1]	Last in spring	First in fall	Growing season[1]	Last in spring	First in fall	Growing season[1]	Last in spring	First in fall	Growing season[1]
			Days			*Days*			*Days*			*Days*			*Days*			*Days*
1899	Mar. 26	Dec. 2	251	Apr. 23	Oct. 11	171	Apr. 21	Oct. 13	175	May 15	Oct. 3	141	May 12	Oct. 10	151	Apr. 23	Dec. 2	223
1900	Apr. 28	Sept. 26	151	Feb. 17	Nov. 19	275	Mar. 6	Nov. 3	242	June 9	Aug. 26	78	Apr. 9	Oct. 1	175	Apr. 8	Nov. 18	224
1901	July 11	Sept. 28	79	Apr. 24	Dec. 11	231		Nov. 9		June 30	Sept. 15	77	Apr. 24	do	160	do	Nov. 26	232
1902	Apr. 23	Oct. 1	161	Apr. 12	Nov. 19	221	Apr. 9	Oct. 31	205	June 5	Aug. 28	84	May 18	Sept. 28	133	Apr. 13	Nov. 20	221
1903	May 24	Nov. 10	170	Apr. 15	Nov. 17	216	Apr. 11	Oct. 3	175	May 1	Sept. 26	148	May 7	Oct. 7	153	Apr. 5	Nov. 16	225
1904	Mar. 27	do	228	Apr. 23	Dec. 3	224	May 4	Oct. 9	158	June 25	Sept. 10	77	May 5	Oct. 17	165	Mar. 26	Dec. 3	252
1905	Apr. 8	Oct. 18	193	Mar. 30	Oct. 18	202	Mar. 28	Oct. 18	204	June 15	Sept. 30	107	Apr. 11	Oct. 10	182	Apr. 10	Oct. 19	192
1906	Apr. 12	Oct. 20	191	Apr. 12	Nov. 19	221	Apr. 11	Oct. 19	191	June 19	Sept. 11	84	Apr. 12	Oct. 18	189	Mar. 17	Nov. 19	247
1907	Apr. 30	Nov. 9	193	Apr. 29	Nov. 27	212	Apr. 28	Nov. 8	194	May 5	Sept. 13	131		Oct. 10		Apr. 28	Nov. 12	198
1908	Apr. 28	Sept. 16	141	Apr. 28	Sept. 24	149	Apr. 4	Sept. 25	174		Sept. 25			Sept. 25		Apr. 7	Oct. 22	198
1909	May 23	Oct. 7	137	Apr. 21	Nov. 14	207	Apr. 7	Oct. 17	193	May 5	Oct. 7	155	May 10	Sept. 18	131	Mar. 21	Nov. 14	238
1910	Apr. 17	Oct. 26	192	Apr. 14	Oct. 26	195	Mar. 29	Oct. 26	211	Apr. 16	Oct. 26	193	May 1	Oct. 21	173	Mar. 6	Oct. 27	235
1911	June 20	Oct. 18	120	Apr. 17	Oct. 27	193	Apr. 15	Oct. 19	187	May 23	Sept. 23	123	May 23	Sept. 23	123	Mar. 3	Oct. 28	239
1912	Apr. 26	Oct. 12	169	Apr. 14	Nov. 25	225	Mar. 23	Oct. 20	211	Apr. 26	Oct. 21	178	Apr. 26	Oct. 7	164	Mar. 21	Oct. 31	224
1913	Apr. 29	Oct. 29	183	Apr. 25	Nov. 12	203	Apr. 29	Oct. 16	170	May 2	Oct. 15	166	May 2	Oct. 3	154	Apr. 2	Dec. 3	245
1914	May 16	Nov. 14	182	Feb. 17	Nov. 18	274	Apr. 1	Nov. 14	227	May 28	Oct. 22	147	Apr. 29	Oct. 21	175	Feb. 18	Nov. 15	270
1915	Apr. 23	Nov. 10	201	Feb. 19	Nov. 27	281	Mar. 26	Nov. 6	225	May 1	Oct. 6	158	Apr. 9	Oct. 7	181	Mar. 26	Nov. 7	226
1916	May 12	Oct. 1	142	Mar. 29	Oct. 4	189	Apr. 23	Oct. 4	164	June 11	Sept. 10	91	May 11	Sept. 28	140	Mar. 14	Oct. 8	208
1917	Apr. 22	Oct. 17	178	Mar. 17	Oct. 18	215	May 17	Oct. 28	164	May 17	Oct. 17	153	May 16	Oct. 17	154	Mar. 30	Oct. 18	202
1918	Apr. 27	Nov. 25	212	Apr. 4	Nov. 27	237		Oct. 22		May 27	Nov. 22	179	May 8	Oct. 22	167	Apr. 3	Nov. 8	219
1919	May 5	Sept. 28	146	Apr. 8	Oct. 19	194	Apr. 15	Sept. 28	166	June 12	Sept. 29	109	May 12	Sept. 29	140	Apr. 15	Oct. 24	192
1920	May 13	Oct. 30	170	Mar. 31	Nov. 5	219		Oct. 31		May 31	Oct. 22	144	Apr. 24	Oct. 13	172	Apr. 3	Oct. 31	211
1921	Apr. 6	Oct. 22	199	Apr. 4	Nov. 20	230	Apr. 9	Oct. 23	197	May 3	Sept. 13	133	May 11	Sept. 12	124	Apr. 4	Oct. 23	202
1922	May 9	Oct. 29	173	Mar. 27	Nov. 3	221	May 9	Oct. 29	173	May 10	Sept. 8	121	May 9	Oct. 28	172	May 9	Oct. 29	173
1923	Mar. 3	Oct. 26	237	Mar. 3	Nov. 18	260	Mar. 14	Oct. 28	228	Apr. 14	Oct. 23	192	May 30	Oct. 23	146	Mar. 18	do	225
1924	Apr. 22	Oct. 10	171	Apr. 24	Oct. 10	169	Apr. 24	Nov. 9	199	Apr. 25	Sept. 11	139	May 5	Oct. 11	159	Apr. 24	Nov. 12	202
1925	Apr. 14	Oct. 13	182	Mar. 23	Nov. 22	244	May 8	Oct. 30	175	do	Sept. 21	149	Apr. 20	Oct. 18	181	Mar. 26	Nov. 1	220
1926	Apr. 1	Sept. 23	175	Mar. 7	Dec. 4	272	Mar. 24	Sept. 23	183	Apr. 23	Sept. 23	153	May 24	Sept. 24	123	Mar. 6	Sept. 24	202
1927	Mar. 29	Oct. 30	215	Apr. 20	Dec. 6	230	Apr. 19	Oct. 30	194	May 7	Oct. 31	177	Apr. 21	Oct. 29	191	Apr. 21	Nov. 22	215
1928	Apr. 6	Oct. 12	189	Apr. 6	Oct. 21	198	Apr. 7	Nov. 1	208	May 2	Sept. 20	141	May 2	Oct. 13	164	Apr. 8	Oct. 12	197
1929	Apr. 9	Oct. 7	181	Apr. 1	Oct. 29	211	Apr. 11	Oct. 28	200	Apr. 25	Sept. 29	157	June 3	Sept. 30	119	Apr. 1	Oct. 29	211
1930	May 8	Oct. 10	155	Mar. 1	Nov. 26	270	Mar. 16	Oct. 14	212	May 26	Oct. 10	137	May 7	Oct. 9	155	Mar. 16	Oct. 30	228
1931	Apr. 19	Oct. 7	171	Mar. 14	Nov. 21	252	Apr. 17	Nov. 2	199	May 8	Oct. 8	153	Apr. 20	Oct. 8	171	Mar. 28	Nov. 12	229
1932	Apr. 21	do	169	Mar. 12	Nov. 10	243	Mar. 12	Oct. 29	231	May 26	Sept. 21	118	do	Sept. 21	154	Mar. 12	Nov. 10	243
1933	Apr. 19	Oct. 31	195	Apr. 10	Nov. 14	218	Apr. 9	Oct. 20	194	Apr. 19	Sept. 27	161	May 6	Sept. 25	142	Apr. 8	Nov. 4	210
1934	Mar. 25	Dec. 5	255	Apr. 3	Dec. 5	246	Mar. 23	Nov. 27	249	May 21	Nov. 11	174	Apr. 3	Nov. 26	237	Mar. 24	Oct. 16	206
1935	Apr. 9	Oct. 29	203	Feb. 25	Oct. 29	246	Apr. 3	Oct. 21	201	May 3	Aug. 16	105	Apr. 20	Oct. 22	185	Apr. 3	Oct. 23	203
1936	Apr. 4	Nov. 1	211	Apr. 1	Nov. 2	215	do	Oct. 29	209	Apr. 2	Oct. 21	202	Apr. 5	Sept. 16	164	Apr. 4	Nov. 1	211
1937	Feb. 20	Nov. 14	267	Feb. 17	Dec. 1	287	Mar. 18	Nov. 13	240	Apr. 21	Aug. 29	130	Apr. 29	Nov. 4	189	Mar. 21	Nov. 19	243
1938	Apr. 5	Oct. 17	195	do	Nov. 11	267	Mar. 27	Nov. 5	223	Apr. 2	Oct. 17	198	May 2	Oct. 17	168	Mar. 29	Nov. 6	222
Mean	Apr. 22	Oct. 22	184	Mar. 30	do	226	Apr. 9	Oct. 25	199	May 13	Sept. 30	140	do	Oct. 10	161	Mar. 31	Nov. 5	219
Extremes	Feb. 20[2]	Sept. 16[4]	[6] 79	Feb. 17[2]	Sept. 24[4]	[6] 149	Mar. 6[2]	Sept. 23[4]	[6] 164	Apr. 2[2]	Aug. 16[4]	[6] 77	Apr. 3[2]	Sept. 12[4]	[6] 119	Feb. 18[2]	Sept. 24[4]	[6] 173
	July 11[3]	Dec. 5[5]	[7] 267	Apr. 29[3]	Dec. 11[5]	[7] 287	May 17[3]	Nov. 27[5]	[7] 249	June 30[3]	Nov. 22[5]	[7] 202	June 3[3]	Nov. 26[5]	[7] 237	May 9[3]	Dec. 3[5]	[7] 270

[1] Number of days between last killing frost in spring and first in fall.
[2] Earliest date in spring.
[3] Latest date in spring.
[4] Earliest date in fall.
[5] Latest date in fall.
[6] Shortest growing season.
[7] Longest growing season.

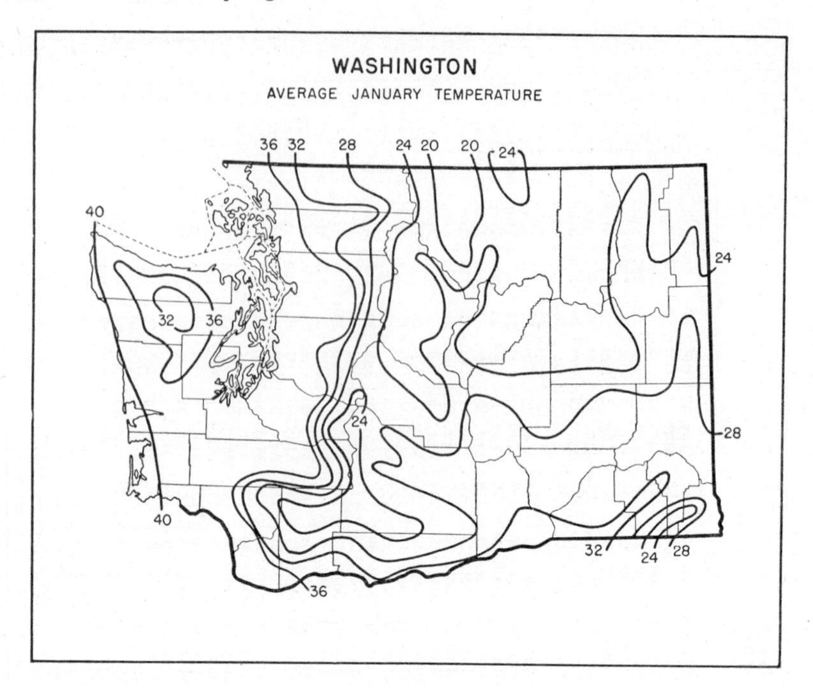
WASHINGTON
AVERAGE JANUARY TEMPERATURE
36
32
28
24
20
20
24
40
32
36
24
24
28
40
32
24
28
36

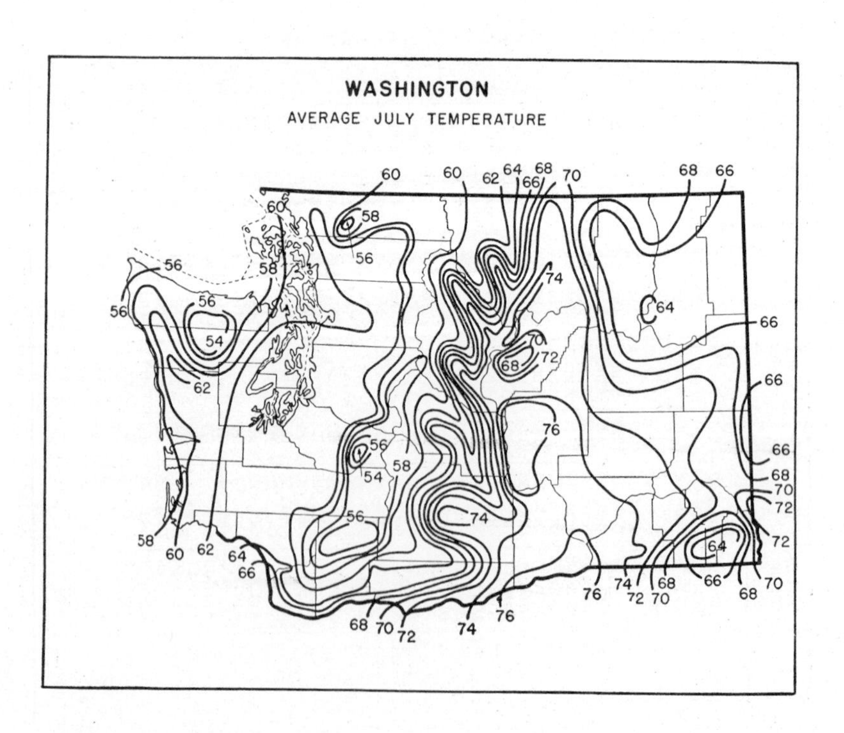
WASHINGTON
AVERAGE JULY TEMPERATURE
60
60
62
64
68
66
70
68
66
60
58
56
56
58
56
56
54
62
74
64
66
70
72
68
66
76
56
58
54
56
74
66
68
70
72
72
58
60
62
64
66
76
74
72
68
70
66
64
68
70
68
70
72
74
76

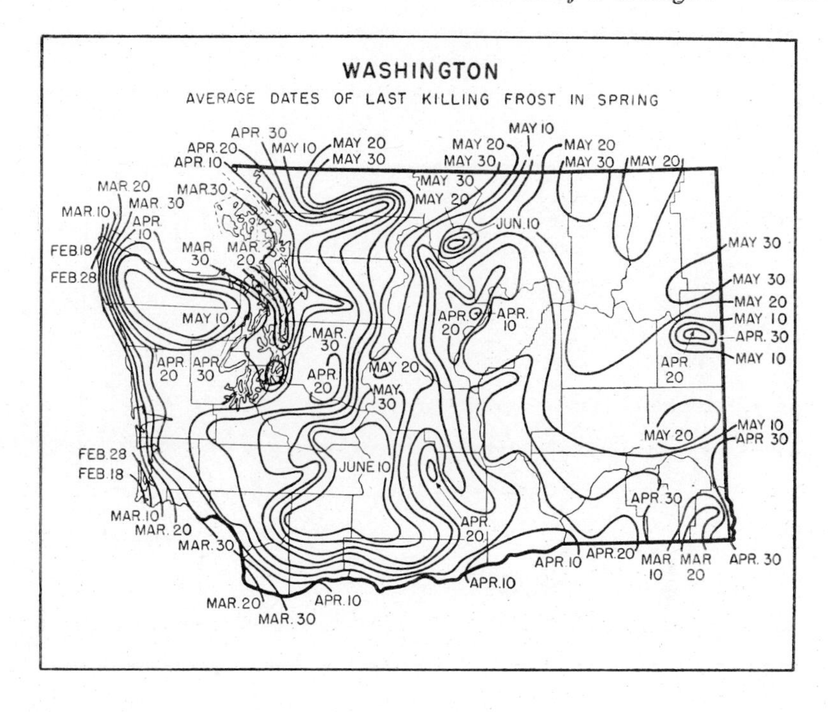
WASHINGTON
AVERAGE DATES OF LAST KILLING FROST IN SPRING
APR. 30
APR. 20
MAY 10
MAY 20
MAY 30
APR. 10
MAY 10
MAY 20
MAY 30
MAY 20
MAY 30
MAY 20
MAR. 20
MAR. 10
MAR. 30
APR. 10
FEB. 18
FEB. 28
MAR. 30
MAR. 20
JUN. 10
MAY 30
MAY 20
MAY 10
APR. 30
MAY 10
APR. 20
APR. 10
MAR. 30
APR. 20
APR. 30
MAY 20
MAY 30
APR. 20
MAY 20
MAY 10
APR 30
FEB. 28
FEB. 18
JUNE 10
APR. 30
MAR. 10
MAR. 20
APR. 20
MAR. 30
APR. 10
APR. 20
MAR. 10
MAR 20
APR. 30
APR. 10
MAR. 20
APR. 10
MAR. 30

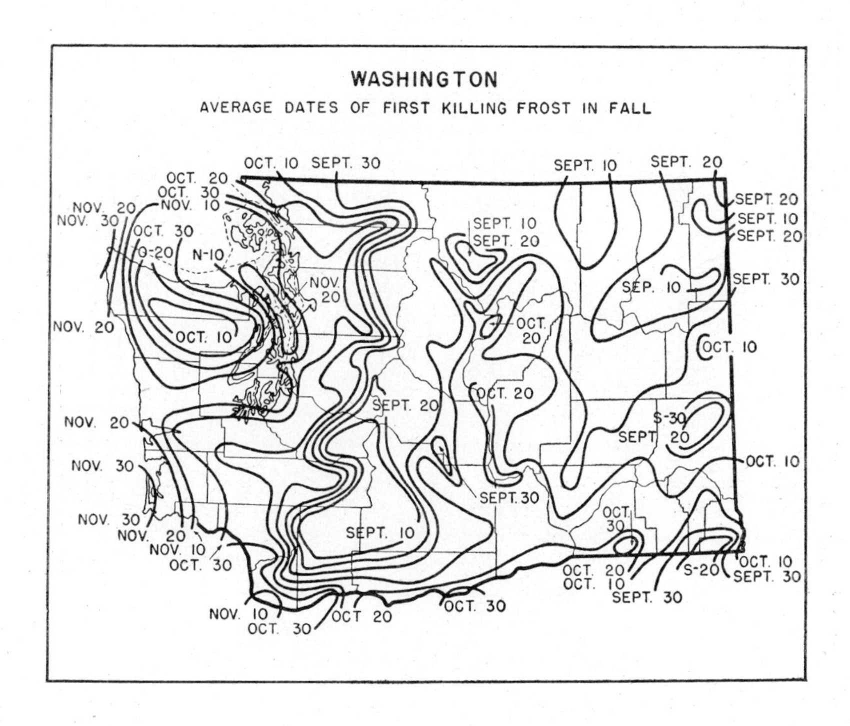
WASHINGTON
AVERAGE DATES OF FIRST KILLING FROST IN FALL
OCT. 10
SEPT. 30
SEPT. 10
SEPT. 20
OCT. 20
OCT. 30
NOV. 20
NOV. 10
NOV. 30
SEPT. 20
SEPT. 10
SEPT. 20
SEPT. 10
SEPT. 20
OCT. 30
O-20
N-10
NOV. 20
SEP. 10
SEPT. 30
NOV. 20
OCT. 10
OCT. 20
OCT. 10
SEPT. 20
OCT. 20
NOV. 20
S-30
SEPT. 20
NOV. 30
OCT. 10
SEPT. 30
NOV. 30
NOV. 20
NOV. 10
OCT. 30
SEPT. 10
OCT. 30
OCT. 20
OCT. 10
S-20
OCT. 10
SEPT. 30
SEPT. 30
NOV. 10
OCT. 30
OCT 20
OCT. 30

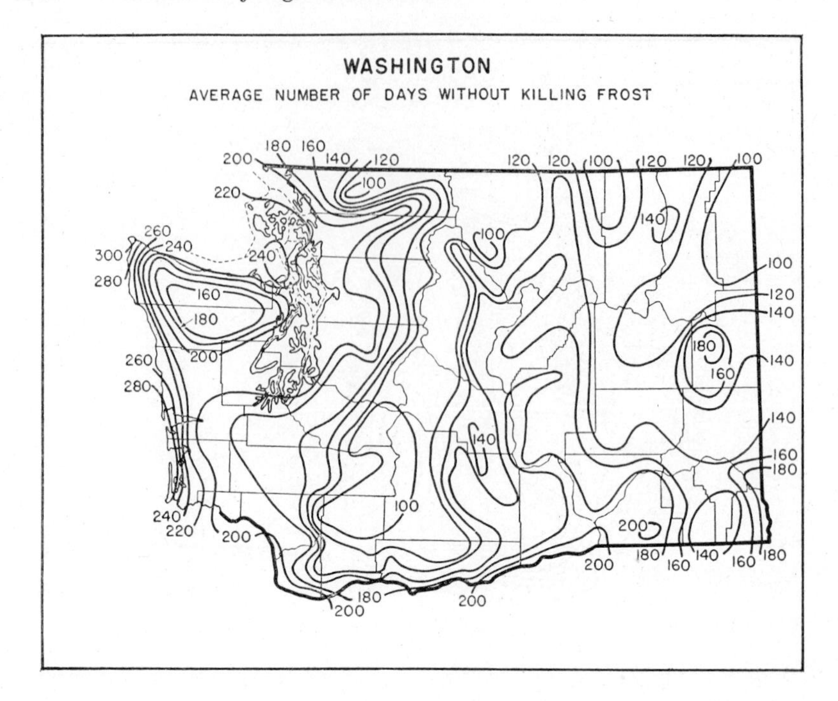
WASHINGTON
AVERAGE NUMBER OF DAYS WITHOUT KILLING FROST

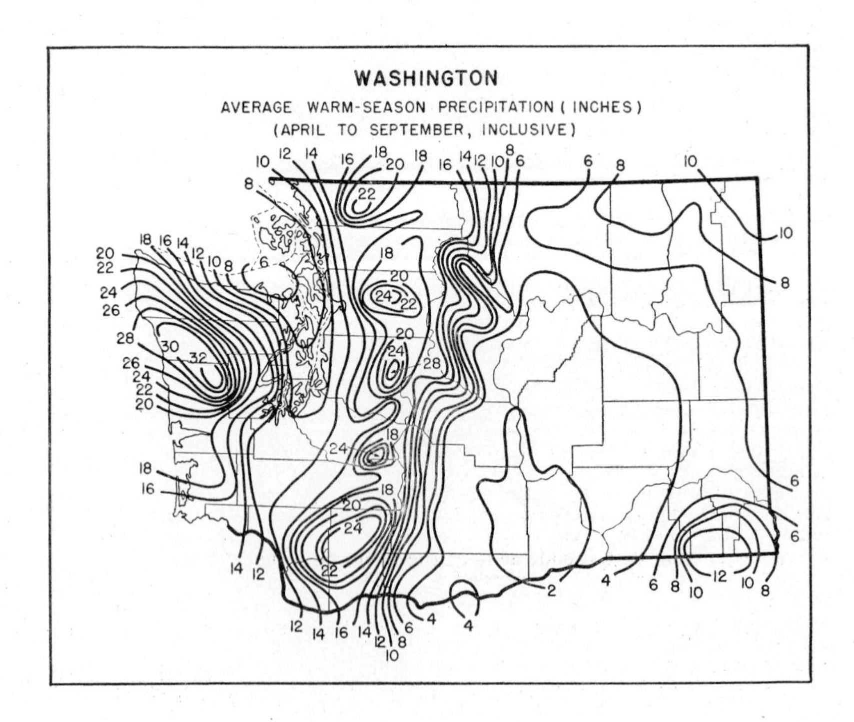
WASHINGTON
AVERAGE WARM-SEASON PRECIPITATION (INCHES)
(APRIL TO SEPTEMBER, INCLUSIVE)

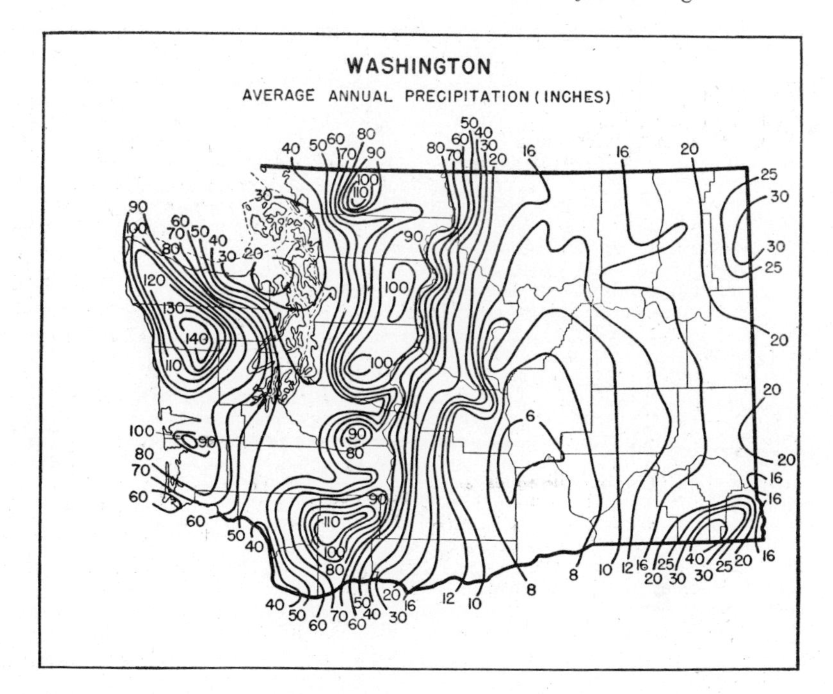

SUPPLEMENTARY CLIMATIC NOTES FOR WASHINGTON

Washington, in the northwestern corner of the United States, borders on the Pacific Ocean and extends eastward more than 350 miles, nearly to the 117th meridian. Its extreme northern boundary is the 49th parallel of latitude and much of its southern boundary is the Columbia River, which extends below the 46th parallel. The Cascade Range, 50 miles or more wide, extends in a north-south direction from British Columbia to the Columbia River and divides the State into a western and an eastern part, whose areas are to each other as 2 is to 3. Several peaks are from 10,000 to 12,000 feet high, while Mount Rainier exceeds 14,000 feet. The Olympic Mountains are the highest in the Coast Range, reaching nearly 8,000 feet. In the northeast is a series of north-south ranges, while in the extreme east are the beginnings of the Rocky Mountains, including the Blue Mountains in the extreme southeast.

The Columbia River enters the State in the northeast and drains all of eastern and part of southwestern Washington. The Chehalis, flowing westward through the Coast Range, drains a part of the west, south of Puget Sound. Other streams in the western part of the State drain into Puget Sound, the inland waters north to the Strait of Georgia, the Strait of Juan de Fuca, and the Pacific Ocean.

The climate of Washington is modified greatly by the influence of the Pacific Ocean and the mountain ranges, which trend north and south and hence lie athwart the prevailing westerly air currents from the ocean as well as the easterly currents from the interior of the continent. Air reaching the State from the west has acquired much water vapor in passing over the ocean and has a cooling effect in summer and is a warming influence in winter. The marine influence is most pronounced on the coast and decreases inland, especially on crossing the Cascade Range, yet even eastern Washington has milder temperatures than the northern Plains. The climate of the western part of the State is much milder than that of any other section of the continent in the same latitude.

Easterly and northeasterly winds from high barometric pressure systems bring cold weather in winter and warm in summer. Some large mountain areas have no residents and no records, while some of the desert regions are not so well represented by climatic data as the more populous lowland areas. Cold spells come on gradually, especially in the west, and warm periods are mostly of short duration.

Precipitation attends low-pressure systems, the west-to-east paths of which lie to the south in winter, while in summer moderately high pressure is more frequent and precipitation is infrequent. The dry season reaches its climax in July and August, after which the rainy season comes on gradually, reaching its peak in November, December, or January.

Precipitation is heaviest near the ocean and on the windward, or southwesterly, slopes of the mountains, and lightest on the leeward slopes. Condensation of moisture in the air is accelerated by dynamic cooling when the air rises to cross the mountains and is diminished by warming through compression when it descends the leeward slopes. Irrigation is vital to agriculture in central Washington valleys and is also practiced locally in the west, owing to the summer dryness. Agricultural pursuits vary greatly according to climatic conditions. The principal wheat-producing section is on the rolling to hilly plateau of east-central and extreme southeastern Washington. West of this to the Columbia River is considerable desert land, which it is proposed to irrigate by the Grand Coulee Dam project.

Great quantities of apples and other fruits of exceptional quality and color are produced under irrigation in the Yakima, Wenatchee, Columbia, Okanogan, and Walla Walla Valleys. Berries, cherries, and prunes thrive in western Washington where there are important garden districts; the Skagit Flats are noted for garden seeds and oats. Sugar beets are produced in the Yakima Valley and in the vicinity of Bellingham, while pears are grown locally for eastern markets, for canning, and for seed. Cattle and sheep are raised in the east near summer mountain pastures, and there is much dairying and condensing of milk in the west. Vast forests still cover the mountains.

The difference between the average temperature for the warmest month and that for the coldest at North Head on the extreme south coast is only 15° F. The corresponding range at Vancouver, which is inland on the Columbia River in western Washington, is 28°. At Kennewick, also on the Columbia River, but located in the south-central interior, the range is 43°. The lowest mean annual temperature for any station is 38° at Paradise Inn, elevation 5,550 feet, on the south slope of Mount Rainier, and the highest is 55° at Mottinger, Benton County, on the Columbia River. Along the coast, temperatures are moderate and equable.

The dates of the last killing frost in spring and the first in autumn and the length of the growing season vary greatly with proximity to water, elevation above sea level, and hill or valley exposure. The longest growing season is on Tatoosh Island, and the longest in the eastern part is around Walla Walla.

The average annual precipitation ranges from 6 inches at Hanford, in south-central Washington on the Columbia River, to 146 at Wynoochee Oxbow in the foothills south of the Olympic Mountains. Thus Washington has by far a greater range in precipitation than is found in any other State. The average annual snowfall ranges from 5 inches on the ocean coast to 600 at Paradise Inn, where the maximum depth on the ground has exceeded 27 feet.

The relative humidity is highest on the coast and lowest in the valleys of south-central Washington. Periods of very low humidity occur at times in the warmer half of the year and create a great fire hazard in the forests and in grain fields about harvest time.

Fogs are rare in summer except on the ocean coast, where they are most frequent in August. Inland they occur with increasing frequency as autumn advances, reaching a maximum in October in the interior of western Washington, where dense fogs occur for an appreciable length of time on an average of 30 days a year. In eastern Washington they occur in winter on about 15 days.

The percentage of the possible amount of sunshine is low in winter and high in summer, when the number of possible hours is double that of winter. There is slightly more sunshine on the coast in winter than at interior stations, even in eastern Washington, but at all other times of the year eastern Washington has the most. July has 85 percent of the possible amount at Walla Walla, as compared with 65 at Seattle and 51 at North Head. The great amount of sunshine, the low humidity, and the comparative absence of rain are favorable for the grain harvest and the curing of hay.

The wind sometimes attains hurricane force on the ocean coast. The inland waters do not experience such winds, but more or less damage does occur at times in the storm season. Tornadoes are unknown in western Washington. Duststorms may occur in the east in the windier months when the light surface soil is dry, while whirlwinds that cause limited damage are sometimes noted. Wind directions are much influenced by local topography. In summer months northerly winds prevail, especially in the daytime.

Thunderstorms are very infrequent and usually feeble in western sections. They occur more often in the warmer eastern part of the State and are most apt to be observed in the mountains in summer. They are often accompanied by little or no rain, when lightning frequently starts forest fires.

LAWRENCE C. FISHER, *Senior Meteorologist and Climatic Section Director for Washington, Weather Bureau, Seattle.*

WEST VIRGINIA

Climatic summary

County [1]	Station	Temperature					Killing frost average dates				Average precipitation													
		Length of record	January average	July average	Maximum	Minimum	Length of record	Last in spring	First in fall	Growing season [2]	Length of record	January	February	March	April	May	June	July	August	September	October	November	December	Annual
		Yr.	°*F.*	°*F.*	°*F.*	°*F.*	*Yr.*			*Days*	*Yr.*	*In.*	*In.*	*In.*	*In.*	*In.*	*In.*	*In.*	*In.*	*In.*	*In.*	*In.*	*In.*	*In.*
Barbour	Philippi	29	33.0	72.3	101	−34	28	May 9	Oct. 13	157	39	4.28	3.27	4.22	3.80	4.42	4.79	4.92	4.29	3.41	3.23	3.00	3.85	47.48
Berkeley	Martinsburg	40	31.0	75.7	112	−19	40	Apr. 22	Oct. 16	177	40	2.70	2.47	3.38	3.30	3.61	4.26	3.61	4.09	3.05	3.11	2.28	2.85	38.71
Boone	Madison	21	36.6	74.8	104	−11					10	4.00	3.23	4.38	4.30	4.32	3.73	5.42	4.10	3.48	2.85	2.50	2.76	45.07
Braxton	Sutton	34	34.3	74.8	105	−21	29	Apr. 30	Oct. 17	170	35	4.71	3.55	4.51	4.16	4.61	4.96	5.64	4.81	3.38	3.21	3.48	4.05	51.07
Brooke	Wellsburg	40	30.2	72.2	106	−26	40	May 3	Oct. 10	160	39	3.32	2.28	3.52	3.35	3.45	4.34	4.46	3.91	3.28	2.77	2.63	2.93	40.24
Cabell	Huntington	40	34.0	76.6	108	−24	39	Apr. 17	Oct. 20	186	39	4.00	3.05	4.29	3.58	4.07	4.22	4.46	3.81	2.58	2.58	2.66	3.47	42.77
Clay	Clay	13	33.8	72.8	104	−13					24	3.62	3.14	4.35	3.53	4.07	4.41	5.06	4.86	3.11	3.19	3.13	3.63	46.10
Doddridge	Central Station	23	32.1	73.1	102	−27	15	May 10	Oct. 2	145	17	3.52	2.69	3.11	3.29	3.67	4.33	4.62	3.50	3.07	2.41	2.43	3.34	39.98
Fayette	Kanawha Falls										20	3.54	2.73	3.69	3.60	4.06	3.97	5.07	4.66	2.93	3.10	2.88	3.22	43.45
	Nuttallburg	23	31.8	71.4	107	−21	18	May 1	Oct. 10	162	18	3.32	2.58	3.77	3.25	3.74	4.50	4.32	3.07	3.18	2.38	2.33	3.09	39.53
	Powellton	36	37.0	74.4	102	−20	31	Apr. 26	Oct. 14	171	22	3.87	2.89	4.45	3.65	4.24	4.61	4.27	4.14	2.88	2.55	2.81	2.93	43.29
Gilmer	Glenville	40	33.8	75.3	107	−29	39	May 2	Oct. 15	166	40	4.52	3.52	4.36	3.78	4.34	4.49	4.88	4.38	3.22	3.14	3.10	3.90	47.63
Grant	Bayard	35	28.8	67.6	95	−30	34	May 25	Sept. 21	119	34	4.90	3.76	4.77	4.15	4.80	5.40	5.12	5.07	3.78	3.87	3.15	4.13	52.90
	Stony River Dam										19	3.14	2.76	3.60	3.79	4.66	4.00	4.17	4.44	2.88	3.38	2.82	3.17	42.75
Greenbrier	Lewisburg	37	32.4	71.0	102	−37	35	May 8	Oct. 5	150	36	3.53	2.79	3.62	3.35	3.36	3.85	4.09	4.03	2.65	2.95	2.45	3.02	39.69
	White Sulphur Springs	27	32.1	71.6	101	−34	22	May 15	Oct. 6	144	22	3.13	2.67	3.54	3.08	3.18	3.40	4.20	3.47	3.07	2.77	2.30	2.87	37.68
Hampshire	Romney	37	31.5	74.9	109	−20	38	May 3	Oct. 7	157	38	2.54	2.05	2.98	3.03	3.37	3.98	3.55	3.82	2.96	2.61	1.84	2.23	34.96
Hancock	New Cumberland	40	28.6	73.0	109	−23	38	May 8	Oct. 12	157	39	3.00	2.22	3.36	3.25	3.38	4.43	3.99	3.60	3.01	2.65	2.30	2.70	37.89
Hardy	Moorefield	34	33.0	74.6	112	−27	36	May 1	Oct. 4	156	33	2.33	2.17	2.63	3.07	3.36	3.88	3.21	3.02	2.46	2.29	1.53	2.10	32.05
	Wardensville	19	30.8	70.6	105	−25	18	May 15	Oct. 1	139	17	2.08	1.76	2.53	2.78	3.08	2.74	3.61	4.34	2.55	3.04	1.64	1.92	32.07
Harrison	Benson	16	34.1	72.5	101	−23					14	4.07	3.07	4.00	3.37	4.25	4.24	4.75	4.87	3.62	3.11	3.10	3.35	45.80
	Clarksburg	16	32.6	73.8	102	−23	16	May 5	Oct. 11	159	16	3.50	2.82	3.44	3.26	3.87	4.06	4.17	4.71	3.41	2.90	2.87	2.96	42.06
	Lost Creek	40	32.9	72.2	104	−35	40	May 10	Oct. 3	146	40	4.08	3.01	3.90	3.43	4.16	4.33	4.22	4.19	3.08	2.94	2.79	3.47	43.60
	West Milford										13	3.86	3.05	3.98	3.74	4.08	4.45	4.32	5.07	3.53	3.18	3.13	3.08	45.47
Jackson	Cuba	21	33.5	73.4	103	−27	20	Apr. 30	Oct. 9	162	21	3.67	2.78	3.93	3.52	3.50	3.97	3.86	3.18	2.26	3.20	2.48	3.36	39.71
	Ravenswood	16	35.4	75.1	109	−22	16	do	Oct. 11	164	16	3.92	2.52	3.60	3.01	3.64	3.84	4.80	3.79	2.68	2.69	2.79	2.88	40.16
Jefferson	Harpers Ferry										40	2.75	2.29	3.05	3.36	3.29	3.67	3.59	4.21	2.86	3.28	2.13	2.65	37.13
Kanawha	Charleston	37	37.9	76.9	108	−17	35	Apr. 20	Oct. 23	186	39	4.13	3.34	4.45	3.88	3.87	4.26	4.95	4.39	2.88	2.97	3.12	3.56	45.80
	Dam No. 6										13	3.53	2.62	3.61	3.14	3.06	3.10	5.03	4.78	2.52	3.07	2.35	2.60	39.41
	Kayford										21	4.10	3.32	4.54	3.99	4.71	5.13	6.07	5.38	3.64	3.84	3.20	3.89	51.81
Lewis	Roanoke										15	3.95	3.02	3.98	3.39	4.64	4.49	4.83	4.95	3.31	3.35	3.19	3.28	46.38
	Weston	40	34.1	74.4	105	−30	32	May 3	Oct. 12	162	38	4.31	3.54	4.39	3.75	4.35	4.64	4.72	4.09	2.95	2.91	3.01	3.83	46.49
Logan	Logan	13	39.0	76.0	102	−9	12	Apr. 16	Oct. 26	193	28	4.25	3.49	5.01	4.20	4.25	4.77	5.10	4.25	2.92	2.78	2.93	3.92	47.87
	Sharples										18	3.29	3.26	4.10	3.75	3.78	4.27	5.12	4.47	3.07	2.77	3.02	3.40	44.30
Marion	Dam No. 10										17	3.56	2.75	4.13	3.65	4.26	4.09	3.94	4.09	3.36	2.94	2.98	3.18	42.93
	Dam No. 15										17	3.61	2.85	3.78	3.45	3.96	3.91	4.10	4.09	3.06	3.00	3.00	3.01	41.82
	Fairmount	33	32.2	74.3	108	−20	34	May 1	Oct. 14	166	40	3.92	2.96	4.00	3.26	4.04	4.42	4.41	3.89	3.01	2.97	2.75	3.45	43.08
	Mannington	38	31.9	71.8	101	−31	37	May 9	Oct. 7	151	37	4.21	2.87	4.06	3.79	4.12	4.29	4.77	4.18	3.39	3.03	2.89	3.50	45.10

Marshall	Dam No. 13										23	3.33	2.35	3.39	3.18	3.55	3.52	4.11	4.13	3.44	2.74	2.75	2.84	39.33
	Moundsville	24	32.0	74.1	107	−21	29	May 4	Oct. 13	162	23	3.15	2.26	3.29	2.95	3.30	3.60	4.29	3.44	3.27	3.07	1.99	2.93	37.54
Mason	Hogsett										2	6.04	2.48	2.22	3.46	4.01	4.78	4.48	3.14	3.48	2.77	2.20	1.60	40.66
	Point Pleasant	40	34.1	76.4	106	−26	39	Apr. 23	Oct. 16	176	40	3.96	3.10	4.15	3.39	4.05	4.19	4.39	3.35	2.55	2.75	2.79	3.51	42.18
McDowell	Elkhorn	21	37.3	72.2	95	−17	18	Apr. 24	Oct. 12	171	19	3.62	3.13	4.54	3.44	3.72	5.28	5.67	3.56	2.88	2.62	2.54	3.27	44.27
	Gary	22	35.1	73.1	102	−9	18	Apr. 27	Oct. 15	171	22	3.53	3.28	4.09	3.55	4.15	4.41	4.62	4.79	2.90	3.12	2.73	3.34	44.51
Mercer	Bluefield	40	34.9	71.6	98	−25	37	Apr. 28	Oct. 11	166	38	3.25	3.10	3.53	3.34	3.30	4.23	4.40	4.07	2.62	2.93	2.30	3.05	40.12
	Princeton	14	33.0	68.5	89	−16					14	5.49	4.12	6.32	5.72	5.24	7.18	6.11	5.26	3.92	3.64	3.57	4.40	60.97
Mineral	Burlington	26	30.8	72.7	109	−27	27	May 6	Oct. 2	149	27	2.64	2.16	3.04	2.70	3.93	3.89	3.41	3.74	2.93	2.08	1.66	2.66	34.84
	Piedmont	23	30.9	72.3	104	−15	23	Apr. 29	Oct. 9	163	23	2.82	2.22	3.09	3.49	3.52	3.55	3.44	3.70	2.48	2.90	2.03	2.33	35.57
Mingo	Williamson	39	36.0	76.1	105	−13	37	Apr. 13	Oct. 26	196	38	4.01	3.28	4.62	3.89	4.12	4.48	4.55	4.13	2.83	2.75	2.89	3.72	45.27
Monongalia	Morgantown	40	32.3	73.5	105	−25	39	May 1	Oct. 13	165	40	3.47	2.60	3.51	3.25	3.90	4.25	4.22	3.96	2.90	3.00	2.48	3.07	40.61
Monroe	Union	36	33.3	71.6	102	−34	32	May 10	Oct. 5	148	34	3.28	2.88	3.44	2.85	2.93	3.73	4.08	3.77	2.49	2.90	2.30	2.74	37.39
Ohio	Wheeling	31	30.4	74.8	110	−18	40	Apr. 25	Oct. 19	177	40	3.15	2.38	3.36	3.20	3.47	4.10	4.38	3.45	3.10	2.60	2.46	2.91	38.56
Pendleton	Brandywine	23	30.9	71.3	102	−28	22	May 15	Sept. 28	136	23	2.20	1.75	2.70	2.93	3.00	3.29	3.40	3.45	2.48	2.43	1.96	1.74	31.33
	Upper Tract	37	32.7	71.7	104	−28	39	May 9	Oct. 3	147	20	1.56	1.47	2.14	2.47	2.49	2.43	3.03	2.60	2.19	2.05	1.55	1.16	25.14
Pleasants	Bens Run	38	32.9	75.1	106	−15	38	Apr. 12	Oct. 20	191	38	3.97	2.94	3.98	3.65	4.15	4.40	4.34	4.42	2.47	2.91	2.81	3.58	43.62
	St. Marys										30	4.10	3.00	3.83	3.54	3.84	4.02	4.27	4.70	2.94	3.00	2.94	3.47	43.65
Pocahontas	Arbovale										14	2.98	2.71	3.51	3.04	3.45	3.71	4.80	3.90	2.62	3.10	3.06	2.82	39.70
	Marlinton	40	28.0	67.6	100	−27	35	May 15	Oct. 3	141	32	3.94	3.25	4.51	3.55	4.07	4.65	4.97	4.76	3.10	3.18	2.94	3.72	46.64
Preston	Bruceton Mills										24	4.73	3.56	4.06	3.78	4.46	4.86	5.14	4.78	3.79	4.06	3.35	4.21	50.78
	Rowlesburg										36	4.73	3.75	4.86	4.17	4.79	5.34	5.44	4.54	3.61	3.41	3.32	4.37	52.33
	Terra Alta	37	27.9	68.2	95	−24	34	May 19	Sept. 26	130	34	4.97	3.64	4.54	4.19	5.04	5.97	5.31	5.09	3.67	4.01	3.15	4.73	54.31
Putman	Bancroft	38	34.3	74.7	106	−19	34	Apr. 24	Oct. 19	178	36	4.20	2.90	3.94	3.54	3.89	4.19	4.56	4.50	2.94	2.93	2.67	3.35	43.61
	Robertsburg	39	33.3	75.4	106	−22	38	Apr. 25	Oct. 15	173	39	3.94	2.89	3.87	3.41	3.49	3.80	3.88	3.64	2.46	2.69	2.57	3.29	39.93
Raleigh	Beckley	34	33.4	71.2	103	−20	31	May 7	Oct. 4	150	32	4.15	3.02	4.28	3.83	3.93	4.52	5.14	3.81	2.84	3.14	2.66	3.45	44.77
Randolph	Elkins	40	30.4	70.3	99	−28	40	May 4	Oct. 12	161	40	4.08	3.14	4.31	3.82	4.48	5.15	5.48	4.14	3.49	3.06	2.83	3.55	47.53
	Pickens	40	30.9	68.6	98	−21	37	May 13	Oct. 3	143	37	6.80	5.62	6.70	5.55	5.89	6.33	6.35	5.97	4.57	4.56	4.55	5.81	68.70
Ritchie	Cairo		34.4	74.3	105	−30	29	May 6	Oct. 7	154	30	4.24	3.06	4.11	3.39	3.69	4.76	4.53	4.10	3.10	2.86	2.86	3.60	44.30
Roane	Ryan	37	33.0	73.1	102	−30					36	4.16	3.21	4.34	3.73	3.78	4.40	4.73	4.19	2.86	3.27	2.79	3.44	44.90
	Spencer	40	33.7	73.6	105	−27	35	May 2	Oct. 9	160	36	4.20	3.16	4.11	3.49	3.91	4.47	4.39	4.31	2.87	3.21	2.72	3.45	44.29
Summers	Green Sulphur Springs.	27	33.1	72.5	105	−22	23	May 5	Oct. 7	155	23	3.47	3.02	4.19	3.79	4.01	4.27	4.02	3.42	2.67	2.44	2.30	3.13	40.73
	Hinton	37	34.5	74.4	105	−13	36	Apr. 24	Oct. 23	182	40	3.38	2.97	4.01	3.19	3.52	4.18	4.19	3.98	2.61	2.75	2.42	3.08	40.28
Taylor	Grafton	38	32.6	72.6	104	−27	35	May 4	Oct. 10	159	36	4.23	3.00	4.17	3.63	4.13	4.46	4.74	4.45	3.14	3.32	2.92	3.57	45.76
Tucker	Cortland										18	4.25	3.53	3.86	4.06	4.59	4.90	5.35	4.13	3.23	3.42	2.84	3.74	47.90
	Davis										25	5.22	4.22	4.41	4.26	4.68	5.32	5.35	4.90	3.81	3.85	3.14	5.10	54.26
	Parsons	40	34.5	70.8	102	−28	39	May 13	Oct. 5	145	40	4.48	3.39	4.44	3.76	4.29	4.86	5.23	4.31	3.12	3.29	2.83	3.86	47.86
Tyler	Alma (near)										12	3.20	2.27	3.77	3.36	3.91	4.47	4.03	5.20	2.88	2.86	2.97	2.79	41.71
Upshur	Aberdeen										14	3.94	3.04	4.30	3.70	4.39	4.43	4.72	5.21	3.35	3.42	3.14	3.15	46.86
	Buckhannon	39	32.5	71.8	99	−31	37	May 5	Oct. 7	155	38	4.49	3.82	4.69	3.96	4.62	5.05	5.09	4.33	3.13	3.24	3.26	4.07	49.75
Wayne	Wayne										14	4.18	3.00	4.52	3.49	3.66	4.23	4.57	4.21	2.75	3.06	3.11	2.76	43.54
Webster	Camden-on-Gauley										20	3.87	3.15	4.58	3.61	5.16	4.84	5.06	5.46	3.26	3.17	3.55	4.06	49.77
Wetzel	New Martinsville	40	33.1	75.2	109	−25	40	Apr. 30	Oct. 16	169	40	3.79	2.89	3.87	3.47	3.76	4.05	4.34	3.98	2.99	2.92	2.79	3.60	42.45
	Smithfield	28	30.3	72.2	106	−25	22	May 8	Oct. 13	158	24	4.81	3.41	3.90	3.67	3.95	4.63	5.14	4.12	3.35	3.39	3.34	3.93	47.64
Wirt	Creston	38	34.1	74.7	105	−26	38	May 3	Oct. 10	160	38	3.99	3.06	4.03	3.74	3.94	4.27	4.29	4.24	2.56	3.10	2.72	3.42	43.36
	Elizabeth										28	4.02	2.77	3.94	3.23	3.67	4.50	4.54	4.86	2.75	3.23	2.73	3.31	43.55
Wood	Dam No. 19										22	3.51	2.48	3.79	3.38	3.96	3.84	3.87	4.55	3.08	2.87	3.03	3.06	41.42
	Dam No. 20										22	3.53	2.74	3.92	3.27	3.67	3.69	3.94	4.33	2.93	2.97	2.86	3.12	40.97
	Parkersburg	40	32.5	75.4	106	−27	40	Apr. 18	Oct. 19	184	40	3.37	2.49	3.53	3.07	3.43	3.96	3.95	3.76	2.57	2.41	2.38	2.97	37.89

[1] The following counties, for which no records are available, are best represented by the stations indicated: Calhoun—Creston; Lincoln—Madison; Morgan—Martinsburg; Nicholas—Camden-on-Gauley; Wyoming—Gary.

[2] Length of growing season between average dates of last killing frost in spring and first in fall.

WEST VIRGINIA—Continued

Precipitation and temperature—State unit values

[This tabulation gives the mean annual, mean monthly, and average seasonal precipitation, 1886–1938, and the mean annual temperatures, 1902–38, for West Virginia]

Precipitation		Precipitation		Precipitation		Precipitation		Temperature		Temperature	
Year	Mean	Year	Mean	Year	Mean	Month	Mean	Year	Mean	Year	Mean
	In.		*In.*		*In.*		*In.*		°*F.*		°*F.*
1886	39.70	1907	52.22	1928	43.28	May	4.09	1902	52.8	1921	55.7
1887	36.45	1908	41.04	1929	46.77	June	4.39	1903	52.2	1922	53.9
1888	48.16	1909	42.18	1930	25.43	July	4.56	1904	51.4	1923	52.8
1889	42.95	1910	39.36	1931	42.36	August	4.09	1905	52.3	1924	50.7
1890	59.58	1911	46.87	1932	43.86	September	3.03	1906	54.0	1925	52.8
1891	45.96	1912	43.18	1933	48.65	October	2.88	1907	52.1	1926	51.6
1892	38.33	1913	48.29	1934	37.61	November	2.80	1908	53.6	1927	53.7
1893	39.82	1914	39.71	1935	51.13	December	3.23	1909	53.0	1928	52.3
1894	34.62	1915	44.14	1936	42.12			1910	52.3	1929	52.7
1895	32.82	1916	45.55	1937	49.86	Annual	43.36	1911	54.5	1930	53.2
1896	43.49	1917	44.11	1938	42.39			1912	51.7	1931	54.7
1897	41.59	1918	45.28					1913	54.1	1932	54.0
1898	47.63	1919	47.89	Month	Mean	Season	Average	1914	52.2	1933	54.4
1899	42.42	1920	42.05					1915	52.7	1934	53.5
1900	38.85	1921	45.46					1916	52.5	1935	53.0
1901	45.91	1922	41.30					1917	50.1	1936	53.3
1902	42.72	1923	45.04		*In.*		*In.*	1918	53.1	1937	52.9
1903	40.66	1924	47.21	January	3.67	Winter	10.08	1919	54.0	1938	54.5
1904	33.38	1925	40.66	February	3.18	Spring	11.53	1920	51.8		
1905	44.34	1926	49.60	March	3.91	Summer	13.04				
1906	44.31	1927	49.14	April	3.53	Fall	8.71				

Dates of last killing frost in spring and first in fall, with length of growing season

Year	Glenville			Hinton			Huntington			Morgantown			Parkersburg			Romney		
	Last in spring	First in fall	Growing season [1]	Last in spring	First in fall	Growing season [1]	Last in spring	First in fall	Growing season [1]	Last in spring	First in fall	Growing season [1]	Last in spring	First in fall	Growing season [1]	Last in spring	First in fall	Growing season [1]
			Days			*Days*			*Days*			*Days*			*Days*			*Days*
1899	Apr. 17	Oct. 1	167	Apr. 17	----	----	Apr. 16	Sept. 30	167	Apr. 13	Oct. 5	175	Apr. 10	Oct. 1	174	Apr. 11	Oct. 1	173
1900	May 10	Oct. 17	160	May 10	Nov. 6	180	May 3	Oct. 17	167	May 10	Oct. 17	160	May 4	Oct. 18	167	May 6	Oct. 18	165

1901	Apr. 22	Oct. 5	166	Apr. 26	Oct. 19	176	Apr. 22	do	178	Apr. 22	Oct. 4	165	Apr. 5	Oct. 4	182	Apr. 17	Oct. 4	170
1902	Apr. 18	Oct. 15	180	Apr. 18	Oct. 15	180	Apr. 14	Oct. 14	183	May 10	Oct. 15	158	Apr. 15	Oct. 15	183	May 10	Sept. 15	128
1903	May 2	Oct. 19	170	May 2			Apr. 4	Oct. 24	203	Apr. 22	Oct. 24	185	Apr. 5	Oct. 24	202	May 2	Oct. 31	182
1904		Oct. 4					Apr. 21	Oct. 26	188	Apr. 21	Oct. 4	166	Apr. 21	Oct. 16	178	Apr. 22	Oct. 4	165
1905		Oct. 13					Apr. 18	Oct. 12	177	May 20	Oct. 22	155	Apr. 19	Oct. 13	177	Apr. 23	Oct. 11	171
1906	May 10	Oct. 10	153		Oct. 11		May 9	Oct. 10	154	May 10	Oct. 11	154	May 10	Oct. 12	155	May 11	do	153
1907	May 28	do	135	Apr. 21	Nov. 8	201	Apr. 20	Oct. 14	177	May 22	Oct. 9	140	Apr. 20	Oct. 15	178	May 21	Oct. 9	141
1908	Apr. 22	Oct. 2	163	Apr. 4	Oct. 31	210	Apr. 3	Oct. 3	183	May 1	Oct. 2	154	Apr. 4	Sept. 30	179	May 2	Sept. 30	151
1909	May 4	Oct. 13	162	Apr. 11	Oct. 13	185	Apr. 11	Oct. 13	185	Apr. 24	Oct. 13	172	Apr. 11	Oct. 13	185	May 12	Oct. 13	154
1910	May 6	Oct. 23	170		Oct. 28		May 6	Oct. 28	175	May 6	Oct. 24	171	Apr. 8	Oct. 24	199	May 16	Oct. 24	161
1911	do	Nov. 2	180	May 3	Nov. 3	184	Apr. 16	Nov. 2	200	May 5	Oct. 31	179	Apr. 2	Oct. 25	206	May 6	Oct. 25	172
1912	Apr. 24	Oct. 16	175	Apr. 10	Oct. 25	198	Apr. 9	do	207	Apr. 8	Oct. 16	191	Apr. 8	Oct. 26	201	Apr. 8		
1913	May 12	Oct. 21	162	May 12	Oct. 14	155	May 11	Oct. 22	164	May 12	Oct. 23	164	May 11	Oct. 14	156			
1914	Apr. 13	Oct. 31	201	Apr. 11	Oct. 27	199	Apr. 11	Oct. 27	199	May 1	Sept. 29	151	Apr. 10	Oct. 27	200			
1915	Apr. 16	Oct. 10	177	Apr. 19	Oct. 10	174	Apr. 14	Oct. 10	179	Apr. 14	Oct. 11	180	Apr. 14	Oct. 10	179	Apr. 18	Oct. 10	175
1916	Apr. 29	Oct. 11	165	Apr. 12	Oct. 23	194	Apr. 11	Oct. 27	199	Apr. 10	Sept. 19	162	Apr. 10	Oct. 11	184	Apr. 11	Sept. 19	161
1917	May 10	Oct. 7	150	Apr. 16	Oct. 10	177	Apr. 15	Oct. 14	182	May 26	Oct. 2	129	Apr. 16	Oct. 9	176	Apr. 16	Sept. 11	148
1918	May 2	Sept. 27	148	Apr. 15	Nov. 3	202	Apr. 11	Oct. 3	175	Apr. 25			Apr. 14	Nov. 3	203	Apr. 28	Oct. 9	164
1919	Apr. 27	Nov. 3	190	Apr. 28	Nov. 6	192	Apr. 26	Nov. 6	194		Oct. 13		Apr. 27	Nov. 6	193	Apr. 27	Oct. 19	175
1920	May 16	Oct. 29	166	May 15	Oct. 29	167	Apr. 14	Oct. 30	199	May 15	Oct. 8	146	Apr. 13	Oct. 30	200	May 16	Oct. 4	141
1921	May 1	Oct. 13	165	Apr. 21	Oct. 9	171	Apr. 12	Oct. 13	184	Apr. 19	Oct. 13	177	Apr. 12	Oct. 13	184	Apr. 12	Oct. 9	180
1922	Apr. 30	do	166	Apr. 30	Oct. 19	172	Apr. 23	Oct. 27	187	Apr. 22	Oct. 19	174	Apr. 22	Oct. 19	180	Apr. 29	Sept. 27	151
1923	May 10	Oct. 8	151	May 10	Oct. 21	164	Apr. 10	Nov. 2	206	May 10	Oct. 5	148	Apr. 11	Nov. 1	204	May 11	Oct. 5	147
1924	Apr. 23	Oct. 21	181	Apr. 19	Oct. 22	186	Apr. 3	Oct. 23	203	Apr. 21	Oct. 21	183	Apr. 8	Oct. 23	198	May 5	Oct. 9	157
1925	May 27	Oct. 11	137	May 27	Oct. 11	137	Mar. 21	Oct. 11	204	May 27	Oct. 10	136	Apr. 3	Oct. 10	190	May 27	Oct. 10	136
1926	May 5	Oct. 26	174		Nov. 4		Apr. 28	Nov. 3	189	May 4	Oct. 25	174	Apr. 27	Nov. 4	191	May 5	Oct. 24	172
1927	May 1	Oct. 22	174	Apr. 25	Nov. 7	196	Apr. 24			Apr. 25	Oct. 15	173	Apr. 25	Nov. 6	195	Apr. 25	Sept. 22	150
1928	May 13	Sept. 26	136	Apr. 26	Oct. 26	183				May 13	Sept. 26	136	Apr. 26	Oct. 26	183	May 14	Sept. 21	130
1929	Apr. 24	Oct. 18	177	Apr. 19	do	190	Apr. 19	Oct. 18	182	Apr. 23	Sept. 19	149	Apr. 19	Oct. 18	182	May 17	Sept. 19	125
1930	Apr. 27	Oct. 1	157	Apr. 27	Oct. 2	158	Apr. 25	Oct. 20	178	Apr. 25	Oct. 1	159	Apr. 25	Oct. 20	178	June 1	Oct. 1	122
1931	Apr. 30	Oct. 18	171	Apr. 9	Nov. 3	208	Mar. 21	Oct. 18	211	May 1	Oct. 30	182	Apr. 8	Oct. 19	194	May 4	Oct. 13	162
1932	May 3	Oct. 29	179	Apr. 28	Oct. 29	184	Apr. 15	Oct. 30	198	Apr. 27	Nov. 2	189	Apr. 18	Nov. 2	198	May 3	Sept. 30	150
1933	Apr. 27	Oct. 26	182	Apr. 27	Oct. 26	182	Apr. 8	Oct. 26	201	do	Oct. 26	182	Apr. 24	Oct. 14	173	Apr. 27	Oct. 26	182
1934	Apr. 29	Oct. 14	168	Apr. 28	Oct. 29	184	Apr. 28	Oct. 14	169	May 28			Apr. 28	do	169	Apr. 29	Oct. 14	168
1935	May 1	Oct. 5	157	Apr. 17	Oct. 7	173	Apr. 17	Oct. 7	173	May 14	Sept. 30	149	Apr. 18	Oct. 4	169	Apr. 27	Sept. 30	156
1936	Apr. 25	Oct. 28	186	Apr. 23	Oct. 28	188	Apr. 23	Oct. 28	188	Apr. 23	Oct. 28	188	Apr. 23	Oct. 28	188	May 29	Oct. 27	151
1937	Apr. 17	Oct. 15	181	Apr. 18	Oct. 15	180	Apr. 12	Oct. 14	185	Apr. 12	Oct. 14	185	Apr. 12	Oct. 15	186	Apr. 29	Sept. 18	142
1938	May 12	Oct. 25	166	Apr. 11	Oct. 25	197	May 12	Nov. 9	181	Apr. 23	Oct. 8	168	May 12	Nov. 1	173	May 13	Oct. 8	148
Mean	May 2	Oct. 15	166	Apr. 24	Oct. 23	182	Apr. 17	Oct. 20	186	May 1	Oct. 13	165	Apr. 18	Oct. 19	184	May 3	Oct. 7	157
Extremes	Apr. 13[2]	Sept. 26[4]	[6] 135	Apr. 4[2]	Oct. 2[4]	[6] 137	Mar. 21[2]	Sept. 30[4]	[6] 154	Apr. 8[2]	Sept. 19[4]	[6] 129	Apr. 2[2]	Sept. 30[4]	[6] 155	Apr. 8[2]	Sept. 11[4]	[6] 122
	May 28[3]	Nov. 3[5]	[7] 201	May 27[3]	Nov. 8[5]	[7] 210	May 12[3]	Nov. 9[5]	[7] 211	May 28[3]	Nov. 2[5]	[7] 191	May 12[3]	Nov. 6[5]	[7] 206	June 1[3]	Oct. 31[5]	[7] 182

[1] Number of days between last killing frost in spring and first in fall.
[2] Earliest date in spring.
[3] Latest date in spring.
[4] Earliest date in fall.
[5] Latest date in fall.
[6] Shortest growing season.
[7] Longest growing season.

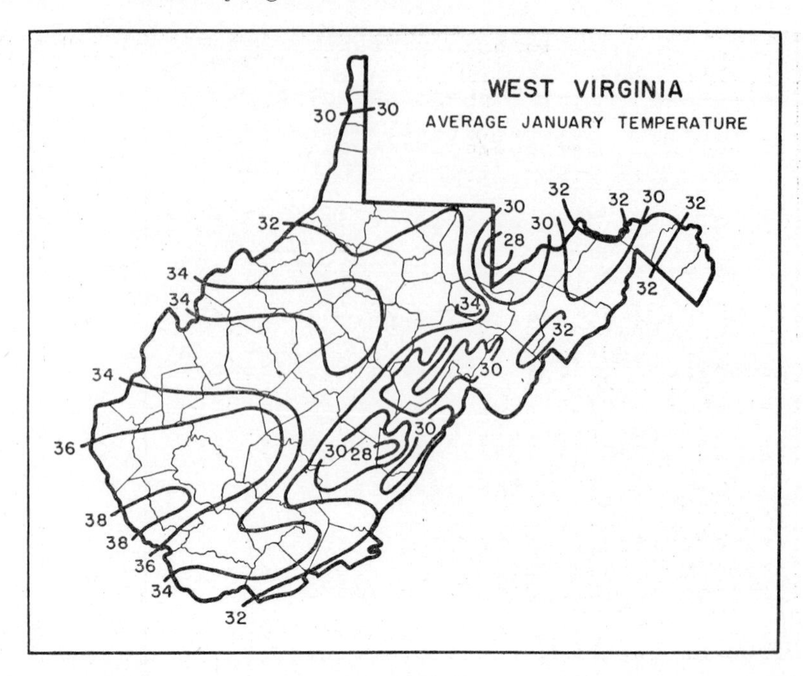
WEST VIRGINIA
AVERAGE JANUARY TEMPERATURE

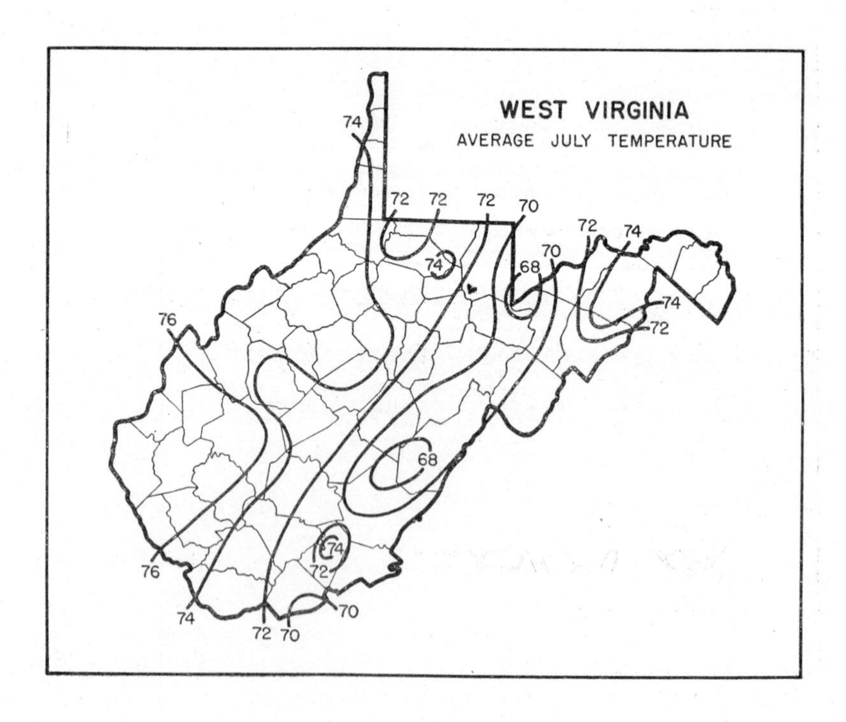
WEST VIRGINIA
AVERAGE JULY TEMPERATURE

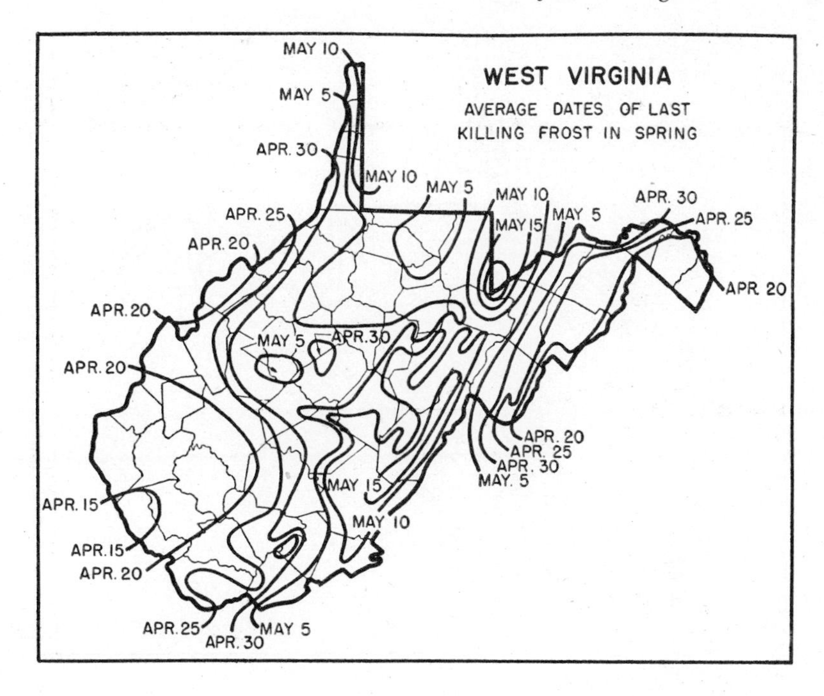
WEST VIRGINIA
AVERAGE DATES OF LAST KILLING FROST IN SPRING
MAY 10
MAY 5
APR. 30
MAY 10
MAY 5
MAY 10
MAY 15
MAY 5
APR. 30
APR. 25
APR. 25
APR. 20
APR. 20
APR. 20
APR. 20
MAY 5
APR. 30
APR. 20
APR. 25
APR. 30
MAY. 5
MAY 15
MAY 10
APR. 15
APR. 15
APR. 20
APR. 25
APR. 30
MAY 5

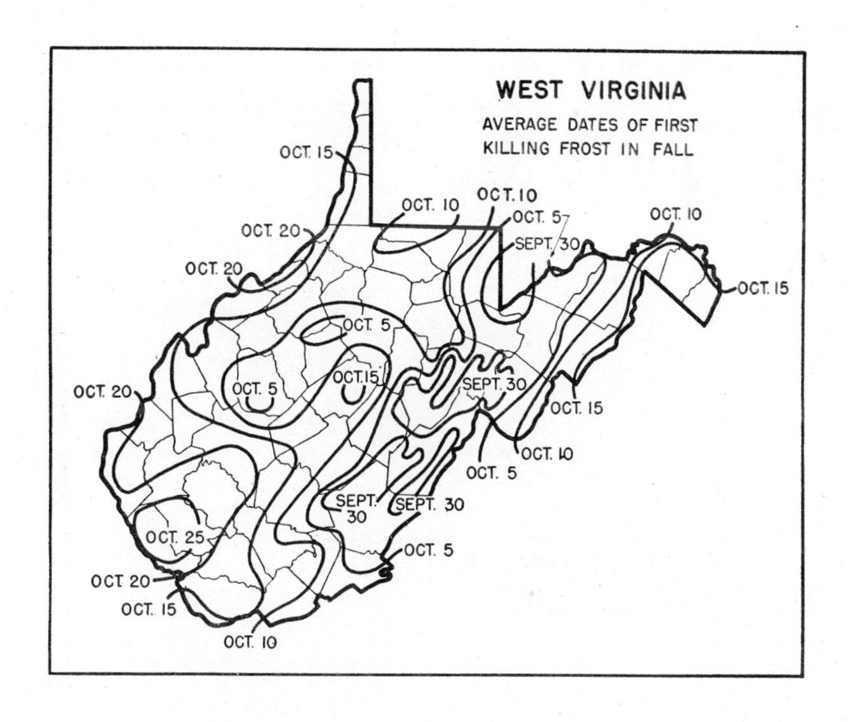
WEST VIRGINIA
AVERAGE DATES OF FIRST KILLING FROST IN FALL
OCT. 15
OCT. 10
OCT. 10
OCT. 5
SEPT. 30
OCT. 10
OCT. 20
OCT. 20
OCT. 15
OCT. 5
OCT. 20
OCT. 5
OCT. 15
SEPT. 30
OCT. 15
OCT. 10
OCT. 5
SEPT. 30
SEPT. 30
OCT. 5
OCT. 25
OCT 20
OCT. 15
OCT. 10

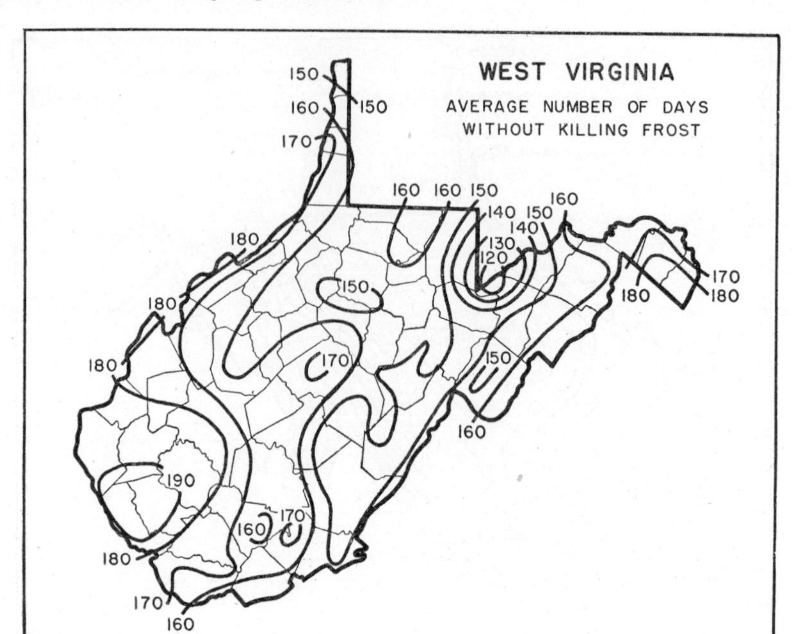
WEST VIRGINIA
AVERAGE NUMBER OF DAYS
WITHOUT KILLING FROST
150
160
170
180
190
140
130
120

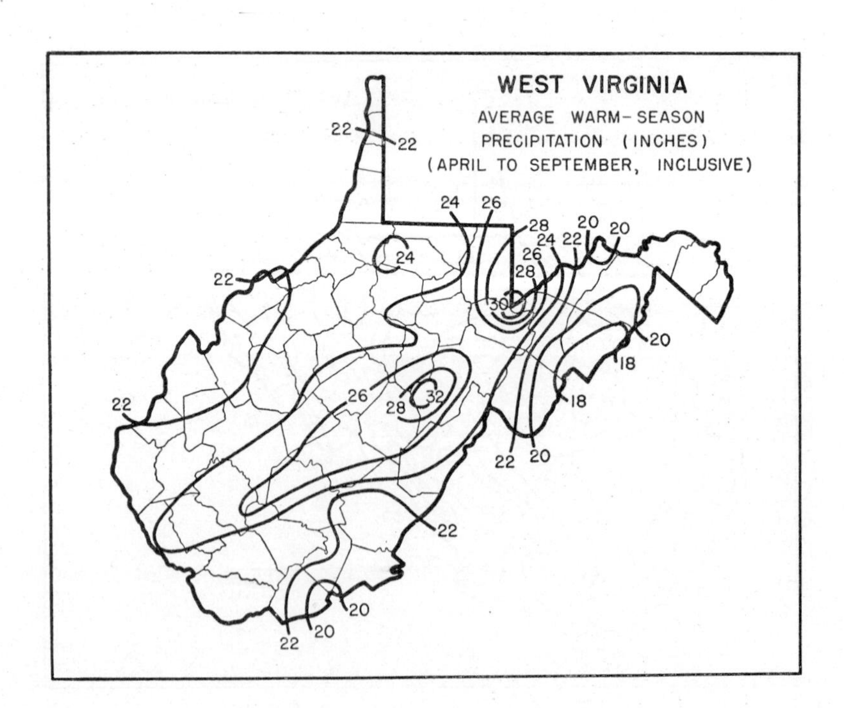
WEST VIRGINIA
AVERAGE WARM-SEASON
PRECIPITATION (INCHES)
(APRIL TO SEPTEMBER, INCLUSIVE)
18
20
22
24
26
28
30
32

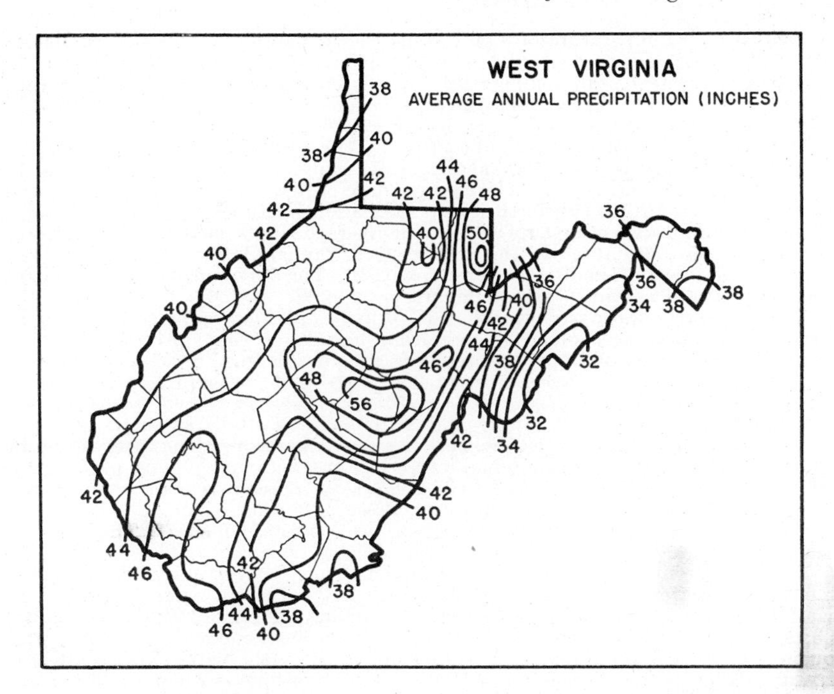

SUPPLEMENTARY CLIMATIC NOTES FOR WEST VIRGINIA

West Virginia has two natural subdivisions—the western plateau and the higher Appalachian section to the east. In the north and west the plateau is well cut by weather and stream erosion into round hills, while in the south it consists of flat-topped hills and canyons, erosion having been retarded by heavy conglomerates. In the eastern mountain area there are persistent ridges of hard strata, relieved by valleys of softer rocks. The greater part of the State forms part of the Ohio River drainage basin, the principal subbasins being the Kanawha, sloping northwestward, and the Monongahela, sloping northward. The remainder of the State, comprising the eastern panhandle, lies in the Potomac River drainage basin.

Topographic characteristics considerably modify the latitudinal control of the climate of West Virginia, with the result that marked variations in temperature and precipitation occur, not only between the mountain, plateau, and hill areas, but also between different parts of the same counties. The seasons are nearly of equal length and are strongly contrasted. In most sections of the State the winters are moderate to rigorous and only occasionally severe except in the mountains. Cold waves occur on an average of three times during the winter, but severely cold spells, as a rule, last only 2 or 3 days.

The summers are usually warm in the low valleys and rather mild in the mountains, where temperatures in excess of 90° are infrequent. However, readings of 100° F. or higher have occurred practically every summer at some station in the State.

Precipitation is ample and well distributed over the State throughout the year. Summer rainfall occurs mostly during thunderstorms or as moderate showers in connection with low-pressure areas that pass north of the State. The thunderstorms are especially extensive and well developed, with sporadic rainfall, and while usually of short duration, they are often violent and attended by excessive falls, causing local flooding of streams. The heaviest precipitation of the fall and winter months occurs during the passage of the general storms that move from the far Southwest northeastward over the Ohio Valley.

The average temperature in winter is 33.6° F., spring 52.3°, summer 71.5°, and fall 54.7.° The coldest part of the State is the Cheat River Basin, with an

298737°—41——76+

average annual temperature of 49.6°, while the warmest is the Tug Fork Basin, with 55.2°.

During the last 47 years temperatures have been 100° or higher at some station in the State in all but 8 years; they have been zero or lower every year, and −10° or lower in all but 5.

The average date of the last killing frost in spring for the State as a whole is May 3; for the northeastern Panhandle, May 7; for the northern section, May 4; and for the southern, May 1. The average date of first killing frost in fall for the State is October 10; for the northeastern Panhandle, October 3; northern section, October 10; and southern, October 11. The average length of the growing season for the State is 160 days. In the northeastern Panhandle it is 153 days; in the northern section, 159; and in the southern, 163. For different localities it ranges from 193 days at Logan to 119 at Bayard.

Normally precipitation ranges from 68.70 inches at Pickens to 25.14 at Upper Tract. On an average, somewhat more than half of the year's precipitation falls during the warm season (April–September), amounting to as much as 60 percent in scattered areas. The average number of days with measurable precipitation for the State is 122.

Approximately 8 percent of the annual precipitation falls as snow, with the percentage varying from 16 at Pickens to 4 at Williamson. The distribution of snowfall is varied, showing a gradual increase from an annual average of less than 20 inches in southwestern counties to 35 in west-central counties, and then a rapid increase in the mountain areas comprising Preston, Tucker, Randolph, Pendleton and Grant Counties, where the average is well over 70 inches. The greatest seasonal average is 105 inches at Pickens.

The average number of days with thunderstorms in West Virginia is 43, the months of greatest frequency being June and July, with an average of 10 each. Hail falls on an average of 1 day a year. Clear days average 147; partly cloudy, 93; and cloudy, 125. Dense fogs, due mainly to local radiation combined frequently with slow air drainage, are quite prevalent in the valleys, especially the Tygart Valley. The average number of hours of sunshine is 2,090, or 46 percent of the possible amount, ranging from 743 hours in summer to 285 in winter.

The prevailing winds are from the west. At the high levels they are westerly throughout the year, but on the lower lands in summer and fall they tend to be southerly. Violent local windstorms, accompanying thunderstorms, occur yearly in some part of the State, but tornadoes are very infrequent.

Stanley S. Schworm, *Associate Meteorologist and Climatic Section Director for West Virginia, Weather Bureau, Parkersburg.*

WISCONSIN

Climatic summary

County [1]	Station	Temperature: Length of record	Temperature: January average	Temperature: July average	Temperature: Maximum	Temperature: Minimum	Killing frost average dates: Length of record	Killing frost average dates: Last in spring	Killing frost average dates: First in fall	Killing frost average dates: Growing season [2]	Average precipitation: Length of record	January	February	March	April	May	June	July	August	September	October	November	December	Annual
		Yr.	°F.	°F.	°F.	°F.	Yr.			Days	Yr.	In.	In.	In.	In.	In.	In.	In.	In.	In.	In.	In.	In.	In.
Ashland	Butternut	11	10.7	66.3	100	−43	9	May 28	Sept. 12	107	10	1.22	1.13	1.83	1.82	3.36	3.87	4.28	4.94	4.89	3.47	1.82	1.45	34.08
	Mellen	13	9.8	68.6	105	−33	12	May 21	Sept. 23	125	12	1.51	.99	.95	1.99	2.76	3.72	3.26	3.56	4.04	2.74	1.89	1.17	28.58
Barron	Barron	22	9.7	68.5	102	−48	22	May 23	Sept. 17	117	23	1.14	.85	1.58	2.22	4.00	4.71	4.27	3.95	3.79	2.82	1.64	.91	31.88
Bayfield	Ashland (near)	36	12.4	66.8	107	−40	34	May 30	Sept. 23	116	39	.97	.93	1.20	1.97	3.07	3.51	3.75	3.06	3.46	2.32	1.61	1.08	26.93
	Cornucopia	26	12.0	64.7	105	−38	26	May 26	Sept. 30	127	25	1.30	.89	1.47	2.09	2.77	3.55	3.02	2.86	3.18	2.30	1.76	1.57	26.76
	Iron River	29	8.6	67.3	109	−42	29	May 19	Sept. 24	128	29	1.07	.95	1.41	2.11	3.13	3.39	3.56	2.89	3.37	2.24	1.79	1.26	27.17
Brown	Green Bay	30	15.7	70.0	104	−36	40	May 5	Oct. 9	157	40	1.21	1.35	1.92	2.50	3.09	3.34	3.17	2.91	3.24	2.15	1.83	1.26	27.97
Buffalo	Mondovi	31	11.8	70.6	110	−43	30	May 13	Sept. 25	135	31	1.15	1.15	1.84	2.68	3.70	5.09	3.47	3.57	4.03	2.12	1.78	1.17	31.75
Burnett	Danbury	20	9.3	68.8	108	−54	20	May 26	Sept. 22	119	19	1.17	.90	1.22	1.87	2.84	4.16	3.65	3.14	3.68	2.14	1.51	1.09	27.37
	Grantsburg	40	10.1	69.6	108	−51	40	May 22	Sept. 19	120	40	1.04	.96	1.24	2.11	3.38	4.45	4.26	3.37	3.79	2.51	1.57	1.01	29.69
Calumet	Brillion	---	---	---	---	---	11	May 5	Oct. 4	152	14	1.60	1.81	1.82	2.03	2.52	3.37	2.26	3.00	3.64	2.14	2.10	1.46	27.75
	Chilton	12	17.2	70.8	100	−34	12	May 6	Oct. 7	154	12	1.59	1.41	2.35	2.74	3.77	3.92	3.72	3.22	3.32	2.24	1.69	1.76	31.73
Chippewa	Stanley	36	11.3	68.0	113	−44	36	May 12	Sept. 24	135	36	1.17	1.11	1.60	2.62	3.93	5.07	3.83	3.72	4.38	2.55	2.07	1.13	33.18
Clark	Neillsville	40	12.7	70.0	106	−46	40	May 15	Sept. 25	133	40	1.19	1.23	1.78	2.53	4.04	4.93	3.68	3.82	4.27	2.73	1.79	1.30	33.29
Columbia	Portage	40	17.5	73.1	111	−37	40	May 3	Oct. 5	155	40	1.07	1.18	1.79	2.73	3.76	3.82	3.62	3.54	4.21	2.48	1.94	1.32	31.46
	Wisconsin Dells	19	16.0	71.6	114	−38	17	May 11	Sept. 27	139	8	1.36	1.28	1.97	2.08	2.83	3.17	3.52	3.71	5.26	2.11	2.34	1.15	30.78
Crawford	Prairie du Chien	40	17.6	73.7	110	−34	40	Apr. 26	Oct. 9	166	40	1.02	1.12	1.84	2.40	3.99	4.29	3.54	4.03	4.26	2.23	1.97	1.23	31.92
Dane	Madison	40	16.7	72.1	107	−29	40	Apr. 29	Oct. 17	171	40	1.23	1.29	1.93	2.55	3.71	3.38	3.49	3.29	4.14	2.28	1.95	1.36	30.60
	Mount Horeb	18	17.0	71.8	103	−30	16	May 10	Oct. 3	146	17	1.43	1.13	1.97	3.14	4.48	4.13	3.71	3.61	4.24	2.61	1.92	1.35	34.12
Dodge	Burnett	36	15.6	70.2	112	−34	36	May 8	do	148	35	1.11	1.12	1.35	2.44	3.55	4.01	2.69	3.15	3.98	2.36	2.06	1.15	28.97
Door	Plum Island	23	19.3	67.3	106	−26	31	May 5	Nov. 1	180	30	1.51	1.43	1.83	2.11	2.39	2.56	2.65	2.57	2.66	2.31	2.30	1.55	25.87
	Sturgeon Bay	36	17.9	66.9	105	−29	34	May 17	Oct. 9	145	34	1.45	1.62	1.95	2.68	3.26	3.19	3.10	2.89	3.45	2.76	2.46	1.75	30.56
Douglas	Solon Springs	33	8.3	66.7	108	−50	33	May 26	Sept. 14	111	33	1.11	1.02	1.10	2.16	3.31	4.12	4.05	3.17	3.30	2.33	1.65	1.09	28.41
	Superior	30	9.8	65.2	105	−35	30	May 11	Oct. 2	144	30	.78	.66	1.25	2.20	3.69	3.49	3.64	2.89	3.42	2.13	1.67	.93	26.75
Dunn	Downing	39	11.1	68.5	106	−49	35	May 23	Sept. 17	117	39	1.36	1.09	1.34	2.13	3.59	4.90	3.85	3.37	3.94	2.79	1.52	1.25	31.13
Eau Claire	Eau Calire	40	13.4	71.5	111	−40	40	May 4	Oct. 1	150	40	1.19	1.14	1.86	2.64	4.06	4.71	3.55	3.81	4.19	2.72	1.84	1.15	32.86
Florence	Breakwater power station.	---	---	---	---	---	12	May 19	Sept. 15	119	14	1.18	1.25	1.40	2.20	2.78	3.81	3.09	3.26	3.56	2.24	2.00	1.16	27.93
	Brule Island	---	---	---	---	---	15	May 25	do	113	17	1.33	1.46	1.54	2.35	2.91	3.73	3.27	3.25	3.95	2.25	1.87	1.43	29.34
	Florence	37	12.3	66.1	104	−39	37	May 30	Sept. 14	107	37	1.18	1.34	1.74	2.42	2.92	3.86	4.13	3.38	3.63	2.42	2.08	1.35	30.45
Fond du Lac	Fond du Lac	40	17.2	71.5	110	−44	40	May 7	Oct. 1	147	40	1.38	1.35	1.85	2.51	3.41	3.74	3.04	3.58	3.71	2.43	2.04	1.40	30.44
	Ripon	16	15.6	72.0	103	−28	15	May 2	Oct. 4	155	14	1.05	1.20	1.81	2.69	4.31	3.98	2.60	3.83	3.91	2.56	2.17	1.25	31.36
Forest	Crandon	16	11.1	66.8	104	−37	16	May 15	Sept. 15	123	18	.91	1.07	1.73	2.23	2.81	3.17	4.22	3.80	3.70	2.60	1.80	.92	28.96
	Laona	12	14.3	68.6	103	−37	11	May 20	Sept. 21	124	11	1.62	1.33	1.41	2.36	3.09	3.45	2.21	3.02	3.68	2.79	1.76	1.27	27.99

[1] The following counties, for which no records are available, are best represented by the stations indicated: Adams—Hancock; Kenosha—Racine; Pepin—Mondovi.

[2] Length of growing season between average dates of last killing frost in spring and first in fall.

WISCONSIN—Continued

Climatic summary—Continued

County	Station	Temperature: Length of record	Temperature: January average	Temperature: July average	Temperature: Maximum	Temperature: Minimum	Killing frost average dates: Length of record	Killing frost: Last in spring	Killing frost: First in fall	Growing season	Average precipitation: Length of record	January	February	March	April	May	June	July	August	September	October	November	December	Annual
		Yr.	*°F.*	*°F.*	*°F.*	*°F.*	*Yr.*			*Days*	*Yr.*	*In.*	*In.*	*In.*	*In.*	*In.*	*In.*	*In.*	*In.*	*In.*	*In.*	*In.*	*In.*	*In.*
Grant	Lancaster	38	16.6	72.1	108	−30	38	Apr. 29	Oct. 1	155	38	1.07	1.14	1.97	2.82	4.10	4.00	3.86	3.63	4.24	2.31	1.90	1.26	32.30
Green	Brodhead	40	19.2	73.4	111	−35	39	May 4	Oct. 7	156	40	1.36	1.47	2.19	2.82	3.70	4.09	3.71	3.68	4.24	2.64	2.18	1.59	33.67
Green Lake	Berlin						14	May 16	Oct. 4	141	16	1.37	1.37	1.41	2.23	3.23	3.94	3.55	2.94	3.81	2.35	1.90	1.16	29.26
Iowa	Dodgeville	18	16.7	70.8	107	−31	13	May 10	Oct. 3	146	10	1.16	1.19	1.68	1.85	5.03	3.87	4.21	2.83	3.97	2.23	1.61	1.23	30.86
Iron	Flambeau residence						13	May 26	Sept. 14	111	13	1.16	1.23	1.40	1.99	3.27	4.13	3.74	3.19	4.12	2.46	2.21	1.36	30.26
Jackson	Hatfield	40	13.2	70.2	108	−51	31	May 19	Sept. 25	129	40	.95	.96	1.40	2.45	3.97	4.60	3.82	3.42	3.96	2.50	1.70	1.10	30.83
	Mather (near)	36	12.4	69.4	106	−44	36	May 16	Sept. 18	125	36	1.24	1.21	1.64	2.47	4.13	4.23	3.57	3.70	4.08	2.33	1.91	1.17	31.68
Jefferson	Lake Mills	40	18.3	71.6	110	−32	32	May 8	Oct. 7	152	40	1.27	1.20	1.78	2.77	4.00	3.72	3.62	3.51	4.14	2.92	2.22	1.38	32.53
	Watertown	40	18.0	71.3	104	−33	40	May 2	Oct. 10	161	40	1.47	1.45	2.07	2.77	3.81	3.78	3.51	3.25	4.04	2.74	2.13	1.52	32.54
Juneau	Mauston						22	May 11	Oct. 2	144	36	1.09	1.21	1.68	2.46	4.38	4.18	3.90	3.57	4.11	2.39	1.71	1.02	31.70
	Meadow Valley	40	13.7	69.5	110	−48	39	May 16	Sept. 19	126	39	.97	.95	1.42	2.39	3.85	4.26	3.62	3.35	4.11	2.50	1.78	1.02	30.22
Kewaunee	Kewaunee	26	18.0	67.1	104	−26	24	May 8	Oct. 14	159	24	1.58	1.74	1.52	2.28	3.16	3.32	2.63	2.82	3.30	2.33	2.40	1.56	28.64
La Crosse	La Crosse	40	16.1	72.8	108	−43	40	Apr. 29	Oct. 9	163	40	1.15	1.10	1.78	2.39	3.98	4.17	3.85	3.79	4.13	2.34	1.83	1.25	31.76
Lafayette	Darlington	34	16.8	72.5	107	−36	34	May 12	Sept. 29	140	34	1.01	1.19	1.85	2.58	3.89	4.06	3.55	3.85	4.70	2.80	2.09	1.20	32.77
	Shullsburg	14	17.9	71.8	102	−28	13	May 13	Oct. 3	143	13	1.76	1.54	1.70	3.28	5.06	3.77	3.22	4.31	5.01	2.76	1.96	1.41	35.78
Langlade	Antigo	40	13.4	68.1	101	−40	40	May 8	Sept. 23	138	40	1.01	1.02	1.38	2.35	3.26	4.26	3.93	3.30	4.06	2.53	1.57	1.00	29.67
	Koepenick	27	11.6	66.8	100	−42	25	May 22	Sept. 19	120	26	1.19	1.15	1.78	2.64	3.58	3.97	4.32	3.78	4.30	2.64	1.89	1.36	32.60
Lincoln	Merrill	34	11.4	69.5	110	−48	33	May 16	Sept. 25	132	33	1.05	1.05	1.57	2.53	3.29	4.00	3.84	3.34	3.89	2.55	2.06	1.15	30.32
	Tomahawk	17	11.4	67.8	104	−43	19	May 17	Sept. 21	127	28	1.20	1.15	1.76	2.44	3.22	4.57	3.65	3.68	3.84	2.50	2.03	.92	30.96
Manitowoc	Manitowoc	40	19.1	68.0	105	−32	40	May 2	Oct. 13	164	40	1.52	1.67	2.23	2.65	3.42	3.47	3.24	2.94	3.63	2.60	2.27	1.70	31.34
Marathon	Wausau	40	14.2	68.4	107	−40	40	May 22	Sept. 29	130	40	1.19	1.12	1.60	2.63	3.50	4.20	3.86	3.59	3.74	2.72	1.75	1.16	31.06
Marinette	High Falls	28	13.2	69.0	104	−40	27	May 27	Sept. 25	121	27	1.36	1.36	1.86	2.57	2.77	3.65	3.66	3.51	3.51	2.44	1.93	1.39	30.01
	Marinette	20	19.0	71.1	108	−28	20	May 8	Oct. 7	152	20	1.51	1.54	1.87	2.76	2.43	3.26	2.64	2.76	3.05	2.40	2.47	1.56	28.25
Marquette	Grand River Lock	31	15.6	71.4	105	−42	31	May 7	Sept. 28	144	40	.99	1.14	1.80	2.51	3.95	4.10	3.51	3.53	4.11	2.49	1.96	1.19	31.28
Milwaukee	Milwaukee	40	20.6	70.1	105	−25	40	Apr. 22	Oct. 23	184	40	1.71	1.61	2.43	2.57	3.37	3.15	2.53	2.72	3.52	2.49	1.94	1.60	29.64
	Milwaukee Airport	13	22.5	71.7	106	−29	12	May 2	do	174	8	1.74	1.28	1.89	1.78	3.29	2.63	2.69	2.74	3.27	1.97	2.21	1.18	26.67
Monroe	Valley Junction	25	14.5	69.5	101	−44	18	May 14	Sept. 18	127	18	1.08	1.18	2.06	2.74	5.47	4.45	4.70	4.00	4.68	3.27	1.87	1.26	36.76
Oconto	Oconto	40	16.6	69.5	105	−31	40	May 8	Oct. 7	152	40	1.59	1.55	1.80	2.47	3.23	3.39	3.35	2.96	3.40	2.45	1.93	1.54	29.66
Oneida	Long Lake	31	9.9	64.8	105	−51	31	June 10	Aug. 28	79	31	1.11	1.10	1.51	2.39	3.04	3.82	3.95	3.69	3.70	2.40	2.06	1.12	29.89
	Minocqua	36	9.6	67.1	106	−48	35	May 22	Sept. 26	127	35	.94	.87	1.40	2.23	3.23	4.28	4.14	3.77	4.21	2.46	1.75	.95	30.23
	Sugar Camp Dam						7	May 28	Sept. 17	112	11	.95	.76	1.46	2.28	3.62	3.70	4.09	4.50	3.05	2.95	1.61	1.08	30.05
	Rhinelander	31	10.4	67.1	108	−44	31	May 20	Sept. 20	123	31	1.05	1.09	1.34	2.36	3.19	4.41	4.26	3.97	3.82	2.54	1.88	.99	30.90
Outagamie	Appleton	27	15.8	70.8	107	−32	30	May 6	Oct. 7	154	32	1.39	1.29	1.81	2.23	3.68	3.43	3.47	2.77	3.78	2.35	2.00	1.35	29.55
Ozaukee	Port Washington						34	May 3	Oct. 14	164	39	1.64	1.76	2.31	2.62	3.54	3.25	2.69	2.96	3.51	2.54	2.09	1.64	30.55
Pierce	River Falls	31	11.2	70.2	109	−47	21	May 16	Sept. 29	136	21	.99	.86	1.60	2.34	3.70	4.73	3.02	3.03	3.82	1.90	1.66	1.01	28.66
Polk	Amery	17	9.5	69.0	108	−46	17	May 12	Sept. 26	137	17	.89	1.00	1.27	1.98	2.78	3.91	2.74	2.93	4.16	2.06	1.52	.93	26.17

	Osceola	31	10.5	70.0	105	−47	22	May 16	Sept. 23	130	22	1.03	.85	1.46	1.82	3.89	4.59	4.35	3.44	4.07	2.85	1.39	1.04	30.78
Portage	Amherst	10	14.1	69.6	99	−48	8	May 14	Sept. 28	137	10	1.13	1.15	1.81	2.31	4.27	4.12	4.71	3.86	3.52	2.89	1.48	1.64	32.89
	Coddington	18	11.5	67.0	106	−43	18	May 30	Sept. 12	105	18	.80	1.17	1.38	2.87	3.18	4.51	3.87	3.65	4.31	2.19	2.03	.95	30.91
	Stevens Point	40	14.9	70.9	108	−48	40	May 13	Sept. 29	139	40	1.30	1.23	2.00	2.96	3.80	4.83	3.47	3.70	3.99	2.46	1.92	1.32	32.98
Price	Park Falls	29	8.7	67.2	106	−45	29	May 27	Sept. 19	115	29	1.30	1.12	1.67	2.63	3.21	4.52	4.38	3.97	4.07	2.46	1.93	1.32	32.58
	Prentice (near)	40	10.5	66.0	107	−48	38	June 2	Sept. 9	99	40	1.18	1.00	1.55	2.46	3.55	4.58	4.17	3.72	4.21	2.75	1.74	1.13	32.04
Racine	Racine	40	22.9	72.0	107	−24	40	Apr. 24	Oct. 21	180	40	1.58	1.47	2.48	2.60	3.58	3.17	2.97	2.88	4.18	2.69	2.15	1.52	31.27
Richland	Richland Center	20	18.0	72.5	110	−40	20	May 13	Sept. 28	138	20	1.02	1.12	1.72	2.53	3.54	4.55	2.86	3.35	5.02	1.93	2.11	1.31	31.06
Rock	Beloit	40	20.3	72.8	110	−27	40	Apr. 25	Oct. 15	173	40	1.50	1.40	2.16	2.67	3.58	3.86	3.62	3.41	4.10	2.60	2.11	1.58	32.59
Rusk	Ladysmith										14	1.12	.94	1.48	2.05	2.89	3.42	3.15	3.38	4.13	2.32	1.83	1.22	27.93
	Weyerhauser	33	10.0	67.3	109	−48	32	May 23	Sept. 20	120	32	1.09	.98	1.58	2.45	3.55	4.61	4.17	3.33	3.90	2.58	1.84	1.04	31.12
St. Croix	New Richmond	15	10.0	70.2	100	−42	13	May 10	Oct. 3	146	13	1.44	1.11	1.42	1.65	3.91	5.36	3.42	2.96	3.21	2.30	1.56	1.04	29.38
Sauk	Prairie du Sac	31	17.6	74.0	107	−26	28	Apr. 19	Oct. 12	176	31	1.01	1.03	1.36	2.54	3.44	3.58	2.85	3.39	4.44	2.04	1.81	.98	28.47
Sawyer	Hayward	26	9.3	67.5	102	−50	25	May 26	Sept. 15	112	25	1.04	.99	1.46	1.88	3.19	4.21	4.31	3.44	3.38	2.67	1.39	.89	28.85
	P. K. Reservoir	24	8.9	65.8	107	−52	24	May 31	Sept. 18	110	16	1.56	1.29	1.79	3.16	4.82	6.37	5.90	4.81	4.97	3.72	2.56	1.50	42.45
Shawano	Shawano	35	15.1	69.5	109	−39	19	May 20	Sept. 23	126	35	1.36	1.26	1.63	2.50	3.16	3.73	3.48	3.10	3.56	2.64	1.99	1.32	29.73
Sheboygan	Plymouth	29	17.3	70.4	107	−27	29	May 8	Oct. 10	155	29	1.29	1.63	1.81	2.58	3.22	3.34	2.35	3.16	3.77	2.83	2.34	1.33	29.65
	Sheboygan	40	20.0	70.5	107	−25	39	Apr. 24	Oct. 22	181	40	1.69	1.73	2.21	2.49	3.41	3.50	2.73	3.15	3.57	2.60	2.17	1.73	30.98
Taylor	Medford	40	12.2	68.6	104	−45	40	May 18	Sept. 26	131	40	1.07	.98	1.48	2.56	3.94	4.67	4.18	3.93	4.30	3.01	1.88	1.11	33.11
Trempealeau	Blair	40	13.4	70.6	109	−49	39	May 14	Sept. 25	134	40	1.34	1.17	1.75	2.34	3.73	4.22	3.50	3.57	4.48	2.21	1.65	1.23	31.19
	Whitehall										24	1.11	1.05	1.83	2.28	4.48	4.13	3.51	3.60	4.15	2.35	1.60	1.31	31.40
Vernon	Hillsboro	40	14.0	69.6	108	−45	40	May 17	Sept. 23	129	40	1.23	1.19	1.78	2.82	4.15	4.28	3.74	3.62	4.34	2.40	1.94	1.28	32.77
	Viroqua	40	15.2	71.2	108	−33	38	May 5	Oct. 4	152	40	1.09	1.16	1.64	2.55	4.33	4.20	4.33	3.70	4.66	2.50	1.90	1.13	33.19
Vilas	Big St. Ger. Dam	29	10.7	65.3	106	−45	29	June 3	Sept. 15	104	29	1.08	.98	1.33	2.24	3.06	4.08	4.10	3.75	4.11	2.52	1.90	1.13	30.28
	Deerskin Dam						28	June 7	Sept. 11	96	29	1.10	.94	1.29	2.05	3.07	3.98	4.03	3.74	4.02	2.59	1.94	1.16	29.91
	Rest Lake	29	9.5	66.1	102	−51	25	May 30	Sept. 16	109	28	1.33	1.06	1.36	2.14	3.09	4.27	4.13	3.72	3.96	2.94	1.98	1.32	31.30
Walworth	Delavan	21	18.7	71.9	103	−29	26	May 7	Oct. 5	151	21	1.12	1.06	1.85	2.86	3.68	3.22	4.00	3.32	4.26	2.53	1.78	1.41	31.09
	Williams Bay	23	18.9	72.2	110	−29	18	May 10	Oct. 15	158	36	1.60	1.35	2.25	2.72	3.29	3.56	3.47	3.75	3.92	2.63	2.15	1.60	32.29
Washburn	Spooner	40	10.3	69.1	110	−46	37	May 15	Sept. 26	134	40	.84	.82	1.43	1.91	3.22	3.69	4.04	3.58	3.44	2.36	1.38	.92	27.63
Washington	West Bend	20	19.5	71.4	107	−28	21	May 7	Oct. 2	148	21	1.32	1.69	2.02	2.36	3.34	3.64	3.34	2.94	3.76	2.67	2.18	1.44	30.70
Waukesha	Waukesha	39	19.0	71.5	109	−27	38	Apr. 29	Oct. 15	169	40	1.55	1.35	2.22	2.70	3.60	3.42	3.04	3.19	3.94	2.62	2.18	1.48	31.29
Waupaca	New London	40	15.9	70.8	109	−37	40	May 6	Oct. 3	150	40	1.36	1.39	2.16	2.68	3.95	4.18	3.77	3.48	3.68	2.48	2.16	1.42	32.71
	Waupaca	40	15.0	71.2	106	−41	38	May 10	Oct. 3	146	40	1.24	1.29	1.85	2.70	3.89	4.15	3.33	3.52	4.05	2.44	2.01	1.26	31.73
Waushara	Hancock	40	14.2	71.3	112	−40	36	May 10	Oct. 3	146	40	1.07	1.16	1.60	2.66	4.08	4.47	3.36	3.38	4.01	2.50	1.72	1.19	31.20
	Pine River	40	15.9	70.3	105	−36	40	May 8	Oct. 2	147	40	1.26	1.38	1.89	2.73	3.87	4.02	2.69	3.25	3.89	2.43	2.00	1.37	31.78
Winnebago	Menasha	19	17.2	71.5	105	−33	18	May 2	Oct. 14	165	40	1.19	1.20	1.57	2.37	3.20	3.53	3.04	2.85	3.64	2.23	1.73	1.21	27.76
	Oshkosh	40	17.2	71.7	107	−34	40	May 4	Oct. 7	156	40	1.32	1.20	1.76	2.68	3.32	4.00	3.23	3.17	3.56	2.20	1.95	1.25	29.64
Wood	Marshfield	26	12.7	68.5	105	−36	32	May 17	Sept. 22	128	26	1.38	1.11	1.51	2.79	3.35	5.02	3.33	3.70	3.70	2.55	2.13	1.18	31.75
	Port Edwards										10	1.54	1.24	1.65	2.60	4.84	4.15	3.31	3.62	4.30	2.69	1.35	1.44	32.73
	Wisconsin Rapids	36	12.9	70.1	107	−43	36	May 14	Sept. 27	136	36	1.24	1.19	1.72	2.64	4.02	4.34	3.42	3.59	4.27	2.38	1.93	1.15	31.89

WISCONSIN—Continued

Precipitation and temperature—State unit values

[This tabulation gives the mean annual, mean monthly, and average seasonal precipitation, 1886–1938, and the mean annual temperatures, 1902–38, for Wisconsin]

Precipitation		Precipitation		Precipitation		Precipitation		Temperature		Temperature	
Year	Mean	Year	Mean	Year	Mean	Month	Mean	Year	Mean	Year	Mean
	In.		In.		In.		In.		°F.		°F.
1886	31.18	1907	30.14	1928	33.09	May	3.57	1902	44.6	1921	47.1
1887	32.19	1908	29.36	1929	28.09	June	3.95	1903	43.1	1922	45.0
1888	31.22	1909	31.43	1930	25.08	July	3.47	1904	41.6	1923	43.7
1889	26.53	1910	21.41	1931	29.68	August	3.29	1905	43.2	1924	41.0
1890	35.21	1911	37.00	1932	25.37	September	3.68	1906	44.8	1925	43.5
1891	26.12	1912	32.51	1933	27.11	October	2.44	1907	42.6	1926	41.8
1892	34.98	1913	32.81	1934	30.56	November	1.83	1908	45.5	1927	43.2
1893	29.80	1914	32.30	1935	30.39	December	1.40	1909	43.4	1928	43.9
1894	27.96	1915	32.79	1936	25.38			1910	44.4	1929	41.6
1895	22.45	1916	33.79	1937	27.41	Annual	30.57	1911	44.8	1930	45.0
1896	32.21	1917	27.35	1938	41.64			1912	41.5	1931	48.6
1897	27.77	1918	29.69					1913	44.2	1932	43.8
1898	28.04	1919	33.22	Month	Mean	Season	Average	1914	43.8	1933	44.8
1899	30.54	1920	29.99					1915	43.5	1934	45.1
1900	35.07	1921	30.73					1916	42.3	1935	43.4
1901	26.34	1922	31.42					1917	39.5	1936	42.6
1902	32.59	1923	26.39		In.		In.	1918	43.6	1937	43.2
1903	35.81	1924	33.06	January	1.35	Winter	4.04	1919	43.9	1938	45.7
1904	31.55	1925	27.62	February	1.29	Spring	7.87	1920	43.2		
1905	35.10	1926	35.05	March	1.79	Summer	10.71				
1906	34.20	1927	30.94	April	2.51	Fall	7.95				

Dates of last killing frost in spring and first in fall, with length of growing season

Year	Spooner			Medford			Waupaca			La Crosse			Madison			Milwaukee		
	Last in spring	First in fall	Growing season [1]	Last in spring	First in fall	Growing season [1]	Last in spring	First in fall	Growing season [1]	Last in spring	First in fall	Growing season [1]	Last in spring	First in fall	Growing season [1]	Last in spring	First in fall	Growing season [1]
			Days			Days			Days			Days			Days			Days
1899	May 20	Sept. 13	116	May 22	Sept. 13	114	Apr. 16	Sept. 23	160	Apr. 10	Oct. 3	176	Apr. 10	Sept. 30	173	Apr. 9	Sept. 30	174
1900	May 19	Oct. 17	151	June 30	Sept. 17	79	Apr. 15	Oct. 17	185	Apr. 9	Nov. 7	212	May 4	Nov. 6	186	Apr. 13	Nov. 5	206

1901				June 8	Oct. 3	117	May 26	Oct. 3	130	Apr. 3	Oct. 4	184	Apr. 21	Oct. 4	166	Apr. 20	Oct. 4	167
1902	May 9			May 9	Sept. 13	127	May 10	Oct. 10	153	Apr. 7	Oct. 14	190	Apr. 15	Oct. 14	182	Apr. 15	Oct. 14	182
1903	May 6			June 12	Sept. 28	108	June 12	Sept. 28	108	Apr. 4	Oct. 24	203	Apr. 30	Oct. 18	171	Apr. 30	Oct. 18	171
1904				May 16	Sept. 15	122	May 15			Apr. 21	Oct. 6	168	Apr. 22	Oct. 27	188	Apr. 21	Oct. 23	185
1905	May 30	Sept. 13	106	May 26	Oct. 13	140	May 1	Oct. 12	164	Apr. 18	Oct. 21	186	Apr. 21	Oct. 21	183	Apr. 22	Oct. 28	189
1906		Sept. 27		May 10	Oct. 6	149	May 9	Oct. 1	145	Apr. 2	Oct. 10	191	Apr. 23	Oct. 10	170	Apr. 23	Oct. 10	170
1907	May 20	Sept. 22	125	May 27	Sept. 22	118	May 11	Sept. 26	138	May 4	Oct. 8	157	May 11	Oct. 13	155	May 11	Oct. 14	156
1908	May 6	Sept. 29	146	May 4	Sept. 29	148	May 4	Sept. 29	148	May 3	Sept. 29	149	May 2	Sept. 29	150	May 2	Oct. 30	181
1909	May 10	Oct. 11	154	May 10	Sept. 1	114	May 11	Sept. 27	139	May 10	Oct. 14	157	May 3	Oct. 12	162	May 3	Oct. 14	164
1910	May 13	Oct. 6	146	May 14	Oct. 6	145	May 14	Oct. 23	162	May 24	Oct. 22	151	Apr. 23	Oct. 28	188	Apr. 23	Oct. 28	188
1911	May 4	Oct. 22	171	May 5	Oct. 20	168	May 13	Sept. 30	140	May 4	Oct. 24	173	May 2	Oct. 24	175	May 2	Oct. 24	175
1912	Apr. 27	Sept. 27	153	May 17	Sept. 27	133	May 14	Sept. 27	136	Apr. 19	Oct. 23	187	Apr. 19	Oct. 23	187	Apr. 19	do	188
1913	May 9	Sept. 23	137	May 19	Sept. 22	126	June 10	Sept. 22	104	Apr. 27	Oct. 18	174	May 10	Oct. 21	164	Apr. 20	Oct. 21	184
1914	May 13	Oct. 14	154	May 15	Oct. 14	152	May 15	Oct. 25	163	Apr. 20	Oct. 27	190	Apr. 20	Oct. 27	190	do	Oct. 27	190
1915	May 18	Oct. 9	144	May 19	Sept. 21	125	May 27	Aug. 27	92	May 9	Oct. 9	153	Apr. 13	Oct. 9	179	Apr. 3	Nov. 12	223
1916	May 12	Sept. 17	128	May 18	Sept. 16	121	Apr. 25	Sept. 16	144	May 2	Sept. 29	150	Apr. 10	Sept. 16	159	Apr. 10	Oct. 22	195
1917	May 28	Aug. 29	93	May 24	Sept. 10	109	May 23	Sept. 10	110	May 23	Sept. 10	110	May 23	Oct. 13	143	May 23	Oct. 8	138
1918	May 13	Sept. 10	120	May 13	do	120	May 1	Sept. 26	148	May 13	Sept. 21	131	Apr. 25	Nov. 2	191	Apr. 25	Nov. 11	200
1919	May 8	Oct. 7	152	May 9	Oct. 11	155	Apr. 29	Oct. 11	165	May 2	Oct. 11	162	Apr. 26	Oct. 17	174	do	Oct. 29	187
1920	May 14	Oct. 1	140	May 15	Sept. 30	138	May 15	Sept. 30	138	Apr. 16	Oct. 1	168	May 14	Oct. 29	168	May 14	do	168
1921	May 16	Oct. 3	140	May 16	Oct. 4	141	May 16			May 16	Oct. 4	141	May 15	Oct. 8	146	Apr. 17	Nov. 5	202
1922	Apr. 27	Oct. 9	165	Apr. 28	Oct. 9	164	Apr. 28	Oct. 9	164	Apr. 22	Oct. 12	173	Apr. 21	Oct. 17	179	Apr. 20	Oct. 18	181
1923	May 13	Sept. 13	123	May 17	Sept. 13	119	May 17	Sept. 14	120	May 9	Sept. 13	127	May 13	Oct. 21	161	May 9	Oct. 21	165
1924	May 21	Sept. 9	111	May 24	Sept. 29	128	May 2	Sept. 30	151	May 11	Sept. 30	142	Apr. 20	Oct. 22	185	Apr. 12	Nov. 8	210
1925	May 25	Sept. 21	119	May 26	Oct. 5	132	May 17	Oct. 7	143	May 25	Oct. 10	138	May 25	Oct. 10	138	Mar. 29	Oct. 10	195
1926	May 22	Sept. 25	126	May 22	Sept. 25	126	May 4	Sept. 25	144	Apr. 26	Sept. 26	153	Apr. 26	Sept. 26	153	Apr. 26	Oct. 23	180
1927	May 16	Sept. 26	133	May 16	Sept. 23	130				Apr. 23	Oct. 14	174	Apr. 23	Nov. 2	193	Apr. 23	Nov. 5	196
1928	May 12	Sept. 23	134	May 12	do	134	Apr. 27	Sept. 26	152	Apr. 28	Sept. 26	151	Apr. 27	Sept. 26	152	Apr. 20	Oct. 29	192
1929	June 3	Sept. 18	107	May 20	Sept. 18	121	May 19	Sept. 18	122	May 19	Sept. 18	122	May 19	Nov. 2	167	Apr. 1	Nov. 5	218
1930	May 17	Sept. 28	134	May 30	Sept. 29	122	May 17	Sept. 30	136	May 17	Oct. 17	153	May 17	Oct. 17	153	Apr. 24	Oct. 18	177
1931	May 23	Oct. 12	142	May 23	Aug. 30	99	May 3	Nov. 2	183	May 23	do	147	Apr. 30	Nov. 6	190	Apr. 23	Nov. 6	197
1932	Apr. 28	Sept. 23	148	May 28	Sept. 24	119	Apr. 27	Oct. 6	162	Apr. 27	Oct. 6	162	Apr. 26	Oct. 6	163	Apr. 12	Oct. 6	177
1933	May 10	Sept. 21	134	May 10	Oct. 2	145	May 4	Oct. 13	162	do	Oct. 13	169	do	Oct. 13	170	Apr. 15	Oct. 20	188
1934	May 15	Aug. 20	97	May 15			May 25	Oct. 28	156	do	Oct. 28	184	Apr. 27	Oct. 28	184	Apr. 28	Oct. 28	183
1935	May 24	Sept. 1	100	May 14	Sept. 27	136	May 4	Oct. 4	153	May 4	Oct. 4	153	May 4	Oct. 4	153	May 4	Oct. 4	153
1936	May 3	Sept. 29	149	Apr. 26	Oct. 1	158	Apr. 24	Oct. 2	161	Apr. 22	Oct. 2	163	Apr. 23	Oct. 2	162	Apr. 23	Oct. 23	183
1937	June 9	Sept. 17	100	May 14	Sept. 19	128	May 14	Oct. 8	147	do	Oct. 8	169	Apr. 16	Oct. 13	180	Apr. 16	Oct. 13	180
1938	May 11	Oct. 24	166	May 12	Oct. 19	160	Apr. 22	Oct. 21	182	do	Oct. 24	185	Apr. 10	Nov. 7	211	Apr. 9	Nov. 9	214
Mean	May 15	Sept. 26	134	May 18	Sept. 26	131	May 10	Oct. 3	146	Apr. 29	Oct. 9	163	Apr. 29	Oct. 17	171	Apr. 22	Oct. 23	184
Extremes	Apr. 27[2]	Aug. 20[4]	[6] 93	Apr. 26[2]	Aug. 30[4]	[6] 79	Apr. 15[2]	Aug. 27[4]	[6] 92	Apr. 2[2]	Sept. 10[4]	[6] 110	Apr. 10[2]	Sept. 16[4]	[6] 138	Mar. 29[2]	Sept. 30[4]	[6] 138
	June 9[3]	Oct. 24[5]	[7] 171	June 30[3]	Oct. 20[5]	[7] 168	June 12[3]	Nov. 2[5]	[7] 185	May 25[3]	Nov. 7[5]	[7] 212	May 25[3]	Nov. 7[5]	[7] 211	May 23[3]	Nov. 12[5]	[7] 223

[1] Number of days between last killing frost in spring and first in fall.
[2] Earliest date in spring.
[3] Latest date in spring.
[4] Earliest date in fall.
[5] Latest date in fall.
[6] Shortest growing season.
[7] Longest growing season.

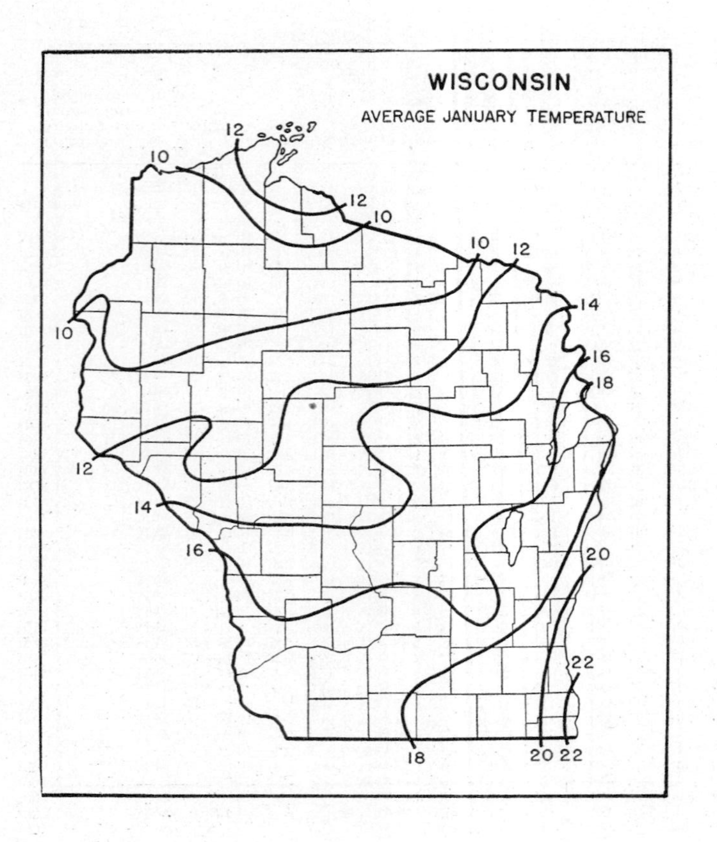
WISCONSIN
AVERAGE JANUARY TEMPERATURE
12
10
12
10
10
12
10
14
16
18
12
14
16
20
22
18
20 22

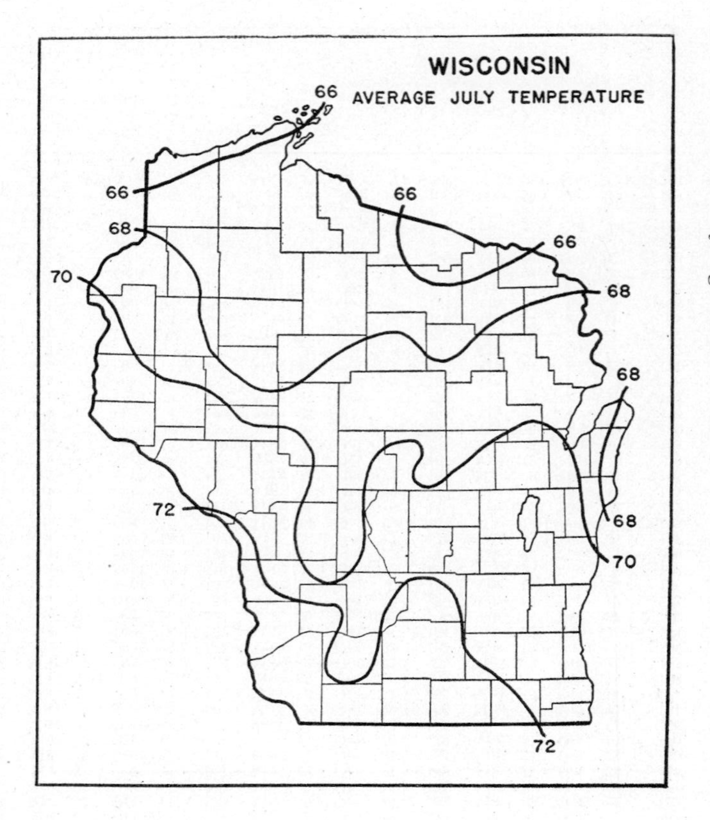
WISCONSIN
AVERAGE JULY TEMPERATURE
66
66
68
70
66
66
68
68
72
68
70
72

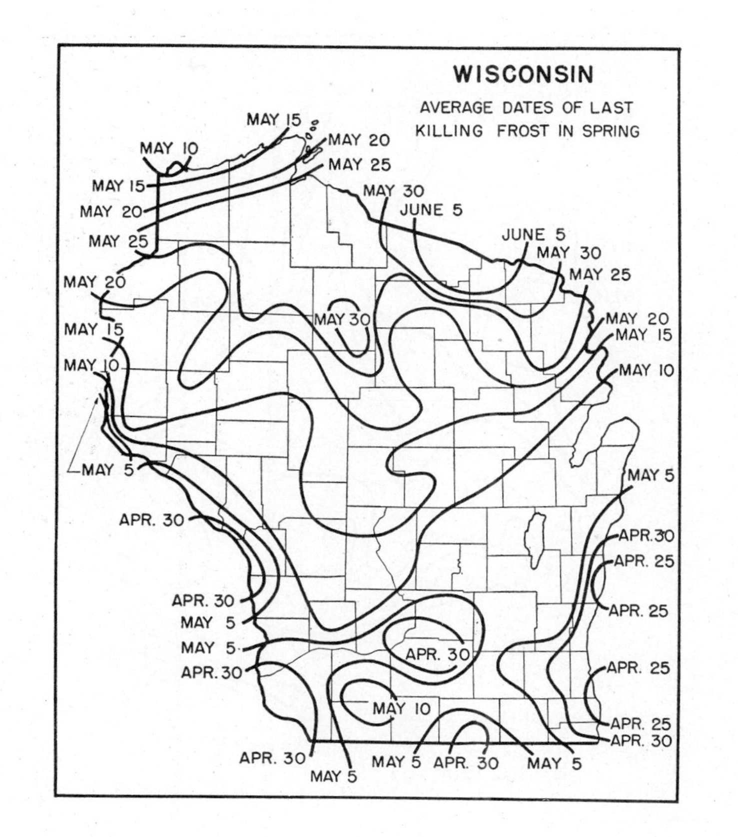
WISCONSIN
AVERAGE DATES OF LAST
KILLING FROST IN SPRING

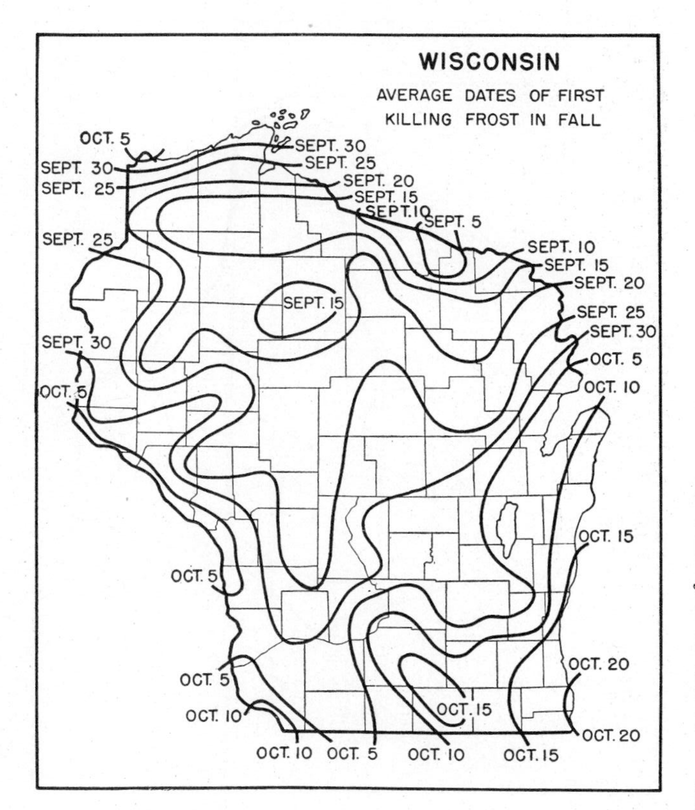
WISCONSIN
AVERAGE DATES OF FIRST
KILLING FROST IN FALL

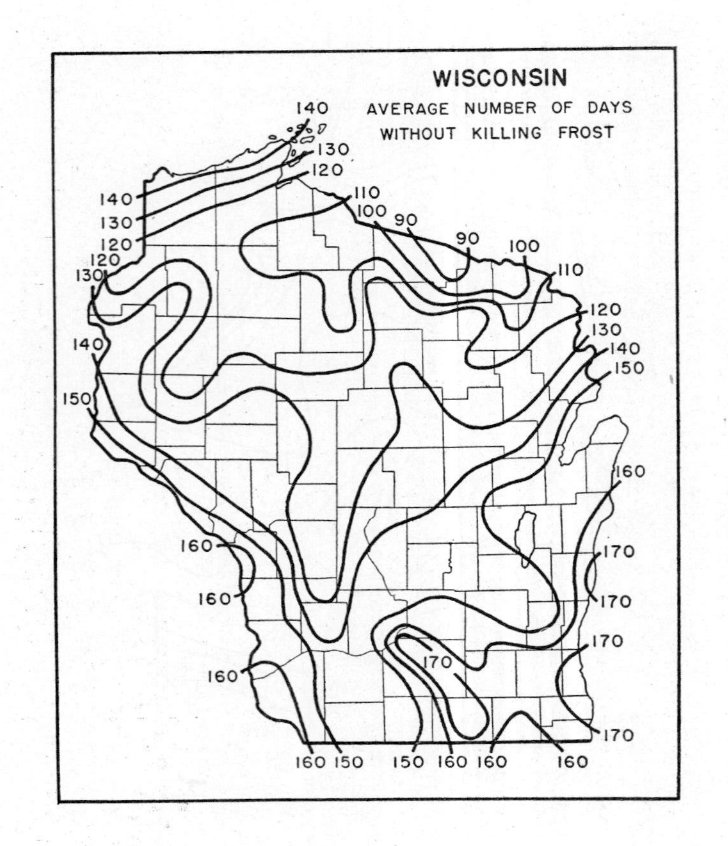
WISCONSIN
AVERAGE NUMBER OF DAYS WITHOUT KILLING FROST
140
130
120
140
130
120
120
130
140
150
110
100
90
90
100
110
120
130
140
150
160
160
160
160
170
170
170
170
170
160 150
150 160 160
160

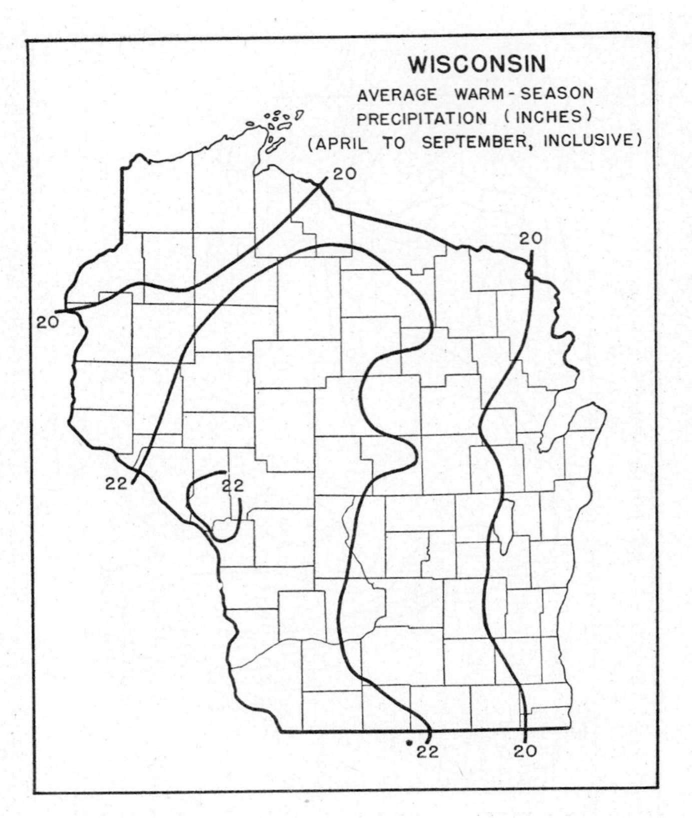
WISCONSIN
AVERAGE WARM-SEASON PRECIPITATION (INCHES)
(APRIL TO SEPTEMBER, INCLUSIVE)
20
20
20
22
22
22
20

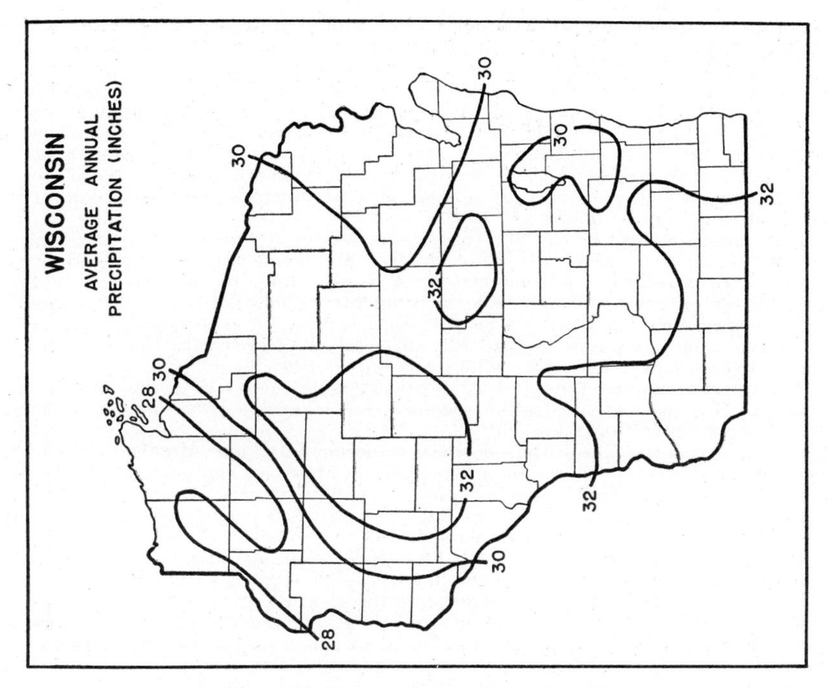

SUPPLEMENTARY CLIMATIC NOTES FOR WISCONSIN

Wisconsin lies between the Great Plains on the west and the Great Lakes on the east, and extends from Lake Superior and the Upper Peninsula of Michigan on the north to the northern boundary of Illinois on the south.

The topography and soils of Wisconsin have been generally determined by the various glaciations to which these lands have been subjected, so that much of the State is rolling or hilly. There is, however, a considerable area in the southwestern and central-western parts which has never been covered by glaciers and is known as the Driftless Area. This is marked by hills and valleys with comparatively steep sides. A considerable area in the central part of Wisconsin is comparatively level, owing to weathering of the soft sandstone and deposits of outwash material during the last glacial period, when this region was covered by water. A marked ridge, or moraine, extends from the Door Peninsula to Walworth County on the southern border, the area east of the ridge being drained by numerous small streams flowing into Lake Michigan.

A relatively high plateau occupies much of the northern part of the State, with elevations ranging from 1,000 to 1,800 feet above sea level. Hills of considerable elevation are occasionally met with in this section; Rib Hill, near Wausau, with an elevation of 1,940 feet above sea level, is the highest point in the State. This northern plateau contains many small lakes, and there the most important rivers of the State have their sources. The slope downward to the level of Lake Superior is quite steep.

The northeastern section of the State drains into Lake Michigan, a large part of it through Green Bay. The Wisconsin River is the main factor in the drainage of the central and north-central parts. The source of the main stream is a small lake, nearly 1,600 feet above sea level, on the Michigan boundary, while most of its tributaries also spring from lakes in the northern part of the State.

Wisconsin is to a large extent an agricultural State, with its southern and central parts in a high state of cultivation. The soil and climate are especially adapted to dairying, and dairy products are the main source of farm income, accounting for over 50 percent of the total. As a consequence, hay, oats, and corn are the main crops. The production of canning peas, dry peas, sugar beets, cabbage, and tobacco is also of importance.

The climate of Wisconsin is influenced by the general storms which move eastward along the northern border of the United States, and by those which move northeastward from the southwestern States to the Great Lakes. The winters, especially in the central and northern parts of the State, are long and severe, while the summers in the south are sometimes very warm. Lake Michigan modifies temperature conditions to some extent in a narrow adjoining southeastern belt, but the influence of the Lake on cold waves in winter that sweep across the State from the Northwest is very limited and not nearly so great as in those parts of Michigan on the leeward side. During such periods, the difference in temperature between the west side of Lake Michigan and the east side in the same latitude may be marked.

In the colder parts of the State minimum winter temperatures are extremely low practically every year. In 36 of the last 50 years a minimum of −40° F. or lower has been recorded in some part of the State, while, on the other hand, there are very few summers during which the temperature does not reach 100° or higher in some localities. Markedly cool periods also may be experienced in summer. For the normally warmest month, July, in nearly half the years, temperatures as low as freezing are recorded at some place in the State.

The average annual temperature is lowest in the extreme north, where it is about 39° F., and increases rather regularly southward to 47° along the southern and southwestern boundaries.

As already noted, the waters of Lake Superior and Lake Michigan affect the temperatures of their shores to a considerable extent. The general effect is to make the adjacent land cooler in summer and warmer in winter. When the onshore winds are due to general cyclonic circulations, the effect of the Lakes may be felt inland as far as 15 to 20 miles.

While there is a very limited area along the central part of the northern border of the State which has an average growing season shorter than 100 days, most of the north averages from 110 to 135 frost-free days, while in the south the growing season ranges from 135 up to about 160 days. Along the southern border of Lake Michigan there are from 160 to 175 days when crops are considered safe from frost.

The average date of the last killing frost in spring is from May 20 to June 1 in the extreme north, and between April 25 and May 5 in the extreme south. In the fall the first killing frost usually occurs in the far north from September 15 to 25, but the average is as late as October 5 to 15 in the extreme south.

The average annual precipitation in Wisconsin ranges from about 26 inches in some parts of the extreme north to about 34 along the extreme southern and southwestern borders. The wettest months are May to September, inclusive, so that moisture during the growing season is usually sufficient for crops. During this period the rainfall is fairly well distributed.

The greatest amount of snowfall occurs in the far north where some sections average 55 to 60 inches. In the extreme south the average snowfall is about 30 inches.

During the summer months thunderstorms occur rather frequently. They are occasionally violent and accompanied by hail and high winds which do considerable damage. Tornadoes are rather infrequent, probably occurring oftenest in that part of the north extending from Polk, St. Croix, and Pierce Counties eastward to Lincoln and Marathon Counties.

For the State as a whole, sunshine averages somewhat over 50 percent of the possible amount a year. The greatest percentage occurs in summer and the least in winter.

The annual average relative humidity, determined from 4 first-order Weather Bureau stations, is 80 percent at 7 a. m., 64 at noon, and 70 at 7 p. m. It is somewhat higher in winter than in summer.

Frank H. Coleman, *Meteorologist and Climatic Section Director for Wisconsin, Weather Bureau, Milwaukee.*

WYOMING

Climatic summary

County	Station	Temperature: Length of record	Temperature: January average	Temperature: July average	Temperature: Maximum	Temperature: Minimum	Killing frost average dates: Length of record	Killing frost average dates: Last in spring	Killing frost average dates: First in fall	Killing frost average dates: Growing season [1]	Average precipitation: Length of record	January	February	March	April	May	June	July	August	September	October	November	December	Annual
		Yr.	*°F.*	*°F.*	*°F.*	*°F.*	*Yr.*			*Days*	*Yr.*	*In.*	*In.*	*In.*	*In.*	*In.*	*In.*	*In.*	*In.*	*In.*	*In.*	*In.*	*In.*	*In.*
Albany	Centennial	31	21.5	61.4	92	−42	32	June 7	Sept. 12	97	36	1.31	1.61	1.61	2.03	1.66	1.19	1.63	1.35	1.27	1.34	0.78	1.13	16.91
	Foxpark	24	14.0	51.5	90	−52	29				26	1.22	1.47	1.70	2.04	1.63	1.12	1.74	1.46	1.45	1.19	1.16	1.31	17.49
	Laramie	40	22.3	63.8	92	−41	40	May 29	Sept. 19	113	40	.39	.46	.71	1.32	1.47	1.07	1.82	1.21	.98	.89	.38	.49	11.19
	Marshall	14	14.7	63.2	94	−47	14	June 13	Sept. 8	87	15	.47	.48	.63	.83	1.87	1.56	1.32	1.24	.99	.69	.46	.45	10.99
	Moore	15	26.4	64.6	97	−34	14	May 26	do	105	16	.49	.67	.73	1.64	2.51	1.67	1.81	1.42	1.48	1.01	.50	.62	14.55
Big Horn	Basin	34	15.8	73.7	114	−51	34	May 11	Sept. 24	136	36	.43	.37	.57	.73	1.06	.87	.49	.41	.62	.57	.32	.35	6.79
	Deaver	23	14.2	72.2	106	−42	23	May 16	do	131	23	.18	.16	.24	.48	.97	.86	.55	.46	.54	.39	.23	.22	5.28
	Hyattville	24	22.9	70.3	105	−34	24	May 23	Sept. 21	121	16	.36	.20	.46	.58	.50	.64	.16	.36	.37	.46	.27	.35	4.71
	Lovell	30	16.0	71.8	111	−51	30	May 16	Sept. 18	125	31	.42	.27	.34	.62	1.12	.87	.59	.48	.69	.51	.33	.28	6.52
Campbell	Echeta	12	20.6	70.0	106	−45	17	May 30	Sept. 15	108	21	.91	.71	1.02	1.80	2.29	2.14	1.84	1.09	1.46	1.26	.96	.90	16.38
	Gillette	27	21.0	70.9	110	−40	26	May 14	Sept. 30	139	28	.62	.40	.95	1.53	2.38	1.98	1.76	1.33	1.18	1.00	.58	.68	14.39
	Rockypoint	16	17.7	71.7	106	−45	26	May 20	Sept. 25	128	28	.91	.75	1.23	1.71	2.63	2.72	2.10	1.24	1.52	1.27	.81	.72	17.61
Carbon	Big Creek	9	18.6	60.9	98	−36	10	June 17	Sept. 3	78	12	1.17	1.20	1.20	1.60	1.49	.95	1.76	1.76	1.46	1.61	.97	1.67	16.84
	Dixon	17	15.5	65.5	97	−50	16	June 7	Sept. 11	96	17	.79	.80	1.03	1.02	1.30	.67	1.19	1.31	1.05	1.19	.89	1.09	12.33
	Elk Mountain						10	June 23	Aug. 31	69	33	1.18	1.52	1.52	2.25	1.86	1.01	1.51	1.36	1.29	1.38	.76	1.22	16.86
	Encampment	30	21.7	65.4	100	−45	29	June 3	Sept. 19	108	30	.66	.80	1.05	1.31	1.41	.87	1.29	1.08	1.26	1.43	.78	.77	12.71
	Leo	19	21.7	65.7	100	−42	14	May 30	Sept. 15	108	20	.65	.55	.83	.93	1.52	1.00	.84	1.00	.87	.81	.48	.60	10.08
	Rawlins	32	21.3	67.8	102	−36	32	June 1	Sept. 21	112	33	.58	.74	1.01	1.23	1.60	.97	1.05	.91	1.12	1.09	.51	.79	11.60
	Saratoga	33	20.0	64.9	103	−55	30	June 6	Sept. 11	97	34	.61	.61	.77	1.03	1.45	.91	1.10	1.05	.93	1.03	.56	.65	10.70
Converse	Douglas	28	23.5	70.9	106	−43	28	May 20	Sept. 21	124	29	.36	.54	.70	1.87	2.41	1.66	1.52	1.12	1.18	1.27	.53	.58	13.74
	Dull Center	11	21.3	73.0	111	−49	12	May 13	Sept. 26	136	12	.21	.36	.75	1.33	3.43	2.02	2.01	2.03	1.07	1.02	.60	.26	15.09
	Ross (near)	14	20.1	69.9	102	−40	14	May 15	Sept. 22	130	13	.27	.46	.67	.94	2.27	2.14	1.25	1.08	.85	.80	.45	.22	11.40
Crook	Colony	24	20.6	72.8	111	−39	24	May 14	Sept. 29	138	25	.50	.41	.91	1.63	2.39	2.72	2.20	1.48	1.37	1.03	.61	.55	15.80
	Knowles						15	May 28	Sept. 25	120	30	.55	.56	1.33	2.22	3.36	3.35	2.65	1.70	2.04	1.36	.83	.73	20.68
	Moorcroft	20	17.9	71.2	108	−42	16	May 22	Sept. 20	121	19	.55	.70	.92	1.35	2.22	2.30	1.66	1.23	1.36	.79	.50	.81	14.39
	Pine Ridge										17	.76	.74	1.10	1.52	2.58	2.48	1.77	1.30	1.42	.96	.49	.87	15.99
	Sundance	24	19.0	68.5	105	−42	26	May 26	Sept. 23	120	25	1.04	.75	1.37	1.53	2.75	2.96	2.33	1.44	1.51	1.50	.92	1.07	19.17
Fremont	Diversion Dam	18	19.2	69.1	100	−45	18	May 15	Sept. 21	129	18	.21	.26	.38	1.21	1.79	.86	1.26	.80	.77	1.23	.35	.22	9.34
	Dubois	30	21.1	60.4	98	−48	26	June 10	Sept. 7	89	31	.46	.47	.53	1.00	1.35	1.09	.83	.86	.84	.81	.36	.33	8.93
	Lander	40	19.2	68.5	102	−40	40	May 18	Sept. 20	125	40	.49	.73	1.12	2.23	2.43	1.05	.82	.59	1.08	1.59	.68	.73	13.54
	Middle Fork	20	22.5	68.4	97	−34	22	May 20	Sept. 24	127	21	.56	.94	1.49	3.10	3.37	1.23	1.39	.97	1.58	2.09	.97	.68	18.37
	Pavillion	19	17.6	72.1	102	−42	20	May 9	Sept. 28	142	22	.22	.19	.44	1.19	1.91	1.05	1.15	1.02	.99	.89	.31	.24	9.60
	Riverton	23	14.8	69.6	103	−46	23	May 15	Sept. 21	129	24	.13	.26	.43	1.23	1.95	1.10	1.06	.70	.91	1.20	.42	.22	9.61
	South Pass City	36	12.5	57.3	102	−46	37				37	1.12	1.14	1.28	1.53	1.33	.89	1.09	.86	1.03	.88	.76	.79	12.70

[1] Length of growing season between average dates of last killing frost in spring and first in fall.

WYOMING—Continued

Climatic summary—Continued

County	Station	Temperature: Length of record	Temperature: January average	Temperature: July average	Temperature: Maximum	Temperature: Minimum	Killing frost average dates: Length of record	Killing frost average dates: Last in spring	Killing frost average dates: First in fall	Killing frost average dates: Growing season	Average precipitation: Length of record	January	February	March	April	May	June	July	August	September	October	November	December	Annual
		Yr.	°*F.*	°*F.*	°*F.*	°*F.*	*Yr.*			*Days*	*Yr.*	*In.*	*In.*	*In.*	*In.*	*In.*	*In.*	*In.*	*In.*	*In.*	*In.*	*In.*	*In.*	*In.*
Goshen	Fort Laramie	39	25.3	71.6	107	−48	38	May 20	Sept. 22	125	39	0.36	0.52	0.77	1.90	2.64	1.97	1.78	1.37	1.29	1.06	0.45	0.48	14.59
	Lagrange	20	25.4	71.1	110	−48	22	May 21	Sept. 25	127	23	.48	.52	.85	2.23	2.59	2.26	1.67	1.56	1.67	1.45	.64	.88	16.80
	Torrington	18	24.1	72.5	104	−43	18	May 13	Sept. 26	136	18	.26	.38	.61	1.99	2.67	2.51	1.51	1.19	1.10	1.14	.53	.37	14.26
Hot Springs	Thermopolis	34	18.6	71.7	107	−44	34	May 19	Sept. 17	121	33	.38	.41	.94	2.06	2.54	1.37	1.09	.81	1.20	1.15	.44	.45	12.84
Johnson	Barnum	17	21.9	68.8	108	−45	19	May 25	Sept. 19	117	25	.39	.31	.77	1.48	2.24	1.25	1.31	.75	.93	1.08	.49	.47	11.47
	Buffalo	32	21.8	68.6	106	−40	30	May 23	Sept. 17	117	32	.48	.46	.86	1.60	2.43	1.89	1.28	1.04	1.23	.78	.48	.54	13.07
	Hunter's Station	28	18.6	58.0	99	−42	32	July 5	Aug. 25	51	30	.75	.72	1.53	2.33	3.18	2.32	2.02	1.50	1.57	1.49	.79	.81	19.01
	Nine Mile Creek	10	21.2	71.0	103	−43	14	May 25	Sept. 20	118	16	.25	.26	.69	1.59	2.28	1.70	1.19	1.08	1.07	.70	.43	.40	11.64
Laramie	Cheyenne	40	26.7	67.0	100	−38	40	May 14	Oct. 2	141	40	.38	.75	1.11	2.29	2.48	1.58	1.99	1.57	1.41	1.07	.57	.62	15.82
	Hecla										28	.41	.92	1.18	2.14	2.42	1.74	2.08	1.87	1.63	1.18	.67	.72	16.96
	Pine Bluffs	34	26.0	70.6	109	−38	33	May 16	Sept. 25	132	36	.24	.51	.91	2.10	2.25	2.13	2.17	2.10	1.63	1.07	.41	.53	16.05
Lincoln	Afton (near)	32	14.3	60.9	98	−55	32	June 30	Aug. 22	53	33	1.46	1.41	1.68	1.41	1.92	1.34	1.21	1.24	1.42	1.71	1.07	1.32	17.19
	Bedford	38	16.7	60.4	97	−46	39	June 27	Aug. 30	64	38	1.93	1.72	1.79	1.62	2.01	1.48	1.00	1.16	1.19	1.56	1.28	1.63	18.37
	Border	36	11.9	63.7	102	−60	37	June 23	do	68	37	1.25	1.25	1.18	1.16	1.23	.96	.75	.84	1.19	1.27	.87	.96	12.91
	Cokeville	10	15.6	61.1	96	−44	12	June 22	Sept. 3	73	12	1.06	1.08	.98	1.33	1.18	.96	.81	.64	1.31	1.28	.74	.79	12.16
Natrona	Casper	28	26.4	72.1	109	−41	28	May 19	Sept. 29	133	29	.62	.79	1.24	2.14	2.28	1.52	1.33	.96	1.20	1.31	.81	.79	14.99
	Ervay	29	20.6	66.0	100	−38	30	June 1	Sept. 14	105	31	.46	.65	1.13	2.16	2.91	1.66	1.60	1.21	1.57	1.70	.77	.69	16.51
	Pathfinder	40	23.1	70.6	107	−39	40	May 18	Sept. 24	129	40	.29	.35	.59	1.21	1.92	1.03	1.16	.89	1.05	.97	.43	.43	10.32
	Salt Creek	16	22.7	71.4	106	−41	16	May 11	Sept. 26	138	17	.53	.49	1.21	1.59	2.37	1.61	1.75	.99	1.14	1.00	.62	.58	13.88
Niobrara	Kirtley (near)	34	21.4	68.4	109	−35	32	May 26	Sept. 21	118	35	.41	.45	.66	1.90	3.15	2.76	1.81	1.53	1.41	1.26	.58	.45	16.37
	Lusk	40	22.7	68.3	105	−35	40	do	Sept. 18	115	39	.43	.50	.82	1.66	2.95	2.40	1.61	1.18	1.07	.85	.43	.60	14.50
	Spencer	20	17.7	73.6	107	−38	18	May 11	Sept. 22	134	20	.43	.46	.63	1.69	2.32	2.59	1.90	1.38	.98	1.12	.51	.38	14.39
Park	Clark	28	25.0	70.5	105	−33	30	May 2	Oct. 5	156	30	.44	.38	.75	1.02	1.77	1.39	1.24	.80	1.02	.85	.71	.45	10.82
	Cody	32	23.6	69.5	105	−46	31	May 17	Sept. 19	125	31	.25	.31	.48	.99	1.35	1.35	1.01	.79	.93	.77	.45	.29	8.97
	Crandall Creek	19	18.2	59.5	94	−49	17	June 23	Aug. 27	65	20	1.32	1.12	1.62	1.86	1.58	2.19	1.93	1.68	1.36	1.63	1.40	.97	18.66
	Powell	30	17.5	69.5	103	−36	32	May 15	Sept. 23	131	32	.17	.12	.22	.50	.97	1.15	.65	.50	.78	.38	.24	.17	5.85
	Quaking Aspen Creek	22	20.9	61.7	100	−43	22	June 10	Sept. 15	97	22	.49	.63	1.13	2.60	3.11	1.89	1.99	1.55	1.36	1.46	.89	.48	17.58
	Shoshone Dam	32	26.4	69.7	100	−42	32	May 10	Sept. 29	142	34	.39	.40	.65	1.10	1.92	1.41	1.22	.97	1.05	.77	.47	.46	10.81
Platte	Chugwater	37	26.8	67.8	110	−45	37	May 29	Sept. 16	110	37	.50	.72	.95	2.11	2.49	2.04	1.50	1.40	1.36	1.11	.58	.80	15.56
	Wheatland	31	28.9	72.3	109	−36	30	May 10	Sept. 28	141	30	.44	.62	.98	2.04	2.43	1.78	1.58	1.05	1.35	1.23	.48	.67	14.65
Sheridan	Dome Lake	28	14.4	55.4	90	−42	26	July 2	Aug. 26	55	28	1.53	1.33	2.76	3.91	3.35	2.66	2.07	1.55	1.96	2.43	1.98	1.62	27.15
	Sheridan	38	19.4	68.9	106	−45	36	May 15	Sept. 22	130	40	.83	.66	1.24	1.94	2.75	1.95	1.26	.75	1.39	1.25	.65	.64	15.31
	Sheridan Field Station.	22	18.9	71.8	107	−38	22	May 14	Sept. 25	134	22	.53	.45	1.20	2.17	2.60	2.12	1.36	.60	1.36	1.40	.79	.53	15.11
	Ulm										25	.86	.67	1.26	1.87	2.51	2.17	1.32	.68	1.60	1.46	.72	.79	15.91
Sublette	Kendall	18	11.4	55.4	103	−52	16	July 11	Aug. 22	42	22	1.73	1.76	1.70	1.29	1.67	1.39	1.29	1.37	1.19	1.14	1.17	1.76	17.46

	Pinedale	26	11.8	60.4	94	−46	28	June 23	Aug. 24	62	28	.71	.71	.70	.67	1.06	1.06	1.10	1.11	1.08	.90	.56	.71	10.37
Sweetwater	Eden	27	9.8	64.2	97	−48	27	June 11	Sept. 8	89	27	.38	.56	.44	.70	.80	.71	.82	.67	.72	.64	.32	.29	7.05
	Green River	33	18.6	69.3	103	−40	34	June 3	Sept. 11	100	34	.32	.54	.53	.84	1.07	.51	.55	.68	.80	.83	.42	.33	7.42
Teton	Alta	28	17.5	61.2	97	−46	30	June 30	Sept. 1	63	29	1.60	1.27	1.35	1.47	1.95	1.80	1.21	1.27	1.48	1.51	1.31	1.43	17.65
	Jackson	22	12.8	61.4	96	−52	17	June 20	Aug. 31	72														
	Moran	28	10.4	57.8	92	−63	28	July 3	Aug. 19	48	28	2.37	2.21	2.25	1.78	1.79	1.69	1.28	1.32	1.66	1.68	1.70	1.87	21.60
Uinta	Evanston	40	18.9	62.3	96	−38	40	June 11	Sept. 7	88	40	1.09	1.29	1.32	1.28	1.39	.89	1.03	1.13	1.04	1.25	.84	.86	13.41
	Lyman	14	17.0	64.9	102	−37	14	June 10	Sept. 10	92	15	.45	.87	.76	1.40	1.08	.60	1.29	1.22	.64	1.03	.62	.58	10.54
Washakie	Worland	28	13.8	72.0	104	−51	28	May 10	Sept. 27	140	29	.33	.27	.41	.89	1.31	1.11	.83	.61	.81	.68	.30	.23	7.78
Weston	Hampshire										18	.43	.25	.50	.98	2.43	1.90	1.58	1.35	.86	.91	.39	.26	11.84
	Newcastle	30	21.6	72.8	108	−37	32	May 15	Sept. 26	134	31	.61	.47	.78	1.24	2.58	2.47	2.31	1.58	1.30	1.07	.60	.51	15.52
	Upton	12	14.7	69.6	105	−45	13	May 30	Sept. 15	108	14	.62	.47	.66	1.14	2.44	2.92	2.28	1.33	1.64	1.44	.79	.68	16.41
Yellowstone National Park.	Buffalo Ranch	31	12.9	57.6	98	−58	31	July 8	Aug. 20	43	32	1.32	1.10	1.18	1.19	2.00	2.06	1.75	1.60	1.25	1.24	1.05	1.13	16.87
	Gallatin	18	11.6	54.9	97	−54	18	do	Aug. 12	35	25	1.39	.97	1.64	1.49	1.72	1.97	1.50	1.55	1.34	1.65	1.32	1.42	17.96
	Lake Yellowstone	30	11.4	55.0	94	−56	31	July 3	Aug. 19	47	31	2.07	1.55	2.07	1.45	1.93	2.01	1.66	1.41	1.37	1.54	1.35	1.56	19.97
	Snake River	28	12.9	58.2	93	−56	26	June 29	Aug. 17	49	29	4.32	2.93	3.53	2.21	2.25	2.30	1.59	1.56	1.62	2.06	2.59	2.89	29.85
	Yellowstone Park	40	18.1	61.4	96	−41	35	May 23	Sept. 16	116	40	1.29	1.00	1.46	1.41	1.82	1.63	1.28	1.19	1.24	1.44	1.07	1.16	15.99
	West Yellowstone (Riverside).	29	12.5	57.7	97	−66	32	July 16	Aug. 15	30	30	2.15	1.61	1.63	1.35	1.60	2.01	1.42	1.25	1.36	1.39	1.58	1.70	19.05

WYOMING—Continued

Precipitation and temperature—State unit values

[This tabulation gives the mean annual, mean monthly, and average seasonal precipitation, 1886–1938, and the mean annual temperatures, 1902–38, for Wyoming]

Precipitation		Precipitation		Precipitation		Precipitation		Temperature		Temperature	
Year	Mean	Year	Mean	Year	Mean	Month	Mean	Year	Mean	Year	Mean
	In.		*In.*		*In.*		*In.*		°*F.*		°*F.*
1886	9.79	1907	14.62	1928	14.23	May	2.07	1902	43.0	1921	43.6
1887	8.02	1908	17.22	1929	15.06	June	1.58	1903	41.4	1922	40.7
1888	13.03	1909	16.36	1930	14.70	July	1.36	1904	42.4	1923	41.2
1889	12.93	1910	12.12	1931	11.57	August	1.10	1905	40.5	1924	40.5
1890	14.81	1911	13.98	1932	13.31	September	1.09	1906	40.8	1925	43.1
1891	15.99	1912	18.40	1933	12.16	October	1.07	1907	41.2	1926	42.9
1892	11.92	1913	16.88	1934	10.85	November	.69	1908	41.2	1927	41.3
1893	10.67	1914	12.32	1935	12.28	December	.73	1909	40.6	1928	41.5
1894	11.87	1915	19.21	1936	13.13			1910	42.8	1929	40.0
1895	16.90	1916	13.50	1937	15.53	Annual	13.93	1911	39.5	1930	41.8
1896	15.00	1917	13.78	1938	15.26			1912	38.6	1931	43.2
1897	12.86	1918	16.13					1913	39.5	1932	40.5
1898	12.50	1919	10.99	Month	Mean	Season	Average	1914	41.7	1933	43.2
1899	13.99	1920	14.18					1915	40.8	1934	45.8
1900	10.95	1921	12.58					1916	39.1	1935	42.2
1901	12.09	1922	14.16					1917	39.5	1936	42.4
1902	9.81	1923	19.31		*In.*		*In.*	1918	41.7	1937	41.4
1903	12.87	1924	12.69	January	0.78	Winter	2.29	1919	42.2	1938	43.0
1904	14.29	1925	15.62	February	.78	Spring	4.75	1920	41.0		
1905	16.23	1926	14.58	March	1.14	Summer	4.04				
1906	17.82	1927	18.16	April	1.54	Fall	2.85				

Dates of last killing frost in spring and first in fall, with length of growing season

Year	Cheyenne			Cody			Green River			Lander			Lusk			Sheridan		
	Last in spring	First in fall	Growing season [1]	Last in spring	First in fall	Growing season [1]	Last in spring	First in fall	Growing season [1]	Last in spring	First in fall	Growing season [1]	Last in spring	First in fall	Growing season [1]	Last in spring	First in fall	Growing season [1]
			Days			*Days*			*Days*			*Days*			*Days*			*Days*
1899	May 17	Sept. 28	134	May 22						June 14	Aug. 14	70	May 17	Sept. 16	122			
1900	May 19	Sept. 26	130	May 20	Sept. 25	128				Apr. 12	Oct. 7	178	May 18	Sept. 19	124		Sept. 25	
1901	May 22	Sept. 16	117							June 6	Sept. 14	100	June 5	Sept. 16	103	June 6	Sept. 17	103

1902	May 21	Sept. 12	114							Apr. 23	Sept. 12	142	June 20	Sept. 11	83			
1903	June 1	Sept. 14	105							May 23	Sept. 9	109	June 9	do	94			
1904	May 17	do	120							May 12	Sept. 14	125	July 6	Aug. 21	46			
1905	May 16	Oct. 9	146				May 12	Sept. 1	112	May 6	Oct. 1	148	May 16	Sept. 18	125	May 17	Sept. 18	124
1906	May 6	Oct. 4	151				June 8	Sept. 12	96	June 8	Oct. 4	118	June 20	Sept. 12	84	May 18	Sept. 16	121
1907	May 14	Sept. 20	129				June 23	Aug. 11	49	May 3	Oct. 1	151	May 27	Sept. 9	105	May 27	Oct. 18	144
1908	May 10	Sept. 26	139				do	Aug. 31	69	May 21	Aug. 31	102	May 21	Sept. 23	125	May 1	Sept. 25	147
1909	May 25	Sept. 22	120		Sept. 18		June 10	Sept. 12	94	May 19	Sept. 23	127	May 17	Sept. 18	124	May 18	Sept. 24	129
1910	May 22	Aug. 25	95	May 17	Aug. 25	100	June 9	Aug. 26	78	May 22	Aug. 25	95	May 22	Aug. 25	95	May 17	Aug. 25	100
1911	May 27	Oct. 19	145	May 28	Aug. 28	92	June 10	Sept. 6	88	May 28	Sept. 8	103	May 26	Sept. 17	114	May 12	Sept. 19	130
1912	May 14	Sept. 15	124	May 13	Sept. 15	125	June 16	do	82	May 24	Sept. 30	129	June 18	Sept. 14	88	May 13	Sept. 17	126
1913	May 3	Sept. 20	140	May 20	Sept. 16	119	May 14	Sept. 20	129	May 3	Sept. 20	140	May 22	Sept. 16	117	May 3	Sept. 20	141
1914	May 7	Sept. 14	130	May 14	Sept. 13	122	June 22	Sept. 12	82	May 13	Sept. 12	122	May 16	Sept. 12	119	May 12	Sept. 2	113
1915	June 13	Oct. 5	114	May 6	Sept. 12	129	June 21	Sept. 15	86	May 8	Sept. 28	143	June 6	Sept. 14	100	May 22	Sept. 15	117
1916	May 17	Sept. 28	134	June 6	Sept. 14	100	June 11	Sept. 4	85	May 23	Sept. 11	111	June 7	Sept. 11	96	May 17	do	120
1917	May 11	Oct. 12	154	June 14	Sept. 25	113	June 13	Sept. 15	94	June 13	Sept. 26	105	June 13	Sept. 19	98	June 1	Sept. 30	121
1918	May 10	Oct. 24	167	June 1	Sept. 16	107	June 2	Aug. 22	81	May 19	Oct. 7	141	May 26	Aug. 30	96	May 22	Sept. 16	117
1919	June 3	Oct. 4	123	June 2	Sept. 22	112	June 5	Sept. 23	110	May 6	Oct. 5	152	June 2	Sept. 20	110	June 2	Sept. 22	112
1920	May 15	Sept. 29	137	do	Aug. 29	88	June 1			June 1	Sept. 25	116	June 3	Sept. 3	92	Apr. 26	Sept. 29	156
1921	May 2	Oct. 7	158	May 13	Sept. 10	120	July 3	Sept. 1	60	May 1	Sept. 17	139	May 14	Sept. 4	113	May 13	Sept. 11	121
1922	May 16	do	144	June 1	Sept. 8	99	June 1	Sept. 8	99	June 1	Oct. 7	128	June 1	Oct. 7	128	Apr. 21	Oct. 5	167
1923	do	Oct. 13	150	May 15	Sept. 18	126	do	Sept. 17	108	May 16	Sept. 18	125	May 16	Oct. 11	148	May 16	Sept. 18	125
1924	May 14	Oct. 5	144	May 27	Sept. 27	123	June 20	Sept. 11	83	May 10	Sept. 28	141	May 27	Sept. 28	124	May 10	Sept. 14	127
1925	May 4	Oct. 8	157	May 16	Sept. 30	137	June 17	Sept. 30	105	May 9	Sept. 23	137	May 16	Oct. 6	143	May 9	Sept. 22	136
1926	May 14	Sept. 24	133	Apr. 25	Sept. 22	150	May 14	Sept. 5	114	Apr. 24	Sept. 24	153	Apr. 28	Sept. 24	149	May 14	do	131
1927	May 10	Sept. 26	139	May 29	Sept. 25	119	June 1	Sept. 2	93	May 10	Sept. 27	140	May 30	Sept. 19	112	May 30	Sept. 19	112
1928	May 4	Oct. 12	161	May 4	Oct. 1	150	June 19	Sept. 10	83	May 4	Sept. 10	129	June 10	Sept. 23	105	May 4	Sept. 21	140
1929	May 12	Oct. 22	163	May 28	Sept. 4	99	June 20	Sept. 9	81	June 20	Sept. 6	78	June 20	Sept. 5	77	May 18	Sept. 8	113
1930	May 18	Oct. 16	151	May 23	Oct. 15	145	May 23	Sept. 26	126	June 14	Sept. 24	102	May 23	Sept. 26	126	May 23	Sept. 26	126
1931	May 22	Oct. 27	158	May 22	Sept. 21	122	May 30	do	119	May 22	Sept. 22	123	May 30	do	119	May 20	Oct. 12	145
1932	May 16	Oct. 4	141	May 1	Sept. 13	135	June 7	Aug. 31	85	June 2	Aug. 31	90	May 16	Sept. 20	127	May 27	Sept. 22	118
1933	May 12	Oct. 16	157	May 28	Sept. 23	118	May 28	Sept. 16	111	May 14	Sept. 16	125	May 13	do	136	May 13	Sept. 23	133
1934	Apr. 20	Sept. 15	148	Apr. 16	Sept. 20	157	Apr. 27	Sept. 21	147	June 2	Sept. 15	105	Apr. 21	Sept. 14	146	do	Sept. 21	131
1935	May 4	Oct. 21	170	May 9	Sept. 27	141	May 15	Sept. 28	136	May 15	Sept. 28	136	May 23	Sept. 28	128	May 9	Oct. 10	154
1936	Apr. 9	Oct. 7	181	Apr. 29	Sept. 16	140	May 6	Sept. 15	132	May 21	Sept. 15	117	Apr. 17	Sept. 16	152	May 1	Sept. 16	138
1937	May 13	Sept. 25	135	Apr. 24	Sept. 25	154	May 1			Apr. 30	Sept. 24	147	Apr. 27	Sept. 24	150	May 22	Sept. 25	126
1938	May 7	Oct. 19	165	May 7	Oct. 17	163	May 9	Oct. 9	153	May 8	Oct. 9	154	May 7	Oct. 19	165	Apr. 28	Oct. 19	174
Mean	May 14	Oct. 2	141	May 17	Sept. 19	125	June 3	Sept. 11	100	May 18	Sept. 20	125	May 26	Sept. 18	115	May 15	Sept. 22	130
Extremes	Apr. 9[2] June 13[3]	Aug. 25[4] Oct. 27[5]	[6] 95 [7] 181	Apr. 16[2] June 6[3]	Aug. 25[4] Oct. 17[5]	[6] 92 [7] 163	Apr. 27[2] July 3[3]	Aug. 11[4] Oct. 9[5]	[6] 49 [7] 153	Apr. 12[2] June 20[3]	Aug. 23[4] Oct. 9[5]	[6] 70 [7] 178	Apr. 17[2] July 6[3]	Aug. 21[4] Oct. 19[5]	[6] 46 [7] 165	Apr. 21[2] June 6[3]	Aug. 25[4] Oct. 19[5]	[6] 100 [7] 174

[1] Number of days between last killing frost in spring and first in fall.
[2] Earliest date in spring.
[3] Latest date in spring.
[4] Earliest date in fall.
[5] Latest date in fall.
[6] Shortest growing season.
[7] Longest growing season.

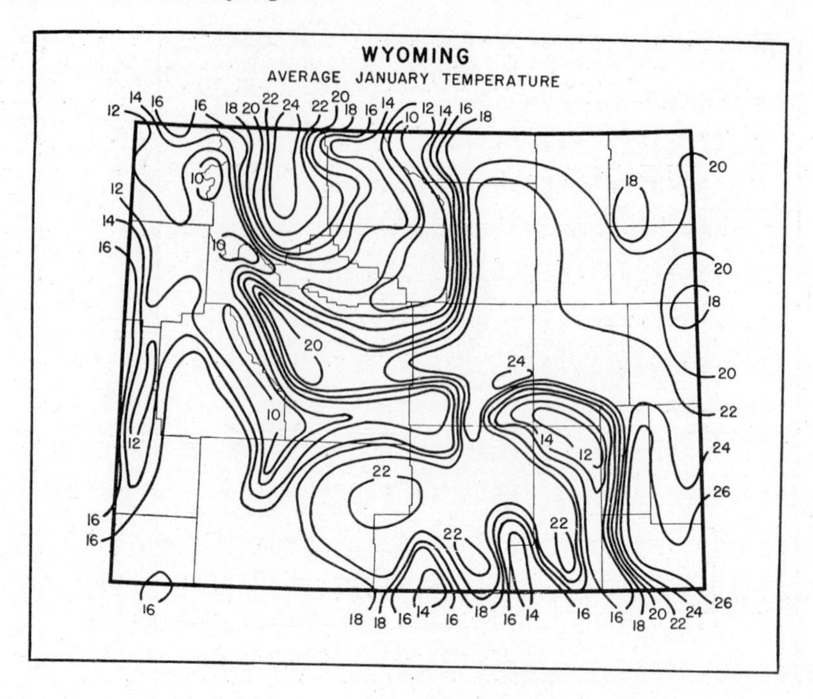
WYOMING
AVERAGE JANUARY TEMPERATURE

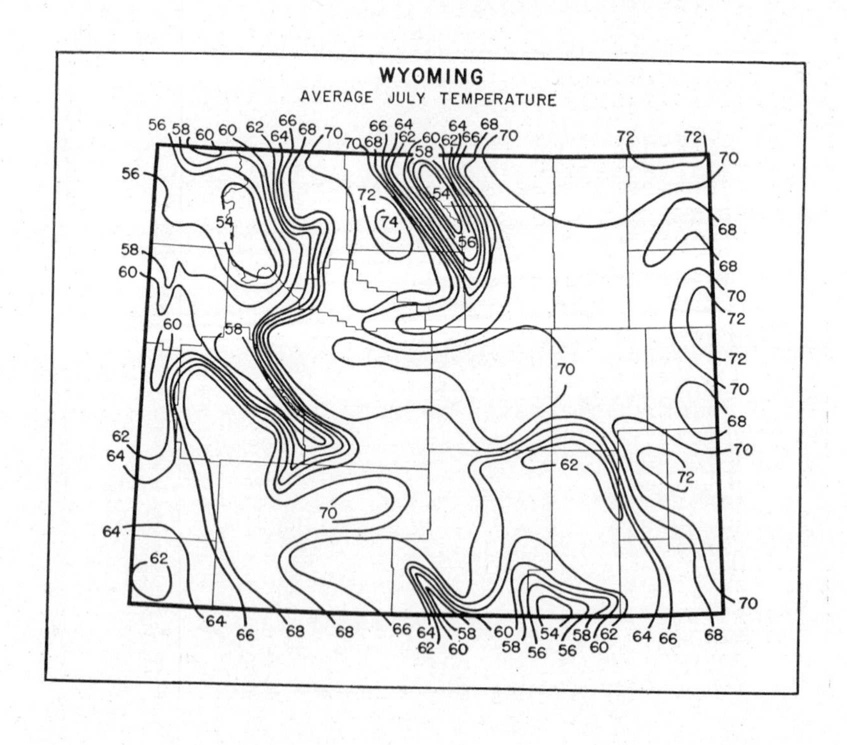
WYOMING
AVERAGE JULY TEMPERATURE

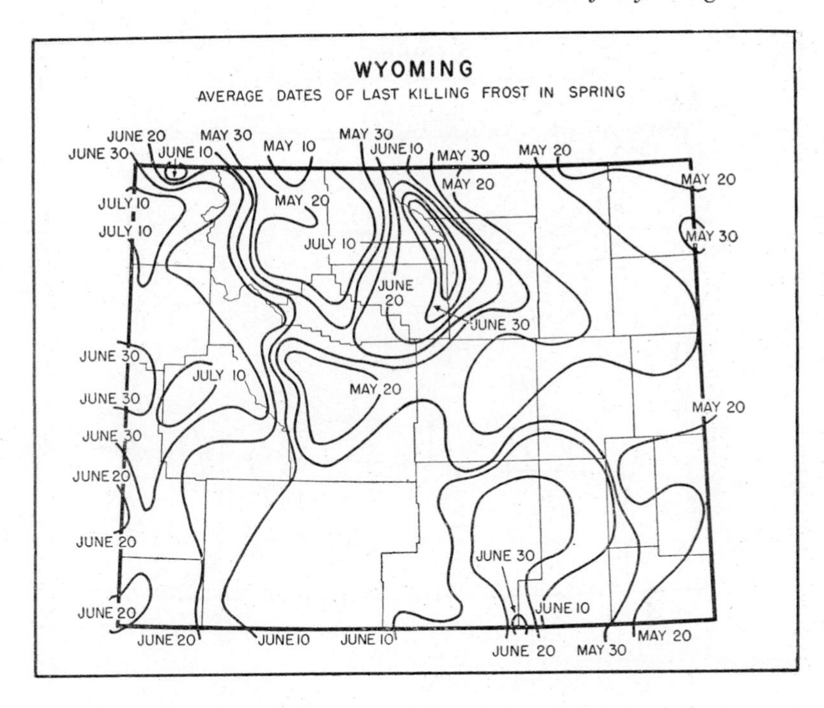
WYOMING
AVERAGE DATES OF LAST KILLING FROST IN SPRING
JUNE 20
JUNE 30
JUNE 10
MAY 30
MAY 10
MAY 30
JUNE 10
MAY 30
MAY 20
MAY 20
MAY 20
MAY 20
JULY 10
JULY 10
JULY 10
MAY 30
JUNE 20
JUNE 30
JUNE 30
JULY 10
MAY 20
JUNE 30
MAY 20
JUNE 30
JUNE 20
JUNE 20
JUNE 30
JUNE 10
JUNE 20
JUNE 20
JUNE 10
JUNE 10
JUNE 20
MAY 30
MAY 20

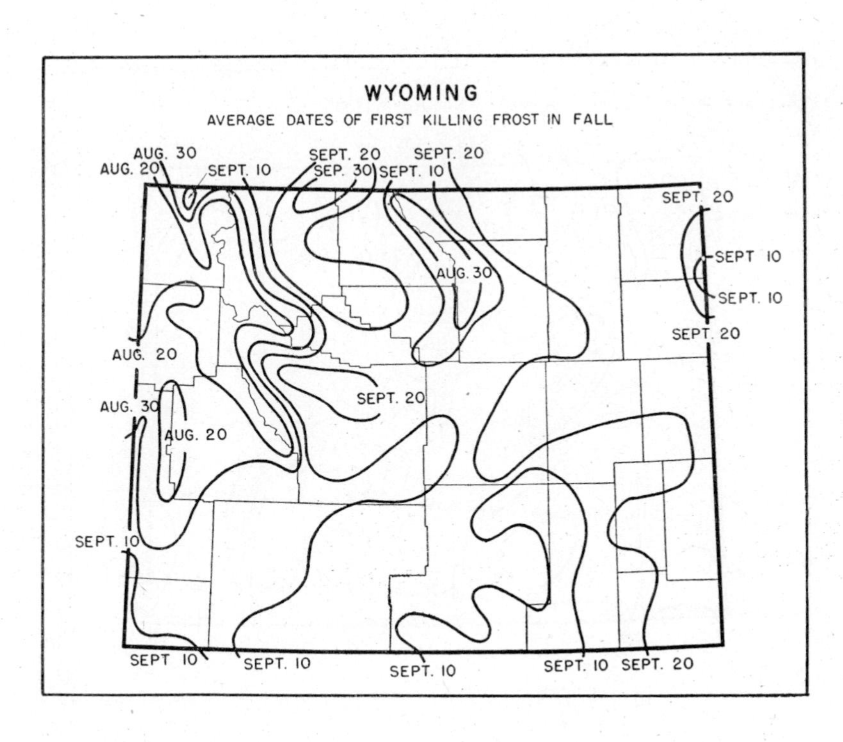
WYOMING
AVERAGE DATES OF FIRST KILLING FROST IN FALL
AUG. 30
AUG. 20
SEPT. 10
SEPT. 20
SEP. 30
SEPT. 10
SEPT. 20
SEPT. 20
SEPT 10
SEPT. 10
AUG. 30
SEPT. 20
AUG. 20
SEPT. 20
AUG. 30
AUG. 20
SEPT. 10
SEPT 10
SEPT. 10
SEPT. 10
SEPT. 10
SEPT. 20

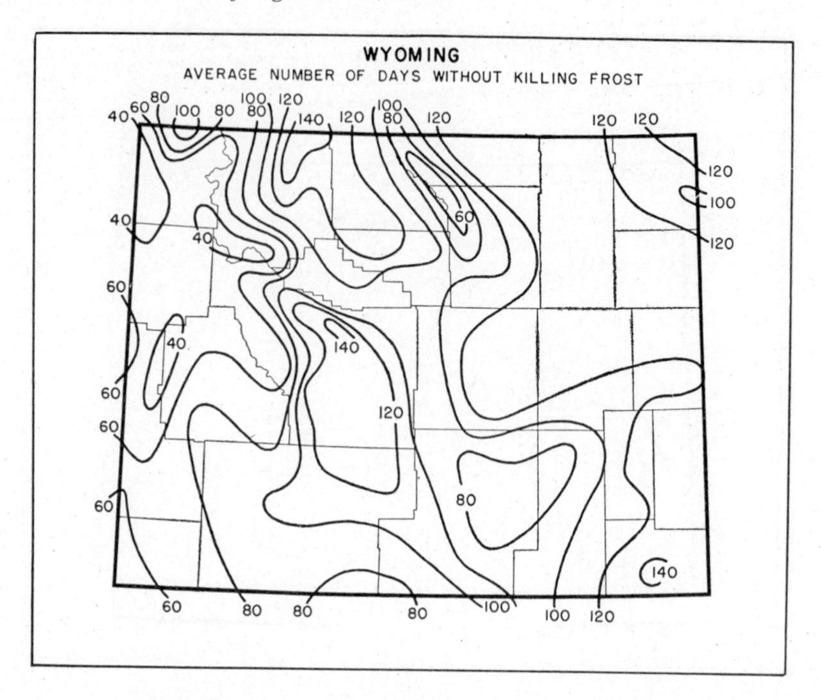
WYOMING
AVERAGE NUMBER OF DAYS WITHOUT KILLING FROST

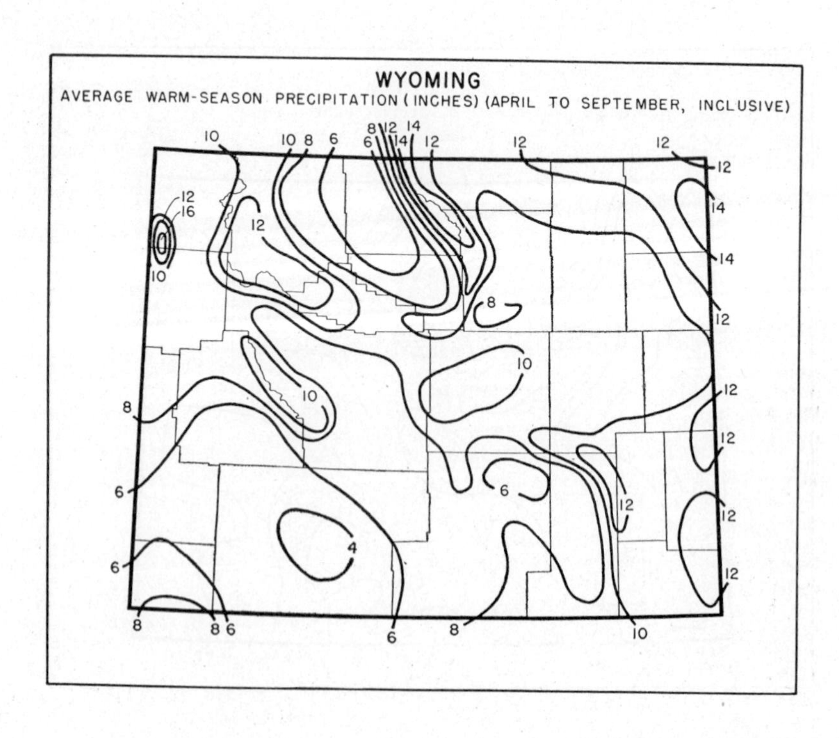
WYOMING
AVERAGE WARM-SEASON PRECIPITATION (INCHES) (APRIL TO SEPTEMBER, INCLUSIVE)

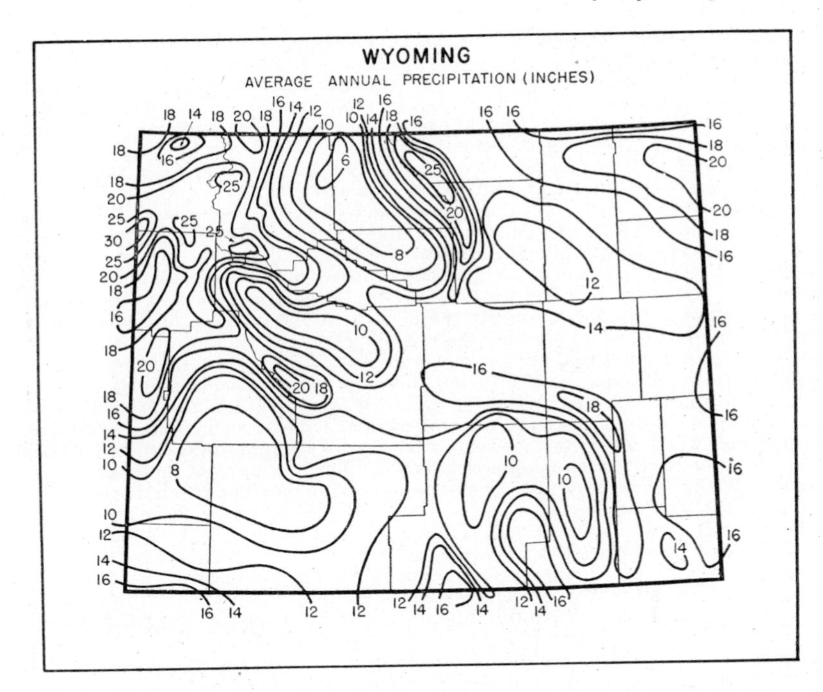

SUPPLEMENTARY CLIMATIC NOTES FOR WYOMING

Except for the Red Desert and the Big Horn Basin in the western part of Wyoming, and the northeastern and extreme eastern sections, which are really an extension of the Great Plains, most of the State is mountainous. Some of the more important systems are the Teton, Absaroka, Wind River, Gros Ventre, Owl Creek, and Sierra Madre Ranges in the western part, the Medicine Bow and Laramie Ranges in the southeast, and the Big Horn Range in the north-central part. The mean elevation of the State is approximately 6,700 feet, varying from 3,125 feet where the Belle Fourche River enters South Dakota, in Crook County, to 13,785 on the summit of Gannett Peak, Fremont County. The Continental Divide crosses the State in a northwest-southeast direction from the Yellowstone Park area to the south-central part.

The drainage of Wyoming is remarkable in that its waters flow in practically every direction, and tributaries of three great river systems have their sources in a rather limited area in the northwest part of the State. The Green River, a tributary of the Colorado, has its source in the northern part of Sublette County, and flows into the Gulf of California. The Snake River has its source in the area adjacent to the southern part of Yellowstone Park and the western slopes of the Wind River and Gros Ventre mountain ranges; it is a tributary of the Columbia. The Missouri and the Yellowstone Rivers have their sources in Yellowstone Park, and the Big Horn, a tributary of the Yellowstone, has its source on the east slope of the Wind River and Absaroka mountain ranges; all these streams are a part of the Mississippi River system.

There are several large completed irrigation projects in Wyoming, which is more or less semiarid. Among the larger is the Jackson Lake project, in Teton County, which furnishes irrigation water principally for the State of Idaho. The Riverton project, on the Big Horn River, and the Shoshone project on the Shoshone River, in Park County, supply irrigation water for a large area in the Big Horn Basin, which extends into Montana. The upper North Platte River has a large storage capacity, and much of its water is used in Nebraska. Additional storage has been provided in the Laramie River Basin, and most of this water is used in the Wheatland project in Platte County, Wyo. The Green is the only river most of the water of which leaves the State by natural flow. However, many projects are planned on the Green which will materially reduce the loss of water to the State.

Owing to the diverse topography of Wyoming, climatic features vary greatly from one section to another. The eastern mountain slopes render the winters less severe in the east than in the valleys in the west. The mean annual temperature ranges from 47.2° F. at Casper, in the central part of the State, to 32.2° at Lake Yellowstone in Yellowstone National Park. Over much of the western part of the State freezing temperatures may be expected every month of the year, with the exception of the extreme lower part of the Green River Basin. The summers in this section are short with temperatures of 100° or higher recorded only on rare occasions, while the winters are long and severe. Over the northeastern and eastern parts of the State temperatures of 100° or higher are frequent during July and August. The winters in these sections are not so severe as many people suppose, as the low humidity tempers the chilling effects of the cold waves that sweep southward along the eastern slope of the mountains. These cold waves average about three or four a winter and normally are of short duration, frequently being broken up after a few days by warm chinook winds.

Owing to the varied topography of the State, the length of the growing season varies greatly. Numerous mountain ranges and valleys occupy the western part of the State, where the growing season varies from a minimum of 30 days in parts of Yellowstone Park to a maximum of 125 at Lander. In many of the more elevated localities in this section frost or freezing temperature may be expected every month of the year. The northeastern and southeastern parts, being more or less level or gently rolling and cut by only a few mountain ranges, have a much longer growing season than the western part. In the northeast the growing season varies from 156 days at Clark, in the lower Big Horn Basin, to 24 at Kirwin, in the Absaroka Mountains, while in the southeast it ranges from a maximum of 133 days at Burns and Casper to a minimum of 78 at Big Creek, in the Medicine Bow Mountains.

The average annual precipitation ranges from 4.71 inches at Hyattville in the lower Big Horn Basin to 39.91 at Bechler River in the southwest corner of Yellowstone National Park. The average annual snowfall varies from 12 inches at Powell, in the lower Big Horn Basin, to more than 200 in some areas of Yellowstone National Park. Over much of the State approximately 70 percent of the total annual precipitation occurs during the growing season, April to September, and this is particularly true in the dry-farming sections of the east and northeast. The heaviest amounts of precipitation are mostly in the form of snow in the higher mountains and provide water for the several irrigation projects in the State. The summer precipitation falls mostly in scattered thundershowers and is quite frequently accompanied by hail in the spring months.

Relative humidity in Wyoming, as in other Mountain States, is considerably lower than over the Plains to the eastward. This dryness of the air serves to temper the penetrating effects of the low temperatures during the winter months, while in summer it produces a cooling effect by facilitating evaporation. For this reason neither the cold of winter nor the heat of summer is as noticeable as in more humid climates.

Tornadoes are less frequent in Wyoming than over the central Plains area and much less destructive. In fact, they are more like overgrown whirlwinds and usually affect only small areas. They rarely occur in the western part of the State and on an average only once a year in the east.

FRED L. DISTERDICK, *Associate Meteorologist and Climatic Section Director for Wyoming, Weather Bureau, Cheyenne.*

ALASKA

Climatic summary

District	Station	Temperature: Length of record	Temperature: January average	Temperature: July average	Temperature: Maximum	Temperature: Minimum	Killing frost average dates: Length of record	Killing frost average dates: Last in spring	Killing frost average dates: First in fall	Killing frost average dates: Growing season[1]	Average precipitation: Length of record	January	February	March	April	May	June	July	August	September	October	November	December	Annual
		Yr.	*°F.*	*°F.*	*°F.*	*°F.*	*Yr.*			*Days*	*Yr.*	*In.*	*In.*	*In.*	*In.*	*In.*	*In.*	*In.*	*In.*	*In.*	*In.*	*In.*	*In.*	*In.*
Southeastern	Annex Creek	21	22.7	54.9	84	−12	20	May 6	Sept. 30	147	22	9.04	7.85	6.20	5.65	5.14	4.33	6.21	10.22	13.42	16.61	13.41	9.36	107.44
	Bell Island	9	29.0	58.2	90	−4	9	May 8	Oct. 28	173	9	10.63	8.51	7.12	6.64	5.33	5.49	5.71	7.19	11.26	15.29	15.11	11.78	110.06
	Haines	15	22.9	57.6	90	−15	14	May 20	Sept. 19	122	15	5.42	5.14	4.76	3.34	2.01	1.58	1.80	2.27	4.98	10.24	7.74	7.15	56.43
	Juneau	40	27.5	56.6	89	−15	23	Apr. 28	Oct. 17	172	40	7.18	5.63	5.41	5.46	5.22	3.95	5.03	7.33	10.15	11.18	9.10	7.61	83.25
	Kassan										13	9.21	7.59	6.32	6.22	5.65	3.76	3.68	4.44	6.30	10.17	10.39	10.27	84.00
	Ketchikan	28	32.6	57.5	96	−8	23	May 5	Oct. 17	165	28	13.71	11.63	12.20	10.79	8.31	6.55	8.24	11.51	12.14	20.13	19.74	15.94	150.89
	Petersburg	8	28.5	55.2	81	−5	6	May 18	Sept. 24	129	9	8.50	9.85	7.29	6.39	5.79	4.49	5.31	6.94	11.97	15.32	12.79	11.81	106.45
	Seclusion Harbor	6	30.3	55.8	92	−2	6	May 6	Oct. 9	156	6	11.89	9.08	8.20	6.68	5.49	4.14	4.70	6.67	8.52	17.45	15.40	12.33	110.55
	Sitka	40	32.4	54.9	87	−5	23	May 10	Oct. 16	159	40	7.84	6.78	5.97	5.58	4.15	3.36	4.29	7.02	10.33	12.64	10.07	9.10	87.13
	Skagway	32	21.1	57.7	92	−19	21	May 27	Sept. 15	111	30	2.05	1.40	1.30	1.46	.89	.92	1.45	1.91	3.52	5.02	4.14	2.79	26.85
	Tree Point	9	34.1	54.4	86	−3	8	May 22	Sept. 23	124	9	10.85	7.23	6.97	6.47	5.46	5.66	5.72	5.41	8.38	12.69	13.45	11.38	99.67
	View Cove	7	35.1	56.0	88	5	6	Apr. 25	Nov. 3	192	7	17.74	12.17	12.36	10.97	9.50	6.65	6.20	7.23	12.58	18.37	22.57	19.18	155.52
	Wrangell	23	29.0	58.2	92	−6	19	Apr. 26	Oct. 12	169	22	7.71	7.25	5.43	4.89	4.38	3.55	4.49	5.31	8.35	11.21	11.79	8.59	82.95
Pacific coast	Cordova	26	27.2	54.8	87	−19	22	May 8	Oct. 4	149	27	9.49	10.70	8.49	8.69	9.09	6.03	8.51	13.24	19.96	22.94	15.51	12.78	145.43
	Kodiak	36	29.8	54.3	85	−12	23	May 5	Oct. 12	160	40	4.66	4.73	3.83	3.93	6.03	4.91	3.60	5.00	5.43	7.55	5.72	6.09	61.48
	Seward	26	22.4	55.3	82	−20	18	May 18	Sept. 27	132	26	4.46	4.91	3.34	4.25	3.39	2.42	2.83	5.92	9.60	11.06	14.85	6.70	73.73
	Valdez	27	19.1	53.3	83	−24	20	May 23	Sept. 16	116	25	4.55	4.92	4.22	2.90	2.81	2.15	3.53	6.18	9.05	8.38	5.99	5.70	60.38
	Whale Island	14	28.8	53.1	83	−9	14	June 3	Sept. 17	106	15	3.87	4.62	2.84	3.52	6.88	4.22	3.16	3.46	3.66	7.43	5.75	4.62	54.03
	Yukutat	17	29.3	52.8	82	5	12	May 9	Oct. 8	152	18	10.77	9.67	8.75	7.80	7.84	4.17	8.18	10.17	14.65	17.73	16.92	12.48	129.13
Southwestern	Atka	12	33.4	49.6							13	6.53	4.43	5.54	5.19	5.13	3.98	5.55	5.41	6.52	7.70	8.26	6.00	70.24
	Dutch Harbor	22	32.2	51.3	80	8	22	May 22	Oct. 14	145	18	5.80	5.24	5.01	4.02	4.41	2.74	1.92	2.35	5.21	7.33	5.71	7.03	56.77
	St. Paul Island	27	25.2	45.8	64	−26	23	June 5	Oct. 10	127	36	2.26	1.61	1.87	1.36	1.52	1.39	2.73	3.25	3.47	3.32	2.94	2.22	27.94
Southern Valley	Anchorage	22	11.2	57.0	92	−36	23	May 25	Sept. 12	110	22	.85	.69	.57	.39	.48	.58	1.65	2.64	2.49	2.08	1.06	.84	14.32
	Bethel	15	8.3	54.5	90	−46	15	June 4	Sept. 5	93	15	1.10	.66	.87	.53	.69	1.15	2.32	3.97	3.30	1.69	.86	.84	17.98
	Kennecott	24	4.5	52.4	80	−39	23	June 6	do	91	20	1.71	1.48	1.08	.65	1.16	1.46	2.39	3.03	3.07	2.15	1.84	1.58	21.60
	Matanuska	19	12.6	57.7	91	−36					19	.94	.80	.61	.47	.62	1.06	1.87	2.88	2.39	1.84	1.05	1.08	15.61
	Susitna	6	9.1	57.7	86	−37					6	1.74	.86	1.00	.94	1.25	1.88	2.38	4.88	4.10	4.07	2.35	1.43	26.88
	Talkeetna	19	7.6	58.0	90	−48	15	June 14	Aug. 25	72	18	1.81	1.98	1.97	.90	.96	1.65	3.64	5.13	4.40	4.02	1.87	1.70	30.03
Bering Sea	Dillingham (near)	22	16.1	55.6	89	−41					21	1.87	1.34	1.78	1.29	1.63	1.70	2.71	3.91	3.93	2.78	1.73	1.45	26.12
	Nome	32	3.4	49.8	84	−47	21	June 19	Aug. 10	52	32	1.16	.83	.88	.64	.66	1.21	2.55	3.36	2.77	1.61	1.00	1.15	17.82
	Teller	6	−.1	52.1	76	−35					6	1.46	.60	.31	.79	.46	.71	1.80	1.47	2.01	.53	.83	.42	11.39
	White Mountain	16	2.7	54.1	89	−55	15	June 9	Aug. 24	76	14	.97	.68	.67	.27	.29	.98	2.10	2.84	3.45	.82	.69	.90	14.66
Yukon Valley	Allakaket	24	−20.3	57.7	90	−70	14	June 13	Aug. 6	54	25	.77	.84	.70	.36	.65	1.32	2.11	2.02	1.55	1.11	.83	.84	13.10
	Dawson	37	−21.0	59.3	92	−66					37	.87	.70	.52	.52	1.02	1.19	1.55	1.58	1.41	1.17	1.12	1.04	12.69
	Fairbanks	34	−11.6	60.0	99	−66	20	May 29	Aug. 26	89	34	.97	.49	.70	.29	.57	1.30	1.92	2.10	1.31	.85	.74	.63	11.87
	Fort Yukon	23	−21.6	61.2	100	−78	18	June 1	Aug. 21	81	23	.40	.41	.26	.27	.49	.80	1.07	1.27	.65	.60	.35	.31	6.88
	Holy Cross	35	−.4	56.5	93	−58	22	May 31	Aug. 29	90	29	1.49	.97	1.29	.66	.67	1.31	2.70	3.78	2.91	1.67	1.29	1.32	20.06
	Hot Springs	9	−11.1	58.3	88	−70					9	1.64	.99	.37	.12	.26	1.46	3.41	4.30	1.64	.91	.85	.74	16.69

ALASKA—Continued

Climatic summary—Continued

District	Station	Temperature					Killing frost average dates				Average precipitation													
		Length of record	January average	July average	Maximum	Minimum	Length of record	Last in spring	First in fall	Growing season [1]	Length of record	January	February	March	April	May	June	July	August	September	October	November	December	Annual
		Yr.	*°F.*	*°F.*	*°F.*	*°F.*	*Yr.*			*Days*	*Yr.*	*In.*	*In.*	*In.*	*In.*	*In.*	*In.*	*In.*	*In.*	*In.*	*In.*	*In.*	*In.*	*In.*
Yukon Valley—Con.	McKinley Park	16	1.9	54.3	89	−54	15	June 9	Aug. 11	63	15	.83	.78	.41	.60	.96	2.09	2.38	3.13	1.68	1.10	.70	.62	15.28
	Nulato	13	−7.5	57.5	90	−62					13	1.40	.96	1.26	.38	.58	.83	2.41	2.64	2.10	1.87	1.21	.86	16.50
	Ruby	6	−7.5	57.5	98	−52					6	1.78	.99	.82	.31	.79	.71	3.06	3.82	2.77	1.06	.83	.83	17.77
	Tanana	37	−12.5	58.3	91	−76	21	June 3	Aug. 26	64	38	.80	.74	.64	.25	.76	1.21	2.37	2.60	1.80	1.07	.75	.64	13.63
	University Experiment Station	34	−10.2	59.9	99	−65					34	.93	.45	.73	.28	.57	1.32	1.85	2.14	1.37	.86	.70	.56	11.76
Arctic drainage	Barrow	25	−17.0	40.2	78	−56	18	July 4	July 21	17	23	.15	.20	.14	.13	.15	.26	.93	.74	.46	.59	.32	.27	4.34
	Kotzebue	14	−9.2	52.4	81	−58	10	June 13	Sept. 14	93	6	.94	.24	.26	.50	.09	.57	1.05	.89	.73	.37	.36	.32	6.32

[1] Length of growing season between average dates of last killing frost in spring and first in fall.

Precipitation—Territorial unit values

[This tabulation gives the mean annual precipitation, 1907–38, for the southern and northern divisions of Alaska separately. The southern division consists of the southeastern, Pacific coast, and southwestern island districts; the northern division consists of the remainder of the Territory]

Precipitation for southern division		Precipitation for southern division		Precipitation for southern division		Precipitation for northern division		Precipitation for northern division		Precipitation for northern division	
Year	Mean	Year	Mean	Year	Mean	Year	Mean	Year	Mean	Year	Mean
	In.		*In.*		*In.*		*In.*		*In.*		*In.*
1907	65.41	1919	80.78	1931	85.82	1907	13.59	1919	15.70	1929	19.35
1908	68.01	1920	81.69	1932	79.54	1908	10.96	1920	15.68	1930	18.44
1909	63.87	1921	83.23	1933	73.01	1909	10.15	1921	14.23	1931	15.21
1910	67.87	1922	82.26	1934	81.78	1910	9.61	1922	17.14	1932	15.74
1911	67.71	1923	91.29	1935	87.84	1911	11.22	1923	14.96	1933	11.07
1912	93.68	1924	91.33	1936	91.97	1912	12.35	1924	17.17	1934	15.43
1913	84.58	1925	85.62	1937	88.83	1913	9.83	1925	17.24	1935	17.77
1914	78.53	1926	104.46	1938	102.75	1914	12.20	1926	13.11	1936	14.86
1915	100.96	1927	83.49			1915	16.31	1927	12.90	1937	16.45
1916	84.74	1928	98.09			1916	16.23	1928	16.95	1938	17.04
1917	105.18	1929	93.54			1917	13.95				
1918	96.79	1930	92.91			1918	15.58				

SUPPLEMENTARY CLIMATIC NOTES FOR ALASKA

Climatically, Alaska is naturally divided into three areas—southeastern and southern, western and northern, and the interior valleys.

The southeastern area is crescent-shaped, with an arc 1,500 miles in length, and is mostly within 20 miles of tidewater. It is mountainous in the extreme, with the land areas cut by innuemrable tidewater bays, sounds, inlets, and fiords, some of which are flanked by huge glaciers descending the mountain passes. Scores of the peaks have elevations above 5,000 feet, and a number rise to from 10,000 to 15,000 feet. From Kodiak Island eastward, the precipitous slopes of the mountains are for the most part clothed to heights of 1,000 to 3,000 feet with luxuriant forests of spruce, hemlock, and some cedar. To the southward of Kodiak Island, however, the Alaska Peninsula and contiguous islands are entirely devoid of forests or any form of tree growth.

Among the larger islands of the Alexander Archipelago, which embraces about half of southeastern Alaska, are Chichagof, Baranof, Admiralty, Revillagigedo, and Prince of Wales, the last-named having a length of 140 miles and a width of 40. The more important tidal watercourses are Portland Canal, 75 miles in length and very narrow, along the southeastern border; Clarence Strait, through which steamers from the States enter this part of the Territory; and Chatham Strait. The largest fresh-water streams in the section are the Stikine and Taku Rivers, which have their sources in British Columbia. A most distinctive as well as picturesque feature of southern Alaska is its glaciers, of which there are scores, if not hundreds. Taku Glacier is only a few miles from the steamer track of the famous inside passage and can be seen from the largest ocean steamers that ply Alaskan waters.

The western and northern area includes the Aleutian Islands, the Bering Sea section and adjacent coast, and the Arctic coast and its drainage basins. The Aleutian Islands are principally a continuation of the Alaskan Peninsula. These are mountainous in the extreme and largely of volcanic origin. The mountains are devoid of timber, but their lower slopes are for the most part covered with a luxuriant growth of native grasses. The Bering Sea area comprises the immediate coast line of the mainland; the coast is of low relief except along the Alaska and Seward Peninsulas. Connecting Bering Sea and the Arctic Ocean and separating the continents of Asia and North America is Bering Strait, about 50 miles wide. The coast line of this area has a length of approximately 1,300 miles, with the southern part of the arctic slope a high, rolling plateau, beginning with the Endicott Mountains. Flowing northward into the Arctic Ocean and having their source in the plateau area of the Endicott Mountains are the Meade, Chipp, Colville, and Canning Rivers.

The interior valleys of Alaska comprise principally those of the Yukon River and its tributaries. The Endicott Mountains, lying north of the Arctic Circle and sloping northward to the ocean and southward into the Koyukuk Valley, form the northern limits of the area, and between these and the Alaska Range lies the drainage basin of the great Yukon. The Alaska Range is a crescent-shaped ridge 50 to 60 miles wide and extending from the vicinity of Lake Clarke on the west to the St. Elias Range on the east. This range is composed of numerous peaks more than 10,000 feet above sea level. Mount McKinley, in the northwestern part of the arc, with an elevation of 20,300 feet, is the highest mountain peak in North America.

The Yukon, rising within 25 miles of tidewater in southeastern Alaska and emptying into the Bering Sea through a course 2,300 miles in length, together with its tributaries, constitutes the fifth largest river system in North America. Its drainage basin has an estimated area of 330,000 square miles, over half of which is in Canada. Features of this basin are the Yukon Flats, on and near the Arctic Circle, and the coastal lowland and delta area, extending inland about 100 miles from Bering Sea. The Tanana River Valley, with an area of about 24,000 square miles, lies to the northward of the Alaska Range, the glaciers of which form the source of most of the southern tributaries of the river. While the upper half of the valley is rough and broken, there is considerable level and gently rolling country in the lower half that is well adapted to agriculture, which has its greatest development in the vicinity of Fairbanks.

Lying north of the Pacific Ocean with a vast expanse of land to the east and separated only by Bering Strait from the larger land mass of Siberia to the west, the main part of Alaska is covered during the winter by relatively high atmospheric pressure. Over the immediate water surface to the south there usually exists a trough of low pressure, with a west-east trend, commonly known as the Aleutian low. Through this pressure valley, so to speak, pass a great many of the cyclonic disturbances of the Northern Hemisphere in their west-to-east movement. Other disturbances originate in it, and altogether it exercises a great influence on the weather of the Territory, as well as on that of the Canadian Provinces to the east and the northern half of the United States to the southeast.

The mountains of British Columbia, with their southeast-northwest trend, present something of a barrier to the eastward movement of these barometric depressions, many of which stagnate in the Gulf of Alaska for days at a time, especially if the Pacific high-pressure area, lying far to the south, manifests a tendency to move northeastward over Oregon and Washington. In fact, after reaching the Gulf of Alaska a cyclonic storm may be forced to pursue a retrograde course and actually to move northwestward.

Whether from a breaking down of pressure over the arctic slope of Alaska, or from the northward thrust of the Pacific high, these Aleutian lows occasionally take a northeastward movement, over Bering Sea, and advance toward the Seward Peninsula, or they may take a similar direction farther east over the Yukon Valley. As long as the lows in winter pursue their normal track over the north Pacific and the Gulf of Alaska, fair and cold weather obtains over the interior valleys of the Territory, with relatively warm and rainy conditions over the southeast. When, however, they take a northeastward course, the temperature of the interior moderates under the influence of southerly winds, and precipitation to a greater or less extent ensues. Occasionally, from some cause not yet definitely known, the arctic high builds up to an exceptional extent; then northerly winds, attended by fair and unusually cold weather, prevail over nearly the entire Territory.

In the summer season, with the building up of pressure over the cooler waters of the North Pacific and the heating of the land surface of the interior under the influence of the long days of high latitudes, the interior pressure is relatively low and the weather becomes warm, sometimes hot, with occasional rains.

The temperature in different parts of Alaska varies greatly. In the extreme southeast, south, and southwest, it is relatively mild and decidedly equable, while the precipitation is heavy. In the most southerly sections the temperature varies from a mean of about 32° F. in January, the coldest month, to about 54° in July, the warmest. The average January temperature corresponds to that in central Maryland, southern Illinois, and southern Kansas. To the north, however, winter temperatures become progressively more severe; extremely cold weather is frequent in the interior basin and the arctic area. In the Yukon and Tanana Valleys the annual temperature range is pronounced, varying from an average of lower than −20° for January in the coldest parts, to about 60° in July, or an annual range of more than 80° compared with one of a little more than 20° in the more southern sections. In the west, the Bering Sea area, the average January temperature ranges from 14° at Naknek to 3° at Nome, with a summer range from 54° to 50°, respectively. On the Arctic coast the average annual range is from −18° in January to about 40° in July.

The average annual minimum temperatures range from 4° to 7° F. in the extreme southeast and 0° along the southern coast to −56° at Tanana and −64° at Allakakat, in the interior on the Arctic Circle. The average annual range of the maxima is smaller, however, increasing from 75° along the southern coast to 85° or 90° in the Yukon Basin. The highest temperatures of record range from 80° in the extreme south to 100° in the upper Yukon Valley, while the lowest of record vary from 5° at Yukutat and slightly below zero in the southeast to −76° at Tanana. It is of interest to note that the lowest temperature of record at Sitka, −5°, compares favorably with the low record at Meridian, Miss., of −6°, and at Tallahassee, Fla., of −2°. Minima in the interior, however, are considerably lower than at any place in the United States, the extreme of −76° at Tanana being 10° lower than the absolute minimum for the United States, −66° in Yellowstone Park, Wyo.

The average number of days annually with minimum temperatures of zero or lower gives a good indication of the relative severity of a climate. In Alaska this ranges from only 2 years in 20 at Ketchikan and Sitka, and 6 in 20 at Juneau, to an average of more than 100 days a year in the Yukon and Tanana Valleys. At Fort Yukon there is an average of 132 days a year with temperatures of zero or below, and at Barrow, on the north coast, 170.

The length of the growing season, or the period between the last freezing weather in spring and the first in fall, has a basic relation to agriculture. In

Alaska the growing season ranges in length from an average of 160 days along the southeastern coast and 140 on the central Pacific coast to 80 to 90 in the central Tanana and upper Yukon Valleys. In the south this period of 140 to 160 days corresponds to the growing season in the central part of the Lower Peninsula of Michigan, southern Minnesota, and central Nebraska, but in the interior valleys it is shorter than in any agricultural area in the United States. Under the influence of prolonged daylight, however, vegetation makes rapid growth. This unusual length of the day compensates to a considerable extent for the shortness of the growing season, though there is much cloudy weather.

The variations in precipitation in Alaska are equally as marked as those in temperature. Along the southern coast rainfall is heavy, being in some sections considerably greater than in any locality in the United States. In the extreme southeast the average annual amount is more than 150 inches, and it is considerably over 100 in some central coast sections. Inland from the coast, however, precipitation decreases very rapidly, ranging generally in the interior basin from about 7 inches in the upper Yukon Valley to about 14 over the central valley sections. In the arctic area precipitation averages less than 5 inches a year.

Snowfall has a relative distribution quite similar to that of rainfall, being heavy along the Pacific coast, and decreasing northward to a minimum along the Arctic coast. The average annual amounts vary from over 100 inches in southeastern sections of the Territory to between 80 and 100 in most of the Bering Sea area, 40 to 60 in the interior valleys, and less than 40 in the arctic area. Barrow is the only recording station showing some snowfall every month in the year. The Pacific coast, in general, has about 4 months without any snow, the Bering Sea coast 3, the interior 2 months, and the far north no month without at least a trace of snow. In the interior, June and July are the months without snow, while in the same latitude along the Bering Sea, July and August are generally snow-free. This illustrates the effect of the cool sea in retarding both the spring and the early summer rise in temperature.

The possible daily hours of sunshine at different latitudes across Alaska vary from a maximum of 8 in the extreme south in December to 16 in the south and 24 in parts of the interior and the north in June. However, the percentage of the possible amount actually received is generally quite low. Very few sunshine data are available, but the figures for Juneau show that even in the long days of summer when the possible hours of sunshine are 17 or 18 a day the actual number is lower than at Boston. Boston has a yearly total of sunshine almost twice that of Juneau. Since observational data are very sparse, the best indication of the amount of sunshine is the number of clear and cloudy days. At practically all Alaska stations the number of clear days is seldom over half the total number, and often less than one-third; the greatest number of clear days is found in the interior, especially during the late winter and early spring months. Nearly all stations, except in the interior, average more cloudy days than clear ones in the course of a year. The Pacific coast is the cloudiest part of the Territory, with an average of 200 cloudy days a year.

Records of foggy days are not available except for Juneau, where the average is only 1 to 2 days a month. However, the pilot chart of the north Pacific shows for the Gulf of Alaska and the Aleutian Islands 15 to 25 percent of the days foggy during the winter season.

J. B. Kincer, *Principal Meteorologist and Chief of Division of Climate and Crop Weather, Weather Bureau, Washington, D. C.*

THE HAWAIIAN ISLANDS

Climatic summary

Island	Station	Temperature					Killing frost average dates[1]				Average precipitation													
		Length of record	January average	July average	Maximum	Minimum	Length of record	Last in spring	First in fall	Growing season[2]	Length of record	January	February	March	April	May	June	July	August	September	October	November	December	Annual
		Yr.	*°F.*	*°F.*	*°F.*	*°F.*	*Yr.*			*Days*	*Yr.*	*In.*	*In.*	*In.*	*In.*	*In.*	*In.*	*In.*	*In.*	*In.*	*In.*	*In.*	*In.*	*In.*
Hawaii	Hakalau (Mauka)	33	69.9	74.7	85	50					38	19.51	17.07	19.86	23.02	16.43	12.64	17.13	18.48	15.40	14.08	22.49	21.98	218.09
	Hilo	34	70.2	74.7	91	51					40	11.77	10.82	15.08	13.06	9.21	7.40	9.89	11.81	10.84	10.97	13.80	12.47	137.12
	Honokaa	34	69.0	74.2	95	52					40	6.76	6.58	8.95	8.00	4.45	2.71	4.27	5.01	3.35	3.46	7.41	7.52	68.47
	Honomu										24	22.54	18.84	21.03	22.67	15.88	12.36	16.88	19.04	18.45	14.68	24.54	23.42	230.33
	Kawainui (upper)										28	16.42	15.63	16.80	22.40	18.72	18.73	23.18	21.69	15.85	12.78	19.49	17.54	219.23
	Kiolakaa	23	68.6	72.7	91	50					25	6.93	4.56	4.97	4.30	3.19	2.68	2.60	3.97	3.76	4.71	4.98	6.52	53.17
	Kohala	34	69.8	74.6	94	51					40	4.99	4.82	5.55	6.56	4.33	3.51	4.51	4.88	3.69	3.36	5.50	5.74	57.44
	Kohala Mission	34	69.1	74.5	91	54					40	5.60	5.22	5.91	6.81	4.37	3.46	4.53	4.94	3.48	3.35	5.54	5.95	59.16
	Kukuihaele	22	69.9	74.3	93	49					40	6.72	6.16	8.58	8.34	4.74	2.96	4.52	5.30	3.57	3.71	6.96	7.16	68.72
	Mahukona	26	74.5	80.0	98	52					27	2.97	1.52	.98	1.65	.84	.45	.39	.48	.53	.53	1.21	2.46	14.01
	Mountain View										35	16.99	13.20	18.02	18.58	13.68	11.31	15.42	17.63	15.07	12.87	19.07	16.60	188.44
	Napoopoo	19	72.2	76.6	93	56					40	2.52	1.98	2.20	2.57	3.63	3.38	3.64	3.73	3.85	3.29	1.87	2.76	35.42
	Niulii	33	71.0	75.5	92	52					40	5.09	4.61	5.80	6.43	4.63	3.38	4.69	5.02	3.93	3.38	5.46	5.63	58.05
	Olaa	34	70.0	74.3	93	48					38	13.16	9.83	14.82	14.15	9.46	7.69	10.70	12.12	11.32	10.38	14.72	15.10	143.45
	Ookala	33	70.4	74.3	92	52					40	10.52	9.53	14.63	13.55	8.12	5.32	8.09	9.68	6.72	7.52	11.85	11.31	116.84
	Pahala	34	68.6	73.3	100	50					40	5.62	4.77	5.70	3.27	2.19	1.07	1.37	3.02	2.53	3.53	5.19	5.05	43.31
	Pepeekeo	34	70.7	74.7	90	56					40	12.40	9.19	14.96	11.68	8.71	6.64	9.73	11.01	10.52	10.03	12.15	12.58	129.60
	Piihonna										11	12.18	16.01	14.88	17.52	15.18	13.47	17.62	20.23	13.81	13.17	18.63	19.04	191.74
	Volcano Observatory	26	57.8	63.0	84	40					26	12.27	7.78	10.76	8.66	5.92	4.18	6.18	7.23	6.68	6.59	9.94	10.72	96.91
	Waimea	30	61.7	64.8	90	34					40	4.86	4.47	4.95	4.25	3.12	2.25	2.99	3.24	2.24	2.59	3.67	5.13	43.76
Kauai	Eleele	21	71.0	76.8	92	52					38	4.38	3.11	3.96	1.74	1.35	1.05	1.29	1.29	1.91	2.12	2.76	3.69	28.65
	Hiloa-Manawaipuna Divide										28	21.38	12.93	17.61	17.27	17.46	16.32	20.74	20.05	19.51	16.23	19.72	19.63	218.85
	Kealia	33	71.0	78.0	93	44					39	5.02	3.70	5.34	2.74	2.32	1.77	2.53	2.00	2.83	3.35	4.23	4.98	40.81
	Kilauea	34	69.4	75.6	94	49					40	6.61	5.46	8.40	5.44	5.08	3.64	4.75	4.64	4.89	5.34	6.99	6.97	68.21
	Koloa	34	69.3	76.0	89	46					40	6.96	5.06	6.90	4.71	4.64	3.91	4.82	4.87	4.62	5.14	6.03	6.44	64.10
	Lihue	34	69.2	76.4	91	46					34	7.32	4.06	5.95	3.62	3.55	2.44	3.30	3.19	4.16	4.80	4.93	6.02	53.34
	Makaweli	34	70.8	78.0	93	50					40	3.54	3.07	3.19	1.10	.90	.71	.68	.90	1.25	1.61	2.47	3.27	22.69
	Mana	33	69.8	77.2	95	48					34	3.70	1.93	3.41	1.01	.95	.77	.68	.90	1.51	1.63	1.90	3.34	21.73
	Summit Camp										12	21.34	8.98	18.91	18.34	15.47	11.82	14.34	13.19	16.54	14.45	18.86	18.12	190.36
	Wahiawa Mountain										38	14.62	12.07	14.82	11.98	12.19	11.44	13.99	14.78	12.48	12.69	13.48	15.21	159.75
Lanai	Koele	18	64.9	70.6	88	49					34	4.03	3.81	3.64	3.36	2.63	1.67	1.29	2.15	2.48	2.96	2.39	4.43	34.84
	Lanai City	9	65.9	70.9	85	46					9	3.30	5.13	4.66	2.18	2.16	1.25	1.34	2.33	3.11	4.12	1.88	2.89	34.35
Maui	Eke										26	22.03	18.36	21.84	26.55	20.81	14.80	21.25	20.94	19.07	15.03	23.00	25.56	249.24
	Haiku	23	70.4	74.8	95	50					23	7.81	6.24	6.65	7.29	5.59	4.03	5.15	4.96	3.73	4.20	6.59	7.27	69.51
	Hana	31	71.7	75.9	95	53					32	7.81	6.31	7.64	9.31	5.24	3.67	4.53	5.38	5.33	4.86	6.34	8.89	75.31

	Honomanu	34	64.1	68.8	95	43				34	18.62	18.46	21.55	26.70	19.53	15.11	18.77	21.29	16.68	14.57	21.13	22.61	235.02
	Kaanapali	33	71.5	78.4	98	47				40	3.43	2.96	2.04	1.45	.66	.24	.36	.75	.43	.70	1.56	3.38	17.96
	Kailiili	14	61.8	67.0	82	42				14	13.21	13.39	13.17	18.23	11.14	8.27	9.60	9.39	7.64	5.44	12.43	15.24	137.15
	Kailua	34	67.7	72.6	90	50				35	11.26	9.91	12.21	13.86	10.00	8.43	9.82	11.52	9.70	9.01	11.34	12.77	129.83
	Keanae	24	65.1	70.1	89	50				34	19.25	18.47	21.21	26.36	19.08	15.37	18.75	20.98	16.23	14.49	21.18	23.40	234.77
	Kula Sanatorium	21	60.7	66.7	89	41				23	4.07	4.24	2.19	3.59	2.19	1.83	1.89	2.23	2.33	2.49	1.62	4.65	33.32
	Puu Kukui (lower)									27	10.64	9.83	9.19	10.87	7.25	5.92	6.94	5.84	5.60	7.11	8.96	11.13	99.28
	Waikamoi Gulch									28	24.01	18.30	22.48	24.92	18.07	13.46	16.74	16.99	14.74	13.41	24.00	24.64	231.76
	Wailuku	33	71.0	77.5		51				37	4.56	3.99	3.66	3.39	1.39	.53	.66	.90	.87	1.28	2.74	4.76	28.73
Molokai	Kalaupapa	6	71.2	76.8	91	53				6	7.79	6.64	8.96	8.38	5.61	2.80	2.65	2.93	1.62	3.62	5.32	7.47	63.79
	Kalawao	27	70.6	76.7	93	48				27	8.04	6.21	6.10	7.89	4.72	3.04	3.29	3.91	3.23	3.65	6.56	7.84	64.48
	Maunaloa	12	68.6	74.2	93	47				13	3.16	3.74	2.69	2.17	1.60	.97	1.60	1.27	1.54	2.55	1.73	3.73	26.75
	Molokai Ranch	32	68.4	75.2	94	49				39	5.13	4.67	3.84	3.17	1.59	.94	.93	.97	1.19	1.78	3.63	4.77	32.61
Oahu	Ewa Plantation	34	70.0	77.0	92	48				40	2.82	3.52	2.44	1.24	.97	.50	.40	.63	1.00	1.36	2.32	3.63	20.83
	Hoaeae (upper)	19	68.2	74.6	94	45				31	4.70	3.93	4.26	2.80	1.86	1.35	1.06	1.71	2.39	2.72	3.15	5.62	35.55
	Honolulu	40	71.1	77.5	90	52				34	4.08	2.59	3.10	1.86	1.04	.73	.90	1.12	1.42	1.88	2.45	4.11	25.28
	Kahuku	34	71.0	77.4	95	49				40	4.25	4.73	4.77	3.01	2.16	1.60	2.01	2.28	2.32	2.93	3.40	4.64	38.10
	Kalihi Valley									30	11.46	9.26	10.27	8.90	7.27	6.42	7.22	8.37	7.94	8.25	10.81	12.36	108.53
	Maunawili Ranch	34	69.3	75.3	92	50				40	8.57	7.61	8.59	8.20	6.54	4.23	4.66	5.80	5.61	6.33	7.49	9.91	83.54
	Opaeula	34	66.9	72.7	95	48				34	7.03	6.22	5.94	5.35	3.94	2.99	3.42	3.39	3.52	3.68	6.09	8.39	59.96
	Pupukea	6	69.2	74.6	90	54				23	6.32	4.13	4.61	5.36	3.58	3.46	3.70	3.82	3.34	3.59	6.35	6.39	54.65
	Schofield Barracks	29	67.6	73.8	91	41				29	5.03	4.28	4.48	3.44	2.39	1.77	1.47	2.00	2.93	2.68	3.76	5.95	40.18
	Tantalus	30	66.6	70.6	93	46				37	9.03	7.95	9.10	8.44	7.67	7.04	8.29	8.45	7.89	7.08	9.57	10.93	101.44
	Tantalus (Isenberg)									11	10.42	11.38	13.01	13.06	12.12	14.10	12.23	13.26	14.07	9.76	15.08	14.86	153.35
	U. S. Magnetic Observatory.	34	70.7	78.6	93	48				37	3.22	2.98	2.51	1.27	.79	.54	.36	.68	.83	1.24	1.93	3.80	20.15
	Wahiawa									38	6.17	5.45	5.81	3.44	2.89	2.15	2.23	3.08	3.38	3.17	4.24	6.50	48.51
	Waialua	34	69.5	76.7	97	47				38	4.07	4.67	3.77	2.45	1.32	1.05	1.05	1.23	1.45	1.76	3.20	5.16	31.18
	Waianae	34	71.8	79.4	95	50				40	2.83	3.49	2.24	1.24	.81	.45	.31	.85	1.03	1.15	2.15	3.25	19.80
	Waianae-Uka									8	21.06	22.64	18.98	19.52	18.82	18.55	20.24	18.03	20.39	18.68	15.47	16.94	229.32
	Waimanalo	34	71.6	78.7	96	52				40	5.55	5.20	5.72	4.01	2.55	1.44	1.44	1.82	1.87	3.12	4.33	6.53	43.58
	Waipahu	33	70.7	77.2	95	50				40	3.44	3.80	3.22	1.70	1.29	.80	.53	1.03	1.22	1.80	2.38	4.20	25.41
Midway I.	Midway	21	65.1	77.8	98	40				18	4.73	3.45	3.36	3.07	2.33	2.15	3.38	4.69	4.30	3.75	3.52	3.86	42.59

[1] Observations have shown that frost never occurs below the 2,500-foot level over the entire group of islands, and rarely below the 4,000-foot level. The lowest temperature of record is 38°, reported at Glenwood Experiment Station on the eastern slope of Mauna Loa and Kilauea, Island of Hawaii, at an elevation of 2,300 feet, on the morning of Jan. 7, 1919; this was the nearest definite approach to frost. Volcano observatory at Kilauea Crater, elevation 3,984 feet, reported frost on the morning of Jan. 7, 1919, with a clear sky prevailing and a minimum temperature of 42°.

[2] Length of growing season between average dates of last killing frost in spring and first in fall.

THE HAWAIIAN ISLANDS—Continued

Precipitation and temperature— Territorial unit values

[This tabulation gives the mean annual and mean monthly precipitation and the mean monthly temperatures for Hawaii, 1905–38]

Precipitation		Precipitation		Precipitation		Preicipitation		Temperature		Temperature	
Year	Mean	Year	Mean	Year	Mean	Month	Mean	Month	Mean	Month	Mean
	In.		*In.*		*In.*		*In.*		°*F.*		°*F.*
1905	69.70	1919	48.03	1933	64.01	April	7.95	January	68.9	July	74.3
1906	68.99	1920	64.05	1934	78.15	May	5.63	February	68.7	August	75.8
1907	90.66	1921	83.51	1935	74.48	June	4.67	March	69.0	September	74.6
1908	65.46	1922	73.57	1936	100.77	July	5.93	April	70.2	October	73.8
1909	73.72	1923	104.39	1937	107.41	August	6.22	May	72.0	November	71.8
1910	79.10	1924	73.57	1938	92.14	September	6.05	June	73.4	December	70.1
1911	87.46	1925	71.74			Ootober	5.32				
1912	60.53	1926	50.43	Month	Mean	November	8.12				
1913	70.67	1927	102.12			December	8.93				
1914	109.79	1928	73.94								
1915	80.10	1929	88.29		*In.*	Annual	82.48				
1916	100.16	1930	99.76	January	8.42						
1917	66.41	1931	73.71	February	7.42						
1918	113.41	1932	88.08	March	7.92						

SUPPLEMENTARY CLIMATIC NOTES FOR THE HAWAIIAN ISLANDS

The main group of the Hawaiian Islands lies between 18°55′ and 22°15′ N., and between 154°49′ and 160°15′ W. They are, therefore, near the northern limit of the Tropics, due south of the Alaskan Peninsula, and directly west of Yucatan. From Honolulu, the capital, it is 2,089 miles to San Francisco, 4,630 to Shanghai, 3,850 to Auckland, and 4,420 to Sydney. A series of about 15 small, uninhabited, and seldom-visited islands, lying to the northwest of the main group, terminates not far from Midway Island. The total area of the main group is 6,435 square miles, slightly more than that of Connecticut and Rhode Island combined.

The islands are the summits of a long, 2,000-mile submarine range of mountains of volcanic origin. Elevations have built up from the ocean floor, some 18,000 feet below sea level, to a maximum height of nearly 14,000 feet above sea level—a total of 32,000 feet. It appears certain that formation of the elevations constituting the islands occurred at various periods, and that the western end of the chain is the oldest and the eastern end the youngest. Decided contrasts in the effects of weathering and erosion can be found within short distances, owing to the marked local variations in rainfall and resultant vegetation. Kauai, the oldest and most northwesterly of the larger islands, is much cut up by gorges and ravines, while Hawaii, the youngest and most southeasterly, shows relatively little evidence of erosion. Owing to volcanoes that are not yet extinct, Hawaii is sometimes referred to as still not altogether beyond the formative stage.

Nearly half of the area of the Territory, including the larger part of all the islands except Hawaii, lies within 5 miles of coast. Approximately one-fourth is at an elevation below 650, one-half below 1,950, and one-fourth above 4,500 feet. All but a small percentage of the population lives in the lower one-fourth of the area, at elevations below 650 feet. Human habitants of the area above 4,500 feet are few, and in fact much of the ground at high elevations is accessible only to experienced climbers. On all islands there is a considerable percentage of land that cannot be utilized for cultivation for various reasons, such as excessive rainfall, deficient rainfall and impracticability of irrigation, thin soil, and topographical unsuitability.

Hawaii, the largest island, from which the group takes its name, has an area of 4,030 square miles. The other seven principal islands, in order of area in square miles, are Maui; 728; Oahu, 604; Kauai, 555; Molokai, 260; Lanai, 141; Niihau, 72; and Kahoolawe, 45.

The outstanding features of the climate of the Hawaiian Islands are the remarkable differences in rainfall over adjacent areas; the persistently equable temperature which passes through the cycle of the seasons devoid of marked or sudden changes and with only a very moderate difference between the averages of winter and summer months; and the tenaciousness of the trade winds over the general locality. The trade-wind influence is dominant throughout all seasons and extends over the greater part of all the islands. There are, however, a number of local influences, such as the size and trend of mountains and valleys, the nearness to or relative remoteness from the sea, and direction from the sea in relation to the prevailing east and northeast trades. In the Kona districts of the Island of Hawaii and over a section of Maui to the southwest of Haleakala, for example, mountains to the east project high above sea level and cut off the trades, resulting in prevailing southwesterly winds, with land and sea breezes in evidence. All these influences have their effects on the weather elements, at some places only local but in others more general, and they make combinations that greatly complicate climatic conditions, particularly the distribution of rainfall.

As a general statement it may be said that the climate of the Hawaiian Islands is unusually pleasant for the Tropics. Owing to the marked marine influence, combined with the persistent trade winds, there is relatively little uncomfortable heat for the latitude. Discomfort is infrequently experienced, although at times the trades temporarily give way to light changeable or southerly winds with resultant comparatively high humidity. In summer the trades blow with a high degree of persistency, and the uncomforable periods are consequently most noticeable in fall. The least comfortable time of the year may, therefore, be experienced some weeks, or possibly a month or two, later than the time when the highest temperatures are recorded. In some areas the large amount of rain that falls may be a somewhat disagreeable feature, but it is ameliorated by the occurrence of a large percentage of the rainfall at night.

Though some of those spectacular weather features that may be found elsewhere are absent, considerable variety in climate may be found within the borders of the Territory. In fact it seems doubtful whether one could find anywhere else, within the short radius of a few miles, such persistently sharp contrasts in the weather elements. For instance, there is practically uninterrupted year-round summer in the lowlands, while at the highest elevations, particularly on the Island of Hawaii, conditions approach the continental type of climate, though the winters are mild. Mountain peaks remain persistently cloud-encircled, while over leeward lowlands nearby the sun shines at least several hours practically every day and on many days uninterruptedly. Frequent and copious showers fall almost daily in windward and upland districts, while rain of sufficient intensity and duration to cause more than temporary inconvenience in the ordinary pursuits of outdoor life is an infrequent occurrence over lower sections of leeward areas.

August and September are the warmest months, while January and February are the coolest. At some windward and upland stations there is only slightly over 5° F. difference between the average temperature of the warmest and that of the coolest month; at a few leeward lowland points the average difference reaches a little more than 8°. Elevation is the major controlling influence in determining the average temperature, but location—whether in a leeward or windward section—is also a noticeable factor. The highest temperatures reached during the day in leeward areas are usually above those attained in windward districts. The daily temperature range, also, is greatest over leeward areas, where, in addition to the maxima being higher, the minima—at least at the lower elevations—are slightly lower. These conditions are probably largely due to less cloudiness over leeward than over windward sections.

Available records show that the average temperature for the first 2,000 feet and more above sea level is approximately 1° F. higher at leeward than at windward points at the same elevation. Some stations that lie near sea level along windward coasts and normally have heavy rainfall show relatively low annual temperature averages. This seems to apply particularly to the area along the windward coast of the Island of Hawaii.

The records indicate that at ground elevations up to about 2,500 feet, and especially at the lower elevations within this range, when average temperature is considered, the decrease with altitude is somewhat in excess of the rate of 1° F. for 300 feet; for the first few hundred feet there appears to be a decrease at the rate of about 1° for 200 feet. The very rapid increase in cloudiness as elevated sections are approached and the resultant moderation of the maximum temperature may well explain this. The average annual temperature at Humuula, Island of Hawaii, elevation 6,685 feet, the highest point in the Islands at which temperature records are available, shows an annual value of 52° which, compared with a sea level figure of 74.9°, gives an average lapse rate approximating 1° for 300 feet.

The highest official temperature of record is 100° F. at Pahala, Island of Hawaii, elevation 850 feet, on April 27, 1931; the lowest is 25° at Humuula, elevation 6,685 feet, on the southern edge of Mauna Kea, Hawaii, on March 6, 1912.

Frost rarely forms below 4,000 feet and probably never below 2,500 feet. In winter, however, it is sufficiently cold for the higher levels of Mauna Loa and Mauna Kea, Hawaii, and Haleakala, Maui, to be frequently covered with snow; and it is not so very unusual to see snow on the crests of Mauna Loa and Mauna Kea even in midsummer. It is reported that ice frequently forms to the thickness of an ordinary windowpane at Puu Oo, on the southeastern slope of Mauna Kea at an elevation of 6,450 feet, and that snow is not unknown in the vicinity, though not common below elevations approaching 9,000 feet.

In the Territory as a whole considerably more rain falls from November to April than from May to October. The Maui isthmus and the leeward west Maui lowlands show this seasonal difference most decidedly, though it is also strongly in evidence over properly located Oahu and Kauai areas. It is not unusual for an entire month to go by in the summer without measurable rain falling at some points on the Maui isthmus, and sometimes considerably longer dry periods may occur in that locality. Over areas where trade winds are predominant—and this includes by far the greater part of the Islands—decidedly more rain falls at night than during the day.

From windward to leeward slopes instances of pronounced and sudden decline in rainfall can be found. This is well illustrated in central Kauai, where near the summit of Mount Waialeale, at an elevation of 5,075 feet, the average amount of rain is over 450 inches, while about 15 miles southwest, on the leeward side, it is less than 20 inches.

Not only does rainfall vary greatly within short distances, but monthly amounts received at a station over a period of years may also show a phenomenal range. Most stations, even many of those where the annual normal is 100 inches or more, occasionally have a dry month when the monthly total is less than an inch. Conversely, some of the driest points, where the annual average is 20 to 30 inches, may occasionally during a single wet month, or sometimes even within a period of a few days, have an amount approaching or surpassing the annual normals.

Available data indicate that the zones of maximum rainfall on windward east Maui and on most of windward Hawaii may be at rather moderate elevations, probably about 2,500 feet on Hawaii, and slightly above 3,000 feet on east Maui. On Kauai and west Maui, however, rainfall apparently increases with elevation to, or nearly to, the summits of the peaks at approximately 5,000 feet; it apparently increases also to the highest elevations in the Kohala Mountains of Hawaii. On Oahu there is an increase from the windward coast to, or slightly beyond, the crest of the Koolau Range, where highest elevations are mostly between 2,500 and 3,000 feet.

Thunderstorms are rather infrequent and practically never severe. Hail seldom occurs. Occasionally local storms are accompanied by winds of sufficient force to do limited damage to trees and other property, but severe storms, such as tornadoes, hurricanes, or typhoons, are entirely absent. So-called thick weather is almost unknown to the extent of seriously interfering with shipping and is usually confined to mist and rain rather than being in the form of fog. On rare occasions in certain localities, however, such weather, including fog, may develop to the extent of disrupting airplane schedules for a day or two.

WALTER F. FELDWISCH, *Associate Meteorologist and Climatic Section Director for the Hawaiian Islands, Weather Bureau, Honolulu.*

298737°—41——78

THE WEST INDIAN ISLANDS (INCLUDING PUERTO RICO)

Climatic summary

District	Station	Temperature					Killing frost average dates [1]				Average precipitation [3]													
		Length of record	January average	July average	Maximum	Minimum	Length of record	Last in spring	First in fall	Growing season [2]	Length of record	January	February	March	April	May	June	July	August	September	October	November	December	Annual
		Yr.	°F.	°F.	°F.	°F.	Yr.			Days	Yr.	In.	In.	In.	In.	In.	In.	In.	In.	In.	In.	In.	In.	In.
Bahama Islands, British West Indies.	Nassau	40	71.7	82.7	94	51					40	1.41	1.15	1.22	2.45	4.15	3.58	2.69	2.70	4.63	5.51	3.20	1.16	33.85
												2.16	1.61	1.53	2.51	5.89	6.66	5.83	6.59	7.55	6.34	8.25	1.49	56.41
Turks and Calicos Islands.	Grand Turk	35	75.2	82.8	92	60					5	1.82	1.58	1.07	1.29	2.44	2.01	2.41	2.01	3.16	3.96	4.87	1.94	28.56
												1.99	1.39	1.05	1.33	1.63	1.22	1.76	1.32	3.12	4.14	4.86	1.38	25.19
Cuba	Havana	34	69.9	80.4	95	50					40	1.61	1.13	1.21	3.23	7.50	2.68	5.48	6.21	6.45	7.69	3.14	1.24	47.57
												2.84	1.84	1.92	2.28	4.45	6.46	4.87	5.48	5.78	6.57	3.15	2.44	48.08
	Camaguey	13	71.6	81.6	102	45					20	1.54	1.40	2.43	3.64	7.62	10.52	5.60	5.54	7.26	5.44	3.12	1.96	56.07
Jamaica	Kingston	37	76.0	81.7	98	57					53	3.69	3.07	3.27	4.81	8.87	6.84	5.23	7.14	7.75	10.43	7.82	4.89	73.81
												.92	.67	.96	1.18	4.16	4.00	1.53	3.37	4.42	6.96	2.80	1.55	32.52
Haiti	Port-au-Prince	40	77.7	83.7	100	59					44	1.64	1.99	2.37	4.86	7.79	6.46	4.78	5.98	6.74	6.81	5.08	1.74	56.24
												1.15	2.41	3.73	6.65	9.42	4.17	2.86	5.30	7.52	6.89	3.61	1.31	55.02
Dominican Republic	Puerto Plata	15	70.9	77.3	94	59					17	2.76	1.85	2.05	3.78	6.90	4.70	4.58	5.70	7.35	5.80	6.07	3.21	54.75
												7.47	6.47	3.24	5.74	3.66	1.66	3.02	3.02	4.68	3.77	14.40	9.20	66.33
	Santo Domingo	34	74.3	81.6	95	57					14	2.01	1.20	2.75	3.68	5.06	5.76	7.22	6.67	7.22	7.29	4.25	2.29	55.40
Puerto Rico												3.74	3.20	3.62	4.29	7.22	6.51	6.24	7.35	8.73	7.98	7.69	4.46	71.03
Coastal stations	San Juan	39	74.8	80.0	94	62					39	2.83	2.55	2.60	3.11	6.33	5.02	4.90	5.42	6.64	6.08	6.46	3.46	55.40
												4.45	2.68	2.88	4.01	5.87	5.28	5.80	6.07	6.35	5.60	6.97	5.38	61.34
Coastal plains and foot hills.	Ponce	32	75.4	81.1	96	55					23	3.56	3.13	3.22	4.09	6.20	5.97	6.17	6.97	8.04	7.64	6.97	4.02	65.98
												1.03	.97	1.42	2.14	2.91	3.85	2.89	4.19	4.92	6.72	3.47	1.36	35.87
Interior	Cayey	36	69.2	75.6	94	44					25	4.75	3.77	4.91	5.63	8.77	8.07	7.53	9.37	11.05	9.83	9.50	5.86	89.04
												3.30	2.90	3.00	3.61	4.53	6.14	6.38	6.34	6.27	6.59	6.13	4.41	59.60
Virgin Islands: St. Thomas	Charlotte Amalie	18	77.1	82.2	92	67					17	3.00	2.21	2.18	2.58	5.01	2.90	3.94	4.48	6.69	6.25	6.20	3.42	48.86
												2.71	1.87	2.41	1.89	2.66	3.19	3.09	3.38	5.44	6.15	4.99	3.16	40.94
St. Croix	Christiansted	40	75.7	81.0	96	64					40	1.95	1.99	2.06	2.20	4.03	5.46	4.13	4.35	5.89	5.94	4.42	2.05	44.47
												2.30	2.05	1.24	2.97	4.39	4.64	3.46	4.26	5.59	5.88	5.89	3.86	46.53
St. John	Antigua	11	76.9	81.3	93	60					40		2.00	2.08	1.98			3.62	4.01	5.85	5.61	4.96	2.97	
												3.25	2.24	2.24	3.20	4.26	3.97	4.65	4.71	5.68	5.74	5.54	3.90	49.38
Tortola, British West Indies.	Roadtown										24	3.75	2.59	2.64	3.24	5.56	3.69	4.19	5.71	6.50	6.84	6.70	3.62	55.03
												3.10	2.92	2.23	2.50	4.24	4.25	4.20	4.15	4.93	7.15	7.02	4.76	51.45
North Caribbean												2.74	1.96	1.74	2.10	3.77	3.17	3.65	4.42	5.08	4.85	5.33	3.38	42.19
St. Martin Island	Philipsburg										31	2.48	1.82	1.45	2.19	3.84	2.91	3.18	4.46	5.82	4.68	5.17	3.08	41.08
												2.44	1.69	1.30	2.32	4.06	2.95	3.03	4.45	5.83	4.80	5.39	3.23	41.49

Saba Island	Bottom										25	**3.08**	**2.15**	**1.79**	**2.00**	**3.98**	**2.68**	**3.67**	**4.24**	**4.40**	**4.68**	**5.83**	**3.60**	**42.10**
												3.41	2.76	2.04	2.06	3.68	3.00	3.42	3.62	4.79	5.96	5.75	4.09	44.58
St. Eustatius Island.	Orangetown										40	**2.64**	**1.91**	**1.96**	**2.13**	**3.49**	**3.94**	**4.08**	**7.09**	**5.02**	**5.18**	**5.00**	**3.46**	**45.90**
												2.58	1.97	1.81	2.11	3.50	3.56	4.01	4.57	4.95	5.15	4.88	3.45	42.54
Leeward Islands												**3.85**	**2.07**	**2.98**	**2.63**	**3.24**	**4.17**	**5.92**	**6.61**	**6.44**	**6.35**	**6.70**	**4.98**	**55.94**
Barbuda	Codrington										14	**2.04**	**1.38**	**1.61**	**2.47**	**2.15**	**2.99**	**3.03**	**3.60**	**4.59**	**5.12**	**5.14**	**3.28**	**37.40**
												2.42	1.46	2.06	2.43	2.83	2.00	3.55	2.75	4.19	6.17	6.28	4.74	40.88
St. Kitts	Basseterre	14	76.4	81.2	92	64					40	**4.51**	**2.85**	**3.48**	**4.22**	**4.59**	**4.92**	**6.03**	**6.92**	**7.62**	**7.03**	**8.10**	**5.91**	**66.18**
												3.48	1.95	2.11	3.18	3.90	4.02	4.34	5.37	6.38	6.11	5.22	3.67	49.73
Nevis												**3.40**	**1.70**	**2.86**	**2.29**	**3.33**	**3.31**	**4.93**	**6.10**	**5.23**	**5.97**	**5.57**		
Monserrat												**3.64**		**3.49**	**2.59**	**3.04**	**4.21**	**5.15**	**6.19**	**6.45**	**6.12**	**6.80**	**4.92**	
Dominica	Roseau	6	77.6	81.2	97	63					27	**5.73**	**2.37**	**3.45**	**2.47**	**3.10**	**5.41**	**10.42**	**10.25**	**8.33**	**7.48**	**7.86**	**5.77**	**72.64**
												4.92	3.43	3.08	2.97	4.44	8.10	10.75	10.04	8.75	7.73	6.97	6.46	77.64
Guadeloupe	Camp Jacob	10	69.4	74.0	87	56					10	**3.42**	**2.44**	**2.56**	**4.10**	**3.87**	**5.55**	**5.90**	**7.03**	**7.38**	**8.80**	**8.26**	**4.75**	**64.06**
												9.49	6.73	7.48	7.99	15.39	14.17	20.20	16.73	17.09	14.61	16.50	9.84	156.22
Martinique	Fort-de-France	17	75.7	80.0	93	59					31	**6.65**	**4.13**	**4.46**	**6.05**	**5.97**	**9.19**	**11.20**	**12.76**	**11.51**	**11.55**	**14.93**	**8.31**	**106.71**
												4.68	4.25	2.91	3.90	4.68	7.44	9.37	10.31	9.25	9.64	7.87	5.91	80.21
Windward Islands												**4.76**	**2.90**	**2.69**	**2.80**	**4.08**	**7.41**	**8.95**	**8.86**	**8.80**	**9.49**	**10.03**	**6.27**	**77.04**
St. Lucia	Castries	27	76.9	80.7	93	66					34	**5.68**	**3.00**	**3.29**	**3.76**	**4.43**	**7.90**	**9.45**	**9.64**	**9.60**	**10.15**	**11.83**	**6.30**	**85.03**
												5.68	3.89	4.12	4.01	6.88	8.98	9.73	10.45	9.73	10.28	9.29	7.96	91.00
St. Vincent	Kingston	16	76.9	81.9	98	57					40	**5.64**	**3.94**	**3.12**	**3.40**	**5.34**	**8.70**	**10.72**	**10.04**	**9.78**	**12.13**	**10.95**	**7.12**	**90.88**
												.92	.67	.96	1.18	4.16	4.00	1.53	3.37	4.42	6.92	2.80	1.55	32.48
Barbados	Bridgetown	14	77.8	80.0	91	61					19	**3.06**	**1.85**	**1.63**	**1.79**	**1.96**	**4.45**	**6.22**	**6.60**	**7.46**	**7.51**	**8.89**	**4.11**	**55.53**
												2.06	1.70	1.64	1.67	1.82	4.36	4.84	6.81	6.60	6.03	4.58	3.47	45.58
Grenada	St. George	12	77.1	79.5	93	68					30	**4.66**	**2.80**	**2.71**	**2.24**	**4.57**	**8.60**	**9.38**	**9.17**	**8.36**	**8.15**	**8.45**	**7.53**	**76.62**
												4.45	2.83	2.82	2.24	4.58	8.35	9.80	9.70	8.26	7.77	8.42	7.44	76.66
Tobago	Botanic Station										23	**4.22**	**2.75**	**1.84**	**2.30**	**4.27**	**8.53**	**8.39**	**8.42**	**9.23**	**7.89**	**11.00**	**8.56**	**77.40**
												3.20	1.83	1.95	1.97	5.00	8.79	9.20	9.03	8.21	8.43	7.58	6.43	71.62
Trinidad	Port of Spain	36	77.1	80.0	101	56					40	**4.07**	**2.29**	**2.39**	**2.45**	**4.68**	**8.66**	**9.61**	**9.55**	**8.34**	**7.91**	**9.08**	**8.22**	**77.25**
												2.75	1.52	1.82	1.84	3.64	7.95	8.85	9.63	7.37	6.65	7.00	4.66	63.68
South Caribbean												**2.45**	**.74**	**.64**	**.40**	**.49**	**.79**	**.93**	**1.08**	**1.82**	**3.01**	**5.20**	**4.26**	**21.81**
Bonaire Island, Dutch West Indies.	Kralendyk										20	**2.36**	**.76**	**.58**	**.31**	**.60**	**.84**	**.70**	**1.00**	**1.80**	**2.76**	**5.15**	**4.93**	**21.79**
												2.28	1.15	.71	.65	.52	.57	1.13	1.03	1.04	3.10	4.14	3.53	19.85
Curacao Island, Dutch West Indies.	Willemstad										40	**3.02**	**.88**	**.72**	**.39**	**.49**	**1.06**	**1.12**	**1.39**	**2.17**	**3.45**	**6.11**	**4.46**	**25.26**
												2.07	.95	.84	1.07	.76	.95	1.47	1.22	1.12	4.20	4.43	3.85	22.93
Aruba, Dutch West Indies.	Oranjestad										24	**1.97**	**.60**	**.60**	**.49**	**.39**	**.47**	**.96**	**.85**	**1.48**	**2.83**	**4.35**	**3.38**	**18.37**
												2.01	.58	.66	.64	.38	.53	.97	1.03	1.28	2.92	3.43	2.98	17.41
British Guiana	Georgetown	40	79.0	79.8	92	68					46	**8.62**	**5.31**	**5.07**	**6.78**	**12.45**	**12.00**	**11.95**	**8.19**	**4.02**	**4.45**	**6.01**	**10.29**	**95.14**
												8.50	5.95	6.77	6.35	11.25	11.87	10.00	6.47	3.05	2.54	5.88	11.75	90.38
French Guiana	Cayenne	23	79.2	80.2	97	65					40	**7.43**	**4.79**	**4.97**	**7.32**	**10.48**	**11.46**	**9.19**	**6.10**	**2.69**	**2.59**	**3.29**	**7.28**	**77.59**
												14.37	12.28	15.83	18.86	21.89	15.15	6.93	2.76	1.22	1.34	4.61	10.71	125.95
Venezuela	Caracas	16	65.8	68.9	91	45					35			**1.95**	**1.45**	**3.35**	**4.41**						**2.31**	
												.84	.35	.61	1.50	2.83	4.24	4.25	4.23	4.03	4.04	3.40	1.74	32.06

[1] The lowest temperatures in the West Indies are not reported from the most elevated stations in Puerto Rico or Jamaica but inland from the middle portion of the northern coast of Cuba, where the readings are 40° F. or slightly below on occasions.

[2] Length of growing season between average dates of last killing frost in spring and first in fall.

[3] Figures in boldface type are average values for the district indicated.

THE WEST INDIES (INCLUDING PUERTO RICO)—Continued

Climatic summary—Continued

District	Station	Temperature: Length of record	Temperature: January average	Temperature: July average	Temperature: Maximum	Temperature: Minimum	Killing frost average dates: Length of record	Killing frost average dates: Last in spring	Killing frost average dates: First in fall	Killing frost average dates: Growing season	Average precipitation: Length of record	January	February	March	April	May	June	July	August	September	October	November	December	Annual
		Yr.	°F.	°F.	°F.	°F.	Yr.			Days	Yr.	In.	In.	In.	In.	In.	In.	In.	In.	In.	In.	In.	In.	In.
Panama Canal Zone	Balboa Heights	31	79.6	80.3	97	63					29	2.17	1.26	1.37	3.53	10.21	11.20	11.44	11.43	10.53	12.40	18.32	8.09	101.95
												.91	.79	.63	2.72	7.91	7.99	7.28	8.07	7.87	10.31	10.08	4.17	68.73
	Colon	20	75.2	80.4	95	66					40	3.74	1.62	1.58	4.30	12.37	13.29	16.00	14.75	12.50	15.13	20.70	11.37	127.35
Central America												8.35	4.70	4.17	4.34	7.40	11.21	11.24	10.76	9.61	12.58	13.25	11.07	108.68
												9.69	4.89	7.16	7.64	8.67	10.51	13.35	10.98	8.38	9.18	19.76	18.18	128.39
Costa Rica	San Jose	5	67.3	69.1	94	47					34	.60	.18	.77	1.76	9.04	9.53	8.27	9.53	12.04	11.78	5.75	1.59	70.84
Nicaragua	Bluefields	8	76.0	78.9							5	5.14	2.24	1.72	2.05	12.06	18.68	17.90	14.94	13.44	14.68	9.27	7.28	119.40
												9.86	6.93	3.61	3.12	8.08	17.00	28.58	16.07	8.74	11.22	11.40	14.28	138.89
Honduras												10.84	6.50	4.70	3.67	3.94	5.82	6.24	8.58	7.73	13.03	20.31	13.81	105.17
British Honduras	Belize	22	76.1	81.4	99	46					24					4.94	7.39	5.84	6.06	8.55	14.51	7.60	7.49	
												7.44	3.22	2.47	2.23	4.91	7.86	8.23	8.23	9.38	10.58	13.29	6.65	84.49
Guatemala												7.70	5.20	1.68	4.00		11.12	12.88	13.25	9.92	11.48	9.32	8.62	
Yucatan, Mexico	Progresso	12	69.6	80.0	102	53					12	1.01	.50	.87	1.51	4.39	7.93	6.10	6.65	8.27	6.20	1.98	1.26	46.67
												.77	.64	.58	.69	1.29	2.74	1.71	3.06	2.61	2.89	1.23	.73	18.94

Precipitation and temperature—Regional unit values

[This tabulation gives the mean annual and mean monthly precipitation, the percentage of normal precipitation for each year, and the mean monthly temperature for the entire West Indies region, 1899-1938]

Precipitation		Precipitation		Precipitation		Annual precipitation (in percent of normal)		Annual precipitation (in percent of normal)		Temperature	
Year	Mean	Year	Mean	Month	Mean	Year	Percent	Year	Percent	Month	Mean
	In.		*In.*		*In.*						*°F.*
1899	80.40	1919	64.02	January	3.65	1899	126	1919	100	January	76.1
1900	77.52	1920	62.94	February	2.37	1900	121	1920	99	February	76.3
1901	93.82	1921	53.21	March	2.41	1901	147	1921	83	March	77.3
1902	82.65	1922	53.87	April	3.41	1902	130	1922	84	April	78.6
1903	69.09	1923	52.09	May	5.89	1903	108	1923	82	May	79.9
1904	75.13	1924	66.63	June	6.62	1904	118	1924	104	June	80.6
1905	72.08	1925	54.21	July	6.57	1905	113	1925	85	July	80.7
1906	68.39	1926	56.02	August	6.73	1906	107	1926	88	August	81.0
1907	63.54	1927	68.14	September	6.76	1907	100	1927	107	September	80.8
1908	66.96	1928	57.30	October	7.10	1908	105	1928	90	October	79.8
1909	79.65	1929	57.46	November	7.27	1909	125	1929	90	November	78.5
1910	66.83	1930	50.25	December	5.02	1910	105	1930	79	December	76.6
1911	74.47	1931	70.88			1911	117	1931	111		
1912	69.25	1932	72.52	Annual	63.80	1912	109	1932	114	Annual	78.8
1913	64.46	1933	72.99			1913	101	1933	114		
1914	65.51	1934	60.10			1914	103	1934	94		
1915	70.00	1935	59.26			1915	110	1935	93		
1916	81.32	1936	68.58			1916	127	1936	107		
1917	64.79	1937	62.51			1917	102	1937	98		
1918	60.30	1938	74.02			1918	95	1938	116		

SUPPLEMENTARY CLIMATIC NOTES ON THE WEST INDIAN ISLANDS

The West Indies lie between latitudes 10° and 25° N. and longitudes 60° and 85° W. They are grouped in the following divisions: Bahama Islands; the Greater Antilles, including Cuba, Haiti, Puerto Rico, and Jamaica; the Lesser Antilles, including the Leeward and Windward Islands; and islands off the middle coast of Venezuela. Nearly all of the islands are mountainous and some are very rugged. The elevations of land are of extreme importance in the control of distribution of rainfall in this trade-wind region. Arranged in order of magnitude the areas in square miles are Cuba, 44,164; Haiti, 29,586; Jamaica, 4,450; Puerto Rico, 3,435; Trinidad, 1,862; Guadeloupe, 532; Curaçao, 403; Martinique, 385; Dominica, 305; St. Lucia, 233.

The mean annual temperature at or near sea level is between 77.5° and 79.5° F. over almost the entire region, though at Nassau and Habana the means are 76.9° and 75°, respectively, and at a few stations are in excess of 80°—Swan Island, 80.5°; Port au Prince, Haiti, 80.7°; and Willemstad, Curaçao, 81°. At Toro Negro Dam, P. R. (2,275 feet), the annual mean is slightly below 70°, and at Hill Gardens, Jamaica (4,900 feet), it is only slightly above 60°.

The highest monthly mean temperature at stations in the northern part of this region occurs in July or August; the highest at stations from Martinique southward generally in September. At low elevations the maximum monthly means are about 81° or 82° F., with extremes of 78° (Camajuani, Cuba) and 84° (Port au Prince, Haiti); for the 1,500-foot level they fall to about 75°, and for the 4,900-foot level there is a further fall to 65°.

The minimum monthly means are found almost without exception in January or February. Near sea level they are, as a rule, 75° to 77° F., with extremes of 68° (Camajuani) and 79° (Willemstad), while for the two higher levels mentioned above they are about 70° and 60°, respectively.

The mean annual range of temperature is 8° to 11° F. in the Bahamas and Cuba, about 5° to 7° in other islands of the Greater Antillean group, and still less in the Lesser Antilles, with a minimum of about 3° at Bridgetown, Barbados, and Port of Spain, Trinidad.

Though maximum temperatures of 100° F. or over have been recorded at some of the stations, the highest observed readings do not exceed 95° at many of the low stations and fall below 90° for the higher elevations. In the Greater Antilles the minimum temperatures recorded near sea level range for the most part between 60° and 50°; in the remainder of the area at the same levels they are generally between 65° and 60°.

In the West Indies there are remarkable differences in the amounts of rainfall received on windward and leeward exposures and in low and elevated areas; the contrasts are, of course, especially great between high windward and low leeward stations. Most of these sharp contrasts are between stations separated by only a few miles; the greatest difference, 190 inches between Mooretown and Kingston in Jamaica, occurs within a distance of only 30 miles. The most striking example of great difference in precipitation within a few miles is found in Dominica. Roseau on the west coast, at an elevation of 25 feet, has a mean annual rainfall of 78 inches, while Shawford, about 3 miles to the northeast, at an elevation of 560 feet, has a mean annual of 185 inches. For the entire West Indian region the extreme range of mean annual rainfall is about 200 inches.

There is very little uniformity as to the month of maximum or minimum rainfall, not only for different parts of the territory as a whole but also for different areas on individual islands. The greatest monthly amounts occur from July to November and the least from January to April. In nearly all of the islands the greatest monthly falls are above 10 inches, and at some stations they reach 20 and even 30, while the lowest monthly means fall below 1 inch.

The figures indicating frequency of precipitation do not admit of strict comparison since they are obtained in different ways. The minimum amount of precipitation characterizing a day as rainy is either 0.01 inch or 0.1 mm. (0.004 inch) for most of the stations. For the Greater Antilles the available data show the following range in number of rainy days in the year: Cuba, 92 to 115; Haiti, 43 to 135; Puerto Rico, 92 to 213; and Jamaica, 76 to 178. For stations in the Lesser Antilles there is a rather considerable range: Christiansted, 136; Bridgetown, 171; Roseau, 209; St. John's, Antigua, 242; Castries, 260; and the elevated stations of Camp Jacob and Morne des Cadets, 288 and 290, respectively.

Data on the number of days with thunderstorms do not cover any considerable period except at a few stations, but these are rather well distributed over the West Indian area. The mean annual number of days with thunderstorms varies rather widely: Port au Prince, 114, Cienfuegos, 101, Habana, 78, Kingston, 54, San Juan, 49, Christiansted, 16, St. John's, 15, St. George, Grenada, 12. These figures show a striking difference between conditions over the Greater Antilles and those over the smaller Leeward and Windward Islands. From November to April, thunderstorms are rare, and in the smaller islands they are practically unknown from January to April. In May and June there is considerable increase in frequency and later a further slight increase to the maximum during the 3-month period beginning with July; at that time the average monthly number of days with thunderstorms is from 15 to 20 for Port au Prince, Cienfuegos, and Habana, but less than 5 for stations on the smaller islands.

The prevailing winds are from the east or northeast, with many stations showing the former direction in all months. At Nassau and Habana there is a slight veering in the prevailing directions in the warmer months (from northeast to southeast and from north-northeast to east, respectively), which is probably connected with the development of the sea breeze. The fact that no change is noted at many stations may be due in part to the small land area or to the choice of hours of observation. The phenomenon of alternation of land and sea breezes reaches a marked development in some sections as, for example, at Cienfuegos, Kingston, and Port au Prince.

Mean annual wind velocities are not strictly comparable on account of differences in the elevation of the anemometer, but it appears that the highest mean value is that of 13 miles an hour at San Juan (open exposure, elevation 54 feet) and that the means range down to 5 miles an hour at Santo Domingo and Roseau. In the Bahamas and Cuba wind velocities have a slightly marked maximum from November to April; at several stations in the remainder of the area the maximum occurs in the period from May to August.

Maximum wind velocities have been recorded for only a few stations; the following (in miles an hour) are the extremes reported: Habana, 134, October 11, 1909; San Juan, 92, August 22, 1916; Basseterre, St. Kitts, 72, August 7, 1899; and Bridgetown, 62, September 10, 1898. These high velocities occur during the passing of the well-known West Indian hurricanes.

Puerto Rico

Shaped like a brick with its longer dimension directly east-west and the southeast corner broken out, Puerto Rico presents an extremely rugged contour from the sea from any direction. The backbone, or main divide, extends the length of the island and is for the most part above 3,000 feet in elevation. The higher parts are from 3,500 to 4,000 feet, with isolated peaks somewhat higher. Passes where highways cross from north to south are mostly above 2,000 feet. This backbone divides the island roughly into two parts, with the northern part about two and one-half times as large as the southern. Thus the long, gradual slopes are toward the north, and the short, abrupt slopes face the south. At the west end of the island the mountains spread out fanwise, filling the width of the island, while in the east the divide curves to the northeast corner, where there is a somewhat detached group of rugged peaks known as the Luquillos. Throughout the middle reaches of the island more or less irregular mountain spurs extend northward, so there is relatively little level terrain anywhere except along the coasts. Thus the divide lies parallel with the flow of the prevailing easterly winds and, except for the broad western section and north-curving eastern section, the mountains offer no great deflection for the moisture-laden air currents.

On the coastal plain of Puerto Rico, and generally on the smaller islands, daily and annual temperature ranges are small. Elevations on none of the smaller islands are sufficient to affect the day temperatures materially, but they do produce somewhat lower night temperatures, with a consequent noticeable increase in the daily range. In Puerto Rico, where elevations up to 4,000 feet are not uncommon, a difference is noted in the day temperatures, and daily ranges increase from an average of 10° or 11° F. on the coast through 15° or 20° in the foothills, to 25° or even 30° in the higher reaches. Temperatures are intimately correlated with humidity, so that in areas of continuous moderately high temperatures, as in this area, personal comfort depends largely upon the rapidity of evaporation. Day temperatures are generally between 80° and 90°, which is conducive to profuse perspiration on the slightest physical exertion. With a relative humidity throughout the 24 hours generally above 75 percent, evaporation is rather sluggish unless the surrounding air keeps in motion. As a consequence, locations protected from the prevailing breezes seem uncomfortably hot, while situations with similar temperature open to the trade winds are cool and pleasant.

Convectional rains—that is, thunderstorms and rains induced by topographic upward deflection of the air currents—account for a large percentage of tropical rainfall throughout the year. Puerto Rico, because of its size and the elevation of its mountains, has extremely varied amounts. The heaviest falls are recorded in the interior of the east and in the west end of the island where the mountains offer the broadest upward deflective front to the winds, and here the annual totals are over 100 inches. In the middle, while actual elevations are higher, the mountain trend is parallel with the prevailing wind and only moderately large totals are reported. The mountain barrier at the south rises rather abruptly and is comparatively free from spurs and foothills, so that the southern coastal plain has a greater contrast of wet and dry seasons than that north of the divide, where the surface is extremely rugged and broken by frequent northward-jutting spurs from the divide.

No discussion of the climate of this region is complete without some mention of the cyclonic developments which frequently traverse the Caribbean Sea and its surrounding islands during the summer months. Much has been written and compiled about these terrific storms, but statements of averages, and especially "average storm tracks," mean little. The violence of these cyclonic developments is well known. They are subject to the laws of cyclonic movement in the Northern Hemisphere, having a counterclockwise direction of rotation and a forward movement of the entire cyclonic whirl at rates varying from less than 5 to more than 15 miles an hour, depending on the position in the trajectory and interference of other storms or anticyclonic areas.

Tables of average frequency of destructive storms give at best a somewhat distorted idea of when a storm may be expected after one has been experienced. For Puerto Rico, the so-called average period of major storms is approximately 30 years, but the Island may not rest content on the assumption that 30 years will pass before another visitation. The north coast has been visited by major catastrophes three times within a 5-year period. One of these, in 1931, was perhaps classified as a moderate storm but its effect in a restricted area was almost tornadic.

August and September are the months of greatest frequency for this part of the hurricane belt and naturally of greatest dread for the inhabitants of the entire area. It is during these months that the storms originate farther east and attain greatest development before they reach the longitude of Puerto Rico and the Virgin Islands. Both earlier and later storms are likely to originate within the Caribbean itself, and these do not attain destructive violence before they have passed Puerto Rico. General terms, however, do not suffice, and there is a more or less constant dread of the hurricane between the first of July and the first of November.

J. B. Kincer, *Chief*, and W. W. Reed, *Assistant Chief, Division of Climate and Crop Weather, Weather Bureau, Washington, D. C.*

INDEX

298737°—41——79

O

THE PATTERN OF

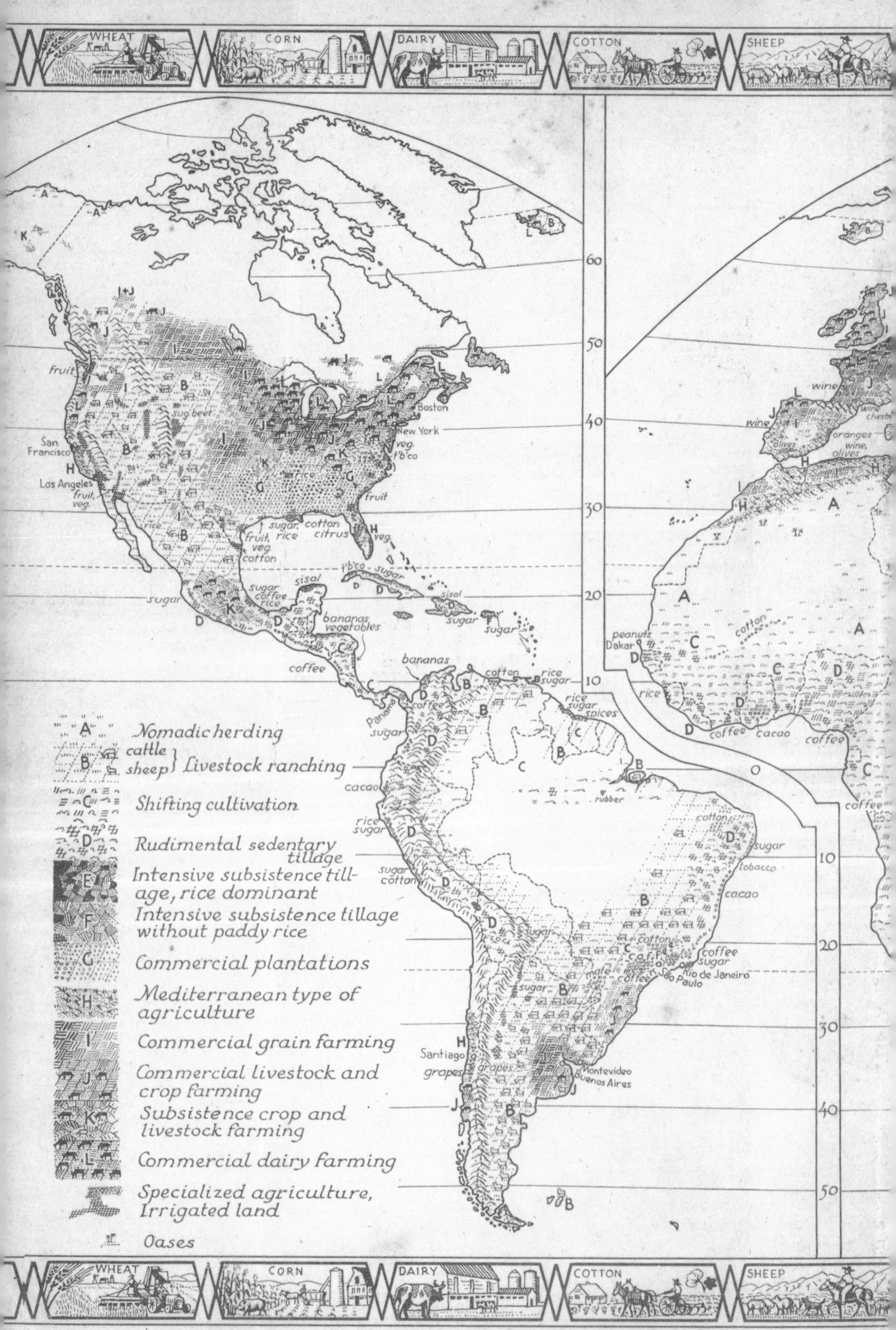
WHEAT
CORN
DAIRY
COTTON
SHEEP
A Nomadic herding
B cattle sheep } Livestock ranching
C Shifting cultivation
D Rudimental sedentary tillage
E Intensive subsistence tillage, rice dominant
F Intensive subsistence tillage without paddy rice
G Commercial plantations
H Mediterranean type of agriculture
I Commercial grain farming
J Commercial livestock and crop farming
K Subsistence crop and livestock farming
L Commercial dairy farming
Specialized agriculture, Irrigated land
Oases
San Francisco
Los Angeles
Boston
New York
Panama
Dakar
Santiago
Montevideo
Buenos Aires
Rio de Janeiro
São Paulo
fruit
veg.
sug. beet
t'b'co
rice
sugar
cotton
citrus
sisal
coffee
bananas
vegetables
cacao
spices
rubber
tobacco
mate
grapes
peanuts
wine
olives
oranges
60
50
40
30
20
10
0
WHEAT
CORN
DAIRY
COTTON
SHEEP